THE OFFICIAL FOOTBALL ASSOCIATION

# NON-LEAGUE CLUB DIRECTORY 2000

EDITOR TONY WILLIAMS

ISBN 1-869833-44-9

Published by Tony Williams Publications Ltd
Printed by WBC Book Manufacturers Ltd., (Bridgend)
Typeset by Nina Whatmore and T.W. Publications
Distributed by Tony Williams Publications Ltd.,
Helland, North Curry, Taunton TA3 6DU
Tel: 01823 490080   Fax: 01823 490281

The main photograph on the front cover shows the Tiverton Town goalkeeper, Paul Edwards (with hair dyed for the occasion), saving at full strength from Bedlington Terriers' Dean Gibb. Photo: Graham Cotterill

# INTRODUCTION

Following the great celebrations for our twenty first edition last season we are now getting our heads down and working towards our fiftieth year! The Directory continues to be a sporting best seller every year and hopefully it helps to give football enthusiasts a better knowledge of the many levels of 'pyramid' football.

Over three million football people are involved with the game outside the four full time leagues and the spirit within most of this huge football 'family' is plain for visitors to enjoy. This book tries to promote the thousands of clubs in the hundreds of semi-professional and amateur competitions all over the country, and the love of the game at these levels is as genuine as you will ever experience. Most characters you will meet at these clubs are contributing to the game of football, as compared to many at higher levels who sadly just take out of the game.

This Directory is dedicated to all those millions who give so much, and, as you will see, this year's edition has again attempted to include many team photos to cover hundreds of semi-professional players at real grass roots level, while also making a very well deserved fuss of the England internationals at the very top of their particular section of the game.

We hope that more and more clubs will be appointing press officers this season and that they will encourage team photos to be taken every year while also sending in news and changes regarding club personnel. This obviously helps us to ensure this Directory remains both useful and enjoyable to you all.

Editorial Team:
Tony Williams (Editor)
George Brown (House Editor)
Jenny Gullick and James Wright
Editorial Address: Tony Williams Publications Ltd.,

Helland, North Curry, Taunton TA3 6DU
Tel: 01823 490080   Fax: 01823 490281

# ACKNOWLEDGEMENTS

Every year the enthusiastic help we receive from all quarters of the game makes the mammoth task of compiling this Directory a happy labour of love.

As House Editor, GEORGE BROWN has not only had the task of working with new computers and new systems, but he has also taken upon himself the job of smartening up the whole presentation and I am extremely appreciative of his efforts and all he has achieved. NINA WHATMORE of Orchard Design has worked with much skill and enthusiasm and also achieved miracles with the minimum of fuss. George and Nina deserve special 'merit awards' of their own!

THE LEAGUE SECRETARIES, often with help from their CHAIRMEN and PRESS OFFICERS, have again helped us with League statistics, photos and reviews at a time when they are battling with their own handbooks. CLUB SECRETARIES, too, have sent in changes to club personnel, records and general news along with the much appreciated programmes and photos. Thanks to you all.

For every year since we first published the little pocket book in 1978, The Football Association's competitions department has been a consistent source of encouragement and help. Thanks again to a team of workers who really do love the game and who show the whole football world that The Football Association really does care for its clubs and competitions.

A bunch of enthusiasts, who have created a terrific reputation for themselves, are the Team Talk Photographers who go out in all weathers to bring you some wonderful photos featuring every level of the game. Thanks to this team, semi-pro football gets the colourful glamour it never received in the old days. Team photos, action and portraits boost the players' images and satisfy the supporters' desire for good club publicity. Many thanks to them all - Paul Barber, Peter Barnes, Clive Butchins, Andrew Chitty, Keith Clayton, Alan Coomes, Graham Cotterill, Paul Dennis, Tim Durrant, Tim Edwards, Keith Gillard, Ken Gregory, Tim Lancaster, Garry Letts, Peter Lirettoc, Eric Marsh, Ian Morsman, Dennis Nicholson, Ray Pruden, Kevin Rolfe, Mark Sandon, Francis Short, Colin Stevens, Neil Thaler, Roger Turner, Alan Watson, Bill Wheatcroft, Gordon Whittington and Martin Wray. What stars!

Most of the helpers come under the headings listed with appreciation above, but we have also received valued contributions from Mike Amos, John Anderson, Jeremy Biggs, Bill Berry, Albert Cole, Stewart Davidson, Arthur Evans, Mike Ford, Rob Grillo, Wally Goss, Tony Incenzo, Dave Phillips, Mike Simmonds, Jenny Thompson, Tom Tyler and Mike Wilson.

Having compiled most of the League and regional news for Team Talk during the last year we also had the knowledge of JAMES WRIGHT to call upon for this year's Non-League Directory. He also produces the quite brilliant Non-League Newsdesk and is one of the most experienced and widely travelled enthusiasts at our level of the game. Congratulations to James and his wife Karen on their lovely daughter Rosie, who was one year old on the day this directory was officially launched.

Thanks to a wonderful team who really love their football. They are really appreciated, one and all.

Tony Williams.

# CONTENTS

# Editorial

We launched the 21st edition of The F.A. Non League Club Directory at a special lunch in London last year at which players, administrators, managers and journalists past and present all thoroughly enjoyed a happy reunion amongst real football people.

By real football people I mean lovers of the game and its traditions and spirit - people who are in the game not because of money or prestige just a basic love of the sport and all that surrounds it.

In a year when money and politics has hit the game's headlines time and time again we are basically lucky that much of our level of the game remains untouched, and every weekend you can guarantee that you can walk into just about any non-League ground, still get a cheerful welcome, much improved facilities to enjoy and a competitive and honest game of football with officials who may not be perfect (anymore than the players are), but who are usually also acting within the spirit of the game and enjoying themselves.

Having set that happy scene, I will say that especially at the games played in front of small crowds, the attitude of club officials on the bench and indeed the touchline can influence the atmosphere of the occasion.

### No excuses for bad behaviour

With the backing of only a sparse crowd, rude and ignorant bully boys amongst managers, coaches, players and sometimes even chairmen can ruin the occasion completely. Families present hear streams of abuse at the officials and weak minded supporters often join in, and before you know it the occasion is ruined, the officials are obviously effected and the more easily influenced players are encouraged to lose their cool.

Chairmen of non-League clubs can eliminate these situations by ensuring that when employing managers they leave them in no possible doubt that their conduct and that of their helpers and players will not be tolerated if below a certain standard. Chairmen give standards to staff, staff give standards to players and anyone falling below these standards should go. Clubs would be happier and more supporters will be attracted to the game.

Most referees and linesmen will react favourably to well behaved, friendly and happy players and every-one benefits.

Our officials at non-League level are quite naturally not always the greatest - as they are officiating for players who also have many faults and also make mistakes. managers and coaches at this level aren't exactly at the top of their profession either, but all involved in the game can reasonably expect officials to avoid the arrogant posturing and bizarre behaviour that a few sad officials bring to the match.

### Ex-players as Referees

How I wish that players of thirty plus, could take up refereeing and have a chance to reach the top. We all accept that just because you have played it doesn't mean you will be a good referee, any more than it will make you a good jour-nalist, coach, manager or TV pundit.

But if you have played and you do have the right characteristics for any of these jobs it MUSt give you an advan-tage over people who have never played and experienced the game at first hand. Referees and their administrators seem determined to keep the competition of such potential quality well away so they cannot compete for senior places in the game.

A perfect example that I saw last season was Steve Baines, an ex-Football League journeyman professional who I saw take the Hednesford Town v Barnet F.A. Cup tie. His relaxed attitude was fair and sensible and quiet words here and there defused awkward situations and obviously soothed players in the heat of `battle'.

I asked him afterwards if he hoped to reach the Premier League and he explained he couldn't get to that level ever as he had started his career after playing professionally, there just wasn't time. What a waste!

Later in the season, a supporter phoned in to 6.06 on BBC5 Live he just had to report the superb performance of the referee he had seen at a Football League match that afternoon. His name was Steve Baines!

First appearances at St Leonards Football Club are always clean, smart and inviting.          Photo: Tim Lancaster

### First impressions at clubs are really important

At a time when non-League grounds are generally becoming more comfortable and well served with ever improving facilities, the semi professional game is benefiting from the massive football boom throughout the county and indeed the world.

As Premier and Football League clubs celebrate the fact they have sold out to season ticket holders for every match, more and more football enthusiasts have to look for alternative clubs, they turn to those that give them the most natural welcome. First impressions are really important, a cheery welcome on the gate, a smart well priced programme, an audible and sensibly manned loudspeaker system plus a warm and cozy well run bar with reasonable refreshments, available before and after the game, with easily accessible car parking, can all add up to a really happy footballing afternoon which can easily persuade the local family man that this is an affordable and enjoyable way of sampling an alternative to big time football.

What's more the new recruit might also be flattered if asked to help at the club and another family may set down its roots within the game where they will be appreciated.

### Beware of the `ego man'

If the previous scenario sounds good - so it should, but just occasionally the `ego man' will also appear. He has realised that football is now socially acceptable for those with or without money and most clubs are easy prey for those with self interest, a little money, a lot of confidence and ambition to be a big fish in a little pond.

Many clubs welcome the potential `money man' who says he will take the club to the top of the pyramid. Maybe his company has done well locally, perhaps he has inherited money or even won the lottery, the club committee or board are usually thrilled to have someone relieving them of the season by season worries.

But in the last couple of years when we have seen Barrow in all sorts of trouble, Gloucester City stagger and fight back and Hastings Town drop a division despite finishing fifth in the Dr. Martens Premier League, we can see clearly what problems can be brought with potential money men even with good intentions and ambitions that although possibly selfish, could also help their clubs to success. We all know the ones who have already hit the headlines for varying reasons good and bad, but think of all the others who have edged in all around the country to see their quotes in the local papers, talking about a sport or club for which they really have no deep concern or interest, just a wish to promote themselves as a local celebrity.

Often they are surrounded by local businessmen who feel that being directors of their town club, gives them extra standing amongst the `round table', `freemasons' or `rotary club'. These `football lovers' rarely go to away games, although they certainly enjoy being seen at home matches.

We all know who they are and they are pleased to find a leader who they want to believe will take them to the promised land and bring extra prestige to them all. To quote one "We no longer want football people with their traditions or spirit, running this club, from now on it's a business being run by sensible business people.

## Integrity needed

Well, I will agree that romantic, fanciful, well meaning football folk may not always face reality full in the face and the hard nosed businessman is often the ideal 'partner', but not replacement. A happy blend will bring results and as I have mentioned before in Team Talk, if you put the twenty-two top millionaires in charge of the Conference Clubs, three will still be relegated. The top clubs will be those where the businessman chairmen have surrounded them-selves with experts who know about football and its administration, publicity, tradition and spirit. The Chairmen will still deserve praise for setting it all up and delegating and that is real success.

Max Griggs at Rushden & Diamonds is an example of how it can be done to just about everyone's benefit and surely it won't be long before we lose them to the Football League.

In the last year The Football Association was disturbed by changes at the top where the Chairman, Chief Executive and Head Coach all moved on bringing the game disturbing headlines .

Also at the same time The Rugby Union (for three years) The National Cricket Board and the World Administrators for the Olympics or indeed world football all seemed to have the most depressing internal problems that could only fill us with doubt about the integrity of sporting administrators. We desperately need sporting leader-ship to be honest and sport needs to be looked after by those who can convince us the good of the games means more to them than personal gratification.

Where are these people?

Never has football a better chance of improving its reputation. Those newly elected to power within the game can compare their role with a manager picking up a club after relegation. The only way is up and we all desperately need some good news and good principles presented by administrators we can respect.

## So let's look at the good news

There is no doubt the Football Association is looking towards a modification and improvement of the pyramid struc-ture of the game below the Football League (although many feel Divisions Two and Three would themselves benefit from change).

The F.A. are also working extremely hard to help clubs, leagues and counties with their administration, sponsor-ship and public relations. National seminars are being held to help with all these facets, while the commercial arm of the F.A. has never been more sophisticated or successful in attracting supportive associates.

Just look at the sponsors who have proved an inspiration at our level. AXA's sponsorship of the F.A. Cup has been a brilliant success while Carlsberg's involvement with the F.A. Challenge Vase has been accepted as having changed the image of the whole competition. The F.A. Trophy and F.A. Sunday Cup have benefited from Umbro's enthusiastic support and look at the progress made by our three main regional feeder leagues as Dr. Martens, Rymans and Unibond extend their support and influence on the Southern, Isthmian and Northern Premier competi-tions.

it's Non-League time at Wembley Towers with the Trophy and Vase sponsors prominently placed.

Photo: Peter Barnes

8

The England squad in Holland:
Back Row: John Owens, Jimmy Conway, Squad Doctor, Murray Fishlock, Lee Charles, Michael Danzey, Paul Gothard, Warren Patmore, Steve Book, Simon Shaw, Steve Stott
Front Row: Tim Ryan, Gary Patterson, Mark Smith, Neil Grayson, Gary Butterworth (captain), Paul Underwood, Barry Williams, Andy Comyn
Photo: Andrew Chitty

### Does anyone care about England?

I know three are some who have heard and read enough of me pleading for a competitive tournament for the England Semi-Professional International squad.

This team represents the largest section of English football (at least 95%) and are the only English International team with no competition. Surely someone thinks its important enough to look after this level of football.

So how about making Inter-League games International trials instead of FAXI games watched by very few and a sponsors trophy, with a little competitive edge this would certainly give John Owens the England manager a chance to see potential internationals in competitive representative games. Come on someone, please show you care!

Vauxhall's long and happy sponsorship of the Conference will be hard to follow and we can only hope that Nationwide enter the spirit of our level of the game and understand the character of its football as well as their predecessors.

### Team Talk Co-operative

It was with sponsors and advertisers in mind that we set up the Team Talk Co-operative. The arrangement should eventually introduce companies who supply all the 200 services that we can think of, needed from time to time by the 1,000 senior non-League clubs with whom we can form a link through the magazine. We aim to promote the services and to assist the clubs to find the help they need.

So please contact Team Talk with any ideas of potential services needed or indeed companies who want their products or skills promoted the the potential thousand clients.

Through Team Talk we do have the opportunity to promote any club or individual with their new ideas, products, publications or special events, so please remember we are there to help everyone succeed in improving this level of the game we all enjoy.

### Non-League Paper

One definite plus last season was the coverage given to non-League football by Sport First, an all sports Sunday newspaper edited by an old friend of local semi-professional football, David Emery.

David had great ideas for increasing the coverage this season, but the owners didn't agree with this and sadly he stepped down from the editorial post.

We have written to all senior clubs to find out whether they would appreciate an all non-League football Sunday edition. If there is general support, then David will be published just such a newspaper, with our support, but we do need to know if you are with us!

Everyone with whom I have discussed the idea is all for it, but very few club officials have written back to promise actual support. It's in your hands!

## Security would be a bonus

Having battled away for twenty-two years working to establish this directory and nearly twelve years with the magazine, I know that a large and very appreciative market does really enjoy our efforts.

However, it is always difficult to hold our own in the modern financial world as many others have found out when starting publications of their own.

Yes, we are lucky to work on a job we love, but no, we are not able to enjoy the security of a pay cheque every month or even the knowledge that the future is secure.

So are we silly to continue? I hope not, I like to think we are providing this level of the game we love with annual and monthly publications that bring it increased credibility, good publicity and respect.

If more people bought the Directory and subscribed to Team Talk we would certainly be more secure and anyone who has seen my 224,000 mile, very battered Alpha Romeo will know what I mean!But we have come a long way and thanks to the wonderful team of photographers, the loyal subscribers and readers who have supported us since the start we are certainly looking forward to celebrating Team Talk 100 in April and a special new directory every year.

We are holding a Presentation Lunch, for the Non-League Footballer of the Year and the Non-League Manager of the Year to launch the book this September. Everyone is welcome and as the years go by I hope the occasion will become a regular celebration for non-League people past and present, so we hope to see you there next year!

thank you for your support once again and don't forget to write in with your ideas, constructive criticism and even articles, statistics or photos of your own.

Have a good season

Tony Williams

"The Dream Team" - A group of Team Talk loyal and hardy photographers on a "day out" at Wembley

Back Row (L-R): Alan Coomes, Neil Thaler, Gordon Whittington, Graham Cotterill
Front Row: Peter Lerittoc, Peter Barnes, Eric Marsh, Roger Turner

Photo by Paul Dennis

# TEAM TALK CO-OPERATIVE

Does your club need to contact companies supplying the following services or maybe you just need advice from the experts handling them. If so, please contact the **TEAM TALK HELP LINE** where you will be put you in touch with the companies in the **TEAM TALK CO-OPERATIVE**.

| | | |
|---|---|---|
| Accountants | Ground Surrounds | Magazines |
| Advertisement Boards | Pitch | Programmes |
| Entertainers | Stadium | Leaflets |
| Players, Coaches, Clubs | Health Care | Programme |
| General Advice | Health Drinks | Advice |
| All Weather Surface | Honours Boards | Clubs Compilers |
| Architects | Hotel Groups | Fairs |
| Awards | Overnight Stops | Statisticians |
| Badges | Pre Match Meals | Rosettes |
| Blazers | Injury Clinics | Scarves |
| Metal, Lapel | Insurance | Shower Gel |
| Beers | Commercial | Showers |
| Blinds | Home | Signwriting |
| Ceilings (Low & High) | Injuries | Sponsorship Advice |
| Clubhouses (Erection & | Motoring | Sports Development |
| Extension) | Travel | Initiatives |
| Club Shop (Gifts) | Investments | Sports Drinks |
| Contract (Advice) | Internet Advice | Sports Injury Clinic |
| Deodorants (Players) | Kit Bags | Sport & Liaision |
| Design | Kit | Consultants |
| Publications | Match | Stadia Development |
| Buildings | Training | Advice |
| Do It Yourself | Leisure Kit | Stands |
| Dressing Rooms | Life Insurance | Large |
| Building | Lights | Small |
| Design | Floodlights | Portable |
| Seating | Security | Surveying |
| Toiletries | Spotlight | Table Football |
| Fixture Cards | Internal | Tickets |
| Floodlights | Local Authority Liaison | Ties |
| Pitch | Lottery Bids | Training Aids |
| Car Park Etc | Lottery Grants | Bibs |
| Flooring | Magazines | Cones |
| Footballs | Magnetic Training Aids | Footwalls |
| Match | Medical Supplies | Goals |
| Training | Overnight Stops | Trophies |
| Indoors | Pensions | Glass |
| Fundraising Advice | Photographers | Sculptured |
| Furniture | Physio's Supplies | Medals |
| Gifts (Shop) | Picture Framing | Plaques |
| Grandstands | Pitch Surrounds | T-Shirts |
| Small | Planning Advice | Web Sites |
| Large | Playground Aids | Youth Football Coaching |
| Extensions | Pool Tables | Youth Football |
| Grant Aid Advice | Printers | Tournaments |
| Grants (Local/National) | Books | |

# HELP LINE: 01823 490080

21st Anniversary 1998

Above: At last year's Presentation Lunch, apart from the awards for season 1997-98, we announced the squad of sixteen players and a manager selected by readers and the editorial team for the twenty-one year period from our first little annual in 1978 to last year's Directory. Those selected, who attended the presentation lunch, were presented with a photographic montage of the squad and manager. In this photo you can see, left to right: Back Row: John Davison (Altrincham and England), Geoff Chapple (Manager - Woking and Kingstonian), Andy Pape (Enfield and England), Antone Joseph (Telford United, Kidderminster Harriers and England), Kevan Brown (Woking and England), Paul Davies (Kidderminster Harriers and England). Front Row: Clive Walker (Woking and Cheltenham Town), Kim Casey (Kidderminster Harriers and England), Tony Jennings (Enfield and England), and Mark Carter (Runcorn, Barnet and England). Photo: Peter Barnes

Above: The 1997-98 Non League Footballer of the Year.
England's record goalscorer Mark Carter presents Tiverton Town's ace goalscorer Phil Everitt with his beautiful award.
Photo: Peter Barnes

Two successful clubs with 'happy' tables.
Above: Kidderminster Harriers (three FA Trophy Finals - one victory, one Conference Championship).
Photo: Peter Barnes
Left: Tiverton Town (three FA Vase Finals and two victories, with four League Championships).
Photo: Keith Clayton

# CLUB DIRECTORY

Above: Non League Footballer of the 21 year era was Clive Walker, and here he receives his award from Alan Smith, who at present is the only player to have won England semi-professional caps and moved on to win full international honours.
Photo: Keith Clayton

Right: Here is Clive again with Sport First newspaper owner Keith Young, and Manager of the 21 year era squad, Geoff Chapple.
Photo: Peter Barnes

Left: Antone Joseph, who played in four FA Trophy Finals, and Paul Davies, the Conference record goalscorer, with Geoff Chapple and Keith Young.
Photo: Keith Clayton

Right: Two of England's very best captains were Tony Jennings (left), who was selected as skipper of the 21 year era squad, and John Davison (right), who holds the record number of England semi-professional caps (24), with Geoff Chapple and Keith Young.
Photo: Keith Clayton

# NSPCC ●

## Cruelty to children must stop. FULL STOP.

During season 1999-2000 Team Talk magazine will be helping to raise funds for The National Society for the Prevention of Cruelty to Children's FULL STOP campaign.

In a very simple exercise from October 99 we will promote a special call line number provided by Dave Boddy of Sportslines, which is **09066 555765.**

Calls cost 60p per minute and the calls will not exceed two minutes.

On the line you will be asked to answer a simple non-league question and name the non-league club you support.

Each month all those giving the correct answer will be entered in a draw and the lucky winner will receive the prize of the month as advertised in Team Talk. The club supported by the winner will also receive a prize as well as the club with most supporters using the call line each month.

The call line number will be promoted in many different ways throughout the season and hopefully the family spirit existing throughout the non-League football world will enable us to raise substantial funds for a very worthy cause.

So why not try your luck each month? As the questions change so will the exciting prizes.

TONY WILLIAMS

NOW IN ITS RECORD 9TH YEAR OF PUBLICATION

# BRITAIN'S MOST POPULAR NATIONAL NON-LEAGUE FOOTBALL MONTHLY

Team Talk should be available from your local non-League football club or your local newsagent and is available by subscription from the publishers.

Team Talk is published by Tony Williams Publications Ltd., Helland, North Curry, Taunton, Somerset TA3 6DU
Tel: 01823 490080  Fax: 01823 490281  e-mail: tony.williams12@virgin.net

# The Non-League Club Directory

# 1998-99
# AWARDS

## ROLL OF HONOUR

### FOOTBALLER OF THE YEAR
Neil Grayson

### MANAGER OF THE YEAR
Brendan Phillips

### ENGLAND PLAYER OF THE YEAR
Gary Butterworth

### INDIVIDUAL MERIT AWARDS
Jim Rogers
David Pace
Doug Gillard
John Milner
Martyn Rogers

### REGIONAL AWARDS

| | |
|---|---|
| North East | Bedlington Terriers |
| North West | Workington |
| Midlands | Cheltenham Town |
| East of England | Spalding United |
| Home Counties North | Hayes |
| Home Counties South | Havant & Waterlooville |
| West of England & Wales | Taunton Town |

# INDIVIDUAL MERIT AWARDS 1998-99

**Jim Rogers (Harrow Borough)** - If ever a man dedicated himself to a football club it is Harrow Borough's president who, has served as secretary and chairman during the clubs climb from Athenian League Division Two and the precarious existence, co-habiting with a darts and social club in a dingy, damp dilapidated club room, to a smart and much respected well presented Ryman Premier League club.

Jim has been backed up by his wife Meg and son Peter, who is now chairman, and their inspiration has encouraged the club to succeed in a traditionally difficult area in which to attract small club loyalty. Harrow Borough is always a happy and friendly club to visit where they obviously have their basic priorities right.

(Left): Jim Rogers presents Vladimir Gusavac with the Harrow Borough
Best Newcomber Award of 1998-99.    Photo: Paul Cash

**David Pace (Chairman/Manager Droylsden)** - Having taken over an ailing club in the mid nineties he met incredible resistance with impressive determination to succeed. He rebuilt the social club (from a burnt out wreck) erected a superb new stand and took the managerial responsibility building a playing squad to match, once he had released the managers who had used his money without success. He took `The Bloods' to promotion and a Presidents Cup success, but lost in the Unifilla First Division Cup Final. The changing room facilities are now second to none in northern semi-professional football and David has backed his ideas with money to produce wonderful results on and off the field.

**Doug Gillard** - is a perfect example of football's massive band of honorary workers who dedicate themselves to the game. He has just completed 20 years as a member of the League's Management Committee. For the past ten years he has been Chairman. During this time he has been responsible for many fine aspects of the Southern Football League, one of which has been the maintenance of magnificent sponsorship for the Competition. The League has enjoyed just two main sponsors in fifteen years!

As well as holding many other positions with local Competitions, Doug has been a member of the Kent County Football Association for more than 20 years.

Since being elected to the Football Association Council six years ago, he has been returned unopposed for the last five years and he has been a committee member, director and chairman of Ashford Town Football club. He is now a Life Member.

**John Milner (Bedlington Terriers)** - The disappointment of being released as an unwanted full back, by Kevin Keegan at Newcastle United must have seemed a long way away last season as John couldn't stop scoring. He was top scorer in the F.A. Vase and second top scorer in the F.A. Cup, he totalled 65 for the season and inspired many of The Terriers great performances. John had a never to be forgotten dream season.

**Martyn Rogers (Manager of Tiverton Town)** - Having dominated the Screwfix Western League for two years and as holders of the F.A. Carlsberg Vase and Team Talk Trophy (by beating Trophy holders Cheltenham Town 2-0), league games were difficult to take seriously at the beginning of last season for some players. However, having brought his squad back to earth, Martyn steadily consolidated in second position which enabled `Tivvy' to gain promotion to the Dr. Martens League and despite a difficult passage to the final the West Country cup fighters beat powerful Bedlington Terriers in the final to retain the Vase.

Bedlington Terriers' John Milner tries a diving header against Workington.   Photo: Neil Thaler

16

# REGIONAL CLUB AWARDS 1998-99

### North East
**BEDLINGTON TERRIERS** were known to have assembled an exciting squad in the North East, but it wasn't until their 4-1 F.A. Cup success against Colchester United that the rest of the country realised what a powerful club they really were. Then a good performance at Scunthorpe and a Vase run to the final at Wembley was accompanied by another Arnott Insurance Northern League Championship.

### North West
**WORKINGTON** were relegated into the North West Counties League and the well lknown ex- Football League name appeared to be falling out of sight down the pyramid. However a wonderful transformation with improved results, attracted the crowds and after a good Vase run an amazing late run saw `The Reds' beat Mossley in their last game to guarantee their immediate return to the Unibond League.

### Midlands
**CHELTENHAM TOWN** - although many people's favourites from the outset, it must be remembered that this was only their second season back in the Conference. The Robins' powerful squad guided by good leadership in the boardroom and manager's office brought Football League status along with the County Cup and an Umbro Trophy run to the Semi Final. They also supplied six members of the England squad.

### East of England
**SPALDING UNITED** produced the form that they had threatened in previous seasons and they won the Uhlsport United Counties Championship by fifteen points! To add to their near perfect season, the Hinchingbroke Cup and the Leicestershire Senior Cup also finished in their cabinet.

### Home Counties North
**HAYES** - play in the West of London where non-League attendances are traditionally sparse. But the way transfer fee income has been used to develop the ground and the squad was so successful that the England v Italy fixture was played at Church Road and a best ever third place was clinched in the Conference with a run in of seven victories in the last ten games.

### Home Counties South
**HAVANT & WATERLOOVILLE** - took their place in the Dr. Martens Southern Division as a result of a merger between the two well known south coast clubs. It is not easy to settle down quickly with any success, on or off the field, so the club's achievement of winning this championship and promotion is particularly credit worthy.

### West of England & Wales
**TAUNTON TOWN** - completed a memorable `double' over Tiverton Town and went onto win the Screwfix Direct Western League championship. They also beat Conference leaders Kettering Town 4-3, in the F.A. Cup and reached The Carlsberg Vase Semi Final for the second consecutive year and were finalists in the Somerset Cup.

### F.A. Cup
**RUSHDEN & DIAMONDS** - After the exciting performances by the real minnows such as Bedlington Terriers, Ford United and Camberley Town, the old FA Cup favourites, Yeovil Town remained in the competition longer than any other non-league club but it was Rushden & Diamonds, who having disposed of Shrewsbury Town, faced Premier League opposition. The club coped with the Leeds United glamour tie, with charm, efficiency and quality of play that nearly brought them victory, and at least provided a trip to Elland Road where they led before eventually losing 1-3 in an entertaining Cup tie.

# ENGLAND PLAYER OF THE YEAR

# GARY BUTTERWORTH

**England's Player of the Year 1998-99**
Selected by The England Semi-Professional
International manager John Owens.

### GARY BUTTERWORTH
(Rushden & Diamonds)

In the two years that I have managed the
England squad, my captain for all four
Internationals has been Gary and not only has
he carried out the skipper's duties in excellent
fashion on and off the field, but he has also managed to be an outstanding performer in all the
matches.

His consistency in all weathers (although it's usually very wet) has been impressive and his com-
batitive mid-field style is laced with impressive
passing skills which usually keeps possession for
the side. His performances for his country have
been even more praiseworthy as he hasn't
always been playing regularly for his club.

This season he was certainly pushed for this
award by colleagues who have also had excellent international seasons, such as Gary
Patterson, Neil Grayson and Warren Patmore,
but on this occasion the skipper gets the nod.

J.O.

'The Skipper' Gary Butterworth, and
(left) with the Dutch Captain

Photos: Andrew Chitty

18

# NON LEAGUE MANAGER OF THE YEAR

## BRENDAN PHILLIPS
### (Nuneaton Borough)

(Left to right): Richie Norman, Brendan Phillips, Steve Burr
Photo: Keith Clayton

## Non League Manager of the Year 1998-99
### Brendan Phillips (Nuneaton Borough)

The performance of Nuneaton Borough throughout the whole of last season was a dream come true, They stormed off to a great start with six consecutive victories, their young striker Malcolm Christie scoring in all six. He was then snapped up by Derby County. Goals then came from all departments (18 players) as an invincable position was built at the top of the Dr.Martens Premier Division and a string of quality clubs never really had the incentive to challenge as they were soon just too far behind. Brendan had built the perfect squad for the competition, with the help of his Assistant Steve Burr and Physio Richie Norman and he obviously had found the right blend of players and coaching staff as Borough were never out of the top spot for the whole season, winning the championship by 23 points! This was a magnificent achievement which will be very hard to match at any level.

### PAST WINNERS

| | |
|---|---|
| 1997-98 | Steve Cotterill   (Cheltenham Town) |
| 1996-97 | Paul Futcher   (Southport) |
| 1995-96 | Paul Fairclough  (Stevenage Borough) |
| 1994-95 | Sammy McIlroy   (Macclesfield Town) |
| 1993-94 | Bill Punton   (Diss Town) |
| 1992-93 | Martin O'Neill   (Wycombe Wanderers) |

# NON LEAGUE FOOTBALLER OF THE YEAR

## NEIL GRAYSON
### (Cheltenham Town)

Photo: Andrew Chitty

Photo: Peter Barnes

### Non League Footballer of the Year 1998-99
### Neil Grayson

You would never believe that the 'fireball' in the No9 shirt for England and Cheltenham Town was thirty let alone a few years older than that!

The energy, enthusiasm and determination he shows in all games, whether he is facing Italy in the mud or Canvey Island in the Trophy, underlines the fact that he never gives less than 100% effort and he is a manager's dream. How a player with his pace and finishing skills was allowed to leave the Football League is a mystery.

In the 1997-98 season Neil was 'cup tied' when The Robins reached Wembley and last season he was most upset to lose in the Trophy semi-final.

Thankfully he had the championship and Conference 'Player of the Season' to celebrate and now he has 'The Non-League Footballer of the Year for 1999. No-one could deserve it more.

### PAST WINNERS

| | |
|---|---|
| 1997-98 | Phil Everett  (Tiverton Town) |
| 1996-97 | Howard Forinton  (Yeovil Town) |
| 1995-96 | Barry Hayes  (Stevenage Borough) |
| 1994-95 | Kevan Brown  (Woking) |
| 1993-94 | Chris Brindley  (Kidderminster Harriers) |
| 1992-93 | Steve Guppy  (Wycombe Wanderers) |
| 1991-92 | Tommy Killick  (Wimborne Town) |
| 1990-91 | Mark West  (Wycombe Wanderers) |
| 1989-90 | Phil Gridelet  (Barnet) |
| 1988-89 | Steve Butler  (Maidstone United) |
| 1987-88 | David Howell  (Enfield) |
| 1986-87 | Mark Carter  (Runcorn) |
| 1985-86 | Jeff Johnson  (Altrincham) |
| 1984-85 | Alan Cordice  (Wealdstone) |
| 1983-84 | Brian Thompson  (Maidstone United) |

# THE TEAM TALK
# TROPHY CHALLENGE

## 1998

Tiverton Town (FA Carlsberg Vase winners 1998)  2
Cheltenham Town (FA Umbro Trophy winners 1998)  0

## 1999

Tiverton Town (FA Carlsberg Vase winners 1999)  3
Kingstonian (FA Umbro Trophy winners 1999)  4

# PECKING ORDER 1998-99
### A J Sarnecki

| 95-6 | 96-7 | 97-8 | 98-9 | Code | League | FA Cup ent | FA Cup xmt | FA Cup won | FA Trophy ent | FA Trophy xmt | FA Trophy won | FA Vase ent | FA Vase xmt | FA Vase won | C pts | T pts | V pts | Total pts |
|---|---|---|---|---|---|---|---|---|---|---|---|---|---|---|---|---|---|---|
| 1 | 1 | 1 | 1 | FC | FOOTBALL CONFERENCE | 22 | 132 | 40 | 88 | 44 | 42 | 0 | 0 | 0 | 194 | 174 | 0 | 368 |
| 2 | 3 | 2 | 2 | ISP | ISTHMIAN Premier | 22 | 88 | 36 | 88 | 22 | 27 | 0 | 0 | 0 | 146 | 137 | 0 | 283 |
| 3 | 2 | 3 | 3 | NPP | NORTHERN PREMIER Premier | 22 | 88 | 23 | 88 | 12 | 34 | 0 | 0 | 0 | 133 | 134 | 0 | 267 |
| 4 | 4 | 4 | 4 | SOP | SOUTHERN Premier | 22 | 88 | 31 | 88 | 12 | 21 | 0 | 0 | 0 | 141 | 121 | 0 | 262 |
| 8 | 6= | 6 | 5 | NP1 | NORTHERN PREMIER First | 22 | 0 | 37 | 88 | 20 | 13 | 0 | 0 | 0 | 59 | 121 | 0 | 180 |
| 6 | 5 | 8 | 6 | SO1S | SOUTHERN Southern | 22 | 0 | 33 | 88 | 20 | 11 | 0 | 0 | 0 | 55 | 119 | 0 | 174 |
| 5 | 8 | 7 | 7 | IS1 | ISTHMIAN First | 22 | 0 | 29 | 88 | 18 | 14 | 0 | 0 | 0 | 51 | 120 | 0 | 171 |
| 7 | 6= | 5 | 8 | SO1M | SOUTHERN Midland | 22 | 0 | 22 | 88 | 12 | 13 | 0 | 0 | 0 | 44 | 113 | 0 | 157 |
| 9 | 10 | 9 | 9 | IS2 | ISTHMIAN Second | 22 | 0 | 21 | 0 | 0 | 0 | 22 | 42 | 32 | 43 | 0 | 96 | 139 |
| 10 | 11 | 10 | 10 | NOR1 | NORTHERN First | 20 | 0 | 19 | 0 | 0 | 0 | 20 | 40 | 26 | 39 | 0 | 86 | 125 |
| 12 | 13 | 11 | 11= | ECOP | EASTERN COUNTIES Premier | 19 | 0 | 14 | 0 | 0 | 0 | 22 | 38 | 26 | 33 | 0 | 86 | 119 |
| 11 | 12 | 13= | 11= | NWC1 | NORTH WEST COUNTIES First | 20 | 0 | 15 | 0 | 0 | 0 | 22 | 28 | 34 | 35 | 0 | 84 | 119 |
| 15 | 15 | 12 | 13= | WESP | WESTERN Premier | 16 | 0 | 17 | 0 | 0 | 0 | 18 | 28 | 24 | 33 | 0 | 62 | 95 |
| 14 | 13 | 13= | 13= | NCEP | NORTHERN COUNTIES EAST Premier | 18 | 0 | 15 | 0 | 0 | 0 | 19 | 20 | 23 | 33 | 0 | 62 | 95 |
| 16 | 18 | 18 | 15 | IS3 | ISTHMIAN Third | 20 | 0 | 20 | 0 | 0 | 0 | 20 | 0 | 27 | 40 | 0 | 47 | 87 |
|  |  | 16 | 16 | SSMP | SPARTAN SOUTH MIDLANDS Premier | 12 | 0 | 9 | 0 | 0 | 0 | 19 | 16 | 18 | 21 | 0 | 53 | 74 |
| 17 | 15 | 15 | 17= | UCOP | UNITED COUNTIES Premier | 18 | 0 | 5 | 0 | 0 | 0 | 19 | 18 | 11 | 23 | 0 | 48 | 71 |
| 18 | 17 | 17 | 17= | SSX1 | SUSSEX COUNTY First | 18 | 0 | 11 | 0 | 0 | 0 | 18 | 10 | 14 | 29 | 0 | 42 | 71 |
| 13 | 16 | 16 | 19 | MDA | MIDLAND ALLIANCE | 19 | 0 | 8 | 0 | 0 | 0 | 20 | 4 | 19 | 27 | 0 | 43 | 70 |
| 21 | 20 | 19 | 20 | WSX1 | WESSEX | 14 | 0 | 1 | 0 | 0 | 0 | 18 | 18 | 17 | 15 | 0 | 53 | 68 |
| 20 | 19 | 20 | 21 | KEN1 | KENT | 12 | 0 | 6 | 0 | 0 | 0 | 16 | 10 | 15 | 18 | 0 | 41 | 59 |
| 25 | 24 | 24 | 22 | HELP | HELLENIC Premier | 5 | 0 | 2 | 0 | 0 | 0 | 18 | 0 | 9 | 7 | 0 | 37 | 44 |
| 27= | 22 | 26 | 23 | COCP | COMBINED COUNTIES | 10 | 0 | 4 | 0 | 0 | 0 | 13 | 6 | 16 | 14 | 0 | 29 | 43 |
| 23= | 23 | 25 | 24 | ESXS | ESSEX Senior | 6 | 0 | 5 | 0 | 0 | 0 | 11 | 4 | 12 | 11 | 0 | 29 | 40 |
| 19 | 21 | 21 | 25 | NOR2 | NORTHERN Second | 12 | 0 | 4 | 0 | 0 | 0 | 14 | 10 | 5 | 16 | 0 | 23 | 39 |
| 35 | 35 | 30 | 26 | LESP | LEICESTERSHIRE SENIOR Premier | 0 | 0 | 0 | 0 | 0 | 0 | 11 | 10 | 15 | 0 | 0 | 36 | 36 |
| 30= | 30 | 29 | 27 | SWE | SOUTH WESTERN | 2 | 0 | 6 | 0 | 0 | 0 | 6 | 0 | 10 | 8 | 0 | 26 | 34 |
| 22 | 25 | 22 | 28= | NCE1 | NORTHERN COUNTIES EAST First | 9 | 0 | 6 | 0 | 0 | 0 | 11 | 0 | 6 | 15 | 0 | 17 | 32 |
| 23= | 27 | 31= | 28= | WES1 | WESTERN First | 6 | 0 | 3 | 0 | 0 | 0 | 12 | 8 | 11 | 9 | 0 | 23 | 32 |
| 32= | 28 | 28 | 30= | ECO1 | EASTERN COUNTIES | 2 | 0 | 1 | 0 | 0 | 0 | 16 | 8 | 11 | 9 | 0 | 23 | 32 |
| 34 | 29 | 31= | 30= | NWC2 | NORTH WEST COUNTIES Second | 6 | 0 | 2 | 0 | 0 | 0 | 8 | 0 | 6 | 3 | 0 | 27 | 30 |
| 32= | 34= | 34= | 32 | CMSU | CENTRAL MIDLANDS Supreme | 0 | 0 | 0 | 0 | 0 | 0 | 11 | 4 | 14 | 8 | 0 | 22 | 30 |
| 29 | 33 | 33 | 33 | SSX2 | SUSSEX COUNTY Second | 0 | 0 | 0 | 0 | 0 | 0 | 9 | 0 | 4 | 0 | 0 | 25 | 25 |
| 26 | 32 | 34= | 34 | WMDP | WEST MIDLAND REGIONAL Premier | 1 | 0 | 0 | 0 | 0 | 0 | 7 | 0 | 4 | 2 | 0 | 17 | 19 |
| 36= | 37 | 39= | 35 | MDCP | MIDLAND COMBINATION Premier | 0 | 0 | 0 | 0 | 0 | 0 | 7 | 4 | 6 | 1 | 0 | 15 | 16 |
| 45= | 36 | 36 | 36 | SMDS | SPARTAN SOUTH MIDLANDS Senior | 0 | 0 | 0 | 0 | 0 | 0 | 7 | 0 | 3 | 0 | 0 | 13 | 13 |
| 36= | 39= | 37 | 37 | WCH1 | WEST CHESHIRE First | 0 | 0 | 0 | 0 | 0 | 0 | 1 | 0 | 1 | 1 | 0 | 10 | 11 |
| 38= | 39= | 39= | 38= | NALP | NORTHERN ALLIANCE Premier | 0 | 0 | 0 | 0 | 0 | 0 | 1 | 1 | 1 | 0 | 0 | 11 | 11 |
| 48= | 46= | 43= | 38= | NTAS | NOTTS ALLIANCE Senior | 0 | 0 | 0 | 0 | 0 | 0 | 1 | 0 | 0 | 0 | 0 | 5 | 5 |
|  |  | 38= | 38= | HAM1 | HAMPSHIRE First | 0 | 0 | 0 | 0 | 0 | 0 | 2 | 0 | 0 | 0 | 0 | 5 | 5 |
|  |  | 41= | 41= | MANP | MANCHESTER Premier | 0 | 0 | 0 | 0 | 0 | 0 | 1 | 0 | 0 | 0 | 0 | 2 | 2 |
| 43= | 44= | 39= | 41= | DVC | DEVON COUNTY LEAGUE | 0 | 0 | 0 | 0 | 0 | 0 | 1 | 0 | 0 | 0 | 0 | 2 | 2 |

The consolidation of the two "premier" divisions of the Spartan South Midlands League has improved the standing of the new division. Last season the Northern section was 23rd and the Southern 27th. The change in the exemption system for the Cup and Trophy has not greatly affected the "Pecking Order" but help the Isthmians to regain the second spot.

# F.A. CHALLENGE CUP

### sponsored by AXA

# 1998-99 REVIEW

## NON LEAGUE HONOURS BOARD 1998-99

### FIRST ROUND PROPER

**NATIONWIDE CONFERENCE (13)**

Cheltenham Town
Doncaster Rovers
Hayes
Hednesford Town
Kidderminster Harriers
Kingstonian
Rushden & Diamonds
Southport
Stevenage Borough
Telford United
Welling United
Woking
Yeovil Town

**DR MARTENS (5)**

Burton Albion
Gresley Rovers
Salisbury City
Tamworth United
Worcester City

**RYMANS (8)**

Basingstoke Town
Boreham Wood
Camberley Town (Div 3)
Dulwich Hamlet
Enfield
Ford United (Div 3)
Hendon
Slough Town

**UNIBOND (4)**

Emley
Lancaster City
Leigh RMI
Runcorn

**ARNOTT INSURANCE NORTHERN LEAGUE (2)**

Bedlington Terriers
West Auckland Town

### SECOND ROUND

Bedlington Terriers
Doncaster Rovers
Hednesford Town
Kingstonian
Rushden & Diamonds
Stevenage Borough
Yeovil Town

### THIRD ROUND

| | | | | |
|---|---|---|---|---|
| Rushden & Diamonds | v | Leeds United | 0-0 | 6,431 |
| Leeds United | v | Rusden & Diamonds | 3-1 | 39,159 |
| Southport | v | Leyton Orient | 0-2 | 4,950 |
| Cardiff City | v | Yeovil Town | 1-1 | 12,561 |
| Yeovil Town | v | Cardiff City | 1-2 aet | 8,101 |

# PRELIMINARY ROUND

| # | Home | | | Away | |
|---|---|---|---|---|---|
| 1 | Ashton United | 5 | v 2 | Willington | 175 |
| 2 | Thackley | 2 | v 1 | Hebburn | 101 |
| 3 | Atherton Collieries | 1 | v 2 | Armthorpe Welfare | |
| 4 | Stockton | 1 | v 4 | Liversedge | 74 |
| 5 | Rossendale United | 0 | v 3 | Brigg Town | 105 |
| 6 | Ashington | 2 | v 1* | Horden CW | 285 |
| 7 | Sheffield | 2 | v 4 | Atherton LR | 34 |
| | (at Ossett Town FC) | | | | |
| 8 | Trafford | 4 | v 1 | Peterlee Newtown | 154 |
| 9 | Ramsbottom United | 0 | v 0 | Maine Road | |
| R | Maine Road | 1 | v 2 | Ramsbottom United | 120 |
| 10 | Harrogate Town | 1 | v 2 | Burscough | 179 |
| 11 | Tadcaster Albion | 1 | v 0 | Ossett Town | |
| 12 | Guisborough Town | 1 | v 3 | Rossington Main | 215 |
| 13 | Shotton Comrades | 1 | v 2 | Jarrow Rfng Boldon CA | 51 |
| 14 | Flixton | 3 | v 0 | Northallerton Town | 75 |
| 15 | Marske United | 1 | v 1 | Billingham Synthonia | 253 |
| R | Billingham Synthonia | 3 | v 0 | Marske United | 232 |
| 16 | Oldham Town | 0 | v 2 | Warrington Town | |
| 17 | Bacup Borough | | v | Blackpool (wren) Rovers | |
| | (walkover for Bacup Borough - Blackpool (wren) Rovers withdrawn) | | | | |
| 18 | Bradford (Park Ave) | 4 | v 1 | Easington Colliery | 148 |
| 19 | Yorkshire Amateur | 1 | v 3 | Witton Albion | 200 |
| 20 | Durham City | 2 | v 0 | Dunston FB | 272 |
| 21 | Sandwell Borough | 0 | v 3 | Blakenall | 112 |
| 22 | Boston Town | 2 | v 0 | Blackstone | 73 |
| 23 | Shepshed Dynamo | 1 | v 1 | Barwell | 215 |
| R | Barwell | 3 | v 3 | Shepshed Dynamo | 167 |
| 24 | Sutton Coldfield Tn | 1 | v 0 | VS Rugby | 162 |
| 25 | Hinckley United | 2 | v 0 | Rushall Olympic | 237 |
| 26 | Lye Town | 0 | v 1 | Racing Club Warwick | 70 |
| 27 | Oldbury United | 2 | v 0 | Shifnal Town | 240 |
| 28 | Stafford Rangers | 3 | v 0 | Boldmere St Michaels | 471 |
| 29 | Matlock Town | 4 | v 1 | Redditch United | 191 |
| 30 | Halesowen Harriers | 2 | v 1 | Stourport Swifts | 75 |
| 31 | Bridgnorth Town | 3 | v 3 | Borrowash Victoria | |
| R | Borrowash Victoria | 0 | v 2 | Bridgnorth Town | 101 |
| 32 | Corby Town | 0 | v 4 | Leek CSOB | 91 |
| 33 | Chelmsford City | 6 | v 0 | Fakenham Town | 358 |
| 34 | Canvey Island | 6 | v 1 | Stansted | 203 |
| 35 | Eynesbury Rovers | 3 | v 3 | Southall | 34 |
| R | Southall | 6 | v 0 | Eynesbury Rovers | 84 |
| 36 | Tring Town | 0 | v 2 | Waltham Abbey | |
| 37 | Bowers United | 5 | v 3 | Wooton Blue Cross | 71 |
| 38 | Felixstowe Pt & Tn | 1 | v 2 | Ford Sports Daventry | 75 |
| 39 | Leyton Pennant | 2 | v 1 | Wembley | 93 |
| 40 | Stotfold | 2 | v 2 | Sudbury Town | 140 |
| R | Sudbury Town | 2 | v 1 | Stotfold | 229 |
| 41 | Harpenden Town | 3 | v 2 | Burnham | 40 |
| 42 | Potton United | 0 | v 3 | Baldock Town | 115 |
| 43 | Hornchurch | 1 | v 1 | London Colney | |
| R | London Colney | 1 | v 0 | Hornchurch | 51 |
| 44 | Marlow | 2 | v 1 | Hemel Hempstead Tn | 161 |

| # | Home | | | Away | |
|---|---|---|---|---|---|
| 45 | Bury Town | 1 | v 1 | Tilbury | 164 |
| R | Tilbury | 3 | v 2 | Bury Town | 133 |
| 46 | Kingsbury Town | 4 | v 4 | Grays Athletic | |
| R | Grays Athletic | 7 | v 0 | Kingsbury Town | 96 |
| 47 | Stowmarket Town | 5 | v 1 | Gorleston | 91 |
| 48 | Potters Bar Town | 2 | v 2 | Wealdstone | 264 |
| R | Wealdstone | 5 | v 3 | Potters Bar Town | |
| 49 | Witney Town | 3 | v 0 | Northwood | 119 |
| 50 | Arlesey Town | 0 | v 2 | Barking | 105 |
| 51 | Welwyn Garden C | 6 | v 1 | East Thurrock United | |
| 52 | Ford United | 2 | v 0 | Wellingborough Town | |
| 53 | Burnham Ramblers | 2 | v 1 | Soham Town Rangers | |
| 54 | Halstead Town | 3 | v 0 | Flackwell Heath | |
| 55 | Wisbech Town | 2 | v 3 | Bedford Town | 585 |
| 56 | Desborough Town | 1 | v 0 | Cheshunt | 119 |
| 57 | Farnham Town | 1 | v 1 | Hailsham Town | 100 |
| R | Hailsham Town | 3 | v 2 | Farnham Town | 145 |
| 58 | Molesey | 1 | v 4 | Oxford City | 72 |
| 59 | Deal Town | 4 | v 1 | Hillingdon Borough | 221 |
| 60 | Egham Town | 2 | v 2 | Fisher Athletic | |
| R | Fisher Athletic | 6 | v 0 | Egham Town | 99 |
| 61 | St Leonards | 2 | v 1 | Wick | 354 |
| 62 | Cowes Sports | 1 | v 2 | Dorking | 139 |
| 63 | Godalming & G'ford | 1 | v 2 | Banstead Athletic | 107 |
| 64 | Dartford | 0 | v 0 | Reading Town | 292 |
| R | Reading Town | 0 | v 3 | Dartford | 110 |
| 65 | Folkestone Invicta | 2 | v 3 | Tonbridge Angels | 328 |
| 66 | Ashford Town | 1 | v 1 | Margate | 515 |
| R | Margate | 1 | v 2 | Ashford Town | 468 |
| 67 | Littlehampton Tn | 1 | v 4 | Fleet Town | 87 |
| 68 | Fareham Town | 0 | v 2 | Croydon | 155 |
| 69 | Portfield | 1 | v 1 | Eastleigh | 99 |
| R | Eastleigh | 1 | v 2 | Portfield | 92 |
| 70 | Abingdon Town | 0 | v 3 | Maidenhead United | 125 |
| 71 | Ashford Town (Mx) | 1 | v 3 | Erith & Belvedere | 90 |
| 72 | Bashley | 4 | v 2 | Ramsgate | 328 |
| 73 | Chatham Town | 1 | v 1 | Horsham | 103 |
| R | Horsham | 3 | v 1 | Chatham Town | 171 |
| 74 | Eastbourne Town | 1 | v 0 | Herne Bay | 100 |
| | (at Herne Bay FC) | | | | |
| 75 | Wokingham Town | 0 | v 2 | Camberley Town | 115 |
| 76 | Burgess Hill Town | 1 | v 0 | Thame United | |
| 77 | Torrington | 0 | v 1 | Melksham Town | 64 |
| 78 | Cirencester Town | 3 | v 2 | Chippenham Town | 163 |
| 79 | Falmouth Town | 1 | v 0 | Devizes Town | 197 |
| 80 | Newport AFC | 0 | v 0 | Weston-super-Mare | 568 |
| R | Weston-super-Mare | 1 | v 0 | Newport AFC | 334 |
| 81 | Elmore | 1 | v 0 | Yate Town | 103 |
| 82 | Paulton Rovers | 2 | v 1 | Bemerton Hth H'quins | 112 |
| 83 | Minehead Town | 4 | v 0 | Frome Town | |
| 84 | Backwell United | 2 | v 1 | Calne Town | |
| 85 | Bideford | 1 | v 2 | Barnstaple Town | 268 |
| 86 | Bridgwater Town | 5 | v 0 | Welton Rovers | 148 |

Molesey's No 4 Lyndon Buckwell clears this Oxford City attack. However City did find the net four times in the 4-1 victory over their League rivals in the FA Cup Preliminary tie at Walton Road. Photo: Andrew Chitty

Guisborough Town's Richie Storr is felled in the box by Rossington Main's Captain Kenny Taylor. No penalty given. (FA Cup Preliminary Round). Photo: Neil Thaler

Duncan Green, Wick's goalkeeper, makes a good save to keep out St Leonards at The Firs. (FA Cup Preliminary Round). Photo: Roger Turner

# FIRST QUALIFYING ROUND

| No. | Home | | v | | Away | |
|---|---|---|---|---|---|---|
| 1 | Billingham Town | 7 | v | 3 | Denaby United | |
| 2 | Ashington | 0 | v | 2 | Louth United | 270 |
| 3 | Atherton L.R. | 0 | v | 4 | Chester-le-Street T. | 63 |
| 4 | Prescot Cables | 5 | v | 2 | Liversedge | 200 |
| 5 | Crook Town | 1 | v | 4 | Farsley Celtic | 115 |
| 6 | Eccleshill United | 2 | v | 2 | Penrith | 40 |
| R | Penrith | 6 | v | 0 | Eccleshill United | 151 |
| 7 | Brigg Town | 1 | v | 0 | Garforth Town | 205 |
| 8 | Tadcaster Albion | 1 | v | 1 | Armthorpe Welfare | 132 |
| R | Armthorpe Welfare | 0 | v | 0* | Tadcaster Albion | |

Tadcaster A. won 4-3 after penalties

| No. | Home | | v | | Away | |
|---|---|---|---|---|---|---|
| 9 | Seaham Red Star | 2 | v | 2 | Netherfield Kendal | 84 |
| R | Netherfield Kendal | 8 | v | 1 | Seaham Red Star | 124 |
| 10 | Warrington Town | 0 | v | 4 | North Ferriby Utd. | 98 |
| 11 | Bootle | 2 | v | 3 | Bradford (Park Ave.) | 109 |
| 12 | Glasshoughton Welf | 3 | v | 1 | Salford City | |

Tie awarded to Salford C. as Glasshoughton used an ineligible player

| No. | Home | | v | | Away | |
|---|---|---|---|---|---|---|
| 13 | Consett | 1 | v | 2 | Newcastle Blue Star | |
| 14 | West Auckland Tn | 5 | v | 0 | Rossington Main | 70 |
| 15 | Chadderton | 1 | v | 1 | Ryhope CA | 76 |
| R | Ryhope CA | 2 | v | 1 | Chadderton | |
| 16 | St Helens Town | 3 | v | 1 | Brandon United | 112 |
| 17 | Radclifffe Borough | 2 | v | 1 | Clitheroe | 188 |
| 18 | Evenwood Town | 4 | v | 1 | Durham City | |
| 19 | Droylsden | 2 | v | 2 | Maltby Main | 143 |
| R | Maltby Main | 0 | v | 2 | Droylsden | 80 |
| 20 | Flixton | 3 | v | 0 | Brodsworth | 96 |
| 21 | Ossett Albion | 1 | v | 1 | Workington | |
| R | Workington | 2 | v | 2* | Ossett Albion | |

Ossett Albion won 4-2 after penalties

| No. | Home | | v | | Away | |
|---|---|---|---|---|---|---|
| 22 | Ashton United | 2 | v | 1 | Tow Law Town | 212 |
| 23 | Great Harwood Tn | 3 | v | 3 | Whitley Bay | 124 |
| R | Whitley Bay | 1 | v | 2 | Gt Harwood Town | 140 |
| 24 | South Shield | 0 | v | 2 | Witton Albion | 120 |
| 25 | Morpeth Town | 2 | v | 0 | Skelmersdale United | 87 |
| 26 | Parkgate | 4 | v | 2 | Cheadle Town | |
| 27 | Ramsbottom Utd | 3 | v | 0 | Shildon | 233 |
| 28 | Trafford | 1 | v | 2 | Mossley | 242 |
| 29 | Bedlington Terriers | 11 | v | 1 | Pickering Town | 150 |
| 30 | Billingham S'thonia | 7 | v | 0 | Darwen | 106 |
| 31 | Gretna | 0 | v | 0 | Harrogate Railway | 101 |
| R | Harrogate Railway | 2 | v | 1 | Gretna | 205 |
| 32 | Whickam | 0 | v | 2 | Stocksbridge P. S. | 133 |
| 33 | Thackley | 2 | v | 0 | Bacup Borough | 105 |
| 34 | Selby Town | 6 | v | 0 | Curzon Ashton | 100 |
| 35 | Burscough | 2 | v | 0 | Jarrow Rfg Boldon CA | 177 |
| 36 | Staveley M.W. | 1 | v | 3 | Leek CSOB | 131 |
| 37 | Racing Club War'k | 1 | v | 0 | Willenhall Town | 145 |
| 38 | Boston Town | 0 | v | 5 | Eastwood Town | 86 |
| 39 | Stapenhill | 1 | v | 0 | Spalding United | 125 |
| 40 | Belper Town | 3 | v | 0 | Alfreton Town | 312 |
| 41 | Rocester | 3 | v | 0 | Holbeach United | 93 |
| 42 | Shepshed Dynamo | 4 | v | 1 | Bloxwich Town | 155 |
| 43 | Glapwell | 1 | v | 2 | Matlock Town | 150 |
| 44 | Lincoln United | 3 | v | 0 | Wednesfield | 177 |
| 45 | Halesowen Harriers | 1 | v | 2 | Nantwich Town | 100 |
| 46 | West Mids Police | 1 | v | 0 | Stratford Town | 69 |
| 47 | Blakenall | 1 | v | 0 | Hinckley United | 199 |
| 48 | Congleton Town | 5 | v | 3 | Bilston Town | 126 |
| 49 | Moor Green | 6 | v | 1 | Pelsall Villa | 150 |
| 50 | Bourne Town | 1 | v | 2 | Glossop North End | |
| 51 | Sutton Coldfield Tn | 2 | v | 1 | Kidsgrove Athletic | 167 |
| 52 | Arnold Town | 3 | v | 1 | Knypersley Victoria | 160 |
| 53 | Stamford | 2 | v | 3 | Buxton | 188 |
| 54 | Newcastle Town | 1 | v | 3 | Chasetown | 126 |
| 55 | Paget Rangers | 1 | v | 1 | Solihull Borough | 215 |
| R | Solihull Borough | 4 | v | 2 | Paget Rangers | 130 |
| 56 | Oldbury United | 1 | v | 6 | Stourbridge | 232 |
| 57 | Bridgnorth Town | 0 | v | 4 | Hucknall Town | 110 |
| 58 | Stafford Rangers | 1 | v | 1 | Bedworth United | 478 |
| R | Bedworth United | 1 | v | 2 | Stafford Rangers | 236 |
| 59 | Wroxham | 3 | v | 0 | Stewarts & Lloyds | 66 |
| 60 | Chalfont St Peter | 3 | v | 3 | St Neots Town | 100 |
| R | St Neots Town | 0 | v | 3 | Chalfont St Peter | 140 |
| 61 | Beaconsf'd SYCOB | 2 | v | 1 | Concord Rangers | 45 |
| 62 | London Colney | 1 | v | 3 | Braintree Town | 120 |
| 63 | Banbury United | 3 | v | 1 | Harpenden Town | 280 |
| 64 | Hertford Town | 0 | v | 0 | Barkingside | |
| R | Barkingside | 3 | v | 2* | Hertford Town | 75 |
| 65 | Leighton Town | 1 | v | 2 | Ford Sports Daventry | 160 |
| 66 | Canvey Island | 5 | v | 3* | Histon | 202 |
| 67 | Edgware Town | 2 | v | 3 | Grays Athletic | 156 |
| 68 | Northampton Spncr | 1 | v | 4 | Chelmsford City | 204 |
| 69 | Boweers United | 1 | v | 3 | Halstead Town | 109 |
| 70 | Burnham Rmblrs | 2 | v | 2 | Basildon United | 98 |
| R | Basildon United | 2 | v | 0 | Burnham Ramblers | 107 |
| 71 | Marlow | 1 | v | 2 | Tiptree United | 166 |
| 72 | Woodbridge Town | 4 | v | 2 | Southall | 56 |
| 73 | Buckingham Town | 0 | v | 1 | Wealdstone | |
| 74 | Bedford United | 0 | v | 3 | Royston Town | |
| 75 | Ford United | 1 | v | 1 | Barton Rovers | |
| R | Barton Rovers | 0 | v | 1 | Ford United | 103 |
| 76 | Yaxley | 2 | v | 5 | Berkhamsted Town | 135 |
| 77 | Clapton | 2 | v | 0 | Tilbury | |
| 78 | Harlow Town | 5 | v | 0 | Diss Town | 184 |
| 79 | Sudbury Town | 4 | v | 0 | Ruislip Manor | 290 |
| 80 | Barking | 3 | v | 2 | Warboys Town | |
| 81 | New,market Town | 0 | v | 0 | Gt Yarmouth Town | 162 |
| R | Gt Yarmouth Town | 2 | v | 2* | Newmarket Town | |

Newmarket T. won 4-2 after penalties

| No. | Home | | v | | Away | |
|---|---|---|---|---|---|---|
| 82 | Ware | 3 | v | 2 | Leyton Pennant | 163 |
| 83 | Ely City | 0 | v | 4 | Harwich & Parkeston | 105 |
| 84 | Brook House | 1 | v | 3 | Aveley | |
| 85 | Yeading | 1 | v | 2 | Welwyn Garden City | 80 |
| 86 | Staines Town | 1 | v | 1 | Lowestoft Town | 298 |
| R | Lowestoft Town | 2 | v | 2* | Staines Town | 211 |

Lowestoft T. won 3-1 after penalties

| No. | Home | | v | | Away | |
|---|---|---|---|---|---|---|
| 87 | Stowmarket Town | 0 | v | 1 | Romford | 206 |
| 88 | Desborough Town | 1 | v | 2 | Raunds Town | 171 |
| 89 | Tring Town | 0 | v | 1 | Wingate & Finchley | |
| 90 | Clacton Town | 1 | v | 1 | Bedford Town | 446 |
| R | Bedford Town | 2 | v | 0 | Clacton Town | 523 |
| 91 | Long Buckby | 1 | v | 2 | Witney Town | 85 |
| 92 | Sudbury Wndrs | 0 | v | 0 | Uxbridge | 102 |
| R | Uxbridge | 3 | v | 2* | Sudbury Wanderers | 129 |
| 93 | Witham Town | 1 | v | 0 | Hitchin Town | |

Top: FA Cup 1st Qualifying Round: Epsom & Ewell 2 Shoreham 1. Shoreham's keeper David Treadwell dives, but fails to stop Andy Rawlinson scoring Epsom's first goal. Photo: Peter Lirettoc

Centre: FA Cup 1st Qualifying Round: Viking Sports 1 Bashley 5. Bashley skipper Riley nods home the third goal of his side's 5-1 demolition of Viking Sports at Avenue Park. Photo: D Nicholson

Bottom: FA Cup 1st Qualifying Round: Gretna 0 Harrogate Railway 0. Harrogate keeper Robert Montgomery thwarts Gretna's Mike Hodgson. Photo: Alan Watson

| | | | | | | |
|---|---|---|---|---|---|---|
| 94 | Brackley Town | 0 | v | 2 | Wivenhoe Town | 122 |
| 95 | Baldock Town | 1 | v | 3 | Gt Wakering Rovers | 209 |
| 96 | Sheppey United | 0 | v | 0 | Lymington & N. Milton | 73 |
| R | Lym'ton & N. Milton | 1 | v | 2 | Sheppey United | 145 |
| 97 | East Preston | 6 | v | 0 | Peacehaven & Tels. | 102 |
| 98 | Thatcham Town | 3 | v | 4 | Ashford Town | 297 |
| 99 | Oxford City | 3 | v | 2 | Chertsey Town | 198 |
| 100 | Bedfont | 5 | v | 2 | Whitstable Town | |
| 101 | Fisher Athletic | 4 | v | 0 | BAT Sports | 87 |
| 102 | Corinthian Casuals | 1 | v | 2 | Worthing | 114 |
| 103 | Havant & W'looville | 1 | v | 0 | Hassocks | 260 |
| 104 | Thamesmead Tn | 3 | v | 0 | Horsham YMCA | |
| 105 | Burgess Hill Town | 1 | v | 3 | Saltdean United | 415 |
| 106 | Arundel | 0 | v | 7 | Camberley Town | 60 |
| 107 | Horsham | 2 | v | 2 | Bracknell Town | 237 |
| R | Bracknell Town | 3 | v | 4* | Horsham | 113 |
| 108 | Gosport Borough | 0 | v | 2 | Croydon | 127 |
| 109 | Slade Green | 2 | v | 4 | Hungerford Town | |
| 110 | Fleet Town | 3 | v | 2 | Dartford | 94 |
| 111 | Chipstead | 2 | v | 0 | Redhill | 86 |
| 112 | Langney Sports | 3 | v | 1 | Hailsham Town | 473 |
| 113 | Newbury AFC | 1 | v | 2 | Tooting & Mitcham U | 100 |
| 114 | Eastbourne Town | 2 | v | 2 | Tunbridge Wells | 211 |
| R | Tunbridge Wells | 2 | v | 4 | Eastbourne Town | 163 |
| 115 | Metropolitan Police | 2 | v | 2 | Canterbury City | 103 |
| R | Canterbury City | 1 | v | 1* | Metropolitan Police | 121 |

Canterbury C. won 4-3 after penalties

| | | | | | | |
|---|---|---|---|---|---|---|
| 116 | Leatherhead | 5 | v | 0 | Whitehawk | 150 |
| 117 | Viking Sports | 1 | v | 5 | Bashley | 85 |
| 118 | Sandhurst Town | 0 | v | 1 | Tonbridge Angels | 211 |
| 119 | Bognor Regis Tn | 2 | v | 4 | Newport (I. of Wight) | 388 |
| 120 | Andover | 2 | v | 5 | Deal Town | 208 |
| 121 | Epsom & Ewell | 2 | v | 1 | Shoreham | 49 |

| | | | | | | |
|---|---|---|---|---|---|---|
| 122 | Windsor & Eton | 1 | v | 1 | Chichester City | 120 |
| R | Chichester City | 0 | v | 4 | Windsor & Eton | |
| 123 | Portsmouth RN | 4 | v | 2 | Raynes Park Vale | 62 |
| 124 | Whyteleafe | 2 | v | 2 | Banstead Athletic | 118 |
| R | Banstead Athletic | 1 | v | 2 | Whyteleafe | |
| 125 | Maidenhead Utd | 2 | v | 1 | Selsey | 213 |
| 126 | Brrockenhurst | 1 | v | 7 | Dorking | 107 |
| 127 | Ash United | 7 | v | 1 | Pagham | 71 |
| 128 | Hythe United | 2 | v | 1 | Croydon Athletic | 158 |
| 129 | Portfield | 1 | v | 2 | Sittingbourne | 81 |
| 130 | Lewes | 1 | v | 2 | Erith & Belvedere | 128 |
| 131 | St. Leonards | 2 | v | 0 | Erith Town | 279 |
| 132 | Ringmer | 1 | v | 0 | Didcot Town | 99 |
| 133 | Falmouth Town | 3 | v | 1 | Wimborne Town | 257 |
| 134 | Tuffley Rovers | 0 | v | 3 | Minehead Town | |
| 135 | Mangotsfield Utd | 2 | v | 1 | Melksham Town | 212 |
| 136 | Tiverton Town | 2 | v | 0 | Weston super Mare | 678 |
| 137 | Paulton Rovers | 8 | v | 1 | Glastonbury | 70 |
| 138 | Taunton Town | 4 | v | 0 | Bournemouth | 467 |
| 139 | Barnstaple Town | 1 | v | 0 | Evesham United | 186 |
| 140 | Bridgwater Town | 1 | v | 0 | Bridport | 197 |
| 141 | Cirencester Town | 2 | v | 2 | Odd Down | 65 |
| R | Odd Down | 0 | v | 2 | Cirencester Town | 145 |
| 142 | St Blazey | 3 | v | 2 | EFC Cheltenham | 103 |
| 143 | Brislington | 3 | v | 3 | Pershore Town | 62 |
| R | Pershore Town | 4 | v | 2 | Brislington | 123 |
| 144 | Westbury United | 3 | v | 3 | Elmore | 109 |
| R | Elmore | 4 | v | 0 | Westbury United | |
| 145 | Backwell United | 10 | v | 1 | Downton | 72 |
| 146 | Clevedon Town | 1 | v | 1 | Cinderford Town | 275 |
| R | Cinderford Town | 0 | v | 0* | Clevedon Town | 256 |

Cinderford T. won 5-4 after penalties

FA Cup 1st Qualifying Round: Stamford 2 Buxton 3. Steve Botchett celebrates scoring for Buxton Town in the first half of the FA Cup tie against Stamford. Photo: Peter Barnes

# SECOND QUALIFYING ROUND

| | | | | | | | | | | |
|---|---|---|---|---|---|---|---|---|---|---|
| 1 | Selby Town | 1 | v | 2 | Frickley Athletic | 27 | Harrogate Railway | 1 | v 1 | Prescot Cables |
| | | Att: 197 | | | | | | Att: 165 | | |
| 2 | Colwyn Bay | 0 | v | 1 | Emley | R | Prescot Cables | 2 | v 0 | Harrogate Railway |
| | | Att: 454 | | | | | | Att: 220 | | |
| 3 | Whitby Town | 4 | v | 2 | Accrington Stanley | 28 | Chester-le-Street Town | 1 | v 1 | West Auckland Town |
| | | Att: 542 | | | | | | Att: 135 | | |
| 4 | Radcliffe Borough | 2 | v | 0 | Ryhope C.A. | R | West Auckland Town | 2 | v 0 | Chester-le-Street Tn |
| | | Att: 153 | | | | | | Att: 160 | | |
| 5 | Billingham Synthonia | 0 | v | 0 | Mossley | 29 | Grantham Town | 4 | v 0 | West Midlands Police |
| | | Att: 167 | | | | | | Att: 572 | | |
| R | Mossley | 1 | v | 0 | Billingham Synthonia | 30 | Cambridge City | 1 | v 1 | Glossop North End |
| | | Att: 233 | | | | | | Att: 265 | | |
| 6 | Louth United | 0 | v | 2 | Brigg Town | R | Glossop North End | 1 | v 1* | Cambridge City |
| | | Att: 163 | | | | | Glossop N.E. won 5-4 after penalties | | | |
| 7 | Ashton United | 1 | v | 1 | Altrincham | 31 | Congleton Town | 1 | v 0 | Boston United |
| | | Att: 539 | | | | | | Att: 231 | | |
| 8 | Flixton | 4 | v | 0 | Spennymoor United | 32 | Parkgate | 0 | v 3 | Sutton Coldfield Town |
| | | Att: 216 | | | | | | Att: 79 | | |
| 9 | Thackley | 1 | v | 1 | Guiseley | 33 | Racing Club Warwick | 0 | v 1 | Stourbridge |
| | | Att: 520 | | | | | | Att: 194 | | |
| R | Guiseley | 2 | v | 1 | Thackley | 34 | Arnold Town | 1 | v 1 | Matlock Town |
| | | Att: 505 | | | | | | Att: 232 | | |
| 10 | Netherfield Kendal | 1 | v | 3 | Lancaster City | R | Matlock Town | 0 | v 2 | Arnold Town |
| | | Att: 335 | | | | | | Att: 276 | | |
| 11 | Bradford Park Avenue | 1 | v | 0 | Stocksbridge Pk Stls | 35 | Belper Town | 1 | v 2 | Stafford Rangers |
| | | Att: 240 | | | | | | Att: 388 | | |
| 12 | Runcorn | 0 | v | 0 | Blyth Spartans | 36 | Blakenall | 1 | v 0 | Lincoln United |
| | | Att: 392 | | | | | | Att: 143 | | |
| R | Blyth Spartans | 2 | v | 4 | Runcorn | 37 | Shepshed Dynamo | 1 | v 2 | Gresley Rovers |
| | | Att: 586 | | | | | | Att: 428 | | |
| 13 | Hyde United | 4 | v | 0 | Gainsborough Trinity | 38 | Nantwich Town | 1 | v 1 | Raunds Town |
| | | Att: 482 | | | | | | Att: 61 | | |
| 14 | Morpeth Town | 0 | v | 0 | Ossett Albion | R | Raunds Town | 2 | v 0 | Nantwich Town |
| | | Att: 94 | | | | | | Att: 165 | | |
| R | Ossett Albion | 2 | v | 2* | Morpeth Town | 39 | Stapenhill | 0 | v 4 | Rothwell Town |
| | Att: 197 Morpeth T. won 3-2 after penalties | | | | | | | Att: 105 | | |
| 15 | Gateshead | 3 | v | 0 | Bishop Auckland | 40 | Ilkeston Town | 2 | v 0 | Moor Green |
| | | Att: 313 | | | | | | Att: 521 | | |
| 16 | Droylsden | 6 | v | 0 | St Helens Town | 41 | Atherstone United | 0 | v 0 | Nuneaton Borough |
| | | Att: 185 | | | | | | Att: 2029 | | |
| 17 | Bedlington Terriers | 1 | v | 1 | Bamber Bridge | R | Nuneaton Borough | 3 | v 0 | Atherstone United |
| | | Att: 230 | | | | | | Att: 3019 | | |
| R | Bamber Bridge | 4 | v | 4* | Bedlington Terriers | 42 | Solihull Borough | 0 | v 1 | Hucknall Town |
| | Att: 262 Bedlington T. won 4-3 after penalties | | | | | | | Att: 149 | | |
| 18 | Penrith | 1 | v | 1 | Chorley | 43 | Halesowen Town | 2 | v 2 | Eastwood Town |
| | | Att: 196 | | | | | | Att: 604 | | |
| R | Chorley | 1 | v | 0* | Penrith | R | Eastwood Town | 0 | v 1 | Halesowen Town |
| | | Att: 246 | | | | | | Att: 322 | | |
| 19 | Stalybridge Celtic | 1 | v | 2 | Worksop Town | 44 | Chasetown | 0 | v 1 | Buxton |
| | | Att: 438 | | | | | | Att: 138 | | |
| 20 | Great Harwood Town | 1 | v | 3 | Marine | 45 | Leek CSOB | 2 | v 3 | Tamworth |
| | | Att: 205 | | | | | | Att: 243 | | |
| 21 | Witton Albion | 7 | v | 2 | Glasshoughton Welf | 46 | Rocester | 0 | v 1 | Burton Albion |
| | | Att: 353 | | | | | | Att: 423 | | |
| 22 | Ramsbottom United | 3 | v | 0 | Billingham Town | 47 | Bromsgrove Rovers | 1 | v 1 | King's Lynn |
| | | Att: 275 | | | | | | Att: 708 | | |
| 23 | North Ferriby United | 5 | v | 3 | Newcastle Blue Star | R | King's Lynn | 2 | v 1* | Bromsgrove Rovers |
| | | Att: 230 | | | | | | Att: 715 | | |
| 24 | Burscough | 2 | v | 2 | Evenwood Town | 48 | Dorking | 0 | v 5 | Carshalton Athletic |
| | | Att: 213 | | | | | | Att: 241 | | |
| R | Evenwood Town | 0 | v | 6 | Burscough | 49 | Sheppey United | 0 | v 0 | Leatherhead |
| | | Att: 209 | | | | | | Att: 127 | | |
| 25 | Leigh R.M.I. | 1 | v | 0 | Winsford United | R | Leatherhead | 3 | v 1* | Sheppey United |
| | | Att: 336 | | | | | | Att: 174 | | |
| 26 | Tadcaster Albion | 1 | v | 2 | Farsley Celtic | 50 | Witney Town | 1 | v 1 | Wroxham |
| | | Att: 209 | | | | | | Att: 133 | | |
| | | | | | | R | Wroxham | 2 | v 3 | Witney Town |

Top left: FA Cup 2nd Qualifying Round: Taunton Town 3 Cinderford Town 1. Goal number three for Taunton Town as Ellis Laight (8) slides home the 75th minute goal which provided the home side with a 3-1 victory over Dr Marten's League visitors Cinderford Town. Photo: Ken Gregory

Top right: Atherstone Utd 0 Nuneaton Borough 0. Atherstone's Kim Green climbs to head on target late in the second half. Photo: Paul Barber

Centre: Stalybridge Celtic 1 Worksop Town 2. Worksop Town's Lee Hirst just beats the Stalybridge defence to head home during his side's 2-1 away victory in the FA Cup. Photo: Colin Stevens

Bottom: Graham Colbourne (Bath City) shoots against Colchester Town.

| | | | | |
|---|---|---|---|---|
| 51 | Grays Athletic | 2 v 0 | Ashford Town | |
| | | Att: 367 | | |
| 52 | Sudbury Town | 0 v 0 | Sittingbourne | |
| | | Att: 261 | | |
| R | Sittingbourne | 1 v 2 | Sudbury Town | |
| | | Att: 276 | | |
| 53 | Bedfont | 0 v 2 | Chipstead | |
| 54 | Dagenham & Redbridge | 4 v 0 | Eastbourne Town | |
| | | Att: 529 | | |
| 55 | Welwyn Garden City | 2 v 2 | Great Wakering Rvrs | |
| | | Att: 200 | | |
| R | Great Wakering Rovers | 3 v 4 | Welwyn Garden City | |
| | | Att: 230 | | |
| 56 | Ash United | 1 v 5 | Walton & Hersham | |
| | | Att: 324 | | |
| 57 | Clapton | 0 v 1 | Purfleet | |
| | | Att: 77 | | |
| 58 | Bishop's Stortford | 0 v 2 | Aldershot Town | |
| | | Att: 719 | | |
| 59 | Banbury United | 2 v 2 | Epsom & Ewell | |
| | | Att: 403 | | |
| R | Epsom & Ewell | 0 v 1 | Banbury United | |
| | | Att: 85 | | |
| 60 | Tooting & Mitcham Utd | 2 v 3 | Lowestoft Town | |
| | | Att: 177 | | |
| 61 | Wivenhoe Town | 1 v 3 | Harlow Town | |
| | | Att: 202 | | |
| 62 | Fisher Athletic | 1 v 2 | Halstead Town | |
| | | Att: 153 | | |
| 63 | Hendon | 1 v 1 | Chelmsford City | |
| | | Att: 488 | | |
| R | Chelmsford City | 2 v 3 | Hendon | |
| | | Att: 459 | | |
| 64 | Slough Town | 1 v 1 | Fleet Town | |
| | | Att: 465 | | |
| R | Fleet Town | 0 vv 2 | Slough Town | |
| | | Att: 236 | | |
| 65 | Romford | 1 v 2 | St Albans City | |
| | | Att: 427 | | |
| 66 | Ware | 1 v 1 | Braintree Town | |
| | | Att: 250 | | |
| R | Braintree Town | 4 v 1 | Ware | |
| | | Att: 283 | | |
| 67 | Boreham Wood | 4 v 0 | Saltdean United | |
| | | Att: 233 | | |
| 68 | Berkhamsted Town | 1 v 1 | Langney Sports | |
| | | Att: 156 | | |
| R | Langney Sports | 0 v 0* | Berkhamsted Town | |
| | | Att: 233  Langney Sports won 4-3 after penalties | | | |
| 69 | Tiptree United | 0 v 1 | Royston Town | |
| | | Att: 159 | | |
| 70 | Barking | 1 v 0 | Beaconsfield SYCOB | |
| | | Att: 87 | | |
| 71 | Witham Town | 5 v 2 | Hythe United | |
| | | Att: 79 | | |
| 72 | Whyteleafe | 2 v 1 | Bedford Town | |
| | | Att: 360 | | |
| 73 | Aylesbury United | 3 v 1 | Horsham | |
| | | Att: 571 | | |
| 74 | St. Leonards | 0 v 1 | Sutton United | |
| | | Att: 683 | | |
| 75 | East Preston | 0 v 2 | Worthing | |
| | | Att: 464 | | |
| 76 | Croydon | 0 v 4 | Enfield | |
| | | Att: 240 | | |
| 77 | Billericay Town | 4 v 0 | Tonbridge Angels | |
| | | Att: 503 | | |
| 78 | Basildon United | 2 v 2 | Barkingside | |
| | | Att: 88 | | |

| | | | | |
|---|---|---|---|---|
| R | Barkingside | 3 v 3* | Basildon United | |
| | | Att: 135  Basildon U. won 4-2 after penalties | | | |
| 79 | Ford Sports Daventry | 2 v 1 | Aveley | |
| | | Att: 122 | | |
| 80 | Crawley Town | 5 v 0 | Canterbury City | |
| | | Att: 906 | | |
| 81 | Wingate & Finchley | 0 v 5 | Canvey Island | |
| | | Att: 225 | | |
| 82 | Heybridge Swifts | 3 v 1 | Bashley | |
| | | Att: 164 | | |
| 83 | Uxbridge | 0 v 5 | Maidenhead United | |
| | | Att: 193 | | |
| 84 | Dulwich Hamlet | 1 v 0 | Deal Town | |
| | | Att: 307 | | |
| 85 | Bromley | 2 v 1 | Chesham United | |
| | | Att: 422 | | |
| 86 | Wealdstone | 0 v 0 | Newport (I. of Wight) | |
| | | Att: 389 | | |
| R | Newport (I. of Wight) | 3 v 2* | Wealdstone | |
| | | Att: 415 | | |
| 87 | Hungerford Town | 6 v 0 | Portsmouth R N | |
| | | Att: 116 | | |
| 88 | Havant & Waterlooville | 5 v 1 | Hampton | |
| | | Att: 310 | | |
| 89 | Harwich & Parkeston | 0 v 2 | Chalfont St. Peter | |
| | | Att: 91 | | |
| 90 | Erith & Belvedere | 0 v 1 | Windsor & Eton | |
| | | Att: 118 | | |
| 91 | Ford United | 1 v 1 | Woodbridge Town | |
| R | Woodbridge Town | 1 v 2 | Ford United | |
| | | Att: 193 | | |
| 92 | Harrow Borough | 3 v 0 | Thamesmead Town | |
| | | Att: 202 | | |
| 93 | Gravesend & Northfleet | 3 v 1 | Oxford City | |
| | | Att: 379 | | |
| 94 | Newmarket Town | 1 v 1 | Hastings Town | |
| | | Att: 320 | | |
| R | Hastings Town | 2 v 1* | Newmarket Town | |
| | | Att: 538 | | |
| 95 | Camberley Town | 2 v 1 | Ringmer | |
| | | Att: 127 | | |
| 96 | Bath City | 3 v 1 | Cirencester Town | |
| | | Att: 626 | | |
| 97 | Dorchester Town | 0 v 3 | Salisbury City | |
| | | Att: 616 | | |
| 98 | Mangotsfield United | 0 v 1 | Worcester City | |
| | | Att: 344 | | |
| 99 | Taunton Town | 3 v 1 | Cinderford Town | |
| | | Att: 462 | | |
| 100 | Pershore Town | 1 v 3 | St. Blazey | |
| | | Att: 183 | | |
| 101 | Minehead Town | 0 v 0 | Bridgwater Town | |
| | | Att: | | |
| R | Bridgwater Town | 0 v 1 | Minehead Town | |
| | | Att: 403 | | |
| 102 | Elmore | 0 v 1 | Barnstaple Town | |
| | | Att: 178 | | |
| 103 | Backwell United | 1 v 1 | Basingstoke Town | |
| | | Att: 230 | | |
| R | Basingstoke Town | 1 v 0 | Backwell United | |
| | | Att: 547 | | |
| 104 | Falmouth Town | 1 v 0 | Tiverton Town | |
| | | Att: 833 | | |
| 105 | Merthyr Tydfil | 0 v 2 | Weymouth | |
| 106 | Gloucester City | 2 v 1 | Paulton Rovers | |
| | | Att: 507 | | |

Top: Droylsden 2 Northwich Victoria 0. Northwich Vic's keeper Dean Greygoose is at full stretch to clear a Droylsden corner. Home side Droylsden shocked their Conference opponents by winning 2-0.
Photo: Colin Stevens

Centre: Paul Adamson (West Auckland) sends another header goalward, under pressure from Dave Robinson (Kings Lynn).
Photo: Keith Clayton

Bottom: Whitby Town v Accrington Stanley. Whitby Town's Graham Robinson tries another acrobatic lob.
Photo: Neil Thaler

# THIRD QUALIFYING ROUND

| 1 | West Auckland Town | 2 v 0 | Hyde United |
|---|---|---|---|
| | Gorman 29, Harrison 34 | Att: 197 | |

| 2 | Mossley | 0 v 1 | Lancaster City |
|---|---|---|---|
| | | Att: 252 | Martin 42 |

| 3 | Whitby Town | 1 v 1 | Bedlington Terriers |
|---|---|---|---|
| | Hudson 48 | Att: 847 | Boon 90 |

| R | Bedlington Terriers | 1 v 1 | Whitby Town |
|---|---|---|---|
| | Middleton 54 | Att: 472 | Francis 29 |
| | Bedlington T. won 3-2 after penalties | | |

| 4 | Doncaster Rovers | 2 v 0 | Flixton |
|---|---|---|---|
| | Kirkwood 77, Hulme 86 | Att: 2048 | |

| 5 | Runcorn | 1 v 1 | North Ferriby Utd |
|---|---|---|---|
| | Nolan 63 | Att: 298 | Stead 53 |

| R | North Ferriby United | 2 v 1 | Runcorn |
|---|---|---|---|
| | Flounders 43, 57 | Att: 300 | Nolan 18 |

| 6 | Gateshead | 2 v 1 | Barrow |
|---|---|---|---|
| | Ryan 67, 89 | Att: 386 | O'Keefe 88 |

| 7 | Bradford Park Ave | 0 v 1 | Ashton United |
|---|---|---|---|
| | | Att: 317 | Elliott 39 |

| 8 | Emley | 0 v 0 | Marine |
|---|---|---|---|
| | | Att: 381 | |

| R | Marine | 1 v 4 | Emley |
|---|---|---|---|
| | Morgan 76 | Att: 219 | Lacey 35, David 40, |
| | | | Reynolds 60, Banks 68 |

| 9 | Morpeth Town | 1 v 0 | Prescot Cables |
|---|---|---|---|
| | | Att: 105 | |

| 10 | Morecambe | 4 v 2 | Farsley Celtic |
|---|---|---|---|
| | Norman 38, 79, Lyons 42 | Att: 520 | Whellens 39, Turner 44 |
| | Healy 88 | | |

| 11 | Frickley Athletic | 1 v 0 | Witton Albion |
|---|---|---|---|
| | Stratford 84 | Att: 230 | |

| 12 | Guiseley | 1 v 1 | Chorley |
|---|---|---|---|
| | Packe 11 | Att: 463 | Potts 78 (p) |

| R | Chorley | 1 v 2 | Guiseley |
|---|---|---|---|
| | McCluskie 33 | Att: 256 | Elam 49, Atkinson 83(p) |

| 13 | Droylsden | 2 v 0 | Northwich Victoria |
|---|---|---|---|
| | Ashton 11, Jones 77 (p) | Att: 635 | |

| 14 | Worksop Town | 1 v 2 | Leigh RMI |
|---|---|---|---|
| | Clark 61 | Att: 618 | Evans 70, Rostron 86 |

| 15 | Radcliffe Borough | 0 v 1 | Burscough |
|---|---|---|---|
| | | Att: 123 | Clandon 76 |

| 16 | Ramsbottom United | 0 v 5 | Southport |
|---|---|---|---|
| | | Att: 829 | Gamble 5, |
| | | | Ross 3 (23, 38, 84) |
| | | | O'Reilly 33 |

| 17 | Kidderminster H'riers | 3 v 1 | Blakenall |
|---|---|---|---|
| | Willetts 15, Deakin 80 | Att: 1141 | Rhodes 61 |
| | Hadley 85 | | |

| 18 | Halesowen Town | 1 v 2 | Gresley Rovers |
|---|---|---|---|
| | Bradley 55 | Att: 652 | Fitzpatrick 75, Pitt 87 |

| 19 | Sutton Coldfield Tn | 1 v 1 | Telford United |
|---|---|---|---|
| | Kirk 18 | Att: 442 | Huckerby 59 |

| R | Telford United | 1 v 0 | Sutton Coldfield Tn |
|---|---|---|---|
| | Huckerby 45 | Att: 590 | |

| 20 | Congleton Town | 1 v 1 | Hednesford Town |
|---|---|---|---|
| | Payne 85 | Att: 480 | Kimmins 22 |

| R | Hednesford Town | 1 v 0 | Congleton Town |
|---|---|---|---|
| | Davies 15 (p) | Att: 501 | |

| 21 | Buxton | 0 v 0 | Leek Town |
|---|---|---|---|
| | | Att: 804 | |

| R | Leek Town | 3 v 0 | Buxton |
|---|---|---|---|
| | Mike 3 (47, 48, 78) | Att: 464 | |

| 22 | Stafford Rangers | 5 v 1 | Arnold Town |
|---|---|---|---|
| | Piggott 3 (32, 37, 85) | Att: 732 | Ricketts 26 |
| | Mitchell 45, Wright 70. | | |

| 23 | Burton Albion | 2 v 1 | Nuneaton Borough |
|---|---|---|---|
| | Holmes 41, Smith 54 | Att: 1894 | Christie 5 |

| 24 | Glossop North End | 2 v 3 | Grantham Town |
|---|---|---|---|
| | Smallwood 59 | Att: 471 | Taylor 50, Speed 67 |
| | Nwadike 77(og) | | Archer 76. |

| 25 | Brigg Town | 0 v 2 | Tamworth |
|---|---|---|---|
| | | Att: 401 | Haughton 19, Yates 56 |

| 26 | Raunds Town | 2 v 2 | Rothwell Town |
|---|---|---|---|
| | York 47, Slinn 88 | Att: 241 | Marshall 12, Jowett 89 |

| R | Rothwell Town | 0 v 1* | Raunds Tn (AET) |
|---|---|---|---|
| | | Att: 300 | Slinn 120 (p) |

| 27 | Ilkeston Town | 1 v 2 | Kings Lynn |
|---|---|---|---|
| | Ball 63 | Att: 793 | Mitchell 24 |
| | | | Bishop 74 (og) |

| 28 | Hucknall Town | 0 v 0 | Stourbridge |
|---|---|---|---|
| | | Att: 410 | |

| R | Stourbridge | 3 v 0 | Hucknall Town |
|---|---|---|---|
| | Hunter 12, 70, Bennett 83 | Att: 296 | |

| 29 | Hastings Town | 0 v 3 | Yeovil Town |
|---|---|---|---|
| | | Att: 1156 | Patmore 27 |
| | | | Hannigan 45 |
| | | | Hayfield 72 (p). |

| 30 | Hereford United | 2 v 3 | Newport I.of Wight |
|---|---|---|---|
| | James 7, Williams 80 | Att: 1841 | Fearon 65, Leigh 81, |
| | | | Soares 89. |

| 31 | Crawley Town | 1 v 0 | Billericay Town |
|---|---|---|---|
| | | Att: 1321 | |

| 32 | Worcester City | 3 v 1 | Falmouth Town |
|---|---|---|---|
| | Bowen 3, Richards 22 | Att: 931 | Band 74 |
| | Griffiths 46 | | |

| 33 | Gravesend & N'fleet | 0 v 0 | Dover Athletic |
|---|---|---|---|
| | | Att: 1058 | |

| R | Dover Athletic | 3 v 2 | Gravesend & N'fleet |
|---|---|---|---|
| | Vansittart 3 (39, 43, 64) | Att: 1034 | Ballard 57 |
| | | | Jackson 85 (p) |

| 34 | Farnborough Town | 2 v 0 | Heybridge Swifts |
|---|---|---|---|
| | Bailey 45 (p), Wingfield 83 | Att: 482 | |

| 35 | Basingstoke Town | 2 v 0 | Chalfont St. Peter |
|---|---|---|---|
| | Manley (2) | Att: 587 | |

| 36 | Taunton Town | 4 v 3 | Kettering Town |
|---|---|---|---|
| | Laight 18 | Att: 1023 | Vowden 8, Wright 39, |
| | Loram 3 (50, 54, 90) | | Norman 74 (p) |

| 37 | Dulwich Hamlet | 2 v 2 | Purfleet |
|---|---|---|---|
| | Thompson 10, PGarland 88 | Att: 308 | Georgiou 19, 37. |

| R | Purfleet | 1 v 3 | Dulwich Hamlet |
|---|---|---|---|
| | Georgiou | Att: | Bartley, Thompson (2) |

| 38 | Welling United | 3 v 2 | Weymouth |
|---|---|---|---|
| | Hynes 43, 61, Linger 63 | Att: 602 | Adcock 55, Laws 82 |

| 39 | Barnstaple Town | 0 v 1 | Cheltenham Town |
|---|---|---|---|
| | | Att: 991 | Victory 39 |

| 40 | Dag. & Redbridge | 2 v 0 | Chipstead |
|---|---|---|---|
| | Cobb 60, Cole 85. | Att: 592 | |

*Top: Byron Miller (Daventry) holds off the attentions of John Ugbah (Sutton United).*
*Photo: Keith Clayton*

*Centre: Whyteleafe's Danny Rose saves well to thwart Worthing's Marc Rice.*
*Photo: Graham Cotterill*

*Bottom: Yeovil Town's Matt Hayfield beats Hasting Town's Tony Kessell from a penalty kick for Yeovil's third goal.*
*Photo: Roger Turner*

| 41 | Rushden & D'monds | 2 | v | 0 | Forest Green Rvrs |
|---|---|---|---|---|---|
| | Mison 19, Collins 31 | | Att: 2376 | | |
| 42 | Welwyn Garden C | 2 | v | 2 | Ford United |
| | | | Att: 242 | | |
| R | Ford United | 4 | v | 2 | Welwyn Garden C |
| | | | Att: 150 | | |
| 43 | Hayes | 1 | v | 0 | Bromley |
| | Hodson 82 | | Att: 629 | | |
| 44 | Maidenhead United | 2 | v | 4 | Kingstonian |
| | Banton 14, Ulasi 43 | | Att: 717 | | Leworthy 9, 40 |
| | | | | | Holligan 46, 65 |
| 45 | Royston Town | 0 | v | 2 | Boreham Wood |
| | | | Att: 239 | | Xavier, McCarthy (p) |
| 46 | Minehead Town | 1 | v | 5 | Woking |
| | Conway 89 | | Att: 1040 | | Hay 4 (30, 42, 77, 88) |
| | | | | | Payne 84 |
| 47 | Witney Town Borough | 1 | v | 2 | Stevenage |
| | Teggart 5 | | Att: 767 | | Meah 45, Love 90 |
| 48 | Gloucester City | 10 | v | 0 | Sudbury Town |
| | Bennett 21, Burns 25, 47 | | Att: 621 | | |
| | Hemmings 44, Callinan 57 | | | | |
| | Mings 3 (67, 73, 88) | | | | |
| | Kemp 72, Hoskins 76 | | | | |
| 49 | Slough Town | 3 | v | 1 | Halstead Town |
| | Pearson, Channing Hammatt | | Att: 540 | | |
| 50 | Braintree Town | 1 | v | 3 | Camberley Town |
| | Bennett | | Att: 345 | | |
| 51 | Langney Sports | 4 | v | 1 | Harrow Borough |
| | M Allen 25, Farrier 50 | | Att: 339 | | Lawford 86 |
| | Ducille 67, Creed 89 | | | | |
| 52 | Worthing | 0 | v | 2 | Whyteleafe |
| | | | Att: 375 | | Cormack 11, Elliott 40 |

| 53 | Leatherhead | 2 | v | 0 | Windsor & Eton |
|---|---|---|---|---|---|
| | Webb, Reed | | Att: 283 | | |
| 54 | Grays Athletic | 0 | v | 1 | Aldershot Town |
| | | | Att: 784 | | John (og) |
| 55 | Walton & Hersham | 2 | v | 2 | Bath City |
| | Sayer 21, Johnson 37 | | Att: 291 | | White 73, Paul 77 |
| R | Bath City | 3 | v | 0 | Walton & Hersham |
| | Bodin 33, Loydon 64 | | Att: 656 | | |
| | Paul 80 (p) | | | | |
| 56 | Aylesbury United | 0 | v | 1 | Carshalton Athletic |
| | | | Att: 809 | | Haynes |
| 57 | St Albans City | 3 | v | 0 | Basildon United |
| | Haworth 2, Gentle | | Att: 503 | | |
| 58 | Lowestoft Town | 4 | v | 2 | Canvey Island |
| | | | Att: 501 | | Reilly, Tilson |
| 59 | Banbury United | 0 | v | 4 | Enfield |
| | | | Att: 1028 | | Caldon, Darlington, Dunwell, Cooper |
| 60 | Hungerford Town | 1 | v | 1 | Salisbury |
| | Sly 50 | | Att: 386 | | Rofe 81 |
| R | Salisbury | 3 | v | 2 | Hungerford Town |
| | Sales 45, 90, Harbut 56 | | Att: 421 | | Sly 30, Toomey 57 |
| 61 | Ford Sports Daventry | 2 | v | 2 | Sutton United |
| | | | Att: 312 | | M Watson, Vines |
| R | Sutton United | 3 | v | 0 | Ford Sports Dav. |
| | Salako (2), Harlow | | Att: 441 | | |
| 62 | Havant & W'looville | 0 | v | 0 | Witham Town |
| | | | Att: 296 | | |
| R | Witham Town | 0 | v | 4 | Havant & W'looville |
| | | | Att: 180 | | |
| 63 | Harlow Town | 2 | v | 4 | Hendon |
| | | | Att: 565 | | |
| 64 | St. Blazey | 1 | v | 0 | Barking |
| | Salmon 50 | | Att: 272 | | |

*Maidenhead United defender Tim Cook heads away powerfully against Kingstonian at York Road. Photo: Eric Marsh*

*Top left: Bedlington Terriers' keeper Paul O'Connor clears under pressure from Stafford Rangers' striker Gary Piggott during their FA Cup 4th Qualifying Round tie at Marston Road. The Northern League side won 2-1.*
*Photo: Chris Elsley*

*Top right: Keith Evans of Leigh RMI finds himself closely marked by Droylsden's Ged Henningan.*
*Photo: Colin Stevens*

*Bottom: Doncaster Rovers v Guiseley. Colin Sutherland's header for Doncaster just misses the target.*
*Photo: Bill Wheatcroft*

# FOURTH QUALIFYING ROUND

| | | | |
|---|---|---|---|
| **Runcorn** | 5 v 3 | Ashton United | |
| Salt 4, 86, Warder 15 | Att: 476 | Clowes 12, Carter 54, 89p | |
| Minally 35, Ross 82 | | | |

| | | | |
|---|---|---|---|
| King's Lynn | 0 v 1 | **West Auckland T** | |
| | Att: 1314 | Adamson 58 | |

| | | | |
|---|---|---|---|
| **Tamworth** | 2 v 1 | Grantham Town | |
| Haughton 74, Shaw 85 | Att: 805 | Twynham 23 | |

| | | | |
|---|---|---|---|
| Droylsden | 1 v 2 | **Leigh RMI** | |
| Kinney 65 | Att: 842 | Matthews 13, Cryer 48 | |

| | | | |
|---|---|---|---|
| **Southport** | 4 v 0 | Stourbridge | |
| Ross 18, 38, Horner 26 | Att: 1057 | | |
| Furlong 42 | | | |

| | | | |
|---|---|---|---|
| Leek Town | 0 v 3 | **Lancaster City** | |
| | Att: 449 | Stuart 41 | |
| | | Thompson 89, 90 | |

| | | | |
|---|---|---|---|
| **Telford United** | 2 v 1 | Burscough | |
| Huckerby 30, Gray 58 | Att: 627 | | |

| | | | |
|---|---|---|---|
| **Doncaster Rovers** | 3 v 1 | Guiseley | |
| Duerden 44, 59 | Att: 2495 | Elam 70 | |
| Kirkwood 56 | | | |

| | | | |
|---|---|---|---|
| Morpeth Town | 0 v 1 | **Burton Albion** | |
| | Att: 534 | Holmes 24 | |

| | | | |
|---|---|---|---|
| Frickley Athletic | 0 v 0 | Gresley Rovers | |
| | Att: 530 | | |
| **Gresley Rovers** | 2 v 1 | Frickley Athletic | |
| Simpson 60, Stratford 70(p) | Att: 621 | Armstrong 3 | |

| | | | |
|---|---|---|---|
| Morecambe | 1 v 2 | **Hednesford Town** | |
| Lyons 34 | Att: 1010 | Davis 50, 77 (p) | |

| | | | |
|---|---|---|---|
| Emley | 1 v 1 | Gateshead | |
| Hurst 67 | Att: 723 | Heron 66 | |
| Gateshead | 0 v 2 | **Emley** | |
| | Att: 403 | Tonks 62, David 90 | |

| | | | |
|---|---|---|---|
| Stafford Rangers | 1 v 2 | **Bedlington Terriers** | |
| Piggott 4 | Att: 1046 | Middleton 5, Gibb 51 | |

| | | | |
|---|---|---|---|
| Aldershot Town | 0 v 0 | Woking | |
| | Att: 6780 | | |
| **Woking** | 2 v 1* | Aldershot Town | |
| Hay 66, Steele 100 | Att: 3867 | Abbott 29 | |

| | | | |
|---|---|---|---|
| St Albans City | 1 v 1 | Kingstonian | |
| Keen 80 | Att: 861 | Stewart 58 | |
| **Kingstonian** | 1 v 1* | St. Albans City | |
| Holligan 17 | Att: 845 | Clark 9 | |
| Kingstonian won 5-4 after penalties | | | |

| | | | |
|---|---|---|---|
| **Enfield** | 2 v 0 | Raunds Town | |
| Richardson 81, Bentley 88 | Att: 443 | | |

| | | | |
|---|---|---|---|
| Dag'ham & Redbridge | 0 v 3 | **Stevenage Borough** | |
| | Att: 763 | Samuels 6, Alford 68, | |
| | | Love 80 | |

| | | | |
|---|---|---|---|
| Havant & Waterlooville | 2 v 2 | Hayes | |
| Wakefield 18, Watts 71(og) | Att: 956 | Flynn 10, Randall 83 | |
| **Hayes** | 1 v 1 | Havant & W'looville | |
| Randall 14 | Att: 623 | Milkins 62 | |
| Hayes won 4-3 after penalties | | | |

| | | | |
|---|---|---|---|
| Lowestoft Town | 1 v 3 | **Ford United** | |
| Ellis 15 | Att: 1057 | Parish 12, Wood 24, | |
| | | Willis 56 | |

| | | | |
|---|---|---|---|
| **Hendon** | 4 v 0 | Bath City | |
| Wyatt 14, Whitmarsh 53 | Att: 357 | | |
| Herd 82, 88 | | | |

| | | | |
|---|---|---|---|
| Basingstoke Town | 2 v 2 | Dover Athletic | |
| Simpson 26, Killick 45 | Att: 1011 | Godden 68, Adams 86 | |
| Dover Athletic | 1 v 2 | **Basingstoke Town** | |
| Reina 18 | Att: 1318 | Lisk 66, Richardson 83 | |

| | | | |
|---|---|---|---|
| **Boreham Wood** | 1 v 0 | Sutton United | |
| Dixon 21 (p) | Att: 420 | | |

| | | | |
|---|---|---|---|
| **Worcester City** | 7 v 0 | Langney Sports | |
| Bowen 23, 68 | Att: 1012 | | |
| Griffiths 55, 65 | | | |
| Chenoweth 62, 82 | | | |
| Owens 85 | | | |

| | | | |
|---|---|---|---|
| **Welling United** | 3 v 1 | Whyteleafe | |
| Cooper 4, Hynes 80, 85 | Att: 421 | Anderson 74 | |

| | | | |
|---|---|---|---|
| **Kid'minster Harriers** | 2 v 1 | Gloucester City | |
| Webb P 21, Yates 87 | Att: 1690 | Webb D 64 | |

| | | | |
|---|---|---|---|
| Leatherhead | 1 v 1 | Rushden & D'monds | |
| Lunn 45 | Att: 1145 | Warburton 90 | |
| **Rushden & D'monds** | 4 v 0 | Leatherhead | |
| Collins 30, West 43 | Att: 1855 | | |
| Heggs 48, Brady 54 | | | |

| | | | |
|---|---|---|---|
| Farnborough Town | 1 v 3 | **Yeovil Town** | |
| Day 7 | Att: 1396 | Piper 40, Hayfield 51 | |
| | | Patmore 69 | |

| | | | |
|---|---|---|---|
| Carshalton Athletic | 0 v 6 | **Salisbury City** | |
| | Att: 278 | Housley 3 (17, 45, 90) | |
| | | Harbut 56, Randall 59, | |
| | | Sales 77 | |

| | | | |
|---|---|---|---|
| **Dulwich Hamlet** | 3 v 2 | Newport (I. o. W.) | |
| Bartley 43 | Att: 628 | Pegler 8, Rew 48 | |
| Thompson 50, 65 | | | |

| | | | |
|---|---|---|---|
| **Cheltenham Town** | 3 v 2 | Taunton Town | |
| Eaton 19, 71, Howells 26 | Att: 1758 | Myers 65, Fowler 70 | |

| | | | |
|---|---|---|---|
| St. Blazey | 0 v 2 | **Camberley Town** | |
| | Att: 597 | Lloyd 32, Bills T 40 | |

| | | | |
|---|---|---|---|
| Crawley Town | 0 v 0 | Slough Town | |
| | Att: 1874 | | |
| **Slough Town** | 3 v 2 | Crawley Town | |
| Deaner 39, 55 | Att: 881 | Abbey 36 | |
| Hammitts 90 | | | Ullathorne 43 |

*Top: Action from Worcester City's AXA Sponsored FA Cup first round tie with Torquay United. City's Steve Hillman challenges United's Ken Veysey.*
*Photo: Tim O'Grady*

*Centre: Doncaster Rovers' goalkeeper Andy Woods punches clear from Southend's Barry Conlon.*
*Photo: Alan Coomes*

*Bottom: Emley's Chris Hurst rises above Rotherham's Ingledon and Garner but his header goes wide.*
*Photo: Bill Wheatcroft*

# FIRST ROUND

**Bedlington Terriers** 4 v 1 Colchester United
Ditchburn 16    Att 1600    Adcock 86
Milner 22, 85p, Cross 59

**Bedlington:** O'Connor,Sokoluk, Pike, Teasdale, Ditchburn, Melrose, Cross, Bond, Gibb, Milner, Middleton. Subs: Renforth, Bowes, Cameron, Ludlow, Egan

**Dulwich Hamlet** 0 v 1 *Southport*
Att 1835    Houghton 56 (og)

**Dulwich:** Cleevely, Humphrey, Cyrus (sub Anderson, 73), Hewitt, Edwards, Garland M, (sub Gorman, 83), Griggs, McKimm, Bartley, Thompson, Houghton. Subs: Akers, Chin, Salih.
**Southport:** Stewart, Farley, Ryan, Gouck (sub Formby, 46), Guyett, Horner, Quinn (sub Thompson, 42), Butler, Ross (sub Furlong, 84), Gamble, O'Reilly. Subs: Bolland, Bagnall

**Hednesford Town** 3 v 1 Barnet
Davis 71, Kimmins 79    Att 1463    Currie 47
Carty 90

**Hednesford:** Morgan, Sedgemore, Colkin, Comyn, Brindley, Bradley, Ware, Lake, Davis (sub Hayward, 84), Carty, Kimmins. Subs: Kelly, Fitzpatrick, Jackson, Reece.

**Kingstonian** 1 v 0 **Burton Albion**
Holligan 65    Att 1505

**Kingstonian:** Farrelly, MMustafa, Luckett, Crossley, Stewart, Harris, Patterson, Pitcher, Rattray, Holligan (sub Leworthy, 90), Akuamoah. Subs: Corbett, Brown, Smith, John.
**Burton:** Goodwin, Davies, Ashby (sub Francais, 87), Marsden, Blount, Grocutt, Lyons, Stride, Holmes, Garner, Spooner. Subs: Smith M, Benton, Smith C, Webster.

**Rushden & Diamonds** 1 v 0 Shrewsbury Town
Underwood 19    Att 4121

**Rushden:** Gayle, Wooding, Bradshaw, Mison, Warburton, Heggs, McElhatton, Butterworth, West, Collins (sub Rawle, 63), Underwood. Subs: Rodwell, Brady, Hanlon, Cramman.

**Runcorn** 1 v 1 **Stevenage Borough**
McNally 85    Att 1114    Alford 58

**Runcorn:** Morris, Ward (sub Carragher, 70), Oliver (sub Callaghan, 22), Warder, Elliis, Ruffer, Salt, McNally, Rose, Nolan (sub Randles, 76), Watson. Subs: Brooks, Williams

**Stevenage:** Taylor, Harvey, Naylor, Smith, Howarth, Beevor, Reinelt, Berry, Alford, Love, Samuels. Subs: Thompson, Coll, Kean, Rogers, Gallagher

**Stevenage Borough** 2 v 0 **Runcorn**
Love 48, Alford 74    Att 3252

**Stevenage:** Taylor, Harvey, Naylor, Smith, Trott, Beevor (sub Meah 10), Reinelt (sub Thompson 83), Berry, Alford (sub Samuels 89), Love, Kean. Subs: Rogers, Gallagher

**Runcorn:** Morris, Ward, Carragher (sub Brooks 60), Warder (sub Whalley 56), Ellis, Ruffer, Salt, McNally, Rose (sub Irving 79), Nolan, Watson. Subs: Williams, Randles

**Yeovil Town** 2 v 2 **West Auckland Tn**
Patmore 39, Hannigan 90    Att 3203    Milroy 9, Adamson 35

**Yeovil:** Pennock, Piper (sub Smith B 63), Fishlock, Brown, Hannigan, Cousins, Thompson, Stott, Patmore, dale (sub Pounder 83), Hayfield (sub Franklin 83). Subs: Mountain, Pickard

**W. Auckland:** Sams, Bainbridge, Stout, Sinclair, Jackson, Fleming, Wheldon, Innes (sub Johnson 59), Milroy, Adamson (sub Gorman 82), Hornsby. Subs: Mellanby, Lowes, Cowell

**West Auckland Tn** 1 v 1 *Yeovil Town*
Milroy 61    Att 2160    Dale 74

**W Auckland:** Sams, Bainbridge, Stout, Sinclair, Jackson, Fleming, Wheldon, Johnson (sub Cowell 114), Milroy (sub Gorman 80), Adamson (sub Innes 93), Hornsby. Subs: Mellanby, Lowes.

**Yeovil:** Pennock, piper (sub Pitman 105), Fishlock, Brown, Hannigan, Cousins, Thompson, Stott, Patmore, Dale, Pounder. Subs: Smith B, Franklin, Appleton, Mountain.

*Action during Kingstonian's victory over Burton Albion in the First Round of the FA Cup. Photo: Peter Lirettoc*

Southend United   0  v  1   *Doncaster Rovers*
Att 3740   Penney 12

**Doncaster:** Woods, Linares, Ybarra, Shaw, Snodin, Warren, Nicol, Maamria, Penney, Duerden (sub Hume, 79), Kirkwood, Wright. Subs: Cauldwell, George, Jones.

Brentford   5  v  0   **Camberley Town**
Bates 30, Quinn 42   Att 4783
Folan 63, 74, Hreidarsson 66

**Camberley:** Gray, Tippins, Heath, SSills, Powell, Xibberas, Todd (sub Ross, 82), Jopling (sub Tomsett, 68), Lloyd, Sills T, Harkness (sub Garrod, 85). Subs: Mason, Wood.

**Basingstoke Town**   1  v  2   Bournemouth
Mancey 57   Att 3830   O'Neill 37, Stein 66

**Basingstoke:** Benstead, Marshall, Redwood, Richardson (sub Coombs, 79), Harris (sub Cleeve, 66), Lisk, Wilkinson, Simpson, Mancey, Killick, Hurdle. Subs: Barker, Lyttle, Huxford.

Bristol Rovers   3  v  0   **Welling United**
Roberts 3 (51,70,71)   Att 5381

**Welling:** Knight, Powell, Copley (sub Hynes, 71), Skiverton, Dolby, Linger, Allardyce, Rutherford, Brown D (sub Watts, 82), Appiah (sub Riviere, 80), Browne S. Subs: Side, Harris.

**Boreham Wood**   2  v  3   Luton Town
Nisbett 54, Xavier 81   Att 1772   Gray 33, 53, Davis 76

**Boreham Wood:** Taylor, Sanders, McCarthy, Shaw J, Nisbet, Brown (sub Daly 88), Grime, Heffer, Dixon, Samuels (sub Xavier 73), Brady (sub Ireland 67). Subs: Hatchett, Sewell.

**Cheltenham Town**   0  v  1   Lincoln City
Att 3589   Thorpe 79

**Cheltenham:** Book, Duff, Victory, Banks, Freeman, Brough, Howells (sub Knight, 83), Bloomer, Eaton (sub Milton, 83), Grayson (sub Smith, 88), Norton. Subs: Walker C, Jackson.

*Boreham Wood v Luton - FA Cup First Round. Junior Samuels in a sandwich of Kofi Nyamah and Marvin Johnson. Photo: Clive Butchins*

*Brentford v Camberley Town - FA Cup First Round. Camberley's Tim Sills looks to evade the challenge of Brentford's Hreidarsson and Bates. Photo: Francis Short*

**Mansfield Town** 2 v 1 **Hayes**
Clarke 6, Lormor 71    Att 2613   Flynn 74

**Hayes:** Meara, Goodliffe, Flynn, Watts, Bunce, Sparks (sub Catlin, 73), Metcalfe, Hall (sub Delisser, 53), Hodson (sub Boothe, 85), Randall, Wilkinson. Subs: Charles, Buglione.

**Northampton Town** 2 v 1 **Lancaster City**
Thomson 55 og    Att4545   Thomson 30
Sampdon 56

**Lancaster:** Thornley, Curwen (sub Lang, 88), Graham (sub Lavelle, 70), Udall, Baldwin, Gelling, Martin, Flannery, Diggle (sub Cheal, 83), Thomson, Parkinson. Subs: Hartley, Taylor.

**Preston North End** 3 v 0 **Ford United**
Rankine 31, Harris 53, 90    Att 10167

**Ford:** Chapman, Deveraux,Fowler, Beck, Gardner (sub Hughes, 69), Wills, Mundy (sub Bly, 72), Riley (sub Waite, 81), Wood, Parish, Lord. Subs: Murphy, Wallduck.

**Salisbury City** 0 v 2 Hull City
   Att 2573   Rioch 55, McGinty 79

**Salisbury:** Matthews, Braybrooke, Ferrett (sub Bright, 65), Rofe, Emms, Randall, Bowers, Sales, Harbut, Chalk, Housley. Subs: Thompson, Reeks, Bush, Coles.

**Telford United** 0 v 2 Cambridge United
   Att 1818   Benjamin 22, Butler 66

**Telford:** Williams, Turner M, Lyne, Fowler, Bentley, Shakespeare, Doyle, Jones, Norbury (sub Gray, 76), Huckerby, Palmer (sub Murphy, 73). Subs: Cartwright, Davies, Blytheway.

Walsall 1 v 0 **Gresley Rovers**
Roper 79    Att 4272

**Gresley:** Ford, Wardell, Kearns, Fitzpatrick (sub Fowkes 84), Carvell, Faulconer, Smith (sub Lonergan 84), Simpson, Pitt, Rowland, Orton. Subs: Sandar, Grant, Brown.

**Woking** 0 v 1 Scunthorpe United
   Att 3359   Forrester 35

**Woking:** Batty, Payne, Hollingdale, Saunders, Smith, Danzey, Girdler, Perkins (sub Bolt 59), Steele, West, Hay. Subs: Goddard, French, Flavahan, Ellis.

**Worcester City** 0 v 1 Torquay United
   Att 3023   Partridge 77

**Worcester:** Higgs, Sandeman, Burnham, Greenman, Talbot (sub Woods 87), Cotterill, Wells, Chenoweth, Bowen (sub Owen 69), Griffiths, Hillman. Subs: Wright, Jones, Watson

**Emley** 1 v 1 Rotherham United
Bambrook 14    Att 6062   Hudson 90

**Emley:** Rhodes, Nicholson (sub Wood 22), Jones, Thompson, Lacey, David, Banks, Hurst, Thorpe (sub Calcutt 68), Bambrook, Reynolds. Subs: Wilson, Tonks, Smith.

Rotherham United 3 v 1 **Emley**
Glover 28, Hurst 82    Att 5077   Bambrook 1
Garner 85

**Emley:** Rhodes, Tonks (sub Calcutt 58), Jones, Thompson, Lacey, David, Wilson, Hurst, Bambrook, Wood, Reynolds. Subs: Smith, Hutson, Thorpe, Bray.

*Salisbury City 0 Hull City 2 - FA Cup First Round. Second-half action from Raymond McEnhill St. Tiger 'keeper Steve Wilson under pressure takes the ball after a Salisbury corner and denies No 5 Roger Emms from a goalscoring chance.*    *Photo: Martin Wray*

Top: Paul Whitmarsh, Hendon, tangles with Notts County's Chris Fairclough.
Photo: Roger Turner

Centre: Leigh RMI v Fulham. Another save from keeper Fellgate.
Photo: M Sandom

Bottom: Enfield v York. Darren Annon and Grant Cooper in defensive action.
Photo: Clive Butchins

**Enfield** 2 v 2 York City
Dunwell 61, Richardson 66   Att 1634   Cresswell 16, 35

**Enfield:** Pape, Annon, Naylor, Cooper G, Terry, Jones, Penn, Bentley, Richardson, Dunwell, Cooper S (sub Deadman, 83). Subs: Protheroe, Morgan, Risley, Hall.

York City 2 v 1 **Enfield**
Jordan 18, Cresswell 45   Att 2131   Dunwell 27

**Enfield:** Pape, Annon, Protheroe, Cooper G, Terry, Jones (sub Clarke 73), Penn, Bentley, Richardson, Dunwell (sub Hall 85), Cooper S (sub Morgan 61). Subs: Risley, Deadman.

Fulham 1 v 1 **Leigh RMI**
Lehmann 36   Att 7965   Whealing 20

**Leigh RMI:** Felgate, Locke, Whealing, Hill, Precott, Turpin, Monk (sub Cryer 81), Ridings, Matthews, Evans, Smythe. Subs: Wallace, James, Rostron, Senior.

**Leigh RMI** 0 v 2 Fulham
Att 7125   Peschisolido 32p, 40

**Leigh RMI:** Felgate, Locke, Whealing, Hill, Prescott, Turpin, Monk, Ridings, Matthews (sub Cryer 75), Evans, Smythe. Subs: James, Carr, Rostron, Senior.

Macclesfield Town 2 v 2 **Slough Town**
Tomlinson 72, Sodje 87   Att 2014   Pierson 24, Deaner 28

**Slough:** Wilkerson, Channing, Hughes (sub Hardyman, 58), Roberts, Pierson, Thorp (sub Bicknell, 73), Denton, Kemp, Deaner (sub Holzman, 80), Hamment, Browne. Subs: Line, Francis.

**Slough Town** 1 v 1 Macclesfield Town

AET Macclesfield won 9-8 after penalties

**Slough:** Wilkerson, Channing (sub Holzman 76), Hughes, Roberts (sub Hardyman 56), Pierson, Thorp, Denton, Kemp (sub Line 100), Deaner, Hamment, Browne. Subs: Francis, Bicknell.

Plymouth Argyle 0 v 0 **Kidderminster Hr's**
Att 4284

**Kidderminster:** Brock, Hinton, Hines, Weir (sub Wolsey, 46), Smith, Yates, Webb, Taylor, Hadley, Arnold, Willetts. Subs: Beard, Bignall, Davies, Acton.

**Kidderminster Hrs** 0 v 0 Plymouth Argyle
Att 4471
AET Plymouth won 5-4 after penalties

**Kidderminster:** Brock, Hinton, Hines, Webb, Smith, Yates, Cunnington (sub Willetts 71), Hadley (sub Deakin 91), May, Arnold, Taylor. Subs: Bignall, Wolsey, Acton.

**Hendon** 0 v 0 Notts County
Att 1627

**Hendon:** McCann, Howard, Clarke, Daly, Bateman, Cox, Pye (sub Heard 81), Hyatt, Whitmarsh (sub Maran 90), Fitzgerald, Lewis. Subs: Kelly T, Gill, Warmington.

Notts County 3 v 0 **Hendon**
Owers 60, Jones 75, 82   Att 2230

**Hendon:** McCann, Howard, Clarke, Daly, Bateman, Cox (sub Heard 78), Pye (sub Warmington), Hyatt, Whitmarsh (sub Kelly T 78), Fitzgerald, Lewis. Subs: Gill, Brady.

Tamworth 2 v 2 Exeter City
Shaw 28, Smith 52   Att 2485   Gittens 15
Richardson 90

**Tamworth:** McNamara, Warner, Shaw, Steele, Batchelor, Howard, Crawford, Walker, Smith, Dixon, Haughton. Subs: Wilson, Hatton, Mitchell, Price, Wood.

Exeter City 4 v 1 **Tamworth**
Rowe 15 og, Flack 52   Att 3152   Smith 75
Rowbotham 31, 45

**Tamworth:** Rowe, Warner, Shaw, Steele, Batchelor, Howard, Crawford, Walker (sub Hatton 69), Smith, Dixon (sub Yates 45), Haughton. Subs: McNamara, Wood, Roddock

*Tamworth (Dr Martens Premier Division) v Exeter City (Nationwide Division Three). Tamworth's Gary Smith (No 9) is about to score as Exeter keeper Ashley Bayes stops a shot but can only paray the ball into the path of Gary Smith who only had to tap it in to put Tamworth 2-1 up. Photo: Paul Barber*

# SECOND ROUND

### Mansfield Town  1  v  2  *Southport*
Lormor 72    Att 3210    Gamble 25p, Ross 46.

**Southport:** Stewart, Farley, Ryan, Butler (sub Futcher 24), Guyett, Horner, Thompson (sub Furlong 75), Gouck (sub Bolland 45), Rosss, Gamble, Formby.

### *Yeovil Town*  2  v  0  Northampton Town
Thompson 14, Patmore 82    Att 5218

**Yeovil:** Pennock, Piper, Fishlock, Brown, Hannigan, Cousins, Thompson, Stott, Patmore, Dale (sub B Smith 90), Pitman (sub Pounder 71). Sub: Mountain

### Doncaster Rovers  0  v  0  **Rushden & Diamonds**
Att 5396

**Doncaster:** Woods, Shaw, Warren, I Snodin (sub Beckett 80), Nicol, Sutherland, Penney, Goodwin, Doerden (sub Hume 72), Kirkwood, Wright. Sub: Maamria.
**Rushden:** Gayle, Wooding, Bradshaw, Mison, Warburton, Heggs, McElhatton, Butterworth, West, Archer, Underwood. Subs: Foster, Hanlon, Hamsher.

### *Rushden & Dia'monds*  4  v  2  **Doncaster Rovers**
Hamsher 6p, West 63, 84    Att 5564    Sutherland 17,
Brady 68                                         Maamria 89

**Rushden:** Gayle, Wooding, Bradshaw, Hamsher, Warburton, Heggs, Brady, Butterworth, West, Collins (sub Mison 76), Underwood.
Subs: Foster, Wilson, Rodwell.
**Doncaster:** Woods, Warren, Maxfield, Nicol, Penney, Sutherland (sub George 87), Beckett (sub Duerden 71), Goodwin, Hume, Kirkwood (sub Maamria 85), Wright. Subs: Cauldwell, Jones.

### Kingstonian  0  v  0  Leyton Orient
Att 3495

**Kingstonian:** Farrelly, Mustafa, Luckett, Crossley, Stewart, Harris, Patterson, Pitcher, Rattray, Leworthy (sub Holligan 61), Akuamoah. Subs: Corbett, Smith, Brown, John.

### Leyton Orient  2  v  1  **Kingstonian**
Waldchaerts 12, Simba 48    Attt 3264    Holligan 75

**Kingstonian:** Farrelly, Mustafa, Luckett, Crossley, Stewart (sub Holligan 57), Harris, Patterson, Pitcher, Rattray (sub Corbett 46), Leworthy (sub John 88), Akuamoah. Subs: Smith, Brown.

### Scunthorpe United  2  v  0  **Bedlington Terriers**
Eyre 54p, Forrester 81.    Att 4719

**Bedlington:** O'Connor, Sokoluk, Pike, Teasdale, Ditchburn, Melrose, Cross (sub Ludlow 82), Bond (sub Boon 57), Gibb, Milner, Middleton (sub Renforth).

### Cardiff City  3  v  1  **Hednesford Town**
Middleton 45, Fowler 59    Att 5638    Carty 87.
Williams 82

**Hednesford:** Morgan, Sedgemore, Colkin, Comyn, Brindley, Bradley, Ware, Beeston (sub Blades 64), Davis (sub Kelly 69), Carty, Kimmins (sub Hayward 63).

### Lincoln City  4  v  1  **Stevenage Boro**
Battersby 22, Alcide 49    Att 4375    Alford 90
Finnigan 66, Holmes 69

**Stevenage:** Taylor, Harvey, Naylor, Smith, Howarth, Beevor (sub Kean 72), Plummer, Berry, Alford, Love, Reineult (sub Samuelas 46). Sub: Trott

*Matt Crossley (No 4) hits the post v Leyton Orient in the FA Cup Second Round. Photo: Eric Marsh*

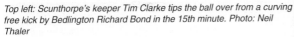

*Top left: Scunthorpe's keeper Tim Clarke tips the ball over from a curving free kick by Bedlington Richard Bond in the 15th minute. Photo: Neil Thaler*

*Top right: Tommy Wright (Doncaster), Michael McElhatton and Carl Heggs (Yellow/Black). Photo: Peter Barnes*

*Bottom left: FA Cup Second Round: Yeovil Town v Northampton Town. Getting in an aerial assault against his former club is Yeovil's striker, Warren Patmore, who scored the second goal in a 2-0 victory. Moving in support is Steve Thompson, scorer of the "Glovers" opening goal. Photo: Ken Gregory*

*Bottom right: Carl Dale - Yeovil's goalscoring hero. Photo: Ken Gregory*

# THIRD ROUND

**Rushden & Diamonds** 0 v 0 Leeds United
Att: 6,431

**Rushden:** Feuer, Wooding, Bradshaw, Hamsher, Rodwell, Heggs, McElhatton, Butterworth, Foster, De Souza, Underwood. Subs: Brady, Corry, Whyte, Wilson, Cooper.

Leeds United 3 v 1 **Rushden & Diamonds**
Smith 22, 51  Att: 39,159  Heggs 11
Hasselbank 67

**Rushden:** Feuer, Wooding, Bradshaw, Hamsher (sub Brady 76), Rodwell, Heggs, McElhatton, Butterworth, Foster (sub West 46), De Souza (sub Whyte 88), Underwood. Subs: Corry, Cooper.

**Southport** 0 v 2 Leyton Orient
Att: 4,950  Smith 60p, Griffiths 71

**Southport:** Bagnall, Farley, Ryan, Bolland, Guyett, Horner, Quinn (sub Newman 75), Futcher (sub Furlong 72), Gouck, Gamble, Thompson. Subs: Formby, Farrell, Taylor.

Cardiff City  1 v 1 **Yeovil Town**
Roberts 84  Att 12,561 Dale 54

**Yeovil:** Pennock, Piper, Pounder (sub Pitman 75), Brown, Hayfield, Cousins, Thompson, Stott, Patmore, Dale (suub Appleton 80), Smith. Subs: Tomkin, Franklin, Mountain.

**Yeovil Town** 1 v 2 Cardiff City
Hayfield 86  Att: 8,081 Eckhardt 43, Nugent 91.

**Yeovil:** Pennock, Piper (sub Hayfield 69), Fishlock, Brown, Hannigan, Cousins, Thompson, Stott, Patmore (sub Pickard 45), Dale (sub Pounder 78), Smith B. Subs: Mountain, Pitman.

*Top: Steve Stott leads out his battling Yeovil team at the start of what was to be a full bloodied, exciting 3rd Round tie. Almost as a prelude heavy thunder and lightning greeted the teams. Photo: Ken Gregory*

*Bottom: Leeds defend in numbers to prevent Diamonds scoring in the FA Cup Third Round. Photo: Peter Barnes*

## FA CUP THIRD ROUND: SOUTHPORT 0   LEYTON ORIENT 2

Brass band; Sandy, the Lion mascot, leading the massed singing of the song celebrating the Sandgrounders' Trophy Final visit to Wembley last season;near capacity and, by some way, their largest crowd of the season; police horses and road closed signs; yes, Haig Avenue, Southport, had all the trappings of F.A. Cup success. Even the season ticket holders grumbled in  a good hearted way about having to vacate their usual seats so that the representatives of such stalwart supporters of the non-League scene as the 'Sun' and the 'News of the World' could be accommodated. Unfortunately the Sandgrounders were not able to enjoy further luck on the field. Twice in the first half Orient's Matthew Joseph headed off his own line, the second time as Southport were giving the Londoners' defence a real battering, with three corners in quick succession. Stuart Quinn and David Gamble had also gone close with forceful shots.

Again, at the opening of the second half, luck was not with the Conference team, at least not all the way. To start with it was as visiting goalkeeper, Chris Mackenzie's, clearance ricocheted off one of his defenders to give Gamble a clear chance from 20 yards. Gamble went for power, as if he wanted to take the net with his shot. Instead his attempt went high and wide and, with it, Southport's last chance of making the 4th Round.

For an hour they had dominated their Third division opponents although obviously missing the strike power of Brian Ross. Scott Guyet pushed forward whenever possible and, despite being well into the veteran stage, player manager Paul Futcher was able to operate effectively in midfield as Southport forced the opposition back. Then, on the hour, fate intervened in the shape of referee Brandwood. O's Carl Griffiths fell theatrically in the area as Phil Horner took the ball, and Mr Brandwood fell for it too, pointing to the penalty spot, much to the delight of Griffiths' team mates who celebrated with appropriately 'luvvy' cuddles. Up stepped serious minded skipper Dean Smith to smash the ball to John Bagnall's right. And that was really it.

Twelve minutes later Junior McDougald left Griffiths with Bagnall to beat. Having spurned a similar chance in the opening half, when he took too much time and allowed Bagnall to dive smartly and push away, Griffiths did not miss a second time. Still in panto mode however, Griffiths jumped the barrier to be engulfed by his own supporters, emerging to feign surprise when the referee rightly booked him. Now Orient threatened to overwhelm the Yellows as Martin Ling and Tony Richards hit the same spot with consecutive shots but Southport dug in and deservedly kept their self respect.

A series of meaningless and time wasting substitutions then whittled away the time as Southport pushed forward. In the dying seconds Dave Thompson swivelled sharply on the six yard line and nudged the ball goalward only to see Mackenzie plunge to his left and palm away even the chance of a consolation. Southport were beaten but far from disgraced.
Arthur Evans

FA Cup reports were first published in Team Talk Magazine

## FA CUP THIRD ROUND: RUSHDEN & DIAMONDS 0   LEEDS UNITED 0

Wasn't it a pleasure to read that prices for entry had not been increased at Nene Park for the visit of Premier Division Leeds United.

Equally pleasing was the lack of conjecture regarding the transfer of the fixture to Elland Road and the complete harmony in which the two clubs undertook pre-match administration and publicity.

Indeed as you can see from this photo, David O'Leary sat by the Rushden & Diamonds Chairman Max Griggs when on a spying mission!

The game itself could, in hindsight, have provided the first Premier scalp for a Conference club as Leeds United were left with only one very young centre half fit to play (and he was to be sent off) and an injury problem that meant Diamonds could not have met their famous visitors at a better time.

Adrian Foster, a striker who had started the season brilliantly had recovered from a recent injury and had to take responsi-bility as the main striker because Colin West (suspended) and Darren Collins (injured) were unavailable.

Little was he to realise that his second minute header that hit the post was to have been so impor-tant, although he did have an even better chance to win the game with just three minutes to go when another unchallenged header sailed over the bar. Surely Leeds wouldn't have come back from a goal at that stage,but such was the spirit between the two clubs on and off the field that you almost felt both sides wanted a draw so they could enjoy Elland Road together in the replay!

Both sides certainly competed well and had their chances for vic-tory. Giant American goalkeeper Ian Feuer was magnificent and so was the stadium, the atmosphere, the colour and the whole occa-sion!

*Right: Rushden & Diamonds v Leeds United. Jimmy Floyd Hasselbank lays the ball off with John Hamsher close by.*
*Photo: Peter Barnes*

## FA CUP THIRD ROUND REPLAY: LEEDS UTD 3   RUSHDEN & DIAMONDS 1

When the first tie at Nene Park was shown over and over again on television Rushden & Diamonds supporters must have become more and more convinced they should have been the first non-League club to have beaten a Premier League club in the F.A. Cup.

A draw was such a good result that the fact that ace marksman Adrian Foster really should have won the game with a clear headed chance from five yards in the last three minutes, didn't really matter.

A trip to Elland Road was great and how the football world sat up when the score flashed up on the Sky TV screen - Leeds United 0 Rushden & Diamonds 1 after 11 minutes.

Miguel de Souza who was something of a non-League journeyman after initial trials at Charlton Athletic and Bristol City and before a lively Football League career mainly inspired by Barry Fry, used his undoubted pace down the right and fired a low cross into a crowded Leeds goal mouth.

Carl Heggs' first shot hit an upright, but eventually it came back to him and he scored through a mass of bodies.

John Hamsher had already gone close with a long range drive so Diamonds deserved their lead and Leeds had to use all their professionalism to wrestle back the initiative.

By the interval they were on level terms thanks to teenager Alan Smith. His excellent strike being tucked just inside a post from a Hasselbaink flick.

Diamonds never gave up and they made Leeds battle all the way. Harry Kewell missed a number of chances and Woodgate just failed with a header. De Souza nearly put in his own goal and Lee Bowyer shot over.

In the second half there was no real doubt that the Premier club would keep on top and perhaps their extra class threatened to build a larger score.

Hasselbaink could have scored twice before providing Smith with his second after 51 minutes and then Kewell's right wing run pulled the visitors defence out of position and the big Dutchman diverted the cross to Smith.

Heggs had a chance in a break away to pull one back for the Conference side, but it was not to be and Hasselbaink wrapped the game up with a low shot under Feuer's body.

Before the end the 'keeper did save well from Bowyer and although well defeated on the night Rushden & Diamonds had proved capable of conducting themselves quite superbly on and off the field while bringing great credit to their club, the Conference and indeed pyramid football in general.

*Diamonds' players applaud their loyal fans at Elland Road, Leeds after their FA Cup Third Round Replay away.*
*Photo: Peter Barnes*

## FA CUP THIRD ROUND: CARDIFF CITY 1   YEOVIL TOWN 1

Do the older readers amongst you sometimes look back at past F.A. Cup ties and wonder whether the modern competition still has that special spirit? Well, a capacity crowd and a good playing surface at Ninian Park, in torrential rain with fervent vocal support from both clubs, created a very special atmosphere that managed to lift everyone present in the Third Round of the competition.

Cardiff City were enjoying a fine run of form and the return of one of their favourite old boys, Carl Dale brought the best out of the home supporters who gave him a standing ovation. Yeovil on an unbeaten run of seven F.A. cup ties against Football League opposition knew the first twenty minutes would be vital and somehow they kept their goal intact long enough to settle down, and gradually you could see the confidence filtering through, especially in mid field where the cup experience of Steve Thompson, the battling of Steve Stott and cheeky skills of Ben Smith began to break up the Bluebirds rhythm.

The last ten minutes of each half is dangerous when part-timers face full-time professionals, but the first danger zone was successfully negotiated and at half time everyone was made well aware that there was nothing to fear. Another burst from the Bluebirds after the break was well held and then came Yeovil's best period. You could almost sense the home supporters confidence waning as the visitors now seemed to be taking control. Yeovil's Smith looked a class act, as he appeared all over the pitch to orchestrate the flow of play which was now testing the home defence.

A corner was won on the right and as Steve Thompson placed the ball, a bright red flare lit up the Yeovil supporters behind the goal. The majestic Warren Patmore met the cross firmly with his head but the block rebounded to Carl Dale and flashed off him, low, into the corner of the Cardiff net. What emotion for the ex-City hero, the crowd behind the goal, the Yeovil players and indeed for the home supporters who now increased the volume of their support, just as their players magnificently increased their work rate.

The Ninian Park roar was now non stop as a blue wave washed over the heroic Yeovil rear guard, but a break away was always a possibility and it was Ben Smith who featured three times in a move that swept the length of the pitch and left David Piper with the chance to shoot past a stranded Jon Hallworth, only to see Mark Delaney clear desperately off the line.

Having given Cardiff 25 minutes to reply, the odds were definitely on an equalizer and it came with six minutes to go from another corner. This time four players rose together and Kevin Nugent timed his jump to perfection. However the looping header would probably have been cleared if substitute Christian Roberts hadn't attempted a deflection. Goalkeeper Tony Pennock hesitated for the change of direction, substitute Jamie Pitman strayed from his post for the same reason, and the header passed Roberts by, didn't change direction and crept in off the far post. Sad for the underdog, but to be truthful it was a goal which in overall play was deserved by City.

The Cardiff supporters who had given Carl Dale an excellent round of applause when he was substituted, despite his the vital goal, were rewarded for their sportsmanship and there were still vital minutes in which a winner could be grabbed. To give Yeovil their due, they appeared just as likely to score as Cardiff,although the nearest anyone came was when Kevan Brown spectacularly cleared another Nugent header away from under the bar. Yeovil substitute Arthur Appleton hit the side netting and when the final whistle came the Glovers were about to take a second successive corner – so they finished on top!

Everyone had enjoyed a truly magnificent F.A. Cup tie which lived up to the best traditions of the famous competition. Yeovil had extended their run to eight unbeaten games against Football League opposition and they were, in fact,disappointed not to have won. But they will have Al James Hannigan and Murray Fishlock back for the replay which should be another wonderful chapter in the Yeovil F.A. Cup saga. TW

*Yeovil Town's Tony Pounder gets the ball away during the exciting tie at Ninian Park which ended all square at 1-1.*          *Photo: Ken Gregory*

## FA CUP THIRD ROUND REPLAY: YEOVIL TOWN 1   CARDIFF CITY 2 a.e.t.

There is no sport that can be so cruel yet so uplifting, so exciting yet so completely deflating! Over 8,000 at Huish Park where Yeovil Town, probably England's most famous club outside the full time ninety-two, and the most successful giant killer,could sense another great F.A. cup occasion. The atmosphere was special - happy, tense but ready to explode into a proud roar as Yeovil were taking their rightful place on the F.A. Cup stage.

Full marks to Frank Burrows' Cardiff City however, as it wasn't easy for them and they settled well and after a quality initial exchange they settled down to look the most dangerous. But as in the first tie the initial storm was weathered and it was Yeovil's classy mid field youngster Ben Smith who waltzed his way into a shooting position, chipped the advancing Jon Hallworth, only to scrape the crossbar.

Neither side really looked likely to break through, but as at Cardiff the League club did look more dangerous from set pieces and perhaps it was no surprise that Kevin Nugent won Richard Carpenter's left wing corner and his header was turned in by centre half Jeff Eckhardt just before half time. The big defender probably enjoyed the moment especially as he had been captain of Fulham when Yeovil had beaten them 1-0 five years ago.

The second half saw Yeovil taking care not to commit too many players going forward for an equaliser. But gradually they did get on top with the back three of Kevan Brown, Rob Cousins and Al-James Hannigan superb and the experience of Steve Stott and Steve Thompson especially important in mid field. Probably the vital loss however was Warren Patmore, off injured at half time,the attacking balance was lost.

Throughout the game Cardiff did carve out regular chances, but on at least five occasions Welsh goalkeeper Tony Pennock spread himself bravely to keep Yeovil in the game. He was an outstanding hero, so when Matt Hayfield picked up a loose ball on the edge of the box and crashed in an equaliser with just five minutes from time it was Pennock more than anyone who had kept his side in the game.

Before the final whistle the whole ground thought Steve Stott had won the tie but somehow Hallworth deflected his shot for a corner and we were into extra time. BBC Five Live were apparently 'very excited' the Yeovil crowd prepared to roar the boys home, Cardiff heads were dropping, Yeovil heads were up, but how the game can 'kick you in the teeth'.

Within a minute Pennock safely fell on a through ball, correctly looked behind him, rolled the ball forward and somehow it didn't spin back and it rolled too far from him. The ever alert striker Nugent pounced like a mongoose on a snake and before the 'keeper realised his error he had blocked his desperate clearance and cushioned the ball just at the right angle back into the net. You could have heard a pin drop - except for a very relieved chorus of 'You're not singing any more' from the distant 'away' end! The game collapsed, Cardiff did all they had to do, Yeovil looked and felt very sad and we all wanted to put an arm round Tony Pennock who looked suicidal. That as they say is football!

Congratulations to Cardiff City who had looked a very good footballing side and had contributed to two quite brilliant F.A. Cup ties. Yeovil will be hoping they get promotion and if Tony Pennock helps his club to Wembley perhaps the season can still be a happy memory.

Another F.A. Cup campaign had come to an end for the non-League clubs, and I'm sure new sponsors AXA will have been proud of them. Technically Yeovil Town had lasted longest as they had played extra time in a Third Round Replay and now they have sampled F.A. Cup thrills again, next season can't come quick enough!          TW

# AXA F.A. CUP SPECIAL AWARDS

## REGIONAL AWARDS

### PRELIMINARY ROUND
**North East** Rossington Main
*(Northern Counties East)*
**North West** Trafford
*(Unibond Division One)*
**Midlands** Bedford Town
*(Ryman Division Two)*
**South East** Camberley Town
*(Ryman Div Three)*
**South West** Elmore
*(Screwfix Direct Western Division One)*

### FIRST QUALIFYING ROUND
**North East** Bedlington Terriers
*(Arnott Insurance Northern League)*
**North West** Mossley
*(North West Counties Division One)*
**Midlands** Stapenhill
*(Interlink Midland Football Alliance)*
**South East** Deal Town
*(Winstonlead Kent Division One)*
**South West** Backwell United
*(Screwfix Direct Western Premier Div)*

### SECOND QUALIFYING ROUND
**North East** Bedlington Terriers
*(Arnott Insurance Northern League)*
**North West** Glossop N.E.
*(North West Counties Division One)*

### SECOND QUALIFYING ROUND cont.
**Midlands** Arnold Town
*(Northern Counties East)*
**South West** Falmouth Town
*(Jewson South West)*

### THIRD QUALIFYING ROUND
**North East** North Ferriby United
*(Northern Counties East)*
**North West** Droylsden
*(Unibond Division One)*
**Midlands** Stafford Rangers
*(Dr Martens Midland Division)*
**South East** Newport (IoW)
*(Dr Martens)*
**South West** Taunton Town
*(Screwfix Direct Western Premier Div)*

### FOURTH QUALIFYING ROUND
West Auckland Town
*(Arnott Insurance Northern League)*
Lancaster City
*(Unibond Premier)*
Hednesford Town
*(Nationwide Conference)*
Hendon
*(Ryman Premier)*
Basingstoke Town
*(Ryman Premier)*

## LAST MAN IN AWARD

Bedlington Terriers were the last remaining team to have started the competition in the Preliminary Round. The team was presented with the AXA Award and a cheque for £10,000 from the F.A.

## GIANT KILLER OF THE ROUND

### FIRST ROUND
Bedlington Terriers received the Award and a cheque for £500 for their 4-1 victory over Colchester United
### SECOND ROUND
Southport United received the Award and a cheque for £500 for their 2-1 away win at Mansfield Town
### THIRD ROUND
Swansea City received the Award and a cheque for £500 for their 1-0 win against West Ham United
### FOURTH ROUND
Fulham received the Award and a cheque for £500 for their 2-0 away win over Aston Villa

## AWARDS PRESENTED AT THE TEAM TALK AWARDS NIGHT

### FASTEST GOAL
George Georgiou of Purfleet won the Award and a cheque for £500 for his 17 second strike against Dulwich in the Third Qualifying Round
### NON-LEAGUE LEADING SCORER
Phil Dean, Welwyn Garden City, scored a total of nine. He was presented with an Award and a cheque for £500
### AXA F.A. CUP NON-LEAGUE TEAM OF THE SEASON
Ford United, minnows of minnows, made it all the way from the Preliminary Round to play Preston North End in the First Round Proper.

## AXA F.A. CUP TOP INDIIVIDUAL GOALSCORERS

| Name | Club | | | | | | Total |
|---|---|---|---|---|---|---|---|
| Phil Dean | Welwyn Garden City | 5 | 1 | 1 | 1 | 1 | = 9 |
| John Milner | Bedlington Terriers | 5 | 1 | 2 | | | = 8 |
| Jody Banam | Flixton | 2 | 1 | 4 | | | = 7 |
| Stuart White | Dorking | 2 | 4 | | | | = 6 |
| Mark Loram | Taunton Town | 3 | 3 | | | | = 6 |
| Dean Gibb | Bedlington Terrier | 3 | 1 | 2 | | | = 6 |
| Brian Ross | Southport | 3 | 2 | 1 | | | = 6 |
| Lee Bajada | Barkingside | 1 | 1 | 3 | | | = 5 |
| Jeff Wood | Ford United | 1 | 1 | 2 | 1 | | = 5 |
| Darren Hay | Woking | 4 | 1 | | | | = 5 |

## HAT TRICK SCORERS

### PRELIMINARY ROUND

| | Name | Club |
|---|---|---|
| 5 | Phil Dean | Welwyn Garden City |
| 3 | Tim Hamley | Fisher Athletic |
| | Wayne Joscelyne | Bowers United |
| | Steve Tilson | Canvey Island |
| | Chris Yeardley | Southall |

### FIRST QUALIFYING ROUND

| | Name | Club |
|---|---|---|
| 5 | John Milner | Bedlington Terriers |
| 4 | Graham Cheeseman | Backwell United |
| | Stuart White | Dorking |
| | Chris Jack | East Preston |
| | Lee Wasdon | Parkgate |
| 3 | Nick Cross | Solihull Borough |
| | Peter Cumiskey | Prescot Cables |
| | Dean Gibb | Bedlington Terriers |
| | Gary Brockwell | Eastbourne Town |
| | Martin Boyle | Poulton Rovers |
| | Steve Botchett | Buxton |
| | Nick Gray | Chester le Street |
| | Matthew Lea | Penrith |
| | Mark Loram | Taunton Town |
| | Trevor McCoy | Leatherhead |

### FIRST QUALIFYING ROUND cont.

| Name | Club |
|---|---|
| Andy Perrott | Paulton Rovers |
| Andy Watts | Backwell United |
| Tony Wood | Billingham Synthonia |
| Andy Sargent | Elmore |

### SECOND QUALIFYING ROUND

| | Name | Club |
|---|---|---|
| 4 | Jody Banin | Flixton |
| 3 | Eddie Bishop | Witton Albion |
| | Nick Kirk | Sutton Coldfield Town |
| | Richard Jowett | Rothwell Town |
| | Lee Guiver | Witham Town |
| | Lee Bajada | Barkingside |

### THIRD QUALIFYING ROUND

| | Name | Club |
|---|---|---|
| 4 | Darren Hay | Woking |
| 3 | Adie Mike | Leek Town |
| | Joff Vansittart | Dover Athletic |
| | Brian Ross | Southport |
| | Gary Piggot | Stafford Rangers |
| | Paul Wood | Havant & Waterlooville |
| | Grant Pierpoint | Lowestoft Town |

*Action from the AXA F.A. Challenge Cup Third Round*
*Top: Yeovil Town v Cardiff City . Photos: Ken Gregory*
*Below: Rushden & Diamonds v Leeds. Photos: Peter Barnes*

# GET ALL THE LATEST NEWS ON THE

**THE FOOTBALL ASSOCIATION**

# COMPETITIONS NEWSLINE

Updated daily with Draws, Match Dates, Change of Venues, Kick-off Times and Midweek Results for the F.A. Cup sponsored by AXA, F.A. Umbro Trophy, F.A. Carlsberg Vase, The Times F.A. Youth Cup, AXA F.A. Women's Cup and F.A. Umbro Sunday Cup. Saturday & Sunday results will be on the Newsline after 6.30pm – Cup draws on Monday after 1.00pm.

## PHONE NOW
# 09066 555 888

Presented by Tony Incenzo

Marketed by Sportslines, Common Road, Evesham on 01386 47302

Calls cost 60p per minute at all times.

# OR FAX-BACK ON
# 09065 511 051

Weekend results, Monday draws and midweek fixtures and results service

Calls cost £1.00 per minute at all times.
Call costing correct at time of going to press (June 1999).

# F.A. UMBRO TROPHY

# 1998-99 REVIEW

# FIRST ROUND
24th October 1998

| | | | | | | |
|---|---|---|---|---|---|---|
| 1 | Belper Town<br>Turner 37 | 1 | v | 3 | Radcliffe Borough<br>**Allen** 3 (44, 53, 75) | 115 |
| 2 | Farsley Celtic<br>Surtees 57 | 1 | v | 1 | Accrington Stanley<br>O'Callaghan 24 | 90 |
| R | Accrington Stanley<br>Tomlinson 7<br>Wells 30,40<br>O'Callaghan 60 | 4 | v | 1 | Farsley Celtic<br>Whellans | 134<br>22 |
| 3 | Ashton United<br>**Bell** 3 (26, 70, 90)<br>Carter 74,76, Coleman 86 | 6 | v | 0 | Bloxwich Town | 125 |
| 4 | Stafford Rangers<br>Eccleston 9, Smith 70<br>Boughey 79, Mitchell 90 | 4 | v | 2 | Lancaster City<br>Thomson 65,67 | 414 |
| 5 | Redditch United<br>Booth 51, Burton 69, 75 | 3 | v | 0 | VS Rugby | 140 |
| 6 | Bilston Town<br>Turner 2, Voyle 30<br>Rollinson 35 | 3 | v | 4 | Hyde United<br>Scargill 20, Taylor 29 (pen)<br>Richardson 42, Wilson 75 | 120 |
| 7 | Hinckley United<br>Drewitt 48, Symonds 57 | 2 | v | 1 | Congleton Town<br>Murphy 8 | 129 |
| 8 | Stalybridge Celtic<br>Sullivan 27, Mitten 84 | 2 | v | 1 | Flixton<br>Beirne 85 | 189 |
| 9 | Sutton Coldfield Tn<br>Biddle 16, Richardson 27 | 2 | v | 2 | Bamber Bridge<br>Carroll 2, 65 | 115 |
| R | Bamber Bridge<br>Maddock 25<br>Borrowdale 94 | 2 | v | 1* | Sutton Coldfield Tn<br>Kink 61 | 206 |
| 10 | Bradford Pk Ave<br>Hey 26, Maxwell 48, 84 | 3 | v | 0 | Stourbridge | 140 |
| 11 | Eastwood Town<br>Morgan 79, Eaton 83 | 2 | v | 2 | Runcorn<br>Irving 46, Nolan 71 | 153 |

| | | | | | | |
|---|---|---|---|---|---|---|
| R | Runcorn<br>Salt 25, Warder 49 | 2 | v | 1 | Eastwood Town<br>Morgan 39 | 138 |
| 12 | Spennymoor Utd | 0 | v | 1 | Trafford<br>Briffa 7 | 146 |
| 13 | Gateshead<br>Kitchen 31, Proudlock 78 | 2 | v | 2 | Paget Rangers<br>Hunt 39, Whitehouse 90 | 198 |
| R | Paget Rangers<br>Neadus 8 | 1 | v | 0 | Gateshead | 84 |
| 14 | Stocksbridge PS<br>Hurlstone 39 | 1 | v | 1 | Boston United<br>Carmichael 10 | 221 |
| R | Boston United<br>Carmichael 75 | 1 | v | 0 | Stocksbridge PS | 527 |
| 15 | Marine<br>Townsend 26, Rooglioso 90 | 2 | v | 3 | Frickley Athletic<br>Armstrong 4, Forthersgill 47<br>Hilton 71 | 141 |
| 16 | Gresley Rovers<br>Rowland 49 | 1 | v | 0 | Stamford | 322 |
| 17 | Blyth Spartans<br>Farret 44, Moat 79 | 2 | v | 2 | Whitby Town<br>Logan 34, 40 (pens) | 343 |
| R | Whitby Town<br>Chillingworth 45<br>Waller 60, Regan 85 | 3 | v | 1 | Blyth Spartans<br>Goodchild 24 (og) | 521 |
| 18 | Burton Albion | 0 | v | 0 | Grantham Town | 588 |
| R | Grantham Town | 0 | v | 3 | Burton Albion<br>Grocutt 21, Smith 31<br>Blount 74 | 570 |
| 19 | Halesowen Town | 0 | v | 2 | Guiseley<br>Atkinson 28 (p), Hinder 55 | 324 |

*Blyth Spartans v Whitby Town. Steve Walker (Blyth) on ground watches Whitby keeper Kelly thwart his goal bound effort.*

| 20 | Blakenall | 2 | v | 0 | Ilkeston Town | 158 |
|---|---|---|---|---|---|---|

Reed 64, Helliwell 82 (og)

| 21 | Gretna | 3 | v | 1 | Solihull Borough | 106 |
|---|---|---|---|---|---|---|

Brown 50, Dubie 57 — Dowling 54
Hodgson 90

| 22 | Winsford Utd | 0 | v | 1 | Gainsboro Trin | 104 |
|---|---|---|---|---|---|---|

Dunn 18

| 23 | Bishop Auckland | 4 | v | 2 | Matlock Town | 92 |
|---|---|---|---|---|---|---|

Banks 6, Shaw 9, 34 — Taylor 69, Tilly 86

| 24 | Dag & Redbridge | 1 | v | 1 | Wealdstone | 576 |
|---|---|---|---|---|---|---|

*(after abandoned tie - waterlogged pitch)*
Cobb — Kent

| R | Wealdstone | 0 | v | 5 | Dag & Redbridge | 404 |
|---|---|---|---|---|---|---|

Cobb, Goodwin, **Shipp** (3)

| 25 | Maidenhead Utd | 1 | v | 1 | Yate Town | 132 |
|---|---|---|---|---|---|---|

Banton 45 — Clark 7

| R | Yate Town | 1 | v | 2 | Maidenhead Utd | 87 |
|---|---|---|---|---|---|---|

Clark 37 — Banton 30, Terry 113

| 26 | Whyteleafe | 3 | v | 1 | Bishops Stortford | 95 |
|---|---|---|---|---|---|---|

Dallie (og), Dillon (2) — McCarthy

| 27 | Dorchester Town | 0 | v | 2 | Bath City | 522 |
|---|---|---|---|---|---|---|

Davis 23, Loyden 84

| 28 | Bashley | 4 | v | 0 | Staines Town | 138 |
|---|---|---|---|---|---|---|

Taylor 15, 73
Laidlaw 20, 65

| 29 | Molesey | 1 | v | 2 | Boreham Wood | 102 |
|---|---|---|---|---|---|---|

Musgrove — Samuels, Nesbett

| 30 | Cirencester Tn | 1 | v | 0 | Cinderford Town | 105 |
|---|---|---|---|---|---|---|

Baverstock 34

| 31 | Braintree Town | 4 | v | 1 | Fleet Town | 183 |
|---|---|---|---|---|---|---|

Gedny (3), Bennett

| 32 | Walton & Hersham | 2 | v | 2 | Weston-s-Mare | 131 |
|---|---|---|---|---|---|---|

Allingson 67, Sawyer 81 — Pritchard 13, 28

| R | Weston-s-Mare | 2 | v | 0 | Walton & Hersham | 100 |
|---|---|---|---|---|---|---|

Relish 20, Thompson 68

| 33 | Salisbury City | 2 | v | 1 | Carshalton Ath | 335 |
|---|---|---|---|---|---|---|

Ferrett 4, Sales 35 — Hynes 58

| 34 | Chertsey Town | 0 | v | 5 | Gloucester City | 246 |
|---|---|---|---|---|---|---|

**Hemmings** 3 (40, 54, 59)
Mings 44, 47

| 35 | Folkestone Invicta | 2 | v | 1 | Hampton | 205 |
|---|---|---|---|---|---|---|

Dent 34, Arter 69 — Stephenson 14

| 36 | Weymouth | 1 | v | 0 | King's Lynn | 497 |
|---|---|---|---|---|---|---|

Laws 2

| 37 | Harrow Borough | 4 | v | 2 | Cambridge City | 169 |
|---|---|---|---|---|---|---|

Greaves 48 og, Kumah 71 — Robbins 14, 25
McCormack 49, Walters 90

| 38 | Leyton Pennant | 4 | v | 3 | Purfleet | 78 |
|---|---|---|---|---|---|---|

Cove (2), Read, Baffom — **Macklin** (3)

| 39 | Canvey Island | 1 | v | 0 | Wisbech Town | 239 |
|---|---|---|---|---|---|---|

Sussex 77

| 40 | Erith & Belvedere | 1 | v | 1 | Newport (IoW) | 112 |
|---|---|---|---|---|---|---|

Fisher 90 — Pegler 46

| R | Newport (IoW) | 4 | v | 3 | Erith & Belvedere | 152 |
|---|---|---|---|---|---|---|

Soares 44, Wilson 46 — Fisher 13, 49, Roberts 86
Pegler 74, 85

| 41 | Croydon | 0 | v | 2 | Baldock Town | 57 |
|---|---|---|---|---|---|---|

Walker 44, De Luca 48

| 42 | Wembley | 1 | v | 2 | Witney Town | 49 |
|---|---|---|---|---|---|---|

Woodruffe 79 — Leach 70, Bourne 87

| 43 | Hastings Town | 2 | v | 2 | Chelmsford City | 298 |
|---|---|---|---|---|---|---|

Jones 81, McRobert 83 — Tovey 14, 67

| R | Chelmsford City | 0 | v | 1 | Hastings Town | 264 |
|---|---|---|---|---|---|---|

Simmonds 50

| 44 | St Leonards | 2 | v | 4 | Enfield | 540 |
|---|---|---|---|---|---|---|

Ramsden 32, 75 — Cooper 14, Naylor 19 (p)
Darlington 82, 89

| 45 | Worcester City | 2 | v | 1 | Billericay Town | 441 |
|---|---|---|---|---|---|---|

Richards 38, Bowen 64 — Aderulh 72

| 46 | Brackley Town | 1 | v | 4 | Grays Athletic | 85 |
|---|---|---|---|---|---|---|

Watts 87 — Hayzeldon 33, Moseley 55
Double 77, John 86

| 47 | Leatherhead | 1 | v | 2 | Crawley Town | 335 |
|---|---|---|---|---|---|---|

Webb 53 — Taylor 51, Abbey 82

| 48 | Newport AFC | 2 | v | 4 | Heybridge Swifts | 325 |
|---|---|---|---|---|---|---|

Bayliss 25 (pen), 40 — McLean 17, Adcock 19
Diddes 23, Deuyne 83

## FIRST ROUND STATISTICS

29 **Home Victories**

19 **Away Victories**

1 Abandoned

**Best Attendance** 588
Burton Albion v Grantham Town

**Average Attendance** 226

**Best Home Victory** 6-0
Ashton United v Bloxwich Town

**Best Away Victory** 0-5
Wealdstone v Dagenham & Redbridge

**Hat Tricks**
Allen (Radcliffe Borough), Bell (Ashton United),
Gedny (Braintree Town), Hemmings (Gloucester Town),
Macklin (Purfleet)

Top: John Hunt (Paget) bursts through the Accrington defence with Derek Highdale (Accrington) ready to tackle. Photo: Keith Clayton

Centre: Blakenhall keeper Matthew Lowe makes an excellent reflex save from Brian Gray (9) of Telford during the first half at the Red Lion Ground. Photo: Martin Wray

Bottom: Worcester's Michael Griffiths takes on the Fisher Athletic defence at the Surrey Dock Stadium. Photo: D Nicholson

# SECOND ROUND

### 21st November 1998

| | | | | | |
|---|---|---|---|---|---|
| 1 | Gainsboro Trin | 4 | v | 1 | Harrogate T 398 |
| | Bennett 20 (p), Olssen 41 | | | | Robson 80 |
| | Down 42, 89 | | | | |
| 2 | Altrincham | 2 | v | 2 | Burscough 566 |
| | Power 4, Robertson 62 | | | | Cowley 79 (pen), Saint 84 |
| **R** | Burscough | 1 | v | 3 | Altrincham 257 |
| | Wilde 8 | | | | Ellenden 24, Harris 35 |
| | | | | | Power 52 |
| 3 | Burton Albion | 5 | v | 0 | Bamber Bridge 676 |
| | Spooner 50, 65, Stryde 54 | | | | |
| | Smith 73, Holmes 90 | | | | |
| 4 | Kidderminster H | 2 | v | 2 | Lincoln United 982 |
| | Yates 32, 57 | | | | Simmons 65, Ramshaw 73 |
| **R** | Lincoln United | 2 | v | 1 | Kidderminster H 302 |
| | Ramshaw 2, 72 | | | | Webb 48 |
| 5 | Hinckley Utd | 2 | v | 0 | Gresley Rovers 397 |
| | Harbttle M 25 (pen) | | | | |
| | Titterton 32 | | | | |
| 6 | Trafford | 1 | v | 3 | Chorley 218 |
| | Russell 87 | | | | Potts 30, Mitchell 79 |
| | | | | | Swailes 81 |
| 7 | Witton Albion | 0 | v | 2 | Bradford PA 279 |
| | | | | | Freeman 39 (pen), Hey 61 |
| 8 | Tamworth | 1 | v | 3 | Stalybridge Celtic 611 |
| | Houseley 68 | | | | Trundle 20, Parr 47 |
| | | | | | Sullivan 50 |
| 9 | Doncaster Rovers | o | v | 2 | Frickley Ath 2003 |
| | | | | | Fuller 39, 54 |
| 10 | Redditch Utd | 3 | v | 2 | Corby Town 205 |
| | Marsh 68, 75, Booth 82 | | | | Tanner 32, Manby 42 |
| 11 | Radcliffe Borough | 5 | v | 1 | Great Harwood Tn 148 |
| | **Carroll** 3 (1, 61, 78) | | | | |
| | Jones 8, Mullin 70 | | | | |
| 12 | Boston United | 1 | v | 1 | Worksop Town 1018 |
| | Carmichael 49 | | | | Clark 66 |
| **R** | Worksop Town | 0 | v | 4 | Boston United 668 |
| | | | | | Stringfellow 35, Watts 61 |
| | | | | | Hardy 63, Munsen 89 |
| 13 | Bromsgrove Rvrs | 1 | v | 2 | Hednesford Town 721 |
| | Payne 44 | | | | Kimmins 29, 61 |
| 14 | Colwyn Bay | 3 | v | 2 | Stafford Rangers 392 |
| | Roberts 45 (pen), 64 | | | | Mitchell 18, Barlow 86 |
| | Lawton 69 | | | | |
| 15 | Bishop Auckland | 1 | v | 1 | Guiseley 242 |
| | Ross 68 | | | | Daly 38 |
| **R** | Guiseley | 3 | v | 1 | Bishop Auckland 314 |
| | Hunter 48, 86, Hook 54 | | | | Rowntree 70 |

| | | | | | |
|---|---|---|---|---|---|
| 16 | Nuneaton Borough | 1 | v | 1 | Hyde United 1207 |
| | Williams 49 | | | | Page 76 |
| **R** | Hyde United | 1 | v | 0 | Nuneaton Borough 472 |
| | Moncrieffe 19 | | | | |
| 17 | Runcorn | 3 | v | 0 | Moor Green |
| | Watson 16, 84, McNally 37 | | | | |
| 18 | Atherstone Utd | 0 | v | 0 | Southport 502 |
| **R** | Southport | 2 | v | 1 | Atherstone Utd 741 |
| | Thompson 26, Ross 90 | | | | Blair 49 |
| 19 | Hucknall Town | 2 | v | 1 | Barrow 515 |
| | Madden 35, Tomlinson 40 | | | | Contes 70 |
| 20 | Alfreton Town | 1 | v | 2 | Droylsden 109 |
| | Connelly 67 | | | | Green 68, Hennigan 76 |
| 21 | Northwich Victoria | 3 | v | 0 | Netherfield Kendal 778 |
| | Illman 2, Vicary 7 | | | | |
| | Owen 40 | | | | |
| 22 | Emley | 1 | v | 0 | Whitley Bay |
| | Bambrook 70 | | | | |
| 23 | Blakenall | 1 | v | 1 | Telford United 316 |
| | Clifton 1 | | | | Huckerby 30 |
| **R** | Telford United | 2 | v | 1 | Blakenall 403 |
| | Huckerby 6, Palmer S 11 | | | | Palmer L 54 |
| 24 | Paget Rangers | 0 | v | 2 | Accrington Stanley 223 |
| | | | | | O'Callaghan 44, Byrne 59 |
| 25 | Ashton United | 1 | v | 0 | Leek Town 316 |
| | Coleman 14 | | | | |
| 26 | Gretna | 1 | v | 1 | Shepshed Dynamo 101 |
| | Dobie 38 | | | | Smaller 35 |
| **R** | Shepshed Dynamo | 2 | v | 0 | Gretna 168 |
| | McGregor 7, McKinchey 69 | | | | |
| 27 | Whitby Town | 4 | v | 0 | Bedworth United 453 |
| | Toman 1, 90, Robinson 11 | | | | |
| | Chillingsworth 30 | | | | |
| 28 | Leigh RMI | 4 | v | 1 | Morecambe 435 |
| | Monk 10, 65, Evans 35 | | | | Lyons 45 |
| | Ridings 46 | | | | |
| 29 | Cirencester Town | 0 | v | 3 | Dulwich Hamlet 131 |
| | | | | | Griggs 7, Bartlet 27 |
| | | | | | Gorman 75 |
| 30 | Stevenage Borough | 4 | v | 0 | Uxbridge 1743 |
| | Alford 47, 51, Love 78 | | | | |
| | Reinett 85 | | | | |
| 31 | Rushden & D'monds | 2 | v | 0 | Bath City 1989 |
| | Vickerman 7(og), Brady 66 | | | | |
| 32 | Hayes | 1 | v | 1 | Folkestone Invicta 504 |
| | Charles 75 | | | | Morris 38 |

*Warren Patmore (9) (Yeovil) flicks the ball on - across a crowded Tonbridge goal area during his team's 1-0 victory. Photo: Ken Gregory*

| R | Folkestone Invicta | 3 | v | 2 | Hayes | 461 |
|---|---|---|---|---|---|---|
| | Charles (og) 24 | | | | Charles 40 (pen), Flynn 45 | |
| | Lawrence 39, Morris 64 (p) | | | | | |
| 33 | Merthyr Tydfil | 0 | v | 2 | Basingstoke Town | 481 |
| | | | | | Redwood 2, Mancey 27 | |
| 34 | Gloucester City | 1 | v | 2 | Kingstonian | 652 |
| | Tucker 41 | | | | Akuamiah 23, Wilgrass 66 (p) | |
| 35 | Ashford Town | 0 | v | 2 | Hastings Town | 531 |
| | | | | | McRobert 68, 89 (pen) | |
| 36 | Aldershot Town | 3 | v | 1 | Bromley | 1587 |
| | Narty (2), Stapleton | | | | Sharman | |
| 37 | Romford | 3 | v | 3 | Worthing | 161 |
| | Paul (3) | | | | Holden, Carrington (2) | |
| R | Worthing | 4 | v | 3 | Romford | 144 |
| | **Carrington** (3), Rice | | | | | |
| 38 | Maidenhead Utd | 1 | v | 0 | Clevedon Town | 208 |
| | Crighton 82 | | | | | |
| 39 | Fisher Athletic | 1 | v | 1 | Worcester City | 204 |
| | Manning 48 | | | | Griffiths 12 | |
| R | Worcester City | 5 | v | 1 | Fisher Athletic | 531 |
| | **Wright** 3 (24, 48, 58) | | | | Gamble 70 | |
| | Woods 56, Cottrill 73 | | | | | |
| 40 | Dover Athletic | 4 | v | 1 | Welling United | 786 |
| | Reina 10, Buddon 28 | | | | | |
| | Strouts 70, Adams 82 | | | | | |
| 41 | Kettering Town | 4 | v | 0 | Andover | 1118 |
| | Brown 21, McNamara 38 | | | | | |
| | Hudson 43, Fisher 56 | | | | | |
| 42 | Forest Green Rvrs | 4 | v | 1 | Boreham Wood | 432 |
| | Birkby 11, Sykes 60 | | | | Samuels | |
| | Hedges 61, Hunt 74 | | | | | |
| 43 | Yeovil Town | 1 | v | 0 | Tonbridge Angels | 1525 |
| | Pounder 45 | | | | | |
| 44 | Leyton Pennant | 0 | v | 3 | St Albans City | 301 |
| | | | | | Haworth, Clark, McLean (og) | |
| 45 | Margate | 1 | v | 3 | Havant & W'loovile | 409 |
| | Sykes 65 | | | | Wakefield 15, 89, Tate 86 | |
| 46 | Slough Town | 3 | v | 1 | Baldock Town | 392 |
| | Pearson 31, 86 | | | | Deller 42 | |
| | Hammats 39 | | | | | |
| 47 | Woking | 2 | v | 1 | Salisbury City | 1640 |
| | West 45, Ellis 87 | | | | Bright 62 | |

| 48 | Farnborough Tn | 1 | v | 1 | Dartford | 474 |
|---|---|---|---|---|---|---|
| | Miller 33 | | | | Payne 48 | |
| R | Dartford | 1 | v | 2 | Farnborough Town | 229 |
| | Spriggs 40 | | | | Underwood 20, Robinson 59 | |
| 49 | Cheltenham Town | 2 | v | 1 | Bashley | 1348 |
| | Grayson 29, 65 | | | | Andrews 18 (pen) | |
| 50 | Newport (IoW) | 1 | v | 0 | Gravesend & N'fleet | 342 |
| | Peglar 6 | | | | | |
| 51 | Hereford Utd | 1 | v | 1 | Hitchin Town | 1382 |
| | Wright 63 | | | | Turner 77 | |
| R | Hitchin Town | 2 | v | 1 | Hereford Utd | 447 |
| | Cretton 36, Deon 70 | | | | Wright 4 | |
| 52 | Heybridge Swifts | 1 | v | 2 | Sutton United | 319 |
| | Hewes | | | | Watson, Vines | |
| 53 | Crawley Town | 2 | v | 2 | Sittingbourne | 677 |
| | McEntegart 18, Payne 65(p) | | | | Malkie 12 (og), Hume 76 (p) | |
| R | Sittingbourne | 1 | v | 5 | Crawley Town | 248 |
| | Miller 10 | | | | Payne 51 (p), Abbot 53, 65 | |
| | | | | | Hawthorne 39, Morris 64 (p) | |
| 54 | Dag & Redbridge | 3 | v | 2 | Barton Rovers | 524 |
| | Matthews, Cook(og), Cubb | | | | Drew, Phillips | |
| 55 | Weymouth | 2 | v | 1 | Braintree Town | 774 |
| | Robinson 23, Vellman 89 | | | | Vincent 90 | |
| 56 | Aylesbury Utd | 1 | v | 1 | Harrow Borough | 655 |
| | Crawshaw | | | | Roberts | |
| R | Harrow Borough | 2 | v | 3* | Aylesbury Utd | 306 |
| | Toussaint, Gavin | | | | Rutherford, King, Cranshaw | |
| 57 | R C Warwick | 1 | v | 1 | Raunds Town | 139 |
| | Sheedy 60 | | | | Slinn 16 | |
| R | Raunds Town | 2 | v | 0 | R C Warwick | 107 |
| | Johnson 32, York 89 | | | | | |
| 58 | Grays Athletic | 2 | v | 3 | Whyteleafe | 142 |
| | Pridoe, Hayzelden | | | | Dillon (2) Scott | |
| 59 | Evesham Utd | 1 | v | 1 | Canvey Island | 121 |
| | Thomas 16 | | | | Parmenter 80 | |
| R | Canvey Island | 5 | v | 0 | Evesham Utd | 153 |
| | Williams 15,56, Britnall 58 | | | | | |
| | Parmenter 43, Walker 79(og) | | | | | |
| 60 | Oxford City | 0 | v | 1 | Enfield | 302 |
| | | | | | Richardson | |
| 61 | Bognor Regis Tn | 1 | v | 3 | Witney Town | 322 |
| | Pickering 85 | | | | Wimble 8, Leach 20 | |
| | | | | | Holbert 43 | |
| 62 | Weston-s-Mare | 1 | v | 1 | Berkhamstead Town | 200 |
| | Power 42 | | | | Swales 72 | |
| R | Berkhamstead T | 0 | v | 2 | Weston-s-Mare | 102 |
| | | | | | Dann 9, Pritchard 12 | |
| 63 | Yeading | 3 | v | 3 | Chesham Utd | 190 |
| | Grieves, Warner, Conroy | | | | Adorne, Thompson, Winston | |
| R | Chesham Utd | 4 | v | 0 | Yeading | 140 |
| | Winston, Bushay (2) | | | | | |
| | Mitchell | | | | | |
| 64 | Hendon | 1 | v | 1 | Rothwell Town | 202 |
| | Hyatt 24 | | | | Hefferman 64 | |
| R | Rothwell Town | 1 | v | 2* | Hendon | 186 |
| | Hefferman 59 | | | | Lewis 87, Whitmarsh 110 | |

*Aldershot Town v Bromley: Mark Harper (Shots) challenges Anthony Latronica. Photo: Ian Morsman*

## SECOND ROUND STATISTICS

**40 Home Victories**

**24 Away Victories**

**Best Attendance** 2003
Doncaster Rovers v Frickley Athletic

**Average Attendance** 514

**Best Home Victory** 5-0
Canvey Island v Evesham United
Burton Albion v Bamber Bridge

**Best Away Victory** 1-5
Sittingbourne v Crawley Town

**Hat Tricks**
Carrington (Worthing), Carroll (Radcliffe Borough),
Paul (Romford), Wright (Worcester City)

# THIRD ROUND

| # | Home | | | | Away | Att |
|---|---|---|---|---|---|---|
| 1 | Radcliffe Borough<br>Carroll 16 | 1 | v | 2 | Northwich Victoria<br>Cooke 45, Vicary 68 | 550 |
| 2 | Colwyn Bay<br>Graham 30 | 1 | v | 1 | Hednesford Tn<br>Carty 89 | 407 |
| R | Hednesford Tn<br>Sedgemore 39 (pen)<br>Ware 117 | 2 | v | 2* | Colwyn Bay<br>Donnelly 61<br>Graham 109 | 391 |
| | *(Colwyn Bay won 5-4 after penalties)* | | | | | |
| 3 | Shepshed Dynamo<br>Bah 15 | 1 | v | 1 | Emley<br>David 45 | 279 |
| *R* | Emley<br>Wilson 35, 70, David 45 | 3 | v | 1 | Shepshed Dynamo | 426 |
| 4 | Altrincham<br>Chambers 74 | 1 | v | 0 | Burton Albion | 825 |
| 5 | Accrington Stanley<br>Bermingham 54 | 1 | v | 3 | Ashton United<br>Baxter 45, Coleman 53, 90 | 349 |
| 6 | Stalybridge Celtic | 0 | v | 3 | Hinckley United<br>Symonds 45, Titterton 50, 69 | 556 |
| 7 | Lincoln United<br>Ranshaw 60, Barker 80 | 2 | v | 5 | Bradford PA<br>Sharpe 20, Ball 47<br>Connor 70, Lee 86, 88 | 280 |
| 8 | Whitby Town<br>Pitman 36, Borthwick 60 | 2 | v | 1 | Frickley Athletic<br>Fothergill 5 | 467 |
| 9 | Droylsden<br>Wright 74, 83 | 2 | v | 3 | Telford United<br>Murphy 43, 90, Bentley 87 | 987 |
| 10 | Chorley<br>Critchley 23 | 1 | v | 1 | Guiseley<br>Parke 89 | 363 |
| R | Guiseley<br>Davison 80, Morrell 84 | 2 | v | 1 | Chorley<br>Mitchell 75 | 335 |
| 11 | Leigh RMI | 0 | v | 1 | Southport<br>Guyett 72 | 864 |
| 12 | Runcorn<br>Salt 3, McNally 79 | 2 | v | 1 | Hyde United<br>Yeo 57 | 534 |
| 13 | Gainsboro Trinity<br>Turnbull 90 | 1 | v | 4 | Boston United<br>Mason 33, Stringfellow 48<br>Venables 80, Costello 89 | 1647 |
| 14 | Hucknall Town<br>Roberts 80 | 1 | v | 3 | Redditch United<br>Gillett 6, Booth 43<br>Gidding 75 | 385 |
| 15 | Basingstoke Tn | 0 | v | 2 | Yeovil Town<br>Pickard 50, Dale 80 | 1617 |
| 16 | Hitchin Town<br>Parker (2), Dixon | 3 | v | 3 | Enfield<br>Darlington, Dunwell<br>Calder | 519 |
| R | Enfield | 0 | v | 1 | Hitchin Town<br>Parker 18 | 302 |
| 17 | Worthing | 0 | v | 2 | Hendon<br>Howard 71, Whitmarsh 90 | 358 |

*The white shirts of Telford United battle it out at Droylsden's Butchers Arms, grabbing two late goals to record a 3-2 victory.* Photo: Colin Stevens

| | | | | | |
|---|---|---|---|---|---|
| 18 | Hastings Town | 0 v | 3 | St Albans City | 380 |
| | | | | Turner 3, Clark 38 | |
| | | | | Gentle 39 | |
| 19 | Weston-s-Mare | 2 v | 2 | Raunds Town | 182 |
| R | Raunds Town | 0 v | 1 | Weston-s-Mare | |
| 20 | Stevenage Boro | 3 v | 2 | Dover Athletic | 2476 |
| | Alford 18, Pearson 41, 90 | | | Le Bihan 6, Hynes 22 | |
| 21 | Forest Green Rvrs | 4 v | 0 | Witney Town | 806 |
| | **Sykes** 3 (8, 14, 25) | | | | |
| | Hunt 69 | | | | |
| 22 | Weymouth | 1 v | 0 | Sutton United | 1060 |
| | Laws 54 | | | | |
| 23 | Kingstonian | 5 v | 2 | Kettering Town | 624 |
| | Akuamoah 25, 90 | | | Brown 12 | |
| | Leworthy 29, 40 | | | McNamara 58 | |
| | Stewart 50 | | | | |
| 24 | Crawley Town | 2 v | 3 | Chesham United | 1138 |
| | Mackie 32, Warden 61 | | | **Winston** 3 (18, 52, 82) | |
| 25 | Dulwich Hamlet | 1 v | 2 | Whyteleafe | 492 |
| | Bartley 80 | | | Dillon 6, Kadi 21 | |

| | | | | | |
|---|---|---|---|---|---|
| 26 | Cheltenham Tn | 2 v | 1 | Canvey Island | 2045 |
| | Grayson 29, Freeman 90 | | | Brett 48 | |
| 27 | Aldershot Town | 1 v | 0 | Maidenhead Utd | 2068 |
| | Sugrue 37 | | | | |
| 28 | Slough Town | 1 v | 2 | Rushden & Dia | 729 |
| | Flore 15 | | | West 23, 73 | |
| 29 | Aylesbury Utd | 2 v | 0 | Newport (IoW) | 468 |
| | Hercules 69, Crawshaw 88 | | | | |
| 30 | Dag & Redbridge | 1 v | 1 | Farnborough Tn | 783 |
| | Shipp 29 | | | Bailey 2 | |
| R | Farnborough Tn | 1 v | 1* | Dag & Redbridge | 452 |
| | West 96 | | | Matthews 120 | |
| | *(Dagenham won 4-2 after penalties)* | | | | |
| 31 | Havant & W'looville | 0 v | 1 | Worcester City | 254 |
| | | | | Owen 43 | |
| 32 | Woking | 8 v | 4 | Folkestone Invicta | 1979 |
| | Hay 4 (40, 45, 80, 88) | | | Dent 22, Lawrence 56 | |
| | Perkins 51, Steele 73 | | | Beal 66, Cuggy 90 | |
| | Payne 81, 84 | | | | |

## THIRD ROUND STATISTICS

**13** Home Victories

**17** Away Victories

**2** Penalty Deciders (Away Winners)

**5** Replays

**Best Attendance** 2476
Stevenage Borough v Dover Athletic

**Average Attendance** 810

**Best Home Victory** 8-4
Woking v Folkestone Invicta

**Best Away Victory** 2-5
Lincoln United v Bradford Park Avenue

*Aldershot v Maidenhead. Roy Young v Tyrone Houston of Maidenhead. Photo: Ian Morsman*

Top: Gainsborough's Ian Dunn and Boston United's Peter Costello get a perfect 10 in the Torvill and Dean department.
Photo: Bill Wheatcroft

Centre: Mark Dearlove (Redditch) muscled out by Pete Kenworthy and Lee Margerison (Hucknall).   Photo: Keith Clayton

Bottom: Ashton Utd open the scoring against Accrington Stanley with a long range shot from Banter. Photo: Andy Ingham

61

## GET ALL THE LATEST NEWS ON THE

**THE FOOTBALL ASSOCIATION**

# COMPETITIONS NEWSLINE

Updated daily with Draws, Match Dates, Change of Venues, Kick-off Times and Midweek Results for the F.A. Cup sponsored by AXA, F.A. Umbro Trophy, F.A. Carlsberg Vase, The Times F.A. Youth Cup, AXA F.A. Women's Cup and F.A. Umbro Sunday Cup. Saturday & Sunday results will be on the Newsline after 6.30pm – Cup draws on Monday after 1.00pm.

## PHONE NOW
# 09066 555 888

Presented by Tony Incenzo

Marketed by Sportslines, Common Road, Evesham on 01386 47302

Calls cost 60p per minute at all times.

## OR FAX-BACK ON
# 09065 511 051

Weekend results, Monday draws and midweek fixtures and results service

Calls cost £1.00 per minute at all times.
Call costing correct at time of going to press (June 1999).

# FOURTH ROUND

Aldershot Town   1   v   2   Altrincham
Nartey 89    Att: 2754    Harris 29, Russell 36
**Aldershot:** Phillips, Smart, Chewins, Fielder, Howard, Watkinson, Sugrue, Champion, Abbott, Young, Hathaway. Subs: Nartey, Cobbett, Cash.
**Altrincham:** Coburn, Hodson, Adams, Timmons, Ellender, Robertson, Gallagher, K Russell, Ward, R Harris, Chambers. Subs: Hardy, Hawkes, Keilty.

Ashton United   2   v   2   St Albans City
Vickers 20 (og)    Att: 443    Gentle 45, Haworth 90
**Ashton:** McKenna, Caswell, Hollis, K Bell, Clowes, J Bell, Elliott, Anderson, Coleman, G Williams, Johnson. Subs: Doolan, Baxter, Philips.
**St Albans:** Newell, Meredith, Carstairs, Vickers, Mudd, Piper, Haworth, Turner, D Gentle, Jones, J Gentle. Subs: Witney, Kane, Keen.

R    St Albans City   2   v   1   Ashton United
Clark 2    Att: 390
**St Albans:** Newell, Meredith, Carstairs, Vickers, Mudd, Piper, Haworth (sub Keen), D Gentle (sub Jones), Clark (sub Polston), Kane, J Gentle.
**Ashton:**

Aylesbury United   0   v   1   Whitby Town
Att: 901    Williams 84
**Aylesbury:** Wilmot, Darlington, Hercules, Kelly, King, Browne, Crawshaw, Soloman, Butler, Rooney, L Harvey. Subs: Mason, Kimble, Dowie.
**Whitby:** Kelly, G Williams, Logan, Goodchild, Hudson, Dixon, Goodrick, Chillingsworth, Robinson, Toman, Pitman. Subs: Borthwick, Waller, Cook.

Boston United   2   v   0   Redditch United
Venables 9    Att: 1426
Carmichael 89
**Boston:** Bastock, Gowshall, L Curtis, Stringfellow, Hardy, Charles, Stanhope, Cogtehow, Carmichael, Venables, Mason. Subs: Watts, Seager, Clyde.
**Redditch:** Arnold, Knight, Laker, Manton, Pugh, Moulders, R Smith, Nicholls, Burton, Marsh, Gillett. Subs: Blain, Hart, Whittington.

Cheltenham Town   0   v   0   Stevenage Borough
Att: 3005
**Cheltenham:** Book, Duff, Victory, Brough, Freeman, R Walker, Howells, Bloomer, Eaton, Watkins, Norton. Subs: Jackson, Knight, Smith.
**Stevenage:** Taylor, Harvey, Rogers, Smith, Trott, Howarth, Berry, Kirby, Alford, Pearson, Love. Subs: Telemarque, Thompson, Naylor.

R   Stevenage Borough   0   v   0   Cheltenham Town
AET    Att: 2,814    Cheltenham won 5-4 after penalties
**Stevenage:** Taylor, Harvey, Kirby, Smith, Trott, Howarth, Plummer, Berry, Alford, Pearson, Love. Subs: Beevor, Thompson, Telemarque, Gallagher, Rogers.
**Cheltenham:** Book, Duff, Victory, Brough, Freeman, R Walker, Eaton, Bloomer, Grayson, Watkins, Norton. Subs: Knight, Smith, C Walker, Jackson, Casey.

Chesham United   0   v   2   Hendon
Att: 521    Whitmarsh 50, Lewis 65
**Chesham:** Jennings, Kelly, Pluckrose, J Mitchell, D Thompson, Gell, Bashir, McAree, Winston, Bushay, Nabil. Subs: Argave, Totten, Lewis.
**Hendon:** McCann, Howard, Clarke, Daly, Bateman, Warmington, Stephenson, White, Watson, Whitmarsh, Fitzgerald. Subs: Lewis, Brady, Heard.

Colwyn Bay   3   v   1   Bradford (Park Ave)
Evans 45, Graham 49    Att: 405    Freeman 58 (pen)
Roberts 52
**Colwyn Bay:** R Roberts, McGosh, M Evans, G Graham, Caton, Price, Limbert, G Roberts, D Graham, Donnelly, Lawton. Subs: Congerton, Mottram, Fuller.
**Bradford:** Lenaghan, Blair, Grayston, Briggs, Bagshaw, Connor, Lee, Benn, Sharpe, Hey, Maxwell. Subs: Freeman, Brandon, Ball.

Dag'ham & Redbridge   4   v   0   Telford United
**Shipp** 3 (1, 11, 38)    Att: 840
Pratt 35
**Dagenham:** Gothard, ICole, Pratt, Howard, Goodwin, L Matthews, Broom, Cobb, Shipp, Game, Bird. Subs: G Blackford, Haywood, Barry.
**Telford:** Williams, Naylor, Fowler, Fee, Bentley, Challinor, Doyle, M Jones, Murphy, Huckerby, Palmer. Subs: Corns, Davis, Shakespeare.

*Aldershot v Altrincham: Roy Young challenges Stuart Coburn.    Photo: Ian Morsman*

Guiseley 0 v 2 Emley
Att: 827     Thompson 68, Tonks 89
**Guiseley:** Dickinson, Atkinson, Gallagher, Nettleton, Hook, Parsley, Airdrie, Williams, Parke, Davison, Hazel, Morrell, Hunter, Phillips.
**Emley:** Rhodes, Wood, Jones, Thompson, Lacey, David, Banks, Hurst, Thorpe, Wilson, Tonks. Subs: Smith, Calcutt, Bray.

Hitchin Town 2 v 1 Weston-super-Mare
Abbey 30, 76     Att: 549     Warton 49
**Hitchin:** Bonfield, Burke, Allpress, Cretton, K Gillard, Fenton, Parker, Meah, A Turner, C Williams, Abbey. Subs: Dixon, M Bates, Bone.
**Weston:** Norville, Llewellyn, Fitzgerald, Gibbins, J Price, Rogers, Withey, White, Pritchard, Warton, Rhodes-Brown. Subs: Price, Wheeldon, Dann.

Northwich Victoria 1 v 0 Worcester City
Cooke 23     Att: 1109
**Northwich:** Greygoose, Simpson, Birch, Crookes, Robertson, Owen, Terry, Webster, Cooke, Tait, Vicary. Subs: Duffy, Devlin, Illman.
**Worcester:** Hicks, Dandeman, Burnham, Greenman, Heeley, Cottrill, Woods, Chenoweth, Purdie, Owen, Lutz. Subs: Davies, Jones, Bowen.

Runcorn 2 v 3 Southport
Worthington 6, Watson 74     Att: 1090     Homer 16, McNally 38(og)
Luckett 80 (pen)
**Runcorn:** Morris, Fleming, Ward, Whalley, McNally, Randles, Salt, Rose, Worthington, Nolan, Watson. Subs: Brady, Collaghan, Irving.
**Southport:** Stewart, Farrelly, Ryan, Guyett, Bolland, Horner, Thompson, Gouck, Ross, Gamble, Furlong. Subs: Formby, Newman, Butler.

Weymouth 1 v 2 Forest Green Rovers
Mason 88     Att: 1415     McGregor 54, 72
**Weymouth:** Myers, Boulton, S Browne, A Browne, Waldock, Powell, Robinson, Hutchinson, Adcock, Laws, Mansell. Subs: Mason, George, Flory.
**Forest Green:** Shuttlewood, Hedges, Forbes, Bailey, Kilgour, Smart, Cook, Coupe, McGregor, Mehew, Sykes. Subs: Wigg, Smith, Catley.

Whyteleafe 0 v 3 Kingstonian

## FOURTH ROUND STATISTICS

7 **Home Victories**

8 **Away Victories**

1 **Penalty Decider** (Away Winner)

3 **Replays**

**Best Attendance**     3005
Cheltenham Town v Stevenage Borough

**Average Attendance**     1475

**Best Home Victory**     4-0
Dagenham & Redbridge v Telford United

**Best Away Victory**     0-3
Whyteleafe v Kingstonian

**Hat Tricks**
Shipp (Dagenham & Redbridge)

Att 945     Leworthy 54, 55
Luckett 80 (pen)
**Whyteleafe:** Lidbury, Fisher, Elliott, Alger, Hopkins, Kadi, Golley, McSherry, Scott, Dillon, Cormack. Subs: Dodman, George, Rose.
**Kingstonian:** Farrelly, Mustafa, Luckett, Crossley, W Brown, Harris, Patterson, Pitcher, Corbett, Leworthy, Akuamoah. Subs: John, Smith, Lester.

Woking 0 v 0 Rushden & Diamonds
Att: 2788
**Woking:** Batty, Taylor, Hollingdale, Saunders, Smith, Danzey, Girdler, Gridelet, Payne, Hay, Steele. Subs: Bolt, Ellis, West.
**Rushden:** M Smith, Wooding, Cramman, McElhatton, Rodwell, Whyte, Hamsher, Butterworth, Foster, Collins, Underwood. Subs: De Souza, Corry, West.

R     Rushden & Dia. 1 v 2 Woking
Warburton 1     Att: 1955     Payne 43, Hay 54
**Rushden:** Smith, Wooding (sub Heggs), Cramman, McElhatton, Rodwell, Warburton, Brady, Butterworth, West (sub Foster), Collins, Underwood.
**Woking:**

Yeovil Town 3 v 2 Hinckley United
Patmore 6, 68     Att: 2351     Titterton 27
Pickard 16     Symmonds 45
**Yeovil:** Pennock, Piper, Fishlock, Brown, Hannigan, Cousins, Thompson, Stott, Patmore, Pickard, B Smith. Subs: Pitman, Heynes, Pounder.
**Hinckley:** Starkey, Daly, Hassall, Thomas, Palmer, Allcock, Doughty, Titterton, Symmonds, D King, Harbottle. Subs: Bindley, Hadland, Stanborough.

*Leroy Chambers (rear), Ricky Harris (centre) and Keith Russell (front) celebrate Altrincham's opening goal from Ricky Harris in the 2-1 victory over Aldershot.*
*Photo: Andrew Chitty*

64

Top: OOPH! St Albans defender Carstairs deflects John Coleman's goalbound effort for Ashton.
Photo: D Nicholson

Centre: Yeovil Town v Hinckley United. Two goal Warren Patmore powers in a header in the tie which was won 3-2 by the Conference side.
Photo: Ken Gregory

Bottom: Whitby Town's Andy Toman battles against the Aylesbury defence.
Photo: Neil Thaler

# FIFTH ROUND

Boston United  2  v  0  Altrincham
Watts 19, 79    Att: 2,575
**Boston:** Bastock, Gowshall, L Curtis, Stringfellow, Hardy, Charles, Stanhope, Costello, Carmichael, Watts, Mason.
**Altrincham:** Coburn, Hodson, Adams, Timmons, Ellender, Robertson, K Russell, Power, Ward, R Harris, Chambers.

Cheltenham Town  3  v  0  Hendon
Victory 41, 45    Att: 2514
Watkins 66
**Cheltenham:** Book, Duff, Victory, Brough, Freeman, R Walker, Jackson, Knight, Grayson, Watkins, Norton.
**Hendon:** McCann, Howard, Clarke, Daly, Bateman, White, Fitzgerald, Hyatt, Watson, Heard, Lewis.

D'ham & Redbridge  1  v  2  St Albans City
Janney 88    Att: 1227    Mudd 27, Gentle 67
**Dagenham:** Gothard, Cole, Pratt, Howard, Mas, L Matthews, Broom, Cobb, Shipp, Game, Blackfold.
**St Albans:** Newell, Meredith, Risley, Keen, Mudd, Piper, Haworth, Turner, Clark, Jones, D Gentle.

Emley  2  v  0  Whitby Town
og 23 (Waller), Calcutt 30    Att: 908
**Emley:** Rhodes, Wood, Jones, Thompson, Lacey, David, Banks, Hurst, Tonks, Calcutt, Smith.
**Whitby:** Kelly, Waller, Logan, Goodchild, Hudson, Dixon, Goodrick, Stout, Chillingworth, Toman, Pitman.

Hitchin Town  1  v  2  Forest Green Rovers
Parker 33    Att: 963    Mehew 4, 5
**Hitchin:** Robinson, Burke, Gillard,Cretton, Allpress, Scott, C Williams, Abbey, Dixon, Parker, Meah.
**Forest Green:** Shuttleworth, Hedges, Forbes, Bailey, Kilgour, Honor, Cook, Drysdale, McGregor, Mehew, Sykes.

Kingstonian  1  v  0  Yeovil Town
Stewart 89    Att: 1783
**Kingstonian:** Farrelly, Mustafa, Nyamah, Crossley, Stewart, Harris, Patterson, Pitcher, Rattray, Leworthy, Akuamoah.
**Yeovil:** Pennock, Chandler, Fishlock, Brown, Hannigan, Cousins, Thompson, Stott, Patmore, Pickard, Simpson.

Northwich Victoria  3  v  1  Colwyn Bay
Vicary 52, Devlin 56    Att: 1402    Lawton 28
Walters 64 (pen)
**Northwich:** Greygoose, Simpson, Birch, Crookes, Robertson, Devlin, Terry, Walters, Cooke, Tait, Vicary.
**Colwyn:** R Roberts, Congerton, McGosh, G Graham, Caton, Price, Limbert, Mottram, D Graham, Donnelly, Lawton.

Woking  0  v  0  Southport
Att: 2783
**Woking:** Flahaven, Perkins, Hollingdale, Saunders, Smith, Danzey, Girdler, Gridelet, Payne, Hay, Steele.
**Southport:** Stewart, Farley, Ryan, Guyett, Bolland, Horner, Thompson, Gouck, Ross, Gamble, Quinn.

R    Southport  1  v  0  Woking
Gamble 41 (pen)    Att: 1217

## FIFTH ROUND STATISTICS

2 **Home Victories**

6 **Away Victories**

1 Replay

**Best Attendance**  2783
Woking v Southport

**Average Attendance**  1705

*Jamie Victory (Cheltenham) volleys his second goal against Hendon.   Photo: Keith Clayton*

*Top: Emley's Neil Lacy clears off of the goal line in the 80th minute after Whitby Town's Carl Chillingworth (on floor) heads towards goal.*
*Photo: Neil Thaler*

*Centre: A brilliant save by Justin Shuttlewood at full stretch to deny an excellent Hitchin effort.*
*Photo: Peter Barnes*

*Bottom: Yeovil wing back Murray Fishlock closes down Kingstonian's Eddie Akuamoah during the 'Ks' 1-0 victory at Kingstonian.*
*Photo: Ken Gregory*

# QUARTER FINALS

Emley   0   v   1   Cheltenham Town

Att: 1239     Howarth 44

**Emley:** Rhodes, Tonks, Jones, Thompson, Lacey, David, Banks, Hurst, Calcutt, Wilson (sub Thorpe 74), Wood.
**Cheltenham:** Book, Knight (sub Casey 90), Victory, Banks, Freeman, Howarth, Howells, Milton, Grayson, Eaton, Norton.

*Emley v Cheltenham Town*
*Photo: Julian Hodgson*

Forest Green Rovers   4   v   1   Southport

Mehew 11, Sykes 27, 46    Att: 1240    Quinn 62
McGregor 29

**Forest Green:** Shuttlewood, Hedges, Forbes, Bailey, Kilgour, Wigg, Coupe (sub Winter 52), Drysdale, McGregor, Mehew (sub Smart 76), Sykes (sub Catley 87). Subs: Perrin, Smith.
**Southport:** Stewart, Thompson, Ryan, Guyett, Bolland (sub Farley 31), Horner, Quinn, Gouck, Ross, Gamble (sub Courney 76), Formby. Subs: Naylor, Taylor, Futcher.

*Forest Green Rovers v Southport: Alex Sykes scores after 46 minutes*
*Photo: Peter Barnes*

# QUARTER FINALS

St Albans City     2    v    1     Boston United
Vickers 33, Meredith 88     Att: 2723     Watts 23

**St Albans:** Lomas, Meredith, Polston, Vickers, Keen (sub Kane 88), Piper, Haworth (sub Carstairs 88), Turner, D Gentle (sub Jones 64), McDougald, J Gentle. Subs: Cain, Cawston.

**Boston:** Bastock, Gowshall, Curtis, Stringfellow, Hardy, Charles, Stanhope, Costello (sub Kelly 88), Carmichael (sub Featherstone 45), Watts, Mason. Subs: Clyde, Melson, Maddison.

*St Albans City v Boston United: Saints beat Boston United at the death. Scorer Tom Meredith in goalmouth
Photo: Eric Marsh*

Northwich Victoria    0    v    2    Kingstonian
Att: 1819     Mustafa 48, Akuamoah 68

**Northwich:** Key, Simpson, Birch, Crookes, Robertson, Devlin, Terry, Walters, Cooke, Illman, Vicary. Subs: Tait, Webster, Williams.

**Kingstonian:** Farrelly, Mustafa, Luckett, Crossley, Stewart, Harris, Patterson, Pitcher, Rattray, Leworthy, Akuamoah. Subs: Corbett, Thomas, Francis.

*Northwich Victoria v Kingstonian: Eddie Akuamoah (yellow, centre) scores Kingstonian's second goal at Northwich*

# SEMI FINALS

### Kingstonian 2 v 2 Cheltenham Town
Stewart 27, Pitcher 69     Att: 2203     Grayson 58, Brough 72

**Kingstonian:** Farrelly, Mustafa, Luckett, Crossley, Stewart, Harris, Patterson, Pitcher, Rattray, Leworthy (sub Francis 85), Akuamoah. Subs: Nyamah, Corbett, Brown, John.

**Cheltenham:** Book, Duff, Victory, Banks, Freeman, Howarth, Howells, Bloomer, Grayson, Brough, Norton. Subs: Milton, C Walker, Knight, Smith, Eaton.

### Cheltenham Town 1 v 3 Kingstonian
Grayson     Att: 4425     Crossley 5, Leworthy 55
                                              Patterson 87

**Cheltenham:** Book, Duff (sub Norton 49), Victory, Banks, Freeman, Brough (sub Eaton 75), Howells, Bloomer, Grayson, C Walker (sub Knight 53), Milton. Subs: Howarth, Smith.

**Kingstonian:** Farrelly, Mustafa, Luckett, Crossley, Stewart, Harris, Patterson, Pitcher, Rattray, Leworthy (sub Nyamah 90), Akuamoah (sub Francis 88). Subs: Brown, Sullivan, John.

*Kingstonian celebrate their 3-1 win at Cheltenham*

# SEMI FINALS

Top: Steve Book punches clear. (Spot Eric Marsh)   Photo: Peter Baarnes

Bottom: Eddy Akuamoah is thwarted by the presence of Steve Book.   Photo: Peter Barnes

# SEMI FINALS

### St Albans City   1   v   1   Forest Green Rovers
Risley 21     Att: 2120     Drysdale 1(pen)

**St Albans:** Lomas, Meredith, Risley, Vickers, Bodley, Pollard (sub Polston 88), Haworth, Turner, Clark, Jones, McDougald. Subs: D Gentle, Keen.

**Forest Green:** Shuttlewood (sub Perrin 38), Hedges, Forbes, Bailey, Kilgour, Honor, Coupe, Drysdale, McGregor, Mehew (sub Birkby 57), Winter (sub Sykes 80).

### Forest Green Rovers   3   v   2   St Albans City
Sykes 45, Hedges 74, Smart 82     Att: 3002     og 2 (Kilgour), Clark 41

**Forest Green:** Perrin, Hedges, Forbes, Bailey, Kilgour, Wigg (sub Winter 62), Cook, Drysdale, McGregor, Mehew, Sykes (sub Smart 79). Subs: Honor, Birkby, Westlake.

**St Albans:** Lomas, Meredith, Risley (sub Keen 83), Bodley, Vickers, Pollard (sub Piper 86), Haworth, Turner, Clark, Jones, McDougall. Subs: Polston, J Gentle, Newall.

*Forest Green Rovers have reached Wembley - what a feeling!*
*Photo: Peter Barnes*

# SEMI FINALS

*Top: Forest Green attack in numbers with Mike Kilgour, Rob Cook and Ian Hedges all prominent. Photo: Peter Barnes*

*Bottom: Ian Hedges scores Forest Green Rovers' equaliser. Photo: Peter Barnes*

# FINAL

# FINAL

*Opposite Page: Top: K's Colin Luckett covers Marc McGregor. Photo: Peter Barnes*
*Centre: Midway through the first half Forest Green Rovers striker Marc McGregor was fouled in the penalty area but shook himself free, steadied himself and cut in towards Steve Farrelly. The referee understandably played the advantage rule, but the big keeper saved brilliantly from point blank range. Photo: Tim Edwards*
*Bottom: Tarfan Mustafa scores the winning goal with this shot to give Kingstonian the FA Trophy. Photo: Roger Turner*

*This page: Top: K's lift the Cup. Photo: Ian Morsman*
*Bottom: Celebrations! Photo: Eric Marsh*

## THIRD ROUND

Radcliffe Borough 1
Northwich Victoria 2

Havant & W'ville 0
Worcester City 1

Colwyn Bay 1,2*
Hednesford Tn 1,2*

Lincoln United 2
Bradford (PA) 5

Dulwich Hamlet 1
Whyteleafe 2

**KINGSTONIAN 5**
Kettering Town 2

Basingstoke Tn 0
Yeovil Town 2

Stalybridge Cltc 0
Hinckley Utd 3

Chorley 1
Guiseley 1

Shepshed D'mo 1,1
Emley 1,3

Aylesbury Utd 2
Newport (IoW) 0

Whitby Town 2
Frickley Ath 1

Cheltenham Tn 2
Canvey Island 1

Stevenage Boro 3
Dover Athletic 2

Crawley Town 2
Chesham Utd 3

Worthing 0
Hendon 2

Dag & R'bridge 1,1°
Farnborough Tn 1,1°

Droylsden 2
Telford United 3

Accrington Stanley 1
Ashton United 3

Hastings Town 0
St Albans City 3

Gainsboro Trinity 1
Boston United 4

Hucknall Town 1
Redditch Utd 3

Aldershot Town 1
Maidenhead Utd 0

Hitchin Town 3,1
Enfield 3,0

Weston-s-Mare 2,1
Raunds Town 2,0

Weymouth 1
Sutton United 0

**FOREST G R 4**
Witney Town 0

Woking 8
Folkestone Invicta 4

Slough Town 1
Rushden & D 2

Runcorn 2
Hyde United 1

Leigh RMI 0
Southport 1

## FOURTH ROUND

Northwich Victoria 1

Worcester City 0

Colwyn Bay 3

Bradford (PA) 1

Whyteleafe 0

**KINGSTONIAN 3**

Yeovil Town 3

Hinckley Utd 2

Guiseley 0

Emley 2

Aylesbury Utd 0

Whitby Town 1

Cheltenham Tn 0,0⁺

Stevenage Boro 0,0⁺

Chesham Utd 0

Hendon 2

Dag & R'bridge 4

Telford United 0

Ashton United 2,1

St Albans City 2,2

Boston United 2

Redditch Utd 0

Aldershot Town 1

Altrincham 2

Hitchin Town 2

Weston-s-Mare 1

Weymouth 1

**FOREST G R 2**

Woking 0,2

Rushden & D 0,1

Runcorn 2

Southport 3

## FIFTH ROUND

Northwich Victoria 3

Colwyn Bay 1

**KINGSTONIAN 1**

Yeovil Town 0

Emley 2

Whitby Town 0

Cheltenham Tn 3

Hendon 0

Dag & R'bridge 1

St Albans City 2

Boston United 2

Altrincham 0

Hitchin Town 1

**FOREST G R 2**

Woking 0,0

Southport 0,1

## SIXTH ROUND

Northwich Victoria 0
**KINGSTONIAN 2**

Emley 0
Cheltenham Tn 1

St Albans City 2
Boston United 1

**FOREST G R 4**
Southport 1

## SEMI FINALS

**KINGSTONIAN 2,3**
Cheltenham Tn 2,1

St Albans City 1,2
**FOREST G R 1,3**

## FINAL

**KINGSTONIAN**

**FOREST GREEN ROVERS**

\* Colwyn Bay won 5-4 after penalties
° Dagenham & Redbridge won 4-2 after penalties
⁺ Cheltenham Town won 5-4 after penalties

76

# FINAL

Saturday 15th May 1999

## FOREST GREEN ROVERS 0 v 1 KINGSTONIAN

Att: 20,037

Referee: A B Wilkie (Chester-le-Street)

| | |
|---|---|
| Justin Shuttlewood | Steve Farrelly |
| Ian Hedges | Tarkan Mustafa |
| Don Forbes | Colin Luckett |
| Danny Bailey (sub Gary Smart 76) | Matt Crossley |
| Mike Kilgour | Simon Stewart |
| Nathan Wigg (sub Rob Cook 58) | Mark Harris |
| Chris Honor (sub Steve Winter 58) | Gary Patterson |
| Jason Drysdale | Geoff Pitcher |
| Marc McGregor | Kevin Rattray |
| David Mehew | David Leworthy (sub Delton Francis 87) |
| Alex Sykes | Eddie Akuamoah |

| | |
|---|---|
| Subs not used: | Subs not used: |
| Steve Perrin | Jerome John |
| Matthew Coupe | Scott Corbett |
| | Danny Brown |
| | Carl Tranter |

**Goalscorer:** Tarkan Mustafa 49 mins.

The Wembley turf looks good at any time but in early May it has even more of the lawn mower advert about it, with its rolled stripes and its freshly painted image. Both sets of supporters were in good voice, aided by the P.A. system and its encouraging music. They even sang the national anthem with the fervour of a rugby crowd. Many were colourfully adorned for the day and there were few non-partisan onlookers. All were in good humour, aided by the romantic vision of two teams who, in their first year at Conference level, had acquitted themselves so creditably and found themselves at the Mecca of English football. Expectations were great but the anticipated feast never arrived, and there was precious little of the bread and butter football either, as both sides gave the ball away so the goalmouth incidents required to raise the temperature were few and far between.

In fat quarter of an hour had gone past before there was any threat to either goal. Alex Sykes had drifted one attempt well wide before David Mehew's neat control and turn put Sykes in for a much closer effort. Marc McGregor next cut down the left, bundled through Matt Crossley's challenge, and closed in on Steve Farrelly. Unfortunately by this time the ball was on his weaker right foot and Farrelly was able to block at the expense of a corner.

Kingstonian's retort came from Eddie Akuamoah's threatening dribble which ended with the ball trickling disappointingly into Justin Shuttlewood's safe clutches. Geoff Pitcher produced a teasing cross to pick out Tarkan Mustafa who shot over. The full back's next effort was on target and Shuttlewood had to punch over. K's were now on top as Kevin Rattray's header brought a save from the keeper.

Respite for Green came when McGregor forced Farrelly to his knees and Sykes twice saw a defender clear for corners. Nathan Wigg and Mehew both hooked over but the best chance of the half fell to Geoff Pitcher at the other end. He had sent a subdued David Leworthy down the left and was on hand to meet the low return but could not keep his shot down, so reaching a scoreless half time.

Four minutes after the restart K's took the lead. Shuttlewood came out to punch a long ball but only managed to flap it to the edge of his area, straight to the lurking Mustafa. He needed no prompting to volley fiercely and send the net corner billowing skywards. K's fans followed but the phlegmatic Geoff Chapple, who had already three trophy wins under his managerial belt, continued, once the score had registered, to sit impassively.

Mehew, McGregor and Sykes each had half chances but nothing to trouble the inscrutable Farrelly who was in full control of anything remotely within his gigantic reach, his best save being to fall on a powerful, low drive from McGregor.

Most of the remaining period Kingstonian were in control, threatening to add to their score through impressive Gary Patterson's volley and Rattray's header. Rovers could not raise their game sufficiently to trouble K's and so the winning of both Vase and Trophy by the same team has still to be accomplished.

*Arthur Evans*

# PAST F.A. TROPHY FINALS

1970    MACCLESFIELD TOWN 2 (Lyond, B Fidler)    TELFORD UNITED 0    Att: 28,000
Macclesfield: Cooke, Sievwright, Bennett, Beaumont, Collins, Roberts, Lyons, B Fidler,Young, Corfield, D Fidler.
Telford: Irvine, Harris, Croft, Flowers, Coton, Ray,Fudge, Hart, Bentley, Murray, Jagger.    Ref: K Walker

1971    TELFORD UTD 3 (Owen, Bentley, Fudge)    HILLINGDON BORO. 2 (Reeve, Bishop)
Telford: Irvine, Harris, Croft, Ray, Coton, Carr, Fudge, Owen, Bentley, Jagger ,Murray.    Att: 29,500
Hillingdon B.: Lowe, Batt, Langley, Higginson, Newcombe, Moore, Fairchild,Bishop, Reeve, Carter, Knox.    Ref: D Smith

1972    STAFFORD RANGERS 3 (Williams 2, Cullerton)    BARNET 0    Att: 24,000
Stafford R.: Aleksic, Chadwick, Clayton, Sargeant, Aston, Machin, Cullerton, Chapman,Williams, Bayley, Jones.
Barnet: McClelland, Lye, Jenkins, Ward, Embrey, King,Powell, Rerry, Flatt, Easton, Plume .    Ref: P Partridge

1973    SCARBOROUGH 2 (Leask, Thompson)    WIGAN ATHLETIC 1 (Rogers) aet    Att:23,000
Scarborough: Garrow, Appleton, Shoulder, Dunn, Siddle, Fagan, Donoghue, Franks,Leask (Barmby), Thompson, Hewitt.
Wigan: Reeves, Morris, Sutherland, Taylor,Jackson, Gillibrand, Clements, Oats (McCunnell), Rogers, King, Worswick. Ref: H Hackney

1974    MORECAMBE 2 (Richmond, Sutton)    DARTFORD 1 (Cunningham)    Att: 19,000
Morecambe: Coates, Pearson, Bennett, Sutton, Street, Baldwin, Done, Webber,Roberts (Galley), Kershaw, Richmond.
Dartford: Morton, Read, Payne, Carr, Burns,Binks, Light, Glozier, Robinson (Hearne), Cunningham, Halleday.    Ref: B Homewood

1975    MATLOCK TOWN 4 (Oxley, Dawson, T Fenoughty, N Fenoughty)    SCARBOROUGH 0    Att: 21,000
Matlock: Fell, McKay, Smith, Stuart, Dawson, Swan, Oxley, N Fenoughy, Scott, T Fenoughty, M Fenoughty.
Scarborough: Williams, Hewitt, Rettitt, Dunn, Marshall, Todd, Houghton, Woodall, Davidson, Barnby, Aveyard.    Ref: K Styles

1976    SCARBOROUGH 3 (Woodall, Abbey, Marshall(p))    STAFFORD R. 2 (Jones 2) aet    Att: 21,000
Scarborough: Barnard, Jackson, Marshall, H Dunn, Ayre (Donoghue), HA Dunn, Dale,Barmby, Woodall, Abbey, Hilley.
Stafford: Arnold, Ritchie, Richards, Sargeant,Seddon, Morris, Chapman, Lowe, Jones, Hutchinson, Chadwick.  Ref: R Challis

1977    SCARBOROUGH 2 (Dunn(p), Abbey)    DAGENHAM 1 (Harris)    Att: 21,500
Scarborough: Chapman, Smith, Marshall (Barmby), Dunn, Ayre, Deere, Aveyard,Donoghue, Woodall, Abbey, Dunn.
Dagenham: Hutley, Wellman, P Currie, Dunwell,Moore, W Currie, Harkins, Saul, Fox, Harris, Holder.    Ref: G Courtney

1978    ALTRINCHAM 3 (King, Johnson, Rogers)    LEATHERHEAD 1 (Cook)    Att: 20,000
Altrincham: Eales, Allan, Crossley, Bailey, Owens, King, Morris, Heathcote,Johnson, Rogers, Davidson (Flaherty).
Leatherhead: Swannell, Cooper, Eaton, Davies,Reid, Malley, Cook, Salkeld, Baker, Boyle (Bailey).    Ref: A Grey

1979    STAFFORD RANGERS 2 (A Wood 2)    KETTERING TOWN 0    Att: 32,000
Stafford: Arnold, F Wood, Willis, Sargeant, Seddon, Ritchie, Secker, Chapman, AWood, Cullerton, Chadwick (Jones).
Kettering: Lane, Ashby, Lee, Eastell, Dixey,Suddards, Flannagan, Kellock, Phipps, Clayton, Evans (Hughes).    Ref: D Richardson

1980    DAGENHAM 2 (Duck, Maycock)    MOSSLEY 1 (Smith)    Att : 26,000
Dagenham: Huttley, Wellman, Scales, Dunwell, Mooore, Durrell, Maycock, Horan,Duck, Kidd, Jones (Holder).
Mossley: Fitton, Brown, Vaughan, Gorman, Salter,Polliot, Smith, Moore, Skeete, O'Connor, Keelan (Wilson).    Ref: K Baker

1981    BISHOP'S STORTFORD 1 (Sullivan)    SUTTON UNITED 0    Att:22,578
Bishop's Stortford: Moore, Blackman, Brame, Smith (Worrell), Bradford, Abery, Sullivan,Knapman, Radford, Simmonds,
Mitchell.
Sutton Utd.: Collyer, Rogers, Green, J Rains,T Rains, Stephens (Sunnucks), Waldon, Pritchard, Cornwell, Parsons.    Ref: J Worrall

1982    ENFIELD 1 (Taylor)    ALTRINCHAM 0    Att:18.678
Enfield: Jacobs, Barrett, Tone, Jennings, Waite, Ironton, Ashford, Taylor,Holmes, Oliver (Flint), King.    Ref: B Stevens
Altrincham: Connaughton, Crossley, Davison, Bailey,Cuddy, King (Whitbread), Allan, Heathcote, Johnson, Rogers, Howard.

1983    TELFORD UTD 2 (Mather 2)    NORTHWICH VICTORIA 1 (Bennett) Att: 22,071
Telford: Charlton, Lewis, Turner, Mayman (Joseph), Walker, Easton, Barnett,Williams, Mather, Hogan, Alcock.
Northwich: Ryan, Fretwell, Murphy, Jones,Forshaw, Ward, Anderson, Abel (Bennett), Reid, Chesters, Wilson.    Ref: B Hill

1984    NORTHWICH VICTORIA 1 (Chester)    BANGOR CITY 1 (Whelan)    Att: 14,200
Replay    NORTHWICH 2 (Chesters(p), Anderson)    BANGOR 1 (Lunn)    Att: 5,805 (at Stoke)
Northwich: Ryan, Fretwell, Dean, Jones, Forshaw (Power 65), Bennett, Anderson,Abel, Reid, Chesters, Wilson.
Bangor: Letheren, Cavanagh, Gray, Whelan, Banks,Lunn, Urqhart, Morris, Carter, Howat, Sutcliffe (Westwood 105) . Same
teams in replay.    Ref: J Martin

1985    WEALDSTONE 2 (Graham, Holmes)    BOSTON UNITED 1 (Cook)    Att: 20,775
Wealdstone: Iles, Perkins, Bowgett, Byatt, Davies, Greenaway, Holmes, Wainwright,Donnellan, Graham (N Cordice 89), A Cordice.
Boston: Blackwell, Casey, Ladd,Creane, O'Brien, Thommson, Laverick (Mallender 78), Simpsom, Gilbert, Lee, Cook.  Ref: J Bray

## F.A. UMBRO TROPHY

1986      ALTRINCHAM 1 (Farrelly)      RUNCORN 0      Att: 15,700
Altrincham: Wealands, Gardner, Densmore, Johnson, Farrelly, Conning, Cuddy,Davison, Reid, Ellis, Anderson. Sub: Newton.
Runcorn: McBride, Lee, Roberts,Jones, Fraser, Smith, S Crompton (A Crompton), Imrie, Carter, Mather, Carrodus.      Ref: A Ward

1987      KIDDERMINSTER HARRIER S 0      BURTON ALBION 0      Att: 23,617
Replay      KIDDERMINSTER 2 (Davies 2)      BURTON 1 (Groves)      Att: 15,685 (at West Brom)
Kidderminster: Arnold, Barton, Boxall, Brazier (sub Hazlewood in rep), Collins (subPearson 90 at Wembley), Woodall,
McKenzie, O'Dowd, Tuohy, Casey, Davies. sub:Jones.
Burton: New, Essex, Kamara, Vaughan, Simms, Groves, Bancroft, Land, Dorsett, Redfern, (sub Wood in replay), Gauden.
Sub: Patterson.      Ref: D Shaw

1988      ENFIELD 0      TELFORD UNITED 0    Att: 20,161, Ref: L Dilkes
Replay      ENFIELD 3 (Furlong 2, Howell)      TELFORD 2 (Biggins, Norris(p))    Att: 6,912 (at W Brom)
Enfield: Pape, Cottington, Howell, Keen (sub Edmonds in rep), Sparrow (subHayzleden at Wembley), Lewis (sub Edmonds at
Wembley), Harding, Cooper, King,Furlong, Francis.
Telford: Charlton, McGinty, Storton, Nelson, Wiggins, Mayman (sub Cunningham inrep (sub Hancock)), Sankey, Joseph,
Stringer (sub Griffiths at Wembley,Griffiths in rep), Biggins, Norris.

1989      TELFORD UNITED 1 (Crawley)      MACCLESFIELD TOWN 0      Att: 18,102
Telford: Charlton, Lee, Brindley, Hancock, Wiggins, Mayman, Grainger, Joseph,Nelson, Lloyd, Stringer. Subs: Crawley, Griffiths.
Macclesfield: Zelem, Roberts, Tobin, Edwards, Hardman, Askey, Lake, Hanton,Imrie, Burr, Timmons. Subs: Devomshire, Kendall.
     Ref: T Holbrook

1990      BARROW 3 (Gordon 2, Cowperthwaite)      LEEK TOWN 0      Att: 19,011
Barrow: McDonnell, Higgins, Chilton, Skivington, Gordon, Proctor, Doherty(Burgess), Farrell (Gilmore), Cowperthwaite, Lowe, Ferris.
Leek: Simpson, Elsby (Smith), Pearce, McMullen, Clowes, Coleman (Russell),Mellor, Somerville, Sutton, Millington      Ref: T Simpson

1991      WYCOMBE W. 2 (Scott, West)      KIDDERMINSTER H. 1 (Hadley)      Att: 34,842
Wycombe: Granville, Crossley, Cash, Kerr, Creaser, Carroll, Ryan, Stapleton,West, Scott, Guppy (Hutchinson). Ref: J Watson
Kidderminster: Jones, Kurila, McGrath, Weir, Barnett, Forsyth, Joseph (Wilcox), Howell (Whitehouse), Hadley, Lilwall, Humphries

1992      COLCHESTER UTD 3 (Masters, Smith, McGavin)      WITTON ALBION 1 (Lutkevitch)      Att: 27,806
Colchester: Barrett, Donald, Roberts, Knsella, English, Martin, Cook, Masters,McDonough (Bennett 65), McGavin, Smith. Ref: K P Barratt
Witton: Mason, Halliday, Coathup, McNeilis, JimConnor, Anderson, Thomas, Rose,Alford, Grimshaw (Joe Connor), Lutkevitch (McCluskie).

1993      WYCOMBE W. 4 (Cousins, Kerr, Thompson, Carroll)      RUNCORN 1 (Shaughnessy)      Att: 32,968
Wycombe: Hyde, Cousins, Cooper, Kerr, Crossley, Thompson (Hayrettin 65),Carroll, Ryan, Hutchinson, Scott, Guppy. Sub: Casey.
Runcorn: Williams, Bates, Robertson, Hill, Harold (Connor 62), Anderson, Brady(Parker 72), Brown, Shaughnessy, McKenna, Brabin
     Ref: I J Borritt

1994      WOKING 2 (D Brown, Hay)      RUNCORN 1 (Shaw (pen))      Att: 15,818
Woking: Batty, Tucker, L Wye, Berry, Brown, Clement, Brown (Rattray 32), Fielder, Steele, Hay (Puckett 46), Walker.      Ref: Paul Durkin
Runcorn: Williams, Bates, Robertson, Shaw, Lee, Anderson, Thomas, Connor, McInerney (Hill 71), McKenna, Brabin. Sub: Parker

1995      WOKING 2 (Steele, Fielder)      KIDDERMINSTER H. 1 aet (Davies)   Att: 17,815
Woking: Batty, Tucker, L Wye, Fielder, Brown, Crumplin (Rattray 42), S Wye, Ellis, Steele, Hay (Newberry 112), Walker. Sub: Read(gk)
Kidderminster: Rose, Hodson, Bancroft, Webb, Brindley (Cartwright 94), Forsyth, Deakin, Yates, Humphreys (Hughes 105),
Davies, Purdie. Sub: Dearlove (gk)      Ref: D J Gallagher

1996      MACCLESFIELD TOWN 3 (Payne, OG, Hemmings)    NORTHWICH VICTORIA 1 (Williams)    Att: 8,672
Macclesfield: Price, Edey, Gardiner, Payne, Howarth(C), Sorvel, Lyons, Wood (Hulme 83), Coates, Power, Hemmings (Cavell 88).
Northwich: Greygoose, Ward, Duffy, Burgess (Simpson 87), Abel (Steele), Walters, Williams, Butler (C), Cooke, Humphries,
Vicary.      Ref: Mike D Reed

1997      DAGENHAM & REDBRIDGE 0      WOKING 1 Hay 112      Att: 24,376
Dagenham: Gothard, Culverhouse, Connor, Creaser, Jacques (sub Double 75), Davidon, Pratt (Naylor 81), Parratt, Broom,
Rogers, Stimson (John 65).
Woking: Batty, Brown, Howard, Foster, Taylor, S Wye, Thompson (sub Jones 115), Ellis, Steele (L Wye 108), Walker, Jackson
(Hay 77).      Ref: J Winter

1998      CHELTENHAM TOWN 1 (Eaton 74)      SOUTHPORT 0      Att: 26,387
Cheltenham: Book, Duff, Freeman, Banks, Victory, Knight (Smith 78), Howells, Bloomer, Walker (sub Milton 78), Eaton,
Watkins. Sub: Wright.
Southport: Stewart, Horner, Futcher, Ryan, Farley, Kielty, Butler, Gamble, Formby (sub Whittaker 80), Thompson (sub Bollard
88), Ross. Sub: Mitten.      Ref: G S Willard

# FA TROPHY OVERALL RECORDS

| | 1998 | 1999 | | S | P | W | L | % | Pts | Best |
|---|---|---|---|---|---|---|---|---|---|---|
| + | 2 | 1 | Altrinchm | 30 | 90 | 62 | 28 | 68.89 | 80 | W x 2 |
| - | 1 | 2 | Telford | 30 | 85 | 58 | 27 | 68.24 | 80 | W x 3 |
| = | 3 | 3 | Runcorn | 30 | 87 | 57 | 30 | 65.52 | 72 | F x 3 |
| = | 4 | 4 | Enfield | 25 | 79 | 56 | 23 | 70.89 | 70 | W x 2 |
| + | 6 | 5 | Northwich Victoria | 30 | 81 | 52 | 29 | 64.20 | 69 | W 84 |
| - | 5 | 6 | Kidderminster Harriers | 30 | 74 | 45 | 29 | 60.81 | 66 | W 87 |
| = | 7 | 7 | Stafford Rangers | 30 | 75 | 47 | 28 | 62.67 | 65 | W x 2 |
| = | 8 | 8 | Macclesfield Town | 28 | 74 | 48 | 26 | 64.86 | 62 | W x 2 |
| + | 11 | 9 | Boston United | 30 | 72 | 42 | 30 | 58.33 | 58 | F 85 |
| + | 13 | 10 | Cheltenham Town | 29 | 85 | 57 | 28 | 67.06 | 57 | W 98 |
| - | 9 | 11 | Dagenham | 18 | 67 | 50 | 17 | 74.63 | 55 | W 80 |
| - | 10 | 12 | Scarborough | 18 | 54 | 39 | 15 | 72.22 | 55 | W x 3 |
| - | 12 | 13 | Kettering Town | 30 | 63 | 33 | 30 | 52.38 | 55 | F 79 |
| = | 14 | 14 | Yeovil Town | 30 | 63 | 33 | 30 | 52.38 | 55 | SF x 2 |
| = | 15 | 15 | Wycombe Wanderers | 19 | 52 | 35 | 17 | 67.31 | 51 | W x 2 |
| = | 16 | 16 | Dartford | 26 | 64 | 38 | 26 | 59.38 | 51 | F 74 |
| = | 17 | 17 | Morecambe | 30 | 76 | 47 | 29 | 61.84 | 50 | W 74 |
| = | 18 | 18 | Burton Albion | 30 | 74 | 44 | 30 | 59.46 | 49 | F 87 |
| + | 22 | 19 | Woking | 25 | 69 | 47 | 22 | 68.12 | 48 | W x 3 |
| - | 19 | 20 | Bangor City | 22 | 53 | 31 | 22 | 58.49 | 47 | F 84 |
| + | 24 | 21 | Weymouth | 30 | 63 | 33 | 30 | 52.38 | 47 | last 8 x 2 |
| - | 20 | 22 | Barrow | 27 | 61 | 35 | 26 | 57.38 | 46 | W 90 |
| - | 21 | 23 | Bromsgrove Rovers | 30 | 68 | 38 | 30 | 55.88 | 46 | last 8 x 2 |
| - | 23 | 24 | Merthyr Tydfil | 30 | 68 | 38 | 30 | 55.88 | 45 | last 8 - 78 |
| = | 25 | 25 | Bath City | 30 | 68 | 38 | 30 | 55.88 | 42 | last 8 - 90 |
| + | 27 | 26 | Slough Town | 25 | 55 | 30 | 25 | 54.55 | 42 | SF x 2 |
| + | 29 | 27 | Worcester City | 29 | 62 | 33 | 29 | 53.23 | 42 | last 8 x 4 |
| - | 26 | 28 | Bishop Auckland | 25 | 63 | 38 | 25 | 60.32 | 41 | last 8 x 2 |
| - | 28 | 29 | Witton Albion | 30 | 79 | 49 | 30 | 62.03 | 40 | F 92 |
| = | 30 | 30 | Marine | 25 | 55 | 30 | 25 | 54.55 | 39 | SF x 2 |
| = | 31 | 31 | Nuneaton Borough | 30 | 61 | 31 | 30 | 50.82 | 38 | last 8 x 3 |
| + | 33 | 32 | Hyde United | 30 | 76 | 46 | 30 | 60.53 | 37 | SF x 3 |
| - | 32 | 33 | Barnet | 22 | 52 | 30 | 22 | 57.69 | 37 | F 72 |
| + | 35 | 34 | Sutton United | 25 | 52 | 27 | 25 | 51.92 | 37 | F 81 |
| + | 36 | 35 | Dover Athletic | 30 | 59 | 29 | 30 | 49.15 | 37 | SF 98 |
| + | 37 | 36 | Chorley | 30 | 67 | 37 | 30 | 55.22 | 36 | SF 96 |
| - | 34 | 37 | Gateshead | 29 | 61 | 32 | 29 | 52.46 | 36 | last 8 x 3 |
| = | 38 | 38 | Blyth Spartans | 25 | 50 | 25 | 25 | 50.00 | 35 | last 8 x 2 |
| = | 39 | 39 | Bedford Town | 13 | 38 | 25 | 13 | 65.79 | 34 | SF 75 |
| = | 40 | 40 | Matlock Town | 30 | 72 | 43 | 29 | 59.72 | 34 | W 75 |
| = | 41 | 41 | Grantham | 30 | 67 | 37 | 30 | 55.22 | 33 | last 8 x 2 |
| = | 42 | 42 | Welling United | 17 | 37 | 20 | 17 | 54.05 | 31 | last 8 - 89 |
| = | 43 | 43 | Chelmsford City | 30 | 62 | 32 | 30 | 51.61 | 30 | SF 70 |
| = | 44 | 44 | Maidstone United | 17 | 43 | 26 | 17 | 60.47 | 29 | last 8 x 2 |
| = | 45 | 45 | Mossley | 26 | 59 | 33 | 26 | 55.93 | 29 | F 80 |
| + | 50 | 46 | Dagenham/Redbridge | 10 | 30 | 20 | 10 | 66.67 | 27 | F 97 |

# F.A. CARLSBERG VASE

# 1998-99
# REVIEW

# FIRST QUALIFYING ROUND
### Saturday 12th September

| 1 | Goole AFC | 1 | v | 0 | Fleetwood Freeport | 255 |
|---|---|---|---|---|---|---|
| 2 | Marske United | 1 | v | 5 | Shildon | 140 |
| 3 | Woodley Sports | | v | | Blackpool (wren) Rovers | |

*walkover for Woodley Sports - Blackpool (wren) Rovers withdrawn*

| 4 | Sheffield | 1 | v | 5 | Consett | 74 |
|---|---|---|---|---|---|---|

*(at Ossett Town FC)*

| 5 | Liversedge | 3 | v | 2 | Chadderton | 94 |
|---|---|---|---|---|---|---|
| 6 | Glasshoughton Welf. | 2 | v | 4 | Maltby Main | 46 |
| 7 | Newcastle Blue Star | 1 | v | 3 | Ossett Town | 90 |
| 8 | Parkgate | 0 | v | 2 | Shotton Comrades | 46 |
| 9 | Kirkby Muxloe | 1 | v | 0 | Stafford Town | 83 |
| 10 | Ludlow Town | 1 | v | 3 | Nettleham | 98 |
| 11 | Boston Town | 1 | v | 2 | Handrahan Timber | 61 |
| 12 | Studley BKL | 0 | v | 8 | Kinton Town | 150 |
| 13 | Malvern Town | 2 | v | 0 | Bilston Comm. Coll. | 75 |
| 14 | Highfield Rangers | 3 | v | 1 | Barrow Town | 32 |
| 15 | Downes Sports | 1 | v | 3 | Stourport Swifts | 23 |
| 16 | Mickleover Sports | 3 | v | 2 | Kings Norton Town | 72 |
| 17 | Mildenhall Town | 4 | v | 1 | Toddington Rovers | 123 |
| 18 | Buckingham Ath. | 4 | v | 1 | Viking Sports | 38 |
| 19 | Kempston Rovers | 0 | v | 1 | Hullbridge Sports | 50 |

| 20 | Bedford United | 1 | v | 2 | Ruislip Manor | 44 |
|---|---|---|---|---|---|---|
| 21 | Sawbridgeworth Tn | 1 | v | 2 | Wivenhoe Town | 101 |
| 22 | Islington St Marys | 2 | v | 1 | Burnham | 37 |

*(at Burnham FC)*

| 23 | Kingsbury Town | 0 | v | 2* | Milton Keynes City | 20 |
|---|---|---|---|---|---|---|
| 24 | Downham Town | 0 | v | 1 | East Thurrock United | 57 |
| 25 | Cockfosters | 1 | v | 2 | Stowmarket Town | 80 |
| 26 | Brimsdown Rovers | 1 | v | 3 | Southend Manor | 45 |
| 27 | Slade Green | 0 | v | 1 | Merstham | 68 |
| 28 | Sheppey United | 3 | v | 2 | Erith Town | 76 |
| 29 | Lordswood | 1 | v | 3 | Newbury AFC | 76 |
| 30 | Greenwich Borough | 1 | v | 2 | Beckenham Town | 65 |
| 31 | East Cowes Victoria | 1 | v | 2 | Hungerford Town | 56 |
| 32 | Redhill | 2 | v | 1 | Whitehawk | 105 |
| 33 | Blackfield & Langley | 1 | v | 4 | Eastleigh | 129 |
| 34 | Cray Wanderers | 0 | v | 1 | Abingdon United | 74 |
| 35 | Fareham Town | 3 | v | 0 | Lancing | 106 |
| 36 | Truro City | 2 | v | 0 | Willand Rovers | 196 |
| 37 | Street | 2 | v | 1 | Frome Town | 123 |
| 38 | Harrow Hill | 1 | v | 3 | Pershore Town | 68 |
| 39 | Highworth Town | 0 | v | 2 | Brislington | 139 |

## FIRST QUALIFYING ROUND STATISTICS

**14 Home Victories**

**24 Away Victories**

1 Walkover

**Best Attendance**  255
Goole AFC v Fleetwood Freeport

**Average Attendance**  83

**Best Home Victory**  4-1
Mildenhall Town v Toddington Rovers
Buckingham Athletic v Viking Sports

**Best Away Victory**  0-8
Studley BKL v Kington Town

**Hat Tricks**
Tony Halliday (Consett), Ian Perry (Stourport Swifts)

*Mildenhall Town (Jewson Eastern Division One) 4 Toddington Rovers (Minerva Spartan South Midlands) 1*
*Stuart Oglivie steers home the fourth Mildenhall goal from close range.*
*Photo: Gordon Whittington*

# SECOND QUALIFYING ROUND
### Saturday 10th October

| | | | | | |
|---|---|---|---|---|---|
| 1 | Shildon | 2 v 3* | Maine Road | 127 | |
| 2 | Crook Town | 2 v 3 | Bootle | 78 | |
| 3 | Pickering Town | 1 v 2 | Washington | 60 | |
| 4 | South Shields | 1 v 0 | Ashington | 78 | |
| 5 | Armthorpe Welfare | 0 v 2 | Goole AFC | 176 | |
| 6 | Prescot Cables | 5 v 1 | Holker Old Boys | 110 | |
| 7 | Tadcaster Albion | 1 v 3 | Selby Town | 120 | |
| 8 | Skelmersdale Utd | 1 v 2 | Liversedge | 123 | |
| 9 | Thackley | 0 v 1 | Brodsworth | 96 | |
| 10 | Stockton | 2 v 4 | Chester-le-Street | 81 | |
| 11 | Cheadle Town | 2 v 3 | Ramsbottom United | 70 | |
| 12 | Rossendale United | 2 v 1 | East Manchester | 114 | |
| 13 | Hall Road Rangers | 1 v 2 | St Helens Town | 87 | |
| 14 | Yorkshire Amateur | 0 v 8 | Vauxhall GM | 58 | |
| 15 | Grimethorpe M. W. | 0 v 3 | Hallam | 35 | |
| 16 | Peterlee Newtown | 2 v 3 | Rossington Main | 32 | |
| 17 | Salford City | 2 v 0 | Northallerton Town | 40 | |
| 18 | Hebburn | 0 v 1 | Ossett Albion | 82 | |
| 19 | Garforth Town | 5 v 1 | Willington | 320 | |
| 20 | Ryhope CA | 0 v 2 | Morpeth Town | 35 | |
| 21 | Louth United | 2 v 1 | Jarrow Roofing Boldon | 48 | |
| 22 | Maltby Main | 0 v 3 | Brandon United | 58 | |
| 23 | Atherton Collieries | 4 v 4* | Harrogate Railway | 80 | |
| R | Harrogate Railway | 2 v 1 | Atherton Collieries | 41 | |
| 24 | Oldham Town | 2 v 5 | Easington Colliery | 39 | |
| 25 | Eccleshill United | 5 v 0 | Penrith | 84 | |
| 26 | Ossett Town | 2 v 0 | Whickham | 73 | |
| 27 | Woodley Sports | 2 v 0 | Prudhoe Town | 80 | |

| | | | | | |
|---|---|---|---|---|---|
| 28 | Shotton Comrades | 1 v 3 | West Allotment Celtic | 45 | |
| 29 | Evenwood Town | 1 v 3 | Consett | 62 | |
| 30 | Bacup Borough | 1 v 3 | Darwen | 72 | |
| | 1st game abandoned due to floodlight failure | | | | |
| 31 | Worsbro Bridge MW | 5 v 3 | Horden CW | 90 | |
| 32 | Nantwich Town | 4 v 1 | Glapwell | 59 | |
| 33 | Rushall Olympic | 3 v 1 | Nettleham | 60 | |
| 34 | Pelsall Villa | 2 v 2* | Sandiacre Town | 76 | |
| R | Sandiacre Town | 1 v 2 | Pelsall Villa | 79 | |
| 35 | Gornal Athletic | 4 v 0 | Walsall Wood | 45 | |
| 36 | Ibstock Welfare | 3 v 1 | Stourport Swifts | 77 | |
| 37 | Lye Town | 4 v 4* | Gedling Town | 30 | |
| R | Gedling Town | 3 v 0 | Lye Town | 65 | |
| 38 | West Mids Police | 2 v 2 | Stewarts & Lloyds | 41 | |
| R | Stewarts & Lloyds | 0 v 1 | West Midlands Police | 52 | |
| 39 | Bridgnorth Town | 1 v 5 | Highfield Rangers | 92 | |
| 40 | Kings Heath | 1 v 2 | Bolehall Swifts | 48 | |
| 41 | Wednesfield | 4 v 5 | Kirkby Muxloe | 65 | |
| 42 | Glossop North End | 2 v 1 | Sandwell Borough | 143 | |
| 43 | Long Eaton United | 1 v 4 | Oldbury United | 83 | |
| 44 | Mickleover Sports | 3 v 3* | Shirebrook Town | 44 | |
| | Shirebrook Town | 1 v 3 | Mickleover Sports | 72 | |
| 45 | Rainworth MW | 3 v 0 | Holbeach United | 60 | |
| 46 | Blackstone | 4 v 2 | Leek CSOB | 76 | |
| 47 | Friar Lane OB | 3 v 4 | Stratford Town | 76 | |
| 48 | Holwell Sports | 10 v 1 | Highgate United | 83 | |
| 49 | Willenhall Town | 2 v 0 | Barwell | 112 | |
| 50 | Meir KA | 8 v 0 | Malvern Town | 68 | |
| 51 | Long Buckby | 2 v 5* | Handrahan Timbers | 67 | |
| 52 | Borrowash Victoria | 0 v 1 | Heanor Town | 130 | |
| 53 | Chasetown | 7 v 0 | Tividale | 71 | |
| 54 | Knypersley Victoria | 1 v 1* | Arnold Town | 90 | |
| | Arnold Town | 2 v 0 | Knypersley Victoria | 157 | |
| 55 | Newcastle Town | 1 v 1* | Desborough Town | 101 | |
| | Desborough Town | 1 v 2 | Newcastle Town | 142 | |
| 56 | Staveley MW | 2 v 1 | Dunkirk | 76 | |
| 57 | St Andrews | 3 v 2 | Halesowen Harriers | 62 | |
| 58 | Stapenhill | 1 v 0 | Anstey Nomads | 63 | |
| 59 | Westfields | 2 v 1 | Shifnal Town | 64 | |
| 60 | Boldmere St Mich's | 3 v 0 | Bourne Town | 90 | |
| 61 | Kington Town | 6 v 4* | Kimberley Town | 188 | |
| 62 | Mildenhall Town | 2 v 0 | Brightlingsea United | 80 | |
| 63 | Swaffham Town | 2 v 1 | Ruislip Manor | 87 | |
| 64 | Flackwell Heath | 1 v 1* | Sttansted | 69 | |
| | Stansted | 4 v 1 | Flackwell Heath | 32 | |
| 65 | Bury Town | 1 v 3 | Beaconsfield SYCOB | 124 | |
| 66 | March Town United | 1 v 2 | Clapton | 56 | |
| 67 | Stowmarket Town | 3 v 0 | Brook House | 130 | |
| 68 | Wingate & Finchley | 0 v 4 | Ilford | 92 | |
| 69 | Yaxley | 7 v 2 | Soham Town Rangers | 139 | |
| 70 | Clacton Town | 3 v 1 | Hadleigh United | 120 | |
| 71 | Islington St Marys | 2 v 1 | Southend Manor | 25 | |
| | (at Southend Manor) | | | | |
| 72 | Barkingside | 2 v 1 | Southall | 50 | |
| 73 | Biggleswade Town | 1 v 4 | Bedford Town | 320 | |
| 74 | Needham Market | 1 v 2 | Saffron Walden Town | 117 | |

*Glossop v Sandwell Borough. Trevor Smallwood of Glossop chases Sandwell Borough's Brett Hayward during his side's 2-1 FA Vase triumph.*
*Photo: Colin Stevens*

| No. | Home | | v | | Away | No. |
|---|---|---|---|---|---|---|
| 75 | Amersham Town | 1 | v | 2 | Tiptree United | 40 |
| 76 | Potton United | 0 | v | 5 | Wellingborough Town | 40 |
| 77 | Somersham Town | 0 | v | 6 | Hornchurch | 56 |
| 78 | East Thurrock Utd | 1 | v | 0 | Felixstowe P & T | 63 |
| 79 | Wivenhoe Town | 2 | v | 4* | Harlow Town | 168 |
| 80 | Tilbury | 4 | v | 0 | Burnham Ramblers | 64 |
| 81 | Thetford Town | 2 | v | 0 | Hoddeson Town | 83 |
| 82 | Fakenham Town | 2 | v | 0 | Norwich United | 130 |
| 83 | Edgware Town | 4 | v | 2 | Harwich & Parkeston | 110 |
| 84 | Concord Rangers | 1 | v | 3* | Ware | 50 |
| 85 | Milton Keynes City | 0 | v | 2 | Letchworth | 45 |
| 86 | Watton United | 1 | v | 0 | Wooton Blue Cross | 84 |
| 87 | Newmarket Town | 3 | v | 0* | Cornard united | 170 |
| 88 | Buckingham Ath | 3 | v | 1 | Witham Town | 48 |
| 89 | Bowers United | 4 | v | 1 | Maldon Town | 69 |
| 90 | St Neots Town | 4 | v | 4* | Hullbridge Sports | 86 |
| R | Hullbridge Sports | 1 | v | 1* | St Neots Town | 104 |
| | (St Neots won 5-4 after penalties) | | | | | |
| 91 | Royston Town | 2 | v | 1 | Banbury United | 93 |
| 92 | Warboys Town | 0 | v | 3 | Chalfont St Peter | 88 |
| 93 | Tring Town | 0 | v | 1 | Ford United | 36 |
| 94 | Gt. Yarmouth Town | 1 | v | 0 | Halstead Town | 135 |
| 95 | Bicester Town | 2 | v | 2* | Hertford Town | 78 |
| R | Hertford Town | 0 | v | 1 | Bicester Town | 60 |
| 96 | Welwyn Garden C | 3 | v | 2* | London Colney | 68 |
| 97 | Waltham Abbey | 3 | v | 0 | Ipswich Wanderers | 86 |
| 98 | Eynesbury Rovers | 4 | v | 1 | Haverhill Rovers | 43 |
| 99 | Basildon United | 2 | v | 1 | Langford | 56 |
| 100 | Ford Sports Dav'try | 4 | v | 2 | Hillingdon Borough | 53 |
| 101 | Whitton United | 0 | v | 3 | Leighton Town | 90 |
| 102 | Harpenden Town | 3 | v | 0 | Stanway Rovers | 41 |
| 103 | Aveley | 3 | v | 0 | Gorleston | 67 |
| 104 | Hanwell Town | 1 | v | 2 | Lowestoft Town | 51 |
| 105 | Hem. Hempstead T | 2 | v | 4* | Cheshunt | 131 |
| 106 | Merstham | 2 | v | 1 | Eastbourne Town | 73 |
| 107 | Ringmer | 2 | v | 0 | Whitchurch United | 80 |
| 108 | Kintbury Rangers | 2 | v | 3 | Hassocks | 64 |
| 109 | Totton AFC | 0 | v | 1 | Cobham | 92 |
| 110 | Epsom & Ewell | 2 | v | 1* | Bracknell Town | 105 |
| 111 | Wick | 5 | v | 0 | Hailsham Town | 108 |
| 112 | Raynes Park Vale | 2 | v | 3* | Croydon Athletic | 50 |
| 113 | Carterton Town | 0 | v | 0* | Sidley United | 35 |
| R | Sidley United | 1 | v | 0 | Carterton Town | 205 |
| 114 | Didcot Town | 5 | v | 3* | Farnham Town | 50 |
| 115 | Ash United | 2 | v | 1 | Three Bridges | 71 |
| 116 | Dorking | 1 | v | 2 | Chichester City | 60 |
| 117 | Redhill | 3 | v | 2 | Hythe United | 109 |
| 118 | Abingdon United | 2 | v | 0 | East Grinstead Town | 63 |
| 119 | Romsey Town | 1 | v | 9 | Hungerford Town | 95 |
| 120 | East Preston | 1 | v | 2* | Pagham | 113 |
| 121 | Portsmouth RN | 0 | v | 2 | Chipstead | 36 |
| 122 | Met Police | 0 | v | 1 | Fareham Town | 89 |
| 123 | Oakwood | 2 | v | 4 | Southwick | 45 |
| | (at Southwick FC) | | | | | |
| 124 | Chatham Town | 2 | v | 4* | Cove | 54 |
| 125 | Ramsgate | 3 | v | 0 | Newbury AFC | 102 |
| 126 | Corinthian Casuals | 5 | v | 1 | Crowborough Athletic | 45 |
| 127 | Saltdean United | 2 | v | 4 | Windsor & Eton | 127 |
| 128 | Sheppey United | 2 | v | 0 | BAT Sports | 73 |
| 129 | Beckenham Town | 0 | v | 2 | Horsham YMCA | 54 |
| 130 | Sandhurst Town | 4 | v | 2* | Bournemouth | 87 |
| 131 | Camberley Town | 1 | v | 0 | Portfield | 70 |
| 132 | Reading Town | 2 | v | 1 | Ashford Town (Middx) | 45 |
| 133 | Bedfont | 3 | v | 1* | Selsey | 50 |

*Langford goalkeeper Ross Silverman takes a cross under pressure from Basildon's Micky Munro.*

Photo: Alan Coomes

| | | | | | | | | | | | | |
|---|---|---|---|---|---|---|---|---|---|---|---|---|
| 134 | Lewes | 1 | v | 4 | Egham Town | 101 | | 148 | Newquay | 3 | v | 2 | Hallen | 94 |
| 135 | Gosport Borough | 1 | v | 0 | Langney Sports | 109 | | 149 | Backwell United | 0 | v | 2 | Paulton Rovers | 103 |
| 136 | Horsham | 0 | v | 2 | Camberley Town | 192 | | 150 | Bideford | 2 | v | 1 | Welton Rovers | 82 |
| 137 | Thamesmead Tn | 1 | v | 0 | Christchurch | 39 | | 151 | Barnstaple Town | 1 | v | 1* | Odd Down | 171 |
| 138 | North Leigh | 4 | v | 1 | Arundel | 84 | | R | Odd Down | 1 | v | 4 | Barnstaple Town | 59 |
| 139 | Godalming & G'ford | 0 | v | 4 | Deal Town | 96 | | 152 | St Blazey | 5 | v | 1 | Almondsbury Town | 83 |
| 140 | Tunbridge Wells | 3 | v | 0 | Wantage Town | 94 | | 153 | Bridport | 7 | v | 2 | Calne Town | 137 |
| 141 | Shoreham | 0 | v | 3 | Eastleigh | 112 | | 154 | Elmore | 1 | v | 4 | Ilfracombe Town | 74 |
| 142 | Brockenhurst | 5 | v | 1 | Chard Town | 94 | | 155 | Wellington Town | 1 | v | 0 | Shortwood United | 50 |
| 143 | Westbury United | 1 | v | 4 | Melksham Town | 220 | | 156 | Bridgwater Town | 0 | v | 1 | Falmouth Town | 199 |
| 144 | Bemerton Hth Hqns | 3 | v | 0 | Warminster Town | 85 | | 157 | Keynsham Town | 1 | v | 3 | Minehead Town | 101 |
| 145 | Street | 0 | v | 2 | Devizes Town | 96 | | 158 | Tuffley Rovers | 0 | v | 1 | Truro City | 70 |
| 146 | Brislington | 4 | v | 0 | Glastonbury | 32 | | 159 | Bishop Sutton | 0 | v | 1 | Dawlish Town | 56 |
| 147 | Downton | 1 | v | 2 | Pershore Town | 53 | | 160 | Fairford Town | 2 | v | 0 | Torrington | 54 |

## SECOND QUALIFYING ROUND STATISTICS

**85 Home Victories**

**74 Away Victories**

1 Decided after Penalties

**Best Attendance**  320
Garforth Town v Willington
Biggleswade Town v Bedford Town

**Average Attendance**  91

**Best Home Victory**  10-1
Holwell Sports v Highgate United

**Best Away Victory**  1-9
Romsey Town v Hungerford Town

**Hat Tricks**

**4**
Kevin Randle (Yaxley), Matt Harby (Holwell Sports),
Kevin Thompson (Vauxhall GM),
Chris Driver (Worsbrough Bridge)

**3**
Kirk Master (Highfield Rangers), Andy Banks (Chasetown),
Dean Culpin (Kirby Muxloe),
David Toomey (Hungerford Town),
John Morton (Blackstone), Nic Andrews (Cove),
Sammy Percival (Stratford Town),
Dennis Greene (Windsor & Eton),
Graham Keast (Holwell Sports), David Logie (Bedfont),
Neil Perks (Handrahan Timbers),
Brian Green (Eastleigh) including his first in 20 seconds

Left: Clinton More, Wick, beats Dave
Winterton, Hailsham Town's goalkeeper
for Wick's fifth goal.
Photo: Roger Turner

Right: Ian Green (Long Buckby) shoots
over the Handrahan bar.
Photo: Keith Clayton

## GET ALL THE LATEST NEWS ON THE

**THE FOOTBALL ASSOCIATION**

# COMPETITIONS NEWSLINE

Updated daily with Draws, Match Dates, Change of Venues, Kick-off Times and Midweek Results for the F.A. Cup sponsored by AXA, F.A. Umbro Trophy, F.A. Carlsberg Vase, The Times F.A. Youth Cup, AXA F.A. Women's Cup and F.A. Umbro Sunday Cup. Saturday & Sunday results will be on the Newsline after 6.30pm – Cup draws on Monday after 1.00pm.

## PHONE NOW
# 09066 555 888

Presented by Tony Incenzo

Marketed by Sportslines, Common Road, Evesham on 01386 47302

Calls cost 60p per minute at all times.

# OR FAX-BACK ON
# 09065 511 051

Weekend results, Monday draws and midweek fixtures and results service

Calls cost £1.00 per minute at all times.
Call costing correct at time of going to press (June 1999).

# FIRST ROUND
### Saturday 7th November

| Clubs | Ely City |
|---|---|
| receiving EXEMPTION | Endsleigh |
| to the First Round Proper | Guisborough Town |
| | Littlehampton Town |
| Arlesey Town | Mangotsfield United |
| Atherton LR | Marlow |
| Barking | Northampton Spencer |
| Billingham Synthonia | Northwood |
| Birstall United | Peacehaven & Telscombe |
| Bodmin Town | Poulton Victoria |
| Brigg Town | Rocester |
| Buckingham Town | Seaham Red Star |
| Chippenham Town | Stotfold |
| Cowes Sports | Thatcham Town |
| Curzon Ashton | Warrington Town |
| Denaby United | West Auckland Town |
| Diss Town | Whitstable Town |
| Durham City | Wimborne Town |

1 West Auckland Town 1 v 0 Bootle 111
Stout 60

2 Maine Road 2 v 2* Brodsworth 49
Radford 17, Perkins 79 Crane 32, Brown 76

*R* Brodsworth 1 v 3* Maine Road 127
Schofield 36 Wadsworth 26, Hall 95,
Thomas 99

3 St Helens Town 2 v 1 Brigg Town 131
Walker 31, Pennington 62 Ward 72

4 Curzon Ashton 1 v 3 Hallam 65
Colley 3, Hopkinson 63
Goddard 80.

5 Poulton Victoria 0 v 2 Louth United 105
West 60, Wilson 70

6 Liversedge 4 v 2 Rossendale United 116
Carter 26, Lawford 45, 72, Butters 6, Heys 82
Toronczak 53.

7 Guisborough Town 1 v 2 Ossett Town 166
Hutchinson 11 Stabb 65, Sayer 82.

8 Chester-le-Street Tn 2 v 1 Durham City 202
Bryson 75, Jewson 80 Todd 44

9 Washington 1 v 6 Prescot Cables 52
O'Donnovan 40 **Eddie Taylor** 10, 33, 55,
Cuminskey 15, 66,
MacDonald 75.

10 Warrington Town 3 v 1* Ossett Albion 115
Nestor 90, Whitehead 103 Day 10
Tyrell 121 (p).

11 Selby Town 2 v 3 Consett 123
Oldfield 63, Collier 84 Halliday 15, Robson 27, 87.

12 Morpeth Town 2 v 1 Denaby United 81
Burgess 18, Leech 61 Hobson 81

13 Rossington Main 2 v 5 Goole AFC 220
Henderson 23, Fern 65 Nevis 10, Horne 4, 43,
Gibson 50, Lanaghan 47

14 Seaham Red Star 3 v 1 West Allotment Celtic 74
Gallagher 43, Taylor 65 Fitzpatrick 30
Holt 80

15 Easington Colliery 2 v 0 Salford City 33
McKenna 10, 53

16 Atherton LR 1 v 5 Billingham Synthonia 100
Cunningham 87 OG 2, Wilkinson 16, 57,
Wood 34, Rowntree 81.

17 Darwen 1 v 3 Eccleshill United 69
Lynch 84 Megson 47, 80, McGowan 90

18 Worsbro Bdge MW 1 v 4 Garforth Town 140
Wetton 69 Watson 34, Allen 62,
Falk 84, Ramsden 88.

19 Ramsbottom United 4 v 1 Woodley Sports 190
Goodall 9, Orrell 47, McNeil 1
O'Brien 77, Langhorn 80.

20 Brandon United 5 v 1 Harrogate Railway 66
Darvill 70

21 Vauxhall GM 1 v 0 South Shields 73
Lacy 31

22 Arnold Town 3 v 1 Kirkby Muxloe 139
Irons 40, OG 48 OG
Williams 86

23 West Mids Police 1 v 3 Holwell Sports 81
Hancox Keast 30, 46, Houghton 59

24 Stratford Town 1 v 2 Chasetown 69
Bradley 90 Tulloch 14, Leadbeater 69

25 Boldmere St Michael 2 v 3 Mickleover Sports 95
Canning 63 (p), Bluck 27 Barnes 78, Hudson 68,
Parkins 90

26 Rainworth MW 0 v 7 Rushall Olympic 105
**Steve Ball** 15, 27 (p), 58,
Pickstone 30, Richards 40,
Gregory 77, Welburn 87.

27 Gornal Athletic 0 v 2 Staveley MW 57
Thomson 14, Godber 48

28 Ibstock Welfare 2 v 1 Westfields 106
Sullivan 50, Hession 53 Eversham 87

29 Stapenhill 1 v 2 St Andrews 70
Freeman 20 Knight 47, Marsden 57

30 Gedling Town 0 v 3 Kington Town 58
Savory 31, Kelly 60, King 85

31 Rocester 5 v 0 Handrahan Timbers 90
Owen 50, OG 68, Booth 80
Langston 85, 90

32 Northampton Spncr 2 v 4 Nantwich Town 42
York 45, Coleman 51 Dawson 15, Griggs 82, 88,
Scarlett 84.

33 Pelsall Villa 1 v 3 Oldbury United 86
Lee 89 Wright 3, Grosvenor 26,
Young 69

34 Heanor Town 7 v 2 Blackstone 139
**Glyn Stacey** 8, 45, 51, Bull 40, Morton 86
Johnson 4, Preston 46,
Townsend 71, 72.

35 Birstall United 3 v 0 Glossop North End 124
White 3, Orme 19
Connolly 87.

36 Bolehall Swifts 2 v 0 Ely City 57
Mayne 30, Casey 90

37 Meir KA 2 v 0 Willenhall Town 75
Moran 5, 48

38 Newcastle Town 0 v 1 Highfield Rangers 85
Master 70

39 Redhill 2 v 1 Sheppey United 122
Newman 15, 60 Toms 89

40 Welwyn Garden City 1 v 3 Windsor & Eton 112
Templeton 65 Evans 37, Murphy 68,
Greene 88

| # | Home | | | Away | # |
|---|------|---|---|------|---|
| 41 | Bowers United<br>Warner 38, 67, Mully 87 | 3 | 0 | Waltham Abbey | 45 |
| 42 | Newmarket Town<br>Ansell 59, 90 | 2 | 2* | Barking<br>O'Sullivan 62, Rogan 58 | 154 |
| R | Barking<br>Haylock 17, Kennedy 70 | 2 | 2* | Newmarket Town | 124 |
| | (Newmarket Town won 4-2 after penalties) | | | | |
| 43 | Ilford | 0 | 3 | Yaxley<br>**David Robertson** 14,25,89(p) | 86 |
| 44 | Swaffham Town<br>Blockwell 86 | 1 | 2 | Royston Town<br>Miles 23, 45 | 106 |
| 45 | Hungerford Town<br>Sly 17 (p) | 1 | 0 | Gosport Borough | 129 |
| 46 | Tunbridge Wells<br>McCarthy 72, OG 75 | 2 | 1 | Leighton Town<br>Walters 41 | 102 |
| 47 | Barkingside<br>Bajada 95 | 1 | 0* | Croydon Athletic | 46 |
| 48 | Fareham Town | 0 | 1 | Letchworth | 123 |
| 49 | Buckingham Town<br>Dowling 18, 43<br>Harmon 40, 52 | 4 | 2 | Marlow<br>Walsh 72, Anson 81 | 116 |
| 50 | St Neots Town<br>Atkins 9, Jons 14,<br>McCreanor 35<br>Pope 86 | 4 | 1 | Pagham<br>Smith 30 (p) | 110 |
| 51 | Lowestoft Town<br>Crick 5 | 3 | 1 | Wellingborough Tn | 238 |
| 52 | Canterbury City | 0 | 1 | Northwood<br>Barnard 27 | 74 |
| 53 | Tiptree United<br>Houghton 10<br>Warwick 18, 70, Devito 80 | 4 | 1 | Cowes Sports<br>Dent 30 | 160 |
| 54 | Sidley United<br>Loft 45, 48<br>Heritage 65, 87 | 4 | 2 | Clapton<br>Allen 26, Thorne 88 | 207 |
| 55 | Basildon United<br>OG 25, Cox 28, Finning 59 | 3 | 0 | Beaconsfield SYCOB | 66 |
| 56 | Ware | 0 | 3 | Hassocks<br>Burt 47, Wilson 45,<br>Emmerson 75 | 101 |
| 57 | Stowmarket Town<br>Trinder 31, Vincent 56<br>Platt 58, Parker 65, 85<br>Burman 70 | 6 | 1 | Littlehampton Town | 147 |
| 58 | Aveley<br>Reed 16, Roudette 119 | 2 | 1* | Whitstable Town<br>Horton 60 | 128 |
| 59 | Fakenham Town<br>Howard 65, 92, Coe 98 | 3 | 2 | Egham Town<br>Whittle 18, 35 | 157 |
| 60 | Merstham<br>Pennels 60 | 1 | 5 | Deal Town<br>Appleton 34, Graham 21, 75,<br>Seager 57, Schweiso 85. | 91 |
| 61 | Saffron Walden Tn<br>Herd 70 | 1 | 0 | Chalfont St Peter | 230 |
| 62 | Buckingham Ath<br>Taibor 5, Quinn 18<br>Broughton 29 | 3 | 2 | Islington St Marys | 40 |
| 63 | Hornchurch | 0 | 1 | Cheshunt<br>Sinclair-Menzies 84 | 65 |
| 64 | Thetford Town<br>Carter 84, 80, Sims 69 | 3 | 2 | Corinthian Casuals<br>Freeborough 40,<br>Raishbrook 62 | 130 |
| 65 | Diss Town<br>Jopling 17 | 1 | 0 | Edgware Town | 241 |
| 66 | Abingdon Town | 0 | 2 | North Leigh | 106 |
| 67 | Horsham YMCA<br>Butcher 79 | 1 | 0 | Ringmer | 100 |
| 68 | Ford United<br>Devereux 51, Wood 59<br>Parish 29, 112 | 4 | 4* | Bedfont<br>**David Logie**<br>50, 72, 80, 115 | 94 |
| R | Bedfont | 0 | 1 | Ford United<br>Wood 50 | 130 |

*Curzon Ashton's Mark Leacock tries an acrobatic kick during his team's 3-1 defeat at home to Hallam FC.*
*Photo: Colin Stevens*

88

# F.A. CARLSBERG VASE

| | | | | | |
|---|---|---|---|---|---|
| 69 | Cobham | 6 v | 2* | Peacehaven & Tels. | 62 |
| | Robinson 1, 80, Gale 8 | | | Wiltshire 35, Merry 89 | |
| | Gray 37, Tilbury 62 | | | | |
| | Petruzziello 77 | | | | |
| 70 | Reading Town | 1 v | 2 | Bicester Town | 46 |
| | Parr 16 | | | Allen 32, Darch 75 | |
| 71 | Thamesmead Town | 5 v | 0 | Watton United | 55 |
| | Heselden 50, 81 | | | | |
| | Waithe 67, 85 | | | | |
| | Simmons 70 | | | | |
| 72 | Cove | 0 v | 6 | Camberley | 84 |
| | | | | J Sills, Powell, Lloyd, | |
| | | | | T Sills 2, Harkness | |
| 73 | Didcot Town | 0 v | 3 | Harlow Town | 88 |
| | | | | Nicholson 63, Samuels 83, | |
| | | | | Salmon 89. | |
| 74 | Tilbury | 1 v | 3 | Wick | 73 |
| | Francois 52 | | | More 8, Smith 38, Moore 89 | |
| 75 | Gt Yarmouth Town | 0 v | 2 | East Thurrock United | 149 |
| | | | | Lee 47, Greaves 80 | |
| 76 | Mildenhall Town | 3 v | 1 | Sandhurst Town | 132 |
| | Brown 24, Allis 73 | | | OG 90 | |
| | Ogilvie 82 | | | | |
| 77 | Chipstead | 3 v | 2 | Arlesey Town | 70 |
| | Maslona 40, 44 | | | OG22, Spring 32 | |
| | Munslow 90 | | | | |
| 78 | Thatcham Town | 4 v | 0 | Chichester City | 124 |
| | Baily 53, Anderson 79 | | | | |
| | Whorriskey 84, Gust 89 | | | | |
| 79 | Eastleigh | 0 v | 1 | Clacton Town | 114 |
| | | | | Hepburn 5 | |
| 80 | Stotfold | 1 v | 0 | Ford Sports Daventry | 133 |
| | Heard 81 | | | | |
| 81 | Harpenden Town | 0 v | 1 | Ramsgate | 84 |
| | | | | Court 8 | |
| 82 | Epsom & Ewell | 1 v | 1* | Stansted | 52 |
| | Tome 23 | | | Ansah 90 | |
| R | Stansted | 0 v | 5 | Epsom & Ewell | 78 |
| | | | | Martyn Jones 63, 66, 83 | |
| | | | | Grant 27, Owen 28 (p) | |
| 83 | Southwick | 2 v | 4 | Ash United | 125 |
| | Woods 50, Hewitt 63 | | | Kean 28, Horton 54, | |
| | | | | Woodhouse 51 (p) 55 (p) | |
| 84 | Bedford Town | 3 v | 1 | Eynesbury Rovers | 460 |
| | Covington 58, Joyce 77 | | | Meeds 52 | |
| | Reed 90 | | | | |
| 85 | Devizes Town | 0 v | 1 | Brislington | 77 |
| | | | | Rose 48 | |
| 86 | Minehead Town | 2 v | 1* | Falmouth Town | 233 |
| | Morgan 25, Burr 107 | | | Sidey 53 | |
| 87 | EFC Cheltenham | 1 v | 2 | Barnstaple Town | 67 |
| | Paul 27 | | | Stevens 45, Gough 90 | |
| 88 | Newquay | 2 v | 0 | Brockenhurst | 124 |
| | Lentern 60, Robins 78 | | | | |
| 89 | Fairford Town | 2 v | 1 | Truro City | 86 |
| | Flynn 22, 24 | | | Wherry 59 | |
| 90 | St Blazey | 1 v | 0 | Mangotsfield United | 134 |
| | Waddell 56 | | | | |
| 91 | Bideford | 2 v | 3* | Wellington Town | 79 |
| | Vittells 2, Shell 80 | | | Prevosi 33, Pocock 40, | |
| | | | | Jenkins 117. | |
| 92 | Pershore Town | 0 v | 2* | Ilfracombe Town | 97 |
| | | | | Burns 95, Brereton 117 | |
| 93 | Dawlish Town | 3 v | 1 | Bodmin Town | 119 |
| | Charlesworth 40, 65 | | | Daly 4 | |
| | Cadwallader 70 | | | | |
| 94 | Bridport | 2 v | 1 | Paulton Rovers | 129 |
| | Drake 23, Carrter 30 | | | Ponfield 58 | |
| 95 | Melksham Town | 3 v | 1 | Wimborne Town | 196 |
| | Brooks 50, Lewis 68, 90 | | | Taylor 70 | |
| 96 | Bemerton Hth Harl. | 2 v | 1 | Chippenham Town | 89 |
| | Brice 35, Maynard 89 | | | Townsend 67 | |

*Ibstock Welfare 2 Westfields 1. First half action from The Welfare Ground as Westfields attack the Ibstock goal.*
*Photo: Martin Wray*

# FIRST ROUND STATISTICS

35 **Home Victories**

28 **Away Victories**

2 Replays
1 Penalty Shoot Out

**Best Attendance** 460
Bedford Town v Eynesbury Rovers

**Average Attendance** 116

**Best Home Victory** 7-2
Heanor Town v Blackstone

**Best Away Victory** 0-7
Rainworth MW v Rushall Olympic

**Hat Tricks**
**(4)** David Logie (Bedford)
**(3)** Eddie Taylor (Prescot Cables),
Steve Ball (Rushall Olympic), Glyn Stacey (Heanor Town),
David Robertson (Yaxley), Martyn Jones (Epsom & Ewell)

*Top: James King, Clapton (stripes) takes the ball around a Sidley United player.*      *Photo: Roger Turner*

*Bottom: Minehead v Falmouth Town. Minehead goalkeeper, Mark Coombe, punches clear in the closely contested tie with Falmouth Town.*      *Photo: Ken Gregory*

# SECOND ROUND
### Saturday 28th November

Clubs receiving
EXEMPTION
to the Second Round

| | |
|---|---|
| Abingdon Town | North Ferriby United |
| Banstead Athletic | Oadby Town |
| Bedlington Terriers | Porthleven |
| Billingham Town | Potters Bar Town |
| Brache Sparta | Spalding United |
| Burgess Hill Town | Sudbury Town |
| Buxton | Sudbury Wanderers |
| Clitheroe | Swindon Supermarine |
| Dunston F.B. | Taunton Town |
| Great Wakering Rovers | Tiverton Town |
| Herne bay | Thame United |
| Histon | Tow law Town |
| Kidsgrove Athletic | Tooting & Mitcham United |
| Lymington & New Milton | Wokingham Town |
| Mossley | Workington |
| | Wroxham |
| | Woodbridge Town |

1   Ossett Town   2   v   3   Seaham Red Star   157
Sayer 17, Stabb 58    Taylor 30, Pearson 75, Holt 115

2   Garforth Town   4   v   2*   Prescot Cables   301
Darren Falk 45, 86, 91    Cuminskey 60 (p), 75 (p)

3   Bedlington Terriers   3   v   0   Ramsbottom United   200
Gibb 13, 68, Milner 55

4   North Ferriby Utd   0   v   1   Workington   236
Gray 47

5   Bill'ham Synthonia   2   v   5*   Tow Law Town   220
Wood 50, Slaven 60    Nelson 18, Nash 25, Moorhead 97, Bailey 100, Robinson 115

6   Clitheroe   1   v   0*   West Auckland Town   210
OG (Bainbridge) 116

7   Eccleshill United   3   v   2   Hallam   69
Cochrane 43, 87, Megson 71

8   Dunston FB   2   v   1   Maine Road   122
Fletcher 26, Keegan 42    Brown 40

9   Vauxhall GM   4   v   2   Easington Colliery   72
Young 17, Spellman 25, Williams 45, Connor 57    Allen 53, 80.

10   Mossley   3   v   1   Consett   172
Mark Murray 28, 73, 87

11   St Helens Town   2   v   2*   Morpeth Town   167
Griffiths 27, 43    Pyle 20, Power 89

R   Morpeth Town   0   v   4   St Helens Town   81
Pennington 44, Griffiths 59, 80, Walker 62

12   Brandon United   3   v   1   Liversedge   63
Clarke 33, 37    Dunderdale 14
Cunningham 75

13   Billingham Town   2   v   1*   Chester-le-Street Town   78
Woodhouse 25, 115    Nixon 5

14   Warrington Town   2   v   0   Louth United   104
Edwards 4, Tyrell 15

15   Heanor Town   4   v   2*   Rushall Olympic   173
Stewart 44, Tomlin 99, Smith 105, Aldred 110    Ball 75, Howells 100

16   Mickleover Sports   2   v   1   Stotfold   185
Yeomans 75, Parkins 87    Price 58

17   Spalding United   5   v   2   Rocester   302

---

Dolby 28, Wilson 39, 63      Ede 41, Poxon 87
Drake 83, 1 OG

18   Birstall United   0   v   1   Oadby Town   203
Hunter 13

19   Highfield Rangers   3   v   1   Holwell Sports   97
Ndokwu 30, 81 Lessett 88    Mogg 70

20   Staveley M.W.   1   v   0   Nantwich Town   107
Godber 8

21   Arnold Town   3   v   4*   Wroxham   195
Irons 2, Gunn 73, Elliott 90    Danby 10, 102, Johnson 28, Pauling 79

22   Chasetown   1   v   0   Histon   111
Jackson 74

23   St Andrews   3   v   2   Buxton   115
Anastasi 12, Wood 20    Wilson 32, OG 55
Marsden 75

24   Goole   2   v   1   Meir KA   323
Nevis 33, 65    Reanes 90

25   Ibstock Welfare   0   v   5   Bedford Town   324
Jaggard 7, Covington 48, 60, Sherlock 76, 87

26   Kidsgrove Athletic   5   v   3   Bolehall Swifts   150
Dundas 7, 44 (p), Evans 9    Cassey 40, 60, Haywood 75
Hobby 24, Jones 37

27   Kington Town   4   v   5   Oldbury United   200
Savory 30, 118    Hesson 7, 46, Murphy 64,
Holmans 75, 89.    Wright 119, Young 118.

28   Fakenham Town   2   v   1   Epsom & Ewell   167
Coe 50, Setchell 87    Tome 81

29   Lowestoft Town   1   v   3   Tooting & Mitcham U.   315
Maguire 81    Pale 23, Kane 54, 84

30   Saffron Walden Tn   1   v   2   Sudbury Town   235
Head 25    Ince 31, 81

31   Tunbridge Wells   2   v   6   Ash United   124
Jenkinson 3, Dunk 11    Shaun Mitchell 9, 26, 88
Horton 16, Mackley 37
Calvert 45

32   Abingdon Town   0   v   1   Letchworth   60

33   Banstead Athletic   2   v   1   Hassocks   101
Leahy 61, Feltham 72    Kitchen 87

34   Thatcham Town   1   v   3   Ramsgate   181
Grist 77    Brown 54, Bowey 60,
Court 72

35   Barkingside   2   v   1   Tiptree United   58
Bajada 5, Gallery 35    Lee 85 (p)

36   Harlow Town   4   v   3*   Gt. Wakering Rovers   189
Theodosiou 36, 87    Ablitt 38, Hampshire 68
Salmon 16, Kelly 111    OG 76

37   Woodbridge Town   3   v   2   Redhill   115
Buckle 35, Gray 87    Newman 41, 66
David 93

38   Mildenhall Town   0   v   1   Herne Bay   203
Gurr 52.

39   Thamesmead Town   1   v   2   Brache Sparta   53
Bradley    Paris 42, George 53

40   Newmarket Town   5   v   0   Aveley   123

41   Northwood   3   v   1   Buckingham Athletic   162
Keith Boreham 5, 44, 82    Fenton 15

42   Clacton Town   3   v   1   Buckingham Town   260
Howe 74, Kemp 83    Harmon 17
Campbell 85

| 43 | Burgess Hill Town | 2 | v | 2* | Camberley Town | 301 |
|---|---|---|---|---|---|---|
| | Carr 23, Geddes 33 | | | | OG 3, Sills J 86 | |
| **R** | Camberley Town | 4 | v | 0 | Burgess Hill Town | 174 |
| | Jopling 53, 56, Sills T 7 | | | | | |
| | Todd 78 | | | | | |
| 44 | Chipstead | 7 | v | 2 | Windsor & Eton | 96 |
| | Sidwell 30, Munslow 40, 69 | | | | | |
| | Maslena 44, 71, Garner 62 | | | | | |
| | Oakins 74 | | | | | |
| 45 | Thetford Town | 0 | v | 4 | Sudbury Wanderers | 130 |
| | | | | | **Brian Deveraux** 3, 62, 89, | |
| | | | | | Day 70 | |
| 46 | Horsham YMCA | 0 | v | 5 | Deal Town | 150 |
| | | | | | Martin 43, Coupland 55, | |
| | | | | | Reid 60, Appleton 88, | |
| | | | | | Bryant 90. | |
| 47 | Royston Town | 1 | v | 0* | North Leigh | 103 |
| | Pugh 107 | | | | | |
| 48 | Potters Bar Town | 0 | v | 1 | Ford United | 152 |
| | | | | | Wood 3 | |
| 49 | Cobham | 5 | v | 2 | Stowmarket Town | 82 |
| | Spence 14, Sergant 53, 85 | | | | Langham 26, Parker 49 | |
| | Robinson 63, Goldie 89 | | | | | |
| 50 | Bowers United | 1 | v | 0 | Basildon United | 156 |
| | Hope 44 | | | | | |
| 51 | Diss Town | 4 | v | 4* | Yaxley | 298 |
| | Stock 50, Trail 47, 79 | | | | | |
| | Jopling 107 | | | | | |
| **R** | Yaxley | 1 | v | 3 | Diss Town | 153 |
| | Randle 63 | | | | Stock 34, Jopling 21, 57 | |
| 52 | Wokingham Town | 0 | v | 1 | Sidley United | 143 |
| | | | | | Loft 15 | |
| 53 | Cheshunt | 0 | v | 1 | Wick | 70 |
| | | | | | Smart 18 | |

| 54 | East Thurrock Utd | 2 | v | 1* | St Neots Town | 112 |
|---|---|---|---|---|---|---|
| | Winney 36, 112 | | | | Johnson 44 | |
| 55 | Bicester Town | 1 | v | 3* | Thame United | 162 |
| | Allen 85 | | | | Holmes 8, Brown 96, | |
| | | | | | Walker 110 | |
| 56 | Bemerton Hth Harl. | 3 | v | 0 | Swindon Supermarine | 80 |
| | **Jason Brice** 16, 35, 85 | | | | | |
| 57 | Newquay | 1 | v | 3 | Hungerford Town | 210 |
| | Lentern 12 | | | | Churchward 61, 82, | |
| | | | | | Morgan 90 | |
| 58 | Taunton Town | 4 | v | 0 | Bridport | 465 |
| | Fowler 13, Loram 15 | | | | | |
| | Lynch 63, 64. | | | | | |
| 59 | Ilfracombe Town | 0 | v | 5 | Tiverton Town | 357 |
| | | | | | Tallow 45, Everett 48, | |
| | | | | | Daly 51 (p), Leonard 60, | |
| | | | | | Pears 77 | |
| 60 | Minehead Town | 0 | v | 2* | Melksham Town | 88 |
| | | | | | O'Pray 97, Campbell 99. | |
| 61 | Dawlish Town | 3 | v | 2 | Fairford Town | 71 |
| | Hancox 25 | | | | Dawson 74, Hodgkiss 89 | |
| | Charlesworth 60 | | | | | |
| | Stocker 71 | | | | | |
| 62 | Lym'ton & N. Milton | 1 | v | 0 | Wellington Town | 175 |
| | Stone 30 | | | | | |
| 63 | Brislington | 3 | v | 3* | Porthleven | 161 |
| | Penny 5, Gould 50, 60 | | | | Thwaites 23, | |
| | | | | | Harrington 74, OG 34. | |
| **R** | Porthleven | 1 | v | 0 | Brislington | 265 |
| | Legg 6 | | | | | |
| 64 | Barnstaple Town | 1 | v | 5 | St Blazey | 283 |
| | Gough 4 | | | | **Chris Hawke** 6, 22, 80 | |
| | | | | | Whaddel 35, Gosling 86 | |

*Left: Ashley Carr (Burgess Hill Town) has the edge over a Camberley Town player     Photo: Roger Turner*

*Right:  Cobham (Combined Counties)  5   Stowmarket Town (Jewson Eastern)  2. Cobham's Harry Tilbury challenges a Stow defender for the ball     Photo: D Nicholson*

## SECOND ROUND STATISTICS

38 **Home Victories**

26 **Away Victories**

4 Replays

**Best Attendance**   465
Taunton Town v Bridport

**Average Attendance**   180

**Best Home Victory**   7-2
Chipstead v Windsor & Eton

**Best Away Victory**   0-5
Ibstock Welfare v Bedford Town
Horsham YMCA v Deal Town
Ilfracombe Town v Tiverton Town

**Hat Tricks**
Darren Falk (Garforth Town), Mark Murray (Mossley),
Shaun Mitchell (Ash United), Keith Boreham (Northwood),
Brian Devereux (Sudbury Wanderers),
Jason Brice (Bemerton Heath Harlequins),
Chris Hawke (St Blazey)

*Top left: Burgess Hill Town's Paul Thomsett and a Camberley Town player challenge for the ball at Leylands Park.*
*Photo: Roger Turner*
*Top right: Northwood's hat trick hero, Keith Boreham  Photo: Neil Thaler*
*Bottom: Heanor Town 4 Rushall Olympic 2. Lee Stewart heads Heanor in front (far left) a minute before the interval.*
*Photo: Gordon Whittington*

# THIRD ROUND
### Saturday 12th December

| 1 | Highfield Rangers | 1 | v | 2 | Garforth | 102 |
|---|---|---|---|---|---|---|
| | Finney 65 | | | | Shaw 85, Watson 42. | |
| 2 | Staveley M.W. | 0 | v | 2 | Dunston Fed. Brewery | 141 |
| | | | | | Elliott 54, Hogg 88 | |
| 3 | Mickleover Sports | 0 | v | 2 | Bedlington Terriers | 675 |
| | | | | | Milner 80, 90 | |
| | (after 2 abandoned ties at Bedlington due to floodlight failure) | | | | | |
| 4 | St. Helens Town | 3 | v | 1 | Eccleshill United | 104 |
| | Pennington 17,76, Reilly 33 | | | | Innes 55 | |
| 5 | Brandon United | 2 | v | 3 | Goole | 114 |
| | Clarke 54, MacDonald 48 | | | | | |
| 6 | Warrington Town | 2 | v | 1* | Heanor Town | 124 |
| | Whitehead 89, 97 | | | | Stacey 70 | |
| 7 | Mossley | 3 | v | 0 | St. Andrews | 208 |
| | Murray 66, Barker 38 | | | | | |
| | Wilkinson 20 | | | | | |
| 8 | Billingham Town | 0 | v | 2 | Clitheroe | 168 |
| | | | | | Hart 1, Gardner 86 | |
| 9 | Seaham Red Star | 0 | v | 2 | Vauxhall GM | 90 |
| | | | | | Young 55, 64 | |
| 10 | Workington | 1 | v | 1* | Tow Law Town | 1160 |
| | Darren 53 | | | | Wilkinson 41 | |
| R | Tow Law Town | 3 | v | 4 | Workington | |
| | Morton 48, Laidler 14, 67 | | | | Williamson 31, Wilson 77, | |
| | | | | | Henderson 52, 55 | |
| 11 | Kidsgrove Athletic | 3 | v | 1 | Oadby Town | 184 |
| | Mountford 18, Walker 40 | | | | McDonald 74 | |
| | Davies 60 | | | | | |
| 12 | East Thurrock Utd | 3 | v | 4* | Harlow Town | 215 |
| | Winney 9, Cockayne 52 | | | | Moore 67, Falana 71, | |
| | Wilson 62 | | | | Cork 76, Salmon 120 | |
| 13 | Royston Town | 0 | v | 3 | Sudbury Town | 216 |
| | | | | | Tracey 52, Smith 64, 81 | |
| 14 | Thame United | 2 | v | 1 | Letchworth | 121 |
| | Sherwood 73, Holmes 80 | | | | | |
| 15 | Sudbury Wanderers | 3 | v | 1 | Brache Sparta | 122 |
| | **Brian Deveraux** 27,33,75 | | | | Walker 74 | |
| 16 | Bowers United | 4 | v | 0 | Diss Town | 100 |
| | Warner 19, 79 | | | | | |
| | Harding 33, Goodwin 73 | | | | | |
| 17 | Barkingside | 1 | v | 7 | Oldbury United | 49 |
| | Bajada 22 | | | | Murphy 7, Young 46, | |
| | | | | | **Andy Wright** 60, 75, 85 | |
| | | | | | Hesson 50, Long 67. | |
| 18 | Spalding United | 2 | v | 2* | Northwood | 432 |
| | Korkma 63, Dolby 93 | | | | Sargent 56, Cooperr 111 | |
| R | Northwood | 2 | v | 1 | Spalding United | 178 |
| | Sargent 61, Fitzgerald 71 | | | | Wilson | |
| 19 | Fakenham Town | 1 | v | 4 | Bedford Town | 417 |
| | Haynes 7 | | | | Covington 74, 77, | |
| | | | | | Sherlock 25, Daniels 45 | |
| 20 | Chasetown | 0 | v | 1 | Wroxham | 122 |
| | | | | | Terrington 49 | |
| 21 | Ford United | 4 | v | 3* | Newmarket Town | 141 |
| | Wood 44, Reilly 85, | | | | Kennedy 76, Lloyd 85, | |
| | Waite 90, 95 | | | | Claydon 89 | |
| 22 | Woodbridge Town | 1 | v | 0 | Clacton Town | 143 |
| | Buckie 60 | | | | | |
| 23 | Melksham Town | 1 | v | 2 | Ash United | 241 |
| | Tweedle 57 | | | | Calvert 9, Everard 40 | |
| 24 | Herne Bay | 0 | v | 2* | Banstead Athletic | 174 |
| | | | | | Myatt 109, Burton 118 | |
| 25 | Taunton Town | 1 | v | 0 | Dawlish Town | 431 |
| | Lynch 47 | | | | | |
| 26 | Deal Town | 1 | v | 2 | Tiverton Town | 478 |
| | Appleton 59 | | | | Nancekivell 5, OG 44 | |
| 27 | St. Blazey | 2 | v | 1 | Porthleven | 323 |
| | Hooper 33, 77 | | | | Legg 20 | |
| 28 | Ramsgate | 0 | v | 3 | Bemerton Heath Harl. | 177 |
| | | | | | Cole 65, Richardson 70, 77 | |
| 29 | Lym'ton & N. Milton | 4 | v | 0 | Hungerford Town | 182 |
| | Stride 8, 75, Stone 52 | | | | | |
| | Oldbury 80 | | | | | |
| 30 | Chipstead | 2 | v | 2* | Tooting & Mitcham U | 175 |
| | Stowell 47, Harmsworth 89 | | | | Kane 28, Thompson 44 | |
| R | Tooting & Mitcham U | 3 | v | 2 | Chipstead | 182 |
| | Bhola 23, Pace 65, Kane 90 | | | | Stowell 37, Garner 68 | |
| 31 | Wick | 3 | v | 2* | Sidley United | 180 |
| | More 16, 98, Moore 97 | | | | Heritage 35, Day 112 | |
| 32 | Cobham | 1 | v | 2 | Camberley Town | 91 |
| | Gale 30 | | | | J Sills 44, T Sills 60 | |

*Workington 1 Tow Law 1*
*Tow Law's Trevor Laidler gets in his header despite the attentions of Reds' Stuart Williamson.*
*Photo: Alan Watson*

## FIRST QUALIFYING ROUND STATISTICS

**15 Home Victories**

**17 Away Victories**

3 Replays

**Best Attendance** 1,160
Workington v Tow Law Town

**Average Attendance** 248

**Best Home Victory** 4-0
Lymington & New Milton v Hungerford Town
Bowers United v Diss Town

**Best Away Victory** 1-7
Barkingside v Oldbury United

**Hat Tricks**
Brian Devereux (Sudbury Wndrs), Andy Wright (Oldbury U)

*Top: Letchworth's Alan Arber firmly grasps the ball. he was the Man of the Match in one of the most entertaining matches of the season.*
*Photo: Steve Ayre*

*Centre: Mickleover Sports v Bedlington Terriers. Sports' keeper Mark Harvey wins this battle.*
*Photo: Bill Wheatcroft*

*Bottom: Ford United 2 Newmarket Town 3. FA Cup heroes Ford and visitors Newmarket served up a Vase cracker after extra time in atrocious conditions. Here, Ford's Lee Parish (10) is outjumped by the "Jockey's" defence.*
*Photo: D Nicholson*

# FOURTH ROUND
### Saturday 9th January

Ash United 1 v 5 Tiverton Town
Joyce 3 **Phil Everett** 8, 35, 55, 73,
Att: 619 Daly 15.

Bedford Town 3 v 1 Wroxham
Lawley 3, Searle 71 Barbrook 76
Williams 89 Att: 848

Bedlington Terriers 7 v 3 Banstead Athletic
**John Milner** 2, 35, 48 Burton 40, 71, Feltham 44.
Boon 26,Bond 49, 70
Pike 82. Att: 350

Bowers United 1 v 2* Woodbridge Town
Warner 83 Att: 151 Dearsley 36, Taylor 108
*(at Billericay Town FC)*

Camberley Town 1 v 0* Tooting & Mitcham Utd
Jopling 119 Att: 237

Clitheroe 1 v 0 St. Helens Town
Rishton 44 Att: 360

Ford United 4 v 2 Kidsgrove Athletic
Wood 7 Dundas 10 (p), 31.
OG (Mountford) 46
Lord 51, Reilly 60 Att: 270

Goole 0 v 1 Bemerton Heath Harl.
Att: 572 Scott 21.
Harlow Town 1 v 2 Taunton Town
Theodosiou 28 Att: 801 Edwards 17, Rinch 72.

Lym'ton & N. Milton 1 v *0 Mossley
Sampson 115p Att: 448

Oldbury United 0 v 4 Workington
Swales 33, 76,
Att: 319 Henry 68, 86.

St.. Blazey 1 v 5 Dunston Fed. Brewery
McMillan 65 **Andy Fletcher**
16 (p), 25, 33, 70 (p),
Att: 384 Elliott 45.

Sudbury Town 0 v 1* Northwood
Att: 422 Sherry 111.

Sudbury Wanderers 2 v 0 Garforth Town
Day 3, Hyde 87 Att: 338

Warrington Town 0 v 2* Thame United
Att: 324 Lolus 112, Maciak 120.

Wick 0 v 5 Vauxhall GM
Att: 271 **Kevin Odger** 52, 58, 66,
Antrobus 85, Young 90.

*Above: Bedford Town v Wroxham. Eddie Lawley and John Edridge in midfield action.*
*Photo: Peter Barnes*

## FOURTH ROUND STATISTICS

7 **Home Victories**

9 **Away Victories**

**Best Attendance** 848
Bedford Town v Wroxham

**Average Attendance** 402

**Best Home Victory** 7-3
Bedlington Terriers v Banstead Athletic

**Best Away Victory** 0-5
Wick v Vauxhall Motors

**Hat Tricks**
Phil Everett (Tiverton Town) (4),
Andy Fletcher (Dunston Federation Brewery) (4),
John Milner (Bedlington Terriers),
Kevin Odger (Vauxhall Motors)

Top: Wroxham attack the Bedford goal.
Photo: Steve Ayre

Centre: Kidsgrove's Wayne Mountford heads over the Ford United bar from this corner.
Photo: Alan Coomes

Bottom: Harlow Town keeper Darren Turpin parries from a Taunton attack in the 17th minute.
Photo: Neil Thaler

# FIFTH ROUND
### Saturday 30th January

**Bedford Town** 1 v 2 **Tiverton Town**
Joyce 87p   Att: 1798   Nancekivell 26, Everett 45.

**Clitheroe** 1 v 0 **Bemerton Heath Harl.**
Welsh 74   Att: 510

**Dunston F. Brewery** 1 v 4* **Lymington & N. Milt.**
Briggs 17    Barnes 62,
     Att: 470   Sampson 95,111, Jones 98

**Ford United** 1 v 2 **Bedlington Terriers**
Gardner 24   Att: 534   Gibb 18, Milner 47.

**Taunton Town** 5 v 2 **Northwood**
Loram 7, Lynch 38    Gell 27, 32.
Laight 41
Edwards 68, 89   Att: 1,139

**Thame United** 2 v 1* **Vauxhall GM**
Paul 1, Lolus 99   Att: 319   Thompson 77.

**Woodbridge Town** 2 v 1 **Camberley Town**
Keeley 17, Oldfield 75   Att: 343   Sills 10.

**Workington** 3 v 0* **Sudbury Wanderers**
Wilson 94, Swales 103
Taylor 120   Att: 1308

## FIFTH ROUND STATISTICS
5 **Home Victories**

3 **Away Victories**

**Best Attendance**   1,566
Bedford Town v Tiverton Town

**Average Attendance**   771

**Best Home Victory**   5-2
Taunton Town v Northwood

**Best Away Victory**   1-4
Dunston Federation Brewery v Lymington & New Milton

*Left: Carlsberg's Customer Development Manager, James Hoare presents the Man of the Carlsberg Match award to Thame United Captain, Martin Brown.*
*Photo: Neil Thaler*

*Opposite page:*
*Top: Clitheroe v Bemerton Heath Harlequins. Colin Hopkins under pressure from Clitheroe forward Brian Welch.*

*Centre: Ford United v Bedlington Terriers. Terriers' Gary Middleton beats Terry Hughes (Ford).*
*Photo: D Nicholson*

*Bottom: Thame United v Vauxhall Motors. Kevin Thompson (Vauxhall) fails with this penalty kick but scores from the rebound off the keeper to put the tie into extra time.*
*Photo: Andrew Chitty*

# SIXTH ROUND
Saturday 20th February

### Bedlington Terriers 1 v 0* Workington
Bowes 116 Att: 1319

**Bedlington:** O'Connor, Cameron, Pike, Teasdale, Melrose, Pearson (sub Bowes 93 mins), Cross, Renforth (sub Bond 75 mins), Gibb (sub Ludlow 93 mins), Milner, Middleton. Subs not used: Harmison, Egan.
**Workington:** Dixon, Gray, Green, Kirkby, Taylor, Williamson, Jones, Henney, Swailes (sub Millar 108 mins), Stewart, Wilson (sub Henderson 58 mins). Subs not used: Corrie, Casson, Goulding.

### Taunton Town 3 v 1 Lymington & New Milton
Lynch 12, Parker 63 , Laight 73 Att: 1608 Stone 4

**Taunton:** Penberthy, Edwards, Fowler, West, Thompson, Kelly, Parker, Laight, Loram, Myers, Lynch. Subs not used: Thorpe, Hadley, Underhay, Ewens, Ayres.
**Lymington:** Shaw, Stride (sub Sims 75 mins), Oldbury, Kemp, Morris, Mottashed, Sheppard, Anderson, Jones (sub Sampson 65 mins), Stone, Phillips. Subs not used: Green, Metcalf, Hubbard.

### Tiverton Town 4 v 0 Clitheroe
Everett 64, 73, Varley 68 Nancekivell 80 Att: 1473

**Tiverton:** Edwards, Fallon, Saunders, Tatterton (sub Smith 83 mins), Tallon, Conning, Nancekivell, Varley (sub Pears 81 mins), Everett, Daly (sub Rogers 80 mins), Leonard. Subs not used: Hynds, Tucker.
**Clitheroe:** Parrott, Norman, Lang (sub Rhodes 79 mins), Bowers, Rishton, Greenwood, Grimshaw, Taylor (sub Howarth 79 mins), Gardner, Welch, Stewart (sub D Hill 71 mins). Subs not used: Dunn, Riley.

### Woodbridge Town 0 v 2* Thame United
Att: 1051 Herbert 94p, Louis 99.

**Woodbridge:** Garnham, Gilbert, Brill, Long, Keeley, Gray (sub Fryer 102 mins), Buckle, Mason (sub Fryett 100 mins), Wark (sub Oldfield 118 mins), David, Wallis. Subs not used: Thorpe, Brighty.
**Thame:** Moores, Gascoyne, Roberts, Tregurtha, Williams A (sub Gregory 102 mins), Joe (sub Williams G 65 mins), Carlisle, Holmes, Herbert, Walker (sub Louis 74 mins). Subs not used: Sutcliffe, Sherwood.

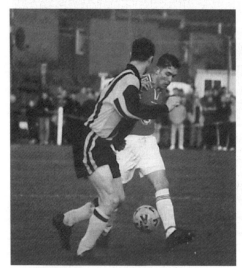 

*Left: Bedlington Terriers' John Milner tries to pass Workington's Marc Green. Photo: Neil Thaler*

*Right: Taunton's Tony Lynch on the attack*

## SIXTH ROUND STATISTICS

| | |
|---|---|
| 3 **Home Victories** | **Best Attendance** 1,608 |
| | Taunton Town v Lymington & New Milton |
| 1 **Away Victories** | |
| | **Average Attendance** 1,383 |

*Top: A lucky escape for Thame United as Ian Moores and two defenders watch second half goal chance go over the bar from Woodbridge captain Carl David (hidden) in the FA VAse 6th Round.*
*Photo: Eric Marsh*
*Bottom: Taunton Town v Lymington & New Milton. Taunton's Ellis Laight rises above Paul Morris to head in the third goal which sealed the 6th Round tie for the home-side 3-1.*
*Photo: Ken Gregory*

# SEMI FINALS

## Taunton Town 0 v 3 Tiverton Town
Att: 3,284    Everett 7, Varley 12, Nancekivell 78

**Taunton:** Penberthy, Edwards (sub Hadley 73 mins), Fowler, West, Thompson, Kelly, Parker, Laight, Loram, Myers, Lynch(sub sub Underhay 79 mins). Subs not used: Thorpe, Fortt, Ayres.
**Tiverton:** Edwards, Fallow, Saunders, Tatterton, Tallow, Conning, Nancekivell, Varley, Everett, Daly (sub Rogers 74 mins), Leonard. Subs not used: Smith, Hynds, Pears, Tucker.

## Tiverton Town 2 v 1 Taunton Town
Daly 57 (p), 69 (p)    Att: 2,896    Laight 45

**Tiverton:** Edwards, Fallon, Saunders, Tatterton, Tallow (sub Smith 77 mins), Conning (sub Rogers 80 mins), Nancekivell, Varley (sub Pears 80 mins), Everett, Daly, Leonard. Subs not used: Hynds, Tucker.
**Taunton:** Penberthy, Bastow (sub Hadley 74 mins), Fowler, West, Thompson (sub Thorpe 16 mins), Kelly, Parkker (sub Underhay 78 mins), Laight, Loram, Myers, Lynch. Subs not used: Fortt, Edwards.

*"WOOF! WOOF! TERRIERS!"*
*Bedlington Terriers FA Vase Finalists celebrate with their travelling fans.*
*Photo: Neil Thaler*

# SEMI FINALS

## Bedlington Terriers 5 v 0 Thame United
John Milner 42, 49, 64 Bond 76, 88      Att: 864

**Bedlington:** O'Connor, Cameron, Pike, Bowes (sub Pearson 45 mins), Melrose, Teasdale, Cross, Renforth (sub Bond 45 mins), Gibb (sub Ludlow 78 mins), Milner, Middleton. Subs not used: Sokoluk, Gowens.
**Thame:** Moores, Gascoyne, Roberts, Brown, Tregurtha, Paul, Joe, Williams A. (sub Maciak 61 mins), Holmes (sub Louis 58 mins), Herbert (sub Gregory 65 mins), Walker. Subs not used: Sherwood, Williams G.

## Thame United 0 v 0 Bedlington Terriers
Att: 431

**Thame:** Moores, G Williams, A Williams, Brown, Tregurtha, Paul, Gascoyne, Maciak, Louis, Herbert, Carlisle.
**Bedlington:** O'Connor, Cameron, Pike, Teasdale, Melrose, Pearson, Cross (sub Bowes 85 mins), Bond (sub Renforth 80 mins), Gibb, Milner, Middleton (sub Ludlow 82 mins). Subs not ussed: Gowens, Egan.

*Super Sub Richie Bond races down the right wing
closely watched by Thame United's Ronnie Joe*

# FINAL

Sunday 16th May 1999

Attendance: 13,878
Referee: W C Burns (North Riding)

## Bedlington Terriers    0    1    Tiverton Town

| | |
|---|---|
| Paul O'Connor | Paul Edwards |
| Andy Bowes | Micky Fallon |
| Martin Pike | Neil Saunders |
| Steve Boon (sub Glen Renforth, 90) | Paul Tatterton |
| Craig Melrose | Darren Tallon |
| Warren Teasdale | Pete Conning (sub Scott Rogers, 70) |
| Mickey Cross | Kevin Nancekivell (sub Richard Pears, 70) |
| Gary Middleton (sub Lee Ludlow, 90) | Pete Varley |
| Dean Gibb | Phil Everett |
| John Milner | Steve Daly |
| Richie Bond | Dave Leonard |

Subs not used:
Laurence Pearson
Mark Cameron
Andy Gowans

Subs not used:
Lee Tucker
Steve Hynds
Martyn Grimshaw

Goalscorer: Scott Rogers 89 mins

*Left: Tiverton Town's Scott Rogers. Photo: Alan Coomes*

*Below: Tiverton lift the Cup. Photo: Ian Morsman*

*Opposite page:*
*Top: Tiverton Town goalkeeper, Paul Edwards holds on to a fierce shot from Bedlington Terriers. Photo: Roger Turner*

*Centre: Bedlington Terriers' Dean Gibb leaps high but Edwards is first to the cross.*

*Goal - Scott Rogers on ground beats Paul O'Connor to give Tiverton the FA Vase. Photo: Roger Turner*

## FA CARLSBERG VASE AT A GLANCE

**THIRD ROUND**

Ford United 4*
Newmarket Town 3*

Kidsgrove Athletic 3
Oadby Town 1

**BEDLINGTON T 0**
Mickleover Sports 2

Herne Bay 0*
Banstead Athletic 2*

Barkingside 1
Oldbury United 7

Workington 1*,3
Tow Law Town 1*,4

Sudbury Wndrs 3
Brache Sparta 1

Highfield Rangers 1
Garforth Town 2

Bowers United 4
Diss Town 0

Woodbridge Town 1
Clacton Town 0

Cobham 1
Camberley Town 2

Chipstead 2,2
Tooting & Mitch. 2,3

Warrington Town 2*
Heanor Town 1*

Thame United 2
Letchworth 1

Wick 3*
Sidley United 2

Seaham Red Star 0
Vauxhall GM 2

East Thurrock Utd 3*
Harlow Town 4*

Taunton Town 1
Dawlish Town 0

Royston Town 0
Sudbury Town 3

Spalding United 2*,1
Northwood 2*,2

St Blazey 2
Porthlevin 1

Staveley MW 0
Dunston FB 2

Lymington & NM 4
Hungerford Town 0

Mossley 3
St Andrews 0

Fakenham Town 1
Bedford Town 4

Chasetown 0
Wroxham 1

Melksham Town 1
Ash United 2

Deal Town 1
**TIVERTON TOWN 2**

Billingham Town 0
Clitheroe 2

St Helens Town 3
Eccleshill United 1

Brandon United 2
Goole 3

Ramsgate 0
Bemerton H H'qns 3

**FOURTH ROUND**

Ford United 4

Kidsgrove Athletic 2

**BEDLINGTON T 7**

Banstead Athletic 3

Oldbury United 0

Workington 4

Sudbury Wndrs 2

Garforth Town 0

Bowers United 1*
Woodbridge Town 2*

Camberley Town 1

Tooting & Mitcham 0

Warrington Town 0

Thame United 2*

Wick 0

Vauxhall GM 5

Harlow Town 1

Taunton Town 2

Sudbury Town 0

Northwood 1

St Blazey 1

Dunston FB 5

Lymington & NM 1*

Mossley 0

Bedford Town 3

Wroxham 1

Ash United 1

**TIVERTON TOWN 5**

Clitheroe 1

St Helens Town 0

Goole 0

Bemerton H H'qns 1

**FIFTH ROUND**

Ford United 1

**BEDLINGTON T. 2**

Workington 3*

Sudbury Wndrs 0

Woodbridge Town 2

Camberley Town 1

Thame United 2*

Vauxhall GM 1

Taunton Town 5

Northwood 2

Dunston FB 1

Lymington & NM 4*

Bedford Town 1

**TIVERTON TOWN 2**

Clitheroe 0

Clitheroe 1

Bemerton H H'qns 0

**SIXTH ROUND**

**BEDLINGTON T. 1***

Workington 0

Woodbridge Town 0

Thame United 2*

Taunton Town 3

Lymington & NM 1

**TIVERTON TOWN 4**

**SEMI FINALS**

**BEDLINGTON T. 5, 0**

Thame United⁺ 0,0

Taunton Town⁺ 0, 1

**TIVERTON TOWN 3, 2**

**FINAL**

**BEDLINGTON T. 0**

**TIVERTON TOWN 1**

* After extra time
⁺ Home in first semi final leg

106

# F.A. CARLSBERG VASE FINAL

## BEDLINGTON TERRIERS 0  TIVERTON TOWN 1
### Att: 13,878          Rogers 88

Just to be playing in a final at Wembley is of course its won reward but nevertheless players and supporters hope that the event itself will be an exciting and quality affair. Sadly that is often not the case and here was another Wembley final which failed to light any fire in fans or participants. Obviously Tiverton Town will be the happier since theirs was the victory and their name will go down in the annals as winners for the second year on the trot. Bedlington will always have the happy memories but tinged with that little niggle that they by no means reached their potential, in front of probably the largest ever crowd to witness their play, and in the national stadium. This after some stirring performances during the season, including that victory over Colchester and again winning the Northern League title. They had slightly the edge in this match, having done the bulk of the attacking, and it was rough justice that their opponents should garb the all important goal with only a minute of normal time to go.

And what a goal to please the Tiverton management it was too. Not only was it scored by a substitute, for that always makes the manager look inspired, but to make it even more special the super sub was none other that Scott Rogers, the manager's cousin's son (who was also his god son). Pleasing for Scott but torture for defender Craig Melrose who was crucially robbed by Rogers on the edge of the area. He had to be consoled by team mates after Rogers had progressed into the area and, with his, maybe slightly scuffed, left foot shot, sent the ball trickling past Paul O'Connor's left hand to nestle cosily in the corner. There was no time for Terriers to come back and by then both sides were pretty well spent forces, for the common Wembley affliction of cramps had tortured a couple of victims.

A couple of minute before Melrose had almost been the hero when he had taken the ball from his own eighteen yard area to that of his opponents, only to roll his attempted shot straight into the grateful arms of Paul Edwards, who, entering into the occasion, had dyed his hair a bright yellow. It did not detract from his performance and he, along with the staunch sweeper, Paul Tatterton, can look back on a satisfactory performance. They certainly gave top scorer John Milner and his competitive and aggressive (controlled and fair) partner, Dean Gibb, little chance to add to their total. Most dangerous for Terriers was Richie Bond with his right wing sorties and low crosses. Mickey Cross and Steve Boon when close with shots, but hard thought their supporters toiled with rolling chants of "Terriers - woof, woof" and though on balance of play Bedlington had more of the ball, the Vase slipped from their clutches.

Tiverton's Pete Varley and Phil Everett forced O'Connor into a couple of diving saves, Kevin Nancekivell showed his customary neat touches but we never saw the power that the Devon side can unleash. Their promotion to the Doc Martens League means they will not be able to go for a third consecutive win but they wouldn't begrudge Bedlington a return visit. May they be able to demonstrate their top form in that eventuality.

Arthur Evans

107

# PAST F.A. VASE FINALS

**1975**    **HODDESDON TOWN 2**      **EPSOM & EWELL 1**        Att: 9,500
Sedgwick 2             Wales                    Ref: Mr R Toseland
Hoddesdon: Galvin, Green, Hickey, Maybury, Stevenson, Wilson, Bishop, Picking, Sedgwick, Nathan, Schofield
Epsom & Ewell: Page, Bennett, Webb, Wales, Worby, Jones, O'Connell, Walker, Tuite, Eales, Lee

**1976**    **BILLERICAY TOWN 1**      **STAMFORD 0**     (aet)       Att: 11,848
Aslett                                        Ref: Mr A Robinson
Billericay: Griffiths, Payne, Foreman, Pullin, Bone, Coughlan, Geddes, Aslett, Clayden, Scott, Smith
Stamford: Johnson, Kwiatowski, Marchant, Crawford, Downs, Hird, Barnes, Walpole, Smith, Russell, Broadbent

**1977**    **BILLERICAY TOWN 1**      **SHEFFIELD 1**     (aet)       Att: 14,000
Clayden                    Coughlan og               Ref: Mr J Worrall
Billericay: Griffiths, Payne, Bone, Coughlan, Pullin, Scott, Wakefield, Aslett, Clayden,Woodhouse, McQueen. Sub: Whettell
Sheffield: Wing, Gilbody, Lodge, Hardisty, Watts, Skelton, Kay, Travis, Pugh, Thornhill,Haynes. Sub: Strutt

**Replay**    **BILLERICAY TOWN 2**      **SHEFFIELD 1**           Att: 3,482
Aslett, Woodhouse        Thornhill               at Nottingham Forest
Billericay: Griffiths, Payne, Pullin, Whettell, Bone, McQueen, Woodhouse, Aslett, Clayden, Scott, Wakefield
Sheffield: Wing, Gilbody, Lodge, Strutt, Watts, Skelton, Kay, Travis, Pugh, Thornhill, Haynes

**1978**    **NEWCASTLE BLUE STAR 2**    **BARTON ROVERS 1**      Att: 16,858
Dunn, Crumplin          Smith                Ref: Mr T Morris
Newcastle: Halbert, Feenan, Thompson, Davidson, S Dixon, Beynon, Storey, P Dixon, Crumplin, Callaghan, Dunn. Sub: Diamond
Barton Rovers: Blackwell, Stephens, Crossley, Evans, Harris, Dollimore, Dunn, Harnaman, Fossey, Turner, Smith. Sub: Cox

**1979**    **BILLERICAY TOWN 4**      **ALMONDSBURY GREENWAY 1**    Att: 17,500
Young 3, Clayden         Price                   Ref: Mr C Steel
Billericay: Norris, Blackaller, Bingham, Whettell, Bone, Reeves, Pullin, Scott, Clayden,Young, Groom. Sub: Carrigan
Almondsbury: Hamilton, Bowers, Scarrett, Sulllivan, Tudor, Wookey, Bowers, Shehean, Kerr,Butt, Price. Sub: Kilbaine

**1980**    **STAMFORD 2**            **GUISBOROUGH TOWN 0**        Att: 11,500
Alexander, McGowan                               Ref: Neil Midgeley
Stamford: Johnson, Kwiatkowski, Ladd, McGowan, Bliszczak I, Mackin, Broadhurst, Hall,Czarnecki, Potter, Alexander. Sub: Bliszczak S
Guisborough: Cutter, Scott, Thornton, Angus, Maltby, Percy, Skelton, Coleman, McElvaney,Sills, Dilworth. Sub: Harrison

**1981**    **WHICKHAM 3**           **WILLENHALL 2**     (aet)        Att: 12,000
Scott, Williamson, Peck og    Smith, Stringer            Ref: Mr R Lewis
Whickham: Thompson, Scott, Knox, Williamson, Cook, Ward, Carroll, Diamond, Cawthra,Robertson, Turnbull. Sub: Alton
Willenhall: Newton, White, Darris, Woodall, Heath, Fox, Peck, Price, Matthews, Smith,Stringer. Sub: Trevor

**1982**    **FOREST GREEN ROVERS 3**    **RAINWORTH M.W 0**      Att: 12,500
Leitch 2, Norman                                 Ref: Mr K Walmsey
Forest Green: Moss, Norman, Day, Turner, Higgins, Jenkins, Guest, Burns, Millard, Leitch, Doughty. Sub: Dangerfield
Rainworth M.W: Watson, Hallam, Hodgson, Slater, Sterland, Oliver, Knowles, Raine, Radzi, Reah, Comerford. Sub: Robinson

**1983**    **V.S. RUGBY 1**           **HALESOWEN TOWN 0**        Att: 13,700
Crawley                                   Ref: Mr B Daniels
VS Rugby: Burton, McGinty, Harrison, Preston, Knox, Evans, ingram, Setchell, Owen,Beecham, Crawley. Sub: Haskins
Halesowen Town: Coldicott, Penn, Edmonds, Lacey, Randall, Shilvock, Hazelwood, Moss, Woodhouse,P Joinson, L Joinson. Sub: Smith

**1984**    **STANSTED 3**            **STAMFORD 2**               Att: 8,125
Holt, Gillard, Reading      Waddicore, Allen           Ref: Mr T Bune
Stanstead: Coe, Williams, Hilton, Simpson, Cooper, Reading, Callanan, Holt, Reevs,Doyle, Gillard. Sub: Williams
Stamford: Parslow, Smitheringate, Blades, McIlwain, Lyon, Mackin, Genovese, Waddicore,Allen, Robson, Beech. Sub: Chapman

**1985**    **HALESOWEN TOWN 3**      **FLEETWOOD TOWN 1**      Att: 16,715
L Joinson 2, Moss         Moran                   Ref: Mr C Downey
Halesowen: Coldicott, Penn, Sherwood, Warner, Randle, Heath, Hazlewood, Moss (Smith),Woodhouse, P Joinson, L Joinson
Fleetwood Town: Dobson, Moran, Hadgraft, Strachan, Robinson, Milligan, Hall, Trainor, Taylor(Whitehouse), Cain, Kennerley

**1986**    **HALESOWEN TOWN 3**      **SOUTHALL 0**              Att: 18,340
Moss 2, L Joinson                                  Ref: Mr D Scott
Halesowen: Pemberton, Moore, Lacey, Randle (Rhodes), Sherwood, Heath, Penn, Woodhouse, PJoinson, L Joinson, Moss
Southall: Mackenzie, James, McGovern, Croad, Holland, Powell (Richmond), Pierre,Richardson, Sweales, Ferdinand, Rowe

**1987**    **ST. HELENS 3**           **WARRINGTON TOWN 2**       Att: 4,254
Layhe 2, Rigby          Reid, Cook                Ref: Mr T Mills
St Helens: Johnson, Benson, Lowe, Bendon, Wilson, McComb, Collins (Gledhill), O'Neill,Cummins, Lay, Rigby. Sub: Deakin
Warrington: O'Brien. Copeland, Hunter, Gratton, Whalley, Reid, Brownville (Woodyer), Cook,Kinsey, Looker (Hill), Hughes

**1988**  COLNE DYNAMOES 1  EMLEY 0  Att: 15,000
Anderson  Ref: Mr A Seville
Colne Dynamoes: Mason, McFafyen, Westwell, Bentley, Dunn, Roscoe, Rodaway, Whitehead (Burke),Diamond, Anderson, Wood (Coates)
Emley: Dennis, Fielding, Mellor, Codd, Hirst (Burrows), Gartland (Cook), Carmody,Green, Bramald, Devine, Francis

**1989**  TAMWORTH 1  SUDBURY TOWN 1  aet  Att: 26,487
Devaney  Hubbick  Ref: Mr C Downey
Tamworth: Bedford, Lockett, Atkins, Cartwright, McCormack, Myers, Finn, Devaney, Moores,Gordon, Stanton. Subs: Rathbone, Heaton
Sudbury Town: Garnham, Henry, G Barker, Boyland, Thorpe, Klug, D Barker, Barton, Oldfield,Smith, Hubbick. Subs: Money, Hunt

Replay  TAMWORTH 3  SUDBURY TOWN 0  Att: 11,201
Stanton 2, Moores  at Peterborough
Tamworth: Bedford, Lockett, Atkins, Cartwright, Finn, Myers, George, Devaney, Moores,Gordon, Stanton. Sub: Heaton
Sudbury Town: Garnham, Henry, G Barker, Boyland, Thorpe, Klug, D Barker, Barton, Oldfield,Smith, Hubbick. Subs: Money, Hunt

**1990**  YEADING 0  BRIDLINGTON TOWN 0  aet  Att: 7,932
Ref: Mr R Groves
Yeading: Mackenzie, Wickens, Turner, Whiskey (McCarthy), Croad, Denton, Matthews, James(Charles), Sweates, Impey, Cordery
Bridlington: Taylor, Pugh, Freeman, McNeill, Warburton, Brentano, Wilkes (Hall), Noteman,Gauden, Whiteman, Brattan (Brown)

Replay  YEADING 1  BRIDLINGTON TOWN 0  Att: 5,000
Sweales  at Leeds Utd FC
Yeading: Mackenzie, Wickens, Turner, Whiskey, Croad (McCarthy), Schwartz, Matthews,James, Sweates, Impey (Welsh), Cordery
Bridlington: Taylor, Pugh, Freeman, McNeill, Warburton, Brentano, Wilkes (Brown), Noteman,Gauden (Downing), Whiteman, Brattan

**1991**  GRESLEY ROVERS 4  GUISELEY 4  aet  Att: 11,314
Rathbone, Smith 2, Stokes  Tennison 2, Walling, A Roberts  Ref: Mr C Trussell
Gresley: Aston, Barry, Elliott (Adcock), Denby, Land, Astley, Stokes, K Smith, Acklam,Rathbone, Lovell (Weston)
Guiseley: Maxted, Bottomley, Hogarth, Tetley, Morgan, McKenzie, Atkinson (Annan),Tennison, Walling, A Roberts, B Roberts

Replay  GUISELEY 3  GRESLEY ROVERS 1  Att: 7,585
Tennison, Walling, Atkinson  Astley  at Bramall Lane
Guiseley: Maxted, Annan, Hogarth, Tetley, Morgan, McKenzie (Bottomley), Atkinson,Tennison (Noteman), Walling, A Roberts, B Roberts
Gresley: Aston, Barry, Elliott, Denby, Land, Astley, Stokes (Weston), K Smith, Acklam, Rathbone, Lovell (Adcock)

**1992**  WIMBORNE TOWN 5  GUISELEY 3  Att: 10,772
Richardson, Sturgess 2, Killick 2  Noteman 2, Colville  Ref: Mr M J Bodenham
Wimborne: Leonard, Langdown, Wilkins, Beacham, Allan, Taplin, Ames, Richardson, Bridle,Killick, Sturgess (Lovell), Lynn
Guiseley: Maxted, Atkinson, Hogarth, Tetley (Wilson), Morgan, Brockie, A Roberts,Tennison, Noteman (Colville), Annan, W Roberts

**1993**  BRIDLINGTON TOWN 1  TIVERTON TOWN 0  Att: 9,061
Radford  Ref: Mr R A Hart
Bridlington: Taylor, Brentano, McKenzie, Harvey, Bottomley, Woodcock, Grocock, A Roberts, Jones, Radford (Tyrell), Parkinson. Sub: Swailes
Tiverton Town: Nott, J Smith, N Saunders, M Saunders, Short (Scott), Steele, Annunziata, KSmith, Everett, Daly, Hynds (Rogers)

**1994**  DISS TOWN 2  TAUNTON TOWN 1  Att: 13,450
Gibbs (p), Mendham  Fowler  Ref: Mr K. Morton
Diss Town: Woodcock, Carter, Wolsey (Musgrave), Casey (Bugg), Hartle, Smith, Barth, Mendham, Miles, Warne, Gibbs
Taunton Town: Maloy, Morris, Walsh, Ewens, Graddon, Palfrey, West (Hendry), Fowler, Durham, Perrett (Ward), Jarvis

**1995**  ARLESEY TOWN 2  OXFORD CITY 1  Att: 13,670
Palma, Gyalog  S Fontaine  Ref: Mr G S Willard
Arlesey: Young, Cardines, Bambrick, Palma (Ward), Hull, Gonsalves, Gyalog, Cox, Kane,O'Keefe, Marshall (Nicholls). Sub: Dodwell
Oxford: Fleet, Brown (Fisher), Hume, Shepherd, Muttock, Hamilton (Kemp), Thomas, Spittle, Sherwood, S Fontaine, C Fontaine. Sub: Torres

**1996**  BRIGG TOWN 3  CLITHEROE 0  Att: 7,340
Stead 2, Roach  Ref: Mr S J Lodge
Brigg: Gawthorpe, Thompson, Rogers, Greaves (Clay), Buckley (Mail), Elston, C Stead, McLean, N Stead (McNally), Flounders, Roach
Clitheroe: Nash, Lampkin, Rowbotham (Otley), Baron, Westwell, Rovine, Butcher, Taylor (Smith), Grimshaw, Darbyshire, Hill (Dunn)

**1997**  NORTH FERRIBY UTD. 0  WHITBY TOWN 3  Att: 11,098
Williams, Logan, Toman  Ref: Graham Poll
North Ferriby: Sharp, Deacey, Smith, Brentano, Walmsley, M Smith, Harrison (Horne), Phillips (Milner), France (Newman), Flounders, Tennison
Whitby Town: Campbell, Williams, Logan, Goodchild, Pearson, Cook, Goodrick (Borthwick), Hodgson, Robinson, Toman (Pyle), Pitman (Hall)

**1998**  TIVERTON TOWN 1  TOW LAW TOWN 0  Att: 13,139
Varley  Ref: M A Riley
Tiverton: Edwards, Felton, Saunders, Tatterton, Smith J, Conning, Nancekivell (Rogers), Smith K (Varley), Everett, Daly, Leonard (Waters)
Tow Law: Dawson, Pickering, Darwent, Bailey, Hague, Moan, Johnson, Nelson, Suddick, Laidler (Bennett), Robinson.

# F.A. CARLSBERG VASE CLUB RECORDS

| Positions 1998 | 1999 | | Pts | Ssns | 98-99 | Best |
|---|---|---|---|---|---|---|
| 1 | 1 | Hungerford Town | 77 | 25 | 3rd | SF x 3 |
| 2 | 2 | Stamford | 73 | 24 | | W80 |
| 5 | 3 | Buckingham Town | 66 | 21 | 2nd | 6th x 2 |
| 3 | 4 | Guiseley | 64 | 17 | | W 91 |
| 4 | 5 | Barton Rovers | 64 | 20 | | F 78 |
| 6 | 6 | North Ferriby United | 63 | 25 | 2nd | F 97 |
| 7 | 7 | Burnham | 60 | 17 | 1st Qual | SF 83 |
| 8 | 8 | Irthingborough D | 58 | 15 | | SF 2 |
| 18 | 9 | Tiverton Town | 58 | 18 | Finalist | W98 |
| 9 | 10 | Hinckley Athletic | 58 | 23 | | 5th x 2 |
| 10 | 11 | Blue Star Newcastle | 57 | 15 | 1st Qual | W 78 |
| 11 | 12 | Whickham | 56 | 19 | 2nd Qual | W81 |
| 12 | 13 | Wisbech Town | 54 | 16 | | SF x 2 |
| 13 | 14 | Brigg Town | 54 | 25 | 1st | W 96 |
| 20 | 15 | Sudbury Town | 53 | 11 | 4th | F89 |
| 14 | 16 | Billericay Town | 52 | 9 | | W x 3 |
| 15 | 17 | Friar Lane Old Boys | 52 | 25 | 2nd Qual | SF x 2 |
| 23 | 18 | Warrington Town | 51 | 19 | 4th | F87 |
| 16 | 19 | Lincoln United | 51 | 21 | | 6th 75 |
| 17 | 20 | Halesowen Town | 50 | 12 | | W x 2 |
| 19 | 21 | Harefield United | 50 | 24 | | 6th 90 |
| 26 | 22 | Banstead Athletic | 50 | 25 | 4th | SF 97 |
| 21 | 23 | Hucknall Town | 49 | 17 | | 6th 86 |
| 22 | 24 | Bridgnorth Town | 48 | 23 | 2nd Qual | 5th x 2 |
| 24 | 25 | Newport IoW | 47 | 18 | | 5th x 2 |
| 41 | 26 | Clitheroe | 47 | 23 | 6th | F 96 |
| 25 | 27 | Gresley Rovers | 46 | 19 | | F 91 |
| 27 | 28 | Molesey | 45 | 15 | | 6th 82 |
| 28 | 29 | Paulton Rovers | 45 | 19 | 1st | 5th 90 |
| 30 | 30 | Arlesey Town | 45 | 25 | 1st | W 95 |
| 31 | 31 | Newbury Town | 44 | 20 | | 6th 94 |
| 39 | 32 | Diss Town | 44 | 22 | 3rd | W94 |
| 29 | 33 | Almondsbury Town | 44 | 23 | 2nd Qual | F 79 |
| 62 | 34 | Eastleigh | 44 | 24 | 1st | 4th x 3 |
| 36 | 35 | Tunbridge Wells | 44 | 25 | 2nd | 4th x 5 |
| 33 | 35 | Guisborough Town | 43 | 13 | 1st | F 80 |
| 40 | 37 | Abingdon Town | 43 | 18 | 2nd | 5th x 3 |
| 35 | 38 | Rainworth MW | 43 | 20 | 1st | F 82 |
| 43 | 39 | Windsor & Eton | 42 | 14 | 2nd | SF 81 |
| 37 | 40 | Wimborne Town | 42 | 17 | 1st | W92 |
| 46 | 41 | Basildon United | 42 | 20 | 2nd | 6th x 2 |
| 32 | 42 | Thackley | 42 | 21 | 2nd Qual | 5th 81 |
| 47 | 43 | Hallam | 42 | 24 | 2nd | 5th 81 |
| 34 | 44 | Sheffield | 42 | 25 | 1st Qual | F 77 |
| 38 | 45 | Eastwood Hanley | 41 | 18 | | 5th x 3 |
| 45 | 46 | Great Yarmouth Town | 41 | 19 | 1st | SF 83 |
| 49 | 47 | Burgess Hill Town | 41 | 22 | 2nd | 5th 98 |
| 42 | 48 | Collier Row | 40 | 11 | | SF 87 |
| 44 | 49 | Yate Town | 40 | 20 | | 5th 92 |
| 55 | 50 | Thatcham Town | 40 | 22 | 2nd | 6th 89 |

# ENGLAND SEMI-PROFESSIONAL REPRESENTATIVE FOOTBALL

Match Reports first published in Team Talk

John Owens' second season in charge of England's semi-professional international squad finished with his selections, still unbeaten, but again a little frustrated, as only friendly internationals had been played and no real challenges had been faced.

Club managers and chairmen are happy and proud to see their players representing their country, but FAXI trial games can becoame an irritant during the season if there is no championship, tournament or cup at which the squad can aim at the end of the campaign. Managers with clubs challenging for promotion or a Wembley appearance can be forgiven if they doubt the importance of the England preparations.

A British championship or end of season European tournament would change all that, and surely our level of the game deserves a worthwhile end of season challenge.

Last season's FAXI games helped John Owens prepare his squad although bad weather prevented the match against The Unibond League taking place.

With the squad built around the excellent Cheltenham Town contingent, this coming season should see a new look for England and there will be every incentive to challenge for International recognition.

Last season's victory over an Italian Under 21 Serie C selection was impressive while a draw in Holland was as much as our team was ever going to be allowed to achieve on the evening. John Owens with helpers Steve Avory and Jimmy Conway have yet to taste defeat, but as soon as the squad begins to develop a spirit they are disbanded and rebuilding takes place. Hopefully more games, preferably in a tournament, will once and for all establish this squad, that represents the biggest section of English football.

*England v Wales*
*Back row (L-R): Jim Conway, Steve Avery, Andy Comyn, Warren Patmore, Tim Ryan, Paul Gothard, Steve Stott, Steve Book, Mark Yates, Chris Banks, Lee Howells, John Owens, Steve Avory*
*Front row: Neil Grayson, Gary Butterworth, Geoff Pitcher, Mark Smith, Barry Williams, Lee Charles, Gary Wormull.  Photo: Keith Clayton*

## FA XI　0　v　0　DR MARTENS LEAGUE
(at Twerton Park, Bath City FC)

**FA SQUAD:** Steve Book, Michael Duff, Jamie Victory and Chris Banks (Cheltenham Town), Rob Cousins (Yeovil Town), Richard Walker, Lee Howells, Russell Milton, Jason Eaton and Dale Watkins (Cheltenham Town), Jason Drysdale (Forest Green Rovers).
**SUBSTITUTIONS:** Stuart Brock (Kidderminster Harriers) for Steve Book, Paul Hunt (Forest Green Rovers) for Dale Watkins, Ian Wright (Hereford United) for Rob Cousins and Chris Honour (Forest Green Rovers) for Jason Drysdale.
**Team Manager:** John Owens　**Assistant Manager:** Steve Avory　**Trainer/Physio:** Jimmy Conway (Kidderminster)

**DR MARTENS SQUAD:** Shane Higgs (Worcester City), Richard Barratt (Atherstone United), Gary Twynham (Grantham Town), Garry Wotton (Bath City), Mark Albrighton (Atherstone United), Ryan Cross (Dorchester Town), Neil Glasser (Grantham Town), Ian Robinson (Ilkeston Town), Graham Colbourne (Bath City), Adrian Randall (Salisbury City), Chris Burns (Gloucester City).
**SUBSTITUTIONS:** Kevin Braybrook (Salisbury City) for Garry Wotton, Dean Bennett (Bromsgrove Rovers) for Graham Colbourne, Richard Gardner (Nuneaton Borough) for Adrian Randall.
**Management:** George Rooney and Ron Bradbury.　**Physio:** Terry Hardwell (Bath City)

## FA XI　1　v　1　RYMANS LEAGUE
Akuamoah　　　　　　St Hilaire
(at Harrow)

**FA SQUAD:** Chris Taylor and Lee Harvey (Stevenage Borough), Murray Fishlock (Yeovil Town), Matt Crossley (Kingstonian), Mark Smith (Stevenage Borough), Michael Danzey and Steve Perkins (Woking), Steve Berry (Stevenage Borough), Warren Patmore (Yeovil Town), Eddie Akuamoah and Gary Patterson (Kingstonian).
**SUBSTITUTIONS:** Steve Farrelly for Chris Taylor, Steve West for Warren Patmore, Barry Miller for Steve Perkins, Stuart Beever for Matt Crossley.
**Team Manager:** John Owens　**Assistant Manager:** Steve Avory　**Trainer/Physio:** Jimmy Conway (Kidderminster)

**RYMAN LEAGUE SQUAD:** Paul Wilkerson (Slough Town), Steve Daly (Boreham Wood), Micky Engwell (Slough Town), Steve Watson (Sutton United), Richard Pierson (Slough Town), Andy Riley and Dave Harlow (Sutton United), Ian King (Aylesbury United), Tony Samuels (Boreham Wood), Leon Gutmore and Martin St Hilaire (Billericay Town).
**SUBSTITUTIONS:** Paul Gothard (Dagenham & Redbridge) for Paul Wilkerson, Graham Kemp (Slough Town) for Steve Watson, Otis Roberts (Harrow Borough) for Micky Engwell.
**Management:** Graham Roberts and Steve Browne.　**Physio:** Kevin McGoldrick (Slough Town)

## FA XI　3　v　0　COMBINED SERVICES
Grayson (2), Cox
(at Burton Albion)

**FA SQUAD:** Adam Sollitt (Kettering Town), Paul Carty (Hednesford Town), Steve Prindiville (Nuneaton Borough), Andy Comyn (Hednesford Town), Colin Vowden and Craig Norman (Kettering Town), Barry Williams (Nuneaton Borough), Neil Grayson (Cheltenham Town), Lee Hudson (Kettering Town), Adrian Foster (Rushden & Diamonds), Steve Taylor (Kidderminster Harriers).
**SUBSTITUTIONS:** Phil Morgan (Hednesford Town) for Adam Sollitt, Paul Cox (Kettering Town) for Craig Norman, Mark Wolseley (Kidderminster Harriers) for Barry Williams, Matt Beard (Kidderminster Harriers) for Steve Taylor.
**Team Manager:** John Owens　**Assistant Manager:** Steve Avory　**Trainer/Physio:** Jimmy Conway (Kidderminster)

**COMBINED SERVICES SQUAD:** Nigel Healy (R.A.F.), Alfie Alford (Army), Davie Wilson (R.N.), Gary Wotton (R.A.F.), Terry Price and Steve Riley (R.N.), Terry Lynch (Army), Paul Willetts and Steve Stacey (R.N.), Dave Hope and Chris Williams (Army).
**SUBSTITUTIONS:** Stuart Adams (R.N.) for Nigel Healy, Brian Kyall (R.A.F.) for Gary Wotton, Ritchie Hope (Army) for Chris Williams.
**Team Manager:** Major W.T.E. Thomson (Army)　**Team Coach:** WOPT T.G. Johnson (R.N.)
**Assistant Coaches:** CPOWEA S. Johnson (R.N.) and WO1 A. Higgins (Army)　**Physio:** Captain M. Healy (Army)

## FA XI 4 v 0 BRITISH UNIVERSITIES
Charles (2), Docking, Pope
(at Soham Town Rangers FC)

**FA SQUAD:** Paul Bastock (Boston United), Ashley Vickers (St Albans City), Chris Sparkes (Hayes), Neil Pope (Histon), Joby Gowshall (Boston United), Darren Haylock (Newmarket Town), Martin St Hilaire (Billericay Town), Neil Docking (Soham Town Rangers), Lee Charles (Hayes), Junior Lewis (Hendon), David Braybrooke (Soham Town Rangers).
**SUBSTITUTIONS:** James Heeps (Bedford United) for Paul Bastock, Andrew Stanhope (Boston United) for Neil Docking), Mark Leonard (Soham Town Rangers) for Joby Gowshall, Zak Nedemovic (Soham Town Rangers) for Neil Pope.
**Team Manager:** Steve Avory

## ENGLAND 4 v 1 ITALY
Grayson (2), Charles, Cavazzana (OG)     Iaquita
(at Hayes. Att: 1026)

England Semi-Professionals recorded their best ever victory over their old footballing rivals and in doing so gave a superb display of football laced with a very definite will to win.

Conditions were difficult as it rained all evening on an already drenched pitch, but the Hayes ground stood up to the deluge well and John Owens' instructions that his side should play passing football from the back and through midfield was upheld to the final whistle. As the Italian squad was selected from their Serie C Under 21s, and were all full time professionals, many a management team would have opted for the safety first tactic of the long ball and condensing space, on such a wet surface. After just five two hour sessions of quality coaching, in which John was assisted by Steve Avory and Jimmy Conway, you could see the players believed in their chosen tactics implicitly and they had the skill, technique and character to carry them out.

In the first half England must have had 70 per cent of the possession and when Italy were allowed the ball they were closed down so well they didn't manage a shot on target until the 45th minute when Steve Book saved well with his feet from Grometti.

The defensive central three saw Michael Danzey outstanding in the air and Tim Ryan tackling as well as ever, marking the twin Italian strikers, with Mark Smith sweeping and reading the game so well he always appeared to be in complete control. Those three and 'keeper Book constantly brought wing backs Simon Shaw and Paul Underwood into play from deep and their use of the wings gave the whole side the space in which to play and pulled the Italians all over the field.

Skipper Garry Butterworth had an oustanding game as he acted as central midfield anchorman and his no non-sense attitude was matched by Mark Yates and Garry Patterson, who were encouraged to go forward to help the wing backs and the two strikers.

After just nine minutes, in which England had dominated without creating any chances, England worked the ball through midfield to the powerful Warren Patmore who held off a double challenge and fed the speeding Simon Shaw down the right. A perfect centre found Neil Grayson diving in low to head home a spectacular goal, and help inspire the England team to produce a quite superb first half display. The front two of Patmore and Grayson, whom John Owen had sensibly put in a hotel room together, had obviously built an understanding as they constantly kept possession and pulled the typically rugged Italian central defenders this way and that, enncouraging many a desperate lunging tackle, and winning many a free kick.

Half time came with even more heavy rain and the mud did threaten the fluency of England's game. The Italians came out with instructions to match England's physical presence and the game threatened to boil over. But common sense prevailed and it wasn't long before the hard working midfield men set up yet another lovely passing move and from Paul Underwood's cross field pass from the left, Garry Patterson's step over and Butterworth's through ball the effervescent Grayson confidently collected his third England goal in two Internationals.

This goal came ten minutes into the second half and within ten more another burst by Shaw down the right was diverted into the net by a sliding Italian defender Terry Cavazzana with Dale Watkins, who had come on for Patmore, desperately trying to get a touch!

With the result now a foregone conclusion both managers were able to award 'caps' to all squad members and John Owens gave his substitutes at least twenty minutes to show what they could do. Local hero Lee Charles came on and thrilled the Hayes supporters with a nearly headed goal from a perfect Watkins cross and Simon Wormull had time to show his class as the right sided wing back. Andy Comyn won his second cap as a substitute in the back three and the only non-Conference member, Paul Gothard, was given time to show his undoubted goalkeeping ability.

Unfortunately for Book, who had dealt with everything he had to do with commendable coolness in the sticky conditions, the passing of the England defenders had produced one mistake and a rasping shot from substitute Vincenzo Iaquinta had given the visitors a consolation goal just before the substitutuion.

Before the final whistle the Italians did 'score' again with a snap shot following a scramble but Gothard appeared to have made an outstanding reaction save for a corner. In fact he had diverted the shot away but it had

England v Italy
Back Row (L-R): Lee Charles, Steve Book, Michael Danzey, Warren Patmore, Paul Gothard, Gary Patterson, Tim Ryan, Simon Shaw, John Owens (manager)
Front Row: Andy Comyn, Dale Watkins, Paul Underwood, Mark Smith, Neil Grayson, Mark Yates, Gary Butterworth (captain)    Photo: Keith Clayton

Centre: On the way to the International in Holland.
Photo: Andrew Chitty

England v Holland
(L-R): Gary Butterworth, Paul Underwood, Simon Shaw, Steve Stott, Warren Patmore, Tim Ryan, Michael Danzey, Neil Grayson, Gary Patterson, Steve Book, Mark Smith, Barry Williams, Andy Comyn, Paul Gothard, Murray Fishlock, Lee Charles

somehow passed through the net, out of the signt of the referee, much to the visitors' frustration.

But a 4-1 scoreline was certainly a fair reflection of the play. It's a result that any English football fan will really relish against Italian opposition and the determination, will to win and general spirit of the squad made you wonder why we hardly ever see the same from their senior counterparts at Wembley?

In just three days this England squad had accepted new coaching methods, a fresh style of play and had taken on board new set pieces and developed understandings with new team colleagues. The squad, although originally possessing six Cheltenham Town players (what a compliment that is to Steve Cotterill and his club), had Lee Howells and Chris Banks unfit and finished up with twelve different clubs represented. John Owens and his team of scouts had certainly scoured the country for talent and had come up with a very well balanced selection.

The only sad concusion that is continually irritating is the lack of a proper competitive tournament for England's impressive Semi-Professional set up to show the football world what they can really achieve. The management and players deserve more and we can only hope that in the very near future we will be given some good news on this subject! There are sponsors standing by, willing to help!

**ENGLAND SQUAD (3-5-2):** Steve Book (Cheltenham Town), Michael Danzey (Woking), Mark Smith (Stevenage Borough), Tim Ryan (Southport), Simon Shaw (Doncaster Rovers), Garry Patterson (Kingstonian), Garry Butterworth (Rushden & Diamonds) (captain), Mark Yates (Cheltenham Town), Paul Underwood (Rushden & Diamonds), Warren Patmore (Yeovil Town), Neil Grayson (Cheltenham Town).
**SUBSTITUTES:** Paul Gothard (Dagenham & Redbridge) for Book, Andy Comyn (Hednesford Town) for Danzey, Simon Wormull (Doncaster Rovers) for Shaw, Lee Charles (Hayes) for Patterson, Dale Watkins (Cheltenham Town) for Patmore.

**ITALY:** Marco Rama, Claudio Riboni, Cristian Benassi, Terry Cavazzana, Maurizio Pellaras, Paolo Gobba, Francesco Montervino, Michele Malpeli, Giuseppe Giglio, Simone Barone, Paolo Giometti.
**SUBSTITUTES:** Lorenzo Di Leo for Rama, Daniele De Batisti for Pellaras, Tiziano Polenghi for Montervino, Vincenzo Iaquinta for Giometti, Mirko Savini for Robini.

## HOLLAND 1 v 1 ENGLAND
Knijn                Patmore
(at Sportclub Genemuiden, Holland. Att: 1,400)

England's second international this season was played at Genemuiden's well appointed ground in the middle of Holland. All amateur clubs appear to have the luxury of a complex with at least three enclosed grounds usually including an all weather pitch and special training facilities plus a central changing room within a club house. Sportclub Genemuiden was obviously a very progressive club, which had been working its way up the Dutch promotional ladder, and many town fans were there to support one of the local stars, who was included in the International squad. The team of 'amateurs' had been training together twice a week for four weeks and had looked good in their practice matches against senior opposition.

England had replaced the injured Simon Wormull, Mark Yates and Dale Watkins with Yeovil Town's Steve Stott and Murray Fishlock, plus Barry Williams from runaway Dr Martens League leaders Nuneaton Borough.

Having met at a Heathrow hotel after matches on the Saturday, a late morning flight to Amsterdam and coach journey to Zwolle gave John Owens and Steve Amory time for 90 minutes training before dinner and a team meeting. Two more taining sessions at excellent facilites saw the new players settling into the roles required of them and hard work was put in on both attacking and defensive set pieces.

Some interesting spelling of the England players' clubs on the official team sheets included Steverage, Jeovil, Cveltenham, but didn't worry the England team that saw just one change from the starting line-up against Italy, Steve Stott (Jeovil) replacing Mark Yates to win his sixth cap and become the most capped player in the team!

Within seconds of the kick off one of the well practised free kicks from Paul Underwood saw Michael Danzy rise to smash a header against the Dutch crossbar and then two minutes later an equally powerful header from Warren Patmore scorched past a helpless goalkeeper only for the big centre forward to be penalised for bumping the centre back as he reached Stott's right wing cross.

This was a very harsh decision but one of many made by a referee, who never allowed the game to flow or gain any rhythm. England's spectacular start was backed up by some excellent flowing football but gradually the whistle won the day, the game deteriorating into a succession of stops and starts. Holland too suffered and one early delightful move of thirty passes was never to be repeated.

The home goalkeeper Schoemaker made two vital saves after excellent centres from Simon Shaw and then after 34 minutes Gary Patterson battled for possession on the left and produced a chance, which Patmore managed to force in from six yards for his first England goal.

The Dutch certainly came out with more resolve for the second half, but neither side could gain enough possession to get on top.

After 57 minutes both strikers Patmore and Neil Grayson joined the defence to face a free kick from 30 yards out. Unfortunately the kick was played to advancing centre back Dick Knijn who drove a powerful low shot into a

**STARS AGAINST SCOTLAND**

*Top left: Warren Patmore was on top form against the Scots and the Welsh. Photo: Garry Letts*
*Top right: Geoff Pitcher joined the squad after a fine display at Wembley.*
*Bottom left: Simon Wormull who enjoyed an excellent first season in the Conference. Photo: Garry Letts*
*Bottom right: Goalscorer: Tim Ryan. Photo: Garry Letts*

packed defence where a deflection resulted in Steve Book diving one way and the ball finishing in the opposite bottom corner, for an equalizer.

The goal spurred the English into a higher gear and Patterson chipped onto the crossbar, and Patmore missed two good chances before the Dutch saw another deflected shot shave the crossbar. Substitutes Lee Charles and Murray Fishlock added effective attacking variations, but a second goal couldn't be found and another satisfactory display meant that John Owens' undefeated record was intact after three games.

The spirit was once again noticably good and another Interntational trip away underlined the fact that the more this squad gets together the more they will obviously develop into a very well coached and successful team.

**NETHERLANDS TEAM:** Schoemaker, Meyerink, Knijn, Homburg, van Rijswijk, Boots, Linger, Bierstekers, Drummend, Wissink, Sepp.
**SUBSTITUTES:** Kremers (Bierstekers 85), van Haagen (van Rijswijk 66), Kreuze (Sepp 57), Lindeboom (Drummen 45), Diteweg.

**ENGLAND TEAM:** Steve Book (Cheltenham Town), Simon Shaw (Doncaster Rovers), Paul Underwood (Rushden & Diamonds) (Sub: Murray Fishlock (Yeovil Town) 73 mins), Michael Danzey (Woking), Mark Smith (Stevenage Borough) (Sub: Barry Williams (Nuneaton Borough) 73 mins), Tim Ryan (Southport), Steve Stott (Yeovil Town), Garry Butterworth (Rushden & Diamonds), Warren Patmore (Yeovil Town) (Sub: Andy Comyn (Hednesford Town) 86 mins), Neil Grayson (Cheltenham Town) (Sub: Lee Charles (Hayes) 59 mins), Garry Patterson (Kingstonian).
**Subs:** not used: Paul Gothard (Dagenham & Redbridge)

## FA XI   1   v   1   HIGHLAND LEAGUE
Ryan                    Murray
(at Chesham. Att: 400 estimated)

The FA recorded an emphatic victory in Scotland on their last meeting, but have still to record a victory against the Highland League at home.

Representative matches can often be rather like pre-season friendlies or exhibition matches with lots of skill, a deal of effort, plenty of short passing and movement, but lacking competitive edge. And that last named is the vital ingredient that gets most spectators involved.

Unfortunately, there was not too much of that about at Chesham, especially from an England point of view, although the several Scots present found more to praise, until Neil Grayson appeared with half an hour to go. His extra pace and evident will to win led to the home team looking more dangerous than they had in the preceding hour. However, they still carved out fewer scoring opportunties than the Highland League lads, who several times forced Paul Gothard to extend himself to field ground and air shots. He was one Englander able to show his attributes of sound handling, good judgement and keeping his defenders alert.

In front of him Mark Smith looked elegant and willing to move forward if the opportunity arose. Skipper Gary Butterworth was busy and energetic in the midfield engine room. He tried to motivate others around him. Warren Patmore looked dangerous in the air and that is where the F.A. should have been able to capitalise. However, Highlanders' David Morland, not possessing Patmore's physique, showed considerable skill and positional sense. Ian Murray down the right side looked the best player on the pitch, so it was a surprise when he was substituted. Up front Derek Nicol, Andy McKay and Colin Milne, well served by Michael Stephen, caused umpteen more problems than the F.A. front line.

Spectators were not pleased by the F.A. XI's performance as demonstrated in the several barbed comments from the Chesham faithful over the qualities of Conference skill compared with the Ryman League. That was a mite unfair since there was no lack of effort but the players admittedly looked tired and lacking sharpness.

Colin Milne should have given the visitors the lead but the ball stuck under his foot only a couple of yards from the gaping goal. Nicol sent Gothard plunging to save at the post, then headed and flicked just over, and Murray's shot was topped over by Gothard stretching back. Despite all these attempts it was the home team who took an undeserved lead. Scott Clark gave away an unnecessary corner. Gary Patterson took a low one which reached Tim Ryan, who juggled the ball on his left foot before shooting home in the 41st minute.

A Colin Milne shot and header at the start of the second half showed the Scots still had the will to win. When Butterworth pulled back Darren Still as he entered the penalty area there was no doubting the penalty with which Murray coolly levelled the scores. His side should have taken the lead when Stephen provided a chance which the sliding McKay was unfortunate to see skid the wrong side of the far post.

The F.A. XI had a slightly better second half. Lee Howells ran 50 yards with the ball before giving Lee Charles a chance which was blocked. The nearest to a second half score for them came when Mark Yates' good long ball was headed strongly by Patmore. Alas, the advertising hoarding took the force as we waited expectantly for the net to bulge. Had it gone in it would have been an unjust ending for our Celtic brothers, who well deserved their draw.

**FA XI SQUAD:** Paul Gothard (Dagenham & Redbridge), Mark Yates (Cheltenham), Simon Wormull (Dover), Andy Comyn (Hednesford), Mark Smith (Stevenage), Tim Ryan (Southport), Lee Howells (Cheltenham) (sub Geoff Pitcher (Kingstonian) 61st minute), Gary Butterworth (Rushden & Diamonds), Warren Patmore (Yeovil Town), Lee Charles (Hayes) (sub Neil Grayson (Cheltenham) 61st minute), Gary Patterson (Kingstonian) (sub Barry Williams (Nuneaton) 79th minute). **Subs:** not used: Chris Banks and Steve Book (both Cheltenham)

**HIGHLAND LEAGUE SQUAD:** Mark McRitchie (Forres Mechanics), Scott Clark (Peterhead) (sub Derek Milne (Fraserburgh) 46th minute), Steve King (Peterhead), David Morland (Huntly), Andy Patterson (Huntly), Ian Murray (Fraserburgh) (sub Kristoffer Hunter (Fraserburgh) 64th minute), Darren Still (Keith), Derek Nicol (Keith), Colin Milne (Peterhead) (sub Russell McBride (Fraserburgh) 86th minute), Andy McKay (Clachnacuddin), Michael Stephen (Fraserburgh) (sub Martin Johnston (Cove) 81st minute). **Subs:** not used: g/k Ivor Pirie (Peterhead)

**Referee:** G K Hegley, assisted by I G Williamson and A Osborne. Reserve official: W Skelton.


# ENGLAND  2  v  1  WALES
Patmore, Pitcher                     Shepherd
(at Clarence Park, St Albans. Estimated attendance: 550)

Out of their FA XI mould and into their England guise the same squad of players, who performed listlessly againt the Highland League two days earlier, was far more positive when they faced their Weslh counterparts and just about deserved their narrow win. Cheltenham were well represented in the crowd, as were Wealdstone although they were there to protest, in an orderly way, at their Ryman promotion being turned down.

England were seldom troubled at the back in the first half where Barry Williams settled in well and Mark Smith again looked very much at ease. Smith kept the lively and bustling Deiniol Graham more or less under control, although Graham and Gary Shepherd looked to have the makings of a successful partnership which would profit from further acquaintanceship.

For half an hour the Welsh kept England at bay but suicidal hesitancy by David Barnhouse, who could have put the ball back to his keeper or well upfield several times over such was his time oon the ball, allowed Neil Grayson to rob him. As Grayson surged into the area, with Barnhouse trailing yet trying to atone for his lethargy, the inevitable happened. There was no guarantee that Grayson would score but Barnhouse brought him down to double his crime. Warren Patmore's penalty beat Gary Wager to his right despite the keeper getting a hand to it.

Twelve minutes later England were two up as Patmore headed down for Geoff Pitcher to volley unerringly home. Their pressure, Williams, Mark Yates and Grayson all going close, had paid off. Two headers by defender Neil O'Brien and one by Shepherd were rare Welsh forays into England territory.

Matters were far more even in the second half. Shepherd had already gone close with a shot from the edge of the penalty area before, in the 55th minute, Graham headed on and Shepherd hooked the ball past a bemused Steve Book. All three goals had hit the same net corner.

Wales now came good. Full back Andrew Thomas made several forward charges and Graham, really enjoying the window shopping, tormented the English defence with his speedy feints and turns. He had one effort cleared off the line and set up a chance which Jonathon Williams was a fraction tardy in spotting. At the other end Simon Wormull's corner and cross were respectively headed on to the bar and past the post by a stooping Patmore.

A flurry of substitutions, in order to give everyone at least a few minutes of action, did not halt the enthusiastic Welsh pursuit of a second goal but England hung on to retain their lead in this thirteenth fixture between the two teams. For the record it is now 8-3 to England, with two drawn.

**ENGLAND TEAM:** Steve Book (Cheltenham Town) (Sub Paul Gothard (Dagenham & Redbridge) 84th min)., Barry Williams (Nuneaton) (Sub Andy Comyn (Hednesford Town) 76th min.), Simon Wormull (Dover) (Sub Steve Stott (Yeovil) 84th min.), Chris Banks (Cheltenham), Mark Smith (Stevenage), Tim Ryan (Southport), Mark Yates (Cheltenham) (Sub Lee Howells (Cheltenham) 84th min.), Garry Butterworth (Rushden & Diamonds), Warren Patmore (Yeovil), Neil Grayson (Cheltenham), Geoff Pitcher (Kingstonian) (Sub Lee Charles (Hayes) 84th min.)

**WALES TEAM:** Gary Wager (Inter Cable) (Sub Neil Thomas (Merthyr) 81st min.), Andrew Thomas (Merthyr), Kevin Lloyd (Caersws), David Barnhouse (Carmarthen), Neil O'Brien (Cwmbran), Craig Lima (Newport) (Sub Anuerin Thomas (Aberystwyth) 46th min.), Adrian Needs (Merthyr) (Sub Neil Davies (INter Cable) 59th min.), Lee Congerton (Colwyn Bay) (Sub Colin Reynolds (Newtown) 70th min.), Deiniol Graham (Colwyn Bay), Gary Shepherd (Merthyr) (Sub Mattie Davies (Cwmbran) 62nd min.), Jonathan Williams (Aberystwyth).

**Referee:** A D'Urso (Billericay) assisted by S Head (Stokenchurch) and J Pettitt (Welling).
Fourth official: L Garrett (Southend)

A third 'friendly' international in one season was a very encouraging improvement of the English Semi-Professional International Squad and, with John Owens' selections still unbeaten, Wales were eagerly welcomed to Clarence Park, St Albans for the last game of the campaign.

Gary Patterson, Paul Underwood and Michael Danzey were unavailable and possible defensive replacements Murray Fishlock, Jamie Victory and Rob Hollingdale were all injured.

However, Kingstonian's 'playmaker' in midfield, Geoff Pitcher, who had been 'man of the match' in their Trophy semi-final at Cheltenham and in the final at Wembley, was called in and was selected to make his England debut.

It was good to see the Welsh squad and their FA Officials so obviously pleased to be back in the International arena and in a lively game we saw two classic goals from Pitcher himself with a spectacular volley after Warren Patmore had leapt to nod down a right wing cross and then with an equally well exectued volley for the Welsh by Gary Shepherd.

Over the weekend England (disguised as the FA XI on Friday) had kept John Owens' unbeaten record and shown in flashes that the form displayed against Italy, and on occasions against Holland, is there to be encouraged and reproduced.

But we do need a competition to bring out the best in everyone concerned; the players, the managers, the spectators and, I suspect, even the administrators as well.

As it was, my man of the weekend was Warren Patmore, who never stopped working for the two full games and led the line superbly. Sadly his partnership with the evergreen Neil Grayson may be split if Neil stays in the Nationwide Football League - but you never can tell!                                                   TW

*Right:*
*Craig Lima (Wales) powers in a header despite the attention of Mark Yates, Gary Patterson and Chris Banks.*
*Photo: Keith Clayton*

*Below:*
*Geoff Pitcher outnumbered by the Welsh. Andrew Thomas (2) and Lee Congerton*

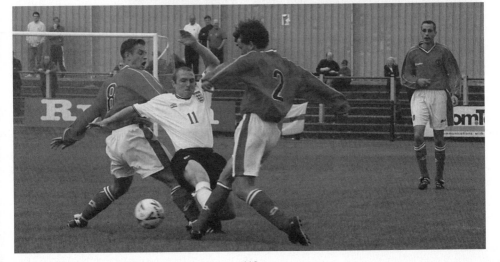

119

*Top left: Steve Stott (Yeovil Town)   Photo: Andrew Chitty*
*Top right: Gary Patterson (Kingstonian)   Photo: Andrew Chitty*
*Bottom left: Barry Williams (Nuneaton Borough)   Photo: Andrew Chitty*
*Bottom right: Paul Gothard (Dagenham & Redbridge, now Hayes)   Photo: Neil Thaler*

# ENGLAND SEMI-PRO CAPS 1979-99

KEY TO COUNTRY CODES:
E - Eire;  I - Italy;  F - Finland;  G - Gibralter;  H - Holland;  N - Norway;  S - Scotland;  W - Wales.
Players capped for the first time during season 1998-99 are in bold.

Gary Abbott  (Welling) 87 I(s), S(s), 92 W(s)  (3)

David Adamson  (Boston Utd) 79 SH, 80 ISH  (5)

Tony Agana  (Weymouth) 86 E  (1)

Carl Alford  (Kettering T. & Rushden & Ds) 96 EH  (2)

Ian Arnold  (Kettering Town) 95 W(s)H  (2)

Jim Arnold  (Stafford Rangers) 79 SH  (2)

Nick Ashby  (Kettering & Rushden & Ds)   94 FN, 95 G 96 EH (5)

Noel Ashford  (Enfield & Redbridge For.) 82 GHS, 83 IHS,
    84 WHSI, 85 WI(s), 86 EE,87 W(s), IHS, 90 WE, 91 I(s)  (21)

John Askey  (Macclesfield) 90 W  (1)

Paul Bancroft  (Kidderminster H.) 89 IW, 90 IWE, 91 W  (6)

Chris Banks  (Cheltenham T.) 98 H, 99 W  (2)

Keith Barrett  (Enfield) 81 HSI, 82 GIHS, 83 IHS,
    84 W(s)HS, 85 IHS  (16)

Laurence Batty  (Woking) 93 F(s), 95 WHG  (4)

Mark Beeney  (Maidstone) 89 I(s)  (1)

Graham Benstead  (Kettering) 94 WFN(s)  (3)

Kevin Betsy  (Woking) 98 H(s)  (1)

Marcus Bignot  (Kidderminster H) 97 H  (1)

Jimmy Bolton  (Kingstonian) 95 G  (1)

**Steve Book (Cheltenham Town) 99 IHW**  **(3)**

Gary Brabin  (Runcorn) 94 WFN  (3)

Mark Bradshaw  (Halifax T.) 98 H  (1)

Colin Brazier  (Kidderminster) 87 W  (1)

Stewart Brighton  (Bromsgrove) 94 W  (1)

Steve Brooks  (Cheltenham) 88 W(s), 90 WE  (3)

Derek Brown  (Woking) 94 F(s)N  (2)

Kevan Brown  (Woking) 95 WHG 96 H 97 E  (5)

Corey Browne  (Dover) 94 F(s)N(s), 95 H(s)  (3)

David Buchanan  (Blyth) 86 E(s)E  (2)

Brian Butler  (Northwich) 93 F  (1)

Gary Butterworth  (Rushden & Diamonds) 97 EH, 98 H,
    99 IHW  (6)

Steve Butler  (Maidstone) 88 W, 89 IW  (3)

Chris Byrne  (Macclesfield T.) 97 H  (1)

Mark Carter  (Runcorn & Barnet)
    87 WIHS, 88 W, 89 IW, 90 IE, 91 IW(s)  (11)

Kim Casey  (Kidderminster) 86 WEE(s), 87 WI  (5)

Paul Cavell  (Redbridge) 92 W, 93 F  (2)

Kevin Charlton  (Telford) 85 WI  (2)

**Lee Charles (Hayes) 99 I(s) H(s) W(s)**  **(3)**

Andrew Clarke  (Barnet) 90 EE  (2)

David Clarke  (Blyth Spartans) 80 IS(s)H, 81 HSI,
    82 IHS, 83 HS, 84 HSI  (14)

Gary Clayton  (Burton) 86 E  (1)

Robert Codner  (Barnet) 88 W  (1)

John Coleman  (Morecambe) 93 F(s)  (1)

Darren Collins  (Enfield) 93 F(s), 94 WFN  (4)

Andy Comyn  (Hednesford T.) 98 H(s), 99 I(s)H(s)W(s)  (4)

Steve Conner  (Dartford, Redbridge & Dagenham & R)
    90 I, 91 IW, 92 W, 93 F  (5)

David Constantine  (Altrincham) 85 IHS, 86 W  (4)

Robbie Cooke  (Kettering) 89 W(s), 90 I  (2)

Scott Cooksey  (Hednesford T.) 97 E 98 H(s)  (2)

Alan Cordice  (Wealdstone) 83 IHS, 84 WS(s), I(s), 85 IHS  (9)

Ken Cramman  (Gateshead & Rushden & Diamonds)
    96 E 97 EH  (3)

Paul Cuddy  (Altrincham) 87 IHS  (3)

Paul Culpin  (Nuneaton B) 84 W, 85 W(s) IHS  (5)

Michael Danzey (Woking) played particularly well against Italy.   Photo: Andrew Chitty

Mark Golley  (Sutton Utd.) 87 H(s)S, 88 W, 89 IW, 92 W    (6)

Paul Gothard  (Dagenham & Redb.) 97 E(s), 99 I(s)W(s)    (3)

Neil Grayson  (Cheltenham T.) 98, H 99 IHW    (4)

Phil Gridelet  (Hendon & Barnet) 89 IW, 90 WEE    (5)

Steve Guppy  (Wycombe W.) 93 W    (1)

Steve Hancock  (Macclesfield) 90 W    (1)

David Harlow  (Farnborough T.) 97 E(s)H    (2)

Barry Hayles  (Stevenage Bor.) 96 EH    (2)

Brian Healy  (Morecambe) 98 H    (1)

Tony Hemmings  (Northwich) 93 F    (1)

Andy Hessenthaler  (Dartford) 90 I    (1)

Kenny Hill  (Maidstone Utd) 80 ISH    (3)

Mark Hine  (Gateshead) 95 W(s)H    (2)

Simeon Hodson  (Kidderminster) 94 WFN    (3)

Colin Hogarth  (Guiseley) 95 WH    (2)

Steven Holden  (Kettering) 94 WFN(s), 95 HG    (5)

Mark Hone  (Welling) 90 I, 93 F, 94 W(s)F(s)N    (5)

Gary Hooley  (Frickley) 85 W    (1)

**Michael Danzey (Woking) 99 IH**    **(2)**

Dean Hooper  (Kingstonian) 98 H    (1)

Paul Davies  (Kidderminster H.) 86 W, 87 WIS, 88 W, 89 W    (6)

Keith Houghton  (Blyth Spartans) 79 S    (1)

John Davison  (Altrincham)
79 SH, 80 IS, 81 HSI, 82 GIHS, 83 IHS,
84 WHIS, 85 IHS, 86 WEE    (24)

Barry Howard  (Altrincham) 81 HSI, 82 GIHS    (7)

Neil Howarth  (Macclesfield) 95 H(s) 97 E    (2)

John Denham  (Northwich Victoria) 80 H    (1)

David Howell  (Enfield)
85 H(s)S(s), 86 WE, 87 WIHS, 88 W,
89 IW, 90 IEE    (14)

Peter Densmore  (Runcorn) 88 W, 89 I    (2)

Phil Derbyshire  (Mossley) 83 H(s)S(s)    (2)

Lee Howells  (Cheltenham T.) 98, H 99 W    (1)

Mick Doherty  (Weymouth) 86 W(s)    (1)

Lee Hughes  (Kidderminster) 96 EH 97 EH    (4)

Neil Doherty  (Kidderminster H.) 97 E    (1)

Delwyn Humphreys  (Kidderminster H.)
91 W(s), 92 W, 94 WFN, 95 WH    (7)

Lee Endersby  (Harrow Bor.) 96 H    (1)

Steve Humphries  (Barnet) 87 H(s)    (1)

Mick Farrelly  (Altrincham) 87 IHS    (3)

Nicky Ironton  (Enfield) 83 H(s), 84 W    (2)

Steve Farrelly  (Macclesfield) 95 H(s)G(s)    (2)

Tony Jennings  (Enfield)
79 SH, 80 ISH, 81 HSI, 82 GIHS    (12)

Trevor Finnegan  (Weymouth) 81 HS    (2)

Murray Fishlock  (Yeovil Town) 99 H(s)    (1)

Jeff Johnson  (Altrincham) 81 SI, 82 GIHS, 83 IHS, 84 HSI,
84 IHS, 86 W(s)EE    (18)

Richard Forsyth  (Kidderminster) 95 WHG    (3)

Paul Furlong  (Enfield) 90 IEE, 91 IW    (5)

Tom Jones  (Weymouth) 87 W    (1)

Mark Gardiner  (Macclesfield T.) 97 E    (1)

Anton Joseph  (Telford Utd. & Kidderminster H.)
84 S(s), 85 WIHS, 86 W(s), 87 WI(s)H,
88 W, 89 IW, 90 IEE    (14)

Jerry Gill  (Yeovil T.)  97 E    (1)

John Glover  (Maidstone Utd) 85 WIHS    (4)

Andy Kerr  (Wycombe) 93 W    (1)

Ged Kimmins  (Hyde Utd.) 96 E(s)H(s) 97 E(s)  (3)

Mike Lake  (Macclesfield) 89 I  (1)

Andy Lee  (Telford U. & Witton A.) 89 I(s), 91 IW  (3)

David Leworthy  (Farnborough & Rushden & Diamonds)
93 W, 94 W 97 EH (4)

Kenny Lowe  (Barnet) 91 IW  (2)

Martin McDonald  (Macclesfield) 95 G(s)  (1)

John McKenna  (Boston Utd)
88 W(s), 90 IEE, 91 IW, 92 W (7)

Leroy May  (Stafford R.) 95 G(s)  (1)

Bobby Mayes  (Redbridge) 92 W  (1)

Paul Mayman  (Northwich Vic) 80 IS  (2)

Stewart Mell  (Burton) 85 W  (1)

Neil Merrick  (Weymouth) 80 I(s)S  (2)

Russell Milton  (Dover) 94 FN  (2)

Trevor Morley  (Nuneaton) 84 WHSI, 85 WS(s)  (6)

Les Mutrie  (Blyth Spartans) 79 SH, 80 ISH  (5)

Mark Newson  (Maidstone U) 84 WHSI, 85 W  (5)

Doug Newton  (Burton) 85 WHS  (3)

Paul Nicol  (Kettering T) 91 IW, 92 W  (3)

Steve Norris  (Telford) 88 W(s)  (1)

Joe O'Connor  (Hednesford T.) 97 EH(s)  (2)

Eamon O'Keefe  (Mossley) 79 SH  (2)

Frank Ovard  (Maidstone) 81 H(s)S(s)I(s)  (3)

Andy Pape  (Harrow Bor. & Enfield)
85 W(s)HS, 86 W(s)E 87 WIHS,
88 W, 89 IW, 90 IWE  (15)

Brian Parker  (Yeovil Town) 80 S  (1)

**Warren Patmore (Yeovil Town) 99 IHW**  **(3)**

**Gary Patterson (Kingstonian) 99 IH**  **(2)**

Steve Payne  (Macclesfield T.) 97 H  (1)

Trevor Peake  (Nuneaton Bor) 79 SH  (2)

David Pearce  (Harrow Bor) 84 I(s)  (1)

Brendan Phillips  (Nuneaton Bor. & Kettering T.)
79 SH, 80 S(s)H  (4)

Gary Philips  (Barnet) 82 G  (1)

Owen Pickard  (Yeovil T.) 98 H(s)  (1)

**Geoff Pitcher (Kingstonian) 99W**  **(1)**

Phil Power  (Macclesfield T.) 96 E(s)H(s)  (2)

Ryan Price  (Stafford R. & Macclesfield)
92 W(s) 93 WF 96 EH 97 H  (6)

Steve Prindiville  98 H(s)  (1)

Simon Read  (Farnborough) 92 W(s)  (1)

Andy Reid  (Altrincham) 95 W  (1)

Carl Richards  (Enfield) 86 E  (1)

Derek Richardson  (Maidstone U) 83 I, 84 W, 86 E  (4)

Ian Richardson  (Dagenham & Red) 95 G  (1)

Kevin Richardson  (Bromsgrove) 94 WFN  (3)

Paul Richardson  (Redbridge) 92 W, 93 WF  (3)

Terry Robbins  (Welling) 92 W, 93 WF, 94 WFN  (6)

Peter Robinson  (Blyth S) 83 IHS, 84 WI, 85 W  (6)

John Rogers  (Altrincham) 81 HSI, 82 I(s)S  (5)

Paul Rogers  (Sutton) 89 W, 90 IE(2), 91 IW  (6)

Colin Rose  (Witton Alb.) 96 E(s)H  (2)

Kevin Rose  (Kidderminster) 94 F(s)N  (2)

Brian Ross  (Marine) 93 W(s)F(s), 94 W(s) 95 WH  (5)

Tim Ryan  (Southport) 98 H, 99 IHW  (4)

*Tim Ryan (Southport) has played in all of manager John
Owens' Internationals*

*Mark Yates (Cheltenham Town)*
*Photo: Neil Thaler*

| | |
|---|---|
| Bob Stockley (Nuneaton Bor) 80 H | (1) |
| Steve Stott (Kettering T., Rushden & Ds & Yeovil T.) 95 WH(s)G, 96 EH, 99 HW(s) | (7) |
| Peter Taylor (Maidstone) 84 HSI | (3) |
| Steve Taylor (Bromsgrove R.) 95 G | (1) |
| Shaun Teale (Weymouth) 88 W | (1) |
| Stuart Terry (Altrincham) W | (1) |
| Brian Thompson (Yeovil & Maidstone) 79 SH, 81 HSI, 82 IHS, 83 IHS, 84 WHSI | (15) |
| Steve Thompson (Wycombe) 93 W | (1) |
| Kevin Todd (Berwick Rangers) 91 W | (1) |
| Mark Tucker (Woking) 96 E | (1) |
| Tony Turner (Telford) 85 W | (1) |
| **Paul Underwood (Rushden & Diamonds) 99 IH** | **(2)** |
| David Venables (Stevenage Bor.) 94 W(s), 95 HG 96 EH(s) | (5) |
| Jamie Victory (Cheltenham T.) 98 H(s) | (1) |
| David Waite (Enfield) 82 G | (1) |
| Paul Walker (Blyth) 86 WEE(s), 87 S(s) | (4) |

| | |
|---|---|
| Neil Sellars (Scarboro) 81 HSI, 82 GH(s)S, 83 IHS | (9) |
| Mark Shail (Yeovil T.) 93 W | (1) |
| **Simon Shaw (Doncaster Rovers) 99 IH** | **(2)** |
| Peter Shearer (Cheltenham) 89 I(s) | (1) |
| Paul Shirtliff (Frickley A. & Boston U.) 86 EE, 87 WIH, 88 W, 89 IW, 90 IWEE, 92 W, 93 WF | (15) |
| Paul Showler (Altrincham) 91 I(s)W | (2) |
| Gordon Simmonite (Boston Utd.) 79 S(s)H(s), 80 ISH | (5) |
| Gary Simpson (Stafford R.) 86 EE, 87 IHS, 90 IWEE | (9) |
| Wayne Simpson (Stafford) 94 FN(s) | (2) |
| Glenn Skivington (Barrow) 90 IWE, 91 IW | (5) |
| Alan Smith (Alvechurch) 82 GIS | (3) |
| Ian Smith (Mossley) 80 ISH(s) | (3) |
| Mark Smith (Stevenage Bor.) 96 EH 98 H, 99 IHW | (6) |
| Ossie Smith (Runcorn) 84 W | (1) |
| Tim Smithers (Nuneaton), 85 W(s)I, 86 W | (3) |
| Simon Stapleton (Wycombe) 93 W | (1) |
| Mickey Stephens (Sutton), 82 GS(s), 86 WEE(s) | (5) |
| Billy Stewart (Southport) 98 H | (1) |

| | |
|---|---|
| Steve Walters (Northwich Victoria) 97 H | (1) |
| Mark Ward (Northwich Victoria) 83 S(s) | (1) |
| Dale Watkins (Cheltenham T.) 98 H, 99 I(s) | (2) |
| John Watson (Wealdstone, Scarborough & Maidstone) 79 S(s)H, 80 ISH, 81 HSI, 82 IHS, 83 IHS, 84 W(s)HSI | (18) |
| Liam Watson (Marine) 95 WH(s) | (2) |
| Paul Watts (Redbridge Forest) 89 W, 90 IEE, 91 I, 92 W, 93 WF | (8) |
| Paul Webb (Bromsgrove R & Kidderminster H) 93 F, 94 WFN(s) 95 WHG 96 EH 97 EH | (11) |
| Mark West (Wycombe W) 91 W | (1) |
| Barry Whitbread (Runcorn & Altrincham) 79 SH, 80 ISH, 81 I | (6) |
| Russ Wilcox (Frickley) 86 WE | (2) |
| **Barry Williams (Nuneaton Borough) 99 H(s)W** | **(2)** |
| Colin Williams (Scarborough & Telford Utd.) 81 HS, 82 IHS | (5) |
| Roger Willis (Barnet) 91 I(s) | (1) |
| Paul Wilson (Frickley) 86 W | (1) |
| **Simon Wormull (Dover Athletic) 99 I(s)W** | **(2)** |
| **Mark Yates (Cheltenham Town) 99 IW** | **(2)** |

# THE NATIONWIDE CONFERENCE

## Founded 1979

**President:** J C Thompson MBIM, Minst.M, FID

**Chairman:** W J King  **Chief Executive:** J A Moules

**Secretary:** M A Annett, The Nationwide Conference, Collingwood House, Schooner Court, Crossways, Dartford, Kent DA2 6QQ
Tel: 01322 303120  Fax: 01322 303121

---

With six games played at the end of August very few would have bet against Rushden & Diamonds in the Conference as they were out on their own with maximum points at the top of the table.

By the end of October the Diamonds had slipped to third place and Cheltenham were beginning to show their power.

Doncaster Rovers, despite being busy rebuilding, were finding life difficult, especially as they rarely seemed to finish with eleven men. Other newcomers Forest Green Rovers were also finding life a little tough, but they knew they would. Geoff Chapple's Kingstonian had started well but well fancied Southport dipped after the first three games.

Surprisingly disappointing in the early months were Woking, Hednesford Town, Stevenage Borough and Morecambe but easing up to take over at the top were the success story of the season - Kettering Town. Peter Morris had rebuilt the squad which had only just survived the previous season and now they had quietly taken over at the top.

The new F.A. Cup structure didn't prevent thirteen Conference clubs reaching the Third Round and Rushden & Diamonds had the thrill of entertaining Premier Division Leeds United. Diamonds' attitude, facilities and indeed standard of play brought great credit to the competition.

In the F.A. Trophy three of the semi-finalists represented the Conference with Cheltenham Town, the favourites, facing Geoff Chapple's club. That in itself must have been a worrying thought and Kingstonian did turn it on for 'the master' with a wonderful 3-1 victory at Whaddon Road. Forest Green Rovers, whose shrewd manager Frank Gregan had by now lifted his squad up to Conference standards, had a chance to enable his club to be first to reach a Trophy final after already having won the F.A. Vase.

Ryman Leaguers St Albans City stood in their way and with 50 minutes gone in the second leg City were 2-0 up with Wembley in their sights. Rovers came back well to win a thrilling tie 3-2 and, of course, their hard fought final finished with Geoff Trophy-Chapple winning again!

The Championship developed into a thrilling climax at the end of the season with four clubs capable of taking the title. Steady Kettering, Glamourous Diamonds, Home-shy Yeovil and Professional Cheltenham.

In a thrilling finish the Professionals deservedly won and good luck to Steve Cotterill and the club in the future. The season finished in style for Doncaster Rovers, who broke up for the close season in great spirits when 7,160 watched them storm to an emphatic Endsleigh Trophy success against luckless Farnborough Town.

At the foot of the table Leek Town and Farnborough had slipped sadly away, while Barrow had thought they had leaped over Welling United on the last day of the season, only to land in all sorts of close season trouble, which even at the time of writing hasn't been settled.

Welling United will live to fight again and there is also a warm welcome back to three 'old boys' returning to the Conference, Altrincham, Nuneaton Borough and Sutton United.

Competition will be as tough as ever and attendances will probably break records for a third consecutive year in the 21st season of Conference (Alliance) football.  TW

# NATIONWIDE CONFERENCE FINAL LEAGUE TABLE 1998-99

| | | P | HOME | | | | | AWAY | | | | | Pts | LEADING SCORERS BY CLUB |
|---|---|---|---|---|---|---|---|---|---|---|---|---|---|---|
| | | | W | D | L | F | A | W | D | L | F | A | | *(these include all goals as reported in the league bulletin)* |
| 1 | Cheltenham Town | 42 | 11 | 9 | 1 | 35 | 14 | 11 | 5 | 5 | 36 | 22 | 80 | Grayson 24, Eaton 12, Watkins 8 |
| 2 | Kettering Town | 42 | 11 | 5 | 5 | 31 | 16 | 11 | 5 | 5 | 27 | 21 | 76 | McNamara 12, Hudson, Norman 10 |
| 3 | Hayes | 42 | 12 | 3 | 6 | 34 | 25 | 10 | 5 | 6 | 29 | 25 | 74 | Charles 20, Randall 11, Flynn 7 |
| 4 | Rushden & Diamonds | 42 | 11 | 4 | 6 | 41 | 22 | 9 | 8 | 4 | 30 | 20 | 72 | Collins 19, Foster 15, West 8 |
| 5 | Yeovil Town | 42 | 8 | 4 | 9 | 35 | 32 | 12 | 7 | 2 | 33 | 22 | 71 | Patmore 26, Pickard 13, Dale 7 |
| 6 | Stevenage Borough | 42 | 9 | 9 | 3 | 37 | 23 | 8 | 8 | 5 | 25 | 22 | 68 | Alford 33, Love 7, Strouts 5 |
| 7 | Northwich Victoria | 42 | 11 | 3 | 7 | 29 | 21 | 8 | 6 | 7 | 31 | 30 | 66 | Tait 18, Illman 12, Vicary 10 |
| 8 | Kingstonian | 42 | 9 | 7 | 5 | 25 | 19 | 8 | 6 | 7 | 25 | 30 | 64 | Leworthy 17, Akuamoah 13, Holligan 11 |
| 9 | Woking | 42 | 9 | 5 | 7 | 27 | 20 | 9 | 4 | 8 | 24 | 25 | 63 | Hay 22, West 13, Payne 11 |
| 10 | Hednesford Town | 42 | 9 | 8 | 4 | 30 | 24 | 6 | 8 | 7 | 19 | 20 | 61 | Kimmins 12, Davis 11, Ware 6 |
| 11 | Dover Athletic | 42 | 7 | 9 | 5 | 27 | 21 | 6 | 4 | 9 | 27 | 27 | 58 | Hynes 12, Vansittart 8, Reina, Carruthers 6 |
| 12 | Forest Green Rovers | 42 | 9 | 5 | 7 | 28 | 22 | 6 | 8 | 7 | 27 | 28 | 58 | McGregor, Sykes 15, Hunt 10 |
| 13 | Hereford United | 42 | 9 | 5 | 7 | 25 | 17 | 6 | 5 | 10 | 24 | 29 | 55 | Leadbeater, Williams, Wright 6 |
| 14 | Morecambe | 42 | 9 | 5 | 7 | 31 | 29 | 6 | 3 | 12 | 29 | 47 | 53 | Norman 23, Lyons 11, Jackson 6 |
| 15 | Kidderminster Harriers | 42 | 9 | 4 | 8 | 32 | 22 | 5 | 5 | 11 | 24 | 30 | 51 | May 12, Hadley 10, Willetts 9 |
| 16 | Doncaster Rovers | 42 | 7 | 5 | 9 | 26 | 26 | 5 | 7 | 9 | 25 | 29 | 48 | Duerden 18, Hume 9, Kirkwood 7 |
| 17 | Telford United | 42 | 7 | 8 | 6 | 24 | 24 | 3 | 8 | 10 | 20 | 36 | 46 | Huckerby 16, Murphy 11, Palmer 8 |
| 18 | Southport | 42 | 6 | 9 | 6 | 29 | 28 | 4 | 6 | 11 | 18 | 31 | 45 | Ross 10, O'Reilly, Guyett, Elam 7 |
| 19 | Barrow | 42 | 7 | 5 | 9 | 17 | 23 | 4 | 5 | 12 | 23 | 40 | 43 | Mutch 10, Foster 7, Coates 5 |
| 20 | Welling United | 42 | 4 | 7 | 10 | 18 | 30 | 5 | 7 | 9 | 26 | 35 | 41 | Brown 8, Hynes 7, Adams, Dolby 6 |
| 21 | Leek Town | 42 | 5 | 5 | 11 | 34 | 42 | 3 | 15 | 9 | 14 | 34 | 32 | McAuley 19, Mike 14, Hawtin 6 |
| 22 | Farnborough Town | 42 | 6 | 5 | 10 | 29 | 48 | 1 | 6 | 14 | 12 | 41 | 32 | Bailey 19, West 11, Wingfield 5 |

# NATIONWIDE CONFERENCE RESULTS & ATTENDANCES 1998-99

| | 1 | 2 | 3 | 4 | 5 | 6 | 7 | 8 | 9 | 10 | 11 | 12 | 13 | 14 | 15 | 16 | 17 | 18 | 19 | 20 | 21 | 22 |
|---|---|---|---|---|---|---|---|---|---|---|---|---|---|---|---|---|---|---|---|---|---|---|
| 1 Barrow | X | 1-1 1773 | 2-2 2050 | 1-0 1290 | 1-0 1530 | 2-1 1176 | 0-1 1518 | 0-2 1232 | 0-1 1775 | 0-0 1443 | 0-4 1738 | 1-0 1730 | 0-0 1047 | 2-1 2073 | 0-1 2015 | 0-2 2003 | 0-0 1191 | 0-1 2096 | 1-1 1604 | 2-1 1401 | 1-2 2176 | 2-0 1202 |
| 2 Cheltenham Town | 4-1 2005 | X | 2428 | 1-0 2575 | 0-0 2265 | 1-1 3058 | 3-3 1879 | 0-0 2168 | 2-2 3341 | 3-0 5202 | 1-0 4518 | 1-0 3184 | 0-0 1912 | 4-1 1959 | 0-1 2060 | 1-0 4051 | 3-0 2594 | 3-0 2772 | 2-0 3027 | 4-1 5400 | 1-1 2406 | 3-2 6150 |
| 3 Doncaster Rovers | 2-1 2617 | 2-2 3082 | X | 5-4 2119 | 3-4 3468 | 0-1 3402 | 0-1 3149 | 0-1 3595 | 3-1 3568 | 4-1 4569 | 0-1 3222 | 0-2 2915 | 1-2 3520 | 2-1 4251 | 2-2 2296 | 1-1 3768 | 0-1 3663 | 1-2 4629 | 1-1 3040 | 4-1 2952 | 0-1 2833 | 0-2 4413 |
| 4 Dover Athletic | 1-1 1117 | 0-0 972 | 1-0 1517 | X | 2-1 860 | 1-1 1017 | 0-0 1035 | 0-0 1126 | 3-1 1001 | 0-1 807 | 0-1 925 | 5-1 1480 | 2-1 974 | 2-3 872 | 0-0 949 | 1-1 1387 | 2-1 792 | 1-1 1394 | 1-1 865 | 1-2 1334 | 3-2 1168 | 1-2 1154 |
| 5 Farnborough | 2-2 758 | 2-4 1067 | 1-0 893 | 1-2 847 | X | 2-2 750 | 1-5 789 | 0-1 541 | 0-4 795 | 1-3 635 | 2-4 733 | 4-2 759 | 2-1 578 | 1-6 682 | 1-6 552 | 1-2 958 | 1-1 559 | 1-0 932 | 3-1 613 | 1-1 683 | 2-1 1057 | 0-0 870 |
| 6 Forest Green R | 1-1 404 | 1-2 1909 | 0-0 1271 | 0-1 492 | 0-0 703 | X | 1-2 634 | 1-0 832 | 2-1 1705 | 1-0 825 | 5-0 1001 | 4-2 784 | 3-1 624 | 1-6 408 | 3-1 684 | 0-2 1120 | 1-0 746 | 1-2 903 | 0-1 951 | 3-2 624 | 3-2 465 | 1-2 860 |
| 7 Hayes | 1-0 578 | 3-2 2105 | 2-0 733 | 1-2 580 | 1-0 703 | 0-3 597 | X | 1-0 570 | 1-2 569 | 0-2 603 | 2-1 553 | 3-0 929 | 2-0 603 | 1-2 422 | 1-0 685 | 2-1 1302 | 3-0 677 | 2-2 665 | 4-3 615 | 1-2 724 | 2-2 1103 | 1-1 692 |
| 8 Hednesford Town | 1-0 794 | 3-2 1651 | 1-1 1542 | 1-2 1026 | 1-2 1100 | 1-1 889 | 0-0 860 | X | 3-1 1736 | 0-2 1608 | 0-1 934 | 0-1 652 | 0-1 943 | 1-0 834 | 1-0 1127 | 1-1 1387 | 3-1 1015 | 2-2 861 | 1-1 887 | 3-2 806 | 2-1 1292 | 2-3 908 |
| 9 Hereford United | 3-0 1521 | 0-2 3480 | 1-0 2115 | 2-0 2139 | 2-0 1788 | 4-0 1735 | 0-1 2053 | 0-0 1610 | X | 0-2 2181 | 1-3 2658 | 2-0 1288 | 2-0 2140 | 2-0 2049 | 2-2 1910 | 3-2 2044 | 2-2 2308 | 0-1 1629 | 0-0 1592 | 1-1 1532 | 1-0 1320 | 0-1 2410 |
| 10 Kettering Town | 2-0 1817 | 0-2 1615 | 0-1 3646 | 1-0 1864 | 4-1 1389 | 2-2 1405 | 1-0 1563 | 1-0 2631 | 1-1 1386 | X | 1-1 1684 | 2-0 1469 | 1-1 1110 | 6-0 2364 | 0-0 1763 | 0-0 5017 | 2-1 1515 | 1-2 2463 | 2-1 1840 | 1-1 2371 | 3-0 2012 | 1-2 1754 |
| 11 Kidderminster H | 1-2 1877 | 0-1 3295 | 3-3 2200 | 1-0 1312 | 2-0 1670 | 2-2 1716 | 0-1 1534 | 1-2 1725 | 1-0 3188 | 1-2 1977 | X | 0-1 1884 | 2-1 1713 | 5-2 1828 | 4-0 1235 | 0-0 2337 | 2-1 1780 | 2-0 2072 | 3-0 2003 | 1-1 1460 | 3-2 2024 | 0-0 2007 |
| 12 Kingstonian | 5-1 1281 | 1-2 1801 | 2-1 1942 | 2-1 904 | 1-0 1063 | 2-1 1008 | 1-1 1129 | 1-1 1293 | 2-0 2104 | 1-2 1068 | 1-0 735 | X | 3-0 606 | 0-0 888 | 1-1 901 | 1-5 2605 | 0-2 492 | 1-0 1745 | 1-0 816 | 2-1 904 | 0-0 2694 | 0-0 1017 |
| 13 Leek Town | 3-1 426 | 0-2 704 | 1-1 1365 | 0-4 533 | 4-0 527 | 1-4 465 | 1-4 465 | 1-3 701 | 3-2 667 | 1-2 717 | 1-4 711 | 2-2 495 | X | 7-0 501 | 0-3 559 | 0-0 806 | 0-0 632 | 1-1 597 | 1-1 672 | 2-4 353 | 0-3 583 | 2-4 253 |
| 14 Morecambe | 3-2 3193 | 0-2 1354 | 1-2 1180 | 0-4 850 | 1-0 1136 | 3-1 812 | 2-3 1016 | 3-1 1256 | 1-0 1012 | 3-1 1055 | 2-1 966 | 0-0 1024 | 2-2 840 | X | 3-1 1107 | 2-3 1099 | 1-1 1356 | 1-1 1010 | 0-1 902 | 2-0 855 | 0-1 1120 | 1-1 1254 |
| 15 Northwich Victoria | 1-0 1107 | 1-0 1155 | 1-3 1402 | 2-2 942 | 1-0 837 | 2-1 866 | 2-1 1150 | 1-1 1002 | 1-0 1068 | 4-0 1385 | 1-0 1122 | 2-3 906 | 0-2 1070 | 1-1 1304 | X | 2-1 1802 | 1-2 1628 | 0-1 910 | 1-1 1008 | 3-0 1032 | 0-3 1003 | 1-2 1150 |
| 16 Rushden & Diamonds | 4-0 2259 | 1-2 6312 | 1-3 4577 | 2-2 2744 | 2-2 2481 | 4-0 1626 | 5-0 3208 | 1-0 3123 | 1-1 3521 | 1-2 4700 | 1-1 2374 | 1-1 1818 | 2-0 2833 | 2-1 2394 | 1-2 2803 | X | 3-1 2135 | 2-1 3169 | 2-3 2909 | 3-1 2261 | 1-2 4307 | 1-2 2367 |
| 17 Southport | 0-4 1426 | 0-2 1224 | 2-2 1450 | 3-0 955 | 2-1 997 | 3-1 961 | 2-1 1203 | 1-1 1144 | 0-0 872 | 0-1 1070 | 1-1 976 | 1-1 1060 | 3-1 1333 | 1-1 1427 | 2-2 1457 | 0-1 1653 | X | 1-1 1056 | 2-1 1282 | 5-2 1035 | 0-0 811 | 2-3 929 |
| 18 Stevenage Borough | 1-2 1701 | 2-2 2576 | 2-2 3513 | 1-1 1458 | 3-1 2379 | 2-1 1976 | 1-1 3203 | 3-1 2329 | 0-3 2832 | 2-2 3937 | 3-0 1915 | 3-3 2261 | 2-0 2614 | 2-2 2266 | 1-3 1923 | 4-3 4319 | 0-0 2433 | X | 2-2 2189 | 1-1 3413 | 5-0 2028 | 2-2 2483 |
| 19 Telford United | 1-1 749 | 0-3 1304 | 0-2 1539 | 1-1 588 | 3-1 662 | 2-1 708 | 2-0 716 | 1-1 954 | 0-1 1086 | 0-2 832 | 0-0 1220 | 1-1 680 | 2-0 847 | 3-2 727 | 3-0 911 | 2-2 867 | 1-0 704 | 0-3 905 | X | 0-0 609 | 1-0 787 | 2-2 757 |
| 20 Welling United | 1-1 700 | 2-1 820 | 1-1 761 | 0-3 962 | 0-0 648 | 0-2 743 | 0-2 663 | 0-2 507 | 2-2 727 | 0-2 455 | 0-0 780 | 1-3 803 | 1-0 524 | 3-2 727 | 3-0 500 | 0-1 667 | 2-3 502 | 1-2 524 | 0-1 745 | X | 0-1 843 | 1-2 531 |
| 21 Woking | 2-3 1917 | 1-0 2738 | 2-0 2530 | 1-2 2263 | 4-0 2101 | 2-1 2057 | 2-1 1997 | 1-1 1453 | 2-5 2541 | 0-0 1647 | 2-1 1982 | 0-1 3772 | 1-0 1926 | 1-0 2740 | 0-3 2059 | 1-0 2808 | 2-3 1900 | 1-2 2776 | 3-0 1677 | 0-0 1477 | X | 0-0 2581 |
| 22 Yeovil Town | 1-0 2588 | 2-2 2955 | 2-2 2300 | 1-1 2211 | 6-3 2924 | 2-1 2437 | 2-1 2560 | 1-0 2008 | 2-2 2263 | 2-1 1718 | 3-1 2112 | 1-3 2339 | 2-0 2442 | 0-1 1966 | 1-2 2075 | 0-1 2876 | 3-1 2158 | 1-3 2936 | 4-0 2253 | 1-3 2903 | 0-1 2465 | X |

# ENDSLEIGH BROKERS CHALLENGE TROPHY 1998-99

## FIRST ROUND

| | | | | | |
|---|---|---|---|---|---|
| Kettering Town | 0 | v | 3 | Hayes | |
| | | Att: 651 | | Hodson 2, 1 og | |
| Barrow | 2 | v | 1 | Leek Town | |
| O'Keefe, Mutch | | Att: 891 | | McAuley | |
| Dover Athletic | 2 | v | 3 | Stevenage Borough | |
| Elliot 2 | | Att: 605 | | Perkins 2, Thompson | |
| Farnborough Town | 4 | v | 2 | Kingstonian | |
| Bailey 2, Baker N, Rowlands | | Att: 540 | | Luckett, Holligan | |
| Forest Green Rovers | 2 | v | 4 | Kidderminster Harriers | |
| Birkby, Drysdale | | Att: 446 | | Hadley 2, May, Willetts | |
| Southport | 2 | v | 1 | Telford United | |
| O'Rielly, Gamble | | Att: 634 | | Murphy | |

## SECOND ROUND

| | | | | | |
|---|---|---|---|---|---|
| Hayes | 3 | v | 2 | Welling United | |
| Charles, Moore 2 | | Att: 227 | | Appiah, Ugbah | |
| Morecambe | 2 | v | 0 | Barrow | |
| Norman, Hughes | | Att: 567 | | | |
| Stevenage Borough | 0 | v | 1 | Cheltenham Town | |
| | | Att: 604 | | Eaton | |
| Doncaster Rovers | 2 | v | 0 | Southport | |
| Hume 2 | | Att: 947 | | | |
| Hednesford Town | 1 | v | 3 | Northwich Victoria | |
| Dennison | | Att: 318 | | Vicary, Illman, Cooke | |
| Farnborough Town | 3 | v | 1 | Rushden & Diamonds | |
| Bailey 3 | | Att: 313 | | Foster | |
| Kidderminster Harriers | 1 | v | 2 | Hereford United | |
| Arnold | | Att: 645 | | Parry, Druce | |
| Woking | 3 | v | 0 | Yeovil Town | |
| Bolt 2, Payne | | Att: 580 | | | |

## QUARTER FINALS

| | | | | | |
|---|---|---|---|---|---|
| Cheltenham Town | 2 | v | 1 | Hayes | |
| Hopkins 2 | | Att: 469 | | Flynn | |
| Doncaster Rovers | 3 | v | 2 | Northwich Victoria | |
| Barret, Edinboro 2, George | | Att: 1877 | | Tait, Vicary | |
| Farnborough Town | 4 | v | 3 | Woking | |
| West 2, Underwood, Bailey | | Att: 592 | | Coward, Bolt 2 | |
| Hereford United | 3 | v | 2 | Morecambe | |
| Cowe, Cook | | Att: 567 | | Lyons, Norman | |

## SEMI-FINALS

| | | | | | |
|---|---|---|---|---|---|
| Farnborough Town | 2 | v | 0 | Cheltenham Town | |
| Robson, Wingfield | | Att: 260 | | | |
| | | (only one leg played) | | | |
| Morecambe | 1 | v | 2 | Doncaster Rovers | |
| Keeling | | Att: 1302 | | Duerden 2 | |
| Doncaster Rovers | 3 | v | 0 | Morecambe | |
| Duerden 2, Sutherland | | Att: 3297 | | | |
| | | (Aggregate score 5-1) | | | |

## FINAL

| | | | | | |
|---|---|---|---|---|---|
| Farnborough Town | 0 | v | 1 | Doncaster Rovers | |
| | | Att: 643 | | Penney | |
| Doncaster Rovers | 3 | v | 0 | Farnborough Town | |
| Duerden 2, Sutherland | | Att: 7160 | | | |
| | | (Aggregate score 4-0) | | | |

# MANAGER OF THE YEAR 1998-99

**STEVE COTTERILL**
**(CHELTENHAM TOWN)**
*Photo: Peter Barnes*

# GOALKEEPER OF THE YEAR 1998-99

**STEVE BOOK**
**(CHELTENHAM TOWN & ENGLAND)**
*Photo: Andrew Chitty*

# RIGHT FULL BACK OF THE YEAR 1998-99

**MIKE DUFF**
**(CHELTENHAM TOWN)**
*Photo: Peter Barnes*

# LEFT FULL BACK OF THE YEAR 1998-99

*(Right)*
**JAMIE VICTORY (CHELTENHAM TOWN)**
*Jamie Victory presented with a memento for achieving 150 appearances for Cheltenham Town.*
*Photo: Peter Barnes*

# CENTRE BACKS OF THE YEAR 1998-99

**MARK SMITH**
**(STEVENAGE BOROUGH & ENGLAND)**

*Photo: Peter Barnes*

**DARREN BRADSHAW**
**(RUSHDEN & DIAMONDS)**
*Photo: Peter Barnes*

# TEAM MATES AND TWO MIDFIELD PLAYERS OF THE YEAR 1998-99

**GEOFF PITCHER**
**(KINGSTONIAN & ENGLAND)**

*Photo: Garry Letts*

**GARY PATTERSON**
**(KINGSTONIAN & ENGLAND)**
*Photo: Andrew Chitty*

# THE THIRD MIDFIELD SELECTION 1998-99

*(Left)*
**STEVE WALTERS  (NORTHWICH VICTORIA)**
*Photo: Andrew Chitty*

# A THIRD OF THE SELECTED STRIKE-FORCE 1998-99

**HUGH McAULEY**
**(LEEK TOWN**
**(NOW CHELTENHAM TOWN)**
*Photo: Peter Barnes*

# CONFERENCE PLAYER OF THE YEAR 1998-99

CONFERENCE
PLAYER OF THE YEAR
AND
CONFERENCE STRIKER
NEIL GRAYSON
(CHELTENHAM TOWN
& ENGLAND)

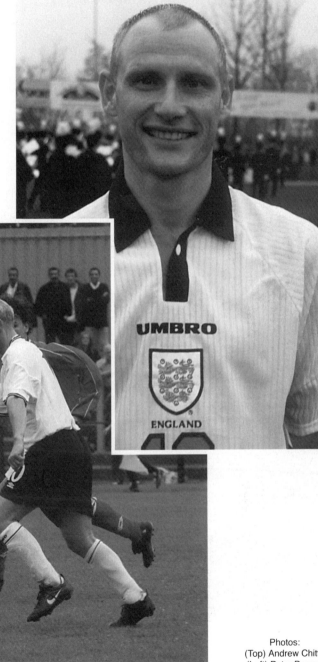

Photos:
(Top) Andrew Chitty
(Left) Peter Barnes

137

# TOP CONFERENCE GOALSCORER 1998-99

**CARL ALFORD**
**(STEVENAGE BOROUGH)**
Photo: Keith Clayton

# ALTRINCHAM

One of the most famous names in semi-professional football is back.
Altrincham were one of the Alliance's first giants and the team building undertaken by Bernard Taylor brought the crowds back to Moss Lane after a very shaky start to the season had left them in 20th position by mid September.

Their first victory was against lowly Spennymoor United, in their ninth game, and a 2-1 scoreline was celebrated not only for the three points but indeed the first league game of the campaign in which they had scored more than one goal.

The form of Leroy Chambers and Paul Power in front of goal and indeed the all round contributions of Paul Ellender hit the headlines while their new goalkeeper from Colne, Stuart Coburn, was also an inspiration. The team grew in confidence and surged up the table to hit top spot by the end of the year and as their challengers were mainly from clubs who hadn't applied for Conference grading, there was little worry for Alty in their excellent form. That treasured Conference place was soon theirs again and now with a new and confident squad could there be another exciting period in the club's history just about to be made?

## CLUB OFFICIALS 1999-2000

| | |
|---|---|
| Chairman: | **Gerry Berman** |
| President: | **Noel White** |
| Deputy Chairman: | **Mark Harris** |
| Vice President: | **Bill King** |
| Secretary: | **Graham Heathcote** |
| Press Officer: | **Mark Harris** |
| Match Secretary | **George Heslop** |

Back Row; Danny Adams, Brendan Burke, Jason Gallagher, Tony Hemmings, Dean Greygoose, Stuart Coburn, Leroy Chambers, Simeon Hodson, Ged Kielty, Mark Maddox. Middle Row: Paul Lake (Physio), Graham Heathcote (Coach), Barry Crowe, Kevin Ellison, Andy Lovelock, Richard Landon, Eddie Turkington, Gary Talbot, Paul Ellender, Ricky Harris, Vic Green (Kitman), Gary Thompson (Physio), George Shepherd (Assistant Coach). Front Row: Mark Harris (Deputy Chairman), Stuart Walker, Chris Timons, Bernard Taylor (Manager), Phil Power, Keith Russell, Gerry Berman (Chairman). Missing from photo Mick Carmody and Martin McDonald

# ALTRINCHAM - Match Facts 1998-99

| No | Date | Venue | Comp | Opponents | Result | Score | Att. | Goalscorers |
|---|---|---|---|---|---|---|---|---|
| 1 | 22.08 | H | NPL | Frickley Athletic | D | 1-1 | 685 | Russell |
| 2 | 25.08 | A | NPL | Winsford United | L | 1-2 | 460 | Chambers |
| 3 | 29.08 | H | NPL | Whitby Town | D | 1-1 | 752 | Chambers |
| 4 | 31.08 | H | NPL | Colwyn Bay | D | 1-1 | 680 | Ellender |
| 5 | 05.09 | A | NPL | Blyth Spartans | D | 0-0 | 603 | |
| 6 | 08.09 | H | NPL | Lancaster City | L | 1-2 | 564 | Chambers |
| 7 | 12.09 | A | NPL | Worksop Town | L | 1-3 | 777 | Chambers |
| 8 | 15.09 | A | NPL | Marine | L | 1-2 | 304 | Hardy |
| 9 | 19.09 | H | NPL | Spennymoor United | W | 2-1 | 635 | Hardy, Russell |
| 10 | 26.09 | A | NPL | Emley | W | 3-0 | 437 | Timons, Chambers, Ramplin(9) |
| 11 | 29.09 | H | NPL | Gainsborough Trinity | D | 1-1 | 590 | Russell |
| 12 | 10.10 | A | NPL | Chorley | W | 2-0 | 454 | Hardy, Chambers |
| 13 | 20.10 | H | NPL | Worksop Town | W | 2-0 | 537 | Hardy, Russell(9) |
| 14 | 24.10 | H | NPL | Chorley | W | 4-0 | 606 | Russell 2, Chambers, Power(9) |
| 15 | 31.10 | H | NPL | Accrington Stanley | W | 2-1 | 691 | Hardy, Chambers |
| 16 | 07.11 | H | NPL | Gateshead | W | 1-0 | 814 | Chambers |
| 17 | 14.11 | A | NPL | Bishop Auckland | L | 1-2 | 268 | R Harris(8) |
| 18 | 28.11 | A | NPL | Accrington Stanley | W | 4-1 | 638 | Timons, Power, Chambers |
| 19 | 05.12 | H | NPL | Blyth Spartans | D | 0-0 | 843 | |
| 20 | 12.12 | H | NPL | Stalybridge Celtic | W | 2-1 | 904 | Timons, R. Harris |
| 21 | 19.12 | A | NPL | Gainsborough Trinity | W | 3-0 | 604 | R. Harris 2, Hardy(6) |
| 22 | 26.12 | A | NPL | Runcorn | W | 3-0 | 630 | Coburn, Robertson, Power |
| 23 | 28.12 | H | NPL | Marine | W | 4-1 | 1001 | Ellender, R. Harris, Power, Chambers |
| 24 | 02.01 | H | NPL | Guiseley | W | 1-0 | 1147 | Ellender |
| 25 | 09.01 | A | NPL | Hyde United | W | 1-0 | 964 | Power |
| 26 | 23.01 | A | NPL | Whitby Town | W | 4-1 | 709 | Chambers |
| 27 | 13.02 | H | NPL | Winsford United | D | 1-1 | 878 | Power |
| 28 | 20.02 | A | NPL | Spennymoor United | W | 2-0 | 327 | Chambers 2 |
| 29 | 09.03 | H | NPL | Runcorn | W | 3-0 | 718 | R. Harris 2, Chambers |
| 30 | 13.03 | A | NPL | Leigh RMI | L | 2-3 | 451 | Ellender |
| 31 | 16.03 | A | NPL | Lancaster | D | 0-0 | 329 | |
| 32 | 20.03 | A | NPL | Bamber Bridge | W | 1-0 | 890 | |
| 33 | 26.03 | H | NPL | Bishop Auckland | D | 0-0 | 872 | |
| 34 | 30.03 | A | NPL | Stalybridge Celtic | L | 1-3 | 802 | |
| 35 | 03.04 | H | NPL | Hyde United | W | 2-1 | 923 | Robertson, R. Harris |
| 36 | 05.04 | A | NPL | Colwyn Bay | D | 1-1 | 459 | Ellender |
| 37 | 07.04 | H | NPL | Leigh RMI | W | 1-0 | 518 | Ellender |
| 38 | 10.04 | H | NPL | Bamber Bridge | D | 1-1 | 780 | Talbot |
| 39 | 17.04 | A | NPL | Gateshead | W | 1-0 | 306 | |
| 40 | 27.04 | A | NPL | Frickley Athletic | W | 3-0 | 385 | Robertson, Power, Rigby |
| 41 | 29.04 | H | NPL | Emley | W | 1-0 | 1526 | Lovelock |
| 42 | 01.05 | A | NPL | Guisley | L | 0-2 | 615 | |

**CUP COMPETITIONS**  ULCC - Unibond Lge. Chall. Cup   ULPC - Unibond Lge. President's Cup   ATS - Lancs. ATS Trophy

| | Date | Venue | Comp | Opponents | Result | Score | Att. | Goalscorers |
|---|---|---|---|---|---|---|---|---|
| | 22.09 | A | UCSC1 | Winsford United | W | 2-1 | 225 | Russell, Chambers |
| | 03.10 | A | FAC 2Q | Ashton United | L | 0-1 | 539 | |
| | 06.10 | H | PC1 | Winsford United | D | 2-2 | 374 | Hardy, C-Excell(9) |
| | 13.10 | A | PC1R | Winsford United | W | 1-0 | 228 | Ellender |
| | 03.11 | A | LCC | Stalybridge Celtic | L | 0-1 | 302 | |
| | 16.11 | H | UCSC2 | Chester | W | 3-0 | 303 | Power, Chambers, Tobin |
| | 21.11 | H | FAT2 | Burscough | D | 2-2 | 566 | Robertson, Power |
| | 24.11 | A | FAT 2R | Burscough | W | 3-1 | 257 | Ellender, Power, R. Harris |
| | 25.01 | H | FAT 3 | Burton Albion | W | 1-0 | 825 | Chambers |
| | 02.02 | H | PC 2 | Leigh RMI | D | 1-1 | 366 | Russell |
| | 06.02 | A | FAT 4 | Aldershot | W | 2-1 | 2754 | Russell, R. Harris |
| | 22.02 | A | UCSC SF | Hyde United | W | 1-0 | 601 | Chambers |
| | 24.02 | A | PC 2R | Leigh RMI | L | 1-2 | 178 | Hardy |
| | 27.02 | A | FAT 5R | Boston United | L | 0-2 | 2575 | |
| | 20.04 | A | UCSC F | Northwich Victoria | W | 1-0 | 964 | |

140

| 1 | 2 | 3 | 4 | 5 | 6 | 7 | 8 | 9 | 10 | 11 | 12 / 14 / 15 | |
|---|---|---|---|---|---|---|---|---|----|----|----|---|
| Dibble | Lyons | Faulkner | Timons | Kilcline | Ellender | Chambers | Power | Russell | Carmody | Gleghorn | S Harris(11), Shepherd(2), France | 1 |
| Dibble | Shepherd | Gleghorn | Timons | Kilcline | Lyons | Chambers | Power | Russell | Carmody | Ellender | France(1), S Harris(6), Faulkner | 2 |
| Dibble | Shepherd | Adams | Timons | Kilcline | France | Ellender | Power | Russell | Carmody | Chambers | Gleghorn(5), S Harris(8), Lyons(2) | 3 |
| Dibble | Shepherd | Adams | Timons | Wright | France | Ellender | Power | Russell | Carmody | Chambers | Gleghorn(10), S Harris(8), Lyons(2) | 4 |
| Dibble | Shepherd | Adams | Timons | Kilcline | France | Ellender | Power | Russell | McNeil | Chambers | Faulkner(6), Gleghorn(2), Lyons(10) | 5 |
| Dibble | France | Robertson | Timons | Kilcline | Adams | Chambers | Ellender | Russell | Power | Gleghorn | Cox, Lyons(8), A Borwn (2) | 6 |
| Dibble | Ramplin | Adams | Timons | Ellender | McNeil | Lyons | Robertson | Russell | Carmody | Chambers | Quigley(8), C-Excell(7), Cox(6) | 7 |
| Dibble | Ramplin | Adams | Timons | Ellender | Faulkner | McNeil | Hardy | Russell | Carmody | Robertson | Brown(6), C-Excell(7), Harris(8) | 8 |
| Dibble | Hodlson | Adams | Timons | Ellender | S Harris | Robertson | Hardy | Russell | Carmody | Chambers | C-Excell(11), France(8), Ramplin | 9 |
| Coburn | Ramplin | Adams | Timons | Ellender | S Harris | Robertson | Hardy | Russell | Carmody | Chambers | C-Excell(8), France(10), Power(6) | 10 |
| Dibble | Hodson | Adams | Timons | Ellender | S Harris | Robertson | Power | Russell | Carmody | Chambers | France(10), Ramplin (9), Ybarra(8) | 11 |
| Coburn | Hodson | Adams | Timons | France | Robertson | Harris | Power | Russell | Ellender | Chambers | Hardy(8), Ramplin, C-Excell(7) | 12 |
| Dibble | Brown | Adams | Timons | France | Robertson | Quigley | S Harris | Hardy | Ellender | Chambers | C-Excell(9), McNeill(7), Faulkner(8) | 13 |
| Coburn | Hodson | Adams | Timons | France | Gallagher | Robertson | Tobin | Hardy | Ellender | Chambers | Quigley(6), Ramplin, C-Excell(9) | 14 |
| Coburn | Hodson | Adams | Timons | Ellender | Quigley | Ward | Robertson | Hardy | Carmody | Chambers | Gallagher(6), Tobin(12), C-Excell(9) | 15 |
| Coburn | Hodson | Adams | Timons | Ellender | Gallagher | Tobin | Robertson | Hardy | Carmody | Chambers | France, R Harris(6), C-Excell(9) | 16 |
| Coburn | Hodson | Adams | Timons | Ellender | Robertson | Ward | Gallagher | Hardy | Carmody | Chambers | Powell(11), Russell(9), R Harris(10) | 17 |
| Coburn | Hodson | Adams | Timons | Ellender | Robertson | Ward | Gallagher | Russell | Carmody | Chambers | Powell(9), Hardy(11), R Harris(7) | 18 |
| Coburn | Hodson | Adams | Timons | Ellender | Robertson | Ward | Gallagher | Hardy | Carmody | Chambers | Powell(9), Goodier, R Harris(7) | 19 |
| Dibble | Hodson | Adams | Timons | Ellender | Robertson | Ward | Gallagher | Hardy | Carmody | Chambers | Powell(9), Goodier, R Harris(3) | 20 |
| Coburn | Hodson | Adams | Timons | Ellender | Robertson | Ward | Gallagher | Russell | Carmody | Chambers | Powell(9), Goodier, R Harris | 21 |
| Coburn | Hodson | Adams | Timons | Ellender | Robertson | Gallagher | Power | Ward | Carmody | Chambers | Hardy(9), Goodier, R Harris(8) | 22 |
| Coburn | R Harris | Adams | Timons | Ellender | Robertson | Gallagher | Power | Ward | Carmody | Chambers | Hardy(9), Tobin, Donnelly(10) | 23 |
| Coburn | Hodson | Adams | Timons | R Harris | Robertson | Gallagher | Power | Ward | Goodier | Chambers | Hardy, Donnelly, Hart (10) | 24 |
| Coburn | Hodson | Adams | Timons | Ellender | Robertson | Gallagher | Power | Ward | R Harris | Chambers | Goodier(6), Hart, Tobin(7), Donnelly | 25 |
| Hawkes | Hodson | Adams | Timons | Ellender | Robertson | Gallagher | Power | Ward | R Harris | Chambers | S Harris(8), Hardy(11), Goodier(9) | 26 |
| Coburn | Hodson | Adams | Timons | Ellender | Robertson | Gallagher | Power | Ward | R Harris | Chambers | Hardy(8), Donnelly, S Harris | 27 |
| Coburn | Hodson | Adams | Timons | Ellender | Robertson | Gallagher | Power | Ward | R Harris | Chambers | Hardy(11), Carmody(7), Donnelly | 28 |
| Coburn | Hodson | Adams | Timons | Ellender | Robertson | R Harris | Power | Ward | Carmody | Chambers | Hardy(6), Donnelly(10),C-Excell(11) | 29 |
| Coburn | Hodson | Adams | Timons | Ellender | Robertson | R Harris | Power | Ward | Carmody | Chambers | Hardy(7), Gallagher(15), Donnelly | 30 |
| Coburn | Hodson | Adams | Timons | Ellender | Robertson | R Harris | Power | Ward | Carmody | Chambers | Hardy(9), Gallagher(5), Donnelly(10) | 31 |
| Coburn | Hodson | Adams | Timons | Ellender | Robertson | R Harris | Power | Ward | Carmody | Chambers | Hardy(6), Gallagher(8), Maddox | 32 |
| Coburn | Hodson | Adams | Timons | Ellender | Robertson | R Harris | Power | Gallagher | Carmody | Chambers | Hardy(8), Keilty(10), Maddox | 33 |
| Coburn | Hodson | Adams | Timons | Ellender | Robertson | Gallagher | Power | Ward | R Harris | Chambers | Keilty(10), Carmody(10), Russell(8) | 34 |
| Coburn | Hodson | Adams | Timons | Ellender | Robertson | Gallagher | Power | Ward | R Harris | Chambers | Hardy(7 ), Donnelly, Russell(2) | 35 |
| Hawkes | Keilty | Adams | Timons | Ellender | Robertson | Gallagher | Power | Ward | Russell | Chambers | Hardy, Shepherd, Maddox(9) | 36 |
| Coburn | Hodson | Adams | Timons | Ellender | Robertson | Gallagher | Russell | Ward | R Harris | Chambers | Hardy(10), Hawkes, Keilty, Maddox | 37 |
| Coburn | Hodson | Adams | Timons | Maddox | Robertson | Gallagher | Powell | Ward | R Harris | Chambers | Hardy, Keilty, Russell(10) | 38 |
| Coburn | Hodson | Adams | Timons | Ellender | Robertson | Gallagher | Powell | Russell | R Harris | Chambers | Hardy, Keilty(9), Maddox | 39 |
| Coburn | Hodson | Adams | Timons | Ellender | Robertson | Russell | Powell | Ward | R Harris | Chambers | Hardy, Maddox, Shepherd | 40 |
| Hawkes | Gallagher | Ashcroft | Shepherd | Maddox | Goodier | Keilty | C-Excell | Hardy | Carmody | Donnelly | Hart(8), Adams(11), Power(9) | 41 |
| Coburn | Hodson | Adams | Timons | Ellender | Robertson | Russell | Power | Ward | R Harris | Chambers | Gallagher(10),Maddox(11),Carmody(9) | 42 |

League Attendances      HIGHEST: 1526      LOWEST: 518

NORTHERN PREMIER: 1st   FA CUP: 2nd Qualifying Round      FA TROPHY: 5th Round

## MANAGER
### BERNARD TAYLOR

## FOOTBALL MANAGEMENT TEAM

| | |
|---|---|
| Coach/Asst Manager: | Graham Heathcote |
| Assistant Coach: | George Shepherd |
| Physiotherapist: | Ian Liversedge |
| Kit Manager: | Vic Green |

## 1998-99

**Top Scorer:** Leroy Chambers

**Players of the Year:** Stuart Coburn &
Paul Ellender

**Captain:** Michael Carmody

Keith Russell celebrates after scoring Altrincham's second goal
in their 2-1 victory over Aldershot in the FA trophy 4th Round.

Photo: Andrew Chitty

## MATCHDAY PROGRAMME

| | |
|---|---|
| Number of pages: | 36 |
| Price: | £1.20 |
| Programme Editor: | Graham Rowley |
| | Tel: 0161 928 1045 |
| Other club publications: | ????? |
| Local Newspapers: | Sale & Altrincham Messenger |
| | Sale & Altrincham Express |
| | Manchester Evening News |
| Local Radio: | GMR (BBC) |
| | Signal Radio |
| | Piccadilly Radio |

# PLAYING SQUAD

| Player | D.O.B. | Signed From | Previous Clubs |
|---|---|---|---|
| **GOALKEEPERS** | | | |
| Stuart Coburn | 05.05.75 | Trafford F.C. | Trafford, Maine Road, Irlam Town |
| Dean Greygoose | 18.12.64 | Northwich Victoria | Cambridge U., Leyton O., Crystal Pal., Crewe Alex., Holywell Town |
| | | | |
| **DEFENDERS** | | | |
| Danny Adams | 03.01.76 | Congleton Town | Bury,Congleton T, NorthwichV, |
| Barry Crowe | 15.06.80 | Tranmere Rovers | Tranmere Rovers |
| Paul Ellender | 21.10.74 | Gainsborough Trinity | Scunthorpe Utd.,Gainsborough Trin |
| Jason Gallagher | 25.03.72 | Hyde United | Hyde United   Marine, Ternia (Belg.),Witton A Northwich V., Runcorn, Caernarfon T. |
| **Simeon Hodson** | **05.02.66** | **Telford United** | **Telford United,Notts Co., Charlton Ath., Lincoln C., Newport Co., W.B.A., Mansfield T., Kidderminster H., Rushden & Diamonds** |
| Mark Maddox | 11.03.73 | Barrow | Barrow, Local football |
| Gary Talbot | 06.10.70 | Winsford United | Winsford United, Rhyl, Wilmslow Alb,Barnton |
| Chris Timons | 08.12.74 | Gainsborough trinity | Clipstone M.W, Mansfield Town Gainsborough Trinity, Mansfield Town |
| Eddie Turkington | 15.05.78 | Stockport County | Stockport Co. |
| | | | |
| **MIDFIELDERS** | | | |
| Ged Kielty | 01.09.76 | Barrow | Barrow, Manchester C., York C., Southport |
| Stuart Walker | 17.03.79 | Brooklands Tap | Local football (Brooklands Tap) |
| Mike Carmody | 09.02.66 | Emley | Huddersfield Town, Tranmere R, Emley |
| Richard Harris | 12.07.67 | Hyde United | Ashton Utd.,Hyde U.,Runcorn, Hyde U., Altrincham |
| **Martin McDonald** | **04.12.73** | **Macclesfield Town** | **Stockport Co., Macclesfield, Southport, Doncaster Rovers, Macclesfield Town** |
| | | | |
| **FORWARDS** | | | |
| Brendan Burke | 13.1070 | Stalybridge Celtic | Manchester U., Oldham T., Mossley, Witton A. |
| Leroy Chambers | 25.10.72 | Macclesfield Town | Sheffield W., Chester C., Boston Utd., |
| Kevin Ellison | 23.02.79 | Conwt Town | Conwy Town |
| Richard Langdon | 22.03.70 | Macclesfield Town | Bedworth, Plymouth A., Stockport C. Macclesfield T., (L) Hednesford T. |
| Keith Russell | 31.01.74 | Blackpool | Blackpool,Tamworth, Atherstone, Hednesford Blackpool (£50,000) |
| **Tony Hemmings** | **21.09.67** | **Gloucester City** | **Burton A., Rochester, Northwich V., Wycombe** |
| **Phil Power** | **25.07.66** | **Macclesfield Town** | **Stalybridge C., Barrow, Chorley, Northwich V.,** Witton Alb., Crewe A., Horwich RMI. |

Players shown in bold are England Semi-Professional Internationals.
Departures: Nathan Comley-Excell (Ashton United -free), Neil Hardy (Morecambe -free)

# ALTRINCHAM

**Formed:** 1903

**Nickname:** The Robins

**Sponsor:** TBA

**Colours:** Red & white striped/black/white

**Change colours:** Yellow/green/green

**Midweek matchday:** Tuesday

**Reserves' League:** Bolton & Dist

**Youth League:** Altrincham Youth

## GROUND DETAILS

Moss Lane
Altrincham,
Cheshire WA15 8AP

**TELEPHONE:** Tel: 0161 928 1045
Fax: 0161 926 9934

**DIRECTIONS:** M6 junction 19; A556/M56 (Manchester Airport) to junction 7; signs Hale and Altrincham; through 1st traffic lights then 3rd right into Westminster Road and continue into Moss Lane. Ground on right.

**CAPACITY:** 6,085
**COVER:** Yes
**SEATS:** 1,154

**Clubhouse:** Bar under the stand open on match days only. Two snack bars on ground for pies, crisps, soft drinks etc

**Club Shop:** Yes

## PREVIOUS

**Leagues:** Manchester 03-11, Lancashire Comb. 11-19, Cheshire County 19-68, Northern Premier 68-79, 97-99 Conference 79-97

**Grounds:** Pollitts Field -1903-1910

**Names:** None

## CLUB RECORDS

**Attendance:** 10,275
Altrincham Boys v Sunderland Boys
English Schools Shield 3rd Round 28.02.25

**Goalscorer:** Jack Swindells 252 - 1965-71
**Appearances:** JohnDavison 677 - 1971-86

**Win** 9-2
v Merthyr Tydfil,Vauxhall Conference, Feb 1991
**Defeat:** Unknown

**Fee Paid:** £15,000
to Blackpool for Keith Russell
**Fee Received:**
From Crewe Alexandra for Paul Edwards - 1988

## BEST SEASON

**FA Trophy:** Winners 77-78, 85-86

**FA Cup:** 85-86 4th Round,
0-2 v York City (A)
League clubs defeated: 10

## Past Players who progressed to the Football League

G Barrow (Wigan Ath. 81), E Bishop (Tranmere R. 88),
F Carrodus (Manchester C. 69), T Carke (Shrewsbury T. 93),
P Conning (Rochdale, 86),
R Dale/ N Daws/ S Johnson/ A Reid (Bury, 51 77 92 92),
P Edwards (Crewe, 88), B Green (Exeter C., 62),
J Hughes/ A Kilner (Stockport Co., 76 90),
J Kennedy/ E Robinson (West Brom, 48 57),
S March (Port Vale, 59),Charlie Mitten (Halifax T., 65),
B Phillips (Middlesbrough, 54), J Rogers(Wigan Ath., 82),
P Showler (Barnet, 91), N Stiffle (Chesterfield, 54),
JStreet (Barrow, 69), C Freeman (Doncaster R. 93).

## HONOURS

Alliance Premier League 79-80, 80-81;
FA Trophy 77-78, 85- 86;
Bob Lord Trophy 80-81;
Northern Prem. Lge       Champions 98-99;
Lge.Cup 69-70 97-98; N.P.L. Shield 79-80;
Cheshire County League      Champions 65-66, 66-67;
Lge Cup 50-51, 52-53, 63-64;
Cheshire Senior Cup 04-05, 33-34,66-67,81-82;
Manchester League 04-05;
Cheshire Amateur Cup 03-04.

# DONCASTER ROVERS

The Rovers, although stepping down a stage to the Conference, obviously found their first season a very difficult one. The support throughout the season was amazing, with their lowest crowd of the season topping many teams' highest.

**CLUB OFFICIALS 1999-2000**

President      **Alick Jeffrey**

Chairman      **John Ryan**

Vice Chairman      **Peter Wetzel**

Club Secretary      **Mrs K J Odale**

c/o the club
Tel: 01302 539441 Fax: 01302 539679

Commercial Executive    **Nigel Reed**

c/o the club
Tel: 01302 539441 Fax: 01302 539679

One of the highlights of the campaign was the brilliant victory over Southend United in the F.A. Cup that was closely followed by a 2-1 victory over Barrow in the league.

Victories over Southport, Northwich, Morecambe and Farnborough (in a two legged) final brought the first silverware of their new non-League life, in the Endsleigh Challenge Trophy.

Doncaster seemed to be able to beat just about every team that the likes of Cheltenham and Yeovil found hard to beat. Coasting their way through victories over Kettering, Rushden, Kidderminster and Northwich, yet still finishing 16th. Indeed there were worries about a second relegation until the second half of the season.

But with exciting new players joining the squad Rovers will surely be the team to beat in the Conference next season.

T.T.

L-R Back: Lee Warren, Simon Shaw, Jason Minett, Glenn Kirkwood, Mark Hume, Colin Sutherland, Ian Duerdan, Mike Newell.
Centre: Dave Penney, Dean Walling, Noureddine Maamrria, Mark Barnard, Andy Warrington, Kevin McIntyre, Matt Cauldwell, Andy Watson, Tommy Wright.
Front: Scott Maxfield, John Ryan (chairman), Shaun Goodwin, Glynn Snodin (coach), Ian Snodin (manager), Martin Foster, Peter Wetzel (vice chairman), David Jones

# DONCASTER ROVERS
## MATCH FACTS 1998-99

| No | Date | Venue | Comp | Opponents | Att | Result | Score | Goalscorers |
|----|------|-------|------|-----------|-----|--------|-------|-------------|
| 1 | 15/08 | A | NC | Dover Athletic | 1517 | L | 0 - 1 | |
| 2 | 18/08 | H | NC | Southport | 3663 | L | 0 - 1 | |
| 3 | 22/08 | H | NC | Kidderminster Harriers | 3222 | W | 1 - 0 | Goodwin 49 |
| 4 | 25/08 | A | NC | Barrow | 2050 | D | 2 - 2 | Maamria 27, Goodwin 82 |
| 5 | 29/08 | A | NC | Kingstonian | 1942 | L | 1 - 2 | Minett 80 |
| 6 | 31/08 | H | NC | Kettering Town | 4569 | D | 1 - 1 | Kirkwood 19 |
| 7 | 05/09 | H | NC | Forest Green Rovers | 3402 | L | 0 - 1 | |
| 8 | 12/09 | A | NC | Hayes | 733 | L | 0 - 2 | |
| 9 | 15/09 | A | NC | Southport | 1450 | L | 2 - 3 | Kirkwood 3, Guyett 16[og] |
| 10 | 19/09 | H | NC | Rushden & Diamonds | 3768 | D | 1 - 1 | Foster 53 |
| 11 | 22/09 | A | NC | Morecambe | 1180 | W | 2 - 1 | Kirkwood 17, Hume 81 |
| 12 | 26/09 | A | NC | Yeovil Town | 2300 | D | 2 - 2 | Hume 32, Goodwin 60 |
| 13 | 03/10 | H | NC | Farnborough Town | 3468 | L | 1 - 2 | Sutherland 90 |
| 14 | 10/10 | H | NC | Woking | 2833 | L | 0 - 1 | |
| 15 | 24/10 | A | NC | Cheltenham Town | 2428 | L | 1 - 2 | Hume 28 |
| 16 | 07/11 | A | NC | Stevenage Borough | 3513 | L | 0 - 2 | |
| 17 | 17/11 | H | NC | Barrow | 2617 | W | 2 - 1 | Kirkwood 7, Maamria 73 |
| 18 | 28/11 | A | NC | Hereford United | 2115 | L | 0 - 1 | |
| 19 | 12/12 | A | NC | Welling United | 761 | D | 1 - 1 | Hume 23 |
| 20 | 19/12 | H | NC | Dover Athletic | 2119 | W | 5 - 4 | Kirkwood 30 84, Penney 52, Maamria 75, Budden 81[og] |
| 21 | 26/12 | H | NC | Leek Town | 3520 | L | 0 - 1 | |
| 22 | 28/12 | A | NC | Hednesford Town | 1542 | D | 1 - 1 | Hume 41 |
| 23 | 02/01 | A | NC | Leek Town | 1365 | D | 1 - 1 | Kirkwood 11 |
| 24 | 09/01 | H | NC | Cheltenham Town | 3082 | D | 2 - 2 | Goodwin 51, Duerden 55 |
| 25 | 16/01 | H | NC | Morecambe | 4251 | W | 2 - 1 | Penney 70 72 |
| 26 | 23/01 | A | NC | Rushden & Diamonds | 4577 | W | 3 - 1 | Duerden 48 50 79 |
| 27 | 30/01 | A | NC | Kettering Town | 3646 | W | 1 - 0 | Duerden 88 |
| 28 | 13/02 | H | NC | Yeovil Town | 4413 | L | 0 - 2 | |
| 29 | 20/02 | A | NC | Forest Green Rovers | 1271 | D | 0 - 0 | |
| 30 | 23/02 | H | NC | Telford United | 3040 | W | 2 - 1 | Goodwin 41, Kirkwood 73 |
| 31 | 27/02 | H | NC | Hereford United | 3568 | W | 3 - 1 | Duerden 14 50, Penney 56[p] |
| 32 | 06/03 | A | NC | Woking | 2530 | L | 0 - 2 | |
| 33 | 13/03 | H | NC | Hayes | 3149 | L | 0 - 1 | |
| 34 | 16/03 | A | NC | Northwich Victoria | 1402 | W | 3 - 1 | Duerden 47 61 90 |
| 35 | 20/03 | H | NC | Welling United | 2952 | W | 4 - 1 | Duerden 9, Wright 43, Watson 89, Penney 90 |
| 36 | 26/03 | H | NC | Stevenage Borough | 4629 | D | 0 - 0 | |
| 37 | 03/04 | A | NC | Kidderminster Harriers | 2200 | D | 3 - 3 | Sutherland 18, Barnwell 57, Maxfield 80 |
| 38 | 05/04 | H | NC | Hednesford Town | 3595 | L | 0 - 1 | |
| 39 | 14/04 | H | NC | Northwich Victoria | 2296 | D | 2 - 2 | Hume 5, Duerden 56 |
| 40 | 17/04 | A | NC | Farnborough Town | 893 | L | 0 - 1 | |
| 41 | 24/04 | A | NC | Telford United | 1539 | W | 2 - 0 | Beckett 85, Penney 89 |
| 42 | 01/05 | H | NC | Kingstonian | 2915 | L | 0 - 1 | |

### CUP COMPETITIONS

| | Date | Venue | Comp | Opponents | Att | Result | Score | Goalscorers |
|--|------|-------|------|-----------|-----|--------|-------|-------------|
| | 17/10 | H | FA Cup Q3 | Flixton | 2048 | W | 2-0 | Kirkwood 77, Hulme 86 |
| | 31/10 | H | FA Cup Q4 | Guiseley | 2495 | W | 3-1 | Duerden 45 61, Kirkwood 58 |
| | 14/11 | A | FA Cup 1 | Southend United | 3740 | W | 1-0 | Penney 12 |
| | 21/11 | H | FA Trophy 2 | Frickley Athletic | 2003 | L | 0-2 | |
| | 01/12 | H | Endsleigh 2 | Southport | 949 | W | 2-0 | Hume 32 55 |
| | 05/12 | H | FA Cup 2 | Rushden & Diamonds | 5396 | D | 0-0 | |
| | 15/12 | H | FA Cup 2 rep | Rushden & Diamonds | 5564 | L | 2-4 | Sutherland 17, Maamria 89 |
| | 02/03 | H | Endsleigh QF | Northwich Victoria | 1877 | W | 3-2 | Barnwell 65 76, George 68 |
| | 30/03 | A | E'sleigh SF 1 | Morecambe | 1302 | W | 2-1 | Duerden(2) |
| | 08/04 | H | E'sleigh SF 2 | Morecambe | 3297 | W | 1-0 | Watson 64 |
| | 20/04 | A | Endsleigh F 1 | Farnborough Town | 643 | W | 1-0 | Penney 89 |
| | 03/05 | H | Endsleigh F 2 | Farnborough Town | 7160 | W | 3-0 | Sutherland, Duerden(2) |

| 1 | 2 | 3 | 4 | 5 | 6 | 7 | 8 | 9 | 10 | 11 | 12/14/15 | |
|---|---|---|---|---|---|---|---|---|---|---|---|---|
| Woods | Shaw | McIntyre | Warren | Hume | Sutherland | Bradley | Goodwin | Wright | Maamria | Maxfield | Beckett ,George, Warren | 1 |
| Southall | Shaw | McIntyre | Snodin | Hume | Sutherland | Minett | Goodwin | Maamria | Wright | Maxfield | Kirkwood, Warren, D Beckett | 2 |
| Southall | Shaw | McIntyre | Snodin | Hume | Sutherland | Minett | Goodwin | Maamria | Wright | Maxfield | Kirkwood, Warren, D Beckett | 3 |
| Southall | Shaw | McIntyre | Warren | Hume | Sutherland | Minett | Goodwin | Maamria | Wright | Maxfield | Kirkwood, Beckett, D George | 4 |
| Southall | Shaw | Maxfield | Snodin | Hume | Sutherland | Wright | Goodwin | Maamria | Sheridan | Penney | Warren, Minett, Kirkwood | 5 |
| Southall | Shaw | Maxfield | Warren | Hume | Sutherland | Minett | Sheridan | Kirkwood | Maamria | Wright | Beckett, D Brookes, George | 6 |
| Southall | Shaw | McIntyre | Warren | Hume | Sutherland | Minett | Sheridan | Kirkwood | Maamria | Wright | D Beckett , Maxfield, George | 7 |
| Southall | Shaw | Maxfield | Snodin | Nicol | Sutherland | Minett | Goodwin | Kirkwood | Sheridan | Warren | Cunningham, George, Hume | 8 |
| Southall | I Snodin | McIntyre | Warren | George | Sutherland | Wright | Minett | Maamria | Kirkwood | Maxfield | G Snodin , Brookes, D Esdaille | 9 |
| Woods | Warren | Nicol | McIntyre | Penney | Sutherland | Minett | Sheridan | Maamria | Kirkwood | Maxfield | George, Hume, D Esdaille | 10 |
| Woods | Warren | McIntyre | Nicol | Penney | Sutherland | Minett | Sheridan | Kirkwood | Hume | Maxfield | George, Beckett, D Esdaille | 11 |
| Woods | Warren | Maxfield | Nicol | Penney | Sutherland | Shaw | Sheridan | Kirkwood | Hume | Minett | Goodwin, Beckett , George | 12 |
| Southall | Shaw | Nicol | McIntyre | Warren | Sutherland | Penney | Goodwin | Hayward | Hume | Sheridan | Maxfield , Minett , Kirkwood | 13 |
| Woods | Shaw | McIntyre | Nicol | Warren | Sutherland | Penney | Minett | Hayward | Maamria | Maxfield | George, Hume, Kirkwood | 14 |
| Woods | Shaw | Maxfield | Nicol | Warren | Sutherland | Wright | Minett | Duerden | Hume | Hayward | Kirkwood, Beckett , Maamria | 15 |
| Woods | Ybarra | Shaw | Nicol | Warren | Sutherland | Maamria | Penney | Duerden | Kirkwood | Wright | George, Snodin, Cauldwell | 16 |
| Woods | Ybarra | Shaw | I Snodin | Warren | Nicol | Maamria | Penney | Duerden | Kirkwood | Wright | Cauldwell, Hume, Jones | 17 |
| Woods | Ybarra | Shaw | I Snodin | Warren | Nicol | Maamria | Penney | Duerden | Kirkwood | Wright | Goodwin, Hume, Jones | 18 |
| Woods | Warren | Maxfield | I Snodin | Penney | Sutherland | Beckett | Goodwin | Duerden | Hume | Wright | Maamria, Cauldwell, Jones | 19 |
| Woods | Shaw | Maxfield | Nicol | Penney | Sutherland | Warren | Goodwin | Hume | Kirkwood | Wright | Cauldwell, Maamria, Duerden | 20 |
| Woods | Shaw | Maxfield | Nicol | Penney | Sutherland | Maamria | Warren | Duerden | Kirkwood | Wright | Hume, Cauldwell, Ybarra | 21 |
| Woods | Linares | Warren | I Snodin | Penney | Sutherland | Maamria | Nicol | Hume | Kirkwood | Wright | Duerden, Cauldwell, Bennett | 22 |
| Woods | Warren | McIntyre | I Snodin | Penney | Nicol | Maamria | Maxfield | Duerden | Kirkwood | Goodwin | Wright, Ybarra , Cauldwell | 23 |
| Woods | Shaw | McIntyre | Nicol | Rimmer | Sutherland | Penney | Goodwin | Duerden | Kirkwood | Warren | Maamria, Ybarra , I Snodin | 24 |
| Woods | Shaw | McIntyre | Nicol | Rimmer | Sutherland | Penney | Goodwin | Duerden | Kirkwood | Warren | Maxfield, Ybarra, Beckett | 25 |
| Woods | Shaw | McIntyre | Nicol | Warren | Minett | Penney | Goodwin | Duerden | Kirkwood | Wright | Maxfield, Maamria, Rimmer | 26 |
| Woods | Shaw | McIntyre | Warren | Penney | Sutherland | Minett | Goodwin | Duerden | Kirkwood | Wright | Hum, Maxfield, Rimmer | 27 |
| Woods | Shaw | McIntyre | Nicol | Penney | Sutherland | Warren | Goodwin | Duerden | Kirkwood | Wright | Maamria, Hume, Maxfield | 28 |
| Woods | Shaw | McIntyre | Nicol | Penney | Sutherland | Warren | Goodwin | Duerden | Hume | Wright | Maamria, Kirkwood , Maxfield | 29 |
| Woods | Shaw | McIntyre | Nicol | Warren | Sutherland | Penney | Goodwin | Duerden | Kirkwood | Maxfield | Maamria, Hume, Cauldwell | 30 |
| Woods | Shaw | McIntyre | Nicol | Warren | Cauldwell | Penney | Maamria | Duerden | Kirkwood | Maxfield | Barnwel, Ybarra, George | 31 |
| Woods | Shaw | McIntyre | Warren | Cauldwell | Sutherland | Penney | Maamria | Duerden | Barnwell | Maxfield | Kirkwood, Beckett , George | 32 |
| Woods | Shaw | McIntyre | Nicol | Warren | Sutherland | Penney | Beckett | Duerden | Kirkwood | Maxfield | Barnwel, Maamria ,Cauldwell | 33 |
| Woods | Shaw | McIntyre | Nicol | Penney | Warren | Wright | Goodwin | Duerden | Maxfield | Cauldwell | Kirkwood, Minett , Barnwell | 34 |
| Woods | Shaw | Cauldwell | Nicol | Penney | Sutherland | Wright | Goodwin | Duerden | Barnwell | Minett | Watson, Beckett, Kirkwood | 35 |
| Woods | Shaw | McIntyre | Nicol | Penney | Sutherland | Warren | Goodwin | Duerden | Barnwell | Wright | Minett, Kirkwood, Maxfield | 36 |
| Woods | Shaw | McIntyre | Warren | Penney | Sutherland | Minett | Goodwin | Duerden | Barnwell | Maxfield | Kirkwood, Foster, George | 37 |
| Woods | Shaw | McIntyre | Warren | Penney | Sutherland | Watson | Minett | Duerden | Barnwell | Maxfield, | Kirkwood, George, Foster | 38 |
| Woods | Shaw | McIntyre | Warren | Penney | Sutherland | Watson | Foster | Duerden | Hume | Maxfield | George, Cauldwell, Goodwin | 39 |
| Woods | Minett | McIntyre | Warren | George | Maxwell | Foster | Goodwin | Kirkwood | Barnwell | Cauldwell | Brookes, Beckett , Jones | 40 |
| Woods | Shaw | McIntyre | Warren | Minett | Sutherland | Watson | Foster | Duerden | Barnwell | Maxfield | Penney, Beckett , Cauldwell | 41 |
| Woods | Shaw | McIntyre | Warren | George | Beckett | Minett | Foster | Kirkwood | Hume | Cauldwell | Maxfield, Brookes, Barnwell | 42 |

League Attendances          HIGHEST: 4629          LOWEST: 2119

CONFERENCE: 16th          FA CUP: 2nd Qualifying Round          FA TROPHY: 2nd Round

## MANAGER
### IAN SNODIN

| | |
|---|---|
| Date of Appointment | 1st August 1998 |
| Date of Birth: | 15th August 1963 |
| Place of Birth: | Rotherham |

PREVIOUS CLUBS
As manager                                      None
As asst. manager/coach                          None
As player          Doncaster Rovers, Leeds Utd., Everton,
Sunderland (loan), Oldham Ath.,Scarborough.

HONOURS
As manager                    Nationwide Cup 98-99
As asst. manager/coach                          N/A
As player                         England: u21 x4.

## FOOTBALL MANAGEMENT TEAM
Assistant Manager/Coach:    Glyn Snodin

Physio:                     Jon Bowden

### 1998-99
**Top Scorer:**        Ian Deurden
**Player of the Year:**  Lee Warren
**Captain:**           Dave Penney

BELOW
Left: manager Ian Snodin
Photo: Roger Turner

Right: Simon Shaw
Photo: Keith Clayton

## MATCHDAY PROGRAMME

| | |
|---|---|
| Number of pages | 36 |
| Price | £2.00 |
| Programme Editor | Nigel Reed c/o the club |
| Other club publications: | Supporters' Club Handbook Two fanzines |
| Local Press | Doncaster Star Yorkshire Post |
| Local Radio Stations: | Radio Hallam Radio Sheffield |

# PLAYING SQUAD

| Player | Birthplace Honours | D.O.B. | Previous Clubs |
|---|---|---|---|
| **GOALKEEPERS** | | | |
| Andy Warrington | Sheffield | 10.0676 | York City |
| | | | |
| **DEFENDERS** | | | |
| Mark Barnard | Sheffield | 27.1175 | Darlington |
| Mark Hume | Barnsley | 21.05.78 | Barnsley |
| Kevin McIntyre | Liverpool | 23.12.77 | Tranmere Rovers |
| **Simon Shaw** | **Middlesbrough** | **21.09.73** | **Darlington** |
| Colin Sutherland | Glasgow | 15.03.75 | Clydebank, Scarborough |
| Dean Walling | Leeds | 17.04.69 | Lincoln City £25,000 |
| Lee Warren | Manchester | 28.02.69 | Leeds Utd., Rochdale, Hull C., Lincoln C., Doncaster R. |
| | | | |
| **MIDFIELDERS** | | | |
| Matthew Caldwell | Chesterfield | 16.10.78 | |
| Harvey Cunningham | Manchester | 11.09.68 | Doncaster Rovers. |
| Martin Foster | Rotherham | 29.10.77 | Greenock Morton |
| David Jones | Bedford | 17.11.78 | Blackpool |
| Noureddine Maamfia | Tunisia | 26.05.71 | Ayr United |
| Scott Maxfield | Doncaster | 13.07.76 | Doncaster Rovers (T), Hull City |
| Jason Minett | Peterborough | 12.08.71 | |
| David Penney | Wakefield | 17.08.64 | |
| Ian Snodin | Rotherham E: B 2, u21 4, Y 4; Div.1 '87 | 15.08.63 | Doncaster Rovers (A), Leeds Utd., Everton, Sunderland (loan), Oldham Ath., Scarborough. |
| Andy Watson | Leeds | 13.11.78 | Garforth |
| | | | |
| **FORWARDS** | | | |
| Ian Duerden | Burnley | 27.03.78 | Halifax Town |
| Shaun Goodwin | Rotherham | 14.06.69 | Rotherham Utd (T), |
| Glenn Kirkwood | Chesterfield | 03.12.76 | Eastwood Town |
| Mike Newall | Liverpool | 27.01.65 | Aberdeen, Blackburn R., Everton, Leicester C., Luton T., Wigan A., Crewe Alex., Liverpool (A) |
| Tommy Wright | Dunfermline S: u21. | 10.01.66 | Leeds Utd.,Oldham Ath., Leicester C.,  Middlesbrough, Bradford C., Oldham Ath., St. Johnstone |

Bold print denotes England semi-professional international.


DEPARTURES (since may 99): Jamie Barnwell-Edinboro,Harvey Cunningham,Robert Wild, Danny George,(Burton Albion),  Darren Brooks ( Worksop), Harvey Cunningham, Duane Becket, Andy Woods (Scarboro), Jamie Barnwell

# DONCASTER ROVERS

**Founded:** 1879

**Nickname:** The Rovers

**Sponsors:** Beazer Homes

**Club Colours:** White shirts with red trim, white shorts with red trim, white socks

**Change Colours:** All blue

**Midweek matchday:** Tuesday

**Reserve Team's League:** No reserve team

## PREVIOUS

**Leagues:** Midland Alliance Lge 1890-91; Midland League 1891-1901, 03-04 & 05-15,20-23; Football League 1901-3, 04-05, 23-Sept 39, 42-44, 45-98; Midland Comb. 1915-16; E Midlands War Lge Oct 1939-40; War Lge North 1940-42, 44-45

**Names:** None

**Ground:** 1880-1916 Intake Ground; 1920-22 Benetthorpe Ground; 1922 > Belle Vue (formerly known as Low Pasture)

## CLUB RECORDS

**Attendance:** 37,149 v Hull City, Div. 3N, 2.10.1948

**Career Goalscorer:** Tom Keetley, 180, 1923-29

**Career Appearances:** Fred Emery, 417, 1925-36

**Win:** 10-0 v Darlington (H), Div. 4, 25.01.64

**Defeat:** 0-12 v Small Heath (A), Division 2, 11.04.03

**Transfer Fee Paid:** £62,500 to Torquay United for Darren Moore, July 1995

**Transfer Fee Received:** £350,000 from Bradford City for Darren Moore, 1997

## GROUND DETAILS

Belle Vue Ground,
Doncaster,
S. Yorks. DN4 5HT

TELEPHONE 01302 539441
Fax 01302 539679

**SIMPLE DIRECTIONS:**
From north & west
Into Doncaster town centre and follow signs to Bawtry (A368) and after 1.2 miles take 3rd exit at roundabout into BawtryRoad.
From east
M18, then A630, A18 and A638 (Bawtry Road)
From south
M18 junct 3, A6182, then A18 and A638 (Bawtry Road)

**CAPACITY:** 8,608
**SEATED:** 1,259
**COVERED TERRACING:** 2,125

**SOCIAL FACILITIES:**
No Clubhouse.
Food outlets on ground on matchdays

**CLUB SHOP:** Open on matchdays, and Mon - Fri 1-4.30pm

## BEST SEASON

**FA Trophy:** 2nd Rd 98-99 (1st season)

**FA Cup:** 5th Rd 1951-52, 53-54, 54-55 & 55-56

**League Cup:** 5th Round 1975-76

## HONOURS

Division 3 N 1934-35, 46-47, 49-50;
Division 4 1965-66, 68-69;
Sheffield County Cup 1890-91, 1911-12, 35-36, 37-38, 55-56, 67-68, 75-76, 85-86;
Yorkshire Electricity Cup 1995-96;
Midland Counties League 1896-97, 98-99;
NorthernIntermediate Lge Cup 1984-95, 86-87

## Past Players who progressed to the Football League
Not applicable at present

# DOVER ATHLETIC

## CLUB OFFICIALS 1999-2000

| | |
|---|---|
| Chairman | **John Husk** |
| Directors | **J T Husk, A G Husk,** |
| | **G A Goodacre,** |
| Associate Directors | |
| | **J F Durrant, K F Stamp,** |
| | **D Hammond, C J Harman** |
| Secretary | **John Durrant** |
| c/o the club | Tel: 01304 822373 |
| Commercial Manager | **Jean Haves** |
| & Press Officer | Tel: 01304 240041 |

Dover always seem to make excellent progress at the start of the season. So with the first two games bringing a maximum six points, probably things could only get worse - and they did!

Their home crowd of 1,517 for the opening game of the season sadly deteriorated to 865 for the last and indeed their support continued to be inconsistent throughout.

After a promising Cup run in the F.A. Trophy reaching Round Three they came up against Stevenage Borough and a last gasp goal from Chris Pearson.

Having enjoyed a wonderful Christmas period beating Kingstonian and Welling, 5-1 and 3-0, the New Year brought great improvement in the Conference, moving from 14th to 4th in just two months. But a further six losses before the end of the season took them to a final league placing of 11th and some rebuilding to do in the close season.

T.T.

Back Row: Simon Elliott, Lee Palmer, Liburd Henry, Neil Le Bihan, Roy Godden, James Virgo, Jason Moore. Centre Row: Frank Brooks (physio), Jake Leberl, Ash Harrison, Jimmy Strouts, Lee Shearer, Charlie Mitten, Dave Clarke, Robin Hastie (Kit Manager). Front Row: Darren Adams, Ricky Reina, Bill Williams (Manager), Scott Daniels (Captain), Clive Walker (Asst. Manager0, Joff Vansittart, John Budden.

# DOVER ATHLETIC
## MATCH FACTS 1998-99

| No | Date | Venue | Comp | Opponents | Att | Result | Score | Goalscorers |
|----|------|-------|------|-----------|-----|--------|-------|-------------|
| 1 | 15/08 | H | NC | Doncaster Rovers | 1517 | W | 1-0 | Daniels 34 |
| 2 | 18/08 | A | NC | Woking | 2263 | W | 2-1 | Vansittart 52, Henry 76 |
| 3 | 22/08 | A | NC | Hereford United | 2139 | L | 0-2 | |
| 4 | 25/08 | H | NC | Stevenage Borough | 1394 | D | 1-1 | Budden 61 |
| 5 | 29/08 | H | NC | Yeovil Town | 1154 | L | 1-2 | Adams 57 |
| 6 | 31/08 | A | NC | Farnborough Town | 847 | W | 2-1 | Adams 26, Budden 87 |
| 7 | 05/09 | A | NC | Telford United | 588 | D | 1-1 | K Adams 8 |
| 8 | 08/09 | H | NC | Rushden & Diamonds | 1387 | D | 1-1 | Virgo 22 |
| 9 | 12/09 | A | NC | Hednesford Town | 1026 | W | 2-1 | Brady 67, Reina 74 |
| 10 | 19/09 | H | NC | Barrow | 1117 | D | 1-1 | Iorfa 88 |
| 11 | 26/09 | A | NC | Leek Town | 533 | L | 0-2 | |
| 12 | 03/10 | A | NC | Cheltenham Town | 2575 | D | 1-1 | Reina 64 |
| 13 | 10/10 | H | NC | Northwich Victoria | 949 | D | 0-0 | |
| 14 | 07/11 | A | NC | Barrow | 1290 | L | 0-1 | |
| 15 | 14/11 | H | NC | Kettering Town | 807 | L | 0-1 | |
| 16 | 28/11 | A | NC | Yeovil Town | 2211 | D | 1-1 | Henry 50 |
| 17 | 05/12 | H | NC | Cheltenham Town | 972 | D | 0-0 | |
| 18 | 12/12 | H | NC | Southport | 792 | W | 2-1 | Hynes 46, Budden 56 |
| 19 | 19/12 | A | NC | Doncaster Rovers | 2119 | L | 4-5 | Vansittart 3 13 27, Hynes 79 |
| 20 | 26/12 | A | NC | Welling United | 962 | W | 3-0 | Farley 10[og], Witter 59[og], Le Bihan 76 |
| 21 | 28/12 | H | NC | Kingstonian | 1480 | W | 5-1 | Carruthers 4 56 75, Virgo 34, Hynes 76 |
| 22 | 02/01 | H | NC | Welling United | 1334 | L | 1-2 | Carruthers 2 |
| 23 | 09/01 | A | NC | Northwich Victoria | 942 | L | 0-2 | |
| 24 | 23/01 | H | NC | Hereford United | 1001 | W | 3-1 | Hynes 52, Leberl 85, Reina 90 |
| 25 | 26/01 | A | NC | Hayes | 580 | W | 2-1 | Wormnull 44, Carruthers 45 |
| 26 | 30/01 | H | NC | Leek Town | 974 | W | 2-1 | Clarke 39, Le Bihan 78 |
| 27 | 06/02 | A | NC | Kettering Town | 1864 | W | 2-0 | Carruthers 22, Hynes 82 |
| 28 | 09/02 | H | NC | Farnborough Town | 860 | W | 2-1 | Le Bihan 23, Shearer 42 |
| 29 | 13/02 | H | NC | Hednesford Town | 1126 | D | 0-0 | |
| 30 | 20/02 | A | NC | Morecambe | 850 | W | 4-0 | Budden 33, Brown 64, Hynes 71 74 |
| 31 | 27/02 | H | NC | Hayes | 1035 | D | 0-0 | |
| 32 | 06/03 | H | NC | Forest Green Rovers | 1017 | D | 1-1 | Reina 85 |
| 33 | 13/03 | A | NC | Southport | 955 | L | 0-3 | |
| 34 | 16/03 | A | NC | Rushden & Diamonds | 2744 | D | 2-2 | Wormnull 36, Hynes 55 |
| 35 | 20/03 | A | NC | Kidderminster Harriers | 1312 | L | 0-1 | |
| 36 | 27/03 | H | NC | Morecambe | 872 | L | 2-3 | Hynes 23, Shearer 77[p] |
| 37 | 03/04 | H | NC | Woking | 1168 | W | 3-2 | Virgo 40 44, Carruthers 62 |
| 38 | 05/04 | A | NC | Kingstonian | 904 | L | 0-1 | |
| 39 | 10/04 | A | NC | Stevenage Borough | 1458 | L | 0-1 | |
| 40 | 17/04 | H | NC | Kidderminster Harriers | 925 | L | 0-1 | |
| 41 | 28/04 | A | NC | Forest Green Rovers | 492 | W | 1-0 | Hynes 48 |
| 42 | 01/05 | H | NC | Telford United | 865 | D | 1-1 | Vansittart 59 |

**CUP COMPETITIONS**

| | Date | Venue | Comp | Opponents | Att | Result | Score | Goalscorers |
|----|------|-------|------|-----------|-----|--------|-------|-------------|
| | 06/10 | H | Endsleigh 1 | Stevenage Borough | 0 | L | 2-3 | |
| | 17/10 | A | FA Cup Q3 | Gravesend & Northfleet | 1058 | D | 0-0 | |
| | 20/10 | H | FA Cup Q3 rep | Gravesend & Northfleet | 1034 | W | 3-2 | Vansittart 38 43 57 |
| | 03/11 | D | FA Cup Q4 | Basingstoke Town | 1011 | D | 2-2 | Godden 28, Adams 86 |
| | 09/11 | H | FA Cup Q4 rep | Basingstoke Town | 1318 | L | 1-2 | Reina 18 |
| | 21/11 | H | FA Trophy 2 | Welling United | 786 | W | 4-1 | Reina 10, Budden 28, Strouts 70, Adams 82 |
| | 16/01 | A | FA Trophy 3 | Stevenage Borough | 2476 | L | 2-3 | Le Bihan 6, Hynes 22 |
| | 02/03 | H | Kent SC QF | Welling United | 355 | L | 0-2 | |

| 1 | 2 | 3 | 4 | 5 | 6 | 7 | 8 | 9 | 10 | 11 | 12 / 14 / 15 | |
|---|---|---|---|---|---|---|---|---|---|---|---|---|
| Mitten | Leberl | Palmer | Budden | Daniels | Le Bihan | Clarke | Strouts | Vansittart | Reina | Adams | Henry, Moore, Godden | 1 |
| Mitten | Leberl | Palmer | Budden | Daniels | Le Bihan | Clark | Strouts | Vansittart | Reina | Henry | Moore, Adams, Elliott | 2 |
| Mitten | Leberl | Moore | Budden | Daniels | Le Bihan | Clarke | Strouts | Vansittart | Reina | Henry | Godden, Adams, Palmer | 3 |
| Mitten | Leberl | Palmer | Budden | Daniels | Le Bihan | Adams | Strouts | Vansittart | Reina | Henry | Moore, Godden, Elliott | 4 |
| Mitten | Moore | Palmer | Budden | Leberl | Le Bihan | Clarke | Strouts | Vansittart | Reina | Virgo | Adams, Elliott, Godden | 5 |
| Mitten | Godden | Palmer | Budden | Leberl | Le Bihan | Clarke | Strouts | Reina | Adams | Virgo | Vansittart, Elliott, Hogg | 6 |
| Mitten | Moore | Palmer | Budden | Leberl | Le Bihan | K Adams | Strouts | D Adams | Reina | Virgo | Brady, Vansittart, Godden | 7 |
| Mitten | Moore | Palmer | Budden | Leberl | Le Bihan | Virgo | Strouts | Vansittart | Reina | Brady | K Adams, D Adams, Elliott | 8 |
| Mitten | Moore | Palmer | Budden | Leberl | Le Bihan | Virgo | K Adams | Vansittart | Reina | Brady | D Adams, Hogg, Godden | 9 |
| Mitten | Moore | Palmer | Budden | Leberl | Le Bihan | Virgo | Strouts | D Adams | K Adams | Brady | Iorfa, Elliott, Hogg | 10 |
| Mitten | Clarke | Palmer | Virgo | Leberl | Le Bihan | K Adams | Strouts | D Adams | Reina | Brady | Wormull, Iorfa, Hogg | 11 |
| Mitten | Moore | Palmer | Virgo | Leberl | Le Bihan | Clarke | Strouts | Iorfa | Reina | Brady | D Adams, K Adams, Elliott | 12 |
| Mitten | Moore | Virgo | Strouts | Leberl | Le Bihan | Clarke | Wormull | Elliott | Reina | D Adams | Henry, Godden, Hogg | 13 |
| Mitten | Moore | Palmer | Budden | Virgo | Le Bihan | Godden | Wormull | Vansittart | Henry | D Adams | Shearer, Clarke, Leberl | 14 |
| A Harrison | Clarke | Palmer | Budden | Shearer | Le Bihan | Wormull | Virgo | Vansittart | Reina | D Adams | Munday, Godden, Henry | 15 |
| Mitten | Clarke | Palmer | Budden | Shearer | Virgo | Wormull | Strouts | Reina | Henry | Le Bihan | Vansittart, Moore, A Harrison | 16 |
| Mitten | Wormull | Palmer | Budden | Shearer | Le Bihan | Clarke | Strouts | Reina | Henry | Virgo | Munday, Hynes, Moore | 17 |
| Mitten | Munday | Palmer | Budden | Shearer | Le Bihan | Wormull | Strouts | Carruthers | Henry | Virgo | Hynes, Moore, Godden | 18 |
| Mitten | Munday | Palmer | Budden | Shearer | Carruthers | Clarke | Wormull | Vansittart | Hynes | Virgo | Strouts, Reina, Henry | 19 |
| Mitten | Munday | Palmer | Budden | Shearer | Wormull | Clarke | Strouts | Reina | Hynes | Le Bihan | Henry, Carruthers, Virgo | 20 |
| Mitten | Munday | Palmer | Budden | Shearer | Clarke | Wormull | Strouts | Carruthers | Hynes | Le Bihan | Virgo, Leberl, Godden | 21 |
| Mitten | Munday | Palmer | Budden | Shearer | Clarke | Wormull | Strouts | Carruthers | Hynes | Virgo | Moore, Reina, Hogg | 22 |
| Mitten | Munday | Palmer | Budden | Shearer | Wormull | Carruthers | Leberl | Reina | Hynes | Virgo | Henry, Godden, Moore | 23 |
| Mitten | Munday | Palmer | Budden | Shearer | Wormull | Clarke | Leberl | Reina | Hynes | Le Bihan | Carruthers, Virgo, Henry | 24 |
| Mitten | Munday | Palmer | Le Bihan | Shearer | Wormull | Clarke | Leberl | Reina | Carruthers | Virgo | Budden, Hynes, Beard | 25 |
| Mitten | Munday | Palmer | Leberl | Shearer | Le Bihan | Clarke | Wormull | Reina | Carruthers | Virgo | Beard, Godden, Moore | 26 |
| Mitten | Munday | Leberl | Le Bihan | Shearer | Wormull | Clarke | Beard | Reina | Carruthers | Virgo | Hynes, Budden, Godden | 27 |
| Mitten | Munday | Beard | Budden | Shearer | Le Bihan | Clarke | Wormull | Reina | Carruthers | Virgo | Hynes, Moore, Palmer | 28 |
| Mitten | Munday | Leberl | Budden | Shearer | Wormull | Clarke | Le Bihan | Brown | Hynes | Virgo | Palmer, Moore, Godden | 29 |
| Mitten | Munday | Beard | Budden | Shearer | Le Bihan | Clarke | Wormull | Brown | Hynes | Virgo | Vansittart, Palmer, Moore | 30 |
| Mitten | Leberl | Palmer | Budden | Shearer | Le Bihan | Clarke | Wormull | Brown | Hynes | Virgo | Godden, Vansittart, Beard | 31 |
| Mitten | Munday | Leberl | Budden | Shearer | Le Bihan | Clarke | Wormull | Brown | Hynes | Virgo | Reina, Palmer, Beard | 32 |
| Mitten | Munday | Beard | Budden | Shearer | Le Bihan | Leberl | Wormull | Brown | Reina | Virgo | Vansittart, Norman, Palmer | 33 |
| Mitten | Munday | Leberl | Budden | Shearer | Le Bihan | Clarke | Wormull | Brown | Vansittart | Virgo | Hynes, Norman, Beard | 34 |
| Mitten | Munday | Leberl | Budden | Palmer | Le Bihan | Clarke | Wormull | Brown | Hynes | Norman | Godden, Virgo, Beard | 35 |
| Mitten | Leberl | Palmer | Budden | Shearer | Le Bihan | Clarke | Wormull | Vansittart | Hynes | Virgo | Henry, Beard, Norman | 36 |
| Mitten | Beard | Palmer | Budden | Shearer | Virgo | Clarke | Wormull | Vansittart | Hynes | Carruthers | Norman, Godden, Hogg | 37 |
| Mitten | Leberl | Palmer | Budden | Beard | Le Bihan | Clarke | Carruthers | Vansittart | Hynes | Virgo | Norman, Godden, Henry | 38 |
| Mitten | Munday | Leberl | Budden | Shearer | Le Bihan | Beard | Wormull | Carruthers | Vansittart | Virgo | Palmer, Norman, Hynes | 39 |
| Mitten | Munday | Budden | Beard | Shearer | Leberl | Clarke | Wormull | Carruthers | Vansittart | Le Bihan | Hynes, Virgo, Palmer | 40 |
| Mitten | Munday | Leberl | Beard | Shearer | Le Bihan | Clarke | Wormull | Vansittart | Hynes | Virgo | Palmer, Elliott, A Hogg | 41 |
| Mitten | Leberl | Beard | Budden | Shearer | Le Bihan | Clarke | Wormull | Vansittart | Hynes | Virgo | Palmer, Carruthers, Elliott | 42 |

League Attendances  **HIGHEST:** 1517  **LOWEST:** 792

**CONFERENCE:** 12th  **FA CUP:** 4th Qualifying Round  **FA TROPHY:** 3rd Round

## MANAGER

### BILL WILLIAMS

| | |
|---|---|
| Date of Appointment | 24.01.97 |
| Date of Birth: | 23rd August 1942 |
| Place of Birth: | Esher, Surrey. |

PREVIOUS CLUBS

| | |
|---|---|
| As manager | Durban City (SA), Sacramento Gold (ASL), Atlanta Chiefs (NASL), Maidstone Utd. |
| As coach | None |
| As player | Portsmouth, West Brom. A., Q.P.R., Gillingham, Maidstone Utd. |

HONOURS

| | |
|---|---|
| As manager | Championships with Durban City (x2), Sacramento (x2), Atlanta. GMVC & F.Lge 4 with Maidstone U. |
| As player | England: Youth (8). |

## FOOTBALL MANAGEMENT TEAM

| | |
|---|---|
| Assistant Manager | Clive Walker |
| Coach | Paul Hyde |
| Reserve Team Managers | |
| | Les Hall & Julian Holmes |
| Youth Team Managers | |
| | Steve Nolan, Jim Gleeson, John Spencer, Savas Pavlou, Tom Smyth |
| Physiotherapist | Frank Brooks |
| Club Doctor | Dr. S F Hodnett MBBCH BAO |

Liburd Henry, after a long and varied career retired at the end of last season.

Photo: Andrew Chitty

## MATCHDAY PROGRAMME

| | |
|---|---|
| Number of pages | 40 |
| Price | £1.50 |
| Programme Editor | Martin Burke 01797 230572 e mail: nicework@compuserve.com m.burke9857@aol.com |
| Local Newspapers: | Dover Express Dover Mercury |
| Local Radio Stations: | Radio Kent Invicta FM |

154

| Player | Birthplace Honours | D.O.B. | Previous Clubs |
|---|---|---|---|
| **GOALKEEPERS** | | | |
| Paul Hyde | Hayes | | Hayes, Hillingdon Borough, Wycombe Wanderers, Leicester City, Leyton Orient. |
| Charlie Mitten | Kent | | Thamesmead Town |
| | | | |
| **DEFENDERS** | | | |
| Lee Shearer | Rochford | 23.10.77 | Leyton Orient |
| Stuart Monday | Newham | 28.09.72 | Brighton & Hove Albion |
| Tony Browne | Sheppey | 28.09.72 | West Ham, Gravesend, Brighton & H.A. |
| Jake Leberl | Manchester | | Crewe Alexandra |
| Scott Daniels | Benfleet | 22.11.69 | Colchester United, Exeter city |
| David Clarke | Nottingham | | Notts Co., Eastwood T., Harrow Borough, £5k to Dover Athletic |
| Simon Beard | Bromley | | West ham, Sittingbourne, Hastings T. |
| | | | |
| **MIDFIELDERS** | | | |
| Anthony Hogg | Kent | | From Youth Team |
| James Virgo | Brighton | | Brighton & Hove A., Sutton United |
| Neil Le Bihan | Croydon | 14.03.76 | Tottenham Hotspur, Peterborough United |
| **Simon Wormull** | **Crawley** | | **Tottenham Hotspur, Brentford** |
| Paul Manning | | | Fisher Athletic |
| | | | |
| **FORWARDS** | | | |
| Simon Elliott | | | Gillingham, Tunbridge Wells |
| Matt Caruthers | Dover | | Ashford Town, Folkestone |
| Steve Norman | Romford | | Gillingham, St. Leonards |
| Roy Godden | Hythe | | From Youth Team |
| Mark Hynes | London | | Whyteleafe, Sutton United, Welling United |
| Joff Vansittart | Sussex | 12.09.74 | Brighton & H.A., Crawley Town, Sutton United, £10k to Dover Athletic |

Departures: John Budden (Brighton Hove A), Simon Elliott, Roy Godden (St Leonards), Ash Harrison (Canvey Island), Anthony Hogg (St Leonards), Lee Palmer (Folkestone Invicta), Ricky Reina (retired)

PLAYERS ON LOAN Steve Norman (St. Leonards), Steve Brown (Macclesfield), Keiron Adams (Barnet), Matt Brady (Barnet)

NON CONTRACT    Dominic Iorfa (Hong Kong)

Bold print indicates England semi-pro international

DEPARTURES    Lee Palmer (Folkestone), John Budden (Brighton), Ash Harrison (Canvey Island),

# DOVER ATHLETIC

**Founded:** 1983

**Nickname:** The 'Whites'

**Club colours:** White shirts
Black shorts, white socks

**Change colours:** Red shirts
red shorts, red socks

**Reserve team's league:** Kent League Div. 2

**Midweek home matchday:** Tuesday

**Club Sponsors:** Daihatsu (UK) Ltd

**Local Newspapers:** Dover Express
East Kent Mercury
**Local Radio:** Radio Kent
Invicta FM

## GROUND DETAILS

Crabble Athletic Ground
Lewisham Road
River, Dover,
Kent. CT17 0JB
**Telephone Number:** 01304 822373

**Simple Directions:**

**Capacity:** 6,500
**Seated:** 1,000
**Terracing -** **Covered:** 4,900
**Uncovered:** None

**SOCIAL FACILITIES:**
Social Club open 7 days a week. Meals available.
Steward: Gavin Hughes 01304 822306.

**CLUB SHOP:**
At the ground. Open matchdays for general souvenirs.
Also at Worthington Street in town, open daily.
Contact Jean Haves 01304 240041.

## PREVIOUS

**Leagues:** Kent League, Southern League

**Grounds:** None

**Names:** Dover FC

## CLUB RECORDS

**Attendance:** 4,035 v Bromsgrove Rovers
Southern League April 92

**Win:** 7-0 v Weymouth 03.04.1990

**Defeat:** 1-7 v Poole Town

**Career Goalscorer:** Lennie Lee 160

**Career Appearances:** Jason Bartlett 539

**Transfer Fees
Paid:** £50,000 for David Leworthy
(Farnborough Town) Aug. 93

**Received:** £50,000 for Ricky Reina
(Brentford) '97

## BEST SEASON

**FA Cup:** 1st Round 81-82
0-2 v Oxford Utd (H)

**FA Trophy:** Semi-Final 97-98

**FA Amateur Cup:** Did not compete

## HONOURS

Southern League     Premier Division 89-90, 92-93
Southern Division 87-88
Championship Match  1990, 1993
Premier Inter League Cup 90-91
Challenge Cup 91-92

Kent Senior Cup 90-91, R-up 93-94, 96-97

## Past Players who progressed to the Football League

Ricky Reina (Brentford) 1997

# FOREST GREEN ROVERS

The Forest Green fairy tale booked yet another chapter in the Conference next season. This season, basically wrote itself as well as making a new record - becoming the first side ever to reach Wembley in an F.A. Vase Final and an F.A. Trophy Final. Sadly they lost out to four times winner Geoff Chapple's managerial magic, but there was much more to their season than this.

## CLUB OFFICIALS 1999-2000

| | |
|---|---|
| President | **E G Smith** |
| Chairman | **Trevor Horsley** |
| Secretary | **David Honeybill** |

c/o The lawn, Nympsfield Road, Forest Green, Nailsworth, Glos. GL6 0ET
Tel: 01453 834860 Fax: 01453 835291

| | |
|---|---|
| Press Officer | **Heather Cook** |
| Tel: 01453 823281 | Mobile 07775 603287 |
| Managing Director | **Colin Peake** |

With Mark McGregor and Alex Sykes both on target fifteen times and clear victories against Kettering, Yeovil, Hayes and Kingstonian in the League, Frank Gregan made it look easy. August brought four losses and two draws, which placed them in the bottom two, but this did not discourage Frank Gregan's men, in fact, if anything it made them more determined to do well. Since then the results kept on coming and by the final game of the season, a win against Southport took them to twelfth position. In just 25 years this historic club has gone from the Gloucestershire County League to the Football Conference, fitting in two Wembley appearances on the way. They should have an even better season this year. T.T.

L - R    Back Row: Dave Tyrell (Physio), Alan McDougall (Scout), Mark Hallam, Chris Honor, Rob Cook, Justin Shufflewood, Martin Woodhouse, Don Forbes, Martin Boyle, Tim Banks (left), Tommy Callinan (Asst. Manager), Mike Kilgour (Coach). Front Row: Tom Jones, Paul Hunt, Grantley Dicks (left), Paul McLoughlin (left), Frank Gregan (Manager), Gary Smart (Captain), Alex Sykes, Matthew Coupe, Toby Jackson, Steve Winter.

# FOREST GREEN ROVERS
## MATCH FACTS 1998-99

| No | Date | Venue | Comp | Opponents | Att | Result | Score | Goalscorers |
|---|---|---|---|---|---|---|---|---|
| 1 | 15/08 | H | NC | Rushden & Diamonds | 1120 | L | 0-2 | |
| 2 | 18/08 | A | NC | Farnborough Town | 750 | D | 2-2 | Hunt 7, McGregor 83 |
| 3 | 22/08 | A | NC | Northwich Victoria | 866 | L | 0-1 | |
| 4 | 26/08 | H | NC | Cheltenham Town | 1909 | L | 1-2 | Smart 87 |
| 5 | 29/08 | H | NC | Stevenage Borough | 903 | L | 1-2 | Hunt 85 |
| 6 | 31/08 | A | NC | Woking | 2057 | D | 1-1 | Sykes 75 |
| 7 | 05/09 | A | NC | Doncaster Rovers | 3402 | W | 1-0 | Hunt 61 |
| 8 | 12/09 | H | NC | Kettering Town | 825 | W | 1-0 | Hunt 31 |
| 9 | 16/09 | H | NC | Hayes | 634 | L | 1-2 | Hallam 61 |
| 10 | 19/09 | A | NC | Telford United | 708 | L | 1-2 | Hunt 50 |
| 11 | 21/09 | A | NC | Kidderminster Harriers | 1716 | D | 2-2 | Hallam 60, Hunt 80 |
| 12 | 26/09 | H | NC | Welling United | 624 | W | 3-2 | Sykes 57, Cook 85, Hallam 90 |
| 13 | 03/10 | A | NC | Hednesford Town | 889 | D | 1-1 | Drysdale 50 |
| 14 | 10/10 | A | NC | Southport | 961 | D | 1-1 | Cook 48 |
| 15 | 07/11 | A | NC | Morecambe | 812 | L | 1-3 | Hedges 70 |
| 16 | 14/11 | H | NC | Northwich Victoria | 684 | W | 3-1 | Hunt 23[p], Cook 28 59 |
| 17 | 28/11 | A | NC | Kettering Town | 1405 | L | 1-2 | Sykes 11 |
| 18 | 05/12 | H | NC | Farnborough Town | 703 | D | 0-0 | |
| 19 | 12/12 | A | NC | Stevenage Borough | 1976 | D | 1-1 | Smart 81 |
| 20 | 19/12 | A | NC | Barrow | 1176 | L | 1-2 | McGregor 70 |
| 21 | 28/12 | H | NC | Hereford United | 1705 | W | 2-1 | Hedges 67, Hunt 69 |
| 22 | 09/01 | A | NC | Welling United | 743 | W | 2-0 | Kilgour 13, McGregor 56 |
| 23 | 23/01 | H | NC | Leek Town | 624 | W | 3-1 | Mehew 1 49, Parker 38[og] |
| 24 | 26/01 | A | NC | Yeovil Town | 2437 | W | 4-0 | Sykes 7, Mehew 64 77, McGregor 84 |
| 25 | 20/02 | H | NC | Doncaster Rovers | 1271 | D | 0-0 | |
| 26 | 06/03 | A | NC | Dover Athletic | 1017 | D | 1-1 | Sykes 90 |
| 27 | 09/03 | A | NC | Hayes | 597 | W | 3-0 | McGregor 24 47 50 |
| 28 | 13/03 | H | NC | Kidderminster Harriers | 1001 | W | 5-0 | Drysdale 45, Cook 49, Hedges 53, Sykes 68 76 |
| 29 | 17/03 | H | NC | Yeovil Town | 860 | L | 1-2 | Drysdale 18 |
| 30 | 20/03 | A | NC | Leek Town | 480 | W | 2-0 | McGregor 17 82 |
| 31 | 24/03 | H | NC | Kingstonian | 784 | W | 1-0 | Winter 24 |
| 32 | 31/03 | H | NC | Hednesford Town | 832 | W | 1-0 | Coupe 88 |
| 33 | 03/04 | H | NC | Telford United | 951 | D | 1-1 | Winter 80 |
| 34 | 05/04 | A | NC | Hereford United | 1735 | L | 0-4 | |
| 35 | 07/04 | H | NC | Woking | 465 | L | 0-2 | |
| 36 | 14/04 | H | NC | Barrow | 404 | D | 1-1 | Mehew 9 |
| 37 | 20/04 | A | NC | Cheltenham Town | 3058 | D | 1-1 | Coupe 80 |
| 38 | 22/04 | H | NC | Morecambe | 408 | D | 2-2 | McGregor 36 56 |
| 39 | 24/04 | H | NC | Kingstonian | 1008 | W | 1-0 | McGregor 5 |
| 40 | 26/04 | A | NC | Rushden & Diamonds | 1626 | L | 0-4 | |
| 41 | 28/04 | H | NC | Dover Athletic | 492 | L | 0-1 | |
| 42 | 01/05 | H | NC | Southport | 746 | W | 1-0 | Sykes 57 |

### CUP COMPETITIONS

| | Date | Venue | Comp | Opponents | Att | Result | Score | Goalscorers |
|---|---|---|---|---|---|---|---|---|
| | 09/08 | H | DML Shield | Margate | 375 | D | 1-1 | Kilgour 35    2 0 |
| | 07/10 | H | Endsleigh 1 | Kidderminster Harriers | 446 | L | 2-4 | Birkby 14, Drysdale 80 |
| | 14/10 | H | Glos SC QF | Bristol Rovers | n/k | W | 2-0 | Hunt 40 89 |
| | 17/10 | A | FA Cup Q3 | Rushden & Diamonds | 2376 | L | 0-2 | |
| | 21/11 | H | FA Trophy 2 | Boreham Wood | 432 | W | 4-1 | Birkby 11, Sykes 60, Hedges 61, Hunt 74 |
| | 17/01 | H | FA Trophy 3 | Witney Town | 806 | W | 4-0 | Sykes 8 14 25, Hunt 69 |
| | 06/02 | A | FA Trophy 4 | Weymouth | 1415 | W | 2-1 | McGregor 54 72 |
| | 16/02 | H | Glos SC SF | Gloucester City | 501 | L | 2-4 | Sykes 56 77 |
| | 27/02 | A | FA Trophy 5 | Hitchin Town | 963 | W | 2-1 | Mehew 4 5 |
| | 27/03 | H | FA Trophy QF | Southport | 1240 | W | 4-1 | Mehew 11, Sykes 27 46, McGregor 29 |
| | 10/04 | A | FA Trophy SF 1 | St Albans City | 2120 | D | 1-1 | Drysdale 1 |
| | 18/04 | H | FA Trophy SF 2 | St Albans City | 3002 | W | 3-2 | Sykes 45, Hedges 74, Smart 82 |
| | 15/05 | A | FA Trophy F | Kingstonian | 20037 | L | 0-1 | Wembley Stadium |

| 1 | 2 | 3 | 4 | 5 | 6 | 7 | 8 | 9 | 10 | 11 | 12 / 14 / 15 | # |
|---|---|---|---|---|---|---|---|---|---|---|---|---|
| uttlewood | Rollo | Forbes | Honor | Kilgour | Wigg | Winter | Smart | Hallam | Hunt | Sykes | | 1 |
| uttlewood | Rollo | Forbes | Honor | Kilgour | Wigg | Winter | Smart | Hallam | Hunt | Sykes | Cook, Jackson, McGregor | 2 |
| uttlewood | Rollo | Forbes | Honor | Kilgour | Wigg | Winter | Smart | Hallam | Hunt | Sykes | Cook, Jackson, McGregor | 3 |
| uttlewood | Callinan | Forbes | Honor | Coupe | Wigg | Winter | Smart | Hallam | Hunt | Sykes | Cook, Mogg, Hodgson | 4 |
| uttlewood | Rollo | Forbes | Honor | Coupe | Wigg | Winter | McGregor | Hodgson | Hunt | Sykes | Catley, Cook, Hedges | 5 |
| uttlewood | Hedges | Forbes | Coupe | Honor | Wigg | Winter | Smart | Hodgson | Hunt | Sykes | Coo, Rollo, McGregor | 6 |
| uttlewood | Hedges | Forbes | Coupe | Honor | Cook | Winter | Smart | Hodgson | Hunt | Sykes | Hallam, McGregor, Rollo | 7 |
| uttlewood | Hedges | Forbes | Coupe | Kilgour | Cook | Winter | Smart | Hallam | Hunt | Sykes | Wigg, Rollo, Hodgson | 8 |
| uttlewood | Hedges | Forbes | Coupe | Honor | Cook | Winter | Smart | Hallam | Hunt | Sykes | Rollo, McGregor, Wigg | 9 |
| uttlewood | Hedges | Forbes | Honor | Kilgour | Cook | Coupe | Smart | Hallam | Hunt | Sykes | Smith, McGregor, Wigg | 10 |
| uttlewood | Hedges | Forbes | Honor | Kilgour | Cook | Coupe | Smart | Hallam | Hunt | Sykes | Wigg, McGregor, Smith | 11 |
| uttlewood | Hedges | Forbes | Bailey | Honor | Wigg | Coupe | Drysdale | Hallam | Hunt | Sykes | Cook, Smith, McGregor | 12 |
| uttlewood | Hedges | Forbes | Bailey | Honor | Wigg | Cook | Drysdale | Hallam | Hunt | Sykes | Coupe, Smith, Birkby | 13 |
| uttlewood | Hedges | Forbes | Bailey | Honor | Wigg | Cook | Drysdale | Hallam | Hunt | Sykes | Smith, Birkby, Winter | 14 |
| uttlewood | Hedges | Forbes | Bailey | Honor | Drysdale | Cook | Smart | Birkby | Hunt | Sykes | Hallam, Wigg, Coupe | 15 |
| uttlewood | Hedges | Forbes | Bailey | Honor | Wigg | Cook | Drysdale | Birkby | Hunt | Sykes | Smart, Hallam, Coupe | 16 |
| uttlewood | Hedges | Smart | Bailey | Honor | Wigg | Cook | Drysdale | Birkby | Hunt | Sykes | Rollo, Hallam, McGregor | 17 |
| uttlewood | Hedges | Forbes | Bailey | Honor | Rollo | Cook | Drysdale | Birkby | Hunt | Sykes | Smith, McGregor, Smart | 18 |
| uttlewood | Hedges | Forbes | Bailey | Kilgour | Wigg | Cook | Drysdale | Hallam | Hunt | McGregor | Smart, Smith, Evans | 19 |
| uttlewood | Hedges | Sykes | Bailey | Kilgour | Wigg | Cook | Drysdale | Hallam | Hunt | McGregor | Smith, Birkby, Smart | 20 |
| uttlewood | Hedges | Forbes | Bailey | Kilgour | Honor | Cooke | Drysdale | McGregor | Hunt | Chapple | Sykes, Smart, Smith | 21 |
| uttlewood | Hedges | Forbes | Bailey | Kilgour | Honor | Cook | Drysdale | McGregor | Hunt | Chapple | Sykes, Smart, Mehew | 22 |
| uttlewood | Hedges | Forbes | Bailey | Kilgour | Honor | Cook | Drysdale | McGregor | Mehew | Sykes | Chapple, Smart, Coupe | 23 |
| uttlewood | Hedges | Forbes | Bailey | Kilgour | Honor | Cook | Drysdale | Chapple | Mehew | Sykes | Coupe, McGregor, Smart | 24 |
| uttlewood | Coupe | Forbes | Bailey | Kilgour | Cook | Chapple | Drysdale | McGregor | Mehew | Catley | Wigg, Smart, Rollo | 25 |
| uttlewood | Hedges | Forbes | Bailey | Kilgour | Wigg | Cook | Drysdale | Mehew | McGregor | Sykes | Smart, Chapple, Rollo | 26 |
| uttlewood | Hedges | Forbes | Bailey | Kilgour | Wigg | Cook | Drysdale | McGregor | Mehew | Sykes | Chapple, Smart, Rollo | 27 |
| uttlewood | Hedges | Chapple | Bailey | Kilgour | Wigg | Cook | Drysdale | Mehew | McGregor | Sykes | Coupe, Rollo, Smart | 28 |
| uttlewood | Hedges | Forbes | Bailey | Kilgour | Wigg | Cook | Drysdale | McGregor | Mehew | Sykes | Chapple, Rollo, Coupe | 29 |
| uttlewood | Hedges | Forbes | Bailey | Kilgour | Wigg | Cook | Drysdale | McGregor | Mehew | Sykes | Coupe, Chapple, Rollo | 30 |
| Perrin | Coupe | Forbes | Rollo | Honor | Chapple | Cook | Winter | Smith | Smart | Catley | Bailey, Drysdale, Sykes | 31 |
| uttlewood | Hedges | Forbes | Bailey | Winter | Wigg | Coupe | Drysdale | McGregor | Mehew | Sykes | Rollo, Chapple, Smart | 32 |
| uttlewood | Hedges | Forbes | Bailey | Winter | Honor | Coupe | Drysdale | McGregor | Mehew | Sykes | Chapple, Smart, Rollo | 33 |
| uttlewood | Hedges | Forbes | Bailey | Winter | Honor | Coupe | Drysdale | McGregor | Chapple | Sykes | Rollo, Smart, Wigg | 34 |
| Perrin | Rollo | Forbes | Coupe | Kilgour | Wigg | Smith | Catley | Birkby | Smart | Sykes | Winter, Bailey, Hedges | 35 |
| Westlake | Honor | Forbes | Bailey | Kilgour | Wigg | Cook | Drysdale | McGregor | Mehew | Sykes | Smart, Birkby, Coupe | 36 |
| Perrin | Hedges | Forbes | Honor | Kilgour | Wigg | Cook | Drysdale | McGregor | Mehew | Sykes | Winter, Coupe, Birkby | 37 |
| Perrin | Hedges | Forbes | Bailey | Kilgour | Honor | Cook | Drysdale | McGregor | Birkby | Smart | Winte, Sykes, Coupe | 38 |
| Perrin | Hedges | Forbes | Bailey | Kilgour | Chapple | Smith | Winter | Birkby | McGregor | Sykes | Coupe, Smart, Wigg | 39 |
| | Perrin | Coupe | Forbes | Bailey | Kilgour | Wigg | Cook | Drysdale | McGregor | Mehew | Sykes Birkby, Winter, Rollo | 40 |
| Perrin | Hedges | Forbes | Honor | Coupe | Wigg | Winter | Drysdale | Birkby | Mehew | Smart | Cook, Sykes, Catley | 41 |
| uttlewood | Hedges | Forbes | Bailey | Kilgour | Wigg | Honor | Drysdale | Winter | Mehew | Sykes | Coupe, Cook, Perrin | 42 |

League Attendances  **HIGHEST:** 1909  **LOWEST:** 404

**CONFERENCE:** 11th  **FA CUP:** 3rd Qualifying Round  **FA TROPHY:** Final

## MANAGER
### FRANK GREGAN

Date of Appointment                    01.01.94

Date of Birth:                         09.08.57
Place of Birth:                        Newcastle-upon-Tyne

PREVIOUS CLUBS
As manager                             None
As player                              None

HONOURS
As manager          Southern League -
                    Southern Div. Championship 96-97
                    Premier Div. Championship 97-98
                    FA Trophy Runners-up 98-99

## FOOTBALL MANAGEMENT TEAM
Assistant Manager:          Mike Kilgour
Coach:                      Chris Smith
Scout:                      Alan McDougall
Physio:                     Bob Baird
College Academy:            Chris Smith &
                            Jason Drysdale

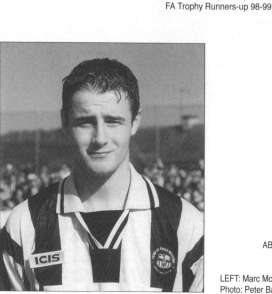

ABOVE: Record signing, Adrian Randall from Salisbury City.
Photo: Eric Marsh

LEFT: Marc McGregor
Photo: Peter Barnes

## MATCHDAY PROGRAMME

Number of pages                52
Price                          £1.50
Programme Editor               Julie Davis
                               Tel: 01453 834860
Other club publications:       None

Local Newspapers:              Stroud News & Journal
                               Gloucester Citizen

Local Radio Stations:          Severn Sound
                               BBC Radio Gloucestershire

# PLAYING SQUAD

**FOREST GREEN ROVERS**

| Player Honours | Birthplace | D.O.B. | Previous Clubs |
|---|---|---|---|
| **GOALKEEPERS** | | | |
| Justin Shuttlewood | Trowbridge | 08.02.71 | Westbury United |
| Steve Perrin | | | |
| Alastair Hines | | | Bristol Rovers (Free) |
| **DEFENDERS** | | | |
| Mike Kilgour | Dartford | 25.05.65 | Bath C., Larkhall Ath., Melksham T., Trowbridge T., Salisbury C., Stroud, Trowbridge T., Gloucester C., Dorchester T., Salisbury C. |
| Chris Honor<br>DMP | Bristol | 5.6.68 | Bristol C, Bath C, Slough T, Bath C, Newport AFC, Airdrie |
| Billy Clark | Christchurch | 19.05.67 | Bournemouth, Bristol Rovers , Bristol City |
| Wayne Hatswell | Swindon | 08.02.75 | Cinderford Town, Witney Town |
| Don Forbes<br>DMP | Bristol | 17.9.68 | Avon St.Phillips, Bath C |
| Ian Hedges | Bristol | 5.2.69 | Bristol Manor F, Gloucester C, AFC Bournemouth, Bath C |
| Jason Drysdale | Bristol | 17.11.70 | Watford, £425k to Newcastle utd., £340k to Swindon T., Northampton T. |
| Rob Cook<br>DMP | Forest Green | 28.3.70 | Shortwood U, Forest Green R, Cinderford T |
| Chris Smith | Christchurch | 28.03.66 | Cheltenham T, Bristol R, Gloucester C, Bath City, Newport AFC,Cinderford Town |
| **MIDFIELDERS** | | | |
| Steve Winter<br>DMP | Bristol | 26.10.73 | Yate T, Walsall, Yate T, Taunton T, Torquay U, Yeovil T, Salisbury C, Forest Green R, Dorchester T |
| Shaun Chapple<br>Wales: B, u21 | Swansea | 12.01.73 | Swansea C., Merthyr Tydfil |
| Adrian Randall | Bournemouth | 10.11.68 | Bournemouth,Aldershot, Burnley, Salisbury City |
| Chris Burns | Manchester | 9.1.67 | Gloucester C, Cheltenham T, Portsmouth, Swansea C,Northampton |
| Alex Sykes<br>British Univ, DMP | Newcastle-u-Lyme | 2.4.74 | Westfields, Mansfield T, Cheltenham T, Endsleigh |
| Andy Catley | Bath | 29.05.79 | Southampton |
| **FORWARDS** | | | |
| David Mehew | Camberley | 29.10.67 | Leeds Utd., Bristol R., Walsall, Yate T., Weston-s-Mare, Bath C., Farnborough T., Rushden & Diamonds. |
| Dennis Bailey | Lambeth | 13.11.65 | Barking, Fulham (NC),Farnborough T, Crystal Palace, Bristol R, Birmingham C, Bristol R, QP.R., Farnborough Town, Cheltenham |
| Marc McGregor | Southend | 30.04.78 | Oxford utd., Endsleigh |
| Adie Mings | | | Chippenham Town, Bath City, Gloucester City |
| Paul Hunt<br>DMP | Swindon | 8.10.70 | Swindon T, Charlton Ath., Cardiff C, Bristol R, Brann (Nor), Cirencester T |

DEPARTURES:Grantley Dicks (Newport), Toby Jackson (Newport), Tommy Callinan (Glos. City), Gary Smart (Newport), Danny Bailey, Martin Boyle (Paulton R.), Mark Hallam (Tamworth), Dean Birkby (released), Jim Rollo (Clevedon), Matthew Coupe (Gloucester C.), Nathan Wigg (Gloucester C.)

# FOREST GREEN ROVERS

**Founded:** 1890

**Nickname:** Rovers

**Sponsors:** Sheffield Insulations

**Club Colours:** Black & white striped shirts, black shorts, red socks.

**Change Colours:** All Yellow.

**Midweek matchday:** Wednesday

**Reserves' League:** College Academy

**Youth League:** Glos. CountyYouth Lge

## GROUND DETAILS

`The Lawn',
Nympsfield Road,
Forest Green,
Nailsworth,
Glos. GL6 0ET

**TELEPHONE NUMBERS:**
01453 834860
(Matchday & Club AdministrationCentre)
Fax: 01453 835291
Lawnside Fitness Suite: 01453 832268
Social Club: 01453 833295

**SIMPLE DIRECTIONS:**
About 4 miles south of Stroud on the A46 towards Bath. InNailsworth turn into Spring Hill from the mini roundabout and the ground is approx. half a mile up the hill on the left. The nearest BR station is Stroud

**CAPACITY:** 3,030
**COVERED TERRACING:** 1050
**SEATED:** 526

**SOCIAL FACILITIES:** Clubhouse open every evening. Bar and lounge. Open before and after Saturday matches.

**CLUB SHOP:** Open only on matchdays selling souvenirs and programmes. ContactAndy Whiting.

## Past Players who progressed to the Football League

G Rogers (Newport Co. 85)
K Gill (Newport Co. 85),
M England (Bristol Rov 85).

## PREVIOUS

**Leagues:** Stroud & Dist. 1890-1921,
Glos Northern Snr 22-67,
Glos Co. 67-73,
Hellenic 73-82,
Southern League 82-98,
Conference 98-.

**Name:** Stroud FC, 1989-92

**Ground:** None

## CLUB RECORDS

**Attendance:** 3,002
v St. Albans City, FA Umbro Trophy 18.04.99

**Win:** 8-0
v Fareham Town Southern Lge. Southern Div. 96-97

**Defeat:** 0-7
v Moor Green, Southern Lge. Midland Div. 85-86.

**Career Goalscorer:** Karl Bayliss

**Career Appearances:** Tommy Callinan

**Transfer Fee paid:** Adrian Randall from Salisbury City

**Transfer Fee Received:** Steve Book to Cheltenham Town

## BEST SEASON

**FA Cup:** Third Qual Round 87-88, 98-99

**FA Trophy:** Runners-up 98-99

**FA Vase:** Winners 81-82.

## HONOURS

FA Trophy R-up 98-99,
FA Vase 81-82,
Southern League - Premier Div . 97-98,
Southern Div . 96-97;
Hellenic Lg 81-82,
Gloucs Nthn Sen Lg 37-38 49-50 50-51,
Gloucs Sen Cup 84-85 85-86 86-87,
Gloucs Sen Amat Cup (N) 26-27 45-46 71-72 75-76 77-78,
Gloucs Sen Prof Cup 84-85 85-86 86-87.

# HAYES

In a season that many thought would be another tough battle, Hayes proved everybody wrong.

They finished in their highest ever League position of third, with exactly the same number of wins as champions Cheltenham and broke their highest League attendance of last season by 900.

## CLUB OFFICIALS 1999-2000

President — **Les Lovering**

Chairman — **Derek Goodall**

Vice Chairman — **Trevor Griffith**

Financial Director — **Roger Harrison**

Directors — **C Porter, E Stevens,**

**C Mackintosh, A Bond, D Goodall.**

Football Secretary — **John Bond** Jnr.

Press Officer — **Trevor Griffith**

c/o the club  Tel: 0181 573 2075

Congratulations must also go to Lee Charles for his inclusion in the England team and for netting a cool 20 goals in the Conference.

Any team going to Hayes found it difficult to pick up points as their emphatic wins over Rushden, Kingstonian, Cheltenham and Doncaster Rovers proved.

The Missioners made it through the qualifying rounds in the F.A. Cup, but reached a halt in the First Round Proper when they met Third Division Mansfield Town. A 74th minute goal from Flynn gave hope to the red and whites, but they soon found that this was not enough. A strong challenge will be mounted by Hayes next season and we may yet see them playing League football.

T.T.

Hayes F.C. 1999-2000 - Back Row: Lee Charles, Dean Coppard, Nathan Bunce, Neil Trebble, Jason Goodliffe, Ben Hodson, Alvin Watts, Ryan Spencer. Front: Steve McKimm, Mark Boyce, Nick Roddis, Lee Flynn, Paul Gothard, Christian Metcalfe, Seb Proctor, Aaron Patton, Barry Moore.

# HAYES
## MATCH FACTS 1998-99

| No | Date | Venue | Comp | Opponents | Att | Result | Score | Goalscorers |
|----|------|-------|------|-----------|-----|--------|-------|-------------|
| 1 | 15/08 | H | NC | Northwich Victoria | 685 | W | 1-0 | Domingos 69 |
| 2 | 17/08 | A | NC | Stevenage Borough | 3203 | L | 1-2 | Buglione 37 |
| 3 | 22/08 | A | NC | Cheltenham Town | 1879 | D | 3-3 | Norton 25[og], Sparks 45, Charles 57 |
| 4 | 25/08 | H | NC | Yeovil Town | 692 | D | 1-1 | Randall 61 |
| 5 | 29/08 | H | NC | Morecambe | 422 | L | 1-2 | Hall 49 |
| 6 | 31/08 | A | NC | Rushden & Diamonds | 3208 | L | 0-5 | |
| 7 | 05/09 | A | NC | Hereford United | 2053 | W | 1-0 | Catlin 88 |
| 8 | 12/09 | H | NC | Doncaster Rovers | 733 | W | 2-0 | Randall 6, Hall 69 |
| 9 | 16/09 | A | NC | Forest Green Rovers | 634 | W | 2-1 | Randall 78, Watts 90 |
| 10 | 19/09 | H | NC | Kidderminster Harriers | 553 | W | 2-1 | Randall 72, Charles 74 |
| 11 | 26/09 | A | NC | Southport | 1203 | W | 2-1 | Randall 6, Charles 60 |
| 12 | 03/10 | H | NC | Leek Town | 603 | W | 2-0 | Hodson 43, Wilkinson 48 |
| 13 | 10/10 | A | NC | Telford United | 716 | L | 0-2 | |
| 14 | 24/10 | H | NC | Barrow | 578 | W | 1-0 | Flynn 56 |
| 15 | 07/11 | A | NC | Kettering Town | 1563 | L | 0-1 | |
| 16 | 28/11 | A | NC | Woking | 1997 | L | 0-2 | |
| 17 | 05/12 | H | NC | Kettering Town | 603 | L | 0-2 | |
| 18 | 12/12 | H | NC | Hereford United | 569 | L | 1-2 | Sparks 76 |
| 19 | 19/12 | A | NC | Morecambe | 1016 | W | 3-2 | Watts 40 58, Hall 54 |
| 20 | 28/12 | H | NC | Welling United | 724 | L | 1-2 | Flynn 88 |
| 21 | 02/01 | H | NC | Farnborough Town | 703 | W | 1-0 | Moore 90 |
| 22 | 09/01 | A | NC | Kingstonian | 1129 | D | 1-1 | Charles 83 |
| 23 | 23/01 | H | NC | Telford United | 615 | W | 4-3 | Hodson 8, Charles 31 59, Randall 45 |
| 24 | 26/01 | H | NC | DOVER ATHLETIC | 580 | L | 1-2 | Charles 28 |
| 25 | 30/01 | A | NC | Kidderminster Harriers | 1534 | W | 1-0 | Bunce 3 |
| 26 | 06/02 | A | NC | Farnborough Town | 789 | W | 5-1 | Charles 5 67 81, Hodson 11, Bunce 44 |
| 27 | 13/02 | A | NC | Barrow | 1518 | W | 1-0 | Norman 45 |
| 28 | 20/02 | H | NC | Woking | 1103 | D | 2-2 | Charles 29, Randall 33 |
| 29 | 23/02 | H | NC | Stevenage Borough | 665 | D | 2-2 | Hodson 7, Smith 72[og] |
| 30 | 27/02 | A | NC | Dover Athletic | 1035 | D | 0-0 | |
| 31 | 06/03 | H | NC | Rushden & Diamonds | 1302 | W | 2-1 | Sparks 47, Bunce 53 |
| 32 | 09/03 | H | NC | Forest Green Rovers | 597 | L | 0-3 | |
| 33 | 13/03 | A | NC | Doncaster Rovers | 3149 | W | 1-0 | Randall 72 |
| 34 | 20/03 | H | NC | Southport | 677 | W | 3-0 | Charles 54 90, Catlin 63 |
| 35 | | Townsend | | | | | | |
| 36 | 27/03 | A | NC | Yeovil Town | 2560 | D | 1-1 | Hodson 90 |
| 37 | 03/04 | H | NC | Kingstonian | 929 | W | 3-0 | Charles 7 77, Randall 72 |
| 38 | 05/04 | A | NC | Welling United | 663 | W | 2-0 | Charles 4, Randall 20 |
| 39 | 10/04 | A | NC | Leek Town | 465 | W | 4-1 | Flynn 35 36, Moore 83, Hodson 87 |
| 40 | 13/04 | H | NC | Hednesford Town | 570 | W | 1-0 | Charles 5 |
| 41 | 17/04 | A | NC | Northwich Victoria | 1150 | L | 1-2 | Key 9[og] |
| 42 | 24/04 | H | NC | Cheltenham Town | 2105 | W | 3-2 | Wilkinson 27, Metcalfe 74, Hodson 90 |
| | 01/05 | A | NC | Hednesford Town | 860 | D | 0-0 | |

### CUP COMPETITIONS

| | | | | | | | | |
|---|---|---|---|---|---|---|---|---|
| | 29/09 | A | Endsleigh 1 | Kettering Town | 651 | W | 3-0 | Hodson 41, Ridgeway 82[og], Hodson 85 |
| | 17/10 | H | FA Cup Q3 | Bromley | 629 | W | 1-0 | Hodson 85 |
| | 09/11 | A | FA Cup Q4 | Havant & Waterlooville | 956 | D | 2-2 | Flynn 10, Randall 83 |
| | 11/11 | A | FA Cup Q4 rep | Havant & Waterlooville | 623 | W | 1-1 | Randall 14 (4-3 on pens) |
| | 14/11 | A | FA Cup 1 | Mansfield Town | 2613 | L | 1-2 | Flynn 74 |
| | 21/11 | H | FA Trophy 2 | Folkestone Invicta | 504 | D | 1-1 | Charles 73 |
| | 24/11 | A | FA Trophy 2 rep | Folkestone Invicta | 461 | L | 2-3 | |
| | 01/12 | H | Endsleigh 2 | Welling United | 272 | W | 3-2 | Charles 14, Moore 70 79 |
| | 05/01 | H | Middx SC 2 | Enfield | 251 | W | 4-0 | |
| | 09/02 | A | Endsleigh QF | Cheltenham Town | 462 | L | 1-2 | Norman 63 |
| | 18/02 | H | Middx SC QF | Wealdstone | n/k | L | 1-2 | No5 60 |

| 1 | 2 | 3 | 4 | 5 | 6 | 7 | 8 | 9 | 10 | 11 | 12 / 14 / 15 | |
|---|---|---|---|---|---|---|---|---|---|---|---|---|
| Meara | Delisser | Flynn | Sparks | Watts | Goodliffe | Hall | Roddis | Charles | Buglione | Wilkinson | Randall, Domingos, Lyons | 1 |
| Meara | Delisser | Hill | Sparks | Bunce | Goodliffe | Domingos | Roddis | Charles | Buglione | Wilkinson | Watts, Randall, Hall | 2 |
| Meara | Bunce | Flynn | Sparks | Watts | Goodliffe | Roddis | Hall | Charles | Buglione | Wilkinson | Domingos, Randall, Delisser | 3 |
| Meara | Delisser | Flynn | Sparks | Bunce | Goodliffe | Moore | Randall | Charles | Buglione | Wilkinson | Catlin, Domingos, Hall | 4 |
| Meara | Delisser | Flynn | Sparks | Bunce | Goodliffe | Moore | Hall | Charles | Randall | Wilkinson | Watts, Roddis, Buglione | 5 |
| Meara | Delisser | Flynn | Sparks | Bunce | Goodliffe | Moore | Hall | Watts | Randall | Wilkinson | Charles, Buglione, Catlin | 6 |
| Meara | Watts | Flynn | Sparks | Bunce | Goodliffe | Metcalf | Hall | Buglione | Randall | Roddis | Moore, Charles, Catlin | 7 |
| Meara | Moore | Flynn | Sparks | Bunce | Goodliffe | Metcalf | Charles | Buglione | Randall | Wilkinson | Roddis, Watts, Hall | 8 |
| Meara | Watts | Flynn | Sparks | Bunce | Goodliffe | Metcalf | Roddis | Charles | Randall | Wilkinson | Buglione, Hall, Moore | 9 |
| Meara | Moore | Flynn | Sparks | Bunce | Goodliffe | Metcalf | Charles | Hall | Randall | Wilkinson | Buglione, Watts, Catlin | 10 |
| Meara | Watts | Flynn | Sparks | Bunce | Goodliffe | Metcalfe | Charles | Hall | Randall | Wilkinson | Hodson, Roddis, Buglione | 11 |
| Meare | Hodson | Flynn | Watts | Bunce | Goodliffe | Metcalfe | Charles | Hall | Randall | Wilkinson | Roddis, Buglione, Davis | 12 |
| Meara | Delisser | Flynn | Watts | Bunce | Goodliffe | Metcalfe | Charles | Hall | Hodson | Wilkinson | Randall, Moore, Buglione | 13 |
| Meara | Delisser | Flynn | Watts | Bunce | Goodliffe | Metcalfe | Charles | Hall | Hodson | Wilkinson | Roddis, Boothe, Domingos | 14 |
| Meara | Delisser | Flynn | Watts | Bunce | Boothe | Metcalfe | Charles | Hall | Hodson | Wilkinson | Buglione, Catlin, Roddis | 15 |
| Meara | Catlin | Flynn | Watts | Sparks | Goodliffe | Moore | Hall | Charles | Hodson | Wilkinson | Randall, Boothe, Roddis | 16 |
| Meara | Boothe | Flynn | Watts | Goodliffe | Sparks | Moore | Hodson | Charles | Randall | Wilkinson | Hall, Roddis, Buglione | 17 |
| Meara | Boothe | Flynn | Watts | Goodliffe | Sparks | Moore | Hall | Roddis | Randall | Wilkinson | Hodson, Buglione, Charles | 18 |
| Meara | Norman | Flynn | Watts | Roddis | Sparks | Moore | Charles | Hall | Randall | Wilkinson | Hodson, Domingos, oothe | 19 |
| Meara | Norman | Flynn | Watts | Roddis | Boothe | Moore | Charles | Hall | Randall | Wilkinson | Hodson, Taylor, Domingos | 20 |
| Meara | Norman | Flynn | Watts | Roddis | Sparks | Moore | Charles | Hall | Randall | Wilkinson | Domingos, Hodson, Boothe | 21 |
| Meara | Metcalfe | Flynn | Watts | Sparks | Goodliffe | Moore | Charles | Roddis | Randall | Wilkinson | Hall, Norman, Boothe | 22 |
| Meara | Metcalfe | Flynn | Watts | Goodliffe | Sparks | Moore | Charles | Hodson | Randall | Wilkinson | Norman, Taylor, Boothe | 23 |
| Meara | Metcalfe | Flynn | Watts | Goodliffe | Sparks | Roddis | Charles | Hodson | Randall | Wilkinson | Moore, Bunce, Norman | 24 |
| Meara | Roddis | Flynn | Goodliffe | Bunce | Sparks | Metcalfe | Charles | Hodson | Randall | Wilkinson | Watts, Taylor, Boothe | 25 |
| Meara | Watts | Flynn | Roddis | Bunce | Sparks | Taylor | Charles | Hodson | Randall | Wilkinson | Goodliffe, Delisser, Boothe | 26 |
| Meara | Norman | Flynn | Goodliffe | Bunce | Sparks | Watts | Charles | Taylor | Randall | Wilkinson | Boothe, Delisser, Ballard | 27 |
| Meara | Watts | Flynn | Goodliffe | Bunce | Sparks | Asselman | Charles | Hodgson | Randall | Wilkinson | Paul, Norman, Boothe | 28 |
| Meara | Norman | Flynn | Goodliffe | Bunce | Asselman | Watts | Charles | Hodson | Randall | Wilkinson | Moore, Coates, Boothe | 29 |
| Meara | Watts | Flynn | Goodliffe | Bunce | Sparks | Asselman | Clarke | Hodson | Coates | Delisser | Randall, Moore, Spencer | 30 |
| Meara | Flynn | Watts | Goodliffe | Bunce | Sparks | Asselman | Charles | Roddis | Randall | Wilkinson | Moore, Norman, Catlin | 31 |
| Meara | Watts | Flynn | Goodliffe | Bunce | Sparks | Asselman | Charles | Hodson | Catlin | Wilkinson | Norman, Moore, Delisser | 32 |
| Hodson | Norman | Flynn | Goodliffe | Watts | Sparks | Moore | Charles | Hodson | Randall | Wilkinson | Asselman, Spencer, Catlin | 33 |
| Meara | Norman | Flynn | Goodliffe | Bunce | Watts | Moore | Charles | Catlin | Randall | Wilkinson | Spencer, B Hodson, | 34 |
| | | | | | | | | | | | | 35 |
| Meara | Norman | Flynn | Watts | Bunce | Sparks | Roddis | Charles | Catlin | Randall | Spencer | B Hodson, Delisser, Metcalfe | 36 |
| Meara | Spencer | Flynn | Watts | Bunce | Sparks | Roddis | Charles | Catlin | Randall | Wilkinson | B Hodson, Norman, Metcalfe | 37 |
| Meara | Watts | Flynn | Goodliffe | Bunce | Sparks | Roddis | Charles | Hodson | Randall | Wilkinson | Metcalfe, Norman, Spencer | 38 |
| Hodson | Metcalfe | Flynn | Goodliffe | Bunce | Sparks | Roddis | Charles | Hodson | Randall | Wilkinson | Norman, Spencer, Moore | 39 |
| Hodson | Watts | Flynn | Goodliffe | Bunce | Sparks | Moore | Charles | Hodson | Randall | Wilkinson | Roddis, Metcalfe, Norman | 40 |
| Hodson | Watts | Flynn | Goodliffe | Bunce | Sparks | Moore | Charles | Spencer | Randall | Wilkinson | Hodson, Metcalfe, Norman | 41 |
| Hodson | Watts | Flynn | Goodliffe | Bunce | Sparks | Roddis | Charles | Hodson | Spencer | Wilkinson | Delisser, Norman, Metcalfe | 42 |
| Hodson | Spencer | Flynn | Watts | Bunce | Sparks | Roddis | Charles | Hodson | Randall | Wilkinson | Metcalfe, Delisser, Norman | |

40[p], Flynn 45

League Attendances     **HIGHEST:** 2105     **LOWEST:** 422

**CONFERENCE:** 10th     **FA CUP:** 1st Round     **FA TROPHY:** 2nd Round

## MANAGER
### TERRY BROWN

| | |
|---|---|
| Date of Appointment | November 1993 |
| Date of Birth | 5th August 1952 |
| Place of Birth | Hillingdon |

PREVIOUS CLUBS
| | |
|---|---|
| As manager | None |
| As coach | Wokingham Town |
| As player | Hayes, Slough Town, Hayes, Wokingham Town |

HONOURS
| | |
|---|---|
| as manager | Isthmian League Cha,mpionship 95-96 |
| As player | None |

## FOOTBALL MANAGEMENT TEAM

| | |
|---|---|
| Assistant Manager | Willy Wordsworth |
| Coach | Dave Killick |
| Physio | Karl Ballard |

LEFT:
Terry Brown

### 1998-99

**Top Scorer:** Lee Charles

**Player of the Year:** Lee Charles

**Captain:** Nathan Bunce

RIGHT:
Lee Flynn

Photo:
Clive Butchins

## MATCHDAY PROGRAMME

| | |
|---|---|
| Number of Pages | 32 |
| Price | £1.50 |
| Programme editor | Robert Frape 0181 848 8848 |
| Other club publications | None |
| Local Newspapers | Hayes Gazette |
| Local Radio stations | Capital Radio Star FM |

# PLAYING SQUAD

| Player<br>Honours | Birthplace | D.O.B. | Previous Clubs |
|---|---|---|---|
| **GOALKEEPERS** | | | |
| Paul Gothard | | 24.06.74 | Dagenham & Redbridge, Grays Athletic, Chelmsford City, ColchesterUnited. |
| Matt Hodson | | 20.09.79 | Youth Team |
| **DEFENDERS** | | | |
| Chris Sparks<br>ILC | London | 28.12.73 | Brentford, Chertsey T £5k to Hayes |
| Jason Goodliffe<br>ILP | Hillingdon | 07.03.74 | Brentford |
| Nathan Bunce | Hillingdon | 02.05.75 | Brentford, Yeading, £2,000 to Hayes |
| Iain Duncan | Oxford | 31.07.72 | Leicester C, Thatcham T, Basingstoke T, Wealdstone, Windsor & Eton, Wokingham T |
| Tony Witter | | 12.08.65 | Welling United,Q.P.R., Millwall,Scunthorpe United |
| Mark Boyce | | 11.08.80 | Watford |
| **MIDFIELDERS** | | | |
| Nick Roddis | Rotherham | 18.02.73 | Nottingham F, Boston FC, Boston U, Yeading |
| Christian Metcalfe | London | 14.12.74 | Chelsea, Harrow Borough £4,000 to Hayes |
| Steve McKimm | | 30.07.75 | Hendon,Molesey, Dulwich Haml;et, Farnborough T,£4,000 to Hayes. |
| Aaron Patton | London | 20.02.79 | Wycombe Wanderers |
| Lee Flynn | | 04.09.73 | Romford, Boreham Wood, Hendon |
| Barry Moore | | 04,02,77 | Hampton |
| Ryan Spencer | | 03.01.79 | Tottenham Hotspur, Ruislip Manor |
| **FORWARDS** | | | |
| **Lee Charles** | **Hillingdon** | **20.08.71** | Chertsey Town, Q.P.R.(£67,500) Barnet (L) |
| Ben Hodson | | 15.01.76 | Wycombe Wanderers, Forest Green Rovers |
| Neil Trebble | Hitchin | 16.02.69 | Scarborough, P.N.E.,Scunthorpe United, Stevenage Borough Welling United |
| Alvin Watts | | 17.06.79 | Yeading |

Bold Print indicates Enlish Semi-Professional Internationals

Departures: Neil Catlin (Chesham United), Andre Delisser Boreham Wood), Perry Norman, Martin Randall (StAlbans City),Darron Wilkinson (Woking)

# HAYES

| | | |
|---|---|---|
| **Founded:** | 1909 | |

**Nickname:** The Missioners

**Club Sponsors:** Taylor Woodrow

**Club colours:** Red & white shirts
black shorts, black socks

**Change colours:** Blue shirts
blue shorts, blue socks

**Reserve team's league:** Suburban Premier

**Midweek home matchday:** Tuesday

**Local Newspapers:** Hayes Gazette

**Local Radio:** Capital Radio

## GROUND DETAILS

Townfield House
Church Road
Hayes
Middx. UB3 2LE

**Telephone Number:** 0181 573 2075

**Simple Directions:** M25, M4, A312 (Hayes By-Pass),
A4020 (Uxbridge Road) and Church Rd. is on the left.
**Capacity:** 6,500
**Seated:** 450
**Terracing -** **Covered:** 2,000
**Uncovered:** 4,050

**SOCIAL FACILITIES:**
Clubhouse open Sat 12 - 3, 4.45 - 11pm.
Sun 12 - 3pm, 7 - 11pm. Midweek 6.30 - 11pm.
Some cold snacks are available.
**CLUB SHOP:**
Wide range of programmes & souvenirs.
Contact Lee Hermitage, c/o the club.

## Past Players who progressed to the Football League

Cyril Bacon (Orient 46), Phil Nolan (Watford 47),
Dave Groombridge (Orient 51),
Jimmy Bloomfield (Brentford 52),
Derek Neale & Les Champleover(Brighton 56 & 57),
Gordon Phillips (Brentford 63), Robin Friday (Reading 74),
Les Smith (A Villa), Cyrille Regis (WBA 1977),
Les Ferdinand (QPR 87),Derek Payne (Barnet 88),
Paul Hyde (Wycombe 91), Dean Hooper (Swindon95),
Jason Roberts (Wolverhampton W. 97)

## PREVIOUS

**Leagues:** Local leagues 1909-14;
Gt. Western Suburban 19-22;
London 22-24;
Spartan 24-30;
Athenian 30-71;
Isthmian 71-96.

**Names:** None

**Ground:** Botwell Common

## CLUB RECORDS

**Attendance:** 15,370 v Bromley
FA Amateur Cup, 10.2.51

**Win:** Unknown
**Defeat:** Unknown
**Career Goalscorer:** Unknown

**Career Appearances:** Reg Leather 701

**Transfer Fees**
**Paid:** £6,000 for
Gary Keen (Hendon) 1990
Joe Francis (Enfield) 1996

**Received:** £30,000 for Les Ferdinand
(Q.P.R.) 1987

## BEST SEASON

**FA Cup:** 2nd Round (replay)
0-1 v Reading (H) after 0-0
also 2nd Round 90-91 & 92-93
League clubs defeated:
Fulham, Bristol Rov., Cardiff C.

**FA Trophy:** Quarter Final
78-79, 1-2 v Runcorn (A)
97-98, 0-1 v Cheltenham Town (A)

**FA Amateur Cup:** Runners Up 1930-31

## HONOURS

Isthmian League 95-96
Athenian League 56-57
Spartan League 27-28
Great Western Suburban League 1920-24 (4 times)
Middlesex Senior Cup 19-20, 20-21, 25-26,
30-31, 35-36, 39-40, 49-50, 81-82, 95-96
London Senior Cup 31-32, 80-81
Middlesex Charity Cup - 15 Times
London Charity Cup 60-61

# HEDNESFORD TOWN

John Baldwin's side proved once again that they are a rock in the Conference. A few `slip ups', sacrificed a place in the top seven or eight and because of the inconsistent results and some dour displays less supporters have been going to see the Pitmen, with their highest attendance decreasing by a further 700 since last season.

## CLUB OFFICIALS 1999-2000

| | |
|---|---|
| Joint Owners | John Baldwin & |
| | Steve Price |
| President | Nigel Tinsley |
| Chairman | Mike Smith |
| General Manager | David Degg |
| Football Secretary | Richard Munning |
| Club Secretary | Sue Thomas |
| Commercial Manager | Terry Brumpton |
| Press Officer | Neil Holden |

Hednesford, known for their excellent runs in the F.A. Cup became giant killers once again this year. After overcoming Congleton Town and Morecambe in the qualifying rounds they were faced with Third Division Barnet. After pushing them aside 3-1, the Pitmen looked towards Cardiff City for another result, but their First Round score was reversed and that was it for another year.

Ged Kimmins, turned out to be top scorer with twelve, although many thought the ex-international would grab more. Overall, a solid season and with a few more summer signings like John Norman, Morecambe's top scorer on 23 last season, Hednesford should be pushing for a place within the top five.

T.T.

Hednesford Town 1999-2000 - Back Row: Scott Goodwin, Dominic Reece, Stuart King, Iain Brunskill, Gary Twynham, Paul Szewcyzk, Nick Amos, Jake Sedgemore, Noel Malcolm, Ross Rhodes. Second Row: Don Drakeley (physio), Stuart Evans, Adie Mike, Russell Bradley, Chris Brindley, Phil Morgan, Paul Hayward (player coach), Stuart Lake, Andy Comyn, Sean O'Connor, Peter Windsor (kit manager). Third Row: Ian Robinson, John Norman, Lee Colkin, James Kelly, John Baldwin (manager), Steve Devine (asst. Manager), Neil Davis, Ged Kimmins, Colin Hunter, Stewart Airdrie. Front Row: Tom Griffiths & Tony Fierro

# HEDNESFORD TOWN
## MATCH FACTS 1998-99

| No | Date | Venue | Comp | Opponents | Att | Result | Score | Goalscorers |
|----|------|-------|------|-----------|-----|--------|-------|-------------|
| 1 | 15/08 | H | NC | Woking | 1292 | W | 2-1 | Fitzpatrick 60, Ware 70 |
| 2 | 18/08 | A | NC | Cheltenham Town | 2168 | D | 0-0 | |
| 3 | 22/08 | A | NC | Yeovil Town | 2008 | W | 2-1 | Fitzpatrick 11, Brindley 45 |
| 4 | 24/08 | H | NC | Hereford United | 1736 | W | 3-1 | Hayward 44 74, Ware 77 |
| 5 | 29/08 | H | NC | Farnborough Town | 1100 | D | 0-0 | |
| 6 | 31/08 | A | NC | Morecambe | 1256 | L | 1-3 | Beeston 33 |
| 7 | 05/09 | A | NC | Welling United | 507 | D | 1-1 | Davis 86 |
| 8 | 07/09 | H | NC | Northwich Victoria | 1127 | W | 1-0 | O'Connor 90 |
| 9 | 12/09 | H | NC | Dover Athletic | 1026 | L | 1-2 | Ware 64 |
| 10 | 19/09 | A | NC | Stevenage Borough | 2329 | L | 1-3 | Brindley 58 |
| 11 | 26/09 | A | NC | Kingstonian | 1293 | D | 1-1 | O'Connor 37 |
| 12 | 03/10 | H | NC | Forest Green Rovers | 889 | D | 1-1 | Davis 31 |
| 13 | 10/10 | A | NC | Leek Town | 701 | W | 3-1 | Kimmins 60 88, Comyn 71 |
| 14 | 24/10 | H | NC | Kidderminster Harriers | 934 | W | 2-1 | Davis 34[p], Kimmins 90 |
| 15 | 07/11 | H | NC | Rushden & Diamonds | 1387 | D | 1-1 | Davis 57 |
| 16 | 28/11 | A | NC | Barrow | 1232 | W | 2-0 | Sedgemore 35[p], Kimmins 80 |
| 17 | 07/12 | H | NC | Telford United | 887 | D | 1-1 | Hayward 51 |
| 18 | 12/12 | A | NC | Northwich Victoria | 1002 | D | 1-1 | Ware 35 |
| 19 | 19/12 | H | NC | Welling United | 806 | W | 3-2 | Bradley 43, Bignall 44, Ware 70 |
| 20 | 26/12 | A | NC | Kettering Town | 2631 | L | 0-1 | |
| 21 | 28/12 | H | NC | Doncaster Rovers | 1542 | D | 1-1 | Comyn 77 |
| 22 | 02/01 | H | NC | Kettering Town | 1608 | L | 0-2 | |
| 23 | 09/01 | A | NC | Hereford United | 1610 | D | 0-0 | |
| 24 | 23/01 | H | NC | Southport | 1015 | W | 3-1 | Kimmins 7, Sedgemore 27[p], O'Connor 31 |
| 25 | 02/02 | A | NC | Telford United | 954 | D | 1-1 | Davis 86 |
| 26 | 06/02 | H | NC | Morecambe | 834 | W | 1-0 | Davis 1 |
| 27 | 13/02 | A | NC | Dover Athletic | 1126 | D | 0-0 | |
| 28 | 20/02 | A | NC | Rushden & Diamonds | 3123 | L | 0-1 | |
| 29 | 27/02 | H | NC | Leek Town | 943 | D | 1-1 | Kimmins 78 |
| 30 | 06/03 | A | NC | Kidderminster Harriers | 1725 | W | 2-1 | Lake 49 76 |
| 31 | 20/03 | H | NC | Yeovil Town | 908 | L | 2-3 | Mike 57, Davies 85 |
| 32 | 22/03 | H | NC | Cheltenham Town | 1651 | W | 3-2 | Mike 7 45, Davis 47 |
| 33 | 27/03 | A | NC | Woking | 1453 | L | 1-2 | Szewczyk 88 |
| 34 | 31/03 | A | NC | Forest Green Rovers | 832 | L | 0-1 | |
| 35 | 03/04 | A | NC | Southport | 1144 | D | 1-1 | Kimmins 84 |
| 36 | 05/04 | A | NC | Doncaster Rovers | 3595 | W | 1-0 | Kimmins 32 |
| 37 | 10/04 | H | NC | Barrow | 794 | W | 1-0 | Brindley 61 |
| 38 | 13/04 | A | NC | Hayes | 570 | L | 0-1 | |
| 39 | 19/04 | H | NC | Stevenage Borough | 861 | D | 2-2 | Carty 39, O'Connor 73 |
| 40 | 24/04 | A | NC | Farnborough Town | 541 | W | 1-0 | Kelly 12[p] |
| 41 | 27/04 | H | NC | Kingstonian | 652 | L | 1-2 | Szewczyk 75 |
| 42 | 01/05 | H | NC | Hayes | 860 | D | 0-0 | |

### CUP COMPETITIONS

| | Date | Venue | Comp | Opponents | Att | Result | Score | Goalscorers |
|--|------|-------|------|-----------|-----|--------|-------|-------------|
| | 17/10 | A | FA Cup Q3 | Congleton Town | 480 | D | 1-1 | Kimmins 22 |
| | 19/10 | H | FA Cup Q3 r | Congleton Town | 501 | W | 1-0 | Davis 15[p] |
| | 31/10 | A | FA Cup Q4 | Morecambe | n/k | W | 2-1 | Davis 50 75[p] |
| | 14/11 | H | FA Cup 1 | Barnet | 1463 | W | 3-1 | Davis 71, Kimmins 79, Carty 90 |
| | 21/11 | A | FA Trophy 2 | Bromsgrove Rovers | 721 | W | 2-1 | Kimmins 29 61 |
| | 30/11 | H | Endsleigh 2 | Northwich Victoria | 0 | L | 1-3 | Simpson 25[og] |
| | 01/12 | H | Birm. SC 2 | Evesham United | 42 | W | 2-1 | Reece 60, Kelly 69 |
| | 05/12 | A | FA Cup 2 | Cardiff City | 5638 | L | 1-3 | Carty 87 |
| | 25/01 | A | FA Trophy 3 | Colwyn Bay | 407 | D | 1-1 | Carty 89 |
| | 27/01 | H | FA Trophy 3 r | Colwyn Bay | 391 | D | 2-2 | Sedgemore 39[p], Ware 117    (4-5 pens) |
| | 03/02 | A | Birm. SC 3 | Bolehall Swifts | n/k | W | 2-0 | |
| | 15/02 | H | Birm. SC QF | Nuneaton Borough | 716 | W | 2-0 | Kimmins 16, Davis 50 |
| | 08/04 | H | Birm. SC SF | Wolverhampton Wndrs | 2000 | L | 0-5 | |

| 1 | 2 | 3 | 4 | 5 | 6 | 7 | 8 | 9 | 10 | 11 | 12 / 14 / 15 | |
|---|---|---|---|---|---|---|---|---|---|---|---|---|
| Cooksey | Carty | Colkin | Blades | Brindley | Bradley | Beeston | Ware | Hayward | Fitzpatrick | Kimmins | Kelly, Comyn, Francis | 1 |
| Cooksey | Carty | Colkin | Blades | Brindley | Bradley | Beeston | Ware | Hayward | Fitzpatrick | Kimmins | Kelly, Comyn, Francis | 2 |
| Cooksey | Carty | Colkin | Blades | Brindley | Bradley | Beeston | Ware | Hayward | Fitzpatrick | Kimmins | Francis, Comyn, Kelly | 3 |
| Cooksey | Carty | Colkin | Blades | Brindley | Bradley | Beeston | Ware | Hayward | Fitzpatrick | Kimmins | Francis, Kelly, Comyn | 4 |
| Cooksey | Carty | Colkin | Blades | Brindley | Bradley | Beeston | Ware | Hayward | Fitzpatrick | Kimmins | Kelly, Francis, Comyn | 5 |
| Cooksey | Carty | Colkin | Comyn | Brindley | Bradley | Beeston | Kelly | Hayward | Fitzpatrick | Ware | Francis, Lake, Dennison | 6 |
| Cooksey | Carty | Colkin | Comyn | Brindley | Bradley | Kelly | Beeston | Hayward | Ware | Davis | Jackson,Fitzpatrick,Sedgemore | 7 |
| Cooksey | Carty | Colkin | Comyn | Brindley | Bradley | Kelly | Beeston | Hayward | Ware | Davis | O'Connor, Sedgemore, Fitzpatrick | 8 |
| Cooksey | Carty | Colkin | Comyn | Brindley | Bradley | Beeston | Ware | Hayward | Fitzpatrick | O'Connor | Dennison, Sedgemore, Kelly | 9 |
| Cooksey | Fitzpatrick | Colkin | Bradley | Brindley | Carty | Beeston | Ware | Dennison | Davis | O'Connor | Kimmins, Comyn, Kelly | 10 |
| Cooksey | Fitzpatrick | Colkin | Bradley | Brindley | Carty | Beeston | Ware | Dennison | Davis | O'Connor | Kimmins, Jackson, Kelly | 11 |
| Cooksey | Fitzpatrick | Bradley | Jackson | Brindley | Kimmins | Ware | Beeston | Davis | Dennison | O'Connor | Sedgemore, Kelly, Comyn | 12 |
| Cooksey | Sedgemore | Colkin | Comyn | Brindley | Bradley | Ware | Beeston | Davis | Fitzpatrick | Kimmins | Kelly, O'Connor, Jackson | 13 |
| Morgan | Sedgemore | Carty | Comyn | Brindley | Bradley | Beeston | Ware | Davis | Fitzpatrick | Kimmins | O'Connor, Kelly, Jackson | 14 |
| Morgan | Sedgemore | Carty | Comyn | Brindley | Bradley | Ware | Beeston | Davis | Lake | Kimmins | Kelly, O'Connor, Fitzpatrick | 15 |
| Morgan | Sedgemore | Colkin | Comyn | Brindley | Bradley | Ware | Beeston | Hayward | Carty | Kimmins | Kelly, Fitzpatrick, Lake | 16 |
| Morgan | Sedgemore | Colkin | Comyn | Brindley | Bradley | Blades | Lake | Hayward | Fitzpatrick | Carty | Kelly, Reece, Broadhurst | 17 |
| Morgan | Sedgemore | Colkin | Comyn | Brindley | Bradley | Blades | Lake | Bignall | Ware | Hayward | Fitzpatrick, Kelly, Bruce | 18 |
| Morgan | Sedgemore | Colkin | Comyn | Brindley | Bradley | Ware | Lake | Bignall | Hayward | Carty | Fitzpatrick, Kelly, Blades | 19 |
| Morgan | Sedgemore | Colkin | Comyn | Brindley | Bradley | Fitzpatrick | Lake | Davis | Hayward | Kelly | Kimmins, Bignall, Beeston | 20 |
| Morgan | Sedgemore | Colkin | Comyn | Brindley | Bradley | Ware | Fitzpatrick | Davis | Kelly | Kimmins | Hayward, Bignall, Blades | 21 |
| Morgan | Fitzpatrick | Colkin | Comyn | Brindley | Bradley | Ware | Kelly | Davies | Carty | Kimmins | Lake, Hayward, Bignall | 22 |
| Morgan | Sedgemore | Reece | Comyn | Brindley | Bradley | Blades | Fitzpatrick | Hayward | Ware | Carty | Jackson, O'Connor, Devine | 23 |
| Morgan | Sedgemore | Reece | Comyn | Brindley | Blades | Ware | Lake | O'Connor | Kelly | Kimmins | Szewczyk, Amos, Broadhurst | 24 |
| Morgan | Sedgemore | Reece | Comyn | Blades | Bradley | Beeston | Ware | O'Connor | Kelly | Amos | Davis, Lake, Broadhurst | 25 |
| Morgan | Sedgemore | Colkin | Comyn | Lake | Bradley | Beeston | Ware | Davis | O'Connor | Kelly | Amos, Broadhurst, Reece | 26 |
| Morgan | Sedgemore | Colkin | Comyn | Brindley | Bradley | Beeston | Kelly | Davis | Ware | Kimmins | Lake, O'Connor, Amos | 27 |
| Morgan | Carty | Colkin | Comyn | Brindley | Lake | Beeston | Ware | Davis | Kelly | Kimmins | O'Connor, Szewczyk, Reece | 28 |
| Morgan | Sedgemore | Colkin | Comyn | Blades | Lake | Ware | Kelly | Davis | Mike | Kimmins | Beeston, Carty, Szewczyk | 29 |
| Morgan | Sedgemore | Reece | Comyn | Brindley | Lake | Ware | Kelly | Davis | Mike | Kimmins | Blades, Beeston, Carty | 30 |
| Morgan | Sedgemore | Colkin | Comyn | Brindley | Lake | Ware | Kelly | Davis | Mike | Kimmins | Szewczyk, Twynham, Reece | 31 |
| Morgan | Ware | Colkin | Comyn | Brindley | Lake | Twynham | Kelly | Davis | Mike | Kimmins | Sedgemore, Reece, Amos | 32 |
| Morgan | Ware | Colkin | Comyn | Brindley | Lake | Kelly | Sedgemore | Davis | Mike | Kimmins | Reece, Szewczyk, Broadhurst | 33 |
| Morgan | Sedgemore | Reece | Comyn | Brindley | Lake | Ware | Beeston | Davis | Mike | Colkin | Bradley, Amos, Szewczyk | 34 |
| Morgan | Ware | Reece | Comyn | Brindley | Bradley | Beeston | Kimmins | Davis | Colkin | Mike | Szewczyk, O'Connor, Amos | 35 |
| Morgan | Kimmins | Colkin | Comyn | Brindley | Bradley | Ware | Beeston | Davis | Lake | Mike | Reece, Sedgemore, Szewczyk | 36 |
| Morgan | Sedgemore | Reece | Bradley | Brindley | Ware | Kelly | Kimmins | Mike | O'Connor | Szewczyk | Amos, Comyn, Devine | 37 |
| Morgan | Sedgemore | Colkin | Comyn | Brindley | Lake | Kelly | Twynham | Mike | Reece | Kimmins | Carty, O'Connor, Szewczyk | 38 |
| Morgan | Sedgemore | Colkin | Bradley | Brindley | Carty | Twynham | Kimmins | Mike | Kelly | Szewczyk | Amos, O'Connor, Devine | 39 |
| Morgan | Lake | Colkin | Comyn | Brindley | Kimmins | Kelly | Twynham | Mike | Reece | Szewczyk | Ware, Sedgemore, O'Connor | 40 |
| Morgan | Sedgemore | Reece | Comyn | Brindley | Lake | Ware | Kelly | Mike | O'Connor | Szewczyk | Amos, Broadhurst, Devine | 41 |
| Morgan | Sedgemore | Devine | Comyn | Brindley | O'Connor | Kelly | Amos | Szewczyk | Kimmins | Reece | King, Griffiths, Broadhurst | 42 |

League Attendances  
CONFERENCE: 10th

HIGHEST: 1735  
FA CUP: 2nd Round

LOWEST: 652  
FA TROPHY: 3rd Round

## MANAGER
### JOHN BALDWIN

Date of Appointment          January 1990
Date of Birth:          05.05.54
Place of Birth:          London

PREVIOUS CLUBS
As manager          Electricity, Harrisons.
As coach
As player          Walsall, Darlaston & Hednesford Town

HONOURS
As manager          Southern League Prem Div. 94-95
As player          England: Youth.
         British Universities

## FOOTBALL MANAGEMENT TEAM

| | |
|---|---|
| First Team Coach | Steve Devine |
| Club Physiothapist | Don Drakeley |
| 2nd Team Manager | TBA |
| Chief Scout | Steve Griffiths |
| Youth Team Co-ordinator | James Thomas |

### 1998-99

**Top Scorer:**          Ged Kimmins (13)

**Player of the Year:**          Phil Morgan
(Supporters', Players' & Travel Club)
**Club Captain:**          Paul Ware

John Baldwin          Photos: Peter Barnes          Paul Carty

## MATCHDAY PROGRAMME

Number of pages          48

Price          £1.50

Programme Editor          Terry Brumpton

Other club publications:          None

Local Newspapers:          Express & Star; Sporting Star;
Chase Post; Cannock Mercury;
Birmingham Evening Mail; Sports Argus; The Chronicle

Local Radio Stations:          Radio WM; BRMB:
WABC; Beacon: Signal;
BBC Radio Stoke

# PLAYING SQUAD

| Player | Birthplace Honours | Signed From | Previous Clubs |
|--------|--------------------|-------------|----------------|
| **GOALKEEPERS** | | | |
| Phil Morgan | | Macclesfield | Ipswich T., Stoke C., Macclesfield T. |
| Paul Hayward | | Stafford | Stafford Rangers |
| | | | |
| **DEFENDERS** | | | |
| **Andy Comyn** | **Wakefield** | **W.B.A.** | **Alvechurch, Aston Villa, £200,000 to Derby Co, Plymouth A, W.B.A.** |
| Chris Brindley | Stoke | Kidderminster | Hednesford T, Wolves, Telford U, £20k to Kidderminster H |
| GMVC, FAT, FA XI | | | |
| Russell Bradley | Birmingham | Hartlepool | Dudley T, Nottingham Forest, Hereford U, Halifax T, Scunthorpe U, Hartlepool U |
| Neil Broadhurst | | | Birmingham City |
| Lee Colkin | Nuneaton | Northampton | Northampton T, Leyton Orient (L) |
| Paul Carty | Birmingham | 22.10.66 | Everton, Nuneaton B, Bromsgrove R, Tamworth |
| SLP | | | |
| Dominic Reece | | Aston Villa | Aston Villa |
| Stuart Evans | | Hererford | Halesowen Town,Hereford United |
| Jake Sedgemore | Birmingham | W.B.A. | W.B.A. |
| | | | |
| **MIDFIELDERS** | | | |
| James Kelly | Liverpool | Wolves | Wrexham, Wolves, Walsall (L), Wrexham (L) |
| Stuart Lake | Stone | Walsall | Walsall |
| SLP | | | |
| Gary Twynham | | Bangor City | Manchester United,Grantham, Bangor City |
| Nick Amos | | Bromsgrove | Rainham Town, Hornchurch, Rushall Olympic, Bromsgrove Rovers |
| Iain Brunskill, | | Leek Town | Liverpool.Leek Town |
| England Schools | | | |
| Scott Goodwin | | Crantham | Coventry City, Grantham Town |
| Ian Robinson | | Ilkeston | Ilkeston Town |
| | | | |
| **FORWARDS** | | | |
| Stewart Airdrie | | Guiseley | Guiseley(£2,000) |
| John Norman | | Morecambe | Tranmere Rovers, Bury, Heswall, Mold, Morecambe |
| **Ged Kimmins** | **Manchester** | **Hyde United** | **Salford C, Flixton, Hyde U** |
| Neil Davis | | Wycombe | Redditch United, Aston Villa, Wycombe Wanderers |
| Paul Szewczyk | | | Youth |
| Sean O'Connor | | | Youth |
| Adie Mike | | Leek Town | Manchester City,Stockport County, Bury, Hartlepool United, |
| England Schools & U19 | | | Doncaster Rovers, Leek Town |
| Colin Hunter | | Guiseley | Harrogate Railway Athletic, Guiseley |

DEPARTURES
Scott Cooksey (Shrewsbury T.), Wayne Simpson (Nuneaton B.), Paul Blades (Gresley R.), Kevin Collins (Hereford U.), Gary Fitzpatrick (Telford U.), Carl Beeston (Stafford R.), Paul Ware (Macclesfield T.), John Jeffers (released), Robbie Dennison (Hereford U.), Joe O'Connor (Nuneaton B.), Tony Eccleston (Stafford R.), Clive Stanbrook.Paul Carty (Worcester City)

Bold print indicates England semi-profesional internationals.

# HEDNESFORD TOWN

**Founded:** 1880

**Nickname:** The Pitmen

**Club Sponsors:** Extra Personnel

**Club colours:** White shirts & black & red trim, black shorts, white trim

**Change colours:** Darkand sky blue quarters, sky blue shorts & socks

**Midweek home matchday:** Monday

**Reserve team league:** Central Conference, and Midland Combination (Reserve Div.).

## GROUND DETAILS

Keys Park,
Hednesford,
Cannock,
Staffordshire

**COMMUNICATION**
Tel: 01543 422870
Fax: 01543 428180
Hotline: 0930 555880

**SIMPLE DIRECTIONS:** M6 J11 to Cannock, through traffic lights to island , 3rd exit, next island, 2nd exit onto Lichfield Rd. Next island 1st exit, next island straight on, next island 3rd exit, continue to mini-island. Keys Park is straight on (signposted from 2nd island.)

**CAPACITY:** 6,000
**SEATED:** 1,000
**COVERED TERRACING:** 1,000

**CLUB SHOP:** Open throughout the week

**SOCIAL FACILITIES:** Strikers Bar
Open matchdays and every evening 7-11 except Sunday
No food available. Chase Suite hold functions

## Past Players who progressed to the Football League

(Post War)
Brian Horton (Port Vale 1970)
Vernon Allatt (Halifax Town 1979)
Chris Brindley (Wolverhampton W. 1986)
Scott Cooksey (Shrewsbury Town 1998)
Dave Hanson (Leyton Orient)
Paul Ware (Macclesfield Town)
Keith Russell (Blackpool 1997)

## PREVIOUS

**Leagues:** Walsall & District; Birmingham Combination 08-15, 45-53; West Midlands 19-39, 53-72, 74-84; Midland Counties 72-74; Southern League 84-95; Conference 95-.

**Grounds:** The Tins (behind Anglesey Hotel) until 1904, Cross Keys until 1995.

**Names:** None

## CLUB RECORDS

**Attendance:** 10,000 v Walsall F.A.Cup 1919-20

**Win:** 12-1 v Birmingham City, Birmingham Wartime League cup 40-41
12-1 v Redditch United, Birmingham Cambination 52-53

**Defeat:** 0-15 v Burton, Birmingham Combination 52-53

**Career goalscorer:** Tosh Griffiths
Joe O'Connor (post-war)
**Career appearances:** Kevin Foster

**Transfer fee paid:** £12,000
for Steve Burr (Macclesfield Town 1991)
**Transfer fee received:** £50,000
for Dave Hanson (Leyton Orient)

## BEST SEASON

**FA Cup:** 1996-97, 4th Round
2-3 v Middlesbrough (A)
**League clubs defeated:** Blackpool, York City, Hull City and Barnet

**FA Trophy:** 1997-98, 3rd Round
1-2 v Grantham Town (A)

## HONOURS

Welsh Cup R-up 91-92:
Southern League     Prem. Div. 94-95;
Midland Div. R-up 91-92,
Lge. Cup R-up 86-87;
West Midlands. Lge 77-78, R-up 83-84; Lge. Cup 83-84;
Birmingham Combination 09-10 50-51, R-up 12-13 52-53;
Staffs Senior Cup 69-70, 73-74; R-up 92-93;
Birmingham Senior Cup 35-36; R-up 93-94.

174

# HEREFORD UNITED

Last season their supporters and players all had dreams of returning to League football, but now that seems a far off cry. Finishing sixth last year and salvaging some pride from the cup visit of Brighton all brought back hopes and memories to the fans at Edgar Street.

## CLUB OFFICIALS 1999-2000

Chairman/Director of Football

**Graham Turner**

Company Secretary     **Joan Fennessy**

Directors     **Tristram Richmond-Sterry**
**Sam Lodh**
**George Hyde**
**Ron Jukes**

Club Secretary     **Joan Fennessy**

c/o the club
Tel: 01432 276666     Fax: 01432 341359

Now, a respectable thirteenth place and some very good victories against some very good teams, but still 25 points away from the champions, there is a lot of work to be done. But nothing passes Graham Turner.

Sadly no cup runs to speak of last season, which is a change from last year's triumphant wins against Brighton and Colchester and that fabulous tie against Tranmere.

Already, Turner has made some very good summer signings and there is a strong feeling that The Bulls will be challenging to regain their old league status very soon.

Watch out for a few vital goals from Steve Pearce.

T.T.

Hereford United 1999-2000 - Back Row: Fewings, May, Elmes, Quy, Wall, Lane, Parry.
Middle Row: Hanson, Snape, James, Clarke, Pearce, Williams, Taylor. Front Row: Rodgerson, Ford, Turner, Thompson, Wright.

# HEREFORD UNITED
## MATCH FACTS 1998-99

| No | Date | Venue | Comp | Opponents | Att | Result | Score | Goalscorers |
|----|------|-------|------|-----------|-----|--------|-------|-------------|
| 1 | 15/08 | A | NC | Kingstonian | 2104 | L | 0-2 | |
| 2 | 18/08 | H | NC | Leek Town | 2140 | W | 1-0 | Wright 29 |
| 3 | 22/08 | H | NC | Dover Athletic | 2139 | W | 2-0 | G Williams 30 90 |
| 4 | 24/08 | A | NC | Hednesford Town | 1736 | L | 1-3 | Taylor 23[p] |
| 5 | 29/08 | A | NC | Welling United | 727 | D | 2-2 | Leadbeater 78, Druce 80 |
| 6 | 31/08 | H | NC | Southport | 2308 | D | 2-2 | Mahon 44, Leadbeater 79 |
| 7 | 05/09 | H | NC | Hayes | 2053 | L | 0-1 | |
| 8 | 12/09 | A | NC | Barrow | 1775 | W | 1-0 | Cook 22 |
| 9 | 15/09 | A | NC | Telford United | 1086 | W | 1-0 | Wright 29 |
| 10 | 19/09 | H | NC | Morecambe | 2049 | W | 2-0 | Fewings 78, Walker 85 |
| 11 | 26/09 | A | NC | Rushden & Diamonds | 3521 | D | 1-1 | Mahon 31 |
| 12 | 29/09 | H | NC | Northwich Victoria | 1910 | D | 2-2 | Mahon 14[p], Fewings 30 |
| 13 | 03/10 | H | NC | Yeovil Town | 2410 | L | 0-1 | |
| 14 | 10/10 | A | NC | Stevenage Borough | 2832 | W | 3-0 | Walker 7 16, Leadbeater 79 |
| 15 | 31/10 | A | NC | Kettering Town | 1386 | D | 1-1 | Wright 50 |
| 16 | 07/11 | A | NC | Leek Town | 667 | L | 2-3 | Druce 22, Leadbeater 90 |
| 17 | 14/11 | H | NC | Farnborough Town | 1788 | W | 2-0 | Leadbeater 55[p], Dyer 89 |
| 18 | 28/11 | H | NC | Doncaster Rovers | 2115 | W | 1-0 | Leadbeater 80[p] |
| 19 | 05/12 | A | NC | Northwich Victoria | 1068 | L | 0-1 | |
| 20 | 12/12 | A | NC | Hayes | 569 | W | 2-1 | Downing 65, Williams 88 |
| 21 | 19/12 | H | NC | Kettering Town | 2181 | L | 0-2 | |
| 22 | 26/12 | A | NC | Kidderminster Harriers | 3188 | L | 0-1 | |
| 23 | 28/12 | A | NC | Forest Green Rovers | 1705 | L | 1-2 | Snape 55 |
| 24 | 02/01 | H | NC | Kidderminster Harriers | 2658 | L | 1-3 | Dennison 15 |
| 25 | 09/01 | H | NC | Hednesford Town | 1610 | D | 0-0 | |
| 26 | 23/01 | A | NC | Dover Athletic | 1001 | L | 1-3 | Druce 5 |
| 27 | 30/01 | H | NC | Stevenage Borough | 1629 | L | 0-1 | |
| 28 | 13/02 | A | NC | Farnborough Town | 795 | W | 4-0 | Wright 3, Dennison 34, James 55, Parry 59 |
| 29 | 16/02 | A | NC | Southport | 872 | D | 0-0 | |
| 30 | 20/02 | H | NC | Cheltenham Town | 3480 | L | 0-2 | |
| 31 | 27/02 | A | NC | Doncaster Rovers | 3568 | L | 1-3 | Cowe 65 |
| 32 | 06/03 | H | NC | Telford United | 1592 | D | 0-0 | |
| 33 | 09/03 | A | NC | Cheltenham Town | 3341 | D | 2-2 | Roberts 40 90 |
| 34 | 13/03 | A | NC | Yeovil Town | 2263 | L | 0-3 | |
| 35 | 20/03 | H | NC | Barrow | 1521 | W | 3-0 | Parry 46, Cook 76, Roberts 87 |
| 36 | 23/03 | H | NC | Woking | 1320 | L | 0-1 | |
| 37 | 03/04 | A | NC | Morecambe | 1012 | L | 0-1 | |
| 38 | 05/04 | H | NC | Forest Green Rovers | 1735 | W | 4-0 | Williams 53, Cook 56, Evans 84, Wright 90 |
| 39 | 08/04 | H | NC | Kingstonian | 1288 | W | 2-0 | Williams 22, Rodgerson 45 |
| 40 | 17/04 | H | NC | Welling United | 1532 | D | 0-0 | |
| 41 | 24/04 | H | NC | Rushden & Diamonds | 2044 | W | 3-2 | Wright 60, Cowe 65, Williams 81 |
| 42 | 01/05 | A | NC | Woking | 2541 | W | 1-0 | Wright 14 |

### CUP COMPETITIONS

| | Date | Venue | Comp | Opponents | Att | Result | Score | Goalscorers |
|----|------|-------|------|-----------|-----|--------|-------|-------------|
| | 14/12 | A | Endsleigh 2 | Kidderminster Harriers | 645 | W | 2-1 | Parry 61, Druce 90 |
| | 23/02 | H | Endsleigh QF | Morecambe | 0 | L | 2-3 | Cowe 17, Cook 35 |
| | 17/10 | H | FA Cup Q3 | Newport IoW | 1841 | L | 2-3 | James 7, Williams 80 |
| | 21/11 | H | FA Trophy 2 | Hitchin Town | 1382 | D | 1-1 | Wright 62 |
| | 30/11 | A | FA Trophy 2 rep | Hitchin Town | 447 | L | 1-2 | |

| 1 | 2 | 3 | 4 | 5 | 6 | 7 | 8 | 9 | 10 | 11 | 12 / 14 / 15 | |
|---|---|---|---|---|---|---|---|---|---|---|---|---|
| Quy | Lane | Walker | Mahon | Wright | Evans | Rodgerson | Taylor | Leadbeater | Snape | Fewings | Cook, Williams, Downing | 1 |
| Quy | Lane | Walker | Mahon | Wright | Evans | Rodgerson | Snape | Leadbeater | G Williams | Fewings | Downing, Cook, Cross | 2 |
| Quy | Lane | Walker | Mahon | Wright | M Taylor | Rodgerson | Snape | Leadbeater | G Williams | Cook | Downing, Fewings, Cross | 3 |
| Quy | Lane | Walker | Mahon | James | M Taylor | Rodgerson | Snape | Leadbeater | G Williams | Cook | Fewings, Cross, Downing | 4 |
| Quy | Lane | James | Mahon | Wright | Taylor | Rodgerson | Snape | Leadbeater | Williams | Cook | Downing, Fewings, Druce | 5 |
| Quy | Lane | Downing | Mahon | Wright | James | Williams | Taylor | Leadbeater | Druce | Fewings | Cook, Snape, Cross | 6 |
| Quy | Lane | Boden | Mahon | Wright | Walker | Williams | Taylor | Leadbeater | Druce | Fewings | Cook, James, Downing | 7 |
| Quy | Rodgerson | Boden | Mahon | Wright | Walker | Williams | Taylor | Leadbeater | Cook | Snape | Druce, Fewings, James | 8 |
| Quy | Rodgerson | Boden | Mahon | Wright | Walker | Williams | Taylor | Druce | Cook | Snape | Fewings, James, Lane | 9 |
| Quy | Rodgerson | Boden | Mahon | Wright | Walker | Williams | Taylor | Druce | Lane | Snape | Evans, Fewings, James | 10 |
| Quy | Rodgerson | James | Mahon | Wright | Walker | Williams | Taylor | Fewings | Lane | Snape | Leadbeater, Evans, Cross | 11 |
| Quy | Rodgerson | James | Mahon | Wright | Walker | Williams | Taylor | Fewings | Lane | Snape | Leadbeater, Evans, Cross | 12 |
| Quy | Lane | James | Mahon | Wright | Walker | Williams | Taylor | Leadbeater | Lane | Snape | Druce, Evans, Cross | 13 |
| Quy | Rodgerson | James | Mahon | Wright | Walker | Williams | Taylor | Leadbeater | Lane | Snape | Druce, Evans, Cook | 14 |
| Jones | Lane | James | Mahon | Wright | Evans | G Williams | Taylor | Leadbeater | Rodgerson | Snape | Druce, Cook, Cross | 15 |
| Jones | Lane | James | Mahon | Wright | Evans | Williams | Taylor | Druce | Rodgerson | Cook | Parry, Leadbeater, Cross | 16 |
| Jones | Lane | James | Downing | Wright | Evans | G Williams | Taylor | Druce | Rodgerson | Leadbeater | Dyer, Cook, Cross | 17 |
| Jones | Lane | James | Downing | Wright | Evans | Dyer | Taylor | Leadbeater | Rodgerson | Druce | G Williams, Cook, Cross | 18 |
| Quy | Clarke | Collins | Downing | Wright | Evans | Druce | Taylor | Leadbeater | Rodgerson | Dennison | Cook, Lane, Snape | 19 |
| Quy | Clarke | Collins | Downing | Lane | Cross | Druce | Taylor | Leadbeater | Rodgerson | Snape | Williams, Jones, Parry | 20 |
| Quy | Clarke | Collins | Snape | Wright | Evans | Downing | Taylor | Druce | Williams | Parry | Dyer, Cross, Leadbeater | 21 |
| Quy | Lane | Parry | Downing | Wright | James | Rodgerson | Taylor | G Williams | Druce | Dennison | Cross, Dyer, Shirley | 22 |
| Quy | Lane | Cross | Snape | Wright | James | Williams | Taylor | Leadbeater | Rodgerson | Dennison | Parry, Druce, Shirley | 23 |
| Quy | Lane | Collins | Snape | Clarke | James | Williams | Taylor | Druce | Rodgerson | Dennison | Dyer, Parry, Cross | 24 |
| Quy | Lane | Collins | Clarke | Wright | James | Martin | Taylor | Druce | Rodgerson | Dennison | Parry, Snape, G Williams | 25 |
| Quy | Lane | Collins | Parry | James | Clarke | Druce | Taylor | Leadbeater | Rodgerson | Dennison | Williams, Cook, Evans | 26 |
| Quy | Lane | Parry | Evans | Wright | James | Williams | Downing | Leadbeater | Rodgerson | Dyer | Cook, Shirley, Dennison | 27 |
| Quy | Lane | Parry | Evans | Wright | James | Downing | Taylor | Leadbeater | Cowe | Dennison | Williams, Cook, Shirley | 28 |
| Quy | Lane | Parry | Evans | Wright | James | Downing | Taylor | Leadbeater | Cowe | Dennison | Cook, Shirley, Williams | 29 |
| Quy | Lane | Parry | Evans | Wright | James | Downing | Taylor | Leadbeater | Cowe | Dennison | Williams, Cook, Shirley | 30 |
| Quy | Lane | Parry | Evans | Wright | James | Rodgerson | Taylor | Roberts | Cowe | Dennison | Cross, Williams, Cook | 31 |
| Quy | Lane | James | Evans | Wright | Cook | Williams | Taylor | Roberts | Cowe | Parry | Cross, Rodgerson, Shirley | 32 |
| Quy | Lane | James | Evans | Wright | Cook | Williams | Taylor | Roberts | Dennison | Parry | Cross, Rodgerson, Shirley | 33 |
| Quy | Rodgerson | Cross | Dennison | James | Cook | Williams | Taylor | Roberts | Cowe | Parry | Dyer, Jones, Shirley | 34 |
| Quy | Lane | James | Evans | Wright | Cook | Williams | Taylor | Roberts | Cowe | Parry | Rodgerson, Cross, Snape | 35 |
| Quy | Lane | James | Evans | Wright | Cook | Williams | Taylor | Roberts | Cowe | Parry | Rodgerson, Snape, Cross | 36 |
| Quy | Lane | James | Evans | Wright | Snape | Warner | Taylor | Roberts | Cowe | Parry | Rodgerson, Dennison, Cross | 37 |
| Quy | Lane | Rodgerson | Evans | Wright | Snape | Williams | Taylor | Cook | Dennison | Parry | Cowe, Roberts, Dyer | 38 |
| Quy | Lane | Rodgerson | Evans | Wright | Snape | Williams | Taylor | Cook | Dennison | Parry | Cowe, Roberts, Cross | 39 |
| Quy | Lane | Rodgerson | Evans | Wright | Snape | Williams | Taylor | Cook | Dennison | Parry | Cowe, Cross, Jones | 40 |
| Quy | James | Rodgerson | Evans | Wright | Snape | G Williams | Taylor | Cowe | Dennison | Parry | Cross, Jones, Dyer | 41 |
| Quy | James | Rodgerson | Evans | Wright | Snape | Lane | Taylor | Cowe | Dennison | Parry | Cross, Jones, Dyer | 42 |

Wright

League Attendances     **HIGHEST:** 3480     **LOWEST:** 1288

**CONFERENCE:** 13th     **FA CUP:** 3rd Qualifying Round     **FA TROPHY:** 2nd Round

# MANAGER
## GRAHAM TURNER

Date of Appointment
Date of Birth:
Place of Birth:

August 1995
5th October 1947
Ellesmere Port

PREVIOUS CLUBS
As manager

Shrewsbury T., Aston Villa,
Wolverhampton W.

As coach

None

As player

Wrexham, Chester City, Shrewsbury T.

HONOURS
As manager

League: Div.3 78-79 (Shrewsbury),
Div.4 87-88, Div.3 88-89; S.V.T. 87-88 (Wolves)

As player

England - Youth cap.

# FOOTBALL MANAGEMENT TEAM

**Chief Scout:** Ron Jukes

**Physio:** Simon Thompson

## 1998-99

**Top Scorer:**          Ian Wright

**Captain:**          Ian Wright

Grahm Turner

Andy Quy          Photo: Garry Letts

# MATCHDAY PROGRAMME

Number of pages          32

Price          £1.50

Programme Editor          Gary Watts

Other club publications:          None

Local Newspapers:          Hereford Journal
Hereford Times
Evening News

Local Radio Stations:          BBC Hereford & Worcester

# PLAYING SQUAD

| Player | Birthplace Honours | Signed From | Previous Clubs |
|--------|--------------------|-------------|----------------|

**GOALKEEPERS**

| Andy Quy | Harlow | Stevenage | Tottenham H, Derby Co, Grimsby T, Stevenage, Kettering T(L) |
| Mark Jones | | Telford | Telford United |

**DEFENDERS**

| Tony James | | W.B.A. | West Bromwich Albion |
| Matthew Clarke | Cardiff | KIdderminster | Wolves,Halesowen Town, £10,000 to Kidderminster H |
| James Wa ll | Derby | Derby | Derby County |
| Robert Warner | Stratford | | From YTS |
| John Cotterill | | Gresley | Gresley Rovers |
| Ian Wright | Lichfield | Hull | Hull City, Bristol Rovers, Stoke City |
| Paul Sturgess | | Brighton | Brighton & Hove Albion |

**MIDFIELDERS**

| Chris Lane | Liverpool | Everton | Everton |
| Ian Rodgerson | | Cardiff | Hereford United, Birmingham City, Cardiff City |
| MarkTaylor | Bimingham | Sheff Wed | Newton Albion, Shrewsbury Town,Walsall,Sheffield Wednesday |
| Gavin Williams | | Youth Team | |
| Paul Parry | | Youth Team | |
| John Snape | Birmingham | Halesowen | West Bromwich Albion, Bromsgrove R, Northfield T, Stourbridge, Halesowen T |

**FORWARDS**

| Steve Piearce | Wolverhampton | Halesowen | Wolverhampton Wanderers,Doncaster Rovers, Halesowen Town |
| Leroy May | | | Kidderminster H., Enfield, Kettering T., Kidderminstrer H, Stafford R., Altrincham,Tividale,Hereford U ,Tividale,Walsall, Tividale. |
| Paul Fewings | | Hull City | Hull City |
| Rob Eimes | | Halesowen T | Boldmere St Michaels, Bromsgrove Rovers, Halesowen Town |
| Craig Hanson | | Derby Co. | Derby County |

Departures: Gary Cook,Matthew Cross, Robbie Dennison, Wayne Dyer, Stuart Evans.

# HEREFORD UNITED

**Founded:** 1924

**Nickname:** The Bulls

**Sponsors:** Sun Valley

**Club Colours:** Black & White Halves
black shorts, white trim; black socks,white tops

**Change Colours:** Red & black quarters;
black shorts; black socks

**Midweek matchday:** Tuesday

**Reserve League:** Central Conference

## GROUND DETAILS

Edgar Street,
Hereford.
HR4 9JU

**COMMUNICATION**
Tel: 01432 276666
Fax 01432 341359
Club Call 0891 121645
E-mail HUFC@msn.com

**SIMPLE DIRECTIONS:** From Hereford city centre
follow signs to Leominster (A49) into Edgar Street.
Car parking for 1000 (approx.) available near the ground.
Nearest railway station Hereford

**CAPACITY:** 8,843
**SEATED:** 2,761
**COVERED TERRACING:** 6,082

**SOCIAL FACILITIES:** Clubhouse open on matchdays

**CLUB SHOP:** Yes

## PREVIOUS

**Leagues:** Birmingham League;
Birmingham Combination;
Southern League 39-72;
Football League 72-97

**Names:** None

**Ground:** None

## CLUB RECORDS

**Attendance:** 18,114
v Sheffield Wed., FA Cup 3rd Rd, 4.1.58

**Career Goalscorer:** Unknown
**Career Appearances:** unknown

**Win:** 6-0 v Burnley (A), Div. 4 24.1.87

**Defeat:** 0-6 v Rotherham Utd (A), Div. 4 29.4.89

**Transfer Fee Paid:** £75,000
to Walsall for Dean Smith, 7.94
**Transfer Fee Received:** £250,000
for Darren Peacock from Q.P.R., 3.91
+ a further £240,000 when he moved to Newcastle Utd. 3.91

## BEST SEASON

**FA Trophy:** 2nd Round 97-98,
0-2 v Dover Athletic (H)

**FA Cup:** 4th Rd 71-72 (as Southern League side),
76-77, 81-82, 89-90, 91-92

## HONOURS

Welsh Cup 89-90, R-up 3 times;

League Div. 3 75-76;

Southern League R-up 71-72

**Past Players** who progressed to the Football League

Since joining the Conference: Gavin Mahon (Brentford)

# KETTERING TOWN

A rebuilt Kettering side led the way for most of the season until eventual champions, Cheltenham's, games in hand finally paid off.
Who said they'd miss Chris Pearson?
Craig Norman and McNamara certainly filled his place, with 24 goals between them and another ten from Hudson, it's no wonder they were so close.

## CLUB OFFICIALS 1999-2000

| | |
|---|---|
| President | **Sid Chapman** |
| Chairman | **Peter Mallinger** |
| Vice Chairman | **Peter Oliver** |
| Directors | **Richard Davis, Michael Leach** |
| Club Secretary/ | **Graham Starmer** |
| Press Officer | c/o the club |
| Tel: 01536 483028/410815 | Fax: 01536 412273 |
| Assistant Secretary | **Andy Thomas** |

Defeat by Taunton and Kingstonian in both major cups didn't help their fantastic form in the league and especially their form away from home lifted the supporters hopes and expectations. Most teams are hard to beat at home, but Kettering are just as hard to beat away, carrying exactly the same record with them, of eleven wins, five draws and five losses.

Only sixteen goals were conceded by goalkeeper Adam Sollitt at home all season.

If Kettering can carry on getting the excellent support given this season, especially like their season's highest 5,039 against local rivals Rushden, Kettering will be up for another challenge for the Conference title.

T.T.

Back Row: Ian Ridgway, Phil Brown, Craig Norman, Carl Adams, Rob Mutchell. Middle: Peter Barnett (physio), Tim Wilkes, Craig Hopkins, Mickey Nuttall (no longer at the club), Adam Sollitt, Steve Wilson, Mark Hone, Adie Hayes, Mark Tucker, Robbie Cooke (asst. manager). Front Row: Paul Cox, Martin Matthews, Peter Mallinger (chairman), Colin Vowden, Peter Morris (manager), Lee Hudson, Matt Fisher.

# KETTERING TOWN
## MATCH FACTS 1998-99

| No | Date | Venue | Comp | Opponents | Att | Result | Score | Goalscorers |
|---|---|---|---|---|---|---|---|---|
| 1 | 15/08 | H | NC | Yeovil Town | 1754 | L | 1-2 | McNamara 74 |
| 2 | 18/08 | A | NC | Telford United | 832 | W | 2-0 | McNamara 58, Norman 78 |
| 3 | 22/08 | A | NC | Farnborough Town | 635 | W | 3-1 | P Brown 44, Norman 60, McNamara 90 |
| 4 | 25/08 | H | NC | Woking | 2012 | W | 3-0 | Mason 7, McNamara 80, Hudson 87 |
| 5 | 29/08 | H | NC | Northwich Victoria | 1763 | D | 0-0 | |
| 6 | 31/08 | A | NC | Doncaster Rovers | 4569 | D | 1-1 | Norman 45 |
| 7 | 05/09 | H | NC | Kidderminster Harriers | 1684 | D | 1-1 | Vowden 89 |
| 8 | 08/09 | H | NC | Cheltenham Town | 1615 | L | 0-2 | |
| 9 | 12/09 | A | NC | Forest Green Rovers | 825 | L | 0-1 | |
| 10 | 19/09 | H | NC | Kingstonian | 1469 | W | 2-0 | Wilkes 45, Norman 89 |
| 11 | 22/09 | A | NC | Welling United | 455 | W | 2-0 | Hudson 43, Brown 90 |
| 12 | 26/09 | A | NC | Barrow | 1443 | D | 0-0 | |
| 13 | 03/10 | H | NC | Southport | 1515 | W | 1-0 | Brown 46 |
| 14 | 10/10 | A | NC | Morecambe | 1055 | L | 1-3 | Adams 86[p] |
| 15 | 24/10 | H | NC | Leek Town | 1110 | W | 2-1 | Norman 47, Hudson 59 |
| 16 | 31/10 | H | NC | Hereford United | 1386 | D | 1-1 | Leadbeater 41[og] |
| 17 | 07/11 | H | NC | Hayes | 1563 | W | 1-0 | Brown 50 |
| 18 | 14/11 | A | NC | Dover Athletic | 807 | W | 1-0 | McNamara 71 |
| 19 | 17/11 | A | NC | Yeovil Town | 1718 | L | 1-2 | McNamara 66 |
| 20 | 28/11 | H | NC | Forest Green Rovers | 1405 | W | 2-1 | Warne 1 49 |
| 21 | 05/12 | A | NC | Hayes | 603 | W | 2-0 | McNamara 14, Hudson 87 |
| 22 | 12/12 | H | NC | Barrow | 1817 | W | 2-0 | Hudson 63 89 |
| 23 | 19/12 | A | NC | Hereford United | 2181 | W | 2-0 | Hudson 45, Fisher 58 |
| 24 | 26/12 | H | NC | Hednesford Town | 2631 | W | 1-0 | Hayes 77 |
| 25 | 28/12 | A | NC | Stevenage Borough | 3937 | D | 2-2 | Hudson 15, McNamara 34 |
| 26 | 02/01 | A | NC | Hednesford Town | 1608 | W | 2-0 | Brown 41 86 |
| 27 | 09/01 | H | NC | Morecambe | 2364 | W | 6-0 | McNamara 24, Norman 34[p] 64, Hudson 81, Brown 89, Rayno |
| 28 | 30/01 | H | NC | Doncaster Rovers | 3646 | L | 0-1 | |
| 29 | 06/02 | H | NC | Dover Athletic | 1864 | L | 0-2 | |
| 30 | 13/02 | H | NC | Telford United | 1840 | W | 2-1 | Vowden 7, Williams 78 |
| 31 | 15/02 | A | NC | Kidderminster Harriers | 1977 | D | 1-1 | Norman 52 |
| 32 | 20/02 | A | NC | Kingstonian | 1068 | W | 2-1 | Williams 54, Crossley 66[og] |
| 33 | 27/02 | H | NC | Welling United | 2371 | D | 1-1 | Williams 54 |
| 34 | 06/03 | A | NC | Northwich Victoria | 1385 | L | 0-4 | |
| 35 | 09/03 | H | NC | Farnborough Town | 1389 | W | 4-1 | Hudson 24, Fisher 31, Brown 46, Adams 75 |
| 36 | 16/03 | A | NC | Woking | 1647 | D | 0-0 | |
| 37 | 20/03 | A | NC | Cheltenham Town | 5202 | L | 0-3 | |
| 38 | 27/03 | H | NC | Rushden & Diamonds | 5017 | D | 0-0 | |
| 39 | 03/04 | A | NC | Leek Town | 717 | W | 2-1 | Norman 43, Matthews 52 |
| 40 | 05/04 | H | NC | Stevenage Borough | 2463 | L | 1-2 | McNamara 74 |
| 41 | 17/04 | A | NC | Southport | 1070 | W | 1-0 | Vowden 90 |
| 42 | 01/05 | A | NC | Rushden & Diamonds | 4700 | W | 2-1 | Norman 45, McNamara 50 |

### CUP COMPETITIONS

| | Date | Venue | Comp | Opponents | Att | Result | Score | Goalscorers |
|---|---|---|---|---|---|---|---|---|
| | 04/08 | H | Maunsell Cup | Peterborough United | 1020 | D | 2-2 | (3-2 pens) |
| | 29/09 | H | Endsleigh 1 | Hayes | 651 | L | 0-3 | |
| | 17/10 | A | FA Cup Q3 | Taunton Town | 1023 | L | 3-4 | Vowden 8, Wright 38, Norman 75[p] |
| | 21/11 | H | FA Trophy 2 | Andover | 1118 | W | 4-0 | Brown 21, McNamara 38, Hudson 43, Fisher 56 |
| | 22/12 | A | N'hants SC QF | Raunds Town | 127 | L | 0-1 | |
| | 19/01 | A | FA Trophy 3 | Kingstonian | 624 | L | 2-5 | Brown 12, McNamara 58 |

| 1 | 2 | 3 | 4 | 5 | 6 | 7 | 8 | 9 | 10 | 11 | 12 / 14 / 15 | # |
|---|---|---|---|---|---|---|---|---|---|---|---|---|
| Wilson | Matthews | Mutchell | Cox | Vowden | Norman | Hone | Brown | Hudson | McNamara | Hayes | Ridgway, Wilkes, Fisher | 1 |
| Sollitt | Matthews | Hayes | Cox | Vowden | Norman | Hone | Fisher | Hudson | McNamara | P Brown | Adams, Mason, Ridgway | 2 |
| Sollitt | Matthews | Adams | Cox | Bowden | Norman | Hone | P Brown | Mason | McNamara | Fisher | Hudson, Ridgway, Wilson | 3 |
| Sollitt | Matthews | Cox | Adams | Vowden | Norman | Hone | P Brown | Mason | McNamara | Fisher | Hudson, Hayes, Wilson | 4 |
| Wilson | Matthews | Adams | Cox | Vowden | Norman | Hone | Brown | Mason | McNamara | Fisher | Ridgway, Hudson, Hayes | 5 |
| Wilson | Matthews | Adams | Cox | Vowden | Norman | Hone | Brown | Hudson | McNamara | Hayes | Mason, Ridgway, Hopkins | 6 |
| Wilson | Matthews | Adams | Cox | Vowden | Norman | Hone | Brown | Mason | McNamara | Hayes | Ridgway, Hudson, Sollitt | 7 |
| Wilson | Matthews | Adams | Cox | Vowden | Norman | Hone | Brown | Hudson | McNamara | Fisher | Mason, Ridgway, Sollitt | 8 |
| Sollitt | Matthews | Hayes | Cox | Vowden | Norman | Hone | Brown | Fisher | McNamara | Adams | Hopkins, Hudson, Wilson | 9 |
| Sollitt | Matthews | Adams | Cox | Vowden | Norman | Hone | Hudson | Brown | McNamara | Fisher | Hayes, Wilkes, Ridgway | 10 |
| Sollitt | Matthews | Adans | Cox | Vowden | Norman | Hone | Brown | Hudson | Wilkes | Fisher | Mutchell, Ridgway, Mason | 11 |
| Sollitt | Matthews | Mutchell | Cox | Vowden | Norman | Hone | Brown | Hudson | Wilkes | Adams | Fisher, McNamara, Wright | 12 |
| Sollitt | Matthews | Raynor | Cox | Vowden | Norman | Hone | Brown | Hudson | Wright | Fisher | Hayes, McNamara, Wilkes | 13 |
| Sollitt | Matthews | Mutchell | Cox | Vowden | Hone | Raynor | Brown | Hudson | Wright | Fisher | Adams, Wilkes, Ridgway | 14 |
| Sollitt | Matthews | Adams | Cox | Vowden | Norman | Raynor | Brown | Hudson | Wright | Fisher | Hone, Wilkes, McNamara | 15 |
| Sollitt | Matthews | Adams | Cox | Vowden | Norman | Raynor | Brown | Hudson | Adams | Fisher | Wright, McNamara, Hopkins | 16 |
| Sollitt | Ridgway | Hone | Cox | Vowden | Norman | Raynor | Brown | Hudson | Warne | Fisher | Wrigh, Ridgway, McNamara | 17 |
| Sollitt | Adams | Hone | Cox | Vowden | Norman | Raynor | Brown | McNamara | Warne | Fisher | Wright, Wilkes, Hopkins | 18 |
| Sollitt | Matthews | Adams | Howe | Vowden | Norman | Raynor | Brown | Warne | McNamara | Fisher | Wrigh, Hudson, Cox | 19 |
| Sollitt | Matthews | Adams | Hone | Vowden | Norman | Raynor | Brown | Warne | McNamara | Fisher | Cox, Hudson, Hopkins | 20 |
| Sollitt | Matthews | Adams | Hone | Vowden | Norman | Raynor | Brown | Hudson | McNamara | Wright | Hayes, Hopkins, Ridgway | 21 |
| Sollitt | Matthews | Adams | Cox | Vowden | Norman | Raynor | Brown | Hudson | McNamara | Fisher | Wright, Hone, Hayes | 22 |
| Sollitt | Matthews | Adams | Cox | Vowden | Norman | Raynor | Brown | Hudson | McNamara | Fisher | Hone, Hayes, Wright | 23 |
| Sollitt | Matthews | Adams | Cox | Vowden | Norman | Raynor | Brown | Hudson | McNamara | Fisher | Hone, Wright, Thompson | 24 |
| Sollitt | Matthews | Adams | Cox | Vowden | Norman | Raynor | Brown | Hudson | McNamara | Fisher | Hone, Wright, Hayes | 25 |
| Sollitt | Matthews | Adams | Cox | Vowden | Norman | Raynor | Brown | Hudson | McNamara | Fisher | Hone, Thompson, Wright | 26 |
| Wilson | Matthews | Adams | Cox | Vowden | Norman | Raynor | Brown | Hudson | McNamara | Hone | Wright, Thompson, Hayes | 27 |
| Sollitt | Matthews | Adams | Cox | Vowden | Norman | Raynor | Brown | Hudson | McNamara | Hone | Wright, Hayes, Ridgway | 28 |
| Sollitt | Matthews | Hone | Cox | Vowden | Norman | Raynor | Brown | Wright | McNamara | Fisher | Adams, Williams, Ridgway | 29 |
| Sollitts | Matthews | Adams | Cox | Vowden | Norman | Raynor | Brown | Hudson | McNamara | Fisher | Eastwood, Hone, Williams | 30 |
| Sollitt | Matthews | Adams | Cox | Vowden | Norman | Raynor | Gynn | Hudson | Williams | Fisher | McNamara, Hone, Eastwood | 31 |
| Wilson | Matthews | Adams | Cox | Vowden | Norman | Raynor | Eastwood | Williams | McNamara | Fisher | Brown, Ridgeway, Hayes | 32 |
| Wilson | Matthews | Adams | Cox | Vowden | Norman | Raynor | Eastwood | Williams | McNamara | Fisher | Hudson, Ridgeway, Hayes | 33 |
| Wilson | Matthews | Adams | Hone | Vowden | Norman | Haydon | Brown | Hudson | McNamara | Fisher | Williams, Eastwood, Sollitt | 34 |
| Sollitt | Haydon | Adams | Cox | Vowden | Norman | Raynor | Brown | Hudson | McNamara | Fisher | Williams, Hone, Wilson | 35 |
| Sollitt | Haydon | Adams | Cox | Vowden | Norman | Raynor | Brown | Williams | McNamara | Fisher | Matthews, Hone, Ridgway | 36 |
| Sollitt | Haydon | Adams | Brown | Vowden | Hone | Raynor | Matthews | Barclay | McNamara | Fisher | Hopkins, Wilde, Tucker | 37 |
| Sollitt | Matthews | Adams | Cox | Vowden | Norman | Raynor | Haydon | Barclay | McNamara | Fisher | Hone, Wilkinson, Wilde | 38 |
| Sollitt | Matthews | Adams | Cox | Vowden | Norman | Raynor | Haydon | Brown | Wilde | McNamara | Williamson, Ridgway, Barclay | 39 |
| Sollitt | Haydon | Adams | Cox | Vowden | Norman | Matthews | Brown | Williams | McNamara | Fisher | Williamson, Wilde, Hudson | 40 |
| Sollitt | Matthews | Wilde | Cox | Vowden | Norman | Raynor | Brown | Williams | McNamara | Fisher | Ridgeway, Williamson, Hone | 41 |
| Sollitt | Matthews | Adams | Cox | Vowden | Norman | Raynor | Brown | Williams | McNamara | Fisher | Hone, Williams, Ridgeway | 42 |

League Attendances  HIGHEST: 5017  LOWEST: 1110

CONFERENCE: 14th  FA CUP: 3rd Qualifying Round  FA TROPHY: 3rd Round

## MANAGER
### PETER MORRIS

Date of Appointment          May 1998
Date of Birth:               8th November 1943
Place of Birth:              New Houghton, Mansfield

PREVIOUS CLUBS
As manager          Mansfield T., Peterborough U., Crewe A.,
                    Southend U., Nuneaton B.,
                    KetteringT., King's Lynn.
As asst. man./coach   Newcastle U., Leicester C.
As player           Mansfield T., Ipswich T., Norwich C.,
                    Mansfield T., Peterborough U.

## FOOTBALL MANAGEMENT TEAM
**Assistant Manager:**          Robbie Cooke
**Physio:**                     Peter Lake
**Youth & Comunity**
 **development:**               Dominic Genovese
**Youth & Reserve Coach:**      Chris Swift

### 1998-99
**Top Scorer:**                 Brett McNamara
**Player of the Year:**         Paul Cox
**Captain:**                    Colin Vowden

Peter Morris

Colin Vowden

---

## MATCHDAY PROGRAMME

Number of pages                          32

Price                                    £1.50

Programme Editor              Fox Design to Print
                              0116 222 8500
Other club publications:
          "Poppies at the Gates of Dawn" (Fanzine)

Local Newspapers:              Evening Telegraph
                               Chronicle & Echo
                               Herald & Post; Citizen
Local Radio Stations:          Radio Northampton
                               Northants 96;  KCBC

# PLAYING SQUAD

| Player | Birthplace Honours | D.O.B. | Previous Clubs |
|---|---|---|---|
| **GOALKEEPERS** | | | |
| Adam Sollitt | Sheffield | 22.6.77 | Barnsley, Gainsborough Trinity |
| Steve Wilson | | 29.11.78 | Leicester City |
| **DEFENDERS** | | | |
| Colin Vowden | Newmarket | 13.9.71 | Newmarket T, Cambridge C, Cambridge U |
| Craig Norman | Perivale | 21.3.75 | Chelsea |
| Mark Tucker | Woking | 27.4.72 | Fulham, Woking, £45k to Rushden & Diamonds |
| Paul Cox | Nottingham | 6.1.72 | Notts Co, Kettering T, Gresley R, Ilkeston T, Halifax T |
| Mark Hone | | 31.03.68 | Lincoln City |
| **MIDFIELDERS** | | | |
| Martin Matthews | Peterborough | 22.12.75 | Derby Co, Northampton T, King's Lynn |
| Ian Ridgway | Nottingham | 28.12.75 | Notts Co |
| Wayne Diuk | Nottingham | 26.05.80 | Notts. Co., Gedling Town |
| Carl Adams | Birmingham | 13.03.74 | Stevenage Borough |
| Ricky Hailstone | | 24.03.81 | Warboys |
| Matt Fisher | Mansfield | | Army, Ashfield U, Gedling T |
| Craig Hopkins | Nottingham | | Shirebrook Coll, King's Lynn, Spalding U |
| Paul Raynor | | 29.04.66 | Leyton Orient, Stevenage Borough |
| **FORWARDS** | | | |
| Brett McNamara | Peterborough | | Stamford, Northampton T, King's Lynn |
| Steve Williams | | 03.11.75 | King's Lynn |
| Phil Brown | Sheffield | 16.1.66 | Chesterfield, Stockport Co, Lincoln C, Kettering T, Boston U, Gainsborough Trin |
| Lee Hudson | GMVC, Div 4 Peterborough | | Moulton Harrox, Spalding U, Boston T, King's Lynn |

DEPARTURES: Rob Mutchell (Tamworth), Adie Hayes (Diss Town), Tim Wilkes (Telford United0, Eddie King, Paul Miles, Ian Stringfellow, Micky Nuttell

PLAYERS ON LOAN: Dominic Barclay (Macclesfield), Nicky Hayton (Colchester Utd.), Phil Eastwood (Burnley), Paul Thompson (Stevenage borough), Paul Warne (Wigan Athletic)

# KETTERING TOWN

| | |
|---|---|
| **Founded:** | 1872 |
| **Nickname:** | Poppies |
| **Club Sponsors:** | Weldon Plant Ltd. |
| **Club colours:** | Red & black shirts, red shorts, black socks |
| **Change colours:** | Green & yellow shirts, green shorts, green & yellow socks |
| **Midweek home matchday:** | Tuesday |

## GROUND DETAILS

Rockingham Road,
Kettering,
Northants, NN16 9AW

**COMMUNICATION**  Tel: 01536 83028/410815 (Office)
01536 410962 (Social Club)
Fax: 01536 412273

**SIMPLE DIRECTIONS:**
From south - M1 junction 15, A43 to Kettering use A14 exit Junct. 7, follow A43 to Corby/Stamford to 1st roundabout, turn right A6003, ground half a mile.
From north - M1 or M6 use junction 19 then A14 to Kettering. Exit Junct. 7 then as above.
British Rail - Inter-City Midland - 50 mins from London (St.Pancras), 20 mins from Leicester

| | |
|---|---|
| **CAPACITY:** | 6,100 |
| **COVERED SEATING:** | 1,800 |
| **COVERED TERRACING:** | 2,200 |

**CLUB SHOP:**  Open before and after matches, & office staff will open on request on non-match days. Situated in front of main stand. Also Ken Burton's Sports in town centre

**SOCIAL FACILITIES:**  Social Club (Poppies), Vice-Presidents Bar & Sponsor'sLounge

## Past Players who progressed to the Football League

Billy Kellock(Peterborough), Gary Wood (Notts Co.),
Dave Longhurst (Nott'm Forest), Scott Endersby (Ipswich),
Steve Fallon (Cambridge U.), Andy Rogers (Plymouth),
MartynFoster (Northampton), Cohen Griffith (Cardiff C.),
Andy Hunt (Newcastle), Richard Brown (Blackburn R.)
Ben Wright (Bristol C.), Kofi Nyamah (Stoke C.)

## PREVIOUS

| | |
|---|---|
| **Leagues:** | Southern League, Northants League, Midland League, Birmingham League Central Alliance, United Counties League |
| **Grounds** | North Park;  Green Lane |

## CLUB RECORDS

| | |
|---|---|
| **Attendance:** | 11,536 |
| | Kettering v Peterborough (pre-Taylor report) |
| **Win:** | 16-0 |
| | v Higham YMCI (FA Cup 1909) |
| **Defeat:** | 0-13 |
| | v Mardy (Southern League Div. 2, 1911/12) |
| **Transfer fee paid:** | £25,000 |
| | to Macclesfield for Carl Alford, 1994 |
| **Transfer fee received:** | £150,000 |
| | from Newcastle United for Andy Hunt |
| **Career goalscorer:** | Roy Clayton 171 (1972 - 1981) |
| **Career appearances:** | Roger Ashby |

## BEST SEASON

| | |
|---|---|
| **FA Trophy:** | Runners-up 78-79 |
| **FA Cup:** | 4th Round |
| | 1988-89, 1-2 v Charlton Ath. |
| | 91-92, 1-4 v Blackburn R |
| League clubs defeated: | Swindon T., Millwall, Swansea C., Halifax T., Maidstone & Bristol Rovers |

## HONOURS

Premier Inter League Cup;
FA Trophy Runners-up 78-79;
Alliance Premier League (Conference) R-up x 4;
Southern League Winners,
County Cup Winners,
Daventry Charity Cup Winners x 2;
Northants Senior Cup x 27;
Maunsell Cup Winners x 12

# KIDDERMINSTER HARRIERS

With an improvement of only two places, to seventeenth, Harriers fans must be feling that things are moving slowly at Aggborough.
Half way through the season Chairman Dave Reynolds resigned,long term manager Graham Allner was sacked and captain Mark Yates joined Cheltenham Town.

Their highest attendance of 3,295 shows that the supporters haven't given up but it will be up to new manager, Jan Molby, to show them the club means business.

The F.A. Cup brought a trip to Plymouth Argyle and defeat only came after a replay and penalties but sadly they did not reach the latter stages of the F.A.Trophy and local rivals prevented them from acuip run in the Endsleigh Trophy

'Kiddy' still have a talented squad and with Jan Molby's influence and some shrewd new signings it could be their turn for a spell at the top.

T.T.

## CLUB OFFICIALS 1999-2000

| | |
|---|---|
| Chairman | **Lionel Newton** |
| Vice Chairman | **Colin Youngjohns** |
| Company Secretary | **J Richard Painter** |
| Directors | **Graham Lane** |
| | **Paul Byrne, Tom Murrant** |
| Chief Executive | **Alan Biggs** |
| Football Secretary | **Roger Barlow** |
| Commercial Manager | **Mark Searl** |

Kidderminster Harriers 1999-2000 - Back Row: Rene Peterson, Martin Weir, Steve Taylor, Stuart Brock, Phil King, Dean Bennett, Mark Druce. Middle: Ginger Jordan (kit manager), Stuart payne, Adie Smith, Craig Hinton, Andrew Brownrigg, Stewart Hadley, Steve Pope, Shaun Cunnington, Jim Conway (physio). Front: Thomas Skovbjerg, Les Hines, Jan Molby (manager), Paul Webb, Gary Barnett (player-asst. manager), Ian Foster, James Collins.
Photo: Dave Clapp

# KIDDERMINSTER HARRIERS
## MATCH FACTS 1998-99

| No | Date | Venue | Comp | Opponents | Att | Result | Score | Goalscorers |
|----|------|-------|------|-----------|-----|--------|-------|-------------|
| 1 | 15/08 | H | NC | Morecambe | 1828 | W | 5-2 | May 9 20, Hadley 11, Arnold 50 53 |
| 2 | 18/08 | A | NC | Northwich Victoria | 1122 | L | 0-1 | |
| 3 | 22/08 | A | NC | Doncaster Rovers | 3222 | L | 0-1 | |
| 4 | 24/08 | H | NC | Telford United | 2003 | W | 3-0 | Willetts 26 88, Robinson 81 |
| 5 | 29/08 | H | NC | Woking | 2024 | W | 3-2 | Willetts 45, May 52 88 |
| 6 | 31/08 | A | NC | Yeovil Town | 2112 | L | 1-3 | May 90 |
| 7 | 05/09 | A | NC | Kettering Town | 1684 | D | 1-1 | Willetts 54 |
| 8 | 19/09 | A | NC | Hayes | 553 | L | 1-2 | Deakin 20 |
| 9 | 21/09 | H | NC | Forest Green Rovers | 1716 | D | 2-2 | Deakin 62, Willetts 79 |
| 10 | 26/09 | H | NC | Stevenage Borough | 2072 | W | 2-0 | May 31 48 |
| 11 | 03/10 | A | NC | Welling United | 780 | D | 0-0 | |
| 12 | 10/10 | H | NC | Kingstonian | 1884 | L | 0-1 | |
| 13 | 24/10 | A | NC | Hednesford Town | 934 | L | 1-2 | Yates 75 |
| 14 | 26/10 | H | NC | Southport | 1780 | W | 2-1 | Gouck 50[og], Arnold 69 |
| 15 | 07/11 | H | NC | Yeovil Town | 2007 | L | 0-1 | |
| 16 | 28/11 | A | NC | Leek Town | 711 | W | 4-1 | Taylor 23 37, Arnold 74, May 78 |
| 17 | 12/12 | A | NC | Woking | 1982 | L | 1-2 | Willetts 40 |
| 18 | 19/12 | A | NC | Southport | 976 | D | 1-1 | Hines 30 |
| 19 | 26/12 | H | NC | Hereford United | 3188 | W | 1-0 | Thomas 89 |
| 20 | 28/12 | H | NC | Cheltenham Town | 3295 | L | 0-1 | |
| 21 | 02/01 | A | NC | Hereford United | 2658 | W | 3-1 | Taylor 46, Hadley 68, May 82 |
| 22 | 09/01 | H | NC | Leek Town | 1713 | L | 1-2 | Arnold 12 |
| 23 | 23/01 | H | NC | Welling United | 1460 | L | 0-1 | |
| 24 | 30/01 | H | NC | Hayes | 1534 | L | 0-1 | |
| 25 | 02/02 | A | NC | Rushden & Diamonds | 2374 | D | 1-1 | Taylor 61 |
| 26 | 13/02 | H | NC | Rushden & Diamonds | 2337 | D | 0-0 | |
| 27 | 15/02 | H | NC | Kettering Town | 1977 | D | 1-1 | Weir 72 |
| 28 | 20/02 | A | NC | Telford United | 1220 | D | 0-0 | |
| 29 | 27/02 | A | NC | Farnborough Town | 733 | W | 4-2 | May 4 75, Payne 45 57 |
| 30 | 06/03 | H | NC | Hednesford Town | 1725 | L | 1-2 | Ford 80 |
| 31 | 09/03 | A | NC | Kingstonian | 735 | L | 0-1 | |
| 32 | 13/03 | A | NC | Forest Green Rovers | 1001 | L | 0-5 | |
| 33 | 20/03 | H | NC | Dover Athletic | 1312 | W | 1-0 | Webb 87 |
| 34 | 27/03 | A | NC | Barrow | 1738 | W | 4-0 | Ford 12, Cunnington 27, Thomas 36, Hadley 50 |
| 35 | 03/04 | H | NC | Doncaster Rovers | 2200 | D | 3-3 | Druce 13, Hadley 52 75 |
| 36 | 05/04 | A | NC | Cheltenham Town | 4518 | L | 0-1 | |
| 37 | 10/04 | A | NC | Morecambe | 966 | L | 1-2 | Hadley 44 |
| 38 | 12/04 | H | NC | Northwich Victoria | 1235 | W | 4-0 | Payne 6 84, Ford 57, Cunnington 71 |
| 39 | 17/04 | A | NC | Dover Athletic | 925 | W | 1-0 | Hadley 7 |
| 40 | 24/04 | A | NC | Stevenage Borough | 1915 | L | 0-3 | |
| 41 | 01/05 | H | NC | Barrow | 1877 | L | 1-2 | Ford 85 |
| 42 | | | | | | | | |

### CUP COMPETITIONS

| | Date | Venue | Comp | Opponents | Att | Result | Score | Goalscorers |
|--|------|-------|------|-----------|-----|--------|-------|-------------|
| | 07/10 | A | Endsleigh 1 | Forest Green Rovers | 446 | W | 4-2 | Hadley 24 43, May 48, Willetts 85 |
| | 17/10 | H | FA Cup Q3 | Blakenall | 1141 | W | 3-1 | Willetts 15, Deakin 80, Hadley 85 |
| | 31/10 | H | FA Cup Q4 | Gloucester City | 1690 | W | 2-1 | Webb 20, Yates 87 |
| | 14/11 | A | FA Cup 1 | Plymouth Argyle | 4284 | D | 0-0 | |
| | 21/11 | H | FA Trophy 2 | Lincoln United | 982 | D | 2-2 | Yates 32 57 |
| | 01/12 | H | FA Cup 1 rep | Plymouth Argyle | 4471 | L | 0-0 | (4-5 pens) |
| | 07/12 | A | FA Trophy 2 r | Lincoln United | 302 | L | 1-2 | Webb 48 |
| | 14/12 | H | Endsleigh 2 | Hereford United | 645 | L | 1-2 | Arnold 76 |
| | 15/03 | A | Worcs SC QF | Paget Rangers | n/k | W | 3-1 | Hines, May(2) |
| | 14/04 | H | Worcs SC SF | Bromsgrove Rovers | 515 | W | 6-1 | Hadley 21 25 32 49, Hinton 60, May 89 |
| | 19/04 | A | Worcs SC F(1) | Worcester City | 1019 | L | 2-3 | Hadley 41, Willetts 70 |
| | 27/04 | H | Worcs SC F(2) | Worcester City | 1176 | W | 2-0 | Hadley 34, Druce 109 |

| 1 | 2 | 3 | 4 | 5 | 6 | 7 | 8 | 9 | 10 | 11 | 12 14 15 | |
|---|---|---|---|---|---|---|---|---|---|---|---|---|
| Brock | Webb | Skelding | Weir | Glover | Yates | Deakin | Hadley | May | Arnold | Willetts | Wolsey, Hinton, Bignall | 1 |
| Brock | Webb | Skelding | Weir | Glover | Yates | Deakin | Hadley | May | Arnold | Willetts | Bignall, Hinton, Wolsey | 2 |
| Brock | Webb | Skelding | Weir | Glover | Yates | Deakin | Davies | Bignall | Arnold | Willetts | Hinton, Robinson, Wolsey | 3 |
| Brock | Webb | Skelding | Weir | Glover | Yates | Deakin | Bignall | May | Arnold | Willetts | Robinson, Hinton, Wolsey | 4 |
| Brock | Webb | Skelding | Weir | Glover | Yates | Deakin | Robinson | May | Arnold | Willetts | Hinton, Wolsey, Bignall | 5 |
| Brock | Webb | Skelding | Weir | Glover | Yates | Deakin | Robinson | May | Arnold | Willetts | Hinton, Wolsey, Bignall | 6 |
| Brock | Hinton | Skelding | Weir | Glover | Yates | Deakin | Bignall | May | Arnold | Willetts | Cunnington, Smith, Robinson | 7 |
| Brock | Hinton | Skelding | Weir | Glover | Cunnington | Deakin | Bignall | May | Arnold | Willetts | Wolsey, Smith, Robinson | 8 |
| Brock | Hinton | Hines | Weir | Glover | Yates | Deakin | Taylor | May | Arnold | Willetts | Smith, Cunnington, Hadley | 9 |
| Brock | Hinton | Hines | Weir | Glover | Yates | Taylor | Hadley | May | Arnold | Willetts | Webb, Deakin, Cunnington | 10 |
| Brock | Hinton | Hines | Weir | Glover | Yates | Taylor | Hadley | May | Arnold | Willetts | Webb, Deakin, Cunnington | 11 |
| Brock | Hinton | Hines | Weir | Glover | Yates | Taylor | Hadley | May | Deakin | Willetts | Bignall, Cunnington, Webb | 12 |
| Brock | Hinton | Hines | Weir | Glover | Yates | Webb | Hadley | Taylor | Arnold | Willetts | Deakin, Bignall, Smith | 13 |
| Brock | Hinton | Hines | Weir | Glover | Yates | Webb | Hadley | Taylor | Arnold | Deakin | Willetts, Smith, Bignall | 14 |
| Brock | Hinton | Hines | Webb | Smith | Yates | Taylor | Hadley | May | Arnold | Willetts | Deakin, Cunnington, Bignall | 15 |
| Brock | Hinton | Hines | Webb | Smith | Yates | Cunningham | Hadley | May | Arnold | Taylor | Willetts, Deakin, Bignall | 16 |
| Brock | Willetts | Hines | Webb | Smith | Yates | Cunnington | Hadley | May | Purdie | Taylor | Wolsey, Arnold, Deakin | 17 |
| Brock | Wolsey | Hines | Weir | Smith | Yates | Webb | Cunnington | May | Arnold | Deakin | Thomas, Hadley, Purdie | 18 |
| Brock | Webb | Hines | Weir | Smith | Yates | Deakin | Cunnington | May | Arnold | Purdie | C Thomas, Hadley, Wolsey | 19 |
| Brock | Webb | Hines | Weir | Smith | Yates | Deakin | Cunnington | Thomas | Arnold | Purdie | Taylor, Hadley, May | 20 |
| Brock | Wolsey | Hines | Webb | Smith | Yates | Deakin | Cunnington | Hadley | Arnold | Purdie | May, Taylor, Thomas | 21 |
| Brock | Webb | Hines | Weir | Smith | Yates | Deakin | Cunnington | Hadley | Arnold | Taylor | Wolsey, May, Purdie | 22 |
| Brock | Hinton | Hines | Weir | Glover | Smith | Deakin | Wolsey | Hadley | May | Taylor | Purdie, Beard, Thomas | 23 |
| Brock | Hinton | Hines | Weir | Glover | Smith | Bennett | Cunnington | Payne | Druce | Taylor | Wolsey, Arnold, Hadley | 24 |
| Brock | Hinton | Wolsey | Weir | Smith | Webb | Bennett | Cunnington | Payne | Druce | Taylor | Arnold, Glover, Hadley | 25 |
| Brock | Hinton | Ford | Smith | Weir | Webb | Bennett | Cunnington | Payne | Druce | Wolsey | Arnold, Glover, May | 26 |
| Brock | Hinton | Ford | Weir | Taylor | Webb | Bennett | Cunnington | Payne | Druce | Wolsey | May, Glover, Beard | 27 |
| Brock | Hinton | Ford | Weir | Taylor | Webb | Bennett | Cunnington | Payne | Druce | Wolsey | Beard, May, Glover | 28 |
| Brock | Hinton | Ford | Weir | Smith | Webb | Taylor | Cunnington | Payne | Druce | May | Deakin, Wolsey, Hadley | 29 |
| Brock | Hinton | Ford | Weir | Smith | Webb | Bennett | Cunnington | Payne | Druce | May | Deakin, Wolsey, Hadley | 30 |
| Brock | Hinton | Ford | Weir | Smith | Webb | Taylor | Cunnington | Payne | Druce | May | Hadley, Bennett, Wolsey | 31 |
| Acton | Hinton | Ford | Weir | Webb | Wolsey | Bennett | Taylor | Payne | Druce | May | Deakin, Thomas, Hadley | 32 |
| Brock | Hinton | Ford | Webb | Smith | Deakin | Taylor | Cunnington | Thomas | Druce | May | Wolsey, Payne, Willetts | 33 |
| Brock | Hinton | Ford | Webb | Smith | Deakin | Taylor | Cunnington | Hadley | Druce | Thomas | Payne, Wolsey, Willetts | 34 |
| Brock | Hinton | Ford | Webb | Smith | Deakin | Taylor | Cunnington | Hadley | Druce | Thomas | Wolsey, Payne, May | 35 |
| Brock | Hinton | Ford | Smith | Weir | Deakin | Taylor | Cunnington | May | Druce | Thomas | Willetts, Wolsey, Payne | 36 |
| Brock | Hinton | Ford | Weir | Smith | Deakin | Taylor | Cunnington | Hadley | Druce | Thomas | Payne, May, Wolsey | 37 |
| Brock | Hinton | Ford | Weir | Webb | Deakin | Taylor | Cunnington | Hadley | Payne | Willetts | Wolsey, May, Druce | 38 |
| Brock | Hinton | Ford | Weir | Smith | Deakin | Taylor | Webb | Hadley | Payne | Willetts | May, Druce, Bennett | 39 |
| Brock | Hinton | Ford | Webb | Smith | Willetts | Deakin | Cunnington | Hadley | Payne | Taylor | Wolsey, May, Bennett | 40 |
| Brock | Hinton | Ford | Weir | Webb | Druce | Deakin | Bennett | Hadley | Payne | May | Hines, Thomas, Cunnington | 41 |
| | | | | | | | | | | | | 42 |

League Attendances      **HIGHEST:** 3295      **LOWEST:** 1312

**CONFERENCE:** 14th      **FA CUP:** 1st Round      **FA TROPHY:** 2nd Round

## MANAGER
### JAN MOLBY

Date of Appointment: 1st June 1999

Date of Birth: 4th July 1963
Place of Birth: Kolding, Jutland

PREVIOUS CLUBS
As player/manager          Swansea C.
As player          Kolding, Ajax, Liverpool, Barnsley (L), Norwich C. (L)

HONOURS
As player/manager          None
As player:          Denmark: 34, u21, Y.
Div. 1 85-86 87-88 89-90; FAC 85-86 91-92

## FOOTBALL MANAGEMENT TEAM

Assistant Manager/Player          Gary Barnett
Physio          Jimmy Conway
Chief Scout          Paul Molesworth
Reserves/
 Youth Team Manager          Geoff Allard

### 1998-99

Top Scorer:          Leroy May

Player of the Year:          Adie Smith

Captain:          Shaun Cunnington

jan Molby

Martin Weir
Photo: V. Robertson

## MATCHDAY PROGRAMME

Number of pages          48
Price          £1.50
Programme Editor          Steve Thomas
Other club publications:          None

Local Newspapers:          Kidderminster Shuttle / Times
Kidderminster Chronicle
Evening Mail; Express & Star
Worcester Evening News
Local Radio Stations:          BBC Hereford & Worcester
Radio Wyvern
Beacon Radio; BRMB

# PLAYING SQUAD

| Player | Birthplace Honours | D.O.B. | Previous Clubs |
|---|---|---|---|
| **GOALKEEPERS** | | | |
| Stuart Brock | Sandwell | 26.09.76 | Aston Villa, Northampton T, Solihull B |
| Daniel Tipton | | 15.04.81 | Watford |
| | | | |
| **DEFENDERS** | | | |
| Les Hines | | 07.01.77 | Aston Villa |
| Steve Pope | | 08.09.76 | Crewe Alexandra |
| Martin Weir | Birmingham | 04.07.68 | Birmingham C |
| GMVC, FA XI, Middx Wanderers | | | |
| Phil King | Bristol | 28.12.67 | Wxwter City, Torquay United,Swindon Town, Nots County,Sheff Wed, Aston Villa, W.B.A., Swansea City, Blackpool, Brighton |
| England B | | | |
| Craig Hinton | | 26.11.77 | Birmingham City |
| Adie Smith | Birmingham | 11.08.73 | Willenhall T, Birmingham C, Bromsgrove R, "10k to Kidderminster H |
| | | | |
| MIDFIELDERS | | | |
| Andrew Brownrigg | | 02.08.76 | Hereford United, £100,000 to Norwich City, Rotherham United |
| Shaun Cunnington | | 04.01.66 | Wrexham, Grimsby Town, £650,000 to Sunderland, W.B.A.Notts Co. |
| **Paul Webb** | **Wolverhampton** | **30.11.67** | **Bilston T, Shrewsbury T, Bromsgrove R, £17,500 to Kidderminster H** |
| **ESP, GMVC, SLP, FA XI** | | | |
| Dean Bennett | | 13.12.77 | W.B.A.,Bromsgrove Rovers (record fee to Kidderminster Harriers) |
| Rene Petersen | Denmark | 22.08.73 | F.C.Kopenhagen, St.Truiden (Belgium) |
| Thomas Skovbierg | Denmark | 25.10.74 | Esbjerg,IKAST,LYNGBY, Esbjerg |
| James Collins | | 28.06.78 | Crewe Alexandra |
| Gary Barnett | Stratford | 11.03.63 | Coventry City,Oxford United, Wimbledon,Fulham, Huddersfield Town,Leyton Orient, Barry Town |
| | | | |
| FORWARDS | | | |
| Stewart Hadley | | 30.12.73 | Derby County, Mansfield Town |
| **Steve Taylor** | | **07.01.70** | **Rushall Olympic, Bromsgrove Rovers, £90,000 to Crystal P., Hednesford Town,Telford United, Bromsgrove Rovers** |
| Mark Druce | | 03.03.74 | Oxford United, Rotherham United, Hereford United. |
| Stuart Payne | | 10.01.74 | Bromsgrove Rovers |
| Andrew Hodgetts | | 05.03.81 | Walsall |
| Ian Foster | Liverpool | 11.11.76 | Liverpool,Hereford United,Barrow |

Bold Print indicates England Semi-Profesional Internationals

Departures: Kevin Willetts and John Deakin (Worcester City), Mark Wolsey and Darren Acton (Tamworth), Leroy May (Hereford United), Jon Ford (Telford United), Dean Glover (Port Vale Youth Team Coach), Clinton Thomas (Halesowen Town), Dean Roberts (Evesham United)an,Matt Beard.

# KIDDERMINSTER HARRIERS

| | |
|---|---|
| Founded: | 1886 |
| Nickname: | Harriers |
| Sponsors: | OGL Computer |
| Club colours: | Red & white shirts, |
| | red shorts, red socks |
| Change colours: | Blue with yellow trim |
| Reserve team's league: | Central Conference |
| Midweek home matchday: | Mondays 7.45pm |

## GROUND DETAILS

Manor Park,
Aggborough Stadium,
Hoo Road,
Kidderminster,
Worcs. DY10 1NB

**COMMUNICATION:**
Tel: 01562 823931
Fax: 01562 827329
E-mail info@harriers.co.uk
Web www.harriers.co.uk

**SIMPLE DIRECTIONS:**
On all the main approach roads into Kidderminster -
follow the yellow & black signs to the ground

| | |
|---|---|
| **CAPACITY:** | 6,293 |
| **COVERED SEATING:** | 1,100 |
| **COVERED TERRACING:** | 3,589 |
| **CLUB SHOP:** | Open Monday to Friday 9am-5pm, |
| | plus 1st XI match days |

**SOCIAL FACILITIES:**
Aggborough Suite (restricted access). Lounge bar.
Social & supporters club (3 bars) open to visiting supporters
before & after the match, temporary admission 50p.
Hot & cold food available

## Past Players who progressed to the Football League

Lee Hughes (WestBrom. A.),
Richard Forsyth (Birmingham C., now Stoke C.),
Paul Jones(Wolverhampton W., now Stockport Co.),
Dave Barnett (Barnet, now BirminghamC.),
Steve Lilwall (West Brom. A.), Marcus Bignot (Crewe Alex.)

## PREVIOUS

| | |
|---|---|
| Leagues: | Birmingham League 1889-1890, 1891-1939, |
| | 1947-1948, 1960-1962, |
| | Midland League 1890-1891, |
| | Southern League 1939-1945 (Abandoned - W.W. II), |
| | 1948-1960, 1972-1983, |
| | Birmingham Combination 1945-1947, |
| | West Midlands League 1962-1972 |
| Grounds: | None |
| Names: | None |

## CLUB RECORDS

| | |
|---|---|
| Attendance: | 9,155 |
| | v Hereford United - FA Cup 1st Rd 27.11.48 |
| Win: | 25-0 |
| | v Hereford (H), 12.10.1889 - Birmingham Sen. Cup 1st Rnd |
| Defeat: | 0-13 |
| | v Darwen (A), 24.01.1891 - FA Cup 1st Rnd Proper |
| Transfer fee paid: | £20,000 |
| | for Chris Brindley from Telford - 1992 |
| Transfer fee received: | £180,000 + apps |
| | for Lee Hughes to West Bromwich Albion |
| Career goalscorer: | Peter Wassall 432, 1963-1974 |
| Career appearances: | Brendan Wassall 686, 1962-1974 |

## BEST SEASON

| | |
|---|---|
| FA Cup: | 5th Round 1993-94. |
| | 0-1 v West Ham United |
| League clubs defeated: | Birmingham City, |
| | Preston North End |
| FA Trophy: | Winners 86-87, |
| | R-up 90-91, 94-95 |

## HONOURS

GMV Conference Champions 1994, R-up 1997;
FA Trophy 1987, Runners-up 1991, 1995;
Spalding Cup 1997,
Welsh FA Cup R-up 1986, 1989;
SouthernLeague Cup 1980;
Worcester Senior Cup (21); Birmingham Senior Cup (7);
Staffordshire Senior Cup (4);
West Midland League (6), Runners-up (3);
West Midland League Cup (7); Southern Premier R-up (1);
KeysCup (7); Border Counties Floodlit League (3),
Camkin FloodlitCup (3); Bass County Vase (1);
Conference Fair Play Trophy (5)

# KINGSTONIAN

In their first season in the Conference, Geoff Chapple's squad certainly earned respect.
Steady, if unspectacular, league performances were punctuated throughout the season with gritty and sometimes explosive 'sudden death' battles of real power and skill.
Having beaten Maidenhead United, St Albans City (only after penalties) and Burton Albion, K's qualified to face Leyton Orient but lost to them away in a replay, in which they produced their best football of the season.

In the midst of their excellent cup run, they had managed to reach the 3rd Round of the F.A.Trophy and a list of some of the clubs they beat on the way to Wembley must represent one of the most difficult paths to the final ever experienced- Kettering Town (H), (who were currently top of the Conference), Yeovil Town (H) (currently with the best conference away record.), Northwich Victoria (A) and Cheltenham Town (H&A).

The Kingstonian mid field duo of Gary Patterson and Geoff Pitcher seemed to get better and better as the season went on and there was no way any club seemed likely to stop Geoff Chapple winning the Trophy for the fourth time or Kingstonian proudly adding their name to the impressive list of winners.

The rest of the Conference know the K's now but with the confidence of their Wembley success behind them, who would bet against Kingstonian challenging for the title this season?

T.T.

## CLUB OFFICIALS 1999-2000

Chief Executive     **Chris Kelly**
& Company Sec.

Directors :
**G Chapple, L Cooley, T Dixon,P Gellard,
C.Kelly,A Kingston,T.Weir, R M Woolfson,**

Football Secretary     **Derek Powell**
30 Warwick Rd., Ash Vale, Aldershot GU12 5PL
    Tel: 01252 675007

Commercial &
    Admin. Manager     **Chris Kelly**

Press Officer     **Alan Kingston**
    Tel: 01737 210032

Back Row (L-R): Clive House, Jerome John, Tarkan Mustafa, Simon Harris, Mark Harris, Steve Farrelly, Matt Crossley, Wayne Baron, Gary Patterson, Scott Corbett, James Pipes, Ian McDonald
Front Row: Danny Smith, Eddie Akuamoah, Kevin Rattray, David Leworthy, Geoff Chapple, Geoff Pitcher, Delton Francis, Colin Luckett

193

# KINGSTONIAN
## MATCH FACTS 1998-99

| No | Date | Venue | Comp | Opponents | Att | Result | Score | Goalscorers |
|----|------|-------|------|-----------|-----|--------|-------|-------------|
| 1 | 15/08 | H | NC | Hereford United | 2104 | W | 2-0 | Leworthy 10, Francis 35 |
| 2 | 18/08 | A | NC | Yeovil Town | 2339 | W | 3-1 | Luckett 21, Stewart 57, Akuamoah 85 |
| 3 | 22/08 | A | NC | Morecambe | 1024 | D | 0-0 | |
| 4 | 25/08 | H | NC | Rushden & Diamonds | 2605 | L | 1-5 | Leworthy 15 |
| 5 | 29/08 | H | NC | Doncaster Rovers | 1942 | W | 2-1 | Mustafa 65, Holligan 90 |
| 6 | 31/08 | A | NC | Telford United | 680 | D | 1-1 | Corbett 9 |
| 7 | 05/09 | A | NC | Northwich Victoria | 906 | W | 3-2 | Luckett 59, Mustafa 84, Corbett 88 |
| 8 | 08/09 | H | NC | Stevenage Borough | 1745 | W | 1-0 | Akuamoah 14 |
| 9 | 12/09 | H | NC | Cheltenham Town | 1801 | L | 1-2 | Luckett 63 |
| 10 | 15/09 | A | NC | Farnborough Town | 759 | L | 2-4 | Brown 78, Holligan 88 |
| 11 | 19/09 | A | NC | Kettering Town | 1469 | L | 0-2 | |
| 12 | 26/09 | H | NC | Hednesford Town | 1293 | D | 1-1 | Harris 83 |
| 13 | 03/10 | H | NC | Barrow | 1281 | W | 5-1 | Patterson 5, Akuamoah 46 90, Holligan 75 82 |
| 14 | 10/10 | A | NC | Kidderminster Harriers | 1884 | W | 1-0 | Leworthy 35 |
| 15 | 24/10 | H | NC | Welling United | 904 | W | 2-1 | Rattray 29, Mustafa 35 |
| 16 | 07/11 | A | NC | Southport | 1060 | D | 1-1 | Holligan 8 |
| 17 | 28/11 | H | NC | Northwich Victoria | 901 | D | 1-1 | Pitcher 40 |
| 18 | 12/12 | H | NC | Yeovil Town | 1017 | D | 0-0 | |
| 19 | 19/12 | A | NC | Leek Town | 495 | D | 2-2 | Leworthy 12, Corbett 39 |
| 20 | 26/12 | H | NC | Woking | 2694 | D | 0-0 | |
| 21 | 28/12 | A | NC | Dover Athletic | 1480 | L | 1-5 | Patterson 37 |
| 22 | 02/01 | A | NC | Woking | 3772 | W | 1-0 | Boylan 76 |
| 23 | 09/01 | H | NC | Hayes | 1129 | D | 1-1 | Luckett 14 |
| 24 | 23/01 | H | NC | Farnborough Town | 1063 | D | 1-1 | Akuamoah 48 |
| 25 | 30/01 | A | NC | Barrow | 1730 | W | 1-0 | Pitcher 10 |
| 26 | 13/02 | A | NC | Stevenage Borough | 2261 | D | 3-3 | Leworthy 35 36, Luckett 63 |
| 27 | 20/02 | H | NC | Kettering Town | 1068 | L | 1-2 | Pitcher 39 |
| 28 | 23/02 | H | NC | Leek Town | 606 | W | 3-0 | Pitcher 34, Crossley 38, Leworthy 49 |
| 29 | 06/03 | H | NC | Morecambe | 888 | D | 0-0 | |
| 30 | 09/03 | H | NC | Kidderminster Harriers | 735 | W | 1-0 | Tranter 25 |
| 31 | 13/03 | A | NC | Welling United | 803 | W | 3-1 | Crossley 4, Akuamoah 51, Leworthy 87 |
| 32 | 20/03 | H | NC | Telford United | 816 | W | 1-0 | Akuamoah 19 |
| 33 | 24/03 | A | NC | Forest Green Rovers | 784 | L | 0-1 | |
| 34 | 03/04 | A | NC | Hayes | 929 | L | 0-3 | |
| 35 | 05/04 | H | NC | Dover Athletic | 904 | W | 1-0 | Rattray 6 |
| 36 | 08/04 | A | NC | Hereford United | 1288 | L | 0-2 | |
| 37 | 13/04 | A | NC | Cheltenham Town | 3184 | L | 0-1 | |
| 38 | 20/04 | A | NC | Rushden & Diamonds | 1818 | D | 0-0 | |
| 39 | 24/04 | H | NC | Forest Green Rovers | 1008 | L | 0-1 | |
| 40 | 27/04 | A | NC | Hednesford Town | 652 | W | 2-1 | Leworthy 8, Pitcher 39 |
| 41 | 28/04 | H | NC | Southport | 492 | L | 0-2 | |
| 42 | 01/05 | A | NC | Doncaster Rovers | 2915 | W | 1-0 | Leworthy 24 |

### CUP COMPETITIONS

| Date | Venue | Comp | Opponents | Att | Result | Score | Goalscorers |
|------|-------|------|-----------|-----|--------|-------|-------------|
| 04/08 | A | Saft Nife Shield | Hampton | n/k | W | 3-1 | Perna 4 48, Holligan 40 |
| 29/09 | A | Ryman Lge CS | Sutton United | 403 | W | 6-1 | Akuamoah 29 44, Luckett 32, Patterson 36, Pitcher 75, Corbett 87 |
| 06/10 | A | Endsleigh 1 | Farnborough Town | 514 | L | 2-4 | Luckett 43[p], Holligan |
| 17/10 | A | FA Cup Q3 | Maidenhead United | 717 | W | 4-2 | Leworthy(2), Holligan(2) |
| 31/10 | A | FA Cup Q4 | St Albans City | 861 | D | 1-1 | Stewart 55 |
| 03/11 | H | FA Cup Q4 rep | St Albans City | 845 | W | 1-1 | Holligan 12    (5-4 pens) |
| 14/11 | H | FA Cup 1 | Burton Albion | 1505 | W | 1-0 | Holligan 65 |
| 21/11 | A | FA Trophy 2 | Gloucester City | 652 | W | 2-1 | Akuamoah 23, Willgrass 66[p] |
| 06/12 | H | FA Cup 2 | Leyton Orient | 3497 | D | 0-0 | |
| 15/12 | A | FA Cup 2 rep | Leyton Orient | 3652 | L | 1-2 | Holligan 74 |
| 22/12 | H | Surrey SC 1 | Cobham | 550 | W | 5-3 | Langley 20, Corbett 25, Thomas 82, Sullivan 84, Patterson 89 |
| 30/12 | H | Surrey SC 2 | Croydon | 131 | D | 2-2 | Smith 35, Pritchard 89 |
| 19/01 | H | FA Trophy 3 | Kettering Town | 624 | W | 5-2 | Akuamoah 25 90, Leworthy 29 40, Stewart 50 |
| 27/01 | A | Surrey SC 2 rep | Croydon | 104 | W | 4-1 | Leworthy, Crossley, Luckett, Pitcher |
| 06/02 | A | FA Trophy 4 | Whyteleafe | 945 | W | 3-0 | Leworthy 54 55, Luckett 80[p] |
| 09/02 | A | Surrey SC QF | Molesey | 200 | W | 1-0 | Akuamoah |
| 27/02 | H | FA Trophy 5 | Yeovil Town | 1783 | W | 1-0 | Stewart 89 |
| 01/03 | H | Surrey SC SF | Carshalton Athletic | 205 | D | 1-1 | Corbett 3 |
| 15/03 | A | Surrey SC SF rep | Carshalton Athletic | 253 | L | 2-3 | Corbett, Leworthy |
| 27/03 | A | FA Trophy QF | Northwich Victoria | 1819 | W | 2-0 | Mustafa 48, Akuamoah 68 |
| 10/04 | H | FA Trophy SF(1) | Cheltenham Town | 2203 | D | 2-2 | Stewart 28, Pitcher 69 |
| 17/04 | A | FA Trophy SF(2) | Cheltenham Town | 4425 | W | 3-1 | Crossley 5, Leworthy 55, Patterson 87 |
| 15/05 | A | FA Trophy F | Forest Green Rovers | 20037 | W | 1-0 | Mustafa 49                (at Wembley Stadium) |

| 1 | 2 | 3 | 4 | 5 | 6 | 7 | 8 | 9 | 10 | 11 | 12 / 14 / 15 | |
|---|---|---|---|---|---|---|---|---|---|---|---|---|
| John | Culverhouse | Luckett | Crossley | Stewart | Harris | Patterson | Pitcher | Francis | Leworthy | Akuamoah | Rattray, Corbett, Holligan | 1 |
| Barrett | Smith | Luckett | Crossley | Stewart | Harris | Patterson | Pitcher | Rattray | Leworthy | Akuamoah | Holligan, Francis, Corbett | 2 |
| Barrett | Smith | Luckett | Crossley | Stewart | Harris | Patterson | Pitcher | Rattray | Leworthy | Akuamoah | Francis, Corbett, Holligan | 3 |
| Barrett | Smith | Luckett | Crossley | Stewart | Harris | Patterson | Pitcher | Rattray | Leworthy | Akuamoah | Corbett, Holligan, Francis | 4 |
| Barrett | Mustafa | Luckett | Brown | Stewart | Harris | Patterson | Pitcher | Francis | Leworthy | Akuamoah | Corbett, Rattray, Holligan | 5 |
| Barrett | Mustafa | Luckett | Brown | Stewart | Harris | Patterson | Pitcher | Francis | Corbett | Akuamoah | Rattray, Holligan, Watkinson | 6 |
| Barrett | Mustafa | Luckett | Brown | Stewart | Harris | Patterson | Pitcher | Francis | Leworthy | Akuamoah | Holligan, Corbett, Rattray | 7 |
| John | Mustafa | Luckett | Crossley | Stewart | Harris | Patterson | Pitcher | Corbett | Leworthy | Akuamoah | Rattray, Holligan, Francis | 8 |
| John | Mustafa | Luckett | Crossley | Stewart | Harris | Patterson | Pitcher | Corbett | Leworthy | Akuamoah | Holligan, Rattray, Francis | 9 |
| John | Mustafa | Luckett | Crossley | Brown | Harris | Patterson | Pitcher | Corbett | Leworthy | Akuamoah | Rattray, Francis, Holligan | 10 |
| S Brown | Mustafa | Luckett | Crossley | Smith | Harris | Rattray | Pitcher | Holligan | Leworthy | Akuamoah | Francis, Corbett, Brown | 11 |
| Brown | Mustafa | Luckett | Crossley | Stewart | Harris | Patterson | Pitcher | Francis | Leworthy | Akuamoah | Holligan, Corbett, Rattray | 12 |
| John | Mustafa | Luckett | Crossley | Stewart | Harrison | Patterson | Pitcher | Francis | Leworthy | Akuamoah | Corbett, Holligan, Rattray | 13 |
| S Brown | Mustafa | Luckett | Crossley | Stewart | Harris | Patterson | Pitcher | Rattray | Leworthy | Holligan | Corbett, Watkinson, W Brown | 14 |
| S Brown | Mustafa | Luckett | Crossley | Stewart | Harris | Patterson | Willgrass | Rattray | Leworthy | Holligan | Akuamoah, Corbett, Smith | 15 |
| Farrelly | Mustafa | Luckett | Crossley | Stewart | Harris | Patterson | Pitcher | Willgrass | Holligan | Akuamoah | Rattray, Corbett, Brown | 16 |
| Farrelly | Mustafa | Luckett | Crossley | Corbett | Harris | Patterson | Pitcher | Willgrass | Holligan | Akuamoah | Leworthy, Smith, Thomas | 17 |
| Farrelly | Mustafa | Luckett | Crossley | Stewart | Harris | Patterson | Pitcher | Rattray | Leworthy | Akuamoah | Willgrass, Holligan, Brown | 18 |
| Farrelly | Mustafa | Luckett | Crossley | Corbett | Harris | Patterson | Pitcher | Willgrass | Leworthy | Boylan | Watkinson, Thomas, Smith | 19 |
| Farrelly | Mustafa | Luckett | Crossley | W Brown | Harris | Corbett | Pitcher | Boylan | Leworthy | Willgrass | Smith, Thomas, Akuamoah | 20 |
| Farrelly | Mustafa | Luckett | Crossley | Brown | Harris | Patterson | Pitcher | Willgrass | Boylan | Thomas | Corbett, Akuamoah, Smith | 21 |
| Farrelly | Mustafa | Luckett | Crossley | Stewart | Harris | Patterson | Pitcher | Rattray | Boylan | Akuamoah | Willgrass, Corbett, John | 22 |
| Farrelly | Mustafa | Luckett | Crossley | Stewart | Harris | Patterson | Pitcher | Rattray | Boylan | Akuamoah | Corbett, Leworthy, Lester | 23 |
| Farrelly | Mustafa | Luckett | Crossley | Stewart | Harris | Patterson | Pitcher | Rattray | Leworthy | Akuamoah | Corbett, Thomas, Lester | 24 |
| Farrelly | Mustafa | Luckett | Crossley | Stewart | Harris | Patterson | Pitcher | Rattray | Leworthy | Akuamoah | Thomas, Corbett, Lester | 25 |
| Farrelly | Mustafa | Luckett | Crossley | Stewart | Harris | Patterson | Pitcher | Rattray | Leworthy | Akuamoah | Corbett, Francis, Nyamah | 26 |
| Farrelly | Mustafa | Nyamah | Crossley | Stewart | Harris | Coates | Pitcher | Rattray | Leworthy | Akuamoah | Corbett, Luckett, Francis | 27 |
| John | Mustafa | Luckett | Crossley | Stewart | Harris | Patterson | Pitcher | Rattray | Leworthy | Akuamoah | Francis, Corbett, Smith | 28 |
| Farrelly | Mustafa | Luckett | Crossley | Stewart | Harris | Patterson | Corbett | White | Leworthy | Akuamoah | Tranter, Smith, Francis | 29 |
| Farrelly | Mustafa | Luckett | Crossley | Stewart | Harris | Patterson | Pitcher | Corbett | Tranter | Francis | Akuamoah, White, Drewett | 30 |
| Farrelly | Mustafa | Luckett | Crossley | Stewart | White | Patterson | Pitcher | Rattray | Tranter | Francis | Akuamoah, Leworthy, Harris | 31 |
| John | Mustafa | Luckett | Crossley | Stewart | Harris | Patterson | Pitcher | Rattray | Leworthy | Akuamoah | White, Francis, Tranter | 32 |
| John | Mustafa | Luckett | Crossley | Stewart | Harris | Patterson | Pitcher | Rattray | Leworthy | Akuamoah | Corbett, Francis, White | 33 |
| Farrelly | Mustafa | Nyamah | White | Stewart | Harris | Langley | Luckett | Rattray | Leworthy | Akuamoah | Pitcher, Tranter, Francis | 34 |
| Farrelly | Mustafa | Luckett | White | Stewart | Harris | Patterson | Pitcher | Rattray | Leworthy | Akuamoah | Nyamah, Tranter, Francis | 35 |
| John | Smith | Luckett | Lester | Brown | Corbett | Langley | Pitcher | Francis | Tranter | Nyamah | Dixon, Thomas, Drewett | 36 |
| John | Mustafa | Luckett | Nyamah | Stewart | Harris | Patterson | Corbett | Rattray | Leworthy | Francis | AkuamoahvBrown, Lester | 37 |
| Farrelly | Mustafa | Luckett | Crossley | Stewart | Harris | Patterson | Pitcher | Rattray | Leworthy | Akuamoah | Francis, Brown, Lester | 38 |
| Farrelly | Mustafa | Luckett | Crossley | Stewart | Harris | Patterson | Pitcher | Rattray | Leworthy | Akuamoah | Brown, Francis, Smith | 39 |
| Farrelly | Mustafa | Luckett | Crossley | Stewart | Harris | Smith | Pitcher | Rattray | Leworthy | Francis | Brown, Drewett, Lester | 40 |
| Farrelly | Smith | Luckett | Crossley | Stewart | Harris | Brown | Pitcher | Rattray | Leworthy | Francis | Lester, Drewett, Tranter | 41 |
| Farrelly | Mustafa | Luckett | Crossley | Stewart | Harris | Patterson | Smith | Rattray | Leworthy | Francis | Brown, Lester, Tranter | 42 |

League Attendances    **HIGHEST:** 2694    **LOWEST:** 492

**CONFERENCE:** 9th    **FA CUP:** 2nd Round    **FA TROPHY:** Final

## MANAGER
### GEOFF CHAPPLE

| | |
|---|---|
| Date of Appointment | May 1997 |
| Date of Birth: | 7th November 1945 |
| Place of Birth: | Farnham, Surrey |

PREVIOUS CLUBS
As manager             Windsor & Eton, Woking.
As player       Woking, Guildford City, Windsor & Eton

HONOURS
As manager

FA Trophy 93-94, 94-95, 96-97, 98-99;
Isthmian League - Premier Div. 91-92, 97-98,
Div. 1 R-up 89-90, Div. 2 S 86-87,
League Cup 90-91, Charity Shield 91-92;
Conference - R-up 94-95, 95-96,
Championship Shield 94-95, R-up 95-96.

Right: Geoff Chapple. Photo: Mark Sandom

Eddie Akuamoah. Photo: Andrew Chitty

## FOOTBALL MANAGEMENT TEAM

| | |
|---|---|
| Assistant Manager | Clive Howse |
| Coach | Ian McDonald |
| Physio | Jim Pearce |
| Youth Team Manager | S.Chamberlain |
| Youth Development Officer | S Chamberlain |

### 1998-99

| | |
|---|---|
| **Top Scorer:** | David Leworthy |
| **Player of the Year:** | Gary Paterson |
| **Captain:** | Matthew Crossley |

## MATCHDAY PROGRAMME

| | |
|---|---|
| Number of pages | 28 |
| Price | £1.50 |
| Programme Editor | Brian Giffard |
| Other club publications: | Tel: 0870 442 5003<br>None |
| Local Newspapers: | Surrey Comet<br>0181 546 2261 |
| Local Radio Stations: | County Sound<br>Southern Counties |

# PLAYING SQUAD

| Player | Birthplace Honours | D.O.B. | Previous Clubs |
|---|---|---|---|
| **GOALKEEPERS** | | | |
| Steve Farrelly | | 27.03.65 | Chester City, Macclesfield Town, Rotherham United, Barrow |
| Richard Hurst | | | Queens Park Rangers |
| | | | |
| **DEFENDERS** | | | |
| Colin Luckett | | 19.01.76 | Millwall |
| RLP | | | |
| Matt Crossley | Basingstoke | 18.03.68 | Overton U, Wycombe W |
| GMVC, FAT, RLP | | | |
| Derek Allan, | | 24.12.74 | Ayr United,Southampton, Brighton& Hove Albion |
| Scotland U21 | | | |
| Luke Basford | | 06.01.80 | Bristol Rovers |
| Mark Harris | | 15.07.63 | Burnley, Swansea City, Gillingham, Cardiff City |
| Michael Lester | | | Youth Team |
| Tarkan Mustafa | | 28.08.73 | Wimbledon, Kettering Town. |
| Simon Stewart | | 01.11.73 | Sheffield Wednesday, Shrewsbury Town,Fulham |
| | | | |
| **MIDFIELDERS** | | | |
| Phil Wingfield | | 11.03.69 | Walton& Hersham,Kingstonian, Hayes, Kingstonian, Farnborough T. |
| **Gary Patterson** | **Newcastle** | **27.11.72** | **Notts County, Shrewsbury T, Wycombe W** |
| RLP | | | |
| Danny Smith | London | 07.09.75 | Tottenham Hotspur, Welling U |
| RLP | | | |
| **Geoff Pitcher** | **Carshalton** | **15.08.75** | **Millwall, Watford, Carshalton Ath, Kingstonian, Colchester U** |
| RLP | | | |
| Junior Kady | | | Coventry City, Whyteleafe |
| | | | |
| **FORWARDS** | | | |
| **David Leworthy** | **Portsmouth** | **22.10.62** | **Portsmouth, Fareham T, Tottenham Hotspur, £175,000 to Oxford U,Reading, Farnborough T, £50,000 to Farnborough T, £15,000 to Rushden & D, £18,000 to Kingstonian** |
| RLP | | | |
| Eddie Akuamoah | London | | Bedfont, Carshalton Ath |
| RLP | | | |
| Dwight Marshall | Jamaica | 03.10,65 | Grays Athletic, Kingsbury, Leyton-Wingate, Hampton, Plymouth Argyle, Luton Town, Plymouth Argyle |
| Dean Thomas | | 12.08.79 | Youth Team |
| Dan Newman | | | A.F.C. Lymington& New Milton |

Bold Print indicates England Semi-Professional Internationals

Departures: Wayne Brown, Jerome John and Kevin Rattray (Enfield) Delton Francis (Nuneaton Borough)

# KINGSTONIAN

**Founded:** 1885

**Nickname:** The Ks

**Sponsors:** Bass Brewers

**Club Colours:** Red & white hooped shirts, white shorts, white socks
**Change Colours:** Yellow shirts, royal blue shorts, white socks

**Midweek matchday:** Tuesday

**Reserves' League:** Suburban

**Newsline:** 0660 666 300
**Geoff Chapple's Buzz Line:** 0660 666 333

## GROUND DETAILS

Kingsmeadow Stadium,
Kingston Road,
Kingston-upon-Thames,
Surrey. KT13PB

TELEPHONE: 0181 547 3335/6

**DIRECTIONS:**
From town centre - Cambridge Rd on to Kingston Rd (A2043) toMalden Rd. From A3, turn off at New Malden, turn left on to A2043 - grd 1 mile on left. Half mile from Norbiton (BR)

**CAPACITY:** 9,000
**COVERED TERRACING:** 3,500
**SEATED:** 690

**SOCIAL FACILITIES:**
Banqueting centre, open 7 days. 3 bars capacity 400. Contact Chris Kelly (0181 547 3335). Banquets & Conference Manager Cathrine Cole Tel: 0181 974 5712

**CLUB SHOP:** Sells programmes, shirts, badges etc. Contact Mrs Ann Dickinson Tel: 0181 747 3336

## Past Players who progressed to the Football League

C Nastri (C Palace), H Lindsay (Southampton 65),
G Still (Brighton 79), D Byrne (Gillingham 1985),
J Power(Brentford 87), Jamie Ndah (Torquay)
Gavin Holligan (West Ham '99)

## PREVIOUS

**Leagues:** Kingston & Dist.; West Surrey Southern Suburban Athenian 1919-29 Isthmian League 29-9

**Names:** Kingston & Surbiton YMCA 1885-87 Saxons 87-90, Kingston Wanderers 1893-1904 Old Kingstonians 08-1

**Grounds:** Several to 1921; Richmond Rd 21-8

## CLUB RECORDS

**Attendance:** 4,582 v Chelsea (Friendly) 22.7.95

**Goalscorer:** Johnny Whing 295
**Appearances:** Micky Preston 555

**Win:** 15-1 v Delft, friendly 5/9/51
Competitive 10-0 v Hitchin (H) Isthmian Lge 19/3/66
**Defeat:** 0-11 v Ilford (A) Isthmian Lge 13/2/37

**Transfer Fee Paid:** £18,000 for David Leworthy to Rushden & Diamonds '97
**Transfer Fee Received:** £150,000 for Gavin Holligan from West Ham Utd. '99

## BEST SEASON

**FA Amateur Cup:** Winners 32-33 R-up 59-60

**FA Trophy:** Winners 98-99

**FA Cup:** 2nd Rd Proper 94-95, v Aylesbury U 95-96, v Plymouth A.
League clubs defeated: Brighton & H.A. 94-95 1-0

## HONOURS

FA Trophy 98-99
Isthmian League 33-34, 36-37, 97-9
R-up 47-48 62-63
Div 1 R-up 84-85
Isthmian Lge. Cup 95-96
Athenian Lge 23-24 25-26, R-up 26-27
LondonSnr Cup 62-63 64-65 86-87, R-up x5
Surrey Snr Cup x9, R-up 90-91

198

# MORECAMBE

Having finished in a creditable 5th position in the previous season, The Shrimps with much the same squad, never quite seemed to match that form.
A terrible start, losing 2-5 to Kidderminster Harriers, didn't help and they always seemed to be working their way away from the bottom for the rest of the season - especially after that other early disaster losing 0-7 to Leek Town!

It took two months to work their way up to 18th place and another two months to reach relative safety.
Defeats by Hednesford Town and Leigh RMI ruined all hopes of successes in The F.A.Cup or F.A. Trophy although the semi-final of the Endsleigh Trophy was reached.
Having enjoyed 7th position in the Conference Jim Harvey's squad were missing the elegant Brian Healy and their league position was once again giving cause for concern. Three wins in the last five games enabled them to reach a final position of 14th but with top scorer John Norman leaving for Hednesford Town, The Shrimps will have to show very real improvement if they are to enjoy the coming campaign.

T.T.

## CLUB OFFICIALS 1999-2000

| | |
|---|---|
| Honorary President | **Jim Bowen** |
| Chairman | **Rod Taylor** |
| Vice Chairmen | **Graham Hodgson** |
| | **Peter Cross** |
| Directors | **Dickie Danson** |
| | **David Derham** |
| | **Peter McMcGuigan** |
| | **Stuart Redman** |
| Company & Club Secretary | **Neil Marsdin** |
| Commercial Manager | **Peter Howard** |

Back: Andy Heald, Paul McGuire, Mark Wright, Barrie Keeling, Tony Hughes, Darren Lyons, Neil Hardy, Phil Eastwood. Middle: Dave Miller, Jeff Udall, Gary Thompson, Wayne Curtis, Andy Farrell, Andy Milner, Steve McIlharghey, Andy Banks, Stewart DRummond, John Hardiker, Paul Rushton, Ryan-Zico Black, Tom Sayer, Lew Dewhurst. Front: Tony Gribbins, Andy Fensome, Dave Swannick, Leon Smith, Dave McKearney, Jim Harvey, Paul Burns, Michael Knowles, Dave Gardner, Neil Morton, Claudia Manfredi.

# MORECAMBE
## MATCH FACTS 1998-99

| No | Date | Venue | Comp | Opponents | Att | Result | Score | Goalscorers |
|----|------|-------|------|-----------|-----|--------|-------|-------------|
| 1 | 15/08 | A | NC | Kidderminster Harriers | 1828 | L | 2-5 | Ceraolo 54, Norman 64 |
| 2 | 18/08 | H | NC | Barrow | 3193 | W | 3-2 | Milner 27, Norman 38, Ceraolo 72 |
| 3 | 22/08 | H | NC | Kingstonian | 1024 | D | 0-0 | |
| 4 | 25/08 | A | NC | Leek Town | 501 | L | 0-7 | |
| 5 | 29/08 | A | NC | Hayes | 422 | W | 2-1 | Norman 57 90 |
| 6 | 31/08 | H | NC | Hednesford Town | 1256 | W | 3-1 | Ceraolo 27 41, A C Banks 78 |
| 7 | 05/09 | A | NC | Cheltenham Town | 1959 | L | 1-4 | Norman 9 |
| 8 | 08/09 | A | NC | Barrow | 2073 | L | 1-2 | Curtis 5 |
| 9 | 12/09 | H | NC | Stevenage Borough | 1010 | D | 1-1 | Curtis 69 |
| 10 | 19/09 | A | NC | Hereford United | 2049 | L | 0-2 | |
| 11 | 22/09 | H | NC | Doncaster Rovers | 1180 | L | 1-2 | Mayers 90 |
| 12 | 26/09 | H | NC | Telford United | 902 | L | 0-1 | |
| 13 | 03/10 | A | NC | Woking | 2740 | W | 3-0 | Shirley 27, Jackson 44, Lyons 72 |
| 14 | 10/10 | H | NC | Kettering Town | 1055 | W | 3-1 | Jackson 7 61, Healy 33 |
| 15 | 24/10 | A | NC | Rushden & Diamonds | 2394 | L | 1-3 | Jackson 14 |
| 16 | 07/11 | H | NC | Forest Green Rovers | 812 | W | 3-1 | Norman 14, Jackson 68 74 |
| 17 | 14/11 | H | NC | Leek Town | 840 | D | 2-2 | Lyons 43, Healy 90 |
| 18 | 28/11 | H | NC | Welling United | 855 | W | 2-1 | Norman 46, Ceraolo 86 |
| 19 | 05/12 | A | NC | Telford United | 604 | W | 3-2 | Norman 55 71 83 |
| 20 | 12/12 | A | NC | Farnborough Town | 682 | W | 6-1 | Norman 31 69, Lyons 51, Shirley 63, Drummond 89, Keeling |
| 21 | 19/12 | H | NC | Hayes | 1016 | L | 2-3 | Mayers 11, Norman 65 |
| 22 | 26/12 | A | NC | Northwich Victoria | 1304 | D | 1-1 | Norman 45 |
| 23 | 28/12 | H | NC | Southport | 1356 | D | 1-1 | Takano 45 |
| 24 | 02/01 | H | NC | Northwich Victoria | 1107 | W | 3-1 | Norman 48 87, Gardner 88 |
| 25 | 09/01 | A | NC | Kettering Town | 2364 | L | 0-6 | |
| 26 | 16/01 | A | NC | Doncaster Rovers | 4251 | L | 1-2 | Lyons 9 |
| 27 | 23/01 | A | NC | Stevenage Borough | 2266 | L | 0-2 | |
| 28 | 30/01 | H | NC | Yeovil Town | 1254 | D | 1-1 | McKearney 65 |
| 29 | 06/02 | A | NC | Hednesford Town | 834 | L | 0-1 | |
| 30 | 13/02 | H | NC | Cheltenham Town | 1354 | L | 0-2 | |
| 31 | 20/02 | H | NC | Dover Athletic | 850 | L | 0-4 | |
| 32 | 06/03 | A | NC | Kingstonian | 888 | D | 0-0 | |
| 33 | 13/03 | H | NC | Woking | 1120 | L | 0-1 | |
| 34 | 20/03 | H | NC | Rushden & Diamonds | 1099 | L | 2-3 | Lyons 46, Norman 67 |
| 35 | 27/03 | A | NC | Dover Athletic | 872 | W | 3-2 | Drummond 62 68, Lyons 84 |
| 36 | 03/04 | H | NC | Hereford United | 1012 | W | 1-0 | Cross 59[og] |
| 37 | 05/04 | A | NC | Southport | 1427 | L | 0-1 | |
| 38 | 10/04 | H | NC | Kidderminster Harriers | 966 | W | 2-1 | Drummond 7, Takano 30 |
| 39 | 22/04 | A | NC | Forest Green Rovers | 408 | D | 2-2 | Curtis 62, Drummond 84 |
| 40 | 24/04 | A | NC | Welling United | 727 | L | 2-3 | Norman 33, Head 77 |
| 41 | 27/04 | A | NC | Yeovil Town | 1966 | W | 1-0 | Gardner 5 |
| 42 | 01/05 | H | NC | Farnborough Town | 1136 | W | 1-0 | Norman 1 |

### CUP COMPETITIONS

| | Date | Venue | Comp | Opponents | Att | Result | Score | Goalscorers |
|---|------|-------|------|-----------|-----|--------|-------|-------------|
| | 20/10 | H | FA Cup Q3 | Farsley Celtic | 0 | W | 4-2 | Norman 37 78, Lyons 41, Healy 90 |
| | 21/11 | A | FA Trophy 2 | Leigh RMI | 435 | L | 1-4 | Lyons 45 |
| | 01/12 | H | Endsleigh 2 | Barrow | 567 | W | 2-0 | Norman 10, Hughes 71 |
| | 13/01 | A | Lancs ATS 2 | Fleetwood Freeport | n/k | W | 4-2 | Haddow 15, Ceraolo 64, Norman 78, Lyons 90 |
| | 02/02 | A | Lancs ATS QF | Chorley | 319 | W | 2-0 | Ceraolo 71, Shirley 80 |
| | 23/02 | A | Endsleigh QF | Hereford United | 0 | W | 3-2 | Lyons 60 99, Norman 67 |
| | 09/03 | H | Lancs ATS SF | Bamber Bridge | 363 | W | 3-2 | Lyons 37, Norman 49, Keeling 59 |
| | 30/03 | H | Endsleigh SF(1) | Doncaster Rovers | 1302 | L | 1-2 | |
| | 08/04 | A | Endsleigh SF(2) | Doncaster Rovers | 3297 | L | 0-1 | |
| | 13/04 | A | Lancs ATS F | Darwen | n/k | W | 2-2 | 4-2 pens (at Chorley) |

| 1 | 2 | 3 | 4 | 5 | 6 | 7 | 8 | 9 | 10 | 11 | 12 / 14 / 15 | |
|---|---|---|---|---|---|---|---|---|---|---|---|---|
| Ilharghey | McKearney | Kennedy | Walter | Mayers | Hall | Drummond | Healy | Milner | Norman | Burns | Rushton, Keeling, Ceraolo | 1 |
| Banks | Rushton | Kennedy | McKearney | Mayers | Hall | Drummond | Healy | Milner | Norman | Ceraolo | Haddow, Curtis, Knowles | 2 |
| Banks | Knowles | Kennedy | McKearney | Mayers | Hall | Drummond | Healy | Ceraolo | Norman | Keeling | Rushton, Curtis, Shirley | 3 |
| Banks | Knowles | Kennedy | McKearney | Mayers | Hall | Healy | Drummond | Ceraolo | Norman | Keeling | Rushton, Curtis, Shirley | 4 |
| Banks | Rushton | Kennedy | Waller | Mayers | Haddow | A C Banks | Healy | Milner | Norman | Shirley | McKearney, Burns, Ceraolo | 5 |
| Banks | Rushton | Kennedy | Waller | Mayers | Haddow | A C Banks | Healy | Ceraolo | Norman | Shirley | Burns, McKearney, Curtis | 6 |
| Banks | Rushton | Kennedy | Waller | Mayers | Haddow | A C Banks | Healy | Ceraolo | Norman | Shirley | Burns, McKearney, Curtis | 7 |
| Ilhargey | McKearney | Kennedy | Waller | Hall | Burns | A C Banks | Healy | Curtis | Norman | Shirley | Drummond, Ceraolo, Haddow | 8 |
| Ilhargey | McKearney | Kennedy | Waller | Hall | Burns | A C Banks | Healy | Ceraolo | Norman | Shirley | Drummond, Keeling, Curtis | 9 |
| Ilhargey | Rushton | McKearney | Waller | Hall | Burns | Keeling | Healy | Curtis | Norman | Shirley | A C Banks, Ceraolo, Drummond | 10 |
| Ilhargey | Rushton | McKearney | Waller | Hall | Burns | Keeling | Healy | Curtis | Norman | Shirley | Takano, Mayers, Ceraolo | 11 |
| Ilhargey | Rushton | Takano | McKearney | Hall | Burns | Lyons | Healy | Ceraolo | Mayers | Shirley | Drummond, Curtis, Norman | 12 |
| Ilhargey | Rushton | Kennedy | Burns | Mayers | Hall | Lyons | Healy | Jackson | Drummond | Shirley | Takano, Norman, Ceraolo | 13 |
| Ilhargey | McKearney | Kennedy | Burns | Mayers | Hall | Lyons | Healy | Jackson | Drummond | Shirley | Curtis, Takano, Ceraolo | 14 |
| Ilhargey | McKearney | Kennedy | Hall | Myers | Burns | Lyons | Drummond | Jackson | Norman | Shirley | Takano, Keeling, T Hughes | 15 |
| Ilhargey | Rushton | Takano | Hall | McKearney | Burns | Lyons | Drummond | Jackson | Norman | Shirley | Gardner, Curtis, Keeling | 16 |
| Ilhargey | Rushton | Takano | Hall | McKearney | Burns | Lyons | Drummond | Curtis | Norman | Shirley | Healy, Gardner, D Hughes | 17 |
| Ilhargey | McKearney | Kennedy | Mayers | T Hughes | Burns | Lyons | Healy | Drummond | Norman | Shirley | Takano, Gardner, Ceraolo | 18 |
| Ilhargey | McKearney | Kennedy | Mayers | T Hughes | Burns | Lyons | Healy | Drummond | Norman | Shirley | Takano, Gardner, Ceraolo | 19 |
| Ilhargey | McKearney | Takano | Mayers | Hughes | Knowles | Lyons | Healy | Drummond | Norman | Shirley | Gardner, Keeling, Ceraolo | 20 |
| Ilhargey | McKearney | Takano | Mayers | Hughes | Knowles | Lyons | Keeling | Drummond | Norman | Shirley | Ceraolo, Burns, Gardner | 21 |
| Ilhargey | McKearney | Takano | Mayers | T Hughes | Burns | Lyons | Knowles | Drummond | Norman | Shirley | Haddow, Ceraolo, Gardner | 22 |
| Ilhargey | McKearney | Kennedy | Mayers | Hughes | Burns | Lyons | Knowles | Drummond | Norman | Takano | Gardner, Curtis, Haddow | 23 |
| Ilhargey | McKearney | Takano | Mayers | Hughes | Burns | Lyons | Knowles | Drummond | Norman | Kennedy | Curtis, Gardner, Haddow | 24 |
| Ilhargey | McKearney | Kennedy | Mayers | Hughes | Burns | Lyons | Drummond | Ceraolo | Norman | Takano | Curtis, Gardner, Haddow | 25 |
| Ilhargey | McKearney | Kennedy | Mayers | Hughes | Burns | Lyons | Knowles | Drummond | Norman | Shirley | Gardner, Rushton, Ceraolo | 26 |
| Banks | Swanwick | Takano | Hall | Hughes | Burns | Lyons | Drummond | Curtis | Norman | Shirley | Keeling, Heald, McGuire | 27 |
| Banks | McKearney | Takano | Hall | Hughes | Burns | Lyons | Keeling | Drummond | Norman | Shirley | Ceraolo, Rushton, Heald | 28 |
| Banks | McKearney | Kennedy | Hall | Hughes | Burns | Lyons | Keeling | Drummond | Norman | Gardner | Ceraolo, Rushton, Takano | 29 |
| Banks | McKearney | Kennedy | Hall | Hughes | Burns | Lyons | Drummond | Ceraolo | Norman | Shirley | Rushton, Takano, Gardner | 30 |
| Banks | Swanwick | Kennedy | Mayers | Hughes | Burns | Gardner | McKearney | Morton | Norman | Shirley | Lyons, Drummond, Takano | 31 |
| Banks | Fensome | Brown | Mayers | Hughes | Drummond | Lyons | McKearney | Morton | Norman | Shirley | Keeling, Rushton, Takano | 32 |
| Banks | Fensome | Brown | Mayers | Rushton | Burns | Lyons | McKearney | Morton | Norman | Shirley | Drummond, Keeling, Takano | 33 |
| Banks | Fensome | Brown | Mayers | Rushton | Burns | Lyons | McKearney | Drummond | Norman | Gardner | Takano, Keeling, Shirley | 34 |
| Ilhargey | Fensome | Brown | Hall | Hughes | Burns | Lyons | McKearney | Drummond | Norman | Gardner | Keeling, Shirley, Takano | 35 |
| Ilhargey | Fensome | Brown | McKearney | Hughes | Burns | Lyons | Drummond | Keeling | Norman | Takano | Gardner, Mayers, Morton | 36 |
| Ilhargey | Fensome | Takano | McKearney | Hughes | Burns | Lyons | Drummond | Keeling | Norman | Gardner | Curtis, Brown, Mayers | 37 |
| Ilhargey | Fensome | Brown | McKearney | Hall | Burns | Lyons | Drummond | Keeling | Norman | Takano | Gardner, Curtis, Mayers | 38 |
| Ilhargey | Fensome | Takano | Mayers | Hall | Keeling | Gardner | Drummond | Curtis | Norman | Shirley | Heald, Hardiker, Maguire | 39 |
| Ilhargey | Fensome | Takano | Mayers | Hall | Keeling | Gardner | Drummond | Curtis | Norman | Shirley | Burns, Hardiker, Heald | 40 |
| Banks | Fensome | Takano | Mayers | Hall | Burns | Lyons | Drummond | Keeling | Norman | Gardner | Heald, Morton, Hardiker | 41 |
| Banks | Fensome | Takano | Hardiker | Hall | Burns | Lyons | Drummond | Morton | Norman | Gardner | Maguire, Shirley, Keeling | 42 |

League Attendances     **HIGHEST:** 3193     **LOWEST:** 812

**CONFERENCE:** 15th     **FA CUP:** 3rd Qualifying Round     **FA TROPHY:** 2nd Round

## MANAGER
### JIM HARVEY

| | |
|---|---|
| Date of Appointment | June 1994 |
| Date of Birth: | 2nd May 1958 |
| Place of Birth: | Lurgan, Northern Ireland |

**PREVIOUS CLUBS**
As manager ... None
As assistant manager ... Morecambe (Jan - June 1994)
As player ... Glenavon, Arsenal, Hereford Utd., Bristol City, Tranmere Rovers, CreweAlexandra.

**HONOURS**
As manager ... Spalding Cup 97-98; NPL R-up 94-95
As player ... N. Ireland - u23., Leyland Daf winner, Mercantile Trophy Winner,

## FOOTBALL MANAGEMENT TEAM

| | |
|---|---|
| Assistant Manager | David Miller |
| Second Team Manager | Jeff Udall |
| 2nd Team Assistant Manager | Tony Gribbins |
| Football in the Community | Derek Quinn |
| Sports Therapist | David Edge |

### 1998-99

**Top Scorer:** John Norman

**Player of the Year:** Stewart Drummond

**Captain:** Dave McKearney

Top: James Harvey
Bottom left: Andrew Milner. Photo: Peter Barnes
Bottom right: Rushden & Diamonds Tim Wooding in action with Morecambes Phil Eastwood. Photo: Colin Stevens

## MATCHDAY PROGRAMME

| | |
|---|---|
| Number of pages | 48 |
| Price | £1.50 |
| Programme Editor | Martin Shaw |
| Other club publications: | "Gazetta de la Shrimpa" |
| Local Newspapers: | Morecambe Visitor |
| | Morecambe Guardian |
| | Lancashire Evening Post |
| | The Citizen |
| Local Radio Stations: | Radio Lancashire |
| | Red Rose Radio; Bay Radio |

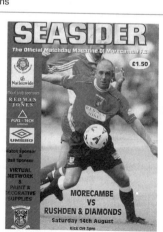

# PLAYING SQUAD

| Player | Birthplace Honours | D.O.B. | Previous Clubs |
|---|---|---|---|

## GOALKEEPERS

| | | | |
|---|---|---|---|
| Steve McIlhargey SC | Glasgow | 10.12.62 | Blantyre Celtic, Walsall, Blackpool |
| Andy Banks | Preston | 21.4.76 | Preston, Bury |

## DEFENDERS

| | | | |
|---|---|---|---|
| Paul Burns SC | Liverpool | 1.10.67 | Grimsby T, Burscough, Prescot, Caernarfon T, Altrincham, Accrington Stanley |
| Dave McKearney SC | Crosby | 20.6.68 | Prescot, Bolton W, Northwich Victoria, Crewe A, Wigan A, Chorley |
| Tony Hughes EY, SC | Liverpool | 3.10.73 | Crewe Alexandra |
| Paul Rushton | | | Crewe Alexandra |
| Andy Farrell | Colchester | 07.10.65 | Rochdale |
| Mark Wright | Manchester | 29.01.70 | Everton, Blackpool, Huddersfield Town, Wigan Athletic |

## MIDFIELDERS

| | | | |
|---|---|---|---|
| Michael Knowles SC | Morecambe | 3.3.74 | From Youth Team |
| Stuart Drummond SC | Preston | 11.12.75 | From Youth Team |

## FORWARDS

| | | | |
|---|---|---|---|
| Justin Jackson | Nottingham | 26.06.75 | Bolton Wanderers, Ayr United, Penrith, Ilkeston Town, Morecambe, Woking, Notts County, Halifax Town £18,000 to Morecambe. |
| Andy Milner SC | Kendal | 10.2.67 | Netherfield, Manchester C, Rochdale, Chester C, Morecambe |
| Paul Eastwood | | | Burnley |
| Neill Hardy | | | Northwich Victoria, Crewe Alexander, Bolton Wanderers, Altrincham |

Departures: Paul Haddow (Lancaster City), Kenny Mayers (Lancaster City), John Normanm (Hednesford Town ), Mark Shirley Accrington Stanley)

# MORECAMBE

**Founded:** 1920

**Nickname:** The Shrimps

**Club sponsor:** Redman Jones

**Club colours:** Red shirts, black shorts, black & white socks

**Change colours:** Yellow shirts, Blue shorts, yellow & blue socks

**Midweek home matchday:** Tuesdays, 7.45pm kick-off

**Reserve Team's League:** Lancashire Lge Div. A & North West All. Yth Div.

## GROUND DETAILS

Christie Park,
Lancaster Road,
Morecambe,
Lancashire LA4 5TJ

**TELEPHONE** 01524 411797
Fax: 01524 411797

**DIRECTIONS:**
From south leave M6 motorway at junction 34. Follow signsfor Morecambe through Lancaster, on A589, go straight across the first 2roundabouts, and at the third (with the Shrimp pub on your left), follow thesigns for Town Centre - Christie Park is approx. 600 metres on your left

**CAPACITY:** 6,000
**SEATED:** 1,200
**COVERED TERRACING:** 4,000

**CLUB SHOP:** On ground and open on matchdays. Also commercial office open Monday to Friday 9.00 - 5.00 selling the same goods

**SOCIAL FACILITIES:** J B's open normal licensing hours

## Past Players who progressed to the Football League

Fred Blondel & MalcolmDarling (Bury 1946 & 78), Herbert Harrison (Accrington 1947), Gordon Milne (Preston 1956), Ray Charnley (Blackpool 1957), Geoff Slack (Stockport 1958), Ron Mitchell (Leeds 1958), Derek Armstrong (Carlisle 1961), Alan Taylor(Rochdale 1973), John Coates (Southport via Burscough & Skelmersdale 1975),Keith Galley (Southport 1975), Brian Thompson (West Ham 1977), David Eyres(Blackpool), Kenny Lowe (Barnet via Barrow), Steve Gardner (Bradford City), Dave Lancaster (Chesterfield)

## PREVIOUS

**Leagues:** Lancs Combination 1920-68, Northern Premier 1968-1995

**Grounds:** Woodhill Lane 1920-25, shared with cricket club who still play there

## CLUB RECORDS

**Attendance:** 9,324 v Weymouth FA Cup 4.1.62

**Win:** 16-0 v Rossendale Utd, Lancs Combination Sept 1967 (Arnold Timmins scored 8)

**Defeat:** 0-7 v Darwen, November 7th 1953

**Transfer fee paid:** £8,000 to Chester City for Andy Milner, November 1997

**Transfer fee received:** £30,000 from Woking for Justin Jackson, January 1997

**Career Goalscorer:** Keith Borrowdale 289 1956-68, 78-79 Lancashire Combination John Coleman 130 1990-1995 (Northern Premier League)

**Career Appearances:** Steve Done 523 + 7 sub 1968-78

## BEST SEASON

**FA Cup:** 3rd Round 1961-62, 0-1 v Weymouth League clubs defeated: Chester City

**FA Trophy:** Winners 73-74, Q-final 72-73, 77-78, 93-94

## HONOURS

FA Trophy 73-74,

Spalding Cup 97-98,

Northern Premier Lge Presidents Cup 91-92,

NPL R-up 94-95,

Lancs Combination x5 24-25 61-63 66-68

R-up 25-26, Lg Cup 26-27 45-46 64-65 66-68;

Lancashire Junior Cup (now ATS Trophy) x8

25-27 61-63 68-69 85-87 92-93, 95-96;

Lancs Senior Cup 67-68,

Lancs League Div 2 83-84

# NORTHWICH VICTORIA

Another solid season was enjoyed at the Drill Field but there was little excitement in the Conference as neither championship or relegation were ever really close.As one of the three clubs to have been ever presents in the Conference, their famous old ground now matches their 'senior ' status with an impressive full length terrace down one side and a smart dining area in the main stand.Their young manager Mark Gardiner settled into the job well with the experienced John Williams available to advise if wanted. An early F.A.Cup exit was forgotten as the F.ATrophy brought victories over Netherfield Kendal, Radcliffe Borough, Worcester City and Colwyn Bay before Kingstonian were drawn at home in the quarter finals. With a Trophy goal tally of 9-2 and recent conference victories over Cheltenham Town, Rushden & Diamonds and Kettering Town it looked as if the Vics tradition in the competition wasn't going to let them down. Sadly on the day K's were just too good, but the form showed augered well for the season ahead. Paul Tait has been snapped up by Crewe but the management are happy with their team building and Northwich will probably be a solid Conference side cabable of great cup results.

## CLUB OFFICIALS 1999-2000

| | |
|---|---|
| Chairman | **Rod J Stitch** |
| Vice Chairman | **Dave Stone** |
| Company Secretary | **Graham Cookson** |
| Chief Executive | **John Stitch** |
| Directors | **Dave Price, Jim Rafferty** |

Associate Directors

**Graham Cookson, Dave Edgeley, Dave Bush, Roger Stubbs.**

President &

Football Secretary **Derek Nuttall**
c/o the club
Tel: 01606 41450  Fax: 01606 330577

Back Row: Val Owen, Mark Birch, Wes Simpson, Chris Duffy, Dean Greygoose, Martin Filson, Ian Cooke, Mark Gardiner, Dominic Crookes. Front Row: Jamie Bates, Stuart Terry, Carwyn Williams, Steve Walters, Neil Illman, Derek Ward, Darren Vicary.
Photo: Courtesy of Northwich Guardian

# NORTHWICH VICTORIA
## MATCH FACTS 1998-99

| No | Date | Venue | Comp | Opponents | Att | Result | Score | Goalscorers |
|----|------|-------|------|-----------|-----|--------|-------|-------------|
| 1 | 15/08 | A | NC | Hayes | 685 | L | 0-1 | |
| 2 | 18/08 | H | NC | Kidderminster Harriers | 1122 | W | 1-0 | Tait 32 |
| 3 | 22/08 | H | NC | Forest Green Rovers | 866 | W | 1-0 | Cooke 55 |
| 4 | 25/08 | A | NC | Southport | 1457 | D | 2-2 | Illman 30, Tait 51 |
| 5 | 29/08 | A | NC | Kettering Town | 1763 | D | 0-0 | |
| 6 | 31/08 | H | NC | Leek Town | 1070 | L | 0-2 | |
| 7 | 05/09 | H | NC | Kingstonian | 906 | L | 2-3 | Walters 38, Filson 72 |
| 8 | 07/09 | A | NC | Hednesford Town | 1127 | L | 0-1 | |
| 9 | 12/09 | A | NC | Yeovil Town | 2075 | W | 2-1 | Tait 77, Vicary 90 |
| 10 | 19/09 | H | NC | Farnborough Town | 837 | W | 3-0 | Owen 26, Tait 47, Walters 53 |
| 11 | 26/09 | H | NC | Woking | 1003 | L | 0-3 | |
| 12 | 29/09 | A | NC | Hereford United | 1910 | D | 2-2 | Williams 76, Illman 87 |
| 13 | 03/10 | A | NC | Rushden & Diamonds | 2803 | W | 2-1 | Walters 55, Terry 71 |
| 14 | 10/10 | A | NC | Dover Athletic | 949 | D | 0-0 | |
| 15 | 24/10 | H | NC | Stevenage Borough | 910 | L | 0-1 | |
| 16 | 07/11 | H | NC | Welling United | 1032 | W | 3-0 | Walters 9, Terry 73, Owen 81 |
| 17 | 14/11 | A | NC | Forest Green Rovers | 684 | L | 1-3 | Terry 38 |
| 18 | 28/11 | A | NC | Kingstonian | 901 | D | 1-1 | Illman 42 |
| 19 | 05/12 | H | NC | Hereford United | 1068 | W | 1-0 | Tait 2 |
| 20 | 12/12 | H | NC | Hednesford Town | 1002 | D | 1-1 | Walters 2 |
| 21 | 19/12 | A | NC | Woking | 2059 | L | 1-2 | Walters 90 |
| 22 | 26/12 | H | NC | Morecambe | 1304 | D | 1-1 | Walters 19 |
| 23 | 28/12 | A | NC | Barrow | 2015 | W | 1-0 | Tait 8 |
| 24 | 02/01 | A | NC | Morecambe | 1107 | L | 1-3 | Cooke 70 |
| 25 | 09/01 | H | NC | Dover Athletic | 942 | W | 2-0 | Cooke 71, Vicary 77 |
| 26 | 23/01 | A | NC | Cheltenham Town | 2060 | W | 1-0 | Tait 22 |
| 27 | 30/01 | H | NC | Rushden & Diamonds | 1802 | W | 2-1 | Crookes 4, Owen 56 |
| 28 | 13/02 | H | NC | Southport | 1628 | L | 1-2 | Tait 46 |
| 29 | 20/02 | A | NC | Welling United | 500 | W | 3-2 | Cooke 35, Terry 52, Walters 78 |
| 30 | 06/03 | H | NC | Kettering Town | 1385 | W | 4-0 | Tait 17 29, Simpson 66, Birch 72 |
| 31 | 13/03 | A | NC | Telford United | 911 | L | 0-3 | |
| 32 | 16/03 | H | NC | Doncaster Rovers | 1402 | L | 1-3 | Illman 88 |
| 33 | 20/03 | A | NC | Farnborough Town | 552 | W | 6-1 | Walters 4, Devlin 6, Illman 13 26 67, Vicary 37 |
| 34 | 03/04 | A | NC | Stevenage Borough | 1923 | W | 3-1 | Devlin 28, Illman 48 77 |
| 35 | 05/04 | H | NC | Barrow | 1107 | W | 1-0 | Vicary 1 |
| 36 | 10/04 | H | NC | Telford United | 1008 | D | 1-1 | Illman 35 |
| 37 | 12/04 | A | NC | Kidderminster Harriers | 1235 | L | 0-4 | |
| 38 | 14/04 | A | NC | Doncaster Rovers | 2296 | D | 2-2 | Peel 12, Tait 76 |
| 39 | 17/04 | H | NC | Hayes | 1150 | W | 2-1 | Simpson 60, Tait 71 |
| 40 | 24/04 | H | NC | Yeovil Town | 1150 | L | 1-2 | Vicary 87 |
| 41 | 27/04 | H | NC | Cheltenham Town | 1155 | W | 1-0 | Tait 50 |
| 42 | 01/05 | A | NC | Leek Town | 559 | W | 3-0 | Tait 14 58, Williams 90 |

**CUP COMPETITIONS**

| | Date | Venue | Comp | Opponents | Att | Result | Score | Goalscorers |
|---|------|-------|------|-----------|-----|--------|-------|-------------|
| | 22/09 | A | Ches. SC 1 | Cheadle Town | n/k | W | 2-0 | Tait 25 42 |
| | 17/10 | A | FA Cup Q3 | Droylsden | 635 | L | 0-2 | |
| | 21/11 | H | FA Trophy 2 | Netherfield Kendal | 778 | W | 3-0 | Illman 2, Vicary 7, Owen 40 |
| | 24/11 | A | Ches. SC QF | Crewe Alexandra | 472 | W | 6-1 | Vicary 5, Owen 11 16, Walters 13 60, Illman 45 |
| | 30/11 | A | Endsleigh 2 | Hednesford Town | 0 | W | 3-1 | Vicary 28, Illman, Terry 83 |
| | 25/01 | A | FA Trophy 3 | Radcliffe Borough | 550 | W | 2-1 | Cooke 45, Vicary 68 |
| | 06/02 | H | FA Trophy 4 | Worcester City | 1109 | W | 1-0 | Cook 24 |
| | 16/02 | A | Ches. SC SF | Runcorn | 248 | W | 2-1 | Illman 25, Tait 32 |
| | 27/02 | H | FA Trophy 5 | Colwyn Bay | 1402 | W | 3-1 | Vicary 53, Devlin 56, Walters 65[p] |
| | 02/03 | A | Endsleigh QF | Doncaster Rovers | 1877 | L | 2-3 | Tait 66, Vicary 85 |
| | 27/03 | H | FA Trophy QF | Kingstonian | 1819 | L | 0-2 | |
| | 20/04 | A | Ches. SC F | Altrincham | 964 | L | 0-1 | (at Witton Albion) |

| 1 | 2 | 3 | 4 | 5 | 6 | 7 | 8 | 9 | 10 | 11 | 12 / 14 / 15 | |
|---|---|---|---|---|---|---|---|---|---|---|---|---|
| Greygoose | D Ward | Birch | Duffy | Robertson | Filson | Terry | Walters | Illman | Cooke | Tait | Vicary, Williams, Simpson | 1 |
| Greygoose | Bates | Birch | Simpson | Robertson | Tait | Terry | Owen | Illman | Cooke | Duffy | Vicary, D Ward, Williams | 2 |
| Greygoose | Bates | Birch | Robertson | Simpson | D Owen | Terry | Walters | Illman | Cooke | Duffy | Tait, Vicary, Williams | 3 |
| Greygoose | Bates | Birch | Robertson | Simpson | D Owen | Terry | Walters | Illman | Cooke | Duffy | Williams, Tait, D Ward | 4 |
| Greygoose | Bates | Birch | Robertson | Simpson | Owen | Terry | Walters | Illman | Tait | Duffy | Williams, D Ward, Filson | 5 |
| Greygoose | Bates | Birch | Robertson | Simpson | V Owen | Terry | Walters | Illman | Tait | Duffy | Filson, Williams, Ward | 6 |
| Greygoose | Bates | Birch | Robertson | Simpson | Filson | Terry | Walters | Williams | Tait | Duffy | Ward, Illman, Vicary | 7 |
| Greygoose | Bates | Birch | Robertson | Simpson | Filson | Terry | Walters | Illman | Williams | V Owen | D Ward, Duffy, Gardiner | 8 |
| Greygoose | Bates | Birch | Robertson | Simpson | V Owen | Terry | Walters | Williams | Tait | Duffy | Vicary, D Ward, Crookes | 9 |
| Greygoose | Bates | Birch | Robertson | Simpson | V Owen | Terry | Walters | Williams | Tait | Vicary | D Ward, Gardiner, Crookes | 10 |
| Greygoose | Bates | Birch | Robertson | Sipson | Owen | Terry | Walters | Williams | Tait | Vicary | Crookes, Duffy, D Ward | 11 |
| Greygoose | Bates | Birch | Robertson | Simpson | Owen | Terry | Ward | Duffy | Tait | Vicary | Williams, Illman, Crookes | 12 |
| Greygoose | Bates | Birch | Robertson | Simpson | Owen | Terry | Walters | Williams | Tait | Duffy | Illman, Vicary, Crookes | 13 |
| Greygoose | Bates | Birch | Robertson | Simpson | Owen | Terry | Walters | Williams | Tait | Duffy | Vicary, Illman, Crookes | 14 |
| Greygoose | Bates | Birch | Robertson | Simpson | Owen | Terry | Walters | Williams | Tait | Vicary | Cooke, Duffy, Crookes | 15 |
| O'Toole | Bates | Birch | Crookes | Simpson | Owen | Terry | Walters | Cooke | Tait | Vicary | Ward, Duffy, C Williams | 16 |
| O'Toole | Bates | Birch | Robertson | Simpson | Owen | Terry | Ward | Cooke | Williams | Vicary | Crookes, Duffy, Gardiner | 17 |
| Greygoose | Bates | Birch | Crookes | Owen | Terry | Walters | Illman | Tait | Vicary | Simpson | Duffy, Cooke, Robertson | 18 |
| Greygoose | Bates | Birch | Crookes | Simpson | Owen | Terry | Walters | Illman | Tait | Vicary | Cooke, Duffy, Robertson | 19 |
| Greygoose | Bates | Birch | Crookes | Simpson | Owen | Terry | Walters | Illman | Tait | Vicary | Robertson, Duffy, Cooke | 20 |
| Key | Duffy | Birch | Crookes | Robertson | Owen | Terry | Walters | Illman | Tait | Vicary | Cooke, Gardner, Ward | 21 |
| Key | Duffy | Birch | Crookes | Robertson | Owen | Terry | Walters | Illman | Tait | Vicary | Cooke, Ward, Simpson | 22 |
| Key | Duffy | Birch | Crookes | Robertson | Ward | Terry | Walters | Illman | Tait | Vicary | Bates, Cooke, Simpson | 23 |
| Key | Duffy | Birch | Crookes | Robertson | Ward | Terry | Walters | Illman | Tait | Vicary | Owen, Cooke, Simpson | 24 |
| Key | Duffy | Birch | Crookes | Robertson | Ward | Terry | Webster | Illman | Peel | Vicary | Simpson, Devlin, Cooke | 25 |
| Greygoose | Simpson | Birch | Crookes | Robertson | Owen | Terry | Webster | Peel | Tait | Vicary | Devlin, Ward, Illman | 26 |
| Greygoose | Simpson | Birch | Crookes | Robertson | Owen | Terry | Webster | Peel | Tait | Vicary | Devlin, Cooke, Illman | 27 |
| Greygoose | Duffy | Birch | Crookes | Simpson | Owen | Terry | Devlin | Peel | Tait | Vicary | Cooke, Gardiner, Webster | 28 |
| Greygoose | Duffy | Birch | Crookes | Robertson | Devlin | Terry | Walters | Cooke | Tait | Vicary | Webster, Illman, Simpson | 29 |
| Key | Simpson | Birch | Crookes | Robertson | Devlin | Terry | Walters | Peel | Tait | Vicary | Duffy, Cooke, Illman | 30 |
| Key | Duffy | Birch | Crookes | Simpson | Devlin | Terry | Walters | Peel | Tait | Vicary | Illman, Cooke, Robertson | 31 |
| Key | Duffy | Birch | Crookes | Robertson | Devlin | Webster | Walters | Peel | Tait | Vicary | Illman, Cooke, Gardiner | 32 |
| Key | Duffy | Birch | Crookes | Simpson | Devlin | Terry | Walters | Cooke | Illman | Vicary | Webster, Bates, Williams | 33 |
| Key | Simpson | Birch | Crookes | Robertson | Devlin | Bates | Duffy | Illman | Tait | Vicary | Webster, Williams, Terry | 34 |
| Key | Simpson | Birch | Crookes | Robertson | Devlin | Bates | Duffy | Illman | Tait | Vicary | Terry, Williams, Webster | 35 |
| Key | Simpson | Birch | Crookes | Robertson | Devlin | Terry | Duffy | Illman | Tait | Vicary | Williams, Bates, Webster | 36 |
| Key | Bates | Birch | Crookes | Robertson | Devlin | Terry | Walters | Peel | Illman | Duffy | Webster, Tait, Simpson | 37 |
| Key | Bates | Birch | Crookes | Robertson | Devlin | Duffy | Walters | Illman | Peel | Vicary | Simpson, Tait, Gardiner | 38 |
| Key | Bates | Birch | Simpson | Robertson | Devlin | Duffy | Walters | Illman | Tait | Vicary | Peel, Terry, Webster | 39 |
| Key | Simpson | Birch | Crookes | Robertson | Devlin | Duffy | Bates | Illman | Peel | Vicary | Cooke, Tait, Terry | 40 |
| Key | Bates | Birch | Simpson | Robertson | Devlin | Duffy | Walters | Illman | Tait | Vicary | Terry, Webster, Fletcher | 41 |
| Key | Crookes | Birch | Simpson | Robertson | Devlin | Duffy | Walters | Illman | Tait | Vicary | Gardiner, Williams, Bates | 42 |

League Attendances      **HIGHEST:** 1802      **LOWEST:** 837

**CONFERENCE:** 8th      **FA CUP:** 3rd Qualifying Round      **FA TROPHY:** Quarter Finals

## MANAGER
### MARK GARDINER

| | |
|---|---|
| Date of Appointment | December 1998 |
| Date of Birth | 25th December 1966 |
| Place of Birth | Cirencester |

PREVIOUS CLUBS
As manager                                                    none
As coach                                                       none
As player          Crewe Alexandra, Chester City, Macclesfield Town,
Swindon Town, Torquay United

HONOURS
As manager                                                    MCSC
As coach
as player                          GM V Conference; F.A. Trophy

## FOOTBALL MANAGEMENT TEAM

| | |
|---|---|
| Director of Football: | John Williams |
| Physio: | Phil Lea |
| Fitness Trainer: | Peter Everson |
| Reserve & Youth Team Manager | Ted Carthy |

## 1998-99

| | |
|---|---|
| **Top Scorer:** | Paul Tait (19) |
| **Player of the Year:** | John Robertson |
| **Captain:** | Steve Walters |

Mark Gardiner

Photos: Andrew Chitty

John Robertson

## MATCHDAY PROGRAMME

| | |
|---|---|
| Number of pages | 44 |
| Price | £1.30 |
| Programme Editor | William Hughes & James Wood |
| Other club publications: | 'Distant Vics' |

(a bi-monthly magazine for exiled Vics' fans)

Local Newspapers:          Northwich Guardian (Wed.)
                           Northwich Chronicle (Wed.)
                           Daily Post
               Manchester Evening News Pink (Sat.)
Local Radio Stations:      GMR (BBC Manchester)
                           Piccadilly Radio; Signal Radio

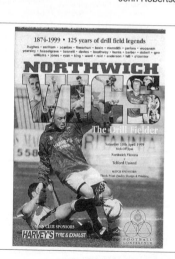

# PLAYING SQUAD

NORTHWICH VICTORIA

| Player<br>Honours | Birthplace | D.O.B. | Previous Clubs |
|---|---|---|---|
| **GOALKEEPERS** | | | |
| Lance Key | Kettering | 13.05.68 | Sheffield Wed., Sheffield Utd., York C., Oldham, Portsmouth, Oxford Utd., Lincoln C., Hartlepool, Dundee utd., Rochdale. |
| John Gann | | | Heswall |
| **DEFENDERS** | | | |
| John Robertson | Liverpool | 08.01.74 | Wigan Ath., Lincoln City |
| Wes Simpson | Winsford | 29.3.77 | Crewe Alexandra |
| Dominic Crookes | Nottingham | 7.12.74 | Mansfield T, Telford U, Dag & Red |
| **Mark Gardiner**<br>**GMVC, FAT** | **Cirencester** | **25.12.66** | **Swindon T, Torquay U, Crewe Alexandra, Macclesfield T** |
| Nick Boothby | | | |
| Steve Walsh | | | |
| Jamie Bates | Manchester | | Maine Road, Runcorn, Stalybridge C. |
| Mark Birch | Stoke | 05.01.77 | Stoke city |
| Chris Royle | | | |
| Rory Prendergast | Pontefract | 06.04.78 | Rochdale, Barnsley, York City. |
| **MIDFIELDERS** | | | |
| **Steve Walters**<br>**EY, ESP** | **Plymouth** | **9.1.72** | **Crewe Alexandra** |
| Mark Devlin | Irvine | 08.01.73 | StokeCity, Exeter city |
| Stuart Terry | | | Bangor City, Altrincham |
| Darren Vicary | Liverpool | | Vauxhall GM, Cammell Lairds |
| Neil Ellis | Chester | 30.04.69 | Tranmere R., Chester C., Chorley, Ashton Utd., Stalybridge C., Oswestry, bangor, Maidstone U., Kettering T., Corby T., Worcester C., Leek Town |
| Val Owen | Manchester | 11.02.71 | Hyde United |
| **FORWARDS** | | | |
| Nathan Peel | Blackburn | 17.05.72 | Preston N.E., Sheffield Utd., Halifax T., Burnley, Rotherham Utd., Mansfield, Doncaster R., Macclesfield, Winsford Utd., Stevenage (L) |
| Ian Cooke | Bebington | 1.11.73 | Cammell Laird |
| Neil Illman | Doncaster | 29.4.75 | Middlesbrough, Eastwood T, £10k to Plymouth A, Eastwood T, Exeter C, Eastwood T |
| Gary Fletcher | | | |
| Liam Robinson | Bradford | 29.12.65 | Nottingham Forest, Huddersfield Town, Tranmere Rovers, Bury, Bristol City, Burnley, Scarborough |
| Phil Eastwood | | | Burnley |
| Damian Logan | | | Everton |

Bold print indicates English Semi-Professional Internationals

DEPARTURES
Dean Greygoose (Altrincham), Derek ward (Stalybridge), Wayne Fairclough (Gainsborough T.), David Clegg (Winsford Utd.), Chris Duffy (Canvey Is. £3k), John Stannard (Droylsden £4k), Paul Tait (Crewe Alex. (Bosman)), Eddie Hussin (Chorley), Carwyn Williams (released), Jaime Webster.

# NORTHWICH VICTORIA

**Founded:** 1874
**Nickname:** The Vics, Greens, Trickies
**Club Sponsors:** Harvey's Tyres
**Club colours:** Green shirts, white shorts and black socks
**Change colours:** Yellow shirts, black shorts & socks
**Midweek home matchday:** Thursday
**Reserve Team's league:** Lancashire League

## GROUND DETAILS

The Drill Field,
Drill Field Road,
Northwich,
Cheshire. CW9 5HN

TELEPHONE: 01606 41450
Fax: 01606 330577.
Club Newsline: 0930 30 122 713
Internet address: www.u-net.com/~sandiway/home.htm

SIMPLE DIRECTIONS: Leave M6 at Junc.19 and follow A556 towards Chester. At second roundabout (approx. 6 miles), turn right onto A533. Ground on right behind Volunteer Public House

CAPACITY: 6,000
SEATED: 660
COVERED TERRACING: 3,500

CLUB SHOP: Located inside ground. Open match days. Manager: Andy Dakin
SOCIAL FACILITIES:
Large social club with members lounge and separate function-room - both available for hire Tel: 0606 43120. Food available on matchdayswith prior notice. Bass beers, Pool, Darts, TV. New suite now available offering matchday & midweek catering

## PREVIOUS

**Leagues:** The Combination 1890-1892, Football League Div.2 1892-94, The Combination 1894-1898, The Cheshire League 1898-1900, Manchester League 1900-12, Lancashire 1912-19, Cheshire County League 1919-68, Northern Premier League 1968-79

**Grounds:** None

## CLUB RECORDS

**Attendance:** 11,290 v Witton Albion, Cheshire League, Good Friday 1949

**Win:** 17-0 v Marple Ass. 15.12.1883
**Defeat:** 3-10 v Port Vale 7.2.1931

**Career Goalscorer:** Peter Burns 160 - 1955-65
**Career Appearances:** 970 by Ken Jones 1969-85

**Transfer Fee paid:** £10,000
to Hyde United for Malcolm O'Connor - August 1988
& to Kidderminster H. for Delwyn Humphreys - Sept. 1995
**Transfer Fee received:** £50,000
from Chester City for Neil Morton - October1990

## BEST SEASON

**FA Cup:** Quarter Finals 1883-84
League clubs defeated: Rochdale, Peterborough, Watford, Chester C., Crewe Alexandra

**FA Trophy:** Winners 83-84
R-up 82-83 95-96

**Past Players** who progressed to the Football League
Tony Hemmings (Wycombe W.), Tony Bullock (Barnsley), Darren Tinson(Macclesfield), Lee Steele (Shrewsbury T.)

## HONOURS

Welsh Cup R-up 1881/82,1888-89;
FA Trophy 1983/84, R-up 1982/83 & 1995/96;
Bob Lord Trophy 1979/80, 92/93;
Northern Premier Lge R-up 1976/77; Northern Premier Lge Cup 1972/73, R-up 1978/79;
Cheshire County Lge 1956/57, R-up 1924/25, 47/48; Cheshire County Lge Cup 1925/35;
Manchester Lge 1902/03, R-up 1900/01, 03/04, 07/08, 08/09, 11/12; The Combination R-up 1890/91;
Cheshire Senior Cup 1880-81, 81/82, 82/83, 83/84, 84/85, 85/86,1928/29, 36/37, 49/50, 54/55, 71/72, 76/77, 78/79, 83/84, 93/94.
R-up 1891/92,96/97, 1905/06, 08/09, 47/48, 50/51, 63/64, 65/66, 69/70, 70/71, 77/78, 85/86; 98/99
Staffordshire Senior Cup 1978/79, 79/80, 89/90, R-up 1986/87, 90/91;
CheshireAmateur Cup 1901/02, R-up 1898/99, 02/93,
Northwich Senior Cup 1948/49, 58/59,59/60, 63/64, 64/65, 65/66, 67/68, 68/69, 69/70, 71/72, 74/75, R-up x7;
Mid Cheshire Senior Cup 1984/85, 85/86, 87/88, 89/90, 91/92, 93/94, 94/95, 96/97,98/99; R-up 1982/83, 83/84, 90/91, 92/93;
North-West Floodlit Lge 1966/67, 75/76;
Cheshire Lge Lancs. Comb. Inter-Lge Cup 1961/62;
Guardian Charity Shield1985/86, 86/87, 87/88

# NUNEATON BOROUGH

Could Borough supporters have imagined a more perfect Dr Martens campaign? Surely not! Brendan Phillips' squad took over at the top of the Division after six consecutive victories and were never threatened. They finished the season 23 points ahead of the runners-up amidst great celebrations and great plans for the battle ahead in the Conference.

Richard Wiliams only conceded 33 goals in the league season (equal best in the four senior leagues) and there were 19 clean sheets, but it was the ability of the whole squad to produce goals from all positions that made Nuneaton such a difficult side to stop.

Barry Williams won his place in the England squad and he will be a vital player in the coming season and of course his manager was in the first ever England semi-professional squad that won the four nations tournament in 1979. He should remember it well as he set up the winning goal for Eamonn O'Keefe in the final against Holland! His assistant Steve Burr will also be remembered for his goals in the F.A.Cup for Macclesfield including a hat trick against Rotherham United.

So the men in charge will be returning to old hunting gounds and it should be an exciting season for all involved with the club.     T.T.

## CLUB OFFICIALS 1999-2000

Chairman:                    **Phil Clayton**

Secretary:                   **Peter Humphreys**
29 Amington Rd, Shirley, Solihull,
West Midlands B90 2RF
Tel: 0121 745 2031

Commercial Director:         **Phil Clayton**

Press Officer:               Chairman & Manager

Back Row: Shaun Wray, Andy Kiwomya, Richard Williams, Terry Angus, Gavin O'Toole, Anton Thomas, Kevin Wilkin, Ian Muir, Andy Kirkup, Joe O'Connor.   Front Row: Barry Williams, Leigh Everitt, Steve Prindiville, Dave Crowley, Wayne Simpson, Jamie March, Kingsley Paul, Brett Healy

# NUNEATON BOROUGH
## MATCH FACTS 1998-99

| No | Date | Venue | Comp | Opponents | Att | Result | Score | Goalscorers |
|----|------|-------|------|-----------|-----|--------|-------|-------------|
| 1 | 22/08 | H | DMP | Hastings Town | 1211 | W | 1-0 | Christie 71 |
| 2 | 25/08 | A | DMP | King's Lynn | 1039 | W | 4-2 | B Williams 15, 68, Christie 43, Wilkin 90 |
| 3 | 29/08 | A | DMP | Boston United | 1159 | W | 3-2 | Simpson 49, 86, Christie 63 |
| 4 | 31/08 | H | DMP | Grantham Town | 1919 | W | 2-0 | Thomas 67, Christie 70 (p) |
| 5 | 05/09 | A | DMP | Crawley Town | 675 | W | 3-0 | Christie 8, Thomas 45, Angus 65 |
| 6 | 08/09 | H | DMP | Burton Albion | 2030 | W | 4-1 | Thomas 16, 85, Christie 40, 64 |
| 7 | 12/09 | A | DMP | Gloucester City | 1010 | L | 0-1 | |
| 8 | 15/09 | H | DMP | King's Lynn | 1564 | W | 4-0 | Christie 16, Thomas 47, Simpson 51, Statham 81 |
| 9 | 19/09 | A | DMP | Worcester City | 1355 | W | 4-0 | Simpson 40, Thomas 74, Christie 75 (p), Wilkin 90 |
| 10 | 22/09 | A | DMP | Grantham Town | 1117 | L | 0-2 | |
| 11 | 26/09 | H | DMP | Tamworth | 2099 | W | 2-0 | Wray 27, Christie 62 (p) |
| 12 | 10/10 | H | DMP | Dorchester Town | 1330 | D | 0-0 | |
| 13 | 24/10 | A | DMP | Bromsgrove Rovers | 608 | W | 4-0 | Wilkin 10, 63, B Williams 16, Landon 89 |
| 14 | 31/10 | H | DMP | Weymouth | 1227 | W | 4-2 | Muir 21, 64 (p), B Williams 62, 89 |
| 15 | 03/11 | A | DMP | Burton Albion | 1059 | D | 1-1 | Gardner 27 |
| 16 | 07/11 | H | DMP | Boston United | 1440 | D | 1-1 | B Williams 83 |
| 17 | 14/11 | A | DMP | Hastings Town | 710 | W | 4-0 | O'Connor 20, Gardner 39, Thomas 51, 76 |
| 18 | 28/11 | H | DMP | Halesowen Town | 1230 | W | 4-3 | B Williams 3, Muir 68 (p), 89, Wray 90 |
| 19 | 05/12 | A | DMP | Rothwell Town | 574 | D | 1-1 | O'Connor 52 |
| 20 | 12/12 | H | DMP | Crawley Town | 1409 | W | 2-1 | Muir 4 (p), B Williams 15 |
| 21 | 19/12 | A | DMP | Cambridge City | 546 | D | 1-1 | O'Toole 7 |
| 22 | 26/12 | H | DMP | Atherstone United | 2242 | W | 1-0 | Thomas 43 |
| 23 | 28/12 | A | DMP | Gresley Rovers | 1490 | W | 3-0 | Thomas 37, og 48, Muir 75 (p) |
| 24 | 01/01 | A | DMP | Halesowen Town | 1521 | L | 0-2 | |
| 25 | 03/01 | H | DMP | Merthyr Tydfil | 1228 | W | 6-1 | Angus 17, Wilkin 19, B Williams 20, Wray 76, Thomas 77, og 86 |
| 26 | 09/01 | A | DMP | Ilkeston Town | 1338 | W | 1-0 | Angus 35 |
| 27 | 23/01 | H | DMP | Salisbury City | 1404 | L | 0-1 | |
| 28 | 30/01 | H | DMP | Bath City | 2018 | D | 1-1 | Muir 80 (p) |
| 29 | 06/02 | A | DMP | Dorchester Town | 802 | W | 1-0 | Kiwomya 77 |
| 30 | 13/02 | H | DMP | Cambridge City | 1515 | W | 4-0 | B Williams 10, Muir 60 (p), Wilkin 68, Wray 70 |
| 31 | 20/02 | A | DMP | Bath City | 1285 | W | 3-1 | Angus 47, Wilkin 54, Wray 76 |
| 32 | 27/02 | A | DMP | Merthyr Tydfil | 582 | L | 1-2 | Thomas 90 |
| 33 | 06/03 | H | DMP | Bromsgrove Rovers | 1533 | W | 6-0 | Muir 31, Kiwomya 56, 64, Wilkin 62, 66, Prindiville 89 |
| 34 | 13/03 | A | DMP | Salisbury City | 1050 | D | 1-1 | O'Toole 87 |
| 35 | 20/03 | H | DMP | Worcester City | 1724 | W | 2-0 | Wilkin 26, B Williams 70 |
| 36 | 27/03 | H | DMP | Ilkeston Town | 1638 | L | 1-3 | Angus 31 |
| 37 | 03/04 | A | DMP | Atherstone United | 2043 | W | 2-0 | Thomas 70, Kiwomya 75 |
| 38 | 05/04 | H | DMP | Gresley Rovers | 2945 | W | 3-1 | Kiwomya 20, Thomas 52, B Williams 68 |
| 39 | 10/04 | H | DMP | Gloucester City | 1538 | W | 2-0 | Kiwomya 55, Paul 89 |
| 40 | 17/04 | A | DMP | Weymouth | 1350 | D | 1-1 | B Williams 37 |
| 41 | 24/04 | H | DMP | Rothwell Town | 2007 | W | 2-0 | Kiwomya 1, Wray 90 |
| 42 | 01/05 | A | DMP | Tamworth | 1404 | D | 1-1 | O'Connor 80 |

### CUP COMPETITIONS

| | Date | Venue | Comp | Opponents | Att | Result | Score | Goalscorers |
|----|------|-------|------|-----------|-----|--------|-------|-------------|
| | 03/10 | A | FAC 2Q | Atherstone United | 2029 | D | 0-0 | |
| | 06/10 | H | FAC 2Qr | Atherstone United | 3019 | W | 3-0 | B Williams 50, Wilkin 80, Christie 90 |
| | 17/10 | A | FAC 3Q | Burton Albion | 1894 | L | 1-2 | Christie 6 |
| | 09/11 | A | DMC 1 1L | Atherstone United | 531 | L | 1-2 | Muir 48 |
| | 21/11 | H | FAT 2 | Hyde United | 1207 | D | 1-1 | B Williams 49 |
| | 23/11 | A | FAT 2r | Hyde United | 472 | L | 0-1 | |
| | 01/12 | A | BSC 2 | Moor Green | 97 | W | 5-2 | Thomas 18, 45, Jennings 22, Wray 52, O'Connor 67 |
| | 15/12 | H | DMC 1 2L | Atherstone United | 558 | L | 1-3 | Prindiville 8 |
| | 12/01 | H | BSC 3 | Stourbridge | 202 | W | 2-1 | Everitt 62, O'Connor 67 |
| | 15/02 | A | BSC QF | Hednesford Town | 718 | L | 0-2 | |

| 1 | 2 | 3 | 4 | 5 | 6 | 7 | 8 | 9 | 10 | 11 | 12 / 14 / 15 | No. |
|---|---|---|---|---|---|---|---|---|----|----|--------------|-----|
| R Williams | Everitt | Prindiville | Statham | B Williams | Crowley | Wray | Andersen | Christie | Muir | Gardner | Thomas, Simpson, Wilkin | 1 |
| R Williams | Everitt | Prindiville | Statham | B Williams | Angus | Wray | Simpson | Christie | Muir | Gardner | Thomas, Wilkin, Andersen | 2 |
| R Williams | Everitt | Prindiville | Statham | B Williams | Angus | Wray | Simpson | Thomas | Christie | Gardner | Muir, Wilkin, Crowley | 3 |
| R Williams | Everitt | Prindiville | Statham | B Williams | Angus | Wray | Simpson | Thomas | Christie | Gardner | Wilkin, Crowley, Muir | 4 |
| R Williams | Everitt | Prindiville | Statham | B Williams | Angus | Wray | Simpson | Thomas | Christie | Gardner | Wilkin, Muir, Healy | 5 |
| R Williams | Everitt | Prindiville | Statham | B Williams | Angus | Crowley | Simpson | Thomas | Christie | Gardner | Wilkin, Muir, Wray | 6 |
| R Williams | Everitt | Prindiville | Statham | B Williams | Angus | Crowley | Simpson | Thomas | Christie | Gardner | Muir, Wilkin, Wray | 7 |
| R Williams | Everitt | Prindiville | Statham | Angus | Crowley | Wray | Simpson | Thomas | Christie | Gardner | Muir, Wilkin, Andersen | 8 |
| R Williams | Everitt | Prindiville | Statham | Angus | Crowley | Wray | Simpson | Christie | Thomas | Gardner | Muir, Wilkin, B Williams | 9 |
| R Williams | Everitt | Prindiville | Statham | Crowley | Angus | Wray | Simpson | Wilkin | Christie | B Williams | Muir, Andersen, Healy | 10 |
| R Williams | Everitt | Prindiville | Statham | Crowley | Angus | Wray | Simpson | Wilkin | Christie | B Williams | Muir, Healy, Andersen | 11 |
| Wood | Everitt | Prindiville | Simpson | Crowley | Angus | Wray | B Williams | Wilkin | Muir | Gardner | W Dyer, Landon, Healy | 12 |
| Wood | Everitt | Prindiville | Simpson | Crowley | Angus | Landon | B Williams | Wilkin | Muir | Gardner | W Dyer, Healy, Statham | 13 |
| Wood | Everitt | Prindiville | Simpson | Crowley | Angus | Wray | B Williams | Landon | Muir | Gardner | Thomas, W Dyer, Simpson | 14 |
| Wood | Everitt | Prindiville | Simpson | Crowley | Angus | Wray | B Williams | Landon | Muir | Gardner | Thomas, Wilkin, W Dyer | 15 |
| R Williams | Everitt | Prindiville | Simpson | B Williams | Angus | Wray | O'Connor | Thomas | Muir | Gardner | Wilkin, Landon, Healy | 16 |
| Shoemake | Everitt | Prindiville | Simpson | B Williams | Angus | Wray | O'Connor | Thomas | Muir | Gardner | Crowley, Wilkin, Straw | 17 |
| Dudley | Everitt | Prindiville | Simpson | B Williams | Angus | Wray | O'Connor | Thomas | Muir | Gardner | O'Toole, Wilkin, Healy | 18 |
| R Williams | Everitt | Prindiville | Simpson | B Williams | Angus | Wray | O'Connor | Thomas | Muir | Gardner | Crowley, Wilkin, O'Toole | 19 |
| R Williams | Everitt | Prindiville | Simpson | B Williams | Angus | Wray | O'Connor | Thomas | Muir | O'Toole | Crowley, Wilkin, Healy | 20 |
| R Williams | Everitt | Prindiville | Simpson | B Williams | Angus | Wray | Gardner | Thomas | Muir | O'Connor | O'Toole, Crowley, Kirkup | 21 |
| R Williams | Everitt | Prindiville | Simpson | Crowley | Angus | Wray | O'Toole | Thomas | Muir | O'Connor | Wilkin, Healy, Kirkup | 22 |
| R Williams | Everitt | Prindiville | B Williams | Crowley | Angus | Wray | O'Toole | Thomas | Muir | O'Connor | Wilkin, Kirkup, Healy | 23 |
| R Williams | Everitt | Prindiville | B Williams | Crowley | Angus | Wray | O'Toole | Thomas | Muir | Wilkin | Kirkup, Healy, Jennings | 24 |
| R Williams | Everitt | Prindiville | B Williams | Crowley | Angus | Wray | O'Toole | Thomas | Muir | O'Connor | Kirkup, Healy, Simpson | 25 |
| Shoemake | Everitt | Prindiville | Simpson | B Williams | Angus | Wray | O'Toole | Thomas | Muir | O'Connor | Crowley, Kiwomya, Wilkin | 26 |
| R Williams | Everitt | Prindiville | Simpson | B Williams | Angus | Wray | Crowley | Thomas | Muir | O'Connor | Kiwomya, Gardner, O'Toole | 27 |
| R Williams | Everitt | Prindiville | Simpson | B Williams | Angus | Wray | Kiwomya | Thomas | Muir | Gardner | Crowley, Wilkin, O'Connor | 28 |
| R Williams | Everitt | Prindiville | Simpson | B Williams | Angus | Wray | Kiwomya | Wilkin | Muir | Crowley | O'Connor, Gardner, Thomas | 29 |
| R Williams | Everitt | Prindiville | Simpson | B Williams | Angus | Wray | Wilkin | Thomas | Muir | Crowley | Gardner, O'Connor, O'Toole | 30 |
| R Williams | Everitt | Prindiville | Simpson | B Williams | Angus | Wray | Wilkin | Thomas | Muir | O'Toole | Kiwomya, O'Connor, Gardner | 31 |
| MacKenzie | Everitt | Prindiville | Simpson | B Williams | Angus | Wray | Kiwomya | Wilkin | Muir | Crowley | O'Connor, O'Toole, Thomas | 32 |
| MacKenzie | Everitt | Prindiville | Simpson | B Williams | Angus | Wray | Wilkin | Thomas | Muir | Crowley | O'Connor, O'Toole, Thomas | 33 |
| R Williams | Everitt | Prindiville | Simpson | B Williams | Angus | Wray | Wilkin | Thomas | Muir | Crowley | O'Connor, O'Toole, Kirkup | 34 |
| R Williams | Everitt | Prindiville | Simpson | B Williams | Angus | Wray | O'Connor | Thomas | Muir | Crowley | Healy, O'Toole, Kirkup | 35 |
| R Williams | Everitt | Prindiville | Simpson | B Williams | Angus | Wray | Kiwomya | Thomas | Muir | Crowley | O'Toole, Kirkup, Paul | 36 |
| R Williams | Everitt | Prindiville | Simpson | B Williams | Angus | O'Toole | Kiwomya | Thomas | Muir | Crowley | Paul, Healy, Kirkup | 37 |
| R Williams | Everitt | Prindiville | Crowley | B Williams | Angus | Wray | Kiwomya | Thomas | Muir | O'Toole | O'Connor, Paul, March | 38 |
| R Williams | March | Prindiville | Crowley | B Williams | Angus | Wray | Kiwomya | O'Toole | Muir | O'Connor | Healy, Paul, Kirkup | 39 |
| R Williams | Everitt | Prindiville | Crowley | B Williams | Angus | Wray | Kiwomya | Thomas | Muir | O'Toole | O'Connor, Healy, Kirkup | 40 |
| R Williams | Everitt | Prindiville | Crowley | B Williams | Angus | Wray | Kiwomya | Thomas | Muir | O'Toole | O'Connor, Healy, Kirkup | 41 |
| R Williams | Everitt | Prindiville | Simpson | B Williams | Angus | Wray | Kiwomya | O'Connor | Muir | Crowley | O'Toole, Paul, Healy | 42 |

League Attendances     **HIGHEST:** 2945     **LOWEST:** 1211

**Dr MARTENS PREMIER:** 1st    **FA CUP:** 3rd Qualifying Rnd     **FA TROPHY:** 2nd Round

| MANAGER | FOOTBALL MANAGEMENT TEAM |
|---|---|

## MANAGER
### BRENDAN PHILLIPS

Date of Appointment

Date of Birth:        16th July 1954
Place of Birth:       West Indies

PREVIOUS CLUBS
As manager:
As Asst. Manager:
As coach:
As player:   Leicester C., Peterborough U., Mansfield T.,
Boston Utd.

HONOURS
As manager          Southern Lge 98-99
As player:          England Semi-Pro

## FOOTBALL MANAGEMENT TEAM

1st Team Coach:        Steve Burr

Physio:          Richie Norman

Reserve Team Manager  Kevin Shoemake

Youth Team Manager:     Dewi Cooke

Coaches:         Jose Ascensao

Chief Scout:        John Halford

Nuneaton Borough applaud their fans at the presentation of the Dr. Martens Championship shield.

Photo: Keith Clayton

## MATCHDAY PROGRAMME

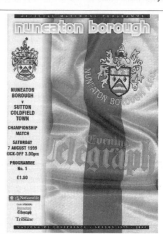

**Number of Pages**          48

**Price**          £1.50

**Programme Editorial Team**   Rod Grubb, John Moore, Andy Pace, Steve Packer, Martin Renshaw and Scott Renshaw

**Other club publications**

**Local Press**     Nuneaton Telegraph & Weekly Tribune

**Local Radio**     Mercia Sound, BBC CWR

# PLAYING SQUAD

| Player | Honours | D.O.B. | Previous Clubs |
|---|---|---|---|
| **GOALKEEPERS** | | | |
| Richard Williams | D.M. | 13.03.73 | Atherstone U, Hednesford T, Atherstone U, Birmingham C |
| Chris MacKenzie | | 14.05. 72 | Nuneaton Borough,Hereford United, Leyton Orient |
| | | | |
| **DEFENDERS** | | | |
| **Barry Williams** | **D.M.** | **06.05.73** | **Redditch U, Ely C, Alvechurch** |
| Leigh Everitt | | 09.09.70 | EveshamU, Atherstone U,Nuneaton, Kevin Elvin (RC Warwick,Nuneaton B |
| Andy Thackeray | V.C. | 13.02.68 | Manchester City, Huddersfield Town,Newport County, Wrexham, Rochdale |
| | | | Halifax Town |
| **Steve Prindiville** | | **26.12.68** | **Leicester C, Chesterfield, Mansfield T, Doncaster R, Wycombe W,** |
| | | | **Halifax Town, Dagenham & Redbridge, Kidderminster Harriers** |
| Terry Angus | D.M. | 14.01.68 | V.S.Rugby, Northampton Town, Fulham,Slough Town |
| **Wayne Simpson** | **D.M.** | **19.09.68** | **Port Vale, Stafford Rangers, Hednesford Town** |
| | | | |
| **MIDFIELDERS** | | | |
| Dave Crowley | | 07.09.68 | Stafford R, Bedworth U, Coventry C |
| Jon Brown | | 08.09.66 | Denaby United, Exeter City |
| Krystof Kotylo | | 28.09.77 | Sheffield Wednesday |
| Perry Norman | | 19.09.80 | Queens Park Rangers |
| Ian Reed | | 04.09.75 | Halesowen Town |
| Ian Muir | D.M. | 05.05.63 | Q.P.R., Birmingham City, Brighton , Tranmere Rovers, Happy Valley (H.K.) |
| Brett Healy | | 06.10.77 | Coventry City |
| Andy Ducros | | 16.09.77 | Coventry City |
| | | | |
| **FORWARDS** | | | |
| Shaun Wray | D.M. | 14.03.77 | Stafford R, Shrewsbury T |
| David Hanson | | 19.11.68 | Bury, Halifax Town, Leyton O,Wellig U (L), Chesterfield (L), Halifax Town |
| Marvin Blake | | 22.08.79 | West Bromwich Albion |
| Delton Francis | F.A.T. | 12.03.78 | Birmingham City, Hednesford Town,Halesowen Town, Kingstonian |
| Joe O'Connor | D.M(2) | 20.10.67 | Lye Town, Stafford Rangers, Hednesford Town |

Bold Print indicates England Semi-Professional Internationals

# NUNEATON BOROUGH

**Formed:** 1937

**Nickname:** The Boro

**Club colours:** Blue & white stripes,blue shorts

**Change colours:** All yellow & green

**Reserve team's league:** Ansells Midland Comb.

**Midweek home matchday:** Tuesday 7.45pm

**Club Sponsors:** Evening Telegraph

## PREVIOUS

**Leagues:** Central Amateur 37-38; B'ham Comb 38-52; West Mids (B'ham) 52-58;Southern 58-79 81-82 88-99. GM Conference (Alliance Premier & Gola) 79-81 82-8

**Names:** None

**Ground:** None

## CLUB RECORDS

**Attendance:** 22,114 v Rotherham, FA Cup 3rd Rd 1967

**Defeat:** 1-8 (55-56 & 68-69)

**Win:** 11-1 (45-46 & 55-56)

**Goalscorer:** Paul Culpin 201 (Career)
55 (Season - 92/93)

**Career Appearances:** Alan Jones 545 (62-74)

**Transfer Fees**
**Paid:** £9,500 for Richard Dixey (Scarborough, 1981)
**Received:** £60,000 for D Bullock (Huddersfield Tn 93)

## GROUND DETAILS

Manor Park,
Beaumont Road,
Nuneaton,
Warks. CV11 5HD

**Telephone Number:** 01203 385738 or 01203 328281
Fax: 01203 342690

**Simple Directions:**
A444 to Nuneaton from M6 junction 3, 2nd exit at 1st round-about, 2nd exit at 2nd r'about, left at 3rd r'bout, 2nd right into Greenmoor Rd, turn right at the end, grd on left.
Parking 100 cars at Manor Park School, Beaumont Rd, 50p each.     Ground 1 mile from Nuneaton Trent Valley (BR)

**Capacity:** 6,500
**Seated:** 520
**Terracing -** **Covered:** 3,000
**Uncovered:** 3,500

**SOCIAL FACILITIES:** Clubhouse open every evening, weekend lunchtimes & matchdays.

**CLUB SHOP:** Sells souvenirs, programmes etc. Commercial department

## BEST SEASON

**FA Cup:** 3rd Rd replay 66-67
1st Rd 19 times

**FA Trophy:** Quarter final- 76-77(rep), 79-80, 86-87

## HONOURS

Alliance Prem Lge R-up (2) 83-85
Southern Lg Premier Div. 98-99, R-up 66-67 74-75
League Cup Win 95-96
Midland Div 81-82 92-93, Champ 95-96
Lg Cup R-up 62-63, Merit Cup 92-93 (jt)
Birmingham Lg 55-56 (Nth Div 54-55)
Birmingham Comb. R-up 3
Birmingham Snr Cup 6, R-up 3

## Past Players who progressed to the Football League

A Morton (Fulham 70), R Edwards Port Vale 72),
K Stephens (Luton 78), T Peake (Lincoln 79),
P Sugrue (Man City 80), M Shotton & T Smithers (Oxford 80),
D Thomas (Wimbledon 81), P Richardson(Derby 84),
P Culpin (Coventry 85), R Hill/T Morley/E McGoldrick/A Harris(Northampton 85/86), D Bullock (Huddersfield 93)

# RUSHDEN & DIAMONDS

With expectations high and seven consecutive victories at the start of the season, The Diamonds appeared to be invincible.

Experienced management, funds to strengthen and good support all made their case just about perfect - but, yes - football is a funny old game!

## CLUB OFFICIALS 1999-2000

| | |
|---|---|
| President | **D Attley** |
| Chairman | **W M Griggs CBE** |
| Managing Director | **M G Darnell** |
| Directors | **A N Gant, S W Griggs,** |
| | **A C Jones, R W Langley, C M Smith** |
| Football Secretary | **David Joyce** |
| | c/o the club |
| Tel: 01933 392821 (H) 01933 6520000 (B) | |
| Press Offiicer | **David Joyce** |
| Retail Sales Manager | **Tom Bungay** |

The next ten games brought just two victories and the favourites were back in fourth position. Victories over Forest Green Rovers, Shrewsbury Town and Doncaster Rovers brought Premier League Leeds United to sample the delights of Nene Park and Adrian Foster could have made history with glorious headed chances in the first and last five minutes. A draw was a wonderful result however and the club's visit to Elland Road lifted everyone.

Defeat by Woking in the F.A.Umbro Trophy left the club free to concentrate on the end of season promotion challenge, but sadly for this beautiful club the pressures proved too much.

Their time will surely come - they certainly deserve it.

T.T.

Back Row (L-R): David Staff, Darren Collins, Jim Rodwell, Michael McElhatton, Paul Underwood, Lee Archer, Adrian Foster, Kenny Cramman

Middle Row: Simon Parsell (Physio), Jon Brady, Colin West, David Mehew, Mark Gayle, Mark Smith, Darren Watts, Chris Whyte, Ritchie Hanlon, Tim Wooding, Mark Cooper, Jeff Vetere (Reserve/Youth Coach)

Front Row: Carel Vandervalden, John Hamsher, Malcolm Ndekwe, Gary Butterworth, Brian Talbot (Head Coach), Darren Bradshaw, Julian

# RUSHDEN & DIAMONDS
## MATCH FACTS 1998-99

| No | Date | Venue | Comp | Opponents | Att | Result | Score | Goalscorers |
|---|---|---|---|---|---|---|---|---|
| 1 | 15/08 | A | NC | Forest Green Rovers | 1120 | W | 2-0 | Whyte 35, Kilgour 49[og] |
| 2 | 18/08 | H | NC | Welling United | 2261 | W | 3-1 | Collins 5 39, Foster 86 |
| 3 | 22/08 | H | NC | Barrow | 2259 | W | 4-0 | Brady 30, Mison 49, Foster 61, Underwood 70 |
| 4 | 25/08 | A | NC | Kingstonian | 2605 | W | 5-1 | Foster 12 60 85, Wooding 73, Collins 90 |
| 5 | 29/08 | A | NC | Southport | 1653 | W | 1-0 | Collins 6 |
| 6 | 31/08 | H | NC | Hayes | 3208 | W | 5-0 | Collins 25 65, Wooding 71, Foster 80 84 |
| 7 | 05/09 | A | NC | Yeovil Town | 2876 | W | 1-0 | Foster 18 |
| 8 | 08/09 | A | NC | Dover Athletic | 1387 | D | 1-1 | Foster 26 |
| 9 | 12/09 | H | NC | Telford United | 2909 | L | 2-3 | Foster 35, Collins 43 |
| 10 | 19/09 | A | NC | Doncaster Rovers | 3768 | D | 1-1 | Hume 89 |
| 11 | 26/09 | H | NC | Hereford United | 3521 | D | 1-1 | Collins 38 |
| 12 | 03/10 | H | NC | Northwich Victoria | 2803 | L | 1-2 | West 44 |
| 13 | 10/10 | A | NC | Farnborough Town | 958 | W | 2-1 | Rodwell 14, Collins 81 |
| 14 | 24/10 | H | NC | Morecambe | 2394 | W | 3-1 | Collins 40, Hamsher 80[p], Heggs 90 |
| 15 | 07/11 | A | NC | Hednesford Town | 1387 | D | 1-1 | Hanlon 77 |
| 16 | 28/11 | A | NC | Cheltenham Town | 4051 | L | 0-1 | |
| 17 | 12/12 | A | NC | Telford United | 867 | D | 2-2 | De Souza 38, Heggs 64 |
| 18 | 19/12 | H | NC | Farnborough Town | 2481 | W | 1-0 | West 28 |
| 19 | 26/12 | A | NC | Stevenage Borough | 4319 | D | 0-0 | |
| 20 | 28/12 | H | NC | Woking | 4307 | W | 2-0 | De Souza 42, Foster 90 |
| 21 | 09/01 | A | NC | Barrow | 2003 | W | 2-0 | Cooper 40, De Souza 87 |
| 22 | 23/01 | H | NC | Doncaster Rovers | 4577 | L | 1-3 | Nicol 40[og] |
| 23 | 30/01 | A | NC | Northwich Victoria | 1802 | L | 1-2 | De Souza 26 |
| 24 | 02/02 | H | NC | Kidderminster Harriers | 2374 | D | 1-1 | Foster 8 |
| 25 | 13/02 | A | NC | Kidderminster Harriers | 2337 | D | 0-0 | |
| 26 | 16/02 | A | NC | Welling United | 667 | W | 1-0 | Collins 20 |
| 27 | 20/02 | H | NC | Hednesford Town | 3123 | W | 1-0 | Collins 90 |
| 28 | 23/02 | H | NC | Southport | 2135 | W | 3-1 | Foster 13, McElhatton 20, Cooper 35 |
| 29 | 06/03 | A | NC | Hayes | 1302 | L | 1-2 | Goodliffe 13[og] |
| 30 | 09/03 | H | NC | Stevenage Borough | 3169 | W | 2-1 | Collins 27 42 |
| 31 | 13/03 | H | NC | Leek Town | 2833 | W | 2-0 | McElhatton 57, Collins 60 |
| 32 | 16/03 | H | NC | Dover Athletic | 2744 | D | 2-2 | Cooper 5, Heggs 20 |
| 33 | 20/03 | A | NC | Morecambe | 1099 | W | 3-2 | Rodwell 6, Cooper 26, McElhatton 89 |
| 34 | 23/03 | A | NC | Leek Town | 806 | W | 3-2 | De Souza 23, Underwood 61, Wooding 66[p] |
| 35 | 27/03 | A | NC | Kettering Town | 5017 | D | 0-0 | |
| 36 | 03/04 | H | NC | Cheltenham Town | 6312 | L | 1-2 | De Souza 22 |
| 37 | 05/04 | A | NC | Woking | 2808 | D | 1-1 | Foster 71 |
| 38 | 13/04 | H | NC | Yeovil Town | 2367 | L | 1-2 | West 90 |
| 39 | 20/04 | H | NC | Kingstonian | 1818 | D | 0-0 | |
| 40 | 24/04 | A | NC | Hereford United | 2044 | L | 2-3 | Cooper 45, Collins 87 |
| 41 | 26/04 | H | NC | Forest Green Rovers | 1626 | W | 4-0 | De Souza 4, Collins 38, Brady 44, Cooper 84 |
| 42 | 01/05 | H | NC | Kettering Town | 4700 | L | 1-2 | McElhatton 20 |

**CUP COMPETITIONS**

| | Date | Venue | Comp | | Opponents | Att | Result | Score | Goalscorers |
|---|---|---|---|---|---|---|---|---|---|
| | 17/10 | H | FA Cup | Q3 | Forest Green Rovers | 2376 | W | 2-0 | |
| | 09/11 | A | FA Cup | Q4 | Leatherhead | 1145 | D | 1-1 | Warburton 90 |
| | 11/11 | H | FA Cup | Q4 r | Leatherhead | 1855 | W | 4-0 | Collins 20, West 45, Heggs 48, Brady 54 |
| | 14/11 | H | FA Cup | 1 | Shrewsbury Town | 4121 | W | 1-0 | Underwood 19 |
| | 21/11 | H | FA Trophy | 2 | Bath City | 1989 | W | 2-0 | Vickerman 7[og], Brady 66 |
| | 01/12 | A | NSC | QF | Rothwell Town | 253 | W | 1-0 | Hamsher 21[p] |
| | 05/12 | A | FA Cup | 2 | Doncaster Rovers | 5396 | D | 0-0 | |
| | 15/12 | H | FA Cup | 2 r | Doncaster Rovers | 5564 | W | 4-2 | Hamsher 6[p], West 63 84, Brady 68 |
| | 22/12 | A | Endsleigh | 2 | Farnborough Town | 313 | L | 1-3 | Foster 64 |
| | 02/01 | H | FA Cup | 3 | Leeds United | 6431 | D | 0-0 | |
| | 13/01 | A | FA Cup | 3 r | Leeds United | 39159 | L | 1-3 | Heggs 11 |
| | 25/01 | A | FA Trophy | 3 | Slough Town | 729 | W | 2-1 | West(2) |
| | 06/02 | A | FA Trophy | 4 | Woking | 2788 | D | 0-0 | |
| | 09/02 | H | FA Trophy | 4 r | Woking | 1995 | L | 1-2 | Warburton 1 |
| | 02/03 | A | NC SF | | Cogenhoe United | n/k | D | 2-2 | Rodwell 57, Cramman 65 |
| | 10/04 | H | NSC SF r | | Cogenhoe United | n/k | W | 3-1 | De Souza 32 41, West 89 |
| | 18/04 | A | NSC F | | Raunds Town | 804 | W | 2-0 | West 18, De Souza 83 |

| 1 | 2 | 3 | 4 | 5 | 6 | 7 | 8 | 9 | 10 | 11 | 12 / 14 / 15 | |
|---|---|---|---|---|---|---|---|---|---|---|---|---|
| Gayle | Wooding | Bradshaw | Mison | P Wilson | Whyte | Brady | Van der Valden | West | Collins | Underwood | | 1 |
| Gayle | Wooding | Bradshaw | Mison | Wilson | Whyte | Brady | Van der Valden | West | Collins | Underwood | Foster, Mehew, Hanlon | 2 |
| Gayle | Wooding | Bradshaw | Mison | Wilson | Whyte | Brady | Van der Valden | Foster | Collins | Underwood | Mehew, Hanlon, McElhatton | 3 |
| Gayle | Wooding | Bradshaw | Mison | Wilson | Whyte | Brady | Van der Valden | Foster | Collins | Underwood | McElhatton, Archer, Hanlon | 4 |
| Gayle | Wooding | Bradshaw | Mison | Wilson | Whyte | Brady | Van der Valden | Foster | Collins | Underwood | McElhatton, Hanlon, Archer | 5 |
| Gayle | Wooding | Bradshaw | Mison | Wilson | Rodwell | Brady | Van der Valden | Foster | Collins | Underwood | Archer, Hanlon, McElhatton | 6 |
| Gayle | Wooding | Bradshaw | Mison | Wilson | Whyte | Brady | Van der Valden | Foster | Collins | Underwood | Archer, Hanlon, McElhatton | 7 |
| Gayle | Wooding | Bradshaw | Mison | Wilson | Whyte | Brady | Van der Valden | Foster | Collins | Underwood | Archer, Hanlon, McElhatton | 8 |
| Gayle | Wooding | Bradshaw | Mison | Wilson | Whyte | Brady | Van der Valden | Foster | Collins | Underwood | McElhatton, West, Hanlon | 9 |
| Gayle | Wooding | Bradshaw | McElhatton | Wilson | Whyte | Brady | Van der Valden | Foster | Collins | Underwood | West, Hanlon, Rodwell | 10 |
| Smith | Wooding | Bradshaw | McElhatton | Wilson | Whyte | Brady | Van der Valden | Foster | Collins | Underwood | West, Rodwell, Hanlon | 11 |
| Smith | Wooding | Rodwell | McElhatton | Wilson | Whyte | Brady | Van der Valden | Foster | West | Underwood | Hanlon, Mison, Mehew | 12 |
| Smith | Hamsher | Underwood | Mison | Rodwell | Whyte | Hanlon | Butterworth | Mehew | Collins | Archer | Foster, Brady, Kiriacou | 13 |
| Smith | Hamsher | Bradshaw | Mison | Rodwell | Brady | McElhatton | Butterworth | Heggs | Collins | Underwood | Archer, West, Hanlon | 14 |
| Gayle | Hamsher | Bradshaw | Mison | Rodwell | Brady | McElhatton | Butterworth | West | Collins | Underwood | Hanlon, Rawle, Wooding | 15 |
| Gayle | Wooding | Bradshaw | Mison | Warburton | Heggs | McElhatton | Butterworth | West | Collins | Underwood | Rawle, Brady, Hanlon | 16 |
| Gayle | Woodling | Bradshaw | Hamsher | Warburton | Heggs | McElhatton | Butterworth | West | De Souza | Underwood | Mison, Brady, Foster | 17 |
| Gayle | Wooding | Bradshaw | Hamsher | Warburton | Heggs | Brady | Butterworth | West | De Souza | Underwood | Mison, Foster, McElhatton | 18 |
| Feuer | Wooding | Bradshaw | Hamsher | Rodwell | Heggs | Brady | Butterworth | West | De Souza | Underwood | Foster, McElhatton, Archer | 19 |
| Corry | Wooding | Bradshaw | Hamsher | Rodwell | Heggs | McElhatton | Butterworth | Foster | De Souza | Underwood | West, Brady, Whyte | 20 |
| Feuer | Wooding | Bradshaw | Hamsher | Rodwell | Heggs | Cooper | Butterworth | Foster | De Souza | Underwood | Brady, P Wilson, West | 21 |
| Feuer | Wooding | Bradshaw | Hamsher | Rodwell | Heggs | McElhatton | Butterworth | Foster | De Souza | Underwood | Brady, Cooper, West | 22 |
| Smith | Wooding | Bradshaw | McElhatton | Rodwell | Wilson | Brady | Butterworth | West | De Souza | Underwood | Hamsher, Heggs, Foster | 23 |
| Smith | Wooding | Wilson | McElhatton | Rodwell | Whyte | Hamsher | Butterworth | Foster | De Souza | Underwood | Brady, Heggs, West | 24 |
| Smith | Heggs | Whyte | McElhatton | Rodwell | Warburton | Brady | Butterworth | De Souza | Collins | Cramman | Foster, Cooper, Wooding | 25 |
| Smith | Heggs | Whyte | McElhatton | Rodwell | Warburton | Brady | Cooper | De Souza | Collins | Underwood | Foster, Butterworth, Wooding | 26 |
| Smith | Heggs | Bradshaw | McElhatton | Rodwell | Warburton | Brady | Cooper | De Souza | Collins | Underwood | Foster, Butterworth, Whyte | 27 |
| Smith | Heggs | Bradshaw | McElhatton | Rodwell | Warburton | Brady | Cooper | Foster | Collins | Underwood | De Souza, Butterworth, Whyte | 28 |
| Smith | Heggs | Bradshaw | McElhatton | Rodwell | Warburton | Brady | Cooper | Butterworth | Collins | Underwood | Foster, Hamsher, Whyte | 29 |
| Smith | Heggs | Bradshaw | McElhatton | Rodwell | Warburton | Brady | Cooper | Foster | Collins | Cramman | Wooding, De Souza, Butterworth | 30 |
| Smith | Heggs | Bradshaw | Warburton | Rodwell | Brady | McElhatton | Cooper | Foster | Collins | Underwood | Hamsher, Whyte, De Souza | 31 |
| Smith | Heggs | Wooding | McElhatton | Rodwell | Whyte | Brady | Cooper | Foster | Collins | Underwood | Hamsher, De Souza, West | 32 |
| Smith | Hamsher | Whyte | McElhatton | Rodwell | Branston | Brady | Cooper | Foster | Collins | Underwood | Butterworth, De Souza, Wooding | 33 |
| Smith | Heggs | Branston | Wooding | Rodwell | Brady | McElhatton | Cooper | De Souza | West | Underwood | Foster, Whyte, Butterworth | 34 |
| Smith | Heggs | Bradshaw | McElhatton | Rodwell | Branston | Brady | Cooper | De Souza | Collins | Underwood | Wooding, Butterworth, Foster | 35 |
| Smith | Heggs | Bradshaw | McElhatton | Rodwell | Branston | Wooding | Cooper | De Souza | Collins | Underwood | West, Hamsher, Berry | 36 |
| Smith | Berry | Bradshaw | McElhatton | Rodwell | Branston | Brady | Cooper | De Souza | Collins | Underwood | Heggs, Wooding, Foster | 37 |
| Smith | Heggs | Bradshaw | McElhatton | Rodwell | Branston | Brady | Cooper | West | De Souza | Underwood | Whyte, Wooding, Berry | 38 |
| Collett | Heggs | Bradshaw | McElhatton | Rodwell | Branston | Brady | Butterworth | West | Collins | Underwood | De Souza, Wooding, Berry | 39 |
| Collett | Wooding | Bradshaw | McElhatton | Rodwell | Branston | Butterworth | Cooper | De Souza | Collins | Underwood | Brady, Heggs, Berry | 40 |
| Collett | Brady | Bradshaw | McElhatton | Rodwell | Branton | Butterworth | Cooper | De Souza | Collins | Underwood | Ndekwe, Berry, Wooding | 41 |
| Collett | Brady | Bradshaw | McElhatton | Rodwell | Branston | Butterworth | Cooper | De Souza | Collins | Underwood | Ndekwe, Wooding, Berry | 42 |

League Attendances   **HIGHEST:** 4700   **LOWEST:** 1626

**CONFERENCE:** 4th   **FA CUP:** 3rd Round   **FA TROPHY:** 4th Round

## CLUB MANAGER
### BRIAN TALBOT

| | |
|---|---|
| Date of Appointment | April 1997 |
| Date of Birth: | 21st July 1953 |
| Place of Birth: | Ipswich |

PREVIOUS CLUBS
As manager — West Bromwich Albion, Kettering T., Hibernians (Malta)
As player — Ipswich T., Arsenal, Watford, Stoke C., Fulham, Aldershot

HONOURS
As manager — Maltese Championship.
As player — England - 6 full, 1 `B' & u23 caps
FA Cup winner x 2, Texaco Cup winner

Above: Brian Talbot, Team Coach.
Photo: Peter Barnes

## FOOTBALL MANAGEMENT TEAM

| | |
|---|---|
| Assistant Head Coach | Terry Westley |
| Chief Scout | Cyril Lea |
| Reserve & Youth Team Coach | Jeff Vetere |
| Physiotherapist | Simon Parsell |
| Asst. Physiotherapist | Nigel Gore |

### 1998-99

| | |
|---|---|
| **Top Scorer:** | Darren Collins |
| **Player of the Year:** | Darren Bradshaw |
| **Captain:** | Ray Warburton |

Gary Butterworth and Paul Underwood proudly display their England shirts
in the presence of their Chairman, Max Griggs. Photo: Peter Barnes

## MATCHDAY PROGRAMME

| | |
|---|---|
| Number of pages | 48 |
| Price | £1.50 |
| Programme Editor | Ted Carrol |
| Other club publications: | None |
| Local Newspapers: | Northants Evening Telegraph Chronicle & Echo, Citizen Herald & Post |
| Local Radio Stations: | Radio Diamonds Radio Northampton KCBC, Northants 96 |

# PLAYING SQUAD

| Player | Birthplace Honours | D.O.B. | Previous Clubs |
|---|---|---|---|
| **GOALKEEPERS** | | | |
| Michael Bertocchi | Cannes (Fra) | 17.07.81 | AS Cannes |
| Mark Smith | Birmingham | 02.01.73 | Nottingham Forest, Crewe Alexandra, Walsall |
| Billy Turley | Wolverhampton | 15.02.73 | Northampton Town, Evesham Utd. |
| **DEFENDERS** | | | |
| Jim Rodwell | Lincoln | 20.11.70 | Darlington, Sabam (Malaysia), Bury, Boston FC, Boston U, Bedworth U, Hednesford T, Nuneaton B, Halesowen T, |
| SLP | | | £40K to Rushden & Diamonds |
| Michael McElhatton | Co.Kerry | 16.04.75 | AFC Bournemouth, Scarborough |
| Tim Wooding | Wellingborough | 05.07.73 | Norwich C, AFC Bournemouth |
| SLP | | | |
| Darren Bradshaw | Sheffield | 19.03.67 | Matlock T, Chesterfield, York C, Newcastle U, Peterborough U, Blackpool |
| John Brady | Newcastle(Aust) | 14.01.75 | Adamstown Rosebuds (Aust), Swansea C, Brentford, Hayes, |
| ILP | | | Mjolner (Nor), Hayes |
| John Hamsher | Lambeth | 14.01.78 | Fulham |
| **Paul Underwood** | **London** | | **Sutton U, Kingstonian, Carshalton A, Enfield,** |
| | | | **£50k to Rushden & Diamonds** |
| Mark Peters | St Asaph | 06.07.72 | Mansfield Town |
| Ray Warburton | Rotherham | 07.10.67 | York City, Northampton Town |
| **MIDFIELDERS** | | | |
| **Gary Butterworth** | **Peterborough** | **08.09.69** | **Peterborough U, Dagenham & Redbridge,** |
| **ESP, SLP** | | | **£20k to Rushden & Diamonds** |
| **Kenny Cramman** | **Gateshead** | **17.08.69** | **Hartlepool U, Bishop Auckland, Gateshead,** |
| **ESP** | | | **£40k to Rushden & Diamonds** |
| Mike Mison | London | 08.11.75 | Fulham |
| Mark Cooper | Wakefield | 18.12.68 | Bristol C, Exeter C, Birmingham C, Fulham, Wycombe W, Exeter C, Hartlepool U, Leyton Orient |
| Carel Van der Velden | Arnheim | 03.08.72 | Den Bosch (Holl), Barnsley, Scarborough, Stevenage B |
| Steven Berry | Liverpool | 04.04.63 | Portsmouth, Swindon T., Sunderland, Newport Co., Aldershot T., Northampton T., Kettering T., Stevenage Bor. (L) |
| Carl Heggs | Leicester | 11.02.70 | Northampton Town, Swansea C., West Bromwich Alb. |
| **FORWARDS** | | | |
| **Darren Collins** | **Winchester** | **24.05.67** | **Petersfield U, Northampton T, Aylesbury U, Enfield,** |
| **ESP, SLP** | | | **£20k to Rushden & Diamonds** |
| Colin West | Wallsend | 13.11.62 | Sunderland, Watford, Glasgow Rangers, Sheffield Wednesday, WBA, Swansea C,Leyton Orient |
| Miguel De Souza | London | 11.02.70 | Peterborough Utd., Wycombe W., Birmingham C. |
| David Town | Boscombe | 09.12.76 | AFC Bournemouth |
| Mark Sale | Burton-on-Trent | 27.02.72 | Colchester Utd., £30k to Rushden & Diamonds |

Young professionals from Youth Team: Andrew Burgess (D),Jon Challinor (D), Gary Mills (MF), Malcolm Ndekwe (F)

Bold print indicates England Semi-Professional Internationals

DEPARTURES
David Mehew (Forest Green), Adrian Foster (Yeovil T.), David Staff (Stafford R.), Chris Whyte (released), Julian Capone (released), Lee Archer, Richie Hanlon, Glen Fuff, Paul Wilson, Mark Gale (Shelbourne), Carol Vandervalden, Chris Whyte(USA)

# RUSHDEN & DIAMONDS

**Founded:** 1992

**Nickname:** Diamonds

**Team Sponsors:** Dr. Martens

**Club colours:** White, red & blue trim, shirts, blue shorts, white socks

**Change colours:** Yellow and black

**Reserve Team's league:**
Capital League/Central Conference

**Midweek home matchday:** Tuesday

## GROUND DETAILS

Nene Park,
Diamond Way,
Irthlingborough,
Northants

TELEPHONE: 01933 652000
Fax: 01933 650418
Newsline: 09068 44 00 33

SIMPLE DIRECTIONS:
South from M1 exit 15, A45 bypassing Northampton until A6 - 1st exit North - ground approx 400 yards right.
North & West from A14 exit A6 South (Bedford),follow A6 for approx 6 miles, ground on left.
East from A14 exit A45 (Northampton) follow A45 for approx 4 miles to A6 - 3rd exit North - ground approx 400 yards on right

CAPACITY: 6,635 - ALL COVERED

SEATED: 4,654

SOCIAL FACILITIES:
Lounge facilities. Open all day, every day. Full restaurant facilities
CLUB SHOP / DOC SHOP:
Sells programmes, replica shirts, scarves, hats, footwear etc.
Contact Tom Bungay (01933 652000, extn.2263)

## Past Players who progressed to the Football League

From Rushden Town: Gordon Inwood (WBA 1949), Robert Peacock (Northampton 1957).

From IrthlingboroughDiamonds: Scott Endersby (Ipswich), Steve Brown & Dave Johnson (Northampton),

## PREVIOUS

**Grounds:**
Rushden Town: Hayden Road, Rushden (pre-1992)
IrthlingboroughDiamonds: Manton Road, Irthlingborough
**Leagues:** Southern League 92-96
Rushden Town : Midland 1894-1901; Utd Co's 01-04, 19-56, 61-83; Central Alliance 61-83
Irthlingborough Diamonds : Rushden Yth; Rushden & Dist; Kettering Amat.; United Counties.
**Names:** Rushden Town (1894-1992) merged with Irthlingborough Diamonds (1946-92) in 1992 to form Rushden & Diamonds

## CLUB RECORDS

**Attendance:** 6,431 v Leeds United
FA Cup 3rd Round, Jan. 1999

**Win:** 7-0 v Redditch Utd (H),
Southern League Midland Div. 7/5/94
**Defeat:** 0-5 v Slough Town (A),
GM Vauxhall Conference 96/97

**Career goalscorer:** Darren Collins 138
**Career appearances:** Darren Collins 242

**Transfer fee paid:** £85,000
to Kettering Town for Carl Alford - 1996
(undisclosed to Northampton T. for Billy Turley - June 1999)
**Transfer fee received:** £18,000
from Kingstonian for David Leworthy - June 1997

## BEST SEASON

**FA Cup:** Third Round replay 98-99,
1-3 v Leeds United (A) after 0-0

**FA Trophy:** Semi-Final 94-95

## HONOURS

Southern League Premier Div 95-96,
Midland Div 94-95,
Northants Senior Cup 94-95 98-99,
Daventry Charity Cup 92-93,
Campri Leisurewear Cup 92-93

Rushden Town: Southern Lg Midland Div R-up 88-89,
Utd Co's Lg 02-03, 26-27,29-30, 31-32, 34-38, 63-64, 72-73,
R-up 12 times, Lg Cup 33-35, 36-38, 46-47,
Northants Snr Cup 25-28, 29-31, 34-35, 36-37, 57-58, 77-78,
FA Vase QF 89-90.

Irthlingborough Diamonds: Utd Co's Lg 70-71, 76-77, 78-79, 82-83, KO Cup 78-79,80-81, Northants Snr Cup 80-81.

# SCARBOROUGH

When that exciting first link was forged with The Football League and the Conference winners of 986-87 season were welcomed into the Fourth Division, Scarborough surprised most experts by coming through on the rails to take that treasured place.
Their manager that season was Neil Warnock who has since made a habit of gaining promotion for clubs at the lower Football League levels.

## CLUB OFFICIALS 1999-2000

| | |
|---|---|
| President | **J R Birley** |
| Chairman | **John Russell** |
| Vice Chairman | **T Milton** |
| Chief Executive | **Kevin Green** |
| Football Secretary | **Mrs G  Russell** |
| Commercial Director | **Russ Green** |

Now it is Colin Addison's turn and he actually took Hereford United into the League before automatic promotion and relegation.

Scarborough had a great F.A. Trophy reputation and they will have their eye on that competition again this season but it will be return to the Football League that will be uppermost in their planning.

To be relegated by a last minute goal from a goalkeeper up for a corner (whose eligibilty was in doubt) was just about as upsetting as you could get, so maybe things can only get better.

Lee Sinnott an experienced defender, has been signed as player-coach and six new players have been added to a squad that had lost eight of last season's regulars.

It may take the club a couple of seasons to re-group and build a strong challenge for the championship but they certainly have the right man as manager for the tough job ahead.

T.T.

## MANAGER
### COLIN ADDISON

Date of Appointment                                    Feb. 1999

Date of Birth                                          18th May 1940
Place of Birth                                              Taunton

PREVIOUS CLUBS
As manager
As coach
As player        York C., Nottm. Forest, Arsenal, Sheff. Utd., Hereford U.

## FOOTBALL MANAGEMENT TEAM

| | |
|---|---|
| Assistant Manager | Ray McHale |
| Player Coach | Lee Sinnott |
| Physiotherapist | Kevin Sullivan |
| Community Officer | Mitch Cook |
| Youth YTeam Coach | Ian Kerr |

### 1998-99

**Top Scorer:**          Chris Tate
**Player of the Year:**  Jamie Hoyland
**Captain:**             Lee Sinnott

ABOVE:
The mural inside the McCain Stadium showing the Championship celebrations in 1987.

LEFT:
The main stand.

Photos: D Nicholson

## MATCHDAY PROGRAMME

Number of pages                                    44

Price                                              £1.50

Programme Editor                          James Hunter

Other club publications:                          None

Local Newspapers:          Scarborough Evening News
                                        The Mercury
Local Radio Stations:                      Radio York
                                        Y.C.R. Radio

# PLAYING SQUAD

| Player | Birthplace Honours | D.O.B. | Previous Clubs |
|---|---|---|---|
| **GOALKEEPERS** | | | |
| Kevin Martin | Bromsgrove | 22.06.76 | |
| Andy Woods | Colchester | 15.01.76 | Halifax Town, Doncaster Rovers |
| Gareth Powell | | | Tranmere Rovers |
| **DEFENDERS** | | | |
| Shaun Rennison | Northallerton | 23.11.80 | |
| Mike McNaughton | Blackpool | 29.01.80 | |
| Scott Middlemass | Worksop | 17.05.72 | Preston N.E. |
| Jamie Hoyland | Sheffield | 23.01.76 | |
| Lee Sinnott | Pelsall | 12.07.65 | Walsall,Watford,Bradford City,Crystal Palace, Huddersfield Town, Oldham Athletic |
| Graeme Carr | Chester-le-Street | 28.10.78 | |
| Mark Tyrrell | Leicester | 15.10.71 | |
| David Tremble | Newcastle | 12.01.81 | |
| Danny Brunton | Bidlington | 13.12.80 | |
| Simon Betts | Middlesbrough | 03.03.73 | Colchester United |
| Leigh Grant | Stockton-on-Tees | 31.01.81 | |
| **MIDFIELDERS** | | | |
| Marcus Jones | Stone | 24.06.74 | Telford United |
| Steve Brodie | Sunderland | 14.01.73 | |
| Andrew Quinn | Halifax | 01.09.79 | Leeds United |
| David Bass | Frimley | 29.11.74 | Rotherham Utd. |
| Alex Gildea | Scarborough | 15.09.80 | |
| Brian McGinty | Glasgow | 10.12.76 | Glasgow Rangers, HUll City |
| Marvin Harriot | Dulwich | 20.04.74 | |
| **FORWARDS** | | | |
| Darren Roberts | Birmingham | 12.10.69 | |
| Gareth McAlindon | Hexham | 06.04.77 | Carlisle United,  Newcastle Utd. |
| Stewart Morris | Newcastle | 21.09.80 | |
| Ian Milbourne | Bradford | 21.01.79 | Newcastle United |

Departures:    Wayne Bullimore, John Kaye, Jason Lydiat, Tony Parks (Halifax Town), Gary Porter (Boston United), Liam Robinson (Northwich Victoria) , Matthew Russell (Halifax Town - £5,000), Andy Saville (Gainsborough Trinity), Chris Tate (Halifax Town -£100,000)

# SCARBOROUGH

**Founded:** 1879

**Nickname:** The Seadogs

**Club Sponsors:** Arnott Insurance

**Colours** Red & white shirts,
white shorts, red socks

**Change colours:** All blue

**Midweek Matchday:** Tuesday

**Reserves' League:** Pontin's League

**Youth League** Youth Aliance

## GROUND DETAILS

McCain Stadium
Seamer Road
Scarborough
N. Yorkshire YO12 4HF

**COMMUNICATION** Tel: 01723 375094
Fax: ????
e-mail: ????

**SIMPLE DIRECTIONS** The ground is situated on the main Scarborough to York road (A64), about half a mile beyond B&Q on the left as you go into Scarborough. Scarborough central (BR) about 2 miles. Car Parking: Ample in streets around the ground.

**CAPACITY** 5,900
**SEATING** 3,500
**COVERED TERRACING** 1,000

**CLUB SHOP:** ???

**SOCIAL FACILITIES:** Clubhouse - opening hours & availability of food??

## Past Players who progressed to the Football League

Not yet applicable

## PREVIOUS

**Leagues:** Northern 1898-1910 14-26
Yorkshire Combination 10-14; Yorkshire 26-27;
Midland 27-40 46-60 63-68
Scarborough & Dist. 45-46
Northern Counties 60-62; North Eastern 62-63;
Northern Premier 68-79
Alliance Premier 79-87 99-
Football League 87-99

**Name:** None

## CLUB RECORDS

**Attendance:** 11,162
v Luton Town, FAC 3rd Rd, 1938

**Victory:** 6-0 v Rhyl Athletic, FA Cup 29.11.30

**Defeat:** 0-8 v Mansfield Town (H), FA Cup 22.11.52

**Career Goalscorer:** Unknown

**Career Appearances:** 196 Steve Richards 87-91

**Transfer Fee Paid:** £100,000
for Martin Russell to Leicester C., Feb. 87

**Transfer Fee Received:** £350,000
for Craig Short from Notts Co. (£150K 7/89 + £250K9/92)

## BEST SEASON

**FA Cup:** 3rd Round 30-31 37-38 75-76 77-78

**FA Trophy:** Winners 72-73 75-76 76-77

**Football League:** 5th in Division 4, 88-89

**League Cup:** 4th Round 92-93

## HONOURS

FA Trophy 72-73 75-76 76-77
Vauxhall Conference 86-87
Bob Lord Trophy 83-84
NPL Lge Cup 76-77
North Eastern Cos Lge 62-63, Lge Cup 62-63
Midland Lge 29-30
Scarborough & Dist. Lge 45-46
E. Riding Cup x 8; N. Riding Sen. Cup x 17

# CHELTENHAM TOWN -
## THANKS FOR THE MEMORIES

1
The 'operations room'
Photo: Peter Barnes

2
Lee Howells
*the midfield 'maestro'*
*who held it all together.*
Photo: Andrew Chitty

3
Dennis Bailey
*whose goals at the end*
*of the season were vital.*
Photo: Ian Morsman

4
Jason Eaton
*who will always be*
*remembered for his win-*
*ning goal at Wembley.*
Photo: Graham Cotterill

**THE TEAM**
who will always remember their two years together

CHELTENHAM TOWN
MEMORIES

**THE BOSS**
who must have
a great future in the game

**THE FANS**
who enjoyed every minute

# SOUTHPORT

As someone who had tipped Southport as a potential championship challenger, I must say I was surprised by The Sandgrounders disappointing Conference campaign.

Like the 'Diamonds', they started the season with a run of victories, in their case just three, but they were up there at the top.

Sadly it was a lack of strike power that proved a severe problem and for four months they failed to score more than a single goal in any Conference match. This was strange as cup ties were no problem as they knocked in twelve goals in a fine F.A.Cup run to the Second Round.

A 2-1 away victory at Mansfield Town was the highlight of the season and hopes were high for a return to Wembley in the Trophy, but a good run ended away at Forest Green in the Sixth Round and all the time they were sinking into the dangerous relegation zone.

In fact with three games remaining, 19th place had been reached. Leek Town were beaten and virtually condemned to the drop, then a 2-0 victory away at Trophy finalists' Kingstonian secured next season's Conference place.

Management knows that the squad will have to be strengthened if another desperate battle is to be avoided.

T.W.

Paul Futcher, Southport manager

229

# SOUTHPORT
## MATCH FACTS 1998-99

| No | Date | Venue | Comp | Opponents | Att | Result | Score | Goalscorers |
|----|------|-------|------|-----------|-----|--------|-------|-------------|
| 1 | 15/08 | H | NC | Telford United | 1282 | W | 2-1 | Ross 27 69 |
| 2 | 18/08 | A | NC | Doncaster Rovers | 3663 | W | 1-0 | O'Reilly 24 |
| 3 | 22/08 | A | NC | Woking | 1900 | W | 3-2 | Bolland 38, Whittaker 41, Horner 90 |
| 4 | 25/08 | H | NC | Northwich Victoria | 1457 | D | 2-2 | Guyett 45, Bolland 61 |
| 5 | 29/08 | H | NC | Rushden & Diamonds | 1653 | L | 0-1 | |
| 6 | 31/08 | A | NC | Hereford United | 2308 | D | 2-2 | Gouck 28, O'Reilly 77 |
| 7 | 05/09 | A | NC | Stevenage Borough | 2433 | D | 0-0 | |
| 8 | 12/09 | H | NC | Welling United | 1035 | W | 5-2 | Guyett 10, Bolland 41 66, O'Reilly 63 89 |
| 9 | 15/09 | H | NC | Doncaster Rovers | 1450 | W | 3-2 | Guyett 69, Gamble 72[p], Horner 79 |
| 10 | 19/09 | A | NC | Cheltenham Town | 2594 | L | 0-3 | |
| 11 | 26/09 | H | NC | Hayes | 1203 | L | 1-2 | Furlong 80 |
| 12 | 03/10 | A | NC | Kettering Town | 1515 | L | 0-1 | |
| 13 | 10/10 | H | NC | Forest Green Rovers | 961 | D | 1-1 | Thompson 72 |
| 14 | 26/10 | A | NC | Kidderminster Harriers | 1780 | L | 1-2 | Quinn 87 |
| 15 | 07/11 | A | NC | Kingstonian | 1060 | D | 1-1 | O'Reilly 88 |
| 16 | 28/11 | A | NC | Farnborough Town | 559 | D | 1-1 | N Baker 17[og] |
| 17 | 12/12 | A | NC | Dover Athletic | 792 | L | 1-2 | Guyett 5 |
| 18 | 15/12 | A | NC | Barrow | 1191 | D | 0-0 | |
| 19 | 19/12 | H | NC | Kidderminster Harriers | 976 | D | 1-1 | Elam 15 |
| 20 | 26/12 | H | NC | Barrow | 1426 | L | 0-4 | |
| 21 | 28/12 | A | NC | Morecambe | 1356 | D | 1-1 | Bolland 90 |
| 22 | 09/01 | H | NC | Yeovil Town | 929 | L | 2-3 | Ryan 59, Elam 67 |
| 23 | 23/01 | A | NC | Hednesford Town | 1015 | L | 1-3 | Ross 58 |
| 24 | 30/01 | H | NC | Cheltenham Town | 1224 | L | 0-2 | |
| 25 | 13/02 | A | NC | Northwich Victoria | 1628 | W | 2-1 | Elam 44 66 |
| 26 | 16/02 | H | NC | Hereford United | 872 | D | 0-0 | |
| 27 | 20/02 | H | NC | Farnborough Town | 997 | D | 2-2 | Arnold 23 57 |
| 28 | 23/02 | A | NC | Rushden & Diamonds | 2135 | L | 1-3 | Gamble 90 |
| 29 | 06/03 | H | NC | Stevenage Borough | 1056 | D | 1-1 | Trundle 9 |
| 30 | 13/03 | H | NC | Dover Athletic | 955 | W | 3-0 | Furlong 6, Guyett 13, Elam 90 |
| 31 | 16/03 | A | NC | Leek Town | 632 | D | 0-0 | |
| 32 | 20/03 | A | NC | Hayes | 677 | L | 0-3 | |
| 33 | 23/03 | A | NC | Yeovil Town | 2158 | L | 1-3 | Furlong 46 |
| 34 | 30/03 | H | NC | Woking | 811 | D | 0-0 | |
| 35 | 03/04 | H | NC | Hednesford Town | 1144 | D | 1-1 | Guyett 13 |
| 36 | 05/04 | H | NC | Morecambe | 1427 | W | 1-0 | Trundle 58 |
| 37 | 10/04 | A | NC | Welling United | 502 | L | 1-2 | Trundle 29 |
| 38 | 13/04 | A | NC | Telford United | 704 | L | 0-1 | |
| 39 | 17/04 | H | NC | Kettering Town | 1070 | L | 0-1 | |
| 40 | 24/04 | H | NC | Leek Town | 1333 | W | 3-1 | Stuart 41, Elam 57 87 |
| 41 | 28/04 | A | NC | Kingstonian | 492 | W | 2-0 | Furlong 67, Trundle 68 |
| 42 | 01/05 | A | NC | Forest Green Rovers | 746 | L | 0-1 | |

### CUP COMPETITIONS

| | Date | Venue | Comp | Opponents | Att | Result | Score | Goalscorers |
|----|------|-------|------|-----------|-----|--------|-------|-------------|
| | 06/10 | H | Endsleigh 1 | Telford United | 631 | W | 2-1 | O'Reilly 48, Gamble 81 |
| | 17/10 | A | FA Cup Q3 | Forest Green Rovers | 2376 | W | 2-0 | |
| | 09/11 | A | FA Cup Q4 | Leatherhead | 1145 | D | 1-1 | Warburton 90 |
| | 11/11 | H | FA Cup Q4 rep | Leatherhead | 1855 | W | 4-0 | Collins 20, West 45, Heggs 48, Brady 54 |
| | 14/11 | H | FA Cup 1 | Shrewsbury Town | 4121 | W | 1-0 | Underwood 19 |
| | 21/11 | H | FA Trophy 2 | Bath City | 1989 | W | 2-0 | Vickerman 7[og], Brady 66 |
| | 01/12 | A | Endsleigh 2 | Doncaster Rovers | 949 | L | 0-2 | |
| | 01/12 | A | N'hants SC QF | Rothwell Town | 253 | W | 1-0 | Hamsher 21[p] |
| | 05/12 | A | FA Cup 2 | Doncaster Rovers | 5396 | D | 0-0 | |
| | 15/12 | H | FA Cup 2 rep | Doncaster Rovers | 5564 | W | 4-2 | Hamsher 6[p], West 63 84, Brady 68 |
| | 02/01 | H | FA Cup 3 | Leeds United | 6431 | D | 0-0 | |
| | 13/01 | A | FA Cup 3 rep | Leeds United | 39159 | L | 1-3 | Heggs 11 |
| | 25/01 | A | FA Trophy 3 | Slough Town | 729 | W | 2-1 | West(2) |
| | 06/02 | A | FA Trophy 4 | Woking | 2788 | D | 0-0 | |
| | 09/02 | H | FA Trophy 4 rep | Woking | 1995 | L | 1-2 | Warburton 1 |
| | 02/03 | A | N'hants SC SF | Cogenhoe United | n/k | D | 2-2 | Rodwell 57, Cramman 65 |
| | 10/04 | H | N'hants SC SF r | Cogenhoe United | n/k | W | 3-1 | De Souza 32 41, West 89 |
| | 18/04 | A | N'hants SC F | Raunds Town | 804 | W | 2-0 | West 18, De Souza 83 |

| 1 | 2 | 3 | 4 | 5 | 6 | 7 | 8 | 9 | 10 | 11 | 12 14 15 | |
|---|---|---|---|---|---|---|---|---|---|---|---|---|
| ewart | Farley | Ryan | Gouck | Guyett | Futcher | O'Reilly | Butler | Ross | Gamble | Formby | Thompson, Whittaker, Bolland | 1 |
| ewart | Farley | Ryan | Gouck | Guyett | Futcher | O'Reilly | Butler | Ross | Gamble | Formby | Thompson, Butler, Bolland | 2 |
| tewart | Farley | Ryan | Gouck | Bolland | Guyett | O'Reilly | Butler | Ross | Gamble | Formby | Thompson, Whittaker, Horner | 3 |
| ewart | Farley | Ryan | Gouck | Bolland | Guyett | O'Reilly | Butler | Thompson | Gamble | Formby | Whittaker, Futcher, Horner | 4 |
| ewart | Farley | Ryan | Guyett | Bolland | Futcher | Thompson | Butler | Furlong | Gamble | Gouck | Whittaker, Formby, Horner | 5 |
| ewart | Farley | Ryan | Gouck | Bolland | Futcher | Thompson | Butler | Furlong | Gamble | O'Reilly | Horner, Whittaker, Newman | 6 |
| ewart | Farley | Ryan | Gouck | Bolland | Guyett | Thompson | Butler | Furlong | Gambles | O'Reilly | Graves, Futcher, Newman | 7 |
| ewart | Farley | Ryan | Gouck | Bolland | Guyett | Thompson | Graves | Furlong | Gamble | O'Reilly | Formby, Newman, Horner | 8 |
| ewart | Farley | Ryan | Gouck | Bolland | Guyett | Thompson | Formby | Furlong | Gamble | O'Reilly | Horner, Graves, Newman | 9 |
| ewart | Farley | Ryan | Horner | Bolland | Guyett | Thompson | Gouck | Ross | Gamble | O'Reilly | Formby, Furlong, Futcher | 10 |
| ewart | Farley | Ryan | Gouck | Horner | Guyett | Formby | Newman | Ross | Gamble | O'Reilly | Bolland, Furlong, Thompson | 11 |
| ewart | Farley | Ryan | Horner | Guyett | Futcher | Thompson | Whittaker | Ross | Gamble | Formby | Furlong, Bolland, Newman | 12 |
| ewart | Farley | Ryan | Horner | Guyett | Futcher | O'Reilly | Gouck | Ross | Gamble | Taylor | Quinn, Thompson, Bolland | 13 |
| ewart | Farley | Ryan | Horner | Guyett | Futcher | Quinn | Gouck | Furlong | Gamble | Thompson | Formby, Whittaker, Bolland | 14 |
| ewart | Farley | Ryan | Gouck | Horner | | Quinn | Furlong | Ross | Gamble | Formby | Bollard, Thompson, O'Reilly | 15 |
| ewart | Thompson | Ryan | Gouck | Guyett | Horner | Elam | Butler | O'Reilly | Gamble | Formby | Quinn, Ross, Bolland | 16 |
| ewart | Farley | Ryan | Gouck | Guyett | Horner | Thompson | Elam | Ross | Gamble | Futcher | Newman, Farrell, Quinn | 17 |
| ewart | Farley | Ryan | Guyett | Bolland | Horner | Elam | Futcher | Thompson | Gamble | Formby | Furlong, Morgan, Newman | 18 |
| ewart | Farley | Ryan | Guyett | Bolland | Horner | Elam | Futcher | Thompson | Gamble | Formby | Furlong, Farrell, Newman | 19 |
| ewart | Farley | Ryan | Dobbin | Guyett | Horner | Elam | Thompson | Trundle | Gamble | Formby | Newman, Gouck, Futcher | 20 |
| ewart | Thompson | Ryan | Bolland | Guyett | Horner | Elam | Dobbin | Trundle | Gouck | Newman | Farley, Formby, Gamble | 21 |
| agnall | Farley | Ryan | Dobbin | Guyett | Horner | Thompson | Butler | Trundle | Gouck | Elam | Gamble, Quinn, Formby | 22 |
| ewart | Farley | Ryan | Butler | Horner | Futcher | Thompson | Gouck | Ross | Gamble | Elam | Formby, Quinn, Mutch | 23 |
| ewart | Guyett | Farley | Butler | Bolland | Horner | Elam | Gouck | Ross | Marsh | Trundle | Gamble, Formby, Thompson | 24 |
| ewart | Farley | Ryan | Guyett | Bolland | Horner | Furlong | Gouck | Trundle | Gamble | Elam | Butler, Ross, Thompson | 25 |
| ewart | Farley | Ryan | Gouck | Guyett | Horner | Arnold | Butler | Trundle | Gamble | Elam | Thompson, Quinn, Ross | 26 |
| ewart | Farley | Ryan | Guyett | Bolland | Horner | Thompson | Arnold | Trundle | Gamble | Elam | Ross, Quinn, Butler | 27 |
| ewart | Farley | Ryan | Guyett | Bolland | Horner | Arnold | Gouck | Trundle | Gamble | Elam | Ross, Butler, Thompson | 28 |
| ewart | Farley | Ryan | Guyett | Bolland | Horner | Arnold | Gouck | Trundle | Gamble | Elam | Thompson, Ross, Quinn | 29 |
| ewart | Farley | Ryan | Butler | Guyett | Horner | Arnold | Gouck | Furlong | Gamble | Elam | Trundle, Thompson, Formby | 30 |
| ewart | Farley | Ryan | Butler | Guyett | Formby | Furlong | Gouck | Trundle | Gamble | Elam | Thompson, Bolland, Ross | 31 |
| ewart | Farley | Morgan | Thompson | Bolland | Futcher | Quinn | Formby | Furlong | Trundle | Elam | Newman, Courtney, Farrell | 32 |
| tewart | Thompson | Ryan | Furlong | Guyett | Horner | Quinn | Gouck | Trundle | Gamble | Elam | Formby, Ross, Futcher | 33 |
| ewart | Bolland | Formby | Butler | Guyett | Horner | Elam | Gouck | Thompson | Ross | Stuart | Quinn, Gamble, Farley | 34 |
| ewart | Bolland | Ryan | Butler | Guyett | Horner | Elam | Gouck | Thompson | Trundle | Stuart | Gamble, Quinn, Ross | 35 |
| ewart | Bolland | Ryan | Butler | Guyett | Horner | Elam | Gouck | Thompson | Trundle | Stuart | Gamble, Ross, Formby | 36 |
| ewart | Bolland | Ryan | Butler | Guyett | Horner | Thompson | Elam | Trundle | Gamble | Stuart | Farley, Furlong, Formby | 37 |
| ewart | Farley | Formby | Gouck | Bolland | Horner | Thompson | Furlong | Trundle | Gamble | Stuart | Elam, Ross, Futcher | 38 |
| ewart | Farley | Ryan | Butler | Bolland | Formby | Furlong | Gouck | Elam | Trundle | Stuart | Thompson, Gamble, Futcher | 39 |
| ewart | Farley | Ryan | Butler | Horner | Formby | Elam | Gouck | Furlong | Trundle | Stuart | Taylor, Gamble, Ross | 40 |
| ewart | Farley | Ryan | Butler | Bolland | Formby | Elam | Gouck | Furlong | Trundle | Stuart | Gamble, Quinn, Ross | 41 |
| ewart | Taylor | Ryan | Butler | Bolland | Formby | Elam | Gouck | Furlong | Trundle | Smart | Lalley, Thompson, Quinn | 42 |

League Attendances     **HIGHEST:** 1653     **LOWEST:** 811

**CONFERENCE:** 18th     **FA CUP:** 3rd Round     **FA TROPHY:** 4th Round

# MANAGER
## PAUL FUTCHER

| | |
|---|---|
| Date of Appointment | June 1997 |
| Date of Birth: | 25th September 1956 |
| Place of Birth: | Chester |

PREVIOUS CLUBS
As manager          Darlington, Gresley Rovers
As player     Chester C., Luton T., Manchester C., Oldham A., Derby Co., Barnsley, Halifax T., Grimsby

HONOURS
As manager          Southern Lge Prem. 1996-97,
Derbys. Sen. Cup (x2) (Gresley R.)
FA Trophy R-up 97-98;
Lancs ATS Trophy 97-98; Liverpool Sen. Cup 98-99

## FOOTBALL MANAGEMENT TEAM

| | |
|---|---|
| Assistant Manager: | Paul Lodge |
| Reserve Team Coach: | Mike Vaughan |
| Physiotherapist: | Max Thompson |
| Youth development: | Dave Hughes |

## 1998-99

| | |
|---|---|
| **Top Scorer:** | Brian Ross |
| **Captain:** | Tim Ryan |

LEFT: Kevin Formby

Photos: Andrew Chitty

BELOW: Tim Ryan

## MATCHDAY PROGRAMME

| | |
|---|---|
| Number of pages | 40 |
| Price | £1.50 |

Programme Editor
     Derek Hitchcock (0976 555782)

Other club publications:      None

Local Newspapers:      Southport Visitor
The Champion

Local Radio Stations:      Dune F.M
Radio Merseyside
Red Rose, Radio City
Radio Lancashire

# PLAYING SQUAD

| Player | Birthplace Honours | D.O.B. | Previous Clubs |
|---|---|---|---|
| **GOALKEEPERS** | | | |
| Steve Dickenson | | | Guiseley |
| **Billy Stewart** | **Liverpool** | **01.01.68** | **Liverpool, Wigan A, Chester C, Northampton T, Chester C** |
| Terry O'Hanlon | | | Runcorn |
| | | | |
| **DEFENDERS** | | | |
| Kevin Formby | Ormskirk | 22.07.71 | Burscough, Rochdale |
| Scott Guyett | Australia | | Brisbane C, Gresley R |
| SLP | | | |
| **Tim Ryan** | **Stockport** | **10.12.74** | **Scunthorpe U, Buxton, Doncaster R** |
| Phil Bolland | Manchester | | Altrincham, Salford C, Trafford, Knowsley U, Altrincham |
| Neil Grayston | | | Bradford City, Bradford (P.A.) |
| Matt Farrell | Liverpool | | Youth Team |
| Bradley Cullen | Liverpool | | Everton |
| Martin Clark | Accrington | 12.09.70 | Southport,Rotherham United |
| James Connelly | | | Preston North End |
| | | | |
| **MIDFIELDERS** | | | |
| Andy Gouck | Blackpool | 08.06.72 | Blackpool, Rochdale |
| John Deary | Ormskirk | 18.10.62 | Blackpool, Burnley, Rochdale |
| Dominic Morley | | | Liverpool, Droylesden |
| Mark Stuart | Chiswick | 15.1266 | Charlton Athletic, Plymouth Argyle, Ipswich Town (L), Bradford City, Huddersfield Town, Rochdale. |
| Paul Taylor | | | Youth Team |
| | | | |
| **FORWARDS** | | | |
| Lee Elam | | | Guiseley |
| Lee Furlong | | | Youth Team |
| **Ian Arnold** | **Durham** | **04.07.72** | **Middlesbrough, Carlisle Utd., Kettering Town, Stalybridge Celtic Kidderminster Harriers** |
| Lee Ellison | | | Darlington |
| Neil Woods | Bradford | 30.07.66 | Doncaster Rovers, Ipswich Town, Glasgow Rangers, Bradford City, Grimsby Town, York City |
| Lee Trundle | Liverpool | | Liverpool, Chorley, Stalybridge Celtic |
| Gerald Courtney | | | Youth Team |

Bold print indicates England Semi-Professional Internationals

Departures: Brian Butler (Leigh RMI), David Gamble (Marine), Phil Horner, Brian Ross (Leigh RMI) David Thompson (Marine)

# SOUTHPORT

**Founded:** 1881

**Nickname:** The Sandgrounders

**Club Sponsors:** Apollo Leisure

**Club colours:** Old Gold & black

**Change colours:** All sky blue

**Midweek home matchday:** Tuesday

**Reserves' League:** Lancashire League

## PREVIOUS

**Leagues:** Northern Premier League
Football League
Lancashire Combination

**Grounds:** Ash Lane

**Names:** Southport Central; Southport Vulcan

## CLUB RECORDS

**Attendance:** 20,010 v Newcastle United
FA Cup - 1932

**Record win:** 8-1 v Nelson - 01.01.31
**Record defeat:** 0-11 v Oldham - 26.12.62

**Career goalscorer:** Alan Spence 98
**Career appearances:** Arthur Peat 401 - 1962-72

**Transfer fee paid:** £20,000
for Martin McDonald from Macclesfield Town - 1995

**Transfer fee received:** £25,000
from Rochdale for Steve Whitehall - 1991

## GROUND DETAILS

Haig Avenue,
Southport,
Merseyside. PR8 6JZ

TELEPHONE: Ground: 01704 533422
Ticket Office: 01704 533422
Fax: 01704 533422

SIMPLE DIRECTIONS:
From M6 - M58 through Ormskirk (A570) to Southport.
Straight on at Tesco/McDonalds roundabout. Right at the mini
roundabout and the ground is on the right

CAPACITY: 6,008
SEATED: 1,660
COVERED TERRACING: 1,100

SOCIAL FACILITIES:
Clubhouse open 7.00-11.00 every night and match days.
Tel: 01704 530182

CLUB SHOP: New shop open this season
Scarves, replica kits and various other souvenirs for sale.
Contact D Hitchcock, c/o Southport F.C or
e-mail: derek@hitchcock98.freeserve.co.uk

## BEST SEASON

**FA Cup:** Quarter Final, 1931-32.
Lost to Newcastle Utd
(The first Division 3 North team to reach the Quarter Finals)

**FA Trophy:** Runners-up 97-98,
0-1 v Cheltenham Town

## HONOURS

FA Trophy R-up 97-98;
Football League Division Four Champions 1972/73
(Runners-up 1966/67);
Northern Premier League 1992/93
(League Cup 1990/91, League Shield 1993/94);
Third Division North Section Cup 1937/38;
Liverpool Senior Cup 1930/31, 1931/32, 1943/44, 1957/58
(shared), 1963/64 (shared), 1974/75, 1990/91, 1992/93
(Runners-up 1993/94 1998/99);
Lancashire Senior Cup 1904/05;
Lancashire Junior Cup 1919/20, 1992/93, 1996-97,
(now ATS ChallengeTrophy) 1997-98
(Runners-up 1993/94)

**Past Players** who progressed to the Football League

Shaun Teale,
Andy Mutch,
Steve Whitehall,
Tony Rodwell

# STEVENAGE BOROUGH

Broadhall Way presents a smart and comfortable ground, Borough supporters are lively, loyal and numerous. Their manager Paul Fairclough was highly respected, so why was the club so unpopular?
The answer can be worked out by last season's diary of events which have been fully reported over the months, but sadly Fairclough had to leave along with some other club officials before a new chairman came in to reorganise the club and hopefully give it a happier image.

Certainly new manager Richard Hill had impressively set about building his own squad from the excellent foundations he inherited. He was well served last season by the top Conference goalscorer, Carl Alford, and there is every indication that Borough will be a power once again in the coming season.

Two tough battles with Cheltenham Town in the F.A.Trophy should have brought them success at the first attempt but they went out after penalties and an F.A.Cup run to the Second Round kept their cup reputation in tact.

Phil Wallace certainly lifted Boreham Wood up into serious Ryman contenders while he was Chairman and their is little doubt that Stevenage Borough will respond to his leadership and carry on where they left off at the end of last season - a 3-1 victory at Yeovil.                    T.T.

## CLUB OFFICIALS 1999-2000

| | |
|---|---|
| Chairman | **Phillip Wallace** |
| Club Administrator | **Roger Austin** |
| (Including Press work) | 01438 278072 |
| Commercial Manager | **Clive Abrey** |
| | 01438 218073 |

1999-2000 Squad - Back Row: Paul Armstrong, Dwayne Plummer, Dominic Naylor, Richard Leadbeater, Jimmy Strouts, Jake Meah, Ross Harrison, Negus Johnson, Michael Love. Middle Row: Chris Pearson, Gordon Barr, Errol Telemaque, Lee Howarth, Chris Taylor, Robin Trott, Bobby Bezhadi, Sam McMahon, Bobby Highton. Front Row: Kevin Levy (kit manager), Carl Alford, Ryan Kirby, Richard Hill (manager), Noel Blackwell (asst. manager), Mark Smith, Lee Harvey, Keith Allinson (physio).

# STEVENAGE BOROUGH
## MATCH FACTS 1998-99

| No | Date | Venue | Comp | Opponents | Att | Result | Score | Goalscorers |
|---|---|---|---|---|---|---|---|---|
| 1 | 15/08 | A | NC | Barrow | 2096 | W | 1-0 | Alford 36 |
| 2 | 17/08 | H | NC | Hayes | 3203 | W | 2-1 | Beevor 45, Alford 81 |
| 3 | 22/08 | H | NC | Leek Town | 2614 | W | 2-0 | Brooker 21, Thompson 76 |
| 4 | 25/08 | A | NC | Dover Athletic | 1394 | D | 1-1 | Beevor 71 |
| 5 | 29/08 | A | NC | Forest Green Rovers | 903 | W | 2-1 | Alford 66, Howarth 75 |
| 6 | 31/08 | H | NC | Welling United | 3413 | D | 1-1 | Alford 17 |
| 7 | 05/09 | H | NC | Southport | 2433 | D | 0-0 | |
| 8 | 08/09 | A | NC | Kingstonian | 1745 | L | 0-1 | |
| 9 | 12/09 | A | NC | Morecambe | 1010 | D | 1-1 | Barnwell 29 |
| 10 | 14/09 | H | NC | Yeovil Town | 2483 | D | 1-1 | Pearson 67 |
| 11 | 19/09 | H | NC | Hednesford Town | 2329 | W | 3-1 | Alford 41 52 75 |
| 12 | 26/09 | A | NC | Kidderminster Harriers | 2072 | L | 0-2 | |
| 13 | 28/09 | H | NC | Farnborough Town | 2379 | W | 3-1 | Barwell 16 60, Alford 38 |
| 14 | 03/10 | A | NC | Telford United | 905 | W | 3-0 | Beevor 27, Barnwell 40, Alford 76 |
| 15 | 10/10 | H | NC | Hereford United | 2832 | L | 0-3 | |
| 16 | 24/10 | A | NC | Northwich Victoria | 910 | W | 1-0 | Trott 89 |
| 17 | 07/11 | H | NC | Doncaster Rovers | 3513 | W | 2-0 | Telemaque 82, Kean 90 |
| 18 | 28/11 | H | NC | Telford United | 2189 | D | 2-2 | Love 17, Alford 63 |
| 19 | 12/12 | H | NC | Forest Green Rovers | 1976 | D | 1-1 | Beevor 61 |
| 20 | 19/12 | A | NC | Cheltenham Town | 2772 | L | 0-3 | |
| 21 | 26/12 | H | NC | Rushden & Diamonds | 4319 | D | 0-0 | |
| 22 | 28/12 | H | NC | Kettering Town | 3937 | D | 2-2 | Plummer 23, Alford 37 |
| 23 | 09/01 | A | NC | Farnborough Town | 932 | L | 0-1 | |
| 24 | 23/01 | H | NC | Morecambe | 2266 | W | 2-0 | Alford 30, Strouts 65 |
| 25 | 30/01 | A | NC | Hereford United | 1629 | W | 1-0 | Alford 48 |
| 26 | 13/02 | H | NC | Kingstonian | 2261 | D | 3-3 | Pearson 16, Alford 20, Love 74 |
| 27 | 20/02 | A | NC | Leek Town | 597 | D | 1-1 | Pearson 84 |
| 28 | 23/02 | A | NC | Hayes | 665 | D | 2-2 | Alford 27 53 |
| 29 | 06/03 | A | NC | Southport | 1056 | D | 1-1 | Leadbeater 27 |
| 30 | 09/03 | A | NC | Rushden & Diamonds | 3169 | L | 1-2 | Alford 56 |
| 31 | 13/03 | H | NC | Cheltenham Town | 2576 | D | 2-2 | Alford 20, Leadbeater 59 |
| 32 | 16/03 | A | NC | Welling United | 524 | D | 1-1 | Dolby 50 |
| 33 | 20/03 | A | NC | Woking | 2776 | W | 2-1 | Harrison 49, Leadbeater 59 |
| 34 | 26/03 | A | NC | Doncaster Rovers | 4629 | D | 0-0 | |
| 35 | 03/04 | H | NC | Northwich Victoria | 1923 | L | 1-3 | Butler 90 |
| 36 | 05/04 | A | NC | Kettering Town | 2463 | W | 2-1 | Alford 12, Leadbeater 64 |
| 37 | 10/04 | H | NC | Dover Athletic | 1458 | W | 1-0 | Alford 84 |
| 38 | 12/04 | H | NC | Woking | 2028 | W | 5-0 | Love 4, Butler 13 53, Alford 48, Strouts 57 |
| 39 | 17/04 | H | NC | Barrow | 1701 | L | 1-2 | Alford 58[p] |
| 40 | 19/04 | A | NC | Hednesford Town | 861 | D | 2-2 | Strouts 26, Trott 71 |
| 41 | 24/04 | H | NC | Kidderminster Harriers | 1915 | W | 3-0 | Alford 3 62, Plummer 87 |
| 42 | 01/05 | A | NC | Yeovil Town | 2936 | W | 3-1 | Alford 15 86, Strouts 20 |

### CUP COMPETITIONS

| | Date | Venue | Comp | Opponents | Att | Result | Score | Goalscorers |
|---|---|---|---|---|---|---|---|---|
| | 06/10 | A | Endsleigh 1 | Dover Athletic | 0 | W | 3-2 | |
| | 18/10 | A | FA Cup Q3 | Witney Town | 767 | W | 2-1 | Meah 45, Love 90 |
| | 04/11 | A | FA Cup Q4 | Dagenham & Redbridge | 763 | W | 3-0 | Samuels 6, Alford 69, Love 80 |
| | 14/11 | A | FA Cup 1 | Runcorn | 1114 | D | 1-1 | Alford 58 |
| | 21/11 | H | FA Trophy 2 | Uxbridge | 1743 | W | 4-0 | Alford 47 51, Love 78, Reinelt 85 |
| | 23/11 | H | FA Cup 1 rep | Runcorn | 3252 | W | 2-0 | Love 48, Alford 74 |
| | 01/12 | H | Endsleigh 2 | Cheltenham Town | 604 | L | 0-1 | |
| | 05/12 | A | FA Cup 2 | Lincoln City | 4375 | L | 1-4 | Alford 90 |
| | 16/01 | H | FA Trophy 3 | Dover Athletic | 2476 | W | 3-2 | Alford 18, Pearson 41 90 |
| | 06/02 | A | FA Trophy 4 | Cheltenham Town | 3005 | D | 0-0 | |
| | 15/02 | H | FA Trophy 4 rep | Cheltenham Town | n/k | D | 0-0 | (4-5 pens) |

| 1 | 2 | 3 | 4 | 5 | 6 | 7 | 8 | 9 | 10 | 11 | 12 / 14 / 15 | |
|---|---|---|---|---|---|---|---|---|---|---|---|---|
| Taylor | Harvey | Naylor | Smith | Trott | Beevor | Brooker | Berry | Alford | Pearson | Barnwell | Thompson, Mahorn, Love | 1 |
| Taylor | Harvey | Naylor | Smith | Howarth | Beevor | Brooker | Berry | Alford | Pearson | Barnwell | Love, Mahorn, Thompson | 2 |
| Taylor | Harvey | Love | Smith | Howarth | Beevor | Brooker | Berry | Alford | Mahorn | Barnwell | Thompson, Dilnut, Perkins | 3 |
| Taylor | Harvey | Love | Smith | Howarth | Beevor | Brooker | Berry | Alford | Thompson | Barnwell | Dilnut, Mahorn, Perkins | 4 |
| Taylor | Harvey | Love | Smith | Howarth | Beevor | Brooker | Berry | Alford | Pearson | Barnwell | Mahorn, Thompson, Perkins | 5 |
| Taylor | Harvey | Love | Smith | Howarth | Beevor | Brooker | Berry | Alford | Mahorn | Perkins | Thompson, Trott, Dilnut | 6 |
| Taylor | Harvey | Love | Smith | Howarth | Beevor | Brooker | Perkins | Alford | Thompson | Barnwell | Kean, Mahorn, Dilnut | 7 |
| Taylor | Harvey | Love | Smith | Howarth | Beevor | Brooker | Perkins | Alford | Samuels | Barnwell | Mahorn, Thompson, Dilnut | 8 |
| Taylor | Harvey | Naylor | Smith | Howarth | Beevor | Brooker | McAree | Alford | Samuels | Barnwell | Love, Pearson, Thompson | 9 |
| Taylor | Dilnut | Naylor | Smith | Howarth | Beevor | Brooker | McAree | Alford | Samuels | Barnwell | Thompson, Pearson, Love | 10 |
| Taylor | Dilnut | Naylor | Smith | Howarth | McAree | Samuels | Berry | Pearson | Alford | Barnwell | Beevor, Thompson, Love | 11 |
| Taylor | Harvey | Naylor | Smith | Howarth | Beevor | Reinelt | Berry | Alford | Thompson | Samuels | Perkins, Trott, Dilnut | 12 |
| Gallagher | Harvey | Naylor | Smith | Howarth | Beevor | Dilnut | Berry | Alford | Love | Barnwell | Perkins, Reinelt, Samuels | 13 |
| Gallagher | Harvey | Naylor | Smith | Howarth | Beevor | Reinelt | Berry | Alford | Love | Barnwell | Trott, Perkins, Thompson | 14 |
| Gallagher | Harvey | Naylor | Smith | Howarth | Beevor | Reinelt | Berry | Alford | Love | Barnwell | Perkins, Trott, Samuels | 15 |
| Taylor | Dilnut | Naylor | Smith | Trott | Beevor | Plummer | Berry | Alford | Love | Barnwell | Howarth, Reinelt, Samuels | 16 |
| Taylor | Harvey | Naylor | Smith | Howarth | Plummer | Reinelt | Berry | Alford | Love | Samuels | Kean, Telemaque, Coll | 17 |
| Taylor | Harvey | Naylor | Smith | Trott | Gridelet | Plummer | Berry | Alford | Love | Peel | Reinelt, Samuels, Rogers | 18 |
| Taylor | Harvey | Rogers | Smith | Trott | Beevor | Peel | Berry | Alford | Love | Telemaque | Reinelt, Howarth, Naylor | 19 |
| Taylor | Dilnut | Rogers | Smith | Trott | Beevor | Plummer | Berry | Alford | Love | Reinelt | Telemaque, Naylor, Kean | 20 |
| Taylor | Harvey | Rogers | Smith | Howarth | Beevor | Plummer | Berry | Alford | Love | Reinelt | Peel, Telemaque, Naylor | 21 |
| Taylor | Harvey | Rogers | Smith | Howarth | Beevor | Plummer | Berry | Alford | Love | Reinelt | Peel, Telemaque, Naylor | 22 |
| Taylor | Harvey | Rogers | Smith | Howarth | Beevor | Plummer | Pearson | Alford | Kean | Love | Samuels, Trott, Kirby | 23 |
| Taylor | Harvey | Rogers | Smith | Trott | Kirby | Plummer | Berry | Alford | Pearson | Strouts | Thompson, Love, Howarth | 24 |
| Taylor | Kirby | Rogers | Smith | Trott | Howarth | Plummer | Berry | Alford | Pearson | Strouts | Telemaque, Beevor, Naylor | 25 |
| Taylor | Harvey | Statham | Smith | Kirby | Berry | Plummer | Love | Alford | Pearson | Strouts | Beevor, Telemaque, Rogers | 26 |
| Gallagher | Harvey | Statham | Smith | Kirby | Berry | Plummer | Harrison | Alford | Pearson | Strouts | Thompson, Beevor, Rogers | 27 |
| Gallagher | Harvey | Statham | Smith | Kirby | Berry | Harrison | Love | Alford | Pearson | Strouts | Rogers, Beevor, Thompson | 28 |
| Gallagher | Harvey | Harrison | Smith | Howarth | Kirby | Love | Berry | Alford | Leadbeater | Strouts | Plummer, Thompson, Naylor | 29 |
| Taylor | Harvey | Harrison | Smith | Howarth | Kirby | Love | Berry | Alford | Leadbeater | Strouts | Plummer, Pearson, Naylor | 30 |
| Taylor | Harvey | Harrison | Smith | Howarth | Kirby | Love | Berry | Alford | Leadbeater | Strouts | Pearson, Thompson, Naylor | 31 |
| Taylor | Harvey | Naylor | Smith | Howarth | Kirby | Love | Berry | Alford | Leadbeater | Strouts | Plummer, Pearson, Thompson | 32 |
| Jackson | Kirby | Harrison | Smith | Trott | Howarth | Plummer | Love | Butler | Leadbeater | Strouts | Pearson, Thompson, Naylor | 33 |
| Jackson | Kirby | Harrison | Smith | Trott | Howarth | Plummer | Love | Alford | Butler | Leadbeater | Naylor, Rogers | 34 |
| Jackson | Kirby | Naylor | Smith | Trott | Howarth | Rogers | Harrison | Butler | Leadbeater | Strouts | Alford, Pearson, Highton | 35 |
| Jackson | Kirby | Harrison | Smith | Trott | Howarth | Plummer | Alford | Naylor | Leadbeater | Strouts | Butler, Rogers, Pearson | 36 |
| Taylor | Harvey | Harrison | Smith | Trott | Howarth | Plummer | Naylor | Alford | Leadbeater | Strouts | Pearson, Butler, Kirby | 37 |
| Taylor | Harvey | Harrison | Smith | Trott | Howarth | Plummer | Kirby | Alford | Butler | Love | Naylor, Strouts, Leadbeater | 38 |
| Taylor | Harvey | Harrison | Smith | Trott | Howarth | Love | Kirby | Alford | Leadbeater | Strouts | Naylor, Plummer, Butler | 39 |
| Jackson | Harvey | Naylor | Smith | Trott | Kirby | Plummer | Love | Alford | Butler | Strouts | Telemarque, Harrison, Rogers | 40 |
| Jackson | Harvey | Harrison | Smith | Trott | Kirby | Plummer | Love | Alford | Butler | Strouts | Howarth, Naylor, Rogers | 41 |
| Taylor | Barr | Alford | Kirby | Smith | Harvey | Leadbeater | Howarth | Love | Strouts | Trott | Plummer, Naylor, Telemarque | 42 |

League Attendances     **HIGHEST:** 4319     **LOWEST:** 1458

**CONFERENCE:** 6th     **FA CUP:** 2nd Round     **FA TROPHY:** 4th Round

## MANAGER
### RICHARD HILL

| | |
|---|---|
| Date of Appointment | January 1999 |
| Date of Birth | 20th September 1963 |
| Place of Birth | Hinckley |

PREVIOUS CLUBS
| | |
|---|---|
| As manager | Wycombe Wanderers (Assistant) |
| As coach | Reading |
| As player | Northampton,Watford and Oxford United |

HONOURS
| | |
|---|---|
| As manager/ coach/ player | None |

## FOOTBALL MANAGEMENT TEAM

| | |
|---|---|
| Assistant Manager | Noel Blackwell |
| Coach | John Harding |
| Reserve Team Manager | Dave Bullock |
| Physiotherapist | Keith Allinson |
| Chief Scout | Robbie Morgan |
| Scouts | Alan Dawson, Steve Williams |
| | Mick Davie, Keith Blackham |

### 1998-99

| | |
|---|---|
| **Top Scorer:** | Carl Alford |
| **Player of the Year:** | Lee Harvey |
| **Captain:** | Mark Smith |

Richard Hill (right) in consultation with Noel Blackwell
Photo: Peter Barnes

Mark Smith
Photo: Mark Sandom

## MATCHDAY PROGRAMME

| | |
|---|---|
| Number of pages | 36 |
| Price | £1.50 |
| Programme Editor | Steve Watkins (01438 318891) |
| Other club publications: | The Borough Yearbook |
| Local Newspapers: | Stevenage Gazette; Comet Stevenage Mercury; Herald |
| Local Radio Stations: | Chiltern Radio BBC Three Counties Radio |

# PLAYING SQUAD

| Player | Birthplace Honours | D.O.B. | Previous Clubs |
|---|---|---|---|

**GOALKEEPERS**

Chris Taylor SC — Bromsgrove — — Everton, Bromsgrove R, Halesowen T, Evesham U, Moor Green, Solihull B,Bromsgrove R, Cheltenham T, Kettering T

**DEFENDERS**

| Player | Birthplace | D.O.B. | Previous Clubs |
|---|---|---|---|
| Lee Harvey | Harlow | 21.12.66 | Harrow Borough, Leyton Orient, Nottingham Forest, Brentford |
| **Mark Smith** ESP, GMVC, ILP | **Luton** | | **Hitchin T, Letchworth GC, Hitchin T, Woking, Hitchin T** |
| Ryan Kirby | Chingford | 6.9.74 | Arsenal, Doncaster R, Northampton T |
| Dominic Naylor | Watford | 12.8.70 | Watford, Halifax T, Barnet, Plymouth Argyle, Gillingham, Leyton O. |
| Robin Trott | Orpington | 17.8.74 | Gillingham, Welling U, £8k to Stevenage B |
| Michael Love | Stockport | 27.11.73 | Bedworth U, Hinckley T, Hinckley Ath., Wigan Ath., Wycombe W Hinckley Ath., Tamworth, Northampton T |
| Lee Howarth | | | Barnet, Peterborough United |

**MIDFIELDERS**

| Player | Birthplace | D.O.B. | Previous Clubs |
|---|---|---|---|
| Dwayne Plummer | | | Bristol City |
| Ross Harrison | Leamington | 28.12.79 | Reading |
| Sam McMahon | | | Cambridge United, Kettering Town (L), Leicester City |
| Jimmy Strouts | | | Harrogate RA, Frickley Athl;etic, Harrogate Town, Sittingbourne, Army, Combined Services, Dover Athletic |

**FORWARDS**

| Player | Birthplace | D.O.B. | Previous Clubs |
|---|---|---|---|
| **Carl Alford** SLP | **Denton** | 11.2.72 | **Rochdale, Stockport , Burnley, Witton Alb, £1,700 to Macclesfield £25k to Kettering T, £85k to Rushden & D** |
| Chris Pearson | Leicester | 5.1.76 | Hinckley T, Notts Co, Hinckley T, £5k to Kettering T, £14k to Stevenage B |
| Richard Leadbetter | | | Hereford United, Wolverhampton Wanderers |
| Tony (Junior) Samuels | | | Boreham Wood |

Bold print indicates
England Semi-Professional Internationals

Departures:
Des Gallagher,
Darren Rogers,
Paul Thompson

Carl Alford,
Stevenage Borough &
Nationwide Conference
top goalscorer in the 1998-99 season.

Photo: Peter Barnes

# STEVENAGE BOROUGH

| | |
|---|---|
| Nickname: | Boro' |
| Club Sponsors: | Sun Banking Corporation |
| Reserve Team's League: | Essex & Herts Border Combination & Capital League |
| Club colours: | White, black & red shirts, black with red & white trim shorts and white with red trim socks |
| Change colours: | Blue & white shirts, blue shorts, blue hooped socks |
| Midweek home matchday: | Monday |

## GROUND DETAILS

Stevenage Stadium,
Broadhall Way,
Stevenage,
Herts SG2 8RH

TELEPHONE: 01438 223223
Fax: 01438 743666

SIMPLE DIRECTIONS:
Stevenage South exit off A1(M) - ground on right at second roundabout.Spectators are however advised to go straight on at this roundabout and park inthe Showground opposite the stadium. The stadium is one mile from Stevenage BRstation.
Buses SB4 and SB5
CAPACITY: 6,546
SEATED: 2,002
COVERED TERRACING: 2,000
Groundsman: Colin Payne
CLUB SHOP: Mon - Sat 9-5.30. 27 Market Place, Stevenage.
01438 218061. Sells acomplete range of club merchandise including a customising service. Mail Order,credit cards accepted, contact Emma Doherty (01438 218061)

SOCIAL FACILITIES:
Tel.: 01438 218079. Clubhouse at ground open Monday to Friday 7 - 11pm,Saturday noon - 2.00 & 4.30 - 11pm, Sunday: All day from noon. Contact: PamTerry

## Past Players who progressed to the Football League

Richard Wilmot & NeilTrebble (Scunthorpe Utd) 1993,
Simon Clark (Peterborough United) 1994,
Leo Fortune West (Gillingham) 1995,
Phil Simpson (Barnet) 1995,
Barry Hayles(Bristol C.) 1997)

## PREVIOUS

| | |
|---|---|
| Leagues: | Chiltern Youth 76-79 Wallspan South Combination 79-80 United Counties 80-84 Isthmian 84-94 |
| Grounds: | King George V Playing Field 1976-80 |

## CLUB RECORDS

| | |
|---|---|
| Attendance: | 6,489 v Kidderminster H., GM Vauxhall Conference 25.1.97 |
| Win: | 11-1 v British Timken Athletic (H), United Counties League Div.1, 1980-81 |
| Defeat: | 0-7 v Southwick (H), Isthmian League Div. 1, 1987-88 |
| Career goalscorer: | Barry Hayles |
| Career appearances: | Martin Gittings |
| Transfer fee paid: | £20,000 for Richard Leadbetter to Hereford United 1999 |
| Transfer fee received: | £300,000 for Barry Hayles (Bristol R.) July 97 |

## BEST SEASON

| | |
|---|---|
| FA Cup: | Fourth Round replay 97-98. 1-2 v Newcastle Utd. (A) after 1-1 also 3rd Round 1996-97. 0-2 v Birmingham City (A) |
| League clubs defeated: | Leyton Orient 96-97; Cambridge Utd., Swindon Town 97-98 |
| FA Trophy: | Semi Final 1996-97. 1-2 v Woking in Replay at Watford |

## HONOURS

GM Vauxhall Conference 95-96,
Isthmian Lge Prem 93-94,
Div 1 91-92, Div 2 (North) 85-86 90-91;
Utd Counties Lg Div 1 80-81 (Div 1 Cup 80-81),
Herts SnrCup R-up 85-86, 93/94;
Herts Charity Cup R-up 93-94,
Herts Charity Shield R-up83-84,
Televised Sports Snr Floodlit Cup 89-90,
Eastern Professional F'lit Cup Group winner
81-82 85-86 86-87 88-89 90-91 91-92,
South Co's Comb. Cup 91-92;
Essex & Herts Border Comb.(Reserves) 94/95
Essex & Herts (Western Div) 95-96

# SUTTON UNITED

There are usually more clubs in the Ryman Premier Division who fancy their promotion chances than in the their Dr.Martens and Unibond counterparts.

Last season was no exception as Aylesbury United, Aldershot, Billericay Town, St.Albans City and Dagenham & Redbridge all had their spells in which they threatened to take over, while Purfleet, Enfield and Hendon were also hovering but never struck.

## CLUB OFFICIALS 1999-2000

Chairman: **Bruce Elliott**

President: **Andrew W Letts**

Secretary: **Brian Williams**, 49 Panmure Rd, Sydenham, London SE26 6NB Tel: 0181 699 2721

Press Officer: **Tony Dolbear** Tel: 0171 782 8644 (daytime) Mobile 0966 507023

Sutton United meanwhile, with the experienced John Rains at the helm, timed their run perfectly and with sensible strengthening of his squad for the vital last push, United finished clear and well deserved champions with a seventeen game unbeaten run.

The striking partnership of Nassem Akrour and Mark Watson was a success but late assistance from Sam Winston made sure goals kept coming.

Akrour has left for neighbours Woking but Rains has a good catchment area in which to build a squad capable of consolidating in the Conference. He's been there before and knows just what is needed.

However, it may take time!

T.T

L-R - Back Row: Tony Rains, Mark Watson, Colin Simpson, Andy Little, Gareth Howells, Paul Harford, John Mackie, John Rains.
Front Row: Geoff Moxy, Richard Skelly, Keith Rowlands, Danny Brooker, Dave Harlow, Andy Salako, Jimmy Dack, Gwynne Berry, Sammy Winston, Micky Cook.

Photo: Garry Letts

# SUTTON UNITED
## MATCH FACTS 1998-99

| No | Date | Venue | Comp | Opponents | Results | Score | Att | Goalscorers |
|----|------|-------|------|-----------|---------|-------|-----|-------------|
| 1 | 22.08 | H | RL | Slough Town | L | 0-1 | 842 | |
| 2 | 24.08 | A | RL | St. Albans City | D | 2-2 | 583 | Riley 2 |
| 3 | 29.08 | A | RL | Billericay Town | W | 2-1 | 725 | Riley, Akrour |
| 4 | 01.09 | H | RL | Hendon | W | 4-1 | 682 | M. Watson 2, Ekrour |
| 5 | 05.09 | H | RL | Heybridge Swifts | D | 1-1 | 702 | Salako |
| 6 | 12.09 | A | RL | Harrow Borough | W | 3-0 | 255 | Akrour 2, M. Watson |
| 7 | 15.09 | H | RL | Boreham Wood | W | 2-1 | 540 | Ekoku 2 |
| 8 | 19.09 | A | RL | Aldershot Town | W | 2-1 | 2796 | M. Watson, Ekoku |
| 9 | 22.09 | A | RL | Bishop's Stortford | W | 2-1 | 210 | Salako, M. Watson |
| 10 | 26.09 | H | RL | Hampton | W | 3-2 | 883 | Riley, Akrour, Blackman |
| 11 | 09.10 | A | RL | Dulwich Hamlet | L | 1-2 | 631 | Akrour |
| 12 | 13.10 | H | RL | Chesham United | W | 2-0 | 688 | S. Watson, Akrour |
| 13 | 07.11 | H | RL | Aylesbury United | L | 1-2 | 1047 | Akrour |
| 14 | 14.11 | A | RL | Bromley | D | 1-1 | 569 | Vines |
| 15 | 28.11 | A | RL | Basingstoke Town | W | 2-1 | 844 | Akrour 2 |
| 16 | 05.12 | H | RL | Harrow Borough | W | 2-1 | 624 | Riley, Simpson |
| 17 | 12.12 | A | RL | Heybridge Swifts | W | 4-2 | 206 | S. Watson 2, Akrour 2 |
| 18 | 19.12 | H | RL | Enfield | D | 1-1 | 917 | Harper |
| 19 | 21.12 | A | RL | Purfleet | W | 3-1 | 276 | Harlow, M. Watson 2 |
| 20 | 28.12 | A | RL | Carshalton Athletic | L | 0-1 | 1807 | |
| 21 | 02.01 | H | RL | Dagenham & Redbridge | W | 3-1 | 959 | Brooker, Riley, M. Watson |
| 22 | 23.01 | H | RL | St. Albans City | L | 2-3 | 924 | Brooker, Riley |
| 23 | 30.01 | A | RL | Slough Town | W | 2-1 | 585 | M. Watson 2 |
| 24 | 13.02 | A | RL | Boreham Wood | L | 0-2 | 459 | |
| 25 | 20.02 | A | RL | Chesham United | W | 3-0 | 494 | M. Watson 2, Akrour |
| 26 | 23.02 | H | RL | Walton & Hersham | W | 5-0 | 611 | Harlow, S. Watson, Dack, M. Watson 2 |
| 27 | 27.02 | H | RL | Dulwich Hamlet | W | 2-0 | 861 | Skelly, Harlow |
| 28 | 06.03 | A | RL | Hampton | W | 3-0 | 380 | Laker, M. Watson 2 |
| 29 | 13.03 | H | RL | Bishop's Stortford | W | 2-0 | 731 | S. Watson, M. Watson |
| 30 | 16.03 | A | RL | Hendon | W | 3-0 | 301 | Dack, M. Watson |
| 31 | 20.03 | H | RL | Purfleet | W | 2-1 | 708 | S. Watson, M. Watson |
| 32 | 23.03 | H | RL | Billericay Town | W | 4-1 | 736 | M. Watson 2, Rowlands 1 |
| 33 | 27.03 | A | RL | Gravesend & Northfleet | L | 1-2 | 536 | Laker |
| 34 | 03.04 | A | RL | Dagenham & Redbridge | D | 0-0 | 1100 | |
| 35 | 05.04 | H | RL | Carshalton Athletic | W | 3-0 | 1454 | Harford, Akrour, Winston |
| 36 | 10.04 | A | RL | Aylesbury United | W | 4-1 | 2216 | Akrour 3 |
| 37 | 13.04 | H | RL | Gravesend & Northfleet | D | 1-1 | 833 | Winston |
| 38 | 17.04 | H | RL | Bromley | W | 2-0 | 1173 | S. Watson, M. Watson |
| 39 | 22.04 | H | RL | Aldershot Town | W | 5-0 | 1156 | Skelly, Harlow, S. Watson, M. Watson, Riley |
| 40 | 24.04 | A | RL | Walton & Hersham | W | 2-0 | 585 | Akrour 2 |
| 41 | 27.04 | A | RL | Enfield | D | 1-1 | 531 | M. Watson |
| 42 | 01.05 | H | RL | Basingstoke Town | L | 1-2 | | |

### CUP COMPETITIONS

| | Date | Venue | Comp | Opponents | Results | Score | Att | Goalscorers |
|--|------|-------|------|-----------|---------|-------|-----|-------------|
| | 08.09 | A | LC1 | Dulwich Hamlet | W | 3-2 | 312 | Ugbah, M Watson |
| | 29.09 | H | ICS | Kingstonian | L | 1-6 | 403 | Tanner |
| | 03.10 | A | FAC 2q | St. Leonards | W | 1-0 | 683 | M. Watson |
| | 17.10 | A | FAC 3q | Ford Sports Daventry | D | 2-2 | 312 | M. Watson, Vines |
| | 20.10 | H | FAC 3qR | Ford Sports Daventry | W | 3-0 | 441 | Harlow, Salako 2 |
| | 31.10 | A | FAC 4q | Boreham Wood | L | 0-1 | 541 | |
| | 03.11 | H | LC2 | Billericay Town | W | 4-0 | 189 | Harlow, S. Watson, Vines, Salako |
| | 17.11 | A | PC1 | Walton & Hersham | L | 1-3 | 246 | Vines |
| | 21.11 | A | FAT 2 | Heybridge Swifts | W | 2-1 | 319 | S. Watson, Vines |
| | 08.12 | H | SS1 | Farnham Town | W | 7-0 | 134 | Riley, Kilner, Salako 3, Akrour |
| | 16.01 | A | FAT 3 | Weymouth | L | 0-1 | 1060 | |
| | 02.02 | H | SSC 2 | Redhill | W | 6-1 | 140 | Harlow, S. Watson, M. Watson 2, Akrour |
| | 09.02 | A | SSC 3 | Ashford Town | W | 2-1 | 78 | S. Watson, Akrour |
| | 16.02 | H | LC3 | Basingstoke Town | W | 2-0 | 178 | S. Watson, M. Watson |
| | 02.03 | H | SSC sf | Woking | W | 6-0 | 352 | Akrour, Riley, M. Watson, Salako |
| | 09.03 | A | LC4 | Maidenhead United | L | 4-5 | 206 | Akrour, Harford, M. Watson, Salako |
| | 03.05 | A | SSC F | Carshalton | W | 3-0 | | |

| 1 | 2 | 3 | 4 | 5 | 6 | 7 | 8 | 9 | 10 | 11 | 12 / 14 / 15 | |
|---|---|---|---|---|---|---|---|---|---|---|---|---|
| Howells | Brooker | Riley | Berry | Skelly | Ugbah | S Watson | Salako | Akrour | Ekoku | Haynes | Laker, Akinbolu, M Watson | 1 |
| Howells | Brooker | Riley | Berry | Skelly | Ugbah | S Watson | Salako | Akrour | M Watson | Ekoku | Laker, Akinbolu, Haynes | 2 |
| Howells | Brooker | Riley | Berry | Skelly | Ugbah | S Watson | Salako | Akrour | M Watson | Ekoku | Laker, Haynes, Blackman | 3 |
| Howells | Brooker | Riley | Berry | Skelly | Ugbah | S Watson | Salako | Akrour | M Watson | Ekoku | Laker, Blackman, Haynes | 4 |
| Howells | Brooker | Riley | Berry | Skelly | Ugbah | S Watson | Salako | Akrour | M Watson | Haynes | Laker, Blackman, Ekoku | 5 |
| Howells | Brooker | Riley | Berry | Skelly | Harlow | S Watson | Salako | Akrour | M Watson1 | Ekoku | Laker, Blackman, Hayes | 6 |
| Howells | Brooker | Laker | Berry | Skelly | Harlow | S Watson | Salako | Akrour | M Watson | Ekoku | Ugbah, Blackman, Hayes | 7 |
| Howells | Laker | Riley | Berry | Skelly | Harlow | Salako | S Watson | Akrour | M Watson | Ekoku | Ugbah, Blackman, Brooker | 8 |
| Howells | Brooker | Laker | Berry | Skelly | Harlow | S Watson | Salako | Akrour | M Watson | Ekoku | Ugbah, Blackman, Antoine | 9 |
| Howells | Brooker | Riley | Berry | Skelly | Harlow | S Watson | Salako | Akrour | M Watson | Ekoku | Ugbah, Blackman, Laker | 10 |
| Howells | Brooker | Riley | Berry | Skelly | Harlow | S Watson | Salako | Akrour | M Watson | Ugbah | Vines, Laker, Blackman | 11 |
| Howells | Brooker | Riley | Berry | Skelly | Harlow | S Watson | Salako | Akrour | M Watson | Ekoku | Vines, Laker, Blackman | 12 |
| Howells | Brooker | Laker | Berry | Skelly | Harlow | S Watson | Harford | Akrour | Vines | Blackman | Salako, Talboys, Kilner | 13 |
| Howells | Brooker | Skelly | Berry | Laker | Harlow | S Watson | Harford | Akrour | Salako | Kilner | Vines, Talboys, Bolton | 14 |
| Howells | Brooker | Riley | Berry | Skelly | Harlow | S Watson | Harford | Akrour | Simpson | Laker | Vines, Talboys, Edwards | 15 |
| Howells | Brooker | Riley | Berry | Talboys | Laker | Salako | Harlow | Akrour | Simpson | Harford | Vines, Skelly, Edwards | 16 |
| Howells | Brooker | Riley | Berry | Skelly | Salako | S Watson | Harlow | Akrour | Simpson | Harford | Vines, Tallboys, Edwards | 17 |
| Howells | Brooker | Riley | Berry | Skelly | Harlow | S Watson | Harper | Akrour | Simpson | Talboys | Vines, Salako, Edwards | 18 |
| Howells | Brooker | Riley | Berry | Skelly | Harlow | S Watson | Salako | Talboys | Simpson | Harford | Harper, M Watson, Vines | 19 |
| Howells | Brooker | Riley | Berry | Skelly | Harlow | S Watson | Salako | Akrour | Simpson | Talboys | Vines, M Watson, Harper | 20 |
| Howells | Brooker | Riley | Berry | Skelly | Harlow | S Watson | Dack | Akrour | Simpson | Salako | Talboys, M Watson, Vines | 21 |
| Howells | Brooker | Riley | Berry | Laker | Harlow | S Watson | Dack | Akrour | Simpson | Ekoku | M Watson, Talboys, Skelly | 22 |
| Howells | Brooker | Riley | Berry | Laker | Harlow | S Watson | Talboys | Ekoku | M Watson | Dack | Akrour, Salako, Skelly | 23 |
| Howells | Brooker | Riley | Berry | Laker | Harlow | S Watson | Harford | Ekoku | M Watson | Harper | Akrour, Skelly, Salako | 24 |
| Howells | Brooker | Skelly | Berry | Laker | Harlow | S Watson | Dack | Ekoku | M Watson | Harford | Harper, Akrour, Salako | 25 |
| Howells | Brooker | Skelly | Berry | Laker | Harlow | S Watson | Dack | Ekoku | M Watson | Harford | Akrour, Harper, Salako | 26 |
| Howells | Brooker | Skelly | Berry | Laker | Harlow | S Watson | Dack | Ekoku | M Watson | Harford | Akrour, Harper, Rowlands | 27 |
| Howells | Brooker | Skelly | Berry | Laker | Harlow | S Watson | Dack | Akrour | M Watson | Harford | Rowlands, Harper, Salako | 28 |
| Howellls | Brooker | Skelly | Berry | Laker | Harlow | S Watson | Harford | Akrour | M Watson | Dack | Rowlands, Harper, Salako | 29 |
| Howells | Brooker | Harper | Berry | Laker | Harlow | S Watson | Dack | Akrour | M Watson | Skelly | Ekoku, Rowlands, Riley | 30 |
| Howells | Brooker | Skelly | Berry | Laker | Harlow | S Watson | Harford | Akrour | M Watson | Dack | Salako, Harper, Rowlands | 31 |
| Howells | Brooker | Skelly | Berry | Laker | Harlow | S Watson | Harford | Akrour | M Watson | Dack | Salako, Riley, Rowlands | 32 |
| Howells | Brooker | Skelly | Berry | Laker | Harlow | S Watson | Dack | Akrour | M Watson | Harford | Riley, Salako, Rowlands | 33 |
| Howells | Brooker | Skelly | Berry | Laker | Harlow | S Watson | Dack | Akrour | M Watson | Harford | Rowlands, Riley, Winston | 34 |
| Pape | Brooker | Skelly | Berry | Laker | Harlow | S Watson | Harford | Akrour | Winston | Riley | Rowlands, M Watson, Harper | 35 |
| Howells | Brooker | Skelly | Berry | Laker | Harlow | S Watson | Harford | Akrour | Winston | Riley | M Watson, Rowlands, Harper | 36 |
| Howells | Brooker | Skelly | Berry | Laker | Harlow | S Watson | Harper | Akrour | Winston | Riley | Rowlands, M Watson, Dack | 37 |
| Howells | Brooker | Skelly | Berry | Laker | Harlow | S Watson | Harper | Akrour | Winston | Riley | Rowlands, M Watson, Ekoku | 38 |
| Howells | Brooker | Skelly | Berry | Laker | Harlow | S Watson | Harper | Akrour | M Watson | Riley | Rowlands, Winston, Ekoku | 39 |
| Pape | Brooker | Skelly | Berry | Laker | Harlow | S Watson | Harper | Winston | M Watson | Riley | Rowlands, Akrour, Ekoku | 40 |
| Howells | Brooker | Skelly | Berry | Laker | Harlow | S Watson | Harper | Akrour | M Watson | Riley | Rowlands, Winston, Ekoku | 41 |
| Pape | Brooker | Salako | Harper | Laker | Harlow | S Watson | Rowlands | Winston | Ekoku | Riley | M Watson, Akrour, Skelly | 42 |

| | | |
|---|---|---|
| **ISTHMIAN LEAGUE** | 1st | |
| **FA CUP** | 4th Qual. Round, 0-1 v Boreham Wood (A) | |
| **FA TROPHY** | 3rd Round, 0-1 v Weymouth (A) | |

League Attendances

| | |
|---|---|
| **HIGHEST** | 1,454 v Carshalton Ath. 5.4.99 |
| **LOWEST** | 540 v Boreham Wood 15.9.98 |

## MANAGER
## JOHN RAINS

| | |
|---|---|
| Date of Appointment | May 1996 |
| Date of Birth: | 25th May 1954 |
| Place of Birth: | Lambeth |

PREVIOUS CLUBS

| | |
|---|---|
| As manager | Epsom, Worthing, Dorking, Molesey, Carshalton Ath. |
| As asst. manager/coach | None |
| As player | Bromley, Sutton Utd. |

HONOURS

| | |
|---|---|
| As manager | Isthmian League Championship 98-99 |
| As player | Isthmian Lge 84-85, 85-86, FA Trophy R-up 81, Anglo-Italian Cup 79 |

## FOOTBALL MANAGEMENT TEAM

| | |
|---|---|
| **Assistant Manager:** | Tony Rains |
| **Coach:** | Micky Cook |
| **Physio:** | Dennis Rose |
| **Youth Team Manager:** | Phil Dunne |

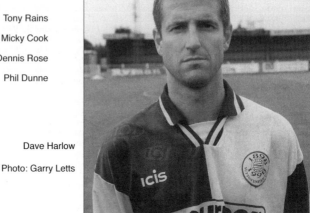

Dave Harlow

Photo: Garry Letts

## MATCHDAY PROGRAMME

| | |
|---|---|
| **Number of Pages** | 48 |
| **Price** | £1.50 |
| **Programme Editor** | Tony Dolbear Tel: 0966 507023 |
| **Other club publications** | 'Touchliner' (Supporters' Club) |
| **Local Press** | Sutton Advertiser, Sutton Guardian Sutton Independent, Sutton Comet |
| **Local Radio** | Thames Radio, County Sound |

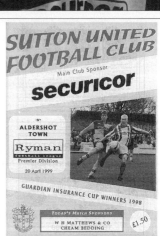

244

| Player | Birthplace<br>Honours | D.O.B. | Previous Clubs |
|---|---|---|---|
| **GOALKEEPERS** | | | |
| Gareth Howells | Guildford | 13.06.70 | Tottenham Hotspur, Torquay United |
| Andy Little | | 03.10.74 | Croydon |
| **DEFENDERS** | | | |
| Gwynne Berry | | 18.12.63 | Welling U,Sutton U, Woking, Sutton U, Whyteleafe |
| John Mackie | | 05.07.76 | Crawley Town |
| Barry Laker | | 03.11.73 | Banstead Ath, Wimbledon |
| Danny Brooker | | 05.12.75 | |
| Richard Skelly | | 24.03.72 | |
| **MIDFIELDERS** | | | |
| **Dave Harlow** | | **02.11.67** | **Farnborough Town** |
| Paul Harford | | 21.10.74 | Welling United |
| Jimmy Dack | | 02.06.72 | Aldershot |
| Paul Sears | | 11.01.80 | Carshalton |
| Ramond Giwa | | 06.02.76 | Youth Team |
| **FORWARDS** | | | |
| Andy Salako | | 08.11.72 | Carshalton Ath, Bromley, Tonbridge, St.Albans C,Croydon, Welling U, Charlton Ath |
| Mark Watson | | 28.12.73 | Welling U, AFC Bournemouth,West Ham U, Sutton U |
| Sammy Winston | | 06.08.78 | Leyton Orient,Yeovil Town,Chesham United |
| Colin Simpson | | 30.04.76 | Leyton Orient |
| Nko Ekoku | | 10.02.69 | Youth Team |
| Keith Rowlands | | 08.11.75 | Farnborough Town |
| Francis Vines | | 31.01.62 | Hampton |
| Joel Rogers | | 07.01.80 | Dunkirk |

Bold print indicates an England Semi-Professional International

DEPARTURES:
Nassim Akrour (Woking), Jimmy Bolton (released), Junior Hayes (Carshalton Ath.), John Ugbah (Welling Utd.),
Steve Talboys (Aldershot T.), Steve Watson (Farnborough T.), Mark Harper (Farnborough T.), Andy Riley (Dulwich H.),
Barry Blackman (released).

# SUTTON UNITED

| | |
|---|---|
| **Formed:** | 1898 |
| **Nickname:** | The U's |
| **Sponsors:** | Securicor |
| **Colours:** | Amber & chocolate/chocolate/ |
| | amber & chocolate |
| **Change colours:** | Green & white/black/black |
| **Midweek matchday:** | Tuesday |
| **Reserve League:** | None |

## GROUND DETAILS

Borough Sports Ground,
Gander Green Lane,
Sutton,
Surrey SM1 2EY

**Telephone Number:** 0181 644 4440
Fax: 0181 644 5120

**Directions:** Gander Green Lane runs between
A232 (Cheam Road - turn by Sutton Cricket Club)
and A217 (Oldfields Road - turn at 'Gander' PH lights).
Ground opposite `The Plough'
50 yards from West Sutton BR station.
Bus 413 passes ground

| | |
|---|---|
| **Capacity:** | 7,032 |
| **Seated**: | 765 |
| **Terracing -** | **Covered:** 1,250 |
| | **Uncovered:** 5,000 |

**Clubhouse:** Open every day, food. Available for hire
**Club Shop:** Open matchdays selling a full range of
souvenirs, etc, contact Tony Cove via club

## Past Players who progressed to the Football League

Numerous including the following since 1980

S Galloway (C Palace 84), P McKinnon (Blackburn 86),
R Fearon (Ipswich 87), PHarding (Notts Co),
E Ekoku (Bournemouth 91), M Golley (Maidstone),
A Barnes (C Palace 91), P Rogers (Sheff U 92),
S Massey (C Palace 92), A & R Scott (Sheff U 93),
O Morah (Cambridge 94), M Watson (West Ham 95)

## PREVIOUS

| | |
|---|---|
| **Leagues:** | Sutton Junior, |
| | Southern Sub 10-21, |
| | Athenian 21-63, |
| | Isthmian 63-86, 91-99, |
| | GMVC 86-91 |
| **Names:** | Sutton Association, Sutton Guild Rovers |
| **Grounds:** | Western Road, Manor Lane, |
| | London Road, The Find. |

## CLUB RECORDS

| | |
|---|---|
| **Attendance:** | 14,000 v Leeds United, |
| | FA Cup 4th Rd 24/1/70 |
| **Victory:** | 11-1 v Clapton 66, & leatherhead 82-83 |
| **Defeat:** | 13-0 v Barking 25-26 |
| **Scorer:** | Paul McKinnon (279) |
| **Appearances:** | Larry Pritchard 781 (65-84) |
| **Fee Paid:** | to Malmo FF for Paul McKinnon 83 |
| **Fee Received:** | £100,000 |
| | for Efan Ekoku (Bournemouth 90) |

## BEST SEASON

| | |
|---|---|
| **FA Amateur Cup:** | Runners-up 62-63 68-69 |
| | SF 28-29 36-37 67-68 |
| **FA Trophy:** | Runners-up 80-81 |
| | SF 92-93 |
| **FA Cup:** | 4th Round |
| | 69-70, 0-6 v Leeds Utd (H) |
| | 88-89, 0-8 v Norwich C. (A) |

## HONOURS

Bob Lord Trophy 90-91;
**Isthmian League** 66-67 84-86 98-99
R-up 67-68 70-71 81-82,
Lge Cup (3) 82-84 85-86 97-98 R-up 79-80;
Loctite Cup 91-92; Carlton Cup 95-96;
**Athenian Lge** 27-28 45-46 57-58 R-up 46-47, Lg Cup
45-46 55-56 61-62 62-63, Res Sec 61-62 R-up 32-33;
Anglo Italian Semi-Pro Cup 79 R-up 80 82;
London Snr Cup 57-58 82-83;
London Charity Cup 69-70 R-up 67-68 68-69 72-73;
Surrey Snr Cup x14 R-up x9; Surrey Intermediate Cup
x4 R-up x6; Surrey Jnr Cup R-up 09-10;
Surrey Snr Charity Shield x3 R-up x6;
Surrey Interm Charity Cup 31-32 R-up 34-35 38-39;
Dylon Charity Shield 84 R-up 80 82 83 85;
Groningen Yth tournament 83 85 R-up 79 81 89 91;
John Ullman Invit. Cup 88-89

# TELFORD UNITED

One of only three founder members of The Conference (Alliance), Telford United enjoyed the relief of being reprieved from the drop to The Dr.Martens League thanks to the collapse of Slough Town in the Summer of 98.

But could they take advantage of their luck and pull away from the danger zone?

## CLUB OFFICIALS 1999-2000

| | |
|---|---|
| President | **Gerald Smith** |
| Chairman | **Tony Esp** |
| Chief Executive | **Andy Shaw** |
| Football Secretary | **Mike Ferriday** |

199 Trench Road, Telford, Shropshire TF2 7DX
Tel: 01952 - 605193(H) 292929(B)

| | |
|---|---|
| Commercial Manager | **Terry Brumpton** |
| | Tel: 01543 468880 |
| Press Officer | **Robert Cave** |
| | Tel: 01952 270767 |

No, not in the full sense as United were never higher than 14th position and spent much of the season in very real danger.

The goals of Huckerby and Murphy proved vital in the end and a reasonably comfortable end to the season could be enjoyed as a point a match from the last ten games saw The Lilywhites finish in 17th position.

The First Round of the F.A.Cup was reached but the run finished with a 0-2 home defeat by Cambridge United and in the F.A.Trophy a disappointingly heavy defeat at Dagenham didn't bring any respite in a hard season.

Perhaps Telford United have now weathered their difficult period and can regain a little of the old glory, but it will take hard work and a strengthening of the squad.

T.T.

# TELFORD UNITED
## MATCH FACTS 1998-99

| No | Date | Venue | Comp | Opponents | Att | Result | Score | Goalscorers |
|---|---|---|---|---|---|---|---|---|
| 1 | 15/08 | A | NC | Southport | 1282 | L | 1-2 | Turner 59 |
| 2 | 18/08 | H | NC | Kettering Town | 832 | L | 0-2 | |
| 3 | 22/08 | H | NC | Welling United | 609 | D | 0-0 | |
| 4 | 24/08 | A | NC | Kidderminster Harriers | 2003 | L | 0-3 | |
| 5 | 29/08 | A | NC | Barrow | 1604 | D | 1-1 | Huckerby 89 |
| 6 | 31/08 | H | NC | Kingstonian | 680 | D | 1-1 | Bentley 87 |
| 7 | 05/09 | H | NC | Dover Athletic | 588 | D | 1-1 | Norbury 53 |
| 8 | 12/09 | A | NC | Rushden & Diamonds | 2909 | W | 3-2 | Huckerby 29, Palmer 47 57 |
| 9 | 15/09 | H | NC | Hereford United | 1086 | L | 0-1 | |
| 10 | 19/09 | H | NC | Forest Green Rovers | 708 | W | 2-1 | Palmer 32, Bentley 77 |
| 11 | 26/09 | A | NC | Morecambe | 902 | W | 1-0 | Campbell 7 |
| 12 | 29/09 | H | NC | Yeovil Town | 757 | D | 2-2 | Huckerby 18, Palmer 62 |
| 13 | 03/10 | H | NC | Stevenage Borough | 905 | L | 0-3 | |
| 14 | 10/10 | A | NC | Hayes | 716 | W | 2-0 | Gray 64, Murphy 77 |
| 15 | 07/11 | A | NC | Farnborough Town | 613 | L | 1-3 | Bentley 2 |
| 16 | 28/11 | A | NC | Stevenage Borough | 2189 | D | 2-2 | Norbury 54, Turner 83 |
| 17 | 05/12 | H | NC | Morecambe | 604 | L | 2-3 | Doyle 25, M Turner 76 |
| 18 | 07/12 | A | NC | Hednesford Town | 887 | D | 1-1 | Murphy 56 |
| 19 | 12/12 | H | NC | Rushden & Diamonds | 867 | D | 2-2 | Huckerby 10, Palmer 46 |
| 20 | 19/12 | A | NC | Yeovil Town | 2253 | L | 0-4 | |
| 21 | 26/12 | H | NC | Cheltenham Town | 1304 | L | 0-3 | |
| 22 | 28/12 | A | NC | Leek Town | 672 | D | 1-1 | Palmer 55 |
| 23 | 02/01 | H | NC | Cheltenham Town | 3027 | L | 0-2 | |
| 24 | 09/01 | H | NC | Woking | 787 | W | 1-0 | Jones 48 |
| 25 | 23/01 | A | NC | Hayes | 615 | L | 3-4 | Murphy 55, Huckerby 70 85 |
| 26 | 30/01 | A | NC | Welling United | 745 | W | 1-0 | Huckerby 85 |
| 27 | 02/02 | H | NC | Hednesford Town | 954 | D | 1-1 | Murphy 83 |
| 28 | 13/02 | A | NC | Kettering Town | 1840 | L | 1-2 | Murphy 44 |
| 29 | 20/02 | H | NC | Kidderminster Harriers | 1220 | D | 0-0 | |
| 30 | 23/02 | A | NC | Doncaster Rovers | 3040 | L | 1-2 | Taylor 90 |
| 31 | 27/02 | H | NC | Barrow | 749 | D | 1-1 | Huckerby 81 |
| 32 | Doyle | | | | | | | |
| 33 | 06/03 | A | NC | Hereford United | 1592 | D | 0-0 | |
| 34 | 13/03 | H | NC | Northwich Victoria | 911 | W | 3-0 | Palmer 1, Bentley 9, Fitzpatrick 86 |
| 35 | 20/03 | A | NC | Kingstonian | 816 | L | 0-1 | |
| 36 | 27/03 | H | NC | Farnborough Town | 662 | W | 3-1 | Fitzpatrick 4 45, Huckerby 79 |
| 37 | 03/04 | A | NC | Forest Green Rovers | 951 | D | 1-1 | Murphy 63 |
| 38 | 05/04 | H | NC | Leek Town | 847 | W | 2-0 | Murphy 52, Huckerby 90 |
| 39 | 10/04 | A | NC | Northwich Victoria | 1008 | D | 1-1 | Huckerby 40 |
| 40 | 13/04 | H | NC | Southport | 704 | W | 1-0 | Fitzpatrick 8 |
| 41 | 17/04 | A | NC | Woking | 1677 | L | 0-3 | |
| 42 | 24/04 | H | NC | Doncaster Rovers | 1539 | L | 0-2 | |
| | 01/05 | A | NC | Dover Athletic | 865 | D | 1-1 | Murphy 74 |

**CUP COMPETITIONS**

| | Date | Venue | Comp | Opponents | Att | Result | Score | Goalscorers |
|---|---|---|---|---|---|---|---|---|
| | 28/07 | A | Shrops SC SF | Bridgnorth Town | n/k | W | 3-0 | |
| | 31/07 | H | Shrops SC F | Shrewsbury Town | n/k | L | 0-1 | |
| | 06/10 | A | Endsleigh 1 | Southport | 631 | L | 1-2 | Murphy 59 |
| | 17/10 | A | FA Cup Q3 | Sutton Coldfield Town | 442 | D | 1-1 | Huckerby 61 |
| | 20/10 | H | FA Cup Q3 rep | Sutton Coldfield Town | 590 | W | 1-0 | Huckerby 45 |
| | 31/10 | H | FA Cup Q4 | Burscough | 627 | W | 2-1 | Huckerby 31, Gray 60 |
| | 14/11 | H | FA Cup 1 | Cambridge United | 1818 | L | 0-2 | |
| | 21/11 | A | FA Trophy 2 | Blakenall | 316 | D | 1-1 | Huckerby 30 |
| | 24/11 | H | FA Trophy 2 rep | Blakenall | 403 | W | 2-1 | |
| | 16/01 | A | FA Trophy 3 | Droylsden | 473 | W | 3-2 | Murphy 43 90, Bentley 87 |
| | 06/02 | A | FA Trophy 4 | Dagenham & Redbridge | 840 | L | 0-4 | |

| 1 | 2 | 3 | 4 | 5 | 6 | 7 | 8 | 9 | 10 | 11 | 12 / 14 / 15 | |
|---|---|---|---|---|---|---|---|---|---|---|---|---|
| Williams | Turner | Fowler | Challinor | Bentley | Hodson | Huckerby | M Jones | Palmer | Gray | Shakespeare | Bytheway, Norbury, Beazlet | 1 |
| Williams | Hodson | Fowler | Challinor | Bentley | M Jones | Turner | Palmer | Huckerby | Murphy | Shakespeare | Gray, Bytheway, Norbury | 2 |
| Williams | Turner | Hodson | Bywater | Bentley | M Jones | Palmer | Bailey | Norbury | Murphy | Shakespeare | Gray, Huckerby, Bytheway | 3 |
| Williams | Hodson | Beazley | Bywater | Bentley | M Jones | Turner | Bailey | Norbury | Murphy | Shakespeare | Huckerby, Palmer, Gray | 4 |
| Williams | Naylor | Beazley | Hodson | Bentley | M Jones | Turner | Bailey | Norbury | Murphy | Shakespeare | Gray, Palmer, Huckerby | 5 |
| Williams | Naylor | J Turner | Cornes | Bentley | M Jones | M Taylor | Bailey | Norbury | Huckerby | Shakespeare | Palmer, Gray, Hodson | 6 |
| Mark Jones | Naylor | Fowler | Fee | Bentley | M Jones | Turner | Bailey | Norbury | Murphy | Palmer | Hodson, Huckerby, Shakespeare | 7 |
| Williams | Naylor | Fowler | Fee | Bentley | M Jones | M Turner | Bailey | Murphy | Huckerby | Palmer | Bywater, Norbury, J Turner | 8 |
| Williams | Naylor | Fowler | Fee | Bentley | Norman | M Turner | Bailey | Murphy | Huckerby | Palmer | Norbury, Gray, J Turner | 9 |
| Williams | Naylor | Fowler | Fee | Bentley | Shakespeare | M Jones | McCord | Murphy | Huckerby | Palmer | Norbury, Bailey, Bytheway | 10 |
| Williams | Naylor | Fowler | Fee | Bentley | Shakespeare | Doyle | McCord | Campbell | Murphy | Palmer | Norman, Huckerby, Gray | 11 |
| Williams | Norman | Fowler | Fee | Bentley | Shakespeare | Doyle | McCord | Campbell | Huckerby | Palmer | Murphy, J Turner, Challinor | 12 |
| Williams | Norman | Fowler | Fee | Bentley | Shakespeare | Doyle | McCord | Campbell | Huckerby | Palmer | Bytheway, Murphy, Jones | 13 |
| Williams | Norman | Lyne | Fee | Bentley | Shakespeare | Doyle | Jones | Campbell | Murphy | Palmer | McCord, Challinor, Gray | 14 |
| Williams | M Turner | Lyne | Fee | Bentley | Norbury | Doyle | Shakespeare | Murphy | Huckerby | Jones | Fowler, Cornes, Gray | 15 |
| Williams | Cartwright | Fowler | Challinor | Norbury | Shakespeare | Doyle | Read | Wilkes | Huckerby | Palmer | Bytheway, M Turner, Murphy | 16 |
| Davies | Bytheway | Fowler | Read | Bentley | Shakespeare | Doyle | Jones | Wilkes | Huckerby | Palmer | M Turner, Murphy, Challinor | 17 |
| Davies | Bytheway | Fowler | Read | Bentley | Shakespeare | Doyle | Jones | Wilkes | Huckerby | Palmer | Challinor, Murphy, M Turner | 18 |
| Davies | Bytheway | Fowler | Read | Bentley | Jones | Doyle | Shakespeare | Murphy | Huckerby | Palmer | Lyne, Gray, Challinor | 19 |
| Davies | Bytheway | Lyne | Read | Bentley | Jones | Doyle | Shakespeare | Murphy | Huckerby | Palmer | Challinor, Gray, J Turner | 20 |
| Williams | Cadette | Lyne | Challinor | Bentley | M Jones | Doyle | Read | Murphy | Huckerby | Palmer | J Turner, Fee, Wilkes | 21 |
| Williams | Cadette | Cornes | Challinor | Fee | Read | Doyle | Shakespeare | Murphy | Huckerby | Palmer | Gray, J Turner, Wilkes | 22 |
| Williams | Cornes | Lyne | Fee | Bentley | Read | Doyle | Shakespeare | Gray | Huckerby | Jones | J Turner, Wilkes, Davies | 23 |
| Williams | Cadette | Lyne | Fee | Bentley | Challinor | Doyle | M Jones | Murphy | Huckerby | Read | Norbury, Cornes, Wilkes | 24 |
| Williams | Taylor | Cornes | Norbury | Bentley | Read | Doyle | M Jones | Murphy | Huckerby | Palmer | Fowler, Fee, Shakespeare | 25 |
| Williams | Corner | Fowler | Fee | Bentley | Challinor | Doyle | Jones | Murphy | Huckerby | Fitzpatrick | Shakespeare, Read, Cartwright | 26 |
| Williams | Naylor | Fowler | Fee | Bentley | Challinor | Doyle | Jones | Murphy | Huckerby | Fitzpatrick | Palmer, Read, Cornes | 27 |
| Williams | McCauley | Fowler | Fee | Bentley | Cornes | Doyle | Jones | Murphy | Huckerby | Fitzpatrick | Shakespeare, Challinor, Palmer | 28 |
| Williams | McCauley | Sandwith | Challinor | Fee | Fowler | Doyle | Fitzpatrick | Murphy | Mutch | Palmer | Naylor, Huckerby, Shakespeare | 29 |
| Williams | McCauley | Sandwith | Challinor | Fee | Fowler | Naylor | Fitzpatrick | Murphy | Mutch | Palmer | Shakespeare, Huckerby, Jones | 30 |
| Williams | McCauley | Sandwith | Challinor | Fee | Jones | Naylor | Fitzpatrick | Murphy | Mutch | Palmer | Huckerby, Shakespeare, | 31 |
|  |  |  |  |  |  |  |  |  |  |  |  | 32 |
| Williams | McCauley | Sandwith | Challinor | Bentley | Fowler | Doyle | Fitzpatrick | Jones | Huckerby | Palmer | Naylor, Shakespeare, Murphy | 33 |
| Williams | McCauley | Sandwith | Naylor | Bentley | Fowler | Doyle | Fitzpatrick | Shakespeare | Huckerby | Palmer | Challinor, Murphy, Mutch | 34 |
| Williams | McCauley | Sandwith | Challinor | Bentley | Fowler | Doyle | Fitzpatrick | Dudley | Huckerby | Palmer | Naylor, Murphy, Fee | 35 |
| Williams | McCauley | Sandwith | Naylor | Challinor | Fowler | Doyle | Fitzpatrick | Shakespeare | Huckerby | Palmer | Murphy, M Jones, Challinor | 36 |
| Williams | McCauley | Sandwith | Naylor | Challinor | Fowler | Doyle | Fitzpatrick | Shakespeare | Huckerby | Palmer | Murphy, M Jones, Cornes | 37 |
| Williams | McCauley | Sandwith | Naylor | Challinor | Fowler | Doyle | Fitzpatrick | Shakespeare | Huckerby | Murphy | Bentley, Jones, Mutch | 38 |
| Williams | McCauley | Sandwith | Naylor | Bentley | Fowler | Doyle | Fitzpatrick | Shakespeare | Huckerby | Murphy | Jones, Challinor, Mutch | 39 |
| Williams | McCauley | Challinor | Naylor | Bentley | Fowler | Doyle | Fitzpatrick | Shakespeare | Huckerby | Murphy | Jones, Palmer, Cornes | 40 |
| Williams | McCauley | Challinor | Naylor | Bentley | Fowler | Doyle | Fitzpatrick | Shakespeare | Huckerby | Murphy | Jones, Cornes, Palmer | 41 |
| Williams | McCauley | Sandwith | Naylor | Bentley | Fowler | Doyle | Fitzpatrick | Cartwright | Huckerby | Murphy | Jones, Palmer, Challinor | 42 |
| Williams | McCauley | Sandwith | Naylor | Bentley | Fowler | Doyle | Fitzpatrick | Palmer | Huckerby | Challinor | Murphy, Cornes, Read | |

erby 6, Palmer 11

League Attendances     **HIGHEST:** 3027     **LOWEST:** 588

**CONFERENCE:** 17th     **FA CUP:** 1st Round     **FA TROPHY:** 4th Round

| MANAGER | | FOOTBALL MANAGEMENT TEAM | |
|---|---|---|---|
| **ALAN LEWER** | | Assistant Manager: | Andy Mutch |
| Date of Appointment | December 1998 | Physiotherapist: | Suzanne Jones |

Date of Birth
Place of Birth

PREVIOUS CLUBS

### 1998-99

| As manager | Haslemere, Windsor & Eton | **Top Scorer:** | Scott Huckerby |
| As coach | Woking | | |
| As player | Arsenal, AFC Bournemouth, Aldershot | **Player of the Year:** | Lee Fowler |

HONOURS

**Captain:** Jim Bentley

As manager/ coach/ player        None

Steve Palmer (left)
and Scott Huckerby
Photo: Peter Barnes

## MATCHDAY PROGRAMME

Number of pages                    32

Price                              £1.30

Programme Editor                   Rollo Sheridan
106 Boulton Grange, Telford TF3 2LF.
01952 406570

Other club publications:           None

Local Newspapers:                  Shropshire Star
Telford Journal

Local Radio Stations:              BBC Radio Shropshire
Beacon Radio, Telford FM

# PLAYING SQUAD

TELFORD UNITED

| Player | Birthplace | Signed From | Previous Clubs |
|---|---|---|---|
| **GOALKEEPERS** | | | |
| Dean Williams | | Gateshead | Birmingham City, Brentford, Doncaster Rovers |
| Justin Bray | | Wolves | Wolverhampton Wanderers |
| **DEFENDERS** | | | |
| Jim Bentley | Liverpool | Man City | Manchester City |
| Stuart Corns | | Shrewsbury | Shrewsbury Town |
| John Ford | Stourbridge | Kidderminster | Cradley Town,Swansea City, Bradford City, Gillingham, Barnet, Kidderminster Harriers. |
| Lee Fowler | Nottingham | Halifax | Stoke C., Preston N.E., Doncaster R., Halifax Town. |
| Kevin Sandwich | Workington | Barrow | Carlisle United,  Barrow |
| Martin Naylor | | Shrewsbury | Shrewsbury Town |
| **MIDFIELDERS** | | | |
| Gary Fitzpatrick | | Hednesford | Manchester City, Hednesford |
| Eire Youth | | | |
| Maurice Doyle | | Shrewsbury | Millwall, Shrewsbury Town |
| Carl Macauley | Liverpool | Barrow | Prescot Cables,Vauxhall G.M., Witton Albion,Manchester City |
| Steve Palmer | Birmingham | Wednesfield | Wednesfield |
| Brian McGorry | Liverpool | Torquay | Weymouth,Bournemouth,Peterborough, Wycombe W, Cardiff City Hereford United, Torquay United |
| Simon Travis | | Stockport | Torquay United, Holywell Town,Stockport County |
| **FORWARDS** | | | |
| Gez Murphy | Leicester | Gresley | Leicester C., VS Rugby, Solihull B., Atherstone U., Gresley Rovers. |
| Ben Henshaw | Wolverhampton | Oxord | Oxford United |
| Scott Huckerby | Nottingham | Ilkeston | Ilkeston town |
| Chris Malkin | Chester | Blackburn | Tranmere Rovers,Millwall, Blackpool, Blackburn Rovers |
| Andy Mutch | Liverpool | Barrow | Southport,Wolverhampton Wanderers, Stockport County, Southport |
| E: u 21 & B | | | |

Departures: Neil Cartwright, Paul Challinor (Bury), Greg Fee ,Brian Gray, Craig Shakespear and Tim Wilkes

# TELFORD UNITED

| | |
|---|---|
| **Founded:** | 1876 |
| **Nickname:** | Lilywhites |
| **Club Sponsors:** | Eastern Generation |
| **Club colours:** | White shirts, black shorts, white socks |
| **Change colours:** | Orange shirts, orange shorts and orange socks |
| **Midweek home matchday:** | Tuesday |
| **Reserves' League:** | Central Conference |

## GROUND DETAILS

Bucks Head Ground,
Watling Street,
Wellington,
Telford,
Shropshire TF12NJ

**TELEPHONE:** 01952 640064
Fax: 01952 640021

**SIMPLE DIRECTIONS:**
M54 Junction 6, A518 to B5061 (Watling Street).
Ground is on several bus routes
Nearest railway station - Wellington

CAPACITY: 7,000
SEATED: 1,200
COVERED TERRACING: 1,500

**SOCIAL FACILITIES:**
Social club adjacent to ground - open matchdays and selected other hours

**CLUB SHOP:**
Telephone 01952 640046 for details

## Past Players who progressed to the Football League

A.Walker (Lincoln City),G.French (Luton Town),
K.McKenna (Tranmere Rovers), S.Norris (Scarborough),
David Pritchard (Bristol Rovers) 1994,
Sean Parrish (Doncaster Rovers) 1994,
Steve Foster (Bristol R.);
Peter Wilding, Roger Preece, Mark Williams & Martyn Naylor
- all to Shrewsbury 1997

## PREVIOUS

| | |
|---|---|
| **Leagues:** | Southern League, Cheshire League, Birmingham League |
| **Name:** | Wellington Town (prior to 1969) |
| **Grounds:** | None |

## CLUB RECORDS

| | |
|---|---|
| **Attendance:** | 13,000 v Shrewsbury Town Birmingham League - 1936 |
| **Win:** | Unknown |
| **Defeat:** | Unknown |
| **Career appearances:** | Unknown |
| **Career goalscorer:** | Jack Bentley |
| **Transfer fee paid:** | £15,000 to Hednesford T. for Mickey Norbury |
| **Transfer fee received:** | £50,000 from Scarborough for Stephen Norris |

## BEST SEASON

**FA Cup:** 5th Round 84-85,
0-3 v Everton (A), 47,402.
Also 4th Rd. 83-84,
3rd Rd.86-87,
2nd Rd. 82-83, 85-86, 91-92

League clubs defeated: Wigan, Rochdale, Stockport C.,
Darlington, Stoke C.,Lincoln U., Bradford C

**FA Trophy:** Winners 71-72, 82-83, 88-89.
R-up 69-70, 87-88

## HONOURS

FA Trophy Winners 71-72, 82-83, 88-89.
R-up 69-70, 87-88;
Birmingham League1920-21, 1934-35, 1935-36;
Cheshire League 1945-46, 1946-47, 1951-52;
Edward Case Cup 1952-53, 1954-55;
Welsh Cup 1901-02, 1905-06, 1939-40;
BirminghamSenior Cup 1946-47;
Walsall Senior Cup 1946-47;
Birmingham League Challenge Cup 1946-47;
Shropshire Senior Cup (30);
Southern League Cup 1970-71;
Midland Floodlit Cup 1970-71, 1982-83, 1988-89,
Runners-up 1969-70, 1987-88

# WELLING UNITED

Only three victories before the new year understandably left Welling in the relegation zone with few willing to give them a chance of survival.
The Kent club are experienced fighters who have battled their way up the pyramid so they were not going to give up their Conference place without a struggle.

## CLUB OFFICIALS 1998-99

| | |
|---|---|
| President | **E Brackstone** |
| Chairman | **Paul Websdale** |
| Vice Chairman | **Steven Pain** |
| General Manager | **Graham Hobbins** |
| Club Secretary | **Barrie Hobbins** |
| | c/o the club |
| Tel: 0181 301 1196 | Fax: 0181 301 5676 |
| Marketing Manager | **Steve Wells** |
| Press Officer | **Paul Carter** |
| | c/o the club |
| Tel: 0181 301 1196 | Fax: 0181 301 5676 |

Two victories over the new year holiday followed by three more points at Kidderminster lifted morale. The Wings had enjoyed an F.A.Cup trip to Bristol Rovers but there was no luck in the Trophy so they only had the survival battle on which to concentrate in the second half of the season.

With just five games to go, and three of them away from home, Welling were in 21st position. However, home victories over Southport and Morecambe plus an away success at Leek and a point at Hereford saw them visit the champions, Cheltenham on the last day of the season, needing a victory to be safe.

A 0-0 draw wasn't enough as Barrow won at Kidderminster, but as we all know now, off the field problems took Barrow away and likeTelford the season before, Welling were reprieved.

So there's a Conference place for Welling United this season but they will have to improve to keep it.                    T.T.

Back Row: Ron Croker (kit manager), Dave McDonald, Tony Dolby, Tyrone King, Terry Skiverton, Glen Knight, Mark Cooper, Len Watts, Richard Vercesi, John Farley, Ken Guiste (coach). Front Row: Sam Appiah, Paul Linger, Dereck Browne (player-coach), Ray Burgess (asst. manager), Kevin Hales (manager), Peter Green (physio), Mike Rutherford, Mark Hynes.

# WELLING UNITED
## MATCH FACTS 1998-99

| No | Date | Venue | Comp | Opponents | Att | Result | Score | Goalscorers |
|----|------|-------|------|-----------|-----|--------|-------|-------------|
| 1 | 15/08 | H | NC | Cheltenham Town | 820 | W | 2-1 | Hynes 26, Appah 87 |
| 2 | 18/08 | A | NC | Rushden & Diamonds | 2261 | L | 1-3 | Vercesi 56 |
| 3 | 22/08 | A | NC | Telford United | 609 | D | 0-0 | |
| 4 | 25/08 | H | NC | Farnborough Town | 648 | D | 0-0 | |
| 5 | 29/08 | H | NC | Hereford United | 727 | D | 2-2 | Hynes 35, Farley 55 |
| 6 | 31/08 | A | NC | Stevenage Borough | 3413 | D | 1-1 | Dolby 79 |
| 7 | 05/09 | H | NC | Hednesford Town | 507 | D | 1-1 | Hynes 81 |
| 8 | 08/09 | H | NC | Yeovil Town | 531 | L | 1-2 | Cooper 18 |
| 9 | 12/09 | A | NC | Southport | 1035 | L | 2-5 | Linger 36 75 |
| 10 | 15/09 | A | NC | Woking | 1477 | D | 0-0 | |
| 11 | 19/09 | H | NC | Leek Town | 524 | W | 1-0 | Linger 57 |
| 12 | 22/09 | H | NC | Kettering Town | 455 | L | 0-2 | |
| 13 | 26/09 | A | NC | Forest Green Rovers | 624 | L | 2-3 | Cooper 74 88 |
| 14 | 03/10 | H | NC | Kidderminster Harriers | 780 | D | 0-0 | |
| 15 | 10/10 | H | NC | Barrow | 700 | D | 1-1 | Dolby 80 |
| 16 | 24/10 | A | NC | Kingstonian | 904 | L | 1-2 | Brown 26 |
| 17 | 07/11 | A | NC | Northwich Victoria | 1032 | L | 0-3 | |
| 18 | 28/11 | A | NC | Morecambe | 855 | L | 1-2 | Browne 57 |
| 19 | 05/12 | H | NC | Woking | 843 | L | 0-1 | |
| 20 | 12/12 | H | NC | Doncaster Rovers | 761 | D | 1-1 | Adams 79 |
| 21 | 19/12 | A | NC | Hednesford Town | 806 | L | 2-3 | Adams 18 19 |
| 22 | 26/12 | H | NC | Dover Athletic | 962 | L | 0-3 | |
| 23 | 28/12 | A | NC | Hayes | 724 | W | 2-1 | Adams 15, Browne 57 |
| 24 | 02/01 | H | NC | Dover Athletic | 1334 | W | 2-1 | Munday 66[og], Browne 85 |
| 25 | 09/01 | H | NC | Forest Green Rovers | 743 | L | 0-2 | |
| 26 | 16/01 | A | NC | Barrow | 1401 | L | 1-2 | Browne 67 |
| 27 | 23/01 | A | NC | Kidderminster Harriers | 1460 | W | 1-0 | Rutherford 61 |
| 28 | 30/01 | H | NC | Telford United | 745 | L | 0-1 | |
| 29 | 16/02 | H | NC | Rushden & Diamonds | 667 | L | 0-1 | |
| 30 | 20/02 | H | NC | Northwich Victoria | 500 | L | 2-3 | Dolby 51 68 |
| 31 | 27/02 | A | NC | Kettering Town | 2371 | D | 1-1 | Dolby 70[p] |
| 32 | 06/03 | A | NC | Farnborough Town | 683 | D | 1-1 | Trebble 59 |
| 33 | 13/03 | H | NC | Kingstonian | 803 | L | 1-3 | Browne 38 |
| 34 | 16/03 | H | NC | Stevenage Borough | 524 | D | 1-1 | Strouts 29 |
| 35 | 20/03 | A | NC | Doncaster Rovers | 2952 | L | 1-4 | Trebble 22 |
| 36 | 03/04 | A | NC | Yeovil Town | 2903 | W | 3-1 | Hanlon 4, Adams 23 77[p] |
| 37 | 05/04 | H | NC | Hayes | 663 | L | 0-2 | |
| 38 | 10/04 | H | NC | Southport | 502 | W | 2-1 | Rowe 21, Browne 38 |
| 39 | 17/04 | A | NC | Hereford United | 1532 | D | 0-0 | |
| 40 | 24/04 | H | NC | Morecambe | 727 | W | 3-2 | Hanlon 19, Ugbah 38, Brown 55 |
| 41 | 26/04 | A | NC | Leek Town | 353 | W | 4-2 | Trebble 21, Hanlon 30 86[p], Rowe 60 |
| 42 | 01/05 | A | NC | Cheltenham Town | 5400 | D | 0-0 | |

### CUP COMPETITIONS

| | Date | Venue | Comp | Opponents | Att | Result | Score | Goalscorers |
|----|------|-------|------|-----------|-----|--------|-------|-------------|
| | 17/10 | H | FA Cup Q3 | Weymouth | 602 | W | 3-2 | Hynes 43 61, Linger 63 |
| | 03/11 | H | FA Cup Q4 | Whyteleafe | 421 | W | 3-1 | Cooper 4, Hynes 80 85 |
| | 14/11 | A | FA Cup 1 | Bristol Rovers | 5381 | L | 0-3 | |
| | 21/11 | A | FA Trophy 2 | Dover Athletic | 786 | L | 1-4 | Ugbah 15 |
| | 01/12 | A | Endsleigh 2 | Hayes | 272 | L | 2-3 | Appiah 42, Ugbah 44 |
| | 02/02 | H | Kent SC 1 | Greenwich Borough | 157 | W | 4-1 | Trebble 34 90, Brown 72[p], Dolby 83 |
| | 23/02 | A | London CC 1 | Hendon | 89 | W | 3-0 | Howard 35[og], S Watts 76, Riviere 78 |
| | 02/03 | A | Kent SC QF | Dover Athletic | 355 | W | 2-0 | Linger 26, Dennis 58 |
| | 23/03 | A | Kent SC SF | Margate | 273 | W | 3-2 | Adams 15, Edwards 44[p], Trebble 115 |
| | 30/03 | H | London CC QF | Bromley | n/k | W | 2-0 | Skiverton 68, Rowe 69 |
| | 28/04 | H | London CC SF | Dulwich Hamlet | n/k | L | 1-3 | Adams 35 |
| | 03/05 | A | Kent SC F | Folkestone Invicta | 712 | W | 1-0 | Adams 76 |

| 1 | 2 | 3 | 4 | 5 | 6 | 7 | 8 | 9 | 10 | 11 | 12/14/15 | # |
|---|---|---|---|---|---|---|---|---|---|---|---|---|
| Knight | L Watts | McDonald | Skiverton | Farley | Vercesi | Linger | Rotherford | Hynes | M Cooper | Appiah | Piper, King, Powell | 1 |
| Knight | L Watts | King | Skiverton | Powell | Vercesi | Piper | Rutherford | Hynes | Brown | Appiah | Farley, Linger, Cooper | 2 |
| Knight | L Watts | McDonald | Skiverton | Farley | Vercesi | Brown | Rutherford | Hynes | Cooper | Appiah | Powell, Linger, King | 3 |
| Knight | L Watts | McDonald | Skiverton | Farley | Vercesi | Brown | Rutherford | Hynes | Cooper | Appiah | Powell, Linger, King | 4 |
| Knight | L Watts | McDonald | Skiverton | Farley | Vercesi | Brown | Rutherford | Hynes | Cooper | Appiah | Dolby, Linger, King | 5 |
| Knight | L Watts | McDonald | Skiverton | Farley | Vercesi | Brown | Rutherford | Hynes | Cooper | Appiah | Linger, Dolby, Side | 6 |
| Knight | L Watts | McDonald | Hunter | Farley | Vercesi | Brown | Rutherford | Hynes | Cooper | Dolby | Linger, King, Piper | 7 |
| Knight | L Watts | McDonald | Hunter | Farley | Vercesi | Brown | Rutherford | Hynes | Cooper | Dolby | Linger, Piper, King | 8 |
| Knight | L Watts | Linger | Hunter | Farley | Vercesi | Brown | Rutherford | Hynes | Cooper | Dolby | Powell, Side, Appiah | 9 |
| nights | L Watts | McDonald | Skiverton | Farley | Hunter | Linger | Rutherford | Appiah | Cooper | Brown | Vercesi, Hynes, Powell | 10 |
| Knight | L Watts | McDonald | Skiverton | Farley | Hunter | Linger | Rutherford | Hynes | Cooper | Brown | Appiah, Dolby, Vercesi | 11 |
| Knight | L Watts | McDonald | Skiverton | Farley | Hunter | Linger | Rutherford | Hynes | Cooper | Brown | Appiah, Dolby, Vercesi | 12 |
| Knight | L Watts | McDonald | Skiverton | Farley | Hunter | Linger | Rutherford | Appiah | Cooper | Brown | Dolby, Vercesi, Powell | 13 |
| Harris | L Watts | Dolby | Skiverton | Witter | Hunter | Linger | Vercesi | Hynes | Cooper | Brown | Appiah, Lewis, Powell | 14 |
| Knight | L Watts | Powell | Skiverton | Dolby | Hunter | Linger | Rutherford | Harford | Cooper | Brown | Hynes, Appiah, Vercesi | 15 |
| Knight | McDonald | Dolby | L Watts | Skiverton | Powell | Linger | Rutherford | Hynes | M Cooper | D Brown | Hunter, Appiah, Lewis | 16 |
| Knight | McDonald | Dolby | D Brown | Skiverton | Allardyce | Linger | Rutherford | Hynes | Cooper | S Brown | Riviere, Appiah, Powell | 17 |
| Knight | McDonald | Dolby | L Watts | Skiverton | Allardyce | Ugbah | Rutherford | Browne | Adams | D Brown | Appiah, Riviere, Powell | 18 |
| Knight | McDonald | Dolby | L Watts | Skiverton | Allardyve | Ugbah | Riviere | D Adams | Browne | D Brown | Farley, Linger, Cooper | 19 |
| Knight | Anderson | Dolby | L Watts | Skiverton | Farley | Ugbah | D Brown | Adams | Browne | Cooper | Linger, Powell, McDonald | 20 |
| Knight | Witter | Dolby | L Watts | Skiverton | Farley | Anderson | D Brown | Adams | Cooper | Ugbah | Browne, Linger, McDonald | 21 |
| Knight | Witter | Dolby | L Watts | Skiverton | Farley | D Brown | Rutherford | Adams | Cooper | Anderson | Ugbah, Browne, Linger | 22 |
| Knight | Witter | McDonald | D Brown | Skiverton | Farley | Anderson | Rutherford | Adams | Browne | Ugbah | Linger, Dolby, Powell | 23 |
| Knight | L Watts | McDonald | Brown | Farley | Dolby | Ugbah | Rutherford | Adams | Anderson | Brown | Powell, Riviere, Side | 24 |
| Knight | L Watts | McDonald | Brown | Farley | Witter | Ugbah | Rutherford | Adams | Browne | Anderson | Dolby, Linger, Powell | 25 |
| Knight | L Watts | Dolby | Brown | Shiverton | Farley | Witter | Rutherford | Adams | Browne | Linger | Cooper, Powell, Riviere | 26 |
| Knight | L Watts | Farley | Brown | Skiverton | Witter | Ugbah | Rutherford | Adams | Browne | Trebble | Cooper, Dolby, Linger | 27 |
| Knight | L Watts | Farley | Brown | Skiverton | Witter | Ugbah | Rutherford | Adams | Browne | Trebble | Dolby, Riviere, Linger | 28 |
| Knight | Watts | Dolby | Brown | Skiverton | Farley | Trebble | Rutherford | Adams | Browne | Dennis | Powell, Riviere, Ugbah | 29 |
| Knight | Watts | Dolby | Brown | Skiverton | Farley | Trebble | Rutherford | Adams | Browne | Dennis | Riviere, Linger, Ugbah | 30 |
| Knight | L Watts | Dolby | Brown | Skiverton | Riviere | Trebble | Ugbah | Adams | Browne | Dennis | Appiah, Linger, Adams | 31 |
| Knight | L Watts | Dolby | Ugbah | Skiverton | Riviere | Trebble | Rutherford | M Cooper | Browne | Dennis | Brown, Linger, Appiah | 32 |
| Knight | Riviere | Dolby | Ugbah | Linger | L Watts | Trebble | Rutherford | Rowe | Brown | Browne | Appiah, Powell, Cooper | 33 |
| Knight | Riviere | Dolby | L Watts | Skiverton | Ugbah | Trebble | Rutherford | Rowe | Browne | Brown | Appiah, Cooper, Linger | 34 |
| Knight | Riviere | Dolby | L Watts | Skiverton | Ugbah | Trebble | Rutherford | Rowe | Browne | Brown | Adams, Appiah, Linger | 35 |
| Knight | Riviere | Harle | L Watts | Skiverton | Hanlon | Trebble | Rutherford | Adams | Rowe | Brown | Browne, Linger, Powell | 36 |
| Knight | Riviere | Harle | L Watts | Skiverton | Hanlon | Trebble | Rutherford | Adams | Rowe | Brown | Browne, Linger, Powell | 37 |
| Knight | Riviere | Harle | L Watts | Skiverton | Hanlon | Trebble | Rutherford | Rowe | Browne | Ugbah | Adams, Brown, Linger | 38 |
| Knight | Riviere | Harle | L Watts | Skiverton | Hanlon | Trebble | Rutherford | Rowe | Browne | Ugbah | Brown, Adams, Powell | 39 |
| Knight | Riviere | Harle | L Watts | Skiverton | Hanlon | Trebble | Rutherford | Rowe | Browne | Ugbah | Brown, Adams, Linger | 40 |
| Knight | Riviere | Harle | L Watts | Skiverton | Hanlon | Trebble | Rutherford | Rowe | Browne | Ugbah | Brown, Adam, Linger | 41 |
| Knight | Riviere | Harle | L Watts | Skiverton | Hanlon | Trebble | Rutherford | Rowe | Browne | Ugbah | Adams, Brown, Linger | 42 |

League Attendances   **HIGHEST:** 962   **LOWEST:** 455

**CONFERENCE:** 19th   **FA CUP:** 1st Round   **FA TROPHY:** 2nd Round

## MANAGER
### KEVIN HALES

| | |
|---|---|
| Date of appointment | August 1995 |
| Date of Birth | 13th January 1961 |
| Place of Birth | Dartford |

**PREVIOUS CLUBS**

| | |
|---|---|
| As manager | None |
| As coach | None |
| As player | Chelsea, Leyton Orient |

**HONOURS**

| | |
|---|---|
| As manager | None |
| As player | None |

## FOOTBALL MANAGEMENT TEAM

| | |
|---|---|
| Assistant Manager | Ray Burgess |
| Coach | Kevin Hales |
| Reserve & Youth Team Manager | Ken Geiste |
| Youth Development | Kevin Hales |
| Physio | Peter Green |

Mark Hynes                    Photos: Keith Gillard

Luke Anderson

## MATCHDAY PROGRAMME

| | |
|---|---|
| Number of Pages | 32 |
| Price | £1.20 |
| Programme Editor | Barrie Hobbins |

Other club publications
"Winning isn't everything" (Fanzine)

| | |
|---|---|
| Local Press | Kentish Times |
| | Bexleyheath & Welling Mercury |

| | |
|---|---|
| Local Radio | Radio Kent |
| | Radio Invicta |
| | R.T.M. |

# PLAYING SQUAD

| Player | Birthplace Honours | D.O.B. | Previous Clubs |
|--------|---------------------|--------|----------------|
| **GOALKEEPERS** | | | |
| Andy Harris | | 25.04.74 | Carshalton athletic, Sutton united, Welling United |
| **DEFENDERS** | | | |
| Russell Edwards | | 21.12.73 | Dulwich Hamlet,Barnet, Crystal Palace |
| Lew Watts | Maidstone | 14.9.74 | Fisher Athletic, Gravesend & Northfleet |
| Anthony Rivere | | 09.11.78 | Faversham |
| Michael Harle | | 31.10.72 | Sittingbourne, Millwall, Barnet |
| **Mark Hone** | | **31.03.68** | **Crystal Palace, Welling United, Southend United,Lincoln City, Kettering Town** |
| John Farley | Greenwich | 18.2.73 | Lewisham Elms |
| Danny Twin | | 19.12.80 | Youth Team |
| **MIDFIELDERS** | | | |
| Michael Harney | | 29.01.80 | Bromley |
| Mike Rutherford | Woolwich | 6.6.72 | Q.P.R. |
| Danny Bailey | London | 21.05.64 | Bournemouth, Dagenham, Torquay United, Exeter City, Fulham (L), Farnborough Town,Slough T,Telford United, Forest Green Rovers |
| John Ugbah | Nigeria | | Fisher Athletic , Carshalton Athletic, Stevenage Borough, Carshalton Athletic, Hendon,  Sutton United |
| Danny Chapman | | | Leyton Orient, Millwall,Hastings Town |
| **FORWARDS** | | | |
| Leke Rowe | | 30.10.73 | Chelsea, Peterborough United |
| Darren Adams | | 12.01.74 | Danson Furnace, Bashley, Cardif City, Aldershot Town , £8,000 to Dover Athletic |
| Leon Braithwaite | | 17.12.72 | Charlton Athletic, St Patricks (Ireland) |
| Richie Hanlon | Keton | 26.5.78 | Chelsea, Southend United, Welling Unied, Rushden & Diamonds, Peterborough United |
| Charlie Side | | 11.02.81. | Youth Team |
| Kevin Dennis | | 14.12.76 | Brentford |
| Jo Baker | London | 19.04.77 | Charlton Athletic, Leyton Orient |

# WELLING UNITED

**Founded:** 1963

**Nickname:** The Wings

**Club Sponsors:**

**Club colours:** Red shirts, red shorts, white socks.

**Change colours:** All jade.

**Midweek home matchday:** Tuesday

**Reserves' League:** Capital League

## PREVIOUS

**Leagues:** Eltham & District League 1963-71
London Spartan League 1971-77,
Athenian League 1977-79
Southern League 1979-86.

**Grounds:** Butterfly Lane, Eltham - 1963-78

## CLUB RECORDS

**Attendance:** 4,100
v Gillingham, FA Cup

**Win:** 7-1
opponents ?? & date ??

**Defeat:** 0-7
opponents ?? & date ??

**Career Goalscorer:** John Bartley - 533

**Career Appearances:** Nigel Ransom - 1,066
& Ray Burgess - 1,044

**Transfer fee paid:** £30,000
for Gary Abbott from Enfield

**Transfer fee received:** £95,000
from Birmingham City for Steve Finnan.1995

## GROUND DETAILS

Park View Road Ground,
Welling,
Kent DA16 1SY

**Communication** Tel: 0181 301 1196
Fax: 0811 301 5676
Welling Wingsline: 0891 80 06 54

**DIRECTIONS:** M25, then A2 towards London.
Take Welling turn-off, ground 1 mile.
By rail to Welling station (BR) - ground 3/4 mile.

**CAPACITY:** 5,500
**SEATED:** 500
**COVERED TERRACING:** 1,500

**SOCIAL FACILITIES:** Clubhouse open on match days

**CLUB SHOP:** Sells programmes (League & non-League),
scarves, mugs, caps, hats, badges, replica kits and
Conference merchandise. Manager Peter Mason.

## BEST SEASON

**FA Cup:** Third Round 1988-89
0-1 v Blackburn Rovers
League clubs defeated: Gillingham

**FA Trophy:** Quarter Final 1988-89
0-1 v Macclesfield

## HONOURS

London Spartan League 197
Southern League Premier Division 1985/86
Kent Senior Cup 1985/86
London Senior Cup 1989/90
London Challenge Cup 1991/92, Runners-up 1993/94

## Past Players who progressed to the Football League

Paul Barron(Plymouth A), Andy Townsend (Southampton),
Ian Thompson (AFC Bournemouth), John Bartley (Millwall),
Dave Smith(Gillingham), Murray Jones (C. Palace),
Kevin Shoemaker (Peterborough), Tony Agana (Watford, ),
Duncan Horton (Barnet), Mark Hone (Southend),
Steve Finnan & Steve Barnes(Birmingham City)

# WOKING

Famous and successful professional footballers often find it difficult to come to grips with management of semi-professional football clubs. So perhaps it wasn't all that surprising that John McGovern didn't enjoy a very successful spell in charge at Woking.

In fact one victory in the first eleven games really put the club under pressure and supporters welcomed the introduction of Brian McDermott, an experienced ex-professional himself but also a man with non league playing and coaching experience.

However four consecutive victories in December were followed by five consecutive defeats, which left supporters a little confused!

The F.A.Cup had brought them two well attended ties with Aldershot but a home defeat to Scunthorpe United wasn't what the Kingfield regulars were accustomed to. They reached the 5th round of the F.A.Trophy and fans had the fun of watching an 8-4 victory over Folkestone Invicta and a 2-1 replay victory at Rushden.

Meanwhile in the Conference the manager was gradually building his squad and accumulating points with the black memory being the 0-5 defeat at Stevenage Borough and the main satisfaction coming from finishing in the top ten.

Life is getting back to normal at Kingfield.

Back Row: Eddie Saunders, Darron Wilkinson, Dante Alighieri, Phil Gridelet, Peter Smith, Damian Panter, Rob Hollingdale
Middle Row: Ian Burns (Youth Team Manager), David Vaughan (Reserve Team Manager), Robert Smith, Steve West, Laurence Batty, Darryl Flahavan, Stuart Girdler, Michael Danzey, Richard Goddard, Malcolm Hague (Kitman), Ron Rawlings (Kitman), Barry Limber (Physiotherapist)
Front Row: Grant Payne, Scott Smith, Scott Steele, Darran Hay, Brian McDermott (Manager), Kevin Hill (Assistant Manager), Nassim Akrour, Danny Bolt, Steve Perkins, Ronell Coward

# WOKING
## MATCH FACTS 1998-99

| No | Date | Venue | Comp | Opponents | Att | Result | Score | Goalscorers |
|---|---|---|---|---|---|---|---|---|
| 1 | 15/08 | A | NC | Hednesford Town | 1292 | L | 1-2 | Goddard 8 |
| 2 | 18/08 | H | NC | Dover Athletic | 2263 | L | 1-2 | Steele 27 |
| 3 | 22/08 | H | NC | Southport | 1900 | L | 2-3 | Hay 57 73 |
| 4 | 25/08 | A | NC | Kettering Town | 2012 | L | 0-3 | |
| 5 | 29/08 | A | NC | Kidderminster Harriers | 2024 | L | 2-3 | Betsy 30 41 |
| 6 | 31/08 | H | NC | Forest Green Rovers | 2057 | D | 1-1 | Danzey 83 |
| 7 | 05/09 | H | NC | Barrow | 1917 | L | 2-3 | Goddard 41, West 45 |
| 8 | 12/09 | A | NC | Leek Town | 583 | W | 3-0 | Bolt 3, Danzey 8, West 25 |
| 9 | 15/09 | H | NC | Welling United | 1477 | D | 0-0 | |
| 10 | 19/09 | H | NC | Yeovil Town | 2581 | D | 0-0 | |
| 11 | 22/09 | A | NC | Cheltenham Town | 2406 | D | 1-1 | West 17 |
| 12 | 26/09 | A | NC | Northwich Victoria | 1003 | W | 3-0 | West 1 18 44 |
| 13 | 03/10 | H | NC | Morecambe | 2740 | L | 0-3 | |
| 14 | 10/10 | A | NC | Doncaster Rovers | 2833 | W | 1-0 | West 86 |
| 15 | 07/11 | H | NC | Cheltenham Town | 2738 | W | 1-0 | Hay 79 |
| 16 | 28/11 | H | NC | Hayes | 1997 | W | 2-0 | Payne 14, Perkins 78 |
| 17 | 05/12 | A | NC | Welling United | 843 | W | 1-0 | Payne 3 |
| 18 | 12/12 | H | NC | Kidderminster Harriers | 1982 | W | 2-1 | Payne 80, Hay 81 |
| 19 | 19/12 | H | NC | Northwich Victoria | 2059 | W | 2-1 | Steele 13, Hay 39 |
| 20 | 26/12 | A | NC | Kingstonian | 2694 | D | 0-0 | |
| 21 | 28/12 | A | NC | Rushden & Diamonds | 4307 | L | 0-2 | |
| 22 | 02/01 | H | NC | Kingstonian | 3772 | L | 0-1 | |
| 23 | 09/01 | A | NC | Telford United | 787 | L | 0-1 | |
| 24 | 30/01 | A | NC | Farnborough Town | 1507 | L | 1-2 | Payne 47 |
| 25 | 13/02 | H | NC | Leek Town | 1926 | W | 1-0 | Hay 12 |
| 26 | 16/02 | A | NC | Yeovil Town | 2465 | W | 1-0 | West 83 |
| 27 | 20/02 | A | NC | Hayes | 1103 | D | 2-2 | Gridelet 19, Hay 62 |
| 28 | 06/03 | H | NC | Doncaster Rovers | 2530 | W | 2-0 | Hay 38 69 |
| 29 | 13/03 | A | NC | Morecambe | 1120 | W | 1-0 | Girdler 26 |
| 30 | 16/03 | H | NC | Kettering Town | 1647 | D | 0-0 | |
| 31 | 20/03 | H | NC | Stevenage Borough | 2776 | L | 1-2 | Hay 88 |
| 32 | 23/03 | A | NC | Hereford United | 1320 | W | 1-0 | Payne 18 |
| 33 | 27/03 | H | NC | Hednesford Town | 1453 | W | 2-1 | Perkins 31, West 37 |
| 34 | 30/03 | A | NC | Southport | 811 | D | 0-0 | |
| 35 | 03/04 | A | NC | Dover Athletic | 1168 | L | 2-3 | Saunders 13, West 48 |
| 36 | 05/04 | H | NC | Rushden & Diamonds | 2808 | D | 1-1 | Payne 43 |
| 37 | 07/04 | A | NC | Forest Green Rovers | 465 | W | 2-0 | Payne 44, Hay 88 |
| 38 | 10/04 | H | NC | Farnborough Town | 2101 | W | 4-0 | Perkins 18, Hollingdale 25, Bolt 34[p], Hay 60 |
| 39 | 12/04 | A | NC | Stevenage Borough | 2028 | L | 0-5 | |
| 40 | 17/04 | H | NC | Telford United | 1677 | W | 3-0 | West 30 43, Bolt 63[p] |
| 41 | 24/04 | A | NC | Barrow | 2176 | W | 2-1 | Bolt 10, Hay 75 |
| 42 | 01/05 | H | NC | Hereford United | 2541 | L | 0-1 | |

**CUP COMPETITIONS**

| | Date | Venue | Comp | Opponents | Att | Result | Score | Goalscorers |
|---|---|---|---|---|---|---|---|---|
| | 17/10 | A | FA Cup Q3 | Minehead Town | 1040 | W | 5-1 | Hay 32 44 50 88, Bolt 57 |
| | 31/10 | A | FA Cup Q4 | Aldershot Town | 6870 | D | 0-0 | |
| | 03/11 | H | FA Cup Q4 rep | Aldershot Town | 3897 | W | 2-1 | Hay 65, Steele 102 |
| | 14/11 | H | FA Cup 1 | Scunthorpe United | 3359 | L | 0-1 | |
| | 21/11 | H | FA Trophy 2 | Salisbury City | 1640 | W | 2-1 | West 45, Ellis 87 |
| | 01/12 | H | Endsleigh 2 | Yeovil Town | 580 | W | 3-0 | Bolt 10[p] 27[p], Payne 42 |
| | 08/12 | A | Surrey SC 1 | Metropolitan Police | n/k | W | 3-1 | |
| | 12/01 | H | Surrey SC 2 | Epsom & Ewell | n/k | W | 5-0 | |
| | 16/01 | H | FA Trophy 3 | Folkestone Invicta | 1979 | W | 8-4 | Hay 44 45 83 89, Perkins 56, Steele 72, Ellis 85, Payne 8 |
| | 02/02 | H | Surrey SC QF | Walton & Hersham | 495 | W | 3-0 | |
| | 06/02 | H | FA Trophy 4 | Rushden & Diamonds | 2788 | D | 0-0 | |
| | 09/02 | A | FA Trophy 4 rep | Rushden & Diamonds | 1995 | W | 2-1 | Payne 43, Hay 54 |
| | 23/02 | A | Endsleigh QF | Farnborough Town | 592 | L | 3-4 | Coward 14, Bolt 59 64e |
| | 27/02 | H | FA Trophy 5 | Southport | 2783 | D | 0-0 | |
| | 02/03 | A | Surrey SC SF | Sutton United | 352 | L | 0-6 | |

260

| 1 | 2 | 3 | 4 | 5 | 6 | 7 | 8 | 9 | 10 | 11 | 12 / 14 / 15 | |
|---|---|---|---|---|---|---|---|---|---|---|---|---|
| ahavan | Betsy | Timothy | Goddard | Sutton | Smith | Ellis | Bolt | Payne | West | Steele | McAree, Kamara, French | 1 |
| ahavan | Timothy | Betsy | Goddard | Sutton | Smith | Bolt | Ellis | West | Payne | Steele | Kamara, McAree, French | 2 |
| ahavan | Betsy | Timothy | Goddard | Sutton | Saunders | Bolt | Taylor | Hay | Payne | Steele | Ellis, Smith, Kamara | 3 |
| ahavan | Betsy | Kamara | Saunders | Sutton | Danzey | Bolt | Turner | Hay | Payne | Steele | Ellis, Timothy, Goddard | 4 |
| ahavan | Kamara | Smith | Saunders | Sutton | Danzey | Bolt | Taylor | Hay | Betsy | Steele | Payne, Goddard, McAree | 5 |
| ahavan | Taylor | Smith | Saunders | Sutton | Danzey | Bolt | Ellis | Hay | Betsy | Steele | Payne, Goddard, McAree | 6 |
| ahavan | Betsy | Smith | Saunders | Goddard | Danzey | Bolt | Taylor | Hay | West | Steele | Payne, Ellis, Timothy | 7 |
| Batty | French | Taylor | Goddard | Smith | Danzey | Bolt | Ellis | Hay | West | Steele | Saunders, Kamara, Payne | 8 |
| Batty | Statham | Taylor | Goddard | Smith | Danzey | Bolt | Ellis | Steele | West | Hay | French, Payne, Saunders | 9 |
| Batty | Statham | Taylor | Goddard | Smith | Danzey | Bolt | Ellis | Steele | West | Hay | French, Payne, Saunders | 10 |
| Batty | Taylor | Statham | Goddard | Smith | Danzey | Bolt | Ellis | Steele | West | French | Hay, Payne, Saunders | 11 |
| Batty | Taylor | Hollingdale | Goddard | Smith | Danzey | Bolt | Ellis | Steele | West | Statham | Girdle, French, Hay | 12 |
| Batty | Taylor | Hollingdale | Goddard | Smith | Girdler | Bolt | Ellis | Steele | West | Statham | Saunders, Hay, French | 13 |
| Batty | Statham | Hollingdale | Goddard | Smith | Danzey | Girdler | Ellis | Steele | West | Hay | Bolt, Saunders, French | 14 |
| Batty | Payne | Hollingdale | Saunders | Smith | Danzey | Girdler | Perkins | Steele | West | Hay | Bolt, Goddard, French | 15 |
| Batty | Perkins | Hollingdale | Saunders | Smith | Danzey | Girdler | Ellis | Payne | West | Bolt | French, Alighieri, Hay | 16 |
| Batty | Perkins | Hollingdale | Saunders | Smith | Danzey | Girdler | Ellis | Payne | West | Bolt | French, Alighieri, Coward | 17 |
| Batty | Perkins | Hollingdale | Saunders | Smith | Danzey | Gridelet | Ellis | Payne | West | Bolt | Hay, Girdler, Steele | 18 |
| Batty | Perkins | Hollingdale | Saunders | Smith | Danzey | Gridelet | Girdler | Payne | West | Steele | Ellis, Hay, Bolt | 19 |
| Batty | Perkins | Hollingdale | Saunders | Smith | Danzey | Girdler | Ellis | Payne | West | Bolt | Hay, Taylor, French | 20 |
| Batty | Perkins | Hollingdale | Saunders | Smith | Danzey | Girdler | Ellis | Payne | West | Bolt | Hay, Taylor, French | 21 |
| Batty | Perkins | Taylor | Saunders | Smith | Danzey | Girdler | Ellis | Payne | West | Bolt | French, Hay, Coward | 22 |
| Batty | French | Taylor | Saunders | Smith | Danzey | Girdler | Ellis | Payne | West | Bolt | Hay, Perkins, Alighieri | 23 |
| Batty | Taylor | Hollingdale | Saunders | Smith | Danzey | Perkins | Ellis | Payne | Hay | Steele | Bolt, West, Girdler | 24 |
| Batty | Taylor | Hollingdale | Saunders | Smith | Danzey | Girdler | Gridelet | Payne | Hay | Steele | Ellis, Perkins, West | 25 |
| Batty | Taylor | Hollingdale | Saunders | Smith | Danzey | Girdler | Gridelet | Payne | Hay | Steele | West, Ellis, Perkins | 26 |
| Batty | Taylor | Hollingdale | Saunders | Smith | Danzey | Ellis | Gridelet | Payne | Hay | Steele | Perkins, West, Coward | 27 |
| Batty | Perkins | Hollingdale | Saunders | Smith | West | Ellis | Gridelet | Payne | Hay | Steele | Bolt, Coward, Girdler | 28 |
| Batty | Perkins | Hollingdale | Saunders | Smith | Danzey | Girdler | Ellis | Payne | Hay | Bolt | Steele, Aligieri, Coward | 29 |
| Batty | Ellis | Hollingdale | Saunders | Smith | Danzey | Girdler | Gridelet | Payne | Hay | Steele | West, Alighieri, Coward | 30 |
| Batty | Ellis | Hollingdale | Saunders | Smith | Danzey | Girdler | Gridelet | Payne | Hay | Steele | Perkins, West, Bolt | 31 |
| Batty | Ellis | Hollingdale | Saunders | Smith | Danzey | Perkins | Gridelet | Payne | West | Bolt | Steele, Girdler, Goddard | 32 |
| Batty | Perkins | Hollingdale | Saunders | Smith | Danzey | Gridelet | Girdler | Payne | West | Bolt | Steele, Hay, Goddard | 33 |
| Batty | Perkins | Hollingdale | Saunders | Smith | West | Ellis | Gridelet | Payne | Hay | Bolt | Girdler, Steele, Goddard | 34 |
| Batty | Perkins | Hollingdale | Saunders | Girdler | Danzey | Ellis | Gridelet | Payne | West | Steele | Bolt, Hay, Goddard | 35 |
| Batty | Perkins | Hollingdale | Saunders | Smith | Danzey | Girdler | Gridelet | Payne | Hay | Bolt | Ellis, Panter, Goddard | 36 |
| ahavan | Perkins | Hollingdale | Saunders | Smith | Danzey | Girdler | Gridelet | Payne | Hay | Bolt | Ellis, Coward, Goddard | 37 |
| ahavan | Perkins | Hollingdale | Saunders | Smith | Danzey | Girdler | Gridelet | Payne | Hay | Bolt | Steele, West, Ellis | 38 |
| ahavan | Perkins | Steele | Saunders | Smith | Danzey | Girdler | Gridelet | Payne | Hay | Bolt | Ellis, West, Coward | 39 |
| ahavan | Kamara | Hollingdale | Goddard | Smith | Danzey | Girdler | Ellis | Coward | West | Bolt | Steele, Panter, Alighieri | 40 |
| ahavan | Ellis | Hollingdale | Saunders | Smith | Goddard | Girdler | Gridelet | Payne | Hay | Bolt | Steele, Perkins, Kamara | 41 |
| ahavan | Perkins | Hollingdale | Saunders | Smith | Goddard | Girdler | Ellis | Payne | Hay | Bolt | West, Kamara, Steele | 42 |

League Attendances  
CONFERENCE: 7th

**HIGHEST:** 3772  
**FA CUP:** 1st Round

**LOWEST:** 1453  
**FA TROPHY:** 5th Round

# MANAGER
## BRIAN MCDERMOTT

Date of Appointment

Date of Birth     8th April 1961
Place of Birth     Slough

PREVIOUS CLUBS
As manager     Slough Town
As coach     None
As player     Arsenal, Oxford Utd., Cardiff C., Exeter C.,
Yeovil T., South China (H.K.), Marlow, Stamco.

HONOURS
As manager     None
As player     England: Youth International

## 1998-99

**Top Scorer:**     Darren Hay

**Player of the Year:**     R Hollingdale

**Captain:**     Michael Danzey

## FOOTBALL MANAGEMENT TEAM

Assistant Manager/Coach:     Brian Finn

Assistant Manager:     Kevin Hill

Reserve Team Manager:     David Vaughan

Youth Team Manager:     Ian Burns

Physio:     Barry Kimber

Top: Brian McDermott
Photo: Eric Marsh

Far left: Darren Hay
Photo: Garry Letts

Left: (L-R) Nassim
Akrour, Steve West,
Darren Hay, Grant Payne

# MATCHDAY PROGRAMME

Number of pages     40

Price     £1.30

Programme Editor     Paul Beard

Other club publications:

"Winning isn't Everything" (fanzine)

Local Newspapers:     Woking News & Mail
Woking Herald
Surrey Advertiser
Local Radio Stations:     BBC Surrey Sussex
County Sound
BBC Southern Counties

# PLAYING SQUAD

| Player | Birthplace Honours | D.O.B. | Previous Clubs |
|---|---|---|---|
| **GOALKEEPERS** | | | |
| **Laurence Batty** **ESP, FAT, ILP** | Westminster | 15.2.64 | Maidenhead U, Fulham, Brentford, Farense (Belg) |
| Darryl Flahavan | | | Southampton |
| **DEFENDERS** | | | |
| Stuart Girdler | | | Fulham |
| Wayne Sutton | Derby | 1.10.75 | Derby Co |
| **Michael Danzey** | **Widnes** | **8.2.71** | **Nottingham Forest, Peterborough U, St.Albans C, Cambridge U, Aylesbury U, £15,000 to Woking** |
| Eddie Saunders | London | | Civil Service, Sutton U, Yeading, Carshalton Ath |
| Richard Goddard | Burnt Oak | 31.3.78 | Arsenal, Brentford, ´'7,500 to Woking |
| Scott Smith New Zealand Int. | Christchurch | 6.3.75 | Rotherham U, Kettering T |
| Peter Smith | Stone | 12.07.69 | Alma Swanley, Brighton. |
| Robert Smith | | | Wycombe Wanderers, Chesham United, Slough Town, Yeovil Town |
| **MIDFIELDERS** | | | |
| Danny Bolt | | | Fulham, Slough Town £15,000 to Woking |
| Scott Steele **FAT(3), SS** | Motherwell | 19.9.71 | Airdrie |
| Grant Payne | Woking | 25.12.75 | Wimbledon |
| **Phil Gridelet** **ESP** | | | **Hendon, £175,000 to Barnsley,Southend United, Stevenage Borough.** |
| Darron Wilkinson | Reading | 24.11.69 | Wokingham Town, Brighton & Hove Albion, Kui Tan (H.K.), Hayes |
| Steve Perkins | Southport | 05.11.75 | Plymouth argyle, Stevenage Borough £10,000 to Woking |
| **FORWARDS** | | | |
| Ronell Coward | | | Youth Team |
| Steve West | Essex | 15.11.72 | Arsenal, Purfleet, Tilbury, Aveley, East Thurrock U, Concord R, Enfield, £35,000 to Woking |
| Darran Hay **FAT** | Hitchin | 17.12.69 | Biggleswade T, Cambridge U |
| Nassim Akrour **FAT** | | | Olympic Noisy-Lesee (France), Sutton United |

*Bold print indicates England semi-professional Internaionals*

*Departures: Desmond Boateng, Andy Ellis (Worcester City), Steve French (Egham), Ben Kamara (Aldershot), David Timothy, Robin Taylor.*

# WOKING

**Founded:** 1889

**Nickname:** The Cards

**Club colours:** Red & white halved shirts & black shorts

**Change colours:** Yellow and navy

**Reserve team's league:** Capital League

**Midweek home matchday:** Tuesday 7.45pm.

**Club Sponsors:** Woking Borough Council

**Local Newspapers:** Woking News & Mail
Woking Herald
Surrey Advertiser

**Local Radio:** BBC Surrey Sussex
County Sound; BBC Southern Counties

## GROUND DETAILS

Kingfield Stadium,
Kingfield,
Woking,
Surrey. GU22 9AA.

**Telephone Number:** 01483 772470

**Simple Directions:**
M25 J10 or 11, signposted from outskirts of Town. Ground 1 mile. Woking B.R. Station & buses from Woking.

**Capacity:** 6,000
**Seated:** 2,500
**Terracing -** **Covered:** 1,400
**Uncovered:** 2,100

**SOCIAL FACILITIES:**
Clubhouse open on matchdays. Food available.

**CLUB SHOP:** Phone 01483 772470 for details.

## PREVIOUS

**Leagues:** Isthmian 1911-92

**Grounds:** Wheatsheaf, Ivy Lane (pre 1923)

## CLUB RECORDS

**Attendance:** 6,000
v Swansea, FA Cup - 1978/79
v Coventry C., FA Cup - 1996-97

**Win:** 17-4 v Farnham, 1912-13

**Defeat:** 0-16 v New Crusaders, 1905-06

**Career Goalscorer:** C Mortimore 331, 1953-65

**Career Appearances:** B Finn 564, 1962-74

**Transfer Fees**
**Paid:** £30,000 for Justin Jackson (Morecambe) - 1996
**Received:** £150,000 for Steve Foster (Bristol Rovers) - May 1997

## BEST SEASON

**FA Cup:** 4th Round 90-91,
0-1 v Everton (H)
League clubs defeated: West Brom. Alb.,
Cambridge U., Millwall (96-97)

**FA Trophy:** Winners 93-94, 94-95, 96-97.

**FA Amateur Cup:** Winners 75-58

## HONOURS

FA Trophy 93-94, 94-95, 96-97
FA Amateur Cup 57-58
GM VauxhallConference R-up 94-95, 95-96
Isthmian League: 91-92, R-up 56-57
Div.2 South 86-87
Isthmian Lge Cup: 90-91, R-up 89-90
Surrey Senior Cup: 12-13, 26-27, 55-56,
56-57, 71-72, 90-91, 93-94, 95-96;
London Senior Cup R-up 82-83
Isthmian League Charity Shield 91-92, 92-93
Vauxhall Championship Shield 94-95, R-up 95-96.

## Past Players who progressed to the Football League

Ray Elliott (M'wall 46), Charlie Mortimore (A'shot 49), Robert Edwards (Chelsea 51), Ron Newman (Portsmouth 55), Mervyn Gill (Southampton 56),John Mortimore (Chelsea 51), Reg Stratton (Fulham 59), George Harris (Newport Co. 61), Norman Cashmore (A'shot 63), Alan Morton (C. Palace 67), William Holmes (Millwall 70), Richard Forbes (Exeter 79), Kevin Rattray (Gillingham 95), Steve Foster (Bristol Rov. 97), Justin Jackson (Notts Co. 98).

# YEOVIL TOWN

Manager Colin Lippiatt's biggest pre season worry last year was how to improve his side's poor away form of the previous season.

This he did magnificently as Yeovil finished with the best away record in the competition and if they had only salvaged half the points lost at home, they could have won the championship by the end of March!

An excellent season saw The Glovers beat Northampton Town and finish up as the last surviving non-league club in the F.A.Cup when they took Cardiff City to extra time in their Third Round Replay

A last minute free kick knocked them out of The F.A.Trophy at Kingstonian at the 5th Round stage, and they were in and out of the promotion race all season as great away results lifted them, before disappointing homer results brought them down again.

## CLUB OFFICIALS 1999-2000

| | |
|---|---|
| Chairman | **John Fry** |
| President | **S N Burfield M.B.E.** |
| Company Secretary | **G R Smith** |
| Club Secretary | **Jean Cotton** |
| c/o the club. | 01935 423662 (Tel) 473956 (Fax) |
| Commercial Manager | **Alan Skirton** |

Warren Patmore enjoyed a great season which earned him a regular England place with Murray Fishlock and Steve Stott (the most capped current semi-professional internbational) also playing for their country.

Possibly the mid season signings could have achieved more with two very unbusinesslike deals bringing in Steve McGrath (£6,000 for two games and a quick departure and Darren Keeling who arrived early in the campaign cost £15,000 and only started 12 games, was transfer listed but not sold.

New players arriving in the close season look impressive however, and if the potentially brilliant Ben Smith hits form there should be another exciting and successful seasson for Yeovil -providing they can win at Huish Park.

Back Row: Paul Steele, Terry Skiverton, Dean Chandler, Tony Pennock, Darren Keeling (now Gloucester City), Matt Hayfield, Ben Smith
Middle Row: Pete Smith, Dave Norton, Jason Eaton, Jamie Pitman, Phil Simpson, Adrian Foster, Tony Pounder, Kevan Brown, Rob Cousins
Front Row: Dave Piper, Steve Thompson, Murray Fishlock, Colin Lippiatt (Coach), Steve Stott, Terry Cotton (Assistant Coach), Warren Patmore

# YEOVIL TOWN
## MATCH FACTS 1998-99

| No | Date | Venue | Comp | Opponents | Att | Result | Score | Goalscorers |
|----|------|-------|------|-----------|-----|--------|-------|-------------|
| 1 | 15/08 | A | NC | Kettering Town | 1754 | W | 2-1 | Pickard 22 55 |
| 2 | 18/08 | H | NC | Kingstonian | 2339 | L | 1-3 | Dale 32 |
| 3 | 22/08 | H | NC | Hednesford Town | 2008 | L | 1-2 | Patmore 49 |
| 4 | 25/08 | A | NC | Hayes | 692 | D | 1-1 | Pounder 49 |
| 5 | 29/08 | A | NC | Dover Athletic | 1154 | W | 2-1 | Thompson 67, Mitten 70[og] |
| 6 | 31/08 | H | NC | Kidderminster Harriers | 2112 | W | 3-1 | Patmore 10 57, B Smith 36 |
| 7 | 05/09 | H | NC | Rushden & Diamonds | 2876 | L | 0-1 | |
| 8 | 08/09 | A | NC | Welling United | 531 | W | 2-1 | Pickard 62, Hannigan 85 |
| 9 | 12/09 | H | NC | Northwich Victoria | 2075 | L | 1-2 | Dale 79 |
| 10 | 14/09 | A | NC | Stevenage Borough | 2483 | D | 1-1 | Patmore 66 |
| 11 | 19/09 | A | NC | Woking | 2581 | D | 0-0 | |
| 12 | 26/09 | H | NC | Doncaster Rovers | 2300 | D | 2-2 | Dale 70, Pickard 82 |
| 13 | 29/09 | A | NC | Telford United | 757 | D | 2-2 | Stott 33, Hayfield 44 |
| 14 | 03/10 | A | NC | Hereford United | 2410 | W | 1-0 | Thompson 18 |
| 15 | 10/10 | H | NC | Cheltenham Town | 2955 | D | 2-2 | Stott 40, Patmore 84 |
| 16 | 07/11 | A | NC | Kidderminster Harriers | 2007 | W | 1-0 | Patmore 19 |
| 17 | 17/11 | H | NC | Kettering Town | 1718 | W | 2-1 | Keeling 16 75 |
| 18 | 28/11 | H | NC | Dover Athletic | 2211 | D | 1-1 | Patmore 32 |
| 19 | 12/12 | A | NC | Kingstonian | 1017 | D | 0-0 | |
| 20 | 19/12 | H | NC | Telford United | 2253 | W | 4-0 | Keeling 49, Hannigan 57 64, Patmore 86 |
| 21 | 28/12 | H | NC | Farnborough Town | 2924 | W | 6-3 | Patmore 17 84 87, Thompson 30, Stott 52 66 |
| 22 | 09/01 | A | NC | Southport | 929 | W | 3-2 | Hannigan 54, Keeling 64, Dale 86 |
| 23 | 23/01 | H | NC | Barrow | 2588 | W | 1-0 | Keeling 74 |
| 24 | 26/01 | H | NC | Forest Green Rovers | 2437 | L | 0-4 | |
| 25 | 30/01 | A | NC | Morecambe | 1254 | D | 1-1 | Patmore 47 |
| 26 | 13/02 | A | NC | Doncaster Rovers | 4413 | W | 2-0 | Patmore 3, Pickard 59 |
| 27 | 16/02 | H | NC | Woking | 2465 | L | 0-1 | |
| 28 | 20/02 | A | NC | Barrow | 1202 | L | 0-2 | |
| 29 | 13/03 | H | NC | Hereford United | 2263 | W | 3-0 | Pickard 55, Fishlock 56, Cross 59[og] |
| 30 | 17/03 | A | NC | Forest Green Rovers | 860 | W | 2-1 | Thompson 52, Patmore 88 |
| 31 | 20/03 | A | NC | Hednesford Town | 908 | W | 3-2 | Pickard 41 77, Patmore 44 |
| 32 | 23/03 | H | NC | Southport | 2158 | W | 3-1 | Pickard 20, Patmore 41, Fishlock 80 |
| 33 | 27/03 | H | NC | Hayes | 2560 | D | 1-1 | Pickard 5 |
| 34 | 03/04 | H | NC | Welling United | 2903 | L | 1-3 | Appleton 86 |
| 35 | 05/04 | A | NC | Farnborough Town | 870 | D | 0-0 | |
| 36 | 13/04 | A | NC | Rushden & Diamonds | 2367 | W | 2-1 | Patmore 26, Piper 30 |
| 37 | 17/04 | H | NC | Leek Town | 2442 | W | 2-0 | Patmore 30, Smith 58 |
| 38 | 22/04 | A | NC | Cheltenham Town | 6150 | L | 2-3 | Pickard 2, Patmore 47[p] |
| 39 | 24/04 | A | NC | Northwich Victoria | 1150 | W | 2-1 | Patmore 56, Pounder 90 |
| 40 | 27/04 | H | NC | Morecambe | 1966 | L | 0-1 | |
| 41 | 29/04 | A | NC | Leek Town | 253 | W | 4-2 | Chandler 10, Franklin 20 58, Cousins 30 |
| 42 | 01/05 | H | NC | Stevenage Borough | 2936 | L | 1-3 | Stott 52 |

**CUP COMPETITIONS**

| | Date | Venue | Comp | Opponents | Att | Result | Score | Goalscorers |
|--|------|-------|------|-----------|-----|--------|-------|-------------|
| | 13/10 | A | Som. PC 1 | Paulton Rovers | 395 | L | 1 - 2 | B Smith 82 |
| | 17/10 | A | FA Cup Q3 | Hastings Town | 1156 | W | 3 - 0 | Patmore 27, Hannigan 45, Hayfield 72[p] |
| | 01/11 | A | FA Cup Q4 | Farnborough Town | 1396 | W | 3 - 1 | Piper 40, Hayfield 51, Patmore 69 |
| | 14/11 | H | FA Cup 1 | West Auckland Town | 3203 | D | 2 - 2 | Patmore 39, Hannigan 90 |
| | 21/11 | H | FA Trophy 2 | Tonbridge Angels | 1525 | W | 1 - 0 | Pounder 45 |
| | 24/11 | A | FA Cup 1 rep | West Auckland Town | 2164 | W | 1 - 1 | Dale 72  (5-3 pens) |
| | 01/12 | A | Endsleigh 2 | Woking | 580 | L | 0-3 | |
| | 05/12 | H | FA Cup 2 | Northampton Town | 5218 | W | 2 - 0 | Thompson 14, Patmore 82 |
| | 02/01 | A | FA Cup 3 | Cardiff City | 12561 | D | 1 - 1 | Dale 54 |
| | 12/01 | H | FA Cup 3 rep | Cardiff City | 8101 | L | 1 - 2 | Hayfield 86 |
| | 16/01 | A | FA Trophy 3 | Basingstoke Town | 1617 | W | 2 - 0 | Pickard 50, Dale 80 |
| | 06/02 | H | FA Trophy 4 | Hinckley United | 2351 | W | 3 - 2 | Patmore 6 68, Pickard 16 |
| | 27/02 | A | FA Trophy 5 | Kingstonian | 1783 | L | 0 - 1 | |

| 1 | 2 | 3 | 4 | 5 | 6 | 7 | 8 | 9 | 10 | 11 | 12 14 15 | |
|---|---|---|---|---|---|---|---|---|----|----|----------|---|
| Pennock | Pitman | Fishlock | Brown | Hannigan | Cousins | Thompson | Stott | Patmore | Pickard | Smith | Dale, Pounder, Piper | 1 |
| Pennock | Pitman | Fishlock | K Brown | Hannigan | Cousins | Thompson | Stott | Patmore | Pickard | Smith | Piper, Dale, Pounder | 2 |
| Pennock | Pounder | Fishlock | Brown | Hannigan | Thompson | Cousins | Stott | Patmore | Dale | B Smith | Birkby, R Smith, Piper | 3 |
| Pennock | Pounder | Fishlock | Brown | Hannigan | Cousins | Thompson | Stott | Patmore | R Smith | B Smith | Dale, Piper, Parmenter | 4 |
| Pennock | Pounder | Fishlock | Brown | Hannigan | Cousins | Thompson | Stott | Patmore | R Smith | B Smith | Dale, Piper, Parmenter | 5 |
| Pennock | Pounder | Fishlock | Brown | Hannigan | Cousins | Thompson | Stott | Patmore | R Smith | B Smith | Parmenter, Piper, Dale | 6 |
| Pennock | Pounder | Fishlock | Brown | Hannigan | Cousins | Thompson | Stott | Patmore | R Smith | B Smith | Dale, Piper, Pickard | 7 |
| Pennock | Pounder | Fishlock | Brown | Hannigan | Cousins | Thompson | Stott | Patmore | R Smith | B Smith | Piper, Pickard, Dale | 8 |
| Pennock | Piper | Fishlock | Brown | Hannigan | R Smith | Thompson | Stott | Patmore | Pickard | B Smith | Cousins, Dale, Pounder | 9 |
| Pennock | Piper | Fishlock | Brown | Hannigan | Cousins | Thompson | Stott | Patmore | Pounder | B Smith | Dale, Pickard, Parmenter | 10 |
| Pennock | Piper | Fishlock | Brown | Hannigan | Cousins | Thompson | Stott | Patmore | McGrath | B Smith | Pickard, Pounder, Dale | 11 |
| Pennock | Hayfield | Fishlock | Brown | Hannigan | Cousins | McGrath | Stott | Patmore | Pickard | B Smith | Winstone, Dale, Piper | 12 |
| Pennock | Piper | Fishlock | Brown | Hannigan | Cousins | Thompson | Stott | Patmore | Pickard | Hayfield | Dale, Winstone, B Smith | 13 |
| Pennock | Piper | Fishlock | Brown | Hannigan | Cousins | Thompson | Stott | Dale | Pickard | Hayfield | Franklin, B Smith, Davey | 14 |
| Pennock | Piper | Fishlock | Brown | Hannigan | Cousins | Thompson | Stott | Patmore | Dale | Hayfield | Winstone, Franklin, B Smith | 15 |
| Pennock | Pounder | Fishlock | Brown | Hannigan | Cousins | Thompson | Stott | Patmore | Keeling | Hayfield | Dale, B Smith, Pounder | 16 |
| Pennock | Piper | Fishlock | Brown | Hannigan | Cousins | Thompson | Stott | Patmore | Keeling | Hayfield | Piper, B Smith, Dale | 17 |
| Pennock | Piper | Fishlock | Brown | Hannigan | Cousins | Thompson | Pounder | Patmore | Keeling | Chandler | B Smith, Pitman, Dale | 18 |
| Pennock | Piper | Fishlock | Brown | Hannigan | Cousins | Thompson | Stott | Patmore | Keeling | Pitman | B Smith, Chandler, Dale | 19 |
| Pennock | Piper | Fishlock | Brown | Hannigan | Cousins | Thompson | Stott | Patmore | Keeling | B Smith | Chandler, Pounder, Dale | 20 |
| Pennock | Piper | Fishlock | Brown | Hannigan | Cousins | Thompson | Stott | Patmore | Keeling | B Smith | Pounder, Hayfield, Dale | 21 |
| Pennock | Piper | Fishlock | Hayfield | Hannigan | Cousins | Thompson | Stott | Patmore | Keeling | B Smith | Dale, Pounder, Chandler | 22 |
| Pennock | Piper | Pounder | Brown | Hannigan | Cousins | Thompson | Stott | Keeling | Pickard | Hayfield | B Smith, Patmore, Pitman | 23 |
| Pennock | Piper | Pitman | Brown | Hannigan | Cousins | Thompson | B Smith | Dale | Pickard | Hayfield | Keeling, Chandler, Pounder | 24 |
| Pennock | Piper | Pounder | Brown | Hannigan | Cousins | Thompson | Stott | Patmore | Pickard | B Smith | Pitman, Keeling, Chandler | 25 |
| Pennock | Piper | Fishlock | Brown | Hannigan | Cousins | Thompson | Stott | Patmore | Pickard | Pitman | Chandler, Dale, B Smith | 26 |
| Pennock | Piper | Fishlock | Brown | Hannigan | Cousins | Thompson | Stott | Patmore | Pickard | Pounder | Dale  B Smith  Chandler | 27 |
| Pennock | Piper | Fishlock | Brown | Hannigan | Cousins | Thompson | Stott | Patmore | Pickard | Simpson | Keeling, Chandler, B Smith | 28 |
| Pennock | Piper | Fishlock | Brown | Hannigan | Cousins | Thompson | Chandler | Patmore | Pickard | Simpson | Pounder, Keeling, B Smith | 29 |
| Pennock | Piper | Fishlock | Brown | Hannigan | Cousins | Thompson | Chandler | Patmore | Pickard | Simpson | Stott, Keeling, B Smith | 30 |
| Pennock | Piper | Fishlock | Brown | Hannigan | Chandler | Thompson | Stott | Patmore | Pickard | Simpson | B Smith, Keeling, Pounder | 31 |
| Pennock | Piper | Fishlock | Chandler | Hannigan | Cousins | Thompson | Stott | Patmore | Pickard | Simpson | Keeling, Smith, Pounder | 32 |
| Pennock | Piper | Fishlock | Chandler | Steele | Cousins | Thompson | Stott | Patmore | Pickard | Simpson | B Smith, Pounder, Keeling | 33 |
| Rigby | Piper | Pounder | Brown | Hannigan | Chandler | Thompson | Stott | Patmore | Pickard | Simpson | Keeling, Tomkin  Appleton | 34 |
| Rigby | Piper | Fishlock | Chandler | Hannigan | Cousins | Thompson | Stott | Keeling | Pickard | Simpson | B Smith, Appleton, Tomkin | 35 |
| Rigby | Piper | Fishlock | Brown | Hannigan | Cousins | Thompson | Stott | Patmore | Pickard | Chandler | Simpson, B Smith, Keeling | 36 |
| Rigby | Piper | Fishlock | Brown | Steele | Cousins | Chandler | Hayfield | Patmore | Keeling | Smith | Pounder, Appleton, Groves | 37 |
| Pennock | Piper | Fishlock | Brown | Steele | Cousins | Chandler | Hayfield | Patmore | Pickard | Smith | Simpson, Keeling, Pounder | 38 |
| Rigby | Piper | Fishlock | Brown | Hannigan | Cousins | Hayfield | Chandler | Patmore | Smith | Simpson | Keeling, Steele, Pounder | 39 |
| Pennock | Piper | Tomkin | Brown | Hannigan | Cousins | Chandler | Hayfield | Patmore | Smith | Pounder | Simpson, R Smith, Franklin | 40 |
| Pennock | Piper | Fishlock | Brown | Chandler | Cousins | Hayfield | Stott | Patmore | Franklin | Simpson | R Smith, Pounder, Smith | 41 |
| Pennock | Piper | Fishlock | Brown | Hannigan | Cousins | Chandler | Stott | Patmore | Franklin | Hayfield | Pounde, Smith, Simpson | 42 |

League Attendances         **HIGHEST:** 2955         **LOWEST:** 1718

**CONFERENCE:** 5th         **FA CUP:** 3rd Round         **FA TROPHY:** 5th Round

## HEAD COACH

### COLIN LIPPIATT

| | |
|---|---|
| Date of Appointment | February 1998 |
| Date of Birth: | 1st January 1942 |
| Place of Birth: | Hayes |

**PREVIOUS CLUBS**

| | |
|---|---|
| As asst. manager/coach | Windsor & Eton, Farnbrough Town, Woking, Kingstonian |
| As player | Hayes, Wokingham & Maidenhead |

**HONOURS**

| | |
|---|---|
| As asst. manager/coach | (Woking) FA Trophy 94, 95, 97, Conf R-up 95, 96; (Windsor & Eton) Athenian Lge (2); FA Vase S-F & Q-F |
| As player | None |

## FOOTBALL MANAGEMENT TEAM

| | |
|---|---|
| Assistant Coach | Terry Cotton |
| Player/Coach: | Steve Thompson |
| Physio: | Peter Smith |
| Youth Development: | Stuart Housley |

### 1998-99

| | |
|---|---|
| **Top Scorer:** | Warren Patmore |
| **Player of the Year:** | Murray Fishlock |
| **Supporters P.o.Y** | Warren Patmore |
| **Captain:** | Steve Stott |

Left: Colin Lippiatt
Right: Talented Yeovil player Ben Smith takes on Tonbridge Angels defenders. Photo: Ken Gregory

## MATCHDAY PROGRAMME

| | |
|---|---|
| Number of pages | 48 |
| Price | £1.50 |
| Programme Editor | Bryan Moore |

| | |
|---|---|
| Other club publications: | "100 Huish Heroes" £3 Centenary Book £14.99 (Both available from the club) |
| Local Newspapers: | Western Gazette Western Daily Press Bristol Evening Post; Sunday Independent |
| Local Radio Stations: | Radio Bristol Somerset Sound Orchard FM |

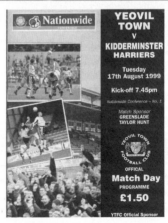

# PLAYING SQUAD

| Player | Birthplace Honours | D.O.B. | Previous Clubs |
|---|---|---|---|
| **GOALKEEPERS** | | | |
| Tony Pennock ILP | Swansea | 10.4.71 | Stockport Co, Wigan A, Hereford U |
| **DEFENDERS** | | | |
| **Kevan Brown** FAT, Div 3 | **Andover** | **25.6.68** | **Southampton, Brighton & H.A., Aldershot, Woking, £7,500 to Yeovil T** |
| Rob Cousins ILP,F.A.XI | Bristol | 9.1.71 | Bristol C, Bath C, ¨£15,000 to Yeovil T |
| **Murray Fishlock** | **Marlborough** | **23.9.73** | **Swindon T, Gloucester C, Trowbridge T, Hereford U.** |
| Dean Chandler | London | 05.06.7 | Charlton Athletic, Torquay United, Lincoln City |
| David Piper | Bournemouth | 31.10.77 | Southampton |
| Terry Skivington | Mile End | 26.06.75 | Chelsea, Wycombe Wanderers,Welling United |
| Jamie Pitman | Trowbridge | 06.01.76 | Swindon Town, Hereford United. |
| Paul Steel | | | Chippenham Town |
| **MIDFIELDERS** | | | |
| David Norton Conf. | Cannock | 03,03,65 | Aston Villa, Notts Co,Hull City,Northampton Town, Cheltenham T. |
| Ben Smith | Chelmsford | 23.11.78 | Arsenal, Reading |
| **Steve Stott** SLP | **Leeds** | **03.02.65** | **Alvechurch, Bromsgrove R, £18,000 to Kettering T, £30,000 to Rushden & D, £9,000 toYeovil T** |
| **Steve Thompson** ESP, GMVC, FAT, ILP | **Plymouth** | **12.01.63** | **Bristol C, Torquay U, Saltash U, Slough T, Wycombe W, Woking, £5,000 to Yeovil T** |
| Matt Hayfield | | | Bristol Rovers |
| Phil Simpson | Lambeth | 10.19.69 | Stevenage Borough, Barnet |
| Tony Pounder ILP | Yeovil | 11.03.66 | Weymouth , Bristol Rovers, Hereford Unitedl |
| **FORWARDS** | | | |
| Jason Eaton F.A.XI, F.A.T.Conf. | Bristol | 29.01.69 | Bristol Rovers, Clevedon Town,Trowbridge Town, Bristol City, Gloucester City, Cheltenham Town £15,000 toYeovil Town. |
| Adrian Foster | Kidderminster | 19.03.71 | W.B.A., Torquay united,£60,000 to Gillingham, Hereford United, Rushden & Diamonds |
| **Warren Patmore** ILP | **Kingsbury** | **14.08.71** | **Northwood, Cambridge U, Millwall, Northampton T, Ards** |

**Bold print indicates England Semi-Professional Internationals**
Departures:Owen Pickard (Dorchester Town), Al James Hannigan (Slough Town),Robert Smith (Woking) , Darren Keeling (Gloucester City),Dean Birkby (Forest Green Rovers), Carl Dale (Newport AFC)

# YEOVIL TOWN

| | |
|---|---|
| Nickname: | Glovers |
| Sponsors: | gateway Computing |
| Club Colours: | Green & white shirts |
| | white shorts & green socks |
| Change Colours: | Navy & red quartered shirts |
| | navy shorts & navy socks |
| Midweek matchday: | Tuesday |
| Reserve League: | Screwfix Direct Western League |
| | Prem. Div |

## PREVIOUS

| | |
|---|---|
| Leagues: | Western League, London Combination, |
| | Southern League, |
| | Alliance Premier,Isthmian, |
| | GMV Conference |
| Names: | Yeovil & Petters Utd |
| Ground: | Pen Mill ground 1895-1921, Huish 1921-1990 |

## GROUND DETAILS

Huish Park,
Lufton Way,
Yeovil
Somerset, BA22 8YF

| | |
|---|---|
| TELEPHONE | 01935 423662 |
| | Fax 01935 473956 |

**SIMPLE DIRECTIONS:**
Leave A303 at Cartgate r'about, take A3088 signposted Yeovil. 1st exit at next r'about, 1st exit at next r'about into Lufton Way.
Railway station - Yeovil Pen Mill (Bristol/Westbury to Weymouth) 2.5 milesfrom ground.
Bus service from stations on Saturday

**CAPACITY:** 8,761
**SEATED:** 5,253
**COVERED TERRACING:** 3,508

**SOCIAL FACILITIES:** Matchdays hot + cold food available. Meals can be orderedprovided advance notice is given. All weather astro turf pitch available forbookings 9am-10pm

**CLUB SHOP:** Open matchdays & 10-4 weekdays, selling a full range of souvenirs, match programmes,scarves, hats, replica kits and badges

## CLUB RECORDS

| | |
|---|---|
| Attendance: | 8,612 |
| | v Arsenal 3rd Rd FA Cup 02/1/93 |
| Career Goalscorer: | Dave Taylor 285 1960-69 |
| Career Appearances: | Len Harris, 691, 1958-72 |
| Win: | 10-0 |
| | v Kidderminster Harriers (H), Southern Lge. 27.12.1955 |
| | v Bedford Town (H), Southern Lge. 4.3.61 |
| Defeat: | 0-8 |
| | v Manchester Utd., FA Cup 5th Rd. |
| | 12.2.49 at Maine Rd. (81,565) |
| Transfer Fee Paid: | £17,500 |
| | to Oxford City for Howard Forinton 1.97 |
| Transfer Fee Received: | £75,000 |
| | for Mark Shail from Bristol City |

## BEST SEASON

| | |
|---|---|
| FA Cup: | 5th Rd 1948-49 |
| | League clubs beaten: (16) |
| FA Trophy: | Semi-Final |
| | 70-71 71-72 |

## Past Players who progressed to the Football League

Over 40 players & 18 managers including,since 1985,

Nigel Jarvis (Torquay), Ian Davies (Bristol Rovers),

Alan Pardew(Crystal Palace), Paul Miller (Wimbledon)

John McGinlay (Bolton), GuyWhittingham (Portsmouth),

Mark Shail (Bristol City), Malcom McPherson (WestHam),

Howard Forinton & Jerry Gill (Birmingham City)

## HONOURS

Southern Lge 54-55, 63-64, 70-71

R-up 23-24, 31-32, 34-35, 69-70, 72-73

Southern Lge Cup 48-49, 54-55, 60-61, 65-66

Vauxhall-Opel Lge (Isthmian) 87-88, R-up 85-86, 86-87

ICIS Prem. (Isthmian) 96-97;

AC Delco Cup 87-88.

Bob Lord Trophy 89-90

R-up 93-94

# NORTHERN PREMIER LEAGUE

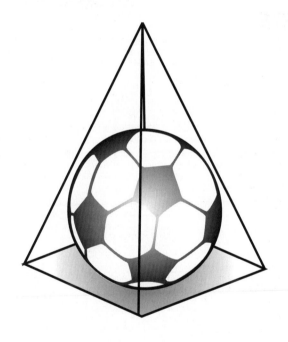

# PYRAMID SECTION

# UniBond
## NORTHERN PREMIER

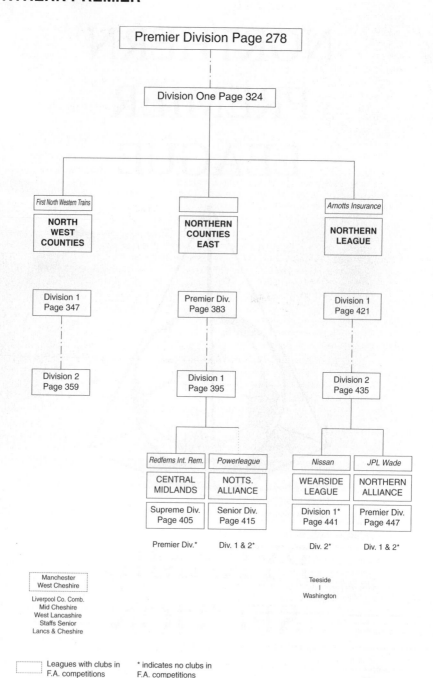

Premier Division Page 278

Division One Page 324

| *First North Western Trains* | | *Arnotts Insurance* |
|---|---|---|
| **NORTH WEST COUNTIES** | **NORTHERN COUNTIES EAST** | **NORTHERN LEAGUE** |

| Division 1 Page 347 | Premier Div. Page 383 | Division 1 Page 421 |
|---|---|---|

| Division 2 Page 359 | Division 1 Page 395 | Division 2 Page 435 |
|---|---|---|

| *Redferns Int. Rem.* | *Powerleague* | *Nissan* | *JPL Wade* |
|---|---|---|---|
| CENTRAL MIDLANDS | NOTTS. ALLIANCE | WEARSIDE LEAGUE | NORTHERN ALLIANCE |
| Supreme Div. Page 405 | Senior Div. Page 415 | Division 1* Page 441 | Premier Div. Page 447 |
| Premier Div.* | Div. 1 & 2* | Div. 2* | Div. 1 & 2* |

Manchester
West Cheshire

Liverpool Co. Comb.
Mid Cheshire
West Lancashire
Staffs Senior
Lancs & Cheshire

Teeside
|
Washington

Leagues with clubs in F.A. competitions

\* indicates no clubs in F.A. competitions

# Unibond League

**President:** N White F.S.C.A.

**Chairman:** Ken Marsden

**Secretary & Treasurer:** R D Bayley,

The two pre-season favourites for the Premier and First Division titles, Altrincham and Droylsden, both duly landed the prizes but not before both had experienced bouts of trepidation.

Indeed, Premier Division Champions Altrincham began the campaign without a victory and with just four points from eight matches to look more like relegation candidates than title favourites. However, manager Bernard Taylor's nerve held and they became the most consistent side in the Division. Although there were a few hiccups on the run-in, the Robins pulled away in the final furlong to win with a bit to spare from surprise package Worksop Town.

The newly promoted "Tigers" proved their rise in status was no fluke and despite being written off several times during the season showed they had the ability to stay the distance and they will surely be there or thereabouts again in the forthcoming campaign. Guiseley, like Altrincham, had their worst start to a campaign since joining the Unibond League but recovered well and were on course for a double until a multitude of games and a long absence through injury of leading scorer Simon Parke took their toll. The Yorkshire outfit faded to finish third and then ended with nothing to show for their efforts when losing in the UniBond League Challenge Cup Final to Stalybridge Celtic who emulated Altrincham's 1998 success in landing the Cup the season after being relegated from the Conference. Celtic will also now doubtless be hoping to again follow in the footsteps of the "Robins" and win back their Conference status!

Another club to have a successful season were Bamber Bridge who have spent most of the time since landing the title in 1996 fighting relegation. But with Tony Greenwood, who took them to that Championship success, back at the helm "Brig" finished a very creditable fourth.

At the other end of the table the club with a household name, Accrington Stanley, unfortunately went down but surely it will only be a matter of time before they bounce back. Accompanying Stanley in the drop to First Division football will be Chorley.

Droylsden spent most of the season looking for a four timer and with an enormous backlog of fixtures it was probably a blessing in disguise when they lost in the quarter-finals of the League Cup to Blyth Spartans. They did, however, lift the President's Cup at the expense of Leigh but had the disappointment of losing in the Unifilla First Division Cup Final to arch rivals Ashton United. And when they lost at Radcliffe Borough in the last week of the season the title was also out of their hands as Hucknall only had to beat Bradford Park Avenue in their final fixture to take the honours at their very first attempt. But a second half equaliser gave Avenue a share of the points leaving the spoils to Droylsden who beat Stocksbridge PS to land the title by virtue of having scored more goals than Hucknall with whom they shared the same number of points and the same goal difference!

Ashton United finished third for the second successive season but had some consolation when winning the Unifilla First Division Cup. However, finishing third and winning a cup isn't good enough to keep a manager in a job at ambitious Ashton and immediately the season had finished the Hurst Cross outfit parted company with John Coleman and installed former Altrincham boss John King.

At the bottom Alfreton Town became the second Derbyshire club in successive seasons after Buxton to nosedive straight through both Divisions and Great Harwood Town will also be relegated despite a brave fightback. In February they looked dead and buried with just thirteen points from 29 games but they took 25 points from their last thirteen games and only failed to stay up on the final day when Stuart Heeps saved a penalty for third bottom Congleton Town against Great Harwood in a relegation decider which finished 1-1.

No doubt about the Unibond League's FA Cup heroes this season with Leigh travelling to Kevin Keegan's Al Fayed backed Fulham and holding them to a draw before losing the replay in front of a capacity 7,500 crowd and Sky TV cameras. Emley maintained their fine FA Cup record by also forcing a replay with Football League outfit Rotherham United whilst Lancaster City led Northampton 1-0 until the second half of their First Round match before bowing out 2-1. Completing the quartet of UniBond representatives was Runcorn who held big spending Conference side Stevenage Borough before losing the replay.

## UNIBOND LEAGUE NEWSLINE
# 09066 555 800
Calls cost 60p per minute

# PREMIER DIVISION
## FINAL LEAGUE TABLE 1998-99

| | | P | W | D | L | F | A | W | D | L | F | A | GD | Pts |
|---|---|---|---|---|---|---|---|---|---|---|---|---|---|---|
| | | | | *Home* | | | | | *Away* | | | | | |
| 1 | Altrincham | 42 | 12 | 8 | 1 | 32 | 13 | 11 | 3 | 7 | 35 | 20 | 34 | 80 |
| 2 | Worksop Town | 42 | 16 | 3 | 2 | 37 | 15 | 6 | 7 | 8 | 29 | 33 | 18 | 76 |
| 3 | Guiseley | 42 | 15 | 3 | 3 | 41 | 17 | 6 | 6 | 9 | 23 | 30 | 17 | 72 |
| 4 | Bamber Bridge✓ | 42 | 9 | 8 | 4 | 39 | 30 | 9 | 7 | 5 | 24 | 18 | 15 | 69 |
| 5 | Gateshead | 42 | 10 | 4 | 7 | 37 | 28 | 8 | 7 | 6 | 32 | 30 | 11 | 65 |
| 6 | Gainsborough Trinity | 42 | 10 | 4 | 7 | 35 | 28 | 9 | 4 | 8 | 30 | 31 | 6 | 65 |
| 7 | Whitby Town | 42 | 10 | 4 | 7 | 38 | 29 | 7 | 9 | 5 | 39 | 33 | 15 | 64 |
| 8 | Leigh | 42 | 6 | 10 | 5 | 30 | 26 | 10 | 5 | 6 | 33 | 28 | 9 | 63 |
| 9 | Hyde United | 42 | 9 | 6 | 6 | 37 | 22 | 7 | 5 | 9 | 24 | 26 | 13 | 59 |
| 10 | Stalybridge Celtic | 42 | 13 | 5 | 3 | 43 | 23 | 3 | 6 | 12 | 28 | 40 | 8 | 59 |
| 11 | Winsford United | 42 | 6 | 8 | 7 | 26 | 27 | 8 | 7 | 6 | 30 | 25 | 4 | 57 |
| 12 | Runcorn | 42 | 6 | 8 | 7 | 21 | 25 | 6 | 11 | 4 | 25 | 24 | -3 | 55 |
| 13 | Emley | 42 | 6 | 9 | 6 | 23 | 24 | 6 | 8 | 7 | 24 | 25 | -2 | 53 |
| 14 | Blyth Spartans | 42 | 7 | 5 | 9 | 29 | 32 | 7 | 4 | 10 | 27 | 32 | -8 | 51 |
| 15 | Colwyn Bay | 42 | 6 | 6 | 9 | 27 | 32 | 6 | 7 | 8 | 33 | 39 | -11 | 49 |
| 16 | Frickley Athletic | 42 | 6 | 6 | 9 | 28 | 32 | 5 | 9 | 7 | 27 | 39 | -16 | 48 |
| 17 | Marine | 42 | 6 | 7 | 8 | 37 | 41 | 4 | 10 | 7 | 24 | 28 | -8 | 47 |
| 18 | Spennymoor United | 42 | 7 | 7 | 7 | 27 | 26 | 5 | 4 | 12 | 25 | 45 | -19 | 47 |
| 19 | Lancaster City | 42 | 7 | 7 | 7 | 28 | 25 | 4 | 6 | 11 | 22 | 37 | -12 | 46 |
| 20 | Bishop Auckland | 42 | 5 | 10 | 6 | 25 | 31 | 5 | 5 | 11 | 24 | 36 | -18 | 45 |
| 21 | Chorley | 42 | 3 | 8 | 10 | 26 | 37 | 5 | 7 | 9 | 19 | 31 | -23 | 39 |
| 22 | Accrington Stanley | 42 | 5 | 5 | 11 | 24 | 37 | 4 | 4 | 13 | 23 | 40 | -30 | 36 |

## PREMIER DIVISION LEADING GOALSCORERS
### (In order of League goals)

| Lge | Cup | Total | | |
|---|---|---|---|---|
| 26 | 10 | 36 | Tony Carroll | (Chorley - 24+10 for Radcliffe) |
| 24 | 5 | 34 | Mark Carter | (Runcorn - 19+5 for Ashton United) |
| 22 | 10 | 32 | Billy O'Callaghan | (Accrington Stanley) |
| 20 | 9 | 29 | Deiniol Graham | (Colwyn Bay) |
| 19 | 7 | 26 | John Morgan | (Marine) |
| 18 | 6 | 24 | Simon Yeo | (Hyde United) |
| 18 | 4 | 22 | Leroy Chambers | (Altrincham) |
| 17 | 7 | 24 | Peter Thomson | (Lancaster City - now NAC Breda) |
| 17 | 5 | 22 | Carl Chillingsworth | (Whitby Town) |
| 17 | 5 | 22 | Paul Heavey | (Accrington Stanley - 11+2 for Congleton Town) |
| 16 | 3 | 19 | Phil Stafford | (Worksop Town) |
| 16 | 1 | 17 | Keith Fletcher | (Blyth Spartans) |

| | | 1 | 2 | 3 | 4 | 5 | 6 | 7 | 8 | 9 | 10 | 11 | 12 | 13 | 14 | 15 | 16 | 17 | 18 | 19 | 20 | 21 | 22 |
|---|---|---|---|---|---|---|---|---|---|---|---|---|---|---|---|---|---|---|---|---|---|---|---|
| 1 | Accrington S | X | 1-4 | 0-5 | 0-1 | 1-3 | 0-0 | 1-2 | 2-0 | 1-1 | 2-1 | 1-3 | 2-0 | 1-1 | 1-1 | 1-2 | 3-2 | 1-2 | 2-3 | 2-0 | 1-1 | 0-2 | 1-3 |
| | | X | 638 | 583 | 370 | 397 | 503 | 446 | 326 | 366 | 388 | 401 | 491 | 419 | 403 | 429 | 343 | 412 | 402 | 417 | 336 | 332 | 434 |
| 2 | Altrincham | 2-1 | X | 1-1 | 0-0 | 0-0 | 4-0 | 1-1 | 1-0 | 1-1 | 1-1 | 1-0 | 1-0 | 2-1 | 1-2 | 1-0 | 4-1 | 3-0 | 2-1 | 2-1 | 1-1 | 1-1 | 2-0 |
| | | 691 | X | 780 | 872 | 843 | 606 | 680 | 1526 | 685 | 590 | 814 | 1147 | 923 | 564 | 518 | 1001 | 718 | 735 | 904 | 752 | 878 | 537 |
| 3 | Bamber Br. | 1-1 | 0-1 | X | 2-2 | 1-0 | 1-0 | 1-1 | 1-2 | 3-2 | 1-4 | 3-1 | 4-1 | 1-1 | 4-3 | 1-1 | 2-2 | 1-2 | 5-1 | 2-1 | 1-1 | 1-1 | 3-2 |
| | | 618 | 890 | X | 413 | 233 | 771 | 215 | 425 | 329 | 251 | 253 | 373 | 373 | 456 | 430 | 225 | 320 | 258 | 349 | 367 | 366 | 405 |
| 4 | Bishop Auck. | 2-1 | 2-1 | 1-1 | X | 2-2 | 0-4 | 0-1 | 1-1 | 2-1 | 2-2 | 1-0 | 0-1 | 1-1 | 0-0 | 0-2 | 2-3 | 1-1 | 3-3 | 1-1 | 0-2 | 2-1 | |
| | | 214 | 268 | 189 | X | 305 | 189 | 207 | 209 | 140 | 181 | 344 | 238 | 201 | 205 | 204 | 207 | 212 | 397 | 151 | 257 | 237 | 283 |
| 5 | Blyth Spart. | 0-1 | 0-0 | 0-1 | 2-1 | X | 0-0 | 4-0 | 0-2 | 2-2 | 0-2 | 1-2 | 4-1 | 1-2 | 1-0 | 4-1 | 2-1 | 1-1 | 4-0 | 3-2 | 0-5 | 0-3 | 0-1 |
| | | 339 | 603 | 327 | 529 | X | 366 | 365 | 380 | 263 | 382 | 1046 | 151 | 525 | 510 | 387 | 411 | 274 | 515 | 336 | 525 | 421 | 362 |
| 6 | Chorley | 4-0 | 0-2 | 0-1 | 1-3 | 0-2 | X | 1-2 | 1-1 | 1-1 | 0-2 | 2-2 | 0-2 | 1-3 | 2-0 | 3-3 | 0-2 | 1-1 | 2-2 | 2-1 | 2-2 | 2-2 | 1-3 |
| | | 354 | 454 | 661 | 236 | 272 | X | 244 | 298 | 310 | 189 | 289 | 224 | 272 | 346 | 227 | 275 | 259 | 249 | 313 | 335 | 262 | 379 |
| 7 | Colwyn Bay | 3-1 | 1-1 | 0-1 | 0-3 | 2-0 | 2-1 | X | 3-3 | 0-2 | 3-4 | 1-1 | 0-0 | 2-1 | 0-0 | 0-1 | 1-0 | 1-3 | 1-3 | 1-2 | 3-1 | 1-2 | 2-2 |
| | | 282 | 459 | 260 | 205 | 286 | 276 | X | 282 | 246 | 275 | 301 | 298 | 164 | 215 | 256 | 251 | 436 | 185 | 385 | 232 | 174 | 217 |
| 8 | Emley | 3-1 | 0-3 | 0-1 | 2-0 | 2-1 | 1-0 | 0-0 | X | 1-1 | 3-2 | 1-2 | 0-1 | 1-1 | 1-1 | 0-2 | 1-1 | 1-1 | 1-0 | 2-2 | 0-1 | 1-1 | 2-2 |
| | | 270 | 437 | 234 | 339 | 326 | 220 | 180 | X | 221 | 383 | 213 | 289 | 175 | 269 | 244 | 301 | 201 | 243 | 347 | 233 | 245 | 413 |
| 9 | Frickley Ath | 0-0 | 0-3 | 0-2 | 0-0 | 2-0 | 2-2 | 2-1 | 0-1 | X | 1-2 | 0-2 | 1-2 | 3-0 | 3-2 | 0-2 | 1-1 | 1-1 | 1-2 | 3-2 | 3-3 | 3-1 | 2-3 |
| | | 219 | 425 | 199 | 181 | 215 | 208 | 151 | 340 | X | 231 | 218 | 249 | 180 | 158 | 174 | 189 | 183 | 161 | 279 | 207 | 120 | 366 |
| 10 | Gainsboro T | 0-4 | 0-3 | 0-1 | 2-1 | 3-4 | 3-0 | 3-1 | 1-2 | 4-1 | X | 1-1 | 2-2 | 0-1 | 1-0 | 2-0 | 3-0 | 1-1 | 3-1 | 1-4 | 2-0 | 0-0 | 3-1 |
| | | 380 | 604 | 449 | 416 | 361 | 485 | 400 | 341 | 471 | X | 429 | 375 | 530 | 484 | 378 | 373 | 485 | 412 | 536 | 390 | 404 | 1003 |
| 11 | Gateshead | 3-0 | 0-1 | 2-0 | 4-1 | 0-1 | 0-0 | 3-2 | 2-1 | 2-3 | 0-2 | X | 1-0 | 0-3 | 7-1 | 1-3 | 2-2 | 2-2 | 0-1 | 2-1 | 1-1 | 2-1 | 3-2 |
| | | 294 | 306 | 308 | 213 | 623 | 324 | 289 | 239 | 212 | 326 | X | 305 | 246 | 284 | 226 | 274 | 304 | 298 | 302 | 406 | 278 | 296 |
| 12 | Guiseley | 4-0 | 2-0 | 3-0 | 1-0 | 1-2 | 4-0 | 2-2 | 1-1 | 3-0 | 2-1 | 3-2 | X | 1-0 | 1-0 | 2-0 | 2-0 | 2-0 | 2-1 | 1-1 | 0-3 | 2-3 | 2-1 |
| | | 388 | 615 | 286 | 296 | 327 | 377 | 231 | 378 | 201 | 287 | 517 | X | 412 | 338 | 366 | 323 | 339 | 247 | 394 | 376 | 293 | 334 |
| 13 | Hyde Utd | 3-2 | 0-1 | 1-1 | 5-0 | 0-1 | 3-4 | 2-2 | 0-1 | 2-0 | 1-2 | 3-0 | 3-1 | X | 1-1 | 1-2 | 1-1 | 2-0 | 3-0 | 1-1 | 3-2 | 2-0 | 0-0 |
| | | 491 | 964 | 467 | 390 | 444 | 525 | 348 | 549 | 357 | 457 | 371 | 483 | X | 575 | 364 | 505 | 424 | 397 | 1357 | 436 | 430 | 507 |
| 14 | Lancaster C | 1-0 | 0-0 | 3-2 | 2-4 | 2-2 | 0-1 | 4-1 | 1-1 | 5-0 | 0-1 | 2-2 | 1-3 | 1-0 | X | 1-2 | 0-0 | 1-1 | 0-3 | 1-1 | 0-1 | 1-0 | 2-0 |
| | | 311 | 329 | 221 | 202 | 247 | 312 | 150 | 225 | 220 | 205 | 206 | 276 | 257 | X | 248 | 224 | 255 | 220 | 280 | 230 | 205 | 270 |
| 15 | Leigh | 1-2 | 3-2 | 0-1 | 1-1 | 3-2 | 0-1 | 3-2 | 0-0 | 0-1 | 3-0 | 2-2 | 3-2 | 2-2 | 0-2 | X | 0-0 | 0-0 | 1-1 | 3-0 | 2-2 | 2-2 | 1-1 |
| | | 239 | 451 | 151 | 183 | 191 | 292 | 245 | 351 | 161 | 201 | 192 | 151 | 287 | 328 | X | 235 | 185 | 278 | 336 | 311 | 161 | 265 |
| 16 | Marine | 2-0 | 2-1 | 1-2 | 2-2 | 1-3 | 4-1 | 1-4 | 2-2 | 1-4 | 1-2 | 0-1 | 1-1 | 1-0 | 2-1 | 1-1 | X | 1-4 | 5-2 | 2-2 | 3-3 | 3-3 | 1-2 |
| | | 303 | 304 | 290 | 273 | 292 | 351 | 191 | 309 | 228 | 262 | 221 | 414 | 249 | 287 | 245 | X | 293 | 231 | 410 | 312 | 237 | 343 |
| 17 | Runcorn | 2-2 | 0-3 | 2-2 | 1-0 | 1-0 | 2-1 | 0-1 | 1-1 | 1-1 | 0-0 | 1-0 | 1-3 | 1-1 | 1-2 | 0-2 | 1-1 | X | 2-0 | 1-0 | 2-3 | 0-1 | 1-1 |
| | | 303 | 630 | 205 | 232 | 257 | 274 | 257 | 375 | 278 | 327 | 298 | 291 | 315 | 192 | 290 | 359 | X | 152 | 349 | 282 | 291 | 347 |
| 18 | Spennymoor | 2-0 | 0-2 | 0-0 | 2-0 | 2-1 | 0-4 | 4-0 | 2-1 | 0-1 | 1-1 | 2-2 | 0-0 | 2-0 | 2-2 | 2-4 | 0-2 | 0-0 | X | 1-0 | 4-5 | 1-3 | 0-2 |
| | | 163 | 327 | 170 | 314 | 314 | 247 | 207 | 229 | 133 | 214 | 384 | 305 | 221 | 175 | 225 | 217 | 219 | X | 231 | 365 | 162 | 263 |
| 19 | Stalybridge | 1-3 | 3-1 | 1-1 | 3-1 | 4-0 | 1-1 | 1-0 | 2-0 | 2-2 | 2-0 | 0-3 | 2-2 | 2-1 | 3-1 | 4-4 | 2-1 | 1-2 | 3-0 | X | 2-0 | 1-0 | 3-0 |
| | | 505 | 802 | 234 | 457 | 443 | 416 | 216 | 536 | 524 | 383 | 488 | 688 | 1640 | 421 | 419 | 427 | 329 | 551 | X | 477 | 572 | 457 |
| 20 | Whitby Town | 3-2 | 1-4 | 1-0 | 2-1 | 2-1 | 1-1 | 4-3 | 1-0 | 4-0 | 5-1 | 1-2 | 0-0 | 2-3 | 1-2 | 0-2 | 0-2 | 0-0 | 4-1 | 4-1 | X | 1-2 | 1-1 |
| | | 469 | 709 | 475 | 791 | 861 | 472 | 494 | 878 | 554 | 507 | 317 | 457 | 429 | 628 | 742 | 521 | 503 | 497 | 549 | X | 641 | 712 |
| 21 | Winsford U | 2-2 | 2-1 | 1-0 | 1-2 | 2-2 | 1-2 | 1-1 | 3-2 | 2-2 | 2-0 | 1-2 | 0-1 | 0-2 | 1-0 | 2-0 | 2-2 | 0-0 | 1-1 | 1-2 | 0-2 | X | 1-1 |
| | | 108 | 460 | 181 | 153 | 181 | 340 | 163 | 180 | 148 | 114 | 181 | 126 | 270 | 126 | 195 | 202 | 240 | 132 | 220 | 175 | X | 250 |
| 22 | Worksop T | 1-0 | 3-1 | 1-1 | 3-1 | 1-0 | 2-0 | 1-2 | 0-2 | 2-0 | 1-1 | 2-0 | 3-1 | 2-0 | 3-0 | 2-1 | 1-1 | 2-1 | 2-1 | 2-1 | 2-1 | 1-0 | X |
| | | 431 | 777 | 439 | 712 | 502 | 420 | 475 | 1070 | 581 | 940 | 620 | 818 | 521 | 412 | 476 | 544 | 410 | 631 | 682 | 582 | 498 | X |
| | Home Ave.rage | 422 | 798 | 396 | 230 | 429 | 307 | 271 | 275 | 222 | 462 | 303 | 349 | 516 | 243 | 247 | 288 | 300 | 242 | 523 | 581 | 197 | 597 |

# LEAGUE CHALLENGE CUP 1998-99

**FIRST ROUND**

| | | | | | | | | |
|---|---|---|---|---|---|---|---|---|
| Accrington Stanley | v | Gretna | 1-0 | | Bradford Park Ave | v | Whitley Bay | 3-1 |
| Burscough | v | Bamber Bridge | 0-0, 2*1 | | Congleton Town | v | Belper Town | 2-3 |
| Droylsden | v | Flixton | 2-0 | | Eastwood Town | v | Alfreton Town | 1-1, 0-1 |
| Great Harwood Town | v | Netherfield Kendal | 1-0 | | Harrogate Town | v | Farsley Celtic | 0-4 |
| Hucknall Town | v | Stocksbridge PS | 4-1 | | Matlock Town | v | Lincoln United | 2-5 |
| Radcliffe Borough | v | Witton Albion | 1-1, 3*4 | | Trafford | v | Ashton United | 0-0, 3-1 |

**SECOND ROUND**

| | | | | | | | | |
|---|---|---|---|---|---|---|---|---|
| Accrington Stanley | v | Great Harwood Town | 2-0 | | Alfreton Town | v | Belper Town | 3-2 |
| Bishop Auckland | v | Farsley Celtic | 3-3, 2-4 | | Blyth Spartans | v | Bradford Park Ave | 3-1 |
| Droylsden | v | Hyde United | 4-1 | | Gainsborough Trinity | v | Lincoln United | 3-1 |
| Guiseley | v | Spennymoor Utd | 1-1, 1-0 | | Hucknall Town | v | Emley | 2-2, 3-2 |
| Lancaster City | v | Trafford | 1-2 | | Leigh | v | Burscough | 0-1 |
| Marine | v | Chorley | 1-1, 1-2 | | Runcorn | v | Colwyn Bay | 0-3 |
| Stalybridge Celtic | v | Altrincham | 1-0 | | Whitby Town | v | Gateshead | 1-2 |
| Winsford United | v | Witton Alb. | 1-1, 2-2, 3p4 | | Worksop Town | v | Frickley Athletic | 1-3 |

**THIRD ROUND**

| | | | | | | | | |
|---|---|---|---|---|---|---|---|---|
| Accrington Stanley | v | Chorley | 0-0, 2-0 | | Colwyn Bay | v | Droylsden | 2-3, 2-2 |
| Gainsborough Trinity | v | Blyth Spartans | 0-0, 0-1 | | Gateshead | v | Farsley Celtic | 0-0, 0-1 |
| Guiseley | v | Frickley Athetic | 3-1 | | Hucknall Town | v | Alfreton Town | 1-0 |
| Stalybridge Celtic | v | Witton Albion | 1-1, 4-1 | | Trafford | v | Burscough | 0-0, 0-1 |

**FOURTH ROUND**

| | | | | | | | | |
|---|---|---|---|---|---|---|---|---|
| Blyth Spartans | v | Droylsden | 4-3 | | Guiseley | v | Accrington Stanley | 1-1, 2-1 |
| Hucknall Town | v | Farsley Celtic | 0-0 | | Stalybridge Celtic | v | Burscough | 5-2 |

**SEMI-FINALS**

| | | | | | | | | |
|---|---|---|---|---|---|---|---|---|
| Blyth Spartans | v | Guiseley | 0-2 | | Hucknall Town | v | Stalybridge Celtic | 1-1, 1-2 |

**FINAL**

| | | | |
|---|---|---|---|
| STALYBRIDGE CELT. | v | GUISELEY | 2-1 |

# PRESIDENT'S CUP 1998-99

**FIRST ROUND**

| | | | | | | | | |
|---|---|---|---|---|---|---|---|---|
| Droylsden | v | Hyde United | 2-2, 0*0, 5p4 | | Eastwood Town | v | Guiseley | 1-3 |
| Farsley Celtic | v | Worksop Town | 2-2, 3*4 | | Gainsborough Trinity | v | Lincoln United | 6-2 |
| Leigh | v | Ashton United | 2-1 | | Stalybridge Celtic | v | Marine | 5-0 |
| Winsford United | v | Altrincham | 2-2, 0-1 | | Witton Albion | v | Runcorn | 1-1, 1-3 |

**SECOND ROUND**

| | | | | | | | | |
|---|---|---|---|---|---|---|---|---|
| Guiseley | v | Droylsden | 1-2 | | Leigh | v | Altrincham | 1-1, 2-1 |
| Stalybridge Celtic | v | Gainsborough T. | 2-2, 2-1 | | Worksop Town | v | Runcorn | 1-3 |

**SEMI-FINALS (Two Legs)**

| | | | | | | | | |
|---|---|---|---|---|---|---|---|---|
| Runcorn | v | Leigh | 0-1, 1-1 | | Stalybridge Celtic | v | Droylsden | 1-1, 2-3 |

**FINAL**

| | | | |
|---|---|---|---|
| LEIGH | v | DROYLSDEN | 1-2 |

# BAMBER BRIDGE

## CLUB OFFICIALS

President: **Arthur Jackson**
Chairman: **D Allan**
Vice Chairman: **Brian Ginty**
Secretary : **Russ Rigby**
c/o B.B.F.C.
Commercial Manager: **Peter Foran**

### FACT FILE

Founded: 1952
Nickname: Brig
Sponsors: Baxi Partnership
Colours: White/black/black
Change Colours: All yellow
Midweek Matches: Tuesday
Reserves' League: Preston & District

## FOOTBALL MANAGEMENT TEAM

Manager: **Tony Greenwood**
Asst Manager: **Phil Entwistle**
Physio: **Liam Royal**

Pages: 36  Price: £1.
Editor: Dave Rowland (01772 465659)

## GROUND

Irongate, Brownedge Road, Bamber Bridge, Preston, Lancs.PR5 6UX
Tel Nos: Club Office 01772-909690; Social Club 01772-909695; Fax No. 01772-909691
Directions: M6 Junct 29, A6 (Bamber Bridge Bypass) towards Walton-le-Dale, to r'bout, A6
London Road to next r'bout, 3rd exit signed Bamber Bridge (Brownedge Road) and first right.
Ground 100 yds at end of road on left. Just over a mile from Bamber Bridge (BR).
Seats: 500        Cover: 800        Capacity: 2,500
Clubhouse: On ground. Open all day Saturday matchdays, every evening and Sunday lunch.
Refreshment cabin on ground serves hot & cold drinks & snacks etc during matches.
Club Shop: Sells various club souvenirs etc plus large selection of programmes. Contact Russ
Rigby (01772 909690)

**PREVIOUS**      Leagues: Preston & District 52-90; North West Counties 90-93.
                  Ground: King George V Ground, Higher Walton 1952-86.  Names: None

**CLUB RECORDS**  **Attendance:** 2,300 v Czech Republic, Pre-Euro 96 Friendly.
                  **Win:** 8-0 v Curzon Ashton N.W.Co. 94-95.   **Defeat:** Unknown
                  **Fee Paid:** £10,000 to Horwich R.M.I.for Mark Edwards.
                  **Fee Received:** £15,000 from Wigan Athletic for Tony Back,  1995.

**BEST SEASON**   **FA Vase:** Semi Final 91-92 (lost 0-2 on agg to Wimborne Tn).
                  **FA Cup:** Third Qualifying Round 96-97 ( 0-5 v Newcastle Town).

**HONOURS**       Nth West Co's Lge R-up 92-93 (Div 2 91-92, F'lit Cup R-up 91-92); Preston &Dist Lge(4) (R-up (3); Guildhall Cup 78-79 80-
                  81 84-85 89-90, R-up 77-78 79-8087-88; Lancs Amtr Shield 81-82, R-up 80-81 89-90; Lancastrian Brigade Cup 76-7789-90
                  90-91; A.T.S.Lancs Trophy 94-95, R-Up 95-96, NPL Chall Cup 94-95; NPL 1st Div R-Up 94-95; NPL Prem Div Champ 95-96.

*Bamber Bridge*

## BAMBER BRIDGE - MATCH FACTS - 1998-99 SEASON

| No | Date | Venue | Comp | Opponents | Att | Result | Score | Goalscorers |
|----|------|-------|------|-----------|-----|--------|-------|-------------|
| 1 | 22/08 | H | ULP | Hyde United | 373 | D | 1-1 | Greenwood 15 |
| 2 | 25/08 | A | ULP | Marine | 290 | W | 2-1 | Nulty 50[og], Borrowdale 87 |
| 3 | 29/08 | A | ULP | Guiseley | 286 | L | 0-3 | |
| 4 | 31/08 | H | ULP | Chorley | 771 | W | 1-0 | Leaver 81 |
| 5 | 05/09 | A | ULP | Gateshead | 308 | L | 0-2 | |
| 6 | 08/09 | H | ULC 1 | **Burscough** | 310 | D | 0-0 | |
| 7 | 12/09 | H | ULP | Blyth Spartans | 233 | W | 1-0 | Milligan 9 |
| 8 | 15/09 | A | ULP | Lancaster City | 221 | L | 2-3 | Smith 28, Leaver 55[p] |
| 9 | 19/09 | H | ULP | Runcorn | 320 | L | 1-2 | Greenwood 18 |
| 10 | 22/09 | A | ULC1r | **Burscough** | 204 | L | 1-2 | **Greenwood 18** |
| 11 | 26/09 | A | ULP | Frickley Athletic | 199 | W | 2-0 | Leaver 5, Borrowdale 20 |
| 12 | 29/09 | H | ULP | Colwyn Bay | 215 | D | 1-1 | Smith 31 |
| 13 | 03/10 | A | FA C Q2 | **Bedlington Terriers** | 230 | D | 1-1 | **Smith 45** |
| 14 | 06/10 | H | FA C Q2 r | **Bedlington Terriers** | 262 | D | 4-4 | **Vickers 72, Turner 74, McHugh 90, Smith 120(3-4 p)** |
| 15 | 10/10 | H | ULP | Gainsborough Trinity | 251 | L | 1-4 | Vickers 61 |
| 16 | 13/10 | H | ULP | Marine | 225 | D | 2-2 | Greenwood 68 70 |
| 17 | 17/10 | A | ULP | Gainsborough Trinity | 449 | W | 1-0 | Vickers 90 |
| 18 | 20/10 | A | ULP | Stalybridge Celtic | 234 | D | 1-1 | Greenwood 50 |
| 19 | 24/10 | A | FA T 1 | **Sutton Coldfield Town** | 115 | D | 2-2 | Carroll 2 65 |
| 20 | 27/10 | H | FA T 1 r | **Sutton Coldfield Town** | 206 | W | 2-1 | **Maddock 72, Borrowdale 95** |
| 21 | 31/10 | H | ULP | Stalybridge Celtic | 349 | W | 2-1 | Maddock 45, Cliff 82 |
| 22 | 07/11 | A | ULP | Colwyn Bay | 260 | W | 1-0 | Greenwood 27 |
| 23 | 14/11 | H | ULP | Spennymoor United | 258 | W | 5-1 | Whittaker 14 43 59, Greenwood 67 84 |
| 24 | 21/11 | A | FA T 2 | **Burton Albion** | 676 | L | 0-5 | |
| 25 | 28/11 | A | ULP | Spennymoor United | 170 | D | 0-0 | |
| 26 | 01/12 | H | ULP | Leigh RMI | 430 | D | 1-1 | Turner 45 |
| 27 | 05/12 | H | ULP | Gateshead | 253 | W | 3-1 | Whittaker 6, Leaver 20[p], Turner 67 |
| 28 | 12/12 | H | ULP | Whitby Town | 367 | D | 1-1 | Cliff 56 |
| 29 | 19/12 | A | ULP | Worksop Town | 439 | D | 1-1 | Whittaker 61 |
| 30 | 26/12 | H | ULP | Lancaster City | 456 | W | 4-3 | Smith 15, Whittaker 27, Turner 62, Leaver 64 |
| 31 | 28/12 | A | ULP | Accrington Stanley | 583 | W | 5-0 | Maddock 29, Vickers 41, Whittaker 45 86, Smith 80 |
| 32 | 02/01 | A | ULP | Chorley | 661 | W | 1-0 | Leaver 19[p] |
| 33 | 05/01 | H | L ATS 2 | **Radcliffe Borough** | 188 | W | 4-0 | **Whittaker 20 28 88, Borrowdale 48** |
| 34 | 09/01 | H | ULP | Bishop Auckland | 413 | D | 2-2 | Cliff 40 45 |
| 35 | 23/01 | A | ULP | Emley | 234 | W | 1-0 | Cliff 90 |
| 36 | 30/01 | H | ULP | Emley | 425 | L | 1-2 | Whittaker 15 |
| 37 | 02/02 | H | L ATS QF | **Great Harwood Town** | 234 | W | 3-1 | **Cliff 42, Leaver 62, Vickers 72** |
| 38 | 06/02 | A | ULP | Bishop Auckland | 189 | D | 1-1 | Cliff 82 |
| 39 | 13/02 | H | ULP | Guiseley | 373 | W | 4-1 | Atkinson 21[og], Vickers 33 55, Whittaker 46 |
| 40 | 20/02 | H | ULP | Frickley Athletic | 329 | W | 3-2 | Vickers 12 27, Borrowdale 64 |
| 41 | 23/02 | A | ULP | Runcorn | 205 | D | 2-2 | Borrowdale 14, Leaver 90 |
| 42 | 27/02 | H | ULP | Winsford United | 366 | D | 1-1 | Whittaker 42 |
| 43 | 09/03 | A | L ATS SF | **Morecambe** | 363 | L | 2-3 | **Borrowdale 15, Cliff 29** |
| 44 | 13/03 | A | ULP | Blyth Spartans | 327 | W | 1-0 | Maddock 59 |
| 45 | 20/03 | H | ULP | Altrincham | 890 | L | 0-1 | |
| 46 | 23/03 | A | ULP | Whitby Town | 475 | L | 0-1 | |
| 47 | 27/03 | A | ULP | Hyde United | 467 | D | 1-1 | Whittaker 90 |
| 48 | 03/04 | A | ULP | Winsford United | 181 | L | 0-1 | |
| 49 | 05/04 | H | ULP | Accrington Stanley | 618 | D | 1-1 | Jones 90 |
| 50 | 10/04 | A | ULP | Altrincham | 780 | D | 1-1 | Whittaker 83 |
| 51 | 13/04 | A | ULP | Leigh RMI | 151 | W | 1-0 | Smith 50 |
| 52 | 17/04 | H | ULP | Worksop Town | 405 | W | 3-2 | Leaver 30, Whittaker 37, Greenwood 85 |

**PLAYING SQUAD 1999-2000:**
GOALKEEPERS: Mike Finch (Burscough)
DEFENDERS: Steve Aspinall (Chorley), Peter Billing (Northwich Victoria), Darren Davies (Accrington Stanley), Shaun McHugh (Radcliffe Borough)
MIDFIELDERS: James Bryson (Rochdale), Dave Carroll (Witton Albion), John Turner (Preston North End)
FORWARDS: Peter Smith (Accrington Stanley), Andy Whittaker (Southport),

# BISHOP AUCKLAND

## FACT FILE

Formed: 1886
Nickname: Bishops
Sponsors:
Colours: Sky & Navy blue
Change colours: Red & white.
Midweek home matchday: Wednesday.
Reserve Team: None.

97-98 Capain: D Lobb
Top scorer: Lee Ellison (32)

Programme:
Pages: 28 Price: £1.
Editor: Bobby Wake (01388 609428)
Local Press: Northern Echo, Evening
Gazette, N'castle Journal. Local Radio:
Radio Cleveland, Radio Tees, Radio Metro,
Radio Newcastle.

### CLUB OFFICIALS

Chairman: **Tony Duffy**
Vice-Chairman: T.B.A.
Secretary: **Tony Duffy,**
8 Ennerdale Grove, West Auckland,
Co.Durham. DL14 9LN.(01388 833410)
Press Officer: **Tony Duffy**
Commercial Manager: **Bryan Collinson**

### FOOTBALL MANAGEMENT TEAM

Manager: Tony Lee
Asst Mgr: Trevor Arnold
Physio: Dave Nesbitt

### GROUND

Kingsway, Bishop Auckland, County Durham          Tel. 01388 603686
Directions: A1 to Scotch Corner (Turn off A68 from A1) or M6 Junc A38 (A685 to Brough),
then follow signs to Bishop Auckland. Ground in town centre (rear off Newgate St.). Half mile
from station.
Capacity: 3,500          Cover: 2,000          Seats: 600
Clubhouse: Open every day noon-4 & 7-11pm, plus Saturday matchdays all day. Large bar,
pool, juke box. Also snack bar within grounds sells hot & cold pies & drinks.
Club Shop: Yes   Metal Badges: £3 . 00.

**PREVIOUS**          Leagues: N East Counties 1889-90/ Northern Alliance 1890-91/ Northern 1893-1988.

**CLUB RECORDS Attendance:** 17,000 v Coventry, FA Cup 2nd Rd 6/12/52.
**Appearances:** Bob Hardisty.
**Win:** 12-3 v Kingstonian, Amateur Cup 55.     **Defeat:** 0-7 v Halifax Tn FA Cup 2nd Rd66-67.
**Fee Paid:** £2,000.          Fee Received: £9,000 for David Laws from Weymouth.

**BEST SEASON**     **FA Amateur Cup:** Winners 8
times
**FA Trophy:** Quarter Finals
78-79, 88-89, 96-97
**FA Cup:** 4th Rd 54-55, 1-3 v
York City (H).
League clubs defeated:
Crystal Palace, Ipswich 54-
55, Tranmere 56-57.

**HONOURS**          FA Amateur Cup 1895-96,
1899-1900 13-14 20-22 34-35
38-39 54-56 57-58 (R-up(8)01-02 05-06 10-11 14-
15 45-46 49-51 53-54); Northern Lg(19) 1898-99
1900-02 08-10 11-12 20-21 30-31 38-39 46-47 49-
52 53-5666-67 84-86, R-up (17) 78-79 86-87 96-97,
Lg Cup(7) 49-51 53-55 59-60 66-67 75-76); D'ham
Chall Cup 1891-92 98-99 1930-31 38-39 51-52 55-
56 61-62 66-67 84-8585-86 87-88 96-97, 98-99
HFS Loans Lg Div 1 R-up 88-89. Plus tournaments
in Isle of Man, Spain, Portugal etc

Players Progressing:    B Paisley (Liverpool), F
Richardson & S O'Connell
(Chelsea 46 & 54), R Hardisty & K Williamson
(Darlimgton 46 & 52), WShergold (Newport 47), N
Smith (Fulham 48), R Steel & K Murray (Darlington
50),A Adey (Doncaster 50), F Palmer & A Stalker
(Gateshead 51 & 58), A Sewell(Bradford City 54), G
Barker (Southend 54), J Major (Hull 55), H
Sharratt(Oldham 56), F McKenna (Leeds 56), J
Barnwell (Arsenal 56), D Lewis (Accrington Stanley
57), C Cresswell (Carlisle 58), W Bradley (Man Utd),
L Brown(Northampton), P Baker (Southampton), M
Gooding (Rotherham), K Nobbs & A
Toman(Hartlepool), P Hinds (Dundee Utd).

# BISHOP AUCKLAND - MATCH FACTS - 1998-99 SEASON

| No | Date | Venue | Comp | Opponents | Att | Result | Score | Goalscorers |
|----|------|-------|------|-----------|-----|--------|-------|-------------|
| 1 | 22/08 | A | ULP | Whitby Town | 791 | L | 1-2 | Bayles 11 |
| 2 | 25/08 | A | ULP | Frickley Athletic | 181 | D | 0-0 | |
| 3 | 29/08 | A | ULP | Lancaster City | 202 | W | 4-2 | Udall 11[og], Mawson 25, Shaw 40[p], Parkinson 75 |
| | 31/08 | A | ULP | Blyth Spartans | 529 | L | 1-2 | Mawson 40 |
| 4 | 05/09 | H | ULP | Runcorn | 212 | L | 2-3 | Mawson 6, Forster 87 |
| 5 | 09/09 | H | ULP | Gateshead | 344 | D | 2-2 | Shaw 14, Parkinson 34 |
| 6 | 12/09 | A | ULP | Winsford United | 153 | W | 2-1 | Mawson 45, Littlefair 86 |
| 7 | 16/09 | H | ULP | Frickley Athletic | 140 | D | 2-2 | Shaw 39[p], Mawson 76 |
| 8 | 19/09 | H | ULP | Colwyn Bay | 207 | L | 0-1 | |
| 9 | 21/09 | A | ULP | Emley | 339 | L | 0-2 | |
| 10 | 26/09 | A | ULP | Worksop Town | 712 | L | 1-3 | Bayles 1 |
| 11 | 30/09 | H | ULP | Whitby Town | 257 | D | 1-1 | Shaw 88[p] |
| 12 | 03/10 | A | FA C Q2 | Gateshead | 313 | L | 0-3 | |
| 13 | 07/10 | A | ULP | Gainsborough Trinity | 416 | L | 1-2 | Shaw 4 |
| 14 | 10/10 | H | ULP | Accrington Stanley | 214 | W | 2-1 | Rowntree 28, Bayles 77 |
| 15 | 14/10 | H | ULP | Emley | 209 | D | 1-1 | Rowntree 39 |
| 16 | 17/10 | H | ULP | Colwyn Bay | 205 | W | 3-0 | Rowntree 63, Shaw 85, Bayles 90 |
| 17 | 21/10 | A | ULP | Gateshead | 213 | L | 1-4 | Gallagher 2 |
| 18 | 24/10 | H | FA T 1 | Matlock T6 | 92 | W | 4-2 | Banks 6, Shaw 9 34, Day 29 |
| 19 | 28/10 | H | DCC 1 | Esh Winning | 81 | W | 9-3 | Shaw(3), Lynch, Rowntree(2), Gallagher, Littlefair, Bayles |
| 20 | 31/10 | H | ULP | Winsford United | 237 | L | 0-2 | |
| 21 | 04/11 | A | ULC 2 | Farsley Celtic | 68 | D | 3-3 | West 27, Rowntree 39, Bayles 79 |
| 22 | 07/11 | A | ULP | Stalybridge Celtic | 457 | L | 1-3 | Banks 42 |
| 23 | 14/11 | H | ULP | Altrincham | 268 | W | 2-1 | Bayles 15, Birch 54 |
| 24 | 16/11 | H | DCC 2 | West Auckland Town | 278 | D | 2-2 | Arnold 70, Rowntree 80[p] |
| 25 | 21/11 | H | FA T 2 | Guiseley | 242 | D | 1-1 | Ross 68 |
| 26 | 24/11 | A | FA T 2 r | Guiseley | 314 | L | 1-3 | Rowntree 70 |
| 27 | 28/11 | A | ULP | Marine | 273 | D | 2-2 | Littlefair 51, Lobb 80 |
| 28 | 05/12 | H | ULP | Gainsborough Trinity | 181 | W | 2-1 | Littlefair 75, Rowntree 90[p] |
| 29 | 08/12 | A | DCC 2 r | West Auckland Town | 193 | D | 1-1 | Ross 102 (won 5-4 on pens) |
| 30 | 12/12 | A | ULP | Leigh RMI | 183 | D | 1-1 | Lynch 60 |
| 31 | 19/12 | H | ULP | Chorley | 185 | L | 0-4 | |
| 32 | 26/12 | A | ULP | Spennymoor United | 314 | L | 0-2 | |
| 33 | 28/12 | H | ULP | Guiseley | 238 | W | 1-0 | West 82 |
| 34 | 02/01 | H | ULP | Spennymoor United | 397 | D | 1-1 | Rowntree 11 |
| 35 | 06/01 | H | DCC QF | Norton & Stockton Ancients | 98 | D | 1-1 | Littlefair 77 |
| 36 | 09/01 | A | ULP | Bamber Bridge | 413 | D | 2-2 | Adams 23, Hellaney 33 |
| 37 | 13/01 | A | D CC QF r | Norton & Stockton Ancients | n/k | W | 7-2 | Gallagher(3), Littlefair(2), Salmon, Shaw |
| 38 | 20/01 | H | Lge C 2 r | Farsley Celtic | 74 | L | 2-4 | Adams 12 79 |
| 39 | 23/01 | H | ULP | Hyde United | 201 | L | 0-1 | |
| 40 | 30/01 | A | ULP | Chorley | 236 | W | 3-1 | Shaw 75 89 90 |
| 41 | 06/02 | A | ULP | Bamber Bridge | 189 | D | 1-1 | Adams 58 |
| 42 | 13/02 | H | ULP | Marine | 207 | L | 0-2 | |
| 43 | 17/02 | A | DCC SF | Consett | n/k | W | 3-2 | Banks 13, Littlefair 35 60 |
| 44 | 20/02 | A | ULP | Hyde United | 390 | L | 0-5 | |
| 45 | 27/02 | H | ULP | Lancaster City | 205 | D | 1-1 | Adams 67 |
| 46 | 06/03 | H | ULP | Worksop Town | 283 | W | 2-1 | Rose 38, Mellanby 68 |
| 47 | 13/03 | A | ULP | Accrington Stanley | 370 | W | 1-0 | Shaw 48 |
| 48 | 20/03 | A | ULP | Leigh RMI | 204 | D | 0-0 | |
| 49 | 23/03 | H | ULP | Blyth Spartans | 305 | D | 2-2 | Gallagher 59 88 |
| 50 | 26/03 | A | ULP | Altrincham | 872 | D | 0-0 | |
| 51 | 03/04 | A | ULP | Guiseley | 296 | L | 0-1 | |
| 52 | 05/04 | A | DCC F | Durham City | 300 | W | 3-2 | Adams 52, Rowntree 93, Littlefair 107 |
| 53 | 07/04 | H | ULP | Stalybridge Celtic | 151 | D | 3-3 | Littlefair 30, West 70, Banks 74 |
| 54 | 10/04 | A | ULP | Runcorn | 232 | L | 0-1 | |

## PLAYING SQUAD 1999-2000:

GOALKEEPERS: Darren Ablewhite (Crook Town), Simon Bishop (Northallerton Town), Steve Jones (Gateshead),
DEFENDERS: Lee Brydon (Darlington), Mark Foster, Stephen Hutt (Hartlepool United), David Lobb, Mark Salmon (Acklam Steelworks)
MIDFIELDERS: George Adams (Shildon), Micky Arnold (Billingham Town), David Bayles (Consett), Chris Birch, David Gallagher (Guisborough Town), Allan Martin (Whitby Town), Andy Mockler, Paul Walton (Hartlepool United), Dave Woodcock
FORWARDS: Danny Brunskill (North Shields Athletic), Gary Hyde, Stuart Irvine (Hartlepool United), Anthony Lee (North Shields Athletic), David Littlefair (Blyth Spartans), Paul Rowntree (Gateshead), Andy Shaw (Spennymoor United), Kevin Todd, Craig Veart (Gateshead)

# BLYTH SPARTANS

## CLUB OFFICIALS

Chairman: **Mike Mitchell**
Secretary: **Scott Sawyer**
53 Ninth Avenue, Blyth, Northumberland
NE24 2TE (01670 355669).
Press Officer: **Ken Teasdale**

## FOOTBALL MANAGEMENT TEAM

Manager: John Gamble
Assistant Manager: TBA

### FACT FILE

Formed: 1899
Nickname: Spartans
Sponsors: Federation Brewery.
Colours: Green & white stripes
Change colours: Orange
Midweek Matches: Tuesday
Reserves' League: Northern Alliance

98-99 Captain: Michael Farrey
Top Scorer: Wayne Edgecumbe
P.o.Y.:Terry Burke (G/K)

Pages: 64 Price: £1
Editor: Brian Grey (0191 2650119)
Local Press: Newcastle Journal
& Evening Chronicle.

## GROUND

Croft Park, Blyth, Northumberland. (01670) 354818 FAX: 01670 545592
Directions: Through Tyne tunnel heading north on A19, take Cramlington turn A1061, follow signs for Newsham/Blyth. Right fork at railway gates in Newsham,down Plessey Rd, ground can be seen on left. Buses X24, X25, X26, X1 from Newcastle.
Seats: 300          Cover: 1,000          Capacity: 6,000
Clubhouse: Open every night plus Saturday & Sunday lunch & matchdays. Available for wedding functions. Pies & sandwiches available.
Souvenir Shop: Large selection. Contact: Malcom Allen (01670 369209)

**PREVIOUS**      Leagues: Northumberland 01-07; Northern Alliance 07-13, 46-47; North Eastern13-14 19-39 47-58 62-64; Northern Combination 45-46; Midland 58-60; Northern Counties 60-62; Northern 62-94. Names: None   Grounds: None

**CLUB RECORDS**  Fee Received: £30,000 for Les Mutrie (Hull City) 1979.   Fee Paid:

**BEST SEASON**   **FA Trophy:** Quarter-Final replay 79-80 82-83.  **FA Amateur Cup:** Semi-Final 71-72.
                  **FA Cup:** 5th Rd replay 77-78 (lost to Wrexham). 1st Round on 47 occasions. League Clubs defeated: Ashington, Gillingham 22-23, Crewe Alexandra,Stockport County 71-72, Chesterfield, Stoke City 77-78, Bury 95-96.

**HONOURS**       Nth Lg(10) 72-73 74-76 79-84 86-88 94-95, (R-up 71-72 73-74 77-78 84-85 94-95),Lg Cup(5) 72-73 77-79 81-82 91-92 94-95, Presidents Cup 96-97; Nth Eastern Lg35-36 (R-up 22-23, Lg Cup 49-50 54-55); Northumberland Lg 03-04; Northern All.08-09 12-13 (R-up 46-47); Northumberland Snr Cup (19); Shields Gazette Cup 95-96.

Players Progressing: William McGlen (Manchester Utd 46), Joe Roddom (Chesterfield 48), Henry Mills (Huddersfield 48), John Allison (Reading 49), James Kelly (Watford 49), Robert Millard (Reading 49), Jim Kerr (Lincoln 52), James Milner (Burnley 52), John Hogg (Portsmouth 54), John Allison(Chesterfield 55), John Inglis (Gateshead 57), John Longland (Hartlepool 58),Alan Shoulder (Newcastle 79), Les Mutrie (Hull City 79), Steve Carney(Newcastle 80), Craig Liddle (Middlesbrough 94), Paul O'Connor (Hartlepool 95). Gustavo Di Lella (Hartlepool 98)

*Back Row (L-R): Glen Martin (Physio), Steve Locker, Ross Lumsden, Matty Hysen, Terry Burke, Willie Moat, Andy Rose, Nicky Peverill, Peter Gamble, Tony Kennedy (Kit Man), Lawrence Fox (G/K Coach)*
*Front Row: Mike Farrey (captain), Steve Hutchinson Tony Skedd, Wayne Edgecumbe, Mike Murr, Ritchie Pitt, Gary O'Hara, Ian Irving, John Atkinson*

# BLYTH SPARTANS - MATCH FACTS - 1998-99 SEASON

| No | Date | Venue | Comp | Opponents | Att | Result | Score | Goalscorers |
|----|------|-------|------|-----------|-----|--------|-------|-------------|
| 1 | 22/08 | H | ULP | Lancaster City | 510 | W | 1-0 | Moat 51 |
| 2 | 25/08 | A | ULP | Guiseley | 327 | W | 2-1 | Farrey 45, Hutchinson 81 |
| 3 | 29/08 | A | ULP | Worksop Town | 502 | L | 0-1 | |
| 4 | 31/08 | H | ULP | Bishop Auckland | 529 | W | 2-1 | Blackstone 18, Hutchinson 73 |
| 5 | 05/09 | H | ULP | Altrincham | 603 | D | 0-0 | |
| 6 | 08/09 | A | ULP | Whitby Town | 861 | L | 1-2 | Ramsey 75 |
| 7 | 12/09 | A | ULP | Bamber Bridge | 233 | L | 0-1 | |
| 8 | 15/09 | H | ULP | Spennymoor United | 515 | W | 4-0 | Moat 21 54, Rose 31, Hutchinson 77 |
| 9 | 19/09 | H | ULP | Hyde United | 525 | L | 1-2 | Edgcumbe 60 |
| 10 | 22/09 | A | ULP | Frickley Athletic | 215 | L | 0-2 | |
| 11 | 26/09 | A | ULP | Colwyn Bay | 286 | L | 0-2 | |
| 12 | 29/09 | H | ULP | Emley | 380 | L | 0-2 | |
| 13 | 03/10 | A | FA C Q2 | Runcorn | 392 | D | 0-0 | |
| 14 | 06/10 | H | FA C Q2 r | Runcorn | 586 | L | 2-4 | Hutchinson 65, McGarrigle 87 |
| 15 | 10/10 | A | ULP | Stalybridge Celtic | 336 | W | 3-2 | Alderson 28, Hutchinson 35, Own-Goal 57 |
| 16 | 13/10 | H | ULP | Whitby Town | 525 | L | 0-5 | |
| 17 | 17/10 | A | ULP | Accrington Stanley | 397 | W | 3-1 | Edgcumbe 19 69, Henderson 85 |
| 18 | 24/10 | A | FA T 1 | Whitby Town | 343 | D | 2-2 | Farrey 44, Moat 79 |
| 19 | 27/10 | A | FA T 1 r | Whitby Town | 521 | L | 1-3 | Goodchild 24[og] |
| 20 | 31/10 | A | ULP | Hyde United | 444 | W | 1-0 | Edgcumbe 80 |
| 21 | 07/11 | H | ULP | Winsford United | 421 | L | 0-3 | |
| 22 | 14/11 | A | ULP | Winsford United | 181 | D | 2-2 | Edgcumbe 26, Alderson 49 |
| 23 | 21/11 | A | ULP | Marine | 292 | W | 3-1 | Edgcumbe 14 61 76 |
| 24 | 28/11 | A | ULP | Leigh RMI | 387 | W | 4-1 | Alderson 63, Edgcumbe 71 86, Earnshaw 82 |
| 25 | 01/12 | H | ULC 2 | Bradford Park Avenue | 282 | W | 3-1 | Skedd 13, Locker 70, Hutchinson 71 |
| 26 | 05/12 | H | ULP | Altrincham | 843 | D | 0-0 | |
| 27 | 12/12 | H | ULP | Marine | 411 | W | 2-1 | O'Hara 11, Skedd 32 |
| 28 | 19/12 | A | ULP | Runcorn | 257 | L | 0-1 | |
| 29 | 26/12 | H | ULP | Gateshead | 1046 | L | 1-2 | Edgcumbe 8 |
| 30 | 28/12 | A | ULP | Emley | 326 | L | 1-2 | Lumsden 30 |
| 31 | 02/01 | A | ULP | Lancaster City | 247 | D | 2-2 | Farrey 18, Rose 90 |
| 32 | 09/01 | H | ULP | Colwyn Bay | 365 | D | 4-4 | Moat 16 88, Edgcumbe 43, Rose 86 |
| 33 | 23/01 | A | ULP | Gainsborough Trinity | 361 | W | 4-3 | Pitt 16, Moat 33, Edgcumbe 38 66 |
| 34 | 26/01 | A | N SC QF | Whitley Bay | 315 | W | 2-0 | Kendal 31[og], Hutchinson 89 |
| 35 | 30/01 | H | ULP | Gainsborough Trinity | 382 | L | 0-2 | |
| 36 | 02/02 | H | ULC 3 | Gainsborough Trinity | 325 | D | 0-0 | |
| 37 | 06/02 | H | ULP | Accrington Stanley | 339 | L | 0-1 | |
| 38 | 10/02 | A | ULC 3 r | Gainsborough Trinity | 224 | W | 1-0 | Moat 57 |
| 39 | 13/02 | A | ULP | Spennymoor United | 314 | L | 1-2 | O'Hara 32[p] |
| 40 | 20/02 | A | ULP | Chorley | 272 | W | 2-0 | Jones 25[og], Hunter 56 |
| 41 | 27/02 | A | ULP | Leigh RMI | 191 | L | 2-3 | Moat 43, Murr 73 |
| 42 | 13/03 | H | ULP | Bamber Bridge | 327 | L | 0-1 | |
| 43 | 15/03 | A | NSC SF | Newcastle Blue Star | 313 | W | 3-0 | Edgcumbe 13, Hysen 21, Pitt 63 |
| 44 | 20/03 | H | ULP | Chorley | 366 | D | 0-0 | |
| 45 | 23/03 | A | ULP | Bishop Auckland | 305 | D | 2-2 | Moat 61, Peverill 70 |
| 46 | 25/03 | H | ULC QF | Droylsden | 289 | W | 4-3 | Edgcumbe 18, Skedd 51 75, Peverill 71 |
| 47 | 03/04 | H | ULP | Worksop Town | 362 | L | 0-1 | |
| 48 | 05/04 | A | ULP | Gateshead | 623 | W | 1-0 | Farrey 78 |
| 49 | 10/04 | A | ULP | Stalybridge Celtic | 443 | L | 0-4 | |
| 50 | 13/04 | H | ULC SF | Guiseley | 313 | L | 0-2 | |
| 51 | 17/04 | H | ULP | Runcorn | 214 | D | 1-1 | Peverill 32 |
| 52 | 20/04 | H | ULP | Guiseley | 151 | W | 4-1 | Farrey 35, Hurr 38, Lumsden 40, Peverill 70 |
| 53 | 01/05 | H | ULP | Frickley Athletic | 263 | D | 2-2 | Edgcumbe 1, Moat 80 |

## PLAYING SQUAD 1999-2000:

GOALKEEPERS: Terry Burke (Whitley Bay)

DEFENDERS: Anth Cole (Gateshead), Alan Colledge (Consett), Paul Harnett (Chester-le-Street Town), Stephen Locker (Bedlington Terriers), Craig Melrose (Bedlington Terriers), Gary O'Hara (Gateshead)

MIDFIELDERS: Dale Anderson (Evenwood Town), David Burt (Newcastle United), Mark Lee (Hibernian), Lawrie Pearson (Bedlington Terriers), Andy Toman (Whitby Town)

FORWARDS: John Atkinson, Andy Blower (Whitley Bay), Wayne Edgcumbe (Bishop Auckland), Ian Irving (local football), Glen Robson (Harrogate Town), Steven Stewart (Chester-le-Street Town)

# COLWYN BAY

## CLUB OFFICIALS

Chairman: **Glynne Owens**
Vice Chairman: **J A Humphreys**
Secretary / Press Officer: **Alan J Banks**
15 Smith Avenue, Old Colwyn, N Wales
LL29 8BE. Tel: 01492 516941 (H)
01492 515133 (B).

## FOOTBALL MANAGEMENT TEAM

Manager: Bryn Jones
01244 531974 (H), 01244 812154 (B)
Assistant Manager: Dave Brett
Physio: John Carmichael

### FACT FILE

Formed: 1885
Nickname: `Bay' or `Seagulls'
Sponsors: Colwyn Shopping Centre
Colours: Maroon with wide blue
stripes/maroon/maroon.
Change colours: White/navy/navy
Reserve Team: None.
Midweek home matchday: Tuesday

98-99 Captain: Craig Lawton
P.o.Y.: Colin Caton
Top scorer: Deiniol Graham (29)

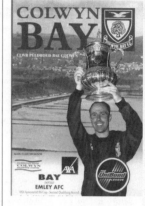

Pages: 28 Price: £1
Editor: Neil Brampton (01492 533341)
Local Press: North Wales Weekly News,
North Wales Pioneer.

## GROUND

Llanelian Road, Old Colwyn, N.Wales.     Tel: 01492 514581
Directions: M55 North Wales Coast - approaching Colwyn Bay take 1st exit signposted Old
Colwyn, left at bottom slip road, straight over r'bout into Llanelian Rd - ground half mile on
right. 2 miles from Colwyn Bar BR station.
Capacity: 2,500          Seats: 250               Cover: 700
Clubhouse: Open matchdays only.
Club Shop: Yes - contact: A Holden 01492 534287 Metal Badges: Yes

**PREVIOUS**          Leagues: Nth Wales Coast 01-21 33-35; Welsh National 21-30; Nth Wales Comb. 30-31; Welsh Lg (Nth) 45-84; North
West Counties 84-91
Grounds: Eiras Park 1930-82; Llanelian Road 82-92; Northwich Victoria FC 92-93; Ellesmere Port Stadium94-95 (2 years
in exile thro' dispute with FAW re League of Wales).

**CLUB RECORDS**     Attendance: 5,000 (at Eiras Park) v Borough United, 1964.
Goalscorer: Peter Donnelly
Appearances: Bryn A Jones

**BEST SEASON**      FA Trophy: Quarter Finals 96-97.
FA Cup: Second Round Proper 95-96.   League
clubs defeated: None.

**HONOURS**          Northern Premier Lg Div 1 91-92 (Div 1 Cup 91-
92); North West Counties Lg R-up90-91 (Div 3
R-up 83-84, Lg Cup 88-89,  Floodlit Cup 90-91;
Welsh Cup SF 91-92;Welsh National Lg R-up
27-28 29-30; Nth Wales Comb. 30-31; Welsh Lg
Nth 64- 6582-83 83-84 (R-up 35-36 45-46 63-
64), Lg Cup 27-28; Alves Cup 63-64; Cookson
Cup 73-74 79-80 80-81 81-82 83-84;
Barritt Cup 79-80 81-82 83-84; Nth Wales Coast
Chal. Cup 30-31 31-32 81-82 82-83 83-84 95-96
97-98; Nth Wales Coast Jnr Cup 1898-99.

Players progressing:   Peter Suddaby (Blackpool), Gareth Davies
(Wrexham).

*Peter Donnelly, Colwyn Bay FC.*
*Photo couresty of North Wales Weekly News*

# COLWYN BAY - MATCH FACTS - 1998-99 SEASON

| No | Date | Venue | Comp | Opponents | Att | Result | Score | Goalscorers |
|---|---|---|---|---|---|---|---|---|
| 1 | 22/08 | A | ULP | Accrington Stanley | 446 | W | 2-1 | Congerton 24, Roberts 84[p] |
| 2 | 25/08 | H | ULP | Runcorn | 436 | L | 1-3 | Graham 1 |
| 3 | 29/08 | H | ULP | Stalybridge Celtic | 385 | L | 1-2 | Donnelly 88 |
| 4 | 31/08 | A | ULP | Altrincham | 680 | D | 1-1 | Donnelly 85 |
| 5 | 05/09 | H | ULP | Frickley Athletic | 246 | L | 0-2 | |
| 6 | 08/09 | A | ULP | Leigh RMI | 245 | L | 2-3 | Graham 8, Limbert 48 |
| 7 | 12/09 | A | ULP | Spennymoor United | 207 | L | 0-4 | |
| 8 | 15/09 | H | ULP | Winsford United | 174 | L | 1-2 | Evans 7 |
| 9 | 19/09 | A | ULP | Bishop Auckland | 207 | W | 1-0 | Graham 33 |
| 10 | 22/09 | H | ULP | Marine | 251 | W | 1-0 | Lawton 51 |
| 11 | 26/09 | H | ULP | Blyth Spartans | 286 | W | 2-0 | Graham 32[p], Lawton 42 |
| 12 | 29/09 | A | ULP | Bamber Bridge | 215 | D | 1-1 | Graham 66 |
| 13 | 03/10 | H | FA C Q2 | Emley | 454 | L | 0-1 | |
| 14 | 06/10 | H | ULP | Lancaster City | 215 | D | 0-0 | |
| 15 | 10/10 | A | ULP | Gateshead | 289 | L | 2-3 | Graham 38, Roberts 86 |
| 16 | 13/10 | H | ULP | Chorley | 244 | W | 2-1 | Roberts 60[p], Evans 77 |
| 17 | 17/10 | H | ULP | Bishop Auckland | 205 | L | 0-3 | |
| 18 | 27/10 | A | ULP | Marine | 191 | W | 4-1 | Limbert 33, Evans 42, Lawton 44, D Graham 84 |
| 19 | 03/11 | A | ULC 2 | Runcorn | 154 | W | 3-0 | Roberts 3, D Graham 62, Evans 75 |
| 20 | 07/11 | H | ULP | Bamber Bridge | 260 | L | 0-1 | |
| 21 | 14/11 | A | ULP | Hyde United | 348 | D | 2-2 | Lawton 20, Graham 49 |
| 22 | 21/11 | H | FA T 2 | Stafford Rangers | 392 | W | 3-2 | Roberts 45[p] 64, Lawton 69 |
| 23 | 05/12 | A | ULP | Frickley Athletic | 151 | L | 1-2 | Limbert 66 |
| 24 | 12/12 | A | NW C QF | Locomotive Llanberis | n/k | W | 7-0 | Roberts 2 8, D Graham 39 48 63, G Graham 44, Lawton 58 |
| 25 | 19/12 | A | ULP | Spennymoor United | 185 | L | 1-3 | Roberts 17[p] |
| 26 | 28/12 | A | ULP | Winsford United | 163 | D | 1-1 | Donnelly 42 |
| 27 | 09/01 | A | ULP | Blyth Spartans | 365 | D | 4-4 | Graham 13 32 80, Roberts 27 |
| 28 | 12/01 | H | NW C QF | Rhyl | 126 | W | 4-1 | Roberts 52, Caton 65, Mottram 79, Lawton 89 |
| 29 | 23/01 | H | ULP | Chorley | 276 | W | 2-1 | Graham 78, Roberts 89 |
| 30 | 25/01 | A | FA T 3 | Hednesford Town | 407 | D | 1-1 | Graham 30 |
| 31 | 27/01 | A | FA T 3 rep | Hednesford Town | 391 | D | 2-2 | Donnelly 61, Graham 109    (won 5-4 on pens) |
| 32 | 06/02 | H | FA T 4 | Bradford Park Avenue | 405 | W | 3-1 | Evans 45, Graham 49, Roberts 52 |
| 33 | 13/02 | A | ULP | Whitby Town | 494 | L | 3-4 | Mottram 57, Graham 68 81 |
| 34 | 16/02 | A | ULC 3 | Droylsden | 110 | D | 2-2 | Graham 1[p] 40 |
| 35 | 20/02 | A | ULP | Worksop Town | 475 | W | 2-1 | Limbert 23, Congerton 47 |
| 36 | 24/02 | H | NW C SF | Bangor City | 345 | W | 3-0 | Limbert 18, Donnelly 24, Lawton 80 |
|  |  |  |  |  |  |  |  | (at Conwy Utd, Colwyn expelled for ineligible player) |
| 38 | 27/02 | A | FA T 5 | Northwich Victoria | 1402 | L | 1-3 | Lawton 28 |
| 39 | 09/03 | H | ULP | Hyde United | 164 | W | 2-1 | Donnelly 76, Graham 79 |
| 40 | 11/03 | H | ULC 2 r | Droylsden | 132 | L | 2-3 | Roberts 32, Limbert 82 |
| 41 | 13/03 | A | ULP | Runcorn | 257 | W | 1-0 | Roberts 16 |
| 42 | 16/03 | A | ULP | Guiseley | 231 | D | 2-2 | Congerton 14, Graham 90[p] |
| 43 | 20/03 | H | ULP | Guiseley | 298 | D | 0-0 | |
| 44 | 23/03 | A | ULP | Lancaster City | 150 | L | 1-4 | Roberts 61 |
| 45 | 27/03 | H | ULP | Accrington Stanley | 282 | W | 3-1 | Graham 43, Roberts 71, Limbert 82 |
| 46 | 30/03 | H | ULP | Leigh RMI | 256 | L | 0-1 | |
| 47 | 03/04 | H | ULP | Gateshead | 301 | D | 1-1 | Donnelly 72 |
| 48 | 05/04 | H | ULP | Altrincham | 459 | D | 1-1 | Caton 62 |
| 49 | 10/04 | H | ULP | Gainsborough Trinity | 275 | L | 3-4 | Donnelly 36, Roberts 41[p], Mottram 56 |
| 50 | 13/04 | A | ULP | Worksop Town | 217 | D | 2-2 | Congerton 51, Roberts 77 |
| 51 | 17/04 | H | ULP | Whitby Town | 232 | W | 3-1 | Graham 8 23 77 |
| 52 | 20/04 | A | ULP | Stalybridge Celtic | 216 | L | 0-1 | |
| 53 | 24/04 | A | ULP | Emley | 180 | D | 0-0 | |
| 54 | 27/04 | A | ULP | Gainsborough Trinity | 400 | L | 1-3 | Evans 38 |
| 55 | 01/05 | H | ULP | Emley | 282 | D | 3-3 | Congerton 2 12, Graham 60 |

**PLAYING SQUAD 1999-2000:**
GOALKEEPERS: Lee Darnborough (Winsford United), Richie Roberts, Richard Sim (Newtown)
DEFENDERS: Peter Donnelly, Jamie Fairhurst (Tns Llansantffraid), David Norman (Bangor City)
MIDFIELDERS: Alun Evans (Ebbw Vale), Robbie Williams (Bangor City)
FORWARDS: Simon Abercrombie (Rhyl), James Mcilvogue (Conwy United), Frank Mottram (Tns Llansantffraid),

# DROYLSDEN

## CLUB OFFICIALS

Chairman: **David Pace**
Secretary: **Bernard King**
22 Hart Street, Droylsden
Manchester M43 7AW.
Tel.0161 285 5232 (H) Fax 0161 370 1426

### FOOTBALL MANAGEMENT TEAM

Manager: David Pace
Asst Manager: Alan Blair

### FACT FILE

Formed: 1892
Nickname: The Bloods
Sponsors:
Alpha Court Windows/ Hastings Taxis
Colours: Red & white/black/black
Change colours: Green/white/green
Midweek matchday: Wednesday
Reserves' League: None

## GROUND

The Butchers Arms Ground, Market Street, Droylsden, Manchester
Tel: 0161 370 1426

**Directions:** **The ground lies** 4 miles east of Manchester via the A662 Ashton New Road, behind Butchers Arms Hotel
Capacity: 3,500       Cover: 2,000       Seats: 500

**Clubhouse:** Pub hours except matchdays. Pool and darts       **Shop:** Yes  Metal Badges: Yes

Pages: 20 Price: 80p
Editor: Martin Crookall
Local Press: Droylsden Reporter, Advertiser
Local Radio: BBC Manchester

**PREVIOUS**       **Leagues:** Manchester; Lancs Com 36-39, 50-68; Cheshire County 39-50, 68-82; NW Counties 82-87

**CLUB RECORDS**       **Attendance:** 4,250 v Grimsby, FA Cup 1st rd 1976
**Scorer:** E Gillibrand 78 (1931-32)       **Win:** 13-2 v Lucas Sports Club
**Fee Received:** £11,000 for Tony Naylor (Crewe)

**BEST SEASON**       **FA Cup:** 2nd Rd 78-79.  League clubs defeated: Rochdale 78-79
**FA Vase:**       **FA Trophy:**

**HONOURS**       Northern Prem Lge Div 1 R-up 89-90 (Div 1 Cup 87-88); NW Counties Lge Div 2 86-87 ; Cheshire County Lge R-up 39-40 45-46 , Lge Cup 77-78 (R-up 76-77);Lancs Comb Div 2 R-up 55-56 58-59 62-63; Manchester Lge 30-31 32-33 (Lge Cup23-24 33-34); Manchester Prem Cup 80-81 (R-up 83-84 90-91 93-94); Manchester Sen Cup 72-73 75-76 78-79 (R-up 72-73 75-76 78-79); Manchester Interm Cup 59-6064-65 69-70; Manchester Chall Shield 46-47

Players progressing: Albert Butterworth & F Letchford (Blackpool 1931), William Davies & Maurice Randall (Crewe 1947), William Mellor (Accrington 1950), Geoff Tonge (Bury 1960), David Campbell (WBA 1962), Kevin Randall (Bury 1965), Peter Litchfield (Preston 1979), Tony Naylor (Crewe 1990)

*Droylsden's Carl Holmes in action against Matlock Town. Holmes was watched by football league scouts earlier this season and has been instrumental in the Bloods' title challenge.  Photo: Colin Stevens*

## DROYLSDEN - MATCH FACTS - 1998-99 SEASON

| No | Date | Venue | Comp | Opponents | Att | Result | Score | Goalscorers |
|---|---|---|---|---|---|---|---|---|
| | 22/08 | H | UL 1 | Harrogate Town | 126 | W | 2-1 | Kinney 8, Stannard 85 |
| | 29/08 | A | UL 1 | Bradford Park Avenue | 177 | W | 5-0 | Cooper 11 39, Stannard 14 87, Holmes 45 |
| | 31/08 | H | UL 1 | Alfreton Town | 190 | W | 1-0 | Stannard 56 |
| | 05/09 | H | UL 1 | Radcliffe Borough | 218 | W | 3-2 | Morley 10, Hennigan 27, Cooper 37 |
| | 08/09 | H | UL C 1 | Flixton | 99 | W | 2-0 | Holmes 28, Quinn 88 |
| | 12/09 | A | UL 1 | Matlock Town | 187 | D | 3-3 | Jones 23, Stannard 47, Kirkham 73 |
| | 15/09 | H | UL 1 | Congleton Town | 102 | L | 2-4 | Holmes 18, Hennigan 26 |
| | 19/09 | H | FA C Q1 | Maltby Main | 143 | D | 2-2 | Lattie 76, Kinney 90 |
| | 22/09 | A | FA C Q1 r | Maltby Main | 80 | W | 2-0 | Cooper 70 81 |
| 10 | 26/09 | A | UL 1 | Eastwood Town | 201 | L | 1-3 | Jones 14 |
| 11 | 29/09 | A | UL 1 | Stocksbridge Park Steels | 140 | W | 3-2 | Cooper 29 77, Wright 86 |
| 12 | 03/10 | H | FA C Q2 | St Helens Town | 185 | W | 6-0 | Holmes 18, Kinney 29 35, Cooper 55, Jones 60 80 |
| 13 | 05/10 | A | PC 1 | Hyde United | 476 | D | 2-2 | Holmes 71, Kinney 86 |
| 14 | 10/10 | A | UL 1 | Farsley Celtic | 157 | D | 3-3 | Kinney 5, Ashton 38 51 |
| 15 | 13/10 | H | PC 1 r | Hyde United | 216 | D | 0-0 | (won 5-4 on pens) |
| 16 | 17/10 | H | FA C Q3 | Northwich Victoria | 635 | W | 2-0 | Ashton 11, Jones 77 |
| 17 | 31/10 | H | FA C Q4 | Leigh RMI | 842 | L | 1-2 | Kinney 65 |
| 18 | 03/11 | H | UL C 2 | Hyde United | 127 | W | 4-1 | Green 11, Wright 20 51, Holmes 47 |
| | 07/11 | A | UL 1 | Hucknall Town | 230 | W | 4-2 | A Wright 32, Marston 38[og], Kinney 50, M Wright 65 |
| 20 | 11/11 | A | UL 1 | Congleton Town | 109 | W | 1-0 | Kinney 75 |
| 21 | 14/11 | A | UL 1 | Farsley Celtic | 77 | D | 1-1 | Wright 58 |
| 22 | 17/11 | H | UL 1 | Witton Albion | 139 | W | 5-0 | Wright 2, Kinney 32, Green 37 68, Jones 72 |
| 23 | 21/11 | A | FA T 2 | Alfreton Town | 109 | W | 2-1 | Green 60, Hennigan 76 |
| 24 | 24/11 | A | Div 1 C 2 | Trafford | 101 | W | 2-0 | Cooper 14, A Wright 72[p] |
| 25 | 28/11 | H | UL 1 | Lincoln United | 337 | W | 5-1 | Wright 42 88, Kinney 48, Holmes 49, Cooper 77 |
| 26 | 08/12 | H | UL 1 | Flixton | 92 | W | 2-1 | Holmes 79, Cooper 83 |
| 27 | 10/12 | A | MPC 1 | Maine Road | 38 | W | 4-2 | Green 38 117, Jones 78, A Wright 102 |
| | | | | | | | | (expelled for fielding ineligible player) |
| 28 | 15/12 | A | UL 1 | Burscough | 108 | W | 3-1 | Cooper 41 71, Kinney 73 |
| | 19/12 | A | UL 1 | Alfreton Town | 117 | W | 2-0 | Kinney 43, Green 90 |
| 30 | 22/12 | A | PC QF | Guiseley | 194 | W | 2-1 | Hannigan 17, Kinney 61 |
| 31 | 28/12 | H | UL 1 | Ashton United | 602 | D | 1-1 | Ashton 45 |
| 32 | 02/01 | H | UL 1 | Belper Town | 307 | W | 4-1 | Wright 34, Holmes 68, Cooper 80, Green 82 |
| 33 | 09/01 | A | UL 1 | Belper Town | 240 | L | 0-3 | |
| 34 | 16/01 | H | FA T 3 | Telford United | 473 | L | 2-3 | Wright 74 84 |
| 35 | 23/01 | A | UL 1 | Eastwood Town | 140 | L | 3-4 | Green 17, Stannard 70, Holmes 74 |
| 36 | 30/01 | H | UL 1 | Whitley Bay | 282 | W | 2-1 | Waring 34, Holmes 53 |
| 37 | 02/02 | H | Div 1 C QF | Bradford Park Avenue | 129 | W | 1-0 | Hinnigan 17 |
| 38 | 06/02 | A | UL 1 | Netherfield Kendal | 93 | W | 2-0 | Holmes 44 80 |
| 39 | 13/02 | H | UL 1 | Netherfield Kendal | 242 | D | 1-1 | Hennigan 85 |
| 40 | 16/02 | H | UL C 3 | Colwyn Bay | 110 | D | 2-2 | Holmes 43[p], Green 71 |
| 41 | 20/02 | A | UL 1 | Lincoln United | 244 | D | 1-1 | Green 82 |
| 42 | 23/02 | H | UL 1 | Great Harwood Town | 116 | W | 3-0 | Green 28, Cooper 45, Wright 74 |
| 43 | 27/02 | A | UL 1 | Gretna | 68 | W | 5-2 | Wright 2 38 76 87, Holmes 16[p] |
| 44 | 06/03 | H | UL 1 | Burscough | 238 | W | 4-2 | Green 18 49, Ashton 27 29 |
| 45 | 11/03 | A | UL C 2 r | Colwyn Bay | 132 | W | 3-2 | Cooper 17, Kinney 29, Stannard 88 |
| 46 | 13/03 | H | UL 1 | Whitley Bay | 140 | D | 1-1 | Wright 38 |
| 47 | 16/03 | A | UL 1 | Trafford | 192 | L | 1-2 | Green 90 |
| 48 | 18/03 | A | Div 1 C SF | Witton Albion | 238 | W | 2-1 | Green 48, Waring 78 |
| 49 | 20/03 | H | UL 1 | Matlock Town | 240 | W | 2-0 | Stannard 17, Cooper 30 |
| 50 | 23/03 | H | PC SF(1) | Stalybridge Celtic | 485 | D | 1-1 | Kinney 44 |
| 51 | 25/03 | A | UL C QF | Blyth Spartans | 289 | W | 3-4 | Cooper 26, Ashton 60, Morley 68 |
| 52 | 27/03 | A | UL 1 | Hucknall Town | 305 | L | 1-3 | Holmes 34 |
| 53 | 30/03 | A | UL 1 | Witton Albion | 307 | W | 2-0 | Holmes 59 83[p] |
| 54 | 01/04 | A | PC SF(2) | Stalybridge Celtic | 547 | W | 3-2 | Kinney 17, Jones 52, Cooper 68 |
| 55 | 03/04 | H | UL 1 | Trafford | 214 | W | 2-0 | Holmes 50[p], Jones 56 |
| 56 | 05/04 | A | UL 1 | Ashton United | 805 | D | 1-1 | Ashton 90 |
| 57 | 10/04 | A | UL 1 | Great Harwood Town | 136 | W | 1-0 | Cooper 17 |
| 58 | 13/04 | H | UL 1 | Gretna | 194 | W | 2-0 | Holmes 45 55 |
| 59 | 15/04 | A | PC F | Leigh RMI | 355 | W | 2-1 | Kinney 12, Jones 30 |
| 60 | 17/04 | H | UL 1 | Harrogate Town | 285 | W | 3-1 | Kinney 45 90, Holmes 66 |
| 61 | 22/04 | H | Div 1 C F | Ashton United | 562 | L | 0-1 | |
| 62 | 24/04 | A | UL 1 | Flixton | 240 | L | 2-3 | Cooper 18, Wright 54 |
| 63 | 26/04 | A | UL 1 | Radcliffe Borough | 128 | L | 2-3 | Waring 59, Stannard 89 |
| 64 | 27/04 | H | UL 1 | Bradford Park Avenue | 138 | W | 2-0 | Harold 51, Hennigan 60 |
| 65 | 01/05 | H | UL 1 | Stocksbridge Park Steels | 250 | W | 3-1 | Kinney 35 45, Cooper 50 |

## PLAYING SQUAD 1999-2000:

GOALKEEPERS: Michael Kinsella (Bootle), David Williams (Bangor City)
DEFENDERS: Dave Ashton, Steve Caswell (Ashton United), Paul Clowes (Ashton United), Ian Harold (Accrington Stanley), Graeme Hughes, Aeon Lattie, Andy Lee, Andrew Taylor (Curzon Ashton), Chris Wareing (Bangor City)
MIDFIELDERS: Ged Hennigan (Barrow), Carl Holmes (Buxton), Franny Hyland (Trafford), Mick Jones (Chorley), John Stannard (Northwich Victoria), Neil Whalley (Runcorn)
FORWARDS: Lee Cooper (Barrow), Nigel Evans (Hyde United), Andy Green (Altrincham), Wes Kinney, Tony Wright (Barrow)

# EMLEY

## CLUB OFFICIALS

Chairman: **Peter Matthews.**
President: **Peter Maude**

Secretary/Press Officer: **Richard Poulain**
17, Smithy Lane, Skelmanthorpe,
Huddersfield HD89DF.
Tel:01484 860323 H, 0411 620726 Mob & B

## FOOTBALL MANAGEMENT TEAM

Manager: Ronnie Glavin.
Asst Manager: Peter Price
Physio: Daryl Brook.

### FACT FILE
Formed: 1903

Nickname: 'The Pewits'

Sponsors: Arrow Self Drive

Colours: Maroon and blue/blue/maroon.

Change Colours: White/maroon/white

Midweek matchday: Monday.

Reserve League: Nth Co's (E) Res Div.

Web:http://www.emleyafc.free-online.co.uk

## GROUND

Emley Welfare Sports Ground, Emley, Huddersfield      Tel: 01924 848398 . Office: 840087
Directions: Follow Huddersfield signs from M1 junct 38, left onto A636 at r'bout, then right
after about 3/4 mile for Emley. 7 miles from Huddersfield (BR) station - buses to Emley Cross.
Capacity: 3,000        Cover: 1,000        Seats: 300
Clubhouse:  (01924 848398). Members' social club open seven nights a week and Saturday &
Sunday. Bingo, discos, occasional cabaret.
Club Shop:  Yes Contact Mrs Linda Sykes (01484 325077)

Pages: 34 Price: £1
Editor: Alan Blackman (01924 403959)

Local Press: Huddersfield Examiner,
Huddersfield & District Chronicle.
Local Radio: Radio Leeds, Radio Sheffield,
Pulse FM, Huddersfield FM.

**PREVIOUS**        Leagues:  Huddersfield; Yorkshire 69-82; Northern Counties East 82-89.  Names: None    Grounds: None.

**CLUB RECORDS**        **Attendance:** 5,134 v Barking, Amateur Cup 3rd Proper 1/2/69.
*18,629 v West Ham Utd, at Upton Pk, 3rd Rd Proper 3/1/99.*
**Win:** 12-0 v Ecclesfield Red Rose9-6-97.        **Defeat:** 7-1 v Altrincham 25-4-98.
**Goalscorer:** Mick Pamment 305.        **Appearances:** Ray Dennis 762.
**Fee Received:** £60,000 for Michael Reynolds (Ayr Utd 98)

**BEST SEASON**        **FA Amateur Cup:** Third Round replay 69-70. **FA Vase:** Runners-up 87-88 (Semi-Final86-87).
**FA Trophy:** Quarter Final 98-99 **FA Cup:** Third Round Proper 97-98 (1-2 v West Ham Utd)

**HONOURS**        FA Vase Runners-up 87-88; Northern Premier Lge Div 1 R-up 90-91; Northern Counties E Lge 87-88, 88-89 (R-up 85-86);
Yorkshire Lg 75-76 77-78 79-80 81-82(R-up(5) 72-74 76-77 78-79 80-81, Lg Cup 69-70 78-79 81-82, Div 2 R-up 69-0;
Sheffield & Hallamshire Senior Cup 75-76 79-80 80-81 83-84 88-89 90-91 91-9297-98; Huddersfield Challenge Cup 82-83
83-84 85-86; Huddersfield Lg(4) 65-69.

Players progressing: A Sweeney (Hartlepool Utd 79), G Cooper(Huddersfield Tn 84), J Francis (Sheffield Utd 88), S Smith (Crewe Alexandra1992), C Alcide
(Lincoln City 95), C Hurst (Huddersfield Tn 97), G Hurst (Ayr Utd 98), M.Reynolds (Ayr United 1998)

*Emley v Rotherham Utd. Simeon Bambrook scores, from Michael Reynolds cross, after 11 minutes to give Emley the lead.   Photo: Bill Wheatcroft*

## EMLEY - MATCH FACTS - 1998-99 SEASON

| No | Date | Venue | Comp | Opponents | Att | Result | Score | Goalscorers |
|---|---|---|---|---|---|---|---|---|
| 1 | 22/08 | A | ULP | Runcorn | 375 | D | 1-1 | Reynolds 37 |
| 2 | 24/08 | H | ULP | Gainsborough Trinity | 383 | W | 3-2 | Reynolds 9, Smith 72, Lacey 86 |
| 3 | 29/08 | A | ULP | Marine | 309 | D | 2-2 | David 20, Thompson 45 |
| 4 | 31/08 | A | ULP | Whitby Town | 878 | L | 0-1 | |
| 5 | 05/09 | H | ULP | Accrington Stanley | 270 | W | 3-1 | Reynolds 48, Bambrook 64, Thompson 86 |
| 6 | 08/09 | A | ULP | Frickley Athletic | 340 | W | 1-0 | Bambrook 26 |
| 7 | 12/09 | H | ULP | Lancaster City | 269 | D | 1-1 | Reynolds 74 |
| 8 | 14/09 | H | ULP | Stalybridge Celtic | 342 | D | 2-2 | Smith 48, Lacey 75 |
| 9 | 19/09 | A | ULP | Winsford United | 180 | L | 2-3 | Hurst 56, Thompson 59 |
| 10 | 21/09 | H | ULP | Bishop Auckland | 339 | W | 2-0 | Reynolds 46, Bambrook 81 |
| 11 | 26/09 | A | ULP | Altrincham | 437 | L | 0-3 | |
| 12 | 29/09 | A | ULP | Blyth Spartans | 380 | W | 2-0 | David 6, Hurst 10 |
| 13 | 03/10 | A | FA C Q2 | Colwyn Bay | 454 | W | 1-0 | Bambrook 85 |
| 14 | 09/10 | A | ULP | Worksop Town | 1070 | W | 2-0 | Lacey 29, Bambrook 37 |
| 15 | 14/10 | A | ULP | Bishop Auckland | 209 | D | 1-1 | Hurst 13 |
| 16 | 17/10 | H | FA C Q3 | Marine | 381 | D | 0-0 | |
| 17 | 20/10 | A | FA C Q3 r | Marine | 219 | W | 4-1 | Lacey 35, David 40, Reynolds 60, Banks 68 |
| 18 | 31/10 | H | FA C Q4 | Gateshead | 723 | D | 1-1 | Hurst 67 |
| 19 | 04/11 | A | FA C Q4 r | Gateshead | 403 | W | 2-0 | Tonks 62, David 90 |
| 20 | 07/11 | A | ULP | Leigh RMI | 351 | D | 0-0 | |
| 21 | 09/11 | A | S SC 1 | Parkgate | 198 | D | 2-2 | Thorpe 40, Smith 108 |
| 22 | 14/11 | H | FA C 1 | Rotherham United | 6062 | D | 1-1 | Bambrook 14          Barnsley |
| 23 | 17/11 | A | S SC 1 r | Parkgate | 128 | W | 4-0 | Lacy 12, Bambrook 34 68, Bray 78 |
| 24 | 21/11 | H | FA T 2 | Whitley Bay | 294 | W | 1-0 | Bambrook 70 |
| 25 | 24/11 | A | FA C 1 r | Rotherham United | 5077 | L | 1-3 | Bambrook 1 |
| 26 | 28/11 | A | ULP | Hyde United | 549 | W | 1-0 | Smith 89 |
| 27 | 30/11 | H | ULC 2 | Hucknall Town | 216 | D | 2-2 | Wilson 32, Bambrook 65 |
| 28 | 05/12 | H | ULP | Spennymoor United | 243 | W | 1-0 | Bambrook 74 |
| 29 | 09/12 | H | S SC 2 | NCB Maltby M. Welfare | 115 | W | 6-0 | Wainman 4 67, Bradley 14 25, Thorpe 32, Fearon 77 |
| 30 | 12/12 | A | ULP | Gateshead | 239 | L | 1-2 | Thorpe 85 |
| 31 | 19/12 | H | ULP | Leigh RMI | 244 | L | 0-2 | |
| 32 | 28/12 | H | ULP | Blyth Spartans | 326 | W | 2-1 | Hurst 15, Wood 78 |
| 33 | 02/01 | H | ULP | Marine | 301 | D | 1-1 | Thompson 38 |
| 34 | 09/01 | A | ULP | Chorley | 298 | D | 1-1 | David 89 |
| 35 | 23/01 | H | ULP | Bamber Bridge | 234 | L | 0-1 | |
| 36 | 27/01 | A | FA T 3 | Shepshed Dynamo | 279 | D | 1-1 | David 45 |
| 37 | 30/01 | A | ULP | Bamber Bridge | 425 | W | 2-1 | David 49, Wilson 65 |
| 38 | 01/02 | H | FA T 3 r | Shepshed Dynamo | 426 | W | 3-1 | Wilson 35 70, David 45 |
| 39 | 06/02 | A | FA T 4 | Guiseley | 827 | W | 2-0 | Thompson 68, Tonks 89 |
| 40 | 13/02 | H | ULP | Gateshead | 213 | L | 1-2 | Jones 85 |
| 41 | 20/02 | A | ULP | Lancaster City | 225 | D | 1-1 | Wilson 37 |
| 42 | 23/02 | H | ULP | Frickley Athletic | 221 | D | 1-1 | David 86 |
| 43 | 27/02 | H | FA T 5 | Whitby Town | 908 | W | 2-0 | Waller 22[og], Calcutt 30 |
| 44 | 08/03 | H | ULC 2 r | Hucknall Town | 144 | L | 2-3 | David 24, Calcutt 52 |
| 45 | 10/03 | A | S SC QF | Sheffield | 0 | W | 3-1 | Calcutt 19, David 31, Sheldon 45 |
| 46 | 12/03 | H | ULP | Worksop Town | 413 | D | 2-2 | Wilson 11 86 |
| 47 | 15/03 | H | ULP | Winsford United | 245 | D | 1-1 | David 31 |
| 48 | 20/03 | A | ULP | Stalybridge Celtic | 536 | L | 0-2 | |
| 49 | 23/03 | A | ULP | Accrington Stanley | 326 | L | 0-2 | |
| 50 | 27/03 | H | FA T QF | Cheltenham Town | 1339 | L | 0-1 | |
| 51 | 29/03 | H | ULP | Runcorn | 201 | D | 1-1 | Wood 82 |
| 52 | 03/04 | H | ULP | Spennymoor United | 229 | L | 1-2 | Hurst 51 |
| 53 | 05/04 | H | ULP | Guiseley | 289 | L | 0-1 | |
| 54 | 10/04 | H | ULP | Whitby Town | 233 | L | 0-1 | |
| 55 | 12/04 | H | ULP | Hyde United | 175 | D | 1-1 | David 64 |
| 56 | 15/04 | A | ULP | Guiseley | 378 | L | 1-1 | Lacey 36 |
| 57 | 17/04 | A | ULP | Gainsborough Trinity | 341 | W | 2-1 | Thorpe 82, David 89 |
| 58 | 19/04 | H | ULP | Chorley | 220 | W | 1-0 | Wilson 50 |
| 59 | 24/04 | H | ULP | Colwyn Bay | 180 | D | 0-0 | |
| 60 | 26/04 | A | S SC SF | Wombwell Main | n/k | W | 2-0 | Jackson 6, Featherstone 86[p]Worsbrough Bridge |
| 61 | 29/04 | A | ULP | Altrincham | 1526 | L | 0-1 | |
| 62 | 01/05 | A | ULP | Colwyn Bay | 282 | D | 3-3 | Tonks 23, Smith 41, Thorpe 66 |
| 63 | 04/05 | A | S SC F | Stocksbridge Park Steels | n/k | L | 0-1 | (at Sheffield Wednesday) |

**PLAYING SQUAD 1999-2000:**

GOALKEEPERS: Andy Rhodes (Airdrieonians)

DEFENDERS: Greg Fee (Telford United), Mark Haran (Frickley Athletic), Simon Jones, Steve Nicholson (Farsley Celtic), Richard Walker, Nicky Wood

MIDFIELDERS: Paul Hutson, Steve Smith (Huddersfield Town), Leon Wainman (Alfreton Town), Andy Wilson (Ossett Albion)

FORWARDS: Danny Day (Ossett Albion), James Featherstone (Scunthorpe United), Scott Jackson, Jamie Robshaw (Denaby United)

# FRICKLEY ATHLETIC

## CLUB OFFICIALS

Chairman: **Mike Twiby**
Tel: 01977 648070
Financial Secretary: **D Fisher**
Tel: 01977 643316 B
Secretary / Treasurer: **D Fisher**
31 Vickers Ave., South Elmsall WF9 3LW.
Tel: 01977 643316

## FOOTBALL MANAGEMENT TEAM

Manager: Ian Thompson
Tel: 01977 609748

**FACT FILE**

Formed: 1910
Nickname: The Blues
Sponsors: Next Distributions
Colours: All blue
Change colours: Yellow & black.
Midweek home matchday: Tuesday
Reserves' League: None

UniBond
PREMIER
LEAGUE
1997-98

FRICKLEY ATHLETIC F.C.

£1 OFFICIAL MATCH PROGRAMME

Berwin
Langthwaite
Official Club Sponsor

Todays Visitors...
COLWYN BAY

## GROUND

Westfield Lane, South Elmsall, Pontefract          Tel/Fax: 01977 642460
Directions: Follow signs for South Elmsall from A1 and A638. Left at Superdrug warehouse,
right at T junction and immediately left up Westfield Lane. Left into Oxford Road (opposite
Westfield Hotel) - ground at bottom on right. Two miles from South Elmsall (BR).
Capacity: 6,000          Cover: 2,500          Seats: 800
Clubhouse: On ground open matchdays, food available.
Club Shop: Yes

Pages: 40 Price: £1
Editor: S Pennock Tel: 01302 835956

Local Press: South Yorks Times, Hemsworth
& South Elmsall Express. Local Radio:
Radio Sheffield, Radio Hallam, Radio Leeds.

**PREVIOUS**          Leagues: Sheffield; Yorkshire 22-24; Midland Counties 24-33 34-60 70-76;Cheshire County 60-70;
Northern Premier 76-80; GMV Conference (Alliance Premier) 80-87.          Name: Frickley Colliery

**CLUB RECORDS**          **Attendance:** 6,500 v Rotherham United, FA Cup First Round 1971.
**Goalscorer:** K Whiteley.  **Defeat:** 0-4   **Fee Paid:** £1,800.
**Fee Received:** £12,500 for Paul Shirtliff (Boston Utd) & £12,500 for Russ Wilcox (Northampton)

**BEST SEASON**          **FA Cup:** 3rd Rd 1985-86 (1-3 v Rotherham H).2nd Rd 84-85 (0-1 at Darlington). 1st Rd 36-37 57-58 63-64 71-72 73-74
83-84 86-87 88-89. League clubs defeated: Hartlepool United 85-86.          **FA Trophy:** Quarter-Finals 84-85.

**HONOURS**          Alliance Premier Lg R-up 85-86, Midland Counties Lg R-up 72-73 (Lg Cup 75-76),Yorkshire Lg R-up 23-24, Sheffield &
Hallamshire Senior Cup 27-28 56-57 60-6162-63 66-67 78-79 85-86 87-88 89-90, Sheffield Assoc. Lg 20-21 (R-up 11-12).
Players Progressing: Dennis Smith & Jack Brownsword (Hull1946), Stan Scrimshaw (Halifax 1947), William Callaghan (Aldershot 1949), Leo Dickens 1950
John Ashley & Graham Caulfield (York 1950 & 67), Ron Barritt(Leeds 1951), John Pickup (Bradford PA 1955), Tom Hymers & Arthur Ashmore &Stewart
Gray (Doncaster 1958 & 66 & 78), Colin Roberts (Bradford City 1959),Derek Downing (Middlesbrough 1965), Graham Reed & Russell Wilcox
(Northampton1985 & 86), Will Foley (Swansea 1986), Gary Brook (Newport 1987), Wayne Scargill (Bradford City 94-95), Andy Hayward (Rotherham Utd.).

Back Row: Ian Thompson, Chris Hilton, Paul Norton, Russ Green, Mark Haran, Dean Jones
Front Row: Mark Whalley, Scott Armstrong, Carl Fothersgill, Lee Stratford, Mark Hancock, Gary Hatto
Photo: Bill Wheatcroft

# FRICKLEY ATHLETIC - MATCH FACTS - 1998-99 SEASON

| No | Date | Venue | Comp | Opponents | Att | Result | Score | Goalscorers |
|---|---|---|---|---|---|---|---|---|
| | 22/08 | A | ULP | Altrincham | 685 | D | 1-1 | Whalley 44 |
| | 25/08 | H | ULP | Bishop Auckland | 181 | D | 0-0 | |
| | 29/08 | H | ULP | Accrington Stanley | 219 | D | 0-0 | |
| | 31/08 | A | ULP | Worksop Town | 581 | L | 0-2 | |
| | 05/09 | A | ULP | Colwyn Bay | 246 | W | 2-0 | Hatto 19, Fothergill 88 |
| | 08/09 | H | ULP | Emley | 340 | L | 0-1 | |
| | 12/09 | H | ULP | Chorley | 208 | D | 2-2 | Stratford 67, Hancock 89 |
| | 16/09 | A | ULP | Bishop Auckland | 140 | D | 2-2 | Fothergill 36, Hatto 89[p] |
| | 19/09 | A | ULP | Lancaster City | 220 | L | 0-5 | |
| 0 | 22/09 | H | ULP | Blyth Spartans | 215 | W | 2-0 | Fuller 72, Fothergill 80 |
| 1 | 26/09 | H | ULP | Bamber Bridge | 199 | L | 0-2 | |
| 2 | 30/09 | A | ULP | Gateshead | 212 | W | 3-2 | Hatto 26[p] 45[p], Frank 31 |
| 3 | 03/10 | A | FA C Q2 | Selby Town | 197 | W | 2-1 | Armstrong 70, Jones 86 |
| 4 | 10/10 | A | ULP | Marine | 228 | W | 4-1 | Field 33, Fuller 55 83, Stratford 89 |
| 5 | 17/10 | H | FA C Q3 | Witton Albion | 230 | W | 1-0 | Stratford 84 |
| 6 | 24/10 | A | FA T 1 | Marine | 141 | W | 3-2 | Armstrong 4, Fothergill 47, Hilton 71 |
| 7 | 31/10 | A | FA C Q4 | Gresley Rovers | 530 | D | 0-0 | |
| 8 | 05/11 | A | FA C Q4 r | Gresley Rovers | 621 | L | 1-2 | Armstrong 3 |
| 9 | 07/11 | A | ULP | Runcorn | 278 | D | 1-1 | Jones 80 |
| 0 | 10/11 | A | S SC 1 | Maltby Main | 0 | W | 3-0 | Green 30, Fothergill 64, Duffty 86 |
| 1 | 14/11 | H | ULP | Guiseley | 249 | L | 1-2 | Green 84 |
| 2 | 21/11 | A | FA T 2 | Doncaster Rovers | 2003 | W | 2-0 | Fuller 39 54 |
| 3 | 05/12 | H | ULP | Colwyn Bay | 151 | W | 2-1 | Hilton 81, Armstrong 84 |
| 4 | 08/12 | H | S SC 2 | Sheffield Bankers | 97 | W | 4-1 | Green 45, Duffty 60 76, Hilton 63 |
| 5 | 12/12 | H | ULP | Runcorn | 183 | D | 1-1 | Duffty 83 |
| 6 | 15/12 | A | ULC 2 | Worksop Town | 270 | W | 3-1 | Hatto 5, Fuller 57, Jones 90 |
| 7 | 19/12 | A | ULP | Accrington Stanley | 366 | D | 1-1 | Field 52 |
| 8 | 26/12 | H | ULP | Whitby Town | 207 | D | 3-3 | Green 16 40, Brooke 78 |
| 9 | 28/12 | A | ULP | Stalybridge Celtic | 524 | D | 2-2 | Field 25, Green 85 |
| 0 | 02/01 | H | ULP | Gateshead | 218 | L | 0-2 | |
| 1 | 09/01 | H | ULP | Leigh RMI | 174 | L | 0-2 | |
| 2 | 19/01 | A | FA T 3 | Whitby Town | 467 | L | 1-2 | Fothergill 5 |
| 3 | 23/01 | A | ULP | Winsford United | 148 | D | 2-2 | Jones 45, Hatto 51 |
| 4 | 30/01 | H | ULP | Stalybridge Celtic | 279 | W | 3-2 | Fuller 10, Hatto 38 46 |
| 5 | 02/02 | A | ULC 3 | Guiseley | 209 | L | 1-3 | Haran 89[p] |
| 6 | 06/02 | A | ULP | Spennymoor United | 133 | W | 1-0 | Fothergill 73 |
| 7 | 13/02 | H | ULP | Lancaster City | 158 | W | 3-2 | Jones 12, Fuller 44, Brooke 54 |
| 8 | 20/02 | A | ULP | Bamber Bridge | 329 | L | 2-3 | Duffty 69, Fothergill 81 |
| 9 | 23/02 | A | ULP | Emley | 221 | D | 1-1 | Hatto 18[p] |
| 0 | 27/02 | H | ULP | Marine | 189 | D | 1-1 | Hatto 74 |
| 1 | 13/03 | A | ULP | Chorley | 310 | D | 1-1 | Collins 89 |
| 2 | 17/03 | H | S SC QF | Denaby United | 87 | W | 1-0 | Fothergill 20 |
| 3 | 20/03 | H | ULP | Hyde United | 180 | W | 3-0 | Green 51, Hatto 79[p] 86[p] |
| 4 | 22/03 | A | ULP | Hyde United | 357 | L | 0-2 | |
| 5 | 26/03 | H | ULP | Worksop Town | 366 | L | 2-3 | Hatto 53[p], Armstrong 68 |
| 6 | 03/04 | A | ULP | Gainsborough Trinity | 471 | L | 1-4 | Fothergill 29 |
| 7 | 05/04 | H | ULP | Spennymoor United | 161 | L | 1-2 | Fothergill 17 |
| 8 | 07/04 | A | ULP | Guiseley | 200 | L | 0-3 | |
| 9 | 10/04 | A | ULP | Leigh RMI | 161 | W | 1-0 | Fothergill 88 |
| 0 | 13/04 | A | ULP | Whitby Town | 554 | L | 0-4 | |
| 1 | 17/04 | H | ULP | Winsford United | 120 | W | 3-1 | Fothergill 51, Green 56, Brookes 85 |
| 2 | 24/04 | H | ULP | Gainsborough Trinity | 231 | L | 1-2 | Haran 62 |
| 3 | 27/04 | H | ULP | Altrincham | 425 | L | 0-3 | |
| 4 | 29/04 | H | S SC SF | Stocksbridge Park Steels | n/k | L | 1-2 | |
| 5 | 01/05 | A | ULP | Blyth Spartans | 263 | D | 2-2 | Brooke 26[p], Hancock 30 |

**PLAYING SQUAD 1999-2000:**

GOALKEEPERS: Paul Norton (Alfreton Town), Derek O'connor (Bradford Park Avenue)
DEFENDERS: David Hilton (Ayr United), Dean Jones (Barnsley)
MIDFIELDERS: Dave Dickinson (local football), Darren Fields (Pontefract Collieries), Simon Fuller (Emley), Paul Hayward (Emley), Mick Priestley (Guiseley), Craig Elkin (Hemsworth Town)
FORWARDS: Danny Drewster (Sheffield Wednesday), Gary Duffty (Matlock Town), Gareth Hooley (Pontefract Collieries), Danny Toronczak (Liversedge), Mark Walley (Nottingham Forest)

# GAINSBOROUGH TRINITY

### CLUB OFFICIALS

Chairman: **Pat Lobley**
President: **Ken Marsden.**
Secretary/Press Officer: **Frank Nicholson**
9 North Street, Morton,
Gainsborough, Lincs DN213AS.
Tel. 01427 615239, Fax 01427 615239.
Commercial Director: **Tim Hanson.**

### FOOTBALL MANAGEMENT TEAM

Manager: Steve Richards
Asst Manager: Paul Olsson.
Physio: Mick Gilbert

### FACT FILE

Formed: 1873
Nickname: The Blues
Sponsors: Eastern Generation.
Colours: All Blue
Change colours: Green/black/green
Midweek home matchday: Tuesday
Reserve Team's League:
98-99Captain: Steve Price
P.o.Y.: Nicky Limber
Top scorer: Iain Quinn

### GROUND
The Northolme, Gainsborough, Lincs DN21 2QW
Tel: 01427 - 613295 (office)  615625 (club)  613295 (Fax)
Directions:  The Northolme is situated opposite the Texaco and Fina petrol stations on the
A159 Gainsborough to Scunthorpe road. Two miles from Lea Road (BR)
Capacity: 3,500          Cover: 2,500          Seats: 515
Clubhouse: Executive `Club on the Park' (01427 615625) open Saturday matchday
lunchtimes. Restaurant facilities.
Club Shop: Yes, contact Nigel Tasker on 01522 542014.

Pages: 32 Price: ¨1
Editor: Basil Godley (01427 611612)

Local Press: Gainsborough News,
Lincolnshire Echo.
Local Radio: BBC Radio Lincs, Lincs FM

**PREVIOUS**     Leagues: Midland Counties 1889-96, 12-60, 61-68, Football Lge 1896-1912,Central Alliance 60-61.
Names: None          Grounds: None

**CLUB RECORDS**     **Attendance:** 9,760 v Scunthorpe Utd. Midland Lge. 1948.
**Fee Paid:** £3,000 for Stuart Lowe (Buxton 89-90).     **Fee Received:** £30,000 for Tony James (Lincoln 1988).
**Win:** 7-0 v Fleetwood Town and Great Harwood Town.     **Defeat:** 2-7 v Hyde Utd.

**BEST SEASON**     FA Cup: 3rd Rd 1886-87, 1st Rd on 33 occasions.     **FA Trophy:** 2nd Rd, 2nd replay86-87.

**HONOURS**     Northern Premier Lge Cup 81-82 96-97 (R-up 71-72); Midland Co's Lge 1890-91,1927-28, 48-49, 66-67 (R-up 1891-92,
1895-96, 13-14, 28-29); Lincs Senior Cup 1889-90, 92-93, 94-95, 97-98, 1903-05, 06-07, 10-11, 46-49, 50-51, 57-59, 63-64

Players Progressing:  Since 1980 - Stewart Evans (Sheffield Utd 80), Tony James, Ian Bowling & John Schofield (Lincoln 88), Dave
Redfern(Stockport 91), Richard Logan (Huddersfield 93), Glenn Humphries (Hull City).

Steve Price heads away for Gainsborough Trinity against Blyth Spartans with support from Nick Lumber (left) and
Rob Hanby.   Photo: Julie Artiss

## GAINSBOROUGH TRINITY - MATCH FACTS - 1998-99 SEASON

| No | Date | Venue | Comp | Opponents | Att | Result | Score | Goalscorers |
|---|---|---|---|---|---|---|---|---|
| | 25/07 | H | L SC QF | Lincoln City | n/k | L | 1-4 | Maxwell 82 |
| | 22/08 | H | ULP | Winsford United | 404 | D | 0-0 | |
| | 24/08 | A | ULP | Emley | 383 | L | 2-3 | Riley 29, Wood 58[og] |
| | 29/08 | A | ULP | Runcorn | 327 | D | 0-0 | |
| | 31/08 | H | ULP | Hyde United | 530 | L | 0-1 | |
| | 05/09 | A | ULP | Leigh RMI | 201 | L | 0-3 | |
| | 09/09 | H | ULP | Guiseley | 375 | D | 2-2 | Dunn 49 84 |
| | 12/09 | H | ULP | Marine | 373 | W | 3-0 | Dunn 24, Marquis 53, Brown 67 |
| | 14/09 | A | ULP | Hyde United | 457 | W | 2-1 | Maxwell 44, Hanby 81 |
| 0 | 19/09 | A | ULP | Gateshead | 326 | W | 2-0 | Reed 54, Dunn 57 |
| 1 | 23/09 | H | P C 1 | Lincoln United | 415 | W | 6-2 | Maxwell 7 16, Reed 34, Dunn 68 72 82 |
| 2 | 26/09 | H | ULP | Chorley | 485 | W | 3-0 | Reed 12, Maxwell 17, Dunn 21 |
| 3 | 29/09 | A | ULP | Altrincham | 590 | D | 1-1 | Dunn 90 |
| 4 | 03/10 | A | FA C Q2 | Hyde United | 482 | | 0-4 | |
| 5 | 07/10 | H | ULP | Bishop Auckland | 416 | W | 2-1 | Hanby 43, Dunn 58 |
| 6 | 10/10 | A | ULP | Bamber Bridge | 251 | W | 4-1 | Dunn 39, Williams 47, Marquis 72, Bennett 87 |
| 7 | 13/10 | A | ULP | Guiseley | 287 | L | 1-2 | Brown 83 |
| 8 | 17/10 | H | ULP | Bamber Bridge | 449 | L | 0-1 | |
| 9 | 31/10 | H | ULP | Spennymoor United | 412 | W | 3-1 | Bennett 37, Reed 77, Brown 83 |
| 20 | 04/11 | A | FA T 1 | Winsford United | 104 | W | 1-0 | Dunn 18 |
| 21 | 07/11 | H | ULP | Lancaster City | 484 | W | 1-0 | Bennett 12[p] |
| 22 | 11/11 | H | ULC 2 | Lincoln United | 411 | W | 3-1 | Reed 33 81, Bennett 76 |
| 23 | 14/11 | A | ULP | Accrington Stanley | 388 | L | 1-2 | Dunn 77 |
| 24 | 21/11 | H | FA T 2 | Harrogate Town | 398 | W | 4-1 | Bennett 20[p], Olsson 41, Dunn 42 89 |
| 25 | 28/11 | H | ULP | Stalybridge Celtic | 536 | L | 1-4 | Brown 8 |
| 26 | 05/12 | A | ULP | Bishop Auckland | 181 | L | 1-2 | Dunn 27 |
| 27 | 09/12 | H | P C QF | Stalybridge Celtic | 266 | D | 2-2 | Norbury 38, Bennett 43[p] |
| 28 | 12/12 | A | ULP | Chorley | 189 | W | 2-0 | Norbury 45, Turnbull 47 |
| 29 | 19/12 | A | ULP | Altrincham | 604 | L | 0-3 | |
| 30 | 22/12 | A | P C QF r | Stalybridge Celtic | 186 | L | 1-2 | Dunn 46 |
| 31 | 26/12 | H | ULP | Worksop Town | 1003 | W | 3-1 | Reid 2, Morrow 17, Allison 84 |
| 32 | 28/12 | A | ULP | Whitby Town | 507 | L | 1-5 | Bennett 5 |
| 33 | 02/01 | H | ULP | Runcorn | 485 | D | 1-1 | Bennett 76 |
| 34 | 16/01 | H | FA T 3 | Boston United | 1647 | L | 1-4 | Turnbull 90 |
| 35 | 23/01 | H | ULP | Blyth Spartans | 361 | L | 3-4 | Hanby 27, Marquis 51, Turnbull 78 |
| 36 | 30/01 | A | ULP | Blyth Spartans | 382 | W | 2-0 | Dunn 64, Ramsden 67[og] |
| 37 | 02/02 | A | ULC 3 | Blyth Spartans | 325 | D | 0-0 | |
| 38 | 06/02 | A | ULP | Winsford United | 114 | L | 0-2 | |
| 39 | 10/02 | H | ULC 3 r | Blyth Spartans | 224 | L | 0-1 | |
| 40 | 13/02 | H | ULP | Leigh RMI | 378 | W | 2-0 | Swailes 43, Marquis 71 |
| 41 | 20/02 | A | ULP | Marine | 262 | W | 2-1 | Norbury 30, Raspin 44 |
| 42 | 27/02 | A | ULP | Stalybridge Celtic | 383 | L | 0-2 | |
| 43 | 02/03 | H | ULP | Whitby Town | 390 | W | 2-0 | Bennett 31[p], Price 79 |
| 44 | 13/03 | H | ULP | Gateshead | 429 | D | 1-1 | Hopkins 14 |
| 45 | 20/03 | H | ULP | Accrington Stanley | 380 | L | 0-4 | |
| 46 | 27/03 | A | ULP | Lancaster City | 205 | W | 1-0 | Price 52 |
| 47 | 03/04 | H | ULP | Frickley Athletic | 471 | W | 4-1 | Morrow 3 67, Bennett 45, Dunn 48 |
| 48 | 05/04 | A | ULP | Worksop Town | 291 | D | 1-1 | Bennett 57 |
| 49 | 10/04 | A | ULP | Colwyn Bay | 275 | W | 4-3 | Allison 2, Sharman 45, Tucker 47, Dunn 85 |
| 50 | 13/04 | A | ULP | Spennymoor United | 214 | D | 1-1 | Norbury 42 |
| 51 | 17/04 | H | ULP | Emley | 341 | L | 1-2 | Norbury 4 |
| 52 | 24/04 | A | ULP | Frickley Athletic | 231 | W | 2-1 | Morrow 35, Sharman 54 |
| 53 | 27/04 | H | ULP | Colwyn Bay | 400 | W | 3-1 | Morrow 5, Allinson 12, Bennett 67 |

## PLAYING SQUAD 1999-2000:

GOALKEEPERS: Steve Curry (Goole), Matt Dixon (Altrincham), Rick Moore (Gateshead), Paul Setterfield (Parkgate), DEFENDERS: Neil Allison (Singapore), Phil Brown (Brodsworth Miners Welfare), Leonard Curtis (Boston United), Ross Hewson (Boston United), Chris James (Leek Town), Neil Lacey (Emley), Nicky Limber (Weymouth), Paul Olsson (North Ferriby United), Neil Sykes (Rossington), Andy Taylor (North Ferriby United), Midfielders:, Troy Bennett (Scarborough), Steve Charles (Boston United), Steve Circuit (Leek Town), Jim Dobbin (Grimsby Town), Rob Hanby (Scarborough), Steve Price (Leek Town), Sam Sharman (Hull City), Nick Tilly (Matlock Town) FORWARDS: Simon Bochenski (Billericay Town), Craig Hopkins (Kettering Town), Jamie Mitchell (Scarborough), Mick Norbury (Telford United), Rory Prendergast (York City), Andy Saville (Scarborough)

# GATESHEAD

## CLUB OFFICIALS

President: **J C Thomas**
Chairman: **John Gibson**
Vice Chairman: **Mark Donnelly**
General Manager: **Mark Donnelly**
Fixture Secretary: **Arthur Waggott**
Press Officer: **Andy Wilson**

## FACT FILE

Founded: 1930
Nickname: The Tynesiders
Sponsors: Cameron Hall Developments Ltd
Club colours: Black & white/black/white
Change colours: All yellow
Midweek home matchday: Wednesday
Reserves League: Vaux Wearside League

**FOOTBALL MANAGEMENT TEAM**

Manager: Matt Pearson
Asst. Man.: Kenny Lowe
Player Coach: Kenny lowe
Physio: Bev Dougherty

**GROUND**

International Stadium, Neilson Road, Gateshead, NE10 0EF.
Tel: 0191 478 3883   Fax : 0191 477 1315.
Directions: From the South follow A1(M) to Granada services (Birtley),take right hand fork marked A194(M) (Tyne Tunnel, South Shields) follow A194 to first roundabout, turn left onto A184 - then 3 miles to stadium. Turn right at traffic lights into Neilson Road.   BY RAIL to Newcastle Central Station,transfer to the Metro System and then to Gateshead Stadium.
Capacity: 11,795       Seats: 11,795       Cover: 3,300
Clubhouse: Bar inside Tyne & Wear stand open before, during and after matches.The Stadium P.H. adjacent to ground. Club Shop: Sells full range of souvenirs, badges, programmes & fanzines.Contact: Mark Donnelly (0191 4783883).

Pages: 36   Price: £1.20
Editor: Andy Wilson (0191 478 3883)

Local Press: Gateshead Post, Newcastle Chronicle & Echo, Sunderland Echo,Sunday Sun. Local Radio: BBC Radio Newcastle, Metro FM, Century Radio.

**PREVIOUS**       Leagues: Football League - Div. 3 N. 30-58, Div.4 58-60, Northern Counties League 60-62, North Regional League 1962-1968, Northern Premier 68-70, 73-83,85-86, 87-90; Wearside 70-71; Midland Lge 71-72; Alliance Premier (Conference)83-85, 86-87, 90-98.       Grounds: Redheugh Park - 1930-1971

**CLUB RECORDS**       Attendance: 11,750 v Newcastle United (Pre-Season Friendly. 7th August 95)
Win: 8-0 v Netherfield, Northern Premier League.       **Defeat:** 0-9 v Sutton United, 22.09.90, GMVC.
Career goalscorer: Bob Topping       **Career appearances:** Simon Smith, 450, 85-94
Fee paid: £9,000 for Paul Cavell (Dagenham &Redbridge).       **Fee received:** For Kenny Cramman from Rushden & D.

**BEST SEASON**       FA Cup: Quarter Final, 1952-53.       **FA Trophy:** Quarter Final, 0-1 v Wycombe W. (A) 13.3.93

**HONOURS**       Football League Div. 3 North R-up 31-32, 49-50; Northern Premier - Champions82-83, 85-86; Runners-up 89-90; Northern Premier League Cup R-up 89-90;Multipart Shield 85-86.

Players Progressing: Osher Williams(Southampton, Stockport, Port Vale, Preston), John McGinley (Sunderland,Lincoln), Billy Askew (Hull City, Newcastle United), Lawrie Pearson (Hull City,Port Vale), Ian Johnson (Northampton Town), Ken Davies (Stockport), Kenny Lowe(Birmingham C., Barnet, Darlington, Stoke C.)

Back Row (L-R): Brian Rowe, Ben Ryan, Sam Kitchen, Tony Hall, Dion Raitt, Graham Pepper, Gary O'Hara, Mark Scott.   Centre Row: Bob Howe (Kit mngr), Arthur Waggott (secretary), Paul Proudlock, Paul Rowntree, Adrian Swan, Chris Heron, Tom Bone (director), Andy Wilson (asst sec./press officer), Bev Dougherty (physio).   Front Row: Richie Watson, Craig Veart, Mattie Pearson (mngr), John Gibson (chairman), Mark Donnelly (director), Kenny Lowe (player/coach), John Watson, Steve Bowey.

## GATESHEAD - MATCH FACTS - 1998-99 SEASON

| No | Date | Venue | Comp | Opponents | Att | Result | Score | Goalscorers |
|---|---|---|---|---|---|---|---|---|
| | 22/08 | H | ULP | Chorley | 324 | D | 0-0 | |
| | 25/08 | A | ULP | Lancaster City | 206 | D | 2-2 | Lowe 48, Bowey 82 |
| | 29/08 | A | ULP | Hyde United | 371 | L | 0-3 | |
| | 31/08 | H | ULP | Guiseley | 305 | W | 1-0 | Fletcher 67 |
| | 05/09 | H | ULP | Bamber Bridge | 308 | W | 2-0 | Fletcher 58, Proudlock 76 |
| | 09/09 | A | ULP | Bishop Auckland | 344 | D | 2-2 | Fletcher 61, O'Hara 89 |
| | 12/09 | A | ULP | Stalybridge Celtic | 488 | W | 3-0 | Rowntree 3, Fletcher 37 61 |
| | 16/09 | H | ULP | Whitby Town | 406 | D | 1-1 | Scott 84 |
| | 19/09 | H | ULP | Gainsborough Trinity | 326 | L | 0-2 | |
| 10 | 22/09 | A | ULP | Spennymoor United | 384 | D | 2-2 | Proudlock 69, Lowe 90 |
| 1 | 26/09 | A | ULP | Runcorn | 298 | L | 0-1 | |
| 2 | 30/09 | H | ULP | Frickley Athletic | 212 | L | 2-3 | Veart 6, Proudlock 48 |
| 3 | 03/10 | H | FA C Q2 | Bishop Auckland | 313 | W | 3-0 | Kitchen 50, Proudlock 61, Lowe 78 |
| 4 | 06/10 | A | ULP | Accrington Stanley | 401 | W | 3-1 | Ainsley 8 84, Norbury 15 |
| 5 | 10/10 | H | ULP | Colwyn Bay | 289 | W | 3-2 | Bowey 2 88, Kitchen 20 |
| 6 | 14/10 | H | ULP | Spennymoor United | 298 | L | 0-1 | |
| 7 | 17/10 | H | FA C Q3 | Barrow | 386 | W | 2-1 | Ryan 67 89 |
| 8 | 21/10 | A | ULP | Bishop Auckland | 213 | W | 4-1 | Ainsley 40, Heron 66, Fletcher 76 80 |
| 9 | 24/10 | H | FA T 1 | Paget Rangers | 198 | D | 2-2 | Kitchen 31, Proudlock 76 |
| 10 | 28/10 | A | FA T 1 r | Paget Rangers | 84 | L | 0-1 | |
| 21 | 31/10 | A | FA C Q4 | Emley | 723 | D | 1-1 | Heron 66 |
| 2 | 04/11 | H | FA C Q4 r | Emley | 403 | L | 0-2 | |
| 3 | 07/11 | A | ULP | Altrincham | 814 | L | 0-1 | |
| 24 | 14/11 | A | ULC 2 | Whitby Town | 435 | W | 2-1 | Fletcher 60, Kitchen 80 |
| 5 | 21/11 | A | ULP | Winsford United | 181 | W | 2-1 | Fletcher 15, Ainsley 62 |
| 26 | 28/11 | A | ULP | Worksop Town | 296 | W | 3-2 | Lowe 6 49, Preen 53 |
| 7 | 05/12 | A | ULP | Bamber Bridge | 253 | L | 1-3 | Raitt 41 |
| 8 | 12/12 | H | ULP | Emley | 239 | W | 2-1 | Bowes 22, Preen 88 |
| 9 | 19/12 | A | ULP | Marine | 221 | W | 1-0 | Raitt 82 |
| 0 | 26/12 | A | ULP | Blyth Spartans | 1046 | W | 2-1 | Fletcher 52, Preen 75 |
| 11 | 28/12 | H | ULP | Runcorn | 304 | D | 2-2 | Fletcher 60, Proudlock 72 |
| 2 | 02/01 | A | ULP | Frickley Athletic | 218 | W | 2-0 | Raitt 46, Green 85 |
| 3 | 09/01 | H | ULP | Lancaster City | 284 | W | 7-1 | Ward 21, Fletcher 58 76, Proudlock 64, Bowey 71p, |
| 4 | | | | | | | | Preen 81, Lynch 89 |
| 5 | 23/01 | H | ULP | Marine | 274 | D | 2-2 | Bowey 43, Fletcher 66 |
| 6 | 26/01 | A | ULC 3 | Farsley Celtic | 76 | D | 0-0 | |
| 7 | 30/01 | A | ULP | Guiseley | 517 | L | 2-3 | Bowey 12 45 |
| 8 | 03/02 | H | ULC 3 r | Farsley Celtic | 116 | L | 0-1 | |
| 9 | 06/02 | H | ULP | Hyde United | 246 | L | 0-3 | |
| 0 | 13/02 | A | ULP | Emley | 213 | W | 2-1 | Bowey 13, Proudlock 80 |
| 1 | 20/02 | H | ULP | Accrington Stanley | 294 | W | 3-0 | Bowey 26, Ward 30, Fletcher 85 |
| 2 | 27/02 | A | ULP | Chorley | 289 | D | 2-2 | Preen 26, Bowey 66[p] |
| 3 | 06/03 | H | ULP | Stalybridge Celtic | 302 | W | 2-1 | Fletcher 11 27 |
| 4 | 13/03 | A | ULP | Gainsborough Trinity | 429 | D | 1-1 | Proudlock 32 |
| 5 | 20/03 | H | ULP | Winsford United | 278 | W | 2-1 | Raitt 18, Lamb 27 |
| 6 | 27/03 | H | ULP | Leigh RMI | 192 | D | 2-2 | Thompson 40[p], Preen 72 |
| 7 | 03/04 | A | ULP | Colwyn Bay | 301 | D | 1-1 | Proudlock 1 |
| 8 | 05/04 | H | ULP | Blyth Spartans | 623 | L | 0-1 | |
| 9 | 10/04 | A | ULP | Worksop Town | 620 | L | 0-2 | |
| 0 | 17/04 | H | ULP | Altrincham | 306 | L | 0-1 | |
| 1 | 20/04 | A | ULP | Whitby Town | 317 | W | 2-1 | Thompson 48, Alderson 85 |
| 2 | 01/05 | H | ULP | Leigh RMI | 226 | L | 1-3 | Alderson 12 |

**PLAYING SQUAD 1999-2000:**

GOALKEEPERS: Philip Naisbett (Sunderland), Adrian Swan (Spennymoor United)

DEFENDERS: Anthony Hall (Queen Of The South), Maurice Hilton (Grantham Town), David Kitchen, Sam Kitchen (Doncaster Rovers), Kenny Lowe (Darlington), Chris Lynch (Bishop Auckland), Graham Pepper (Spennymoor United), Brian Rowe (Doncaster Rovers), Mark Scott (Stockton), Richie Watson (Spennymoor United)

MIDFIELDERS: Jason Ainsley (Jurong (Singapore)), Richard Alderson (Blyth Spartans), Steve Bowey (Bristol Rovers), Gary Robson (Bradford City), Justin Robson (Chester-le-Street Town), Phil Ross (Bishop Auckland), Ben Ryan (Seaham Red Star), Jon Sunderland (Scarborough)

FORWARDS: Keith Fletcher (Jurong (Singapore)), Paul Harkus (Blyth Spartans), Chris Heron (Bishop Auckland), Nick Peverill (Blyth Spartans), Steven Preen (Tow Law Town), Paul Proudlock (Carlisle United), Kris Trevor (Middlesbrough)

# GUISELEY

## CLUB OFFICIALS

Chairman: **Philip Rogerson**
Secretary: **Bruce Speller**
71 Oxford Avenue, Guiseley,
Leeds LS20 9BY
Tel: 01943 874534
Commercial Manager: **Les Wood**
Tel: 01132 509181
Press Officer: **John Martin**
Tel: 01943 879473
Directors: **P.Rogerson, S.Allen, N.Jukes.**

## FACT FILE

Formed: 1909
Sponsors: OHS Ltd.
Colours: White/blue/white.
Change colours: Yellow/Navy
Midweek home matchday: Tuesday.
Reserves' League: Bolton & Dist Comb,
Alliance Div.

## FOOTBALL MANAGEMENT TEAM

Manager: Bobby Davison
Asst Manager: Neil Parsley
Physio: John Rhodes

**GROUND** Nethermoor, Otley Road, Guiseley, Leeds LS20 8BTTel: 0943 873223
Directions: Via M1 to M62 junction 28, follow Leeds road to Leeds ring-road to junction of A65
at Horsforth. At r-about turn left onto A65 through Rawdon to Guiseley centre. Ground 1/4 mile
past traffic lights, on the right,entrance on A65 opposite Silver Cross factory. Further car park-
ing available off Ings Crescent. 5 mins walk from Guiseley (BR/Metro) station.
Capacity: 3,000          Cover: 1,040          Seats: 427
Clubhouse: (01943 872872) Open before and after all games (closes 11pm). Snack bar within
ground open before and during matches.
Club Shop: Sells programmes, various items of clothing, key rings, badges, mugs etc. Phone
Jennifer Rogerson 01943 879236

Pages: 40 Price: £1
Editor: Les Wood (01532 509181)
Local Press: Yorkshire Evening Post,
Bradford Telegraph & Argus, Airedale
&Wharfedale Observer, Wharfe Valley Times.

**PREVIOUS**      **Leagues:** West Riding Co. Amtr; West Yorks; Yorkshire 68-82; Northern Co's East82-91.

**CLUB RECORDS**      **Attendance:** 2,486 v Bridlington Town, FA Vase Semi Final 1st Leg 89-90.

**BEST SEASON**      **FA Cup:** First Round Proper 1994-95 (lost 1-4 at Valley Parade).
**FA Vase:** Winners 1990-91 (R-up 91-92, S.F.94-95).
**FA Trophy:** Semi-Final 1994-95.

**HONOURS**      FA Vase 90-91 (R-up 91-92), Northern Premier Lg Div 1 94-95 (Presidents Cup 94-95, Div 1 Cup 92-93), Northern Counties
(East) Lg 90-91 (Lg Cup 90-91), West Riding County Cup(5 inc 94-95), Yorkshire Lg R-up 79-80 81-82 (Lg Cup 79-80).

Players Progressing: Keith Walwyn (York City), Frank Harrison (Halifax Town),Dean Walling (Carlisle United), Richard Annan (Crewe Alexandra).
Dave Hanson (Halifax Town)

Simon Phillips celebrates scoring his first goal of the season for Guiseley against Marine in front of Granada TV
cameras who were filming material for a documentary on Marine.   Photo: Darren Thomas

# GUISELEY - MATCH FACTS - 1998-99 SEASON

| No | Date | Venue | Comp | Opponents | Att | Result | Score | Goalscorers |
|---|---|---|---|---|---|---|---|---|
| 1 | 22/08 | A | ULP | Stalybridge Celtic | 688 | D | 2-2 | Parke 38, Elam 62 |
| 2 | 25/08 | A | ULP | Blyth Spartans | 327 | L | 1-2 | Atkinson 20[p] |
| 3 | 29/08 | H | ULP | Bamber Bridge | 286 | W | 3-0 | Atkinson 64, Hunter 71, Hook 73 |
| 4 | 31/08 | A | ULP | Gateshead | 305 | L | 0-1 | |
| 5 | 05/09 | H | ULP | Winsford United | 293 | L | 2-3 | Elam 31 47 |
| 6 | 09/09 | A | ULP | Gainsborough Trinity | 375 | D | 2-2 | Elam 8 43 |
| 7 | 12/09 | A | ULP | Runcorn | 291 | W | 3-1 | Parke 54 55 69 |
| 8 | 15/09 | H | ULP | Worksop Town | 334 | W | 2-1 | Parke 45, Elam 83 |
| 9 | 19/09 | H | ULP | Leigh RMI | 366 | W | 2-0 | Davison 51, Hunter 77 |
| 10 | 23/09 | A | P C 1 | Eastwood Town | 105 | W | 3-1 | Parke 18, Norrell 75 82 |
| 11 | 26/09 | A | ULP | Accrington Stanley | 491 | L | 0-2 | |
| 12 | 29/09 | H | ULP | Spennymoor United | 247 | W | 2-1 | Cooke 45, Parke 90 |
| 13 | 03/10 | A | FA C Q2 | Thackley | 520 | D | 1-1 | Hayer 35[og] |
| 14 | 06/10 | H | FA C Q2 r | Thackley | 505 | W | 2-1 | Parke 7 54 |
| 15 | 10/10 | H | ULP | Hyde United | 412 | W | 1-0 | Hazel 86 |
| 16 | 13/10 | H | ULP | Gainsborough Trinity | 287 | W | 2-1 | Morrell 2, Elam 28 |
| 17 | 17/10 | H | FA C Q3 | Chorley | 463 | D | 1-1 | Parke 11 |
| 18 | 20/10 | A | FA C Q3 r | Chorley | 256 | W | 2-1 | Elam 49, Atkinson 83[p] |
| 19 | 24/10 | A | FA T 1 | Halesowen Town | 324 | W | 2-0 | Atkinson 28, Hunter 55 |
| 20 | 31/10 | A | FA C Q4 | Doncaster Rovers | 2495 | L | 1-3 | Elam 70 |
| 21 | 07/11 | H | ULP | Chorley | 377 | W | 4-0 | Parke 10 37, Hunter 65, Daly 90 |
| 22 | 14/11 | A | ULP | Frickley Athletic | 249 | W | 2-1 | Parke 48 81 |
| 23 | 17/11 | A | ULC 2 | Spennymoor United | 139 | D | 1-1 | Hook 51 |
| 24 | 21/11 | A | FA T 2 | Bishop Auckland | 242 | D | 1-1 | Daly 38 |
| 25 | 24/11 | H | FA T 2 r | Bishop Auckland | 314 | W | 3-1 | Hunter 48 86, Hook 54 |
| 26 | 01/12 | H | ULC 2 r | Spennymoor United | 193 | W | 1-0 | Egege |
| 27 | 05/12 | H | ULP | Runcorn | 339 | W | 2-0 | Airdrie 84 88 |
| 28 | 09/12 | A | W R SC 2 | Harrogate Town | 98 | W | 5-3 | Wilkes 6, OG 34, Mitchell 82, Bower 88, Jong 90 |
| 29 | 15/12 | H | ULP | Whitby Town | 376 | L | 0-3 | |
| 30 | 19/12 | H | ULP | Winsford United | 126 | W | 1-0 | Parke 49 |
| 31 | 22/12 | H | P C QF | Droylsden | 194 | L | 1-2 | Parke 83 |
| 32 | 28/12 | A | ULP | Bishop Auckland | 238 | L | 0-1 | |
| 33 | 02/01 | A | ULP | Altrincham | 1147 | L | 0-1 | |
| 34 | 09/01 | H | ULP | Accrington Stanley | 388 | W | 4-0 | Davison 9, Atkinson 27[p], Hook 28, Morrell 79 |
| 35 | 16/01 | A | FA T 3 | Chorley | 363 | D | 1-1 | Parke 89 |
| 36 | 19/01 | H | FA T 3 r | Chorley | 335 | W | 2-1 | Davison 80, Morrell 84 |
| 37 | 23/01 | A | ULP | Lancaster City | 276 | W | 3-1 | Davison 11 40, Gallagher 75 |
| 38 | 30/01 | H | ULP | Gateshead | 517 | W | 3-2 | Atkinson 42[p], Davison 53, Airdrie 83 |
| 39 | 02/02 | H | ULC 3 | Frickley Athletic | 209 | W | 3-1 | Morrell 21 69, Williams 66 |
| 40 | 06/02 | H | FA T 4 | Emley | 827 | L | 0-2 | |
| 41 | 13/02 | A | ULP | Bamber Bridge | 373 | L | 1-4 | Parke 3 |
| 42 | 17/02 | A | W R SC QF | Farsley Celtic | n/k | L | 2-3 | Parke 10 65 |
| 43 | 20/02 | H | ULP | Stalybridge Celtic | 394 | D | 1-1 | Parke 30 |
| 44 | 27/02 | A | ULP | Hyde United | 483 | L | 1-3 | Morrell 51 |
| 45 | 09/03 | A | ULP | Leigh RMI | 151 | L | 2-3 | Parke 20 44 |
| 46 | 13/03 | A | ULP | Spennymoor United | 305 | D | 0-0 | |
| 47 | 16/03 | H | ULP | Colwyn Bay | 231 | D | 2-2 | Hunter 51, Hook 60[p] |
| 48 | 18/03 | A | ULC QF | Accrington Stanley | 152 | D | 1-1 | Morrell 14 |
| 49 | 20/03 | A | ULP | Colwyn Bay | 298 | D | 0-0 | |
| 50 | 23/03 | A | ULP | Chorley | 224 | W | 2-0 | Morrell 23, Davison 56 |
| 51 | 27/03 | H | ULP | Marine | 323 | W | 2-0 | Phillips 4, Morrell 84 |
| 52 | 30/03 | H | ULC QF r | Accrington Stanley | 265 | W | 2-1 | Davison 68 82 |
| 53 | 03/04 | H | ULP | Bishop Auckland | 296 | W | 1-0 | Hunter 45 |
| 54 | 05/04 | A | ULP | Emley | 289 | W | 1-0 | Jordan 63 |
| 55 | 07/04 | H | ULP | Frickley Athletic | 200 | W | 3-0 | Atkinson 2[p], Poole 33, Airdrie 90 |
| 56 | 10/04 | H | ULP | Lancaster City | 138 | W | 1-0 | Airdrie 6 |
| 57 | 13/04 | A | ULC SF | Blyth Spartans | 313 | W | 2-0 | Airdrie 37, Wilkes 70 |
| 58 | 15/04 | H | ULP | Emley | 378 | D | 1-1 | Airdrie 12 |
| 59 | 17/04 | A | ULP | Marine | 414 | D | 1-1 | Hook 64 |
| 60 | 20/04 | A | ULP | Blyth Spartans | 151 | L | 1-4 | Atkinson 66 |
| 61 | 24/04 | A | ULP | Worksop Town | 818 | L | 1-3 | Morrell 70 |
| 62 | 27/04 | A | ULC F | Stalybridge Celtic | 722 | L | 1-2 | Poole 50 |
| 63 | 29/04 | A | ULP | Whitby Town | 457 | D | 0-0 | |
| 64 | 01/05 | H | ULP | Altrincham | 615 | W | 2-0 | Phillips 11[p], Morrell 66 |

## PLAYING SQUAD 1999-2000:

GOALKEEPERS: Nigel Muttick, James Shutt

DEFENDERS: Peter Atkinson, James Blunt (Leeds United), Matthew Daley (Barrow), James Elliott, Ben Gallagher (Manchester City), Colin Hogarth, Neil Parsley (Exeter City), Steve Sanders (Harrogate Town), Simon Trevitt (Hull City)

MIDFIELDERS: Brian Brooks, James Nettleton (Bradford City), Jamie Proctor (Worcester Wildfire (us))

FORWARDS: Tony Agana (Leek Town), Andy Carlton, Simon Ireland (Boreham Wood), Mick Morrell (Guiseley), Simon Parke

# HUCKNALL TOWN

### CLUB OFFICIALS

Chairman: **JohnBeharall**
Vice-Chairman: **Glen Lathell**
President: **Andy Stewart**
Secretary: **Brian Scothern**
95 Brookfield Ave., Shortwood Estate,
Hucknall, Notts NG15 6FF
Tel: 0115 956 3151

### FOOTBALL MANAGEMENT TEAM

Manager: John Ramshaw
Assistant Manager: Billy Millar
Physio: Ken Burton

**FACT FILE**
Founded: 1987
Nickname: The Town
Sponsors: Doff-Portland
Colours: Yellow/black/black
Change colours: All red
Midweek matches: Tuesday
Reserves' League: Mid Reg Alliance Prem
1998-99
Captain: Dave McCarthy
P.o.Y.: Dave McCarthy
Top Scorer: Gary Briscoe 20

**GROUND** Watnall Road, Hucknall, Notts NG15 7LP Tel: 0115 956 1253
**Directions:** M1 jct 27, A608 to lights, right onto A611 to Hucknall, right at r'bout (new by-pass), over next r'bout, right at next r'bout into Watnall Rd -grd on right. From M1 jct 26 follow Nottm signs to lights on island, left onto A610, right at Three Ponds Pub onto B600 towards Watnall, 200 yds past Queens Head turn right signed Hucknall, follow over motorway and past Rolls Royce -ground on left. Nearest station Hucknall
**Capacity:** 5,000     Seats: 270     Cover: 2,200     Floodlights: Yes
**Clubhouse:** Every night and weekend lunchtimes     **Club Shop:** Yes

Pages: 64 Price: 50p
Editor/Press Officer: Simon Matters
Tel: 0115 956 1336
Local Press : Hucknall & Bulwell Dispatch;
Nottm Evening Post; Nottm Football Post

**PREVIOUS**     **Leagues:** Bulwell & Dist. 46-59 60-65; Central All. 59-60; Notts Spartan65-70; Notts All. 70-89; Central Midlands 89-92 Northern Counties East 92-97, Unibond 97-
            **Ground:** Wigham Park 46-54 Name: Hucknall Colliery Welfare (until pit closure 1988)

**CLUB RECORDS**     **Attendance:** 1,305 v Macclesfield, FA Cup 2nd Qual 26/9/92.     **Appearances:** Paul Tomlinson 210(80s -90s)
            **Goals:** Maurice Palethorpe approx 400 (80s & (0s)
**BEST SEASON**     **FA Cup:** 3rd Q Rd v Stourbridge 98-99 lost 0-3 after 0-0 **FA Vase:** Quarter Final 85-86 **FA Trophy:** 3rd Rd v Redditch 98-99

**HONOURS**     Northern Counties (East) Lg Div 1 R-up 92-93 (Lg Cup 93-94 96-97)Presidents Cup 96-97; Central Mids Lg(2) 89-91 (R-up 91-92, Lg Cup(3) 89-92);Notts All.Sen (4) 76-78 87-89, Div 1 72-73 80-81 86-87 Div 2 70-71;Intermediate Cup 72-73 78-81 84-84; Lge Cup 78-79; Notts Snr Cup 84-85 90-91(R-up 83-84 85-86 87-88 89-90), Unibond Lg.: Div 1 R-Up 98-99

Simon Martin of Hucknall watches as his shot is saved by Droylsden's keeper Mike Kinsella. Photo: Bill Wheatcroft

# HUCKNALL TOWN - MATCH FACTS - 1998-99 SEASON

| No | Date | Venue | Comp | Opponents | Att | Result | Score | Goalscorers |
|----|------|-------|------|-----------|-----|--------|-------|-------------|
| 1 | 22/08 | A | UL 1 | Netherfield Kendal | 116 | W | 2-0 | Maddison 50, Hoy 90 |
| 2 | 25/08 | H | UL 1 | Lincoln United | 250 | D | 2-2 | Maddison 6, Hoy 39 |
| 3 | 29/08 | H | UL 1 | Burscough | 187 | W | 2-0 | Hoy 37, Tomlinson 65 |
| 4 | 31/08 | A | UL 1 | Farsley Celtic | 155 | W | 3-0 | Maddison 12, Edwards 29 31 |
| 5 | 05/09 | H | UL 1 | Gretna | 190 | L | 0-1 | |
| 6 | 08/09 | H | ULC 1 | **Stocksbridge Park Steels** | 112 | W | 4-1 | **Maddison 47, Roberts 50, Edwards 70 85** |
| 7 | 12/09 | A | UL 1 | Ashton United | 190 | D | 0-0 | |
| 8 | 15/09 | H | UL 1 | Stocksbridge Park Steels | 128 | D | 2-2 | Roberts 44[p], Edwards 50 |
| 9 | 19/09 | A | FA C Q1 | **Bridgnorth Town** | 173 | W | 4-0 | **Slawson 23, Edwards 75, Tomlinson 84, Roberts 88** |
| 10 | 23/09 | A | UL 1 | Belper Town | 316 | D | 0-0 | |
| 11 | 26/09 | H | UL 1 | Great Harwood Town | 140 | W | 1-0 | Edwards 81 |
| 12 | 29/09 | H | UL 1 | Matlock Town | 290 | W | 1-0 | Margerison 43 |
| 13 | 03/10 | A | FA C Q2 | **Solihull Borough** | 149 | W | 1-0 | **Roberts 50** |
| 14 | 06/10 | H | Div 1 C 1 | **Harrogate Town** | 111 | W | 5-3 | **Brown 1, Davies 2, Roberts 14[p], Soar 42, Place 45** |
| 15 | 10/10 | A | UL 1 | Trafford | 187 | W | 2-1 | Hoy 5, Edwards 11 |
| 16 | 13/10 | H | UL 1 | Farsley Celtic | 167 | W | 2-1 | Brown 53, Place 60 |
| 17 | 17/10 | H | FA C Q3 | **Stourbridge** | 410 | D | 0-0 | |
| 18 | 20/10 | A | FA C Q3 r | **Stourbridge** | 296 | L | 0-3 | |
| 19 | 27/10 | H | N SC 1 | **Gedling Town** | 135 | W | 6-1 | **Marsh 5[og], Maddison 40, Briscoe 42 70 82, Soar 65** |
| 20 | 31/10 | H | UL 1 | Radcliffe Borough | 170 | W | 2-1 | Maddison 38, Rafferty 85 |
| 21 | 07/11 | A | UL 1 | Droylsden | 230 | L | 2-4 | Maddison 55, Rafferty 90 |
| 22 | 10/11 | H | UL 1 | Alfreton Town | 207 | W | 2-1 | Brown 50, Roberts 86 |
| 23 | 14/11 | H | UL 1 | Whitley Bay | 173 | D | 2-2 | Maddison 16, Place 62 |
| 24 | 17/11 | H | UL 1 | Lincoln United | 252 | W | 2-1 | Tomlinson 38, Roberts 56[p] |
| 25 | 21/11 | H | FA T 2 | **Barrow** | 515 | W | 2-1 | **Maddison 35, Tomlinson 40** |
| 26 | 28/11 | H | UL 1 | Burscough | 188 | W | 3-0 | Briscoe 19 65, Tomlinson 68 |
| 27 | 30/11 | A | Div 1 C 2 | **Emley** | 216 | D | 2-2 | **Briscoe 21 46** |
| 28 | 05/12 | H | N SC 2 | **Southwell City** | 107 | W | 7-1 | **Tomlinson 29, Brown 38, Maddison 45 56, Roberts 47[p], Shaw 80 89** |
| 29 | 12/12 | A | UL 1 | Bradford Park Avenue | 190 | D | 2-2 | Hoy 7 52 |
| 30 | 26/12 | H | UL 1 | Belper Town | 182 | W | 1-0 | Kenworthy 60 |
| 31 | 28/12 | A | UL 1 | Eastwood Town | 518 | D | 0-0 | |
| 32 | 02/01 | H | UL 1 | Congleton Town | 207 | W | 4-2 | Edwards 65 75, Maddison 85 89 |
| 33 | 09/01 | A | UL 1 | Stocksbridge Park Steels | 178 | D | 0-0 | |
| 34 | 16/01 | H | FA T 3 | **Redditch United** | 385 | L | 1-3 | **Roberts 78** |
| 35 | 23/01 | A | UL 1 | Congleton Town | 170 | W | 4-2 | Thacker 15, Martin 45 55, Roberts 87[p] |
| 36 | 30/01 | A | UL 1 | Ashton United | 254 | W | 4-0 | Martin 1, Briscoe 40 65, Roberts 80[p] |
| 37 | 06/02 | H | UL 1 | Flixton | 186 | W | 3-0 | Briscoe 55 75, Maddison 78 |
| 38 | 13/02 | A | UL 1 | Radcliffe Borough | 168 | W | 3-1 | Martin 8, Briscoe 48, Tomlinson 88 |
| 39 | 16/02 | H | N SC QF | **Eastwood Town** | 260 | W | 3-1 | **Martin 42, Roberts 60[p], Tomlinson 90** |
| 40 | 20/02 | H | UL 1 | Netherfield Kendal | 216 | W | 6-3 | Briscoe 32, Thacker 42 61, Tomlinson 60, Roberts 70[p], Martin 90 |
| 41 | 24/02 | H | Div 1 C QF | **Radcliffe Borough** | 162 | L | 1-2 | **Maddison 96** |
| 42 | 27/02 | A | UL 1 | Harrogate Town | 298 | L | 0-1 | |
| 43 | 08/03 | A | ULC 2 r | **Emley** | 144 | W | 3-2 | **Briscoe 12, Brown 36, Maddison 55** |
| 44 | 10/03 | H | ULC 3 | **Alfreton Town** | 119 | W | 1-0 | **Tomlinson 60** |
| 45 | 13/03 | A | UL 1 | Gretna | 74 | D | 1-1 | Briscoe 16 |
| 46 | 16/03 | H | N SC SF | **Blidworth Welfare** | 150 | W | 4-1 | **Martin 50 72 88, Brown 59** |
| 47 | 20/03 | A | UL 1 | Great Harwood Town | 102 | L | 0-1 | |
| 48 | 23/03 | H | ULC QF | **Farsley Celtic** | 140 | D | 0-0 | |
| 49 | 27/03 | H | UL 1 | Droylsden | 305 | W | 3-1 | Briscoe 20, Soar 42, Kenworthy 60 |
| 50 | 01/04 | A | ULC QF r | **Farsley Celtic** | 59 | W | 1-0 | **Hoy 54** |
| 51 | 03/04 | A | UL 1 | Flixton | 66 | W | 3-2 | Soar 12, Martin 50, Hoy 74 |
| 52 | 05/04 | H | UL 1 | Eastwood Town | 530 | W | 3-0 | Place 16, Martin 40 42 |
| 53 | 07/04 | H | UL 1 | Witton Albion | 153 | L | 0-1 | |
| 54 | 10/04 | A | UL 1 | Witton Albion | 301 | W | 2-0 | Martin 74, Hoy 80 |
| 55 | 13/04 | A | ULC SF | **Stalybridge Celtic** | 276 | D | 1-1 | **Hoy 84** |
| 56 | 15/04 | H | ULC SF r | **Stalybridge Celtic** | 217 | L | 1-2 | **White 52** |
| 57 | 17/04 | H | UL 1 | Trafford | 266 | D | 1-1 | Marginson 62 |
| 58 | 22/04 | A | UL 1 | Alfreton Town | 159 | W | 2-1 | Wood 45[og], Tomlinson 76 |
| 59 | 24/04 | A | UL 1 | Whitley Bay | 179 | W | 3-2 | Martin 14 35, Marginson 31 |
| 60 | 27/04 | H | UL 1 | Matlock Town | 283 | W | 1-0 | Tomlinson 65 |
| 61 | 29/04 | H | UL 1 | Harrogate Town | 243 | W | 3-0 | Hoy 15, Tomlinson 44, Roberts 70 |
| 62 | 01/05 | H | UL 1 | Bradford Park Avenue | 494 | D | 1-1 | Davies 30 |
| 63 | 05/05 | A | N SC F | **Arnold Town** | 576 | L | 1-2 | **Briscoe 43**            (at Eastwood Town) |

## PLAYING SQUAD 1999-2000:

GOALKEEPERS: Dean Lowe (Borrowash Victoria), Dave Mccarthy (AFC Bournemouth)

DEFENDERS: Kieron Begley (local football), Peter Kenworthy (Oakham United), Lee Margerison (Eccleshill United), Marvin Marston (Sheffield United), Jason Pascoe (Leek Town), Mark Place (Matlock Town)

MIDFIELDERS: Simon Brown (Notts County), Danny Marshall (Boston United), Dean Rafferty (Gedling Town), Jamie Roberts (Eastwood Town), Lee Soar (Gainsborough Trinity), Colin Thacker (Oakham United), Chris White (Arnold Town)

FORWARDS: Mick Godber (Staveley Miners Welfare), David Harbottle (Hinckley United), Kristian Hoy (Armthorpe Welfare), Craig Maddison (Grantham Town), Simon Martin (Lincoln United), Paul Tomlinson (Arnold Town)

# HYDE UNITED

### CLUB OFFICIALS

Chairman: **S C Hartley**
Vice Chairman:
Secretary / Press Officer: **Ray Stanley**
136 Lumn Road, Hyde, Cheshire SK14 1PR
Tel No: 0161 366 5154
Commercial Manager: **Rod Buxton**

### FOOTBALL MANAGEMENT TEAM

Manager: Mike McKenzie
Coach: Osher Williams
Physio: G Clowes

**FACT FILE**

Formed: 1919
Nickname: The Tigers
Club Sponsors: T.B.A.
Colours: All Red
Change colours: Yellow,blue,yellow
Midweek home matchday: Monday

official match programme 1998/9

Pages: 32 Price: £1.
Editor: M Dring
Local Press: North Cheshire Herald
& Hyde Reporter.
Local Radio: GMR, Picadilly.

**GROUND**
Tameside Stadium, Ewen Fields, Walker Lane, Hyde SK14 5PL (0161 368 1031).
Directions: On entering Hyde follow signs for Tameside Leisure Park - in Walker Lane take
2nd car park entrance nr Leisure Pool, follow road around to the stadium. Quarter of a mile
from Newton (BR).
Capacity: 4,000Cover: 2,000Seats: 400
**Clubhouse:** (0161 368 1621). Open most nights, full facilities, 150 seats.Stewards: Lil &
Doug. **Club Shop:** Replica shirts, scarves, sports shirts, baseball caps, bronx hats,badges.
Contact Ray Stanley (0161 366 5154)

**PREVIOUS**        **Leagues:** Lancs & Cheshire 19-21; Manchester 21-30; Cheshire County 30-68, 70-82;  Northern Prem. 68-70

**CLUB RECORDS**    **Attendance:** 9,500 v Nelson, FA Cup 1952.  **Scorer:** P O'Brien 247. **Appearances:** S Johnson 623.
**Defeat:** (as Hyde F.C.) 0-26 v Preston North End, F.A. Cup.
**Fee Paid:** £8,000 for Jim McCluskie (Mossley, 1989).  **Fee Received:** £50.000 for Colin Little (Crewe Alexandra) 1995.

**BEST SEASON**     **FA Cup:** 1st Rd 54-55 (v Workington), 83-84 (v Burnley),94-95 v Darlington.
**FA Trophy:** Semi Final 88-89 94-95 95-96

**HONOURS**         Prem Inter-Lge Cup R-up(2) 88-90; NPL R-up(2) 87-89 (Lg Cup 85-86 88-89 95-96(R-up 83-84 94-95), Chal. Shield 96-97, (R-up
86-87 90-91); Cheshire Co. Lg(3)54-56 81-82 (Lg Cup 33-34 52-53 54-55 72-73 81-82, Lg Chal. Shield(2) 80-82;Manchester Lg(5)
20-23 28-29 29-30 (Lg (Gilgryst) Cup(4) 27-29 49-50 70-71);Cheshire Snr Cup 45-46 62-63 69-70 80-81 89-90 96-97; Manchester
Prem. Cup 93-94, 94-95, 95-96, 98-99,Snr Cup 74-75, Int Cup 55-56 56-57(jt), Jnr Cup 21-22 68-69;Lancs & Cheshire F'lit Cup(2)
54-56; Ashton Chal. Cup(6) 30-34 39-40 47-48;Hyde Chal Cup(2) 27-29; Reporter Cup(3) 72-74 75-76; Gavin Nicholson Mem
Trophy79-80; Lancs F'lit Trophy(2) 86-88; Edward Case Cup(4)

**Players P rogressing:** C McClelland & J Webber & P Barry (B'burn 1946 & 47 & 48),L Battrick (Manc. City 1968), J Hilton (Wrexham 1950), D Teece (Hull
1952), R Calderbank & William Bell & Neil Colbourne (R'dale 1953 & 74 & 80), Jeff Johnson (Stockport 1976), David Constantine & Donald Graham (Bury
1979), George Oghani (Bolton 1983), Kevin Glendon (Burnley 1983), Peter Coyne (Swindon 1984),Colin Little (Crewe Alex. 1995),Lutel James (Bury)

Back Row (L-R): Gus Wilson, Paul Cox, Scott Brenchley, Darren Washington, Kurt Edginton, Alan Pringle, Peter
Band, Tony Rodwel, Ian Lamb (coach)
Front Row: Richard Annan, Simon Yeo, Prince Moncrieffe, Steve Haw, Don Page, Chris Dolby, Ko Joe Taylor

# HYDE UNITED - MATCH FACTS - 1998-99 SEASON

| No | Date | Venue | Comp | Opponents | Att | Result | Score | Goalscorers |
|---|---|---|---|---|---|---|---|---|
| 1 | 22/08 | A | ULP | Bamber Bridge | 373 | D | 1-1 | Moncrieffe 87 |
| 2 | 24/08 | H | ULP | Worksop Town | 507 | D | 0-0 | |
| 3 | 29/08 | H | ULP | Gateshead | 371 | W | 3-0 | Richardson 42, Pace 58, Wilson 72 |
| 4 | 31/08 | A | ULP | Gainsborough Trinity | 530 | W | 1-0 | Richardson 85 |
| 5 | 05/09 | H | ULP | Spennymoor United | 397 | W | 3-0 | Taylor 45, James 67, Haw 85 |
| 6 | 08/09 | A | ULP | Runcorn | 315 | D | 1-1 | Highfield 34 |
| 7 | 12/09 | A | ULP | Accrington Stanley | 419 | D | 1-1 | Wilson 83 |
| 8 | 14/09 | H | ULP | Gainsborough Trinity | 457 | L | 1-2 | James 38 |
| 9 | 19/09 | H | ULP | Blyth Spartans | 525 | W | 2-1 | Traylor 36, Dolby 49 |
| 10 | 21/09 | H | C SC 1 | **Nantwich Town** | **269** | W | **5-1** | **Band 84 110, Preece 102[og], James 114, Dolby 117** |
| 11 | 26/09 | H | ULP | Marine | 505 | D | 1-1 | Band 19 |
| 12 | 29/09 | A | ULP | Chorley | 272 | W | 3-1 | James 20, Edey 33, Haw 45 |
| 13 | 03/10 | H | FA C Q2 | **Gainsborough Trinity** | **482** | W | **4-0** | **Bond 3, Page 45, James 66, Haw 77** |
| 14 | 05/10 | H | P C 1 | **Droylsden** | **476** | D | **2-2** | **Band 23, James 52** |
| 15 | 10/10 | A | ULP | Guiseley | 412 | L | 0-1 | |
| 16 | 13/10 | A | P C 1 rep | **Droylsden** | **216** | D | **0-0** | **(4-5 pens)** |
| 17 | 17/10 | A | FA C Q3 | **West Auckland** | **197** | L | **0-2** | |
| 18 | 27/10 | A | FA T 1 | **Bilston Town** | **120** | W | **4-3** | **Scargill 20, Taylor 29, Richardson 42, Wilson 75** |
| 19 | 31/10 | H | ULP | Blyth Spartans | 444 | L | 0-1 | |
| 20 | 03/11 | H | ULC 2 | **Droylsden** | **127** | L | **1-4** | **Wilson 75** |
| 21 | 07/11 | A | ULP | Marine | 249 | L | 0-1 | |
| 22 | 09/11 | H | M PC 1 | **Mossley** | **369** | W | **2-0** | **Page 4, Washington 82** |
| 23 | 14/11 | A | ULP | Colwyn Bay | 348 | D | 2-2 | Washington 46, Moncrieffe 58 |
| 24 | 17/11 | A | C SC QF | **Stalybridge Celtic** | **535** | W | **2-1** | **Haw 82, Moncrieffe 115** |
| 25 | 21/11 | A | FA T 2 | **Nuneaton Borough** | **1207** | D | **1-1** | **Page 76** |
| 26 | 23/11 | H | FA T 2 r | **Nuneaton Borough** | **472** | W | **1-0** | **Moncrieffe 19** |
| 27 | 28/11 | H | ULP | Emley | 549 | L | 0-1 | |
| 28 | 30/11 | H | ULP | Runcorn | 424 | W | 2-0 | Page 9, Moncrieffe 15 |
| 29 | 04/12 | A | ULP | Leigh RMI | 287 | D | 2-2 | Yeo 15 86 |
| 30 | 12/12 | H | ULP | Winsford United | 430 | W | 2-0 | Band 32, Yeo 68 |
| 31 | 19/12 | A | ULP | Whitby Town | 429 | W | 3-2 | Band 13, Annan 67, Yeo 72 |
| 32 | 26/12 | H | ULP | Stalybridge Celtic | 1357 | D | 1-1 | Yeo 27 |
| 33 | 28/12 | H | ULP | Worksop Town | 521 | L | 0-2 | |
| 34 | 01/01 | A | ULP | Stalybridge Celtic | 1640 | L | 1-2 | Yeo 32 |
| 35 | 09/01 | H | ULP | Altrincham | 964 | L | 0-1 | |
| 36 | 16/01 | A | FA T 3 | **Runcorn** | **428** | L | **1-2** | **Yeo 57** |
| 37 | 23/01 | A | ULP | Bishop Auckland | 201 | W | 1-0 | Band 10 |
| 38 | 30/01 | H | ULP | Accrington Stanley | 491 | W | 3-2 | Yeo 19 36 90 |
| 39 | 01/02 | H | M PC QF | **Cheadle Town** | **320** | W | **6-1** | **Yeo 29 38 68 70, Haw 46, Moncrieffe 78** |
| 40 | 06/02 | A | ULP | Gateshead | 246 | W | 3-0 | Band 22, Yeo 67, Haw 75 |
| 41 | 13/02 | H | ULP | Chorley | 525 | L | 3-4 | Page 30, Yeo 80, Moncrieffe 90 |
| 42 | 20/02 | H | ULP | Bishop Auckland | 390 | W | 5-0 | Yeo 2 14 55 86, Dolby 30 |
| 43 | 22/02 | H | C SC SF | **Altrincham** | **601** | L | **0-1** | |
| 44 | 27/02 | H | ULP | Guiseley | 483 | W | 3-1 | Yeo 2 85, Haw 46 |
| 45 | 09/03 | A | ULP | Colwyn Bay | 164 | L | 1-2 | Price 58[og] |
| 46 | 13/03 | A | ULP | Winsford United | 270 | W | 2-0 | Moncrieffe 19, Taylor 39 |
| 47 | 16/03 | A | M PC SF | **Glossop North End** | **n/k** | W | **3-1** | **Richardson 12, Dolby 13 30** |
| 48 | 20/03 | A | ULP | Frickley Athletic | 180 | L | 0-3 | |
| 49 | 22/03 | H | ULP | Frickley Athletic | 357 | W | 2-0 | P Taylor 26, Moncrieffe 87 |
| 50 | 27/03 | H | ULP | Bamber Bridge | 467 | D | 1-1 | Yeo 90 |
| 51 | 03/04 | A | ULP | Altrincham | 923 | L | 1-2 | Annan 47 |
| 52 | 05/04 | H | ULP | Whitby Town | 436 | W | 3-2 | Moncrieffe 9, Brenchley 75, Turner 80 |
| 53 | 10/04 | A | ULP | Spennymoor United | 221 | L | 0-2 | |
| 54 | 12/04 | A | ULP | Emley | 175 | D | 1-1 | Moncrieffe 50 |
| 55 | 19/04 | H | ULP | Leigh RMI | 364 | L | 1-2 | Haw 88 |
| 56 | 24/04 | A | ULP | Lancaster City | 257 | L | 0-1 | |
| 57 | 28/04 | H | M PC F | **Maine Road** | **n/k** | W | **1-0** | **Yeo 56**                        (at Oldham Athletic) |
| 58 | 01/05 | H | ULP | Lancaster City | 575 | D | 1-1 | Page 19 |

## PLAYING SQUAD 1999-2000:

GOALKEEPERS:
Graham Bennett (Flixton/Morecambe), Kurt Edgington (Flixton), John Morrey (Maine Road), Jonathan Scargill (Flixton)

DEFENDERS: Brendan Aspinall (Coleraine), Jeff Brewer (local football), Cec Edey (Macclesfield Town), Darren Esdaille (Doncaster Rovers), Kojo Taylor (Curzon Ashton), Paul Taylor (Castleton Gabriels), Gordon Tucker (Scunthorpe United), Gus Wilson (Accrington Stanley)

MIDFIELDERS: Chris Dolby (Stalybridge Celtic), Neil Hall (Droylsden), Jason Hardy (Hyde United/Oldham Town), Mark Howard (Fakenham Town), Steve Hughes (Salford City), Alan Pringle (Sheffield Wednesday), Lloyd Richardson (Oldham Athletic) , Tony Rodwell (Marine)

FORWARDS: Peter Band (Bollington Athletic), Jody Banim (Flixton/Atherton Collieries), Steve Haw (Accrington Stanley), Prince Moncrieffe (Doncaster Rovers), Don Page (Stafford Rangers), Mike Turner (Witton Albion), Simon Yeo (Atherton Collieries)

# LANCASTER CITY

## CLUB OFFICIALS

Chairman: **Ian Sharpe**
President: **M Woodhouse**
Vice-Chairman: **K Lancaster**
Secretary: **Mike Sparks**
30 Salisbury Road, Lancaster LA1 5PJ
Tel: 01524 33483
Commercial Man./Press Officer:
**Dave Horner**
(c/o the club)

## FACT FILE

Formed: 1902
Nickname: Dolly Blues
Sponsors: Reebok
Colours: Blue/white/blue
Change colours: All white
Midweek matchday: Tuesday
Reserve League: Lancashire League
98-99 Captain: J.Baldwin
Top Scorer: P,Thomson
P.o.Y: J.Udall

## FOOTBALL MANAGEMENT TEAM

ManagerTony Hesketh
Coach: Barry Stimpson
Physio: J.Udall

## GROUND

Giant Axe, West Road, Lancaster LA1 5PE
Tel: 01524 382238 (Office). Directions: M6 junc 33, follow into city, left at lights immediately after Waterstones bookshop, 2nd right, pass railway station on right, follow road down hill, ground 1st right. 5 mins walk from both bus & rail stations
Capacity: 2,500    Cover: 800    Seats: 300
**Clubhouse:** "The Dolly Blue Tavern" just outside the ground. Also a new tea bar inside ground serving food and drinks.    **Club Shop:** Inside ground, selling metal badges, pennants, programmes and other souvenirs etc. Contact Dave Crawford at club.

Pages: 32 Price: £1
Editor: Paul Wilkinson (c/o the club)
Fanzines: The Mad Axeman, Bambula Azzurri
Local Press: Lancaster Guardian, Morecambe Visitor, Lancashire Evening Post,Lancaster Citizen. Local Radio: Red Rose , Radio Lancashire and Bay Radio

**PREVIOUS**    **Leagues:** Lancs Combination 05-70; Northern Premier 70-82; North West Counties 82-87.
**Name:** Lancaster Town.    **Ground:** Quay Meadow 05-06 (club's 1st 2 games only!)

**CLUB RECORDS**    **Attendance:** 7,500 v Carlisle, FA Cup 1936.
**Goalscorer:** David Barnes 130 League & cup.    **Appearances:** Edgar J Parkinson, 591 league & cup.
**Win:** 8-0 v Leyland Motors (A), 83-84.    **Defeat:** 0-10 v Matlock T, NPL Division One, 73-74

**BEST SEASON**    **FA Vase:** Second Rd 86-87 90-91.
**FA Trophy:** Third Rd 74-75 75-76.    **FA Cup:** 2nd Rd 46-47 (1-4 v Gateshead) 72-73 (1-2 v Notts County)
League Clubs defeated: Barrow, Stockport County 21-22

**HONOURS**    Northern Prem. Lg Cup R-up 79-80 (Div 1 Cup R-up 90-91), Lancs Combination 21-22 29-30 34-35 35-36 (R-up 19-20 22-23 27-28 51-52, Lg Cup 21-22, Div 2 R-up14-15), Lancs Jun. Cup (ATS Challenge Trophy) 27-28 28-29 30-31 33-34 51-52 74-75 (R-up 06-07 08-09 19-20 26-27), Lancs Yth (u18) Cup 87-88 88-89 (R-up 86-87 89-90), President's Cup 1994-95. Unibond Div 1 95-96, Lge Cup 95-96.

Players Progressing: J McNamee (Workington 75), B O'Callaghan (Stoke C.), I Stevens (Stockport Co. 86), G Johnstone (P.N.E. 93), M Clark & W Collins (Crewe Alex.), G Wilson (Crewe Alex.). P.Thomson (NAC Breda 99)

Back Row (L-R): S Hartley, J Udall, M Thornley, P Thompson, S Diggle, G Taylor.   Middle Row: D McKevitt, S Trainor, B Curwen, B Lavelle, T McDonald, M Cheal, J Graham, S Phillips, C Lee, H Sharkey, F Charlton.   Front Row: M Parkinson, P Rigby, B Stimpson, J Flannery, A Tinsley, M Hoyle, J Baldwin, A Bent, S Parkinson

# LANCASTER CITY - MATCH FACTS - 1998-99 SEASON

| No | Date | Venue Comp | Opponents | Att | Result | Score | Goalscorers |
|---|---|---|---|---|---|---|---|
| 1 | 22/08 | ULP | Blyth Spartans | 510 | L | 0-1 | |
| 2 | 25/08 | ULP | Gateshead | 206 | D | 2-2 | Udall 54, Diggle 74 |
| 3 | 29/08 | ULP | Bishop Auckland | 202 | L | 2-4 | Cheal 82, Taylor 89 |
| 4 | 31/08 | ULP | Accrington Stanley | 403 | D | 1-1 | Flannery 64 |
| 5 | 05/09 | ULP | Stalybridge Celtic | 280 | D | 1-1 | Diggle 32 |
| 6 | 08/09 | ULP | Altrincham | 564 | W | 2-1 | Thomson 43 72 |
| 7 | 12/09 | ULP | Emley | 269 | D | 1-1 | Thomson 73 |
| 8 | 15/09 | ULP | Bamber Bridge | 221 | W | 3-2 | Thomson 58 78[p], Diggle 69 |
| 9 | 19/09 | ULP | Frickley Athletic | 220 | W | 5-0 | Thomson 4 54[p], Martin 49, Taylor 80 89 |
| 10 | 25/09 | ULP | Leigh RMI | 328 | W | 2-0 | Flannery 29, Thomson 76 |
| 11 | 29/09 | ULP | Accrington Stanley | 311 | W | 1-0 | Thomson 68[p] |
| 12 | 03/10 | FA C Q2 | **Netherfield Kendal** | **335** | W | **3-1** | **Diggle 11, Thomson 83 90** |
| 13 | 06/10 | ULP | Colwyn Bay | 215 | D | 0-0 | |
| 14 | 10/10 | ULP | Whitby Town | 628 | W | 2-1 | Graham 24, Thomson 45 |
| 15 | 20/10 | FA C Q3 | **Mossley** | **252** | W | **1-0** | **Martin 42** |
| 16 | 24/10 | FA T 1 | **Stafford Rangers** | **414** | L | **2-4** | **Thompson 65 67** |
| 17 | 04/11 | FA C Q4 | **Leek Town** | **449** | W | **3-0** | **Parkinson 41, Thomson 89 90** |
| 18 | 07/11 | ULP | Gainsborough Trinity | 484 | L | 0-1 | |
| 19 | 14/11 | FA C 1 | **Northampton Town** | **4545** | L | **1-2** | **Thomson 30** |
| 20 | 21/11 | ULP | Spennymoor United | 220 | L | 0-3 | |
| 21 | 01/12 | ULC 2 | **Trafford** | **104** | L | **1-2** | **Cheal 67** |
| 22 | 05/12 | ULP | Winsford United | 205 | W | 1-0 | Flannery 81 |
| 23 | 12/12 | ULP | Worksop Town | 270 | W | 2-0 | Thompson 27, Diggle 49 |
| 24 | 15/12 | ULP | Runcorn | 192 | W | 2-1 | Thomson 19, Flannery 89 |
| 25 | 19/12 | ULP | Stalybridge Celtic | 421 | L | 1-3 | |
| 26 | 26/12 | ULP | Bamber Bridge | 456 | L | 3-4 | Thomson 47 48 90 |
| 27 | 28/12 | ULP | Chorley | 312 | L | 0-1 | |
| 28 | 02/01 | ULP | Blyth Spartans | 247 | D | 2-2 | Flannery 38, Thomson 79 |
| 29 | 09/01 | ULP | Gateshead | 284 | L | 1-7 | Martin 19 |
| 30 | 16/01 | ULP | Winsford United | 126 | L | 0-1 | |
| 31 | 21/01 | L ATS 2 | **Marine** | **102** | W | **3-2** | **Parkinson 31 65, Martin 57[p]** |
| 32 | 23/01 | ULP | Guiseley | 276 | L | 1-3 | Parkinson 79 |
| 33 | 30/01 | ULP | Spennymoor United | 175 | D | 2-2 | Flannery 56[p], Cheal 52 |
| 34 | 02/02 | L ATS QF | **Southport** | **337** | L | **0-2** | |
| 35 | 06/02 | ULP | Marine | 224 | D | 0-0 | |
| 36 | 13/02 | ULP | Frickley Athletic | 158 | L | 2-3 | Flannery 46 70 |
| 37 | 20/02 | ULP | Emley | 225 | D | 1-1 | Barnes 69 |
| 38 | 27/02 | ULP | Bishop Auckland | 205 | D | 1-1 | Martin 90 |
| 39 | 06/03 | ULP | Marine | 287 | L | 1-2 | Diggle 49 |
| 40 | 13/03 | ULP | Whitby Town | 230 | L | 0-1 | |
| 41 | 16/03 | ULP | Altrincham | 329 | D | 0-0 | |
| 42 | 20/03 | ULP | Worksop Town | 412 | L | 0-3 | |
| 43 | 23/03 | ULP | Colwyn Bay | 150 | W | 4-1 | Evans 21, Gelling 45, Taylor 48 88 |
| 44 | 27/03 | ULP | Gainsborough Trinity | 205 | L | 0-1 | |
| 45 | 03/04 | ULP | Runcorn | 255 | D | 1-1 | Udall 90 |
| 46 | 05/04 | ULP | Chorley | 346 | L | 0-2 | |
| 47 | 10/04 | ULP | Guiseley | 138 | L | 0-1 | |
| 48 | 17/04 | ULP | Leigh RMI | 248 | L | 1-2 | Kennedy 33 |
| 49 | 24/04 | ULP | Hyde United | 257 | W | 1-0 | Kennedy 50 |
| 50 | 01/05 | ULP | Hyde United | 575 | D | 1-1 | Kennedy 29 |

## PLAYING SQUAD 1999-2000:

GOALKEEPERS: Glenn Johnstone (Gretna)

DEFENDERS: Jez Baldwin (Bamber Bridge), Martin Eatough, Paul Fleming (Runcorn), Steve Hartley, Phil Horner (Southport), John Kennedy (Morecambe), Farrell Kilbane (Stafford Rangers), Ben Lavelle (Accrington Stanley), Kenny Mayers (Morecambe)

MIDFIELDERS: Mark Ashton (Warrington Town), Paul Haddow (Barrow), Dean Martin (Stalybridge Celtic), Stuart Parkinson (Morecambe), Steve Trainor (Bamber Bridge), Graham Yeo

FORWARDS: Peter Borrowdale, Gary Parkinson,

# LEEK TOWN

FACT FILE

## CLUB OFFICIALS

President: **Godfrey Heath**
Chairman: **Linden Davies**
Vice Chairman: **Mike Cope**
Directors: **Robin Halton, Carl France,
Warren France, Tony Pickford**

Football Secretary: **Mike Rowley**
62 London Rd., Chesterton, Newcastle,
Staffs. ST5 7DY Tel: 01782 562890
Commercial Manager: **Ken Warburton**
Press Officer: **Mike Cope**

### FOOTBALL MANAGEMENT TEAM

Manager: Ernie Moss
Assistant Manager: Phil Tingay
Physio: K Birch-Martin

Founded: 1946
Nickname: The Blues
Club Sponsors: Kerrygold
Club colours: All blue
Change colours: All yellow
Reserve team league: Manchester League
Midweek home matchday: Tuesday
Newsline: 0930 55 54 53
98-99 Captain:
Top scorer:
P.o.Y.:

**GROUND**    Harrison Park, Macclesfield Road, Leek ST13 8LD
Tel: 01538 399278 Fax: 01538 399826
**Directions:**    Opposite Courtaults chemical works on A523 Macclesfield to Buxton
road half a mile out of Leek heading towards Macclesfield.
Capacity: 3,600    Seated: 625    Covered Terracing: 2,675
Club Shop: Contact club on 01538 399278.
Clubhouse: `Blues' Bar open nightly & weekend lunchtimes. 01538 383734

Programme:
Pages: 40    Price: £1.50
Editor: Dave Stringer
Local Newspapers: Leek Post & Times,
Evening Sentinel
Local Radio: Radio Stoke, Signal Radio

**PREVIOUS**    **Leagues:** Staffs County, Manchester 51-54 57-73, West Mids (B'ham) 54-56,Cheshire County 73-82, North West Counties 82-87, Northern Premier 87-94 95-97,Southern League 94-95, Conference 97-99
**Names:** Abbey Green Rovers/ Leek Lowe Hamil.    **Grounds:** None
**CLUB RECORDS    Attendance:** 5,312 v Macclesfield Town, F.A. Cup Second Qualifying Round 73-74    **Win:** Unknown    **Defeat:** Unknown
**Transfer fee paid:** £2,000 for Simon Snow (Sutton Town)    **Transfer fee received:** £30,000 for Tony Bullock (Barnsley)
**Career goalscorer:** Dave Suttons 144    **Career appearances:** Gary Pearce 447.
**BEST SEASON    FA Cup:** 2nd Rd 90-91, 0-4 v Chester (A) after 1-1    League clubs defeated: Scarborough 90-91.
**FA Trophy:** Runners-up 89-90, Q-F 85-86.
**HONOURS**    FA Trophy R-up 89-90; Northern Premier Lg 96-97, R-up 93-94 (Div 1 89-90, Div 1Cup R-up 88-89, Presidents Cup R-up 93-94, Lg Shield 90-91); North West Co's LgCup 84-85 (Charity Shield 84-85); Cheshire County Lg 74-75 (Challenge Shield74-75); Manchester Lg 51-52 71-72 72-73 (Lg Cup 72-73); Staffs Snr Cup 95-96,R-up 54-55 81-82 95-96, Jnr Cup 51-52 70-71 (R-up 47-48 48-49 49-50)); StaffsCo. Lg 50-51 69-70 70-71 73-74 (R-up 47-48 49-50, Lg Cup 70-71 73-74); LeekPost Charity Shield 46-47; Leek Cup 47-48 52-53 70-71 71-72 (R-up 46-47); MayBank Cup 47-48 50-51 71-72; Hanley Cup 48-49 70-71 (R-up 49-5); Mid Cheshire LgDiv 2 87-88 (Div 2 Cup 87-88); Evans Halshaw Floodlit Cup Winners 93-94 94-95; Southern Lge Cup R-up 94-95; Unibond Lge Chall Cup R-up 95-96
Players progressing:    Geoff Crosby (Stockport 52), Bill Summerscales (70), Mark Bright (81) & Martyn Smith (84) allto Port Vale, Paul Edwards (Crewe 89), Tony Bullock (Barnsley 97)

Hugh McAuley (now Cheltenham Town) shows good control with Jon Brady and Darren Bradshaw watching closely.
Photo: Peter Barnes

## LEEK TOWN - MATCH FACTS - 1998-99 SEASON

| No | Date | Venue | Comp | Opponents | Att | Result | Score | Goalscorers |
|----|------|-------|------|-----------|-----|--------|-------|-------------|
| 1 | 15/08 | H | NC | Farnborough Town | 527 | W | 4-0 | Hawtin 22, McAuley 36, Ellis 39, Cunningham 45 |
| 2 | 18/08 | A | NC | Hereford United | 2140 | L | 0-1 | |
| 3 | 22/08 | A | NC | Stevenage Borough | 2614 | L | 0-2 | |
| 4 | 25/08 | H | NC | Morecambe | 501 | W | 7-0 | Circuit 13, Kennedy 26, Cunningham 56 77, McAuley 78 86 90 |
| 5 | 29/08 | H | NC | Cheltenham Town | 704 | L | 0-2 | |
| 6 | 31/08 | A | NC | Northwich Victoria | 1070 | W | 2-0 | Mike 17, McAuley 77 |
| 7 | 05/09 | A | NC | Farnborough Town | 578 | L | 1-2 | McAuley 72 |
| 8 | 12/09 | H | NC | Woking | 583 | L | 0-3 | |
| 9 | 15/09 | H | NC | Barrow | 426 | W | 3-1 | McAuley 39, Mike 52 84 |
| 10 | 19/09 | A | NC | Welling United | 524 | L | 0-1 | |
| 11 | 26/09 | H | NC | Dover Athletic | 533 | W | 2-0 | Beeby 19, Mike 79 |
| 12 | 03/10 | A | NC | Hayes | 603 | L | 0-2 | |
| 13 | 06/10 | A | Endsl. 1 | Barrow | 591 | L | 1-2 | Price 13 |
| 14 | 10/10 | A | NC | Hednesford Town | 701 | L | 1-3 | Mike 63 |
| 15 | 13/10 | A | S SC 1 | Blakenall | 68 | W | 2-1 | Mike 54, Hawtin 83 |
| 16 | 17/10 | A | FA C Q3 | Buxton | 814 | D | 0-0 | |
| 17 | 20/10 | A | FA C Q3 r | Buxton | 464 | W | 3-0 | Mike(3) |
| 18 | 24/10 | A | NC | Kettering Town | 1110 | L | 1-2 | Mike 3 |
| 19 | 04/11 | H | FA C Q4 | Lancaster City | 449 | L | 0-3 | |
| 20 | 07/11 | H | NC | Hereford United | 667 | W | 3-2 | Parker 19, McAuley 49, Mike 82 |
| 21 | 14/11 | A | NC | Morecambe | 840 | D | 2-2 | Mike 9, Ellis 20 |
| 22 | 21/11 | A | FA T 2 | Ashton United | 316 | L | 0-1 | |
| 23 | 28/11 | H | NC | Kidderminster Harriers | 711 | L | 1-4 | Agana 43 |
| 24 | 05/12 | A | NC | Barrow | 1047 | L | 1-2 | McAuley 90 |
| 25 | 12/12 | A | NC | Cheltenham Town | 1912 | D | 0-0 | |
| 26 | 19/12 | H | NC | Kingstonian | 495 | D | 2-2 | Mike 52, McAuley 63 |
| 27 | 26/12 | A | NC | Doncaster Rovers | 3520 | W | 1-0 | Hawtin 41 |
| 28 | 28/12 | H | NC | Telford United | 672 | D | 1-1 | McAuley 90 |
| 29 | 02/01 | H | NC | Doncaster Rovers | 1365 | D | 1-1 | McAuley 56 |
| 30 | 09/01 | A | NC | Kidderminster Harriers | 1713 | W | 2-1 | McAuley 18, Mike 26 |
| 31 | 23/01 | A | NC | Forest Green Rovers | 624 | L | 1-3 | McAuley 4[p] |
| 32 | 30/01 | A | NC | Dover Athletic | 974 | L | 1-2 | McAuley 17 |
| 33 | 02/02 | H | S SC 2 | Bilston Town | 156 | W | 3-0 | Hawtin 27, Diskin 35, Hebberin 84 |
| 34 | 13/02 | A | NC | Woking | 1926 | L | 0-1 | |
| 35 | 20/02 | H | NC | Stevenage Borough | 597 | D | 1-1 | McAuley 18 |
| 36 | 23/02 | A | NC | Kingstonian | 606 | L | 0-3 | |
| 37 | 27/02 | A | NC | Hednesford Town | 943 | D | 1-1 | Ellis 83 |
| 38 | 13/03 | A | NC | Rushden & Diamonds | 2833 | L | 0-2 | |
| 39 | 16/03 | H | NC | Southport | 632 | D | 0-0 | |
| 40 | 20/03 | H | NC | Forest Green Rovers | 480 | L | 0-2 | |
| 41 | 23/03 | H | NC | Rushden & Diamonds | 806 | L | 2-3 | Agana 50, Callan 90 |
| 42 | 30/03 | A | S SC QF | Rushall Olympic | 54 | W | 3-1 | Riley 20, Heverin 39, Williams 75 |
| 43 | 03/04 | H | NC | Kettering Town | 717 | L | 1-2 | McAuley 56 |
| 44 | 05/04 | H | NC | Telford United | 847 | L | 0-2 | |
| 45 | 10/04 | H | NC | Hayes | 465 | L | 1-4 | Hawtin 64 |
| 46 | 15/04 | H | S SC SF | Port Vale | n/k | W | 3-1 | |
| 47 | 17/04 | A | NC | Yeovil Town | 2442 | L | 0-2 | |
| 48 | 22/04 | H | S SC F | Stoke City | n/k | L | 1-3 | |
| 49 | 24/04 | A | NC | Southport | 1333 | L | 1-3 | McAuley 75[p] |
| 50 | 26/04 | A | NC | Welling United | 353 | L | 2-4 | Agana 2, Morgan 57 |
| 51 | 29/04 | H | NC | Yeovil Town | 253 | L | 2-4 | Morgan 11, Heverin 72 |
| 52 | 01/05 | H | NC | Northwich Victoria | 559 | L | 0-3 | |

**PLAYING SQUAD 1999-2000:**

GOALKEEPERS: Scott Bentley (Kidsgrove Athletic), Kevin Taylor (Newcastle Rangers)
DEFENDERS: Matt Beeby (Kidsgrove Athletic), Karl Breen (Ex-Crewe Alexandra), John Diskin (Nantwich Town), Dale Hawtin (Crewe Alexandra), Wayne Mountford (Kidsgrove Athletic), Darryl Wilkes (Kidsgrove Athletic)
MIDFIELDERS: Aidan Callan (Stoke City), Stuart Leicester (Radcliffe Borough), Craig Lovatt (Kidsgrove Athletic), Lee Morgan, Scott Williams
FORWARDS: Darren Baker (Leek CSOB), Andrew Bourne (Kidsgrove Athletic), Scott Dundas (Kidsgrove Athletic), Mike Heverin (Northwich Victoria), Dave Sutton (Newcastle Town),

# LEIGH R.M.I.

## CLUB OFFICIALS

Chairman: **Chris Healey**
President: **G H Fisher**
Secretary: **Alan Robinson**
55 Janice Drive, Fulwood, Preston,
Lancs. PR2 9TY.
Tel: 01772 719266 (H)
01942 743743 (Club)

## FOOTBALL MANAGEMENT TEAM

Manager: Steve Waywell
Coach: Gerry Luska

### FACT FILE

Formed: 1896
Nickname: Railwaymen
Sponsors: Gosome Ltd
Colours: Red & white stripes/black/black
Change colours: All Yellow
Midweek home matchday: Tuesday
Reserves' League: Preston & District
98-99 Captain: Dave Felgate
P.o.Y.: Dave felgatel
Top Scorer: Neil Matthews

**GROUND**

Hilton Park, Kirkhall Lane, Leigh. WN7 1RN.
Tel: 01942 743743(Office). Directions: From M61
at junction 5, follow the Westhoughton sign to r'about, then follow signs to Leigh. Keep on
main road to the traffic lights, left into Leigh Road, carry on about 3 miles to the traffic lights.
Turn left and first right to the next set of lights. Right onto Atheleigh Way,A579 at the first set of
traffic lights, turn left (B & Q on right), at the next set of lights turn right (Leigh town centre), at
the 2nd opening on right turn into Prescott St., carry on to top, turn right, ground on left.
Capacity: 8000          Cover: 4,000          Seats: 2,000
Clubhouse: Yes.          Club Shop: Yes

Pages: 32  Price: £1
Editor: Stephen Culshaw (01257 427144)
Local Press: Bolton Evening News.
Local Radio: Radio Lancs, Red Rose Radio,
G.M.R.

**PREVIOUS**          **Leagues:** Lancs Alliance 1891-97; Lancs 1897-1900; Lancs Comb 17-18, 19-39, 46-68; Cheshire County 68-82;
North West Counties 82-83.          **Name:** Horwich R.M.I. to 1995.          **Ground:** Grundy Hill, Horwich to 1994.

**CLUB RECORDS**          Attendance: 8,500 v Wigan Ath (at Horwich) Lancs Jnr Cup 54: 980 v Runcorn (at Leigh) FA Cup:1st Rd v Fulham(7,125).
Win: Unknown          Defeat: 2-9 v Brandon Utd FA Cup.          at Leigh 1998-99
Fee Paid: £4,000 to Hyde Utd for Keith Evans95-96.          Fee Received: £10,000 for Marcus Hallows.

**BEST SEASON**          **FA Trophy:** Quarter Final 90-91          **FA Cup:** 1st Rd 28-29, 82-83,98-99(replay)

**HONOURS**          Premier Inter League (GMAC) Cup 87-88; Cheshire County Lg 78-79 (Challenge Shield 78-79); Lancs Combination 57-58
(R-up 29-30 55-56 66-67), Lg Cup 28-2953-54 56-57 65-66, Div 2 R-up 48-49 50-51; West Lancs Lg 10-11 11-12; Lancs
Junior Cup 24-25 29-30 (R-up x 4); Lancs Floodlit Trophy 84-85 (R-up 83-84); Lancs FA Cup 84-85, NPL Div 1 R-up 96-97.

Players  Progressing: Harold Lea (Stockport 58), David Holland (Stockport 59),Jim Cunliffe (Stockport 60), Frank Wignall (Everton 58), Gary
Cooper (Rochdale73), Tony Caldwell (Bolton 83), Raymond Redshaw (Wigan 84), Tony Ellis (Oldham86).

Anthony Whealin (No 3) gives Leigh the lead from a free kick. Photo: Mark Sandom

# LEIGH R.M.I. - MATCH FACTS - 1998-99 SEASON

| No | Date | Venue | Comp | Opponents | Att | Result | Score | Goalscorers |
|----|------|-------|------|-----------|-----|--------|-------|-------------|
| 1 | 22/08 | A | ULP | Worksop Town | 476 | L | 1-2 | Matthews 90 |
| 2 | 25/08 | H | ULP | Stalybridge Celtic | 336 | W | 3-0 | Matthews 12, Evans 20, Monk 85 |
| 3 | 29/08 | A | ULP | Winsford United | 195 | L | 0-2 | |
| 4 | 31/08 | A | ULP | Spennymoor United | 225 | W | 4-2 | Evans 16, Matthews 22, Riding 53, Smyth 60 |
| 5 | 05/09 | H | ULP | Gainsborough Trinity | 201 | W | 3-0 | Evans 5, Matthews 10 30 |
| 6 | 08/09 | H | ULP | Colwyn Bay | 245 | W | 3-2 | Evans 9, Matthews 20, Rostron 44 |
| 7 | 12/09 | A | ULP | Whitby Town | 742 | W | 2-0 | Evans 60, Brady 73 |
| 8 | 15/09 | H | ULP | Accrington Stanley | 239 | L | 1-2 | Ridings 75 |
| 9 | 19/09 | A | ULP | Guiseley | 366 | L | 0-2 | |
| 10 | 22/09 | H | P C 1 | **Ashton United** | 156 | W | 2-1 | **Monk 23, Matthews 50** |
| 11 | 25/09 | A | ULP | Lancaster City | 328 | L | 0-2 | |
| 12 | 29/09 | A | ULP | Marine | 245 | D | 1-1 | Evans 68 |
| 13 | 03/10 | H | FA C Q2 | **Winsford United** | 336 | W | 1-0 | **Evans 32** |
| 14 | 09/10 | A | ULP | Runcorn | 290 | W | 2-0 | Turpin 58, Rostron 76 |
| 15 | 17/10 | A | FA C Q3 | **Worksop Town** | 618 | W | 2-1 | **Evans 70, Rostron 86** |
| 16 | 20/10 | H | ULP | Winsford United | 161 | D | 2-2 | Ridings 11, Evans 70 |
| 17 | 27/10 | A | ULP | Chorley | 227 | D | 3-3 | Cryer 8 11, Turpin 18 |
| 18 | 31/10 | A | FA C Q4 | **Droylsden** | 842 | W | 2-1 | **Matthews 13, Cryer 48** |
| 19 | 03/11 | A | ULC 2 | **Burscough** | 133 | L | 0-1 | |
| 20 | 07/11 | H | ULP | Emley | 351 | D | 0-0 | |
| 21 | 15/11 | A | FA C 1 | **Fulham** | 7965 | D | 1-1 | **Whealing 20** |
| 22 | 17/11 | A | L ATS 1 | **Skelmersdale United** | 129 | L | 1-2 | **Evans 30** |
| 23 | 21/11 | H | FA T 2 | **Morecambe** | 435 | W | 4-1 | **Monk 10 65, Evans 35, Ridings 46** |
| 24 | 24/11 | A | FA C 1 r | **Fulham** | 7125 | L | 0-2 | |
| 25 | 28/11 | A | ULP | Blyth Spartans | 387 | L | 1-4 | Ridings 47 |
| 26 | 01/12 | A | ULP | Bamber Bridge | 430 | D | 1-1 | Monk 19 |
| 27 | 04/12 | H | ULP | Hyde United | 287 | D | 2-2 | Ridings 26, Evans 90 |
| 28 | 12/12 | H | ULP | Bishop Auckland | 183 | D | 1-1 | Evans 44 |
| 29 | 19/12 | A | ULP | Emley | 244 | W | 2-0 | Keary 66, Cryer 72 |
| 30 | 28/12 | H | ULP | Spennymoor United | 278 | D | 1-1 | Rostron 90 |
| 31 | 02/01 | A | ULP | Whitby Town | 311 | D | 2-2 | Evans 44, Hill 90 |
| 32 | 09/01 | A | ULP | Frickley Athletic | 174 | W | 2-0 | Matthews 16, Monk 76 |
| 33 | 16/01 | H | FA T 3 | **Southport** | 864 | L | 0-1 | |
| 34 | 23/01 | H | ULP | Worksop Town | 268 | D | 1-1 | Wallace 82 |
| 35 | 02/02 | A | P C QF | **Altrincham** | 366 | D | 1-1 | **Locke 23[p]** |
| 36 | 06/02 | A | ULP | Stalybridge Celtic | 419 | D | 4-4 | Statham 62[og] 90[og], Locke 70, Turpin 73 |
| 37 | 13/02 | A | ULP | Gainsborough Trinity | 378 | L | 0-2 | |
| 38 | 24/02 | H | P C QF r | **Altrincham** | 178 | W | 2-1 | **Matthews 31 61** |
| 39 | 27/02 | H | ULP | Blyth Spartans | 191 | W | 3-2 | Matthews 1 20, Carr 83 |
| 40 | 09/03 | H | ULP | Guiseley | 151 | W | 3-2 | Hill 12, Own-Goal 30, Ridings 40 |
| 41 | 13/03 | A | ULP | Altrincham | 451 | W | 3-2 | Black 12, Smyth 24, Monk 46 |
| 42 | 16/03 | H | P C SF(1) | **Runcorn** | 171 | W | 1-0 | **Black 15** |
| 43 | 20/03 | A | ULP | Bishop Auckland | 204 | D | 0-0 | |
| 44 | 23/03 | A | P C SF(2) | **Runcorn** | 205 | D | 1-1 | **Matthews 75** |
| 45 | 27/03 | H | ULP | Gateshead | 192 | D | 2-2 | Ward 8[og], Ridings 57 |
| 46 | 30/03 | H | ULP | Colwyn Bay | 256 | W | 1-0 | Matthews 76 |
| 47 | 03/04 | A | ULP | Accrington Stanley | 429 | W | 2-1 | Black 55, Tobin 78 |
| 48 | 05/04 | H | ULP | Marine | 235 | D | 0-0 | |
| 49 | 07/04 | A | ULP | Altrincham | 518 | L | 0-1 | |
| 50 | 10/04 | H | ULP | Frickley Athletic | 161 | L | 0-1 | |
| 51 | 13/04 | H | ULP | Bamber Bridge | 151 | L | 0-1 | |
| 52 | 15/04 | H | P C F | **Droylsden** | 355 | L | 1-2 | **Black 80** |
| 53 | 17/04 | A | ULP | Lancaster City | 248 | W | 2-1 | Ridings 17, Tobin 75 |
| 54 | 19/04 | A | ULP | Hyde United | 364 | W | 2-1 | Tobin 10, Matthews 22 |
| 55 | 22/04 | H | ULP | Runcorn | 185 | D | 0-0 | |
| 56 | 24/04 | A | ULP | Chorley | 292 | L | 0-1 | |
| 57 | 01/05 | H | ULP | Gateshead | 226 | W | 3-1 | Black 7, Ridings 48, Evans 54 |

## PLAYING SQUAD 1999-2000:

GOALKEEPERS:

David Felgate (Crewe Alexandra), Ian Senior (Mossley/Leigh RMI)

DEFENDERS: Graham Hill (Runcorn), Simon Turpin (Witton Albion), Mick Wallace (Netherfield Kendal), Anthony Whealing (Blackburn Rovers)

MIDFIELDERS: Brian Butler (Southport), David German (Winsford United), Dave Ridings (Crewe Alexandra), Eric Rostron (Daisy Hill), Brett Storey (Alfreton Town), Steve Tobin (Stalybridge Celtic)

FORWARDS: Tony Black (Chorley), Steve Jones (Chorley), Neil Matthews (Guiseley), Ian McInerney (Halifax Town), Ian Monk (Morecambe), Brian Ross (Southport)

# MARINE

## CLUB OFFICIALS

Chairman: **Tom Culshaw**

President: **Dennis Hargreaves**

Secretary: **John Wildman**

4 Ashbourne Avenue, Blundellsands,
Liverpool L23 8TX   Tel: 0151 924 5248

Press Officer: **David Wotherspoon**

## FOOTBALL MANAGEMENT TEAM

Manager: Roly Howard
Asst Mgr/Coach: Roger Patience
Physio: John Bradshaw

**FACT FILE**

Formed: 1894
Nickname: The Mariners
Sponsors: Johnsons the Cleaners
Colours: White/black/black
Change colours: Yellow & Green
Midweek matchday: Tuesday
Reserves' League: Lancs. League Div. One

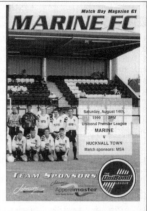

Pages: 24 Price: 80p
Editor: David Wotherspoon
Local Press: Crosby Herald, Liverpool Echo,
Daily Post Local Radio: BBC Radio
Merseyside, Radio City

**GROUND** Rossett Park, College Road, Crosby, Liverpool(Tel: 0151 924 1743)
Directions: College Road is off main Liverpool-Southport road (A565) in Crosby. Ground ten
minutes walk from Crosby & Blundellsands (Mersey Rail). Bus No. 92
Capacity: 2,800    Cover: 1,400             Seats: 400

**Clubhouse:** Open daily. Concert Hall (250 seats), Members Lounge (100 seats).
**Club Shop:** Sells replica kit and range of souvenirs.Metal Badges in home and away colours.
Contact Dave Rannard 0151474 9848

**PREVIOUSLeagues:** Liverpool Zingari; Liverpool
Co. Comb.; Lancs Combination 35-39, 46-69; Cheshire County 69-79.
             **Name:** Waterloo Melville       **Ground:** Waterloo Park1894-1903

CLUB RECORDS   **Attendance:** 4,000 v Nigeria, Friendly 1949
             **Goalscorer:** Paul Meachin 200   **Win:** 14-2 v Rossendale Utd (A), Cheshire County Lge 25/2/78
             **Appearances:** Peter Smith 952    **Defeat:** 2-11 v Shrewsbury Town F.A.Cup 1st Rd 1995
             **Fee Paid:** £6,000 for Jon Penman (Southport Oct. 1995)  **Fee Received:** £20,000 for Richard Norris (Crewe 96)

BEST SEASON   **FA Trophy:** Semi Final 83-84, 91-92   **FA Amateur Cup:** Runners up 31-32 (SF 46-47)
             **FA Cup:** 3rd Rd 92-93, 1-3 v Crewe Alex. (A)       League clubs defeated: Barnsley 75-76, Halifax T. 92-93

HONOURS       FA Amateur Cup R-up 31-32; Northern Prem Lg 94-95, R-up 85-86 91-92, Lg Cup 84-85 91-92 (R-up 80-81 85-86);
             Presidents Cup R-up 83-84 86-87; Cheshire Co. Lg73-74 75-76 77-78 (R-up 72-73); Lancs Comb. R-up 46-47 (Lg Cup 46-
             47 63-64 68-69); Liverpool Comb. 27-28 30-31 33-34 34-35 (Lg Cup 30-31); Lancs Tphy 87-8890-91; Lancs Jnr Cup 78-79;
             Lancs Amtr Cup (5); Liverpool Snr Cup 78-79 84-8587-88 89-90 94-95; Liverpool Non-Lge Cup 68-69 75-76 76-77;
             Liverpool Chal. Cup42-43 44-45 71-72.

Players Progressing: A Sharrock, S Brooks (Southport 73 &77), A Jones (Leeds 60), G Williams (Preston 72), J Lacy (Fulham), P Beesly (Sheffield Utd), M
Kearney (Everton 81), A Finlay (Shrewsbury 81), P Cook (Norwich), P Edwards (Crewe), I Nolan (Tranmere), J McAteer(Bolton W.), R Norris (Crewe 96).

Back Row (L-R): Richard Jones, Barry McMillan, Chris Price, Terry Bowker, John Morgan, Chris Clarke, David
Gamble, Gary Randles, Rick Bainbridge, Joe Morgan   Front Row: Danny Worthington, Terry Fearns, Michael
Douglas, Mark Schofield, Ritchie Townsend, Eddie Hussin. Photo: Peter Hyler

## MARINE - MATCH FACTS - 1998-99 SEASON

| No | Date | Venue | Comp | Opponents | Att | Result | Score | Goalscorers |
|----|------|-------|------|-----------|-----|--------|-------|-------------|
| 1 | 22/08 | A | ULP | Spennymoor United | 217 | W | 2-0 | Bainbridge 38, Morgan 48 |
| 2 | 25/08 | H | ULP | Bamber Bridge | 290 | L | 1-2 | Townsend 60 |
| 3 | 29/08 | H | ULP | Emley | 309 | D | 2-2 | Gautrey 59[p], Camden 70 |
| 4 | 31/08 | A | ULP | Runcorn | 359 | D | 1-1 | Morgan 30 |
| 5 | 05/09 | H | ULP | Worksop Town | 343 | L | 1-2 | Camden 90 |
| 6 | 08/09 | A | ULP | Winsford United | 202 | D | 2-2 | Camden 55, Fearns 76 |
| 7 | 12/09 | A | ULP | Gainsborough Trinity | 373 | L | 0-3 | |
| 8 | 15/09 | H | ULP | Altrincham | 303 | W | 2-1 | Rodwell 30, Morgan 69 |
| 9 | 19/09 | H | ULP | Whitby Town | 312 | D | 3-3 | Morgan 32 62 84 |
| 10 | 22/09 | A | ULP | Colwyn Bay | 251 | L | 0-1 | |
| 11 | 26/09 | A | ULP | Hyde United | 505 | D | 1-1 | Camden 49 |
| 12 | 29/09 | H | ULP | Leigh RMI | 245 | D | 1-1 | Townsend 71 |
| 13 | 03/10 | A | FA C Q2 | Great Harwood Town | 205 | W | 3-1 | Edwardson 10, Price 20, Morgan 60 |
| 14 | 06/10 | A | P C 1 | Stalybridge Celtic | 207 | L | 0-5 | |
| 15 | 10/10 | H | ULP | Frickley Athletic | 228 | L | 1-4 | Edwardson 8 |
| 16 | 13/10 | A | ULP | Bamber Bridge | 225 | D | 2-2 | Rigoglioso 53 76 |
| 17 | 17/10 | A | FA C Q3 | Emley | 381 | D | 0-0 | |
| 18 | 20/10 | H | FA C Q3 r | Emley | 219 | L | 1-4 | Morgan 76 |
| 19 | 24/10 | H | FA T 1 | Frickley Athletic | 141 | L | 2-3 | Townsend 26, Rigoglioso 90 |
| 20 | 27/10 | H | ULP | Colwyn Bay | 191 | L | 1-4 | Schofield 12 |
| 21 | 31/10 | A | ULP | Whitby Town | 521 | W | 2-0 | Rigoglioso 78, Kelly 88[og] |
| 22 | 03/11 | A | ULC 2 | Chorley | 170 | D | 1-1 | Rigoglioso 26 |
| 23 | 07/11 | H | ULP | Hyde United | 249 | W | 1-0 | Bainbridge 12 |
| 24 | 14/11 | A | ULP | Worksop Town | 544 | D | 1-1 | Sang 8 |
| 25 | 21/11 | H | ULP | Blyth Spartans | 292 | L | 1-3 | Camden 86[p] |
| 26 | 24/11 | H | ULC 2 r | Chorley | 128 | L | 1-2 | Blackhurst 89 |
| 27 | 28/11 | H | ULP | Bishop Auckland | 273 | D | 2-2 | Bainbridge 37, Sang 50 |
| 28 | 05/12 | A | ULP | Chorley | 275 | W | 2-0 | Morgan 40, Rigoglioso 73 |
| 29 | 12/12 | A | ULP | Blyth Spartans | 411 | L | 1-2 | Blackhurst 27 |
| 30 | 15/12 | H | LSC 1 | Warrington Town | 102 | W | 3-2 | Townsend 1 42, Bold 75[og] |
| 31 | 19/12 | H | ULP | Gateshead | 221 | L | 0-1 | |
| 32 | 26/12 | H | ULP | Accrington Stanley | 303 | W | 2-0 | Morgan 23 32 |
| 33 | 28/12 | A | ULP | Altrincham | 1001 | L | 1-4 | Nulty 76 |
| 34 | 02/01 | A | ULP | Emley | 301 | D | 1-1 | Bainbridge 70 |
| 35 | 09/01 | H | ULP | Stalybridge Celtic | 410 | D | 2-2 | Townsend 15, Nulty 82 |
| 36 | 16/01 | H | ULP | Spennymoor United | 231 | W | 5-2 | Townsend 30, Morgan 45[p] 85, Bainbridge 73 87 |
| 37 | 21/01 | A | L ATS 2 | Lancaster City | 102 | L | 2-3 | Morgan 11, Fearns 87 |
| 38 | 23/01 | A | ULP | Gateshead | 274 | D | 2-2 | Morgan 15, Fearns 38 |
| 39 | 30/01 | H | ULP | Winsford United | 237 | D | 3-3 | Morgan 21[p], Sang 37, Fearns 42 |
| 40 | 06/02 | A | ULP | Lancaster City | 224 | D | 0-0 | |
| 41 | 13/02 | A | ULP | Bishop Auckland | 207 | W | 2-0 | Bainbridge 6, Morgan 56[p] |
| 42 | 20/02 | H | ULP | Gainsborough Trinity | 262 | L | 1-2 | Townsend 71 |
| 43 | 24/02 | A | L SC QF | Burscough | 197 | L | 1-2 | Nulty 24 |
| 44 | 27/02 | A | ULP | Frickley Athletic | 189 | D | 1-1 | Morgan 53[p] |
| 45 | 06/03 | H | ULP | Lancaster City | 287 | W | 2-1 | Townsend 38, Talbot 74 |
| 46 | 13/03 | A | ULP | Stalybridge Celtic | 427 | L | 1-2 | Fearns 28 |
| 47 | 27/03 | A | ULP | Guiseley | 323 | L | 0-2 | |
| 48 | 03/04 | H | ULP | Chorley | 351 | W | 4-1 | Rigoglioso 12 80, Morgan 78[p], Fearns 90 |
| 49 | 05/04 | A | ULP | Leigh RMI | 235 | D | 0-0 | |
| 50 | 10/04 | A | ULP | Accrington Stanley | 343 | L | 2-3 | Rigoglioso 20, McMillan 61 |
| 51 | 13/04 | H | ULP | Runcorn | 293 | L | 1-4 | Morgan 72[p] |
| 52 | 17/04 | H | ULP | Guiseley | 414 | D | 1-1 | Morgan 68 |

**PLAYING SQUAD 1999-2000:**
GOALKEEPERS: Danny Embleton (Flint Town United) , Terry Hollywood, Richard Jones (Wigan Athletic)
Defenders: Ian Baines, Terry Fearns (Wigan Athletic), Darren Hughes (Newcastle Town), Eddie Hussin (Chorley), Joe Morgan (Southport/Prescot Cables), Mark Schofield (Leigh RMI) , Tom Barnicle, Alex Chvalovsky (FK Chmel Bisany), Danny Gabrielson (Wigan Athletic), David Gamble (Southport), John Gautrey (Southport), Chris Price (Clitheroe), Adriano Rigoglioso (Liverpool)
FORWARDS: Chris Camden (Holywell Town), Stuart Rimmer (Chester City), David Thompson (Southport)

# RUNCORN

Pages: 32 Price: £1.20
Editor: Alex Keenan Tel. 01928 590425
Local Press: Runcorn Weekly News,
Liverpool Echo, Runcorn World, Manchester
Evening News.
Radio: Radio Merseyside, GMR.Wire F.M

## CLUB OFFICIALS

Chairman: **Dr David Robertson**

Vice Chairman: **Tony Bamber**

Secretary: **Chris Henshall**

58 Minerva Close, Warrington,
Cheshire WA4 2XN.
Tel.01925 650311 or 241975 (H)
Tel/Fax 01928 560076 (Sec office)
Asst Secretary: **Rob Ellison**

24 Cross Lane, Grappenhall,
Warrington, Cheshire WA4 2LR.
Tel. 01925 266999 (H) 0802 480313 (Mob)

## FACT FILE

Formed: 1918
Nickname: The Linnets
Midweek matchday: Tuesday
Colours: Yellow/&green/black
Change colours: All red
Reserve's league: Lancashire
Youth's league: Northwest Alliance
97-98 Captain: Carl Ruffer
P.o.Y.: Peter Ellis
Top scorer: Liam Watson (20)

## FOOTBALL MANAGEMENT TEAM

Manager: Derek Brownbill
Assistant Manager: Alan Blair

**GROUND**

Canal Street, Wivern Place, Runcorn, Cheshire WA7 1RZ.
Tel. 01928 560076. Fax01928 560076.

Directions: From South: Leave M56 (junct 11). Follow A56 to Warrington for 1.5miles. Turn left at r'about onto A558 signed Liverpool for 3 miles. Take left hand slipway signed Football Ground. From North: Leave M62 (junct 7).Travel via Widnes and over Runcorn bridge. Follow signs for Northwich for 1mile. Take left hand slipway signed Football Ground.
Capacity: 3,928Cover: 1,327Seats: 499
Clubhouse: Open on matchdays. Light snacks available.
Club Shop: Sells range of club memorabilia. Contact Roy Pickering Tel. 01928568665.

**PREVIOUS**     **Leagues:** Lancs Combination; Cheshire Co. Lg; Northern Prem. Lge. 68 -81;Alliance Premier (Conference) 81-96.
**Names:** None.    **Grounds:** None

**CLUB RECORDS**    **Attendance:** 10,111 v Preston - FA Cup 1938-39.
**Goalscorer:** Alan Ryan (66 goals in 64 appearances 67-68).
**Win:** 11-1 v Congleton Town 64-65. **Defeat:** 0-9 v Wellington 46-47.
**Fee Paid:** £17,000 for Simon Rudge, Hyde Utd, 1989. **Fee Received:** £80,000 for Ian Woan, Nottm Forest, 1990.

**BEST SEASON**    **FA Trophy:** Runners-up 85-86, 92-93, 93-94. **FA Cup:** Second Round Replay 85-86,0-4 v Wigan Ath. (A), after 1-1.
Second Round also 47-48, 67-68, 77-78, 86-87,87-88, 88-89. League clubs defeated: Scunthorpe Utd., Notts. Co.,
Chester City,Wrexham.

**HONOURS**    Lancs Jnr Cup 1918-19; Cheshire Lg 1919-20, 36-37, 38-39, 39-40, 62-63;Cheshire Snr Cup 24-25, 35-36, 61-62, 64-65, 67-68, 73-74, 74-75, 84-89 (5times), R-up 93-94; Cheshire Co. Bowl 37-38; Northern Premier Lg 75-76, 80-81(R-up 74-75); NPL Chall Cup 74-75, 79-80, 80-81; NPL Challenge Shield 80-81,81-82; Alliance Premier Lg 81-82, Gola Lg Championship Shield 82-83, 85-86; Bob Lord Trophy 82-83, 84-85, R-up 91-92. FA Trophy R-up 85-86, 92-93, 93-94.NPL Pres.Cup 98-99

**Players Progressing:** Mark McCarrick, Eddie Bishop, Jim Cumbes, Graham Abel,Barry Knowles, Mark Jones, Don Page, David Pugh, Ian Woan, Gary Brabin, Paul Robertson, Mike Smith,Mark Carter

Runcorn skipper Carl Ruffer wins the ball despite the attention of Guiseley's Stephen Hook during Guiseley's 2-0 victory.
Photo: Darren Thomas

# RUNCORN - MATCH FACTS - 1998-99 SEASON

| No | Date | Venue | Comp | Opponents | Att | Result | Score | Goalscorers |
|---|---|---|---|---|---|---|---|---|
| 1 | 22/08 | H | ULP | Emley | 375 | D | 1-1 | Watson 82 |
| 2 | 25/08 | A | ULP | Colwyn Bay | 436 | W | 3-1 | Whalley 33, McNally 65, Rose 75 |
| 3 | 29/08 | H | ULP | Gainsborough Trinity | 327 | D | 0-0 | |
| 4 | 31/08 | H | ULP | Marine | 359 | D | 1-1 | Watson 15 |
| 5 | 05/09 | A | ULP | Bishop Auckland | 212 | W | 3-2 | Watson 8, Irving 13, Brooks 82 |
| 6 | 08/09 | H | ULP | Hyde United | 315 | D | 1-1 | McNally 8 |
| 7 | 12/09 | H | ULP | Guiseley | 291 | L | 1-3 | Watson 57 |
| 8 | 15/09 | A | ULP | Chorley | 259 | D | 1-1 | Brooke 65 |
| 9 | 19/09 | A | ULP | Bamber Bridge | 320 | W | 2-1 | Callaghan 21, Watson 61[p] |
| 10 | 22/09 | H | C SC 1 | **Woodley Sports** | **166** | W | **3-2** | Watson 7 81[p] 82 |
| 11 | 26/09 | A | ULP | Gateshead | 298 | W | 1-0 | Watson 66 |
| 12 | 29/09 | A | ULP | Winsford United | 240 | D | 0-0 | |
| 13 | 03/10 | H | FA C Q2 | **Blyth Spartans** | **392** | D | **0-0** | |
| 14 | 06/10 | A | FA C Q2 r | **Blyth Spartans** | **586** | W | **4-2** | Nolan 9, McNally 21, Ruffer 53, Brooks 73 |
| 15 | 09/10 | H | ULP | Leigh RMI | 290 | L | 0-2 | |
| 16 | 13/10 | H | P C 1 | **Witton Albion** | **220** | D | **1-1** | Nolan 20 |
| 17 | 17/10 | H | FA C Q3 | **North Ferriby United** | **298** | D | **1-1** | Nolan 63 |
| 18 | 20/10 | A | FA C Q3 r | **North Ferriby United** | **300** | L | **1-2** | Nolan 18 (Re-instated due to ineligible player) |
| 19 | 24/10 | A | FA T 1 | **Eastwood Town** | **153** | D | **2-2** | Irving 46, Nolan 71 |
| 20 | 27/10 | H | FA T 1 r | **Eastwood Town** | **138** | W | **2-1** | Salt 25, Warder 49 |
| 21 | 31/10 | H | FA C Q4 | **Ashton United** | **476** | W | **5-3** | Salt 4 86, Warder 15, McNally 35, Ross 82 |
| 22 | 03/11 | H | ULC 2 | **Colwyn Bay** | **154** | L | **0-3** | |
| 23 | 07/11 | H | ULP | Frickley Athletic | 278 | D | 1-1 | Nolan 60 |
| 24 | 14/11 | H | FA C 1 | **Stevenage Borough** | **1114** | D | **1-1** | McNally 85 |
| 25 | 17/11 | H | C SC QF | **Macclesfield Town** | **240** | W | **4-2** | McNally 9 42, Nolan 96 104 |
| 26 | 21/11 | H | FA T 2 | **Moor Green** | **350** | W | **3-0** | Watson 16 89, McNally 37 |
| 27 | 23/11 | A | FA C 1 r | **Stevenage Borough** | **3252** | L | **0-2** | |
| 28 | 30/11 | A | ULP | Hyde United | 424 | L | 0-2 | |
| 29 | 05/12 | A | ULP | Guiseley | 339 | L | 0-2 | |
| 30 | 09/12 | A | P C 1 r | **Witton Albion** | **139** | W | **3-1** | Whalley 15, Worthington 25, Irving 82[p] |
| 31 | 12/12 | H | ULP | Frickley Athletic | 183 | D | 1-1 | Whalley 47 |
| 32 | 15/12 | H | ULP | Lancaster City | 192 | L | 1-2 | Watson 55 |
| 33 | 19/12 | H | ULP | Blyth Spartans | 257 | W | 1-0 | Irvine 32 |
| 34 | 26/12 | H | ULP | Altrincham | 630 | L | 0-3 | |
| 35 | 28/12 | A | ULP | Gateshead | 304 | D | 2-2 | Whalley 30, Randles 37 |
| 36 | 02/01 | H | ULP | Gainsborough Trinity | 485 | D | 1-1 | Watson 45 |
| 37 | 09/01 | H | ULP | Whitby Town | 282 | L | 2-3 | Worthington 8, Salt 60 |
| 38 | 16/01 | H | FA T 3 | **Hyde United** | **428** | W | **2-1** | Salt 3, McNally 79 |
| 39 | 23/01 | A | ULP | Accrington Stanley | 412 | W | 2-1 | Randles 20, Nolan 55 |
| 40 | 30/01 | H | ULP | Worksop Town | 347 | D | 1-1 | Salt 74 |
| 41 | 02/02 | A | P C QF | **Worksop Town** | **332** | W | **3-1** | Worthington 7 61, Nolan 75 |
| 42 | 06/02 | H | FA T 4 | **Southport** | **1090** | L | **2-3** | Worthington 6, Watson 74 |
| 43 | 13/02 | H | ULP | Stalybridge Celtic | 349 | W | 1-0 | Carter 46 |
| 44 | 16/02 | H | C SC SF | **Northwich Victoria** | **248** | L | **1-2** | Rose 88 |
| 45 | 23/02 | H | ULP | Bamber Bridge | 205 | D | 2-2 | Watson 18, Carter 89 |
| 46 | 27/02 | A | ULP | Worksop Town | 410 | L | 1-2 | Randles 20 |
| 47 | 09/03 | A | ULP | Altrincham | 718 | L | 0-3 | |
| 48 | 13/03 | H | ULP | Colwyn Bay | 257 | L | 0-1 | |
| 49 | 16/03 | A | P C SF(1) | **Leigh RMI** | **171** | L | **0-1** | |
| 50 | 20/03 | A | ULP | Whitby Town | 503 | D | 0-0 | |
| 51 | 23/03 | H | P C SF(2) | **Leigh RMI** | **205** | D | **1-1** | Hill 38[og] |
| 52 | 27/03 | H | ULP | Chorley | 274 | W | 2-1 | McNally 26, Rose 88 |
| 53 | 29/03 | A | ULP | Emley | 201 | D | 1-1 | Irving 62 |
| 54 | 03/04 | A | ULP | Lancaster City | 255 | D | 1-1 | Irvine 44 |
| 55 | 05/04 | H | ULP | Winsford United | 291 | L | 0-1 | |
| 56 | 10/04 | H | ULP | Bishop Auckland | 232 | W | 1-0 | Moseley 85 |
| 57 | 13/04 | H | ULP | Marine | 293 | W | 4-1 | Carter 42, Ward 55, Watson 69[p] 78 |
| 58 | 17/04 | H | ULP | Blyth Spartans | 214 | D | 1-1 | Carter 33 |
| 59 | 20/04 | H | ULP | Spennymoor United | 152 | W | 2-0 | McNally 34, Johnson 76 |
| 60 | 22/04 | A | ULP | Leigh RMI | 185 | D | 0-0 | |
| 61 | 24/04 | H | ULP | Accrington Stanley | 303 | D | 2-2 | Watson 28[p], Carter 76 |
| 62 | 29/04 | A | ULP | Stalybridge Celtic | 329 | W | 2-1 | Watson 53, Rose 59 |
| 63 | 01/05 | A | ULP | Spennymoor United | 219 | D | 0-0 | |

## PLAYING SQUAD 1999-2000:

GOALKEEPERS: Richard Acton (Woodley Sports), Mark Morris, Kevin O'Brien (Marine), David Williams (Everton)

DEFENDERS: Ian Brady (Leigh RMI), Gary Burke (Woodley Sports), Peter Ellis, Eddie Langton (Colwyn Bay), David Robinson (Ashton United), Mark Seagraves (Barrow)

MIDFIELDERS: John Imrie (Woodley Sports), David Nolan (Hyde United), Colin Rose (Gateshead), Mike Smith (Barrow)

FORWARDS: Mark Carter (Ashton United), Richard Irving (Nottingham Forest), Paul Jackson (Maghull), Michael O'Donnell (Maghull)

# SPENNYMOOR UNITED

## CLUB OFFICIALS
Chairman: **Barrie Hindmarch**
Vice Chairman: **P.Fletcher**
Secretary: **Brian Boughen**,141Durham
Road,Spennymoor, Co.Durham. DL16 6JU
Tel No: 01388 811874)
Commercial Manager: **Des Beamson**
Press Officer.: Chairman

## FOOTBALL MANAGEMENT TEAM
Manager: Colin Richardson
Physio: Alan Jackson
Coach: Managerial team

## FACT FILE
Founded: 1904
Nickname: The Moors
Sponsors: Rothmans (Spennymoor).
Club colours: Black & white
stripes/black/white.
Change colours: All red
Midweek home matches: Tuesday
Reserve Team: None
98-99 Captain: Mark Hine
P.o.Y.: David Campbell
Top scorer: Martin Bowes

**GROUND**　　　　Brewery Field, Durham Road, Spennymoor, County Durham DL16 6JN
Tel: 01388 811934　　Directions: From South; A1(M), A167, A688,
straight on at mini-r'bout, 3rd exit at next large r'bout (St Andrews church opposite), pass Asda
on left, straight on at junction, pass Salvin Arms (Durham Rd), ground 200 yds on left. From
A167North - leave at Croxdale (N.E.S.S. factory), right at cemetery on left - this is Durham Rd
- ground half mile on right. Nearest rail station is Durham -buses from there.
Seats: 300　　　　Cover: 2,000　　　　Capacity: 7,500
**Clubhouse:** (01388 814100) Open eves. 7-11pm, Sat 12-11pm (matchdays only), Sun12-2 &
7-10.30pm. Bar snacks. Private functions. Tea bar in ground.　　**Club Shop:** Sells replica kit,
memorabilia, programmes etc. Contact Peter Fletcher (01388 814100).

Pages: 44　Price: £1
Editor: Gary Nunn
Local Press: Northern Echo; The Journal.

**PREVIOUS**　　**Leagues:** Northern 05-08 60-90; North Eastern 08-37 38-58; Wearside 37-38;Midland Counties 58-60;
Northern Counties East 90-93.　　**Ground:** Wood Vue 1901-1904.　　**Names:** None.
**CLUB RECORDS**　　**Attendance:** 7,202 v Bishop Auckland, Durham County Challenge Cup 30/3/57.
**Win:** 19-0 v Eden Colliery, North Eastern Lge 6/2/37.　**Defeat:** 0-16 v Sunderland`A', Durham Snr Cup 4.1.02 (H.T.: 0-10)
**Goalscorer:** Dougie Humble 200+.　　　　　　　**Appearances:** Ken Banks 600+.
**Fee Paid:** £3,500 for Don Prattie (Gretna)　　　**Fee Received:** £20,000 for Michael Heathcote (Sunderland, 88).
**BEST SEASON**　　**FA Trophy:** Semi Final 77-78
**FA Cup:** 3rd Rd 36-37, 1-7 v West Bromwich Albion(A).　League clubs defeated : Hartlepool 27-28, Southport 75-76.
**HONOURS**　　Northern Premier Lg Cup 93-94 (Div 1 R-up 93-94); Northern Lg(6) 67-68 71-7273-74 76-79 (R-up(3) 74-75 79-81), Lg
Cup(5) 65-66 67-68 79-81 86-87; Turney Wylde Cup 80-81; J R Cleator Cup 80-81 86-87; Northern Counties (East) Lg 92-
93(Lg Cup 92-93); Durham Challenge Cup 29-30 44-45 45-46 53-54 62-63 67-68 72-7373-74 74-75 75-76 78-79 82-83 93-
94 94-95 95-96 97-98; Durham Benevolent Bowl26-27 29-30 31-32 47-48 58-59 60-61; North Eastern Lg(4) 09-10 44-46 56-
57 (Lg Cup 28-29).

Players Progressing: Over fifty, including: H. Hubbick (Burnley, 3.25), T .Dawson (Charlton, 3.39), T. Flockett (Charlton, 4.49), J. Smallwood(Chesterfield,
12.49), J. Oakes (Aldershot, 5.54), J. Adams (Luton Town, 53),Alan Moore (Chesterfield), Michael Heathcote (Sunderland, 5.87), Jason Ainsley(Hartlepool,
94), Richie Alderson (York City 97), Graeme Paxton (Newcastle Utd 97)

Whitby Town's Dave Logan prepares to test Spennymoor keeper Dave Campbell. Photo: Andrew Snaith

# SPENNYMOOR UNITED - MATCH FACTS - 1998-99 SEASON

| No | Date | Venue | Comp | Opponents | Att | Result | Score | Goalscorers |
|----|------|-------|------|-----------|-----|--------|-------|-------------|
| 1 | 22/08 | H | ULP | Marine | 217 | L | 0-2 | |
| 2 | 25/08 | H | ULP | Whitby Town | 365 | L | 4-5 | Bowes 55 74 81, Robson 87 |
| 3 | 29/08 | A | ULP | Chorley | 249 | D | 2-2 | Preen 1, Bangura 30 |
| 4 | 31/08 | H | ULP | Leigh RMI | 225 | L | 2-4 | Bowes 12, Preen 88[p] |
| 5 | 05/09 | A | ULP | Hyde United | 397 | L | 0-3 | |
| 6 | 08/09 | A | ULP | Worksop Town | 631 | L | 1-2 | Shotton 31 |
| 7 | 12/09 | H | ULP | Colwyn Bay | 207 | W | 4-0 | Preen 64 74, Bowes 28 55 |
| 8 | 15/09 | A | ULP | Blyth Spartans | 515 | L | 0-4 | |
| 9 | 19/09 | A | ULP | Altrincham | 735 | L | 1-2 | Preen 35 |
| 10 | 22/09 | H | ULP | Gateshead | 384 | D | 2-2 | Preen 30 56 |
| 11 | 26/09 | H | ULP | Stalybridge Celtic | 231 | W | 1-0 | Shotton 45 |
| 12 | 29/09 | A | ULP | Guiseley | 247 | L | 1-2 | Beasley 38 |
| 13 | 03/10 | A | FA C Q2 | Flixton | 216 | L | 0-4 | |
| 14 | 10/10 | A | ULP | Winsford United | 132 | D | 1-1 | Parkin 81 |
| 15 | 14/10 | A | ULP | Gateshead | 298 | W | 1-0 | Hine 75 |
| 16 | 17/10 | H | ULP | Winsford United | 162 | L | 1-3 | Bangura 48 |
| 17 | 31/10 | A | ULP | Gainsborough Trinity | 412 | L | 1-3 | Bangura 65 |
| 18 | 02/11 | H | FA T 1 | Trafford | 146 | L | 0-1 | |
| 19 | 07/11 | A | ULP | Worksop Town | 263 | L | 0-2 | |
| 20 | 10/11 | H | D CC 1 | Silksworth CA | 125 | W | 5-2 | Laidler 5 29 31, Bowes 32, Pearson 57 |
| 21 | 14/11 | A | ULP | Bamber Bridge | 258 | L | 1-5 | Robson 64 |
| 22 | 17/11 | A | D CC 2 | Evenwood Town | n/a | (walkover) | | |
| 23 | 17/11 | H | ULC 2 | Guiseley | 139 | D | 1-1 | Bowes 18 |
| 24 | 21/11 | A | ULP | Lancaster City | 220 | W | 3-0 | Howarth 33, Richardson 69, Robson 83 |
| 25 | 28/11 | H | ULP | Bamber Bridge | 170 | D | 0-0 | |
| 26 | 01/12 | A | ULC 2 r | Guiseley | 193 | L | 0-1 | |
| 27 | 05/12 | A | ULP | Emley | 243 | L | 0-1 | |
| 28 | 12/12 | H | ULP | Accrington Stanley | 163 | W | 2-0 | Howarth 68[p], Robson 87 |
| 29 | 19/12 | H | ULP | Colwyn Bay | 185 | W | 3-1 | Shotton 19, Richardson 67, Bowes 82 |
| 30 | 26/12 | H | ULP | Bishop Auckland | 314 | W | 2-0 | Richardson 56 68 |
| 31 | 28/12 | A | ULP | Leigh RMI | 278 | D | 1-1 | Shotton 35 |
| 32 | 02/01 | A | ULP | Bishop Auckland | 397 | D | 1-1 | Taylor 21 |
| 33 | 16/01 | A | ULP | Marine | 231 | L | 2-5 | Robson 37, Richardson 58 |
| 34 | 23/01 | A | ULP | Stalybridge Celtic | 551 | L | 0-3 | |
| 35 | 30/01 | H | ULP | Lancaster City | 175 | D | 2-2 | Bowes 23 36 |
| 36 | 06/02 | H | ULP | Frickley Athletic | 133 | L | 0-1 | |
| 37 | 13/02 | H | ULP | Blyth Spartans | 314 | W | 2-1 | Howarth 27[p] 44 |
| 38 | 20/02 | H | ULP | Altrincham | 327 | L | 0-2 | |
| 39 | 27/02 | A | ULP | Accrington Stanley | 402 | W | 3-2 | Vine 24, Bowes 35 84 |
| 40 | 13/03 | H | ULP | Guiseley | 305 | D | 0-0 | |
| 41 | 03/04 | H | ULP | Emley | 229 | W | 2-1 | Hine 29, Bowes 46 |
| 42 | 05/04 | A | ULP | Frickley Athletic | 161 | W | 2-1 | Taylor 1 90 |
| 43 | 10/04 | H | ULP | Hyde United | 221 | W | 2-0 | Howarth 27[p] 87 |
| 44 | 13/04 | H | ULP | Gainsborough Trinity | 214 | D | 1-1 | Vine 72 |
| 45 | 17/04 | H | ULP | Chorley | 247 | D | 0-0 | |
| 46 | 20/04 | A | ULP | Runcorn | 152 | L | 0-2 | |
| 47 | 24/04 | A | ULP | Whitby Town | 497 | L | 1-4 | Taylor 19 |
| 48 | 01/05 | H | ULP | Runcorn | 219 | D | 0-0 | |

## PLAYING SQUAD 1999-2000:

GOALKEEPERS: Sebastien Delaunay

DEFENDERS: Gary Andison (Whitley Bay/South Shields), Derek Ord (Gateshead), Mark Taylor (Whitby Town), Lee Tucker (Whitby Town), Ian Williams (Guisborough Town)

MIDFIELDERS: Mark Hine (Stalybridge Celtic), Gary Pearson (Gateshead), John Ramsay (Crook Town), Luke Todd (Gainsborough Trinity)

FORWARDS: Martin Bowes (Middlesbrough), Leon Green (Prudhoe Town), Andy Hayward (Barrow), Trevor Laidler (Tow Law Town), Peter Wiklund (Ronnskars IF), Jeff Wrightson (Kingstonian)

# STALYBRIDGE CELTIC

## CLUB OFFICIALS
President: **Joe Jackson**
Chairman: **Peter Barnes**
Vice Chairman: **Peter Dennerley**
Football Secretary: **Martyn Torr**
c/o the club. Tel: 0161 628 3387 (H)
0161 338 2828 (B) 0161 338 8256 (Fax)
Commercial Manager: **Keith Mogford**
Tel: 0161 338 2828 (B)
Press Officer: **Keith Trudgeon**
Tel: 0161 331 4426 (B) 0161 304 8934 (H)

## FOOTBALL MANAGEMENT TEAM
Manager: Phil Wilson
Asst. Man.: Peter Ward
Physio: Dave Pover

## FACT FILE
Sponsors: Manro Ltd.
Formed: 1909
Nickname: Celtic
Club colours: Blue & white/blue/blue
Change colours: Green & white
hoops/green/green
Midweek home matchday: Tuesday
Reserves' League: None
98-99 Captain & Top Scorer: Brendan Burke
P.O.Y.: Steve Jones

**GROUND**      Bower Fold, Mottram Road, Stalybridge, Cheshire SK15 2RT
Tel: 0161 338 2828 Fax: 0161 338 8256.
Directions: M6 to A556 to M63 to M67; end of Motorway through roundabout to traffic lights,
left; left at end into Mottram Road, up hill, down hill into Stalybridge, ground on left next to
Hare & Hounds pub.
Capacity: 6,000      Seats: 1,300      Cover: 1,300
**Clubhouse:** Open matchdays and evenings during the week. Food available on matchdays.
**Club Shop:** Contact Keith Mogford for details (0161 338 2828)

Pages: 40 Price: £1.30
Editor: Nick Shaw (0161 633 1117)
Local Press: Manchester Evening News,
Manchester Evening News Pink (Sat.eve.),
Aston Reporter, Ashton Advertiser
Local Radio : G.M.R. (BBC Manchester),
Piccadilly Radio

**PREVIOUS**      **Leagues:** Lancashire Combination 1911-12, Central Lge 1912-21, Football Lge1921-23, Cheshire Co. Lge 1923-1982, North West Co's 1982-87, Northern Prem.Lge 1987-92.    **Grounds:** None      **Names:** None

**CLUB RECORDS**      **Attendance:** 9,753 v WBA, FA Cup replay, 22-23
**Win:** 16-2 twice; v Manchester NE 1.5.26; v Nantwich 22/10/32    **Defeat:** 0-6 vNorthwich Victoria
Career appearances: Kevin Booth 354    **Career goalscorer:** Unknown    **Goalscorer(season):** Chris Camden 45, 91-92
**Fee paid:** £15,000 to Kettering Town for Ian Arnold 95    **Fee received:** £3,000 for Martin Filson from Halifax Town

**BEST SEASON**      **FA Cup:** Second Round 93-94, 1-3 v Carlisle Utd.(A)    League clubs defeated: None
**FA Trophy:** Third Round 1991-92, 0-1 v Witton Albion (A).

**HONOURS**      Northern Premier Lg Prem Div 91-92, R-up 90-91 (Div.1 R-up 87-88); Cheshire Cnty Lg 79-80 (R-up 77-78), Lg Cup 21-22 (R-up 46-47,81-82); Challenge Shield77-78 (R-up 79-80), Res Div R-up 81-82; NW Co's Lg 83-84, 86-87 (Lge Cup R-up83-84), Champions v Cup Winners Trophy 83-84; Lancs Comb Div 2 11-12; Cheshire Snr Cup 52-53 (R-up 54-55, 80-81); Manchester Snr Cup 22-23, Intermediate Cup57-58, 68-69 (R-up 56-57, 67-68, 69-70); Challenge Shield 54-55, (Junior Cup62-63); Lancs Floodlit Cup 88-89 (R-up 89-90); Reporter Cup R-up 74-75; Edward Case Cup 77-78.

Players Progressing : Too numerous to list.

## STALYBRIDGE CELTIC - MATCH FACTS - 1998-99 SEASON

| No | Date | Venue | Comp | Opponents | Att | Result | Score | Goalscorers |
|----|------|-------|------|-----------|-----|--------|-------|-------------|
| 1 | 22/08 | H | ULP | Guiseley | 688 | D | 2-2 | Scott 14, Mitten 16 |
| 2 | 25/08 | A | ULP | Leigh RMI | 336 | L | 0-3 | |
| 3 | 29/08 | A | ULP | Colwyn Bay | 385 | W | 2-1 | Burke 44[p], S Jones 78 |
| 4 | 31/08 | H | ULP | Winsford United | 572 | W | 1-0 | Hall 49 |
| 5 | 05/09 | A | ULP | Lancaster City | 280 | D | 1-1 | Hall 48 |
| 6 | 08/09 | H | ULP | Chorley | 416 | D | 1-1 | Jones 12[og] |
| 7 | 12/09 | H | ULP | Gateshead | 488 | L | 0-3 | |
| 8 | 14/09 | A | ULP | Emley | 342 | D | 2-2 | Sullivan 20, Burke 90 |
| 9 | 19/09 | H | ULP | Accrington Stanley | 505 | L | 1-3 | S Jones 30 |
| 10 | 23/09 | A | C SC 1 | Congleton Town | 154 | W | 4-1 | **Trundle 65 75, S Jones 85, Crossland 90** |
| 11 | 26/09 | A | ULP | Spennymoor United | 231 | L | 0-1 | |
| 12 | 03/10 | H | FA C Q2 | Worksop Town | 458 | L | 1-2 | Trundle 79 |
| 13 | 06/10 | H | P C 1 | Marine | 207 | W | 5-0 | **Hall 30, Trundle 32 63[p] 87, P Jones 73** |
| 14 | 10/10 | A | ULP | Blyth Spartans | 336 | L | 2-3 | Sullivan 83, Trundle 86 |
| 15 | 13/10 | A | ULP | Worksop Town | 682 | L | 1-2 | Powell 73[p] |
| 16 | 20/10 | H | ULP | Bamber Bridge | 234 | D | 1-1 | S Jones 14 |
| 17 | 24/10 | H | FA T 1 | Flixton | 221 | W | 2-1 | **Sullivan 27, Mitten 84** |
| 18 | 31/10 | A | ULP | Bamber Bridge | 349 | L | 1-2 | Lunt 83 |
| 19 | 03/11 | H | ULC 2 | Altrincham | 302 | W | 1-0 | **Trundle 32** |
| 20 | 07/11 | H | ULP | Bishop Auckland | 457 | W | 3-1 | Filson 9 65, Trundle 44 |
| 21 | 14/11 | A | ULP | Chorley | 313 | L | 1-2 | Trundle 80 |
| 22 | 17/11 | H | C SC QF | Hyde United | 535 | L | 1-2 | **Powell 85[p]** |
| 23 | 21/11 | A | FA T 2 | Tamworth | 611 | W | 3-1 | **Trundle 20, Parr 47, Sullivan 50** |
| 24 | 28/11 | A | ULP | Gainsborough Trinity | 536 | W | 4-1 | Jones 6, Trundle 18, Parr 22, Mason 45 |
| 25 | 01/12 | H | ULP | Worksop Town | 457 | W | 3-0 | Parr 3, Trundle 73, Burke 85 |
| 26 | 09/12 | A | P C QF | Gainsborough Trinity | 266 | D | 2-2 | **Powell 57[p], Trundle 75** |
| 27 | 12/12 | A | ULP | Altrincham | 904 | L | 1-2 | Burke 65 |
| 28 | 19/12 | H | ULP | Lancaster City | 421 | W | 3-1 | Sullivan 20, Filson 32, Mason 88 |
| 29 | 22/12 | H | P C QF r | Gainsborough Trinity | 186 | W | 2-1 | **Mason 17, Burke 70** |
| 30 | 26/12 | A | ULP | Hyde United | 1357 | D | 1-1 | France 67 |
| 31 | 28/12 | H | ULP | Frickley Athletic | 524 | D | 2-2 | France 23, Filson 84 |
| 32 | 01/01 | H | ULP | Hyde United | 1640 | W | 2-1 | Sullivan 17 25 |
| 33 | 09/01 | A | ULP | Marine | 410 | D | 2-2 | Sullivan 58, Powell 83[p] |
| 34 | 16/01 | H | FA T 3 | Hinckley United | 556 | L | 0-3 | |
| 35 | 19/01 | A | ULC 3 | Witton Albion | 315 | D | 1-1 | **Parr 1** |
| 36 | 23/01 | A | ULP | Spennymoor United | 551 | W | 3-0 | Parr 1, Jones 78, Mason 85 |
| 37 | 30/01 | A | ULP | Frickley Athletic | 279 | L | 2-3 | Mason 48, Sullivan 72 |
| 38 | 02/02 | H | ULC 3 r | Witton Albion | 292 | W | 4-1 | **Filson 24, Burke 34 57, Mason 87** |
| 39 | 06/02 | A | ULP | Leigh RMI | 419 | D | 4-4 | Marginson 22 48, Burke 31, Powell 60[p] |
| 40 | 13/02 | A | ULP | Runcorn | 349 | L | 0-1 | |
| 41 | 20/02 | A | ULP | Guiseley | 394 | D | 1-1 | Marginson 14 |
| 42 | 27/02 | H | ULP | Gainsborough Trinity | 383 | W | 2-0 | Marginson 7, Sullivan 80 |
| 43 | 06/03 | A | ULP | Gateshead | 302 | L | 1-2 | Marginson 22 |
| 44 | 13/03 | H | ULP | Marine | 427 | W | 2-1 | Burke 20, Mason 90 |
| 45 | 16/03 | H | ULC QF | Burscough | 188 | W | 5-2 | **Burke 44, Jones 57 65 84, Marginson 90** |
| 46 | 20/03 | H | ULP | Emley | 536 | W | 2-0 | Marginson 30, Burke 44 |
| 47 | 23/03 | A | P C SF(1) | Droylsden | 485 | D | 1-1 | **Burke 78** |
| 48 | 27/03 | A | ULP | Whitby Town | 549 | L | 1-4 | Powell 36[p] |
| 49 | 30/03 | H | ULP | Altrincham | 802 | W | 3-1 | Bauress 35, Scott 36, Parr 90 |
| 50 | 01/04 | H | P C SF(2) | Droylsden | 547 | L | 2-3 | **Marginson 28, Jones 33** |
| 51 | 03/04 | H | ULP | Whitby Town | 477 | W | 2-0 | Mason 16, Pickford 36 |
| 52 | 07/04 | A | ULP | Bishop Auckland | 151 | D | 3-3 | Burke 16, Mason 34, Sullivan 60 |
| 53 | 10/04 | H | ULP | Blyth Spartans | 443 | W | 4-0 | Burke 2 58, Mason 19, Parr 31 |
| 54 | 13/04 | H | ULC SF | Hucknall Town | 276 | D | 1-1 | **Filson 52** |
| 55 | 15/04 | A | ULC SF r | Hucknall Town | 217 | W | 2-1 | **Burke 7, Marginson 11** |
| 56 | 17/04 | A | ULP | Accrington Stanley | 417 | L | 0-2 | |
| 57 | 20/04 | H | ULP | Colwyn Bay | 216 | W | 1-0 | Marginson 14 |
| 58 | 24/04 | A | ULP | Winsford United | 220 | W | 2-1 | Burke 9, Bauress 45 |
| 59 | 27/04 | H | ULC F | Guiseley | 722 | W | 2-1 | **Filson 69, Mason 82** |
| 60 | 29/04 | H | ULP | Runcorn | 329 | L | 1-2 | Burke 47 |

## PLAYING SQUAD 1999-2000:

GOALKEEPERS: Russ Hughes (Vauxhall Gm/Northwich (Dual)), Gary Ingham (Leek Town), Mark Statham (Northwich Victoria), Gary Walker (Buxton)

DEFENDERS: Lee Coathup (Barrow), Martin Filson (Bangor City), Dave Higgins (Barrow), Eddie Johnston (Barrow), Mark Ogley (Emley), Gavin Walker (Sheffield), Derek Ward (Northwich Victoria)

MIDFIELDERS: Gary Bauress (Barrow), Steven Jones (Leek Town), Kevin Parr (Glossop North End), Steve Pickford (Leigh RMI), Ben Pollard (Poulton Victoria - dual), Jamie Ramplin

FORWARDS: Karl Marginson (Barrow), Andy Mason (Kettering Town), Paul Mitten, Winfield Steele (Chorley) , Tony Sullivan (Prescot Cables)

# WHITBY TOWN

## CLUB OFFICIALS

Chairman: **Graham Manser.**
President: **Brooks Mileson**
Secretary: **Charlie Woodward**
6 Westlands Ave, Whitby,
North Yorks YO21 3DZ Tel: 01947 602312
Press Officer: Secretary

## FOOTBALL MANAGEMENT TEAM

Manager: Harry Dunn
Asst Manager: Mitch Cook
Physio: I Jackson

### FACT FILE
Formed: 1926
Nickname: Seasiders
Sponsors: Arnott Insurance
Colours: All Royal Blue
Change Colours: All white.
Midweek matchday: Tuesday
Reserve League: Teeside League

98-99 Captain: David Logan
P.o.Y.: Chris Hudson
Top scorer: Carl Chillingsworth (24)

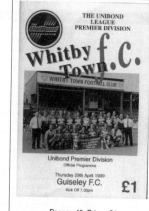

THE UNIBOND LEAGUE PREMIER DIVISION

**Whitby f.c. Town**
WHITBY TOWN FOOTBALL CLUB

Unibond Premier Division
Official Programme

Thursday 29th April 1999
**Guiseley F.C.**
Kick Off 7.30pm

**£1**

## GROUND

Turnbull Ground, Upgang Lane, Whitby, North Yorks
Tel: 01947 604847

Directions: Take A174 road from town centre. Ground on offside travelling towards Sandsend.
Capacity: 3,200          Cover: 500          Seats: 300

Pages: 40 Price: £1
Editor: C Woodward (01947 602312)
Local Press: Whitby Gazette, Northern Echo.
Local Radio: Yorkshire Coast Radio

**Clubhouse:** Mon-Fri 7-11pm, Sat 12-11pm, Sun 12-2 & 7-10.30.
**Club Shop:** Yes

**PREVIOUS**
**CLUB RECORDS**

**Leagues:** Northern League 1926-97.

**Attendance:** 4,000 v Scarborough, N Riding Senior Cup 18.4.65
**Career Goalscorer:** Paul Pitman (375)
**Win:** 11-2 v Cargo Fleet Works 1950
**Defeat:** 3-13 v Willington 24.3.28

**Name:** Whitby United (pre 1950).

**Grounds:** None

**Career Appearances:** Paul Pitman (468)
**Fee Paid:** £2,500 for John Grady (Newcastle Blue Star 90)
**Fee Received:** £5,000 for Graham Robinson (Gateshead 97)

**BEST SEASON**

**FA Vase:** Winners 97.
**FA Trophy:** QuarterFinals 1983-84

**FA Amateur Cup:** Runner-up 1964-65
**FA Cup:** 2nd Round 83-84

**HONOURS**

FA Amateur Cup Runners-up 64-65; FA Vase Winners 96-97; NPL Div 1 97-98; Northern Lge 92-93 96-97 (R-up 27-28 63-64 67-68 81-82 82-83), Lg Cup 28-29 63-64 69-70 76-77 84-85 95-96; Rothmans National Cup 75-76 77-78; Nth Riding SnrCup 64-65 67-68 82-83 89-90, 98-99; N Riding Bene Cup 92-93; J R Cleator Cup 84-85 92-93 95-96 96-97; Mickey Skinner Trophy [5]

Players Progressing: Malcolm Poskett (Hartlepool), Sammy Kemp (Huddersfield), Jimmy Mulvaney (Hartlepool, Barrow, Stockport), Bobby Veart (Hartlepool), Derek Hampton & Trevor Smith & John Linacre & Phil Linacre(Hartlepool), Mark Hine (Grimsby). David Logan (Mansfield)

Whitby Town - post match celebrations.   Photo: Neil Thaler

# WHITBY TOWN - MATCH FACTS - 1998-99 SEASON

| No | Date | Venue | Comp | Opponents | Att | Result | Score | Goalscorers |
|----|------|-------|------|-----------|-----|--------|-------|-------------|
| 1 | 29/07 | H | Nth R SF | Middlesbrough Res. | 1342 | W | 3-0 | **Ellison, Goodrick, Borthwick** |
| 2 | 11/08 | H | Nth R F | York City | 700 | W | 3-1 | **Toman, Francis, Robinson** |
| 3 | 22/08 | H | ULP | Bishop Auckland | 791 | W | 2-1 | Borthwick 9 46 |
| 4 | 25/08 | A | ULP | Spennymoor United | 365 | W | 5-4 | Bangura 36[og], Logan 47, Robinson 60 77, Chillingworth 86 |
| 5 | 29/08 | A | ULP | Altrincham | 752 | D | 1-1 | Robinson 80 |
| 6 | 31/08 | H | ULP | Emley | 878 | W | 1-0 | Borthwick 53 |
| 7 | 05/09 | A | ULP | Chorley | 335 | D | 2-2 | Francis 64, Robinson 77 |
| 8 | 08/09 | H | ULP | Blyth Spartans | 861 | W | 2-1 | Bottomley 37, Alderson 43 |
| 9 | 12/09 | H | ULP | Leigh RMI | 742 | L | 0-2 | |
| 10 | 16/09 | A | ULP | Gateshead | 406 | D | 1-1 | Chillingworth 59 |
| 11 | 19/09 | A | ULP | Marine | 312 | D | 3-3 | Borthwick 10, Robinson 48 90 |
| 12 | 26/09 | H | ULP | Winsford United | 641 | L | 1-2 | Logan 90 |
| 13 | 30/09 | A | ULP | Bishop Auckland | 257 | D | 1-1 | Robinson 45 |
| 14 | 03/10 | H | FA C Q2 | Accrington Stanley | 542 | W | 4-2 | **Toman 7, Logan 57, Robinson 64 82** |
| 15 | 06/10 | H | ULP | Worksop Town | 712 | D | 1-1 | Borthwick 83 |
| 16 | 10/10 | H | ULP | Lancaster City | 628 | L | 1-2 | Toman 60 |
| 17 | 13/10 | A | ULP | Blyth Spartans | 525 | W | 5-0 | Borthwick 5, Chillingworth 19 30 79, Robinson 57 |
| 18 | 17/10 | H | FA C Q3 | Bedlington Terriers | 847 | D | 1-1 | Hudson 48 |
| 19 | 21/10 | A | FA C Q3 r | Bedlington Terriers | 472 | D | 1-1 | Francis 29        **(3-4 pens)** |
| 20 | 24/10 | A | FA T 1 | Blyth Spartans | 343 | D | 2-2 | **Logan 34[p] 40[p]** |
| 21 | 27/10 | H | FA T 1 r | Blyth Spartans | 521 | W | 3-1 | **Chillingworth 45, Waller 60, Regan 85** |
| 22 | 31/10 | H | ULP | Marine | 521 | L | 0-2 | |
| 23 | 07/11 | H | ULP | Accrington Stanley | 469 | W | 3-2 | Logan 23, Chillingworth 30 41 |
| 24 | 14/11 | H | ULC 2 | Gateshead | 435 | L | 1-2 | Bottomley 42 |
| 25 | 21/11 | H | FA T 2 | Bedworth United | 453 | W | 4-0 | **Toman 1 90, Robinson 11, Chillingworth 30** |
| 26 | 28/11 | H | ULP | Chorley | 472 | D | 1-1 | Robinson 8 |
| 27 | 12/12 | A | ULP | Bamber Bridge | 367 | D | 1-1 | Goodchild 49 |
| 28 | 15/12 | A | ULP | Guiseley | 376 | W | 3-0 | Logan 17 56[p], Peverill 29 |
| 29 | 19/12 | H | ULP | Hyde United | 429 | L | 2-3 | Peverill 29, Logan 70[p] |
| 30 | 26/12 | A | ULP | Frickley Athletic | 207 | D | 3-3 | Logan 55[p], Borthwick 68, Chillingsworth 69 |
| 31 | 28/12 | H | ULP | Gainsborough Trinity | 507 | W | 5-1 | Goodrick 32 37, Pitman 46, Chillingsworth 59, Robinson 82 |
| 32 | 02/01 | A | ULP | Leigh RMI | 311 | D | 2-2 | Dixon 75, Pitman 80 |
| 33 | 09/01 | A | ULP | Runcorn | 282 | W | 3-2 | Toman 25, Chillingworth 43, Pitman 67 |
| 34 | 19/01 | H | FA T 3 | Frickley Athletic | 467 | W | 2-1 | **Pitman 36, Borthwick 60** |
| 35 | 23/01 | H | ULP | Altrincham | 709 | L | 1-4 | Pitman 31 |
| 36 | 27/01 | A | N R SC QF | Stockton | 101 | W | 5-0 | **Barker 14, Chillingworth 41, Pitman 53, Toman 57, Waller 86** |
| 37 | 03/02 | H | N R SC SF | Northallerton Town | 349 | W | 4-0 | **Pitman 27 78, Toman 79, Logan 87[p]** |
| 38 | 06/02 | A | FA T 4 | Aylesbury United | 901 | W | 1-0 | **Williams 82** |
| 39 | 13/02 | H | ULP | Colwyn Bay | 494 | W | 4-3 | Chillingworth 30 68, Pitman 76 78 |
| 40 | 20/02 | H | ULP | Winsford United | 175 | W | 2-0 | Dixon 29, Pitman 74 |
| 41 | 27/02 | A | FA T 5 | Emley | 908 | L | 0-2 | |
| 42 | 02/03 | A | ULP | Gainsborough Trinity | 390 | L | 0-2 | |
| 43 | 13/03 | A | ULP | Lancaster City | 230 | W | 1-0 | Chillingworth 20 |
| 44 | 20/03 | H | ULP | Runcorn | 503 | D | 0-0 | |
| 45 | 23/03 | H | ULP | Bamber Bridge | 475 | W | 1-0 | Chillingworth 3 |
| 46 | 27/03 | H | ULP | Stalybridge Celtic | 549 | W | 4-1 | Robinson 9 41, Borthwick 13, Ward 77 |
| 47 | 30/03 | A | ULP | Worksop Town | 582 | L | 1-2 | Ward 81 |
| 48 | 03/04 | A | ULP | Stalybridge Celtic | 477 | L | 0-2 | |
| 49 | 05/04 | A | ULP | Hyde United | 436 | L | 2-3 | Chillingworth 33, Logan 60[p] |
| 50 | 10/04 | A | ULP | Emley | 233 | W | 1-0 | Logan 30 |
| 51 | 13/04 | H | ULP | Frickley Athletic | 554 | W | 4-0 | Chillingworth 1 50, Stout 45, Ward 85 |
| 52 | 17/04 | A | ULP | Colwyn Bay | 232 | L | 1-3 | Goodchild 89 |
| 53 | 20/04 | H | ULP | Gateshead | 317 | L | 1-2 | Goodrick 33 |
| 54 | 24/04 | H | ULP | Spennymoor United | 497 | W | 4-1 | Goodrick 18, Logan 37[p], Chillingworth 70, Borthwick 75 |
| 55 | 27/04 | H | N R SC F | Guisborough Town | 314 | W | 2-0 | **Chillingworth 22 25** |
| 56 | 29/04 | H | ULP | Guiseley | 457 | D | 0-0 | |
| 57 | 01/05 | A | ULP | Accrington Stanley | 336 | D | 1-1 | Logan 45 |

## PLAYING SQUAD 1999-2000:

GOALKEEPERS: David Campbell (Whitby Town), Stuart Dawson (Tow Law Town), Christopher Hill (Bridlington Town)

DEFENDERS: David Goodchild (North Ormesby Sports), Chris Hudson (Pickering Town), David Logan (Bishop Auckland), Glen Moan (Harrogate Town), Micky Waller (Morecambe), Stephen West (Bishop Auckland), Graeme Williams (Guisborough Town)

MIDFIELDERS: Andy Banks (Guisborough Town), Mitch Cook (Scarborough), Brian Crawley (Guisborough Town), Kenny Goodrick (Spennymoor United), Neil Hodgson (Guisborough Town)

FORWARDS: Carl Chillingworth (Guisborough Town), Jonathon Milroy (Bishop Auckland), Paul Pitman (North

# WINSFORD UNITED

## CLUB OFFICIALS

Chairman: **M Morgan**
President: **A Bayliss**
Vice Chairman: **D Cotterill**
Secretary: **Peter Warburton**
3 Massey Avenue, Winsford,
Cheshire CW7 3DU (01606554295)

### FOOTBALL MANAGEMENT TEAM

Manager: Dalton Steele
Asst Manager: John Imrie

### FACT FILE

Founded: 1883
Nickname: Blues
Sponsors: Dickson Motors Ltd, Winsford(Ford).
Colours: Royal/white/royal
Change colours: Maroon/white/white.
Midweek home matchday: Monday.

### GROUND
Barton Stadium, Wharton, Winsford, Cheshire CW7 3EU (01606 593021).
Directions: From north; M6 junction 19, A556 towards Northwich to Davenham,then A5018 to Winsford. From south; M6 junction 18, A54 through Middlewich to Winsford. Ground quarter mile off main road in Wharton area of town. 1 mile from Winsford (BR).
Capacity: 6,000Cover: 5,000Seats: 250
Clubhouse: Mon-Sat 8-11pm, Sun 8-10.30pm
Club Shop: Yes, contact E Welch

Programme:
Pages: 24 Price: 80p
Editor: A Maylor Tel: 01606 552763
Local Press: Winsford Chronicle, Winsford Guardian.
Local Radio: Signal, Piccadilly.

**PREVIOUS**    **Leagues:** The Combination 02-04; Cheshire County 19-40, 47-82; North West Counties 82-87.
**Name:** Over Wanderers (prior to 1914).

**CLUB RECORDS**    **Attendance:** 7,000 v Witton Albion 1947.
**Goalscorer:** Graham Smith 66. **Appearances:** Edward Harrop 400.
**Fee Paid:** Nil. **Fee Received:** £6,000 for Neville Southall from Bury.

**BEST SEASON**    **F.A. Cup:** 2nd Rd 1887-88. 1st Rd 1975-76 1991-92.    **F.A. Trophy:** Qtr Finals 77-78.
League clubs defeated: None.

**HONOURS**    Northern Premier Lg R-up 92-93, Div 1 R-up 91-92, Lg Cup 92-93, Presidents Cup92-93, Div 1 Cup SF 89-90; Cheshire County Lg 20-21 76-77 (R-up 74-75 79-80),Lg Cup 49-50 55-56 59-60 76-77 78-79 79-80 80-81 (R-up 36-37 68-69 77-78); Cheshire Snr Cup 58-59 79-80 92-93; Mid-Cheshire Snr Cup 90-91 92-93 (R-up 88-89); Cheshire Amateur Cup 00-01 02-03; Lancs Comb/Cheshire County Inter-Lg Cup 62-63.

Players P rogressing: W Foulkes (Chester 48), C Marsh (Leeds U. 48), B Nicol(Rochdale 49), E Johnson (Coventry 52), W Hughes (Liverpool 54), R Lewis (Luton54), W Heggie (Accrington 55), J Richardson (Birmingham C. 59), J Abbott (CreweAlex. 61), R Walters (Shrewsbury 62), P Mullington (Rochdale 78), Neville Southall (Bury 80), Mark Came (Bolton Wanderers 84), Dave Bamber (Blackpool),Bob Sutton (West Ham U.), J Richardson (Sheffield U.), Stanley Wood (W.B.A.), R Pearce (Luton T.).

Marine top scorer John Morgan slots home a penalty for Marine against Winsford. Photo: Dave Knowles

# WINSFORD UNITED - MATCH FACTS - 1998-99 SEASON

| No | Date | Venue | Comp | Opponents | Att | Result | Score | Goalscorers |
|---|---|---|---|---|---|---|---|---|
| | 22/08 | A | ULP | Gainsborough Trinity | 404 | D | 0-0 | |
| | 25/08 | H | ULP | Altrincham | 460 | W | 2-1 | Steele 27, Hussin 37 |
| | 29/08 | H | ULP | Leigh RMI | 195 | W | 2-0 | Steele 44, Shaughnessy 71 |
| | 31/08 | A | ULP | Stalybridge Celtic | 572 | L | 0-1 | |
| | 05/09 | A | ULP | Guiseley | 293 | W | 3-2 | Steele 9, Lambert 29, Talbot 62 |
| | 08/09 | H | ULP | Marine | 202 | D | 2-2 | Hibbert 37, Peel 88 |
| | 12/09 | H | ULP | Bishop Auckland | 153 | L | 1-2 | Aspinall 51 |
| | 15/09 | A | ULP | Colwyn Bay | 174 | W | 2-1 | Shaughnessy 22 90 |
| | 19/09 | H | ULP | Emley | 180 | W | 3-2 | Hussin 27, Shaughnessy 38, Hibbert 70 |
| 0 | 22/09 | H | C SC 1 | Altrincham | n/k | L | 1-2 | Peel 47 |
| 1 | 26/09 | A | ULP | Whitby Town | 641 | W | 2-1 | Shaughnessy 53, Pool 89 |
| 2 | 29/09 | H | ULP | Runcorn | 240 | D | 0-0 | |
| 3 | 03/10 | A | FA C Q2 | Leigh RMI | 336 | L | 0-1 | |
| 4 | 06/10 | A | P C 1 | Altrincham | 370 | D | 2-2 | Peel 48, Shaughnessy 49 |
| 5 | 10/10 | H | ULP | Spennymoor United | 132 | D | 1-1 | Hussin 45 |
| 6 | 13/10 | H | P C 1 r | Altrincham | 228 | L | 0-1 | |
| 7 | 17/10 | A | ULP | Spennymoor United | 162 | W | 3-1 | Lambert 38, Peel 69, Steele 75 |
| 8 | 20/10 | A | ULP | Leigh RMI | 161 | D | 2-2 | Shaughnessy 17, Talbot 90 |
| 9 | 31/10 | A | ULP | Bishop Auckland | 237 | W | 2-0 | Thomas 20, Peel 75 |
| 0 | 04/11 | H | FA T 1 | Gainsborough Trinity | 104 | L | 0-1 | |
| 1 | 07/11 | A | ULP | Blyth Spartans | 421 | W | 3-0 | Peel 19, Lambert 26, Shaughnessy 33 |
| 2 | 14/11 | H | ULP | Blyth Spartans | 181 | D | 2-2 | Shaughnessy 34, McDonald 81 |
| 3 | 21/11 | H | ULP | Gateshead | 181 | L | 1-2 | Shaughnessy 85 |
| 4 | 01/12 | A | ULC 2 | Witton Albion | 235 | D | 1-1 | Steele 22 |
| 5 | 05/12 | A | ULP | Lancaster City | 205 | L | 0-1 | |
| 6 | 12/12 | A | ULP | Hyde United | 430 | L | 0-2 | |
| 7 | 15/12 | H | ULC 2 r | Witton Albion | 129 | D | 2-2 | Steele 55, Aspinall 96          (3-4 pens) |
| 8 | 19/12 | H | ULP | Guiseley | 126 | L | 0-1 | |
| 9 | 26/12 | A | ULP | Chorley | 262 | D | 2-2 | Shaughnessy 45, Steele 75 |
| 0 | 28/12 | H | ULP | Colwyn Bay | 163 | D | 1-1 | Wheeler 45 |
| 1 | 02/01 | H | ULP | Accrington Stanley | 352 | W | 2-0 | Talbot 7, Hibbert 65 |
| 2 | 09/01 | A | ULP | Worksop Town | 498 | L | 0-1 | |
| 3 | 16/01 | H | ULP | Lancaster City | 126 | W | 1-0 | Talbot 64 |
| 4 | 23/01 | H | ULP | Frickley Athletic | 148 | D | 2-2 | Shaughnessy 27, Steele 74 |
| 5 | 30/01 | A | ULP | Marine | 237 | D | 3-3 | Steele 16, German 80, Thomas 90 |
| 6 | 06/02 | H | ULP | Gainsborough Trinity | 114 | W | 2-0 | Lambert 14, Jones 56 |
| 7 | 13/02 | A | ULP | Altrincham | 878 | D | 1-1 | Thomas 54 |
| 8 | 20/02 | H | ULP | Whitby Town | 175 | L | 0-2 | |
| 9 | 27/02 | H | ULP | Bamber Bridge | 366 | D | 1-1 | Whittaker 15 |
| 0 | 13/03 | H | ULP | Hyde United | 270 | L | 0-2 | |
| 1 | 15/03 | A | ULP | Emley | 245 | D | 1-1 | Talbot 55 |
| 2 | 20/03 | A | ULP | Gateshead | 278 | L | 1-2 | Whittaker 16 |
| 3 | 03/04 | H | ULP | Bamber Bridge | 181 | W | 1-0 | Roberts 25 |
| 4 | 05/04 | H | ULP | Runcorn | 291 | W | 1-0 | Bridge 51 |
| 5 | 09/04 | H | ULP | Chorley | 340 | L | 1-2 | Hockenhull 4 |
| 6 | 13/04 | H | ULP | Accrington Stanley | 108 | D | 2-2 | Jones 33, Roberts 69 |
| 7 | 17/04 | A | ULP | Frickley Athletic | 120 | L | 1-3 | Whittaker 38 |
| 8 | 22/04 | A | MC F | Northwich Victoria | 0 | D | 0-0 | |
| 9 | 24/04 | H | ULP | Stalybridge Celtic | 220 | L | 1-2 | Hibbert 57 |
| 0 | 01/05 | H | ULP | Worksop Town | 250 | D | 1-1 | Critchley 60 |

**PLAYING SQUAD 1999-2000: (Squad at time of compilation)**
GOALKEEPERS: John Bagnall (Radcliffe Borough), Steve Crompton, Scott Flinders (Ilkeston Town), Phil Ventre
DEFENDERS: Mark Powell (Stalybridge Celtic), Warren Thompson (Mossley/Wilmslow Albion)
MIDFIELDERS: Darren Quick (Chorley)
FORWARDS: Sam Harris (Altrincham), Paul Higginbotham (Chorley), Chris Willcock (Mossley)

# WORKSOP TOWN

1998-99 season
WORKSOP TOWN F.C.
Tigers

Programme sponsored by UniBond LEAGUE
Guardian NEWSPAPERS
Official Match Day Programme
£1

## CLUB OFFICIALS
Chairman: **Rick Knowles**
Vice Chairman: **John Shuker**
Club Secretary: **Keith Illett**, 2 Mount Ave.,
Worksop, Notts (01909 487934)
General Manager:**Danny Hague**
Company Secretary: **Mel Bradley**
Press Officer: **Mel Bradley**
Commercial Manager: **Kevin Barratt**

## FOOTBALL MANAGEMENT TEAM
Team Manager: Paul Mitchell
Coach: Peter Rinkcavage
Physio: Graham Bacon

## FACT FILE
Formed: 1861 Nickname:The Tigers
Sponsors: D.T.H. Engineers/Eyres of
Worksop/Norwood Fisheries/Erriccsons
Colours: Amber & black/white/white
Change colours: All white/amber/black trim
Midweek home matchday: Tuesday.
Reserves' League: County Sen.B.I.R.
Worksop Ladies: Northen Division
Youth Teams' Lge: U21's Central Mid
U18's Notts Imp.
98-99 Captain: Linden Whitehead
P.o.Y.: Phil Stafford

## GROUND
Babbage Way, off Sandy Lane, Worksop, Notts S80 1UJ (01909 501911).
Directions: M1 jct 31 (from north) jct 30 (from south), follow Worksop signs,join A57 and follow
signs for Sandy Lane Industrial Estate - ground on left. 5mins walk from station.
Capacity: 3,000    Cover: 1,000          Seats: 900
Clubhouse: Tigers Club. Normal licensing hours. Pool, quiz nights, disco etc.
Club Shop: `The Tigershop' 30 page catalogue from Steve Jarvis, 10 Wood End Drive,
Ravenshead, Notts NG15 9EJ.

Pages: 28-32 Price: £1
Editor: Mel Bradley (01909 500491/500500)
Local Press: Worksop Guardian, Worksop
Star, Nottingham Football Post.
Local Radio: Radio Sheffield, Radio Hallam,
Radio Lincoln.

**PREVIOUS**    **Leagues:** Midland (Counties)1896-98 1900-30 49-60 61-68 69-74, Sheffield Assoc. 1898-99 1931-33, Central Comb. 33-35, Yorkshire 35-39, Central All. 47-49 60-61, Northern Premier 68-69,74-
**Grounds:** Netherton Road, Bridge Meadow, Central Ave. (pre 1989), The Northolme (Gainsborough Trin. - shared) 89-92.
**CLUB RECORDS    Attendance:** 1,503 v Sheffield Utd, friendly. Central Avenue: 8,171 v Chesterfield, FA Cup 1925 .
**Goalscorer:** Kenny Clark, 287. **Appearances:** Kenny Clark 347. **Win:** 20-0 v Staveley, 1/9/1894.**Defeat:** 1-11 v Hull City
Res., 55-56. **Fee Received:** £10,000 Martin Hardy, Boston U. 87.**Paid:** £5,000 for Kirk Jackson to Grantham Town, 98-99

**BEST SEASON    FA Cup:** 3rd Rd: 07-08 v Chelsea (A) 1-9, 21-22 v Southend (H) 1-2, 22-23 v Spurs (A) 0-0, 0-9, 55-56 v Swindon (A) 0-1.
2nd Rd: 25-26, 1st Rd: 20-21, 26-27, 61-62, 78-79. **League Clubs defeated:** Rotherham T. 1894-95, Grimsby T. 94-95,
Nelson 1921-22, Chesterfield 22-23, Coventry C. 25-26, Bradford C. 55-56.          **FA Trophy:** 2nd Rd replay 73-74.

**HONOURS**    N.P.L. Presidents Cup 85-86 95-96, Midland Cos Lg 21-22 65-66 72-73 (R-up 62-6366-67 73-74), Sheffield Assoc. Lg
1898-99, Sheffield & Hallamshire Snr Cup 23-24 52-53 54-55 65-66 69-70 72-73 81-82 84-85 96-97, Mansfield Charity Cup
22-23.Unibond Div One Runners-up 97-98,Unibond Premier Division Runners-up 98-99

**Players P rogressing:** J Brown (Sheff Wed), G Dale (Chesterfield 48), A Daley(Doncaster 50), K Wood (Grimsby 51), H Jarvis (Notts Co. 51), B Taylor (Leeds51), S Rhode
51, D Gratton 52, A Hodgkinson 53, J Harrison 67 (Sheffield Utd),S Lloyd & P Marshall (Scunthorpe 54), A Rhodes (QPR 54), R Moore (Rotherham55), H Mosby (Crew
1956), L Moore (Derby 1957), H Bowery (Nottm Forest 75), T Moore (Rochdale 84), S Adams (Scarborough 87), D Moss (Doncaster 93).

Back Row (L-R): Kirk Jackson, Dave McNicholas, Phil Stafford, Gavin Smith, Jamie Holmshaw, Martin Francis,
Kenny Clark, Lee Hobson, Ryan Jones, Terry Harris.   Front Row: Matt Walsh, Gary Townsend, Steve Johnson,
Gary Thorpe, Linden Whitehead, Andy Womble, Ian Askey, Darren Field.   Photo: Sarah Jones

| No | Date | Venue | Comp | Opponents | Att | Result | Score | Goalscorers |
|---|---|---|---|---|---|---|---|---|
| 1 | 22/08 | H | ULP | Leigh RMI | 476 | W | 2-1 | Johnson 31, Todd 81[p] |
| 2 | 24/08 | A | ULP | Hyde United | 507 | D | 0-0 | |
| 3 | 29/08 | H | ULP | Blyth Spartans | 502 | W | 1-0 | Stafford 2 |
| 4 | 31/08 | H | ULP | Frickley Athletic | 581 | W | 2-0 | Johnson 39, Clark 81 |
| 5 | 05/09 | A | ULP | Marine | 343 | W | 2-1 | Stafford 56, Whitehead 85 |
| 6 | 08/09 | H | ULP | Spennymoor United | 631 | W | 2-1 | Morris 44, Whitehead 54 |
| 7 | 12/09 | H | ULP | Altrincham | 777 | W | 3-1 | Jones 40[p], Clark 55, Whitehead 57 |
| 8 | 15/09 | A | ULP | Guiseley | 334 | L | 1-2 | Stafford 39 |
| 9 | 19/09 | A | ULP | Chorley | 379 | W | 3-1 | Stafford 4, Whitehead 70, Johnson 82 |
| 10 | 22/09 | H | P C 1 | Farsley Celtic | 444 | D | 2-2 | Townsend 34, Harris 57 |
| 11 | 26/09 | H | ULP | Bishop Auckland | 712 | W | 3-1 | Whitehead 66, Stafford 78 89 |
| 12 | 30/09 | A | P C 1 rep | Farsley Celtic | 86 | W | 4-3 | Hirst 33, Dye 83, Whitehead 87, Stafford 109 |
| 13 | 03/10 | A | FA C Q2 | Stalybridge Celtic | 458 | W | 2-1 | Hirst 48, Johnson 60 |
| 14 | 06/10 | A | ULP | Whitby Town | 712 | D | 1-1 | Clark 24 |
| 15 | 09/10 | H | ULP | Emley | 1070 | L | 0-2 | |
| 16 | 13/10 | H | ULP | Stalybridge Celtic | 682 | W | 2-1 | Whitehead 34, Stafford 72 |
| 17 | 17/10 | H | FA C Q3 | Leigh RMI | 618 | L | 1-2 | Clark 61 |
| 18 | 20/10 | A | ULP | Altrincham | 532 | L | 0-2 | |
| 19 | 31/10 | H | S SC 1 | Treeton Welfare | 276 | W | 7-1 | Stafford 7, Whitehead 21 65 82 88, Johnson 34, Jones 86 |
| 20 | 07/11 | A | ULP | Spennymoor United | 263 | W | 2-0 | Stafford 36, Hutchinson 73 |
| 21 | 14/11 | H | ULP | Marine | 544 | D | 1-1 | Jones 88 |
| 22 | 21/11 | A | FA T 2 | Boston United | 1018 | D | 1-1 | Clark 66 |
| 23 | 24/11 | H | FA T 2 r | Boston United | 668 | L | 0-4 | |
| 24 | 28/11 | A | ULP | Gateshead | 296 | L | 2-3 | Todd 9[p] 80[p] |
| 25 | 01/12 | A | ULP | Stalybridge Celtic | 457 | L | 0-3 | |
| 26 | 05/12 | H | ULP | Accrington Stanley | 431 | W | 1-0 | Townsend 51 |
| 27 | 12/12 | A | ULP | Lancaster City | 270 | L | 0-2 | |
| 28 | 15/12 | H | ULC 2 | Frickley Athletic | 270 | L | 1-3 | Johnson 45 |
| 29 | 19/12 | H | ULP | Bamber Bridge | 439 | D | 1-1 | Askey 31 |
| 30 | 26/12 | A | ULP | Gainsborough Trinity | 1003 | L | 1-3 | Johnson 16 |
| 31 | 28/12 | H | ULP | Hyde United | 521 | W | 2-0 | Whitehead 12, Robson 66 |
| 32 | 09/01 | H | ULP | Winsford United | 498 | W | 1-0 | Womble 52 |
| 33 | 16/01 | A | S SC 2 | Harworth Colliery Institute | 110 | W | 4-1 | Clark 3, Stafford 43, Townsend 54, Johnson 83 |
| 34 | 23/01 | A | ULP | Leigh RMI | 268 | D | 1-1 | Stafford 55 |
| 35 | 30/01 | A | ULP | Runcorn | 347 | D | 1-1 | Johnson 17 |
| 36 | 02/02 | H | P C QF | Runcorn | 332 | L | 1-3 | Stafford 40 |
| 37 | 06/02 | H | ULP | Chorley | 420 | W | 2-0 | Whitehead 4 39 |
| 38 | 13/02 | A | ULP | Accrington Stanley | 434 | W | 3-1 | Stafford 23 90, Whitehead 82 |
| 39 | 20/02 | H | ULP | Colwyn Bay | 475 | L | 1-2 | Brooks 90 |
| 40 | 27/02 | H | ULP | Runcorn | 410 | W | 2-1 | Townsend 51, Clark 80 |
| 41 | 06/03 | A | ULP | Bishop Auckland | 283 | L | 1-2 | Askey 29 |
| 42 | 12/03 | A | ULP | Emley | 413 | D | 2-2 | Clark 30[p], Whitehead 83 |
| 43 | 20/03 | H | ULP | Lancaster City | 412 | W | 3-0 | Womble 25[p], Clark 62, Jackson 76 |
| 44 | 23/03 | H | S SC QF | Stocksbridge Park Steels | 353 | L | 1-2 | Jackson 60 |
| 45 | 26/03 | A | ULP | Frickley Athletic | 366 | W | 3-2 | S Johnson 4, Womble 69[p], Townsend 86 |
| 46 | 30/03 | H | ULP | Whitby Town | 582 | W | 2-1 | Clark 15, Townsend 45[p] |
| 47 | 03/04 | H | ULP | Blyth Spartans | 362 | W | 1-0 | Jackson 13 |
| 48 | 05/04 | H | ULP | Gainsborough Trinity | 291 | D | 1-1 | Jackson 1 |
| 49 | 10/04 | H | ULP | Gateshead | 620 | W | 2-0 | Stafford 30, Jackson 69 |
| 50 | 13/04 | A | ULP | Colwyn Bay | 217 | D | 2-2 | Townsend 6 21 |
| 51 | 17/04 | A | ULP | Bamber Bridge | 405 | L | 2-3 | Womble 42[p], Townsend 65 |
| 52 | 24/04 | H | ULP | Guiseley | 818 | W | 3-1 | Stafford 15 47, Townsend 50 |
| 53 | 01/05 | A | ULP | Winsford United | 250 | D | 1-1 | Jackson 28 |

# ACCRINGTON STANLEY - MATCH FACTS - 1998-99 SEASON

| No | Date | Venue | Comp | Opponents | Att | Result | Score | Goalscorers |
|----|------|-------|------|-----------|-----|--------|-------|-------------|
| 1 | 22/08 | H | ULP | Colwyn Bay | 446 | L | 1-2 | O'Callaghan 85 |
| 2 | 25/08 | A | ULP | Chorley | 354 | L | 0-4 | |
| 3 | 29/08 | A | ULP | Frickley Athletic | 219 | D | 0-0 | |
| 4 | 31/08 | H | ULP | Lancaster City | 403 | D | 1-1 | Black 12 |
| 5 | 05/09 | A | ULP | Emley | 270 | L | 1-3 | Borland 23 |
| 6 | 08/09 | H | ULC 1 | Gretna | 178 | W | 1-0 | Byrne 12 (p) |
| 7 | 12/09 | H | ULP | Hyde United | 419 | D | 1-1 | O'Callaghan 4 |
| 8 | 15/09 | A | ULP | Leigh RMI | 239 | W | 2-1 | O'Callaghan 6, 44 |
| 9 | 19/09 | A | ULP | Stalybridge Celtic | 505 | W | 3-1 | Doherty 24, 49, O'Callaghan 62 |
| 10 | 22/09 | H | ULP | Chorley | 503 | D | 0-0 | |
| 11 | 26/09 | H | ULP | Guiseley | 491 | W | 2-0 | Black 42, O'Callaghan 76 |
| 12 | 29/09 | A | ULP | Lancaster City | 311 | L | 0-1 | |
| 13 | 03/10 | A | FAC Q2 | Whitby Town | 542 | L | 2-4 | Black 16, O'Callaghan 90 |
| 14 | 06/10 | H | ULP | Gateshead | 401 | L | 1-3 | Doherty 61 |
| 15 | 10/10 | H | ULP | Bishop Auckland | 214 | L | 1-2 | Black 36 |
| 16 | 17/10 | H | ULP | Blyth Spartans | 397 | L | 1-3 | Brown 84 |
| 17 | 24/10 | A | FAT 1 | Farsley Celtic | 90 | D | 1-1 | O'Callaghan 24 |
| 18 | 27/10 | H | FAT 1 r | Farsley Celtic | 134 | W | 4-1 | Tomlinson 7, Welch 30, 40, O'Callaghan 60 |
| 19 | 31/10 | A | ULP | Altrincham | 691 | L | 1-2 | Bermingham 40 |
| 20 | 03/11 | H | ULC 2 | Great Harwood Town | 262 | W | 2-0 | O'Callaghan 4, Highdale 90 |
| 21 | 07/11 | A | ULP | Whitby Town | 469 | L | 2-3 | O'Callaghan 22, Bermingham 54 |
| 22 | 14/11 | H | ULP | Gainsborough Trinity | 388 | W | 2-1 | O'Callaghan 3, 23 (p) |
| 23 | 21/11 | A | FAT 2 | Paget Rangers | 333 | W | 2-0 | O'Callaghan 44, Byrne 59 |
| 24 | 28/11 | H | ULP | Altrincham | 638 | L | 1-4 | Daughtrey 87 |
| 25 | 05/12 | A | ULP | Worksop Town | 431 | L | 0-1 | |
| 26 | 12/12 | A | ULP | Spennymoor United | 183 | L | 0-2 | |
| 27 | 19/12 | H | ULP | Frickley Athletic | 366 | D | 1-1 | O'Callaghan 55 |
| 28 | 26/12 | A | ULP | Marine | 303 | L | 0-2 | |
| 29 | 28/12 | H | ULP | Bamber Bridge | 583 | L | 0-5 | |
| 30 | 02/01 | H | ULP | Winsford United | 352 | L | 0-2 | |
| 31 | 05/01 | H | L ATS 2 | Skelmersdale United | 202 | W | 4-0 | O'Callaghan 28, 45, Daughtrey 84, Gough 89 |
| 32 | 09/01 | A | ULP | Guiseley | 388 | L | 0-4 | |
| 33 | 16/01 | H | FAT 3 | Ashton United | 349 | L | 1-3 | Bermingham 55 |
| 34 | 23/01 | H | ULP | Runcorn | 412 | L | 1-2 | O'Callaghan 53 |
| 35 | 26/01 | A | ULC 3 | Chorley | 198 | D | 0-0 | |
| 36 | 30/01 | A | ULP | Hyde United | 491 | L | 2-3 | O'Callaghan 78, Heavey 90 |
| 37 | 02/02 | A | L ATS QF | Darwen | 235 | L | 2-3 | Heavey 3, 7 |
| 38 | 06/02 | H | ULP | Blyth Spartans | 339 | W | 1-0 | O'Callaghan 67 |
| 39 | 13/02 | H | ULP | Worksop Town | 434 | L | 1-3 | O'Callaghan 71 |
| 40 | 16/02 | H | ULC 3 r | Chorley | 172 | W | 2-0 | O'Callaghan 40, Seddon 65 |
| 41 | 20/02 | A | ULP | Gateshead | 294 | L | 0-3 | |
| 42 | 27/02 | A | ULP | Spennymoor United | 402 | L | 2-3 | Hine 6 (og), James 72 |
| 43 | 13/03 | H | ULP | Bishop Auckland | 370 | L | 0-1 | |
| 44 | 18/03 | H | ULC QF | Guiseley | 152 | D | 1-1 | O'Callaghan 88 |
| 45 | 20/03 | A | ULP | Gainsborough Trinity | 380 | W | 4-0 | Heavey 15, O'Callaghan 20, 24, Howard 27 |
| 46 | 23/03 | H | ULP | Emley | 325 | W | 2-0 | Heavey 45, O'Callaghan 58 |
| 47 | 27/03 | A | ULP | Colwyn Bay | 282 | L | 1-3 | Warder 49 |
| 48 | 30/03 | A | ULC QF r | Guiseley | 265 | L | 1-2 | O'Callaghan 84 (p) |
| 49 | 03/04 | H | ULP | Leigh RMI | 429 | L | 1-2 | O'Callaghan 68 |
| 50 | 05/04 | A | ULP | Bamber Bridge | 618 | D | 1-1 | Langhorn 6 |
| 51 | 10/04 | H | ULP | Marine | 343 | W | 3-2 | O'Callaghan 7, 81, Heavey 14 |
| 52 | 13/04 | A | ULP | Winsford United | 108 | D | 2-2 | O'Callaghan 89, 90 |
| 53 | 17/04 | H | ULP | Stalybridge Celtic | 417 | W | 2-0 | Heavey 4, Raines 6 |
| 54 | 24/04 | A | ULP | Runcorn | 303 | D | 2-2 | Heavey 53, Seddon 85 |
| 55 | 01/05 | H | ULP | Whitby Town | 336 | D | 1-1 | Heavey 8 (p) |

# CHORLEY - MATCH FACTS - 1998-99 SEASON

| No | Date | Venue | Comp | Opponents | Att | Result | Score | Goalscorers |
|---|---|---|---|---|---|---|---|---|
| 1 | 22/08 | A | ULP | Gateshead | 324 | D | 0-0 | |
| 2 | 25/08 | H | ULP | Accrington Stanley | 354 | W | 4-0 | Potts 29, Swailes 39, 43, 45 |
| 3 | 29/08 | H | ULP | Spennymoor United | 249 | D | 2-2 | Grimshaw 48, 82 |
| 4 | 31/08 | A | ULP | Bamber Bridge | 771 | L | 0-1 | |
| 5 | 05/09 | H | ULP | Whitby Town | 335 | D | 2-2 | Potts 83, McCluskie 90 |
| 6 | 08/09 | A | ULP | Stalybridge Celtic | 416 | D | 1-1 | Potts 43 |
| 7 | 12/09 | A | ULP | Frickley Athletic | 208 | D | 2-2 | Mitchell 17, Critchley 19 |
| 8 | 15/09 | H | ULP | Runcorn | 259 | D | 1-1 | Grimshaw 48 |
| 9 | 19/09 | H | ULP | Worksop Town | 379 | L | 1-3 | McCluskie 64 |
| 10 | 22/09 | A | ULP | Accrington Stanley | 503 | D | 0-0 | |
| 11 | 26/09 | A | ULP | Gainsborough Trinity | 485 | L | 0-3 | |
| 12 | 29/09 | H | ULP | Hyde United | 272 | L | 1-3 | Ollerton 88 |
| 13 | 03/10 | A | FAC Q2 | **Penrith** | **196** | **D** | **1-1** | **Higginbotham 85** |
| 14 | 06/10 | H | FAC Q2 r | **Penrith** | **246** | **W** | **1-0** | **Swailes 111** |
| 15 | 10/10 | H | ULP | Altrincham | 454 | L | 0-2 | |
| 16 | 13/10 | H | ULP | Colwyn Bay | 244 | L | 1-2 | Swailes 89 |
| 17 | 17/10 | A | FAC Q3 | **Guiseley** | **463** | **D** | **1-1** | **Potts 78 (p)** |
| 18 | 20/10 | H | FAC Q3 r | **Guiseley** | **256** | **L** | **1-2** | **McCluskie 33** |
| 19 | 24/10 | A | ULP | Altrincham | 606 | L | 0-4 | |
| 20 | 27/10 | H | ULP | Leigh RMI | 227 | D | 3-3 | Black 13, Quick 31, Mitchell 70 |
| 21 | 03/11 | H | ULC 2 | **Marine** | **170** | **D** | **1-1** | **Swailes 61** |
| 22 | 07/11 | A | ULP | Guiseley | 377 | L | 0-4 | |
| 23 | 14/11 | H | ULP | Stalybridge Celtic | 313 | W | 2-1 | McCluskie 79, 90 |
| 24 | 21/11 | A | FAT 2 | **Trafford** | **218** | **W** | **3-1** | **Potts 30, Mitchell 79, Swailes 81** |
| 25 | 24/11 | A | ULC 2 r | **Marine** | **128** | **W** | **2-1** | **Mitchell 61, Ollerton 90** |
| 26 | 28/11 | A | ULP | Whitby Town | 472 | D | 1-1 | Mitchell 42 |
| 27 | 05/12 | H | ULP | Marine | 275 | L | 0-2 | |
| 28 | 12/12 | H | ULP | Gainsborough Trinity | 189 | L | 0-2 | |
| 29 | 19/12 | A | ULP | Bishop Auckland | 185 | W | 4-0 | Quick 8, West 38 (og), Potts 48, Swailes 82 |
| 30 | 26/12 | H | ULP | Winsford United | 262 | D | 2-2 | Gray 12, Black 76 |
| 31 | 28/12 | A | ULP | Lancaster City | 312 | W | 1-0 | Potts 65 |
| 32 | 02/01 | H | ULP | Bamber Bridge | 661 | L | 0-1 | |
| 33 | 05/01 | A | L ATS 2 | **Burscough** | **181** | **W** | **1-0** | **Gray 83** |
| 34 | 08/01 | H | ULP | Emley | 298 | D | 1-1 | Black 47 |
| 35 | 16/01 | H | FAT 3 | **Guiseley** | **363** | **D** | **1-1** | **Critchley 24** |
| 36 | 19/01 | A | FAT 3 r | **Guiseley** | **335** | **L** | **1-2** | **Mitchell 75** |
| 37 | 23/01 | A | ULP | Colwyn Bay | 276 | L | 1-2 | Potts 4 |
| 38 | 26/01 | H | ULC 3 | **Accrington Stanley** | **198** | **D** | **0-0** | |
| 39 | 30/01 | H | ULP | Bishop Auckland | 236 | L | 1-3 | Black 23 |
| 40 | 02/02 | H | L ATS QF | **Morecambe** | **319** | **L** | **0-2** | |
| 41 | 06/02 | A | ULP | Worksop Town | 420 | L | 0-2 | |
| 42 | 13/02 | A | ULP | Hyde United | 525 | W | 4-3 | Black 53, 73, Potts 65, Gray 90 |
| 43 | 16/02 | A | ULC 3 r | **Accrington Stanley** | **172** | **L** | **0-2** | |
| 44 | 20/02 | H | ULP | Blyth Spartans | 272 | L | 0-2 | |
| 45 | 27/02 | H | ULP | Gateshead | 289 | D | 2-2 | Hussin 5 (p), Lambert 48 |
| 46 | 13/03 | H | ULP | Frickley Athletic | 310 | D | 1-1 | Shaughnessy 52 |
| 47 | 20/03 | A | ULP | Blyth Spartans | 366 | D | 0-0 | |
| 48 | 23/03 | A | ULP | Guiseley | 224 | L | 0-2 | |
| 49 | 27/03 | A | ULP | Runcorn | 274 | L | 1-2 | Shaughnessy 85 |
| 50 | 03/04 | A | ULP | Marine | 351 | L | 1-4 | Steele 49 |
| 51 | 05/04 | H | ULP | Lancaster City | 346 | W | 2-0 | Hussin 23 (p), Carroll 45 |
| 52 | 09/04 | A | ULP | Winsford United | 340 | W | 2-1 | Lambert 39, Harmer 90 |
| 53 | 17/04 | A | ULP | Spennymoor United | 247 | D | 0-0 | |
| 54 | 19/04 | A | ULP | Emley | 220 | L | 0-1 | |
| 55 | 24/04 | A | ULP | Leigh RMI | 292 | W | 1-0 | Carroll 12 |

## DIVISION ONE FINAL LEAGUE TABLE 1998-99

|    |                          | P  | W  | D  | L  | F  | A  | GD  | Pts |
|----|--------------------------|----|----|----|----|----|----|-----|-----|
| 1  | Droylsden                | 42 | 26 | 8  | 8  | 97 | 55 | 42  | 86  |
| 2  | Hucknall Town*           | 42 | 26 | 11 | 5  | 80 | 38 | 42  | *86 |
| 3  | Ashton United            | 42 | 22 | 12 | 8  | 79 | 46 | 33  | 78  |
| 4  | Lincoln United           | 42 | 20 | 12 | 10 | 94 | 65 | 29  | 72  |
| 5  | Eastwood Town            | 42 | 20 | 8  | 14 | 65 | 69 | -4  | 68  |
| 6  | Radcliffe Borough        | 42 | 19 | 8  | 15 | 78 | 62 | 16  | 65  |
| 7  | Burscough                | 42 | 19 | 8  | 15 | 67 | 61 | 6   | 65  |
| 8  | Witton Albion            | 42 | 18 | 9  | 15 | 70 | 63 | 7   | 63  |
| 9  | Bradford Park Avenue     | 42 | 17 | 11 | 14 | 64 | 55 | 9   | 62  |
| 10 | Stocksbridge Park Steels | 42 | 16 | 13 | 13 | 64 | 60 | 4   | 61  |
| 11 | Harrogate Town           | 42 | 17 | 7  | 18 | 75 | 77 | -2  | 58  |
| 12 | Gretna                   | 42 | 16 | 10 | 16 | 73 | 80 | -7  | 58  |
| 13 | Belper Town              | 42 | 15 | 11 | 16 | 58 | 57 | 1   | 56  |
| 14 | Trafford                 | 42 | 14 | 11 | 17 | 50 | 58 | -8  | 53  |
| 15 | Netherfield Kendal       | 42 | 13 | 10 | 19 | 51 | 64 | -13 | 49  |
| 16 | Flixton                  | 42 | 12 | 12 | 18 | 50 | 64 | -14 | 48  |
| 17 | Matlock Town             | 42 | 14 | 6  | 22 | 53 | 72 | -19 | 48  |
| 18 | Farsley Celtic           | 42 | 11 | 13 | 18 | 56 | 73 | -17 | 46  |
| 19 | Whitley Bay              | 42 | 10 | 9  | 23 | 53 | 77 | -24 | 39  |
| 20 | Congleton Town           | 42 | 8  | 15 | 19 | 65 | 91 | -26 | 39  |
| 21 | Great Harwood Town       | 42 | 10 | 8  | 24 | 51 | 73 | -22 | 38  |
| 22 | Alfreton Town            | 42 | 9  | 8  | 25 | 53 | 86 | -33 | 35  |

\* 3 pts deducted for breach of rule

## RESULTS CHART 1998-99

| HOME TEAM | 1 | 2 | 3 | 4 | 5 | 6 | 7 | 8 | 9 | 10 | 11 | 12 | 13 | 14 | 15 | 16 | 17 | 18 | 19 | 20 | 21 | 22 |
|-----------|---|---|---|---|---|---|---|---|---|----|----|----|----|----|----|----|----|----|----|----|----|----|
| 1 Alfreton Town | X | 1-7 | 0-3 | 2-2 | 0-1 | 2-1 | 0-2 | 3-0 | 2-2 | 0-0 | 1-3 | 0-1 | 1-1 | 1-2 | 2-2 | 3-2 | 1-2 | 1-1 | 1-3 | 0-3 | 2-1 | 1-3 |
| 2 Ashton United | 4-2 | X | 1-0 | 1-0 | 3-1 | 1-1 | 1-1 | 2-0 | 3-0 | 2-0 | 3-0 | 4-2 | 3-2 | 0-0 | 1-1 | 1-0 | 1-1 | 2-1 | 0-2 | 1-1 | 6-3 | 0-2 |
| 3 Belper Town | 1-2 | 0-2 | X | 3-1 | 2-0 | 2-2 | 3-0 | 0-3 | 2-1 | 1-1 | 1-1 | 2-1 | 2-2 | 0-0 | 4-1 | 1-0 | 1-0 | 1-1 | 0-1 | 1-2 | 5-3 | 2-2 |
| 4 Bradford P.A. | 2-1 | 0-3 | 2-0 | X | 1-1 | 4-0 | 0-5 | 3-1 | 1-2 | 2-1 | 0-1 | 4-2 | 0-1 | 2-2 | 3-1 | 3-1 | 1-1 | 1-2 | 1-1 | 0-0 | 0-0 | 5-0 |
| 5 Burscough | 2-1 | 2-3 | 2-1 | 1-1 | X | 3-2 | 1-3 | 2-0 | 1-0 | 3-0 | 0-2 | 2-0 | 2-0 | 0-3 | 2-1 | 0-1 | 0-1 | 1-0 | 1-2 | 2-2 | 2-1 | 4-0 |
| 6 Congleton Town | 2-1 | 2-2 | 1-0 | 0-0 | 3-2 | X | 0-1 | 1-2 | 3-1 | 1-2 | 1-1 | 2-2 | 1-0 | 2-4 | 2-2 | 3-4 | 0-0 | 2-6 | 0-4 | 3-1 | 2-2 | 1- |
| 7 Droylsden | 1-0 | 1-1 | 4-1 | 2-0 | 4-2 | 2-4 | X | 1-3 | 3-3 | 2-1 | 3-0 | 2-0 | 2-1 | 4-2 | 5-1 | 2-0 | 1-1 | 3-2 | 3-1 | 2-0 | 2-1 | 5- |
| 8 Eastwood Town | 2-2 | 2-1 | 1-0 | 4-5 | 2-2 | 2-0 | 4-3 | X | 1-1 | 1-3 | 3-1 | 1-0 | 1-1 | 0-0 | 2-2 | 3-0 | 3-0 | 2-0 | 2-2 | 1-0 | 0-1 | 2- |
| 9 Farsley Celtic | 3-1 | 1-1 | 2-1 | 0-2 | 1-4 | 2-2 | 1-1 | 2-0 | X | 4-0 | 3-1 | 5-3 | 1-2 | 0-3 | 0-0 | 1-1 | 2-0 | 0-0 | 2-0 | 0-2 | 1-2 | 0- |
| 10 Flixton | 2-0 | 2-0 | 0-0 | 0-2 | 2-2 | 2-0 | 3-2 | 3-2 | 0-2 | X | 1-0 | 2-3 | 3-4 | 2-3 | 1-1 | 2-2 | 0-0 | 1-0 | 0-0 | 1-2 | 2-0 | 2- |
| 11 Gt. Harwood Tn. | 5-1 | 1-1 | 0-1 | 3-4 | 2-5 | 2-2 | 0-1 | 0-2 | 2-0 | 0-1 | X | 2-2 | 0-1 | 1-0 | 1-4 | 0-1 | 4-0 | 1-2 | 0-0 | 1-2 | 2-1 | 1- |
| 12 Gretna | 2-1 | 0-2 | 1-1 | 3-2 | 1-1 | 5-2 | 2-5 | 2-4 | 0-0 | 1-2 | 3-0 | X | 2-2 | 1-1 | 2-5 | 3-2 | 1-3 | 2-2 | 1-1 | 4-1 | 2-0 | 2- |
| 13 Harrogate T. | 0-4 | 1-4 | 5-3 | 0-1 | 1-2 | 4-2 | 1-3 | 2-2 | 2-2 | 3-2 | 2-0 | 2-4 | X | 1-0 | 1-1 | 4-0 | 0-2 | 1-2 | 1-0 | 4-2 | 5-1 | 2- |
| 14 Hucknall T. | 2-1 | 4-0 | 1-0 | 1-1 | 2-0 | 4-2 | 3-1 | 3-0 | 2-1 | 3-0 | 1-0 | 0-1 | 3-0 | X | 2-2 | 1-0 | 6-3 | 2-1 | 2-2 | 1-1 | 2-2 | 0- |
| 15 Lincoln Utd. | 4-0 | 1-1 | 1-2 | 1-3 | 2-0 | 1-7 | 1-1 | 7-0 | 2-1 | 2-1 | 4-1 | 3-1 | 4-0 | 1-2 | X | 6-0 | 2-0 | 2-4 | 4-3 | 5-3 | 1-0 | 3- |
| 16 Matlock Town | 0-3 | 1-0 | 1-3 | 0-1 | 2-0 | 2-2 | 3-3 | 1-2 | 3-0 | 3-0 | 1-2 | 2-0 | 2-5 | 0-1 | 0-2 | X | 0-1 | 3-1 | 2-0 | 2-1 | 2-3 | 1- |
| 17 Netherfield Kendal | 1-0 | 1-1 | 1-2 | 1-0 | 4-5 | 1-1 | 0-2 | 3-0 | 4-0 | 1-1 | 3-2 | 0-1 | 2-3 | 0-2 | 1-2 | 1-2 | X | 0-3 | 0-4 | 4-2 | 1-3 | 1- |
| 18 Radcliffe Bor. | 2-3 | 2-1 | 3-3 | 2-0 | 1-0 | 1-1 | 3-2 | 4-0 | 5-2 | 2-2 | 2-4 | 1-3 | 3-2 | 1-3 | 0-1 | 3-1 | 1-1 | X | 0-1 | 4-1 | 2-1 | 3- |
| 19 Stocksbridge P.S. | 2-2 | 0-3 | 0-0 | 2-2 | 0-1 | 3-2 | 2-3 | 1-2 | 2-2 | 1-1 | 2-1 | 2-3 | 2-1 | 0-0 | 3-2 | 0-0 | 0-3 | 2-4 | X | 1-0 | 4-1 | 2- |
| 20 Trafford | 3-2 | 2-1 | 1-1 | 0-1 | 0-1 | 1-1 | 2-1 | 0-1 | 0-1 | 1-0 | 2-1 | 1-1 | 3-0 | 1-2 | 0-1 | 0-0 | 1-0 | 1-0 | 1-3 | X | 1-1 | 1- |
| 21 Whitley Bay | 0-2 | 1-3 | 1-0 | 1-0 | 1-1 | 4-0 | 1-1 | 0-1 | 4-3 | 2-0 | 4-1 | 0-2 | 0-2 | 2-3 | 0-4 | 1-2 | 2-2 | 0-1 | 1-2 | 1-1 | X | 0- |
| 22 Witton Alb. | 4-0 | 1-2 | 4-2 | 2-1 | 3-3 | 5-0 | 0-2 | 5-1 | 4-0 | 1-1 | 1-1 | 5-1 | 0-3 | 0-2 | 1-1 | 1-3 | 1-0 | 1-0 | 4-1 | 0-1 | 2-0 | X |

# ACCRINGTON STANLEY

## CLUB OFFICIALS

Chairman: **Eric Whalley**
President: **J C Prescott/J Hudson**
Secretary: **Philip Terry**
8 Princess Street, Colne, Lancs BB8 9AN.
Tel: 01286 866768 (H), 01282 864000 (B).
Commercial Director: **John de Maine**

## FOOTBALL MANAGEMENT TEAM

Manager: John Coleman
Asst Manager: Jimmy Bell
Osteopath: Martin Dixon D.O.

## FACT FILE

Formed: 1968
Nickname: Reds
Sponsors: Asda.
Newsline: 09068 543 121
Colours: Red/white/red
Change colours: Yellow/Blue/Blue
Midweek home matchday: Tuesday
Youth Lge: Lancs Youth Floodlit League.
1998-99
Player of the Year: Billy O'Callaghan
Players Player of the Year: Jamie Speare
Young Player of the Year: Matt Holdsworth

## GROUND

Crown Ground, off Livingstone Road, Accrington.                  Tel: 01254383235.
Directions: Arriving on A680 from Clayton-le-Moors Livingstone Rd is on left 50 yds past Crown Hotel. From M62/M66, through town centre on A680 -Livingstone Rd 500 yds on right after Victoria Hospital. 1 1/2 miles from Accrington(BR).
Capacity: 4,000          Cover: 1,650                  Seats: 700
Clubhouse: Open two nights and matchdays. Private functions. Well stocked tea-bar in ground.
Club Shop: Sells replica kits, sweaters, t-shirts, videos, photos etc. Contact: Liz Rackstraw

Programme - Pages: 32 Price: £1
Editor: P Terry/D Ellis. (01282 866768)
Local Press: Accrington Observer, Lancashire
Evening Telegraph. Local Radio: Radio
Lancashire, Red Rose Radio.

**PREVIOUS** Leagues: Lancs Combination 70-78; Cheshire County 78-82; North West Counties 82-87.
Names: None.     Grounds: None.

**CLUB RECORDS** **Attendance**: 2,270 v Gateshead 14/11/92 FA Cup 1st Rd
(10,081 v Crewe Alexandra, F.A. Cup Second Round Proper 5/12/92 - played at Ewood Park,Blackburn).
**Career Goalscorer**: David Hargreaves 318.   **Career Appearances:** Chris Grimshaw 352.
**Win**: 9-0 v Ashton Town, Lancashire Combination 75-76.   **Defeat**: 1-9 v Runcorn (A), FA Cup 2nd Qual Rd replay 85-86.
**Fee Paid** :£3,000 Billy O'Callaghan from Droylsden 98-99.   **Fee Received**: £50,000 for Brett Ormerod (Blackpool March 97)

**BEST SEASON** **FA Trophy**: 1st Rd 72-73 78-79 92-93.   **FA Cup**: Second Rd Proper 92-93, 1-6 v Crewe Alexandra (H).
League clubs defeated: None.

**HONOURS** N West Counties Lg R-up 86-87; Cheshire County Lg Div 2 80-81 (R-up 79-80);Lancs Comb 73-74 77-78 (R-up 71-72 75-76), Lg Cup 71-72 72-73 73-74 76-77;George Watson Trophy 71-72 73-74 74-75; John Duckworth Trophy 85-86; Lancs Junior Cup (now ATS Trophy) R-up 85-86 96-97; Lancs U18 Cup 89-90;N.W.All Div Cup 94-95; Anglo-Barbados Cup 95.

Players Progressing: David Hargreaves (Blackburn R. 77), Ian Blackstone (York C.), Gus Wilson (Crewe), Glen Johnstone (Preston), DarrenLyons (Bury), Martin Clark (Crewe 92-93), Mark Wright (Wigan 93-94), Paul Collings (Bury 93-94), Brett Ormerod (Blackpool 96-97), Harvey Cunningham(Doncaster R.).

Photo: R Gabryszak

# ASHTON UNITED

### CLUB OFFICIALS
Chairman: T N Styring
President: D C N Jones
Vice Chairman: J Milne
Secretary: Debbie Quaile
19 Quickwood, off Carrhill Road,
Mossley, Lancs OL5 0SF
Tel: 01457 834208 (H) 0161 200 4925 (B)
Mob 07970 175652
Press Officer: T Liversidge

### FOOTBALL MANAGEMENT TEAM
Manager: John Coleman
Asst Manager: Jimmy Bell
Physio: Chris Moseley

### FACT FILE
Formed: 1878
Club Sponsors:
Nickname: Robins
Colours: Red & white halves/black/red
Change colours: All yellow
Midweek matchday: Monday

1997-98
Captain: Paul Clowes
Top Scorer: Eamonn Elliott/Jimmy Bell
P.o.Y.: John McKenna

OFFICIAL MATCHDAY PROGRAMME £1
SEASON 1998-1999
ASHTON UNITED FOOTBALL CLUB

THE ROBINS

THE UNIBOND FOOTBALL LEAGUE
DIVISION ONE

Ashton United
v
Altrincham
FA Cup Sponsored by AXA 2nd Qualifying Rd
Saturday 3rd October 1998 Kick Off 3pm

"THE ROBINS WELCOME YOU TO HURST CROSS"

**GROUND**                    Surrey Street, Hurst Cross, Ashton-u-Lyne OL6 8DY.
Tel; 0161339 4158. (office) 01613 301511 (Social Club). Fax 0161 339 4158

**Directions:** M62 jct 20, A627(M) to Oldham, keep in right hand 2 lanes, leave at Ashton sign after 2 miles passing Belgrade Hotel, take A627 at next island,keep in left lane and take slip road signed Ashton-under-Lyme, at island follow Stalybridge/Park Road sign, go straight ahead for 3 miles to ground at Hurst Cross. BR to Charles Street (Ashton), or Stalybridge. Buses 331, 332, 337, 408(Ashton-Stalybridge) all pass ground

Pages: 22 Price: £1
Editor: Debbie Quaile (Secretary)
Local Press: Ashton Reporter, Ashton
Advertiser  Local Radio: GMR

Capacity: 4,500          Seats: 250          Cover: 750
**Clubhouse:** Open 11am-11pm. Refreshment bar open matchdays
Club Shop: Yes - contact Mr K Lee (0161 330 9800)

**PREVIOUS**      **Leagues:** Manchester; Lancs Comb 12-23, 48-64, 66-68; Midland 64-66; Cheshire Co. 23-48, 68-82; Nth West Count 82-92.
**Name:** Hurst 1878-1947. Ground: Rose Hill 1878-1912

**CLUB RECORDS Attendance:** 11,000 v Halifax Town, FA Cup First Round 1952.
**Scorer:** Mark Edwards, 37        **Appearances:** Micky Boyle, 462.
**Win:** 11-3 v Staylbridge Manchester Interm Cup 55      **Defeat:** 11-1 v Wellington Town Cheshire Lge 46-47.
**Fee Paid:** £9,000 for Andy Whittaker (Netherfield, 1994)    **Fee Received:** £15,000 for Karl Marginson (Rotherham, Mar. 1993)

**BEST SEASON**   **FA Trophy:** Qtr Final v Dagenham (0-1) (A0 96-97
**FA Cup:** 1st Rd replay 52-53, 1-2 v Halifax T (A), after 1-1. Also 1st Rd 55-56, 1-6 v Southport (A)

**HONOURS**       Northern Prem Lge Div 1 Cup 94-95; Manchester Sen Cup 1884-85 13-14 75-76 77-78; Manchester Lge 11-12; Lancs Comb. Div 60-61 (Lge Cup 62-63);Manchester Prem. Cup 79-80 82-83 92-93; North West Counties Lge 91-92;Challenge Cup 91-92, Div 2 87 88; Floodlit League 90-91; Challenge Shield 92-93; Manchester Chall Shield 35-36 38-39 49-50 53-54 (R-up 34-35 39-40), Manchester Interm Cup 58-59 62-63 65-66, R-up 60-61 64-65; Manchester Jnr Cup 1894-95 10-12 32-33; Unifilla Div 1 Cup 96-97

Players progressing: A Ball (Blackpool), J Mahoney (Stoke C.), B Daniels(Manchester C.), R Jones (Rotherham U.), A Arrowsmith (Liverpool), N Stiffle(Crystal Palace), K Marginson (Rotherham U), P Wilson (Plymouth Argyle)

Ashton United's new aquisition last season, Mark Ceraolo, being closely watched by Lincoln United's Stuart Reddington during their 1-1 draw in March this year.

Photo: Colin Stevens

# ELPER TOWN

## CLUB OFFICIALS

Chairman: **Phil Varney**
President: **Alan Benfield**
Secretary: **Brian Ruskin**
121 Marsh Lane, Belper, Derbys, DE56
1GU. Tel: 01773 827091 Mobile: 0410
444195
Press Officer: **Nigel Oldrini**

## FOOTBALL MANAGEMENT TEAM

Manager: Martin Rowe
Asst Manager: Steve Dolby

### FACT FILE

Formed: 1883
Nickname: Nailers
Colours: Yellow/black/black & yellow
Change colours: All white
Midweek home matchday: Tuesday
Reserves' League: Midlands Reg All
1998-99
Captain:Richard Denby
P.o.Y.: Brendan Morgan
Top scorer: Carl Cunningham

### GROUND

GROUND Address: Christchurch Meadow, Bridge Street, Belper DE56 1BA (01773856556).
Directions: From M1 North, Jnct 28 onto A38 towards Derby, turn off at A610
Ripley/Nottingham), then 4 exit at roundabout towards Ambergate. At junction with A6 (Hurt
Arms Hotel) left to Belper. Ground on right past traffic lights. 400 yards from Belper (BR)
Capacity: 2,640Cover: 1,000Seats: 200
Clubhouse: Open matchdays, bar, hot & cold food available
Club Shop: No

Pages: 36  Price £1.00
Editor: Andy Darlington ( 01773 822993)
Local Press: Belper News, Derby Evening
Telegraph, Belper Express
Local Radio: BBC Radio Derby

### PREVIOUS

**Leagues:** Central Alliance 57-61; Midland Co's 61-82
**Grounds:** Acorn Ground prior to 1951
**Names:** None

### CLUB RECORDS

**Attendance:** 3,200 v Ilkeston Town, 1955
**Goalscorer:** Mick Lakin 231      **Appearances:** Gil Rhodes
Fee **Received:** £700 forBrian Hall (Mansfield Town 59) **Fee Paid:** Nil.
**Victory:** 15-2 v Nottingham Forest 'A'1956    **Defeat:** 0-12 v Goole Town 1965

### BEST SEASON

**FA Vase:** Semi-final 94-95    **FA Amateur Cup:** Not entered
**FA Trophy:** 3rd Qual Rd 97-98
**FA Cup:** 1st Rd Prop 1887-88 (4th Qual. Rnd 1964-65)

### HONOURS

Northern Counties East Lge 84-85, Midland Counties Lg 79-80; Central Alliance Lge 58-59;
Derbys Snr Cup 58-59 60-61 62-63 79-80

Players progressing: None

L-R Back Row: Doug Rowland, Martin Rowe (manager), Dean Smith, Richard Cope, Paul Galloway, Mark Wilson, Craig Smithurst, Mark Wood, Andy Mitchell, Steve Dolby (asst. man.) Peter Walker (physio). Front Row: Darren Turner, Steve Orr, Brendan Morgan, Richard Denby, Craig Weston, Karl Paine, Carl Cunningham.    Photo courtesy of the Derby Evening Telegraph

# BRADFORD PARK AVENUE

**CLUB OFFICIALS**
Chairman: **Mike Firth**
President: **Charlie Atkinson**
Secretary: **Alan Hirst**
24 Quarryfields, Mirfield, W.Yorks WF14 0NT
Tel.01924 480349 (H) 01924 474477 (B)
Press Officer: **Tim Clapham**
Commercial Manager: **Chris Higgins**

**FOOTBALL MANAGEMENT TEAM**

Manager: Trevor Storton
Asst Manager: Clive Freeman
Physio: Ray Killick

**FACT FILE**
Formed: 1907        Reformed: 1988
Nickname: Avenue
Club Sponsor: Allied Colloids
Colours: Green & white/white/green & white
Change colours: Red, amber &
black/black/black
Midweek Matches: Wednesday
Reserves' league: N/A
98-99 Captain: Wayne Benn
Top Scorer:Chris Brandon
P.o.Y.: Neil Grayston

Pages: 36 Price: £1.20
Editor: Martin Worthy
01924 384477
Local Press: Telegraph & Argus
Local Radio: Radio Leeds

## GROUND

Horsfall Stadium, Cemetery Road, Bradford, West Yorks BD6 2NG

**Directions:** M62 Jct 26. Along M606 to the end. At roundabout takeA6036 (signed Halifax) and pass Odsal Stadium on left hand side. At next roundabout take 3rd exit A6036 (Halifax), in approx. 1 mile turn left into Cemetery Rd (by Kings Head Pub). Ground 150 yards on left
Capacity: 5,000            Cover: 2,000            Seats: 1,247
**Club Shop:** Yes - contact Trevor Hutchinson (01274 785657)        **Clubhouse:** No

**PREVIOUS**        **Leagues:** Southern 07-08; Football League 08-70; Northern Premier 70-74; West Riding County Amtr 88-89; Central Mids 89-90; N. W. Counties 90-95
**Grounds:** Park Avenue 07-73; Valley Parade 73-74; Manningham Mills 88-89; Bramley R.L.F.C.,McLaren Field 89-93; Batley 93-96
**CLUB RECORDS**        **Attendance:** 1,007 v Bradford City 97 (Centenary Chall). 32,810 v Blackpool, War Cup 1944
**Win:** 11-0 v Denby Dale FAC 1908        **Defeat:** 0-7 v Barnsley 1911
**Scorer:** Len Shackleton 171 1940-46        **Appearances:** Tommy Farr 542 1934-50
**Fee Received:** £34,000 for K Hector (Derby County 1966)
**Fee Paid:** £24,500 for L Leuty (Derby County 1950)
**BEST SEASON**        **FA Vase:** 2nd Rd Prop 94-95
**FA Trophy:** 3rd Rd 98-99
**FA Cup:** Qtr finals 12-13, 19-20, 45-46
**HONOURS** Football Lge Div 2 R-up 1914; 3rd Div N 28; Yorkshire Lge 21, 23;Midland Lge 32; West Riding Snr Cup 11,13,25,27,32,36,51,53,63, County Cup 29,90-91, N.W.C. Lg Champions 94-95, N.W.C. Carling Challenge Trophy 94-95

Action from Park's league match with Gretna.

Photo: Alan Watson

# BURSCOUGH

## CLUB OFFICIALS

Chairman: **Frank Parr**
Vice Chairman: **Stuart Heaps**
President: **Ken Griffin**
Secretary: **Stan Strickland**
109 Redgate, Ormskirk, Lancs L39 3NW
(H 01695574722) (B 01695 574722)
Press Officer: Secretary

### FOOTBALL MANAGEMENT TEAM
Manager: John Davison
Asst Manager: Peter King
Physio: Kevin Downie

### FACT FILE

Founded: 1946
Nickname: Linnets
Sponsors: Seyfert Ltd.
Colours: Green/white/green
Change colours: Yellow/blue/blue
Midweek Matches: Tuesday
1998-99
Captain: Ged Nolan
Top Scorer Mark Wilde
P.o.Y.: Mark Wilde

Pages: 40 Price £1.00
Editor: Stan Strickland
(01695 574722)
Radio: Radio Lancs,Red Rose.Dune F.M.

**GROUND** Victoria Park, Bobby Langton Way, Mart Lane, Burscough, Ormskirk, Lancs L40 0SD Tel: 01704 893237
**Directions:** M6 Jct 27, follow signs thru Parbold A5209, right into Junction Lane (signed Burscough & Martin Mere) to lights, right onto A59 to Burscough Village, 2nd left over canal bridge into Mart Lane to ground. 200 yards from Burscough Bridge BR station (Wigan-Southport line). Half mile from Burscough Junction (Ormskirk Preston line)
Capacity: 3,000      Seats: 220      Cover: 1,000
**Clubhouse:** `Barons Club' (privately owned, access outside grd). Mon-Thurs 7-11pm, Fri 4-11pm, Sat 1-11pm, Sun noon-3 & 7-10.30pm. No food      **Club Shop:** No

**PREVIOUS** Leagues: Liverpool County Comb. 46-53, Lancs Comb. 53-70, Cheshire Co.70-82, North West Counties 82-98
**CLUB RECORDS** **Attendance:** 4,798 v Wigan Athletic,F.A.Cup 3rd Qual.Rd.1950-51
**Goalscorer:** Johnny Vincent 60 53-54. Most Goals in Game: Louis Bimpson 7. In Career: Wes Bridge 188
**Win:** 10-0 v Cromptons Recreation 1947 & v  Nelson 1948-49, both Lancs. Comb.
**Defeat:** 0-9 v Earlstown,Liverpool County Comb.1948-49      **Fee paid:** Undisclosed for Arthur Green. Burton Alb. 48
**Fee Received:** £10,000 for Gary Martindale (Bolton Wanderers), &Kevin Formby (Rochdale)
**BEST SEASON** **FA Cup:** 1st Rd 59-60 77-78 79-80 80-81
**FA Trophy:** 1982-83
**FA Vase:** 1994-95 (Last 16)
**HONOURS** Liverpool Challenge Cup 47-48 50-51,54-55; George Mahon Cup 47-48;Liverpool County Comb Div 1, 49-50 (Div 2 53-54, 67-68); Lancs Comb.Div 2 53-54; Lancs Comb Div 1 55-56 69-70; Lord Wavertree Cup 67-68; Cheshire County Lge R-up 70-71, League Cup 74-75 (R-up 73-74); Lancs Jnr Cup 47-4849-50 66-67; Liverpool Snr Cup 55/56, 71-72; Nth West Co's League 82-83, Lge Cup 92-93 95-96(R-up 91-92); Challenge Shield 82-83, 95,96; Bill Tyrer Memorial Trophy 90; Liverpool Snr Non-League Cup Finalist 92-93, 95-96,98-99.
**Players progressing:**      L Bimpson, B Parker (Liverpool 53), B Pilson (Stoke 53-54), A Green (Huddersfield), K Waterhouse (Preston), K Spencer (Everton), F Gamble (Derby 80), Tony Rigby (Bury), S Teale (Aston Villa), L Watson(Preston), K Formby A Russell (Rochdale 94), G Martindale (Bolton 94), S Perkins (Plymouth A. 97)

Back Row: Ryan Lowe, Paul Dawson, Ged Nolan, Billy Knowles, Andy McMullen, Paul Blasbery, Michael Clandon, Ryan Bowen, Robbie Armstrong, Neil Hanson, Mark Wilde.
Front Row: Darren Saint, Andy Howard, Michael Yates, Simon Jennings, Robbie Cowley, Ray Birch.

# CHORLEY

### CLUB OFFICIALS

Chairman: **Jack Kirkland**
President: **Dr P J Wren.**
Commercial Manager: **Dawn Fowler**
Secretary / Press Officer: **Mick Wearmouth**
6 Avondale Road, Chorley, Lancs. PR72ED
Tel: 01257 271395

### FOOTBALL MANAGEMENT TEAM

Manager: Ken Wright

**FACT FILE**

Formed: 1883
Founded: The Magpies
Sponsors: Coloroll.
Colours: White & black stripes/black/black
& white
Change colours: All yellow
Midweek matchday: Tuesday
Reserve League: Alliance League.

### GROUND

Victory Park, Duke Street, Chorley, Lancs    Tel: 01257 263406
**Directions:** M61 jct 6, A6 to Chorley, going past Yarrow Bridge Hotel on Bolton Rd turn left
at 1st lights into Pilling Lane, 1st right into Ashley St..,ground 2nd left. From M6; jct 27, follow
signs to Chorley, left at lights,continue for 2 1/2 miles on A49, right onto B5251, on entering
Chorley turn right into Duke Street 200yds after Plough Hotel. 1/4 mile from Chorley (BR).
Capacity: 4,100        Cover: 2,800        Seats: 900
**Clubhouse:** 01257 275662. Open every evening. Weekend entertainment, Snacks available
Club Shop: Yes.

Pages: 32  Price: £1.
Editor:Dawn Fowler
Local Press: Lancs Evening Post,
Chorley Guardian.
Local Radio: Radio Lancs, Red Rose.

**PREVIOUS**        Leagues: Lancs Alliance 1890-94; Lancs 94-1903; Lancs Comb. 03-68, 69-70;Northern Premier 68-69, 70-72, 82-88;
Cheshire County 72-82; GMV Conference 88-90.
Grounds: Dole Lane 1883-1901; Rangletts Park 01-05; St George's Park 05-20.  Name: None

**CLUB RECORDS**   **Attendance:** 9,679 v Darwen, 1931-32.  **Goalscorer:** Peter Watson.
**Fee Paid:** Undisclosed to Marine for Brian Ross 1995.  **Fee Received:** £22,500 for Paul Mariner (Plymouth, 1973).

**BEST SEASON**   **FA Cup:** 2nd Rd 86-87 (lost in replay at Preston), 90-91 (lost at Shrewsbury).  **FA Trophy:** Semi-Final 1995-96.

**HONOURS**        Northern Premier Lg 87-88, Cheshire Co. Lg 75-76 76-77 81-82, Lancs Comb. 19-2022-23 27-28 28-29 32-33 33-34 45-46
59-60 60-61 63-64 (R-up 21-22 26-27 48-4962-63 64-65 65-66, Lg Cup 24-25 58-59 62-63), Lancs Lg 1896-97 98-99,
Lancs Alliance 1892-93 (R-up 94-95), Lancs Jnr Cup 1894-95 1908-09 23-24 39-40 45-4657-58 58-59 60-61 63-64 64-65
75-76 79-80 81-82 82-83.

Players Progressing:   Charles Ashcroft (Liverpool 1946),William Healey (Arsenal 49), Stan Howard (Huddersfield 52), Derek Hogg (Leicester 52),
William Norcross (Southport 59), Micky Walsh (Blackpool 71),Paul Mariner (Plymouth 73), Graham Barrow (Wigan 76),
Steve Galliers (Wimbledon77), Kevin Tully (Bury 80), Geoff Twentyman (Preston 83), Gary Buckley (Bury84), Chris Hunter (Preston 84).

**Back Row:** P Porter, J Hyde, I Cain, P Ashcroft, J Cross, J Price, A Hardman. **Middle Row:** N Bailey, K Hagan, I Leather, M Swailes, C
Shattock, S Marsh, D Quick, A Critchley, S Abraham, L Taylor. **Front Row:** C Potts, I Harold, A Grimshaw, B Griffiths, J McCluskie, P
Higginbotham        J M B Photography

# CONGLETON TOWN

### CLUB OFFICIALS

Chairman: **Peter Evans**
Vice Chairman: **Steve Burgess**
Secretary and Press Officer: **David Wilcock**
4,Maxwell Rd., Congleton
Cheshire CW12 3HY.
Tel: 01260 276347 (H) 01260 270275 (B)

### FOOTBALL MANAGEMENT TEAM

Manager: Tommy Lawson
Asst Mgr: Andy Gray
Physio: Paul Kelly

### FACT FILE
Formed: 1901
Nickname: Bears
Colours: White & black flashes/black/black
& white
Change colours:Red & White
Midweek home matchday: Tuesday
Reserve Team: N/A
1997-98
Captain: Simonm Rudge
P.o.Y.: Russell Payne
Top Scorer: Graham Dodd

**GROUND**   Booth Street Ground, Crescent Road, Congleton, Cheshire Tel: 02602 74460

**Directions:**   On approach to Congleton via Clayton bypass take second right after fire
station, into Booth Street. Two miles from Congleton (BR)
Capacity: 5,000            Cover: 1,200              Seats: 250
**Clubhouse:** Open match days only        **Club Shop:** Yes. Contact:Gerry Brocklehurst

Pages: 48 Price:£1.00
Editor: Ken Mead c/oClub
Local Press: Congleton Chronicle,
Staffs Evening Sentinel
Local Radio: Radio Stoke, Signal

**PREVIOUS**        **Leagues:** Crewe & Dist; North Staffs; Macclesfield; Cheshire 20-39, 46-65, 78-82; Mid Cheshire 68-78; Nth West Co 82-87.
**Name:** Congleton Hornets (prior to current club's formation in 1901)

**CLUB RECORDS**    **Attendance:** 7,000 v Macclesfield, League 53-54
**Goalscorer:** MickBiddle 150+      **Appearances:** Ray Clack 600+ & Graham Harrison 600+
**Fee Paid:** None.        **Fee Received:** £5,000 for D Frost (Leeds)

**BEST SEASON**     **FA Trophy:** 3rd Qualifying Rd 89-90 90-91.  **FA Vase:** 4th Rd 76-77 80-81
**FA Cup:** 1st Rd 89-90, 0-2 v Crewe Alex. (A)        League clubs defeated: None

**HONOURS**         North West Counties League R-up 85-86; Cheshire County League R-up 20-2121-22 (Div 2 81-82); Mid Cheshire League
73-74 75-76 77-78 (R-up 69-70 71-7276-77, League Cup 71-72; Cheshire Senior Cup 20-21 37-38

Players progressing: Ron Broad (Crewe 1955), Jack Mycock (Shrewsbury 1958),Steve Davies (Port Vale 1987), L Hamlet (Leeds), Jimmy Quinn
West Ham, N Ireland), Ian Brightwell (Man City)

**L-R Back Row:** Paul Abbey, Andy Smolenski, Grahm Dodd, Dave Oxton, Stuart Heeps, Colin Webster, Craig Murphy, Russell Payne,
Pete Evans (chairman), Chris Bermingham. **Front Row:** Kevin Garforth, Robbie Hope, Chris Woodward, Andy Mead (mascot), Simon
Rudge, Rod Thornley, Lee Ellis.
                                                      Photo courtesy of Congleton Chronicle

# EASTWOOD TOWN

### CLUB OFFICIALS

Chairman: **George Belshaw**

Vice Chairman: **Roy Cheatle**

President:

Secretary / Press Officer: **Paddy Farrell**
7 Primrose Rise, Newthorpe,
Notts.NG16 2BB Tel/Fax: 01773 786186

### FOOTBALL MANAGEMENT TEAM
Manager: Bryan ChambersAssistant
Manager: Carl Hanson
Physio: Dave Nicholls

### FACT FILE

Formed: 1953

Nickname: The Badgers

Sponsors: Digraph Transport Supplies

Colours: Black & white stripes/black/black

Change Colours: Yellow/blue/yellow

Midweek matchday: Tuesday

BADGERS
SET PIECES
1998 - 1999

THE F.A. CUP

EASTWOOD TOWN F.C.
v
HALESOWEN TOWN F.C.
F.A. CUP 2nd Qualifying Round Replay
Wednesday 7th October 1998
Kick-Off 7.30pm

Official Programme
Price 70r

Pages:50 Price: £1.00
Editor: Jim McVea  01773 717745
Local Press: Eastwood Advertiser
Nottingham Evening Post, Derby Telegraph
Local Radio: Radio Nottingham, Radio Trent

### GROUND
Coronation Park, Eastwood, Notts. Tel: 01773 715823

**Directions:** From North - M1 jct 27, follow Heanor signs via Brinsley to lights in Eastwood.
Turn left then first right after Fire Station - ground entrance on Chewton Street. From South -
M1 jct 26, A610 to Ripley, leave at 1st exit(B6010), follow to Eastwood, left at lights, first left
at `Man in Space' -ground entrance on Chewton Street. Nearest station - Langley Mill. Buses
every10 mins (R11, R12 or R13) from Victoria Centre, Nottingham - approx 40 mins
**Capacity:** 5,500        **Cover:** 1,150        **Seats:** 200
**Clubhouse:** Social club open normal licensing hours (Sat 11am-11pm, midweek matches
6.30-11pm). Hot & cold food available. Steward; Richard James (01773715823)
**Club Shop:** Sells programmes, mugs, scarves, badges etc. Contact R K Storer - 0115 9199596

| | | |
|---|---|---|
| **,98-99PREVIOUS** | **Leagues:** Notts Alliance 53-61; Central Alliance 61-67; East Midlands 67-71; Midland Counties 71-82; N.C.E. 82-87. | |
| | **Names:** None -predecessors Eastwood Collieries disbanded in 1953 | |
| | **Ground:** Coronation Park 1953-65 - previous pitch now town bowling green | |
| **CLUB RECORDS** | **Attendance:** 2,723 v Enfield, FA Amateur Cup, February 1965. | |
| | **Goalscorer:** Martin Wright. Appearances: Arthur Rowley, over 800 1st team games, but not a single booking, 1955-76 | |
| | **Win:** 21-0 v Rufford Colliery 26/10/54 & Ilkeston Town 10/5/69    **Defeat:** 1-8 v Ransome & Marples 2/2/57 | |
| **BEST SEASON** | **Fee Paid:** £500 for Jamie Kay, Gainsborough Trin.90-91    **Fee Received:** £72,500 for Richard Liburd, Middlesbrough 92-93 | |
| | **FA Amateur Cup:** Third Round replay 1967-68.       **FA Trophy:** First Round1978-79 | |
| | **FA Cup:** Final Qual. Rd replay 75-76 (0-1 at Wycombe W.) | |
| **HONOURS** | Northern Counties (East) Lg R-up 82-83 84-85; Midland Counties Lg 75-76(R-up 74-75 77-78), Lg Cup 77-78 79-80; Central Alliance 63-64 (R-up 64-65);Notts Alliance 56-57 (R-up 53-54 54-55 55-56 57-58 58-59 59-60), Lg Cup 55-56;East Midlands Lg R-up 68-69; Notts Senior Cup 75-76 77-78 78-79 79-80 82-83 83-84 88-89 89-90 91-92 (R-up 57-58 63-64 65-66); Evans Halshaw Floodlit Cup 94-95R-up 89-90 97-98; Notts Intermediate Cup 86-87; Ripley Hospital Charity Cup(6)76-81 | |

Players progressing: J Butler (Notts Co 57), A Woodcock A Buckley Andrew Todd (Nottm F ), P Richardson (Derby), S Buckley (Luton), R Liburd
(Middlesbrough 92-93), Martin Bullock (Barnsley 94-95), Neil Illman (Plymouth 95-96), Lee Marshall (Scunthorpe 97), Glenn Kirkwood( Donc"ter R)

Goalkeeper Danny Bryant
punches clear during this
Gretna attack.

Photo: Alan Watson

# FARSLEY CELTIC

## CLUB OFFICIALS

Chairman: **John E Palmer**
Vice Chairman:
Secretary: **Mrs Margaret Lobley**
29 Spring Bank Road, Farsley, Leeds,
West Yorks LS28 5LS
Tel: 01132 575675

**FOOTBALL MANAGEMENT TEAM**

Manager: Martin Haresign
Coach: Darren Foreman/Gary Chapman
Physio: Nick Smith

### FACT FILE
Formed: 1908
Nickname: Villagers
Colours: Sky & navy/navy/navy
Change colours: All white
Midweek home matchday: Wednesday
Reserves' League: N.C.E.Res. Div
1998-99
Captain: Wayne Noteman
P.o.Y.: Matthew Surtees
Top scorer: Robbie Whellans

Pages: 32 Price £1 Editor: Howard Stevenson
Local Press: Yorkshire Evening Post,
Telegraph & Argus, Pudsey Times Local
Radio: Radio Leeds, Radio Aire,
Radio Pennine

**GROUND** Throstle Nest, Newlands, Farsley, Pudsey, Leeds LS28 5BE Tel: 01532 561517
**Directions:** From North East: A1 south to Wetherby, A58 to Leeds, at1st island (approx 8 miles) take 3rd exit (A6120 ring-rd), follow Bradford signs to 12th r'bout (approx 12 miles) - 1st exit (B6157 Stanningley). From M62jct 26, M606 (Bradford) to r'bout, 4th exit (A6177) passing McDonalds on left,continue on Rooley Lane - Sticker Lane passing Morrisons store on left to lights (approx 3 miles) - right onto A647 (Leeds) to 2nd r'bout, 2nd exit(B6157 Stanningley). Continue 800yds passing Police & Fire Stations on left.Turn left down New Street at Tradex warehouse before turning right into Newlands. Ground at bottom of road. 1 mile from New Pudsey (BR)
Capacity: 4,000          Cover: 1,000          Seats: 430
**Clubhouse:** Lounge, games room and committee room open every evening and Friday and weekend lunchtimes. New multi-purpose Leisure Centre available evenings and afternoons
**Club Shop:** League & non-League progs & magazines. Club badges, scarves,ties, sweaters, training suits, polo & T-shirts. Various souvenirs & photos.Contact Brian Falkingham, 27 Rycroft Ct., Leeds LS13 4PE. 0113 255 0749

**PREVIOUS**        **Leagues:** West Riding County Amateur; Leeds Red Triangle; Yorkshire 49-82; Northern Counties East 82-87
                    **Grounds:** Red Lane, Farsley; Calverley Lane,Farsley (prior to 1948)

**CLUB RECORDS**    **Attendance:** 11,000 (at Elland Road) v Tranmere Rovers, FA Cup 1st Rd 1974

**BEST SEASON**     **FA Amateur Cup:** Third Round, 34-35
                    **FA Cup:** 1st Rd 74-75 (see above). Lost 0-2. **FA Vase:** Quarter Final 87-88

**HONOURS**         West Riding County Cup 57-58 59-60 66-67 70-71 83-84 87-88 95-96 96-97; Yorkshire League 59-60 68-69 (R-up 57-58 58-59 70-71 71-72); Div 2 51-52;League Cup 62-63 63-64 66-67 96-97

Players progressing: Barry Smith (Leeds 1951), Paul Madeley (Leeds 1962),William Roberts (Rochdale 1988), Stuart McCall (Bradford City)

Back: Simon Woodhead, Ian Blackstone, Matthew Surtees, Paul Allen, Mark Stimpson, Andy Watson, Wayne Metcalf, Alastair Long.
Front: Pav Singh, Phil Turner, Robbie Whellans, Matthew Flanagan, Nigel Smith, Ben Thackeray.          Photo: Bill Wheatcroft

# FLIXTON

## CLUB OFFICIALS

Chairman:Peter Dentith

President: **F H Eadie**

Secretary: **Stuart Nichols**

20 Brompton Rd.,Stretford, Manchester M329PR Tel: 0161747 5288 (H)

07987108022 (M)

## FOOTBALL MANAGEMENT TEAM

Manager: Alan McGreevy

## FACT FILE

Formed: 1960
Nickname: Valley Roaders
Colours: Blue & white stripes/blue/blue
Change Colours: Gold/black/black
Midweek home matchday: Tuesday
Reserves' League: North West Alliance

**PROGRAMME**
Pages: 36 Price: £1.00
Editor: T.B.A.

## GROUND

Valley Road, Flixton, Manchester M41 8RQ
Tel: 0161 748 2903

**Directions:** M60 Jct10, B5214 (signed Urmston), follow Trafford General Hosp.signs, at 4th r'bout take 3rd exit (Woodbridge Rd), ground at top. 1¼ miles from Flixton BR station (trains from Manchester Oxford Rd) - turn right out of station onto Flixton Rd, left after 1/4 mile into Woodsend Rd,at r'bout after 1/4 mile take 2nd exit into Woodbridge Rd - ground at top.Take any bus from Manchester Picadilly bus station to Flixton and alight at Flixton Red Lion
Capacity: 2,000          Cover: 650          Seats: 250

**Clubhouse:** Open daily 1.00pm-11pm. Sandwiches available most eves
**Club Shop:** No

| | |
|---|---|
| **PREVIOUS CLUB RECORDS** | **Leagues:** South Manchester & Wythenshawe 60-63; Lancs & Cheshire 63-73; Manchester 73-86; North West Counties 86-96 |
| | **Attendance:** 1,543 v Brigg Town FA Vase Semi-Final 95-96 |
| | **Goalscorer:** John Mitchell **Appearances:** John Mitchell & Stan Matthews |
| | **Win:** 10-2 v Irlam 94-95     **Defeat:** 1-10 v Knowsley Utd 90-91 |
| **BEST SEASON** | **FA Cup:** 1st Qual. Rd replay 91-92, 1-2 v Mossley (A) after 1-1     **FA Vase:** Semi-final 95-96 v Brigg Town |
| **HONOURS** | N.W.Co Div I Champions & Cup 95-96, Div 2 94-95 Lg.Cup 94-95, (R-up 87-88), Div 3 R-up 86-87, Cup SF 86-87, Res. Chal. Cup 87-88 90-91 (R-up 88-89 89-90 91-92 92-93), Res. Div East 89-90, Res. Div Sth 92-93; Manc. Lg R-up 78-7981-82 85-86, Div 1 77-78, Div 2(res) 82-83 85-86, Open Tphy 80-81; Lancs AmtrCup 79-80 (R-up 80-81); Manc. Chal. Tphy 83-84 (R-up x2 84-86); Manc. Prem. CupR-up 86-87 91-92; Manc. Amtr Cup R-up 88-89 |

Photo: Bill Wheatcroft

# GRETNA

## CLUB OFFICIALS

Chairman: **Brian Fulton**

President: **Thomas Kerr**

Secretary: **Ron MacGregor**
Brackenhurst, Lochmaben, Lockerbie,
Scotland DG111QA (01387 811820)

## FOOTBALL MANAGEMENT TEAM

Manager: Michael McCartney
Physio: William Bentley

### FACT FILE
Formed: 1946
Nickname: Black & whites
Club colours:
Black & white hoops/black/black & white
Change colours: All maroon (b & w trim)
Midweek matchday: Tuesday
Reserves' league: Carlisle & District

1998-99
Captain: Paul O'Hagan
Top Scorer: Shane Bird
Supporters P.o.Y.: Ross Milligan
Players P.o.Y.: Richard Close

Pages: 28 Price: 80p
Editor: R MacGregorTel: 01387 811820

Local Press : Cumberland News
Evening News & Star ,Dumfries & Galloway
Standard  Local Radio: C.F.M.; Radio
Cumbria,West Sound Radio,BBC Solway

**GROUND**  Raydale Park, Dominion Rd., Gretna, Dumfriesshire
Tel: 01461 337602

**Directions:** 8 miles north of Carlisle on A74. Take slip road to Gretna over border bridge, left at Crossways Inn for Township along Annan Rd for quarter of a mile, left into Dominion Rd, ground on right. Buses leave Carlisle on the half hour. Also trains from Carlisle
Capacity: 2,200      Cover: 800      Seats: 385
**Clubhouse:** Bar in ground-visitors most welcome.
**Club Shop**: Yes, contact Alan Watson 01387 251550, matchdays & postal sales

**PREVIOUS**  **Leagues:** Dumfriesshire Amateur 46-47; Carlisle & District 47-51;Cumberland 51-52; Northern 83-92

**CLUB RECORDS**  **Attendance:** 2,307 v Rochdale, F.A. Cup First Round Proper,16/11/91.
**Scorer:** Denis Smith  **Appearances:** William Cross
**Win:** 20-0 v Silloth 62-63  **Defeat:** 0-6 v Worksop Town 94-95
**Fee Received:** £10,000 from Queen of the South for Derek Townsley 96

**BEST SEASON**  **FA Trophy:** 2nd Rd 84-85 88-89 90-91 93-94
**FA Cup:** 1st Rd Prop 91-92 (lost 1-3 in replay at Rochdale) & 93-94 (lost 2-3 to Bolton Wanderers)
**FA Vase:** 2nd Rd 80-81 83-84

**HONOURS**  Northern Lg 90-91 91-92 (Lg Cup 90-91); Cumberland Senior Cup (9); JR Cleator Cup 89-90 90-91 91-92; Craven Cup 91-92; Carlisle & Dist. Lg (28)(Charity Shield (25), Lg Cup (20); Benevolent Cup (15)
Players progressing: John Hamilton (Hartlepool Utd) 1982, Russell Black &Don Peattie (Sheffield Utd) 1984, Mark Dobie (Cambridge Utd) derek Townsley (Queen of South,Motherwell),Craig Potts (Queen of South)

L-R  **Back:** Billy Bentley (physio), George Norrie (coach), Richard Close, Steve Hodgson, Gary Milne, Paul O'Hagan, Glenn Johnstone, Andy Martin, Ian Armstrong, Marcus Thompson, Mike McCartmey (player-manager).  **Front:** Eddie Harrison, Ross Milligan, Tony Monaghan, Mike Hodgson, Mark Dobie, Lee Marshall, Stephen Monaghan (mascot).  Photo: Alan Watson

# HARROGATE TOWN

TOWN REVIEW

The Official Programme of HARROGATE TOWN AFC

Main Sponsors to
Harrogate Town AFC

CRYSTAL MOTORS
HARROGATE

## CLUB OFFICIALS

Chairman: **Maurice Hammond**
President: **Peter McCormick**
Director of Football:**GrahamShepherd**
General Secretary: **Roy Dalby**
123a Dene Park, Harrogate
N. Yorkshire HG14JX Tel: 01423 567973

## FOOTBALL MANAGEMENT TEAM

Team Manager/Coach: **Paul Ward**
General Manager(Football): **Dave Fell**

**GROUND**

### FACT FILE

Formed: 1919

Nickname: Town

Club Sponsors: Crystal Motors

Colours: Yellow/black/yellow

Change colours: Blue & white

Midweek home matchday: Tuesday

Youths: Northern Youth Aacademy Lg.

Wetherby Road, Harrogate.
Tel: 01423 883671 (01423 880675-Press & Commercial)

**Directions: From Leeds** turn right at traffic lights (Appleyard's) into Hookstone Road, continue to Woodlands Hotel (traffic lights) turn left into Wetherby Road, ground on the right. From Harrogate (BR), turn left and left again, cross road (Odeon Cinema), proceed for about 400yds to main road, crossover to The Stray (open land) using footpath which leads to Wetherby Rd, ground200yds on left.
**From the West** on A59 srtaight on to Wetherby Rd from Empress roundabout. ground on left.
**From North: A**59 exit from M1 then southern bypass to Wetherby Rd
Capacity: 3,800          Cover: 900          Seats: 450
**Clubhouse:** On ground, open every match day and for functions & special events.
**Club Shop:** Sells scarves, ties, pens shirts metal badges & other souvenirs (Phil Harrison)

Pages: 32 Price: £1.00
Editor: R Chambers/T Moseley

Local Press: Yorkshire Post Group
Harrogate Advertiser Series
Local Radio: Radio Leeds, Radio York
Stray FM.

| | |
|---|---|
| **PREVIOUS** | **Names:** Harrogate FC 26-34; Harrogate Hotspurs 36-50     **Ground:** Starbeck Lane 1919-20 |
| | **Leagues:** Yorkshire 20-21, 22-31, 51-82; Midland 21-22; Northern31-32; Harrogate & District 36-46; West Yorkshire 46-51; Northern Counties East 82-87 |
| **CLUB RECORDS** | **Attendance:** 3,208 v Starbeck LNER (now Harrogate R.A.), Whitworth Cup final 1948. |
| | **Win:** 9-1 v Winsford          **Defeat:** 0-7 v Hyde Utd & v Lancaster City |
| **BEST SEASON** | **FA Vase:** 4th Round 89-90          **FA Cup:** 3rd Qual. Rd 94-95 (0-3 at Bishop Auckland) |
| **HONOURS** | Northern Premier Lge Div 1 Cup 89-90; Northern Counties (East) Div 1(Nth) R-up 84-85 (Reserve Div 85-86, Reserve Div Cup 86-87); Yorkshire League Div 1 26-27 (Div 2 81-82, Div 3 R-up 71-72 80-81); West Riding County Cup 62-6372-73 85-86; West Riding Challenge Cup 24-25 26-27 |

Players progressing: Tony Ingham (Leeds 47), Stewart Ferebee (York C. 79),Tim Hotte (Halifax T. 85), Andy Watson (Halifax T. 88), Ian Blackstone(York C. 95)

Gary Edmunds just manages to get the ball away from Droylsden's Dave Ashton in this early season league match.

Photo: Colin Stevens

# LINCOLN UNITED

## CLUB OFFICIALS

Chairman: **M.Wilson**
President: **A Simpson**
Vice Chairman: **W.White**
Commercial Manager: **S Eastmead**

Secretary/Press Officer: **Steve Eastmead**
23 Woodvale Avenue,
Doddington Park,Lincoln LN6 3R
Tel: 01522 885112 H, 01522 696400 B

## FOOTBALL MANAGEMENT TEAM

Managers: John Wilkinson & Tony Simmons
Physio: Anthony Adams

### FACT FILE

Formed: 1938
Nickname: United
Sponsors: City Tyre Experts
& Willie White Accomodation
Colours: All white
Change Colours: Tangerine
Midweek home matchday: Tuesday
Reserves ' League: Lincolnshire

**GROUND**  Ashby Avenue, Hartsholme, Lincoln  Tel: 01522 690674
**Directions:** From Newark A46 onto Lincoln relief road (A446), right at 2nd r'bout for
Birchwood (Skellingthorpe Rd), go for 1 mile passing lake and Country Park, 1st right 10yds
after 30mph sign into Ashby Ave., ground entrance200 yds, opposite Old Peoples home.
From north follow A57 via Saxilby until reaching A46 Lincoln Relief Road - continue on this
and turn left at r'bout signed Birchwood then as above. 3 miles from Loncoln Central (BR)
Capacity: 2,714        Seats: 400        Covered: 1,084
**Clubhouse:** Open daily normal licensing hours. Matchday snack bar -hot &cold food & drinks
**Club Shop:** Yes. Contact Jane Eastmead (01522 885112)

**PREVIOUS**  **Leagues:** Lincs 45-48 60-67; Lincoln 48-60; Yorks 67-82; Northern Co'sEast 82-86, 92-95; Central Mids 82-92
  **Grounds:** Skew Bridge (40s); Co-op Sports Ground (to mid 60s); Hartsholme Cricket Ground (to 82)
  **Name:** Lincoln Amateurs (until an ex-pro signed in 1954)

**CLUB RECORDS**  **Attendance:** 2,000 v Crook Town, FA Amateur Cup 1st Rd Proper, 1968
  **Scorer:** Tony Simmons 215    **Appearances:** Steve Carter 447
  **Win:** 12-0 v Pontefract Colls 95.    **Defeat:** 0-7 v Huddersfield Town FA Cup 1st Round Proper16-11-91
  **Fee Paid:** £250 for Dean Dye (Sutton Town, 7.90) - only player ever bought.
  **Fee Received:** £3,000 for Dean Dye (Charlton Ath., 7.91)

**BEST SEASON**  **FA Cup:** First Round Proper 91-92 (0-7 at Huddersfield Town), 97-98 v Walsall (0-2 Away)
  **FA Trophy:** 3rd 3Rd    **F.A.Vase:**

**HONOURS**  Northern Counties East - Prem Div. 94-95, Div 1 92-93, Div 1 Sth 82-83,Div 2 85-86, Presidents Cup 94-95; Yorks Lg 70-71
  73-74 (Lg Cup 70-71); Lincs Lg 63-64; Lincs Snr `A' Cup 72-73 85-86 95-96, R-up 91-92 94-95, `B' Cup 63-6470-71;
  Central Mids Lg 91-92 (Wakefield Cup 90-91); Evans Halshaw Floodlit Cup R-up 92-93; Lincs I'mediate Cup(7) 67-73 80-
  81; Blankney Hunt Inter Lge 95-96,Cup 95-96 Lincs Sen Cup: R-up 97-98 Uniflla Div 1 Cup R-up 97-98

Stuart Reddington getting
in his tackle to block
Ashton United's Jimmy
Bell's shot on goal.

Photo: Colin Stevens

337

# MATLOCK TOWN

## CLUB OFFICIALS

Chairman: **Donald T Carr**
Vice Chairman: **G Michael Tomlinson**
Secretary: **Keith F Brown**
`Barncroft', 1 Malvern Gardens
Matlock, Derbyshire DE4 3JH
01629 584231 (H) 01335 390301 (B)
Press Officer: **Ian Richardson**
01629 56042(H)
Commercial Manager: **Tom Wright**

## FOOTBALL MANAGEMENT TEAM

Manager: Gary Marrow
Physio: Michael Cunningham

### FACT FILE

Formed: 1885
Nickname: The Gladiators
Sponsors: Westons of Wirksworth/
Panasonic/ Tarmac
Colours: Royal/white
Change colours: All yellow
Midweek home matchday: Tuesday
Reserves' League: Beauvale Mid All

**GROUND**

Causeway Lane, Matlock, Derbyshire
Tel: 01629 583866 (& Fax)

**Directions:** On A615, 500 yds from town centre and Matlock (BR)
Capacity: 7,500          Cover: 2,000          Seats: 240
**Clubhouse:** Gladiators Social Club, on ground, open matchdays only
**Club Shop:** Yes. Contact: Sue Tomlinson (01629 583866)

Pages 40          Price 80p
Editor: Ian Richardson Tel: 01629 56042
Local Press: Matlock Mercury
Derbyshire Times, Derby Evening Telegraph,
Chesterfield Express
Local Radio: Radio Derby

PREVIOUS          **Ground:** Hall Leys (last century).          **Leagues:** Midland Counties 1894-96; Matlock & District; Derbys Senior;
Central Alliance 24-25 47-61; Central Combination 34-35; Chesterfield & District 46-47; Midland Counties 1961-69

CLUB RECORDS          **Attendance:** 5,123 v Burton Albion, FA Trophy 1975
**Win:** 10 v 0 Lancaster (A) **74**          **Defeat:** 1-8 v Chorley (A) 71
Career **Goalscorer:** Peter Scott. **Career**          **Appearances:** Mick Fenoughty
**Fee Paid:** £2,000 for Kenny Clarke1996          **Fee Received:** £10,000 for Ian Helliwell (York)

BEST SEASON          **FA Trophy:** 74-74
**FA Cup:** 3rd Rd 76-77. 1st Rd 1885-86 86-87 86-8787-88 1959-60 74-75 75-76 89-90
League clubs defeated: Mansfield Town 76-77

HONOURS          Northern Prem Lge R-up 83-84, Lge Cup 77-78, Shield 78-79; Midland Counties Lge 61-62 68-69; Central All (North) 59-60
60-61, R-up 61-62 62-63,Div 1 Cup R-up 61-62, Div 2 59-60, Div 2 Cup 59-60 60-61; Derbyshire Sen Cup74-75 76-
77 77-          78 80-81 83-84 84-85 91-92, R-up 60-61 72-73 73-74 75-76 80-8181-82 82-83 89-90 93-94 97-98;
Derbyshire Div Cup          (North) 61-62 R-up 62-63;Evans Halshaw Floodlit Cup 88-89 91-92; Anglo-Italian Non-League Cup 79

Players progressing: Keith Haines (Leeds 1959), Wayne Biggins (Burnley 1984),Darren Bradshaw (Chesterfield 1987), Les McJannet
(Scarborough 1987), Ian Helliwell (York 1987)

Billy Heath shielding the ball
well from Droylsden's Lee
Cooper.

Photo: Colin Stevens

# NETHERFIELD KENDAL

## CLUB OFFICIALS

Chairman: **David Willan**
President: **M Macklin**
Secretary: **Dale Brotherton**
Lime House, Holme Hill, Dalston, Carlisle.
CA5 7DH (Mobile 07977 759903)

Match Secretary: **Craig Campbell**
34 High Sparrowmire, Kendal Cumbria LA9 5PD
01539 725557 (H)

Press Officer: **Peter Savage** (01539 726488)

### FOOTBALL MANAGEMENT TEAM
Manager: Alan Cook
Asst Manager: Keith Galley
Physio: Stan Casey

### FACT FILE
Formed: 1920
Nickname: The Field
Sponsors: Peter Hunt's Bakery Foods
Colours: Black & white stripes/black/black & white
Change colours: Yellow/blue/yellow
Midweek home matchday: Tuesday
1998-99
Club Captain: David Burrow
Player of the Year: John George
Top Goalscorer: Brian Hatton

Saturday 3 April
1 9 9 9
**ALFRETON**

**GROUND**  Parkside Road, Kendal, Cumbria  Tel: 01539 727472

**Directions:** M6 junction 36, follow signs for Kendal (South), right at lights, left at r-bout to `K' Village - Parkside Rd on right opposite factory main offices - ground 400 yds. A mile & a half from Oxenholme (BR) station - bus service to `K' village, No 41 or 41A
Capacity: 2,490        Cover: 1,000        Seats: 250
**Clubhouse:** The Park, open all matchdays. Pies & pasties available        **Club Shop:** No

Pages:32 Price: £1.00
Editor: Peter Savage Tel: 01539 726488
Local Press: Westmorland Gazette
Lancaster Evening Post
Local Radio: Radio Cumbria, The Bay.

**PREVIOUS**        **Leagues:** Westmorland; North Lancs; Lancs Combination 45-68; Northern Premier 68-83; North West Counties 83-87

**CLUB RECORDS**        **Attendance:** 5,184 v Grimsby Town, FA Cup 1st Rd 1955
**Goalscorer:** Tom Brownlee.  **Win:** 11-0 v Great Harwood 22/3/47.  **Defeat:** 0-10 v Stalybridge Celtic 1/9/84
**Fee Paid:** Undisclosed for Tom Brownlee (Bradford C., 66).  **Fee Received:** £10,250 for Andy Milner (Man. City 95)

**BEST SEASON**        **FA Vase:** 3rd Rd 89-90        **FA Trophy:** 2nd Rd 80-81.
**FA Cup:** 2nd Rd replay 63-64, 1-4 v Chesterfield(A) after 1-1. 2nd Rd 49-50, 1st Rd 45-4648-49 52-53 54-55 55-56 64-65

**HONOURS**        Lancs Comb. 48-49 64-65 (R-up 45-46 53-54 61-62 63-64, Lg Cup 55-56 60-61), Westmorland Snr Cup(12) 24-25 31-33 35-36 46-48 63-64 65-66 71-72 86-8789-89 90-91

Players progressing: John Laidlaw (Carlisle 1946), Louis Cardwell (Crewe 1947),Herbert Keen (Barrow 1953), Alec Aston (Preston 1955), Horace Langstreth(Torquay 1956), John Simpson (Lincoln 1957), Dennis Rogers (Accrington 1959),Tom Brownlee (Bradford City 1965), Peter McDonnell (Bury 1973), Keith Silken(Workington 1973), Roger Wicks (Darlington 1981), Andy Milner (Man City)

Jamie Close trying 'not' to obstruct Belper Town's Paul Green during the January league meeting of the two clubs at Parkside Road.
Photo: Alan Watson

# OSSETT TOWN

**CLUB OFFICIALS**

President: **Paul Jervis**

Chairman: **Graham Firth**

Football Chairman: **Peter Wilkinson**

Vice Chairman: **Bruce Saul**

Commercial Manager:**Graham Willis**

Secretary: **Frank Lloyd**,
27 Park Close, Mapplewell,
Barnsley S75 6BY
Tel: 01226 382415

**FOOTBALL MANAGEMENT TEAM**

Manager: Gary Brook

Asst Manager:Lindsey Dawson

Coach: Mick Polli

**FACT FILE**

Founded: 1936
Sponsors: Action Stations
Colours: All red
Change colours: All sky
Midweek matches: Tuesday
Reserves' League: N.C.E. Res Div
Programme: 12 pages, 50p
Editor/Press Off.: Bruce Saul
Tel: 01924 277652
Local Press: Dewsbury Reporter,
Wakefield Express

**GROUND:** Ingfield, Prospect Road, Ossett, Wakefield WF5 8AN Tel: 01924 272960
**Directions:** M1 jct 40, B6129 to Ossett, left into Dale Street, left again at lights opposite bus station on ring road, ground on left. Nearest stations Dewsbury or Wakefield Westgate - both three miles from. Buses 116, 117, 126 and127 from Wakefield, buses 116, 126 and 127 from Dewsbury, buses 117, 118 or 216 from Leeds
Capacity: 4,000          Seats: 360          Cover: 650          Floodlights: Yes
**Clubhouse:** Open Fri & Sun lunchtimes, all day Sat and every evening. Pie & peas, chips, soup from tea bar          **Club Shop:**

**PREVIOUS**          **Leagues:** Leeds 36-39; Yorkshire 45-82; N.C.E. 83-99          **Ground:** Fern House (pre-1958)

**RECORDS**          **Attendance:** 2,600 v Manchester Utd, friendly 1988
**Win:** 10-1 v Harrogate RA (H), N.C.E. Lge Prem. Div. 27/4/93
**Defeat:** 0-7 v Easington Colliery, FA Vase 8/10/83
**Fee received:** £1,350 for Derek Blackburn (Swansea 1957)
**Appearances:** Steve Worsfold          **Goalscorer:** Dave Leadbeater

**HONOURS**          Northern Counties East - Lg Cup 89-90, Div 2 88-89, Res. Div 88-89, Res.Cup 87-88 88-89;
West Riding County Cup 58-59 81-82.

Players progressing: Arnold Kendall (Bradford C.) 1949, Ron Liversidge(Bradford C.) 56, Derek Blackburn (Swansea) 57, Simon Lowe (Barnsley) 83, Gary Chapman (Bradford C.) 88, Mick Norbury (Scarborough) 1989, Mike Williams(Sheffield W.) 90, Dean Trott (Northampton) 98, Paul Cuss (Huddersfield Town) 98.

Photo: Phil Watkins

# RADCLIFFE BOROUGH

## CLUB OFFICIALS

Chairman: Bernard Manning Jnr
President: A A Swarbrick
Vice Chairman: R Doyle
Company/Club Secretary: Graham E
Fielding, c/o Radcliffe Borough

## FOOTBALL MANAGEMENT TEAM

Manager: Kevin Glendon
Coach:Mike Farrelly
Physio: Roy Davies

### FACT FILE
Formed: 1949
Sponsors: Martin Darlington Transport
Nickname: Boro'
Colours: Blue/blue/white
Change colours: All white
Midweek home matchday: Tuesday
Reserve Team:No
1998-99
Captain: Mark Dempsey
P.o.Y.: Jason Astley
Top scorer: Tony Carroll

70p
BORO REVIEW
RADCLIFFE
BOROUGH
FOOTBALL CLUB
UNIBOND
FIRST DIVISION
1998-99

**GROUND**     Stainton Park, Pilkington Road, Radcliffe, Lancs M26 3PE
Tel: 0161 724 5937 (club)   0161 724 8346 (Office)   0161 723 3178(Fax)
Directions: M62 junction 17 - follow signs for Whitefield and Bury . Take A665to Radcliffe.
Thro' town centre, turn right into Unsworth St. (opposite Turf Hotel). Ground on left half mile
Colshaw Close East. 1/2 mile from Radcliffe(BR)
Capacity: 3,000      Cover: 1,000      Seats: 350
NClubhouse: (0161 724 5937) `The Boro'- public house on ground. Food available
Club Shop: Yes - contact Ryan Davies at ground.(0161-724-5937)

Pages: 28 Price: 80p
Editor: Ian Hannay
Local Press: Radcliffe Times, Bolton Evening
News, Manchester Evening News
Local Radio: Greater Manchester Radio
(GMR), Piccadilly

**PREVIOUS**     **Leagues:** South East Lancs; Manchester53-63; Lancs Comb. 63-71; Cheshire County 71-82; North West Counties 82-87
             **Ground:** Bright Street 1949-70.

**CLUB RECORDS**     **Attendance:** 1,468 v Caernarfon Town, N.W.C. Lge 83
             **Goalscorer:** Gary Haworth        **Appearances:** Chris Lilley.
             **Fee Paid:** £5,000 for Gary Walker(Buxton, 1991). **Fee Received:** £5,000 for Kevin Hulme (Bury, 1989)

**BEST SEASON**     **FA Trophy:** 3rd Rd v Gateshead 1995-96
             **FA Cup:** 2nd Qual. Rd replay75-76 (1-4 at Rossendale Utd after 2-2 draw). FA Vase: 4th Rd v Boston Town 93-94

**HONOURS**     Unibond Lge Div One Champ 96-97; North West Counties Lg 84-85 (Div 2 82-83); Lancs Combination Lg Cup 69-70;
             Manchester Lg R-up 55-56 (Lg Cup 58-59joint); Manchester Prem Cup R-up 97-98

Players progressing:    Jim Hayman (Bury 50), Ian Wood (Oldham Athletic 65), Robert Hutchinson (Rochdale 74),
                      Gary Haworth (Rochdale 84),Kevin Hulme (Bury 89)

Steve Berryman safely collects the ball,
to the relief of the defence, from this
Alfreton Town corner.
Photo: Bill Wheatcroft

# STOCKSBRIDGE PARK STEELS

**CLUB OFFICIALS**
President: **C D Sedgwick**
Chairman: **A Bethel**
Vice-Chairman: **M Grimmer**
Secretary: **Michael Grimmer**
48 Hole House Lane, Stocksbridge
Sheffield S36 1BT Tel: 0114 288 6470
Press Officer: **Edwin O'Sullivan**
Commercial Manager: Andrew Horsley
Tel: 0114 288 3867

**FOOTBALL MANAGEMENT TEAM**
Manager: Mick Horne
Asst Manager: Trevor Gough
Physio: Sean Hird

**FACT FILE**

Formed: 1986
Nickname: Steels
Sponsors:Weatherglaze
Colours: Yellow/blue/yellow
Change colours: All blue
Midweek matches: Tuesday
Reserves' League: Beefeater County Senior
1997-98
Captain: Sean Dunphy
P.o.Y.: Simon Marples
Top Scorer: Gary Hurlestone (24)

Pages: 28 Price:50p
Editor: Edwin O'Sullivan
(0114 2884218)
Local Press: Sheffield Trader,
Green'un, The Star

## GROUND

Bracken Moor Lane, Stocksbridge, Sheffield Tel: 0114 288 2045 Fax: 0114 288 8305
**Directions:** M1 jct 35a (from S), 36 (from N), A616 to Stocksbridge. On arrival in
Stocksbridge turn left into Nanny Hill under the Clock Tower and continue up the hill for about
500 yds - ground on left
Capacity: 3,500          Cover: 700          Seats: 450
**Clubhouse:** Open 7 days (lunchtime & evenings). No food. Separate foodbar for matches
**Club Shop:** badges, mugs, shirts, progs and scarves . Contact: H.O'Sullivan(0114 2884218)

**PREVIOUS**     **Ground:** Stonemoor 49-51 52-53     **Names:** Stocksbridge Works, Oxley Park;clubs merged in 1986
**Leagues:** Sheffield Amateur/ Sheffield Association/Yorkshire 49-82

**CLUB RECORDS**     **Attendance:** 2,000 v Sheffield Wed., Floodlight opening Oct '91
**Fee Received:** £15,000 for Lee Mills (Wolves, 1992)     **Fee Paid:** Nil
**Win:** 5-0 v Warrington Town NPL 96-97     **Defeat:** 0-5 v Whitley Bay NPL 97-98
**Scorer:** Trevor Jones (145)     **Appearances:** Not known

**BEST SEASON**     **FA Cup:** 4th Q 50-1, 56-7 **FA Trophy:** 3rd Q 96-97 **FA Vase:** 4th Rd 95-96.

**HONOURS**     Northern Co's East Prem Div 93-94, R-up 95-96, Div 1 91-92, Lg Cup 94-95; Sheffield Snr Cup 92-93 95-96,98-99.
Oxley Park F C: County Sen Div 1 85-86:Stocksbridge Works FC: Yorkshire Lge Div 1 51-52 54-55 55-56 56-57 57-58
61-62 62-63, Div 2 50-51 64-65, Div 3 70-71 74-75, Lge Cup 61-62 Sheffield Snr Cup 51-52
Players progressing: Peter Eustace (Sheffield Wednesday) 1960 (from Stocksbridge Works) , Lee Mills (Wolverhampton W.) 1992

L-R  **Back Row:** Steve Taylor, Mark Highfield, Richard Fidler, John Tesh, Mark Garrett, Andy Carney, Wayne Biggins, Sean Dunphy,
Richard March. **Front Row**: Sean Hird, Simon Marples, Gavin Bailey, Mick Horne, Trevor Gough, Mark Todd, Kevin Ronan, Steve Shutt.
Photo: Bill Wheatcroft

# TRAFFORD

## CLUB OFFICIALS

Chairman: **David Brown**

President: **David Roberts**

Secretary: **Graham Foxall**
62 Grosvenor Road, Urmston M41 5AQ
Tel: 0161 746 9726

### FOOTBALL MANAGEMENT TEAM

Manager: Mark Molyneux
Asst Manager: Peter Freakes
Coach: Dave Higgs

### FACT FILE
Formed: 1990
Nickname: The North
Sponsors: Dawn Processing Ltd
Colours: All White
Change colours: Azure & black,black,black
Midweek Matchday: Tuesday
Reserve League: Mid Cheshire Div 2
1998-99
Captain: Garry Vaughan
P.o.Y.: Jim O'Donnell
Top Scorer: Garry Vaughan (10)

**GROUND**
Shawe View, Pennybridge Lane, Flixton, Urmston, Manchester M415DL Tel: 0161 747 1727

**Directions:** M60 jct 9, B5158 towards Urmston, at 1str/about take 1st exit, 1st lights turn
right into Moorside Road, at nextr/about 2nd exit into Bowfell Rd, at next lights turn sharp left,
thenimmediately right into Pennybridge Lane next to Bird-in-Hand Pub, parking onleft 100 yds
Capacity: 2,500         Cover: 732         Seats: 284
**Clubhouse:** Yes      **Club Shop:** Yes

Pages: 44         Price: 75p
Editor: David Murray (0161 775 7509)

Local Press: Stretford & Urmston Messenger,
Manchester Evening News
Local Radio: GMR Talk,
Piccadilly Radio, Century 105

**PREVIOUS**         **Leagues:** Mid Cheshire 90-92; North West Counties 92-97.   Name: NorthTrafford 90-94.

**CLUB RECORDS**     **Attendance:** 803 v Flixton (NPL Div 1 27/12/97)
**Goalscorer:** ColinSmall 74                                    **Appearances:** Garry Vaughan 247
**Win:** 10-0 v Haslingden St Mary's (LancsAmt Shield 91)        **Defeat:** 0-6 v Oldham Town (NWCL Div 2 93)
**Fee Paid:** Undisclosed for Jock Russell (Radcliffe Borough)   **Fee Received:** Undisclosed for Mike Turner (Witton A.)

**BEST SEASON**      **FA Vase:** 5th Rd 95-96   **FA Trophy:** 2nd Rd 98-99
**FACup:** 2nd Rd Qual 95-96

**HONOURS**          Lamont Pils Trophy 93-94; NWCL Div 1 96-97, Div 2 R-up 93-94; Lge ChallCup R-up 96-97;  Res Div 93-94; Carling Chall
Cup R-up 94-95; Manchester PremCup R-up 94-95, R-up 96-97, Res Div Champ 96-97, Cup 96-97; Manchester Amt
Cup96-97. Unifilla 1st Div Cup 97-98

Players progressing: Anthony Vaughan (Ipswich & Manchester City))

Mark Molyneaux (asst. man.), Dave Law (manager), Steve Jackson, Steve Burns, Steve Raffell, jim O'Donnell, Chris Patterson, Paul
Varley, Dave Higgs (coach), John Crane (kit man.), Roger Finn (sponsor). Front: Ian Tunnicliffe, Darren Wilson, Tony Briffa, Chris
Adams, Garry Vaughan (capt.), Mike Dunphy, Mark Stewart, Chris Simms.

# WHITLEY BAY

## CLUB OFFICIALS

Chairman: **Michael Robinson**

Vice Chairman: **Peter Siddle**

President: **J Hedworth**

Secretary: **Derek Breakwell**
27 Kings Road, Whitley Bay, Tyne And
Wear, NE26 3BDTel: 0191 252 7940

Press Officer: **Gavin Miller**

### FOOTBALL MANAGEMENT TEAM

Manager: Dave Styles
Asst Manager: Dave Rooney
Coach: Colin Holloway
Physio: Joe Jabs

## FACT FILE

Formed: 1897
Nickname: The Bay
Colours: Blue & white stripes/blue/blue
Change colours: Yellow/sky blue
Midweek home matchday: Tuesday
PROGRAMME
Pages: 24          Price: £1.00
Editor: Sean Robinson (0191 251 0356)
Local Press: The News, Guardian
Herald & Post
Local Radio: Radio Newcastle, Metro

1998-99
Captain: Philip Hildreth
P.o.Y.: Phillp Hildreth
Top scorer: Mickey Barkas

**GROUND**   Hillheads Park, Rink Way off Hillheads Road, Whitley Bay, Tyne& Wear NE25 8HR
Tel: 0191 291 3637 (Club) Fax (& matchday office) 0191 291 3636
**Directions:** 1 mile walk from bus station - leave St Pauls Church southward,turn right at
r-about, ground 3rd left at rear of ice rink. Whitley Bay (25mins from Newcastle) or Monkseaton
metro stations, both 1 mile
Capacity: 4,500          Cover: 650          Seats: 450
**Clubhouse:** Open 7-11pm, except Wed. Bar & concert room. Darts, pool
**Club Shop:** Sells programmes, scarves, hats, metal badges etc.
Contact Tom Moody (0191 291 1618)

**PREVIOUS**          **Name:** Whitley Bay Athletic 1950-58
**Leagues:** Tyneside 09-10, Northern Alliance 50-55, North Eastern League 55-58, Northern League 58-88

**CLUB RECORDS**          **Attendance:** 7,301 v Hendon, FA Amateur Cup 1965
**Win:** 12-0 v Shildon 1961          **Defeat:** 1-8 v Bishop Auckland 1979
**Goalscorer:** Billy Wright 307          **Appearances:** Bill Chater 640
Fee Paid: £500 for Paul Walker from Blyth Spartans    Received: £10,000 for Kevin Todd from Berwick Rangers

**BEST SEASON**          **FA Amateur Cup:** Semi Final 65-66 68-69          **FA Trophy:** 3rd Rd 86-87
**FA Cup:** 3rd Rd 89-90 (0-1 v Rochdale [A]). 2nd Rd 90-91 (0-1 v Barrow [H])
League clubs defeated: Scarborough, Preston North End 89-90

**HONOURS**          Northern Premier Lg Div 1 90-91 (Div 1 Cup 88-89 90-91), Northern Lg 64-65 65-66 (R-up 59-60 66-67 68-69 69-70), League
Cup 64-65 70-71 (R-up 67-68);Northern Alliance 52-53 53-54 (Lg Cup 52-53 53-54); Northumberland Senior Cup52-53 60-
61 63-64 64-65 67-68 68-69 69-70 70-71 72-73 86-87 (R-up 53-54 54-5555-56 65-66 76-77 85-86 90-91)

Players progressing:          W Dodd (Burnley 56), W Younger (Nottm Forest 57), R Brown(Blackpool 65), J Ritchie (Port Vale 65),
John Brodie & A McCaffery (Carlisle67 & 88), M Spelman (Wolves 69), T Harrison (Southport 77),
M Miller(Gillingham 81), G Haire (Bradford City 83), S Ferebee (Darlington 87),
David John Cullen (Hartlepool 97, Sheffield Utd), Kevin Todd (Berwick Rangers), Kevin Henderson (Burnley 1998)

Bay's Andy Smith holds off
a determined Shane Bird of
Gretna

Photo: Alan Watson

# WITTON ALBION

## CLUB OFFICIALS

President: **T Stelfox**

Chairman: **D T Lloyd**

Secretary: **Phil Chadwick**
29 Jack Lane, Davenham, Northwich,
Cheshire CW9 8LF Tel: 01606 44845

## FOOTBALL MANAGEMENT TEAM

Manager: Kevin Tully
Coach: Rob Brown
Physio: John Bird

### FACT FILE

Formed: 1887

Nickname: The Albion

Colours: Red & white stripes

Change colours: All yellow

Midweek matchday: Tuesday

Reserve League: None

Pages: 32          Price: £1
Editor: Phil Chadwick  (01606 44845)

Local Press: Northwich Guardian,
Northwich Chronicle
Local Radio: BBC GMR, BBC Radio Stoke

**GROUND**          Wincham Park, Chapel St, Wincham, Northwich. Tel/Fax: 01606 43008

**Directions:** M6 junc 19. A556 towards Northwich, after 3 miles turn onto A559 at beginning of dual carriageway, after 3/4 mile turn left opposite Black Greyhound Inn, grd 1/2 mile on left immediately after crossing Canal Bridge

Capacity: 4,500          Seated: 650          Cover: 2,300

**Clubhouse:** Concert room and Vice-Presidents room open matchdays, Tuesday,Thursday, Friday and Sunday evenings. Food available for private functions          **Club Shop:** Yes

**PREVIOUS**          **Leagues:** Lancs Comb.; Cheshire County -79; Northern Premier 79-91, GMV Conference 91-94
          **Grounds:** Central Ground, Witton Street, Northwich

**CLUB RECORDS**          **Attendance:** 3,940 v Kidderminster Harriers - FA Trophy Semi-Final
          **Win:** 6-0 v Stafford Rangers - 1992/93          **Defeat:** 0-5 v Welling United (H), GMVC12/3/94
          **Fee Paid:** £12,500 to Hyde Utd for Jim McCluskie 91          **Fee Received:** £11,500 for Peter Henderson from Chester City.
          Goalscorer: Frank Fidler 122.          Appearances: John Goryl 652

**BEST SEASON**          **FA Trophy:** Runners-up 91-92, Semi-Finals 90-91, 92-93
          **FA Cup:** 91-92 Second Round 91-92, 1-5 v Preston North End (A). League clubs defeated: Halifax Town91-92

**HONOURS**          Northern Prem Lge 90-91; Cheshire County Lge 48-49 49-50 53-54 (R-up 50-51),Lge Cup 53-54 75-76; Cheshire County
          Sen Cup (7); FA Trophy R-up 91-92 (SF 90-91 92-93)
Players progressing:          P Henderson (Chester C.), Chris Nicholl (Burnley - ex-Southampton manager), Phil Power (Crewe), Neil Parsley &
          Mike Whitlow (Leeds)

L-R   **Back Row:** Rob Brown (coach), Danny Gee, Andy Bridge, Brian Pritchard, Scott Brenchley, Scott Healey, Kevin Langley, Wayne Johnson, Darren Twigg, Peter Ward (manager). **Front Row**: Chris Bermingham, Andy Smolenski, Joey Roberts, Bryan Griffiths, Jon Hassall, Richard Carter          Photo: Keith Clayton

# WORKINGTON

## CLUB OFFICIALS

Chairman: **Bill Wilson**

President: **Eric Fisher**

Vice Chairman: T.B.A.

Match Sec: **Steve Durham** (01946 61380)

Secretary: **Tom Robson**
12 Derwent Bank, Seaton,
Workington CA14 1EE Tel: 01900 605208

## FOOTBALL MANAGEMENT TEAM

Manager:Peter Hampton

Ass.Man & Physio: Keith Hunton

## FACT FILE

Formed: 1884 (reformed 1921)
Nickname: Reds
Sponsors: AXA Homesearch Direct
Colours: All red
Change colours: yellow & black/black/yellow
Midweek matchday: Tuesday
Reserves' League:Vaux Wearside
PROGRAMME
Pages: 36     Price: £1
Press Off/ Ed: Steve Durham (01946 61380)

Local Press: Evening News & Star, Times & Star
Local Radio: BBC Radio Cumbria, C.F.M

1998-99
Captain Martin Kirkby
P.o.Y.: Martin Kirkby
Top Scorer: Darren Wilson

## GROUND

Borough Park, Workington, Cumbria CA14 2DT     Tel: 01900 602871
**Directions:**     A66 into town, right at 'T' junction, follow A596 for 3/4 mile - ground is then
visible and signposted. Ground is north of town centre 1/4 mile from
Workington (BR) station &1/2 mile from bus station
Capacity: 2,500     Cover: 800     Seats: 300     Floodlights: Yes
**Clubhouse:** Open matchdays and for private functions. Food on matchdays restricted menu
**Club Shop:** Sells programmes, badges, magazines, pennants, photographs, replica kit,
T-shirts. etc.   Contact Keith Lister (01900 812867)

**HONOURS**     Football League: 5th in Div 3 65-66, 3rd Div 4 63-64,  Cumberland County Cup 1886-91(x5) 95-99(x4) 1906-08(x2) 09-10 24-25
34-35 36-38(x2) 49-50 53-54 67-68 85-86 95-96  (R-up 1885-86 91-92 1899-1901(x2) 02-03 08-09 11-12 23-24 26-27 29-30 46-
47 68-69 78-79) Football League Cup QF 63-64 64-65; N.P.L. Presidents Cup 83-84; North Eastern Lge R-up 38-39, Lge Cup
34-35 36-37 R-up 37-38; N.W. Trains Lg Div 1 98-99

**PREVIOUS**     **Leagues:** Cumberland Assoc. 1890-94; Cumberland Sen. Lge 94-1901, 03-04; Lancashire Lge 1901-03;
Lancashire Comb. 04-10; North Eastern 10-11, 21-51; Football League 51-77
**Grounds:** Various 1884-1921, Lonsdale Park 21-37

**BEST SEASON**     FA Cup: 4th Rd 33-34. 1st Rd - 53 occasions.
FA Trophy: 1st Round replay 77-78     **FA Vase:** 6th Rd, 98-99 (1st season)

**RECORDS**     **Attendance:** 21,000 v Manchester Utd, FA Cup 3rd Rd 4/1/58
**Goalscorer:** Billy Charlton 193
**Appearances:** Bobby Brown 419     **Win:** 17-1 v Cockermouth Crusaders, Cumb-erland Sen. Lge 19/1/01
**Fee Paid:** £6,000 for Ken Chisholm (Sunderland,'56)     **Defeat:** 0-9 v Chorley (A), NPL Prem. Div., 10/11/87
**Fee Received:** £33,000 for Ian McDonald (Liverpool, '74)

Players progressing: Numerous, the best known being John Burridge.

All smiles as the Workington team are presented with the North West Counties trophy.

# First North Western
## North Western
# FIRST NORTH WESTERN TRAINS LEAGUE

**President:** W J King    **Chairman:** D Tomlinson
**Secretary:** M Darby
87 Hillary Road, Hyde, Cheshire SK14 4EB    Tel/Fax: 0161 368 6243 (H)

It is a credit to the North Western Trains Football League that so many clubs have been involved in the title race with both the first and second division championships not decided until the final week of the season.

In Division One, reigning Champions Kidsgrove Athletic were the early season leaders, Mossley briefly reached the summit in September as did Newcastle Town. Early October saw the Hollinwood Road club regain top spot before being replaced by arch rivals Newcastle Town, who were in pole position at Christmas and well into the New Year.

Mossley took over on the 20th February and were there until the last day of the season when their final day opponents Workington stole the show and promotion to the Unibond League Division One courtesy of their fourteenth straight league victory. 'The Reds' thus became the first club to regain their Northern Premier League status at the first attempt.

While it was success for one Cumbrian outfit the Division's other club was suffering its worst season. Holker Old Boys completed their league campaign without picking up a single point away from home and will now play their football in Division Two next season.

In League Division Two Fleetwood Freeport, under the guidance of Brian Wilson, made it to the top flight along with newcomers Abbey Hey whose last day win at Darwen secured their place in Division One. On the same afternoon Warrington Town will have been disappointed to lose surprisingly at Maghull to scupper their chances of a quick return, while Castleton Gabriels and Woodley Sports will be thinking what might have been. Surprise package Squire Gate kept well among the challengers late in the season and will be hoping they can re-create this season's form next term.

Ramsbottom United were one of the last member clubs to be knocked out of the Axa Sponsored FA Cup in their first ever venture in the competition. They eventually bowed out to Conference outfit Southport at the Third Qualifying Round stage - as did Prescot Cables and Mossley.

In the FA Carlsberg Vase, Clitheroe and Workington were the league's last survivors going out on the same day at the Sixth Round stage to eventual finalists and winners, Bedlington Terriers and Tiverton Town respectively.

In domestic cup competitions Fleetwood Freeport held aloft the Division Two Trophy at the Anchorground when they overcame Warrington Town 2-1, before going on to complete a league and cup double! The Floodlit Trophy saw Clitheroe victorious over Kidsgrove Athletic while the Shawbridge outfit's Reserves lifted the Reserve Division Cup with a 4-3 success over Maine Road. The League Challenge Cup finally saw Vauxhall GM erase the disappointment of last season's defeat by Kidsgrove as they ran out 1-0 winners over first time finalists Prescot Cables. The Gigg Lane final fell foul of a floodlight failure as the teams were about to take penalties following a 1-1 extra time draw - Vauxhall edging the replay at Skelmersdale United's White Moss Park.

In County Cup competitions Prescot Cables reached the semi-finals of the Liverpool Senior Cup, while both Glossop North End and Maine Road reached the same stage of the Manchester Premier Cup, the latter reaching the Boundary Park final before losing 1-0 to Hyde United.

By far the greatest achievement in County Cup competitions was by Darwen who reached the Final of the Lancashire ATS Trophy. Steve Wilkes' side eventually lost on penalties to Conference side Morecambe following a 2-2 extra time draw. Their run in the competition saw them winners at Southport in the semi-finals.

Newcastle Town's Dave Sutton hit the first goal of the season - opening his account with a second minute effort at Workington back in August. Mossley's Darrell Dicken had the satisfaction of scoring the League's first hat trick of the campaign doing so in an early 4-1 win at Nantwich Town.

Brian Smith became the first managerial casualty of the campaign when he stepped down from the Atherton Collieries hot-seat before the end of August.

Fleetwood Freeport recorded the biggest league win when they trounced unfortunate Oldham Town 13-0 in a Division Two encounter, while in the First Division Vauxhall GM's 8-0 defeat of Glossop North End was the biggest winning margin.

Warrington Town youngster Damien Whitehead emerged as the League's top scorer with 52; while in Division One St Helens Town's Steve Pennington hit 35 goals to finish at the top of the leader board in the top flight.

Our congratulations go to all this season's winners and commiserations to all those who didn't quite make it. August, and the new season, will bring fresh hope of success as every club starts with an equal chance in the chase for honours.

John McKiernan

# FINAL LEAGUE TABLES 1998-99

## DIVISION ONE

| | P | W | D | L | F | A | GD | Pts |
|---|---|---|---|---|---|---|---|---|
| Holmer Green | 42 | 30 | 6 | 6 | 121 | 42 | 79 | 96 |
| Workington | 40 | 27 | 9 | 4 | 86 | 28 | 90 | 58 |
| Mossley | 40 | 27 | 7 | 6 | 91 | 38 | 88 | 53 |
| Vauxhall GM | 40 | 26 | 7 | 7 | 92 | 40 | 85 | 52 |
| Newcastle Town | 40 | 25 | 9 | 6 | 86 | 33 | 84 | 53 |
| Kidsgrove Athletic | 40 | 24 | 7 | 9 | 90 | 47 | 79 | 43 |
| Prescot Cables | 40 | 21 | 9 | 10 | 78 | 44 | 74 | 34 |
| Skelmerdale Utd | 40 | 21 | 8 | 11 | 82 | 48 | 71 | 34 |
| St Helens Town | 40 | 22 | 5 | 13 | 77 | 58 | 71 | 19 |
| Leek CSOB | 40 | 14 | 11 | 15 | 52 | 58 | 53 | -6 |
| Salford City | 40 | 15 | 7 | 18 | 63 | 73 | 52 | -10 |
| Ramsbottom Utd | 40 | 14 | 8 | 18 | 54 | 64 | 50 | -10 |
| Clitheroe | 40 | 14 | 6 | 20 | 68 | 58 | 48 | 10 |
| Maine Road | 40 | 14 | 6 | 20 | 50 | 71 | 48 | -21 |
| Rossendale Utd | 40 | 14 | 5 | 21 | 59 | 81 | 47 | -22 |
| Nantwich Town | 40 | 12 | 6 | 22 | 54 | 68 | 42 | -14 |
| Glossop Nth End | 40 | 12 | 6 | 22 | 53 | 81 | 42 | -28 |
| Cheadle Town | 40 | 12 | 6 | 22 | 56 | 97 | 42 | -41 |
| Atherton LR | 40 | 10 | 9 | 21 | 45 | 73 | 37 | -28 |
| Atherton Collieries | 40 | 9 | 7 | 24 | 50 | 88 | 34 | -38 |
| Bootle | 40 | 9 | 7 | 24 | 41 | 84 | 34 | -43 |
| Holker Old Boys | 40 | 4 | 3 | 33 | 21 | 116 | 15 | -95 |

## DIVISION TWO

| | P | W | D | L | F | A | PT | GD |
|---|---|---|---|---|---|---|---|---|
| Fleetwood Freeport | 36 | 20 | 8 | 7 | 102 | 34 | 71 | 68 |
| Abbey Hey | 36 | 20 | 6 | 10 | 70 | 35 | 66 | 35 |
| Squires Gate | 36 | 17 | 14 | 5 | 53 | 31 | 65 | 22 |
| Warrington Town | 36 | 18 | 9 | 9 | 82 | 46 | 63 | 36 |
| Woodley Sports | 36 | 17 | 10 | 9 | 60 | 38 | 61 | 22 |
| Castleton Gabriels | 36 | 17 | 10 | 9 | 71 | 56 | 61 | 15 |
| Formby | 36 | 17 | 7 | 12 | 81 | 59 | 58 | 22 |
| Darwen | 36 | 13 | 12 | 11 | 64 | 53 | 51 | 11 |
| Chadderton | 36 | 11 | 17 | 8 | 42 | 38 | 50 | 4 |
| Tetley Walker | 36 | 14 | 8 | 14 | 62 | 64 | 50 | -2 |
| Bacup Borough | 36 | 11 | 14 | 11 | 47 | 61 | 47 | -14 |
| Daisy Hill | 36 | 12 | 9 | 15 | 51 | 63 | 45 | -12 |
| Nelson | 36 | 11 | 11 | 14 | 51 | 46 | 44 | 2 |
| Curzon Ashton | 36 | 12 | 7 | 17 | 56 | 58 | 43 | -2 |
| Maghill | 36 | 11 | 10 | 15 | 50 | 70 | 43 | -20 |
| Colne | 36 | 11 | 7 | 18 | 54 | 71 | 40 | -17 |
| Ashton Town | 36 | 11 | 6 | 19 | 35 | 59 | 39 | -24 |
| Oldham Town | 36 | 5 | 7 | 24 | 34 | 99 | 22 | -66 |
| Blackpool Mechs | 36 | 4 | 6 | 26 | 39 | 121 | 18 | -82 |

## PREMIER DIVISION RESULTS CHART 1998-99

| | | 1 | 2 | 3 | 4 | 5 | 6 | 7 | 8 | 9 | 10 | 11 | 12 | 13 | 14 | 15 | 16 | 17 | 18 | 19 | 20 | 21 |
|---|---|---|---|---|---|---|---|---|---|---|---|---|---|---|---|---|---|---|---|---|---|---|
| 1 | Atherton Coll. | X | 0-1 | 2-0 | 1-1 | 0-2 | 5-2 | 4-1 | 2-2 | 1-0 | 1-2 | 0-3 | 2-1 | 0-5 | 0-2 | 0-2 | 1-4 | 1-3 | 2-3 | 0-5 | 2-2 | 0-2 |
| 2 | Atherton LR | 2-2 | X | 1-5 | 1-0 | 1-1 | 1-0 | 6-0 | 2-2 | 0-1 | 1-1 | 0-1 | 0-0 | 1-5 | 0-1 | 1-0 | 1-2 | 0-1 | 2-2 | 1-0 | 2-4 | 1-2 |
| 3 | Bootle | 2-3 | 0-0 | X | 1-2 | 1-2 | 3-1 | 1-0 | 0-3 | 0-1 | 0-1 | 0-6 | 1-2 | 1-1 | 1-2 | 1-2 | 1-3 | 0-4 | 1-3 | 4-2 | 0-2 | 0-2 |
| 4 | Clitheroe | 3-1 | 4-0 | 6-0 | X | 5-0 | 5-1 | 5-1 | 3-1 | 0-1 | 4-1 | 1-3 | 1-3 | 0-0 | 2-3 | 0-1 | 2-3 | 0-1 | 3-1 | 0-2 | 0-0 | 0-1 |
| 5 | Cheadle T | 1-6 | 5-1 | 2-3 | 2-0 | X | 2-0 | 1-0 | 0-2 | 1-1 | 0-4 | 0-3 | 2-1 | 2-0 | 2-6 | 1-2 | 3-3 | 0-5 | 0-4 | 2-0 | 1-6 | 1-1 |
| 6 | Glossop NE | 4-1 | 2-1 | 1-2 | 1-0 | 1-3 | X | 5-0 | 2-1 | 1-2 | 1-1 | 2-1 | 1-3 | 1-2 | 0-3 | 1-2 | 0-1 | 0-2 | 2-2 | 3-0 | 0-3 | |
| 7 | Holker OB | 2-0 | 1-1 | 1-1 | 2-5 | 2-4 | 1-2 | X | 0-5 | 1-0 | 0-2 | 1-2 | 0-4 | 0-4 | 0-0 | 1-0 | 1-2 | 1-4 | 1-0 | 1-2 | 0-3 | 0-2 |
| 8 | Kidsgrove A | 5-1 | 4-0 | 0-2 | 2-1 | 0-0 | 3-1 | 8-1 | X | 3-4 | 1-0 | 0-0 | 4-0 | 1-1 | 3-1 | 2-0 | 2-0 | 2-1 | 3-2 | 1-0 | 2-1 | 1-1 |
| 9 | Leek CSOB | 1-4 | 1-2 | 0-0 | 3-1 | 2-0 | 3-0 | 1-0 | 2-1 | X | 1-1 | 1-2 | 1-0 | 1-1 | 1-1 | 1-3 | 5-2 | 1-3 | 0-2 | 1-1 | 0-1 | 1-1 |
| 10 | Maine Rd | 1-0 | 2-0 | 0-3 | 4-1 | 0-0 | 1-2 | 3-0 | 0-4 | 2-1 | X | 0-3 | 2-1 | 0-1 | 0-2 | 1-2 | 3-3 | 0-1 | 2-1 | 3-2 | 0-5 | 0-1 |
| 11 | Mossley | 6-0 | 2-0 | 5-0 | 1-0 | 3-1 | 3-1 | 4-0 | 2-1 | 4-0 | 1-0 | X | 4-1 | 3-3 | 3-1 | 4-1 | 2-0 | 2-1 | 3-1 | 2-2 | 1-0 | 0-3 |
| 12 | Nantwich T | 1-1 | 1-2 | 0-0 | 1-2 | 2-1 | 1-3 | 4-1 | 2-2 | 0-0 | 4-1 | 1-4 | X | 0-2 | 1-5 | 4-2 | 3-1 | 1-0 | 0-0 | 0-1 | 1-2 | 0-2 |
| 13 | Newcastle T | 1-0 | 2-1 | 4-0 | 3-1 | 2-0 | 0-1 | 3-0 | 2-0 | 4-1 | 1-3 | 1-1 | 2-1 | X | 1-0 | 1-2 | 3-1 | 5-0 | 2-3 | 4-1 | 0-1 | 1-1 |
| 14 | Prescot Cbls | 3-0 | 3-2 | 2-2 | 1-0 | 3-1 | 4-1 | 3-0 | 0-1 | 1-0 | 6-1 | 4-0 | 0-2 | 0-3 | X | 1-1 | 5-1 | 4-1 | 5-1 | 1-1 | 1-2 | 0-0 |
| 15 | Ramsbottom U | 0-1 | 2-2 | 1-2 | 2-2 | 4-2 | 1-1 | 3-0 | 1-3 | 2-1 | 1-0 | 1-1 | 0-3 | 0-5 | 1-2 | X | 2-1 | 2-3 | 0-1 | 3-0 | 0-2 | 0-0 |
| 16 | Rossendale U | 1-0 | 0-1 | 1-0 | 2-1 | 3-2 | 1-3 | 3-1 | 3-3 | 1-3 | 1-1 | 1-1 | 4-2 | 2-4 | 1-0 | 0-2 | X | 1-0 | 1-3 | 2-0 | 1-2 | 0-1 |
| 17 | St Helens T | 2-2 | 1-0 | 3-0 | 1-2 | 4-1 | 1-0 | 5-0 | 0-3 | 4-0 | 3-1 | 3-2 | 3-1 | 0-0 | 0-0 | 2-2 | 3-0 | X | 2-2 | 0-6 | 1-2 | 0-4 |
| 18 | Salford City | 3-2 | 3-5 | 3-1 | 2-0 | 1-0 | 4-0 | 3-4 | 0-4 | 4-1 | 1-3 | 2-1 | 0-1 | 1-2 | 0-2 | 1-1 | 0-0 | 3-2 | X | 2-2 | 0-6 | 1-2 |
| 19 | Skelmersdale | 2-1 | 3-1 | 5-1 | 1-1 | 4-1 | 5-0 | 4-0 | 2-0 | 0-1 | 2-3 | 2-1 | 3-0 | 1-2 | 0-2 | 1-1 | 0-0 | 3-2 | 1-3 | X | 1-1 | 1-3 | 1-2 |
| 20 | Vauxhall GM | 1-1 | 3-0 | 1-1 | 2-0 | 5-2 | 8-0 | 3-0 | 1-4 | 4-4 | 5-1 | 3-0 | 1-0 | 0-0 | 0-0 | 3-2 | 3-1 | 1-2 | 4-0 | 4-1 | X | 2-1 |
| 21 | Workington | 4-0 | 4-1 | 4-0 | 2-2 | 6-1 | 0-3 | 3-1 | 2-2 | 2-0 | 2-1 | 3-2 | 1-2 | 3-1 | 3-2 | 4-0 | 4-2 | 5-0 | 1-1 | 1-1 | | X |

## LEAGUE CHALLENGE CUP 1998-99

**FINAL**

| | | |
|---|---|---|
| Prescot Cables | 1*1, 0-1 | Vauxhall GM |

## FLOODLIT TROPHY 1998-99

**FINAL**

| | | |
|---|---|---|
| Clitheroe | 2-1 | Kidsgrove Athletic |

## SECOND DIVISION TROPHY 1998-99

**FINAL**

| | | |
|---|---|---|
| Fleetwood Freeport | 2-1 | Warrington Town |

# ABBEY HEY

**Secretary:** Tony McAllister, 10 Walmer Street, Abbey Hey, Gorton M18 8QP
Tel: 0161 230 7098

**Ground:** Abbey Stadium, Goredale Avenue, Gorton, Manchester 18
Tel: 0161 231 7147 (Club) Fax: 01823 490281

**Directions:** A57 towards Hyde, right into Woodland Avenue approx one & a half miles past Belle Vue junction, right again into Ryder Brow Rd, 1st left after bridge into Goredale Ave.

Capacity: 1000   Seats: 100   Cover: 300   Floodlights: Yes

**HONOURS** Manchester Amat. Lge 65-66: S.E. Lancs Lge 66-67, 68-69 R-up 67-68; Div.2 68-69; Lge Shield 65-66: Manc. Co. Amat. Cup 64-65, 67-68, 68-69, R-up 63-64: Manchester Lge Prem. Div. 81-82, 88-89, 90-91, 93-94, 94-95; Div. 1 70-71; Div.2 88-89, 92-93, 93-94; Gilcryst Cup 76-77, 88-89, R-up 97-88; Open Tphy 78-79,79-80, 92-93: Manchester Chall. Tphy 82-83, 95-96, 96-97. N.W. Trains Div 2 R-up 98-99

**PREVIOUS** **Leagues:** Manchester Amateur; South East Lancs; Manchester Lge.

### FACT FILE

Formed: 1902
Colours:Red/black/black&red
Midweek matchday: Tuesday

**CLUB PERSONNEL**

Chairman: J E Whittaker
0161 445 0036

Emergency Contact; G.Lester
0161 370 0270 or 0161 236 3311 ext 2800

---

# ATHERTON COLLIERIES

**Secretary:** Emil Anderson, 109 Douglas Street, Atherton, Gtr Manchester M46 9EB(01942 87209 (H), 0161 288 6216 (B)

**Ground:** Atherton Colls Football Ground,Alder St., Atherton, Gt ManchesterTel:01942884649.
**Directions:** M61 Jct 5, follow sign for Westhoughton, left onto A6, right ontoA579 (Newbrook Rd/Bolton Rd) into Atherton. At first set of lights turn leftinto High Street, 2nd left into Alder St. to ground. Quarter mile from AthertonCentral (BR).

Seats: 300   Cover: 1,000   Capacity: 2,500   Floodlights: Yes
**Clubhouse:** Open Mon-Fri 7-11pm, Sat 11am-11pm, Sun noon-3 & 7-10.30pm. Hot &cold food on matchdays. **Club Shop:** No, but programmes & badges are available

**HONOURS:** BNWCFL 3rd Div Champ 86/87; Bridge Shield 85/86; Lancs County FA Shield19/20, 22/23, 41/42, 45/46. 56/57, 64/65; Tennents F/lit Trophy Finalist 94/95; NWCFL Div 2 R/up 95/96
**RECORDS** **Attendance:** 3,300 in Lancs Combination, 1920's
**PREVIOUS** **Leagues:** Bolton Combination 20-50, 52-71; Lancs Combination 50-52, 71-78; Cheshire County 78-82.
Players Progressing: J Parkinson (Wigan), Russell Beardsmore(Manchester Utd).

### FACT FILE

Founded: 1916
Nickname: Colls
Club Sponsors: Kensite
Colours: Black & white stripes/black/black.
Change colours: All blue
Reserves' Lge: NWTL Res Div
Midweek Matches: Tuesday
Programme: 40 pages, 60p
Editor: Frank Anderson.
Captain 97-98: Simon O'Brien
P.o.Y.: Scott Dowds
Top Scorer: Alan Shawcross

**CLUB PERSONNEL**

Chairman: Steve Payne
Vice Chairman:
President: J Fielding
Manager: Tommy Harrison/Brian Smith
Physio: Ernie Ackers

---

# ATHERTON L.R.

**Secretary:** Steve Hartle, 32 Greensmith Way, Westhoughton,Bolton BL5 3DR (01942840906-H)
**Ground:** Crilly Park, Spa Road, Atherton, Greater Manchester (01942 883950).
**Directions:** M61 to Jct 5, follow signs for Westhoughton, left onto A6, right onto A579 (Newbrook Rd/Bolton Rd) over the railway bridge, right into Upton Rd passing Atherton Central Station, left into Springfield Rd and again into Hillside Rd into Spa Rd and ground.
Capacity: 3,000Seats: 250Cover: 3 sections Floodlights: Yes
**Clubhouse:** Open normal licensing hours.   **Club Shop:** Yes

**HONOURS:** North West Counties Lge 92-93 93-94, Champions Trophy 92-93 93-94,F/Lit Trophy 93-94; Northern Premier Lge Div.1 Cup R-up 95-96

**PREVIOUS** **Name:** Laburnum Rovers 54-79 **Leagues:** Bolton Comb.; Cheshire County 80-82; NWCL 82-94; NPL 94-97. **Grounds:** Laburnum Road 54-56; Hagfold 56-66.

**BEST SEASON FA Cup:** 3rd Qual Rd 96-97, 0-2 v Bamber Bridge
**FA Vase:** Semi-Final rep. 94-95, 1-2 v Diss Town.
**FA Trophy:** 1st Qual Rd 96-97

**RECORDS** **Attendance:** 1,856 v Aldershot Town, FA Vase Quarter-Final replay 5/3/94.
**Appearances:** Jimmy Evans **Fee Paid:** £500 for Joey Dunn from Warrington T.
**Scorer:** Shaun Parker **Fee Received:** £1,500 for Stuart Humphries to Barrow

### FACT FILE

Formed: 1954
Nickname: The Panthers
Sponsors: T B A
Colours: All Yellow
Change colours: Red & white/black/black
Midweek Matches: Tuesday
Reserves' League: North West Alliance.
Programme: 48 pages 70p
Editor: Tim Lees & Chris Green

**CLUB PERSONNEL**

Chairman:Alan Grundy
Treasurer: Jack Hetherington
Manager: Gerry Luczha
Assistant Manager: Ian Senior
Coach: Steve Walton

# BOOTLE

**Secretary:** Jay Siadankay, 52 Rawson Road,Seaforth,Lliverpool L211BY Tel: 0151 474 8957
**Ground:** Bucks Park, Northern Perimeter Road, Netherton, Bootle. L307PT (0151 526 1850)
**Directions:** End of M57 & M58 follow signs to Bootle and Docks A5063. Turn right at next lights by Police station. Entrance 100 yds on right. Old Roan station 300yds. Bus 55 (150yds from grd), 302 341 345 350 (350yds).
Capacity: 5,000          Seats: 400          Cover: 1,400          Floodlights: Yes
**Clubhouse:** Normal pub hours. Darts & pool          **Club Shop:** Yes

**HONOURS**          N.W.C. Lge Div 2 R-up 92-93 (Floodlit Trophy 93-94), Liverpool Chall. Cup 64-65 75-76 78-79, Liverpool Amtr Cup 65-66 67-68 73-74, Lancs Amtr Cup 69-70, Liverpool County Comb. (x9) 64--66 67-74, George Mahon Cup (x6) 66--68 68-70 72--74, Lancs Comb. 75-76 76-77, Lge Cup 75-76, Cheshire County Lge Div 2 78-79.
**PREVIOUS**          **Leagues:** Liverpool Shipping, Liverpool County Comb., Lancs Comb. 74-78, Cheshire Lge 78-82.  **Name:** Langton 1953-73  **Grounds:** Edinburgh Park 1953-73, Orrell Mount Park 1973-78
**BEST SEASON  FA Cup:**          **FA Vase:**
**RECORDS**          **Attendance:** 750 v Carshalton Ath., FA Trophy 2nd Rd 31/1/81
**Win:** 9-1 v Glossop (H), NWC Lge 8/2/86  **Defeat:** 1-8 v Accrington Stanley (A), NWC Lge 83
**Appearances:** Peter Cumiskey (almost 400)

**FACT FILE**

Founded: 1954
Nickname: Bucks
Sponsors: Taximex
Colours: All royal blue with amber trim
Change colours: Yellow/black/black
Midweek matchday: Tuesday
Reserves' League: Liverpool Co. Combination
Programme: 32 pages, 50p
Editor: Secretary
Local Press: Bootle Times
97-98 Captain: Billy Loughlin
Top Scorer :
Marcel Anzani & Ronnie Morgan 14
P.o.Y: Ronnie Morgan

**CLUB PERSONNEL**

Chairman: Frank Doran
Manager: T.B.A.

# CHEADLE TOWN

**FACT FILE**

Founded: 1961
Colours: White/black/black
Change colours: All blue.
Midweek Matches: Tuesday
Reserves' Lge: NW Counties Lge
Programme: 24 pages,80p.
Editor: Stuart Crawford
98-99 Captain: Ian Henderson
P.o.Y.: Paul Mannion
Top Scorer:Tony Coyne

**Secretary:** Susan Burton, 2 Lavington Ave., Cheadle, Stockport, Cheshire SK8 2HH
          Tel: 0161 491 0823

**Ground:** Park Road Stadium, Park Road, Cheadle, Cheshire SK8 2AN (0161 4282510).
**Directions:** M60 Jct 2, follow signs towards Cheadle (A560), first left after lights into Park Road, ground at end. 1 mile from Gatley (BR), buses from Stockport.
Capacity: 2,500Seats: 300Cover: 300Floodlights: Yes
**Clubhouse:** Open every night. Food available          **Club Shop**: No

**HONOURS**          Manchester Lg Div 1 79-80 (R-up 80-81 81-82); Manchester Amtr Cup 79-80;Lamot Pils R-up 90-91; NWCFL Div 2 Trophy R-up 95-96:

**PREVIOUS**          **Leagues:** Manchester (pre 1987)

**RECORD**          **Attendance** : 1,700 v Stockport County, August 1994.
          **Scorer:** Peter Tilley          **Appearances:** John McArdle
Players progressing: Ashley Ward (Crewe), Steve Bushell (York), Dean Crowe(Stoke).

**CLUB PERSONNEL**

President: Freddie Pye
Chairman: Chris Davies
Vice-Chairman: Clive Williams
Press Officer: Chris Davies (0161 428 2510).
Manager:Chris Bailey
Physio: Simon Cave

# CLITHEROE

**Secretary:** Colin Wilson, 4 Moss Street, Clitheroe, Lancs BB7 1DP(01200 424370).

**Ground:** Shawbridge, Clitheroe, Lancs (01200 423344).
**Directions:** M6 jct 31, A59 to Clitheroe (17 miles), at 5th r'bout continue for half a mile and turn left at Pendle Road. Ground one mile, behind Bridge Inn' on the right. 11 miles from Blackburn BR station: Clitheroe
Capacity: 2,000          Seats: 300          Cover: 1200          Floodlights: Yes
**Clubhouse:** Open during matches. Snacks available          **Club Shop:** Yes.

**HONOURS**          FA Vase Runners-up 95-96; Lancs Comb. 79-80, Lg Cup 34-35; Lancs Challenge Tphy 84-85; NW C Lge 85-86, Div 2 84-85, Div 3 83-84; East Lancs Floodlit Trophy 94-95.N.W.Trains Floodlit Cup: 98-99
**PREVIOUS**          Leagues: Blackburn & Dist.; Lancs Comb. 03-04 05-10 25-82.
**BEST SEASON**          FA Cup:          FA Vase: Runners-up 95-96
**RECORDS**          Attendance: 2,000 v Mangotsfield, FA Vase Semi/F 95-96.
          Goalscorer: Don Francis          Appearances: Lindsey Wallace.
Players progressing Ray Woods (Leeds 1950), Chris Sims (Blackburn 1960), Lee Rogerson (Wigan Ath), Carlo Nash (Crystal Palace).

**FACT FILE**

Formed: 1877.
Nickname: The Blues
Colours: Blue & white stripes/blue/blue
Change colours: All yellow
Midweek matchday: Monday
Reserves' Lge: N.W.C.L.
Programme: 12 pages, 60p
Editor: Ian Rimmer

**CLUB PERSONNEL**

Chairman: S Rush
President: Jer Aspinall
Press Officer: Colin Wilson
Manager:Steve Parry
Assistant Manager: Malcolm Holt
Physio: Keith Lord.

# FLEETWOOD FREEPORT

**FACT FILE**

Founded: 1997
(amalgamation of Fleetwood F.C. and
Fleetwood Town who had disbanded at the
end of season 1995-96)
Colours: Red & white/black/red & white
Midweek Matchday: Tuesday

**Secretary:** Kevin Pennington, 1 Carlisle Avenue, Fleetwood, Lancs. FY7 8LP.
Tel: 01253 771602 (H); 01253 861687 (B)

**Ground:** Highbury Stadium, Park Avenue, Fleetwood, Lancs (01253 770702)

**Directions:** From M55, junction 3, follow signs (A585) to Fleetwood. At Nautical College campus (onleft) traffic island take first left, at second island take 6th exit. Stadium is 3/4 mile on left.

Floodlights: Yes

**PREVIOUS**    **Leagues:** None    **Names:** Fleetwood Wanderers (97-98)

**RECORD**    **Attendance:** 6,150 v Rochdale F.A.Cup 1st Round 65-66

**HONOURS**    NWCFL v 2 Champions: 98-99 Div 2 trophy Winners: 98-99

**CLUB PERSONNEL**

Chairman: J Betmead
31 St. Peters Place, Fleetwood, Lancs. FY7 6EB.
Tel: 01253 771550 (H); 0966 414750 (B)

# GLOSSOP NORTH END

**FACT FILE**

Founded: 1886 Re-formed 1992
Nickname: Hillmen
Sponsor: Davis Blank Furniss Solicitors
Colours: All royal Blue
Change colours: All gold.
Midweek Matches: Tuesday
Reserves' League: North Western Alliance
Programme: 32 pages, 40p
Editor: Mr P Heginbotham (0161 439 3932)

**Secretary:** Peter Hammond, 15 Longmoor Road, Simmondley, Glossop, Derbys SK139NH
Tel: 01457 863852(H) 01457 854411(B)

**Ground:** Surrey Street, Glossop, Derbys (01457 855469).

**Directions:** A57 (Manchester-Sheffield) to Glossop town centre, turn into Shrewsbury Street, follow to top of the hill, left at T-junction for ground.700 yds from Glossop (BR). Buses 236 & 237 from Manchester.

**Capacity:** 2,374    Seats: 209    Cover: 509    Floodlights: Yes

**Clubhouse:** Licensed bar. Hot & cold drinks and pies etc on matchdays.    **Club Shop:** Yes

**HONOURS**    NWC Lge Lamot Pils Tphy 90-91; Manchester Lg 27-28(Gilgryst Cup 22-23 29-30 34-35 74-75); FA Amateur Cup QF 08-09.

**PREVIOUS**    **Leagues:** Midland 1896-98; Football Lge 1898-1915; Manchester Lge 15-56 66-78; Lancs Combination 56-66; Cheshire County 78-82.
**Names:** Glossop North End 1886-1898; Glossop FC 1898-1992.

**BEST SEASON**    FA Cup:    FA Vase:
**RECORDS**    **Attendance:** 10,736 v Preston North End, FA Cup 1913/14
**Fee paid:** £3,000 for Andy Gorton (Lincoln City, 1989).
**Fee received:** £3,000 for Andy Gorton (Oldham Athletic, 1990).
Players progressing: Jimmy Rollands (Rochdale), Ray Redshaw (Wigan Athletic).

**CLUB PERSONNEL**

Chairman: J Dillon
President: C T Boak
Press Officer: Secretary
Manager: Ged Coyne
Asst Manager: Tommy Martin
Physio: TBA.

# GREAT HARWOOD TOWN

**FACT FILE**

Formed: 1965
Nickname: Robins
Club Sponsors: None
Colours: All red
Change colours: All blue
Midweek Matches: Monday
Reserves' league: West Lancs Lge
Programme: Pages: 20 Price: 20p
Editor: D Bennet

**Secretary:** Mark Jones, 15 Elm Close, Rishton,Blackburn, BB1 4HN Tel: 01254 876822(H)
**Ground:**    The Showground, Wood Street, Great Harwood, Lancs Tel: 01254 883913
**Directions:** M66 from Manchester to Haslingden exit, A680 through Baxenden, Accrington to Clayton-le-Moors, left at the Hyndburn Bridge Hotel into Hyndburn Road and right into Wood Street to ground. Or M6 jct 31,Clitheroe/Skipton road to Trafalgar Hotel, A677 to Blackburn, left at Moat House Hotel and follow ring-road to M65 junction, A678 to Rishton, left at lights (B6536) to Gt Harwood, right at Town Gate into Queen Str., follow signs for Lomax Square, left into Park Rd, right into Balfour Street to ground. 3miles from Rishton (BR), 6 miles from Blackburn (BR).
Various buses from Heyes Lane & Park Road to Blackburn & Accrington
**Capacity:** 2,500    Cover: 700    Seats: 200
**Clubhouse:** The Sportsman just outside ground. Normal licensing hours. Full bar facilities. Squash courts and gym. Hot & cold snacks & drinks on matchdays from tea bar in ground
**Club Shop:** Sells programmes, badges, key rings, shirts. Contact: J McKay (c/o club)

**HONOURS**    North West Counties League R-up 91-92 (Div 2 90-91, Lamot Pils Tphy 89-90 (R-up 90-91), Tennents Floodlit Trophy 91-92), Lancs ATS Challenge Trophy 91-92 (R-up 90-91)
**PREVIOUS Leagues:** West Lancashire; Lancs Comb. 79-82; N.W.C. 82-92; N.P.L. 92-99

**CLUB RECORDS**    **Attendance:** 5,397 v Manchester Utd, 1980.
**BEST SEASON**    **FA Cup:** 1st Qual. Round replay 92-93, 1-2 v Atherton LR (H), after 1-1
**FA Vase:** Quarter Finals 90-91, 1-2 v Littlehampton Town (A)

**CLUB PERSONNEL**

Chairman: William Holden
Press Officer: K Lambert
Commercial Manager: Mark Smith
Manager: M Crabbe
Asst Manager: Dave Sargent

ATHERTON L.R. - the first winners of the Goldline trophy.

**Kidsgrove Athletic** 'keeper, Scott Bentley, prepares to beat away this goal attempt from Ford United's Jeff Wood, in the FA Vase 4th Round.
Photo: Denis Nicholson.

NEWCASTLE TOWN L-R Back Row: Martin Smith (asst. man.), Paul Heath (youth coach), Neil Pesteridge, Rob Myatt, Dean Gillick, Chris Holmes, rob Wade, Darren Hughes, Harry Walshaw (physio), Ian Banks, Ray Walker (player manager). Front Row:John Brown, Peter Weston, Adrian Dunn, Dave Sutton, Barry Roden (shirt sponsor), Andy Holmes (capt.), John Burndred, Michael Bate, Anthony Buckle.

# KIDSGROVE ATHLETIC

**Secretary:** Christine Osmond, 451 New Inn Lane, Trentham, Stoke-on-Trent, ST48BN (01782 644241).

**Ground:** Clough Hall, Hollinswood Road, Kidsgrove, Stoke-on-Trent, Staffs (01782782412).
**Directions:** M6 Jct 16, A500 towards Stoke, 2nd jctn onto A34 towards Manchester, turn right at 1st lights into Cedar Ave., 2nd right into Lower Ash Rd, 3rd left into Hollinwood Rd to ground. B R Kidsgrove (5mins)
Capacity: 4,500   Seats: 250   Cover: 600   Floodlights: Yes

**Clubhouse:** Yes

### FACT FILE

Formed: 1952
Colours: Blue & white/blue/blue
Change Colours:
Midweek Matches: Tuesday

### CLUB PERSONNEL

Chairman: Leslie Wagg
President: Ernie Langford
Manager: Peter Ward
Coach: Jack Heath
Physio: Arthur Duckworth.

**HONOURS**     NWC Div. 1 97-97; NWC Chall. Cup 97-98; Mid Cheshire Lg 70-71 78-79 86-87 87-88, R-up 68-69 85-86; Lg Cup 67-68 69-70 85-86, R-up 84-85 86-87;  Staffs County Lge; Burslem & Tunstall Lge. Floodlit Trophy R-up: 1999

**PREVIOUS**     **Leagues:** Staffordshire County, Mid Cheshire Lge.

**BEST SEASON   FA Cup:**              **FA Vase:** Semi-Final 1997-98

**RECORDS**     **Attendance:** 1,903 FA Vase S-F 1998.

---

# LEEK C.S.O.B.

**Secretary:** Stan Lockett, 5 Fitzherbert Close, Swynnerton, Stone, Staffs ST150PQ,
                        Tel:  01782 796551,
**Ground:** Harrison Park, Macclesfield Road, Leek, Staffs, (01538 383734)
**Directions:** M6 south Junc 17, A534 to Congleton - follow signs for Leek (A54),carry on until junction with A523, turn right on to A523, this road is direct to Leek, ground is 8 miles, on right just into Leek.
Capacity: 3,600            Seating: 625            Covered Terracing: 2,675    Floodlights: Yes

### FACT FILE

Founded: 1945
Colours: Yellow/Black/Yellow
Change colours: White&Red, Red, White
Midweek Matchday: Wednesday
Programme: Yes
Editor: Stan Lockett
98-99 Captain: Steve Callear

### CLUB PERSONNEL

Chairman: K J Hill, 11 Springfield Drive, Leek, Staffs ST13 (01538 371859)
Manager: Chris McMullen
Assistant Manager: Andrew Walters
Physio: Noel Carroll

**HONOURS**     Refuge Midland Lge 95-96. Lge Cup 94-95 95-96; Leek Cup 94-95 95-96; Midland Ref Charity Shield 95-96; Sportsline Chall Cup 95-96.

**PREVIOUS**     **Leagues:** Leek & Moorland Lge, Staffs County North, Refuge Midland Lge.

**BEST SEASON   FA Cup:** 3rd Q 98-99

**RECORDS**     **Attendance:** 293 v Tamworth F.A.Cup 1998-99

---

# MAINE ROAD

**Secretary:** K Hunter, 157 Aston Ave., Fallowfield, Manchester M14 7HN (0161 226 9937)
**Ground:** Manchester County FA Ground, Brantingham Rd., Chorlton-cum-Hardy, Manchester
             M21 0TT (0161 861 0344)
**Directions:** M60 Jct 7, A56 towards City Centre, right onto A5145 Chorlton/Stockport, thro' lights, left at next lights into Wilbraham Rd(A6010) to Chorlton, thro' lights for approx 1 mile. Left into Withington Rd,first left into Brantingham Rd, ground 300 yds on left. 2 miles from Stretford (Metrolink (tram)), 3 miles from Piccadilly & Victoria , Virgin & First North Western trains.
Buses16 16A 85 87 87A 168 188  275. **Clubhouse:** Matchdays (Snacks on ground) **Shop:** No.
Capacity: 2,000            Seats: 200            Cover: 700            Floodlights: Yes.

### FACT FILE

Founded: 1955
Nickname: Blues
Sponsors: Surface Engineers
Colours: Bloe & Black stripes, Black, Black
Change Colours: Yellow, Green,Yellow
Midweek matchday: Tuesday
Reserves ' League: NW Co's Lge Res. Div.
Programme: 48 pages ,50p
Editor: Mr P,Ramsden (0161 448 1659)

### CLUB PERSONNEL

Chairman: R Meredith
President: F G Thompson
Press Officer: P Ramsden
Manager: G Whittingham
Asst Manager:Ossie Smith
Physio: E Jenkinson

HONOURS     Manc. Prem. Lg(4) 82-86, Cup 82-83 83-84;98-98 Man.Co Prem. Cup 87-8 Chal. Cup(4) 82-83 84-87; NW Co's Lg Div 2 89-90 (R-up 88-89).
PREVIOUS     **Leagues:** Rusholme Sunday 55-66; Manchester Amtr Sunday 66-72; Manchester 72-87              **Name:** City Supporters Rusholme
                        **Grounds:** Hough End PF 55-73; Ward Street O.B. 73-75; Tootal Spts Ground 75-79; Leesfield 79-80
BEST SEASON   **FA Cup:** 2nd Qual. 2nd replay 92-93   **FA Vase:** 4th Rd 94-95
RECORDS     **Attendance:** 875 v Altrincham, FA Cup 2nd Qual. Rd 29/9/90
             **Goalscorer:** John Wright 140      **Appearances:** Gordon Wood 455
             **Win:** 15-0 v Little Hulton 2/9/86   **Defeat:**0-7 v Newcastle Town

# MOSSLEY

**Secretary:**David Buckley, 18 Chellow Dene, Mossley,Ashton -under-Lyne, Lancs. OL5 0NB tel No: 01457 835989

**Ground:** Seel Park, Market Street, Mossley, Lancs. (Grd 01457 832369), (Club01457 836104)

**Directions:** From north; M62 Junc 20, A627M/A627 to Ashton-U-Lyne, A670 to Mossley- ground behind market place. From south; M6 Junc 19,A556, M56 to Junc 3, A5103 to M'chester, then Mancunian Way (A57M) to A635.Follow Ashton signs 5m, the Mossley signs via A670 to town centre. Rail:Mossley BR. Buses 153 from Manchester, 343 from Oldham, 350 from Ashton

Capacity: 4,500          Cover: 1,500          Seats: 200          Floodlights: Yes

**Clubhouse:** Open nights and matchdays          **Club Shop:** Yes

**HONOURS**          FA Trophy Runners-up 79-80; Northern Premier League 78-79 79-80 (R-up 80-81 81-82 82-83, Chall Cup 78-79; NWC Floodlit Trophy R-up 95-96 NWTL Div 1 R-up 98-99

**BEST SEASON**     **FA Cup:** 2nd Rd replay 49-50, also 2nd Rd 80-81 & 1st Rd 6 times.
                    **FA Trophy:** Runners-up 79-80          **FA Vase:** 6th Rd 96-97

**PREVIOUS**          **Leagues:** Ashton; South East Lancs; Lancs Comb. 18-19; Cheshire County 19-72; Northen Prem.   **Names:** Park Villa 03-04; Mossley Juniors 04-09.

**RECORDS**          **Attendance:** 7,000 v Stalybridge, 1950          **Fee Paid:** £2,300
                    **Fee Received:** £25,000 for Eamon O'Keefe (Everton, 1979)

### FACT FILE

Formed: 1903
Nickname: Lilywhites
Colours: White/black/black
Change colours: Yellow/green/green
Midweek matchday: Tuesday
Programme: 28 Pages £1.0
Editor: John A Cawthorne
98-99- Captain: jimmy Birch
Top scorer: Ian Barker
P.o.Y.: Paul Taylor
Local Press : Oldham Evening Chronicle,
Saddleworth & Mossley Reporter
Local Radio: Radio Manchester, Piccadilly

### CLUB PERSONNEL

Chairman: S Rigby
President: J Wharmby
Manager: Benny Phillips

# NANTWICH TOWN

**Secretary:** Alan Thompson, 7Sandown Road, Crewe CW1 3TE Tel/Fax: 01270256588

**Ground:** Jackson Avenue, off London Road, Nantwich, Cheshire.   Tel: 01270 624098

**Directions:** M6 Jct 16, A500 for Nantwich (about 8 miles), continue on A52 over railway crossing (London Rd), second right after railway crossing into Jackson Ave. From Chester, A51. Threee miles from Crewe (BR).

Capacity: 1,500          Seats: 150          Cover: 555          Floodlights: Yes

**Clubhouse:** Every night except Sunday 8pm-11pm. Hot pies available          **Club Shop:** Yes

**HONOURS**          Cheshire Co. Lg 80-81; Ches. Snr Cup 75-76; N.W. Co.Lg.Cup 94-95

**PREVIOUS**          **Leagues:** Shropshire & Dist.; The Combination 1892-94; Lancs Comb. 12-15; Cheshire Combination 19-38; Manchester; Mid-Cheshire; Cheshire County 68-82.          **Name:** Nantwich FC (pre 1973)

**BEST SEASON** **FA Cup:**          **FA Vase:**

**RECORDS**          **Attendance:** 2,750 v Altrincham, Cheshire Senior Cup 66-67
                    **Fee received:** £4,000 from Stafford Rangers for D.Dawson
                    **Record Goalscorer in Season:** Gerry Duffy, 42 in 61-62

### FACT FILE

Founded: 1884
Nickname: Dabbers
Club Sponsors: Jim Barrie Plant Hire
Colours: Black & white/black/black
Change colours: All green
Midweek matchday: Thursday
Reserves' League:Springbank Midland
Programme: 18 pages, 65
Editor: Che Kerrin (01270 624098)

### CLUB PERSONNEL

Chairman: R Tilley
Vice Chairman: Peter Palmer
President: T.B.A.
Manager: Paul Cuddy
Asst Manager:T.B.A.
Physio: Ivan Robertson

# NEWCASTLE TOWN

**Secretary:** John F Cotton, 293 Weston Rd., Weston Coyney, Stoke-on-Trent, Staffs. St3 6HA Tel: 01782 333445

**Ground:** Lyme Valley Parkway Stadium, Lilleshall Rd, Clayton, Newcastle-under-Lyne, Staffs (01782 662351) (Club 01782 662350)

**Directions:** M6 jct 15, A500 for Stoke, left at r'bout A519 for Newcastle, rightat 2nd r'bout into Stafford Ave., 1st left into Tittensor Road to ground. 3miles from Stoke-on-Trent (BR).

Seats: 300          Cover: 1,000          Capacity: 4,000     Floodlights: Yes     **Club Shop:** Yes

**Clubhouse:** Saturday matchdays 12-7.30pm, midweek 5-11pm. Hot & cold food available.

**HONOURS:** Nth West Co's Lg Div 1 R-up 95-96 96-97, Div 2 R-up 91-92, Challenge Cup 96-97, F/Lit Trophy R-up 96-97; Lamot Pils Tphy 91-92; Mid Cheshire Lg Div1 85-86, R-up 86-78, Div 2 82-83, 90-91, Lge Cup 84-85; Walsall Snr Cup 93-94 94-95 R-up 95-96; Sentinel Cup 94-95; Tennents Floodlit Trophy 92-93 95-96; Staffs Snr Cup R-up 95-96; Staffs M/W F/Light Lge 94-95 R-up 95-96; Umbro Over 35 Chall Cup 94-95.

**RECORDS - Attendance:** 3,948 v Notts County FA Cup Nov 96   **Win:** 8-1 v Holker Old Boys

**Defeat:** 0-5 v Eastwood Hanley (A)   **Appearances:** Neil Pesteridge 275 (NWCL only)

**Goalscorer:** Shaun Wade 105 (NWCL only)

**PREVIOUS - Leagues:** Hanley & Dist. Sunday; North Staffs Sunday; Potteries & Dist.Sunday; Res Refuge Ass Mid; Newcastle & Dist/ Staffs Co.; Mid Cheshire.   **Names:** Parkway Hanley (founded 1964, later Clayton Park, ParkwayClayton); Newcastle Town (founded 1980) - clubs merged in 1986.

### FACT FILE

Founded: 1964
Nickname: Castle.
Club Sponsors: A.N.C.Ltd
Colours: All Royal with red & white trim
Change colours: All yellow
Midweek Matches: Tuesday
Reserve Team: Burslem & Newcastle Dist Lge
Programme: 40 pages, 50p
Editor: Peter Tindall (01260 28093)

### CLUB PERSONNEL

Chairman: J W Walker
Vice-Chairman: K G Walshaw
President: K H Walshaw.
Press Officer: Ray Tatton (01782 644916)
Player/Manager: Ray Walker
Asst Manager: Martin Smith
Physio: Lee Arnold

Lee Wilkinson of Mossley being closely watched by John Dilkes of Holker O.B.

Photo: Colin Stevens

NANTWICH TOWN 1998-99

Photo: Keith Clayton

Goalmouth action as Ramsbottom United (dark shirts) attack the Workington goal during their league match in March.

Photo: Alan Watson

# PRESCOT CABLES

**Secretary:** John Tasker, 15 Cremorne Hey, Liverpool L28 7RA (Tel No: 0151 480 0950)

**Ground:** Valerie Park, Hope Street, Prescot. L34 6HD (Tel No: 0151 430 0507)
**Ground:Directions:** M62 Jct 7. A57 to Prescot. Take 2nd exit at roundabout after two and a half miles. Turn right after another 1/2 mile. Right at Hope & Anchor pub, into Hope Street..
Capacity: 4,400          Seats: 200          Cover: 550          Floodlights: Yes

**Clubhouse:** Refreshment bar, open matchdays/evenings for hot & cold refreshments
**Club Shop:** No but metal badges available.

| | |
|---|---|
| **HONOURS** | Lancs Comb. 56-57 (Lg Cup 47-48); Ches. Lg Div 2 76-77; Mid Ches. Lg 76-77; L'pool Non-League Cup(4) 51-53 58-59 60-61; L'pool Chal. Cup(5) 28-30 48-4961-62 77-78; George Mahon Cup 36-37. |
| **PREVIOUS** | **Leagues:** Liverpool Co. Comb.; Lancs Comb. 1897-98 18-20 27-33 36-67; Ches. Co. 33-36 78-82; Mid Cheshire 67-78.<br>**Names:** Prescot Athletic; Prescot Cables 46-65 80-90; Prescot Town 65-80. |
| **BEST SEASON** | **FA Cup:** 2nd Rd 57-58 59-60          **FA Vase:** 2nd Rd 1998-99 |
| **RECORDS** | **Attendance:** 8,122 v Ashton National, 1932 |

### FACT FILE

Founded: 1886
Nickname: Tigers
Colours: Gold/black/black
Change colours: Blue/blue/gold
Midweek Matches: Wednesday
Programme: 30 pages,70p
Editor: J.Pilnick

### CLUB PERSONNEL

President: Mr B F Taylor
Chairman: Ted Mercer
Vice Chairman: G.Hayward
Commercial Manager: Arthur McCumiskey
Manager: Arthur McCumiskey
Asst Manager: Derek Hughes

---

# RAMSBOTTOM UNITED

**Secretary:** John Maher, 75 Ramsbottom Road, Hawkshaw, Bury BL8 4JS. Tel: 01204852742

**Ground:** Riverside Ground, Acre Bottom, Ramsbottom. Tel: 01706 822799(Cricket Club)
          Answe Phone: 01204 852742 (for match details)
**Directions:** M6r (North) to junction 1, take A56 towards Ramsbottom. After one mile turn left into Bury New Road. Turn left after the Danisco Paper Mill along the road running parallel with the East Lancs Railway.
**Floodlights:** Yes

| | |
|---|---|
| **HONOURS:** | Bolton Comb. Div. One Champs 72-73; Bolton Comb. Prem Div. 76-77, 86-87; Manchester Lge Div. One Champs 90-91; Manchester Lge Div. 1 Cup Winners 90-91; Gilgryst Cup Winners 94-95; NWCFL Div 2 Champ 96-97, Trophy 95-96 |
| **RECORDS** | **Attendance:** 829 v Southport F.A.C. 3Q 98-99 NWCFL Div 2 29/3/97 |
| **PREVIOUS** | **Leagues:** Bury Amateur League, Bolton Combination, Manchester Lge. |
| **BEST SEASON:** | **F.A.Cup:** 3rd Q 1998-99          **F.A.Vase:** 2nd Round 98-99 |

### FACT FILE

Formed: 1966
Colours: Blue with white trim/blue/white
Midweek Matchday: Tuesday

### CLUB PERSONNEL

Chairman: H Williams (01706 822799)

---

# ROSSENDALE UNITED

**Secretary:** Wendy Ennis, 4 Brow Edge, Newchurch, Rossendale, Lancs BB4 7TT(01706 212634)

**Ground:** Dark Lane, Staghills Rd, Newchurch, Rossendale, Lancs BB4 7UA
          Tel: 01706 215119 (Ground);  01706 213296 (Club)
**Directions:** M66 Junc 18, M66 north following signs for Burnley, then A682 to Rawstenstall, take 2nd exit sign Burnley A682, at 1st lights turn right into Newchurch Rd, 1.5 miles turn right into Staghills Rd, grd 800 yards right
Capacity: 2,500          Cover: Yes          Seats: 500          Floodlights: Yes
**Clubhouse:** Evenings & matchdays. Hot snacks. Snooker room, Pool, darts, satellite TV, concert room

| | |
|---|---|
| **HONOURS** | NWC Lg Div 1 88-89 (R-up 87-88 93-94), Div 2 R-up 85-86, Chall Cup 93-94 |
| **PREVIOUS** | **Leagues:** N.E. Lancs Comb.; Lancs Comb. 1898-99 1901-70; Central Lancs 1899-1901; Cheshire County 70-82; NWC 82-89; NPL 89-93. |
| **BEST SEASON** | **FA Cup:** 2nd Rd 71-72, 1-4 v Bolton W. at Bury FC. Also 1st Rd 75-76<br>**FA Trophy :** 2nd Rd 81-82          **FA Vase:** 5th Rd  86-87,88-89 |
| **RECORDS** | **Attendance:** 12,000 v Bolton Wanderers FA Cup 2nd Rd 71<br>**Appearances:** Johnny Clarke 770, 1947-65 **Goalscorer:** Bob Scott<br>**Fee Paid:** £3,000 for Jimmy Clarke (Buxton, 1992)<br>**Fee Received:** £1,500 for Dave O'Neill (Huddersfield Town, 1974)<br>**Win:** 17-0v Ashton Town, Lancs Comb.1911-12<br>**Defeat:** 0-14 v Morecambe, Lancs Comb. 67-68 |

### FACT FILE

Founded: 1898
Nickname: The Stags
Sponsors: Hurstwood Developments
Colours: Blue & white stripes/blue/blue
Change cols: White stroipes/red/red
Midweek matchday: Tuesday
Reserves ' League: First N.W.Reserve
Programme: 28 pages-£1.00
Editor: David Hawarth
Local Radio: Red Rose, Radio Lancashire.
Local Press : Lancs Evening Telegraph,
Rossendale Herald &Post, Rossendale Mail.

### CLUB PERSONNEL

Chairman: A Connelly
Vice-Chairman: Lee Brierley
President: David White
Manager: Mickey Graham
Coach: John HughesPhysio: Syd Parkinson
Capt: Simon O'Brien P.o.Y. & Top Scorer:
Craig Sargesson(22 goals)

# ST HELENS TOWN

**Secretary:** W J Noctor, 95 Sutton Park Drive, Marshalls Cross, St Helens WA9 3TR
Tel: 01744 816182

**Ground:** Hoghton Road, Sutton, St Helens, Merseyside.
Tel: 01744 817225 (Ground), 01744 812721(Club). **Directions:** M62 Jct 7, take 4th exit (St Helens Linkway), exit Linkway at 3rd r/about (Sherdley) follow signs for Sutton, continue to Sutton Village, Ground just beyond St Helens Junc station 150 yards
**Capacity:** 4,400        **Seats:** 200        **Cover:** 550        **Floodlights:** Yes

**Clubhouse:** Weekdays 8-11pm, Saturday matchdays 2-6.30pm. **Club Shop:** Yes

**HONOURS**        FA Vase 86-87; George Mahon Cup 49-50; Lancs Comb. 71-72, Div 2 50-51, Lg Cup R-up 70-71;Liverpool Snr Non Lge Cup R-up 76-77; Lancs Jnr Cup R-up 66-67; Bass Charrington Cup 73-74; Carling Chall Cup r-up 93-94; N.W.C. Floodlit Trophy r-up 97-98.

**PREVIOUS**        **Leagues:** Lancs Comb. 03-14 49-75; Liverpool County Comb. 49-74; Cheshire County 74-82.        **Grounds:** Park Road 01-52; City Road 52-53.

**BEST SEASON**    **FA Cup:**   4th Q Rd 85-86        **FA Vase:** Winners 86-87

**RECORDS**        **Gate:** 4,000 v Manchester City, Bert Trautmann transfer match,April 1950.
**Goalscorer:** S Pennington    **W in:** 10-4 v Everton `B' 1952
**Appearances:** Alan Wellens    **Defeat** : 1-8 v Liverpool Res., L'pool Snr Cup 1950

### FACT FILE

Founded: 1946
Nickname: `Town'
Colours: Blue & white/white/blue
Change colours: All yellow
Midweek Matches: Wednesday
Reserve League:
Programme: 24 pages, 50p
Editor: John McKiernan (01744 600612)
Local Press: Reporter, Star, Leader, Echo.

### CLUB PERSONNEL

President: J Jones
Chairman/Press Officer: J Barrett
Manager: James McBride
Asst Manager: G Walker
Coach: John Neary

---

# SALFORD CITY

**Secretary:** Bill Taylor , 23 Westwood Drive, Pendlebury, Salford M27 4JJ

**Ground:** Moor Lane, Kersal, Salford, Manchester. Tel: 0161 792 6287

**Directions:** M62 jct 17, A56 Bury New Road to Manchester, continue thro' 4 sets of lights, right into Moor Lane, ground 500 yds left. 4 miles from Manchester Victoria (BR). Buses 96, 139, 94, 95 to Moor Lane
**Capacity:** 8,000        **Seats:** 260        **Cover:** 600        **Floodlights:** Yes

**Clubhouse:** Open matchdays only. Hot snacks

**HONOURS**        Lancashire Amateur Cup 72-73 74-75 76-77; Manchester Senior Cup, Manchester Challenge Cup, Manchester Lg 74-75 75-76 76-77 78-79.

**PREVIOUS**        **Leagues:** Manchester 63-80; Cheshire Co. 80-82.
**Names:** Salford Central 40-63; Salford Amateurs 1963 until merger with Anson Villa; Salford FC.
**Ground:** Crescent, Salford

**BEST SEASON**    **FA Cup:**        **FA Vase:**

**RECORDS**        **Attendance:** 3,000 v Whickham FA Vase 1981

### FACT FILE

Founded: 1940
Nickname: Ammies
Colours: Tangerine/white/white
Change colours: Blue & white stripes/blue/blue
Midweek Matches: Tuesday
Reserves' League: NWC Res. Div. S.
Programme: 24 pages, 50p
Editor: Scott White

### CLUB PERSONNEL

Chairman: D.Taylor
Managers: Tom Foster & Matt Wardrop
Press Officer: Scott White
Commercial Manager: Stevie Plant

Mick Gilmore powers in a header for St. Helens Town's fourth goal against Ramsbottom united.        Photo: Malcolm Thacker

# SKELMERSDALE UUNITED

**Secretary:** Arthur Gore, 7 Hilltop Walk, Ormskirk, Lancs L39 4TH    Tel: 01695 575643

**Ground:** White Moss Park, White Moss Road, Skelmersdale, Lancs    Tel: 01695 722123

**Directions:** M58 Jct 3, at 2nd r'bout take 3rd exit towards Skelmersdale,continue for approx 1 mile, ground on the right. 4 miles from Ormskirk (BR)

**Capacity:** 10,000          **Seats:** 250          **Cover:** 1,000          **Floodlights:** Yes

**Clubhouse:** None. Matchday food bar sells hot drinks, soup, pies & pasties etc **Club Shop:** No

**HONOURS**    FA Amateur Cup 70-71 R-up 66-67; Ches. Co. Lg 68-69 69-70, Jubilee Cup 69-70; Lancs F'lit Cup 69-70; Lancs Jnr Cup 69-70 70-71; Ashworth Cup 70-71; Barassi Anglo-Italian Cup 70-71; Lancs Non-Lge Cup 73-74 74-75; North West Co's Lg Cup R-up 82-83.N.W.Co Div 2 R-Up: 97-98

**PREVIOUS**    **Leagues:** Liverpool County Comb., Lancashire Comb. 1891-93, 03-07, 21-24 55-68, 76-78, Cheshire County 68-71 78-82, Northern Premier 71-76.

**BEST SEASON**    **FA Cup:** 1st Rd 67-68, 0-2 v Scunthorpe(A), 68-69, 0-2 v Chesterfield(A), 71-72, 0-4 v Tranmere R. (A)          **FA Amateur Cup:** Winners 70-71

**RECORDS**    **Attendance:** 7,000 v Slough, FA Amat Cup Q-F '67

### FACT FILE

Founded: 1882
Nickname: Skem
Sponsors:Matalan
Colours: Blue & white/blue/blue
Change colours: Red & white/red/red
Midweek Matches: Thursday
Programme: 20 pages, 50p
Editor: Team effort

### CLUB PERSONNEL

Chairman: D Tomlinson
Vice Chairman: T Garner
Press Officer: Secretary
Manager: Russ Perkins
Asst Manager: Alan Kershaw
Physio: Billy Leigh

# VAUXHALL G.M.

**Secretary:** Mrs carole Paisey, 26 South Rd., West Kirby, Wirral CH48 3HQ (Tel:0151 625 6936)

**Ground:** Vauxhall Sports Ground, Rivacre Road, Hooton, Ellesmere Port, South Wirrall. Tel:  0151 327 1114 (Ground)  0151 327 2115 (Club)

**Directions:** M53 junction 5, take A41 to Chester. At the first set of lights turn left into Hooton Green. Left at T-junction, right at next T-junction into Rivacre Rd, ground is 250 yards on right. Floodlights: Yes

**HONOURS**    N.W.C. Lge. 2nd Div Champ 88-89 95-96; Raab Karcher Chall Cup 90-91.

**PREVIOUS**    **Leagues:** North West Counties League, West Cheshire League (to 1995)

**BEST SEASON**    **FA Cup:**          **FA Vase:** 5th Rd 98-99 v Thame U (A) 0-1 aet

**RECORDS**    **Attendance:** 1,500 v English F.A. XI, 1987

### FACT FILE

Formed: 1987
Re-formed 1995
Club Sponsors: James Edwards
Colours: All White
Midweek Matchday: Tuesday

### CLUB PERSONNEL

Chairman: Tony Woodley
Vice Chairman: Len Jones
Treasurer:Steven McInerney
N.W.Trains League Administrator:Ken Triggs
13 Brentwood St., Wallasey, Wirral.
Ch48 3HQ
Tel: 0151 638 4106 (H)
0191 355 2632 (B)

VAUXHALL G.M. 1998-99

Photo: Andrew Chitty

# ALSAGER

**Secretary:** Steve Whittaker, 2 Lea Close, Sandbach, Cheshire
Tel: 01270 753654 (H) 01477 532116 (B)

**Ground:** The Town Ground, Wood park, Alsager. Tel: 01270 872917

**Directions:** M6, Junction 16, A500 towards Stoke. Leave A500 at 2nd exit (A34 to Congleton),
at 2nd set of lights turn left for Alsager. Turn right opposite Caradon/Twyfords
(500 yds), into Moorhouse Ave., Woodlaid Court 1/2 mile on right.
Nearest Railway station: Alsager
Floodlights: No

**HONOURS** Jt R-up Mid Cheshire div. 2, R-up Springbank Vending Lge.

**PREVIOUS** **Leagues:** Mid Cheshire Div. 2; Springbank Vending Lge.

**RECORD** **Attendance:** 50

### FACT FILE
Founded: 1968
Colours: Black & white/black/black
Change colours: Yellow & sky blue/yellow/yellow
Midweek Matches: Monday

### CLUB PERSONNEL
Chairman: A Smart
Tel: 01270 872917 (H)
1st Team Sec.: Pauline Matthews
Tel: 01782 834296 (H)

---

# ASHTON TOWN

**Secretary:** Stephen Speakman, 7 Birchfield Avenue, Atherton, M46 0HR
Tel: 01942 793250 (H&W)

**Ground:** Edge Green Street, Ashton-in-Makerfield, Wigan WN4 8SY (01942 510677)
**Directions:** M6 Jct 23, A49 to Ashton-in-M. Right at lights onto A58 towards Bolton.
After 3/4 mile turn right at `Rams Head' P.H. into Golbourne Rd. After 200
yds right into Edge Green Str. Ground at end.
Floodlights: No

**HONOURS** Warrington Lg Guardian Cup.

**PREVIOUS** **Leagues:** Warrington, Lancs Comb. 03-11 71-78, Ches. Co. 78-82.

**BEST SEASON** **FA Vase:** Prelim. Rd 84-85

**RECORD** **Gate:** 600 v Accrington Stanley 76-77

### FACT FILE
Founded: 1962
Colours: Red with white trim/red/red
Change colours: All sky blue
Midweek Matches: Tuesday

### CLUB PERSONNEL
President: W Pomfrett
Chairman:J.L.Riley
Manager: Norman Hickson

---

# BACUP BOROUGH

**Secretary:** Frank Manning, 38 Acre Avenue, Stacksteads, Bacup OL13 0HN
Tel: 01706 877460 (H)

**Ground:** West View, Cowtoot Lane, Blackthorn, Bacup, Lancashire (01706 878655).
**Directions:** From M62, M66 onto A681 through Rawtenstall to Bacup centre, leftonto A671
towards Burnley, after approx 300 yds right (immed. before the IrwellInn) climbing Cooper
street, right into Blackthorn Lane then first left intoCowtoot Lane to ground.
**Capacity:** 3,000    **Seats:** 500    **Cover:** 1,000    **Floodlights:** Yes
**Clubhouse:** Open matchdays and private functions (for which buffets can beprovided). Pies
and sandwiches on matchdays.    **Club Shop:** Not yet
**HONOURS** Lancs Jnr Cup 10-11 (R-up 22-23 74-75); Lancs Comb. 46-47 (Lg Cup R-
up46-47 80-81; NW Co's Lg Div 2 R-up 89-90.
**PREVIOUS** **League:** Lancs Comb. 03-82Name: Bacup FC.Grounds: None
**BEST SEASON** **FA Cup:** **FA Vase:**
**RECORD** **Gate:** 4,980 v Nelson 1947    **Scorer:** Jimmy Clarke

### FACT FILE
Founded: 1875
Nickname: The Boro
Club Sponsors:B&EBoys Ltd
Colours:White with black trim,black,black
Change colours:Yellow,Blue,Blue
Midweek Matches: Tuesday.
Programme: 22Pages 50p
Editor: D Whatmough (0706 875041)
### CLUB PERSONNEL
President: W.Shufflebottom
Chairman: H.Connolly
Vice Chairman: D.Whatmough
Manager: Brent Peters
Assistant Manager: Simon Holding

---

# BLACKPOOL MECHANICS

**Secretary:** William Singleton, c/o Club. Tel: 01253 313444(H) 01253 761721(B)
**Ground:** Jepson Way, Common Edge Rd, Blackpool, Lancs FY4 5DY (01253 761721).
**Directions:** M6 to M55, follow Airport signs. Left at r'bout along A583 (Preston New Rd) to
lights, right into Whitehill Rd, becomes School Rd, to lights.Straight over main road & follow
signs for Blackpool Mechanics F.C. to ground.Rail to Blackpool North - then bus 11c from Talbot
Rd bus station (next to rail station) to Shovels Hotel, Common Edge Rd.
**Capacity:** 2,000    **Seats:** 250    **Cover:** 1,700    **Floodlights:** Yes
**Clubhouse:** Match days, training nights. Dancehall. Matchday, hot food.
**Club Shop:** Manager Andrew Sneddon (01253 729962). Ties, sweaters, old programmes, badges.
**HONOURS** Lancs Comb Bridge Shield 72-73; NW Co's. Lg Div 3 85-86; W Lancs Lg 60-
61 62-63; Lancs County FA Shield 57-58 60-61:
**PREVIOUS** **Leagues:** Blackpool & Fylde Comb., West Lancs, Lancs Comb. 62-68.
**BEST SEASON** **FA Cup:**    **FA Vase:**
**RECORD** **Gate:** 1,200 v Morecambe, Lancs Comb, August 1968

### FACT FILE
Founded: 1947    Nickname: Mechs
Sponsors: Yates Wine Lodge, Blackpool.
Club colours: Tangerine/white/tangerine
Change colours: All blue
Midweek matchday: Tuesday
Programme: 10 pages, 50p
Editor: John Barlow

### CLUB PERSONNEL
Chairman: Henry Baldwin
Vice Chairman: John Sanderson
President: Gregory Gregorio
Commercial Manager: John Sanderson
Manager: Dave Rump
Asst Man.: Gary Collings
Coach: William Singleton.

# CASTLETON GABRIELS

**Secretary:** David Lord, 34 Fairway, Castleton, Rochdale OL11 3BU    Tel: 01706 522719
**Ground:** Butterworth Park, Chadwick Lane, off Heywood Rd., Castleton, Rochdale. Tel: 01706 527103)    **Directions:** M62 Jct 20, A6272M to r'bout. Left towards Castleton (A664Edinburgh Way) to next r'bout, keeping Tesco Superstore to the left, take 1st exit to next r'bout, take 2nd exit into Manchester Rd (A664), after just under mile turn right at `Top House' P.H. into Heywood Rd., to end & ground on right
Capacity: 1,500         Seats: 250         Cover: 500         Floodlights: Yes
**Clubhouse:** Open seven nights a night and all day Saturday. Pie & peas and sandwiches available matchdays (pie & peas only at Reserve matches)    **Club Shop:** No
**HONOURS**        Manchester Lge 86-87, Murray Shield 86-87; Res Div Cup 95-96.
**PREVIOUS**        **Leagues:** Rochdale Alliance 24-84; Manchester 84-89.
                    **Name:** St Gabriels (pre-1960s)  **Ground:** Park pitches; Springfield Pk 60-81.
**RECORDS**         **Gate:** 640 v Rochdale, pre-season friendly 1991  **Win:** 8-0 v Squires Gate
                    N.W.Co.Div 2 94    **Defeat:** 1-10 v Blackpool Mechanics N.W.Co.Div 2 95

### FACT FILE
Founded: 1924        Nickname: Gabs
Club Sponsors: Dale Mill
Colours: Royal/black/black
Change colours: Red/white/red
Midweek matchday: Tuesday
Reserves ' League: N.W.C. Res. Div.
Programme: 28 pages, 50p
Editor: Peter Wilson (01616 249602)

### CLUB PERSONNEL
Chairman: T E Butterworth
Vice Chairman: R Butterworth
Press Officer: Peter Wilson (01616 249602)
Manager/Coach: Peter Freakes
Assistant Manager: Dave Jones
Coach: Neil Mills

---

# CHADDERTON

**Secretary:** Ronald Manton,77 Denton Lane, Chadderton, Oldham OL9 8AC
**Ground:** Andrew Street, Chadderton, Oldham, Lancs (0161 624 9733)
**Directions:** M62 Jct 20, A627(M) to Oldham. M'way becomes dual carriageway. Left at 1st major traffic lights A669 Middleton Rd, then first left into Butterworth Street. Andrew Street is second right. Oldham Werneth (BR) 1 m. Buses 458 & 459 (Oldham-Manchester) stop at the Harlequin
Capacity: 2,500        Seats: 200        Cover: 600        Floodlights: Yes
**Clubhouse:** Matchdays only. Hot & cold snack during & after games        **Club Shop:** No
**HONOURS** Manchester Amat Lg 62-63, North Div 55-56, Manchester Prem Cup R-up 82-83, Challenge Tphy 71-72, R-up 72-73, Manchester Lg Div 1 66-67, Div 2 64-65, Gilgryst Cup 69-70, Murray Shield 65-66, Lancs Comb. Cup R-up 81-82, Alfred Pettit & Hulme Celtic Cup 61-62, NWC F/lit Tphy R-up 92-93
**PREVIOUS  Leagues:** Oldham Amat., Manchester Amat., Manchester 64-80, Lancs Comb. 80-82
**RECORD Gate:** 1,500 v Guinness Ex'ts 1969 **Appearances:** Billy Elwell 750+ (64-90)
Players progressing: (include) David Platt (Crewe), John Pemberton (Crewe)

### FACT FILE
Founded: 1947        Nickname: Chaddy
Sponsors: Royton Metals,
Nationwide Building Society and Asda
Colours: All red
Change colours: All Yellow
Midweek Matches: Tuesday
Reserves' Lge: NWC Res. Div.
Programme: 28-32 pages  Editor: David Greaves
**98-99 Top Scorer:** David Kershaw
**Captain:** Tony Lucas **P.o.Y:** Steve Patterson
### CLUB PERSONNEL
Chairman: Harry Muall
President: Derek Glynn
Press Officer: John Fitton
Manager:Martin Farrell & Glynn Mellor
Asst Man.: Paul Dixon

---

# COLNE F C

**Secretary:** Jean Moore, 5 Haverholt Close, Colne, BB8 9SN        Tel: 01282 868857

**Ground:** Holt House Stadium, Holt House, Colne. (Tel: 01282 862545)
**Directions:** Enter Colne from M65 to roundabout, keep left follow signs for Keighley. At next roundabout turn left, continue on Harrison Drive over mini roundabout & follow road to ground. Nearest Railway station - Colne.
Capacity: 1,800         Seats: 100         Cover: 1000         Floodlights: Yes

**Clubhouse:**Yes,Small Lounge Bar open on matchdays        **Club Shop:** No
**HONOURS**        BEP Cup Winners 96-97
**BEST SEASON**    **FA Cup:**          **FA Vase:**
**RECORDS**        **Attendance:**150v Nelson 97-98
                   **Scorer:** Geoff Payton    **Appearances:** Nick Roscoe
**PREVIOUS**       **Leagues:** East Lancashire League

### FACT FILE
Formed: 1996
Colours: All red
Change colours: All yellow
Midweek Matchday: Thursday
Programme: Yes    Editor: Ray Moore
98-99 Captain: Gary Dalton
98-99 P.o.Y.: Steve Gavin
98-99 Top Scorer: Steve Gavin

### CLUB PERSONNEL
Chairman: D Blacklock (01282 696340)
Press Officer: Ray Moore(01282  868857)
Manager:Denzil Hart

---

# CURZON ASHTON

**Secretary:** Graham Shuttleworth, 42 Southgate Road, Chadderton, Oldham, OL9 9PT.
            Tel: 0161 682 1137 (H)0161 438 2416 (W)
**Ground:** National Park, Katherine Street, Ashton-under-Lyne OL7 6DA (0161 3306033)
**Directions:** Behind Ashton police station off Manchester Rd (A635),Ashton-under-Lyne, one and a half miles from Ashton-under-Lyne (BR)
Capacity: 5,000         Cover: 450         Seats: 350         Floodlights: Yes
**Clubhouse:** Every night. Food on matchdays. **Club Shop:** Contact Roy Howe, 0161 220 8345
**PREVIOUS**        **Leagues:** Manchester Amat.; Manchester (-1978); Cheshire Co. 78-82;
                    N.W.C. 82-87, Northern Prem. Lge. 87-97, N.C.E. 97-98, N.W.C. 98-.
**BEST SEASON**     **FA Cup:** 3rd Qual. Rd replay 89-90, 1-3 v Mossley (A) after 1-1
                    **FA Vase:** Semi-Final 79-80 **FA Trophy:** 2nd Qual. Rd 82-83, 84-85.
**HONOURS**         Cheshire Co. Lge Div 2 R-up 78-79: Manchester Lge 77-78, R-up 74-75 75-
                    76; Lge Cup 77-78, R-up 74-75 75-76; Murray Shield R-up 75-76:
                    Manchester Amat. Lge 63-64 65-66, R-up 64-65: Manchester Prem. Cup  x 5:
**RECORD**          **Attendance:** 1,826 v Stamford, FA Vase SF 1980

### FACT FILE
Formed: 1963
Nickname: Curzon
Colours: Royal Blue/white/white
Change colours: Yellow/green/yellow
Midweek matches: Tuesday
Programme: 16pages 50p
Editor: Robert Hurst (0161 775 3883)

### CLUB PERSONNEL
Chairman: Harry Galloway
Chief Executive: Harry Twamley
President: Peter Mayo
Manager: Dave Denby
Physio: Malcolm Liptrot
Press Officer: Barry Thorpe

DAISY HILL

Dowe scores from the spot in the derby match at Nelson.

TETLEY WALKER  (L-R)  Back Row: Bobby Fitzpatrick, Lee Webster, Neil Maher, Gary Swann, Steve Hunt, Tony Plant, Rob Preidt, Justin Farrelly.  Front Row: Paul Adawee, Paul Gwyther, John Sanson, Kevin dack, Karl Jones, Lee Holden.        Photo: Garry Clarke

# DAISY HILL

**Secretary:** Bob Naylor, 8 Bailey Fold, Westhoughton, Bolton, Lancs BL5 3HH(01942 813720)
**Ground:** New Sirs, St James Street, Westhoughton, Bolton, Lancs (01942 818544)
**Directions:** M61 Jct 5, A58 (Snydale Way/Park Road) for 1.5 miles, left into Leigh Road (B5235) for 1 mile, right into village then left between Church and School into St James Street. Ground 250 yds on the left. Half mile from Daisy Hill (BR)

| Capacity: 2,000 | Seats: 200 | Cover: 250 | Floodlights: No | Club Shop: No |
|---|---|---|---|---|

**Clubhouse:** Open normal licensing hours during any football activity. Snacks on matchdays
**HONOURS** Bolton Comb Prem Div 62-63 72-73 75-76 77-78, Lg Cup 59-60 61-62 71-72 72-73; Lancs Shield 61-62 71-72 86-87:
**PREVIOUS** **Leagues:** Westhoughton; Bolton Comb.; Lancs Combination. 78-82.
**Name:** Westhoughton Town **Record Goals & Apps:**Alan Roscoe 300-450
**BEST SEASON** FA Cup: FA Vase:
**RECORD** **Attendance:** 2,000 v Horwich RMI, Westhoughton Charity Cup final May
**PLAYERS PROGRESSING:** Barry Butler (Chester C ) + Phil Priestley(Rochdale)via AthertonLR

### FACT FILE
Founded: 1894
Reformed: 1952
Colours: All royal blue
Change:All amber
Midweek Matches: Tuesday
Reserves' Lge CNWL Res Div
Programme: 38 pages 50p
Editor: Committee

### CLUB PERSONNEL
Chairman: Tony Veitch
Manager: John Hulton
Asst Mgr: Tony Riley

---

# DARWEN

**Secretary:** Lynn Atkinson, 58 Harwood St.., Darwen, Lancs BB3 1PD (01254761755)
**Ground:** Anchor Ground, Anchor Road, Darwen, Lancs BB3 0BB, (01254 705627)
**Directions:** A666 Blackburn / Bolton road, 1 mile north of Darwen town centre,turn right at Anchor Hotel, ground 200 yds on left. One and a half miles from Darwen (BR), bus 51 to Anchor Hotel

| Capacity: 4,000 | Seats: 250 | Cover: 2,000 | Floodlights: Yes |
|---|---|---|---|

**Clubhouse:** Matchday only **Club Shop:** No
**HONOURS** Lancs Comb 31 32 73 75: Comb Cup 30 31 75; Lancs Jun Cup 73; Geo Watson Trophy 73; LFA Yth Cup 75; NWC Cup 83; Lancs F/Lit Trophy 90; NWC Res Div Cup 94; Blackburn & Dist Yth Lge 94 95 97, Cup 94 95 97; NW All Chall Cup 96.
**PREVIOUS** **Leagues:**Football Alliance 1889-91, Football Lg 1891-99, Lancs Lg 99-03,Lancs Comb. 03-75, Ches. Co. 75-82. **Ground:** Barley Bank
**RECORD** **Gate:** (Anchor Ground) 10,000 v Fleetwood Lancs Jun Cup 1920
**BEST SEASON** FA Cup: Semi Finals

### FACT FILE
Founded: 1875
Sponsors: Prince Moran
Colours: Red & white/white/red
Change colours: All blue
Midweek Matches: Tuesday
Reserves' League: NWC Res. Div.
Programme: 20 pages, 60p
Editor: D Marah

### CLUB PERSONNEL
President: E Devlin
Chairwoman: Mrs K Marah
Manager: S Wilkes
Asst Manager: M Atkinson
Physio: Mick Sharples

---

# FORMBY

**Secretary:** Dave Dickenson, 2 Seafield, Formby, Merseyside,L37 4EL Tel: 01704 870944 (H)
**Ground:** Brows Lane, Formby, Merseyside (01704 833505)**Directions:** A565 Liverpool-Southport, turn left for Formby at lights opposite Tesco into Altcar Rd, left at T junction to r'bout (opposite Blundell Arms Hotel), take 2nd exit then sharp left into Duke Street, 1st right into Elbow Lane, ground 50yds on left. Formby (BR) 1/2m, buses from Formby &Southport stations

| Capacity: 2,000 | Seats: 200 | Cover: 500 | Floodlights: No |
|---|---|---|---|

**Clubhouse:** None. Matchday refreshment bar stocks hot food & drinks
**Club Shop:** Sells programmes, badges & souvenirs. Contact Paul Lawler (01704878409)
**HONOURS** Liverpool Co. Comb. 48-49, R-up 64-65; Liverpool Senior Cup 77-78, R-up 84-85; Challenge Cup 52-53 63-64 67-68, R-up 64-65; Amtr Cup 29-30 47-48 48-49;Lamot Pils Trophy 94-95; George Mahon Cup 64-65, R-up 55-56 56-57; Lancs Co FA Amt Cup 34-35.
**PREVIOUS Leagues:** Liverpool Co. Comb. 19-68/ Lancs Comb. 68-71, Ches. Co. 71-82.
**BEST SEASON** **FA Cup:** 1st Rd 73-74, 0-2 v Oldham Ath. (H) **FA Trophy:** 1st Rd 73-74, lost to Stalybridge Celtic **FA Vase:** 2nd Rd 96-97, lost to Tetley Walker

### FACT FILE
Founded: 1919 Nickname: Squirrels
Club Sponsors: DKS Packaging
Colours: Yellow/blue/yellow
Change: White/black/black
Midweek Matches: Tuesday
Programme: 36 pages, 50p
Editor: Paul Lawler, (01704 878409)

### CLUB PERSONNEL
Chairman: Chris Welsh
Comm. Man.: Dave Dickinson (01704 870944)
Press Officer: Paul Lawler (01704 878409)
Managers: Peter Hennerty & Mike Scott
Physio: Keith Johnson

---

# HOLKER OLD BOYS

**Secretary:** Allan Wilson, 56 Fairfield Lane, Barrow-in-Furness, Cumbria. LA13 9HL
Tel: 01229 822751 (W) 01229 822983 (H)

**Ground:** Rakesmoor Lane, Hawcoat, Barrow-in-Furness, Cumbria (01229 828176)
**Directions:** M6 Jct 36, A590 to Barrow-in-Furness, on entering Barrow, continue across r'bout, 2nd right (Dalton Lane) to top of road, right into Rakesmoor Lane, ground on right.

| Capacity: 2,500 | Seats: 220 | Cover: 500 | Floodlights: Yes |
|---|---|---|---|

**Clubhouse:** Mon-Fri 8-11pm, Sat noon-11pm, Sun normal licensing. Pies & peas on matchdays
**Club Shop:** No

**HONOURS** W Lancs Lg 86-87, R-up 85-86; Lancs Junior Shield 88-89 90-91.
**PREVIOUS** **Leagues:** North Western; Furness Premier; West Lancs 70-91.
**RECORDS** **Attendance:** 1240 v Barrow ATS Trophy 95-96 **Win:** 12-0
**Defeat:** 1-8 v Newcastle T. (H) 91-92 **Scorer:** Dave Conlin

### FACT FILE
Founded: 1936 Nickname: Cobs
Club Sponsors: Kitchen Design Studio
Colours: Green & white stripes/green/green
Change colours: Blue/red
Midweek Matches: Tuesday
Programme: 8 pages, 30p

### CLUB PERSONNEL
President: R Brady
Chairman: Ron Moffatt
Vice Chairman: Ray Sharp
Press Officer: John Taylor
Manager: Des Johnson
Asst Manager: Jim Capstick
Coach: Jim Ballantyne
Physio: Mark Hetherington

# NELSON

**Secretary:** Cyril King, 1 Grange Ave, Barrowford, Nelson, Lancashire BB9 8AN(01282 695578)

**Ground:** Victoria Park, Lomeshaye Way, Nelson, Lancs (01282 613820)
**Directions:** M65 jct 13, 1st left (A6068 Fence), 2nd left (B6249 for Nelson),2nd right sign
Lomeshaye Village to grd
**Capacity:** 1500    Seats:150Cover: 200    Floodlights: Yes
**Clubhouse:** Bar open matchdays    **Club Shop:** No.

**HONOURS**    Lancs Lge 54-55; Lancs Comb. 1949-50 51-52; Lg Cup 49-50 50-51 59-60;
Bridge Shield 75-76 81-82; Lancs Jnr Cup 54-55; N.W.C. Div 2 Cup 96-97.

**BEST SEASON**    **FA Cup:** 2nd Rd Proper 30-31(replay) **FA Vase:**

**PREVIOUS**    **Leagues:** Lancashire 1889-98 1900-01; Football League 1898-1900;
Lancashire Comb. 01-16 46-82; N.W.C. 82-88; West Lancashire 88-92.

### FACT FILE

Founded: 1881
Nickname: Blues
Colours: Blue & white stripes/black/blue
Change colours: White/red
Midweek matchday: Wednesday
Reserve League: N.W.C. Res. Div.

### CLUB PERSONNEL

Chairman: A.T.Barnes
Vice-Chairman: A Barnes
Manager: John Bailey
Assistant Manager:Andy Wych

---

# OLDHAM TOWN

**Secretary:** Joan Cooper, 1 Hannerton Rd., Shaw, Oldham. Tel/Fax: 01706 8406649
**Ground:** Whitebank Stadium, Whitebank Rd, Hollins, Oldham, Lancs OL8 3JH
Tel: 0161 624 2689 **Directions:** M62 jct 18, M66 to Heaton Pk, right on to A576, left
2nd lights on to A6104, follow Victoria Ave. on to Hollinwood Ave. under bridge to roundabout
take 2nd exit onto Hollins Rd, follow Hollins Rd for one & a half miles to Fire Station, left on
rough gate leading onto Elm Rd and follow to next left, Whitebank Rd on left.
**Capacity:** 1,000    Seats: 101    Cover: Yes    Floodlights: Yes
**Clubhouse:** Open evenings and matchdays
**HONOURS**    NWC: Div 2 97-98, R-up 94-95; Div 3 R-up 85--86; Lg.Champions 97-98
Res Div R-up 94-95, Cup 94/95:

**PREVIOUS**    **Leagues:** Manchester Amateur; Lancashire Comb. 81-82.

**BEST SEASON**    **FA Cup:**    **FA Vase:**

**RECORD**    **Attendance:** 495 v Halifax Town, '96.

### FACT FILE

Founded: 1964
Colours: Blue,white,blue
Change Colours:
Midweek Matches: Tuesday
Programme: 16 pages, 50p
Editor: Secretary
98-99Captain: Steve Hughes
Top Scorer: Bradley Coe

### CLUB PERSONNEL

Chairman: Ken Hughes
Manager: Len Cantello

---

# SQUIRES GATE

**Secretary:** Ian Farish, 19 Brocklewood Ave., Poulton-le-Fylde, Lancs. FY6 8BZ.
Tel/Fax: 01253 899245

**Ground:** School Road, Marton, Blackpool, Lancs.    Tel: 01253 798584
**Directions:** M6 to M55 jct 4, left onto A583, right at 1st lights (Whitehall Rd) follow signs for air-
port. Ground approx 1.5 miles on right. Nearest station Blackpool South.
**Capacity:** 1000    Seats: 2 rows    Cover: One side    Floodlights: Yes
**Clubhouse:** Yes

**HONOURS**    West Lancs Lg: Div 2 80-81, Richardson Cup 86-87
**PREVIOUS**    **Leagues:** W. Lancs (pre-1991)
**BEST SEASON**    **FA Cup:**    **FA Vase:**
**RECORD**    **Attendance:** 600 v Everton 95

### FACT FILE

Formed: 1948
Colours: Royal/black/royal
Midweek Matches: Tuesday
Programme: 20 pages

### CLUB PERSONNEL

Chairman: P Mack
Vice President: Brian Addison
ManagerGordon Fell
Assistant Manager: John Chippendale

---

# TETLEY WALKER

**Secretary:** Gary Clarke, 183 Liverpool Road, Gt.Sankey, Warrington, Cheshire Wa5 1QU
**Ground:** Tetley Walker Club, Long Lane, Orford, Warrington, Ches. WA2 9PB  (01925 634904)
**Directions:** M6 Junc 21A to M62 Junc 9, follow signs for Warrington town centre on A49. After 1
1/2 miles turn left at 2nd r'bout ground about 500yds on left. Nearest station Warrington Central
**Capacity:** 2,000    Seats: 40    Cover: 150    Floodlights: No    Shop: No
**Clubhouse:** Open noon-midnight. Food includes sandwiches & pies, (01925 634904)
**HONOURS**    NWC Div 2 Trophy 97-98; Guardian Cup 84-85 85-86 93-94 95-96 96-97;
Jubilee Cup 84-85 93-94; Warrington Lge 86-87 93-94:
**PREVIOUS**    **League:** Warrington & District 1974-94    **Grounds:** None
**BEST SEASON**    **FA Vase:** 4th Rd 96-97    **FA Cup:**
**RECORDS**    **Attendance:** 200 v Durham C., FA Vase 96-97
**Appearances:** Ray Arnold   **Win:** 15-2 v Nelson, NWCL 96-97
**1998-99 Captan:** Neil Maher   **Top Scorer:** Tony Plant

### FACT FILE

Founded: 1974    Nickname: Walkers
Sponsor: Adobe Systems/
Colours: Navy blue with yellow trim
Change Cols: White & Red
Midweek matches: Tuesday
Reserves' Lge: Mid Cheshire Div 2.
Programme: 40 pages 50p
Editor: Garry Clarke
### CLUB PERSONNEL
President: T.B.A.
Chairman: Bob McLaughlin
Treasurers;Tony Healey & John Hackney
Managers: Jimmy Drewery & Ian Street
Physio: Harry Peacey
Press Officer: Garry Clarke

# WARRINGTON TOWN

**Secretary:** Harry Boden, 10 Landseer Ave, Warrington Tel: 01925 659796 (H) 0589 512675(M)
**Ground**: Cantilever Park, Common Lane, Latchford, Warrington WA4 2RS01925 631932
(Club), 01925-653044 (Office). **Directions:** M6 junction 20, then A50 towards Warrington. After
2 miles turn left immediately after swing bridge into Station Road, ground 600yds on left. From
town centre travel 1 mile south on A49, left at lights into Loushers Lane, ground quarter mile on
right. 2miles from Warrington Bank Quay (BR)
Capacity: 2,000    Cover: 650    Seats: 350    Floodlights: Yes    **Club Shop:** Yes
**Clubhouse:** Weekdays 1-11pm, Sat. 12-11pm, Sun. 12-3pm, 7-10.30pm.  Bar food on matchdays
**HONOURS:** FA Vase R-up 86-87; N.W.C. Lge 89-90 (Lg Cup 85-86 87-88 88-89 (R-up 89-90),
Div 2 R-up86-87, Div 3 R-up 82-83; Mid-Cheshire Lg 60-61 (R-up 57-58, Lg Cup 54-55 55-56)
11-12 72-73, Altrincham Amat. Cup 54-55,
**PREVIOUS    Leagues:** Warrington & Dist. 49-52; Mid-Cheshire 52-78; Cheshire Co. 78-82;
N.W.C. 82-90; N.P.L 90-97. **Name:** Stockton Heath 1949-62. **BEST SEASON  FA Cup:** 4th
Qual. Rd 94-95 **FA Vase:** Runners-up 86-87 **FA Trophy:** Quarter-Finalists 92-93

### FACT FILE
Formed: 1948        Nickname: The Town
Colours: Blue & yellow/blue/blue
Change colours:Blue & yellow squares/blue
Midweek matchday: Tuesday
Reserves' League: Mid-Cheshire
Programme 36 Pages 50p
Editor: Rick Barker 01925 604101 Tel/Fax

### CLUB PERSONNEL
Chairman: Harry Boden
Vice Chairman: M P McShane
Press Officer: Colin Serjent
Manager: Alan Lord
Asst Manager: Dave Entwhistle
Coach: Gary Bradley  Physio: Lynda Roberts

# WOODLEY SPORTS

**Secretary:** Ian Woodhouse, 4 Firethorn Drive, Godley, Hyde SK14 3SN
Tel: 0161 3511631 (H), 0161 330 6837 (B)

**Ground:** Lambeth Grove Stadium, Lambeth Grove, Woodley, Stockport.  Tel: 0161 494 6429
**Directions:** M60 Jct 25, follow signs (A560) Bredbury, take left filter atlights which brings you
onto A560 Stockport Road for approx 1 mile, turn leftat pub, Lowes Arms into Mill Street which
goes into Mill Lane. Over bridge take2nd right into Woodlands Avenue, then 1st leftinto
Lambeth Grove. Ground 200 yards ahead.
Floodlights: Yes

RECORD        **Attendance:** 1,500 v Stockport County
PREVIOUS      **Leagues:** Lancashire & Cheshire, Manchester League.
BEST SEASON   **FA Cup:**        **FA Vase:** 1st Round 1998-99

### FACT FILE

Founded: 1970
Colours: Red & royal blue/royal/white
Midweek Matchday: Tuesday

### CLUB PERSONNEL

Chairman: Ian Campbell
14 Gloucester Rd., Gee Cross, Hyde.
Tel: 0161 368 4834 (H), 0467 290561 (M)

Warrington Town's Tague is closely watched by Berry of Curzon Ashton during this league game which the visitors, Warrington Town, won 4-1.
Photo: Colin Stevens

# FRANK ARMITT
# LIVERPOOL COUNTY FOOTBALL COMBINATION

## Secretary: J F Deal

The 1998-99 season has been a traumatic and extremely successful one for our League. The demise of five teams in Division Two, prior to and during the season, left this Division with only seven teams, which is an unacceptable number. The Management Committee met on 1st June to format a proposal for the constitution for next season. My personal opinion is that one division is the only option. If you recall, Crystal Villa resigned before the season started, Rainhill Town were expelled due to gross maladministration, while Avon Athletic, Manweb Reserves and Mossley Hill Reserves resigned due to shortage of players. A further set back has been received with the decision of Stockbridge to disband and Manweb and Maghull Reserves to resign and apply to join the West Cheshire League.

The past season has been horrendous for the number of postponements due to waterlogged pitches. Congratulations to all our successful Clubs in the County FA Competitions. Waterloo Dock and St Dominics gave an excellent account of themselves in the Final of the Liverpool County FA Challenge Cup which Waterloo Dock won 3-2. League newcomers St Aloysius had a tremendous 4-0 win against St Philomenas in the Final of the Liverpool County FA Junior Cup and St Dominics regained the Lancashire FA Amateur Cup with a 1-0 extra time win over Aigburth Peoples Hall, to register their sixth success in this competition.

St Dominics also retained the First Division Championship in fine style, winning the League by twelve points to equal Waterloo Dock and Bootle (Langton) with nine Championship victories. St Aloysius capped a remarkable season by not only adding the Second Division Championship to their County FA Cup success, but they also won the Lord Wavertree Cup and were narrow losers in the Final of the Fred Micklesfield Cup which was won by Cheshire Lines.

Stockbridge retained the George Mahon Cup with a narrow 1-0 win over Lucas Sport and Speke caused a shock, knocking out St Dominics on the way to a 2-1 extra time win over Crawfords UB in the Final of the Andy Nolan Memorial Cup.

On behalf of the League Management Committee I thank all our sponsors - Mike Armitt for the League Championship, Peter Coyne for the George Mahon Cup, Carlsberg/Tetley for the Lord Wavertree Cup and Kevin Nolan for the Andy Nolan League Cup.

The shortage of fixtures in the Second Division required another competition to be organised which was won by Prescot BICC and thanks to go Rewardaward for the donation of the Trophy. The introduction of the Reg Kirkpatrick Sportsmanship Trophy sponsored by Vice-President Mick Glancy has been won by Second Division Birchfield.

The individual Division goalscoring awards were won by Brian Burns of Plessey GPT in Division One and Anthony Davidson of Prescot BICC in Division Two. Dave Hughes of Prescott BICC is the Secretary of the Year and Joe Chappell won the coveted Referee of the Season.

J F Deal, Secretary

## HONOURS LIST 1998-99

| | Winners | Runners up/Finalists |
|---|---|---|
| DIVISION ONE<br>Sponsored by Frank Armitt & Son Ltd | St Dominics | Manweb |
| GEORGE MAHON CUP<br>Sponsored by Peter Coyne Ltd | Stockbridge | Lucas Sports |
| DIVISION TWO<br>Sponsored by Frank Armitt & Son Ltd | St Aloysius | Prescot BICC |
| LORD WAVERTREE CUP<br>Sponsored by Carlsberg/Tetley | St Aloysius | Cheshire Lines |
| ANDY NOLAN CUP<br>Sponsored by Kevin Nolan | Speke | Crawfords U.B. |
| FRED MICKLESFIELD CUP | Cheshire Lines | St Aloysius |
| SECOND DIVISION SUPPLEMENTARY SHIELD<br>Sponsored by Rewardaward Ltd | Prescot BICC | |
| REG KIRKPATRICK SPORTSMANSHIP TROPHY<br>Sponsored by Mick Glancy | Birchfield | |
| LIVERPOOL COUNTY FA CHALLENGE CUP | Waterloo Dock | St Dominic |
| LIVERPOOL COUNTY FA JUNIOR CUP | St Aloysius | |
| LANCASHIRE FA AMATEUR CUP | St Dominics | |

# FINAL LEAGUE TABLES 1998-99

## DIVISION ONE

| | P | W | D | L | F | A | Pts |
|---|---|---|---|---|---|---|---|
| St Dominics | 30 | 23 | 3 | 4 | 79 | 26 | 72 |
| Manweb | 30 | 18 | 6 | 6 | 72 | 41 | 60 |
| Plessey GPT | 30 | 16 | 9 | 5 | 93 | 48 | 57 |
| Waterloo Dock | 30 | 16 | 8 | 6 | 89 | 45 | 56 |
| Crawfords UB | 30 | 14 | 10 | 6 | 69 | 44 | 52 |
| Royal Seaforth | 30 | 14 | 8 | 8 | 87 | 59 | 50 |
| Stockbridge | 30 | 14 | 8 | 8 | 63 | 50 | 50 |
| Speke | 30 | 15 | 5 | 10 | 69 | 63 | 50 |
| Ford Motors | 30 | 12 | 5 | 13 | 64 | 80 | 41 |
| Lucas Sports | 30 | 10 | 6 | 14 | 50 | 57 | 36 |
| Bootle Res | 30 | 9 | 3 | 18 | 57 | 67 | 30 |
| BRNESC | 30 | 7 | 4 | 19 | 39 | 83 | 25 |
| Mossley Hill Athletic | 30 | 7 | 4 | 19 | 49 | 100 | 25 |
| South Liverpool | 30 | 6 | 5 | 19 | 46 | 65 | 23 |
| Yorkshire CT* | 30 | 7 | 4 | 19 | 41 | 101 | 22 |
| Ayone | 30 | 5 | 6 | 19 | 42 | 80 | 21 |

\* points deducted

## DIVISION TWO

| | P | W | D | L | F | A | Pts |
|---|---|---|---|---|---|---|---|
| St Aloysius | 12 | 8 | 2 | 2 | 36 | 16 | 26 |
| Prescot BICC | 12 | 6 | 2 | 4 | 35 | 16 | 20 |
| Halewood Town | 12 | 6 | 2 | 4 | 30 | 28 | 20 |
| Cheshire Lines | 12 | 5 | 4 | 3 | 19 | 16 | 19 |
| Plessey GPT Res | 12 | 4 | 2 | 6 | 19 | 24 | 14 |
| Birchfield | 12 | 3 | 2 | 7 | 13 | 31 | 11 |
| Maghull Reserves | 12 | 2 | 2 | 8 | 8 | 29 | 8 |

### SECOND DIVISION SUPPLEMENTARY SHIELD

| | P | W | D | L | F | A | Pts |
|---|---|---|---|---|---|---|---|
| Prescott BICC | 6 | 5 | 0 | 1 | 21 | 6 | 15 |
| St Aloysius | 6 | 4 | 2 | 0 | 17 | 10 | 14 |
| Cheshire Lines | 6 | 3 | 2 | 1 | 12 | 7 | 11 |
| Birchfield | 6 | 3 | 0 | 3 | 11 | 12 | 9 |
| Plessey GPT Res | 6 | 2 | 0 | 4 | 4 | 11 | 6 |
| Halewood Town | 6 | 1 | 1 | 5 | 7 | 15 | 4 |
| Maghull Reserves | 6 | 0 | 1 | 5 | 2 | 17 | 1 |

## GEORGE MAHON CUP 1998-99

### FIRST ROUND

| | | | | | | |
|---|---|---|---|---|---|---|
| Ford Motors | v | Plessey GPT | 7-5 | Lucas Sports | v | St Dominics | 2-1 |
| Mossley Hill Athletic | v | BRNESC | 2-4 | Royal Seaforth | v | Crawfords UB | 3-2 |
| South Liverpool | v | Bootle Reserves | 2-5 | Stockbridge | v | Ayone | 7-3 |
| Waterloo Dock | v | Speke | 3-2 | Yorkshire CT | v | Manweb | 1-5 |

### SECOND ROUND

| | | | | | | |
|---|---|---|---|---|---|---|
| Manweb | v | Bootle Reserves | 1-2 | Lucas Sports | v | BRNESC | |
| Stockbridge | v | Ford Motors | | Royal Seaforth | v | Waterloo Dock | 3-3, 3-1 |

### SEMI FINALS

Bootle Reserves v Lucas Sports  0-1      Stockbridge v Royal Seaforth  1-0

### FINAL

LUCAS SPORTS v STOCKBRIDGE  0-1

## LORD WAVERTREE CUP 1998-99

### SEMI FINALS

Halewood Town v St Aloysius  2-6      Prescot BICC v Cheshire Lines  0-2

### FINAL

CHESHIRE LINES v ST ALOYSIUS  3-4

## FRED MICKLESFIELD CUP 1998-99

### SEMI FINALS

Cheshire Lines v Prescot BICC  1-1, 4p3      St Aloysius v Halewood Town  10-1

### FINAL

CHESHIRE LINES v ST ALOYSIUS  2-1

## ANDY NOLAN LEAGUE CUP 1998-99

### FIRST ROUND

| | | | | | | |
|---|---|---|---|---|---|---|
| Birchfield | v | BRNESC | 2-4 | Lucas Sports | v | St Aloysius | 0-2 |
| Maghull Reserves | v | Bootle Reserves | 0-2 | Manweb | v | Ford Motors | 2-1 |
| Prescot BICC | v | Mossley Hill Athletic | 2-0 | Plessey GPT Res | v | Mossley Hill Ath Res | 11-1 |
| St Dominics | v | Waterloo Dock | 2-1 | Speke | v | Plessey GPT | 4-3 |
| Yorkshire CT | v | Cheshire Lines | 3-1 | | | | |

### SECOND ROUND

| | | | | | | |
|---|---|---|---|---|---|---|
| Ayone | v | Prescot BICC | 2-1 | Crawfords UB | v | Stockbridge | 2-1 |
| Halewood Town | v | Yorkshire CT | 2-2, 2-2, 6p5 | Plessey GPT Res | v | South Liverpool | 1-3 |
| Royal Seaforth | v | BRNESC | 7-2 | St Aloysius | v | Bootle Reserves | 2-0 |
| St Dominics | v | Manweb | 1-0 | Speke | v | Avon Athletic | 3-0 |

### THIRD ROUND

| | | | | | | |
|---|---|---|---|---|---|---|
| Ayone | v | St Dominics | 2-2, 0-5 | Halewood Town | v | Speke | 1-7 |
| Royal Seaforth | v | Crawfords UB | 1-1, 0-4 | South Liverpool | v | St Aloysius | 2-3 |

### SEMI FINALS

Crawfords v St Aloysius  1-1, 2-1      Speke v St Dominics  3-2

### FINAL

CRAWFORDS UB v SPEKE  1-2

# CARLSBERG WEST CHESHIRE A.F.L.

**President:** K Halsall    **Chairman:** R Prescott

**Hon. Secretary:** L Bullock
8 Cambridge Road, Bromborough, Wirral L62 7JA
Tel: 0151 334 3545

The most memorable season in the history of the Carlsberg West Cheshire AFL began with the re-introduction of a Third Division after a 90 year gap and ended with the League receiving the tremendous honour of representing England in the inagural UEFA Regions cup. The invitation from the Cheshire F.A. to fly the flag on both the region's and the country's behalf gave little time for preparation and the League's proximity to Wales meant that a number of players who had appeared there were ineligible. Nevertheless manager Ken Meadows and his squad flew out in mid June to Dublin to play in Group 8 of the 32 country competition. England's group opponents were Republic of Ireland, Scotland and the Netherlands with the professionally run tournament featuring two games on each of three days. On arrival it was learnt that The Netherlands would feature seven Ajax players and that some of the squad earned a "sponsored" living from the game while The Republic actually represented the whole of their country rather than a region. Undaunted the England squad met the challenge and a group of players drawn from six different clubs improved with each game. They were helped to this end by the experience of Medical Officer Dr. Mike Freeman and physiotherapist Rick Carter of Crewe Alexandra who were added to the party at the suggestion of The Football Association, who also supported the squad by supplying a large amount of training and playing equipment. First opponents, The Netherlands, took a 2-0 lead but after Heswall's Nick Dillon had pulled one back for England the Dutch side were left to hang on grimly before claiming victory. Two days later a very even encounter with hosts Republic of Ireland finished all square at 1-1 after Paul Wiggans headed a late equaliser from one of many corners forced by England. By now the spirit in the camp was sky high and "The Auld Enemy" Scotland were brushed aside in the final game as a first half strike by Stork's Wiggans and a second period penalty from Mike Riley of Poulton Victoria took England to a comprehensive 2-0 win. Under the circumstances the final group placing of runners up to The Netherlands, who thereby qualify for the final stages to be played in Southern Europe later this year, was a superb achievement. The players truly relished appearing in "the big time", training virtually every day, transported everywhere in their own team bus, given advice on what to eat etc, they were so overwhelmed they even gave up drinking for most of the week! Undoubtedly a long lasting experience for all including those most generous of hosts the Irish Junior F.A., who were full of praise for the attitude and behaviour of an English party who in the true spirit of the amateur game gained new friendships with their opponents.

The season had opened with four new clubs and four new Reserve sides helping to get the expanded League under way but it was an old name who were to take the major honours. Cammell Laird carried virtually everything before them during the 70's and 80's and under new manager Mike Keeley they collected the League and Pyke Cup double this time round. Ashville were defeated in the final of the Pyke while nearest challengers for the title were runners up Heswall who gained some consolation by winning their fourth consecutive Wirral Senior Cup final in a final contest with Stork that went to extra time. Champions for the previous three seasons had been Poulton Vics who following a considerable change in personnel finished in third place but who can still count the season as a success thanks to becoming the eighth consecutive West Cheshire side to win the prestigious Cheshire Amateur Cup. Their 1-0 final success coming at the expense of Mid Cheshire outfit, Linotype. The Division One campaign ended on a sad note when bottom club Bromborough Pool decided to call it a day after being in existence for 115 years.

Division Two also featured a title battle between Lairds and Heswall with the Village side gaining the upper hand on this occasion as their second string were crowned champions leaving Lairds to pick up the West Cheshire Bowl following a single goal success over New Brighton. Division Three witnessed a terrific three way contest as new boys BICC Helsby, Aintree Villas and Pavillions strived to gain promotion at the 1st attempt. As it was BICC took the title and Villa will join them in Division Two having become runners up. Pavillions also missed out in the Shield final which was won by BICC who thereby claimed the treble having defeated First Division General Chemicals in the final of the Runcorn Senior cup.

The season opened with Poulton Vics collecting the Bill Wight Trophy, the proceeds of which go to charitable causes, while the 36 gallons of beer from sponsors Carlsberg, went to Shell for winning the penalty shoot out competition. The annual Inter-League game with Mid Cheshire was played as part of the build up for the UEFA Regions competition with our opponents winning through by the only goal of the game, scored in the first minute.

Next season will also be of great significance as we celebrate the centenary of the Pyke Cup. The partnership between ourselves and Pykes and Jewellers is such that the original trophy presented by company founder John Pyke is still played for today and the family firm have continued to supply the mementos for all cup final participants. For the new campaign Maghull (North West Trains), Mallaby (South Wirral League) and MANWEB (Liverpool County Combination) will be joining us for the first time, St. Werburghs (Chester & District) return to the league and five Reserve sides will be added. This means that just twelve months after extending to three Divisions the Carlsberg West Cheshire AFL will have its full complement of sixteen teams in each sphere.

# FINAL LEAGUE TABLES 1998-99

## DIVISION ONE

| | P | W | D | L | F | A | Pts |
|---|---|---|---|---|---|---|---|
| Cammell Laird | 30 | 23 | 5 | 2 | 82 | 25 | 74 |
| Heswall | 30 | 22 | 5 | 3 | 74 | 34 | 71 |
| Poulton Victoria | 30 | 19 | 5 | 6 | 93 | 51 | 62 |
| Vauxhall Motors | 30 | 15 | 7 | 8 | 78 | 62 | 52 |
| Stork | 30 | 16 | 3 | 11 | 64 | 37 | 51 |
| Ashville | 30 | 14 | 6 | 10 | 51 | 45 | 48 |
| Mersey Royal | 30 | 13 | 4 | 13 | 59 | 47 | 43 |
| General Chemicals | 30 | 13 | 3 | 14 | 57 | 52 | 42 |
| Shell | 30 | 8 | 10 | 12 | 48 | 55 | 34 |
| Capenhurst | 30 | 9 | 5 | 16 | 54 | 77 | 32 |
| Christleton | 30 | 9 | 4 | 17 | 44 | 68 | 31 |
| Blacon Youth Club | 30 | 9 | 3 | 18 | 41 | 78 | 30 |
| Mond Rangers | 30 | 8 | 5 | 17 | 48 | 76 | 29 |
| Merseyside Police | 30 | 7 | 7 | 16 | 60 | 83 | 28 |
| Newton | 30 | 7 | 7 | 16 | 45 | 70 | 28 |
| Bromborough Pool | 30 | 7 | 3 | 20 | 38 | 76 | 24 |

## DIVISION TWO

| | P | W | D | L | F | A | Pts |
|---|---|---|---|---|---|---|---|
| Heswall Res. | 26 | 22 | 1 | 3 | 75 | 22 | 67 |
| Cammell Laird Res. | 26 | 20 | 3 | 3 | 70 | 26 | 63 |
| Poulton Victoria Res. | 26 | 14 | 8 | 4 | 72 | 41 | 50 |
| New Brighton | 26 | 13 | 6 | 7 | 65 | 44 | 45 |
| Stork Res. | 26 | 11 | 3 | 12 | 57 | 64 | 36 |
| Castrol Social | 26 | 10 | 4 | 12 | 55 | 55 | 34 |
| Ashville Res. | 26 | 10 | 3 | 13 | 65 | 63 | 33 |
| Capenhurst Res. | 26 | 9 | 5 | 12 | 41 | 51 | 32 |
| Shell Res. | 26 | 10 | 2 | 14 | 50 | 69 | 32 |
| Upton Athletic Association | 26 | 9 | 4 | 13 | 48 | 50 | 31 |
| Mersey Royal Res. | 26 | 9 | 3 | 14 | 44 | 61 | 30 |
| Christleton Res. | 26 | 7 | 6 | 13 | 35 | 60 | 27 |
| West Kirby | 26 | 6 | 5 | 15 | 41 | 65 | 23 |
| Moreton | 26 | 4 | 3 | 19 | 36 | 83 | 15 |

## DIVISION ONE RESULTS CHART 1998-99

| | | 1 | 2 | 3 | 4 | 5 | 6 | 7 | 8 | 9 | 10 | 11 | 12 | 13 | 14 | 15 | 16 |
|---|---|---|---|---|---|---|---|---|---|---|---|---|---|---|---|---|---|
| 1 | Ashville | X | 2-0 | 2-0 | 1-2 | 2-1 | 1-0 | 0-2 | 1-1 | 2-2 | 4-0 | 1-3 | 1-1 | 1-3 | 1-0 | 2-1 | 0-2 |
| 2 | Blacon Youth Club | 1-3 | X | 3-1 | 1-2 | 1-2 | 1-2 | 0-1 | 0-5 | 2-1 | 2-2 | 3-1 | 3-2 | 5-3 | 0-5 | 0-6 | 1-2 |
| 3 | Bromborough Pool | 3-3 | 0-4 | X | 2-1 | 4-6 | 2-1 | 3-2 | 0-2 | 1-0 | 2-1 | 2-0 | 2-3 | 0-4 | 3-1 | 1-2 | 2-2 |
| 4 | Cammell Laird | 3-0 | 3-0 | 4-1 | X | 2-1 | 4-1 | 2-1 | 0-2 | 4-1 | 1-1 | 2-0 | 3-0 | 2-2 | 2-2 | 2-0 | 5-0 |
| 5 | Capenhurst | 1-2 | 5-0 | 5-1 | 0-4 | X | 3-2 | 0-2 | 1-1 | 0-5 | 3-3 | 4-0 | 1-3 | 2-3 | 0-1 | 3-2 | 2-2 |
| 6 | Christleton | 1-8 | 0-1 | 3-2 | 0-5 | 5-1 | X | 2-1 | 2-4 | 1-4 | 1-3 | 1-1 | 0-2 | 1-5 | 1-1 | 1-0 | 4-2 |
| 7 | General Chemicals | 3-4 | 1-2 | 1-0 | 1-5 | 2-3 | 0-3 | X | 1-2 | 0-2 | 3-2 | 4-0 | 2-0 | 2-2 | 10-05 | 1-3 | 2-2 |
| 8 | Heswall | 1-0 | 4-1 | 2-0 | 1-5 | 4-1 | 2-1 | 3-0 | X | 3-0 | 4-0 | 2-1 | 2-1 | 2-2 | 3-0 | 1-2 | 2-2 |
| 9 | Mersey Royal | 1-2 | 6-1 | 2-1 | 1-2 | 2-0 | 5-0 | 1-2 | 0-1 | X | 7-3 | 1-0 | 3-0 | 2-1 | 0-0 | 2-1 | 1-2 |
| 10 | Merseyside Police | 2-4 | 3-1 | 4-1 | 1-5 | 3-4 | 2-2 | 1-2 | 2-3 | 2-2 | X | 2-3 | 4-2 | 1-6 | 5-2 | 2-1 | 3-1 |
| 11 | Mond Rangers | 3-0 | 3-4 | 0-0 | 1-2 | 1-1 | 0-3 | 3-3 | 0-3 | 2-1 | 3-3 | X | 4-0 | 3-5 | 1-0 | 1-4 | 3-2 |
| 12 | Newton | 1-1 | 2-0 | 2-1 | 1-1 | 4-0 | 1-0 | 1-4 | 2-4 | 1-2 | 0-0 | 3-4 | X | 2-5 | 1-1 | 1-6 | 1-1 |
| 13 | Poulton Victoria | 4-0 | 6-0 | 2-0 | 1-2 | 4-0 | 0-2 | 4-1 | 4-4 | 2-1 | 4-2 | 6-2 | 5-3 | X | 2-1 | 1-0 | 2-2 |
| 14 | Shell | 1-1 | 2-2 | 5-0 | 1-3 | 4-2 | 1-1 | 0-4 | 1-3 | 0-0 | 3-0 | 5-1 | 1-1 | 5-4 | X | 0-1 | 1-5 |
| 15 | Stork | 0-1 | 1-1 | 5-1 | 0-3 | 1-1 | 2-1 | 1-0 | 2-3 | 6-0 | 4-2 | 2-0 | 4-0 | 0-1 | 1-1 | X | 3-2 |
| 16 | Vauxhall Motors | 2-1 | 2-1 | 4-2 | 1-1 | 7-1 | 4-2 | 1-3 | 2-0 | 5-4 | 3-1 | 7-4 | 5-4 | 3-0 | 1-3 | 2-3 | X |

## DIVISION TWO RESULTS CHART 1998-99

| | | 1 | 2 | 3 | 4 | 5 | 6 | 7 | 8 | 9 | 10 | 11 | 12 | 13 | 14 |
|---|---|---|---|---|---|---|---|---|---|---|---|---|---|---|---|
| 1 | Ashville Reserves | X | 1-3 | 5-1 | 2-4 | 0-1 | 0-3 | 3-0 | 3-3 | 0-1 | 1-5 | 3-1 | 5-2 | 2-3 | 1-1 |
| 2 | Cammell Laird Res | 4-2 | X | 4-0 | 1-1 | 2-1 | 3-2 | 3-0 | 3-1 | 4-2 | 5-2 | 4-1 | 2-1 | 2-0 | 4-0 |
| 3 | Capenhurst Res | 3-2 | 0-1 | X | 1-3 | 3-0 | 0-5 | 0-2 | 5-2 | 1-1 | 0-0 | 1-2 | 1-4 | 2-2 | 5-2 |
| 4 | Castrol Social | 1-2 | 1-6 | 2-3 | X | 3-0 | 1-4 | 2-0 | 0-2 | 1-1 | 1-2 | 5-0 | 4-0 | 2-2 | 3-6 |
| 5 | Christleton Res | 2-5 | 0-3 | 0-3 | 0-0 | X | 3-1 | 1-0 | 3-2 | 2-2 | 0-2 | 2-5 | 3-4 | 0-0 | 3-1 |
| 6 | Heswall Res | 1-0 | 3-0 | 4-0 | 3-2 | 7-1 | X | 5-1 | 3-0 | 2-1 | 0-0 | 5-0 | 2-3 | 3-1 | 6-0 |
| 7 | Mersey Royal Res | 2-6 | 0-2 | 0-3 | 5-1 | 3-1 | 2-3 | X | 4-4 | 2-0 | 5-2 | 3-0 | 2-5 | 2-4 | 1-1 |
| 8 | Moreton | 5-2 | 1-3 | 0-0 | 0-5 | 0-2 | 0-1 | 1-2 | X | 2-5 | 0-2 | 2-7 | 4-6 | 1-0 | 1-0 |
| 9 | New Brighton | 3-1 | 2-0 | 0-3 | 4-1 | 4-0 | 1-2 | 3-1 | 8-1 | X | 1-1 | 3-4 | 1-0 | 3-1 | 3-2 |
| 10 | Poulton Victoria Res | 4-4 | 1-1 | 5-1 | 1-0 | 2-2 | 0-3 | 5-0 | 7-1 | 5-3 | X | 9-1 | 3-1 | 3-0 | 3-3 |
| 11 | Shell Reserves | 1-4 | 2-2 | 2-0 | 2-3 | 2-2 | 1-3 | 0-1 | 6-1 | 1-4 | 1-2 | X | 0-4 | 4-1 | 2-0 |
| 12 | Stork Reserves | 1-4 | 1-8 | 2-2 | 4-5 | 2-1 | 1-2 | 1-1 | 2-1 | 3-3 | 3-1 | 0-1 | X | 0-3 | 2-3 |
| 13 | Upton Athletic Assoc. | 7-3 | 1-0 | 0-2 | 2-0 | 2-2 | 0-2 | 3-4 | 3-1 | 1-3 | 1-2 | 5-1 | 2-3 | X | 2-0 |
| 14 | West Kirby | 1-4 | 0-1 | 2-1 | 2-4 | 2-3 | 1-2 | 2-1 | 1-0 | 3-3 | 3-3 | 0-3 | 1-2 | 4-2 | X |

## ASHVILLE

**Secretary:** Dave Walton, 15 Wellesley Road, Wallasey, Wirral,
Merseyside, L445UR Tel: 0151 639 9196
**Ground:** Villa Park, Cross Lane, Wallasey Village, Wallasey,
Tel: 0151 638 2127
**Colours:** White/black/black      Formed: 1949

## BLACON YOUTH CLUB

**Secretary:** Ron Paddock
71 Blacon Avenue, Blacon, Chester CH1 5BB Tel: 01244 371240
**Ground:** Cairns Crescent Playing Fields,
Cairns Crescent, Blacon, Chester.
**Colours:** Black & white stripes/black/black      Formed: 1964

## CAMMELL LAIRD

**Secretary:** Ray Steele
46 Croft Ave, Bromborough, Wirral L62 2BR Tel: 0151 334 8998
**Ground:** Kirklands, St Peters Road, Rock Ferry, Birkenhead
Tel: 0151 645 5991
**Colours:** All blue      Formed: 1900

## CAPENHURST

**Secretary:** Martin Williams, 157 Hope Farm Road, Great Sutton,
South Wirral L662TJ Tel: 0151 339 8935
**Ground:** Capenhurst Sports Ground, Capenhurst Lane, Capenhurst
Tel: 0151 339 4101
**Colours:** Sky & claret/claret/claret & sky      Formed: 1952

## CHRISTLETON

**Secretary:** Ken Price, 35 Canadian Ave, Hoole, Chester CH2 3HQ
Tel: 01244 313513

**Ground:** Little Heath, Christleton Tel: 01244 332153
**Colours:** Red/navy/navy.      Formed: 1966

## GENERAL CHEMICALS

**Secretary:** Tony Riley
171 Cotton Lane, Runcorn, Cheshire WA7 5JB Tel: 01928 565390
**Ground:** Pavilions Club, Sandy Lane, Weston Point, Runcorn
Tel: 01928 590508
**Colours:** Black & White/black/black

## HESWALL

**Secretary:** Jake Horan
13 Reedville Road, Bebington, Wirral L63 2HS Tel: 0151 644 0459
**Ground:** Gayton Park, Brimstage Road, Heswall, Wirral
Tel: 0151 342 8172
**Colours:** Yellow/royal blue/yellow      Formed: 1891

## MAGHULL

**Secretary:** Danny Sherlock, 14 Alexander Drive, Lydiate, Merseyside
L31 2NJ(0151 526 2306)
**Ground:** Old Hall Field, Hall Lane, Maghull, Merseyside (0151 526
7320) **Directions:** M57 or M58 to end (Switch Island), A59 towards
Preston (Northway)to lights at Hall Lane, turn right following signs for
Maghull Station. Ground 200 yds on the left. Half mile from Maghull
(Merseyrail)      **Colours:** Blue & red stripes/blue/blue

## MERSEY ROYAL

**Secretary:** Dave Lawson
7 Mount Park, Higher Bebington, Wirral L63 5RD Tel: 0151 608 2261
**Ground:** Unilver Sports Ground, Bromborough
**Colours:** Navy blue and sky blue.      Formed: 1946

## MERSEYSIDE POLICE

**Secretary:** George Todd, 14 Crowther Street, St Helens, Merseyside
WA10 4NH Tel: 01744 755845
**Ground:** Police Club, Fairfield, Prescot Road, Liverpool L7 0JD
Tel: 0151 228 2352
**Colours:** All navy b lue with red trim.      Formed: 1885

## MOND RANGERS

**Secretary:** Pat Crowe, 2 Fairfax Drive, Runcorn, Cheshire WA7 5NN
Tel No: 10928 574689 (H) 01928 512483 (W)
**Ground:** Pavilions Club, Sandy Lane, Weston Point, Runcorn
Tel: 01928 590508
**Colours:** Navy & azurte/navy/azure      Formed: 1967

## NEWTON

**Secretary:** Alan Dabner, 79A Eleanor Road, Bidston, Wirral CH43
7RW. Tel NOs: 0151 653 2151 (H) 0151 227 2151 (W)
**Ground:** Millcroft, Frankby Road, Greasby, Wirral Tel: 0151 677 8382
**Colours:** Yellow & green stripes/green/yellow    Formed: 1933

## POULTON VICTORIA

**Secretary:** Gerry Hillhouse, 2 Gerard Road, Wallasey, Wirral CH44
6RB Tel No: 0151 638 2422 (H)
**Ground:** Victoria Park, Rankin Street, Wallasey Tel: 0151 638 3559
**Colours:** All Royal Blue      Formed: 1935

## SHELL TESSUTI F.C.

**Secretary:** Martin Wood, 23 Whitefields, Elton, Chester CH2 4LS
Tel Nos: 01928 725689 (H) 01244 284254 (W)
**Ground:** Chester Road, Whitby, Ellesmere Port, South Wirral
Tel: 0151 200 7080
**Colours:** Yellow /blueblue. Formed: 1924

## STORK

**Secretary:** Steve Carter
7 Elm Road, Bebington, Wirral L63 8PF Tel: 0151 645 6697
**Ground:** Unilever Sports Ground, Bromborough
**Colours:** All green      Formed: 1920

## VAUXHALL MOTORS

**Secretary:** Carole Paisey, 26 South Road, West Kirby, Wirral L48
3HQ (0151 6256 936)
**Ground:** Vauxhall Sports Ground, Rivacre Road, Hooton, Ellesmere
Port (0151 3281114)
**Colours:** All white      Formed: 1963

| WEST CHESHIRE LEAGUE DIV. 2 | WEST CHESHIRE LEAGUE DIV. 3 |

**WEST CHESHIRE LEAGUE DIV. 2**

**AINTREE VILLA**

**BICC HELSBY**

**CASTROL SOCIAL FC**
Secretary: Dave Bebbington, 490 Overpool Rd, Whitby, Ellesmere Port, SouthWirral L66 2JJ (0151 357 1979)
Ground: Castrol Sports & Social Club, Chester Road, Whitby, Ellesmere Port(0151 355 1730)
Colours: Blue & white/black/blackFormed: 1954

**NEW BRIGHTON**
Formed: 1993
Secretary: Russell Holmes, 10 Rudgrave Square, Wallasey, Wirral L44 0EL (0151638 9506)
Ground: Harrison Drive, Wallasey Village, Wallasey
Colours: Red & white/white/red & white

**UPTON ATHLETIC**
Formed: 1964
Secretary: Bary Gaulton, 24 St Marks Crescent, Whitby, Ellesmere Port L66 2XD (0151 339 1504)
Ground: Cheshire County Council Sports & Social Club, Plas Newton Lane, Chester (01244 318367)
Colours: White/black/black

**WEST KIRBY**

**plus**

| | |
|---|---|
| Ashville Reserves | Cammell Laird Reserves |
| Capenhurst Reserves | Christleton Reserves |
| Heswall Reserves | Mersey Royal Reserves |
| Poulton Victoria Reserves | Shell Reserves |
| Stork Reserves. | |

**WEST CHESHIRE LEAGUE DIV. 3**

MALLABY (ex South Wirral League)

**MANOR ATHLETIC**
Secretary: Stewart Galtress, 3 Centurion Close, Meols, Wirral L47 7BZ (0151 6323211)
Ground: Octel Sports Club, Bridle Road, Bromborough
Colours: White/black/redFormed: 1968

MANWEB (ex Liverpool County Combination)

**MORETON FC**
Formed: 1900
Secretary: Jeff Williams-Lloyd, 46 Burrell Drive, Moreton, Wirral L46 0TQ (0151677 9840)
Ground: Elm Grove, Hoylake
Colours: Red/black/black

PAVILIONS

ST. WERBURGH'S (ex Chester & District League)

SHAFTESBURY

WILLASTON

plus

| | |
|---|---|
| Aintree Villa Reserves | Castrol Reserves |
| Maghull Reserves | Mond Rangers Reserves |
| New Brighton Reserves | Newton Reserves |
| Upton Ath. Assoc. Reserves | |

# GREEN CONTRACT SERVICES MID-CHESHIRE LEAGUE

**President:** R Atherton Esq.

**Hon. Secretary:** E B Davies
34 Rye Bank Road, Firswood, Manchester M16 0FP
Tel: 0161 881 5732

ollowing the departure of Alsager, Hanley Town and Wilmslow Albion from the previous season's list of member clubs the
ague were able to welcome Crews FC, Ellesmere Port United, Trafford FC Res. and Walkers Sports & Social Club into the
econd Division with Garswood United and Middlewich (Town formally (Athletic) being accepted back into Division One. A late
esignation from Bramhall FC resulted in Division One running with sixteen members and seventeen in Division Two. By the
nd of September 98 in Division One Barnton were back in the position they had made their own over the previous two sea-
ons, Garswood United had topped the table initially following their first three games resulting in wins but two defeats followed
opping them down the table. Linotype were fifth after spending the first month in the bottom four, both Rylands and Chorlton
own made good starts holding second and third spots. By the end of the year Barnton were first followed by Knutsford but
ith a nine point gap whilst at the bottom Whitchurch had edged up two places after spending four months in the bottom two
ith Lostock Gralam who had now been joined by Warrington Boro. Despite a strong position but with other clubs having a
ring of games still to play Barnton only clinched their hat trick of titles with a 1-0 win at Garswood on the 1st May 1999. The
nners up spot decider went until the last match of the season on the 25th May with Poynton's victory over Garswood deny-
g them and allowing Linotype to secure this position after they too had only managed a draw at Poynton five evenings earli-
r when a win would have then have killed off any chance that Garswood may have had. With no improvement on their results
nce the start of the new year both Lostock Gralam and Warrington Borough were relegated.

The Division Two league produced many good games in a highly competitive nature probably the best since the start of
iis Division, Padsgate St Oswalds, Grove United, Garswood United Res. and Trafford Res were all in the early running for hon-
urs. Padgate had six wins on the run before dropping their first point at home to Garswood United Res. on the 3rd October
8 Ellesmere Port United in their first season topped this table for the whole of November whilst Linotype Res also showed their
terest taking over top spot for the whole of December and three weeks into January 99. Walkers S & S also showed their
etal moving into second position but they had actually by this time had played a lot more games than their lower placed rivals.
he title race ran until early May 99 with Padgate the eventual winners over Grove United by five points, Trafford Res. finished
ell to finished third only two points adrift. When it came to the Cup Competitions Barnton and Padgate St Oswalds the respec-
ve Division One and Division Two winners never lost their league form although the scores of 1-0 in each of the finals gave
oth Beeches and Broadheath Central more than just hope right up to the final whistle. This season saw the first of hopefully
any President's Cup Competitions and Garswood United lift the new trophy following a 2-1 win over Whitchurch Alport. After
any sleepless nights over the on/off/on/off Inter League fixture with the West Cheshire League I am more than pleased to
cord a famous 1-0 victory and return to more normal sleeping habits.

Having recorded the on pitch events throughout the season remarkably easy it would be wrong not to record the terrible
eather that gave everyone a fixture headache. From the second to last week in October when the league had a complete
ash-out until the early weeks of May 1999 when postponed night matches caused a fixture pile-up not experienced before,
total of 116 matches were either postponed or abandoned including several due to clubs failure to fulfil the rearranged fixtures
ith an evening K O, these all had to be re-arranged and played.

The Jubilee Book became available in early October 98 and although not yet a sell-out has received outstanding reviews.
gain our thanks to Paul Lavelle who accomplished a brilliantly researched book and to all who supported its publication.

For season 1999-2000 the League lose Billington Athletic Res who failed to get the necessary support from the members
nd welcome Flixton FC Res in their place. In the Second Division both Padgate St Oswalds and Grove United are promoted
hilst Lostuck Gralam and Warrington Borough make way for them taking their plans in the Second Division.

eft: Barnton: Division One Cup Winners 1998-99,
played at Trafford FC

Right: Garswood United, Winners, President's Cup 1998-99
2-1 v Whitchurch Alport

371

# FINAL LEAGUE TABLES 1998-99

## DIVISION ONE

| | P | W | D | L | F | A | Pts |
|---|---|---|---|---|---|---|---|
| Barnton | 30 | 26 | 2 | 2 | 97 | 11 | 80 |
| Linotype | 30 | 20 | 3 | 7 | 72 | 41 | 63 |
| Garswood United | 30 | 19 | 4 | 7 | 85 | 40 | 61 |
| Knutsford | 30 | 14 | 10 | 6 | 47 | 35 | 52 |
| Beeches | 30 | 15 | 6 | 9 | 48 | 45 | 51 |
| Chorlton Town | 30 | 14 | 8 | 8 | 60 | 46 | 50 |
| Poynton | 30 | 13 | 10 | 7 | 65 | 47 | 49 |
| Rylands | 30 | 14 | 4 | 12 | 69 | 57 | 46 |
| Middlewich Town | 30 | 11 | 7 | 12 | 41 | 40 | 40 |
| Pilkington | 30 | 11 | 7 | 12 | 60 | 61 | 40 |
| Bollington Athletic | 30 | 10 | 5 | 15 | 48 | 79 | 35 |
| Cheadle Heath Nomads | 30 | 9 | 6 | 15 | 45 | 62 | 33 |
| Whitchurch Alport | 30 | 9 | 0 | 21 | 35 | 61 | 27 |
| AFC Zeneca | 30 | 7 | 5 | 18 | 42 | 84 | 26 |
| Warrington Borough | 30 | 5 | 2 | 23 | 52 | 82 | 17 |
| Lostock Gralam | 30 | 2 | 3 | 25 | 46 | 121 | 9 |

## DIVISION TWO

| | P | W | D | L | F | A | Pts |
|---|---|---|---|---|---|---|---|
| Padgate St Oswalds | 32 | 22 | 6 | 4 | 86 | 24 | 72 |
| Grove United | 32 | 20 | 7 | 5 | 95 | 41 | 67 |
| Trafford Res. | 32 | 19 | 8 | 5 | 92 | 34 | 65 |
| Garswood United Res. | 32 | 20 | 4 | 8 | 98 | 47 | 64 |
| Linotype Res. | 32 | 17 | 10 | 5 | 56 | 34 | 61 |
| Walker Sports | 32 | 17 | 6 | 9 | 84 | 55 | 57 |
| Rylands Res. | 32 | 15 | 3 | 14 | 68 | 66 | 48 |
| Malpas | 32 | 15 | 2 | 15 | 79 | 83 | 47 |
| Ellesmere Port United | 32 | 15 | 1 | 16 | 58 | 60 | 46 |
| Broadheath Central | 32 | 14 | 3 | 15 | 70 | 55 | 45 |
| Chester Nomads | 32 | 11 | 9 | 12 | 60 | 54 | 42 |
| Crewe | 32 | 11 | 5 | 16 | 69 | 83 | 38 |
| Poynton Res. | 32 | 8 | 2 | 22 | 55 | 84 | 26 |
| Chorlton Town Res. | 32 | 8 | 2 | 22 | 45 | 102 | 26 |
| Styal | 32 | 7 | 5 | 20 | 64 | 140 | 26 |
| Littlemoor | 32 | 7 | 4 | 21 | 47 | 96 | 25 |
| Bollington Athletic Res. | 32 | 6 | 3 | 23 | 43 | 111 | 21 |

## DIVISION ONE RESULTS CHART 1998-99

| | | 1 | 2 | 3 | 4 | 5 | 6 | 7 | 8 | 9 | 10 | 11 | 12 | 13 | 14 | 15 | 16 |
|---|---|---|---|---|---|---|---|---|---|---|---|---|---|---|---|---|---|
| 1 | AFC Zeneca | X | 0-1 | 3-1 | 2-1 | 1-1 | 0-4 | 1-5 | 2-0 | 1-2 | 3-3 | 0-1 | 2-2 | 0-4 | 1-8 | 3-2 | 0-2 |
| 2 | Barnton | 6-1 | X | 2-2 | 5-0 | 4-0 | 2-0 | 6-0 | 1-0 | 5-0 | 4-0 | 4-0 | 4-0 | 1-0 | 6-0 | 3-0 | 1-2 |
| 3 | Beeches | 3-1 | 1-5 | X | 2-3 | 3-2 | 0-0 | 1-0 | 5-1 | 1-4 | 3-1 | 0-0 | 0-3 | 0-2 | 3-2 | 4-2 | 2-1 |
| 4 | Bollington Athletic | 1-1 | 1-2 | 2-0 | X | 2-1 | 2-1 | 1-2 | 0-1 | 1-2 | 3-1 | 1-4 | 2-5 | 2-2 | 1-5 | 0-7 | 1-2 |
| 5 | Cheadle Heath N | 3-2 | 0-7 | 1-2 | 0-1 | X | 2-2 | 0-6 | 1-1 | 1-0 | 8-0 | 0-2 | 0-3 | 0-0 | 2-3 | 1-0 | 2-0 |
| 6 | Chorlton T | 3-0 | 0-2 | 0-0 | 0-1 | 2-1 | X | 2-1 | 1-1 | 1-2 | 8-4 | 2-1 | 1-1 | 1-0 | 2-5 | 2-0 | 2-1 |
| 7 | Garswood United | 8-1 | 0-1 | 2-1 | 11-0 | 0-0 | 2-0 | X | 0-0 | 1-0 | 9-1 | 2-0 | 4-1 | 2-0 | 2-2 | 2-1 | 4-0 |
| 8 | Knutsford | 2-1 | 1-1 | 1-0 | 2-0 | 1-0 | 1-0 | 5-2 | X | 1-6 | 3-1 | 0-0 | 0-0 | 0-0 | 0-1 | 8-1 | 1-0 |
| 9 | Linotype | 3-1 | 1-3 | 1-2 | 7-1 | 2-1 | 2-2 | 2-1 | 2-0 | X | 4-2 | 1-0 | 4-2 | 3-1 | 1-2 | 3-2 | 3-0 |
| 10 | Lostock Gralam | 1-3 | 0-4 | 1-2 | 2-3 | 2-2 | 4-6 | 3-5 | 2-6 | 0-4 | X | 2-4 | 1-2 | 4-4 | 0-3 | 3-2 | 2-1 |
| 11 | Middlewich Town | 3-2 | 0-1 | 1-1 | 1-2 | 1-2 | 2-2 | 2-3 | 2-2 | 0-1 | 1-0 | X | 1-1 | 4-3 | 0-1 | 3-1 | 1-0 |
| 12 | Pilkington | 0-3 | 1-0 | 1-2 | 3-2 | 2-3 | 3-5 | 1-1 | 3-3 | 1-1 | 4-0 | 3-1 | X | 1-3 | 2-3 | 3-2 | 0-3 |
| 13 | Poynton | 2-2 | 0-3 | 1-1 | 2-2 | 5-1 | 2-2 | 4-1 | 0-2 | 3-3 | 4-0 | 1-0 | 3-2 | X | 1-1 | 3-2 | 5-1 |
| 14 | Rylands | 5-1 | 0-3 | 0-2 | 1-1 | 2-4 | 0-3 | 0-2 | 1-2 | 2-5 | 9-2 | 0-1 | 4-3 | 2-4 | X | 5-2 | 2-0 |
| 15 | Warrington Boro | 3-4 | 0-6 | 2-3 | 4-3 | 3-5 | 2-3 | 1-2 | 0-1 | 3-2 | 3-2 | 1-1 | 1-2 | 1-2 | 0-0 | X | 2-0 |
| 16 | Whitchurch Alp | 4-0 | 1-2 | 0-1 | 1-6 | 3-1 | 0-1 | 1-3 | 0-1 | 0-1 | 4-2 | 1-4 | 2-5 | 1-4 | 1-0 | 2-1 | X |

## DIVISION ONE LEAGUE CUP 1998-99

**SEMI FINALS**

Knutsford v Barnton 2-2, 2*4

Poynton v Beeches p-p

**FINAL**

Barnton v Beeches 1-0

## DIVISION TWO LEAGUE CUP 1998-99

**SEMI FINALS**

Broadheath Central v Malpas 0-0, 1-1, 5p4

Padgate St Oswalds v Walkers S & S 2-1

**FINAL**

Broadheath Central v Padgate St Oswalds 0-1

## PRESIDENT'S CUP 1998-99

**SEMI FINALS**

Chorlton Town v Garswood United 1-3

Rylands Reserves v Whitchurch A 0-2

**FINAL**

Garswood United v Whitchurch Alport 2-1

## ASTRA ZENECA

**Chairman:** David Lea **Manager:** Chris Owen
**Secretary:** David Stubbs, 11 Petunia Grove,
Macclesfield, Cheshire SK11 7YY (01625
423160)
**Ground:** Mulberry Leisure Centre, Alderley Edge
**Colours:** All Green
**Change Colours:** Yellow/Black

## BARNTON AFC

**Chairman:** William Perrin **Manager:** Mark Emmerson
**Secretary:** Michael Webster, 92 Church Road, Barnton
CW8 4JE (01606 782960)
**Ground:** Townfield, Townfield Lane, Barnton
**Colours:** Black & White Stripes/Black
**Change Colours:** Amber/Blue

## BEECHES FC

**Chairman:** Gordon Rigby **Manager:** A Hockenhull
**Secretary:** David Corrigan, 7 Burrows Ave, Haydock,
St Helens WA11 0DE (01744 757273)
**Ground:** Cowley Fields, Wynne Road, St Helens
**Colours:** Claret & Blue/Claret
**Change Colours:** Red & Blue Halves/Blue

## BOLLINGTON ATHLETIC FC

**Chairman:** Albert Hall
**Secretary:** Anthony Holmes, 1 Princess Drive, Bollington,
Macclesfield SK10 5ES (01625 574913)
**Ground:** Recreation Ground, Bollington
**Colours:** Green & White Stripes/White
**Change Colours:** Blue & White Hoops/Blue

## CHEADLE HEATH NOMADS

**Chairman:** Roy Welsh **Manager:** Peter Blundell
**Secretary:** George Gibbons, 3 Hurley Drive,
Cheadle Hulme, Stockport SK8 6DH
**Ground:** The Heath, Norbreck Ave, Cheadle, Stockport
**Colours:** Maroon & Sky Blue/Maroon
**Change Colours:** Black & White Stripes/Black

## CHORLTON TOWN

**Chairman:** TBA **Manager:** Graham Wright
**Secretary:** Jim Calderbank, 21 South Meade, Timperley,
Altrincham, Cheshire WA15 6QL
**Ground:** Parkway Ground, Rylstone Avenue, Chorlton
**Colours:** Red & Black/White
**Change Colours:** Yellow or Blue/Blue

## GARSWOOD UNITED FC

**Chairman:** Barry Mavers **Manager:** Alan Aspinall
**Secretary:** John Anelay, 128 Victoria Road, Garswood,
Wigan WN4 0RE (01942 492623)
**Ground:** The Wooders, Simms Lane End, Garswood
**Colours:** Blue & White Halves/Blue
**Change Colours:** All Yellow

## GROVE UNITED FC

**Chairman:** Mark Boothby **Manager:** John Whiteley
**Secretary:** Bernard Jordan, 25 Bean Leach Road, Hazel
Grove, Stockport SK7 4LD (0161 456 2542)
**Ground:** Half Moon Lane, Offerton, Stockport
**Colours:** Red/Black
**Change Colours:** Lt Blue & Claret Stripes/Claret

## KNUTSFORD FC

**Chairman:** TBA **Manager:** Ken Harrison
**Secretary:** Kevin Deeley, 28 East Street, Guide Bridge,
Manchester, M34 5DX (0161 320 9650)
**Ground:** Manchester Road, Knutsford
**Colours:** Red & Black Stripes/Black
**Change Colours:** White/Blue

## LINOTYPE FC

**Chairman:** James Barry **Manager:** Jim Vince
**Secretary:** Brian McGuiness, 36 Barrington Road,
Altrincham, Cheshire (0161 929 0021)
**Ground:** British Airways Club, Clay Lane, Timperley
**Colours:** White/Black
**Change Colours:** Red & Black/White

## MIDDLEWICH TOWN FC

**Chairman:** Steven Morris **Manager:** David Twite
**Secretary:** Vic Knop, Ashford, 5 Hough Lane, Aderton,
Northwich CW9 6AB (01606 76545)
**Ground:** Seddon Street, Middlewich (01606 835842)
**Colours:** Red/White
**Change Colours:** All Blue

## PADGATE ST OSWALDS FC

**Chairman:** Graham Millins **Manager:** Mick Armitage
**Secretary:** Brian Hughes, 13 Jubilee Ave, Padgate,
Warrington WA1 3JY (01925 490924)
**Ground:** Bennets Rec. Ground, Station Rd, Padgate
**Colours:** Black & White Stripes/Black
**Change Colours:** Yellow/Green

## PILKINGTON AFC

**Chairman:** Barry Meadows **Manager:** David Burrows
**Secretary:** Paul Pinder, 629 Eltonhead Road, Sutton
Heath, St Helens WA9 5SX (01744 816158)
**Ground:** Ruskin Drive, St Helens
**Colours:** Blue & Black Stripes/Black
**Change Colours:** Red & Black Stripes/Red

## POYNTON FC

**Chairman:** David Corcoran **Manager:** Paul Cunningham
**Secretary:** Mark Warburton, 27 Alderley Close, Hazel
Grove, Stockport SK7 6BS (01625 873872)
**Ground:** London Road North, Poynton
**Colours:** Red & Black/Black
**Change Colours:** Blue & White/Blue

## RYLANDS FC

**Chairman:** Alan Jackson **Manager:** Terry Selby
**Secretary:** Ian Finchett, 31 Elizabeth Drive, Padgate,
Warrington WA1 4JQ (01925 816911)
**Ground:** Rylands Rec. Club, Gorsey Lane, Warrington
**Colours:** Blue & Black/Black
**Change Colours:** Red & Royal Blue/Blue

## WHITCHURCH ALPORT

**Chairman:** P Wainwright **Manager:** Alan Smith
**Secretary:** Robert Dutton, 7 Nessina Grove, Crewe,
Cheshire CW2 8EL (01270 663015)
**Ground:** Yockings Park, Blackpark Rd, Whitchurch
**Colours:** Green & White/Black
**Change Colours:** Red/Black

# DIVISION TWO
# CLUBS 1999-2000

## BROADHEATH CENTRAL FC
**Chairman:** Ian Beresford  **Manager:** Peter Cavanagh

**Secretary:** Graham Anderson, 1 Foxglove Drive, Broadheath, Altrincham  (0161 718 9093)
**Ground:** Viaduct Road, Broadheath, Altrincham
**Colours:** Black & Red Stripes/Black
**Change Colours:** Blue & White Stripes/White

## CHESTER NOMADS FC
**Chairman:** Phil Darlington **Manager:** Jerry Ireland
**Secretary:** Ritz Ritzema, 22 Cross Green Upton, Chester CH2 1QR  (01244 379791)
**Ground:** Garrison Ground, Eaton Rd, Handbridge
**Colours:** Amber/Black
**Change Colours:** Grey/Red

## CHORLTON TOWN RESERVES
**Chairman:** TBA  **Manager:** Graham Wright
**Secretary:** Jim Calderbank, 21 South Meade, Timperley, Altrincham, Cheshire WA15 6QL
**Ground:** Parkway Ground, Rylstone Avenue, Chorlton
**Colours:** Red & Black/White
**Change Colours:** Yellow or Blue/Blue

## CREWE FC
**Chairman:** Patrick Slack  **Manager:** Ian O'Reilly
**Secretary:** Mrs M Vickers, 59 Hall-o-Shaw St, Crewe (01270 581578)
**Ground:** Cumberland Sprts Grnd, Thomas St, Crewe
**Colours:** Blue/Blue
**Change Colours:** Yellow/Black

## ELLESMERE PORT UNITED FC
**Chairman:** TBA  **Manager:** TBA
**Secretary:** Tony Wallace, 39 Gantby Road, Birkenhead, Merseyside L41 7DS  (083117 9065)
**Ground:** Ellesmere Port Stadium
**Colours:** All Blue
**Change Colours:** All White

## FLIXTON FC RESERVES
**Chairman:** Peter Dentitch  **Manager:** Len Heywood
**Secretary:** Stuart Nichols, 20 Brompton Rd, Stretford, Manchester M32 9PR  (0161 747 5288)
**Ground:** Valley Rd, Flixton, M'chester  (0161 7477757)
**Colours:** Blue & White/Blue
**Change Colours:** Gold/Black

## GARSWOOD UNITED FC RESERVES
**Chairman:** Barry Mavers  **Manager:** Alan Clarke
**Secretary:** John Anelay, 128 Victoria Road, Garswood, Wigan WN4 0RE  (01942 492623)
**Ground:** The Wooders, Simms Lane End,  Garswood
**Colours:** Blue & White Halves/Blue
**Change Colours:** All Yellow

## LINOTYPE FC RESERVES
**Chairman:** James Barry  **Manager:** Philip Deadman
**Secretary:** Brian McGuiness, 36 Barrington Road, Altrincham, Cheshire  (0161 929 0021)
**Ground:** British Airways Club, Clay Lane, Timperley
**Colours:** White/Black
**Change Colours:** Red & Black/White

## LITTLEMOOR FC
**Chairman:** Arthur McClelan **Manager:** Frank Sanders
**Secretary:** Stanley McQuarrie, 96 Mottram Towers, Mottram St, Hillgate, SK1 3NY (0161 2925461)
**Ground:** Warth Meadow, Welkin Rd, Lower Bredbury
**Colours:** Black & White Stripes/Black
**Change Colours:** All Maroon

## LOSTOCK GRALAM FC
**Chairman:** D Washburn  **Manager:** Andy Hough
**Secretary:** Andy Hough, 31 Beechwood Drive, Wincham, Northwich CW9 6EY  (01565 733383)
**Ground:** Slow & Easy Hotel, Manchester Rd, Lostock G.
**Colours:** All Blue
**Change Colours:** Green & Yellow Halves/Black

## MALPAS FC
**Chairman:** Robert Leslie  **Manager:** Martin Holden
**Secretary:** Bernard Lloyd, 15 Springfield Ave, Malpas, Cheshire SY14 8QD  (01948 860812)
**Ground:** Malpas & Dt SC, Oxheys, Wrexham Rd, Malpas
**Colours:** Green & White Hoops/White
**Change Colours:** Red/Black

## POYNTON FC RESERVES
**Chairman:** David Corcoran **Manager:** Mark Warburton
**Secretary:** Mark Warburton, 27 Alderley Close, Hazel Grove, Stockport SK7 6BS  (01625 873872)
**Ground:** London Road North, Poynton
**Colours:** Red & Black/Black
**Change Colours:** Blue & White/Blue

## RYLANDS FC RESERVES
**Chairman:** Alan Jackson  **Manager:** Alan Blackstone

**Secretary:** Ian Finchett, 31 Elizabeth Drive, Padgate, Warrington WA1 4JQ  (01925 816911)
**Ground:** Rylands Rec. Club, Gorsey Lane, Warrington
**Colours:** Red & Royal Blue/Blue
**Change Colours:** Blue & Black/Black

## STYAL FC
**Chairman:** Barry Green  **Manager:** TBA
**Secretary:** Alan Jones, 1 Oak Brow Cottages, Altrincham Rd, Styal, Wilmslow SK9 4JE (01625 530270)
**Ground:** Altrincham Road, Styal
**Colours:** Yellow/Blue
**Change Colours:** Blue/Black

## TRAFFORD FC RESERVES
**Chairman:** David Brown  **Manager:** Dave Norman
**Secretary:** Graham Foxhall, 62 Grosvenor Rd, Urmston, Manchester M41 5AQ  (0161 746 9726)
**Ground:** Shawe View, Pennybridge Lane, Urmston
**Colours:** All White
**Change Colours:** Red/Navy

## WALKERS SPORTS & SOCIAL FC
**Chairman:** Tom Tandy  **Manager:** John Green
**Secretary:** Billy Cowell, 55 Fleetwood Close, Gt Sankey, Warrington WA5 2US  (01925 721494)
**Ground:** Tetley Walkers SC, Long Lane  01925 634904
**Colours:** White/Red
**Change Colours:** All Blue

## WARRINGTON BOROUGH FC
**Chairman:** Harry Buden  **Manager:** Derek Holden
**Secretary:** John Kent, 126 Cumberland ST, Warrington, WA4 1EX  (01925 482970)
**Ground:** Cantilever Park  (01925 724421)
**Colours:** Blue & Yellow Halves/Blue
**Change Colours:** All Red

# SGL SEAT CARS
# WEST LANCASHIRE LEAGUE

**President:** D Procter

**Chairman & Secretary:** W Carr
60 Selby Avenue, Blackpool, Lancashire FY4 2LZ
Tel: 01253 348450

The League was re-organised into three Senior Divisions for the first time since the formation of the league in 1904. The First and Second Divisions were slimmed down to sixteen teams in each and the bottom six teams formed the basis for the new Division Two; four new clubs Barrow Rangers, Coppull United, Fleetwood Anchor and Millom were recruited, but British Aerospace (Samlesbury) resigned before the season commenced. Division One was renamed Premier Division, Division Two became Division One, three new clubs, Askam Utd. from Cumbria along with Burnley Belvedere and Heywood from East Lancashire will join Division Two next season to make the new division eleven strong. Also the two reserve divisions will have four more teams to make a total of 29 reserve teams of member clubs.

Fulwood Amateurs retained the Hollands Lancashire Challenge Shield by beating Division One colleagues Garstang, by 4 goals to 1, further to enhance the league's record of ten wins and nine runners-up but had the disappointment of not being promoted due to the decision to reduce the two senior divisions; they made sure of promotion this time by finishing champions with Norcross & Warbreck runners-up, and it was good to see the success of these two long-serving clubs. Wrens were founder members when the league was re-formed in 1959, and they also won the Fair Play Trophy for the second year in succession. Carnforth Rangers members since 1962 took Division One opponents Milnthorpe Corinthians to extra time before conceding the Presidents Cup Final by 2 goals to 1. The Wilson Carradus trophy for Hospitality was again won by Bootle (Cumbria).

Eagley won the Houston Cup for the first time after a close game against Freckleton, and they also achieved the Double by winning the Reserve Div. One Championship.

Roy Tomlinson that dedicated club Chairman/Secretary/everything-else was the popular winner of the League's Exceptional Merit award, and Barbara Knagg for her excellent work as Secretary of Vickers won the Secretary of the Season award.

The League are delighted that all our Sponsors will be continuing next season with S.G.L Leyland the Sponsor of the League and the President's Cup.

Derrick Procter

## FINAL LEAGUE TABLES 1998-99

### PREMIER DIVISION

| | P | W | D | L | F | A | Pts |
|---|---|---|---|---|---|---|---|
| Fulwood Amateur | 30 | 23 | 5 | 2 | 87 | 23 | 74 |
| Charnock Richard | 30 | 21 | 5 | 4 | 98 | 43 | 68 |
| Vickers Sports Club | 30 | 20 | 3 | 7 | 72 | 35 | 63 |
| Kirkham & Wesham -3 | 30 | 20 | 5 | 5 | 86 | 33 | 62 |
| Lansil | 30 | 15 | 4 | 11 | 61 | 54 | 49 |
| Dalton United | 30 | 14 | 5 | 11 | 59 | 48 | 47 |
| Wyre Villa | 30 | 12 | 4 | 14 | 54 | 65 | 40 |
| Leyland Motors Athletic | 30 | 12 | 3 | 15 | 66 | 56 | 39 |
| Feniscowles | 30 | 11 | 5 | 14 | 43 | 49 | 38 |
| Eagley | 30 | 11 | 3 | 16 | 58 | 75 | 36 |
| Burnley United | 30 | 10 | 3 | 17 | 46 | 67 | 33 |
| Freckleton -3 | 30 | 10 | 4 | 16 | 44 | 56 | 31 |
| Blackrod Town | 30 | 9 | 4 | 17 | 42 | 63 | 31 |
| Springfields | 30 | 9 | 4 | 17 | 50 | 88 | 31 |
| Padiham | 30 | 9 | 2 | 19 | 41 | 70 | 29 |
| Fleetwood Hesketh | 30 | 2 | 5 | 23 | 33 | 115 | 11 |

### DIVISION ONE

| | P | W | D | L | F | A | Pts |
|---|---|---|---|---|---|---|---|
| Barnoldswick United | 30 | 21 | 5 | 4 | 91 | 39 | 68 |
| Norcross & Warbreck | 30 | 19 | 6 | 5 | 74 | 38 | 63 |
| Tempest United | 30 | 17 | 5 | 8 | 59 | 47 | 56 |
| BAC Preston | 30 | 14 | 7 | 9 | 59 | 46 | 49 |
| Milnthorpe Corinthians | 30 | 12 | 11 | 7 | 60 | 39 | 47 |
| Whinney Hill | 30 | 14 | 4 | 12 | 64 | 50 | 46 |
| Hesketh Bank | 30 | 12 | 7 | 11 | 55 | 63 | 43 |
| Poulton Town -3 | 30 | 13 | 6 | 11 | 58 | 44 | 42 |
| Wigan College -6 | 30 | 13 | 5 | 12 | 59 | 54 | 38 |
| Thornton C'leys Inter -3 | 30 | 11 | 7 | 12 | 60 | 64 | 37 |
| Preston West End | 30 | 8 | 10 | 12 | 45 | 65 | 34 |
| Lancashire Constab | 30 | 8 | 7 | 15 | 45 | 58 | 31 |
| Haslingden St Mary's | 30 | 8 | 5 | 17 | 44 | 73 | 29 |
| Garstang | 30 | 6 | 10 | 14 | 53 | 67 | 28 |
| Turton | 30 | 7 | 7 | 16 | 44 | 64 | 28 |
| Lytham St Annes | 30 | 4 | 4 | 22 | 32 | 91 | 16 |

## PREMIER DIVISION RESULTS CHART 1998-99

| | | 1 | 2 | 3 | 4 | 5 | 6 | 7 | 8 | 9 | 10 | 11 | 12 | 13 | 14 | 15 | 16 |
|---|---|---|---|---|---|---|---|---|---|---|---|---|---|---|---|---|---|
| 1 | Blackrod Town | X | 3-1 | 0-2 | 1-2 | 6-0 | 1-3 | 3-1 | 2-1 | 1-1 | 2-3 | 4-2 | 1-0 | 0-2 | 2-2 | 1-2 | 1-3 |
| 2 | Burnley United | 1-0 | X | 1-5 | 1-0 | 4-1 | 2-1 | 1-1 | 1-3 | 0-1 | 1-5 | 0-2 | 0-3 | 2-1 | 4-0 | 1-5 | 1-3 |
| 3 | Charnock Richard | 3-0 | 6-2 | X | 1-1 | 4-0 | 1-2 | 9-2 | 1-0 | 2-0 | 4-5 | 2-1 | 3-2 | 7-0 | 5-1 | 0-0 | 4-2 |
| 4 | Dalton United | 6-0 | 3-1 | 2-2 | X | 2-1 | 2-0 | 3-4 | 1-2 | 1-2 | 1-5 | 0-1 | 2-0 | 5-0 | 1-0 | 1-2 | 1-1 |
| 5 | Eagley | 1-2 | 1-0 | 2-2 | 5-3 | X | 2-1 | 2-3 | 4-1 | 1-3 | 0-2 | 1-2 | 3-1 | 1-3 | 5-0 | 3-2 | 4-1 |
| 6 | Feniscowles | 0-2 | 4-2 | 0-6 | 0-3 | 3-0 | X | 2-2 | 0-0 | 0-1 | 0-3 | 0-1 | 0-2 | 1-0 | 1-3 | 0-0 | 1-1 |
| 7 | Fleetwood Hesketh | 2-2 | 1-4 | 0-5 | 1-5 | 1-3 | 1-2 | X | 1-2 | 0-6 | 1-7 | 0-2 | 1-2 | 3-3 | 0-1 | 1-4 | 1-1 |
| 8 | Freckleton | 0-0 | 3-5 | 2-3 | 0-3 | 3-0 | 0-1 | 3-1 | X | 0-0 | 1-5 | 3-3 | 4-1 | 3-0 | 2-4 | 1-0 | 2-1 |
| 9 | Fulwood Amateurs | 3-0 | 2-0 | 6-0 | 0-0 | 4-2 | 3-2 | 9-0 | 3-0 | X | 3-2 | 2-2 | 4-0 | 5-1 | 8-0 | 0-0 | 3-0 |
| 10 | Kirkham & Wesham | 4-0 | 1-1 | 2-1 | 4-0 | 2-2 | 2-0 | 3-0 | 2-0 | 5-0 | X | 0-1 | 2-2 | 1-0 | 2-3 | 2-1 | 0-0 |
| 11 | Lansil | 3-2 | 4-0 | 1-5 | 1-2 | 2-4 | 2-2 | 7-1 | 3-1 | 1-5 | 1-3 | X | 3-2 | 4-1 | 1-3 | 2-1 | 1-3 |
| 12 | Leyland Motors Ath | 3-0 | 0-3 | 4-5 | 1-3 | 1-1 | 2-3 | 9-1 | 2-1 | 2-3 | 2-0 | 2-2 | X | 4-1 | 4-1 | 2-3 | 5-2 |
| 13 | Padiham | 2-1 | 3-1 | 1-3 | 2-3 | 3-1 | 1-3 | 3-1 | 1-3 | 0-2 | 1-1 | 1-0 | 0-1 | X | 4-0 | 2-3 | 0-4 |
| 14 | Springfields | 4-1 | 0-0 | 4-0 | 3-3 | 7-1 | 1-5 | 4-0 | 2-0 | 0-4 | 2-9 | 2-3 | 0-5 | 0-3 | X | 0-3 | 1-2 |
| 15 | Vickers SC | 4-1 | 3-2 | 0-1 | 4-0 | 2-4 | 2-1 | 5-2 | 3-2 | 0-1 | 2-1 | 1-0 | 2-1 | 4-0 | 4-2 | X | 7-0 |
| 16 | Wyre Villa | 2-3 | 2-4 | 0-2 | 3-0 | 5-3 | 1-5 | 3-0 | 3-1 | 1-3 | 1-3 | 1-3 | 2-1 | 3-2 | 2-0 | 1-3 | X |

## DIVISION ONE RESULTS CHART 1998-99

| | | 1 | 2 | 3 | 4 | 5 | 6 | 7 | 8 | 9 | 10 | 11 | 12 | 13 | 14 | 15 | 16 |
|---|---|---|---|---|---|---|---|---|---|---|---|---|---|---|---|---|---|
| 1 | BAC Preston | X | 2-4 | 0-2 | 3-1 | 4-4 | 1-3 | 3-0 | 3-0 | 1-1 | 2-0 | 1-2 | 4-2 | 4-3 | 4-4 | 2-1 | 1-1 |
| 2 | Barnoldswick Utd | 0-0 | X | 1-1 | 3-2 | 4-1 | 2-0 | 8-0 | 3-0 | 4-1 | 2-1 | 4-0 | 0-2 | 5-1 | 5-1 | 5-3 | 2-0 |
| 3 | Garstang | 1-1 | 2-5 | X | 6-0 | 2-2 | 3-4 | 7-2 | 1-1 | 1-1 | 0-5 | 1-1 | 2-3 | 2-2 | 1-3 | 1-2 | 3-1 |
| 4 | Haslingden St Marys | 1-7 | 1-2 | 2-0 | X | 1-5 | 1-0 | 1-2 | 2-0 | 1-1 | 6-3 | 2-2 | 0-6 | 3-4 | 2-0 | 1-0 | 4-5 |
| 5 | Hesketh Bank | 0-4 | 1-3 | 2-1 | 2-0 | X | 3-2 | 3-0 | 2-1 | 1-2 | 2-1 | 0-0 | 4-2 | 2-4 | 2-1 | 3-4 | 2-0 |
| 6 | Lancashire Constab. | 0-1 | 1-0 | 1-2 | 1-1 | 2-4 | X | 2-1 | 1-2 | 3-2 | 1-4 | 1-2 | 0-2 | 3-4 | 2-2 | 1-3 | 1-1 |
| 7 | Lytham St Annes | 3-2 | 0-3 | 1-3 | 2-1 | 0-1 | 1-5 | X | 1-3 | 0-4 | 1-1 | 2-2 | 1-2 | 1-3 | 1-4 | 0-4 | 0-1 |
| 8 | Milnthorpe Corinthians | 2-0 | 3-3 | 3-0 | 5-0 | 2-2 | 1-1 | 4-1 | X | 0-0 | 1-1 | 3-2 | 4-1 | 1-1 | 4-0 | 2-3 | 2-2 |
| 9 | Norcross & Warbreck | 2-0 | 7-2 | 3-3 | 2-0 | 6-1 | 3-1 | 4-0 | 2-2 | X | 2-1 | 4-2 | 1-0 | 3-2 | 4-2 | 2-1 | 1-0 |
| 10 | Poulton Town | 0-1 | 4-4 | 0-0 | 1-1 | 3-0 | 3-0 | 3-2 | 1-0 | 3-0 | X | 2-2 | 2-0 | 3-0 | 2-1 | 1-3 | 1-3 |
| 11 | Preston West End | 2-0 | 1-6 | 5-5 | 3-1 | 0-0 | 1-1 | 1-4 | 1-4 | 0-5 | 0-4 | X | 0-2 | 2-1 | 1-1 | 1-2 | 5-0 |
| 12 | Tempest United | 0-0 | 0-1 | 2-0 | 4-2 | 3-1 | 0-3 | 1-1 | 2-1 | 0-5 | 3-2 | 2-2 | X | 5-3 | 3-0 | 2-1 | 3-2 |
| 13 | Thornton Cleveleys | 2-0 | 0-5 | 4-2 | 1-3 | 2-2 | 1-1 | 4-0 | 1-1 | 0-2 | 3-1 | 3-1 | 1-2 | X | 1-1 | 4-3 | 1-2 |
| 14 | Turton | 1-2 | 1-4 | 3-0 | 0-0 | 2-2 | 0-1 | 2-0 | 2-4 | 3-1 | 1-2 | 0-1 | 1-1 | 0-4 | X | 5-4 | 3-1 |
| 15 | Whinney Hill | 1-2 | 1-1 | 4-0 | 0-2 | 3-0 | 4-0 | 4-4 | 0-0 | 3-1 | 3-2 | 1-2 | 2-3 | 0-0 | 1-0 | X | 3-1 |
| 16 | Wigan College | 3-4 | 2-0 | 3-1 | 3-2 | 4-1 | 3-3 | 5-1 | 0-4 | 1-2 | 0-1 | 4-1 | 1-1 | 4-1 | 4-0 | 2-0 | X |

## LANCASHIRE CHALLENGE SHIELD 1998-99

| Winners | Runners Up |
|---|---|
| Fulwood Amateur | Garstang |

## RICHARDSON CUP 1998-99

| Winners | Runners Up |
|---|---|
| Kirkham & Wesham | Blackrod Town |

## PRESIDENT'S CUP 1998-99

| Winners | Runners Up |
|---|---|
| Milnthorpe Corinthians | Carnforth Rangers |

## LEADING GOALSCORERS 1998-99

**PREMIER DIVISION**

| 37 | S Walker | Vickers Sports |
|---|---|---|
| 31 | T Speak | Lansil |
| 30 | P Nicholson | Kirkham & W |

**DIVISION ONE**

| 46 | P Corrigan | Barnoldswick U |
|---|---|---|
| 22 | P Hutchinson | Tempest United |
| 20 | L Catlow | Norcross & W |

**DIVISION TWO**

| 32 | D Barron | Blackpool WR |
|---|---|---|
| 25 | L Watson | Carnforth Rgrs |
| 17 | D Donaldson | Preston WE |

# MANCHESTER FOOTBALL LEAGUE

**President:** P Morris

**Secretary:** Paul Bishop, 21 Church Walk, Stalybridge, Cheshire SK15 1DL
Tel: 0161 303 1581

The 1998-99 Manchester Football League season proved to be one of the most eventful and entertaining in many years. Unfortunately, it also saw the League lose one of football's genuine characters in Secretary Jim Warrington, who passed away in November, leaving amateur football in the Manchester area bereft of one of its most tireless administrators, and a true friend.

On the park, the League's constitution, of two divisions of sixteen and twenty clubs respectively, changed before a ball was kicked as Lostock, previously known as British Aerospce, resigned. The Indian summer saw Prestwich Heys and Wythenshawe Amateurs make the early running in the Premier Division, whilst Willows, pipped for promotion at the end of the previous season, and Wilmslow Albion both set off in determined form in the First Division.

As the season reached its hectic climax, the Premier Division title shoot-out turned into a two horse race as Stand Athletic and East Manchester slugged it out, but East's' crucial defeat at Prestwich Heys allowed Stand to nudge ahead and the Whitefield based side eventually cantered home to win the title by a massive twelve point margin, providing Manger Nick Davis with some silverware in only his second season in charge. With Tottington's early exit, only one team faced the drop, and Stockport Georgians just fell short in a thrilling run in, finishing the season bottom as Failsworth Town and Little Hulton United both dug deep to get the points that would leave them safe. With only twelve points separating sixth placed Prestwich Heys from Stockport Georgians at the bottom, the Premier Division proved a much tighter affair then usual, boding well for the coming season. Monton Amateurs claimed third place in what was a good campaign for the Eccles club, but the gloss was taken off their season when vandals burnt down their excellent facilities in April. Last season's Champions Springhead could not rekindle their cracking form, ending the season in seventh, whilst both the Division's new boys, Failsworth Town and Urmston, survived their debut season. The recovery of the year came from Elton Fold, who rallied from relegation candidates in February to finish eighth as they look forward to moving to a brand new ground later in 1999.

So the Manchester League, one of the oldest and most respected competitions in the country, looks forward to the 1999-2000 season, which promises to be yet another fascinating campaign. Ambitious Stand Athletic will be looking to repeat their Premier Division triumph, but with East Manchester and Wythenshawe Amateurs waiting in the wings, plus any from a group of top quality clubs in the chasing pack, they will have to battle all the way to keep the Championship trophy. The First Division should also continue to provide a gripping contest with Tintwistle Villa, Gamesley, Wilmslow Albion, Whitworth Valley, Milton and Breightmet United likely to be among the front runners, and with the Gilgryst Cup and Murray Shield dispensing their usual quota of shocks the new millennium should see the Manchester League going from strength to strength, and continuing to provide a high standard of football at county level across the Greater Manchester area.

## FINAL LEAGUE TABLES 1998-99

### PREMIER DIVISION

| | P | W | D | L | F | A | Pts |
|---|---|---|---|---|---|---|---|
| Stand Athletic | 28 | 19 | 5 | 4 | 76 | 35 | 62 |
| East Manchester | 28 | 15 | 5 | 8 | 56 | 45 | 50 |
| Monton Amateurs | 28 | 13 | 7 | 8 | 47 | 37 | 46 |
| Wythenshawe Am | 28 | 12 | 9 | 7 | 43 | 36 | 45 |
| Mitchell Shackleton | 28 | 13 | 4 | 11 | 57 | 47 | 43 |
| Prestwich Heys | 28 | 11 | 6 | 11 | 52 | 48 | 39 |
| Springhead | 28 | 10 | 6 | 12 | 43 | 40 | 36 |
| Elton Fold | 28 | 11 | 3 | 14 | 40 | 50 | 36 |
| Dukinfield | 28 | 10 | 6 | 12 | 38 | 49 | 36 |
| Atherton Town | 28 | 9 | 8 | 11 | 44 | 43 | 35 |
| BICC | 28 | 8 | 11 | 9 | 62 | 62 | 35 |
| Urmston | 28 | 9 | 5 | 14 | 44 | 60 | 32 |
| Railsworth Town | 28 | 9 | 5 | 14 | 42 | 61 | 32 |
| Little Hulton Utd | 28 | 8 | 6 | 14 | 43 | 55 | 30 |
| Stockport Georgians | 28 | 7 | 6 | 15 | 33 | 52 | 27 |

Tottington United - Record expunged

### FIRST DIVISION

| | P | W | D | L | F | A | Pts |
|---|---|---|---|---|---|---|---|
| Willows* | 34 | 27 | 5 | 2 | 116 | 42 | 83 |
| Pennington | 34 | 21 | 6 | 7 | 81 | 48 | 69 |
| Wilmslow Albion* | 34 | 20 | 8 | 6 | 78 | 53 | 66 |
| Whitworth Valley | 34 | 18 | 11 | 5 | 93 | 56 | 65 |
| Breightmet Utd | 34 | 18 | 5 | 11 | 82 | 55 | 59 |
| Tintwistle Villa** | 33 | 18 | 3 | 12 | 84 | 64 | 57 |
| Gamesley** | 33 | 16 | 5 | 12 | 81 | 64 | 54 |
| Milton | 34 | 14 | 8 | 12 | 67 | 56 | 50 |
| Avro | 34 | 14 | 4 | 16 | 56 | 59 | 46 |
| Manchester Royal | 34 | 12 | 9 | 13 | 55 | 73 | 45 |
| Sacred Heart | 34 | 12 | 5 | 17 | 65 | 77 | 41 |
| Hindsford | 34 | 10 | 6 | 18 | 66 | 75 | 38 |
| Old Alts | 34 | 9 | 9 | 16 | 50 | 75 | 38 |
| Whalley Range | 34 | 11 | 5 | 18 | 74 | 112 | 36 |
| Ashton Athletic | 34 | 10 | 6 | 18 | 64 | 65 | 36 |
| New Mills | 34 | 8 | 10 | 16 | 56 | 75 | 34 |
| Wythenshawe Town | 34 | 5 | 11 | 18 | 32 | 59 | 26 |
| Hollinwood | 34 | 1 | 6 | 27 | 29 | 121 | 9 |

GM Police - Record expunged
* Points deducted
** Gamesley v Tintwistle Villa fixture subject to FA Inquiry

# PREMIER DIVISION RESULTS CHART 1998-99

| | | 1 | 2 | 3 | 4 | 5 | 6 | 7 | 8 | 9 | 10 | 11 | 12 | 13 | 14 | 15 | 16 |
|---|---|---|---|---|---|---|---|---|---|---|---|---|---|---|---|---|---|
| 1 | Atherton Town | X | 2-2 | 2-1 | 1-1 | 0-1 | 8-0 | 0-0 | 3-4 | 0-3 | 3-2 | 2-2 | 1-1 | 0-2 | 0-2 | 1-1 | 2-1 |
| 2 | BICC | 2-2 | X | 2-3 | 2-4 | 2-2 | 4-2 | 2-3 | 0-4 | 1-1 | 4-4 | 2-1 | 4-4 | 4-1 | A-A | 2-1 | 2-2 |
| 3 | Dukinfield Town | 0-1 | 0-4 | X | 1-2 | 2-1 | 1-2 | 3-1 | 2-0 | 1-0 | 3-3 | 0-0 | 0-4 | 3-1 | 2-1 | 3-2 | 1-1 |
| 4 | East Manchester | 2-1 | 3-1 | 1-0 | X | 2-2 | 2-4 | 5-1 | 2-1 | 1-2 | 1-1 | 1-0 | 1-2 | 5-2 | 2-1 | 1-0 | 2-2 |
| 5 | Elton Ford | 1-4 | 2-1 | 3-3 | 2-3 | X | 3-2 | 3-0 | 1-3 | 1-3 | 1-0 | 2-1 | 0-2 | 2-1 | A-A | 1-2 | 0-1 |
| 6 | Failsworth Town | 2-0 | 2-2 | 1-2 | 1-1 | 0-2 | X | 0-5 | 1-0 | 1-1 | 2-0 | 2-0 | 1-3 | 1-2 | 3-2 | 2-2 | 0-1 |
| 7 | Little Hulton United | 2-0 | 1-1 | 1-1 | 3-2 | 4-0 | 5-2 | X | 1-2 | 1-2 | 0-6 | 0-1 | 3-2 | 0-1 | A-A | 2-1 | 1-1 |
| 8 | Mitchell Shackleton | 2-3 | 5-1 | 3-1 | 2-3 | 2-0 | 1-0 | 5-4 | X | 2-0 | 0-1 | 1-4 | 1-3 | 1-1 | 4-2 | 2-1 | 1-3 |
| 9 | Monton Amateurs | 1-2 | 1-1 | 0-1 | 3-2 | 0-3 | 3-5 | 1-1 | 1-1 | X | 2-0 | 3-0 | 1-5 | 2-1 | A-A | 4-1 | 2-0 |
| 10 | Prestwich Heys | 2-1 | 2-4 | 1-2 | 1-0 | 4-1 | 1-3 | 2-1 | 1-1 | 1-4 | X | 3-0 | 0-3 | 2-1 | 1-1 | 1-1 | 1-2 |
| 11 | Springhead | 1-1 | 2-1 | 3-1 | 1-0 | 0-1 | 5-0 | 3-0 | 3-2 | 0-3 | 1-4 | X | 3-3 | 7-1 | 2-1 | 3-1 | 1-1 |
| 12 | Stand Athletic | 1-0 | 2-3 | 3-0 | 5-0 | 3-2 | 3-1 | 0-0 | 1-6 | 3-0 | 1-2 | 2-1 | X | 3-1 | 2-1 | 6-1 | 1-1 |
| 13 | Stockport Georgians | 2-0 | 1-4 | 3-1 | 0-1 | 3-1 | 0-2 | 3-2 | 1-2 | 1-1 | 1-1 | 0-0 | 1-1 | X | A-A | 0-1 | 1-2 |
| 14 | Tottington United | A-A | A-A | 2-2 | A-A | 0-1 | 0-6 | A-A | 2-2 | A-A | 3-3 | A-A | 2-1 | A-A | X | A-A | A-A |
| 15 | Urmston | 4-1 | 4-3 | 1-1 | 2-5 | 2-1 | 1-1 | 5-1 | 3-1 | 0-2 | 2-5 | 1-0 | 2-4 | 2-0 | 1-1 | X | 0-3 |
| 16 | Wythenshawe Ams | 0-3 | 1-1 | 3-1 | 2-3 | 0-1 | 3-2 | 1-0 | 2-2 | 1-1 | 3-1 | 2-0 | 0-4 | 1-1 | 0-2 | 4-0 | X |

Tottington United - Record expunged

# GILGRYST CUP 1998-99

**FIRST ROUND**

| | | | | | | | |
|---|---|---|---|---|---|---|---|
| Springhead | v | Stand Athletic | 0-2 | Stockport Georgians | v | Little Hulton Utd | 2-3 |
| Elton Fold | v | East Manchester | 1-5 | Atherton Town | v | Failsworth Town | 1-2 |
| Mitchell Shackleton | v | Prestwich Heys | 2-3 | Monton Amateurs | v | Dukinfield Town | 2-1 |
| BICC | v | Wythenshawe Amat | 2-3 | | | | |

**SECOND ROUND**

| | | | | | | | |
|---|---|---|---|---|---|---|---|
| East Manchester | v | Urmston | 2-1 | Failsworth Town | v | Prestwich Heys | 5-3 |
| Wythenshawe Amat | v | Little Hulton United | 3-1 | Stand Athletic | v | Monton Amateurs | 0-1 |

**SEMI-FINALS**

| | | | | | | | |
|---|---|---|---|---|---|---|---|
| East Manchester | v | Failsworth Town | 1-2 | Monton Amateurs | v | Wythenshawe Amat | 1-5 |

**FINAL**

| | | | | |
|---|---|---|---|---|
| Failsworth Town | v | Wythenshawe Amat | 1-2 | at Stockport Georgians |

# MURRAY SHIELD 1998-99

**PRELIMINARY ROUND**

| | | | | | | | |
|---|---|---|---|---|---|---|---|
| Tintwistle Villa | v | Breightmet United | 2-1 | Hollinwood | v | Wythenshawe Town | 1-5 |
| Old Alts | v | Pennington | 1*1, 4p2 | Ashton Athletic | v | New Mills | 1-0 |

**FIRST ROUND**

| | | | | | | | |
|---|---|---|---|---|---|---|---|
| Gamesley | v | Hindsford | 3-1 | Willows | v | Tintwistle Villa | 4-1 |
| Old Alts | v | Milton | 0-1 | Wilmslow Albion | v | Wythenshawe Town | 5*3 |
| GM Police | v | Whalley Range | 3*3, 3p4 | Ashton Athletic | v | Sacred Heart | 2*2, 0p3 |
| Manchester Royal | v | Whitworth Valley | 6-4 | | | | |

**SECOND ROUND**

| | | | | | | | |
|---|---|---|---|---|---|---|---|
| Avro | v | Sacred Heart | 3-2 | Gamesley | v | Whalley Range | 5-4 |
| Manchester Royal | v | Willows | 1-3 | Milton | v | Wilmslow Albion | 2-3 |

**SEMI-FINALS**

| | | | | | | | |
|---|---|---|---|---|---|---|---|
| Gamesley | v | Willows | 3-2 | Avro | v | Wilmslow Albion | 1-0 |

**FINAL**

| | | | | |
|---|---|---|---|---|
| Avro | v | Gamesley | 1-3 | at Springhead |

# LEADING GOALSCORERS 1998-99

**PREMIER DIVISION**

| | | |
|---|---|---|
| Micky Bartholomew | Stand Athletic | 29 |
| Mark Mitchell | Wythenshawe Amat | 22 |
| Chris Lowery | Mitchell Shackleton | 19 |
| Phil Hornby | Little Hulton United | 18 |
| Mike Platt | Monton Amateurs | 18 |

**FIRST DIVISION**

| | | |
|---|---|---|
| John Smith | Willows | 34 |
| Rory McDowell | Whitworth Valley | 31 |
| Daniel Christie | Pennington | 26 |
| Noel Green | Tintwistle Villa | 24 |
| Gamma Tembo | Whalley Range | 23 |

# ATHERTON TOWN

**Secretary:** G Butler, 43 Hope Fold Ave., Atherton, Lancs M29 0BW
**Tel:** 01942 870326
**Ground:** Howe Bridge Spts Centre, Howe Bridge, Atherton
**Tel:** 01942 884882
**Directions:** A579 Atherton to Leigh road - Sports Centre 800 yds on left
**Colours:** Royal/white/royal

# B.I.C.C.

**Secretary:** L. Stone, 51 Coppleridge Drive, Crumpsall, Manchester M8 4PB   **Tel:** 0161 740 6621
**Ground:** B.I.C.C. Works, Blackley New Road, Blackley.
**Directions:** Follow Rochdale Rd A664 from Manchester. Turn left at Brackley intoOld Market St, then fork right into Blackley New Rd, ground 300yards on left.(0161 740 9151)
**Colours:** Blue & white/blue/blue

# DUKINFIELD TOWN

**Secretary:** Paul Bishop, 21 Church Walk, Stalybridge, Cheshire
**Tel:** 0161 303 0398
**Ground:** Blocksages Playing Fields, Birch Lane, Dukinfield.
**Directions:** From Ashton centre follow Kings St, turn left into Chapel St. thenright turn into Foundry St/Birch Lane. Ground 880 yds on right, behind publicbaths.
**Colours:** All yellow

# EAST MANCHESTER

**Secretary:** D Wilkinson, 76 Sandy Lane, Dukinfield, Cheshire SK16 5NL   **Tel:** 0161 330 4450
**Ground:** Gorton League Complex, Kirkmanshulme Lane, Gorto.
**Directions:** Turn into Kirkmanshulme Lane at Belle Vue (A57) junction, groundapprox 880 yards on left after Pink Bank Lane.
**Colours:** All royal blue

# ELTON FOLD

**Secretary:** Guy Mallinson, 14 Lonsdale St, Bury BL8 2QD
**Tel:** 0161 797 7090
**Ground:** Bolton Rd Sports Club, Bolton Rd, Bury
**Directions:** A58 from Bury to Bolton. 1 mile from Bury pass Wellington Pub onright 200 yards turn left into Connaught St. Halfway down turn right in betweenhouses into car park
**Colours:** Blue & black/black/black

# FAILSWORTH TOWN

**Secretary:** David Walton, 45 Woodend Street, Oldham, Lancs
**Tel:** 0161 627 5480
**Ground:** GMT White House, Heaton Park, Manchester
**Directions:** M66 junc 5 towards Manchester, ground approx 1mile on right behindWhite House GMT Club.
**Colours:** Black & white/white/white

# MITCHELL SHACKLETON

**Secretary:** Ian Street, 11 Senior Road, Peel Green, Eccles, M30 7PZ
**Tel:** 0161 789 7061
**Ground:** Salteye Park, Peel Green, Eccles Tel: 0161 788 8373
**Directions:** Leave M63 at Peel Green r'bout (jct 2), take A57 Liverpool Roadtowards Irlam, ground entrance half mile on left behind Kara Cafew opposite Barton airport. Or, follow A57 from Manchester via Salford & Eccles, then follow Irlam signs.
**Colours:** Green & white/black/black

# MONTON AMATEURS

**Secretary:** T Lee, 28 Wheatley Rd, Swinton, Manchester M27 3RW
**Tel:** 0161 793 8033
**Ground:** Granary Lane, Worsley
**Directions:** From Eccles Centre turn right into Worsley Rd at Patricroft Bridge.Ground approx 1 mile on left, entrance just before Bridgewater Hotel
**Colours:** All royal

# PRESTWICH HEYS

**Secretary:** Stephen Howard, 28 Brandram Road, Prestwich, Manchester M25 1HJ  **Tel:** 0161 773 4408
**Ground:** Sandgate Rd, Prestwich   **Tel:** 0161 773 8888
**Directions:** Follow Old Bury Rd (A665) from Manchester to Prestwich, right intoHeywood Rd, 3rd left into Mount Rd/Sandgate Rd - ground on right.
**Colours:** Red & white/red/red

# SPRINGHEAD

**Secretary:** K Gibson, 1 Little Oak Close, Lees, Oldham OL4 3LW
**Tel:** 0161 627 3760
**Ground:** St John St, Lees, Oldham (0161 627 0260).
**Directions:** From Oldham (Mumps r'bout) follow A669 towards Lees for approx onemile, left into St John St, ground 500yds on right.
**Colours:** Black & red/black/black

# STAND ATHLETIC

**Secretary:** T H Edwards, 3 Burndale Drive, Unsworth, Bury BL9 8EN
**Tel:** 0161 766 3432
**Ground:** Elms Playing Fields, George Street, Whitefield.
**Directions:** From Manc. city centre proceed via Bury New Rd (A56) to Whitefield.George St. is on right just before Fire Station. Car park & changing facilitiesare at Whitefield Community Centre in Green Lane, off George Str.   **Colours:** Yellow/black/yellow

# STOCKPORT GEORGIANS

**Secretary:** Ged Newcombe, 7 Chiltern Close, Hazel Grove, Stockport SK7 5BQ Tel: 0161483 0004
**Ground:** Cromley Rd, Stockport, Tel: 0161 483 6581
**Directions:** Follow A6 from Stockport centre, turn right at Cemetery intoBranhall Lane. After 1 mile turn left at r/about into Woodsmoor Lane. Take 1st right Flowery Fields then right into Cromley Road
**Colours:** Purple/white/black

# URMSTON

**Secretary:** Sean Brett, 3 Shuttleworth Close, Whalley Range, Manchester  **Tel:** 0161 881 1962
**Ground:** Flixton Park, Flixton Road.
**Directions:** M63 junc 3 take Barton Rd to r/about. Then 3rd turning intoBayswater Rd. To r/about, take 2nd left Bowfell Rd, joins Flixton Rd, ground onleft.
**Colours:** Royal & white/royal/royal

# WYTHENSHAWE AMATEURS

**Secretary:** John Sobierajsh, 5 Wensley Drive, Withington, Manchester  **Tel:** 0161 445 3415
**Ground:** Longley Lane, Northenden  **Tel:** 0161 998 7268
**Directions:** Princess Parkway from Manchester to Post House hotel, via PalatineRd & Moor End Rd to Longley Lane - ground entrance opposite Overwood Rd.
**Colours:** Blue & white stripes/blue/blue

# PENNINGTON

**Secretary:** Joanne Hindley, 30 Sycamore Road, Atherton, Manchester (01942897273)
**Ground:** Jubilee Park, Leigh Rd, Atherton (01942 894703).
**Directions:** The entrance to the pathway to the ground is approx. 1 mile from Leigh Centre on the left hand side of the B5215 Atherton Road, the entrance is directly opposite the GMT depot.
**Colours:** White/blue/blue

# WILLOWS

**Secretary:** Frank Miller, 11 Edmund Street, Salford, Manchester (0161 737 2411)
**Ground:** Salteye Park, Peel Green, Eccles
**Directions:** From Eccles town centre take A57 and pass under M63 at Peel Green Roundabout, after approx. 400 yds turn left into a lay-by, the changing rooms are just behind Kara Cafe. For matchday contacts telephone Willows Club 0161 736 1451
**Colours:** All red

# UNOFFICIAL PYRAMID OF NORTH WEST AMATEUR LEAGUES
# BELOW NORTH WEST COUNTIES LEAGUE
## compiled by Alan Wilson

| | 1 | 2 | 3 | 4 | 5 |
|---|---|---|---|---|---|
| **A** | LIVERPOOL CO COMB | WEST CHESHIRE | MID-CHESHIRE | MANCHESTER | WEST LANCASHIRE |
| **B** | I ZINGARI LEAGUE | | | LANCASHIRE AMATEUR | |
| **C** | I ZINGARI COMB | SOUTH WIRRAL | LANCASHIRE & CHESHIRE AMAT | | PRESTON & DIST |
| **D** | ST HELENS & DIST COMBINATION (and column 3) | BIRKENHEAD & WIRRAL | CREWE & DISTRICT | BOLTON & DISTRICT AMAT. COMB. | |
| | | | | STOCKPORT | NORTH LANCS & DISTRICT |
| | WIGAN & DISTRICT AMATEUR (and column 5) | CHESTER & DISTRICT | WARRINGTON & DISTRICT (and column 1) | EAST LANCASHIRE | |
| **E** | ACCRINGTON COMBINATION (5)  ALTRINCHAM & DISTRICT (3-4)  BLACKBURN & DISTRICT COMB (5) BLACKPOOL & FYLDE COMBINATION (5)  BURNLEY & DISTRICT (5)  BURY & DIST. AMATEUR (4-5) CHORLEY & DISTRICT AMATEUR (5)  DARWEN AMATEUR (5)  EAST CHESHIRE (3-4) LEIGH & DISTRICT AMATEUR (4)  LIVERPOOL C.M.S. (1)  LIVERPOOL OLD BOYS AMATEUR( 1) MANCHESTER AMATEUR (4)  ROCHDALE ALLIANCE (4)  SOUTHPORT & DISTRICT AMATEUR (1 & 5) SOUTH EAST LANCASHIRE (4)<br><br>( ) Column position | | | | |

**Notes about the Pyramid:**
Level A represents the highest playing standard. most of those listed at Level E are leagues whose quality of play is unknown to me, therefore they may be placed at either Level C, D or E.

Of the 37 leagues listed altogether, just six have provided the following number of clubs, during the North West Counties' 1 seasons:

| | | | | | |
|---|---|---|---|---|---|
| Manchester | 9 | Mid-Cheshire | 5 | West Lancashire | 5 |
| Liverpool Combination | 1 | Preston | 1 | Warrington | 1 |

Three of these clubs have gained promotion to the Northern Premier League:
Bamber Bridge (P)          Flixton (M)          Trafford (MC)

**Sources:**
Lancashire FA and Manchester FA Directories
Lancashire Evening Post, Liverpool Echo, Manchester Evening News
Non-League Club Directory (various)

**Further Reading**
West Cheshire League 100 Years History, Dave Edmunds, 1991
Mid-Cheshire League Golden Jubilee History, Paul Lavell, 1998
I. Zingari League Centenary, Reg Kirkpatrick, 1997
85 Years of the Lancashire Amateur League, Alan Thompson, 1984
A Centenary of Warrington Football, Bob Smith, 1996

# NORTH WESTERN SATURDAY FINAL LEAGUE TABLES 1998-99

## I-ZINGARI LEAGUE

| Premier Division | P | W | D | L | F | A | PT |
|---|---|---|---|---|---|---|---|
| Aigburth Peop'S H | 26 | 21 | 2 | 3 | 76 | 35 | 65 |
| REMYCA Utd | 26 | 18 | 5 | 3 | 77 | 38 | 59 |
| Quarry BankOB | 26 | 12 | 7 | 7 | 48 | 30 | 43 |
| Edge Hill BCOB | 26 | 12 | 7 | 7 | 44 | 36 | 43 |
| East Villa | 25 | 13 | 3 | 9 | 59 | 45 | 42 |
| Sacre Coeur FP | 26 | 12 | 4 | 10 | 64 | 50 | 40 |
| Roma | 26 | 11 | 6 | 9 | 50 | 45 | 39 |
| Old Xaverians | 26 | 11 | 4 | 11 | 55 | 53 | 37 |
| NELTC | 26 | 9 | 6 | 11 | 45 | 50 | 33 |
| St. Philomenas | 26 | 9 | 2 | 15 | 59 | 67 | 29 |
| Warbreck | 26 | 8 | 3 | 15 | 42 | 49 | 27 |
| St Marys Cob | 26 | 7 | 4 | 15 | 37 | 61 | 25 |
| Stoneycroft | 26 | 5 | 4 | 17 | 39 | 82 | 19 |
| Kirkby Boulevard | 25 | 2 | 5 | 18 | 30 | 84 | 11 |

| Division One | P | W | D | L | F | A | PT |
|---|---|---|---|---|---|---|---|
| Mills | 22 | 18 | 1 | 3 | 63 | 30 | 55 |
| Dista | 22 | 15 | 3 | 4 | 63 | 42 | 48 |
| Leyfield | 22 | 15 | 2 | 5 | 68 | 36 | 47 |
| Focus | 22 | 14 | 1 | 7 | 65 | 45 | 43 |
| Sefton and District | 22 | 11 | 2 | 9 | 52 | 54 | 35 |
| Collegiate OB | 22 | 11 | 1 | 10 | 59 | 45 | 34 |
| Old Holts | 22 | 10 | 2 | 10 | 43 | 49 | 32 |
| Maghull Town | 22 | 7 | 5 | 10 | 56 | 58 | 26 |
| Dela Salle OB | 22 | 6 | 3 | 13 | 32 | 50 | 21 |
| Home Office | 22 | 5 | 2 | 15 | 42 | 62 | 19 |
| Essemmay OB | 22 | 5 | 0 | 17 | 42 | 79 | 15 |
| Liverpool Nalgo | 22 | 2 | 4 | 16 | 23 | 58* | 9 |

| Division Two | P | W | D | L | F | A | PT |
|---|---|---|---|---|---|---|---|
| Kinsellas | 20 | 14 | 2 | 4 | 78 | 37 | 44 |
| Aerospace Luca | 20 | 13 | 3 | 4 | 55 | 30 | 42 |
| Thirlmere | 20 | 11 | 3 | 6 | 67 | 47 | 36 |
| Rockville Wallasey | 20 | 10 | 4 | 6 | 62 | 45 | 34 |
| Finn Harps | 20 | 9 | 5 | 6 | 59 | 38 | 32 |
| Waterloo GSOB | 20 | 8 | 4 | 8 | 33 | 39 | 28 |
| Alsop OB | 20 | 6 | 4 | 10 | 47 | 61 | 25 |
| Blueline | 20 | 8 | 2 | 10 | 57 | 53 | 23 |
| Laburnum Vics | 20 | 6 | 4 | 10 | 52 | 56 | 22 |
| Orchard | 20 | 5 | 2 | 13 | 24 | 60 | 17 |
| Oaks Institute OB | 20 | 3 | 1 | 16 | 26 | 93 | 10 |

## I ZINGARI COMBINATION

| Division One | P | W | D | L | F | A | PT |
|---|---|---|---|---|---|---|---|
| Aigburth Peop. Hall | 26 | 21 | 3 | 2 | 100 | 36 | 66 |
| REMYCA Utd | 26 | 20 | 3 | 3 | 107 | 38 | 63 |
| Old Xaverians | 26 | 18 | 2 | 6 | 73 | 53 | 56 |
| EastVilla | 26 | 14 | 8 | 4 | 77 | 31 | 50 |
| Warbreck | 26 | 12 | 5 | 9 | 56 | 53 | 41 |
| Quarry BankOB | 26 | 11 | 5 | 10 | 63 | 50 | 38 |
| Aintree Villa | 26 | 11 | 5 | 10 | 64 | 56 | 38 |
| Sacre Coeur FP | 26 | 10 | 4 | 12 | 64 | 66 | 34 |
| Liverpool Nalgo | 26 | 9 | 3 | 14 | 54 | 71 | 30 |
| St Marys Coll. OB | 26 | 8 | 3 | 15 | 53 | 66 | 27 |
| Merseyside Police | 26 | 9 | 3 | 14 | 55 | 85 | 27* |
| Stoneycroft | 26 | 6 | 3 | 17 | 45 | 72 | 21 |
| Bluecoat OB | 26 | 3 | 5 | 18 | 44 | 92 | 14 |
| Essemmay OB | 26 | 2 | 4 | 20 | 38 | 124 | 10 |

## ST HELENS & DISTRICT COMBINATION

| Premier Division | P | W | L | D | PT |
|---|---|---|---|---|---|
| Child | 20 | 18 | 2 | 0 | 56 |
| The Anchor | 20 | 17 | 0 | 3 | 51 |
| Rifle | 20 | 13 | 1 | 6 | 40 |
| Pilkington Reg | 20 | 11 | 4 | 5 | 37 |
| Shoe | 20 | 9 | 4 | 7 | 31 |
| Gerard Arms | 20 | 9 | 4 | 7 | 31 |
| East Sutton Labour | 20 | 8 | 2 | 10 | 26 |
| Rainford North End | 20 | 3 | 7 | 10 | 16 |
| Prescott BICC Rec | 20 | 3 | 2 | 15 | 11 |
| Beeches Res | 20 | 3 | 2 | 15 | 8* |
| Engine | 20 | 2 | 0 | 18 | 4 |

## SOUTH WIRRAL LEAGUE

| Premier Division | P | W | D | L | PT |
|---|---|---|---|---|---|
| Mallaby | 24 | 22 | 2 | 0 | 46 |
| Charing Cross | 24 | 17 | 5 | 2 | 39 |
| Pavilions Res | 24 | 16 | 3 | 5 | 35 |
| Grange Athletic | 24 | 16 | 2 | 6 | 34 |
| Avon Athletic | 24 | 11 | 2 | 11 | 24 |
| Rangers Breaks | 24 | 11 | 1 | 12 | 23 |
| Manor Athletic Res | 24 | 9 | 4 | 11 | 22 |
| West Kirby Res | 24 | 8 | 4 | 12 | 20 |
| AFC Tanner | 24 | 7 | 6 | 11 | 18* |
| Halfway Athletic | 24 | 8 | 1 | 15 | 17 |
| Mersey Ferries | 24 | 7 | 3 | 14 | 17 |
| Bronze Social | 24 | 2 | 4 | 18 | 8 |
| Ellesmere Port Utd Res | 24 | 3 | 2 | 19 | 6* |

## BIRKNHEAD AND WIRRAL LEAGUE

| Division One | P | W | D | L | F | A | PT |
|---|---|---|---|---|---|---|---|
| FC Pensby | 18 | 17 | 1 | 0 | 83 | 27 | 35 |
| Abbotsford | 18 | 15 | 0 | 3 | 86 | 36 | 30 |
| Nue Ave | 18 | 14 | 1 | 3 | 79 | 22 | 29 |
| Royal Liver | 18 | 8 | 1 | 9 | 65 | 73 | 17 |
| Parkfield BA | 18 | 8 | 1 | 9 | 46 | 55 | 17 |
| Old Bank | 18 | 8 | 0 | 10 | 59 | 47 | 16 |
| Archers | 18 | 7 | 1 | 10 | 53 | 65 | 15 |
| Beehive | 18 | 6 | 2 | 10 | 39 | 70 | 14 |
| Belta | 18 | 3 | 1 | 14 | 40 | 79 | 7 |
| Vitt Vaults | 18 | 0 | 0 | 18 | 21 | 97 | 0 |

## SOUTHPORT & DISTRICT AMATEUR LEAGUE

| | P | W | D | L | F | A | PT |
|---|---|---|---|---|---|---|---|
| Leisure Sports | 24 | 18 | 4 | 2 | 106 | 40 | 40 |
| Birchfield Res | 24 | 19 | 2 | 3 | 89 | 39 | 40 |
| High Park | 24 | 17 | 4 | 3 | 107 | 31 | 38 |
| Formby Dons | 24 | 16 | 3 | 5 | 104 | 42 | 31* |
| St Pauls | 24 | 12 | 6 | 6 | 67 | 46 | 30 |
| Southport YMCA | 24 | 11 | 5 | 8 | 68 | 47 | 27 |
| Sporting Argyle | 24 | 8 | 2 | 14 | 74 | 84 | 18 |
| The Dales | 24 | 7 | 4 | 13 | 76 | 90 | 18 |
| Formby JSCOB Res | 24 | 7 | 4 | 13 | 50 | 106 | 18 |
| Formby JSCOB | 24 | 6 | 4 | 14 | 41 | 56 | 16 |
| Blowick | 24 | 8 | 0 | 16 | 50 | 96 | 16 |
| Formby Dons Res | 24 | 3 | 4 | 17 | 32 | 90 | 12* |
| Redgate Rovers | 24 | 2 | 2 | 20 | 38 | 135 | 6 |

## LIVERPOOL C M S LEAGUE

| Division One | P | W | D | L | F | A | PT |
|---|---|---|---|---|---|---|---|
| Tapes for Industry | 28 | 23 | 1 | 4 | 100 | 38 | 70 |
| Clifton | 28 | 20 | 4 | 4 | 104 | 42 | 64 |
| Dunningsbridge Pk | 28 | 20 | 4 | 4 | 87 | 46 | 64 |
| Anne | 28 | 17 | 3 | 8 | 64 | 35 | 54 |
| Dog and Gun | 28 | 16 | 6 | 6 | 67 | 47 | 54 |
| The Monty | 28 | 14 | 6 | 8 | 60 | 53 | 48 |
| Seaview Chaucer | 28 | 13 | 6 | 9 | 55 | 56 | 45 |
| Dow | 28 | 12 | 3 | 13 | 46 | 65 | 39 |
| Sam Dodds | 28 | 12 | 2 | 14 | 59 | 58 | 38 |
| Marlow Construction | 28 | 10 | 2 | 16 | 64 | 88 | 32 |
| Al- Rahma | 28 | 9 | 4 | 15 | 66 | 75 | 31 |
| Florence Albion | 28 | 6 | 4 | 18 | 42 | 77 | 22 |
| Shakespear | 28 | 5 | 3 | 20 | 55 | 109 | 18 |
| Gee Bee Sports | 28 | 3 | 5 | 20 | 30 | 65 | 14 |

## SOUTHPORT & DISTRICT SUNDAY LEAGUE

| Division One | P | W | D | L | F | A | PT |
|---|---|---|---|---|---|---|---|
| Bedford Rangers | 22 | 18 | 1 | 3 | 90 | 26 | 35 |
| Packaging DKS | 22 | 16 | 3 | 3 | 63 | 24 | 35 |
| Ship | 22 | 17 | 1 | 4 | 68 | 30 | 35 |
| Churchtown | 22 | 14 | 3 | 5 | 78 | 27 | 31 |
| Formby Dons | 22 | 15 | 1 | 6 | 61 | 34 | 31 |
| Greaves Hall | 22 | 9 | 4 | 9 | 44 | 38 | 22 |
| Scarisbrick Hotel | 22 | 8 | 3 | 11 | 38 | 72 | 19 |
| Metro Ainsdale | 22 | 7 | 3 | 12 | 40 | 48 | 17 |
| Wyke Cop Albion | 22 | 6 | 2 | 14 | 38 | 76 | 14 |
| Running Horses | 22 | 4 | 3 | 15 | 26 | 77 | 11 |
| Dell Rangers | 22 | 2 | 5 | 15 | 20 | 69 | 9 |
| Redgate Rovers | 22 | 1 | 1 | 20 | 14 | 59 | 3 |

## LIVERPOOL FORMERS SUNDAY LEAGUE

| Division One | P | W | D | L | F | A | PT |
|---|---|---|---|---|---|---|---|
| Senator | 21 | 18 | 3 | 0 | 85 | 31 | 57 |
| Mount Vernon | 21 | 11 | 5 | 5 | 53 | 37 | 38 |
| New Crescent | 21 | 10 | 5 | 6 | 65 | 56 | 35 |
| The Grammar | 21 | 9 | 2 | 10 | 64 | 61 | 29 |
| Omega Villa | 21 | 7 | 4 | 10 | 41 | 51 | 25 |
| Club Kiosk | 21 | 6 | 5 | 10 | 53 | 70 | 23 |
| Dovedale Kipper | 21 | 6 | 3 | 12 | 55 | 65 | 21 |
| Robeck | 21 | 3 | 1 | 17 | 23 | 66 | 10 |

## CROSBY & DISTRICT SUNDAY LEAGUE

| Division One | P | W | D | L | F | A | PT |
|---|---|---|---|---|---|---|---|
| Eden Vale | 21 | 16 | 5 | 0 | 57 | 21 | 37 |
| Freehouse | 21 | 16 | 2 | 3 | 68 | 18 | 34 |
| Saltbox | 22 | 11 | 7 | 4 | 36 | 27 | 29 |
| Fitness Conn. | 22 | 12 | 4 | 6 | 44 | 22 | 28 |
| Cabbage | 22 | 8 | 5 | 9 | 47 | 47 | 21 |
| Wynstay | 22 | 8 | 4 | 10 | 35 | 47 | 20 |
| St William Of York | 22 | 7 | 5 | 10 | 53 | 59 | 19 |
| Osset Sound | 22 | 5 | 8 | 9 | 32 | 45 | 18 |
| Database | 22 | 7 | 2 | 13 | 41 | 58 | 16 |
| Ninos | 22 | 5 | 5 | 12 | 37 | 55 | 15 |
| Tom Jones | 22 | 5 | 5 | 12 | 34 | 58 | 15 |
| Dominion | 22 | 3 | 4 | 15 | 30 | 57 | 10 |

## ST HELENS COMBINATION (SUNDAY SECTION)

| Premier Division | P | W | D | L | F | A | PT |
|---|---|---|---|---|---|---|---|
| Ex-Serv. Rainhill | 15 | 9 | 2 | 4 | 47 | 26 | 29 |
| Oddfellows | 15 | 9 | 2 | 4 | 48 | 35 | 29 |
| East Sutton Lab | 15 | 8 | 2 | 5 | 39 | 33 | 26 |
| Rose and Crown | 15 | 7 | 2 | 6 | 42 | 39 | 23 |
| OC Ravenhead | 15 | 3 | 3 | 9 | 33 | 50 | 12 |
| Toll Bar | 15 | 1 | 5 | 9 | 28 | 54 | 8 |

## WALLASEY SUNDAY LEAGUE

| Premier Division | P | W | D | L | PT |
|---|---|---|---|---|---|
| St Josephs | 18 | 13 | 4 | 1 | 30 |
| Gt Float Social | 18 | 14 | 0 | 4 | 28 |
| The Queens | 18 | 12 | 3 | 3 | 27 |
| Poulton Royal | 18 | 10 | 4 | 4 | 24 |
| Millhouse | 18 | 9 | 1 | 8 | 19 |
| Old Bank | 18 | 9 | 1 | 8 | 19 |
| Horizon | 18 | 7 | 3 | 8 | 17 |
| St Marys | 18 | 4 | 1 | 13 | 9 |
| The Leasowe | 18 | 1 | 3 | 14 | 5 |
| Gorsedale | 18 | 0 | 2 | 16 | 2 |

## LIVERPOOL & DISTRICT SUNDAY LEAGUE

| Premier Division | P | W | D | L | F | A | PT |
|---|---|---|---|---|---|---|---|
| Sandon | 19 | 15 | 1 | 3 | 58 | 27 | 46 |
| Allerton | 16 | 14 | 1 | 1 | 68 | 25 | 43 |
| Britannia | 19 | 12 | 4 | 3 | 57 | 28 | 40 |
| Pineapple | 20 | 8 | 3 | 9 | 39 | 46 | 27 |
| Blue Union | 19 | 7 | 4 | 8 | 39 | 45 | 25 |
| Lobster | 19 | 6 | 5 | 8 | 32 | 39 | 23 |
| Rob Roy | 20 | 7 | 2 | 11 | 39 | 48 | 23 |
| Fairfield | 19 | 6 | 3 | 10 | 41 | 54 | 21 |
| TitheBarn | 19 | 6 | 3 | 10 | 40 | 55 | 21 |
| Seymour | 19 | 5 | 4 | 10 | 44 | 56 | 19 |
| Newfield | 19 | 2 | 2 | 15 | 29 | 65 | 8 |

| Division One | P | W | D | L | F | A | PT |
|---|---|---|---|---|---|---|---|
| Almithak | 20 | 13 | 4 | 3 | 69 | 33 | 43 |
| Oyster | 20 | 12 | 5 | 3 | 53 | 31 | 41 |
| Western App. | 20 | 12 | 3 | 5 | 58 | 30 | 39 |
| Dengo United | 20 | 10 | 5 | 5 | 49 | 45 | 35 |
| Cunard | 20 | 9 | 6 | 5 | 72 | 44 | 33 |
| Garston Wood's | 20 | 8 | 5 | 7 | 53 | 50 | 29 |
| Elm House | 20 | 8 | 54 | 8 | 62 | 54 | 28 |
| Caldway | 20 | 5 | 4 | 11 | 38 | 64 | 19 |
| Edinburgh | 20 | 4 | 6 | 10 | 37 | 52 | 18 |
| Hippodrome | 20 | 3 | 3 | 14 | 28 | 64 | 12 |
| Speke Argyle | 20 | 3 | 1 | 16 | 35 | 87 | 10 |

## ORMSKIRK SUNDAY LEAGUE

| Division One | P | W | D | L | F | A | PT |
|---|---|---|---|---|---|---|---|
| Plan-It | 18 | 12 | 4 | 2 | 54 | 23 | 40 |
| RNA Kirkby | 18 | 12 | 2 | 4 | 51 | 36 | 38 |
| Melling Victoria | 18 | 10 | 2 | 6 | 42 | 35 | 32 |
| Memorial | 18 | 8 | 3 | 7 | 43 | 35 | 27 |
| RAOB Kirkby | 18 | 8 | 3 | 7 | 38 | 33 | 27 |
| North Coach | 18 | 6 | 4 | 8 | 36 | 37 | 22 |
| Altway Valentine | 18 | 6 | 3 | 9 | 26 | 40 | 21 |
| Alt Park United | 18 | 5 | 4 | 9 | 33 | 49 | 19 |
| Croftmere S A | 18 | 4 | 5 | 9 | 33 | 37 | 17 |
| Coach & Horses | 18 | 3 | 2 | 13 | 32 | 63 | 11 |

# NORTHERN COUNTIES EAST FOOTBALL LEAGUE

## FEEDER TO: NORTHERN PREMIER LEAGUE

**President:** H F Catt    **Chairman:** C Morris

**Secretary/Treasurer:** B Wood, 6 Restmore Avenue, Guiseley, Leeds LS20 9DG
Tel/Fax: 01943 874558

y review of the 1998-99 season as usual begins with a look at the playing records of our clubs outlining the successes
d failures throughout that time.

The promotion/demotion system between the NCE and the Unibond League at the end of the 1997-98 season worked
the advantage of Champions and Cup winners, Hucknall Town, and as an example of the quality of clubs we have pro-
ded over the years to the higher Unibond League they finished second in Division One and could be promoted to their
emier Division if ground grading allows. Moving in the other direction to us were Buxton who had slid down from
ibond Premier to Division One and to the NCE in successive seasons. Although they were tipped for a straight return to
e Unibond League, an early change of Manager may have contributed to their mid-table position at the end of the sea-
n.

Early pace-setters in the Premier Division were promoted club Garforth Town playing at their new Wheatley Park
adium, but they did suffer along with a number of clubs from the very wet season we have had and I believe that this
oblem did have a bearing on the eventual championship destination.

However important the matches in the first part of the Premier Division season might have been to the eventual desti-
ation of the Championship, there is no denying that the last month's run-in of fixtures were the most exciting in the history
the top division for players and spectators alike. Any club from a group of almost seven clubs could have taken the
ampionship with the odds in favour of North Ferriby United in early April through their series of eleven matches in the
al five weeks of the season eventually took its toll. In the end, the town of Ossett can be very proud of its two clubs
nich, for the very first time, have come out on top of the NCE soccer world. Ossett Albion took the championship with
eir very last fixture at rivals North Ferriby enabling them to leapfrog over Ossett Town and Brigg Town. Albion's success
me with the help of new Manager, Jimmy Quinn, appointed at the beginning of the season, whilst Town surprisingly
anged Managers in mid-stream when striker Gary Brook took over from Trevor Best. There's been disappointment for
ampions Albion, though, as their ground was ruled unsuitable for promotion to the Unibond League, but Town hope to
ake the move up the 'Pyramid' if they can complete ground improvements in time with Alfreton Town likely to be relegat-
d to fill their place.

Despite considerable improvements to their ground, our most northerly club, Pickering Town, failed to match that
vance on the field and will be relegated as bottom club along with Pontefract Collieries who have been in the top flight
r three seasons.

Harrogate Railway took the Division One leader's spot towards the end of February and maintained their superiority to
e end with a nine point advantage over nearest rivals Brodsworth MW. It was a close thing for the Doncaster side,
ough, for they needed to win their final match against Winterton Rangers to reach a promotion place on goal difference
the expense of Glapwell with Parkgate taking fourth position. Rossington Main and Winterton Rangers will be applying
r re-election to the Division which really lacked an adequate number of fixtures for all clubs with just thirteen teams. It is
ped that there will be three additions to the Division next season with Bridlington Town and Mickleover Sports already
proved and an additional club (Goole FC) expected to be nominated from the Central Midlands League.

Just as their first team were enjoying a great season, the second string of North Ferriby United took the Reserve
vision title to show that there is strength in depth at the East Riding club. Emley Reserves were runners-up just ahead of
ssett Town Reserves. Harrogate Town Reserves will not be competing in the Division next season but there have been a
mber of applicants which are shown on the AGM Agenda.

In our own NCE League Cup Competition Denaby United defeated Selby Town 1-0 with a 95th minute extra-time
rike from Bob Moorwood in the League Cup Final at Garforth Town. This Final will probably go down in the records as
e Monsoon Cup Final as the heavens opened at Garforth's new Wheatley Park Stadium and all concerned should be
ngratulated for completing the match. The President's Cup was won by North Ferriby United who completed a 6-1
ggregate victory over Garforth Town at the end of March.

The Wilkinson Sword Trophy saw Yorkshire Amateurs secure a fairly easy 8-2 aggregate victory at the expense of
arkgate whilst the Reserve Division Cup was won by Emley Reserves, who defeated Yorkshire Amateurs Reserves 2-1
Thackley.

In outside competitions Buxton proved our most successful side in the FA Cup losing out to Conference Leek Town in
Third Qualifying Round replay whilst North Ferriby United actually defeated Runcorn in that same replay round but were
minated by the FA after having played an ineligible player. Garforth Town reached the Fourth Round of the FA Vase
ping out 2-0 in a controversial mid-week away game at Sudbury Wanderers after suffering controversial postponements
cause of a wet ground in Suffolk.

The League had the following successes in County Cup competitions:
East Riding Senior Cup - North Ferriby United defeated Filey Town 5-1 at Boothferry Park;
Notts Senior Cup - Arnold Town beat Unibond side Hucknall Town 2-1 in the Final;
West Riding County Cup - Ossett Albion beat another Unibond side, Bradford PA, by 2-0.
In addition, Louth United were Runners-up in the Lincs Senior 'A' Cup Final at Spalding United.

383

## PREMIER DIVISION

| | P | W | D | L | F | A | PT |
|---|---|---|---|---|---|---|---|
| Ossett Albion | 38 | 23 | 5 | 10 | 86 | 50 | 74 |
| Ossett Town | 38 | 22 | 7 | 9 | 76 | 44 | 73 |
| Brigg Town | 38 | 20 | 12 | 6 | 78 | 43 | 72 |
| Hallam | 38 | 22 | 5 | 11 | 95 | 63 | 71 |
| North Ferriby United | 38 | 19 | 12 | 7 | 92 | 50 | 69 |
| Liversedge | 38 | 21 | 4 | 13 | 87 | 63 | 67 |
| Arnold Town | 38 | 19 | 7 | 12 | 78 | 56 | 64 |
| Denaby United | 38 | 15 | 12 | 11 | 66 | 60 | 57 |
| Garforth Town | 38 | 15 | 9 | 14 | 74 | 70 | 54 |
| Buxton | 38 | 14 | 10 | 14 | 54 | 53 | 52 |
| Selby Town | 38 | 15 | 7 | 16 | 59 | 61 | 52 |
| Sheffield | 38 | 15 | 6 | 17 | 55 | 58 | 51 |
| Armthorpe Welfare | 38 | 13 | 11 | 14 | 46 | 50 | 50 |
| Glasshoughton Welfare | 38 | 13 | 9 | 16 | 58 | 71 | 48 |
| Thackley | 38 | 14 | 5 | 19 | 65 | 77 | 47 |
| Eccleshill United | 38 | 12 | 6 | 20 | 56 | 74 | 42 |
| Staveley MW | 38 | 9 | 11 | 18 | 50 | 84 | 36* |
| Maltby Main | 38 | 8 | 6 | 24 | 51 | 87 | 26 |
| Pontefract Colls | 38 | 7 | 7 | 24 | 37 | 86 | 26* |
| Pickering Town | 38 | 5 | 7 | 26 | 44 | 107 | 22 |

## DIVISION ONE

| | P | W | D | L | F | A | PT |
|---|---|---|---|---|---|---|---|
| Harrogate Railway Ath | 24 | 15 | 6 | 3 | 58 | 29 | 51 |
| Brodswrth MW | 24 | 13 | 3 | 8 | 52 | 42 | 42 |
| Glapwell | 24 | 12 | 6 | 6 | 47 | 39 | 42 |
| Parkgate | 24 | 12 | 5 | 7 | 61 | 32 | 41 |
| Borrowash Victoria | 24 | 12 | 5 | 7 | 48 | 38 | 41 |
| Worsbrough Bridge MW | 24 | 9 | 6 | 9 | 49 | 42 | 33 |
| Hall Road Rangers | 24 | 9 | 6 | 9 | 44 | 49 | 33 |
| Hatfield Main | 24 | 10 | 3 | 11 | 27 | 47 | 31* |
| Louth United | 24 | 9 | 3 | 12 | 37 | 33 | 30 |
| Yorskshire Amat | 24 | 6 | 7 | 11 | 41 | 49 | 25 |
| Tadcaster Albion | 24 | 6 | 6 | 12 | 33 | 51 | 24 |
| Rossington Main | 24 | 6 | 4 | 14 | 37 | 51 | 22 |
| Winteron Rangers | 24 | 3 | 8 | 13 | 22 | 54 | 17 |

* points deducted

## RESERVE DIVISION

| | P | W | D | L | F | A | PT |
|---|---|---|---|---|---|---|---|
| North Ferriby Utd Res | 26 | 21 | 2 | 3 | 95 | 33 | 65 |
| Emley Res | 26 | 16 | 8 | 2 | 68 | 30 | 56 |
| Ossett Town Res | 26 | 18 | 2 | 6 | 93 | 32 | 54* |
| Farsley Celtic Res | 26 | 12 | 8 | 6 | 55 | 37 | 44 |
| Thackley Res | 26 | 13 | 4 | 9 | 61 | 54 | 43 |
| Liversdge Res | 26 | 11 | 7 | 8 | 55 | 45 | 40 |
| Ossett Albion Res | 26 | 13 | 2 | 11 | 55 | 56 | 39* |
| Yorkshire Amat Res | 26 | 10 | 5 | 11 | 47 | 50 | 35 |
| Selby Town Res | 26 | 10 | 5 | 11 | 61 | 73 | 35 |
| Glasshoughton Welf R | 26 | 9 | 1 | 16 | 50 | 72 | 28 |
| Harrogate Town Res | 26 | 6 | 4 | 16 | 39 | 59 | 22 |
| Eccleshill Utd Res | 26 | 6 | 5 | 15 | 40 | 66 | 19 |
| Garforth Town Res | 26 | 5 | 2 | 19 | 37 | 87 | 15* |
| Tadcaster Albion Res | 26 | 4 | 1 | 21 | 22 | 84 | 13 |

## PREMIER DIVISION RESULTS CHART 1998-99

| | | 1 | 2 | 3 | 4 | 5 | 6 | 7 | 8 | 9 | 10 | 11 | 12 | 13 | 14 | 15 | 16 | 17 | 18 | 19 | 20 |
|---|---|---|---|---|---|---|---|---|---|---|---|---|---|---|---|---|---|---|---|---|---|
| 1 | Armthorpe Welf | X | 1-2 | 1-1 | 3-0 | 0-1 | 1-0 | 4-0 | 2-2 | 2-1 | 0-3 | 3-2 | 0-0 | 0-1 | 0-1 | 3-2 | 2-0 | 1-2 | 2-0 | 0-0 | 0-2 |
| 2 | Arnold Town | 4-2 | X | 1-2 | 0-0 | 1-3 | 4-1 | 2-1 | 1-2 | 6-0 | 4-0 | 3-1 | 3-3 | 1-3 | 5-2 | 3-0 | 2-0 | 1-3 | 1-0 | 1-2 | 4-2 |
| 3 | Brigg Town | 1-1 | 0-0 | X | 1-1 | 5-0 | 2-3 | 3-3 | 4-0 | 2-2 | 1-0 | 6-1 | 2-2 | 3-1 | 0-1 | 4-0 | 1-1 | 3-2 | 4-1 | 1-0 | 2-0 |
| 4 | Buxton | 3-0 | 0-2 | 0-0 | X | 2-3 | 4-0 | 2-2 | 2-3 | 3-2 | 3-1 | 2-1 | 0-0 | 3-1 | 1-6 | 2-1 | 2-2 | 0-1 | 2-3 | 2-1 | 1-0 |
| 5 | Denaby Utd | 0-2 | 2-2 | 0-2 | 1-1 | X | 1-0 | 1-0 | 2-6 | 2-0 | 2-4 | 4-0 | 1-1 | 4-0 | 2-2 | 4-2 | 3-2 | 1-2 | 2-1 | 1-2 | 0-0 |
| 6 | Eccleshill Utd | 2-0 | 2-1 | 2-3 | 3-1 | 1-1 | X | 1-1 | 0-1 | 1-0 | 2-4 | 5-2 | 0-2 | 3-6 | 0-4 | 1-1 | 1-2 | 1-0 | 4-0 | 2-1 | 1-2 |
| 7 | Garforth Town | 3-1 | 3-2 | 1-3 | 2-1 | 2-2 | 3-1 | X | 1-1 | 0-4 | 0-4 | 3-0 | 3-2 | 2-3 | 2-2 | 3-0 | 5-1 | 4-1 | 2-1 | 1-2 | 6-1 |
| 8 | Glasshoughtn W | 1-1 | 2-3 | 1-2 | 2-1 | 1-4 | 1-2 | 2-1 | X | 1-5 | 1-1 | 3-0 | 0-2 | 2-2 | 0-1 | 5-2 | 2-0 | 2-0 | 1-2 | 1-1 | 1-0 |
| 9 | Hallam | 1-1 | 3-1 | 2-1 | 0-1 | 0-2 | 2-0 | 2-1 | 5-0 | X | 4-6 | 3-3 | 0-5 | 3-3 | 5-2 | 2-0 | 6-1 | 1-0 | 1-1 | 6-1 | 3-1 |
| 10 | Liversedge | 1-1 | 1-3 | 0-2 | 2-0 | 1-1 | 0-3 | 5-3 | 4-2 | 0-3 | X | 3-0 | 3-0 | 2-1 | 3-1 | 5-0 | 1-1 | 3-1 | 3-5 | 5-1 | 1-2 |
| 11 | Maltby Main | 0-1 | 1-2 | 1-1 | 1-2 | 3-1 | 1-1 | 1-2 | 0-2 | 2-3 | 1-2 | X | 1-4 | 2-4 | 0-2 | 1-3 | 1-0 | 1-0 | 1-1 | 5-2 | 6-2 |
| 12 | North Ferriby Utd | 0-0 | 3-2 | 1-2 | 2-0 | 2-2 | 1-1 | 3-4 | 6-2 | 1-3 | 5-0 | 6-3 | X | 1-3 | 0-0 | 5-0 | 2-0 | 6-1 | 2-2 | 2-1 | 5-1 |
| 13 | Ossett Albion | 2-0 | 1-1 | 3-4 | 1-1 | 3-1 | 4-1 | 1-1 | 2-1 | 0-1 | 0-2 | 4-0 | 0-2 | X | 3-1 | 3-0 | 4-1 | 1-0 | 2-0 | 4-1 | 2-3 |
| 14 | Ossett Town | 4-1 | 0-0 | 0-0 | 1-1 | 0-3 | 3-2 | 3-0 | 2-0 | 1-0 | 3-1 | 0-1 | 4-0 | 0-2 | X | 3-1 | 1-0 | 1-0 | 1-0 | 2-2 | 4-2 |
| 15 | Pickering Town | 1-1 | 2-4 | 1-4 | 0-1 | 3-5 | 2-0 | 2-2 | 1-0 | 2-8 | 2-4 | 2-1 | 1-6 | 0-4 | 0-2 | X | 0-0 | 2-2 | 2-3 | 2-2 | 1-0 |
| 16 | Pontefract Colls | 2-4 | 2-1 | 0-0 | 1-4 | 2-1 | 5-3 | 2-0 | 1-2 | 0-1 | 0-3 | 1-1 | 0-3 | 0-4 | 2-7 | 2-0 | X | 1-3 | 0-1 | 0-2 | 3-1 |
| 17 | Selby Town | 1-1 | 3-0 | 3-1 | 1-0 | 1-1 | 4-4 | 0-2 | 1-1 | 2-3 | 2-1 | 1-1 | 1-1 | 1-3 | 3-2 | 4-2 | 2-0 | X | 1-2 | 3-1 | 3-4 |
| 18 | Sheffield | 2-0 | 2-2 | 0-2 | 1-0 | 1-1 | 0-1 | 1-3 | 4-1 | 1-4 | 2-1 | 0-1 | 1-2 | 0-2 | 1-0 | 4-3 | 4-1 | 1-0 | X | 1-2 | 6-0 |
| 19 | Staveley MW | 1-2 | 0-1 | 3-2 | 1-4 | 2-0 | 2-0 | 2-2 | 2-2 | 1-4 | 1-4 | 1-3 | 1-1 | 2-1 | 0-4 | 1-1 | 1-1 | 1-3 | 0-0 | X | 3-3 |
| 20 | Thackley | 1-2 | 1-2 | 4-1 | 1-1 | 1-1 | 2-1 | 1-0 | 1-1 | 6-2 | 0-3 | 2-1 | 2-3 | 0-2 | 1-3 | 3-0 | 5-0 | 0-1 | 1-0 | 7-1 | X |

# LEAGUE CUP 1998-99

**FIRST ROUND**

| Hatfield Main | v | Tadcaster Albion | 2-3 |
|---|---|---|---|

**SECOND ROUND**

| Armthorpe Welfare | v | Glasshoughton Wel | 5-4 | | Arnold Town | v | Rossington Main | 4-2 |
|---|---|---|---|---|---|---|---|---|
| Brodsworth MW | v | Harrogate Railway | 0-5 | | Buxton | v | Brigg Town | 3-1 |
| Denaby United | v | Borrowash Victoria | 7-0 | | Eccleshill United | v | Ossett Town | 1-2 |
| Garforth Town | v | Liversedge | 2-1 | | Louth United | v | Ossett Albion | 0-3 |
| Maltby MW | v | Hall Road Rangers | 3-0 | | Parkgate | v | North Ferriby Utd | 0-3 |
| Sheffield | v | Glapwell | 1-0 | | Staveley MW | v | Thackley | 0-2 |
| Tadcaster Albion | v | Pickering Town | 1-0 | | Winterton Rangers | v | Selby Town | 0-1 |
| Worsbrough Bridge | v | Pontefract Colls. | 1-2 | | Yorkshire Amateur | v | Hallam | 1-2 |

**THIRD ROUND**

| Armthorpe Welfare | v | Tadcaster Albion | 2-0 | | Arnold Town | v | Harrogate Railway | 6-2 |
|---|---|---|---|---|---|---|---|---|
| Buxton | v | North Ferriby United | 0-4 | | Denaby United | v | Sheffield | 3-0 |
| Maltby Main | v | Ossett Albion | 1-7 | | Ossett Town | v | Hallam | 3-2 |
| Selby Town | v | Pontefract Colls. | 3-0 | | Thackley | v | Garforth Town | 3-3, 0-3 |

**FOURTH ROUND**

| Armthorpe Welfare | v | Garforth Town | 1-0 | | Arnold Town | v | North Ferriby Utd | 3-6 |
|---|---|---|---|---|---|---|---|---|
| Ossett Albion | v | Denaby United | 1-2 | | Selby Town | v | Ossett Town | 1-0 |

**SEMI-FINALS**

| Denaby United | v | North Ferriby Utd | 2-1 | | Selby Town | v | Armthorpe Welfare | 1-0 |
|---|---|---|---|---|---|---|---|---|

**FINAL**

| Denaby United | v | Selby Town | 1-0 |
|---|---|---|---|

# PRESIDENT'S CUP 1998-99

**FIRST ROUND**

| Tadcaster Albion | v | North Ferriby United | 2-4 |
|---|---|---|---|

**SECOND ROUND**

| Armthorpe Welfare | v | Rossington Main | 3-2 | | Arnold Town | v | Buxton | 0-3 |
|---|---|---|---|---|---|---|---|---|
| Brodsworth MW | v | Worsbrough Bridge | 1-2 | | Eccleshill United | v | Brigg Town | 1-2 |
| Garforth Town | v | Glasshoughton Welf | 3-1 | | Hallam | v | Glapwell | 6-3 |
| Harrogate Railway | v | Pontefract Colls. | 0-2 | | Hatfield Main | v | Staveley MW | 1-4 |
| Liversedge | v | Ossett Albion | 0-4 | | Louth United | v | Denaby United | 2-0 |
| Maltby Main | v | Borrowash Victoria | 1-0 | | Parkgate | v | Sheffield | 0-3 |
| Pickering Town | v | Ossett Town | 3-2 | | Thackley | v | Selby Town | 3-1 |
| Winterton Rangers | v | North Ferriby United | 1-2 | | Yorkshire Amateur | v | Hall Road Rangers | 0-3 |

**THIRD ROUND**

| Brigg Town | v | Maltby Main | 0-4 | | Buxton | v | Hall Road Rangers | 2-3 |
|---|---|---|---|---|---|---|---|---|
| Hallam | v | Ossett Albion | 2-1 | | Louth United | v | Pontefract Colls. | 3-1 |
| North Ferriby United | v | Sheffield | 4-1 | | Staveley MW | v | Armthorpe Welf | 2-2, 1-4 |
| Thackley | v | Pickering Town | 1-0 | | Worsbrough Bridge | v | Garforth Town | 0-2 |

**FOURTH ROUND**

| Armthorpe Welfare | v | Thackley | 4-0 | | Hallam | v | Garforth Town | 1-3 |
|---|---|---|---|---|---|---|---|---|
| Maltby Main | v | Hall Road Rangers | 2-0 | | North Ferriby Utd | v | Louth United | 3-1 |

**SEMI-FINALS**

| Armthorpe Welfare | v | North Ferriby Utd | 2-3 | | Garforth Town | v | Maltby Main | 2-0 |
|---|---|---|---|---|---|---|---|---|

**FINAL 1st Leg**

| North Ferriby Utd | v | Garforth Town | 4-1 |
|---|---|---|---|

**FINAL 2nd Leg**

| Garforth Town | v | North Ferriby Utd | 0-2 | North Ferriby United won 6-1 on aggregate |
|---|---|---|---|---|

# WILKINSON SWORD TROPHY 1998-99

**FIRST ROUND**

| | | | | | | | |
|---|---|---|---|---|---|---|---|
| Hall Road Rangers | v | Brodsworth MW | 2-3 | Harrogate Railway | v | Borrowash Victoria | 2-1 |
| Winterton Rangers | v | Hatfield Main | 0-3 | Worsbrough Bridge | v | Glapwell | 1-4 |
| Yorkshire Amateur | v | Rossington Main | 2-0 | | | | |

**SECOND ROUND**

| | | | | | | | |
|---|---|---|---|---|---|---|---|
| Harrogate Railway | v | Tadcaster Albion | 0-0, 2-3 | Hatfield Main | v | Louth United | 3-2 |
| Parkgate | v | Glapwell | 4-3 | Yorkshire Amateur | v | Brodsworth MW | 2-1 |

**SEMI-FINALS**

| | | | | | | | |
|---|---|---|---|---|---|---|---|
| Hatfield Main | v | Parkgate | 0-2 | Yorkshire Amateur | v | Tadcaster Alb | 0-0, 2-1 |

**FINAL 1st Leg**

| | | | |
|---|---|---|---|
| Parkgate | v | Yorkshire Amateur | 0-3 |

**FINAL 2nd Leg**

| | | | | |
|---|---|---|---|---|
| Yorkshire Amateur | v | Parkgate | 5-2 | Yorkshire Amateur won 8-2 on aggregate |

# RESERVE DIVISION CUP 1998-99

**FIRST ROUND**

| | | | | | | | |
|---|---|---|---|---|---|---|---|
| Eccleshill Utd Res | v | Ossett Albion Res | 3-2 | Emley Res | v | Thackley Res | 1-0 |
| Farsley Celtic Res | v | Selby Town Res | 5-2 | Glasshoughton W R | v | Ossett Town Res | 0-4 |
| Harrogate Town Res | v | Yorkshire Amat Res | 0-1 | North Ferriby Utd R | v | Garforth Town Res | 6-2 |

**SECOND ROUND**

| | | | | | | | |
|---|---|---|---|---|---|---|---|
| Eccleshill Utd Res | v | Ossett Town Res | 0-1 | Farsley Celtic Res | v | Emley Res | 2-5 |
| Tadcaster Alb Res | v | North Ferriby Utd Res | 0-2 | Yorks Amat Res | v | Liversedge Res | 1-0 |

**SEMI-FINALS**

| | | | | | | | |
|---|---|---|---|---|---|---|---|
| North Ferriby Utd Res | v | Emley Res | 0-4 | Ossett Town Res | v | Yorks Amat Res | 1-2 |

**FINAL**

| | | | |
|---|---|---|---|
| Emley Res | v | Yorks Amat Res | 2-1 |

# LEADING GOALSCORERS 1998-99

### PREMIER DIVISION

| | | | | | |
|---|---|---|---|---|---|
| A J Flounders | North Ferriby United | 43 | G M Ricketts | Arnold Town | 21 |
| D Day | Ossett Albion | 42 | S P Bambrook | Garforth Town | 20 |
| M Goddard | Hallam | 30 | M Godber | Staveley MW | 20 |
| J M Robshaw | Denaby United | 23 | T J Whitman | Arnold Town | 20 |
| S Taylor | Thackley | 23 | M A Tennison | North Ferriby Utd | 19 |
| G Brook | Ossett Town | 22 | S S Johnson | Armthorpe Welfare | 18 |
| G N Evans | Brigg Town | 22 | M A Smith | Armthorpe Welfare | 18 |
| S Lowe | Hallam | 22 | | | |

### DIVISION ONE

| | | | | | |
|---|---|---|---|---|---|
| R Beardshaw | Yorkshire Amateur | 19 | W Gamble | Glapwell | 16 |
| R Blake | Louth United | 18 | C Darvill | Harrogate Railway | 15 |
| C G Sambrook | Brodsworth MW | 17 | J I Little | Harrogate Railway | 13 |
| L I Wasden | Parkgate | 17 | | | |

### RESERVE DIVISION

| | | | | | |
|---|---|---|---|---|---|
| P A Gilbertson | Ossett Albion Res | 32 | C A Hodgson | Selby Town Res | 22 |
| L R Lambert | North Ferriby Utd Res | 26 | A Watt | Thackley Res | 21 |
| L D Bradley | Emley Res | 23 | A Gibson | Ossett Town Res | 20 |
| W Freeman | Farsley Celtic Res | 23 | D P Watts | Ossett Town Res | 20 |
| V Nikolaidis | North Ferriby Utd Res | 23 | | | |

# ALFRETON TOWN

**Secretary:** Roger Taylor, 9 Priory Rd, Alfreton, Derbys. DE55 7JT  Tel: 01773 835121
**Ground:** Town Ground, North Street, Alfreton, Derbyshire Tel: 01773 830277.
**Directions:** M1 junction 28 and follow A38 towards Derby for 1 mile,left onto B600, right at main road to town centre and after half a mile turn left down North Street - ground on right. Half mile from Alfreton (BR) station.Buses 242 & 243 from both Derby and Mansfield
　　　　　　　　Capacity: 5,000　　Cover: 1,000　　　Seats: 350　　　Floodlights: Yes
**Clubhouse:** H & c food & drinks on ground. Supporters Club outside ground open match days
**Club Shop:** Programmes & club souvenirs. Contact Brian Thorpe Tel: 01773 836251

**HONOURS**　　N.C.E. Lg 84-85 (Lg Cup 84-85); Midland Co. Lg 69-70 73-74 76-77 (R-up 71-72 80-81 81-82), Lg Cup 71-72 72-73 73-74; Derbyshire Sen Cup 60-61 69-70 72-73 73-74 81-82 94-95 (R-up 62-63 64-65 77-78 79-80 84-85 87-88 92-93) Div Cup (N) 64-65; Evans Halshaw Floodlit Cup 87-88 95-96; Cent All Lg.R-Up 63-64; NPL Div 1 R-Up 95-96
**PREVIOUS**　　**Leagues:** Central All.(pre-reformation 21-25) 59-61; Midland (Counties) 25-27 61-82; N.C.E. 82-87; Northern Premier 87-99
**BEST SEASON**　**FA Trophy:** 1st Rd Proper 94-95.
**FA Cup:** 1st Rd 3rd replay 69-70. Also 1st Rd 73-74. - League clubs defeated: Lincoln 24-25
**RECORDS**　　**Attendance:** 5,023 v Matlock Tn, Central All 60.
　　　　　　**Scorer:** J Harrison 303　**Win:** 15-0 v Loughborough, Midland Lge. 69-70
**Appearances:** J Harrison 560　　　**Defeat:** 1-9 v Solihull FAT 97, 0-8 v Bridlington 92.

### FACT FILE

Formed: 1959
Nickname: The Reds
Sponsors: Coldseal Windows
Colours: Red & white/red/red
Change colours: Yellow/blue/yellow
Midweek home matchday: Tuesday
Reserve League: None, Under 13s & 12s
Programme: Pages: 32 Price: £1
Editor: Chris Tacey (01302 722415)

### CLUB PERSONNEL

Chairman: Sean Egan
Vice Chairman: Dave Gregory

Manager: Ernie Oliver
Physio: Kevin Grundy

# ARMTHORPE WELFARE

**Secretary:** Maureen Cottam, The Orchards, Whiphill Lane, Armthorpe, Doncaster DN3 3JP.
　　　　　　Tel: 01302 832514 (H)
**Ground:** Welfare Ground, Church St, Armthorpe, DoncasterDN3 3AG.Tel:(M)07771853899 (match days only)
**Directions:** M18 junc 4, A630, left at r'bout then proceed to next r'bout and turn right. Ground 400yds on left behind Plough Inn. Doncaster (BR) 2 1/2 miles. Buses A2, A3 & 181 pass ground
Capacity: 2,500　　Seats: 200　　　Cover: 400　　　Floodlights: Yes　**Club Shop:** No
**Clubhouse:** No. Refreshments on ground. Wheatsheaf Hotel used after matches

**HONOURS**　　Northern Co's East Lg r-up 87-88 (Lg Cup R-up 91-92, Div 1 R-up 83-84, East Central Div 1 84-85); Doncaster & Dist.
Lg 82-83 (Div 1 81-82, Div 2 79-80, Div 3 78-79; Lg Cup 79-80 80-81 81-82 82-83; Challenge Cup 82- 83); West Riding Chall. Cup 81-82 82-83; Goole & Thorne Dist. Cup 82-83
**PREVIOUS**　　**League:** Doncaster Senior
**BEST SEASON**　**FA Cup:**　　**FA Vase:**
**RECORD**　　　**Attendance :** 2,000 v Doncaster R., Charity match 85-86
　　　　　　**Appearances:** Gary Leighton　　　**Scorer:** Martin Johnson
　　　　　　**Win:** 7-0　　　　　　　　**Defeat:** 1-7

### FACT FILE

Founded: 1926
(Disbanded 1974, re-formed 1976)
Nickname: Wellie
Club Sponsors: Houston Transport
Colours: White/navy/white
Change colours: Navy/white/navy
Midweek matches: Tuesday
Programme: 24 pages
Editor: John Morgan, 01302 834475 (H)

### CLUB PERSONNEL

Chairman: Alan Bell, Tel: 01302 833882 (H)
Vice Chairman: James Houston
Comm. Manager: Peter Camm
Press Officer: Sharon Morgan
Manager: Carl Leighton
Asst Manager: John McKeown
Coach: Steve Taylor
Physio: Joey Johnson

# ARNOLD TOWN

**Secretary:** Tony Beale, 6 Elms Gardens, Ruddington, Nottm NG11 6DZ (0115 9211451)
**Ground:** King George V Recreation Ground, Gedling Rd, Arnold, Notts (0115 9263660)
**Directions:** From M1 jct 26, take A610 to B6004 (Stockhill Lane) 3 miles to A60. Right at A60, immediate left (St Albans Rd), thru lights by Sainsburys, left at rear of Sainsburys, ground on right adjacent to market. From A1(M)/A614/A60 to lights (Harvester on right), left thru lights to, St Albans Rd then as above. Nottingham Midland (BR) 4 miles. Buses 53, 55, 59 pass ground,buses 25, 40, 51, 57, 58, 90 stop within 200yds
**Capacity:** 3,400      **Seats:** 150      **Cover:** 950      **Floodlights:** Yes
**Clubhouse:** Licensed bar open matchdays & training night. Also tea-bar on matchdays
**Club Shop:** Sells prog, scarves, badges, pennants etc, contact Rob Hornby (0115 974 6769)

**HONOURS** (Arnold & Arnold Town): Central Mids Lg 92-93 (R-up 88-89, Lg Cup 87-88 (R-up 90-91), F/lit Cup 89-90); NCE Lg 85-86, R-up 83-84, 94-95; Div 1 94-95; Presidents Cup 94-95; Central All 62-63; Notts Snr Cup x 9, r-up x 5; Midland Co's Lg R-up 70-71 75-76, Lg Cup 74-75 (R-up 68-69 70-71 80-81). **PREVIOUS Leagues:** Central Mids 89-93. Arnold FC: Bulwell & Dist, Notts Spartan, Notts Comb (pre 55), Central All. 55-63/ Midland 63-82/ NCE 82-86/ Central Mids 86-89. Kingswell: Notts Yth/ Notts Amat./Notts Spartan/ E. Mids Reg.(pre'76)/Midland 76-82/ NCE 82-86/ Central Mids 86-89. **Names:** Arnold FC (founded 1928 as Arnold St Marys) merged with Arnold Kingswell(founded 1962) 1989
**BEST SEASONS FA Cup:** 1st Rd replay 77-78  **F.A,Vase.:** 3rd Rd(3)  **FA Trophy:** 2nd Rd (3)

## FACT FILE

Founded: 1989      Nickname: Eagles
Sponsors: Mapperley Sports/Neartone Printers
Colours: Yellow (blue trim)/blue/yellow
Change Colours: All white (blue trim)
Midweek matches: Tuesday
Reserves' Lge: Midland Reg. All
Programme: 48-52 pages 70p
Editor: Rob Hornby (0115 974 6769)
98-99- Captain: Bryn Gunn
Top Scorer : Gary Ricketts (30)
Sup.porters P.o.Y : Gary Ricketts.
Players P.o.Y :. Stuart Hammonds

## CLUB PERSONNEL

President: Alan Croome
Chairman: David Law
Vice-Chairman: Roy Francis
General Manager: Ray O'Brien
Comm. Manager: John Scott
Team Man: Iain McCulloch
Asst Man: Bill Brindley
Physio John Scott

John Scott (physio), Iain McCulloch (manager), Daniel Heverin, Mark Bradshaw, Peter davey, Matt Irons, Stuart Hammonds, Andy Elliott, James Mason, Lee Walshaw, Lee Holmes, Gary Ricketts (now Hinckley Utd.), Pete McCann, Wesley Bush, Alan Bush (2nd team manager). Front: Darren Bogan, Mark Clarke, Adrian Thorpe, Bryn Gunn, Brett Williams, Tristram Whitman.

Photo: Nottingham Post Group

# BRIGG TOWN

**Secretary:** Robert B Taylor, `Highfield House', Barton Rd, Wrawby, Brigg, Lincs DN20 8SH
        Tel: 01652 652284 (H)

**Ground:** The Hawthorns, Hawthorn Avenue, Brigg (01652 652767)

**Directions:** From M180 Junc 4 Scunthorpe East, A18 through Brigg leaving on Wrawby Rd, left into East Parade/Woodbine Ave, follow houses on right into Hawthorn Ave. Brigg (BR) 1 mile.
**Capacity:** 4,000      **Seats:** 250      **Cover:** 2 Stands      **Floodlights:** Yes
**Clubhouse:** Licensed club open matchdays

**HONOURS**      F.A. Challenge Vase 95-96; Northern Co's East Lg Presidents Cup R-up 91-92 92-93, R-up 95-96; Lincs Lg 49-50 53-54 73-74 75-76 (Div 1 68-69 69-70 70-71 71-72, Lg Cup 49-50 65-66 68-69 69-70 72-73); Mids Co's Lg 77-78 (Lg Cup 77-78); Lincs `A' Snr Cup 75-76 76-77 94-95; Lincs `B' Snr Cup 54-55 56-57 66-67 68-69 84-85

**PREVIOUS**      Leagues: Lindsey; Lincs 48-76; Midland Counties 76-82
        **Grounds:** Manor House Convent, Station Rd (pre 1939); Brocklesby Ox 1939-59

**BEST SEASON  FA Vase:** Winners 95-96      **FA Cup:**

**RECORD**      Attendance: 2,000 v Boston U. 1953 (at Brocklesby Ox)

## FACT FILE

Formed: 1864
Nickname: Zebras
Colours: Black & white stripes/black/red
Change colours: Orange shirts
Midweek Matchday: Wednesday
Programme: 16 pages
Editor: Match Secretary

## CLUB PERSONNEL

President: B Robins
Chairman: David Crowder, Tel: 01724 864742 (H)
Match Sec: John Martin. Tel: 01652 654526 (H)
Manager: Ralph Clayton
Coach: John Kaye

# BRODSWORTH WELFARE

**Secretary:** Robert Beswick, 75 Coniston Drive, Bolton-on-Dearne, Rotherham S63 8NE
Tel: 01709 890913

**Ground:** Welfare Ground, Woodlands, Nr. Doncaster (01302 728380).

**Directions:** From A1 take A638 to Doncaster, take left after Woodlands Pub into Welfare Road, ground 50yds on left.
Regular bus service from North Bridge Bus Station, Doncaster.
Capacity: 3,000    Seats: 228    Cover: 400    Floodlights: Yes

**Clubhouse:** Yes, Matchday drinks and snacks    **Club Shop:** No

**HONOURS**    Yorks Lg 24-25, Donc. & Dist. Lg 84-85 (Lg Cup 85-86, Div 2 78-79, Div 2Cup 78-79), Sheffield Jnr Cup 83-84, Mexborough Montagu Cup 91-92 92-93.R-up N.C.E. Div 1 98-99

**PREVIOUS**    **Leagues:** Doncaster Snr; Sheffield; Yorkshire.
**Name:** Brodsworth Main

**BEST SEASON** FA Cup:    **FA Vase:** 3rd Rd 97-98

**RECORD**    **Fee received:** £2,550 (+ Payments for apps) forDanny Schofield fromHuddersfield Town, Jan 99

### FACT FILE
Founded: 1912
Nickname: Brody
Colours: Green & yellow stripes/yellow/yellow
Change colours: Purple & White
Midweek home matchday: Wednesday
Programme: 20 pages
Editor: Match Sec.
98-99 Captain: Craig Smith
Top scorer: Chris Sambrook (17)

### CLUB PERSONNEL
Chairman: Gordon Jennings Tel: 01302 781121
Press Officer: John Muldowney
Match Sec: John Muldowney, Tel: 01302 721274
Manager: Neil Brandon
Physio: J Bedford

---

# BUXTON

**Secretary / Press Officer:** Julie Misk, 21 Errwood avenue, Buxton. Sk17 9BD
**Tel No 7 Fax :** 01335 346211 (office hours)
**Tel NO:** (H) 01246 236537  (W) 01246 455158
**Ground :** The Silverlands, Buxton, Derbyshire (01298 24733)
**Directions:** 200 yards of Buxton Market Place, opp. County Police HQ. Buxton (BR) 1/2 mile.
**Capacity:** 4,000 **Cover:** 2,500 **Seats:** 490 **Floodlights:** Yes **Shop:**Yes Pete Scott (01298 9582)
**Clubhouse:** (01298 23197). Open nightly + Sunday lunchtimes. licensed, no hot food .

**HONOURS**    N.P.L Lg Cup 90-91, Presidents Cup 81-82; Cheshire County 72-73(R-up 46-47 62-63, Lg Cup 56-57 57-58 68-69); Manchester Lg 31-32 (R-up 04-05 28-29 29-30 30-31, Lg Cup 25-26 26-27); Derbys. Sen. Cup 38-39 44-45 45-46 56-57 59-60 71-72 80-81 85-86 86-87.

**PREVIOUS**    **Leagues:** The Combination 1891-99; North Derbyshire; E Cheshire; Manchester 07-32; Cheshire County 32-73; NLP 73-98.]

**BEST SEASON**    **FA Trophy:** Qtr Finals 70-71 71-72.    **FA Vase:** 98-99
**FA Cup:** 3rd Rd 51-52. 2nd Rd 58-59, 1st Rd 62-63League clubs defeated: Aldershot 51-52

**RECORDS**    **Attendance:** 6,000 v Barrow, FA Cup 1st rd 51-52
**Goalscorer:** Dave Herbert  **Fee Paid:** £5,000 for Gary Walker (Hyde Utd 89)
**Appearances:** Mick Davis  **Fee Received:** £23,500 for Ally Pickering (Rotherham 89)

### FACT FILE
Formed: 1877
Nickname: The Bucks
Sponsors: Eagle Hotel, Buxton
Colours: Royal & white halves/royal/royal
Change colours: All yellow with blue trim
Midweek matchday: Tuesday
Programme: 36 pages 60p
Editor: Secretary
98-99- Captain:R.Bevan
P.O.Y.: R.Bevan
Top scorer: S Botchett
### CLUB PERSONNEL
Chairman: K Perrins
Vice Chairman: B.Goodwin
Manager: Tony Hodkinson
Asst Manager/Coach: David Bainbridge
Reserve Team Manager: Mike Dodd
Physio: Peter Walker

---

# DENABY UNITED

**Secretary:** Steve Pearce, 16 Calcot Green, Swinton, Mexborough, S. Yorks. S64 8SY
Tel:01709 589464 (H) 0370 745495 (M)
**Ground:** Tickhill Square, Denaby Main, Doncaster. Tel: 01709 864042    **Directions:** From Conisbrough take first left in Denaby along Wadworth St. From Mexborough take first right after Milestone Public House, left on to Bolton St. then left on to Wheatley Street. Rail to Conisbrough
**Capacity:** 6,000    Seats: 250    Cover: 350    Floodlights: Yes
**Clubhouse:** None    **Club Shop:** Yes
**HONOURS**    Yorks Lg R-up 67-68, Div 2 R-up 66-67, Div 3 R-up 81-82, Lg Cup 71-72; N.C.E. Prem Div. 96-97, Cup Winners 98-99Div 1 South R-up 83-84; Midland Lg R-up 07-08; Sheffield & Hallamshire Snr Cup 1905-06,09-10, 32-33 35-36 86-87; Thorn EMI Floodlight Comp. R-up 83-84; Sheffield Assoc. Lg 40-41; Mexborough Montague Cup 1914-15.
**PREVIOUS**    **Leagues:** Sheffield Ass 1900-02 15-18 19-20 40-45; Midland 02-13 20-40 45-60 61-65; Doncaster & Dist. 18-19; Central Alliance 60-61; Yorks 65-82.
**Ground:** Denaby Recreation Ground 1895-1912.**Name:** Shirebrook Miners W
**BEST SEASON**    **FA Vase:** 4th Rd 83-84**FA Cup:** 1st Rd Proper (3) **F.A.Trophy:** 2nd Rd 71-72
**RECORDS** **Attendance:** 5,200 v Southport, FA Cup 1st Rd 1927  **Win:** 20-0 v Shirebrook Colliery (H), Cen. All. 60-61  **Fee paid:** £350 for Kevin Deakin, Mossley 1984  **Fee received:** £3,000 for Jonathan Brown (Exeter, 1990)
Players progressing: S Cowan (Doncaster 23), R Attwell (West Ham 38), W Ardron (Rotherham 43), J Barker (Derby), K Burkinshaw (Liverpool 53), A Barnsley (Rotherham 85), C Beaumont (Rochdale 88), J Brown (Exeter 90)

### FACT FILE
Founded: 1895
Nickname: Reds
Colours: Red & white/red/red
Change colours: Yellow & jade/yellow
Reserves' League: B.I.R. County Sen. Lg.
Midweek matches: Wednesday
Programme: 64 pages 70p
Editor: David Green (01709 862319)
Local press : South Yorks Times, Doncaster Free Press, Dearne Valley Weekender

### CLUB PERSONNEL
Chairman: J Gordon Westwood
Vice Chairman: Jim Dainty
President: Alan Wilson
Manager: Gary Gillatt
Joint Manager: Jason Maybury
Physio: Jack Bramhall

# ECCLESHILL UNITED

**Secretary:** Ian Gardiner, 14 Tivoli Place, Little Horton, Bradford BD5 0PQ. Tel:01274 226052 (H)
**Ground:** Plumpton Park, Kingsway, Wrose, Bradford BD2 1PN (01274 615739)
**Directions:** M62 jct 26 onto M606, right on Bradford Ring Road A6177, left on to A650 for Bradford at 2nd r'bout. A650 Bradford Inner Ring Road onto Canal Rd,branch right opposite Woodheads Builders Merchants into Kings Rd, fork right after 30mph sign to junction with Wrose Rd, across junction - continuation of Kings Rd, 1st left onto Kingsway - ground 200 yds on right. 2 miles from Bradford (BR). Buses 686 or 687 for Wrose
**Capacity:** 2,225      Seats: 225      Cover: 225      Floodlights: Yes
**Clubhouse:** Open normal licensing hours. Bar, lounge, games room, kitchen (hot &cold snacks), committee room      **Club Shop:** Sells range of souvenirs. Contact Roy Maule Snr, 01274662428
**HONOURS**      N.C.E. Div 2 R-up 86-87, Res Div 86-87 89-90, R-up 87-88 94-95)); Bradford Amtr Lg Cup 61-62; Bradford & Dist. Snr Cup 84-85;Bradford & Dist. FA Snr Cup 85-86; W. Riding County Amat. Lg 76-77
**PREVIOUS**      **Leagues:** Bradford Amat; W Riding Co Amat.
**Ground:** Myers Lane      **Name:** Eccleshill FC
**BEST SEASON**      **FA Cup:**      **FA Vase:** 98-99, 3rd Rd at least
**RECORDS**      **Attendance:** 600 v Bradford City 90-91      **Goalscorer:** Paul Viner
Appearances: Paul Viner      **Win:** 7-1 v Yorkshire Main (H), N.C.E. Lge Div. 2 86-87.      **Defeat:** 0-6 v Rossington Main (A), N.C.E. Lge Cup 2nd Rd 92-93, & v Gt. Harwood T. (A), FA Cup Prel. Rd 91-92

**FACT FILE**
Founded: 1948
Nickname: Eagles
Colours: Blue & white stripes/blue/blue
Change colours: All yellow
Midweek matches: Tuesday
Reserves' Lge: NCE Res. Div
Programme: 24-28 pages, 50p
Editor: Raymond Maule (01274 634317)
Local Press: Bradford Telegraph & Argus, Bradford Star Free Press

**CLUB PERSONNEL**
Chairman: Keith Firth Tel: 01274 787057 (H)
Press Officer: Bill Rawlings (01274 635753)
Manager: Barry Gallagher
Physio: Gordon McGlynn

# GARFORTH TOWN

**Secretary:** Paul Bracewell, 24 Coupland Rd, Garforth, Leeds LS25 1AD (0113 2863314)
**Ground:** Wheatley Park, Brierlands Lane, Aberford Road, Garforth, Leeds (01132864083)
**Directions:** From North, A642 from A1 to Wakefield/Garforth, follow signs to Garforth. Over r/about, top of hill turn sharp left, grd end of lane. From South, M1 to M18, north on A1, Left A63 Leeds at PH Boot & Shoe, at r/about right onto A656, next r/about left A642 Garforth. Top of hill turn left into lane. From West, M62 jct 30, A642 to Rothwell Follow to Garforth, thru Garforth on A642, ground on right 1 mile on from lights just past new housing developement & Indian restaurant
**Capacity:** 3,000      Seats: 278      Cover: 200      Floodlights: Yes
**Clubhouse:** Full Licensing Hours      **Club Shop:** Yes
**HONOURS**      Northern Co's East Lg Div 1 97-98, R-up 96-97, Div 2 R-up 85-86; Yorks Lg Div 3 R-up 79-80; Barkston Ash Snr Cup 80-81 84-85 85-86 86-87 92-93 94-95; Wilkinson Sword Trophy 96-97; West Riding County FA Cup 97-98.
**PREVIOUS**      **Leagues:** Leeds Sunday Comb 64-72; West Yorks 72-78; Yorks 78-82.
**Names:** Miners Arms 64-78, Garforth Miners 78-79
**BEST SEASON**      **FA Vase:** Q-F 85-86      **FA Cup:**
**RECORDS**      **Attendance:** 817 v Leeds Utd, friendly 1987
**Goalscorer:** Vinnie Archer      **Appearances:** Philip Matthews (82-93)
**Win:** 11-0 v Blidworth Welf, N.C.E.Div. 1 97-98      **Defeat:** 1-7 v Lincoln Utd (A), N.C.E. Div. 1 92-93

**FACT FILE**
Founded: 1964
Nickname: The Miners
Sponsors: Aagrah Restaurants
Colours: Red/black/red
Change colours: Blue & yellow
Midweek matches: Tuesday
Reserves' League: NCE Res. Div.
Programme: 28 pages, 50p
Editor: K Strangeway (0113 286 6500)
97-98 Captain: Brendan Ormsby
P.o.Y.: Brendan Ormsby
Top Scorer: Darren Falk (31)

**CLUB PERSONNEL**
President: Norman Hebbron
Chairman: Stephen Hayle
Press Officer: Secretary
Manager/Coach: Dave Parker
Asst Manager: Dave Harrison
Physio: Jack Coup

# GLASSHOUGHTON WELFARE

ecretary: Eric Jones, `Marrica', Westfields Ave, Cutsyke, Castleford WF10 5JJ.
Tel: 01977 556257 (H)  01623 629123 (B)

ound: Glasshoughton Welfare, Leeds Rd, Glasshoughton, Castleford (01977518981)

rections: From M62 use either Junct. 31 or 32 towards Castleford. From Junction 32 the road
mes into Glasshoughton. From Junct. 31 turn right at 2nd roundabout at Whitwood Tech.
ollege. The ground is on the left in Leeds Road. Car park on ground. Castleford (BR) 1 mile.
apacity: 2,000          Seats: None          Covered: 250          Floodlights: Yes

ubhouse: Bar & refreshment facilities          **Club Shop:** No

ONOURS          West Riding County Cup 93-94

REVIOUS          **League:** West Yorkshire  **Name:** Anson Sports 1964-76
**Ground:** Saville Park 1964-76

EST SEASON   **FA Vase:**                    **FA Cup:**

ECORD          **Attendance:** 300 v Bradford C, 90

## FACT FILE

Founded: 1964
Club colours: Blue and white stripes/blue/blue
Change colours: All yellow
Midweek Matchday: Tuesday
Reserves' Lge: N.C.E. Res. Div.
Programme: 20 pages, 20p
Programme Editor: Nigel Lee (01977 516615)

### CLUB PERSONNEL

President: R Rooker
Chairman: Gordon Day
Tel: 01977 514178 (H)
Match Sec: Barry Bennett
Tel: 01977 682593 (H)
Manager: Wayne Day
Asst Manager/Coach: M Ripley

---

# HALLAM

cretary: Richard L Groves, 22 Moorgate Crescent, Dronfield, Sheffield, S181YF.
Tel: 01246 413548 (H)

ound: Sandygate (The oldest club ground in the world 1860), Sandygate Road, Crosspool,
effield S10 (0114 230 9484). Two new stands and full access & facilities for wheelchair users.

ections: A57 Sheffield to Glossop Rd, left at Crosspool shopping area signed`Lodge Moor' on
Sandygate Rd. Ground half mile on left opposite Plough Inn.51 bus from Crucible Theatre
pacity: 1,000          Seats: 250          Cover: 400          Floodlights: Yes  **Club Shop:** Yes

ubhouse: No, use Plough Inn opposite. Hot & cold snacks on ground for matches
ONOURS          Northern Counties (East) Lg Div 1 R-up 90-91 94-95, Yorkshire Lg Div 2 60-
61 (R-up 56-57), Sheffield & Hallamshire Snr Cup 50-51 61-62 64-65 67-68.
ST SEASON     **FA Vase:** 5thRd 80-81**FA Cup:** 3Rd Q Rd 1957 **Previous Lg:** Yorks 52-82
UB RECORDS **Attendance:** 2,000 v Hendon, FA Amtr Cup 3rd Rd 59
13,855 v Dulwich at Hillsborough, FA Amtr Cup 55)
**Goalscorer:** A Stainrod 46  **Appearances:** P Ellis 500+  **Win:** 7-0 v Hatfield Main
92-93, & v Kiveton Park(H) 69-70          **Defeat:** 0-7 v Hatfield Main (A) 88-89

yers progressing:Sean Connelly (Stockport C 92-93), Howard Wilkinson (Sheff. Wed) -The F.A.'s
:hnical Director, L Moore (Derby C.)

## FACT FILE

Formed: 1860
Nickname: Countrymen
Sponsors: Hallamshire Holdings Ltd.
Colours: Blue & white hoops/white/blue
Change colours: Red &black/black/red
Midweek Matches: Wednesday
Programme: Yes 50p
Editor: Mark Radford (Press Off.)
Local Press: Star, Green'Un, Sheffield
Telegraph, Yorkshire Post

### CLUB PERSONNEL

Chairman: Tony Scanlan
Tel: 01246 415471 (H)
Vice Chairman: P Fuller
President: A Cooper
Press Officer: Mark Radford
Tel: 0114 249 7287 (H)
Manager: K Johnson
Physio: P Fuller

---

# HARROGATE RAILWAY ATHLETIC

cretary:          W Douglas Oldfield, 80 Stonefall Ave., Harrogate, Nth Yorks HG2 7NP
Tel: 01423 540786

ound:          Station View, Starbeck, Harrogate.          Tel: 01423 885539

ections:          A59 Harrogate to Knaresborough road. After approx 1.5 miles turn left just
before railway level crossing. Ground is 150 yds up the lane
Adjacent to Starbeck (BR).
Served by any Harrogate to Knaresborough bus.
Capacity: 3,000          Seats: 300          Cover: 600          Floodlights: Yes

ubhouse: Games, TV room, lounge. Open normal pub hours. Hot food available.
ub Shop: Yes

NOURS          Northern Co's (East) Lg Cup 86-87

EVIOUS          **L eagues:** West Yorkshire; Harrogate District; Yorkshire 55-73 80-82.
CORD          **Attendance:** 1,400; 1962 FA Amateur Cup

## FACT FILE

Founded: 1935          Nickname: The Rail
Sponsors: Crest Homes
Colours: Red & green/green/red
Change: White/red/white
Midweek matchday: Monday
Programme Editor: Gordon Ward
Tel: 01423 880423 (H)
Local Press: Yorkshire Post, Harrogate Herald
& Advertiser, York Press

### CLUB PERSONNEL

President: J Robinson
Chairman: Dennis Bentley
Comm. Man: Wendy Rock (01423 883104)
Press Officer/Prog. Editor: Gordon Ward
Tel: 01423 880423 (H)
Manager: A Vincent Coach: A Canham
Physio: J Tope

# LIVERSEDGE

**Secretary:** Michael Balmforth, 7 Reform St., Gomersal, Cleckheaton BD19 4JX (01274 862123)

**Ground:** Clayborn Ground, Quaker Lane, Hightown Rd, Cleckheaton, W. Yorks (01274 862108)
**Directions:** M62 jct 26, A638 into Cleckheaton, right at lights on corner of Memorial Park, through next lights & under railway bridge, 1st left (Hightown Rd) and Quaker Lane is approx 1/4 mile on left and leads to ground. From M1jct 40, A638 thru Dewsbury and Heckmondwike to Cleckheaton, left at Memorial Park lights then as above. Buses 218 & 220 (Leeds-Huddersfield) pass top of Quaker Lane

Capacity: 2,000    Seats: 250    Cover: 750    Floodlights: Yes
**Clubhouse:** Matchdays, Tues, Thursday. Pool, TV. Snacks **Club Shop:** No

HONOURS    West Riding Co. Chal. Cup 48-49 51-52 69-70; West Riding County Cup 89-90; North Counties East Lg Div 1 R-up 89-90 (Div 2 R-up 88-89); West Riding Co.Amtr Lg(6) 23-24 25-27 64-66 68-69 (Lg Cup 57-58 64-65).

PREVIOUS    **Leagues:** Spen Valley; West Riding County Amateur 22-72; Yorkshire 72-82.
**Ground:** Primrose Lane, Hightown.    **Name:** None
BEST SEASON    **FA Cup:**    **FA Vase:**
Players progressing: Garry Briggs (Oxford), Martin Hirst (Bristol City) Leigh Bromby (Sheffield Wed)

### FACT FILE
Nickname: Sedge
Founded: 1910
Colours: All blue
Change colours: Red & white
Midweek Matches: Wednesday
Reserves League: NCEL Res. Div.
Programme: 28 pages, 50p
Editor: Secretary
Local Press: Yorkshire Evening Post, Telegraph & Argus, Spenbrough Guardian

### CLUB PERSONNEL
Chairman: Robert Gawthorpe
Press Officer: Secretary
Manager: Eric Gilchrist
Asst Mgr: Tony Passmore

# MALTBY MAIN

**Secretary:** Nick Dunhill, 10 Conrad Drive, Maltby, Rotherham, Sth Yorks S66 8RS
Tel: 01709 815676 01977 669534 (B)
**Ground:** Muglet Lane, Maltby , Rotherham. Tel: 01709 812462 (match days)
**Directions:** Exit M18 at junct 1 with A631. Two miles into Maltby, right at traffic lights at Queens Hotel corner on to B6427 Muglet Lane. Ground 3/4mile on left. Bus 101 from Rotherham stops at ground. Bus 287 from Sheffield to Queens Hotel, then follow as above
Capacity: 2,000Seats: 150Cover: 300Floodlights: Yes
**Clubhouse:** No, Miners Welfare Club opposite    **Club Shop:** No

HONOURS    Sheffield & Hallamshire Snr Cup 77-78, Northern Counties East Lg Presidents Cup 92-93 (SF 90-91), Mexborough Montague Cup 76-77 80-81 90-91,Yorks Lg R-up 77-78, Sheffield Wharncliffe Cup 80-81.
PREVIOUS    **Leagues:** Sheffield County Senior; Yorkshire 73-82.
**Name:** Maltby Main 1916-65 (disbanded); Maltby Miners Welfare 1970-96.
BEST SEASON    **FA Cup:**    **FA Vase:**
CLUB RECORDS    **Attendance:** 1,500 v Sheffield Wed., June 91-92 (friendly) 940 v Thackley, Yorks Lg Cup 77-78. (competitive)
Win: 6-0    Defeat: 0-5
Players progressing: Michael Williams (Sheffield Wednesday) 1991-92

### FACT FILE
Founded: 1916
Nickname: Miners
Sponsors: RJB Mining & Morrell Tyres
Colours: Black & white/black/black
Change colours: Red/white/white
Midweek matchday: Tuesday
Reserve League: None
Programme: 36 pages, 50p
Editor: Secretary
98-99 Top Scorer:Nathan Clayton
P.o.Y.: Darren Bonnington

### CLUB PERSONNEL
Chairman: G McCormick
Vice Chairman: M Richardson
President: H Henson
Press Officer: Secretary
Manager: Glyn Kenny
Asst Manager: Glyn Reeve
Coach: Les Harris

# NORTH FERRIBY UNITED

**Secretary:** Stephen Tather, 16 Peasholme, Heads Lane, Hessle, E Yorks HU13 0NY
Tel: 01482 642046 (H) Fax 01482 647244; 01482 351903 (B)
**Ground:** Grange Lane, Church Road, North Ferriby HU14 3AA (01482 634601)
**Directions:** Main Leeds-Hull road A63 or M62, North Ferriby is 8 miles west of Hull. Into North Ferriby, thru village past the Duke of Cumberland Hotel, right down Church Rd, ground half mile on left. One mile from North Ferriby (BR)
Capacity: 5,000    Seats: 250    Cover: 1,000    Floodlights: Yes
**Clubhouse:** Bar, lounge, TV, pool õ open every night    **Club Shop:** Yes

HONOURS    FA Vase Finalist 96-97; Yorkshire Lg R-up 75-76 (Lg Cup 74-75) (Div 270-71), N.C.E. Prem Div R-up 97-98, Div 1 85-86 (Lg Cup R-up) 90-91 97-98, Presidents Cup 90-91, Div 1 (North), R-up 82-83, Res. Div R-up 90-91); E. Riding Snr Cup 70-71 76-77 77-78 78-79 90-91 96-97 97-98; E. Riding Church Lg 37-38.
PREVIOUS    L eagues: East Riding Church; East Riding Amateur; Yorks 69-82.
BEST SEASON    **FA Cup:** 3rd Q 97-98.=99 **FA Vase:** R-up 96-97, SF 88-89, QF 89-90
RECORDS    **Attendance:** 1,800 v Tamworth, FA Vase Semi-Final, 1989
**Goalscorer:** Andy Flounders 50,98-99 **Appearances:** Richard Woomble, 74-94
**Win:** 9-0 v Hatfield Main, N.C.E. Lge Prem 97-98. **Defeat:** 1-7 v North Shields,N.C.E. Lge Prem 91. **Fee received:** £3,000 for Tim Hotte (Hull City,1988)
Players progressing: T Hotte (Hull) 88, I Ironside (Halifax) 88, D France, D Windass & M Matthews (Hull) 91.

### FACT FILE
Founded: 1934    Nickname: United
Sponsors: Dransfield Developments
Colours: All white
Change colours: All yellow
Midweek matches: Tuesday
Reserves League: N.C.E. Res Div
Programme: 40 pages, 75p
Editor: Jeff Frank (01482 633387)
98-99 Captain: Andy Smith
P.o.Y.: Paul Sharp
Top Scorer: Andy Flounders 50
Local Press: Hull Daily Mail

### CLUB PERSONNEL
President: Jeff Frank
Chairman: Les Hare
Vice Chairman: Roy Wallis
Press Officer: Les Hare
Manager: Brian France
Asst Mgr: John Deacey
Coach/Physio: Martin Woodmansey

# OSSETT ALBION

**Secretary:** David Chambers, 109 South Parade, Ossett, Wakefield, WF5 0BE. Tel:01924 276004 (H)
**Ground:** Dimple Wells, Ossett (01924 273618-club, 01924 280450-grd)
**Directions:** M1 jct 40. Take Wakefield road, right at Post House Hotel down Queens Drive. At
end right then second left down Southdale Rd. At end right,then first left down Dimple Wells
(cars only). Coaches take second left following the road for 200yds bearing left twice. Four
miles from both Wakefield and Dewsbury BR stations. Buses 116 and 117
**Capacity:** 3,000          Seats: 200          Cover: 500          Floodlights: Yes
**Clubhouse:** 3 bars + function room, open 7 days per week - catering available
**Club Shop:** Selling various souvenirs & programmes. Contact chairman

| | |
|---|---|
| **HONOURS** | Yorks Lg 74-75 (R-up 59-60 61-62, Lg Cup 75-76, 76-77, Div 2 78-79, 80-81 (R-up 58-59)); N.C.E. Div 1 86-87 (Lg Cup 83-84); West Yorks Lg 53-54 55-56 (Div 2 52-53, Lg Cup 52-53); W. Riding County Cup 64-65 65-66 67-68; Wheatley Cup 56-57 58-59 |
| **PREVIOUS** | **Leagues:** Heavy Woollen Area 44-49; West Riding Co. Amtr 49-50; West Yorks 50-57; Yorks 57-82.   **Ground:** Fearn House |
| **BEST SEASON** | **FA Cup:**          **FA Vase:** |
| **RECORDS** | **Attendance:** 1,200 v Leeds Utd, floodlight opening 1986.   **Win:** 12-0 v British Ropes(H), Yorks. Lge Div. 2 6/5/59   **Defeat:** 2-11 v Swillington (A), W. Yorks. Lge Div. 1 25/4/56   **Goalscorer:** John Balmer   **Appearances:** Peter Eaton, 800+ (22 yrs) |

**FACT FILE**

Founded: 1944
Nickname: Albion
Sponsors: Arco
Colours: Old gold & black/black/gold
Change colours: All white
Midweek matches: Tuesday
Reserves' Lge: NCEL Res Div
Programme: 44 pages, 50p
Editor: N Wigglesworth (01924 275630)
Local Press: Wakefield Express

**CLUB PERSONNEL**

President: Miss Helen Worth
Chairman: Neville A Wigglesworth
Vice-Chairman: S B Garside
Commercial Man: D Riley  01924 240247
Press Off. Neville Wigglesworth 01924 275630
Manager: Jimmy Martin
Physio: John Hirst
Coach: Peter Eaton

# SELBY TOWN

**Secretary:** Paul Atkin, 6 The Link, Carlton, Goole, E York DN14 9QE  Tel: 01405 861829 (H)
**Ground:** Flaxley Road Ground, Richard Street, Scott Road, Selby, North Yorkshire YO8 0BS.
Tel: 01757 210900
**Directions:** From Leeds, left at main traffic lights in Selby down Scott Rd.then 1st left into
Richard St. From Doncaster go straight across main traffic lights into Scott Road then 1st left.
From York right at main traffic lights into Scott Rd, and 1st left. 1 mile from Selby (BR)
**Capacity:** 5,000    Seats: 220    Cover: 350    Floodlights: Yes
**Clubhouse:** Bar at ground open first and second team matchdays          **Club Shop:** Yes

| | |
|---|---|
| **HONOURS** | Yorkshire Lg 32-33 34-35 35-36 52-53 53-54 (R-up 24-25 25-26 27-28 28-29 30-31 31-32 50-51 55-56, Div 3 R-up 74-75, Lg Cup 37-38 53-54 54-55 62-63); N.C.E. Div 1 95-96, Div 2 R-up 89-90; W. Riding Snr Cup 37-38; W. Riding Co Cup 27-28 48-49; W. Riding Chall. Cup 34-35 35-36 |
| **PREVIOUS** | **League:** Yorkshire (1920-82) Ground: Bowling Green, James St. 1920-51 |
| **BEST SEASON** | **FA Cup:** Second Round Proper 54-55   **FA Vase:** Prel Round 89-90 |
| **RECORD** | **Attendance:** 7,000 v Bradford Park Avenue (FA Cup 1st Rnd 1953-54) |

Players progressing: Numerous

**FACT FILE**

Founded: 1919
Nickname: The Robins
Sponsors: T.B.A.
Colours: All red
Change colours: Amber/black/amber
Midweek Matches: Tuesday
Reserves' League: N.C.E. Res. Div.
Programme: 30 pages, 50p
Editor: Mark Fairweather, 01757 705376 (H)
Local Newspaper: Selby Times

**CLUB PERSONNEL**

Chairman: Ralf Pearse, Tel: 0836 336481(M)
President: A Carter
Match Sec: T.B.A.
Manager: B Lyon
Asst Manager:
Coach: P Dooley

# SHEFFIELD

**Secretary:** Stephen Hall, 23 Regent Court, Bradfield Rd, Hillsborough, Sheffield S6 2BT
     Tel:  0114 233 4441 (H), 01246 450255 ext 300 (B)
**Ground:** Don Valley Stadium, Worksop Rd, Sheffield S9 3TL (0114 256 0607)
**Directions:** M1 Junc 33, turn onto dual carriageway sign City centre, take 2nd exit A57. Turn right at bottom of slip road, at bottom of hill turn right again at lights. Left at lights at rear of Morrison's supermarket. Follow  road passing under bridge, ground on right
Capacity: 25,000     Seats: 25,000     Cover: 13,000     Floodlights: Yes
**Clubhouse:** Licensed Bar     **Club Shop:** No

**HONOURS**     FA Amateur Cup 03-04; FA Challenge Vase Runners-up 76-77;
     Northern Co's East Lg Cup 94-95 (Div 1 88-89 90-91); Yorkshire Lg Div 2 76-77

**PREVIOUS**     **League:** Yorks 49-82  Grounds: Abbeydale Park, Dore (1956-1989);Sheffield
     Amateur Sports Club, Hillsborough Park 1989-91; Sheffield International
     (Don Valley) Stadium 1991-94; Sheffield Sports Stadium 94-97.

**BEST SEASON**     **FA Cup:**     **FA Vase:** R-up 76-77
**RECORD**     **Attendance:** 2,000 v Barton Rovers, FA Vase SF 76-77

Player progressing: Richard Peacock, Hull 94-95

### FACT FILE
Founded: 1857
Nickname: The Club
Sponsors: Bumford Heating
Colours: Red & black quarters/black/black
Change: All blue
Midweek matchday: Wednesday
Programme: 16 pages, 50p
Editor: David Dean (0114 232 5901)
98-99 - Captain: Paul Sykes
P.o.Y.: Martin Thomson
Top scorer: Jamie Creaghan

### CLUB PERSONNEL
Chairman: Peter Beeby
Tel: 0114 251 2509 (B)
President: Alan Methley
Manager: John Pearson
Asst Manager:

---

# STAVELEY MINERS WELFARE

**Secretary:** Roy Berry, 11 Thorpleigh Rd, Woodthorpe, Chesterfield, DerbyshireS43 3BJ.
     Tel: 01246 281827 (H)
**Ground:** Inkersall Road, Staveley, Chesterfield, Derbyshire (01246 471441)
**Directions:** M1 jct 30, follow A619 Chesterfield - Staveley is 3 miles from jct30. Turn left at GK Garage in Staveley town centre into Inkersall Rd - ground200yds on right at side of Speedwell Rooms. Frequent buses (47, 70, 72, 75, 77) from Chesterfield stop in Staveley town centre - 3 mins walk to ground
Capacity: 5,000Cover: 400Seats: 220  Floodlights: Yes
**Clubhouse:** The Staveley Miners Welfare, 500 yds from ground, open before and after games
**Club Shop:** Yes, contactRod Walker 01246 473655

**HONOURS**     County Sen Lg Div 2 92-93, Div 3 91-92, Chesterfield & D. Amat Lg R-up89-
     90 90-91, Byron (Lge) Cup 89-90, R-up 90-91.NCE Div 1 R-up 97-98

**PREVIOUS**     **Leagues:** Chesterfield & D. Amat 89-91; County Sen 91-93.

**BEST SEASON**     **FA Cup:**     **FA Vase:** 98-99, 3rd Rd at least
**RECORDS**     **Attendance:** 280 v Stocksbridge, Sheffield Snr Cup 22/1/94
     **Goalscorer:** Mick Godber
     **Appearances:** Shane Turner

### FACT FILE
Founded: 1989
Nickname: The Welfare
Colours: All red
Change colours: All yellow
Midweek matches: Wednesday
Reserves' League: Beauvale Midlan Regiona
Alliance: Premier Division
Programme: 32pages, 50p
Editor: Secretary

### CLUB PERSONNEL
PChairman: John Atkin
Tel: 01246 551155(H)
Vice-Chairman: Phil White

---

# THACKLEY

**Secretary:** Stewart Willingham, 3 Kirklands Close, Baildon, Shipley, West Yorks BD17 6HN
     Tel: 01274 598589
**Ground:** Dennyfield, Ainsbury Avenue, Thackley, Bradford (01274 615571). **Directions:** On main Leeds/Keighley A657 road, turn off at Thackley corner which is 2 miles from Shipley traffic lights and 1 mile from Greengates lights.Ainsbury Avenue bears to the right 200yds down the hill. Ground is 200yds along Ainsbury Avenue on the right. 3 miles from Bradford Interchange (BR), one and ahalf miles from Shipley (BR). Buses to Thackley corner (400 yds)
Capacity: 3,000     Seats: 300     Cover: 600     Floodlights: Yes
**Clubhouse:** Tue-Sun evenings, matchdays and w/e lunchtimes. Hot & cold snacks on matchdays
**Club Shop:** Progs, souvenirs. Metal badges- £2.50 + s.a.e.Contact Geoff Scott (01274 611520)

**HONOURS**     N.C.E. Lg R-up 94-95 (Lg Cup R-up 94-95), Yorks Lg Div 273-74, West Yorks Lg
     66-67, W. Riding Co. Amtr Lg (x3) 57-60, W. Riding Co. Cup 73-74 74-75, W.
     Riding Co. Chal. Cup 63-64 66-67,(R-Up 94-95); Bradford & Dist. Snr Cupx 11.
**PREVIOUS**     **Leagues:** Bradford Amateur, W. Riding County Amateur, W. Yorks, Yorks 67-82.
     **Name:** Thackley Wesleyians 1930-39
**BEST SEASON**     **FA Vase:** 5th Rd 80-81 (01-2 v Whickham)     **FA Cup:**
**RECORD**     **Attendance:** 1,500 v Leeds Utd 1983

Players progressing: Tony Brown (Leeds), Ian Ormonndroyd (Bradford City).

### FACT FILE
Founded: 1930
Sponsors: Diamond International Shipping
Colours: Red & white/white/red
Change colours: All white
Midweek matches: Tuesday
Programme: 20 pages, 50p Editor: Secretary
Local Press: Bradford Telegraph & Argus,
BradfordStar, Aire Valley Target.

### CLUB PERSONNEL
Chairman: John Myers
Treasurer: Steven Paley
Secretary: T.B.A.
Manager/Coach: Trevor Best
Asst Manager: David Holmes
Physio: Neil Corker

## STAVELEY MINERS WELFARE

Photo: Bill Wheatcroft

## LOUTH UNITED

Photo: Gordon Whittington

## PARKGATE

Photo: Gordon Whittington

# BORROWASH VICTORIA

**Secretary./Press Officer:** Ian Collins, 30 Margreave Road, Chaddesden, Derby DE21 6JD
Tel: 01332 739437
**Ground:** Asterdale Bowl, Borrowash Road, Spondon, Derby (01332 668656).
**Directions:** M1 jct 25, A52 towards Derby, 3rd left off by-pass into Borrowash Rd, ground 400 yds on left. 2 miles from Spondon (BR). Nottingham to Derby buses pass nearby.
Capacity: 5,000          Seats: Yes          Covered: 500          Floodlights: Yes
**Clubhouse:** Normal pub hours. Hot & cold food.          **Club Shop:** No
**HONOURS**          N.C.E. Lg Div 1 Sth 83-84 (R-up 84-85, Div 2 Sth R-up 82-83), Derby Comb. 77-78 (R-up(10) 65-66 68-74 75-77 78-79, Lg Cup 68-69 75-76(R-up 63-64 66-67), Midland Co's Lg Div 80-81 (Div 1 Cup 80-81), Derbys Snr Cup R-up 90-91, Derbys Div. Cup 73-74 (R-up 70-71 72-73), Cen. Midl Lg B E Webbe Cup R-up 88-89 (Res. Cup 94-95),
**BEST SEASON     FA Cup** 3rd Qual. Rd 91-92.          **FA Vase:**
**PREVIOUS Leagues:** Derby Sun. School & Welf. 52-57; Derby Comb.; Midland 79-82; N.C.E.
**RECORDS          Attendance:** 2,000 v Nottingham Forest, floodlight opening 22/10/85.

**FACT FILE**
Founded: 1911 ( Reformed 1963)
Nickname: Vics
Club Sponsors: Robinson Construction
Colours: Red & white stripes/black/black
Change Colours: Yellow/sky/yellow
Midweek matches: Tuesday
Programme: 16 pages, 50p
Editor: Michael Smith 01332 573832

**CLUB PERSONNEL**
Chairman: Ian Anderson
Vice Chairman: Peter Erwin
Manager/Coach:Mick Rodgers
Asst Manager:Gary Adul
Physio: Geoff Woolley

---

# BRIDLINGTON TOWN

**Secretary**          Chris Bemrose, 16 North Back Lane, Bridlington, E. Yorks. YO16 7BA
Tel: 01262 604036 (H & Fax)  01262 676836 (B)

**Ground**   Queensgate Stadium, Queensgate, Bridlington YO16 5LN  Tel: 01262 606879

**Directions**          From south on A165 - Pass golf course, straight over lights. Turn right at r'about by B&Q. Turn left at next lights & over rlwy bridge. At r'about bear left and then straight on up Quay Road. After lights turn right into Queensgate & ground is 800yds on right.
From south & west via A614 (formerly A166) - Straight on at lights (Hosp. on right). At r'about straight on to mini-r'about & bear right (2nd exit). Over the first lights, left at next lights (just after Kwikfit) into Queensgate & ground is 800yds on right.
**PREVIOUS          League:** East Riding Co. Lge.

**FACT FILE**
Founded: 1994
Colours: Redwith 1 black stripe/red/red
Midweek Matchday: Tuesday
Prog. Editor: Jonathon Bemrose

**CLUB PERSONNEL**
Chairman: Gordon Reed
Tel: 01262 673967 (H, B & Fax)
Match Sec.: Jonathon Bemrose
Tel: 01262 604748 (H & Fax)
01262 401487 (B)

---

# GLAPWELL

**Secretary:** Ellen Caton, 111 The Hill, Glapwell, Chesterfield. S44 5LU.
Tel: 01246 854648 (H & Fax)  01623 629123 (B)

**Ground:** Hall Corner,  Glapwell, Chesterfield, Derbyshire (01623812213).

**Directions:** M1 Junc 29 A617 towards Mansfield, after Young Vanish Inn take filter lane left onto Bolsover Road, ground facing, use rear entrance next to garden centre
Floodlights: Yes

**HONOURS**          Central Midlands Lg 93-94,Floodlit Cup 93-94,
Derbyshire Senior Cup SF93-94.

**FACT FILE**
Founded: 1980
Colours: Black & white stripes/white/white
Change colours: All yellow
Midweek matches: Tuesday
Programme: 16 pages,50p
Editor: Club Secretary

**CLUB PERSONNEL**
Chairman: Roger Caton
Manager: Graham Gladwin

---

# GOOLE AFC

**Secretary:** Mike E Norman, Ashville Lodge, 10 High Ash Drive, Leeds LS17 8QY
Tel: 0113 266 4900 (H, B & Fax)

**Ground:** Victoria Pleasure Grounds, Marcus St, Goole DN14 6AR Tel: 01405 762794

**Directions:** M62 Junc 36 follow signs for town centre. Turn right at 2nd lights into Boothferry Rd, 300 yards right again into Carter St, ground at end of road.

Capacity: 3000          Seats: 200          Cover: 800          Floodlights: Yes
**Club Shop:** Yes          **Clubhouse:** Matchdays only
**PREVIOUS          League:** Central Midlands

**FACT FILE**
Founded: 1997
Colours:
White with red sleeves with black trim/black/black & white
Change Colours:  Gold/black/gold & black
Midweek Matchday: Tuesday
Programme Editor: Malcolm Robinson
01405 761078 (H) 07801 092952 (M)

**CLUB PERSONNEL**
Chairman/Secretary: M.E.Norman
Match Sec.: Tim Harness
Tel: 01405 762458 (H & Fax)
Manager:  John Reed

# HALL ROAD RANGERS

**Secretary:** David J Simmons, 24 Gorton Road, Willerby. Hull HU10 6LT.
Tel: 01482658998 (H), 01482 653203 (B & Fax)

**Ground:** Dene Park, Dene Close, Beverley Rd, Dunswell, Nr Hull (01482 850101).
**Directions:** M62 to A63, turn left before Humber Bridge onto A164 to Beverley,after approx 5 miles turn right onto A1079. In 2 miles turn left at large roundabout to ground 20 yards on right.
**Capacity:** 1,200 **Seats:** 250 **Cover:** 750 **Floodlights:** Yes
**Clubhouse:** Open all week for drinks and bar snacks. Snooker, pool,darts. **Club Shop:** Yes

**HONOURS** N.C.E. Lg Div 2 90-91, Yorks Lg Div 3 72-73 79-80, E. Riding Snr Cup 72-73 93-94.

**PREVIOUS** **Leagues:** East Riding; Yorks 68-82 **Ground:** Hull Co-Op (until 1968)

**BEST SEASON** **FA Cup:** **FA Vase:**

**RECORDS** **Attendance:**1,200 v Manchester City Aug 93
**Scorer:** G James **Appearances:** G James

Players progressing: Gerry Ingram (Blackpool, Sheff Wed). Mark Greaves (Hull City)

### FACT FILE
Founded: 1959     Nickname: Rangers
Sponsor: Admiral Signs of Hull Ltd.
Colours: Blue & white
Change Colours: Red & Black Stripes,black
Midweek Matches: Wednesday
Reserves' League: East Riding Co.League
Programme: 36 pages, 50p
Editor/Press Officer: Secretary

### CLUB PERSONNEL
Chairman: Robert Smailes
Tel: 01482821354 (H)
Player-Manager: Chris Lewis
Asst Mgr: Peter Smurthwaite
Coach: Ian Davis

---

# HATFIELD MAIN

**Secretary:** Bruce Hatton, 92 Ingram Rd, Dunscroft, Doncaster, Sth Yorks DN7 4JE
Tel: 01302 841648 (H) 0831 179095 (M)

**Ground:** Dunscroft Welfare Ground, Dunscroft, Doncaster, Sth Yorks    Tel: 01302 841326
**Directions:** From Doncaster (A18) Scunthorpe Rd to Dunsville, left at Flarepath Hotel down Broadway. Ground half mile on right.
Stamforth & Hatfield (BR) 1/2 mile. Buses every 15 mins. from Doncaster.
**Capacity:** 4,000 **Seats:** 200 **Cover:** 600 **Floodlights:** Yes
**Clubhouse:** Full licensing hrs. Hot/cold drinks/snacks **Club Shop:** Yes
**HONOURS** Northern Counties East Prem Div 95-96, R-up 88-89, Div One 94-95;
Yorks Lge Div 1 R-up 65-66; W Riding Cup 61-62 63-64.
**PREVIOUS** **League:** Doncaster Dist, Yorkshire 55-82.
**BEST SEASON** **FA Vase:** **1998-99 P.o.Y. & Capt:** Gary Lockwood
**RECORDS** **Gate:** 1,000 v Leeds, A Jones testimonial. Competitive: 750 v Bishop Auckland,
FA Amtr Cup **Appearances:** Lal Dutt **Fee received:** £1,000 for Mark Hall (York C.)

### FACT FILE
Founded: 1936    Nickname: The Main
Sponsors: Manor Tyres, (Stainforth)
Colours: All red    Change Colours: All blue
Midweek matchday: Tuesday
Reserves' League: None
Programme: 25 pages, 50p
Editor: Tony Ingram (01302 842795)

### CLUB PERSONNEL
President: Russell Wright
Chairman: Peter Wright
Vice Chairman/Treasurer: David Sanderson
Manager: James Goltz
Asst Manager:Mark Taylor
Physio: Anthony Hatton

---

# LOUTH UNITED

**Secretary:** Ken Vincent, 64 Frederick St, Grimsby DN31 1XQ: Tel Nos: 01472 344411(H)
0589 874857 (M) and 01469 553266 **Match day Secretary:** Albany Jordan(01507 607356)
**Albany Jordan Ground:** Park Avenue, Louth, Lincs    Tel: 01507 607351
**Directions:** A16 To Louth Market Place, exit via Eastgate/Eastfield Rd, to Fire Station turn right into Park Avenue. Ground at bottom of avenue of prefabricated bungalows.
**Capacity:** 2,500 **Seats:** None **Cover:** 400 **Floodlights:** Yes **Club Shop:** No
**Clubhouse:** Weekdays 6.30-11.45, Sat 12-11.45. Full bar facilities. Snacks available.

**HONOURS** Lincs Lg Prem 72-73 85-86 86-87 (Div 1 57-58 66-67 67-68; Lg Challenge
Cup 73-74 86-87; Lg Charity Cup 55-56 56-57 67-68; Central Mids Lg Cup R-up 92-93;
Wakefield F'lit Cup R-up 91-92; Lincs Snr `A' Cup 77-78.

**PREVIOUS** **Leagues:** Lincs 47-75 82-88; Central Midlands 88-93.
**Names:** Louth Nats & Louth Town - merged **Grounds:** None
**BEST SEASON** **FA Cup:** **FA Vase:** 4th Rd v Halesowen Town 85-86
**RECORDS** **Goalscorer:** Peter Rawcliffe 39 **Appearances:** Gary Smith 476 **Attendance:** 2,500

### FACT FILE
Founded: 1947    Nickname: The Lions
Sponsors: Foxhall Plant Hire
Colours: Royal with white stripes/royal/red
Change:All Yellow
Midweek matches: Tuesday
Reserves League: Lincolnshire
Programme: 50p
Editor/Press Officer: Albany Jordan (Sec.)

### CLUB PERSONNEL
Chairman: George Horton
Vice-Chairman: Andrew Sylvester
President: Dave Fairburn
Manager: Steve Newby
Coaches: Nigel Fanthorpe/D Cole
Physio: Kenny Vincent

---

# MICKLEOVER SPORTS

**Secretary:** Tony Shaw, 80 Onslow Road, Mickleover, Derbys. DE3 5JB
Tel: 01332 512826 (H & Fax)

**Ground:** Mickleover Sports Ground, Station Rd, Mickleover, Derby(01332 521167).
**Directions:** Derby ring road A38 to A52, turn off at Markeaton Park Island.Take turn to Ashbourne A52, then 2nd left into Radbourne Lane. Take 3rd left into Station Road, ground on corner.

**Capacity:** 1,500 **Seats:** None **Cover:** 200

**Clubhouse:** Open Thursdays and Fridays (7-11 p.m) Saturdays and Sundays (11am-11pm) Snacks available only on Matchdays

**Club Shop:** No
**PREVIOUS** **League:** Central Midlands

### FACT FILE
Founded: 1948
Colours: Red & White stripes/black/red
Change Colours: All blue
Midweek Matchday: Tuesday
Programme Editor: Stephen Pritchard
Tel: 01332 516271

### CLUB PERSONNEL
Chairman Keith Jenkinson
Match Sec.: Stephen Brown (01332 516978-H)
Manager: Mark Kelsey

# PARKGATE

**Secretary:** Bruce Bickerdike, 2 Cardew Close, Rawmarsh, Rotherham S62 6LB
Tel: 01709 522305 Fax: 01709 528583.
**Ground:** Roundwood Sports Complex, Green Lane, Rawmarsh, Rotherham Tel: 01709 826600
**Directions:** From Rotherham A633 to Rawmarsh. From Doncaster A630 to Conisbrough, then A6023 through Swinton to Rawmarsh. Grd at Green Lane - right from Rotherham, left from Conisbrough at the Crown Inn. Grd 800yds right
**Capacity:** 1,000    **Seats:** 300    **Cover:** 300    **Floodlights:** Yes    **Club Shop:** No.
**Clubhouse:** Licensed bar, 2 lounges. Meals available lunchtime Wed-Sat.

**HONOURS** S&HSC Finalists 0-3 v Emley 97-98, Wilkinson Sword Trophy R-up 98-99

**PREVIOUS Leagues:** B.I.R. County Senior Lge; Yorkshire 74-82
**Ground:** None  **Names:** BSC Parkgate (until mid-eighties); RES Parkgate (pre-1994).

**BEST SEASON    FA Cup:        FA Vase:**

**RECORDAttendance:** v Worksop 1982

### FACT FILE
Founded: 1969
Nickname: The Gate or The Steelmen
Kit Sponsors: JBB Investigations
Colours: All red&White    Change : All sky
Midweek matches: Tuesday
Programme: 20 pages, 50p
Editor: Stuart Bisby (01709 817524)

### CLUB PERSONNEL
President:
Chairman: Albert T DudillTel: 01709 524533 (H)
Vice Chairman: Les Taylor
Press Officer: Secretary
Manager: Wilfred Pace
Asst Manager: Vincent Brad
Physio: Eric Beaumont

# PICKERING TOWN

**Secretary:** T.B.A.

**Ground:** Recreation Club, Mill Lane (off Malton Rd), Pickering, North Yorkshire (01751 473317)
**Directions:** A169 from Malton. On entering Pickering take 1st left past Police Station and B.P. garage into Mill Lane, ground 200 yards on right
**Capacity:** 2,000    **Seats:** 200    **Cover:** 500    **Floodlights:** Yes
**Clubhouse:** Open 1.30pm for Saturday games, 6pm for midweek games. Food available from Football Club Kitchen at half-time and after games.    **Club Shop:** No

**HONOURS** Northern Co's East Lg R-up 92-93 (Div 2 1987-88, Div 1 R-up 91-92),Yorks Lg Div 3 73-74, North Riding Snr Cup R-up 93-94 94-95, N. Riding County Cup 90-91.
**PREVIOUS Leagues:** Beckett; York & District; Scarborough & District; Yorkshire72-82.
**RECORD    Attendance:** 1,412 v Notts County, friendly, August 1991
**Players progressing:** Chris Short (Stoke City), Craig Short (Everton) both via Scarborough

### FACT FILE
Founded: 1888    Nickname: Pikes
Club Sponsors: Flamingoland
Colours: Royal/white/royal
Change colours: Amber/black/amber
Midweek matches: Tuesday
Reserves' League: Beckett League
Programme: 32 pages, 50p
Editor: Anthony Dunning (Chairman)

### CLUB PER SONNEL
Chairman: Anthony Dunning (01751 473697)
President:J.P.Jennison
Manager:Jimmy Reid
Assistant Manager: Steve Brown
Physio: Clive Reynolds

# PONTEFRACT COLLIERIES

**Secretary:** Frank Maclachlan, 188 Watling Road, Ferry Fryston, Castleford WF102QY
Tel: 01977 512085 (H), 01977 601327 (B), 0410 586447 (M)
**Ground:** Skinner Lane, Pontefract, West Yorkshire (01977 600818)
**Directions:** M62 jct 32 towards Pontefract. Left at traffic lights opposite Racecourse entrance (travelling through Pontefract follow Racecourse/Leeds signs to traffic lights and turn right) - ground past Territorial Army unit. 1 mile from Monkhill (BR). All Leeds and Castleford buses stop near ground
**Capacity:** 1,200    **Seats:** 300    **Cover:** 400    **Floodlights:** Yes
**Clubhouse:** Fully licensed. Hot & cold snacks. Open before and after games    **Club Shop:** No
**HONOURS** N.C.E. Lg Div 1 83-84 95-96 (Div 2 R-up 82-83); Floodlit Comp 87-88 88-89; Yorks Lg Div 3 81-82; W. Riding Co. Cup R-up 87-88 90-91;Embleton Cup 82-83    86-87 95-96; Castleford FA Cup 82-83 86-87,94-95; Wilkinson Sword 95-96
**PREVIOUS    Leagues:** West Yorkshire 58-79; Yorkshire 79-82
**RECORDS    Attendance:** 1,000 v Hull City, floodlight opening 1985

### FACT FILE
Founded: 1958  Nickname: Colls
Sponsors: John Betts Quality Used Cars
Colours: Blue & black/black/black
Change Colours: White/blue/blue
Midweek Matches: Tuesday
Reserve League: N.C.E. Res. Div.
Programme: 16 pages, 50p
Editor/Press Officer: Secretary

### CLUB PERSONNEL
Chairman:Steve Lloyd (01977 795581)
President: J Betts
Manager: Jim Kenyon
Asst Mgr: Frank Maclachlan
Physio: Alan Dean

# ROSSINGTON MAIN

**Secretary:**  Gerald Parsons, 15 Seaton Gardens, Rossington, Doncaster DN11 0XA
Tel: 01302 867542 (H)
**Ground:**  Welfare Ground, Oxford Street, Rossington, Doncaster    Tel: 01302 865524
**Directions:** Enter Rossington and go over the railway crossings. Pass the Welfare Club on right, Oxford Street is next right - ground is at bottom. 8miles from Doncaster (BR).
**Capacity:** 2,000    **Seats:** 200    **Cover:** 500    **Floodlights:** Yes
**Clubhouse:**  Evenings & matchdays, Sandwiches, rolls, satellite TV, pool.    **Club Shop:** No
**HONOURS**  Sen Lge 44-45, Cup 44-45, Cen. Mids. Prem Div. 84-85, Cup 83-84 84-85, DDSALShield 90-91 R-up 89-90.

**PREVIOUS    Leagues:** Doncaster Sen, Yorkshire Lge, Sheffield County Sen, Cent Mids.
**BEST SEASON    FA Cup:        FA Vase:**
**RECORDS    Attendance:** 864 v Leeds United 8/91.
**Goalscorer:** Mark Illman    **Appearances:** Darren Phipps

### FACT FILE
Founded: 1920    Nickname: The Colliery
Sponsor: RJB Mining
Colours: All blue
Change colours: Blue & black
Midweek matches: Tuesday
Reserves' League: Beefeater County Sen
Programme: 50p
Editor: David Clark (01302 863190)

### CLUB PERSONNEL
Chairman: Gerald Murden (01302 867225)
Joint Managers: D Ridley & L Ostle
Physio: J White

# TADCASTER ALBION

**Secretary:** Mrs Angela J Burnett, 6 Beech Grove House, Ouston Lane, Tadcaster LS24 8DP.
Tel: 01937 832802 (H/Fax)

**Ground:** The Park, Ings Lane, Tadcaster, LS24 9AY.     Tel: 01937 834119

**Directions:** From West Riding and South Yorks, turn right off A659 at John Smith's Brewery Clock. From East Riding turn left off A659 after passing over river bridge and pelican crossing (New Street).

Capacity: 1,500     Seats: Planned this season     Cover: 400     Floodlights: Yes
**Clubhouse:** No
**Club Shop:** No
**Honours:**
**BEST SEASON:     FA Vase:RECORD** Attendance:1,200 v Wincanton F.A.Vase 4th Rd 1996-7

### FACT FILE

Founded: 1892
Colours: Red & blue/red/blue
Change colours: Green & Yellow halves
Midweek Matchday: Tuesday
Programme: 20 pages
Programme Editor: Mrs Angela Burnett (Sec.)

### CLUB PERSONNEL

Chairman: Michael R Burnett
Tel: 01937 832802 (H/Fax)
President: Lord Edward Stourton
Match Sec: Howard Clarke 01937 832887 (H/B)
Manager: Wayne Day

---

# WINTERTON RANGERS

**Secretary:** G Spencer, 2 Dale Park Ave., Winterton, Scunthorpe, N Lincs. DN15 9UY
Tel: 01724 732039 (H)
**Ground:** West Street, Winterton, Scunthorpe, South Humberside (01724 732628).
**Directions:** From Scunthorpe take A1077 Barton-on-Humber for 5 miles. On entering Winterton take 2nd right (Eastgate), 3rd left (Northlands Rd)and 1st right (West St.). Ground 200yds on left
Capacity: 3,000     Seats: 200     Covered: 200     Floodlights: Yes     **Club Shop:** No.
**Clubhouse:** Open matchdays & evenings Mon-Sat, hot & cold food available on matchdays

| | |
|---|---|
| HONOURS | Lincs Jnr Cup 47-48 61-62; Lincs Snr `B' Cup 69-70; Yorks Lg 71-72 76-77 78-79 (Lg Cup 80-81); N.C.E. Div 2 89-90; S'thorpe Lg & Cup many times. |
| PREVIOUS | **Leagues:** Scunthorpe & Dist. 45-65; Lincs 65-70; Yorkshire 70-82. **Ground:** Watery Lane 1930-48. |
| BEST SEASON | **FA Vase:** QF 76-77 **FA Cup:** 4th Qual Rd replay 76-77, 2-3 after 3-3 |
| RECORD | **Attendance:** 1,200 v Sheffield Utd, official floodlight opening, Oct. 78. **Fee received:** £5,000 for Henry Smith (Leeds United, 1979) |

### FACT FILE

Founded: 1930     Nickname: Rangers
Sponsors: Finaction Ltd
Colours: Navy & white/navy/navy
Change colours: All red
Midweek matches: Monday
Programme: 28-36 pages, 50p
Editor: M Fowler (01724 734570)
Local press: Scunthorpe Evening Telegraph

### CLUB PERSONNEL

President: J W Hiles
Chairman: G Spencer
Vice Chairman: A Smith
Press Officer: Secretary
Managers:A.Irvine & M.Newell
Asst Manager/Coach: Peter Lea

---

# WORSBROUGH M.W. & ATHLETIC

**Secretary:** Garry Wiggan, 9 Pantry Well, Worsbrough Bridge, Barnsley, S. Yorks S70 4SW
Tel: 01226 247023
**Ground:** Park Road, Worsbrough Bridge, Barnsley Tel: 01226 284452
**Directions:** On the A61 Barnsley-Sheffield road two miles south of Barnsley, 2miles from M1 jnt 36 opposite Blackburns Bridge. Two and a half miles from Barnsley (BR). Yorkshire Traction run buses every 10 mins thru Worsbrough Bridge.
Capacity: 2,000     Seats: 175     Cover: 175     Floodlights: Due
**Clubhouse:**     **Club Shop:**

| | |
|---|---|
| HONOURS | Northern Co's East Div 1 R-up 90-91 (Div 3 R-up 85-86); Sheffield SnrCup R-up 72-73; County Snr Lg 65-66 69-70 (R-up 62-63, Lg Cup 65-66); Barnsley Lg 52-53 58-59 59-60, Lg Cup 56-57 58-59 (R-up 53-54), Beckett Cup 57-58. |
| PREVIOUS | **Leagues:** Barnsley 52-61; County Snr 62-70; Yorks 71-82. |
| BEST SEASON | **FA Cup: FA Vase:** |
| RECORD | **Attendance:** 2,300 v Blyth Spartans, FA Amateur Cup 1971 |

### FACT FILE

Founded: 1923
Reformed: 1947
Colours: All red
Change colours: Yellow/blue
Midweek Matchday: Wednesday
Programme: 20 pages, 20p
Editor: Secretary

### CLUB PERSONNEL

Chairman: Mr J Wright
Press Officer: Mr A Wright (01226 243418).
Manager: K Paddon

---

# YORKSHIRE AMATEUR

**Secretary:** Colin Guest, c/o Ground address.
**Ground:** The Bracken Edge, Roxholme Road, Leeds LS8 4DZ Tel: 0113 262 4093
**Directions:** From South M1 to Leeds, then A58 Wetherby Road to Fforde Green Hotel, left at lights and proceed to Sycamore Ave. (on right). From East A1 to Boot & Shoe Inn then to Shaftesbury Hotel, turn right into Harehills Lane, then to Sycamore Avenue. Two and a half miles from Leeds (BR). Buses 2, 3 & 20 from Briggate to Harehills Ave.
Capacity : 1,550     Seats: 200     Cover: 160     Floodlights: Yes     **Club Shop:** Yes
**Clubhouse:** Bar, tea bar, games, lounge. Every night 8.30-11, Sat matchdays 12-11, Sun 12-3.

| | |
|---|---|
| HONOURS | FA Amtr Cup SF 31-32; West Riding Co. Cup(3); Yorks Lg 31-32, Div 2 58-59 (R-up 52-53 71-72), Div 3 77-78, Lg Cup 32-33; Leeds & Dist. Snr Cup. |
| PREVIOUS | **League:** Yorks 20-24 30-82.     **Ground:** Elland Road 1919-20 |
| BEST SEASON | **FA Cup:     FA Vase:** |
| RECORD | **Attendance:** 4,000 v Wimbledon, FA Amateur Cup QF 1932. |

### FACT FILE

Founded: 1919     Nickname: Ammers
Sponsors: Screeching Parrot
Colours: White/navy/red
Change colours: All red
Midweek Matches: Tuesday
Programme: 12 pages, 50p
Editor: C.A.Sharman( 0113 293 8894)

### CLUB PERSONNEL

Chairman: Andrew Wilkinson(0113 2650841)
President: Rayner Barker
Manager: Denis Metcalfe
Coach: jim McKay
Physio: Terry Davies

Brigg Town's first goal in their FA Cup 2nd Qual. Rd. tie against Louth United (stripes).

Photo: Gordon Whittington

First half action from Tickhill Square where eventual Champions Ossett Albion (in stripes with dark shorts) were well beaten by Denaby United in April.

The bottom photo shows Albion 'keeper, John Wood, making a fine reflex save.

Photos: Martin Wray

ABOVE: Ramsbottom United's all-seater stadium is still in the planning stages.

Photo: Bill Wheatcroft

BELOW: Look at me when I'm talking to you - I promise I am not going to steal your ball!

Photo: Colin Stevens

OPPOSITE:
Mark Gardiner is now manager of Northwich Victoria but is seen here playing for Macclesfield Town in the '96 Trophy final. He also played for England semi professionals but perhaps he found balance a problem!

Photo: Gary Letts

BELOW:
Who needs a fourth official?

Photo: Graham Brown

## BRITAIN'S MOST POPULAR NATIONAL NON-LEAGUE FOOTBALL MONTHLY

# TEAM TALK

**Team Talk provides comprehensive coverage of the whole spectrum of non-League football from the Nationwide Conference to County League**

including extensive coverage of

the FA Carlsberg Vase

the FA Umbro Trophy

non-League involvement in

the AXA sponsored FA Cup

and the

England Semi-Professional team
(Team Talk is the ONLY magazine to give such support and coverage to this England team)

Team Talk should be available from your local non-League football club or your local newsagent and is available by subscription from the publishers.

Team Talk is published by Tony Williams Publications Ltd., Helland, North Curry, Taunton, Somerset TA3 6DU
Tel: 01823 490080  Fax: 01823 490281  e-mail: tony.williams12@virgin.net

**MICKLEOVER SPORTS** (L-R) **Back Row:** Holness, Harvey, Priestley, Wacoed, Boothe, Mighty, Yeomans, McGinty, Briscoe, Flanner. **Front Row:** Barnes, Hudson, Mable, Taplin, Scully, Poplar, Kelsey (manager). Photo courtesy Derby Evening Telegraph

Frank Harwood, chairman of the Redferns International Removers Central Midlands Football League presenting the Travis Perkins Supreme Division Championship Cup to the captain of Mickleover Sports, ex Derby County player, Robbie Briscoe.

Photo courtesy Derby Evening Telegraph

# REDFERNS INTERNATIONAL REMOVERS
# CENTRAL MIDLANDS LEAGUE

## FEEDER TO: NORTHERN COUNTIES LEAGUE

**President:** Mr R Holmes    **Vice President:** Mr D Capenerhurst
**Chairman & General Secretary:** Frank Harwood
103 Vestry Road, Oakwood, Derby DE21 2BN    Tel: 01332 832372

Once again we can be proud of the achievements of the League both on and off the field. Mickleover Sports deservedly won the Travis Perkins Supreme Division Championship but this was only after a tremendous finish, with Sports taking the title with only two games remaining. Goole looked to have all three trophies within their grasp, as they won the League Challenge Cup and Wakefield Floodlit Cup, but they failed at the final hurdle in the League and were pipped into runners up position by Nottinghamshire club Dunkirk. Both Mickleover Sports and Goole were promoted to the Northern Counties East League. Second placed Dunkirk did not wish to leave the Central Midlands League.

Newcomers Lincoln Moorlands won the Premier Fit Premier Division. Under Manager Paul Goddard they took all before them going through the complete League programmed without losing a game, and they finished an incredible 21 points in front of second placed Welbeck Colliery MW with Shardlow St James third, Selston fourth and Blackwell Miners Welfare fifth. Lincoln Moorlands, Welbeck Colliery MW, Selston and Blackwell MW all gained promotion to the Supreme Division for Season 1999-2000, but unfortunately Graham St Prims have been relegated from the Supreme Division for failing to have floodlights erected as per League Rule.

Gedling Town Reserves won both the Reserve Premier Division and Reserve League Cup and Sandiacre Town Reserves took the Reserve Division One title.

Mickleover Sports, Goole and Heanor Town did well in the FA Vase, with Mickleover Sports only going out to the final runners up Bedlington Terriers after a controversial tie, which was replayed after Sports had cruelly been made to play again after the floodlights at Bedlington had failed, with Sports 3-0 in front and only fourteen minutes remaining . . .

The Cox League Cup Final was played at Staveley MW, and ex CMFL club Staveley's ground and facilities helped to make this one of the best finals for many years, Goole winning 3-1 after extra time against South Normanton Athletic. South Normanton staged the Wakefield Floodlit Cup Final and Goole won again, also when extra time was required, Goole taking the trophy after a 3-1 victory over Premier Division side Selston. The Reserve Final at Dunkirk's ground saw Gedling Town Reserves win convincingly 7-2 against Sandiacre Town Reserves. A feature of the finals was a record attendance at all three games.

The League continues to be grateful to all its sponsors, our main benefactors being Redfern International Removers, Travis Perkins who sponsor the Supreme Division, Cox Accommodation the League Cup, Ready Mixed Concrete the Reserves Cup, and MJT Promotions the Wakefield Floodlit Cup.

Again I have the pleasure in continuing as both Chairman and General Secretary of the League and I am proud to have been Chairman for the past twenty years; the rest of the officials and council are the same, so the League looks forward with confidence to the new season.

Frank Harwood

## ROLL OF HONOUR 1998-99

**Travis Perkins Supreme Division Champions**
Mickelover Sports

**Cox League Cup Winners**
Goole AFC

**Premier Fit Premier Division Champions**
Lincoln Moorlands

**Wakefield Floodlit Cup Winners**
Goole AFC

**Reserve Premier Division Champions**
Gedling Town Reserves

**Reserve Division One Champions**
Sandiacre Town Reserves

**Promoted Clubs to Supreme Division**
Lincoln Moorlands, Welbeck Colliery Miners Welfare,
Selston FC, Blackwell Miners Welfare

**Secretary of the Year**
Sharon Smedley (Stanton Ilkeston)

**Frank Harwood Trophy**
**Programme of the Year Award**
Selston FC

**Sportsmans Award:**
**Travis Perkins Supreme Division**
Heanor Town

**Premier Fit Premier Division**
Selston FC

405

# FINAL LEAGUE TABLES 1998-99

## SUPREME DIVISION

| | P | W | D | L | F | A | Pts |
|---|---|---|---|---|---|---|---|
| Mickleover Sports | 36 | 28 | 3 | 5 | 134 | 44 | 87 |
| Dunkirk | 36 | 26 | 4 | 6 | 109 | 38 | 82 |
| Goole | 36 | 24 | 9 | 3 | 93 | 23 | 81 |
| Nettleham | 36 | 21 | 7 | 8 | 69 | 38 | 70 |
| Heanor Town | 36 | 21 | 6 | 9 | 98 | 41 | 69 |
| Gedling Town | 36 | 18 | 6 | 12 | 76 | 52 | 60 |
| Shirebrook Town | 36 | 16 | 10 | 10 | 72 | 51 | 58 |
| South Normanton Ath | 36 | 17 | 7 | 12 | 74 | 57 | 58 |
| Hucknall Rolls Royce | 36 | 17 | 5 | 14 | 64 | 47 | 56 |
| Sandiacre Town | 36 | 16 | 7 | 13 | 65 | 70 | 55 |
| Clipstone Welfare | 36 | 15 | 5 | 16 | 75 | 86 | 50 |
| Blidworth Welfare | 36 | 14 | 5 | 17 | 51 | 70 | 47 |
| Sneinton | 36 | 13 | 6 | 17 | 61 | 71 | 45 |
| Long Eaton United | 36 | 12 | 6 | 18 | 53 | 74 | 42 |
| Graham Street Prims | 36 | 9 | 6 | 21 | 46 | 92 | 33 |
| Collingham | 36 | 7 | 6 | 23 | 38 | 101 | 27 |
| Kimberley Town | 36 | 5 | 5 | 26 | 51 | 116 | 20 |
| Grimethorpe M Welfare | 36 | 3 | 7 | 26 | 27 | 92 | 16 |
| Harworth Colliery Inst | 36 | 4 | 2 | 30 | 36 | 129 | 14 |

## PREMIER DIVISION

| | P | W | D | L | F | A | Pts |
|---|---|---|---|---|---|---|---|
| Lincoln Moorlands | 28 | 26 | 2 | 0 | 96 | 17 | 80 |
| Welbeck Colliery Welfare | 28 | 18 | 5 | 5 | 67 | 40 | 59 |
| Shardlow St James | 28 | 17 | 4 | 7 | 78 | 48 | 55 |
| Selston | 28 | 16 | 5 | 7 | 79 | 45 | 53 |
| Blackwell Miners Welfare | 28 | 14 | 5 | 9 | 51 | 46 | 47 |
| Holbrook | 28 | 12 | 6 | 10 | 58 | 49 | 42 |
| Thorne Colliery | 28 | 10 | 9 | 9 | 59 | 44 | 39 |
| Yorkshire Main | 28 | 10 | 9 | 9 | 41 | 59 | 39 |
| Askern Welfare | 28 | 11 | 3 | 14 | 59 | 55 | 36 |
| Stanton Ilkeston | 28 | 11 | 3 | 14 | 55 | 64 | 36 |
| Radford | 28 | 9 | 6 | 13 | 48 | 63 | 33 |
| Greenwood Meadows -1 | 28 | 8 | 4 | 16 | 47 | 75 | 27 |
| Teversal Grange | 28 | 5 | 4 | 19 | 38 | 70 | 19 |
| Mexborough Athletic | 28 | 3 | 5 | 20 | 29 | 77 | 14 |
| Mickleover RBL | 28 | 4 | 2 | 22 | 34 | 87 | 14 |

# TRAVIS PERKINS SUPREME DIVISION RESULTS CHART 1998-99

| | | 1 | 2 | 3 | 4 | 5 | 6 | 7 | 8 | 9 | 10 | 11 | 12 | 13 | 14 | 15 | 16 | 17 | 18 | 19 |
|---|---|---|---|---|---|---|---|---|---|---|---|---|---|---|---|---|---|---|---|---|
| 1 | Blidworth Welfare | X | 3-2 | 2-1 | 0-3 | 0-1 | 2-7 | 5-0 | 2-0 | 2-0 | 2-3 | 1-1 | 2-0 | 3-2 | 0-2 | 1-1 | 1-2 | 0-2 | 0-1 | 0-5 |
| 2 | Clipstone Welfare | 3-3 | X | 1-0 | 0-3 | 1-2 | 0-2 | 1-0 | 4-1 | 4-0 | 3-1 | 4-0 | 1-0 | 2-2 | 3-4 | 1-2 | 1-2 | 2-1 | 3-2 | 2-5 |
| 3 | Collingham | 0-3 | 2-4 | X | 0-5 | 0-2 | 1-1 | 4-3 | 2-0 | 1-4 | 1-3 | 0-0 | 1-1 | 0-3 | 1-5 | 1-5 | 1-5 | 2-1 | 0-4 | 0-2 |
| 4 | Dunkirk | 2-0 | 2-3 | 5-0 | X | 3-1 | 0-1 | 5-3 | 8-0 | 5-1 | 2-1 | 0-2 | 3-2 | 3-1 | 3-2 | 1-1 | 9-0 | 1-2 | 1-0 | 3-1 |
| 5 | Gedling Town | 1-4 | 6-1 | 3-1 | 1-2 | X | 1-3 | 8-2 | 2-1 | 6-3 | 1-2 | 2-0 | 4-0 | 0-2 | 1-1 | 1-0 | 1-1 | 2-2 | 3-0 | 2-1 |
| 6 | Goole | 2-2 | 6-0 | 4-0 | 1-1 | 1-2 | X | 5-0 | 2-0 | 7-0 | 3-1 | 1-1 | 1-1 | 4-0 | 2-1 | 2-0 | 0-1 | 1-0 | 1-0 | 2-0 |
| 7 | Graham St Prims | 1-0 | 5-2 | 1-1 | 1-4 | 1-1 | 1-2 | X | 2-1 | 0-1 | 0-4 | 0-5 | 1-0 | 1-2 | 2-2 | 0-2 | 4-3 | 4-1 | 0-1 | 0-3 |
| 8 | Grimethorpe M Welf | 0-1 | 2-1 | 1-1 | 0-3 | 0-4 | 2-2 | 0-0 | X | 0-0 | 0-3 | 1-3 | 3-0 | 2-3 | 1-4 | 2-0 | 2-2 | 1-1 | 1-3 | 1-2 |
| 9 | Harworth Colliery Inst | 2-3 | 1-2 | 1-3 | 1-5 | 0-7 | 0-2 | 0-3 | 2-0 | X | 1-2 | 1-7 | 1-0 | 1-4 | 2-7 | 1-2 | 1-2 | 2-2 | 0-4 | 1-7 |
| 10 | Heanor Town | 4-1 | 2-2 | 6-0 | 2-1 | 2-0 | 1-1 | 6-0 | 5-0 | 6-0 | X | 2-0 | 7-1 | 4-0 | 1-2 | 1-1 | 3-1 | 0-1 | 6-0 | 1-1 |
| 11 | Hucknall Rolls | 0-1 | 4-1 | 1-2 | 0-1 | 3-0 | 1-1 | 4-1 | 1-0 | 2-1 | 1-3 | X | 3-1 | 3-0 | 0-4 | 3-1 | 3-1 | 0-3 | 1-4 | 1-3 |
| 12 | Kimberley Town | 3-1 | 4-4 | 2-3 | 0-10 | 1-1 | 0-7 | 1-2 | 11-0 | 4-3 | 1-4 | 1-3 | X | 3-6 | 0-4 | 1-2 | 4-1 | 1-6 | 3-1 | 2-2 |
| 13 | Long Eaton United | 0-1 | 1-5 | 4-2 | 1-4 | 2-2 | 0-4 | 2-1 | 0-0 | 4-0 | 2-2 | 0-0 | 1-0 | X | 1-2 | 0-2 | 1-4 | 3-5 | 2-1 | 0-3 |
| 14 | Mickleover Sports | 10-1 | 4-5 | 8-0 | 3-1 | 3-0 | 2-1 | 5-1 | 7-0 | 4-0 | 2-1 | 2-1 | 6-1 | 3-1 | X | 2-2 | 1-2 | 4-2 | 5-1 | 6-1 |
| 15 | Nettleham | 1-0 | 1-3 | 1-0 | 3-4 | 1-2 | 0-0 | 4-0 | 3-1 | 4-0 | 2-1 | 2-1 | 5-0 | 1-1 | 0-2 | X | 0-0 | 3-0 | 3-0 | 3-2 |
| 16 | Sandiacre Town | 0-3 | 3-0 | 3-0 | 1-2 | 3-1 | 1-3 | 2-2 | 1-0 | 2-0 | 4-2 | 0-3 | 4-1 | 1-0 | 1-3 | 2-3 | X | 1-3 | 2-2 | 1-1 |
| 17 | Shirebrook Town | 1-1 | 3-0 | 5-2 | 1-1 | 2-1 | 0-3 | 1-3 | 3-2 | 7-1 | 1-1 | 1-0 | 5-0 | 1-0 | 1-4 | 0-1 | 6-2 | X | 1-1 | 0-0 |
| 18 | Sneinton | 4-0 | 3-3 | 1-1 | 0-0 | 1-3 | 0-6 | 3-0 | 2-1 | 6-2 | 0-3 | 1-3 | 2-1 | 4-1 | 3-6 | 1-3 | 1-2 | 1-1 | X | 0-0 |
| 19 | South Normanton Ath | 3-1 | 4-1 | 1-4 | 2-3 | 2-1 | 1-2 | 1-1 | 2-1 | 3-2 | 3-2 | 0-3 | 6-0 | 0-1 | 2-1 | 0-4 | 2-2 | 0-0 | 2-1 | X |

## COX CENTRAL MIDLANDS LEAGUE CUP 1998-99

**PRELIMINARY ROUND**

| | | | | | | | | |
|---|---|---|---|---|---|---|---|---|
| Dunkirk | v | Kimberley Town | 0-0, 2-0 | | Grimethorpe MW | v | Long Eaton Utd | 2-0 |
| Sneinton | v | Askern Welfare | 3-3, 4-3 | | Thorne Colliery | v | Heanor Town | 0-5 |
| Welbeck Colliery MW | v | Holbrook | 7-0 | | | | | |

**FIRST ROUND**

| | | | | | | | | |
|---|---|---|---|---|---|---|---|---|
| Goole | v | Mickleover RBL | 8-0 | | Harworth Coll Inst. | v | Heanor Town | 0-4 |
| Mexborough Athletic | v | Dunkirk | 1-5 | | Mickleover Sports | v | Blidworth Welfare | 7-0 |
| Radfordd | v | South Normanton Ath | 1-2 | | Selston | v | Graham Street P | 3-2 |
| Shardlow St James | v | Hucknall Rolls | 0-0, 2-1 | | Shirebrook Town | v | Greenwood Mdws | 0-1 |
| Sneinton | v | Gedling Town | 2-4 | | Stanton Ilkeston | v | Clipstone Welfare | 5-4 |
| Teversal Grange | v | Grimethorpe MW | 0-0, 5-2 | | Welbeck Coll. MW | v | Blackwell MW | 2-0 |
| Yorkshire Main | v | Nettleham | 0-2 | | | | | |

**SECOND ROUND**

| | | | | | | | | |
|---|---|---|---|---|---|---|---|---|
| Dunkirk | v | Stanton Ilkeston | 6-0 | | Gedling Town | v | Welbeck Coll. MW | 3-2 |
| Goole | v | Heanor Tn | 0-0, 2*2, 4p3 | | Mickleover Sports | v | Lincoln Moorlands | 1-2 |
| Nettleham | v | Greenwood Meadows | 1-0 | | Shardlow St James | v | Selston | 0-1 |
| South Normanton A | v | Collingham | 0-0, 4-0 | | Teversal Grange | v | Sandiacre Town | 1-2 |

**THIRD ROUND**

| | | | | | | | | |
|---|---|---|---|---|---|---|---|---|
| Nettleham | v | Lincoln Moorlands | 1-1, 1-0 | | Sandiacre Town | v | Goole | 0-1 |
| Selston | v | Dunkirk | 2-7 | | South Normanton A | v | Gedling Town | 4-2 |

**SEMI FINALS**

| | | | | | | | | |
|---|---|---|---|---|---|---|---|---|
| Nettleham | v | South Normanton Ath | 0-2 | | Dunkirk | v | Goole | 1-3 |

**FINAL**

| | | | | | |
|---|---|---|---|---|---|
| Goole | v | South Normanton Ath | 3-1 | | AET. At Staveley Miners Welfare FC |

## WAKEFIELD FLOODLIT CUP 1998-99

| | P | W | D | L | F | A | Pts | | | P | W | D | L | F | A | Pts |
|---|---|---|---|---|---|---|---|---|---|---|---|---|---|---|---|---|
| **GROUP A** | | | | | | | | | **GROUP C** | | | | | | | |
| Goole | 6 | 3 | 1 | 2 | 12 | 5 | 10 | | Heanor Town | 6 | 3 | 2 | 1 | 13 | 7 | 11 |
| Selston | 6 | 3 | 1 | 2 | 13 | 10 | 10 | | South Normanton A* | 6 | 4 | 0 | 2 | 20 | 9 | 9 |
| Mickleover Sports | 6 | 1 | 3 | 2 | 5 | 7 | 6 | | Nettleham | 6 | 2 | 3 | 1 | 14 | 9 | 9 |
| Sandiacre Town | 6 | 1 | 3 | 2 | 7 | 15 | 6 | | Kimberley Town | 6 | 0 | 1 | 5 | 8 | 30 | 1 |
| **GROUP B** | | | | | | | | | **GROUP D** | | | | | | | |
| Blidworth Welfare | 8 | 6 | 1 | 1 | 18 | 13 | 19 | | Dunkirk | 6 | 4 | 1 | 1 | 20 | 7 | 13 |
| Stanton Ilkeston | 8 | 4 | 2 | 2 | 13 | 18 | 14 | | Shirebrook Town | 6 | 2 | 2 | 2 | 13 | 9 | 8 |
| Gedling Town | 8 | 2 | 3 | 3 | 17 | 13 | 9 | | Long Eaton Utd | 6 | 2 | 1 | 3 | 7 | 13 | 7 |
| Collingham | 8 | 2 | 3 | 3 | 12 | 10 | 9 | | Harworth Coll Inst | 6 | 2 | 0 | 4 | 9 | 20 | 6 |
| Grimethorpe MW | 8 | 0 | 3 | 5 | 17 | 23 | 3 | | *points deducted | | | | | | | |

**SECOND ROUND**

| | | | | | | | | |
|---|---|---|---|---|---|---|---|---|
| Blidworth Welfare | v | Sth Normanton A | 2*2, 4p3 | | Dunkirk | v | Selston | 0-1 |
| Goole | v | Shirebrook Town | 3-0 | | Heanor Town | v | Stanton Ilkeston | 5-0 |

**SEMI FINALS**

| | | | | | | | | |
|---|---|---|---|---|---|---|---|---|
| Blidworth Welfare | v | Selston | 1-4 | | Goole | v | Heanor Town | 2-0 |

**FINAL**

| | | | | | |
|---|---|---|---|---|---|
| Goole | v | Selston | 3-1 | | AET. At Lees Lane, South Normanton Atheltic FC |

# BLACKWELL MINERS WELFARE

Colours: Red & black stripes/red/red
Change colours: Green/white/green
Midweek Matchday: Tuesday

**Secretary:** Steve Harris, 6 Pennine Close, Newton, Alfreton, Derbys DE55 5UD.
Tel Nos: 01773 872038(H) 01246501561(W)

**Ground & Directions:** Welfare Ground, Primrose Hill, Blackwell, Derbyshire DE55 5JE. (01773 811295). M1 Junc 28, A38 towards Mansfield, left onto B6406, left again at Hilcote Arms, ground 1 mile on left just past Miners Welfare.

Manager:Graham Brentnall

# CLIPSTONE WELFARE

Founded 1927
Colours: Black & white,black,black
Change Colours: Amber & navy/navy/amber
Midweek Matchday: Tuesday or Wednesday
Programme: Yes

**Secretary:** Barry Clarke, 40 Church Road, Clipstone, Mansfield, NG21 9DG (01623640829).
**Ground & Directions:** Clipstone Lido Ground Clipstone Road West, Mansfield,Notts (01632 655674). B6030 from Mansfield, between Forest Town & Clipstone, on left entering Clipstone.
**Capacity: 3000   Seats: 90   Cover: 200   Floodlights: No   Club Shop: No**
**Honours:** Notts Snr Cup 85-86 94-95, Notts Alliance 72-73 73-74 74-75 92-93 94-95 (Lg Cup 72-73 73-74 74-75 94-95 (R-up 92-93)), Notts I'mediate Cup 55-56. Central Midlands Premier Championship 94-95 96-97

Chairman: Gordon Costall
Manager: Peter Burns

# COLLINGHAM

Colours:Yellow & Black.
Change Colours:  Blue & white/blue/blue
Midweek Matchday:  Tuesday

**Secretary:** Darren Goivannetti, 34 Armstrong Road, Retford, Notts DN22 6QY
Tel No: 01777 705893
**Ground & Directions:** Collingham FC, Station Road, Collingham, Newark, Notts. (01636 892303) Take A46 Newark to Lincoln road (Newark bypass). Turn left into Collingham on the A1133 road. In village turn right at traffic lights.Ground 100 yards on left.

Manager:  Paul Hyde

# DUNKIRK

Founded: 1946
Colours:  Red/black/black
Change Colours:  Black & whitestripes/white/red
Midweek Matchday:  Tuesday
Programme : Yes
Chairman: Dave Howes
Managers:  Steve Hardie
Players Progressing: Roger Willis and Matthew McKemzie (Grimsby T)

**Secretary:** Steve Trossell, 24 Kingfisher Wharf, Castle Marina, Nottingham NG71GA (0115 947903 or 07930 806891
**Ground & Directions:** The Ron Steel Sports Ground, Trentside Farm, Clifton Bridge, Nottingham (0602 850803). Ring Road - Clifton Bridge (North End),Ind Estate, Lenton Lane.
**Honours:** FA Vase 5th Rd 93-94; Cen Mid Sup Div R-up 96-97, Prem Div R-up 95-96,KO Cup 97-98;Notts Alliance Div 1 84-85, Div 2 82-83, Lg Cup R-up 84-85; Notts I'mediate Cup 83-4
**Capacity:**1,500  **Seats:** No  **Cover**: 200  **Floodlights:** Yes  **Shop:**  No **Clubhouse:** Yes
**Record Attendance:** 821 v Tiverton Town, F.A.Vase 5th Rd 93-94

# GEDLING TOWN

Founded: 1989
Colours:  Yellow & navy/navy/yellow
Change colours:  All red
Midweek Matchday:  Wednesday
Prog 32 pages 50p  Editor: Paul Dobson
Manager: Paul Elrick   Ass Man: Junior Glave
Physio: Trevor Wells/Pete Tyers

**Secretary:** Paul Dobson, 26 Chevin Gardens, Top Valley Estate, Nottingham NG59ES (0115 9274790) **Ground & Directions:** Riverside Ground, rear Ferryboat Inn, Stoke Lane, Stoke Bardolph, Gedling, Nottm (01159 402145). A612 Nottingham-Lowdham-Southwell road. just before Burton Joyce turn right into Stoke Lane to Ferryboat P.H. Approx 1.5 miles. Ground at rear of pub.  Capacity: 2,000   Seats: None   Cover: 500   Floodlights: Yes
**Clubhouse:** Matchdays only. Hot & cold food. Licensed bar.       Shop: No(Gedling Town)
Best season FA Vase: 3rd Rd 96-97    **Honours:** Central Mids Lg Prem 97-98 R-up 91-92, Div 1 90-91, (Res Prem 96-9797-98); Wakefield Floodlit Trophy 92-93 R-up 95-96; Ken Marsland Cup(Res) 93-94; Notts Amtr Lg 89-90 (Snr Cup R-up 89-90).Res Lg & Cp Winners 98-99

Club Record Goalscorer: Rob Orton 98 in 124
Record Appearances: Gary Ball 216

# GRIMETHORPE MINERS WELFARE

Colours: All Blue & black
Change Colours: All red
Midweek Matchday: Tuesday or Wednesday

**Secretary:** Keith Donkin, 13 Brierley Road, Shafton, Barnslry, S.Yorks. S72 8QQ
**Ground & Directions:** Grimethorpe Miners Welfare, Cemetery Road, Grimethorpe.(01226 711544), A1M to A635 Hickleton to Thurnscoe, turn right to Houghton, At Robin Hood, turn left to Grimethorpe M1 junc 36. A628 to Shafton traffic lights, turn right to Grimethorpe.

Manager: Alan Billingham

# HARWORTH COLLIERY INSTITUTE

**Secretary:** Tom Brogan, 30 Lindsey Road, Harworth, Doncaster, Sth Yorks DN11 8QH(01302 750132).
**Ground & Directions:** Recreation Ground, Scrooby Rd, Bircotes, Doncaster (01302750614).
Off A1(M) at Blyth, head towards Bawtry for approx 2 miles, take third left, ground in village at top of hill on left. Or, from Doncaster to Bawtrythen head for A1(M) and turn left after caravan site - ground at top of hill.
**Honours:** Wharncliffe Charity Cup 62-63 74-75, Central Midlands League 87-88(Runners-up 86-87, Challenge Cup 86-87 87-88, F'lit Cup 91-92 (Runners-up 89-90)), Sheffield Senior League 64-65 74-75, Sheffield & Hallamshire Senior Cup SF 87-88

Colours: Amber & black/black/amber & black
Change Colours: Red & blue/red/red
Midweek Matchday: Wednesday

Manager: Alan Needham

# HEANOR TOWN

**Secretary:** Keith Costello, 45 Stainsby Avenue, Heanor, Derbys. DE75 7EL(01773 719446).
**Ground & Directions:** The Town Ground, Mayfield Avenue, Heanor (01773713742/715815).
M1 (J26), take A610 onto A608, ground 200yds from Market Square
**Capacity:** 3,000 and new stand being built `Cover: 1,000+ new stand **Floodlights:** Yes
**Honours:** Central Midlands League Cup 94-95 (Runners-up 86-87 92-93, B E Webbe Removals Cup 88-89), West Midlands Reg. League Runners-up 72-73; Midland Co's League Runners-up 65-66 67-68; Derbys Senior Cup(9) 1892-94 1946-47 65-69 70-7178-79; FA Cup 1st Rd 58-59 63-64.Central Midlands Supreme Champions:94-5,96-7 Central All.Lg(2) R-up4

Nickname: The Lions
Colours: Black& white stripes/black/black
Midweek Matchday: Wednesday
Programme: 32pages 50p
Press Officer & Editor: Stan Wilton
(01332 880199)
Club House: On ground,hot food,open daily
Chairman: John McCulloch
Manager: Paul Aklam

# HUCKNALL ROLLS

**Secretary:** Peter Williams, 38 Tiverton Close, Hucknall, Nottingham NG15 6JT
Tel: 0115 956 33691
**Ground & Directions:** Rolls Royce Sports & Social Club, Watnall Road, Hucknall Notts (0115 963 0134). M1 Junc 27. Follow sign A611 to Hucknall. Turn right onto by-pass. 2nd r/about turn right on to Watnall Road. Take 2nd left after fire station on R.R. Sports Ground.
**Capacity:** 1,000 **Cover:** yes **Floodlights**: No **Clubhouse:** Social Club always open with food

Colours: Yellow,Blue,Blue
Change colours: Blue,black,black
Midweek Matchday: Wednesday
Programme: yes

Chairman: Darryl Claypole
Manager: Roger Dawkins & Wayne Lear
Reserves: Peter Needham & Paul Hopkins

# KIMBERLEY TOWN

**Match Secretary:** Alan Jennings, 8 Watchwood Grove, Calverton, Nottingham NG146HX
Tel: 0115 965 6100
**Ground & Directions:** Stag Ground, Nottingham Road, Kimberley (0115 9382788).Through Nuthall from M1 jct 26 to Kimberley, ground entrance 150 yds after Stag Inn.
Capacity: 2,500    Seats: None    Cover: 150    Floodlights: Yes
**Clubhouse:** Evenings (Except Sun) & matchdays. Hot & cold snacks available
**Honours:** Notts Amateur Lg Div 1 54-55, Central Alliance Div 2 R-up 57-58.

Nickname: Stags
Colours: All Blue
Change colours: All Yellow
Midweek Matchday: Tuesday
Programme: 40 pages 50p
Editor: George Brown
Chairman: George Giddens
Manager: Julian Garmston
Gen Manager: Brian Harrison

# LINCOLN MOORLANDS

**Secretary:** Colin Edwards, 5 Lansdowne Ave, Lincoln LN6 7PU (01522 520857)

**Ground & Directions:** Moorland Sports Ground, Newark Rd, Lincoln (01522 520184).
From Newark enter Lincoln on A1434, go past Forum Shopping Centre 500yds.
Ground on left sign Moorland Club.

Colours: Yellow & blue/yellow & blue/blue
Change colours: Navy Blue with yellow trim

Manager: Garry Goddard

# LONG EATON UNITED

**Secretary:** David Hampson, 4 Airedale Close, Long Eaton, Nottingham. NG10 3HW(0115-9726343. **Ground & Directions:** Grange Park, Station Road, Long Eaton, Nottingham (01159735700). M1 Junc 25, take A52 towards Nottingham, to island by `Bardills Garden Centre', left onto B6003 to t/lights. Turn right A453 and take 2nd left into Station Rd. Entrance on left opposite the Speedway Stadium
Capacity: 5,000    Seats: None    Cover: 500    Floodlights: Yes    Shop: No
**Clubhouse:** Open matchdays, snacks available Record Attendance: 2,000 1973 FA Cup
**Honours:** Derbys Snr Cup 64-65 75-76, Midland Co's Lg R-up 76-77, Central Alliance Div South 58-59, Northern Co's (East) Div 1 South 84-85.

Founded: 1956    Nickname: Blues
Sponsor: Beeston Suite Co
Colours: Blue & black/black/black
Change colours: Yellow/green/blue
Midweek Matchday: Tuesday
Programme: 20 pages 50p
Editor: G Whitehead
Chairman: J C Fairley
Manager: John Bartlett
Physio: John Burns

409

# NETTLEHAM

**Secretary:** John Wilson, 21 Chancer Drive, Lincoln LN2 4LN (01522 884051).

**Ground & Directions:** Mulsanne Park, Field Close, Nettleham (01522 750007). A46approx. 3 miles north of Lincoln, right at Brown Cow Pub, proceed past Church2nd turning on right, ground at end

**Honours:** Central Mids Lg Premier Division Cup R-up 87-88, Village Tphy, Nursing Cup, Kelly Read Cup, Blankney Hunt Cup, Lincoln & Dist. Amtr Cup R-up, Joe Miller Tphy(2).

Colours: Lighgt blue/navy blue/b lue
Change Colours: yellow & navy blue.
Midweek Matchday: Tuesday

Manager: Ian Musson

# SANDIACRE TOWN

**Secretary:** Mel Williams, 38 Pasture Rd.,Stapleford, Nottingham NG9 8GL(0115 9174079)
**Ground & Directions:** St Giles Park, Stanton Road, Sandiacre, Nottingham NG105EP (0115 939 2880). M1 jct 25, follow signs to Sandiacre passing Post House Hotel on right, straight over crossroads into Rushy Lane and towards Stanton Rd, 1st right after 1000yds into Stanton Rd, ground at bottom after another1000yds.
**Capacity:** 2,000    Seats: None    Cover: 250    Floodlights: Yes    Shop: No
**Clubhouse:** Members Club 8-11pm. Sunday lunch, Saturday 3.45-11pm. Snacks available
**Honours:** Central Mids Lg Premier Div 92-93 (Lg Cup 92-93), Midlands Regional Alliance R-up 91-92, Central Mids Lge Cup R-up 95-96.

Founded: 1978    Nickname: Saints
Colours: Red/navy/red
Change colours: Yellow/sky/yellow
Midweek Matchday: Tuesday
Programme: 44 pages 50p
Editor: Mel Williams (0115 917 4079)
Press Officer: Mel Williams
Manager: Andy freeman
Asst Manager:

# SELSTON

**Secretary:** Alan Jones, 6 Derwent Drive, Selston, Nott NG16 6QU (01773 580436)

**Ground & Directions:** Mansfield Hosiery Mills Sports Ground, Mansfield Road,Sutton in Ashfield, Notts (01623 552376).
M1 junc 28, take A38 Mansfield, passthrough 7 sets of lights to island (Kings Mill Hospital), ground opositeMcDonalds on left

Colours:
Black & white/black & blue/black & white
Change Colours:
Yellow & green/sky/yellow & green

Manager: Wayne Bradley

# SHIREBROOK TOWN

**Secretary:** Steve Wall, 26 Carter Lane West, Shirebrook, Mansfield, Notts NG208NA (01623 747638).
**Ground & Directions:** BRSA Sports Ground, Langwith Rd, Shirebrook, Mansfield(01623 742535). M1 jct 29, A617 to Mansfield, onto B6407 to Shirebrook, through town to Langwith Rd. Clubhouse with refreshments at the ground.
**Capacity:** 2,000    Seata: None    Cover: 400    Floodlights: Yes    Club Shop:No
**Honours:** Central Midlands Lg Res Prem Div 94-95 95-96. Floodlit Cup winners  97-98
**Most Appearances for club:** G.Quincey 262

Founded 1985
Colours: All Red & black
Change Colours: Blue & black/blue/blue
Midweek Matchday: Tuesday
Prog  Editor: Mr Sharnworth (01623 748 375)

Chairman: Mr S.T. Brown (01623 743661)
Managers: S Greenwood, G Charlesworth

# SNEINTON

**Secretary:** Albert Graves, 32 Shelford Road, Gedling, Nottingham NG4 4HW ( 01159878185)

**Ground & Directions:** Stoke Lane Gedling, Nottingham, A612 Nottingham to Southwell Road. Stoke Lane is situated off A612 between Gedling & Burton Joyce(signed Stoke Bardolph). Ground 200 yards on left over level crossing. BR. Nearest Station is Carlton.
**Capacity:** 1000 Seats: None Cover: 100    Floodlights: No    Club Shop: No
**Clubhouse:** No but snacks at Tea Bar.

Founded: 1904
Colours: Blue & black/black/black
Change Colours: All Red
Midweek Matchday: Tuesday
Programme: Yes

Chairman: John W Stokeld
Manager: Tom Brookbanks

# SOUTH NORMANTON ATHLETIC

**Secretary:** Lindon davison, 5 The Brockwell, Broadmeadows, South Normanton, Alfreton, Derbys. DE55 3BA Tel Nos: 01773 510380 (H) 07930 233210 (W)
**Ground & Directions:** South Normanton Athletic FC, Lees Lane, South Normanton,Derby (01773 581491). M1 Junc 28, B6019 towards South Normanton, right after 1mile (in South Normanton) at BP garage into Market Street, after quarter mile turn left immediately after The Clock pub into Lees Lane, ground at bottom on right. (Food available on matchdays)
         **Capacity:** 3000    Seats: 150    Cover: 300    Floodlights:Yes
**Clubhouse** Yes - open on matchdays **Club Shop:** No

Formed: 1875
Colours: Yellow/navy/yellow
Change colours: Black & white/black/white
Programme: Yes - The Shiner
Midweek Matchday: Tuesday

Chairman: Glindon Davison
Manager: Rob Aitkin

# WELBECK COLLIERY M.W.

Colours: White & navy/navy/white
Change colours: Black & yellow/black/black

**Secretary:** Les Graham, 10 saville Way, Warsop, Mansfield, Notts. NG20 0DZ. Tel: 01623 844299

**Ground:** Elksley Road, Meden Vale, Mansfield. (01623 842611)
Directions: 1 1/2 miles off A60 between Worksop and Mansfield. Signed Meden vale. (do NOT follow signs for Welbeck Colliery.) Turn off at Warsop Church.

Manager: Kevin Gee

**Honours:** Notts Alliance Div 2 93-94 (Intermediate Cup 93-94), Chesterfield & District Lg 92-93

BLACKWELL M.W. Back Row: G Brentall (manager), Noble, Slater, Bowater, Wall, Harris (Sec.), Ryan, Wass (Sponsor), Armstrong, L Downing, Bush, Atkin, G Hopkinson. Front: M Downing, Shaw, Bott, Marshall, Greenslade, Statton, McGrath, Clark (asst. man.), Harper (trainer).

HEANOR TOWN Back Row: Simon Smith, Aslam Javid (asst. man.), Chris Atwood, Richard Preston, Lee Thomas, Paul Standring, Alan Rigby, Lee Aldred, Steve Heighway, Matt Johnson, Paul Acklam (manager). Front: Lee Stewart, Paul Tomlin, Ian Townsend, Glyn Stacey, Simon Gordon, Graham Smith, Clive Ingram (physio).
Photo: Gordon Whittington

## ASKERN WELFARE

**Secretary:** Jon Stewart, 43 Sutton Road, Askern, Doncaster S.Yorks. DN6 0AG Tel Nos: 01302 702502 (H) 01302 703035 (W)
**Ground & Directions:** Askern Welfare Sports Ground, Doncaster Road, Askern,Doncaster (01302 700957). A1/A639 Pontefract. Follow sign for Askern/Campsall.At T-junction right. Left at Anne Arms, right at Supersave, ground on right.
Colours: White (navy trim)/navy/navy & white
Change colours: Orange/white/yellow
Manager: Paul Curtis          Midweek Matchday: Wednesday

## BLIDWORTH WELFARE

**Secretary:** Paul Deakin, 8 Birks Road, Ladybrook Estate, Mansfield, Notts. NG19 6JU (01623 453812)
**Ground & Directions:** Welfare Ground, Mansfield Rd, Blidworth, Mansfield (01623 793361). On B6020, Rainworth side of Blidworth. From M1 jct 27 take A608 to Kirby and Annesley Woodhouse, at lights follow A611 to Kirby then take B6020through Ravenshead to Blidworth - thru village and ground at top of hill on right. From A1 follow A614 and A617 to Rainworth, left at lights then 1st right on to B6020 to Blidworth - ground on left at top of hill.

## GRAHAM STREET PRIMS

**Secretary:** David Wright, 6 Athol Close, Sinfin Moor, Derby DE24 9LZ Tel: 01332 606837
**Ground & Directions:** Asterdale Spoprts Complex, Borrowash Rd., Spondon, Derby. M1, J 25 towards derby on A52. Third left (directly under a pedestrian footbridge) Borrowash Rd.. asterdale Sports complex 400 yds on left. Ground at rear.
Colours: Red, white sripes/black/black
Manager: Paul Baxter

## GRANTHAM RANGERS

**Secretary:** Geoffrey Green, 67 High Road, Barrowby, Grantham, Lincs. NG32 1BJ. Tel: 01476 563186 (H) 0976 977165 (B)
**Ground & Directions:** S.K.D.C. Stadium, The Meres, Trent Road, Grantham, Lincs. A52 to Grantham over A1 to r'about - turn right into Barrowby Gate, go to next junction, turn right and then immediate left on to Trent Road. Stadium on the left.
Colours: Green & yellow/green/green or yellow
Managers: Geoffrey Green & Dave Newboult.

## GREENWOOD MEADOWS

**Secretary:** Brain Hall, 34 Sullivan Close, Marmion Estate, St Ann's, NottinghamNG3 2HX (0115 958 2459)
**Ground & Directions:** Greenwood Meadows (0115 986 5913). M1 Junc 24 take A453Nottingham-Clifton Bridge to Lenton Ind Estate. Left into Old Lenton Lane.Ground second on right on lane.
Colours: Green & white/green/green
Change Colours: Red & black/black/black
Managers: Brian Cawthorn & Chris Nicholson

## HOLBROOK

**Secretary:** Stevan Broadhurst, 35 Laund Hill, Belper, Derbys. DE56 1FH (01773821483)
**Ground & Directions:** The Welfare Ground, Shaw Lane, Holbrook, Derbyshire (01332880259), From A38 take B6179 for Kilburn, turn left at lights for Belper. 1mile on left at Bulls Head for Holbrook. 2 miles on turn right at Venturegarage into Shaws Lane.
Colours: Blue & white/blue/blue&white Change: Red & white/red/red
Manager: Mark Webster

## KIVETON PARK

**Secretary:** Nev Wheeler, 15 Holmshaw Drive, Sheffield, South Yorkshire S13 8UJ(0114 2694142).
**Ground & Directions:** Mexborough Athletic Club, New Oxford Road, Mexborough(01709 583426). M18 Junc 2, join A1 for 1 junc. Take Sheffield/Rotherham roadto Conisborough, take right beside castle to Denaby. Go through Denaby tor/about at Mexborough, take right turn into Adwick Road, ground on left
Colours: All blue & white Change colours: Red and Navy/black/black.
Manager: Nev Wheeler          Midweek Matchday: Tuesday

## MEXBOROUGH TOWN ATHLETIC

**Secretary:** Nev Wheeler, 15 Holmshaw Drive, Sheffield, South Yorkshire S13 8UJ(0114 2694142).
**Ground & Directions:** Mexborough Athletic Club, New Oxford Road, Mexborough(01709 583426). M18 Junc 2, join A1 for 1 junc. Take Sheffield/Rotherham roadto Conisborough, take right beside castle to Denaby. Go through Denaby tor/about at Mexborough, take right turn into Adwick Road, ground on left
Colours: All blue & white Change colours: Red and Navy/black/black.
Manager: Nev Wheeler          Midweek Matchday: Tuesday

## MICKLEOVER ROYAL BRITISH LEGION

**Secretary:** Ray Taylor, 15 Inglwood Avenue, Mickleover, Derby DE3 5RT (01332515047).
**Ground & Directions:** Mickleover RBL, Ypres Lodge, Western Road, Mickleover(01332 513548). On west side of Derby off A38, 1/2 mile from Mickleover Villagecentre.
Colours: Yellow/royal/royal
Change Colours: Tangerine/black/black
Manager: Ken Thoresen.          Midweek Matchday: Tuesday

## RADFORD

**Secretary:** Karon Scott, 130 Melbourne Road, Aspley, Nottingham. NG8 5HN. Tel No; 0115 913 7868
**Ground & Directions:** Radford Road, Radford, Nottm (0115 943250). M1 Junc 26,take A610 to Nottingham, at duel carriageway turn left. Move to right lane andgo immediately right into Wilkinson St. At top turn right & right again at 2ndcrossing.
Colours: Black & white/black/black
Change colours: Blure & white/white/white
Manager: Colin Coultan Midweek Matchday: Tuesday

## RIPLEY TOWN

**Secretary:** Michael E Boam, 5 Valley Drive, Newthorpe, Notts. NG16 2DT. Tel: 01773 715277 (H)  0374 876794 (B)
Ground & Directions: Waingroves Brick Works, Peasehill Road, Ripley, Derbys. M1, J 28, A38 south to A610 signed Nottingham. Continue approx. 1 mile. Turn right into Steam Mill Lane, continue to Peasehill Road to brickworks.
Colours: Royal & white halves/royal/royal.
Manager: Kevin Jackson

## SHARDLOW ST JAMES

**Secretary:** Reg Symcox, 22 West End Drive, Shardlow, Derby DE7 2GY (01332792733).
**Ground & Directions:** The Wharf, Shardlow, Derby. (01332 799135), M1 Junc 24, A6Derby/Leicester, 6 miles out of Derby at Shardlow take next left after Shardlowchurch (on right), ground 100yds on left.
Colours: White & blue/white/blue.
Change colours: Tangerine/black/tangerine
Manager: Trevor Hammond   Midweek Matchday: Wednesday

## STANTON ILKESTON
**Secretary:** Mrs S Smedley, 4 Queens Avenue, Ilkeston, Derbyshire DE7 4DL (01159323772)
**Ground & Directions:** Hallam Fields Sports Ground, Stanton Club, Hallam Fields,Nr Ilkeston, Derbys (0115 9323244), M1 (J26) take A52 Nottingham, then A6002for Ilkeston. Follow road through t/lights, turn right at next lights. Followroad to Rutland Windows. Turn left into Thurman St, to top turn left ground 200yds right.
Colours: Blue & white/blue/blueChange Colours: Yellow/blue/blue
Manager: J Smedley/C Trueman    Midweek Matchday: Mon. or Wed.

## THORNE COLLIERY
**Secretary:** Glyn Jones, Top Town Social, Frederick Street, Grimsby DN31 1RG(01472 350554)
**Ground & Directions:** Miners Welfare, Grange Road, Moorends, Thorne, Doncaster.(01374 996474), M18 Junc 6, in THorne, turnat lights to Moorends, go almostthrough village, Grange Road on right.
Colours: Green/black/black
Change Colours: Yellow/green/yellow
Manager: Paul Morrell    Midweek Matchday: Tuesday

## TEVERSAL GRANGE
**Secretary:** Kevin Newton, 8 Vere Ave., Sutton in Ashfield, Notts NG17 2ES (01623511402).
**Ground & Directions:** Teversal Grange Country Inn, Carnarvon Street, Teversal, Sutton-in-Ashfield, Notts. (01623 442021)  M1, J28, A38 towards Mansfield. At r'about take A6075 Mansfield Woodhouse. Next lights left B6014, Stanton Hill. At r'about take A6014 Tibshelf. 2nd on right Carnarvon St., ground at the top.
Colours: Red & black/black    Managers: John Courtie & Andrew Farby

## YORKSHIRE MAIN
**Secretary:** Dennis Tymon, 22 Pamela Drive, Warmsworth, Doncaster DN4 9RP (01302852455)
**Ground & Directions:** Yorkshire Main Welfare, Edlington Lane, Edlington,Doncaster (01709 864075). A1M junc 36. Proceed on A630 towards Rotherham. At1st lights turn on to B6376. Ground on left after Fire Station.
Colours: Red/black/redChange colours: All White
Manager: Derek Wynne    Midweek Matchday:

**TEVERSAL GRANGE**                                    Photo: Bill Wheatcroft

**YORKSHIRE MAIN**                                    Photo: Bill Wheatcroft

LINCOLN MOORLANDS- Back Row: Stuart Gordon (general manager), Darren Chapman, Peter Shelley, Mark Porter, Lee Cooper, Darren Crookes, Simon Daniels, Rob Kinsella, Sean O'Callaghan, Garry Goddard (manager), Stuart Park (asst. man.), Colin Edwards (sec./treas.).  Front: Matt Clayton, Glenn Pearson, Simon Whittle, Jamie Chesham, Stuart Aspin, Sean Maloney                                        Photo: Bill Wheatcroft

SNEINTON - Back Row: G Chulan, C Yeomans, D Marshall, M Dickinson, S Newell, R Cutts, J Bentley, N Berrington, M Strong, P McCaughey, M Jepson (coach).
Front: J Richards, A Douglas, M Chafer, M Corbett, D Jepson, T Brookbanks.

Photo: Gordon Whittington

# POWERLEAGUE NOTTS FOOTBALL ALLIANCE

Founded 1894
**Chairman:** Alan Wright

10 Farady Road, Mansfield NG18 4ES   Tel: 01623 624379 (H)   01623 553237 (B)

**General Secretary & Treasurer:** Godfrey Stafford
7 The Rushes, Gotham, Nottingham NG11 0HY   Tel: 01509 820737

ENIOR DIVISION: Once again the Senior Division was dominated by Boots Athletic, losing only once. Southwell City nished runners-up, this was their best position for many seasons. After gaining promotion from the First Division the revious season Basford United sadly found the pressures too much for them and were relegated along with Thoresby W.

IRST DIVISION: The season saw the resurgence of Clifton FC and IDP Newark. After many seasons of relegation nd near-relegation, Clifton FC put it all together and became champions, IDP Newark were runners-up. City & herwood and Rainworth MW Reserves were relegated.

ECOND DIVISION: One of the new members of the League, Bottersford St Marys, dominated this division, winning by a margin of ten points; the runners-up were Chaffoteux FC, who were playing in youth football just two seasons go.

ENIOR CUP: IDP Newark of the First Division caused major upset by beating Linby CW of the Senior Division 1-0 in he final.

NTERMEDIATE CUP: Bottesford St Mary's completed a league and cup double by beating Pelican Reserves 3-0 in he final.

IOTTINGHAMSHIRE FA CUP: The League once again acquitted itself well in these competitions, Notts Police narpwly losing in the Senior Cup whilst Chaffoteux were successful in the Junior Cup.

## FINAL LEAGUE TABLES 1998-99

### SENIOR DIVISION

| | P | W | D | L | F | A | Pts |
|---|---|---|---|---|---|---|---|
| oots Athletic | 30 | 25 | 4 | 1 | 87 | 37 | 79 |
| outhwell City | 30 | 18 | 4 | 8 | 66 | 36 | 58 |
| inby C.W. | 30 | 16 | 7 | 7 | 65 | 45 | 55 |
| lotts Police | 30 | 15 | 6 | 9 | 58 | 43 | 51 |
| eyworth Utd | 30 | 14 | 4 | 12 | 61 | 58 | 46 |
| ainworth M.W. | 30 | 13 | 7 | 10 | 47 | 49 | 46 |
| etford Utd | 30 | 11 | 11 | 8 | 59 | 40 | 44 |
| elican F.C. | 30 | 12 | 6 | 12 | 54 | 53 | 42 |
| ilsthorpe C.W. | 30 | 11 | 7 | 12 | 44 | 42 | 40 |
| uddington Utd | 30 | 11 | 4 | 15 | 55 | 65 | 37 |
| llerton Town | 30 | 11 | 4 | 15 | 40 | 54 | 37 |
| ollaton F.C. | 30 | 9 | 9 | 12 | 50 | 45 | 36 |
| ttenborough F.C. | 30 | 9 | 7 | 14 | 39 | 54 | 34 |
| otgrave C.W. | 30 | 9 | 2 | 19 | 59 | 77 | 29 |
| horesby C.W. | 30 | 4 | 9 | 17 | 37 | 81 | 21 |
| asford Utd | 30 | 2 | 9 | 19 | 30 | 72 | 15 |

### FIRST DIVISION

| | P | W | D | L | F | A | Pts |
|---|---|---|---|---|---|---|---|
| Clifton F.C. | 30 | 22 | 6 | 2 | 76 | 22 | 72 |
| I.D.P.Newark | 30 | 20 | 6 | 4 | 94 | 49 | 66 |
| Abacus F.C. | 30 | 19 | 3 | 8 | 76 | 44 | 60 |
| Bestwood M.W. | 30 | 16 | 6 | 8 | 78 | 50 | 54 |
| Matrixgrade F.C. | 30 | 15 | 5 | 10 | 83 | 56 | 50 |
| Beeston Town | 30 | 13 | 9 | 8 | 54 | 49 | 48 |
| Kimberley M.W. | 30 | 13 | 7 | 10 | 75 | 53 | 46 |
| Magdala AMS | 30 | 13 | 6 | 11 | 64 | 60 | 45 |
| Southbank F.C. | 30 | 14 | 3 | 13 | 68 | 70 | 45 |
| Wollaton F.C. Res | 30 | 10 | 5 | 15 | 48 | 48 | 35 |
| Radcliffe OLY | 30 | 9 | 8 | 13 | 50 | 61 | 35 |
| Gedling M.W. | 30 | 10 | 4 | 16 | 49 | 75 | 34 |
| Boots Ath. Res | 30 | 8 | 5 | 17 | 41 | 52 | 29 |
| Awsworth Villa | 30 | 6 | 9 | 15 | 36 | 58 | 27 |
| City & Sherwood | 30 | 4 | 3 | 23 | 39 | 100 | 15 |
| Rainworth M.W. Res | 30 | 4 | 3 | 23 | 28 | 113 | 12* |

### SECOND DIVISION

| | P | W | D | L | F | A | Pts |
|---|---|---|---|---|---|---|---|
| ottesford St Mary's | 28 | 24 | 2 | 2 | 90 | 19 | 74 |
| haffoteaux F.C. | 28 | 21 | 1 | 6 | 77 | 38 | 64 |
| elican F.C. Res | 28 | 19 | 5 | 4 | 64 | 30 | 62 |
| outhwell City Res | 28 | 20 | 1 | 7 | 87 | 38 | 61 |
| uddington Utd Res | 28 | 14 | 4 | 10 | 66 | 48 | 46 |
| D.P. Newark Res | 28 | 13 | 6 | 9 | 62 | 44 | 45 |
| ewark Town | 28 | 13 | 4 | 11 | 68 | 61 | 40* |
| alverton M.W. | 28 | 10 | 4 | 14 | 57 | 68 | 34 |

| | P | W | D | L | F | A | Pts |
|---|---|---|---|---|---|---|---|
| East Leake M.W. | 28 | 10 | 4 | 14 | 45 | 58 | 34 |
| Pinxton N. End | 28 | 10 | 2 | 16 | 66 | 82 | 32 |
| Basford Utd Res | 28 | 8 | 4 | 16 | 39 | 67 | 28 |
| Attenborough F.C.Res | 28 | 6 | 3 | 19 | 41 | 81 | 21 |
| Keyworth Utd Res | 28 | 6 | 2 | 20 | 58 | 96 | 20 |
| Retford Utd Res | 28 | 5 | 5 | 18 | 43 | 90 | 20 |
| Melton Mowbray | 28 | 4 | 7 | 17 | 29 | 72 | 19 |
| * Points deducted | | | | | | | |

## ATTENBOROUGH

**Secretary:** Terry Allen, 5 Coningsby Road,Woodthorpe, Nottingham NG54LG Tel: 0115 920 0698
**Ground & Directions:** The Village Green, The Strand, Attenborough, Beeston,Nottingham. Midway between Beeston & Long Eaton on A6005 - adjacent to NatureReserve (via Attenborough Lane).
**Colours:** Green/navy/navy
**Change colours:** White/black/black.

## BILSTHORPE COLLIERY WELFARE

**Secretary:** Les Lee,18 The Hollies, Rainworth, Mansfield NG21 0FZ Tel: 01623 490053 Mobile: 0411 384711

**Ground:** Eakring Road, Bilsthorpe, Notts

**Colours:** All royal blue

## BOOTS ATHLETIC

**Secretary:** Ian Whitehead
21 Rosthwaite Close, West Bridgford, Nottingham NG26RA
Tel: 0115 981 2830 (H)  0115 968 7535 (B)
**Ground:** Lady Bay, West Bridgford, Nottingham Tel: 0115 981 2392
**Colours:** Blue&white stripes, bue,blue.

**Honours:** Notts Alliance Div 1 91-92 (Lg Cup 91-92), Notts Snr Cup R-up 93-94,Notts Inter R-up 91-92.

## CLIFTON

**Secretary:** Keith Elliott, 61 Greencroft, Clifton,Nottingham. NG11 9BX (0115 9215401)

**Ground:** Green Lane, Clifton Est., Nottm Tel: 0115 984 4903

**Colours:** All white

## COTGRAVE COLLIERY WELFARE

**Secretary:** Kevin Whitehead, 51 Cross Hill, Cotgrave, Nottinham. NG12 3NB Tel: 0115 989 4043

**Ground:** Cotgrave Welfare. Scheme Sports Ground

**Colours:** All red

## I.D.P. NEWARK

**Secretary:** Kevin Presland, Appleby Lodge, Barnby Road, Newark, Nottingham NG24 2NE Tel: 01636 704606,  07771 507065

**Ground:** Lowfield Works, off hawton Lane, Balderton, Newark, Nottingham. Tel: 01636 702672

**Colours:** Orange/blue/orange

## KEYWORTH UNITED

**Secretary:** Stuart Douglas
29 Ashley  Crescent, Keyworth, Nottm. NG12 5GF
Tel: 0115 937 5358

**Ground:** Platt Lane, Keyworth (0115 937 5998)

**Colours:** Green/black/white

## LINBY COLLIERY WELFARE

**Secretary:** Paul Capewell
7 Thorn Grove, Hucknall, Nottm. NG15 6AT
Tel: 0115 840 1063

**Ground:** Church Lane, Linby, Nottingham

**Colours:** Red & white/white/red

## NOTTINGHAMSHIRE POLICE

**Secretary:** John Beeston
17 Alandene Ave, Watnall, Nottingham NG16 1HH
Tel: 0115 938 2110
**Ground:** Police Training Centre, Epperstone, Notts.
**Colours:** Navy & sky/navy/navy
**Honours:** Notts Snr R-up 91-92, Notts All. Div 1 & Lge Snr Cup R-up 85-86, PAANNat. K-O Comp 63-64.

## OLLERTON TOWN

**Secretary:** Colin Gibson, 10 Manor Close, Boughton, nr Newark, Nottm. NG22 9JS Tel: 01623 860816
**Match Secretary:** Jack Graham, 77 Petersmith Drive, New Ollerton. Tel: 01623 863127
**Ground:** Walesby Lane, New Ollerton, Notts

**Colours:** Red & white/red/red

## PELICAN

**Secretary:** Malcolm Goodwin
64 Chadwick Road, Bobbersmill, Nottingham.
Tel: 0115 910 6815
**Ground:** Brian Wakefield Sports Ground, Lenton Lane, Nottingham
Tel: 0115 986 8255
**Colours:** All Blue
**Honours:** Notts Alliance Lg Cup 90-91 (R-up 91-92 93-94).

## RAINWORTH MINERS WELFARE
**Secretary:** Alan Wright, 10 Faraday Road, Mansfield NG18 4ES
Tel: 01623 624379 (H)  01623 553237 (B)
**Ground:** Kirklington Road, Rainworth, Notts
**Directions:** On A617 Mansfield - Newark Road
**Colours:** All white
**Honours:** Notts Alliance 77-78 78-79 79-80 80-81 81-82 82-83 (R-up 93-94, Lg Cup81-82), Notts Snr Cup 80-81 81-82 (R-up 82-83 92-93), FA Vase R-up 82-82, ThornEMI F'lit Cup R-up 82-83 83-84 84-85

## RETFORD UNITED

**Secretary:** Jeff Lamb
18 Northumbria Drive, Retford, Notts, DN22 7PR
Tel: 01777 705833

**Ground:** Oaklands Lane (Off London Road), Retford, Notts.
(enter via Caledonian Road)
**Colours:** Black & white stripes/black/black

## RUDDINGTON

**Secretary:** John Fisk, 3 Savages Rd., Ruddington, Nottm NG11 6EW
Tel: 0115 9842552
**Ground & Directions:** The Elms Park Ground, Loughborough Road, Ruddington (0115 984 4976) On A60 Nottm to Loughborough, 5 miles out of Nottingham.
**Colours:** Yellow & blue/blue/blue
**Honours:** Notts Comb. Lg 79-80, Lg Cup 70-71 76-77 80-81

## SOUTHWELL CITY

**Secretary:** Pat Johnson
63 The Ropewalk, Southwell, Notts NG25 0AL
Tel: 01636 812594

**Ground:** War Memorial Recreation G round, Bishops Drive, Southwell, Notts. 01636 814386

**Colours:** Black& White stripes/black/black.

## WOLLATON

**Secretary:** Jonathon Hunt
17 Chapman Court, Beechdale Mews, Nottingham NG8 3FQ
Tel: 0115 916 0174
**Ground:** Wollaton Sports Association, Wollaton Village, Nottm
Tel: 0115 9133 134
**Colours:** Sky Blue
**Honours:** Notts All. Div 1 R-up 92-93, Div 2 91-92, I'mediate Cup R-up 91-92.

This Division also includes the Reserve sides of:

Boots Athletic & Wollaton

## ABACUS

**Secretary:** Trevor Lissaman, 43 Carlton St., Mansfield, Notts NG18 2BG Tel Nos: 01623 462993 (H)    0797 0722194 (M)
**Ground:** Sherwood Colliery Sports Ground, Debdale Lane, Mansfield Woodhouse,Notts.Tel: 01623 631747
**Colours:** Green & white stripes

## AWSWORTH VILLA

**Secretary:** Paul Wilkinson, 15 Barlow Drive North, Awsworth, Nottingham NG16 2RQ. Tel: 0115 930 4905 (H)  0115 932 8721 (B)
**Ground:** Shilo Park, off Attewell Road, Awsworth, Nottm.
**Colours:** Red & white/red/red.

## BASFORD UNITED

**Secretary:** Nev Sheldon, 12 Clipstone Ave., Mapperley, Nottm. (0115 926 6100)    **Ground:** Greenwich Ave., Bagnall Rd, Basford, Nottm (0115 942 3918). **Directions:** M1, J26 follow signs A610 Nottingham then B6004 Arnold into Mill St.    **Colours:** Yellow/black/yellow

## BEESTON TOWN

**Secretary:** Andy Meakin, 26 Redland Drive, Chilwell, Nottingham NG9 5LE Tel: 0115 967 7520
**Ground:** University Ground, Nottingham Tel: 0115 967 5517
**Colours:** All white

## BESTWOOD MINERS WELFARE

**Secretary:** Alan Fisher,5 Skipton Close, Ilkeston, Derbyshire DE7 9HX (0115 932 7717)
**Ground:** Bestwood Workshops, Park Rd, Bestwood
**Colours:** Gold & black/black/black.

## BOTTESFORD ST. MARYS

**Secretary:** Miss M Angeloni, 129 Stamford St., Grantham, Lincs. NG31 7BF  Tel: 07476 593581
**Ground:** Village hall Playing Fields, Belvoir Rd., Bottesford
**Colours:** Blue & black stripes/black/black

## CHAFFOTEAUX

**Secretary:** Mark Nicholls, 31 Telford Drive, Newthorpe, Nottm. NG16 3NN 01773 534169 (H) 0115 942 2400(B)
**Ground:** Basil Russell Playing Fields, Maple Drive, Nuthall, Nottingham 0115 938 4765 **Colours:** Red&black/black/black

## GEDLING MINERS WELFARE

**Secretary:** Norman Hay, 182 Gedling Rd., Arnold, Nottm. NG5 6NY
Tel: 0115 926 5598
**Ground:** Gedling C.W., Plains Road, Mapperley, Nottm. (0115 926 6300)    **Colours:** Yellow/blue/yellow

## KIMBERLEY MINERS WELFARE
**Secretary:** Mick Walker, 33 Maws Lane, Kimberley, Nottm. NG16 2JB. Tel: 01159138199 (H) 07771 567145 (B)
**Ground:** Digby Street, Kimberley, Nottingham (0115 938 2124)
**Colours:** Black & red/black/black & red

## MAGDALA AMATEURS
**Secretary:** Alan Gilmour, 9 Adbolton Grove, West Bridgford, Nottingham NG2 5AR Tel: 0115 982 1071
**Ground:** Civil Service Sports Ground, Wilford Lane, W Bridgford.
**Colours:** Maroon & sky/sky/maroon

## MATRIXGRADE
**Secretary:** Barrie Kerry, 132 Common Lane, Hucknall, Nottm. NG15 6TG. Tel: 0115 953 3268
**Ground:** Carrington Sports Ground, Mansfield Rd., Nottm.
**Colours:** Yellow & black/black/black

## RADCLIFFE OLYMPIC
**Secretary:** C Johnson, 2 The Firs, Holme Pierrepoint, Nottingham NG12 2LT Tel: 0115 933 3791
**Ground:** Wharf Lane, Radcliffe-on-Trent, Nottingham
**Colours:** All green

## SOUTHBANK
**Secretary:** Gerry Bishop, 4 Foxearth Ave., Clifton, Nottm. NG11 8JQ Tel: 0115 984 2363
**Ground:** Haywood Comprehensive School, Edwards lane, Sherwood, Nottingham.    **Colours:** All Red

## THORESBY COLLIERY WELFARE
**Secretary:** Barry Reece,125 Henton Road, Edwinstowe, NottinghamNG219LD (01623 822415)
**Ground:** Thoresby Colliery, Fourth Avenue, Edwinstowe, Nr Mansfield
**Colours:** All pale blue

**ARNOLD KINGSWELL**
**Secretary:** Phil Smith, 95 Denewood Crescent, Bilborough, Nottingham NG8 3DF. Tel: 0115 913 5495 (H)

**CALVERTON M.W.**
**Secretary:** Dean Wilkinson, 46 Pepper Road, Calverton, Nottingham. Tel: 0115 965 4985

**CITY & SHERWOOD HOSPITAL**
**Secretary:** Alan Bird, 72 Bilborough Road, Bilborough, Nottingham NG8 4DW Tel: 0115 928 5507

**EASTLAKE ATHLETIC**
**Secretary:** Andrew Fletcher, 62 Suthers Road, Kegworth, Derby DE74 2DF Tel: 01509 674752

**MELTON MOWBRAY**
**Secretary:** Anne Gibbon, 39 Main Street, Kirby Bellars, Melton Mowbray, Leics. LE14 2EA Tel: 0116 481 2675

**NEWARK TOWN**
**Secretary:** David Wildes, Forest Cottage, Brough, Newark, Nottingham NG23 7QZ Tel: 01636 676038

**PINXTON NORTH END**
**Secretary:** Terry Gospel, 16 PeelRoad, Mansfield, Nottingham NG19 6HB Tel: 01623 634915

Plus the Reserve sides of:
Attenborough, Basford United, I.D.P. Newark, Keyworth United, Ollerton Town, Pelican, Rainworth M.W., Ruddington United and Southwell City.

## SCUNTHORPE & DISTRICT LEAGUE

### DIVISION ONE

| | | | | | | | |
|---|---|---|---|---|---|---|---|
| Brumby Hotel | 22 | 19 | 0 | 3 | 61 | 18 | 57 |
| AFC Friendship | 22 | 15 | 0 | 7 | 75 | 37 | 45 |
| AFC McIntosh | 22 | 14 | 2 | 6 | 65 | 39 | 44 |
| Crowle | 22 | 11 | 6 | 5 | 45 | 39 | 39 |
| Scunthonians | 22 | 12 | 1 | 9 | 86 | 55 | 37 |
| Swinefleet | 22 | 9 | 5 | 8 | 41 | 37 | 32 |
| Scawby | 22 | 8 | 4 | 10 | 43 | 49 | 28 |
| Barton Town O B Res. | 22 | 8 | 4 | 10 | 38 | 56 | 28 |
| Lincoln Imp | 22 | 8 | 3 | 11 | 44 | 48 | 27 |
| New Holland Villa | 22 | 7 | 1 | 14 | 38 | 78 | 22 |
| Bottesford Town Sports | 22 | 5 | 2 | 15 | 44 | 63 | 17 |
| Messingham Trinity | 22 | 1 | 2 | 19 | 27 | 87 | 5 |

## TRAVIS PERKINS NORTHANTS COMBINATION

### PREMIER DIVISION

| | | | | | | | |
|---|---|---|---|---|---|---|---|
| Brixworth All Saints | 28 | 17 | 9 | 2 | 57 | 21 | 60 |
| Harpole | 28 | 18 | 5 | 5 | 82 | 37 | 59 |
| Milton (Northants) | 28 | 17 | 5 | 6 | 62 | 35 | 56 |
| Towcester Town | 28 | 16 | 1 | 11 | 46 | 33 | 49 |
| Spencer United | 28 | 14 | 5 | 9 | 69 | 44 | 47 |
| Heyford Athletic | 28 | 13 | 7 | 8 | 54 | 39 | 46 |
| Moulton | 28 | 12 | 6 | 10 | 56 | 46 | 42 |
| Cold Ashby Rovers | 28 | 11 | 6 | 11 | 55 | 47 | 39 |
| Earls Barton United | 28 | 11 | 6 | 11 | 57 | 55 | 39 |
| Potterspury | 28 | 8 | 8 | 12 | 56 | 67 | 32 |
| Spratton | 28 | 7 | 10 | 11 | 45 | 51 | 31 |
| Weedon | 28 | 7 | 5 | 16 | 53 | 83 | 26 |
| West Haddon -3 | 28 | 8 | 4 | 16 | 45 | 59 | 25 |
| Northants Police | 28 | 5 | 3 | 20 | 41 | 95 | 18 |
| Kislingbury | 28 | 4 | 4 | 20 | 29 | 95 | 16 |

## DEEJAYS LINCOLNSHIRE LEAGUE

| | | | | | | | |
|---|---|---|---|---|---|---|---|
| Limestone Rangers | 36 | 27 | 5 | 4 | 112 | 32 | 86 |
| Barton Town Old Boys | 36 | 24 | 6 | 6 | 124 | 47 | 78 |
| Boston United Res. | 36 | 22 | 6 | 8 | 118 | 59 | 72 |
| Grimsby & Im'ham Ams | 36 | 19 | 14 | 3 | 69 | 28 | 71 |
| Lincoln United | 36 | 22 | 3 | 11 | 80 | 50 | 69 |
| Alstom Sports | 36 | 19 | 4 | 13 | 84 | 68 | 61 |
| Sleaford Town | 36 | 17 | 6 | 13 | 88 | 65 | 57 |
| Epworth Tn Leis. Centre | 36 | 17 | 5 | 14 | 60 | 54 | 56 |
| Lincoln Moorlands | 36 | 16 | 8 | 12 | 55 | 57 | 56 |
| Grantham Town Res. -3 | 36 | 16 | 9 | 11 | 73 | 53 | 54 |
| Appleby Frodingham A | 36 | 14 | 8 | 14 | 86 | 71 | 50 |
| BRSA Retford | 36 | 13 | 7 | 16 | 55 | 79 | 46 |
| Skegness Town +3 | 36 | 12 | 6 | 18 | 64 | 88 | 45 |
| Louth United Res. +3 -3 | 36 | 12 | 6 | 18 | 73 | 81 | 42 |
| Bottesford Town | 36 | 10 | 5 | 21 | 65 | 88 | 35 |
| Wyberton | 36 | 9 | 5 | 22 | 62 | 97 | 32 |
| Hykeham Town | 36 | 10 | 2 | 24 | 53 | 101 | 32 |
| Horncastle Town | 36 | 7 | 5 | 24 | 42 | 97 | 26 |
| Nettleham Res. | 36 | 0 | 2 | 34 | 18 | 166 | 2 |

Chris Partridge of GPT Coventry (white), heads the ball against the Meir KA bar during this 2-2 draw in the Endsleigh Combination Premier Division.

Photo: Keith Clayton

**HIGHFIELD RANGERS**

**THURMASTON TOWN**

Leicestershire Senior League
Photo: Gordon Whittington

# NORTHERN LEAGUE
## Founded 1889

**President:** George Courtney    **Chairman:** M Amos
**Hon. Secretary & Treasurer:** A Golightly
85 Park Road North, Chester-le-Street, Co Durham DH3 3SA
Tel: 0191 388 2056

Since even in the Directory's long and ever more fulsome history no one is ever likely to have mentioned the Royal Academy of Art, let us begin beneath those fabled arches in Piccadilly where a painting by Craigie Aitchison called "Bedlington Terrier in Red" hangs in the summer exhibition.

Bedlington Terrier in Red? Every picture tells a story.

Once again it was principally Bedlington Terriers' year in the Arnott Insurance Northern League. For the second successive season they won the first division championship, in the FA Cup they thrashed Colchester 4-1 before going out 2-0 at Scunthorpe, and in the Vase they became the third AINL side in successive seasons to reach Wembley.

All the time, or most of it, their exploits were accompanied by a wholly different football chant - "Woof, Woof, Terriers" started at the back of someone's throat behind the bottom goal, carried round the ground and now it is a Northumberland anthem. All right, they also became the second successive AINL side to lose 1-0 to Tiverton in the Vase final - but that's what's called woof with the smooth, is it not?

Uniquely among leagues at this level, West Auckland made it two clubs in the first round proper of the FA Cup, came within seconds of a famous win at Yeovil (what a wonderful set-up that is), sang Vindaloo (unfortunately) all the way home and went out on penalties in the replay. Part of their AXA/FA sponsorship money has been spent on splendid new wrought iron gates, incorporating a motif of West's 1909 and 1911 World Cup. Like Dr Graeme Forster's team, well worth seeing.

If the animal world may be allowed a mixed metaphor, Terriers had long made the First Division a one horse race. Tow Law, second, were 26 points behind their record points total. Since neither was interested in promotion, and since Whitley Bay found salvation in the last minute of the season thanks to a goal from someone called Christen Priest, the League's constitution remains the same in the new season.

Durham City were also runaway winners of the Second Division after being relegated by one goal the previous year, and will be anxious to get more fans into their splendid stadium. Shotton, promoted for the first time, and Peterlee join them in the First Division. Penrith's relegation, incidentally, means that Tow Law are now the only First Division side never to have played in the Second. Shildon and Newcastle Blue Star joined the cortege downwards.

Dunston Fed, having earlier in the season established a record for the longest journey made by a visiting team in an English Cup competition (St Blazey, in deepest Cornwall, proved warmly welcoming), won the AINL Cup for the second successive season by beating Jarrow Roofing.

In the Craven Cup, for Second Division sides, Ashington not only narrowly beat Evenwood Town but proved that it's possible to have both boisterous and musical fans - half the Northern Sinfonia seemed to be behind the goal - without ever once swearing, or ever once causing offence. The future of their historic Portland Park ground remains as annoyingly uncertain as the new shopping mall which may or may not be built on it. As they say in the world of town planning, we shall just have to see what develops.

None leave the League in either direction, none join us by promotion from the feeders. There will, however, be two new names. Ryhope CA have merged with Kennek Roker from the Wearside League and become Kennek Roker CA and Stockton, who've played over the river in Thornaby since their re-formation, finally became Thornaby-on-Tees. There's talk of a handsome new ground there, too, but still a lot of water to go under the bridge.

The non-League game's politics have, happily, largely passed us by, though the AINL played a key role in the campaign against the proposed Conference second division and was naturally delighted when the FA rejected it. Relationships with those immediately above and below us remain good, the Curzon Ashton business being likely to have proved both educative and chastening. A quote from Unibond chairman Duncan Bayley deserves to become a watchword - "we aren't in the business of putting people out of business".

Though never in question, the League's own survival has greatly been guaranteed by an extension and enhancement to the end of 2002-03 of the sponsorship deal with Arnott Insurance. Since the Arnott chairman is much ribbed by the League chairman about the amount he smokes, the agreement was written on the inside flap of a Marlboro packet and is worth its weight in Gold Leaf.

Other sponsors continue generously, not least the Northern Echo which meets the now four figure difference between the cost of producing the League magazine and of continuing to sell it at 30p. Northern Ventures Northern Gains celebrates its tenth birthday in October, begun with just 60 copies produced on a manual typewriter and painstakingly photocopied and stapled by volunteers. Now it sells almost 2000 copies each issue.

The anniversary will be marked with a special issue, with extra pages and more colour, reflecting the huge changes in a decade in the life of the world's second oldest league. Still, thanks to yet more sponsorship it will cost just 30p. Subscriptions remain just £3.30, including postage, for the season's six issues (Don Warner, 18 The Riggs, Hunwick, Crook, Co Durham)

The League is also launching The Northern League Club, an attempt to raise its profile and to keep followers both regionally and nationally more informed about what's going on. The initiative was launched, with full media coverage, by former England manager Bobby Robson. Membership includes a badge, regular copies of both of the League magazines and Club newsletter - fixtures, results, tables, gossip - with membership card, 40 page grounds guide, competitions an discounts from league sponsors and from clubs. It costs £10 and is going well. Details from Martin Haworth, 17 The Turr Morpeth, Northumberland.

There are still problems, of course, not least from vandals and arsonists. The League helped organise a specia match for Murton, the most famously affected, only for the lights to go out 20 minutes before the end. It was Friday the 13th, we should have known. Other clubs survive with just two or three heroes at the helm, a picture of true dedicatio doubtless reflected across the country.

The annual dinner, at which the decision to dispense with ex-professionals on automatic pilot was richly vindicated was a particular success. West Auckland's Frank Patrick, 71, won the "Unsung Hero" award for 50 years unstinted servic to the club, Guisborough Town's was voted best tea hut - their prizes included fifty quids' worth of tea bags from the Co-o - and Crook won the award for being the most hospitable to visiting clubs.

Shotton Comrades won both fair play and administration awards, tribute to manager Kevin Stonehouse and secretar Billy Banks, and John Milner's 65 goals for Bedlington almost inevitably made him player of the season.

At the end of 1999-2000, of course, the AINL looks forward to a fourth successive trip to Wembley. Hitherto these weekends have been mostly spent in the capital's pubs and restaurants. Who knows, next time, what we might find in the Royal Academy?

*Mike Amos*

## FINAL LEAGUE TABLES 1998-99

### DIVISION ONE

| | P | W | D | L | F | A | Pts |
|---|---|---|---|---|---|---|---|
| Bedlington Terriers | 38 | 33 | 2 | 3 | 128 | 37 | 101 |
| Tow Law Town | 38 | 23 | 6 | 9 | 80 | 49 | 75 |
| Chester-le-Street Town | 38 | 17 | 14 | 7 | 71 | 46 | 65 |
| West Auckland Town | 38 | 19 | 8 | 11 | 65 | 57 | 65 |
| Dunston Fed Brewery | 38 | 18 | 10 | 10 | 73 | 51 | 64 |
| Guisborough Town | 38 | 18 | 5 | 15 | 68 | 65 | 59 |
| Seaham Red Star | 38 | 16 | 7 | 15 | 62 | 59 | 55 |
| Consett | 38 | 15 | 7 | 16 | 72 | 64 | 52 |
| Morpeth Town | 38 | 15 | 6 | 17 | 54 | 60 | 51 |
| Stockton | 38 | 15 | 6 | 17 | 68 | 76 | 51 |
| Billingham Synthonia* | 38 | 15 | 7 | 16 | 60 | 56 | 49 |
| Marske United | 38 | 13 | 9 | 16 | 58 | 63 | 48 |
| Crook Town | 38 | 13 | 7 | 18 | 51 | 60 | 46 |
| Billingham Town* | 38 | 13 | 9 | 16 | 66 | 81 | 45 |
| South Shields | 38 | 9 | 16 | 13 | 54 | 66 | 43 |
| Jarrow Rfng Boldon CA | 38 | 11 | 10 | 17 | 62 | 85 | 43 |
| Easington Colliery | 38 | 11 | 6 | 21 | 67 | 78 | 39 |
| Newcastle Blue Star* | 38 | 12 | 5 | 21 | 59 | 83 | 38 |
| Penrith -3 | 38 | 10 | 8 | 20 | 59 | 82 | 35 |
| Shildon | 38 | 6 | 8 | 24 | 48 | 107 | 26 |

### DIVISION TWO

| | P | W | D | L | F | A | Pts |
|---|---|---|---|---|---|---|---|
| Durham City | 36 | 29 | 4 | 3 | 101 | 28 | 91 |
| Shotton Comrades | 36 | 22 | 7 | 7 | 89 | 44 | 73 |
| Peterlee Newtown | 36 | 21 | 8 | 7 | 80 | 43 | 71 |
| Northallerton Town | 36 | 20 | 6 | 10 | 73 | 33 | 66 |
| Norton & Stockton Anc. | 36 | 20 | 6 | 10 | 73 | 43 | 66 |
| Brandon United | 36 | 17 | 8 | 11 | 87 | 49 | 59 |
| Hebburn | 36 | 18 | 4 | 14 | 66 | 54 | 58 |
| Evenwood Town | 36 | 15 | 10 | 11 | 82 | 63 | 55 |
| Whickham | 36 | 15 | 8 | 13 | 51 | 43 | 53 |
| Prudhoe Town | 36 | 14 | 10 | 12 | 70 | 61 | 52 |
| Ashington | 36 | 14 | 9 | 13 | 64 | 47 | 51 |
| Alnwick Town | 36 | 15 | 5 | 16 | 63 | 66 | 50 |
| Horden Colliery Welfare | 36 | 13 | 11 | 12 | 53 | 56 | 50 |
| Willington | 36 | 13 | 10 | 13 | 58 | 53 | 49 |
| Esh Winning | 36 | 9 | 10 | 17 | 59 | 73 | 37 |
| Washington | 36 | 10 | 6 | 20 | 55 | 79 | 36 |
| Ryhope Comm. Assn | 36 | 5 | 3 | 28 | 29 | 90 | 18 |
| Murton | 36 | 4 | 2 | 30 | 33 | 167 | 14 |
| Eppleton Coll Welfare* | 36 | 4 | 1 | 31 | 26 | 120 | 7 |
| * points deducted | | | | | | | |

## DIVISION ONE RESULTS CHART 1998-99

| | | 1 | 2 | 3 | 4 | 5 | 6 | 7 | 8 | 9 | 10 | 11 | 12 | 13 | 14 | 15 | 16 | 17 | 18 | 19 | 20 |
|---|---|---|---|---|---|---|---|---|---|---|---|---|---|---|---|---|---|---|---|---|---|
| 1 | Bedlington Terriers | X | 2-0 | 6-0 | 2-1 | 3-0 | 2-0 | 4-0 | 5-1 | 5-2 | 6-1 | 3-1 | 1-1 | 3-1 | 7-0 | 1-1 | 8-1 | 5-0 | 2-1 | 2-1 | 3-0 |
| 2 | B'ham Synthonia | 1-2 | X | 2-2 | 0-1 | 1-0 | 2-2 | 2-1 | 0-3 | 1-3 | 1-3 | 5-1 | 1-0 | 0-0 | 5-0 | 1-0 | 2-0 | 1-1 | 3-0 | 0-2 | 2-3 |
| 3 | Billingham Town | 6-2 | 1-1 | X | 0-4 | 0-3 | 2-1 | 2-2 | 2-2 | 3-0 | 0-2 | 1-2 | 5-1 | 0-2 | 1-5 | 2-2 | 2-2 | 2-2 | 3-2 | 4-2 | 0-1 |
| 4 | Chester le Street | 0-3 | 2-1 | 0-1 | X | 1-0 | 2-1 | 1-1 | 1-1 | 1-0 | 2-2 | 1-0 | 2-2 | 3-2 | 8-4 | 2-2 | 1-1 | 6-1 | 0-1 | 1-1 | |
| 5 | Consett | 2-1 | 2-1 | 4-0 | 2-1 | X | 0-1 | 3-4 | 6-0 | 3-0 | 0-0 | 1-1 | 1-1 | 4-2 | 5-2 | 2-3 | 0-3 | 4-3 | 1-4 | 1-2 | |
| 6 | Crook Town | 1-2 | 1-1 | 2-1 | 1-2 | 1-0 | X | 5-2 | 1-0 | 0-2 | 2-1 | 3-1 | 0-1 | 0-2 | 1-1 | 0-0 | 1-3 | 0-0 | 1-2 | 0-2 | 2-2 |
| 7 | Dunston Fed. | 1-2 | 0-1 | 3-2 | 3-1 | 3-1 | 2-0 | X | 2-3 | 0-0 | 2-1 | 4-1 | 1-1 | 5-0 | 1-0 | 1-0 | 1-1 | 3-0 | 3-1 | 3-3 | 3-3 |
| 8 | Easington Coll. | 1-3 | 4-1 | 1-3 | 0-2 | 4-0 | 0-1 | 1-1 | X | 3-1 | 0-3 | 0-1 | 1-4 | 3-2 | 2-3 | 4-1 | 0-0 | 3-1 | 3-1 | 0-3 | 1-2 |
| 9 | Guisborough Tn | 2-3 | 2-1 | 2-0 | 1-2 | 3-1 | 3-1 | 2-2 | 5-2 | X | 0-0 | 2-2 | 3-2 | 2-0 | 4-1 | 1-0 | 1-2 | 3-1 | 4-2 | 3-1 | 1-2 |
| 10 | Jarrow Roofing | 2-1 | 1-1 | 3-3 | 2-2 | 4-6 | 1-5 | 1-2 | 0-2 | 3-3 | X | 1-2 | 1-3 | 2-12 | 2-1 | 1-2 | 2-2 | 0-0 | 2-4 | 1-2 | 1-2 |
| 11 | Marske United | 2-3 | 3-2 | 1-2 | 1-2 | 2-2 | 4-1 | 2-1 | 4-1 | 1-2 | 3-0 | X | 1-2 | 1-0 | 1-2 | 2-2 | 2-2 | 2-1 | 1-1 | 0-1 | 1-2 |
| 12 | Morpeth Town | 1-4 | 4-2 | 0-2 | 0-3 | 0-0 | 2-3 | 0-2 | 2-1 | 2-1 | 3-0 | 2-1 | X | 3-2 | 1-2 | 0-0 | 3-2 | 1-2 | 2-0 | 1-1 | 4-0 |
| 13 | Newcastle BS | 0-3 | 0-2 | 1-2 | 2-2 | 0-2 | 2-2 | 1-5 | 0-10 | 3-1 | 1-2 | 1-1 | 3-2 | X | 2-1 | 2-3 | 2-1 | 3-1 | 3-0 | 1-5 | 0-1 |
| 14 | Penrith | 2-5 | 3-1 | 3-3 | 1-1 | 3-2 | 2-5 | 0-1 | 2-2 | 2-0 | 0-3 | 0-0 | 2-0 | 0-2 | X | 1-3 | 5-2 | 3-1 | 0-1 | 2-2 | 2-3 |
| 15 | Seaham RS | 0-1 | 0-2 | 6-0 | 0-3 | 2-0 | 4-0 | 1-0 | 3-2 | 1-2 | 4-1 | 3-1 | 0-1 | 3-1 | 2-1 | X | 2-1 | 2-2 | 0-1 | 2-3 | 0-1 |
| 16 | Shildon | 0-5 | 1-6 | 2-4 | 0-4 | 0-4 | 0-4 | 1-5 | 3-2 | 0-3 | 1-2 | 1-3 | 0-2 | 1-2 | 3-1 | 1-2 | X | 2-1 | 2-2 | 0-1 | 2-3 |
| 17 | South Shields | 0-5 | 0-1 | 1-0 | 3-3 | 3-3 | 3-0 | 1-0 | 3-1 | 1-2 | 3-3 | 1-1 | 1-0 | 2-0 | 1-1 | 1-1 | 5-1 | X | 3-1 | 1-3 | 5-2 |
| 18 | Stockton | 2-6 | 0-3 | 3-2 | 0-0 | 1-1 | 2-0 | 1-1 | 3-1 | 4-0 | 0-1 | 4-1 | 2-1 | 1-2 | 1-1 | 0-2 | 5-2 | 3-3 | X | 1-4 | 3-2 |
| 19 | Tow Law Town | 1-2 | 5-1 | 2-1 | 1-1 | 0-1 | 2-0 | 3-1 | 3-2 | 2-0 | 5-2 | 1-2 | 2-1 | 2-0 | 1-0 | 3-1 | 2-3 | 1-1 | 1-5 | X | 1-2 |
| 20 | West Auckland | 1-5 | 1-2 | 1-2 | 1-1 | 3-2 | 0-2 | 1-3 | 0-0 | 4-2 | 0-2 | 0-2 | 3-1 | 3-0 | 2-1 | 5-0 | 6-0 | 1-0 | 1-3 | 1-1 | X |

BEDLINGTON TERRIERS - NORTHERN LEAGUE CHAMPIONS 1998-99

Back Row (L-R): Shaun Campbell (assistant secretary), Steve Boon, Tony Lowery (management), Glen Renforth, Andy Bowes, Mark Cameron, Paul O'Connor, Craig Melrose, Dean Gibb, Archie Gourlay, Andy Gowans, Keith Perry (management), Jon Egan, Gary Middleton.
Front Row: Mel Harmison, John Milner, Richie Bond, Lawrie Pearson, Warren Teasdale, Martin Pike, Mickey Cross, Lee Ludlow, G I Johnny (Kitman).

DUNSTON FEDERATION BREWERY FC - NORTHERN LEAGUE CHALLENGE CUP WINNERS 1998-99

Back Row (L-R): N Peverell, P Hugg, B Irwin, E Melburn, D Hagan, S Jones, C Keegans, K Mills, N Scaife
Front Row: P Symm, C Bone, M Pugh, G Forbes, P Briggs, A Elliott

# NORTHERN LEAGUE CUP 1998-99

**FIRST ROUND**

| | | | | | | | | |
|---|---|---|---|---|---|---|---|---|
| Ashington | v | Jarrow Roofing | 1-2 | | Durham City | v | Norton & SA | 3-1 |
| Esh Winning | v | Consett | 0-2 | | Guisborough | v | Horden CW | 2-0 |
| Bedlington Terriers | v | Murton | 5-0 | | Brandon United | v | Northallerton | 5-0 |

**SECOND ROUND**

| | | | | | | | | |
|---|---|---|---|---|---|---|---|---|
| B'ham Synthonia | v | Billingham Town | 1-2 | | Dunston Fed | v | Evenwood Town | 2-1 |
| Durham City | v | South Shields | 0-1 | | Easington Colliery | v | Crook Town | 4-3 |
| Jarrow Roofing | v | Washington IH | 3-0 | | Marske United | v | Penrith | 2-1 |
| Morpeth Town | v | Chester le Street | 1-0 | | Newcastle BS | v | Tow Law Town | 0-4 |
| Shotton Com. | v | Eppleton CW | 2-1 | | West Auckland | v | Peterlee | 3-0 |
| Bedlington Terriers | v | Prudhoe Town | 2-1 | | Brandon United | v | Consett | 2-3 |
| Guisborough | v | Alnwick Town | 2-0 | | Ryhope CA | v | Seaham RS | 0-3 |
| Shildon | v | Stockton | 3-5 | | Willington | v | Whickham | 4-2 |

**THIRD ROUND**

| | | | | | | | | |
|---|---|---|---|---|---|---|---|---|
| Easington Coll. | v | Jarrow Roofing | 0-1 | | Marske United | v | Dunston Fed. | 0-1 |
| Shotton Com. | v | Guisborough | 2-3 | | West Auckland | v | Stockton | 2-1 |
| Seaham RS | v | Consett | 0-2 | | Tow Law Town | v | South Shields | 0-1 |
| Willington | v | Bedlington Terriers | 0-5 | | Morpeth Town | v | Billingham Town | 5-0 |

**FOURTH ROUND**

| | | | | | | | | |
|---|---|---|---|---|---|---|---|---|
| South Shields | v | Consett | 2-1 | | Bedlington Terriers | v | Morpeth Town | 0-1 |
| Guisborough | v | Dunston Fed. | 2-3 | | Jarrow Roofing | v | West Auckland | 2-1 |

**SEMI-FINALS**

| | | | | | | | | |
|---|---|---|---|---|---|---|---|---|
| Jarrow Roofing | v | South Shields | 2-2, 5p3 | | Morpeth Town | v | Dunston Fed. | 0-3 |

**FINAL**

| | | | | | |
|---|---|---|---|---|---|
| Dunston Fed | v | Jarrow Roofing | 4*1 | | at Peterlee Newtown FC |

# CRAVEN CUP 1998-99

**FIRST ROUND**

| | | | | | | | | |
|---|---|---|---|---|---|---|---|---|
| Esh Winning | v | Alnwick Town | 2-1 | | Shotton Com. | v | Hebburn | 2-4 |
| Norton & SA | v | Horden CW | 3-2 | | | | | |

**SECOND ROUND**

| | | | | | | | | |
|---|---|---|---|---|---|---|---|---|
| Ashington | v | Whickham | 3-2 | | Durham City | v | Eppleton CW | 5-1 |
| Brandon United | v | Norton & SA | 6-1 | | Evenwood Town | v | Murton | 7-1 |
| Prudhoe Town | v | Esh Winning | 3-4 | | Ryhope CA | v | Washington IH | 3-6 |
| Willington | v | Hebburn | 2-0 | | Northallerton | v | Peterlee | 5-0 |

**THIRD ROUND**

| | | | | | | | | |
|---|---|---|---|---|---|---|---|---|
| Ashington | v | Brandon United | 1-1, 4p3 | | Esh Winning | v | Willington | 4-3 |
| Washington IH | v | Durham City | 0-1 | | Northallerton | v | Evenwood Town | 0-1 |

**SEMI-FINALS**

| | | | | | | | | |
|---|---|---|---|---|---|---|---|---|
| Durham City | v | Ashington | 0-1 | | Esh Winning | v | Evenwood Town | 0-2 |

**FINAL**

| | | | | | |
|---|---|---|---|---|---|
| Ashington | v | Evenwood Town | 1-0 | | at Brandon United FC |

# BEDLINGTON TERRIERS

**Secretary:** Eric Young, 6 Millbank Place, Bedlington, Northumberland NE22 5AT
Tel: 01670 829196
**Ground:** Welfare Park, Park Rd., Bedlington, Northumberland. Tel: 01670 825485
**Directions:** Into Bedlington, turn left at `Northumberland Arms' on Front St.,then 2nd Right,
ground on right 100 yds
Capacity: 1,500     Seats: 150     Cover: 200     Floodlights: Yes
**Clubhouse:** Open every evening, 11-11pm Sat. & Sun lunch. Pool, darts etc
**Club Shop:** No

| | |
|---|---|
| **HONOURS** | Northern League Div 2 94-95 (R-up 84-85), Northern Alliance 66-67 (R-up 67-68 69-70 71-72, Lge Cup 57-58 66-67 69-70 81-82, Lge Chall Cup 96-97, Northumberland Sen Cup 96-97. |
| **PREVIOUS** | **Leagues:** Northern Alliance     **Names:** Bedlington Mechanics 49-53; Colliery Welfare 53-56; Mechanics 56- 61; Bedlington United 61-65; Bedlington Colliery 65-68; Bedlington Town 68-74. |
| **BEST SEASON** | **FA Cup:**          **FA Vase:** |
| **RECORDS** | **Attendance:** 1,013 v Blyth Spartans, Northern Lg 85-86 |
| | **Win:** 11-0 v West Auckland, (H) Lge 96-97     **Scorer:** John Milner 33 |

### FACT FILE

Formed: 1949
Colours: Red & white/white/white
Change colours: All blue
Midweek Matches: Wednesday
Programme: 40 pages, 70p
97-98 Captain: Andy Gowens
P.O.Y.: Warren Teasdale
Top Scorer: John Milner (33)

### CLUB PERSONNEL

Chairman: David Perry
Tel: 01670 820049 (H) 01670 530578 (B)
Press Officer: Secretary
Manager: Keith Perry
Assistant Manager: Steven Locker
Coach: Tony Lowery
Physio: Dave Robertson

---

# BILLINGHAM SYNTHONIA

**Secretary:** Graham Craggs, 2 Ribble Close, Billingham, Cleveland TS22 5NT Tel: 01642 535856
**Ground:** The Stadium, Central Avenue, Billingham, Cleveland (Press Box 01642 532348)
**Directions:** Turn off A19 onto A1027 signposted Billingham, Norton (this applies from either
north or south), continue straight on along Central Avenue, ground on left
opposite office block. 1 mile from Billingham (BR)
Capacity: 1,970     Seats: 370     Cover: 370     Floodlights: Yes
**Clubhouse:** 200yds across car park. Normal club hours     **Club Shop:** No

| | |
|---|---|
| **HONOURS** | Northern Lg 56-57 88-89 89-90 95-96, R-up 49-50 50-51  51-52, Lg Cup 51-52 87-88 89-90, Div 2 86-87, Teeside Lg 36-37 (Lg Cup 34-35 38-39), Durham Chall. Cup 88-89 90-91, North Riding Snr Cup 66-67 71-72, North Riding Amat. Cup 38-39 56-57 62-63 63-64. |
| **PREVIOUS** | **League:** Teeside (1923-War)     **Name:** Billingham Synthonia Recreation |
| **BEST SEASON** | **FA Amateur Cup** 4th Rd 48-49     **FA Vase:** |
| | **FA Trophy:** Q-F replay  93-94, 1-2 v Woking after 1-1 (A) |
| | **FA Cup:**1st Rd 48-49 51-52 56-57 57-58 87-88 89-90 |
| **RECORDS** | **Attendance:** 4,200 v Bishop Auck. 6/9/58 |
| | **Scorer:** Tony Hetherington **Appearances:** Andy Harbron |

### FACT FILE

Founded: 1923
Nickname: Synners
Sponsors: Billingham Arms Hotel
Colours: Green & White quarters/white/white
Change colours: Blue & White
Midweek Matches: Tuesdays
Programme: 40 pages (+ads),75p
Editor: Nigel Atkinson (01642 342469)
98-99Captain: Drew Coverdale
Top Scorer: Kraig Wilkinson

### CLUB PERSONNEL

Chairman: Stuart Coleby
President: Frank Cook
Press Officer: Secretary
Manager: Stuart Coleby
Physio: Tommy Cushley
Coach: Lenny Gunn

---

# BILLINGHAM TOWN

**Secretary**: Tom Donnelly, 36 Cumberland Crescent, Billingham,Cleveland TS23 1AY
Tel: 01642 555332

**Ground:** Bedford Terrace, Billingham, Cleveland. Tel: 01642 560043

**Directions:** Leave A19 on A1027 (signed Billingham). Turn left at 3rd r/bout,over bridge 1st left,
1st left again to grd
Capacity: 3,000     Seats: 176     Cover: 600     Floodlights: Yes
**Clubhouse:** Open matchdays. Hot & cold food     **Club Shop:** No

| | |
|---|---|
| **HONOURS** | Durham Amateur Cup 76-77 77-78, Teesside Lg 77-78 81-82, Nth Riding Snr Cup R-up 76-77 81-82, Stockton & Dist. Lg(3) |
| **PREVIOUS** | **Leagues :** Stockton & Dist. 68-74; Teesside 74-82. |
| | **Name:** Billingham Social Club (pre-1982)     **Ground:** Mill Lane (pre-1974) |
| **BEST SEASON** | **FA Cup:** 1st Rd Proper 55-56 |
| | **FA Vase:** |
| **RECORDS** | **Attendance:** 1,500 v Manchester City, FA Youth Cup 1985 |
| | **Scorer:** Paul Rowntree 100 |
| | **Appearances:** Darren Marsh, 250 in Northern League |

Players progressing: Gary Pallister (Middlesbrough), Gerry Forrest (Southampton), Dave Robinson (Halifax), Tony Barratt (Hartlepool), Mark Hine (Grimsby), Tony Hall(Middlesbrough), Graham Hall (Arsenal).

### FACT FILE

Founded: 1967
Nickname: The Social
Colours: All Blue
Change colours: Yellow/green/yellow
Midweek Matches: Tuesday
Reserves' Lge: Stockton & Dist Sunday
Programme: 28 pages, 50p
Editor: Alex Matthews (01642 653621)

### CLUB PERSONNEL

Chairman: Peter Martin
Hon.President: F Cook M.P.
President: G A Maxwell
Press Officer: Secretary
Manager: Trevor Arnold
Asst Manager/Coach: Neal Granycome

# CHESTER-LE-STREET TOWN

**Secretary:** Melvin Atkinson, 1 St Marys Close, Chester-le-Street, Co Durham DH2 3EG
Tel: 0191 288 3664
**Ground:** Moor Park, Chester Moor, Chester-le Street, County Durham (0191 388 3363)
**Directions:** Ground lies approx 2 miles south of town on A167 (C.-le-S. to Durham). Regular buses from C.-le-S. and Durham pass ground. Railway station 2 miles distant in town centre
Capacity: 3,500      Seats: 150        Cover: 1,500      Floodlights: Yes
**Open Matchdays**- midweek 6.30p.m.- 11.00 p.m. Saturday 12.00p.m.-7.00.Open Monday
7..30-11.00pm      **Club Shop:** No, but old programmes available from editor

**HONOURS**          Northern Lg Div 2 83-84 97-98; Wearside Lg 80-81 (R-up 82-83);
Monkwearmouth Cup 80-81 81-82; Washington Lg; Durham Minor Cup; Washington AM Cup.
**PREVIOUS**        **Leagues:** Newcastle City Amtr 72-75; Washington 75; Wearside 77-83
                   **Names:** Garden Farm 72-78
**BEST SEASON**    **FA Cup: 4th Qual. Rd. 86-87, 2-3 v Caernarfon Town (H)**
                   **FA Vase :** 5th Rd v Fleetwood Town 84-85 (1-1,2-0,0-3)
**RECORD**         **Gate:** 893 v Fleetwood FA Vase 18/2/85,
                   (3000 Sunderland v Newcastle,Bradford appeal match 85)
                   **Appearances:** Dean Ferry 219 (+38 subs)
                   **Win:** 9-0 v Washington N.L. 28/2/98    **Defeat:** 0-7 v Consett 6/11/96

**FACT FILE**
Founded: 1972
Nickname: Cestrians
Colours: Blue & white hoops/white/white
Change colours: All yellow
Midweek Matches: Tuesday
Programme: 40 pages, 50p
Editor/Press Officer:J.Thornback
98-99 Captain: Colin Wake
P.o.Y.: Colin Wake
Top Scorers: Stephen Lewis (20)

**CLUB PERSONNEL**
Chairman: John Tomlinson
Vice Chairman: Jack Thornback
President: John Holden
Press Off.: Jack Thornback (0191 3883554)
Manager: Paul Bryson
Asst Mgr/Coach: Stuart Sherwood
Physio: Ray Hartley

---

# CONSETT

**Secretary:** Ian Hamilton, 29 Grange Street, Delves Lane, Consett, Co. Durham DH87AG
Tel: 01207 509366
**Ground:** Belle Vue Park, Ashdale Road, Consett, County Durham (01207 503788)
**Directions:** Quarter of mile north of town centre - along Medomsley Rd, left down Ashdale Rd, ground 100m yards on left. Follow signs for Sports Centre and Baths
Capacity: 4,000          Seats: 400          Cover: 1,000        Floodlights: Yes
**Clubhouse:** Matchdays, and evenings on request. Darts & pool      **Club Shop:** No

**HONOURS**          North Eastern Lg 39-40 (Div 2 26-27, Lg Cup 50-51(jt) 53-54), Durham
Challenge 5, (R-up 2), Northern Lg R-up 76-77 (Div 2 88-89, Lg Cup 78-79 80-81), Northern
Counties Lg 61-62, Sunderland Shipowners Cup 67-68, Monkwearmouth Charity Cup 67-68,
Wearside Lg R-up 68-69 69-70.
**PREVIOUS**        **Leagues:** Northern Alliance 19-26 35-37; North Eastern 26-35 37-58 62-64;
                   Midland 58-60; Northern Counties 60-62; Wearside 64-70
                   **Grounds:** Vicarage Field (pre-1948); Leadgates Eden Colliery 48-50
**BEST SEASON**    **FA Cup:** 1st Rd 58-59, 0-5 v Doncaster Rov. (A)
                   **FA Trophy:** 2nd Rd 78-79.   **FA Vase:**
**RECORD Gate:** 7,000 v Sunderland Reserves, first match at Belle Vue, 1950.
Players progressing: Tommy Lumley (Charlton), Alan Ellison (Reading), Laurie Cunningham
(Barnsley), Jimmy Moir (Carlisle), Jackie Boyd (West Bromwich Albion).

**FACT FILE**

Founded:  1899
Nickname: Steelmen
Colours:  Red with black & white trim/black/red
Change colours: Sky blue/dark blue/sky blue
Midweek Matches:  Wednesday
Programme: 16 pages, 30p
Programme Editor:  Colin French
Local Press: Journal, Northern Echo,
Consett Advertiser.

**CLUB PERSONNEL**

Chairman:  Jack Kay
Vice Chairman:  I Hamilton
President:  D McVickers
Press Officer:  Andrew Pearson
Tel:  01207 506194
Manager:  Colin Carr
Physio:  Joe Darroch

---

# CROOK TOWN

**Secretary:** Alan Stewart, The Wardens Flat, 47 Grasmere Grove, Crook, Co Durham DL15 8NX
Tel: 01388 763425

**Ground:** Millfield Ground, West Road, Crook, County Durham (01388 762959)
**Directions:** 400 yds west of town centre on Wolsingham Road (A689). Nearest BR station is
Bishop Auckland (5 miles). Buses 1A & 1B from Bishop Auckland or X46& X47 from Durham
Capacity: 3,500          Seats: 400          Cover: 300        Floodlights: Yes
**Clubhouse:** Lic Bar open matchdays. Hot & Cold Food available from Shop   **Club Shop:** Yes

**HONOURS**    FA Amateur Cup Winners 00-01 53-54 58-59 61-62 63-64; Northern Lg 5, (R-up 4),
             Lg Cup 3, (R-up 4); Durham Challenge Cup 26-27 31-32 54-55 59-60;
             Durham Benevolent Bowl 5; Ernest Armstrong Mem Trophy 97.
**PREVIOUS**  **Leagues:** Auckland & Dist. 1894-96; Northern 1896-28 29-30; DurhamCentral 28-
29; North Eastern 30-36; Wartime Durham & Northumberland 40-41;Durham Cen. 41-45.
**BEST SEASON**    **FA Cup:** 3rd Rd, v Leicester 31-32. 2nd Rd(4), 1st Rd.(10)
                   **FA Trophy:** 3rd Rd 76-77   **FA Vase:** 2nd Rd 93-94, 95-96
                   **FA Amateur Cup:** Winners 5 times, plus S-F x 3
**RECORD Attendance:** 17,500 v Walton & Hersham, FA Amateur Cup Q-F, 24/02/52
             **Scorer:** Ronnie Thompson 118, 52-62   **Appearances:** Jimmy McMillan 505, 51-68
             **Win:** 12-0 v South Bank twice, (H) 5/4/58 & (A) 12/4/58, Northern Lge.
             **Defeat:** 0-11 v Bishop Auckland (A), Northern Lge 17/12/38

**FACT FILE**
Formed: 1889    Nickname: Black & Ambers
Sponsors: Savers
Colours: Amber/black/black
Change colours: All White
Midweek Matches: Wednesday
Reserves' League: Auckland & Dist
Programme: Yes
Editor: Secretary
98-99 Captain: Michael Vasey
Top Scorer: David Bellamy
P.o.Y.:Danny Key
Commercia Manager: John Phelan
**CLUB PERSONNEL**

Chairman: William Penman
Vice-Chairman:Stephen Buddle
President: Sir Tom Cowie O.R.E.
Press Officer: Secretary
Manager: Alan Shoulder
Physio: Alan Stokeld

# DUNSTON FEDERATION BREWERY

**Secretary:** Bill Montague, 12 Dundee Close, Chapel House, Newcastle-upon-Tyne NE5 1JJ
Tel: 0191 267 2250
**Ground:** Federation Park, Wellington Road, Dunston, Gateshead    Tel: 0191 493 2935
**Directions:** Dunston/Whickham exit off A1(M), ground 400 yds north along Dunston Rd on left.
¼ mile from Dunston or Metrocentre stations. Buses from Gateshead & Metrocentre stop outside ground
**Capacity:** 2,000    **Seats:** 120    **Cover:** 400    **Floodlights:** Yes
**Clubhouse:** Matchdays only. Hot & cold snacks, darts, pool    **Club Shop:** No

**HONOURS**    Northern Lg Div 2 92-93, Northern Amtr Lg 77-78 (R-up 2), Lg Cup 77-78 78-79 (R-up 75-76), Lg Shield 78-79 79-80), Wearside Lg 88-89 89-90 (R-up 90-91, Lg Cup 90-91), Northern Comb. 86-87 (R-up 3), Lg Cup 83-84 86-87 (R-up 3),Sunderland Shipowners Cup 87-88, Durham County Tphy 81-82 (R-up 2), Minor Cup79-80 (R-up 78-79)), Gateshead Charity Cup 77-78 80-81, Heddon Homes Cup 80-81.
**PREVIOUS**    **Ground:** Dunston public park 75-86
**Names:** Whickham Sports; Dunston Mechanics Sports
**BEST SEASON**    **FA Vase:** Quarter-Finals 92-93, 0-2 v Gresley Rov. (A)
**FA Cup:** 3rd Qual. Rd 92-93, 0-3 v Northallerton T.
**RECORDS**    **Attendance:** 1,550 - Sunderland Shipowners Cup Final 1/4/88
**Win:** 11-0 v Willington (A), Northern Lge Div. 2, 92-93    **Scorer:** Paul King
**Defeat:** 1-6 v Billingham Synthonia (A), Northern Lge Div. 1, 94-95 **Appearances:** Paul Dixon

**FACT FILE**
Founded: 1975
Nickname: The Fed
Sponsors: Federation Brewery
Colours: All blue (white trim)
Change colours :All red
Midweek matchday: Tuesday
Reserve s' League : None
Programme: 28 pages, 30p
Editor: Ian McPherson (0191 420 5583)

**CLUB PERSONNEL**
Chairman: Malcolm James
Vice-Chairman: Fred Fowles
President: John Smart
Press Officer: Ian McPherson (0191 420 5583)
Commercial Secretary: Malcolm James
Manager: Bobby Scaife
Asst Manager: Mike Hodgson
Physio: Wayne Farridge

# DURHAM CITY

**Secretary:** Bob Major, 11 Sherwood Close, Glebe Village, Washington Tyne & Wear NE38 7RJ
Tel: 0191 416 8679 (H) & FAX,  0191 477 1011 Ext 3105 (B)

**Ground:**    New Ferens Park, Belmont Durham (0191 386 9616)
**Directions**
**Capacity:**    **Seats:**    **Cover:** 300    **Floodlights: Yes**
**HONOURS**    Northern Lg 94-95 (R-up 70-71, Div 2 R-up 30-31 91-92), Durham Benevolent Bowl 55-56, Durham Challenge Cup R-up (2).Northern Div 2 Champions 98-99, Durham Challenge Cup R-up (3)
**PREVIOUS**    **Leagues:** Victory 18-19; N Eastern 19-21 28-38; Football Lge 21-28; Wearside 38-39 50-51.    **Grounds:** Garden House Park 18-21; Holliday Park 21-38; Ferens Park 49-94. NB club disbanded in 1938
**BEST SEASON**    **FA Cup:** 2nd Rd 25-26 57-58 (Also 1st Rd 27-28 55-56)
**FA Vase:** QF 87-88    **FA Amateur Cup:** 2nd Rd rep. 57-58
**FA Trophy:** 1st Rd 83-84
**RECORD**    **Appearances:** Joe Raine, 552
Players progressing: Harry Houlahan (Newcastle 51), Derek Clark (Lincoln 51),Leo Dale & David Adamson (Doncaster 54/70), Stan Johnstone (Gateshead 54),Dennis Coughlan (Barnsley 57), John Wile (Sunderland 66), Brian Taylor(Coventry 68), Paul Malcolm (Rochdale 84)

**FACT FILE**
Reformed: 1949
Nickname: City
Sponsors: Durham City Housing Partnership
Colours: All Navy
Change colours:Red & White Stripes,black
Midweek Matches: Tuesday
Programme: 30 pages
Editor: Mike Allen 0191 3886768
Local Press: Northern Echo,
Sunderland Echo, Evening Chronicle

**CLUB PERSONNEL**

Chairman: David Asberry
Vice Chairman: A Thompson
President: Stuart Dawson

Commercial Manager: D Willis
Press Officer: Secretary
Manager: Tony Harrison
Asst Manager/Coach: Kevin Todd
Physio: Joanne Dowson

# EASINGTON COLLIERY

**Secretary:** Alan Purvis, 12 Wark Crescent, Jarrow, Tyne & Wear, NE32 4SH (0191489 6930)

**Ground:** Easington Colliery Welfare Ground, CW Park, Easington, Co Durham. (0191527 3047)

**Directions:** A19 Easington turn-off, B1284 thru Easington till Black Diamond PH(next to zebra crossing), grd right
**Capacity:** 2,450    **Seats:** 175    **Cover:** 475    **Floodlights:** Yes
**Club Shop:** No
**Clubhouse:** Normal licensing hours. Pies, soup and sandwiches available

**HONOURS**    Northern Lg Div 2 R-up 85-86; Wearside Lge 29-30 31-32 32-33 47-48 48-49, R-up 28-29 46-47 73-74, Lg Cup 32-33 45-46 61-62; Monkwearmouth Cup 30-31 47-48 75-76; Sunderland Shipowners Cup 74-75 79-80.
**PREVIOUS**    **Leagues:** Wearside 13-37 39-64 73-88
**BEST SEASON**    **FA Cup:** 1st Round Proper 55-56
FA Trophy: 2nd Qual. Rd replay 88-89    **FA Vase:** 4th Rd replay 82-83
**RECORD**    **Attendance:** 4,500 v Tranmere Rovers, FA Cup 1st Round 1955
**Scorer:** Andrew McKenna    **Appearances:** David Howard
Players progressing: Ron Greener (Newcastle 1951), Frank Wayman (Darlington1957), John Langridge (Hartlepool 1982).

**FACT FILE**
Founded: 1913
Nickname: The Colliery
Sponsors: T.B.A.
Colours: Green & white stripes/green/green
Change colours: Yellow/green/yellow
Midweek Matches: Tuesday
Reserves' League : None
Programme: Yes    Editor: Charlie Dodds
98-99 Captain: Chris Pearson
P.O.Y.: David Moore
Top Scorer: Andrew McKenna

**CLUB PERSONNEL**

Chairman: Tommy Goodrum
Vice-Chairman: T.B.A.
Press Officer: Alan Purvis
Manager: Vin Pearson
Asst Mgr/Coach: John Cullen

Jarrow's Michael Haley challenges Dunston's 'keeper Steve Jones

Photo: Alan Watson

Durham City celebrate the Division Two Championship.                    Photo: John Lindsey

The Bedlington Terriers team before the FA Carlsberg Vase Semi-Final, home leg, against Thame United.
Photo: Neil Thaler

# GUISBOROUGH TOWN

**Secretary:** Keith Smeltzer, 55 Thames Ave., Guisborough, Cleveland TS14 8AR(01287 638993)

**Ground:** King George V Ground, Howlbeck Rd, Guisborough, Cleveland (01287636925)

**Directions:** From west: bear left at 2nd set of lights, left into Howlbeck Rd after quarter mile, ground at end. Buses from Middlesbrough

Capacity: 3,500       Seats: 150       Cover: 400       Floodlights: Yes       Club Shop: Yes

**Clubhouse:** Open evenings & weekends. Hot & cold snacks & drinks from kitchen on matchdays

**HONOURS**   FA Vase R-up 79-80; Northern Lg Cup 87-88 (Div 2 R-up 86-87),Northern Alliance
79-80 (R-up 78-79, Lg Cup 78-79); N. Riding Sen. Cup 89-90 90-91 91-9292-93 94-95.

**PREVIOUS**       **Leagues:** Middlesbrough & District; South Bank; Northern Alliance 77-80;
Midland Counties 80-82; Northern Counties (East) 82-85.

**BEST SEASON   FA Cup:** 1st Round Proper 88-89, 0-1 v Bury       **F.A.Vase:** Finalists 79-80
**FA Trophy:** 1st Rd Proper 90-91 91-92 92-93
**RECORD   Gate:** 3,112 v Hungerford, FA Vase SF, 1980
(at Middlesbrough FC - 5,990 v Bury, FA Cup 1st Rd 1988)
**Goalscorer:** Mark Davis 323       **Appearances:** Mark Davis 551
**Win:** 6-0 v Ferryhill & v Easington       **Defeat:** 0-4 v Billingham Synthonia

**1998-99**
**Captain:** Mickey Driscoll       **P.o.Y.:**Matthew Coddington   **Top Scorer:** Darren Mowbray

## FACT FILE
Founded: 1973    Nickname: Priorymen
Sponsors: K.Home Engineering
Colours: Red & white stripes/Black/Red
Change colours: Yellow
Midweek matchday:Tuesday
Reserves ' League: Teesside Strongarm
Programme: 32 pages,50p
Editor: M Hollinworth (01287 637737)
Local Press: Northern Echo,
Middlesbrough Evening Gazette

### CLUB PERSONNEL
Chairman:Trevor Arnold
Vce Chairman: Keith Watson
President: Vacant
Press Officer: K Smeltzer
Manager: Mark Forster
Asst Manager: Steve Corden
Physio: Steve Carter

---

# JARROW ROOFING BOLDON C.A.

**Secretary/Manager:** Richard McLoughlin, 8 Kitchener Terrace, Jarrow NE32 5PU
Tel: 0191 489 9825

**Ground:** Boldon CA Sports Ground, New Road, Boldon Colliery (0191 519 1391)

**Directions:** A19 to junction with A184 (Sunderland/Newcastle). Follow signs to Boldon Asda
stores, then to North Road Social Club. Ground behind. East Boldon(BR) 800 yds.
Capacity: 3,500       Seats: 150       Cover: 800       Floodlights: Yes       Club Shop: Yes
**Clubhouse:** Open eves.& w/e lunchtimes. Hotdogs, burgers etc from tea bar on matchdays

**HONOURS**       Wearside Lg Div 2 R-up 91-92 95-96; Sunderland Shipowners Cup R-up
93-94, 94-95; Tyneside Amtr Lg R-up 90-91, Chal. Shield 90-91 (R-up 89-
90); Bill Dixon Cup 90-91; Mid-Tyne Lg 87-88; Fred Giles Cup R-up 87-88;
Gateshead Charity Cup SF 90-91; Monkwearmouth Cup 94-95;
Craven Cup 96-97, Northern League Div One Cup R-Up 98-98

**PREVIOUS**       **Leagues:** Mid-Tyne; Tyneside Amtr 88-91; Vaux Wearside

**RECORD**       **Attendance:** 500 v South Shields
**Appearances:** Mick Haley   **Goalscorer:** Paul Thompson

## FACT FILE

Founded: 1987
Nickname: Roofing
Sponsors: Jarrow Roofing Co
Colours: All blue with red trim
Change colours: Yellow & Black
Midweek matchday: Wednesday
Programme: 20 pages, free with entry
Editor: Brian Marshall (0191 4217011)

### CLUB PERSONNEL

Chairman: Richard McLoughlin
Press Officer/Treasurer: Rose McLoughlin
Manager/ Secretary: Richard McLoughlin
Coach: John Oliver
Physio: Fred Corner/Alan Leslie

---

# MARSKE UNITED

**Secretary:** Ian Rowe, 19 High Row, Loftus, Saltburn By The Sea, Cleveland. TS134SA
Tel: 01287 643440 (H) 01642 230546 (B) 01642 241273 (Fax)

**Ground:** Mount Pleasant, Mount Pleasant Ave., Marske, Redcar, Cleveland. Tel: 01642 471091
**Directions:** From A19 take A174 exit marked Yarm, Teesport, Redcar, Whitby and head east
towards Saltburn until Quarry Lane r/about. Take 1st left (A1085) into Marske, 1st right (Meadow
Rd) then 1st left (Southfield Rd),then 1st left again Mount Pleasant Ave directly into car park.
By train: Darlington to Saltburn, Marske station 300 yds from ground.
Capacity: 2,500       Seats: 169       Cover: 300       Floodlights: Yes
**Clubhouse:** Open every night and weekend lunchtimes. Food served after all games
Club Shop: Yes, contact Pat Hodgson (01642 484006)
**HONOURS**       N Riding Sen Cup 94-95; N Riding County Cup 80-81 85-86; Teesside Lg
80-81 84-85; Wearside Lg 95-96, R-up 93-94 94-95 96-97, Cup 92-93 94-95
95-96;M/mouth Charity Cup 93-94 95-96; Sunderland Ship. Cup 95-96 96-97.

**PREVIOUS**       **Leagues:** Cleveland, South Bank & Dist, Teesside, Vaux Wearside.
**BEST SEASON   FA Cup:**                       **FA Vase:**
**RECORDS   Attendance:** 950 v Sunderland (friendly) 1983       **Win:** 16-0 v North Shields
**Defeat:** 3-9   **Goalscorer:** Chris Morgan 169   **Appearances:** John Hodgson 476
Players progressing: Peter Beagrie (Middlesbrough), Tony Butler (Blackpool),
Roy Hunter (Northampton), Dave Logan (Mansfield T.)

## FACT FILE
Founded: 1956   Nickname: The Seasiders
Sponsors: Arnott Insurance
Colours: Yellow/royalblue/white
Change: Royal/sky/yellow
Midweek matchday: Tuesday
Programme: 32 pages 50p
Editor: John Hodgson (01642 484006)
97-98 Leading scorer: Ben Thompson (22)
P.o.Y.: Graham Shaw
Local Press: Sunday Sun, Middlesbrough
Evening Gazette, Northern Echo

### CLUB PERSONNEL
Chairman: John Hodgson
Vice Chairman: John Corner
President: Raymond Jarvis
Comm.Manager: Chris Sharratt/Steve Davies
Manager: Charlie Bell
Asst Manager: Stephen Dowling
Physio: Barry Schollay
Coaches: Charlie Bell & Stephen Dowling

Action from the Good friday local derby between Jarrow Roofing and South Shields (white shirts)

Photo: Graham Brown

Darren Jackson of West Auckland (all white) being shadowed by Glyn Stockport of Shildon, during their league encounter in April this year.
Photo: Alan Watson

Neil Ollerton of Chorley (dark shorts) and Jamie Howard of Penrith both seem intent in getting to the ball first in this FA Cup 2nd Qual. Round match.
Photo: Alan Watson

# MORPETH TOWN

**Secretary:** Joe Hobin, 23 Princes Gardens, Malvins Close, Blyth, Northumberland.NE24 5HJ.
Tel: 01670 360820

**Ground:** Craik Park, Morpeth Common, Morpeth, Northumberland. (01670 513785)

**Directions:** Morpeth is signed off the A1 onto A197. Take the B6524, right at Mitford sign, then right after about a mile into the ground, next to Morpeth Common
**Capacity:** 1000    Seated: 150    Cover: 150    Floodlights Yes:    Club Shop: No
Clubhouse: Yes
**HONOURS**    Northern Alliance 83-84, 93-94 (R-up 37-38, 65-66, 73-74, 81-82, 84-85);
Challenge Cup Winners 38-39, 85-86, 93-94 (R-up 36-37, 62-63, 73-74).

**PREVIOUS**    **Leagues:** Northern Alliance pre 1994
**Ground:** Storey Park, Morpeth. pre 1992

**BEST SEASON**    **FA Cup:** 4th Q Rd v Burton Albion 1998-99    **FA Vase:**

**RECORDS**    **Attendance:**

### FACT FILE
Founded:
Colours: Yellow & black stripes/black/black
Change colours: Blue,white,blue
Midweek Matchday: Tuesday
Programme:
Editor: George Leggett (01670 512464)
### CLUB PERSONNEL
Chairman: Ken Beattie Tel.: 01670 515271
(H), 01670 520565 (B)
Press Officer: Secretary

---

# PETERLEE NEWTOWN

**Secretary:** Danny Cassidy, 23 Melbury Str, Seaham, Co. Durham SR7 7NF    0191 581 4591

**Ground:** Eden Lane, Peterlee, County Durham (0191 586 3004)

**Directions:** From town centre Fire Station, turn left into Edenhill Rd, thenright into Robson Ave. Left at the next junction and ground is on the right
Capacity: 6,000    Seats: 50    Cover: 200    Floodlights: Yes    Club Shop: No
**Clubhouse:** Open normal licensing hours. Sandwiches etc available

**HONOURS**    Northern Lg Div 2 82-83, North Eastern F'lit League, 4th Qual Rd FA Cup

**PREVIOUS**    **Leagues:** Northern Alliance 76-79; Wearside 79-82

**RECORD**    **Attendance:** 2,350 v Northern, Hillsborough Fund match 1989
**Scorer** : Keith Fairless    **Appearances** : Keith Bendelow

**BEST SEASON**    **FA Cup:** 4th Qual. Rd replay 85-86    **FA Vase:**

Players progressing: Keith Fairless (Scarborough) 1986, Brian Honour(Hartlepool) 1988)

### FACT FILE
Formed: 1976
Nickame: Newtowners
Sponsors: Artix Ltd
Colours: Sky/navy/sky
Change colours: Yellow/black/yellow
Midweek Matches: Wednesday
Programme: 10 pages, 30p
Editor: Secretary
Local Press: Hartlepool Mail,
Sunderland Echo, Northern Echo

### CLUB PERSONNEL
Chairman: Carl Paylor
Vice-Chairman: Bill Burnett
President: David Brown
Press Officer: Ray Matthews (0191 587 0727)
Manager: Tommy Smith
Asst Manager: Eddie Freeman
Physio: Ron Lamdrel

---

# SEAHAM RED STAR

**Secretary:** John McBeth, 29 Frederick Street, Seaham, Co. Durham SR7 7HX(0191 581 5712)

**Ground:** Seaham Town Park, Stockton Road, Seaham, Co. Durham (0191 581 2540)

**Directions:** From Tyne Tunnel: A19 Teeside approx 8 miles; B1404 Seaham slip road, left at top of slip road. Right at traffic lights & first left past school into ground
Capacity: 4,000    Seats: 60    Cover: 200    Floodlights: Yes    **Club Shop:** No
**Clubhouse:**    Mon-Sat 11am-11pm, Sun 12-2, 7-10.30pm  Bars & restaurant, snooke & pool

**HONOURS**    Northern Lg Cup 92-93, Phillips F'lit Tphy 78-79, Durham Chal. Cup 79-80,
Wearside Lg 81-82 (Lg Cup 81-82, Div 2 R-up 87-88, Monkwearmouth Charity
Cup R-up 79-80).
**PREVIOUS**    **Name:** Seaham Colliery Welfare Red Star 78-87
**Leagues:** Sunday f'tball; Houghton & Dist. 73-74; Northern Alliance74-79; Wearside 79-83.
**Grounds:** Deneside Recreation Recreation Park 73-75; Vane Tempest Welfare 75-78.
**BEST SEASON    FA Cup:        FA Vase:** 5th Rd 78-79    **FA Trophy** 2nd Rd 89-90
**RECORDS**    **Attendance:** 1,500 v Guisborough, Wearside Lg
v Sunderland, floodlight opener 1979
**Scorer:** Tom Henderson    **Appearances:** Michael Whitfield
Players progressing: Bobby Davison (Huddersfield 1980), Nigel Gleghorn (Ipswich1985), Billy Stubbs
(Nottm Forest 1987), Paul Nixon (Bristol Rovers (1989), Mick Smith (Hartlepool).

### FACT FILE
Formed: 1973
Nickname: The Star
Colours: All Red
Change colours: All blue
Midweek matchday: Wednesday
Reserves ' League: Banks Youth League
Programme: 20 pages
Editor: David Copeland (0191 581 8514)
Local Press : Sunderland Echo, Journal,
Northern Echo, Football Echo,
Washington Times

### CLUB PERSONNEL
Chairman: Reg Atkinson
President: Michael English
Press Officer: Secretary
Manager: Chris Copeland
Asst Manager: Paul Walker
Physio: Allan Jackson

# SHOTTON COMRADES

**Secretary:** Billy Banks, 30 Hamilton Court, Shotton Colliery, Durham DH6 2NL (0191 526 7134)

**Ground:** Shotton Rec. Ground, Station Road, Shotton Colliery, Co. Durham(0191 526 2859)
**Directions:** A19 to Peterlee to Shotton, right at the War Memorial t-junction, follow round 800yds, ground on right
Capacity: 1,700    Seats: 80        Cover: 400        Floodlights: No
Clubhouse: No                    Club Shop: No

**HONOURS** Houghton & District  Lg 78-79, Lg Cup x 2, Northern Alliance Lg Cup SF, Hetton Charity Cup 78-79, Peterlee Sunday Lg 75-76, Div 2 74-75; Northern Lg.Div 2 Cup R-Up. 94-95.

**PREVIOUS** **Leagues:** Peterlee Sunday 74-76; Houghton & Dist. 76-80; Northern Alliance 80-83.

**BEST SEASON** **FA Cup:** 2nd Qual. Rd 85-86, 0-2 v Wingate(H)
**FA Vase** 1st Rd 86-87 90-91

**RECORDS** **Attendance:** 1,726 v Dennis Waterman XI
**Win:** 8-0 v Bedlington Ter. (H), '92
**Defeat:** 1-7 v Brandon Utd (A), FA Cup Prel. Rd 91-92
**Goalscorer:** Keith Willets 50        **Appearances:** J Cudlip
**Transfer Fee received**: £500 for G Gudlip (Shildon)

**FACT FILE**
Formed: 1973
Nickname: Coms
Colours: Black & white stripes/black/black
Change colours: All orange
Midweek matches: Wednesday
Reserves' Lge: Banks u-19 Yth
Programme: 12 pages, 20p
Editor: E A Jones

**CLUB PERSONNEL**
Chairman: John Maddison
Vice Chairman: T Robinson
President: G Taylor
Commercial Manager: T Robinson
Press Officer: Secretary
Manager: B Huntingdon
Physio: W Banks

---

# SOUTH SHIELDS F.C.

**Secretary/Press Officer:** David Fall, 50 Basil Way, South Shields NE34 8UD
Tel: 0191 426 2135

**Ground:** Mariners Club, Filtrona Park, Shaftesbury Avenue, Jarrow, Tyne & Wear NE34 9PH.
Tel: 0191 427 9839

**Directions:** From A1(M) take A194(M) to South Shields, A194 town centre road for 5 miles, ignore A1300 (Sunderland & coast) & turn left at next lights beside Co-op store into Simonside Ind. Est. (Shaftesbury Ave.), grd at bottom
Capacity: 2,500    Seats: 150        Cover: 400        Floodlights: Yes
**Clubhouse:** Two function suites, club kitchen        **Club Shop:** Yes

**HONOURS** Northern Lge Div 2 R-up 95-96, Northern Alliance 74-75 75-76, Wearside Lg 76-77 92-93 94-95, Monkwearmouth Charity Cup 86-87 (R-up 94-95), Shipowners Cup 92-93 (R-up 83-84)), Durham Chal. Cup 76-77 R-up 94-95.

**PREVIOUS** **Leagues:** Northern Alliance 74-76
**Ground:** Jack Clarke Park 74-92

**BEST SEASON** **FA Cup:**        **FA Vase** QF 75-76

**RECORD** **Attendance:** 1,500 v Spennymoor, Durham Challenge Cup Final 94-95

**FACT FILE**
Founded: 1974
Nickname: Mariners
Colours: Claret & blue/white/white
Change: All white
Midweek matchday: Tuesday
Reserve team: None
Programme:50p
Editor: Steve Leonard
Local Press: Shields Gazette, Newcastle Journal, Chronicle

**CLUB PERSONNEL**
Chairman: John Rundle
Vice Chairman: George Scott
President:
Manager: David Clark
Asst Manager:Paul Brown
Physio: Jim Wilkinson

---

# THORNABY-ON-TEES (ex Stockton)

**Secretary:** Peter Morris, 20 Wheatear Lane, Ingleby Barwick, Stockton-on-Tees,Cleveland TS17 0TB (01642 760779)

**Ground:** Teesdale Park, Acklam Road, Thornaby, Stockton-on-Tees TS17 8TZ (01642 606803)

**Directions:** A19 to Thornaby turn off, ground half mile on right. One mile fromThornaby BR station. Any Stockton-Middlesbrough bus - stop at Acklam Rd,Thornaby
Capacity: 5,000    Seats: 150        Cover: 350        Floodlights: Yes
**Clubhouse:** 150+ seater social club with concert room, pool/games room and bar. Open every night and Sunday lunchtimes and all day Saturday. Sandwiches avai. in bar, canteen in ground sells pies, burgers, soup, drinks etc

**HONOURS** Northern Lg Div 2 87-88 91-92, Nth Riding Co. Cup 85-86, Inaguralwinners of Craven Cup (Northern Div 2 clubs) 94-95.

**PREVIOUS** **Leagues:** Stockton & District 80-81; Wearside 81-85.
**Names:** Stockton Cricket Club 65-80; Stockton 80-99
**Grounds:** Grangefield Youth & Community Centre, Stockton 80-82; Tilery Sports Centre 82-83.

**BEST SEASON** **FA Vase:** 2nd Rd        **FA Trophy:** 1st Rd
**FA Cup:** 4th Qual. Rd replay 92-93,1-2 v Blyth (H) after 1-1

**RECORD** **Attendance:** 3,000 v Middlesbrough, pre-season friendly August 1986
**Appearances:** Michael Watson    **Win:** 11-0 v Horden C.W.(H) Buchanan Cup 94-95

**FACT FILE**
Club Shop: No
Formed: 1980
Colours: Red & black stripes/black/red
Change colours: All sky
Midweek Matches: Wednesday
Reserves' Lge: Wearside & Teesside Lgs
Programme: 24 pages, 50p
Editor: Peter Morris (01642 585625)
Local Press : Northern Echo, Evening Gazette

**CLUB PERSONNEL**
Chairman: Lol Lyons
Press Officer: Peter Morris
Manager: Michael Watson
Asst Mgr: Peter May
Coach: Paul Sharkey

# TOW LAW TOWN

**Secretary:** Bernard Fairbairn, 3 Coppice Walk, Mowden Park, Darlington, Co. Durham DL3 9DP
Tel: 01325 350743

**Ground:** Ironworks Road, Tow Law, Bishop Auckland Tel: 01388 731443

**Directions:** Just of High Street in Tow Law town centre
Capacity: 6,000    Seats: 200    Cover: 300    Floodlights: Yes
**Clubhouse:** Every evening 8.30 -10.30    **Club Shop:** Yes

**HONOURS** **FA Vase R-up 97-98;** Rothmans National Cup 1977,
Northern League Champions 23-24 24-25 94-95, R-up 28-29 88-89, Lg Cup 73-74;
Rothmans Overseas Cup 76-77, Durham Chal. Cup 1895-96, Durham Amtr Cup 1892-93.

**PREVIOUS** **Leagues:** None
**BEST SEASON** **FA Cup:** 2nd Rd rep. 67-68, 2-6 v Shrewsbury T. (A) after 1-1. Also 1st Rd
68-69 84-85 89-90.    League Clubs defeated:Mansfield Town 67-68
**FA Amateur Cup:** 3rd Rd rep. 70-71    **FA Trophy:** 2nd Rd rep. 82-83
FA Vase: Runners-up 1997-98
**RECORD** **Gate:** 5,500 v Mansfield Town, FA Cup 1967

Players progressing: Reuben Cook & Ralph Guthrie (Arsenal 1951 & 53), Gordon Hughes, Terry Melling
& Chris Waddle (Newcastle 1956 & 65 & 80), EricJohnstone & Kevin Dixon (Carlisle 1963 & 83), Keith
Adamson (Barnsley 1966),Tom Henderson (Bradford PA 1969), Vincent Chapman (Huddersfield 1988)

**FACT FILE**
Founded: 1890
Nickname: Lawyers
Colours:
Black & white stripes/black/black & white
Change colours: Red & white
Midweek Matches: Tuesday
Programme: Yes
Editor:Chairman
Local Press : Northern Echo

**CLUB PERSONNEL**
Chairman: John Flynn
Press Officer: John Flynn (01388 730525)
Manager: Peter Quigley
Assistant Manager: Tony Heslop

# WEST AUCKLAND TOWN

**Secretary:** Allen Bayles, 11 Edith Terrace, West Auckland, Co.Durham.DL14 9JT
Tel: 01388 833783 (H)  & FAX,  01388 605221 (B) 01388 661366

**Ground:** Darlington Road, West Auckland, Co.Durham Tel: 01388 834403

**Directions:** Leaving West Auckland take A68-ground on right before leavingvillage. Bus route
via Bishop Auckland fron Newcastle or Darlington
Capacity: 3,000    Seats: 250    Cover: 250    Floodlights: Yes    **Club Shop:** No
**Clubhouse:** On Gound. ( The Thomas Lipton Trophy  is on display  at the local Working Mans
Club five minutes away). Tel No: 01388 661366

**HONOURS** FA Amateur Cup Finalists 60-61; Northern League Champions 59-60, 60-61
Div 2 90-91,Lg Cup 59-60,62-639r-UP;48-49,61-62,63-64)
Durham Challenge Cup 63-64 Durham Benevolent Bowl 62-63; Sir Thomas
Lipton Tphy`First World Cup'(as featured in `The Captains Tale') 1909, 1911.
**PREVIOUS** League: Auckland & District
Names: St Helens Utd (1919 only), West Auckland Town.
**BEST SEASON** **FA Cup:** 1st Rd 58-59, 61-62,98-99    **FA Trophy:** 3rd Rd. 77-78
**FA Vase:**    **FA Amateur Cup:** Runners-up 60-61; Q-F 59-60
**RECORD** **Gate:** 6,000 v Dulwich Hamlet, FA Amateur Cup 58-59
**Victory:** 11-0 in Durham County Cup

**FACT FILE**

Founded: 1892
Nickname: West
Sponsors:Rushlift Mechanical Handling and
F.Hudson Transport
Colours: All white
Change Colours: All Yellow
Midweek Matches: Tuesday

**CLUB PERSONNEL**

Chairman: Jim Polfreyman
Press Officer: Secretary
Manager: Dr. Graeme Forster
Ass.Manager: Dale Swainston
Coach: Paul Adamson

TOP: Damien Maw, Chester-le-Street (hoops) and Scott Oliver, Crook Town, chasing the ball during their early season league encounter.

LEFT: Esh Winning's Paul Charlton closes in on Brandon United's Daryl Smith.

BOTTOM: Jason Photopolous (Norton & Stockton Ancients) manages to get the ball away despite the attention of Graham Dawson of Willington (stripes).

All photos:

Alan Watson

# ALNWICK TOWN

Secretary:Darren Middleton, 1 Fire Station Houses, Alnwick, NE66 2PB
Ground: St James' Park, Alnwick, Northumberland Tel: 01665 603162
Directions: 35 miles north of Newcastle on A1, take the slip road to Alnwick,then first left. At roundabout turn left, ground is then on your left.
Capacity: 2,500    Seats: 100        Cover: 200        Floodlights: Yes
HONOURS    Northern Lg Div 2 R-up 88-89, Northern Alliance 37-38 62-63 63-64 65-66 67-68 68-69 69-70 70-71 71-72 (R-up 59-60 61-62 66-67 72-73, Lg Cup 61-62 65-6667-68 68-69 70-71, Subsidiary Cup 80-81), Durham Central Lg Cup 64-65, Northumberland Benevolent Bowl 86-87, Northumberland SNR Cup R-up 61-62,Northumberland Amtr Cup 71-72.
PREVIOUS        League: Northern Alliance 35-39 46-64 64-82
                Names: Alnwick United Services; Alnwick United.
BEST SEASON    FA Cup: 3rd Qual. Rd 51-52 (3-4 at Blyth), 57-58 (4-6 at Easington Coll.).
               FA Trophy: 3rd Qual. Rd 90-91.
RECORD         Attendance: 600 v Bedlington Terriers, Northern Alliance 1971.

## FACT FILE
Founded: 1879
Colours: Black & white stripes/black/black
Change colours: Green and yellow
Midweek Matches: Tuesday

Local Press: Northumberland Gazette

## CLUB PERSONNEL
Chairman: Robert Miller
Manager: Malcolm Beusle

---

# ASHINGTON

Secretary: Brian Robinson, 80 Milburn Road, Ashington, N/thumberland NE63 0PG
Tel: 01670 852832 (H) 01670 521212 (B) FAX: 01670 852832
Ground: Portland Park, Ashington NE63 9XG (01670 811991 Social Club)
Directions: 200 yds north at traffic lights in centre of town
Capacity: 2,000    Seats: 350        Cover: 2,200        Floodlights: Yes
Clubhouse: Open 6-11 evening & from11am on Tuesdays(market days) Not open Weds and Sun, darts, jukebox, snacks etc. Club Shop No but jumpers, baseball caps etc. behind bar
HONOURS    Northumberland Snr Cup (9) , Northumberland Chall. Bowl (6) , Midland Lg 58-59, North Eastern Lg Cup 33-34(jt with Sunderland Res.) 39-40; Northern Alliance x 4, R-up x 6; Lg Cup 47-48, Craven Cu p Winners 98-99
PREVIOUS        Leagues: Northern Alliance 1892-93 1902-14 69-70; Football League; North Eastern 14-21 29-58 62-64; Midland 58-60; Northern Counties 60-62;Wearside 64-65; N.P.L. 68-69.
BEST SEASON    FA Cup: 3rd Rd 26-27    FA Amateur Cup SF 73-74
RECORD         Attendance: 13,199 v Rochdale, FA Cup 2nd Rd 9/12/50

## FACT FILE
Formed: 1883    Nickname: The Colliers
Sponsors: Liteon
Club colours: Black & white stripes/black/white
Change colours: Blue/white
Midweek Matches: Tuesday
Programme: Yes, 50p
Editor: A Marchett (01670 854585)

## CLUB PERSONNEL
Chairman: T Reed
Jt Presidents: Sir Bobby Charlton & Jackie Charlton OBE
Press Officer: Brian Bennett (01670 856606)
Manager: John Connelly
Asst.Manager: Iain Scott
Physio: Bob Robinson

---

# BRANDON UNITED

Secretary: Brian Richardson, Flat 2, 30 Commercial St, Brandon, Durham DH7 8PL 0191 378 1373
Ground: Welfare Ground, rear of Commercial Street, Brandon, Durham (0191 3782957)
Directions: A690 - 3 miles west of Durham City. Buses 49 & 49A from Durham
Capacity: 3,000    Seats: 200        Cover: 300        Floodlights: Yes    Club Shop: No
&Clubhouse: Open every day, lunch & evening. Pool  Entertainment at weekends
HONOURS        FA Sunday Cup 75-76, Northern Lg Div 2 84-85  Northern All.(2) 77-79, Lg Cup 77-78 79-80  Sunderland Shipowners Cup 81-82, Durham Co. Sunday Cup 73-74 75-76 76-77,Durham & Dist Sunday Lg(4) 73-77 (Div 2 69-70, Div 3 68-69), Staffieri Cup 75-76.
PREVIOUS        Leagues: Durham & Dist. Sunday 68-77; Northern All. 77-80; Northern Amtr 80-81; Wearside 81-83.
BEST SEASON    FA Cup: 1st Rd replay 88-89 (lost to Doncaster). Also 1st Rd 79-80
               FA Vase: QF 82-83 83-84    FA Trophy: 3rd Qual. Rd 87-88 89-90
RECORD         Gate: 2,500, FA Sunday Cup SF Record Goalscorer: Tommy Holden
Most Appearances: Derek Charlton 1977-86 1998-99 Captain: Andrew Cunningham

## FACT FILE
Founded: 1968    Nickname: United
Sponsors: Bramble Down Landscapes
Colours: All red    Change colours: All blue
Midweek Matches: Wednesday
Programme: 40 pages, 30p
Editor: Keith Nellis (0191 378 0704)

## CLUB PERSONNEL
Chairman: Neil Scott
Vice Chairman: John Dickenson
President: Brian Hewitt
Press Officer: Secretary
Manager: Ken Lindoe
Asst Mgr: Roli Bell
Physio: Bev Dougherty

---

# EPPPLETON COLLIERY WELFARE

Secretary: John Gibson, Avondene, Houghton Road, Hetton-le-Hole, Tyne & Wear DH5 9PH
Tel: 0191 526 3782 & FAX
Ground: Eppleton Welfare Park, Park View, Hetton-le-Hole, Tyne & Wear (01915261048)
Directions: Situated behind Front Street Post Office & directly behind Hetton swimming baths, Hetton-le-Hole on A182. Buses 194, 535, 231, X5, X94 in Front Street. 8 miles from Durham BR station; buses 154 and 254 from Durham
Capacity: 2,500    Seats: 250        Cover: 500        Floodlights: Yes
Clubhouse: Bar & lounge on ground. Normal opening hours. Whitbread beers
Club Shop: Club sweaters, polo shirts, metal lapel badges available
HONOURS    Northern Lg Div 2 R-up 92-93, Wearside Lg 90-91 91-92 (Lg Cup 74-75 78-79 87-88, Sunderland Shipowners Cup 47-48 85-86 90-91 (R-up 91-92), Monkwearmouth Charity Cup 90-91 91-92), Durham Challenge Cup 89-90.
PREVIOUS    Leagues: Wearside 51-65 74-92; Houghton & District 65-74.
BEST SEASON    FA Cup:                FA Vase:
RECORD         Attendance: 1,250 - Monkwearmouth Charity Cup Final 1987-88

## FACT FILE
Founded: 1929    Nickname: Welfare
Club Sponsors: E & N Ritchie
Colours: Black & sky/black/black
Change colours : Yellow/green/green
Midweek matchday: Wednesday
Programme: 16 pages, 20p Editor:

## CLUB PERSONNEL
Chairman: Ralph Lawson
President: J.Storey
Commercial Mgr: Secretary
Press Officer: Secretary
Manager: Alan Hurst
Asst Manager: Derek Waters

# ESH WINNING

**Secretary:** Alan Morton, 20 Durham Road, Esh Winning, Durham Tel: 0191 373 3611
**Ground:** West Terrace, Waterhouses, Durham Tel: 0191 373 3872
**Directions:** Durham to Ushaw Moor, to Esh Winning; ground 1 mile further at Waterhouses
**Capacity:** 3,500    **Seats:** 160    **Cover:** 160    **Floodlights:** Yes
**Clubhouse:** Open daily. Snacks served                **Club Shop:** No

**HONOURS**        Durham & Dist. Sunday Lg 78-79 79-80, Durham Co. Sun. Cup R-up 78-79,Staffieri Cup 74-75, Guards Cup 72-73, N. Durham Yth Lg 94-95, Auckland Yth Lge94-95.
**PREVIOUS**        **Leagues:** Durham & Dist Sunday; Northern Alliance 81-82.
                **Grounds:** None      **Names:** Esh Winning Pineapple (pre-1982)
**BEST SEASON**     **FA Cup:** 2nd Qual Rd 90-91          **FA Vase:** 2nd Round 83-84
**RECORDS**      **Gate:** 900 v Liverpool Fantail, FA Sunday Cup 1982
          **Goalscorer:** Paul Ward 31      **Appearances:** Paul Hewitson 40
          **Win:** 9-0 v Langley Park (H)      **Defeat:** 0-10 v Shotton Comrades
          **Fee Paid:** Nil  **Fee Received:** £500 for Paul Ward (Brandon Un ited)

**FACT FILE**
Formed: 1967
Nickname: `Esh'
Sponsors: Renault Trucks (North East)
Colours: Yellow/green/yellow & green
Change colours: Purple & Black
Midweek Matches: Tuesday
Programme: 20 pages, 50p
Editor/Press Officer: As Secretary

**CLUB PERSONNEL**
Chairman: Charles Ryan
Vice Chairman: R.Hird
President: Jack Lumsden
Manager: Roli Bell
Physio: Lee Sullivan

# EVENWOOD TOWN

**Secretary:** Jim Coates, 19 Wellgarth, Evenwood, Bishop Auckland, Co Durham DL149QU
        Tel: 01388 833035
**Ground:** Welfare Ground, Stones End, Evenwood, County Durham Tel: 01388 832281
**Directions:** In village centre by Sports & Social club in Stones Rd
**Capacity:** 3,500    **Seats:** 32 **Cover:** 200    **Floodlights:** Yes
**Clubhouse:** Open lunch & evening every day

**HONOURS**    Northern Lg 48-49 69-70 70-71 (Lg Cup 35-36), Durham Challenge Cup 69-70.
**PREVIOUS**    **Leagues:** Barnard Castle & Dist. 1894-95; Auckland & Dist. 1894-96 1903-04
        08-23 28-31; Wear Valley 1896-99 1904-06 24-25; Gauntlett Valley 06-07;
        South Durham 27-28.        **Names:** None
**BEST SEASON**    **FA Cup:** 1st Rd 1936        **FA Vase:**
**RECORD**        **Gate:** 9,000 v Bishop Auckland, FA Amtr Cup 1931
Players progressing: Too numerous to record

**FACT FILE**

Founded: 1890
Nickname: The Wood
Sponsors: C A Roofing
Club colours: All blue
Change: Red & white sleeves/white/red
Midweek Matches: Wednesday
Programme: None

**CLUB PERSONNEL**

Chairman: Matt Robinson
President: N Colegrove
Press Officer: G Forster (0191 373 5143)
Manager: Dr Graeme Forster

# HEBBURN

**Secretary:** Tom Derrick, 63 Staneway, Felling, Gateshead, NE10 8LS.Tel: 0191 442 1563
**Ground:** Hebburn Sports & Social Ground, Victoria Road West, Hebburn Tel: 0191 483 5101
**Directions:** On the main road through the town about 1 mile from railway station. Hebburn lies on the Metroline - excellent bus service from Heworth Metro
**Capacity:** 2,000    **Seats:** 153    **Cover:** 420    **Floodlights:** Yes    **Club Shop:** No
**Clubhouse:** Open 7-11pm weekdays, Sat 11am-1pm, Sun noon-2.30pm. Pool, darts etc
**HONOURS Leagues-** Tyneside 38-39, Northern Comb. 43-44, Wearside 66-67; **Cups-**Durham Challenge 42-43 91-92, Monkwearmouth Charity 68-69, Shields Gazette 91-92, Palmer Hospital, Hebburn Aged Miners, Gateshead Charity, Hebburn Infirmary x4, Heddon Homes,
**PREVIOUS Leagues:** Jarrow & Dist. Jnr 12-14; South Shields Comb. 19-22; Tyneside Comb. 22-27; Tyneside 27-39; Northern Comb. 41-44 45-59; North Eastern 44-45 59-60; Wearside 60-89.
        **Names:** Reyrolles; Hebburn Reyrolles (pre-1988)**Grounds:** None
**BEST SEASON FA Vase:** 2nd Rd 91-92 **FA Cup:** 2nd Qual. Rd rep. 89-90, 0-3 v South Bank (A)
**RECORD**        **Attendance:** 503 v Darwen, FA Cup Prel. Rd replay 7/9/91

**FACT FILE**
Founded: 1912
Nickname: Hornets
Colours: Yellow & black trim/royal/yellow
Change colours:Blue and White stripes/black
Midweek Matches: Wednesday
Programme: 24 pages, 30p
Editor: Steve Newton

**CLUB PERSONNEL**
Chairman: Bill Laffey
Vice-Chairman:Brian Errington
Press Officer: Alan Armstrong 0191 430 0078
Manager: Tony Robinson
Assistant Manager:Brian Hill

# HORDEN COLLIERY WELFARE

**Secretary:** Robert Wood, 29 Morpeth St., Horden, Peterlee, County Durham SR84BE
        Tel: 0191 586 8802
**Ground:** Welfare Park Ground, Park Road, Horden, Peterlee, Co. Durham  Tel: 0191 518 2692
**Directions:** A19 to Peterlee, signposted from there                (Club)
**Capacity:** 3,000    **Seats:** 220    **Cover:** 370    **Floodlights:** Yes
**Clubhouse:** Normal licensing hours. Hot & cold snacks, darts, pool

**HONOURS**Durham Challenge Cup 35-36 63-64 80-81 81-82, Durham Benevolent Cup 33-34, Wearside Lg 11-12 12-13 13-14 33-34 64-65 67-68 69-70 70-71 71-72 72-73 (Lg Cup 33-34 49-50, Monkwearmouth Charity Cup 12-13 23-24 32-33 69-70 72-73,Sunderland Shipowners Cup 65-66 72-73), North Eastern Lg 37-38 63-64 (`Non-Reserve' Medal 50-51).
**PREVIOUS**      **Leagues:** Wearside  07-35 63-75; N. Eastern 35-58 62-64; Midland (Co's)58-60; Northern Co's 60-62.    **Names:** Horden Athletic
**BEST SEASON FA Cup:** 2nd Rd 38-39, 2-3 v Newport Co. (H)
**RECORD Attendance:** 8,000 - FA Cup 1937    Player progressing: Paul Dobson (Hartlepool Utd)

**FACT FILE**

Reformed : 1980
Nickname: Colliers
Colours: Red/black/red
Change colours:Sky,navy,navy
Midweek Matches: Tuesday
Programme: 10 pages, 50p

**CLUB PERSONNEL**

Chairman:John McCoy
Press Officer:M.Burgon ( 041 089 064417)

# KENNEK RYHOPE C.A.

**Secretary:** Rob Jones,17Aspatria Avenue, Blackhall, Hartlepool TS27 4EG
Tel No: 0191 5870949
**Ground:** Meadow Park, Stockton Road, Ryhope, Sunderland (0191 523 6555)
**Directions:** From Sunderland follow signs for A19 South, ground adj to Cherry Knowle Hopital
in Ryhope
    Capacity: 2,000   Seats: 150    Cover: 200    Floodlights: Yes

**HONOURS**  Wearside Lg 61-62 62-63 63-64 65-66(Lg Cup 63-64 77-78),
      Durham Chal.Cup 77-78, Monkwearmouth Charity Cup 09-10 65-66 66-67,
      Sunderland Shipowners Cup 61-62 (S.C.Vaux) 86-87
**PREVIOUS Names:** Ryhope C.W. (est.1898, prev.Ryhope Villa) merged with Sporting Club
Vaux (est.1968 as Monkwearmouth, later Bishopwearmouth, South Hetton) in 1988;
Sunderland Vaux Ryhope C.W. 88-93.  **Leagues:** S. C. Vaux: Tyne & Wear; N.Eastern Amat.
**BEST SEASON**   **FA Cup** 1st Rd Proper 67-68     **FA Vase** 1st Rd 81-82
**RECORD**      Gate: 2,000; Ryhope Colliery Welfare v Workington, FA Cup 1967

**FACT FILE**

Founded: 1988
Colours: Red & white/black/red Change
colours: All Blue

**CLUB PERSONNEL**

Chairman: W.Mathieson
Tel: 0191 534 5496 (H)
Press Officer: Secretary

# MURTON

**Secretary:** Tom Turnbull, 15 Dalton Terrace, Murton, Seaham, Co Durham SR7 9BZ
          Tel: 0191 526 6488 (H) 0191 581 9874 (B)
**Ground:** Recreation Park, Church Lane, Murton, Co. Durham (0191 517 0814)  **Directions:**
Exit A19 onto B1285 heading west into Murton - Church Lane on left opposite catholic church
Capacity: 3,500   Seats: 100    Cover: 320    Floodlights: Yes  Club Shop: No
**Clubhouse:** `The International' 300 yards from ground on B1285. Normal pub hours.
Restaurant upstairs. Matchday snacks at ground
**HONOURS**     Northern Lg Div 2 89-90, Wearside Lg 28-29 36-37 59-60 (Lg Cup 58-59
70-71), Sunderland Shipowners Cup 59-60 69-70 70-71, Monkwearmouth Charity Cup 21-22
28-29 34-35 35-36 63-64 70-71 87-88, Durham Chall. Cup 92-93, Durham Jnr Cup 50-51.
**PREVIOUS**   **Leagues:** Wearside 13-46 51-88; North East Counties 46-51.
**BEST SEASON**   FA Cup:        FA Vase:
**RECORD**      Gate: 3,500 v Spennymoor Utd, Durham Challenge Cup 1951
         **Appearances:** Robert Welch 500 (1962-78)

**FACT FILE**
Founded: 1904     Nickname: Gnashers
Club Sponsors: John Hellyns
Colours: All white with red trim
Change colours: Red/black/red
Midweek matchday: Wednesday
Programme: 12 pages, 30p
Programme Editor: Stuart Upperton
**CLUB PERSONNEL**
Chairman: Tom Torrence
Vice Chairman: J Hudson
President: John Hellens
Press Officer: Secretary
Commercial Mgr: T Carr
Manager: Jeff Cranson
Asst Mgr: Brian Burlinson
Coach: Richie Madden Physio: Vince Symmonds

# NEWCASTLE BLUE STAR

**Secretary:** Jim Anderson, 7 Whitbeck Rd, Statyford, Newcastle-on-Tyne NE5 2XA (0191 243 1025)
**Ground:** Wheatsheaf Sports Ground, Woolsington, Newcastle-on-Tyne. NE13 8DF (0191 286 0425)
**Directions:** From central station follow airport signs for 7 miles - ground next to Wheatsheaf Hotel
on left, approx. 800yds before airport. Callerton Parkway metro station is 400yds from ground
Capacity: 2,000   Seats: 300    Cover: 500    Floodlights: Yes  **Club Shop:** Yes
**Clubhouse:** Matchdays only. Hotdogs, soup, sandwiches available
**HONOURS**     FA Vase 77-78; Northern Lg R-up 87-88, Lg Cup 85-86, R-up(1), Div 2 85-86;
Wearside Lg 73-74 75-76 82-83 83-84 84-85, R-up 74-75 77-78 79-80, Lg Cup76-77 79-80 80-
81 82-83 83-84; Sunderland Shipowners Cup 82-83 84-85; Monkwearmouth Charity Cup 74-75
79-80 82-83 88-89; Northern Comb. 62-63 68-69,Lg Cup 66-67 71-72; Northumberland Snr Cup
76-77 82-83 85-86 87-88, R-up 74-75 78-79 80-81, Minor Cup 64-65; J R Cleator Cup 86-87.
**PREVIOUS Leagues:** Newcastle Business Houses 32-38; North East Amateur; Tyneside
Amateur; Northern Comb.; Wearside 75-85  **BEST SEASON FA Trophy:** Qtr-finals 88-89, 1-4
v Telford Utd (H) **FA Vase:** Winners 77-78, SF 81-82 **FA Cup:** 1st Rd 84-85, 0-2 v York C. (A)
**RECORD**      Attendance: 1,800 v Almondsbury Greenway, FA Vase SF 77-78

**FACT FILE**
Founded: 1930     Nickname: `Star'
Sponsors: RTM
Colours: Blue/white/blue
Change colours: Black & White stripes
Midweek matchday: Monday
Reserve s' League: None
Programme: 28 pages,50p Editor: M.Galt

**CLUB PERSONNEL**
Chairman: Tom Brash
Vice-Chairman:
Press Officer: Secretary
Manager/Coach: S.Leeming
Assistant Manager: P.Johnson
Physio: T.B.A.

# NORTHALLERTON TOWN

**Secretary:** Ken Lomer, 28 Aysgarth Grove, Romanby, Northallerton, North Yorks DL7 8HY Tel
No: 01609 7786869 (H) 01609 773970 (W)
**Ground:** Ainderby Rd, Romanby, Northallerton, North Yorks Tel: 01609 772418
**Directions:** Leave A1 at Leeming Bar (A684) follow signs to Northallerton,approaching town
take B1333 signed Romanby - ground 250yds on left. 3/4 a mile from Northallerton BR station -
local bus from town centre(1 1/2 miles) passes ground
Capacity: 3,000   Seats: 150    Cover: 500    Floodlights: Yes
**Clubhouse:** Mon-Fri 7.30-11pm, Sat noon-7.30pm, Sun 12-2 & 7.30-10.30pm
Club Shop: Yes, Contact Nigel Taylor 01748 836017
**HONOURS**     Northern Lg Cup 93-94 (Div 2 R-up 89-90), Harrogate & Dist. Lg,N.Riding
Snr Cup R-up 83-84, Northern Lg.Div 2 champions 96-97 Harrogate Invit; Alverton Tpy.
**PREVIOUS**   **Leagues:** Allertonshire; Vale of Mowbray; Ripon& Dist.; Teesside; North
Yorks; Darlington & Dist.; Harrogate & Dist.
**BEST SEASON**   FA Cup: 4th Qual. Rd 92-93 FA Trophy: 3rd Rnd 92-93   FA Vase:
**RECORD**      Gate: 671 v Farnborough, FA Tphy 3rd Rd 20/2/93

**FACT FILE**
Founded: 1994     Nickname: Town
Colours: Black & White stripes,white
Change colours: Yellow/blue/yellow
Midweek matchday: Wednesday
Reserves ' League: Harrogate& District
Programme: 16 pages, 50p
Programme Editor: Ian Bolland

**CLUB PERSONNEL**
Chairman: T.B.A.
Vice Chairman: RalphAlderson
President: Ian Butler
Press Officer: Ian Bolland(01609 776900)
Manager: Peter Mulcaster
Physio: Miss Sandy Ainsley

# NORTON & STOCKTON ANCIENTS

**Secretary:** Andrew Boynton, 37 Wollaton Road, Billingham, TS23 3AU (01642862039)

**Ground:** Station Road, Norton, Stockton-on-Tees, Cleveland (01642 530203)

**Directions:** Norton village 2 miles from Stockton centre, turn into Station Road on outskirts of village

**Capacity:** 2,000    **Seats:** 200    **Cover:** Yes    **Floodlights:** Yes

**Clubhouse:** Full bar facilities, 150 yds from ground

**HONOURS**    Northern Lg Cup 81-82

**PREVIOUS**    **Leagues:** Teesside (pre-1982)

**Name:** Norton & Stockton Cricket Club Trust

**BEST SEASON**    **FA Cup:** 1st Qual Rd(4) 88-89 90-93    **FA Vase:**

**RECORD**    **Attendance:** 1,430 v Middlesbrough, Friendly 88

### FACT FILE

Formed: 1959
Nickname: Ancients
Colours: Amber, white & black/black & amber/black
Change colours: White with amber trim
Midweek Matches: Wednesday
Programme: 12 pages with entry
Editor:

### CLUB PERSONNEL

Chairman: Steve Warnes
President: Barry Lee
Press Officer: Secretary

# PENRITH

**Secretary:** John Balmer, 58 Castle Hill Road, Penrith, Cumbria    Tel: 01768 866736

**Ground:** Southend Road Ground, Penrith, Cumbria    Tel: 01768 863212

**Directions:** M6 Jct 40, onto dual carriageway to Appleby & Scotch Corner, first left at next r'bout, approx 1/2 mile into Penrith on A6 into town, take 1st left for ground. 3/4 mile from Penrith (BR)

**Seats:** 200    **Cover:** 1,000    **Capacity:** 4,000    **Floodlights:** Yes    **Club Shop:** No

**Clubhouse:** Open Thurs, Fri & Sat 9.30pm-2am, & Sat 2-6pm, Wed match nights 6.30-10.30pm

**HONOURS**    Northern Lg R-up 61-62; NW Co's Lg R-up 83-84; NW Co's F/Light Trophy 95-96 96-97; Cumberland Snr Cup [12], 46-48 50-51 60-66 70-71 72-73 74-75

**PREVIOUS**    **Leagues:** Carlisle & Dist., Northern 48-82, N.W.C. 82-87, 90-97, N.P.L. 87-90.

**BEST SEASON**    FA Cup: 2nd Rd 81-82    League Clubs beaten: Chester 81-82

**RECORDS**    **Attendance:** 2,100 v Chester 1981

**Goalscorer:** C Short    **Appearances:** Lee Armstrong

**Win:** 13-2 v Parton Utd    **Defeat:** 0-13 v Bishop Auckland

### FACT FILE

Founded: 1894    Nickname: Blues
Sponsors: British Gypsum
Colours: Blue/white/blue
Change colours: White/red/white
Midweek Matches: Wednesday
Reserve team: None
Programme: 24 pages, 50p
Editor/ Press Officer: J Bell (01768 63898)
Local Press: Cumberland & Westmorland Herald, Cumberland News

### CLUB PERSONNEL

Chairman: Walter Brogden
Vice Chairman: M Robson
Manager: Geoff Byers
Physio: Les Cornwell

# PRUDHOE TOWN

**Secretary:** Brian Tulip, 12 Orchard Close, Prudhoe NE42 5LP    Tel: 01661 833169

**Ground:** Kimberley Park, Broomhouse Road, Prudhoe, Northumberland NE42 5EH

**Tel/Fax:** 01661 835900    **Directions:** Approach Prudhoe along A695, turn right at `Falcon' Inn, 200 yds down Eastwood Rd., left into Broomhouse Rd., ground on right

**Capacity:** 5,000    **Seats:** 150    **Cover:** Yes    **Floodlights:** Yes

**Clubhouse:** Open every evening plus Sat/Sun lunchtimes

**HONOURS**    Hexham & Dist. Lg 68-69 (Lg Cup 68-69), Newcastle & Dist. Lg 69-70 70-71, Lg Cup 69-70, Charity Shield 69-70 70-71), Northern Comb. 79-80, Northern AmtrLg 71-72, Clayton Charity Cup 68-69, Northumberland Minor Cup 78-79, Northumberland Benevolent Bowl 79-80, Heddon Homes Charity Cup 81-82

**PREVIOUS**    **Leagues:** Hexham & Dist 59-69; Newcastle & Dist 69-71; N. Comb.; N.Amtr; Northern All. 84-88    **Names:** Ovington 1969-75; Prudhoe East End 75-94

**BEST SEASON**    FA Cup:    FA Vase:

**RECORD**    **Attendance:** 2,500 v Blyth, Northumberland Snr Cup 1981

### FACT FILE

Founded: 1959
Nickname: Citizens
Sponsors: Swinton Insurance
Colours: Purple & jade halves/purple/purple
Change: White & blue chevrons/navy/sky
Midweek Matches: Wednesday
Programme: 8 pages, 20p
Editor: J Smith

### CLUB PERSONNEL

Chairman: Alex Waters
Press Officer:Nigel Barton (0191 273 1400)
Manager: Terry Hunter
Asst Manager: Kenny Barton
Physio: Ernie Goodfellow

# NORTHERN VENTURES
# NORTHERN GAINS

Northern Ventures Northern Gains is published six times a season - seven if an Arnott insurance Northern League side reaches Wembley.

For more than ten years now the cover price has stayed at 30p.

Subscriptions: £3.30, including postage, from
Don Warner, 18 The Riggs, Hunwick, Crook, Co. Durham DL15 0JQ

# SHILDON

**Secretary:** Mike Armitage, 22 Hambleton Ct, Byerley Park, Newton Aycliffe, Co.Durham DL5 7HR
**/Press Officer**          Tel: 01325 316322
**Ground:** Dean Street, Shildon, County DurhamTel: 01388 773877    **Directions:** In the town centre 1 mile from BR station and 300yds from Darlington-Bishop Auckland bus stop
Capacity: 4,000    Seats: 400    Cover: 500    Floodlights: Yes    **Club Shop:** No
**Clubhouse:** Every eve. 7.30-11pm (earlier match nights), 1-11pm Sat. matchdays. Pool&Darts
**HONOURS**    Northern Lg 33-34 34-35 35-36 36-37 39-40 (R-up 32-33 38-39, Lg Cup 33-34
          34-35 37-38 38-39 39-40 52-53), Durham Challenge Cup 07-08 25-26 71-72,
          Durham Amateur Cup 01-02 02-03, Durham Benevelopment Bowl 24-25.
**PREVIOUS**    Leagues: Auckland & District 1892-96; Wearside 96-97; North Eastern 07-32.
**BEST SEASON    FA Cup:** 2nd Rd 36-37 1st Rd 27-28 29-30 34-35 36-37 55-56 59-60 61-62
**FA Trophy:** 3rd Qual. Rd 74-75    **FA Amateur Cup:** 4thRd 58-59    **FA Vase:** 1st Rd 86-87
**RECORDS**    **Attendance:** 13,000 - Leeholme v Perkinsville, schoolboys game, 1920s.
          (Shildon game); 11,000 Shildon v Ferryhill Ath., Durham Sen. Cup 1922

### FACT FILE
Founded: 1890    Nickname: Railwaymen
Sponsors: Atkinsons Stairs
Colours: Red & green halves,red,red & white.
Change colours: All blue
Midweek Matches: Wednesday
Programme: 48 pages, 50p
Editor: Neil Bennett (01325 332310)

### CLUB PERSONNEL
Chairman: Bill Aisbitt
Vice Chairman: G. Elliott
President: John Atkinson
Manager:Ray Gowan
Assistant: John Harland  Physio: Jimmy Smalls
Captain: JohnHarland
P.O.Y. & Top Scorer: Charlie Watson

---

# WASHINGTON IKEDA HOOVER

**Secretary:** George Abbott, 14 Grosvenor Street, Southwick, Sunderland SR5 2DG
          Tel: 0191 549 1384

**Ground:** Albany Park, Spout Lane, Concord, Washington          Tel: 0191 417 7779

**Directions:** Ground situated  opposite bus station

Capacity: 3,000    Seats: 25Cover: Yes    Floodlights: Yes    Club Shop: No
**Clubhouse:** Open normal licensing hours, with live entertainment, pool etc

**PREVIOUS**    **Leagues:** Washington Amateur; Northern Alliance 67-68; Wearside 68-88
          **Ground:** Usworth Welfare Park
**RECORD**    **Gate:** 3,800 v Bradford Park Avenue, FA Cup 1970

### FACT FILE
Founded: 1949
Nickname: Mechanics
Colours: All red
Change colours: All blue
Midweek Matches: Wednesday
Programme: 8 pages, 10p
Editor: Secretary

### CLUB PERSONNEL
Chairman: Derek Armstrong
Press Officer: Ray Lish (0191 415 7071)

---

# WHICKHAM

**Secretary:** Harry Hodgson, 2, Dockendale Hall,Dockendale Lane, Whickham, Newcastle upon Tyne,NE16 4EN Tel: 0191 488 2493
**Ground:** Glebe Ground, Rectory Lane, Whickham (0191 420 0186)    **Directions:** A692
(Consett) from A69. Left at r'bout signed Consett/Whickham. Uphill and right at  mini-r'bout.
Continue along & turn left into Rectory Lane (by Lloyds Bank) for 500 yds, clubhouse on right
Capacity: 4,000Seats: 100Cover: YesFloodlights: Due
**Clubhouse:** Mon-Fri. 12-3 & 7-11, Sat.11-11, Sun. 12-2, 7.30-11    Souvenir Shop: No
**HONOURS**    FA Vase 80-81, Wearside Lg 77-78 87-88 (R-up 80-81 84-85, Lg Cup 86-87,
          Monkwearmouth Charity Cup 76-77, Sunderland Shipowners Cup 77-78 80-81),
          Northern Comb. 69-70 72-73 73-74 (Lg Cup 60-61 73-74)
**PREVIOUS**    **Leagues:** Derwent Valley -55; Northern Comb. 55-57 59-74; Tyneside Amtr 57-
          59; Wearside 74-88    **Ground:** Rectory Rec. Field
**BEST SEASON    FA Cup:** 1st Qual. Rd. 89-90    **FA Vase:** Winners 80-81
**RECORD**    **Gate:** 3,165 v Windsor & Eton, F.A. Vase SF 81

### FACT FILE
Founded: 1944
Colours: All black & white
Change colours: All white
Midweek Matches: Wednesday
Programme: 20p
Local Press : Newcastle Journal, Sunday Sun,
Evening Chronicle

### CLUB PERSONNEL
Chairman: Tommy Thompson
Manager: Keith Sheardown
Press Officer: As Secretary

---

# WILLINGTON

**Secretary:** Bob Nichols, 46 Cavendish Ct, Brandon,Durham DH7 8UW Tel/ FAX 0191378 1981
**Ground:** Hall Lane, Hall Lane Estate, Willington, County Durham (01388 746221)
**Directions:** Willington is on A690 7 miles west of Durham City & 2 miles east of Crook. Off main
through road at `The Black Horse Tavern' corner turn off Commercial St, then into Hall Lane after
100yds. Northern Bus Co. operates a service through Willington from Crook or Durham City
Capacity: 2,680    Seats: 350    Cover: 400    Floodlights: Yes    Club shop: Occasionally
**Clubhouse:** Open eves 7-11pm &Sat. matchdays 1-11pm. Bar facilities.Tea shop on matchdays
**HONOURS**    FA Amateur Cup 49-50, R-up 38-39; Northern League 13-14 25-26 29-30,
          R-up 12-13 57-58 75-76, Lge Cup 24-25 25-26 27-28 30-31 31-32 48-49 56-57 74-75;
          Durham Benevolent Cup 48-49 50-51 57-58.
**BEST SEASON FA Cup:** 1st Rd rep. 73-74, 1-6 v Blackburn R (A) after 0-0.Also 1st Rd 45-46
          **FA Trophy** 3rd Qual Rd 75-76    **FA Amat. Cup:** Winners 49-50          & 50-51
**PREVIOUS**    **Leagues:** Auckland & Dist. 1906-11    **Names:** Willington Temperance 1906-11
**RECORD Attendance:** 10,000 v Bromley, FA Amateur Cup 2nd Rd 24/1/53
          **Goalscorer:** J `Boxer' Taylor 55-69    **Appearances:** S Rutherford 47-61

### FACT FILE
Founded: 1906  Nickname: Blue & Whites
Sponsor: Rackwood Park Drift Mine
Colours: Blue & white stripes/blue/blue
Change colours: Yellow/green/yellow
Midweek Matches: Wednesday
Youth League: Auckland & Dist League
Programme: 40p  Editor: Christina Jackson

### CLUB PERSONNEL
Chairman: Anne Robson
Vice-Chairman: Alistair Melville
President: Hilary Armstrong M.P.
Press Officer: Secretary
Player/Manager: Dave Taylor
Joint Manager: Les Ryder

# BEDLINGTON TERRIERS

## A TRIBUTE TO THEIR WONDERFUL
## F.A. CARLSBERG VASE SEASON

LEFT: Terriers' Dean Gibb bears down on the
Ford United goal during their 5th Round tie.
Photo: D Nicholson

### JOY AT THAME!

LEFT;
The goalscorers - John Milner
(left) who got three and Ritchie
Bond who got the other two.

BELOW;
The team and the fans cele-
brate after the match.
Photo: Peter Barnes

# NISSAN WEARSIDE LEAGUE

### FEEDER TO:
### ARNOTT INSURANCE NORTHERN LEAGUE

**President:** W Robson    **Chairman:** P J Maguire

**Secretary:** E Hargreaves, 4 South Mews, Shadforth, Durham DH6 1NS
Tel: 0191 372 2844

It will be all change in the Wearside League this season following the closure of Vaux Breweries of Sunderland and with it the end of a seventeen year sponsorship of the League.

After negotiations with one of the country's leading car manufacturers the League was able to announce on July 1st a new three year sponsorship deal with Nissan Motors, which will ensure the financial stability of the competition well into the millennium.

Bill Robson, secretary of the League for the past eleven seasons, announced his retirement on health grounds at the Annual General Meeting, the position being taken up by Edwin Hargreaves who, among his other positions in football, is treasurer of the County Referees' Association.

On the domestic front the League returned to two divisions last season with North Shields Athletic proving to be runaway winners of Division One, while Red House WMC of Sunderland in their first season in Saturday football, after a long association at Sunday level, clinched the Division Two tittle.

The League has been hit by a number of resignations, namely Kennek Roker, who have merged with Ryhope CA of the AINL, Hartlepool BWOB, Horden CW Athletic, South Shields Reserves and Silksworth CA.

To bring Division One up to its required minimum strength of sixteen clubs, New Marske SC and Workington Reserves were promoted along with champions Red House WMC, while Division Two, with the addition of Stokesley SC from the Teesside League, will operate with eight teams. To this end the clubs will play each other three times next season with the Divisional Cup being played on a league basis of two groups up to the semi-final stages.

Windscale were winners of the League Cup defeating Nissan on a penalty shoot out after the sides had finished at one all after extra time in the Final. In the Monkwearmouth Charity Cup Red House WMC defeated Wolviston 2-1 and North Shields Athletic were to prove to be too strong Boldon CA in the final of the Sunderland Shipowners Cup winning 4-1.

On the County Cup scene North Shields proved to be worthy winners of the Northumberland Senior Benevolent Bowl while Red House were defeated finalists in the Durham Trophy.

As in other levels of football lack of discipline accompanied with strict application of the Laws of the Game by match officials resulted in cautions reaching an all time high, although dismissals did show a slight decrease on recent years. Workington Reserves clinched the award for Sportsmanship with only four cautions logged against them during the campaign.

## FINAL LEAGUE TABLES 1998-99

### DIVISION ONE

|  | P | W | D | L | F | A | Pts |
|---|---|---|---|---|---|---|---|
| North Shields Ath | 28 | 24 | 3 | 1 | 92 | 24 | 75 |
| Wolviston | 28 | 19 | 4 | 5 | 75 | 31 | 61 |
| Nissan* | 28 | 20 | 5 | 3 | 88 | 36 | 59 |
| Hartlepool BWOB | 28 | 16 | 5 | 7 | 56 | 35 | 53 |
| Kennek Roker | 28 | 15 | 6 | 7 | 65 | 40 | 51 |
| Birtley Town | 28 | 16 | 2 | 10 | 57 | 50 | 50 |
| Windscale* | 28 | 15 | 4 | 9 | 52 | 35 | 46 |
| Boldon CA | 28 | 14 | 4 | 10 | 63 | 47 | 46 |
| Cleadon SC | 28 | 10 | 3 | 15 | 45 | 60 | 33 |
| Annfield Plain | 28 | 9 | 4 | 15 | 64 | 82 | 31 |
| Harton & Westoe CW | 28 | 7 | 2 | 19 | 48 | 79 | 23 |
| Jarrow | 28 | 6 | 3 | 19 | 36 | 62 | 21 |
| Stanley United | 28 | 4 | 2 | 22 | 33 | 88 | 14 |
| Whitehaven* | 28 | 4 | 4 | 20 | 39 | 105 | 13 |
| Ryhope CW* | 28 | 4 | 3 | 21 | 30 | 69 | 12 |

### DIVISION TWO

|  | P | W | D | L | F | A | Pts |
|---|---|---|---|---|---|---|---|
| Red House WMC | 24 | 19 | 1 | 4 | 125 | 40 | 58 |
| New Marske SC | 24 | 16 | 6 | 2 | 86 | 29 | 54 |
| Workington Res | 24 | 17 | 2 | 5 | 89 | 28 | 53 |
| Redcar Town | 24 | 14 | 5 | 5 | 85 | 37 | 47 |
| Herrington CW | 24 | 13 | 3 | 8 | 67 | 48 | 42 |
| Simonside SC | 24 | 12 | 4 | 8 | 74 | 51 | 40 |
| Silksworth CA | 24 | 11 | 5 | 8 | 69 | 45 | 38 |
| Ferryhill Athletic | 24 | 10 | 4 | 10 | 50 | 56 | 34 |
| South Shields Res | 24 | 7 | 4 | 13 | 45 | 65 | 25 |
| Horden CW Athletic | 24 | 6 | 3 | 15 | 44 | 101 | 21 |
| Southbank | 24 | 5 | 2 | 17 | 51 | 96 | 17 |
| Whitburn | 24 | 5 | 2 | 17 | 44 | 102 | 17 |
| Wallsend Town | 24 | 0 | 1 | 23 | 12 | 143 | 1 |

* points deducted

# DIVISION ONE RESULTS CHART 1998-99

| | | 1 | 2 | 3 | 4 | 5 | 6 | 7 | 8 | 9 | 10 | 11 | 12 | 13 | 14 | 15 |
|---|---|---|---|---|---|---|---|---|---|---|---|---|---|---|---|---|
| 1 | Annfield Plain | X | 2-3 | 2-5 | 3-4 | 1-0 | 0-1 | 1-3 | 6-1 | 1-0 | 4-3 | 7-1 | 1-5 | 5-1 | 4-2 | 2-5 |
| 2 | Birtley Town | 5-1 | X | 3-1 | 1-0 | 2-0 | 0-3 | 1-0 | 3-2 | 3-1 | 2-3 | 3-1 | 3-7 | 7-3 | 0-1 | 1-5 |
| 3 | Boldon CA | 5-0 | 3-1 | X | 1-1 | 1-0 | 1-2 | 1-0 | 3-4 | 4-0 | 0-2 | 2-0 | 1-1 | 6-0 | 2-2 | 0-5 |
| 4 | Hartlepool BWOB | 1-1 | 1-1 | 2-3 | X | 3-0 | 0-0 | 2-1 | 2-0 | 3-1 | 1-2 | 1-0 | 1-1 | 6-0 | 0-3 | 1-0 |
| 5 | Jarrow | 7-1 | 1-4 | 0-1 | 2-1 | X | 1-3 | 2-3 | 2-1 | 5-1 | 2-3 | 0-2 | 0-5 | 5-0 | 2-2 | 0-2 |
| 6 | North Shields Athletic | 5-0 | 4-0 | 3-1 | 5-0 | 3-0 | X | 1-0 | 7-1 | 6-1 | 1-1 | 3-1 | 4-1 | 7-1 | 2-0 | 0-2 |
| 7 | Cleadon SC | 2-1 | 0-1 | 2-2 | 1-3 | 0-2 | 1-3 | X | 2-1 | 3-0 | 0-6 | 5-3 | 0-1 | 3-1 | 0-3 | 3-5 |
| 8 | Harton & Westoe | 3-4 | 0-3 | 1-6 | 0-4 | 5-1 | 1-3 | 1-3 | X | 5-1 | 1-3 | 2-0 | 1-2 | 1-0 | 2-2 | 1-4 |
| 9 | Stanley United | 2-2 | 1-2 | 4-2 | 2-4 | 1-1 | 1-4 | 1-4 | 2-6 | X | 0-1 | 2-0 | 0-5 | 5-1 | 0-4 | 1-2 |
| 10 | Kennek Roker | 2-2 | 3-1 | 2-4 | 2-5 | 1-0 | 2-2 | 4-2 | 4-1 | 3-1 | X | 3-0 | 0-0 | 8-0 | 0-0 | 1-2 |
| 11 | Ryhope CW | 3-3 | 1-3 | 1-2 | 0-3 | 1-1 | 0-6 | 1-2 | 0-1 | 1-3 | 0-1 | X | 1-4 | 5-2 | 1-0 | 0-0 |
| 12 | Nissan | 1-0 | 2-1 | 1-3 | 2-0 | 5-2 | 4-5 | 7-1 | 3-2 | 7-0 | 2-0 | 5-3 | X | 3-1 | 2-1 | 2-2 |
| 13 | Whitehaven | 6-7 | 2-2 | 3-2 | 1-3 | 2-0 | 2-3 | 2-2 | 1-1 | 2-1 | 2-2 | 2-1 | 2-5 | X | 1-2 | 0-2 |
| 14 | Windscale | 3-1 | 2-0 | 2-0 | 1-2 | 3-0 | 1-3 | 3-1 | 2-1 | 4-1 | 3-2 | 2-1 | 0-4 | 3-0 | X | 0-1 |
| 15 | Wolviston | 3-2 | 0-1 | 3-1 | 1-2 | 5-0 | 1-2 | 1-1 | 6-2 | 3-0 | 2-1 | 1-2 | 2-2 | 8-1 | 2-1 | X |

# LEAGUE CUP 1998-99

**FIRST ROUND**

| Harton & Westoe CW | v | Southbank | 3-0 | Stanley United | v | Hartlepool BWOB | 1-5 |
|---|---|---|---|---|---|---|---|
| Windscale | v | Wallsend Town | 13-0 | Jarrow | v | Whitehaven Ams | 3-0 |
| Kennek Roker | v | Silksworth CA | 3-1 | Horden CW Ath | v | Herrington CW | 0-4 |
| Redcar Town | v | Whitburn | 16-0 | Cleadon SC | v | Ryhope CW | 4-2 |
| Ferryhill Athletic | v | South Shields Res | 2-4 | Boldon CA | v | Workington Res | 3-4 |
| Red House WMC | v | Simonside SC | 3-2 | North Shields Ath | v | Nissan | 0-1 |

**SECOND ROUND**

| South Shields Res | v | Herrington | 0-5 | Jarrow | v | Workington Res | 0*2 |
|---|---|---|---|---|---|---|---|
| Annfield Plain | v | Hartlepool BWOB | 1-3 | Harton & Westoe | v | Wolviston | 1-4 |
| Cleadon SC | v | Kennek Roker | 5-0 | Red House WMC | v | Redcar Town | 3-2 |
| Birtley Town | v | Windscale | 1-2 | Nissan | v | New Marske SC | 9-1 |

**THIRD ROUND**

| Red House WMC | v | Windscale | 1-3 | Herrington | v | Nissan | 1-4 |
|---|---|---|---|---|---|---|---|
| Wolviston | v | Cleadon SC | 1-2 | Workington Res | v | Hartlepool BWOB | 3-2 |

**SEMI FINALS**

| Windscale | v | Workington Res | 1-2 | Cleadon | v | Nissan | 1-3 |
|---|---|---|---|---|---|---|---|

**FINAL**

| Nissan | v | Windscale | 1-1, 2p4 |
|---|---|---|---|

# MONKWEARMOUTH CHARITY CUP 1998-99

**SEMI FINALS**

| Red House WMC | v | Windscale | 1-0 | Wolviston | v | North Shields | 3-3, 11p10 |
|---|---|---|---|---|---|---|---|

**FINAL**

| Wolviston | v | Red House WMC | 1-2 |
|---|---|---|---|

# SUNDERLAND SHIPOWNERS CUP 1998-99

**SEMI FINALS**

| Boldon CA | v | Hartlepool BWOB | 1-0 | Red House WMC | v | North Shields | 0-3 |
|---|---|---|---|---|---|---|---|

**FINAL**

| Boldon CA | v | North Shields | 1-4 |
|---|---|---|---|

# ANNFIELD PLAIN

**Secretary:** M Lawson, 24 Northgate, Annfield Plain, Stanley, Co. Durham DH9 7UY
Tel: 01207 235879

**Ground:** Derwent Park, Annfield Plain. **Directions:** On A693 road to Consett, 200yds west of junction with A6067. Ground behind new housing estate. 6 miles fromDurham (BR). Buses from Sunderland, Newcastle & Durham.

Capacity: 6,000     Seats: 20     Cover: 200     Floodlights: No

**HONOURS**     Wearside Lg 84-85 (Monkwearmouth Charity Cup 92-93), FA Cup 1st Rd 26-27 28-29 64-65.

Founded: 1890.
Colours: Claret/white/white
Change colours: All blue.
Programme: 16 pages, 20p

Chairman: Frank Ross
Manager: D Longstaff
Press Officer: Frank Ross

# BIRTLEY TOWN

**Secretary:** Kevin McConnell, 8 Leyburn Place, Birtley, DH3 1PL (0191 4100495)
Commercial Manager: Ray Stafford.

**Ground:** Birtley Sports Complex. **Directions:** (From Durham) Off A1(M) signpstedfor Chester-le-Street, take 2nd turn off r-bout signed Birtley, take last turnoff next r-bout (still signed Birtley), after one and a half miles take 1stleft after AEI Cables - ground at rear of sports complex.

Capacity: Unknown     Seats: None     Cover: None     Floodlights: No.

Clubhouse: Matchdays only

HONOURS: Wearside Lg 45-46 (Lg Cup 35-36), Northern Alliance 23-24 (R-up 13-14).

Founded: 1890     Reformed: 1986
Colours: Green&white/white/white
Change colours: Yellow/blue/red.
Midweek matches: Wednesday
Sponsors: C & C Coachworks
Chairman: J Heslington
Vice-Chairman: J Grainger.
Manager: Barry Fleming
Asst Manager: David Smith
Coach: Malcolm Thompson

# BOLDON COMMUNITY ASSOCIATION

**Secretary:** Frank Clennell, 31 Fenwicks Srreet, Boldon Colliery (0191 5190424)

**Ground:** Boldon Community Association, New Road, Boldon Colliery.. **Directions:** A19 to junc A184 Sunderland/Newcastle. Follow signs to Boldon Asdastores, then to North Road Social Club (SHACK). Ground behind. 800 yds fromEast Boldon (BR). Buses 533, 531, 319, 528.

Capacity: 3,500Seats: 100Cover: 400Floodlights: NoPress Off./Comm Mgr:

Clubhouse: Matchdays only. Bar snacks

Sponsors: Tyne Dock Engineering Co., South Shields.

HONOURS: Wearside Lg 3, (Lg Cup 3), M/mouth Char Cup 2, Shipowners Cup 6.

Founded: 1892.     Nickname: Villa
Colours: Red& Navy/navy/navy
Change: Scarlet & black
Chairman:K.Oliver
Vice Chairman: G Smith
President: A Brewster.
Manager: Bill Newham
Asst Manager: P Quinn
Coach: Tommy Frazer.
Press Off. / Comm. Man.: Secretary

# JARROW

**Secretary:** Susan Scott,46 Breamish Street, Jarrow. NE32 5SH (0191 4248610)

**Ground:** Perth Green Community Centre.

**Directions:** From A19 or A1(M) followdrections to South Shields, right onto John Reid Road. First slip road ontoBrockley Whinns Estate, follow road past Red Hackle pub, third left left ontoInverness Road, then right into Perth Green Community Centre.

**HONOURS:** Sth Tyne Lg & Lg Cup, Washington Lg R-up 89-90 (Lg Cup 90-91, Aged Peoples Tphy R-up 90-91), Gateshead Charity Cup 90-91, Durham Tphy R-up 90-91.

Founded: 1980.
Colours: Blue & white/blue/blue
Change: Green/black/green

Chairman: B.Tyreman
Treasurer: Jimmy Kane

# NEW MARSKE

**Secretary:** Peter Whitaker, 28 High Street, Marske, Redcar TS11 7BE
Tel: 01642 486770

**Ground:** Pontac Road, New Marske.

**Directions:** A19 south onto A174 Redcar- Teesport. Follow A174 towards Saltburn turn right at r'about with footbridge overroad. Ground 500 yds on left.

Colours: Yellow & black/navy/navy
Change colours: Blue &black/navy/navy

Charmain: Errol Richter
Tel: 01947 600296

# NORTH SHIELDS

**Secretary:** Dave Thompson, 38 Barnstable Road, North Shields. Tel: 0191 259 0249

**Ground:** Ralph Gardner Park, West Percy Rd., N.Shields, Tyne & Wear, NE29 OES

**Directions:** A19 northbound through Tyne Tunnel. Take 1st slip round to 1str/about & take 3rd exit & over next r/about. Take 3rd exit again at nextr/about into Waterville Rd. Over another r/about and 2nd left into Silkey'sLane. 1st right into West Percy Rd, grd on right.

**Clubhouse:** None

**HONOURS:**     FA Amateur Cup 68-69, Northern Lge 68-69, N.C.E. Prem. Div. 91-92, R-up 89-90, 90-91, Lge. Cup 90-91, Presidents Cup 91-92.

Founded: 1896
Nickname: New Robins
Sponsors: Wilkinson Stores
Colours: All red
Change colours: Blue & black/black/black

Chairman: Alan Matthews.
Manager: Bob Weir.
Coach: Wilf Keilty.

## SOUTH SHIELDS CLEADON SOCIAL CLUB

**Secretary:** Steve Wright, 16 Mitford Close, North Lodge, Chester-le-Street. DH3 4BL
Tel NO: 0191 3884189
**Ground:** Jack Clarke Park, South Shields.
**Directions:** Enter South Shields on A194 to r'bout taking you on to A1300 JohnReid Rd. 2nd left at 3rd r'bout into King George Rd then Sunderland Rd, rightat lights into Grosvenor Rd, left into Horsly Hill Rd. Ground on right
Clubhouse: Cleadon Social Club, Fulwell Ave, S Shields. Normal pub hours except Saturday.
**HONOURS:** Wearside Lg Div 2 90-91, Shields & Dist. Lg, Washington Lg 77-78 84-85

Nickname: The Club
Sponsors: Cleadon & Dist. Soc. Club
Colours: All Amber
Change: All red
Midweek matches: Wednesday
Chairman: Gordon Ferries
Vice-Chairman/Press Off . /Manager:
David Wood (0191 455 4607).
Asst Man: Steve Duguid
Commercial Manager: Joan Wood

## SOUTH SHIELDS HARTON & WESTOE

**Secretary:** Ronald Wightman, 12A Rockville, Grosvenor Road, South Shields.NE33 3JH
Tel No: 0191 4540425
**Groun:** Harton Colliery Welfare.

**Directions:** A1M at Whitemare Pool take A194 to South Shields for 2 1/2 miles.At third round-about turn right onto A1300. At 2nd roundabout turn left ontoBoldon Lane. Ground 50 yards on right

Colours: Royal blue & white halves/ royal blue
& blue & white.
Change colours: All red
Chairman: Ronald Wightman
Treasurer: Steven Camm

## STANLEY UNITED

**Secretary:** V Kirkup, 9 Brookes Rise, Regents Green, Langley, Durham DH7 8XY
Tel: 0191 378 0921
**Ground:** High Road, Stanley, near Crook (nicknamed Hill Top Ground). **Directions:** Teeside on A689 to Bishop Auckland and onto Crook, turn left atMarket Place then 1st right for Tow Law to Billy Row and Stanley, right at topof bank then 1st left, grd 250 yards on left.
**Clubhouse:** Open matchdays.     **Club Shop:** No
**HONOURS:** Northern Lg 3, R-up 62-63, Lg Cup 3,
**BEST SEASON:** FA Cup 1st Rd 53-54.     FA Amateur Cup Semi Final 19-20.

Nickname: The Nops
Sponsors: Company Cars Direct
Colours: Red & white stripes/black/red
Change colours: Sky/navy/navy

President: A Westgarth
Vice-President: B Waiting.
Asst Manager/ Coach: K Finnegan
Physio: J Burn

## SUNDERLAND RED HOUSE WMC

**Secretary:**     John Wake, 4 Kenilworth Square, Downhill Estate, Sunderland SR5 4AN
Tel: 0191 536 5284

**Ground:**     Billy Hardy Complex, Castletown, Sunderland

**Directions:**     From south A19 heading for Tyne tunnel. Exit A1231 signposted Stadium of Light. Follow road and pass wessington Hotel, Reg Vardy car showroom, then petrol station. Turn left and at junction turn left, then quick left after 2 houses. (Map provided if reqd.)

Colours: All red
Change: all white

Chairman: Charlie Sumner
Tel: 0191 549 1120
Treasurer: Cliff McGuinness
Tel: 0191 537 1477

## SUNDERLAND RYHOPE C.W.

**Secretary:** George McKitterick, 8 Kilburn Close, Ryhope Village, Sunderland. SR2 0QU
Tel: 0191 523 8436)
**Ground:** Ryhope Recreation Park, Ryhope Street, Ryhope, Sunderland Tel: 0191 521 2843
**Directions:** Take A19 (3 miles south of Sunderland centre) to Ryhope village, atVillage Green turn into Evelyn Terrace/Ryhope Street and carry on up bank pastPresto's for 600 yds - ground appears on left. 3 miles from Sunderland Central(BR), bus every 10 mins from Sunderland centre.
Capacity: 1,000     Seats: No          Cover: No          Floodlights: Yes
**HONOURS:** Wearside Lg 4, (Lg Cup 2), Durham Chall Cup 77-78, M/mouth Charity Cup3, S/land Shipowners Cup 2

Founded: 1988.

Colours: Yellow/black/black & red
Change colours: Red/white/red & white

Chairman:T.B.A.
Press Officer: Secretary

## WASHINGTON NISSAN

**Secretary:**     Harry English, 193 Newcastle Road, Fulwell Mill, Sunderland SR5 1NR
Tel: 0191 548 7194
**Ground:**     Nissan Sports Complex.
**Directions:** North along A1 (M) use A690 (sign post Sunderland) connect withA19, north on A19, after passing the A1231 turn off, plant on the left. Pastplant & follow signs 'Nissan Offices'.
**Clubhouse:** Open Mon-Fri 5-11pm, Sat 11am-11pm, Sun noon-3 & 7-10.30pm
**HONOURS:**     Wearside Lg Div 1 93-94 (Lg Cup R-up 91-92, Div 2 Cup 92-93 93-94), Nissan European Trophy 3.

Founded: 1988
Colours: Blue & yellow/ blue/blue
Change colours: Red & white/white/white.
Chairman: A Hill
Treasurer: P Bevington
Press Officer: Secretary
Manager: Stan Fenwick
Assistant Manager: Keith Robertson.
Coach: Darren Ward

# WHITEHAVEN AMATEURS

**Secretary:** Richard Stamp, Johnson House, Hillcrest Avenue, Whitehaven, CA28 6SU
Tel No: 01946 61877
**Ground:** Whitehaven County Ground, Coach Road, Whitehaven

**Directions:** Barrow on A595, ignore branch to town centre at B.P. garage turnright at t/lights on
A5094. 1/2 mile turn left at Esso garage into Coach Rd.Narrow lane ent immed after l/ crossing
to grd behind Rugby Lge Stadium.
**HONOURS:** Cumberland Cup 90-91, County League 87-88 88-89, Wearside Lg Div 2
Cup R-up 93-94.

Colours: Yellow/blue/yellow
Change colours: White/navy/white

Chairman: Bill Robson.
Press Officer: Secretary
Manager: Ian Green
Assistant Manager: Ian Atkins

# WINDSCALE

**Secretary:** Geoff Turrell, 65 Leathwaite, Loop Road South, Whitehaven, CumbriaCA28 7UG
Tel: 01936 62229
**Ground:** Falcon Field, Egremont.
**Directions:** A66 to Bridgefoot. A595 Barrow,bottom of hill approaching Egremont take
3rd turn off island (signed)Smithfield/Gillfoot, ground in housing estate
**HONOURS:** Furness Senior Cup 1985-86

Founded: 1950

Colours:All Purple.
Change: Blue & white/royal/royal

Chairman: R Napier
Press Officer: Secretary
Treasurer: A Barwise

# WOLVISTON

**Secretary:** Keith Simpson, 14 Lodore Grove, Acklam, Middlesbrough TS5 8PB  01642 823734
**Ground:** Metcalfe Way, Wynyard Road, Wolviston, Billingham, Cleveland TS22 5NE.
**Directions:** On Wynyard Road between Thorpe Thewles & Wolviston. A19 onto A689 into Wolviston
village, take Wynyard Road towards Thorpe Thewles, grd left before Sir John Halls Estate.
**Capacity:** 2,000    Seats: None    Cover: 200    Floodlights: No    Club Shop: No.
**Clubhouse:** Licensed bar. Hot & cold meals. Open 11am-11pm on matchdays.
**HONOURS:** Wearside Lg Div 2 89-90, Lg Cup R-up 92-93, Teesside Lg R-up 84-85, Lg Cup
86-87, Durham FA Trophy R-up 89-90, Stockton & Dist. Lg 3, LgCup 3, Lg Charity Cup 79-80.
**Record Gate:** 500 v Middlesbrough 27/7/93

Founded: 1910    Nickname: Wolves
Sponsors: R.C.I. Industrial Cleaners
Colours: Royal blue/blue/white
Change: Red & white/red/white
Chairman: Eddie Poole    President: Bob Smith
Vice Chairman: Derek Stockton
Press Officer: Secretary
Manager: John Johnson
Asst Manager: Kevin Smith
Coach: Alan Lucas

# WORKINGTON RESERVES

**Secretary:** Tom Robson, 12 Derwent Bank, Seaton, Workington CA14 1EE
Tel; 01900 605208 (H)    01900 65566 (B)
**Ground:** Borough Park, Workington, Cumbria CA14 2DT (01900 602871).
**Directions:** A66 into town, right at `T' junction, follow A596 for 3/4 mile - ground is then visible
and signposted. Ground is north of town centre 1/4 mile from Workington (BR) station &1/2 mile
from bus station
**Capacity:** 2,500    Cover: 800    Seats: 300    Floodlights: Yes
**Clubhouse:** Open matchdays

Colours: All red
Change colours: Blue/white/blue

Chairman: Bill Wilson (01494 671974)
Match Secretary: Steve Durham
10 Grant Drive, Bleach Green, Whitehaven
CA28 6JS Tel: 01946 61380

**FERRYHILL ATHLETIC (1998)**
**Secretary:** Norman Bellwood, 49 Rush park, Bishop Auckland DL14 6NS  Tel: 01388 451065
**HERRINGTON C.W.**
**Secretary:** Keith Stafford, 12 Grasmere, Fulwell, Sunderland SR5 7LL  Tel: 0191 516 9017
**REDCAR TOWN**
**Secretary:** Keith Markham, 2 Riccall Court, Redcar TS10 4HL  Tel: 01642 481966
**SOUTH SHIELDS SIMONSIDE SOCIAL CLUB**
**Secretary:** David Convery, 118 Durham Drive, Fellgate Estate, Jarrow NE32 4QZ  Tel: 0191 536 7298
**STOKESLEY SPORTS CLUB**
**Srecretary:** Peter Grainge, 77 Darnton Drive, Easterside, Middlesbrough TS4 3RF  Tel: 01642 273934
**THORNABY ON TEES**
**Secretary:** Peter Livingstone, 5 Guisborough Road, Thornaby on Tees TS17 8BE  Tel: 01642 646428
**WALLSEND TOWN**
**Secretary:** Brian White, 1 Bray Close, Battlehill Estate, Wallsend NE28 9RJ  Tel: 0191 262 9432 (H)  0191 200 7268 (B)
**WHITBURN**
**Secretary:** John Anthony Allen, 26 Myrtle avenue, Whitburn, Tyne & Wear SR6 7DP  Tel: 0191 529 5919 (H) 0191 529 4202 (B)

# JPL WADE
# NORTHERN ALLIANCE FOOTBALL LEAGUE

**President:** Les Todd    **Chairman:** G F Dobbins
**Secretary:** John McLackland
92 Appletree Gardens, Walkerville, Newcastle upon Tyne NE6 4SX   Tel: 0191 2621636
**Press Officer:** Bill Gardner   Tel/Fax: 0191 4883422

West Allotment Celtic claimed what was their fifth Northern Alliance title and completed a notable treble by also picking up the Premier Division Challenge Cup and the Stan Seymour League Cup.

This triple triumph once again underlined the managerial qualifications of Celtic's Ken Scott who can justifiably claim to be the North East's most consistently successful team boss on the non-League scene.

To retain the Premier Division championship West Allotment had to see off the challenge of Barrie Wardrobe's Ponteland United side. The race went right up to the wire and a packed house at Ponteland's Leisure Centre Ground for the last game of the season saw Celtic triumph in what was a nail-biting decider.

Ponteland have recently been referred to as the 'nearly men' and that seems an apt title. Once again they finished as runners-up and, despite dominating for much of the League Cup Final, succumbed again to a late winner for traditional rivals West Allotment.

Ryton, relative newcomers to the league's top flight, finished in third spot. But their disappointment in missing out in the title race and losing to West Allotment in the Challenge Cup Final was offset by a Durham FA Trophy triumph at Chester-le-Street.

During the season Ryton also celebrated the official opening of their new ground Kingsley Park at Crawcrook which overlooks the Tyne Valley from the south. The facilities include a brand new club house and the ambitious club is now planning for the installation of floodlights.

Lemington Social, champions in 1996-97, learned the harsh lesson that success can be fleeting. Progress off the field in the form of improvements to their Tavern Ground wasn't matched on the park. Several players departed after a bright start and when manager Derek Bell also left the early title challenge evaporated.

The humbling process is due to be completed in the 1999-2000 campaign and Lemington, with a name switch to Cowgate Sports Club, are due to commence team rebuilding down in the Alliance's Second Division.

Carlisle City, despite only an average season on the league front, almost lifted the Cumberland FA Senior Cup but were narrowly beaten by Cleator Moor Celtic in a final replayed following a 1-1 stalemate at the first attempt.

Spittal Rovers also lost out at their last hurdle in the Northumberland FA Senior Bowl Final where Wearside League opponents North Shields were the victors, but there was County Cup success for league newcomers Amble Vikings.

In their first season the Vikings were Northumberland FA Minor Cup winners, Second Division champions and also lifted the lower division's Amateur Cup. Here is a team expected to rise rapidly through the ranks.

At the end of the season some wholesome changes were announced in the divisional constitutions. North Shields St Columbas merged with Benfield Park under the latter team's banner in the Premier Division while Lemington requested to step down.

Shiremoor and Hexham Border Counties resigned and Gosforth Bohemians will be suspending membership for a season hopefully to rebuild. First Division champions Percy Main have returned to the top division along with Heaton Stannington whose facilities at Newton Park have been expensively upgraded. And Newbiggin Central Welfare have also regained Premier Division status.

Nine clubs have been admitted as newcomers from feeder leagues to operate in the Second Division and to accommodate this 'invasion' three clubs along with champions Amble Vikings and runners-up Cullercoats have been elevated into the middle division.

Bill Gardner, League Press Officer

# FINAL LEAGUE TABLES 1998-99

## PREMIER DIVISION

| | P | W | D | L | F | A | Pts |
|---|---|---|---|---|---|---|---|
| West Allotment | 28 | 21 | 4 | 3 | 75 | 31 | 67 |
| Ponteland | 28 | 20 | 4 | 4 | 71 | 25 | 64 |
| Ryton | 28 | 17 | 5 | 6 | 63 | 35 | 56 |
| Northbank | 28 | 15 | 3 | 10 | 52 | 38 | 48 |
| Reyrolle | 28 | 12 | 3 | 13 | 52 | 52 | 39 |
| Benfield Park | 28 | 11 | 4 | 13 | 38 | 51 | 37 |
| Shankhouse | 28 | 11 | 6 | 11 | 41 | 36 | 36* |
| Lemington | 28 | 11 | 3 | 14 | 36 | 51 | 36 |
| Seaton Delaval | 28 | 9 | 7 | 12 | 49 | 53 | 34 |
| Carlisle City | 28 | 10 | 4 | 14 | 44 | 51 | 34 |
| Spittal | 28 | 9 | 6 | 13 | 41 | 59 | 33 |
| St Columbas | 28 | 8 | 7 | 13 | 46 | 56 | 31 |
| Winlaton | 28 | 8 | 4 | 16 | 50 | 68 | 28 |
| Walker Central | 28 | 8 | 4 | 16 | 33 | 56 | 25* |
| Walker L'wood | 28 | 6 | 4 | 18 | 27 | 56 | 19* |

## DIVISION ONE

| | P | W | D | L | F | A | Pts |
|---|---|---|---|---|---|---|---|
| Percy Main | 26 | 20 | 4 | 2 | 83 | 20 | 64 |
| Coxlodge SC | 26 | 17 | 3 | 6 | 100 | 42 | 54 |
| N University | 26 | 15 | 7 | 4 | 90 | 35 | 52 |
| Heaton Stann. | 26 | 11 | 9 | 6 | 68 | 49 | 42 |
| Newbiggin | 26 | 12 | 5 | 9 | 56 | 57 | 41 |
| Amble Town | 26 | 13 | 3 | 10 | 58 | 55 | 39* |
| Procter & G. | 26 | 11 | 6 | 9 | 44 | 49 | 39 |
| Heddon | 26 | 10 | 7 | 9 | 64 | 60 | 37 |
| Morpeth 'A' | 26 | 9 | 5 | 12 | 45 | 50 | 32 |
| Highfields | 26 | 9 | 3 | 14 | 56 | 72 | 30 |
| Bohemians | 26 | 7 | 5 | 14 | 33 | 65 | 26 |
| Ashington Hirst | 26 | 6 | 4 | 16 | 41 | 68 | 22 |
| Hexham S. | 26 | 6 | 2 | 18 | 41 | 101 | 20 |
| Newton Park | 26 | 3 | 3 | 20 | 44 | 100 | 9* |

## DIVISION TWO

| | P | W | D | L | F | A | Pts |
|---|---|---|---|---|---|---|---|
| Amble Vikings | 22 | 16 | 6 | 0 | 62 | 23 | 54 |
| Cullercoats | 22 | 15 | 3 | 4 | 81 | 32 | 48 |
| Chopwell TC | 22 | 14 | 6 | 2 | 66 | 25 | 48 |
| Rutherford | 22 | 12 | 6 | 4 | 52 | 26 | 42 |
| Wark | 22 | 9 | 7 | 6 | 42 | 34 | 34 |
| Northern SC | 22 | 9 | 2 | 11 | 55 | 66 | 29 |
| Wallington | 22 | 8 | 6 | 8 | 39 | 47 | 27* |
| Otterburn | 22 | 6 | 5 | 11 | 44 | 44 | 20* |
| Hexham BC | 22 | 4 | 5 | 13 | 41 | 78 | 17 |
| Newcastle BT | 22 | 5 | 3 | 14 | 32 | 49 | 15* |
| Stobhill | 22 | 3 | 6 | 13 | 32 | 72 | 15 |
| Shiremoor GH | 22 | 2 | 3 | 17 | 32 | 82 | 6* |

* Points deducted

# PREMIER DIVISION RESULTS CHART 1998-99

| | | 1 | 2 | 3 | 4 | 5 | 6 | 7 | 8 | 9 | 10 | 11 | 12 | 13 | 14 | 15 |
|---|---|---|---|---|---|---|---|---|---|---|---|---|---|---|---|---|
| 1 | Carlisle City | X | 1-2 | 0-2 | 3-2 | 0-3 | 2-3 | 1-2 | 2-5 | 1-0 | 2-1 | 0-4 | 5-0 | 1-1 | 3-4 | 3-3 |
| 2 | Hebburn Reyrolle | 0-1 | X | 2-0 | 2-4 | 1-0 | 4-0 | 1-3 | 1-2 | 3-2 | 1-1 | 2-4 | 4-0 | 1-2 | 4-3 | 4-3 |
| 3 | Lemington Soc. | 0-2 | 1-1 | X | 3-2 | 3-0 | 0-0 | 0-2 | 0-4 | 0-2 | 2-3 | 1-0 | 2-1 | 3-2 | 1-3 | 3-5 |
| 4 | Benfield Park | 2-1 | 0-3 | 2-1 | X | 0-1 | 1-1 | 2-2 | 0-2 | 4-0 | 1-2 | 0-0 | 3-2 | 1-0 | 0-4 | 2-0 |
| 5 | Northbank | 1-2 | 2-0 | 1-0 | 0-2 | X | 3-2 | 0-3 | 3-1 | 4-2 | 4-0 | 3-1 | 4-0 | 3-2 | 2-3 | 2-1 |
| 6 | N S St Columbas | 1-5 | 4-0 | 2-2 | 0-1 | 2-3 | X | 0-0 | 0-3 | 3-1 | 7-1 | 1-2 | 0-4 | 1-2 | 2-1 | 2-0 |
| 7 | Ponteland United | 2-0 | 4-1 | 0-1 | 6-1 | 3-0 | 1-0 | X | 1-1 | 1-2 | 3-1 | 7-1 | 4-1 | 4-0 | 1-3 | 4-2 |
| 8 | Ryton | 1-0 | 2-3 | 5-0 | 3-1 | 1-2 | 4-3 | 2-0 | X | 3-2 | 1-2 | 5-0 | 3-1 | 3-2 | 0-1 | 1-1 |
| 9 | Seaton Delavel | 0-0 | 2-1 | 1-3 | 6-1 | 1-1 | 4-2 | 1-4 | 3-3 | X | 0-1 | 2-1 | 0-0 | 2-1 | 2-2 | 2-3 |
| 10 | Shankhouse | 4-0 | 0-0 | 3-0 | 0-1 | 1-0 | 0-0 | 1-1 | 0-0 | 0-1 | X | 2-0 | 4-0 | 5-1 | 0-1 | 1-3 |
| 11 | Spittal Rovers | 2-2 | 3-4 | 2-3 | 1-0 | 2-2 | 3-3 | 0-2 | 2-0 | 2-2 | 2-0 | X | 0-1 | 1-0 | 0-2 | 2-5 |
| 12 | Walker Central | 0-3 | 3-2 | 3-0 | 1-1 | 2-1 | 0-1 | 1-2 | 0-1 | 1-4 | 1-1 | 2-2 | X | 2-0 | 0-3 | 4-1 |
| 13 | Walker Ledwood | 2-1 | 0-3 | 0-1 | 2-0 | 0-5 | 1-3 | 0-3 | 2-3 | 2-2 | 1-0 | 0-1 | 2-1 | X | 1-2 | 0-3 |
| 14 | West Allotment | 3-1 | 2-1 | 3-0 | 4-1 | 2-1 | 2-2 | 2-4 | 1-1 | 3-2 | 3-0 | 7-0 | 3-1 | 0-0 | X | 3-0 |
| 15 | Winlaton | 1-2 | 3-1 | 0-4 | 1-3 | 1-1 | 6-1 | 0-2 | 2-3 | 3-1 | 0-7 | 1-3 | 0-1 | 1-1 | 1-5 | X |

# PREMIER DIVISION CLUBS 1999-2000

## CARLISLE CITY FC

**Chairman:** Jackie Ewbank      **Manager/Coach:** Willie Armstrong
**Secretary:** Jackie Williamson, 14 Etterby Street, Stanwix, Carlisle   (01228 531654)
**Ground:** The Sheepmount Sports Complex, Carlisle   (01228 526569)
**Directions:** Take B6264 Brampton-Carlisle road. Follow Workington sign. Continue past Carlisle Castle on right. Where road intersects double back and turn left just before Castle, follow road down keeping left till you reach ground.
**Colours:** Blue & Navy Hoops/Navy      **Change Colours:** White/Navy

## HEATON STANNINGTON FC

**Chairman:** William Pitt      **Manager/Coach:** Colin Atchinson
**Secretary:** Bob Grounsell, 73 Cleveland Gardens, High Heaton, Newcastle NE7 7QH   (0191 2667464)
**Ground:** Newton Park, Newton Road, High Heaton, Newcastle upon Tyne NE7 7HP   (0191 2819230)
**Directions:** From Newcastle turn left at Corner House Hotel traffic lights into Newton Rd. Continue to r'bout and bear left for 30 yds. Ground is on the right behind the shops. From South Gosforth go past Freeman Hospital, turn left at next roundabout. The ground is on the left approx 250 yards further on.
**Colours:** Black & White Quarters/Black      **Change Colours:** Blue with Black Sleeves/Blue

## HEBBURN REYROLLE FC

**Chairman:** Alan Graham      **Manager/Coach:** Steve Scullion
**Secretary:** Gordon Taylor, 29 Crawley Avenue, Hebburn, Tyne & Wear NE31 2LT   (0191 4834537)
**Ground:** Hebburn Sports Ground, Victoria Road West, Hebburn, Tyne & Wear
**Directions:** From Newcastle and Gateshead via the Felling Bypass to Heworth Roundabout, take A195 signed Hebburn/Jarrow. Ground 2 miles on left. From Tyne Tunnel take Jarrow/Hebburn road A195. Ground 2 miles on right.
**Colours:** Red & Blue/Blue      **Change Colours:** Green & Blue/Navy

## NEWBIGGIN CENTRAL WELFARE FC

**Chairman:** Henry Callan      **Manager/Coach:** Peter Crichton
**Secretary:** George Penman, 10 Vernon Place, Newbiggin-by-the-Sea, NE64 6ED   (01670 854278)
**Ground:** Newbiggin Welfare, Cleveland Terrace, Newbiggin-by-the-Sea, Northumberland
**Directions:** Enter Newbiggin from Spine Road (A189). Continue towards town centre. After 2nd pedestrian crossing turn left between Library and Chemist's. Drive 800 metres and just before school turn right before bungalow.
**Colours:** White/Red      **Change Colours:** Blue & Yellow/Blue

## NEWCASTLE BENFIELD PARK FC

**Chairman:** Jimmy Rowe      **Manager/Coach:** Tommy Sword
**Secretary:** Tony Baird, 23 Balkwell Avenue, North Shields, Tyne & Wear NE29 7JN   (0191 2580833)
**Ground:** Benfield Park, Benfield Road, Newcastle upon Tyne
**Directions:** From Newcastle towards the coast take second slip road after Corner House public house traffic lights and turn right into Benfield Road. The ground is on the left opposite Walkergate Hospital and adjacent to the school.
**Colours:** All White      **Change Colours:** All Red

## NORTHBANK CARLISLE FC

**Chairman:** Kenny Brown      **Manager/Coach:** Kenny Dixon/Neil Rudd
**Secretary:** Bob Lancaster, 25 South Street, Carlisle, Cumbria CA1 2EW   (01228 539383)
**Ground:** Sheepmount Sports Complex, Carlisle   (01228 526569)
**Directions:** Take B6264 Brampton-Carlisle road. Follow Workington sign. Continue past Carlisle Castle on right. Where road intersects double back and turn left just before Castle, follow road down keeping left till you reach ground.
**Colours:** Red with White Sleeves/Red      **Change Colours:** Yellow with Navy Sleeves/Navy

## PERCY MAIN AMATEURS FC

**Chairman:** George Mooney      **Manager/Coach:** B Rodgerson/J Humberstone
**Secretary:** Graham Marsh, 32 Selkirk Way, Chirton Park, North Shields NE29 8DD   (0191 2911526)
**Ground:** Purvis Park, St John's Green, Percy Main, North Shields, Tyne & Wear
**Directions:** From Tyne Tunnel take Royal Quays signs, after school take 2nd left. Ground 1st on right
**Colours:** All White      **Change Colours:** All Red

## PONTELAND UNITED FC

**Chairman:** Frank Smith      **Manager/Coach:** Barrie Wardrobe/Steve Baxter
**Secretary:** Leo McMahon, 1 Wardle Drive, Annitsford, Cramlington, Tyne & Wear NE23 7DB   (0191 2500463)
**Ground:** Ponteland Leisure Centre, Ponteland   (01661 825441)
**Directions:** Enter Ponteland from Newcastle, turn left at traffic lights, ground 100 metres on left.
**Colours:** Black & White Stripes/Black      **Change Colours:** All White

## RYTON FC

**Chairman:** Philip K Hall      **Manager/Coach:** Steven Murray
**Secretary:** Les Robson, 31 Park View Gardens, Runhead, Ryton, Tyne & Wear NE40 3JD (0191 4137628)
**Ground:** Kingsley Park, Crawcrook, Tyne & Wear
**Directions:** From Newcastle & East through Blaydon & Ryton to Crawcrook. At lights turn right onto Wylam & Clara Vale road. Ground 400 yds on right. From West via Prudhoe & Crawcrook and turn left at lights.
**Colours:** Blue & Black Stripes/Black      **Change Colours:** Orange/Black

## SEATON DELAVAL AMATEURS FC

**Chairman:** Tom Ashburn      **Manager/Coach:** Ian Watts
**Secretary:** Brian Plant, 17 Doddington Drive, Hall Close Dale, Cramlington NE23 6DE (01670 715209)
**Ground:** Wheatridge Park, Seaton Delaval, Northumberland
**Directions:** A189 from Newcastle to Annitsford r'bout. A190 to Seaton Delaval, at r'bout in Seaton Delaval turn left. Ground 1/4 mile on right behind Dale Garage and the Market Garden.
**Colours:** Red & Blue Halves/Blue      **Change Colours:** Yellow/Black

## SHANKHOUSE FC

**Chairman:** George Davison      **Manager/Coach:** Garry Kirkup
**Secretary:** Syd Ramsey, 6 Brinkburn Avenue, Cramlington, Northumberland NE23 6TB (01670 715943)
**Ground:** Wheatridge Park, Seaton Delaval (temporary)
**Directions:** A189 from Newcastle to Annitsford r'bout. A190 to Seaton Delaval, at r'bout in Seaton Delaval turn left. Ground 1/4 mile on right behind Dale Garage and the Market Garden.
**Colours:** Black & Yellow Quarters/Black      **Change Colours:** White/Blue

## SPITTAL ROVERS FC

**Chairman:** Noel Evans      **Manager/Coach:** Carl Hudson
**Secretary:** Graeme Burn, 7 Sea Road, Spittal, Berwick upon Tweed, TD15 1RN (01289 306049)
**Ground:** Newfields, Berwick-upon-Tweed
**Directions:** From South take Berwick bypass to 3rd r'bout. Safeway store on right. For pitch take 2nd left on r'bout. NB: Do NOT park in Newfields Estate beside clubhouse.
**Colours:** Black & White Stripes/Black      **Change Colours:** Red/Red

## WALKER CENTRAL FC

**Chairman:** Robert Morton      **Manager/Coach:** Allan Bell
**Secretary:** Bob Mulroy, 116 Lancefield Avenue, Walker, Newcastle upon Tyne NE6 3ER (0191 2873189)
**Ground:** Lightfoot Sports Centre, Walker, Newcastle upon Tyne
**Directions:** From City take Shields Road to Union Rd, then to Welbeck Rd. Turn right onto St Anthonys Rd and onto Warrier St. Lightfoot Centre on right.
**Colours:** All Blue      **Change Colours:** Green & White/White

## WALKER LEDWOOD FOSSE FC

**Chairman:** W A Callanan      **Manager/Coach:** Ian Wall
**Secretary:** S Gate, 12 Meadwalk, Walkerdene, Newcastle upon Tyne NE6 4HB (0191 2763514)
**Ground:** Miller's Dene, Walkergate, Newcastle upon Tyne
**Directions:** From Newcastle through Byker to r'bout at top of Shields Rd & turn right. Left at B&Q store down Fossway. Ground 2nd one down Fossway past Fire Station and on left.
**Colours:** Red with White Sleeves/Red      **Change Colours:** Yellow with Navy Sleeves/Navy

## WEST ALLOTMENT CELTIC FC

**Chairman:** Joe Mather      **Manager/Coach:** Ken Scott
**Secretary:** John Jackson, 4 Rosewood Crescent, Seaton Sluice, Whitley Bay NE26 4BL (0191 2370416)
**Ground:** Hillheads Park, Whitley Bay (0191 2913637)
**Directions:** From Newcastle take A1058 to Foxhunters PH. Turn right follow A191 to Whitley Bay Ice Rink on right. Ground next to Ice Rink.
**Colours:** Green & White Hoops/ Green      **Change Colours:** All Blue

## WINLATON HALLGARTH FC

**Chairman:** Robert Young      **Manager/Coach:** Stephen Breen/Jeff Wightman
**Secretary:** Sid Batey, 6 Wylam View, Winlaton, Tyne & Wear NE21 4RJ (0191 4147970)
**Ground:** Shibdon Park, Shibdon Road, Blaydon-on-Tyne
**Directions:** From A1 North: Over Tyne Bridge at Scotswood take 1st exit for signed Consett. Right at 1st r'bout to next r'bout at Swalwell. Right for Blayton & Winlaton. Ground quarter mile on right. Turn into Blaydon Baths car park.
**Colours:** Green & White/White      **Change Colours:** Blue & White Stripes/Blue

# TEESSIDE STRONGARM FOOTBALL LEAGUE

## FEEDER TO: NORTHERN LEAGUE

**President:** K P Moore    **Chairman:** L Crossman
**Secretary:** R D Marsay
12 Aislaby Court, Wilton Lane, Guisborough, Cleveland TS14 6TG
Tel: 01287 637087

## FINAL LEAGUE TABLE 1998-99

| | P | W | D | L | F | A | Pts | GD |
|---|---|---|---|---|---|---|---|---|
| Grangetown BC | 32 | 29 | 2 | 1 | 118 | 38 | 89 | 80 |
| Acklam SW | 32 | 22 | 5 | 5 | 95 | 38 | 71 | 57 |
| Dormans Ath | 32 | 22 | 3 | 7 | 84 | 40 | 69 | 44 |
| Cargo Fleet | 32 | 18 | 5 | 9 | 83 | 66 | 56* | 17 |
| Stokesley SC | 32 | 17 | 4 | 11 | 79 | 59 | 55 | 20 |
| Fishburn Park | 32 | 16 | 5 | 11 | 62 | 46 | 53 | 16 |
| Bedale Ath | 32 | 15 | 0 | 17 | 65 | 79 | 45 | -14 |
| Carlin How | 32 | 13 | 5 | 14 | 68 | 60 | 44 | 8 |
| Thornaby YC | 32 | 14 | 5 | 13 | 69 | 74 | 44* | -5 |
| Nunthorpe Ath | 32 | 13 | 4 | 15 | 68 | 61 | 43 | 7 |
| Whitby Town Res | 32 | 12 | 7 | 13 | 53 | 53 | 43 | 0 |
| Beads FC | 32 | 13 | 3 | 16 | 53 | 59 | 42 | -6 |
| British Steel | 32 | 12 | 6 | 14 | 76 | 88 | 39* | -12 |
| Thornaby | 32 | 10 | 3 | 19 | 57 | 79 | 33 | -22 |
| Richmond Town | 32 | 6 | 2 | 24 | 34 | 80 | 20 | -46 |
| Guisb Town Res | 32 | 3 | 6 | 23 | 32 | 90 | 15 | -58 |
| New Marske SC | 32 | 3 | 3 | 26 | 36 | 122 | 6** | -86 |

## RESULTS CHART 1998-99

| | 1 | 2 | 3 | 4 | 5 | 6 | 7 | 8 | 9 | 10 | 11 | 12 | 13 | 14 | 15 | 16 | 17 |
|---|---|---|---|---|---|---|---|---|---|---|---|---|---|---|---|---|---|
| 1 Acklam SW | X | 2-1 | 3-0 | 2-2 | 5-0 | 3-2 | 0-2 | 1-0 | 3-3 | 2-2 | 4-1 | 3-0 | 3-1 | 3-3 | 4-0 | 4-1 | 3-0 |
| 2 Beads FC | 1-2 | X | 5-0 | 4-1 | 2-0 | 1-3 | 0-3 | 0-1 | 0-6 | 6-0 | 2-0 | 3-0 | 1-0 | 0-3 | 1-2 | 2-1 | 2-0 |
| 3 Bedale ATH | 2-6 | 5-2 | X | 3-2 | 2-0 | 0-2 | 2-1 | 0-6 | 6-3 | 5-0 | 0-2 | 4-0 | 1-3 | 2-0 | 1-3 | 6-2 | |
| 4 Bsc sports | 1-5 | 1-0 | 1-7 | X | 6-3 | 1-4 | 0-8 | 0-5 | 1-4 | 2-1 | 3-3 | 3-0 | 3-1 | 1-1 | 3-3 | 5-7 | 3-2 |
| 5 Cargo Fleet | 3-2 | 3-2 | 4-1 | 3-5 | X | 3-3 | 3-1 | 1-1 | 1-3 | 4-0 | 1-0 | 2-1 | 5-2 | 2-0 | 1-0 | 6-3 | 2-4 |
| 6 Carlin How | 0-3 | 2-2 | 1-2 | 1-1 | 2-4 | X | 0-2 | 2-1 | 2-3 | 3-0 | 5-1 | 3-3 | 7-3 | 1-5 | 2-0 | 0-3 | 1-2 |
| 7 Dormans Ath | 0-5 | 3-1 | 3-0 | 2-1 | 1-2 | 3-2 | X | 3-0 | 2-3 | 3-1 | 3-0 | 2-1 | 1-3 | 2-4 | 3-1 | 3-3 | 3-1 |
| 8 Fishburn park | 1-1 | 0-0 | 4-0 | 2-1 | 3-3 | 0-3 | 1-3 | X | 0-2 | 2-1 | 4-1 | 2-0 | 3-1 | 1-3 | 4-2 | 2-1 | 0-0 |
| 9 Grangetown BC | 5-1 | 4-1 | 6-1 | 5-1 | 4-0 | 4-2 | 1-0 | 4-2 | X | 3-0 | 2-1 | 3-2 | 4-1 | 5-1 | 4-1 | 6-0 | 0-0 |
| 10 Guisbrough Tn | 1-2 | 0-1 | 0-2 | 2-6 | 0-3 | 1-1 | 0-6 | 0-4 | 1-4 | X | 1-0 | 1-6 | 4-2 | 1-1 | 0-1 | 1-2 | 0-0 |
| 11 New Marske SC | 2-9 | 2-2 | 4-1 | 0-5 | 1-5 | 0-1 | 2-6 | 3-5 | 0-6 | 4-1 | X | 0-4 | 5-2 | 1-8 | 1-6 | 2-2 | 0-3 |
| 12 Nunthorpe Ath | 0-3 | 0-3 | 5-1 | 3-5 | 1-1 | 2-1 | 0-3 | 0-1 | 9-4 | 2-2 | 4-0 | X | 4-1 | 0-1 | 4-2 | 2-2 | 4-2 |
| 13 Richmond Town | 2-1 | 0-1 | 2-0 | 1-4 | 0-1 | 0-3 | 0-3 | 1-4 | 0-1 | 2-0 | 2-0 | 1-3 | X | 0-3 | 1-2 | 1-4 | 2-1 |
| 14 Stokesley SC | 1-3 | 3-1 | 2-4 | 0-4 | 3-6 | 4-1 | 3-4 | 2-4 | 3-4 | 1-3 | 3-0 | 1-0 | 1-1 | X | 4-2 | 0-2 | 3-1 |
| 15 Thornaby FC | 1-4 | 2-3 | 5-1 | 3-2 | 2-5 | 1-4 | 1-1 | 0-3 | 0-3 | 2-1 | 6-1 | 3-5 | 0-0 | 1-3 | X | 4-1 | 0-3 |
| 16 Thornaby YC | 2-1 | 5-1 | 0-4 | 2-1 | 4-3 | 0-4 | 1-3 | 3-0 | 2-3 | 2-2 | 7-0 | 1-0 | 2-1 | 0-3 | 2-5 | X | 1-1 |
| 17 Whitby T Res | 0-1 | 3-1 | 0-2 | 1-1 | 3-3 | 2-0 | 0-0 | 2-1 | 0-5 | 5-2 | 7-0 | 0-1 | 2-0 | 0-3 | 3-2 | 3-1 | X |

## MACMILLAN BOWL 1998-99

**SEMI-FINALS**

| Dormans Athletic | v | Nunthorpe Ath | 1-3 | | Acklam SW | v | Grangetown BC | 1-0 |
|---|---|---|---|---|---|---|---|---|

**FINAL**

| Acklam SW | v | Nunthorpe Ath | 1-2 |
|---|---|---|---|

## R T RAINE TROPHY 1998-99

**SEMI FINALS**

| Cargo Fleet | v | Guisborough Tn Res | 6-0 | | Thornaby | v | Richmond Town | 1-0 |
|---|---|---|---|---|---|---|---|---|

**FINAL**

| Cargo Fleet | v | Thornaby | 2-1 |
|---|---|---|---|

 # NON-LEAGUE NEWSDESK

## FOR RESULTS, TABLES AND NEWS
## FROM THE NON-LEAGUE PYRAMID

Now entering its fifth full season, Non-League Newsdesk has become firmly established as the number one magazine for up-to-date news and statistics from the Pyramid world.

Founded in 1995 by former Non-League Club Directory editor James Wright, Non-League Newsdesk will in 1999-2000 celebrate its 200th edition. The magazine is delivered to subscribers every midweek (usually Wednesday) carrying all the previous week's results, together with current tables, from around FIFTY leagues.

For many of the more senior competitions, full match details (such as goalscorers and attendances) are supplied. County and League Cup competitions are also extensively featured, as are the FA Umbro Trophy and FA Carlsberg Vase, and the involvement of the non-League clubs in the AXA sponsored FA Cup.

But Non-League Newsdesk is not just a statistical work. Each week the magazine carries up-to-date news stories and listings of managerial changes and transfers.

The magazine is therefore particularly popular with -
      * Clubs, who find much of the information extremely useful for matchday programmes and in checking on forthcoming opponents, particularly those from outside their own league.
      * Statisticians, who see the weekly stats as the most extensive, accurate and up-to-date available.
      * Groundhoppers, who find it invaluable in picking their games.
      * The more general non-League enthusiast who likes to keep abreast of the most current news.
If you would like to see a free sample copy from 1998-99, please send an SAE to James Wright at the address below.

Leagues featured in Non-League Newsdesk include: Nationwide Conference, UniBond, Ryman, Dr Martens, First NW Trains NWCL, SGL West Lancs, Manchester, Carlsberg West Cheshire, Green Contract Services Mid-Cheshire, Arnott Insurance Northern, Northern Co's (East), Redferns Central Midlands, Powerleague Notts Alliance, West Yorkshire, Deejays Lincs, Everards Leics, Vaux Wearside, JPL Wade Northern Alliance, Herts, A Quote Insurance Reading, Courage Combined Co's, Cherry Red Chiltonian, Minerva SSML, Essex Senior, Essex Intermediate, Kent Blaxill Essex & Suffolk Border, Interlink Alliance, Endsleigh Midland Comb, Banks's West Mids, Springbank Vending Midland, Complete Music Hellenic, Glos. County, Somerset Senior, Screwfix Western, Jewson SW, Jolly's Cornwall Combination, Cornish Guardian East Cornwall, Westward Developments Devon, Jewson Wessex, Keyline Dorset Comb., Dorset Co., Hampshire, Unijet Sussex, Bass Kent, British Energy Kent Co., Jewson ECL, Lovewell Blake Anglian Combination, McGinty's Suffolk & Ipswich, Uhlsport UCL, Optimum Interiors Capital and Central Conference, League of Wales, CC Sports Welsh League, Cymru Alliance.

JAMES WRIGHT, 13 NORTHFIELD AVENUE, TAUNTON, SOMERSET TA1 1XF
TEL/FAX: 01823 327720  MOBILE: 0421 004219  E-MAIL:NLNEWSDESK@ZETNET.CO.UK

# BRITISH INDUSTRIAL RECLAMATION SHEFFIELD COUNTY FOOTBALL LEAGUE

**President:** M Matthews Esq.    **Chairman:** F Wright Esq.

**Secretary:** R Beadsworth Esq., 32 Cockayne Place, Norton Lees, Sheffield S8 9DG
Tel/Fax: 0114 2551275

he 1998-99 League and League Cup kicked off in September with 42 competing clubs. However, by the time that Woodhouse West End and Sheffield Centralians played the last game in May both Brinsworth Athletic and Elsecar Market Hotel had resigned leaving 40 clubs to complete a total of 496 League fixtures and 40 Cup ties. Difficulties prevailed throughout the season and only the efforts of club secretaries ensured that the season was completed by he deadline.

Wombwell Main and Phoenix led the Premier Division throughout the season. Two results at the end of May - Vombwell Main 3 Phoenix 2, and Parkgate 3 Phoenix 0 - ensured that Wombwell Main took the coveted League Championship.

Hare & Hounds and Athersley Recreation were tied at the top of the First Division when they met to conclude heir fixtures. With Hare & Hounds eventually winning the game 3-2 the First Division title was decided.

Throughout the second half of the campaign Thorpe Hesley and Norton Woodseats were leaders in the chase or the title of Second Division Champions. Again we had to wait for the last week in May when a 3-1 home defeat of South Kirkby Colliery proved to be a title winning result for Norton Woodseats. A late run of wins ensured the runners-up spot for Woodhouse West End.

Frecheville CA and Phoenix won five League Cup ties to reach the final round at Stocksbridge Park Steels' Bracken Moor Ground. An hour before kick-off the conditions were ideal. But it was not to last as an unexpected blizzard nearly caused the game to be abandoned. The players and officials persevered and a single goal gave recheville CA the British Industrial Reclamation County Senior League Cup trophy and as time was to tell the first of wo runners-up awards for Phoenix.

Athersley Recreation's and Wombwell Main's achievement in reaching the latter stages of the County Senior Cup must also be noted. Athersley Recreation's excellent run came to an end when they lost their Quarter Final encounter with Wombwell Main. Main then failed at the penultimate round when losing to Emley.

Of the 496 League fixtures played 182 from the Premier Division realised 692 goals at an average of 3.8 per ame; the 182 games played in the First Division realised 750 goals averaging 4.1 per game, whilst the Second Division provided 132 games and 591 goals at an average of 4.5 per game.

Davy's Lee Machin, with 25 goals, won The Hague & Ibbotson leading individual goalscorer award. Other notable erformers were David Moore - Avest Sheffield (24), Simon Broomhead - Davy (24), Nicky Struggles - Phoenix (23), Alan mith - Athersley Recreation (21), Russell Bailey - ABS Kilnhurst (18) and Andrew Ogden - Sheffield Lane Top (14).

## FINAL LEAGUE TABLES 1998-99

### PREMIER DIVISION

| | P | W | D | L | F | A | Pts |
|---|---|---|---|---|---|---|---|
| Wombwell Main | 26 | 16 | 2 | 8 | 56 | 38 | 50 |
| Phoenix | 26 | 13 | 8 | 5 | 78 | 40 | 47 |
| Parkgate Res. | 26 | 15 | 1 | 10 | 59 | 39 | 46 |
| Frecheville CA | 26 | 12 | 6 | 8 | 54 | 37 | 42 |
| Ecclesfield Red Rose | 26 | 12 | 5 | 9 | 52 | 39 | 41 |
| Denaby United Res. | 26 | 11 | 8 | 7 | 47 | 48 | 41 |
| The Wetherby | 26 | 11 | 6 | 9 | 45 | 39 | 39 |
| Wombwell Town | 26 | 10 | 7 | 9 | 37 | 53 | 37 |
| Mexborough Ath Res. | 26 | 9 | 9 | 8 | 39 | 35 | 36 |
| Sheffield Lane Top | 26 | 10 | 5 | 11 | 55 | 50 | 35 |
| Worksop Town Res. | 26 | 10 | 1 | 15 | 56 | 53 | 31 |
| Penistone Church | 26 | 9 | 4 | 13 | 45 | 61 | 31 |
| Stocksbridge P S Res. | 26 | 6 | 3 | 17 | 37 | 64 | 21 |
| Caribbean Sports | 26 | 3 | 5 | 18 | 32 | 96 | 14 |

### DIVISION ONE

| | P | W | D | L | F | A | Pts |
|---|---|---|---|---|---|---|---|
| Hare & Hounds | 26 | 20 | 4 | 2 | 62 | 17 | 64 |
| Athersley Rec | 26 | 20 | 1 | 5 | 79 | 35 | 61 |
| Hallam Res. | 26 | 18 | 3 | 5 | 61 | 27 | 57 |
| NCB Maltby M Welfare | 26 | 11 | 5 | 10 | 50 | 56 | 38 |
| High Green Villa | 26 | 11 | 4 | 11 | 45 | 47 | 37 |
| Treeton Welfare | 26 | 10 | 5 | 11 | 48 | 62 | 35 |
| Parramore Sports | 26 | 10 | 3 | 13 | 59 | 58 | 33 |
| Wickersley Old Boys | 26 | 9 | 4 | 13 | 52 | 52 | 31 |
| Sheffield Res. | 26 | 9 | 4 | 13 | 51 | 56 | 31 |
| Swinton Athletic | 26 | 8 | 7 | 11 | 47 | 60 | 31 |
| Oughtibridge W M Spts | 26 | 9 | 3 | 14 | 45 | 62 | 30 |
| Avesta Sheffield | 26 | 8 | 3 | 15 | 53 | 64 | 27 |
| Grapes Roy Hancock | 26 | 8 | 2 | 16 | 55 | 89 | 26 |
| Sheffield Bankers | 26 | 6 | 2 | 18 | 43 | 65 | 20 |

# PREMIER DIVISION RESULTS CHART 1998-99

|  |  | 1 | 2 | 3 | 4 | 5 | 6 | 7 | 8 | 9 | 10 | 11 | 12 | 13 | 14 |
|---|---|---|---|---|---|---|---|---|---|---|---|---|---|---|---|
| 1 | Caribbean Sports | X | 0-0 | 0-2 | 1-1 | 1-3 | 2-8 | 0-5 | 3-3 | 0-0 | 2-1 | 0-4 | 1-2 | 0-5 | 1-2 |
| 2 | Denaby United | 3-2 | X | 1-1 | 0-2 | 2-0 | 3-0 | 0-3 | 3-2 | 2-2 | 2-0 | 5-4 | 1-3 | 1-1 | 3-2 |
| 3 | Ecclesfield Red Rose | 4-0 | 2-2 | X | 3-3 | 1-1 | 2-0 | 2-4 | 2-2 | 3-2 | 3-1 | 2-1 | 4-1 | 3-0 | 1-0 |
| 4 | Frecheville CA | 2-1 | 4-1 | 1-4 | X | 1-0 | 5-4 | 6-0 | 0-2 | 4-0 | 2-3 | 1-0 | 3-1 | 0-0 | 2-4 |
| 5 | Mexborough M St | 3-4 | 0-0 | 4-1 | 2-2 | X | 0-1 | 1-2 | 2-2 | 2-0 | 2-2 | 1-1 | 0-0 | 1-2 | 3-0 |
| 6 | Parkgate | 5-0 | 3-0 | 2-1 | 3-1 | 5-0 | X | 4-0 | 3-0 | 2-0 | 2-1 | 3-4 | 3-2 | 0-1 | 4-1 |
| 7 | Penistone Church | 2-1 | 2-3 | 1-6 | 1-1 | 1-2 | 0-1 | X | 2-5 | 2-1 | 5-2 | 0-3 | 0-2 | 1-1 | 2-1 |
| 8 | Phoenix | 15-1 | 4-1 | 2-1 | 1-1 | 1-1 | 6-0 | 3-3 | X | 0-4 | 2-1 | 0-0 | 2-0 | 7-1 | 3-2 |
| 9 | Sheffield Lane Top | 7-3 | 2-3 | 4-0 | 3-2 | 1-2 | 2-1 | 3-1 | 0-5 | X | 1-0 | 2-1 | 0-1 | 1-1 | 3-5 |
| 10 | Stocksbridge PS | 3-3 | 1-2 | 0-2 | 0-3 | 0-1 | 2-1 | 5-1 | 2-5 | 1-7 | X | 2-1 | 0-4 | 0-1 | 2-1 |
| 11 | The Wetherby | 1-2 | 1-1 | 1-0 | 0-3 | 2-4 | 1-1 | 3-2 | 2-1 | 1-1 | 1-1 | X | 3-1 | 2-0 | 2-3 |
| 12 | Wombwell Main | 3-1 | 2-0 | 2-0 | 1-4 | 0-0 | 2-1 | 4-2 | 3-2 | 4-3 | 5-2 | 1-2 | X | 5-1 | 4-1 |
| 13 | Wombwell Town | 3-2 | 4-4 | 3-2 | 1-0 | 2-1 | 2-0 | 1-3 | 0-0 | 2-2 | 1-4 | 2-3 | 1-0 | X | 1-7 |
| 14 | Worksop Town | 9-1 | 1-4 | 1-0 | 1-0 | 1-3 | 1-2 | 0-0 | 2-3 | 2-4 | 4-1 | 0-1 | 1-3 | 4-0 | X |

# BRITISH INDUSTRIAL RECLAMATION COUNTY SENIOR LEAGUE CUP 1998-99

## FIRST ROUND

| Penistone Church Rs | v | Oughtibridge WMSC | 0-1 |
| Worksop Town | v | Parramore Sports | 1-3 |
| Frecheville CA | v | Caribbean Sports | 4-0 |
| Hare & Hounds | v | South Kirkby Colliery | 0-1 |
| Hallam | v | ABS Kilnhurst | 2-0 |

| Sheffield | v | Queens Hotel | 4-1 |
| Sheffield Lane Top | v | Old Ewardians | 5-3 |
| Norton Woodseats | v | Treeton Welfare | 0-2 |
| Phoenix | v | Grapes Roy Hancock | 8-1 |
| Woodhouse W End | v | Brinsworth Athletic | 4-1 |

## SECOND ROUND

| Denaby United | v | Swinton Athletic | 3-3, 3p5 |
| High Green Villa | v | Ecclesfield Red Rose | 1-2 |
| Stocksbridge Pk St | v | Parramore Sports | 7-3 |
| NCB Maltby MW | v | Frecheville CA | 1-3 |
| Wombwell Main | v | Parkgate | 4-1 |
| Phoenix | v | Athersley Recreation | 2-1 |
| Woodhouse W End | v | Wombwell Town | 6-2 |
| Sheffield Bankers | v | Davy | 3-3, 5p4 |

| Penistone Church | v | Oughtibridge WMSC | 0-1 |
| Sheffield | v | Harworth C I | 6-1 |
| Sheffield Lane Top | v | Rossington Main | 7-2 |
| Avesta Sheffield | v | Treeton Welfare | 4-3 |
| Thorpe Hesley | v | South Kirkby Colliery | 0-2 |
| The Wetherby | v | Hallam | 0-2 |
| Mexborough Mn St | v | Wickersley | 2-1 |
| Sheffeild Centralians | | bye | |

## THIRD ROUND

| Swinton Athletic | v | Oughtibridge WMSC | 4-3 |
| Stocksbridge Park St | v | Sheffield Lane Top | 2-1 |
| Wombwell Main | v | Sheffield Centralians | 3-0 |
| Hallam | v | Woodhouse W End | 6-0 |

| Ecclesfield R Rose | v | Sheffield | 4-2 |
| Frecheville CA | v | Avesta Sheffield | 2-1 |
| South Kirkby Coll. | v | Phoenix | 2-3 |
| Mexborough M St | v | Sheffield Bankers | 4-2 |

## FOURTH ROUND

| Swinton Athletic | v | Ecclesfield Red Rose | 2-0 |
| Wombwell Main | v | Phoenix | 1-2 |

| Stocksbridge P St | v | Frecheville CA | 1-3 |
| Hallam | v | Mexborough M St | 4-1 |

## SEMI FINALS

| Swinton Athletic | v | Frecheville CA | 0-1 |

| Phoenxi | v | Hallam | 2-1 |

## FINAL

| Frecheville CA | v | Phoenix | 1-0 |

# WEST YORKSHIRE ASSOCIATION FOOTBALL LEAGUE

## Founded 1928

**President:** J Hill   **Chairman:** B Chaplin

**Secretary:** Kevin Parkinson, 9 Lake Lock Drive, Stanley, Wakefield WF3 4HN

The structure of the League was to see the first and reserve teams of clubs compete in separate divisions, which provided a base for a high standard of football in the quest for honours. Those who ended the season as divisional champions will acknowledge that their fellow clubs have all contributed to a most competitive and exciting season.

The enjoyment experienced by clubs in the League Cup Finals is obvious to see and these competitions do provide an opportunity for every team to have a special day. With one exception, the final ties were close encounters with the Premier Division Greenwood Trophy being decided by a penalty shoot-out after extra time. It is in these competitions where the Club Secretary's awareness and authority must particularly be counted to prevent the expulsion of his or her team through the playing of ineligible players. Sadly, and again, some clubs were not meticulous in this area which automatically denied themselves the chance of a cup final place.

This has been an excellent year where many clubs have distinguished themselves by their achievements in District and County FA Cup Competitions. The status and strength of the league can be measured by this success and all clubs are to be congratulated on their excellent performances during the season.

All fixtures have had an official referee appointed in addition to Premier Division matches being allocated two assistant referees. It is pleasing to note that clubs and referees have given good feedback which does recognise the mutual respect demanded and given from both sides. Throughout the season, all referees have received a banding mark based on club markings. This is an additional measure to monitor performance which will benefit everyone if the reporting is accurately and fairly carried out. A number of referees officiating Premier Division matches have had West Riding County FA assessors in attendance as part of the system for their progression. The number of referees who cancel an appointment, having confirmed their availability, gives cause for concern and this does prompt consideration on the appointments system currently employed. The solution though is not easily visualised.

Almost by default, most clubs do provide after-match hospitality and are to be commended. However, there has occasionally been cause for concern when some visiting clubs have paid the consequences for returning home to base after previously indicating otherwise.

Despite a resolute display in our annual fixture with the West Riding County Amateur Football League, we were to experience defeat following last minute scores by our visitors. Although we would wish to be victorious, this match does provide players with the honour to represent the League and to match their skills at a higher level.

In conducting the business of the League, members of the Council and other Committees have fairly and conscientiously attended to the many issues and matters that have come before them. I would particularly like to record my thanks to my fellow officials who have given their best and supported me in the administration of the League.

I have continued to represent the League's interests on the Leeds and District Football Association and this relationship does benefit the majority of clubs as well as both our organisations. Through our dealings with the West Riding County FA, we have continued to offer and receive support which has been of mutual benefit.

We are pleased that Briggsports have continued their sponsorship of the Premier Division Cup Competition and that clubs are being rewarded with their competitive sporting products and services.

As far as publicity is concerned, we have explored the usual avenues which has maintained the League's profile in local footballing circles. Our thanks are extended to the numerous agencies who have assisted us in this important task.

On reflection, the season just ended has been one where the League has consolidated its position in the football pyramid. This is a wonderful standpoint from which we can now further enhance the West Yorkshire League to share a bright and exciting future in the new millennium.

## FAIRPLAY TROPHY 1998-99

**PREMIER DIVISION**

| | |
|---|---|
| Nestle Rowntrees | 245 |

**DIVISION ONE**

| | |
|---|---|
| Willowfield Celtic | 220 |

**DIVISION TWO**

| | |
|---|---|
| Adel | 100 |

**PREMIER RESERVE DIVISION**

| | |
|---|---|
| Horbury Town | 75 |

**RESERVE DIVISION**

| | |
|---|---|
| Whitkirk Wanderers A | 125 |

## GOLDEN BOOT AWARD 1998-99

**PREMIER DIVISION**

| | | |
|---|---|---|
| Brent Terry | Nestle Rowntrees | 32 |

**DIVISION ONE**

| | | |
|---|---|---|
| Lee Parker | Mount St Mary's | 35 |

**DIVISION TWO**

| | | |
|---|---|---|
| James Duval | Churwell Lions | 52 |

**PREMIER RESERVE DIVISION**

| | | |
|---|---|---|
| Gareth Thornton | Whitkirk Wanderers | 26 |

# LEAGUE HONOURS 1998-99

| | CHAMPIONS | RUNNERS UP |
|---|---|---|
| PREMIER DIVISION | Nestle Rowntrees | Carlton Athletic |
| DIVISION ONE | Wetherby Athletic | Magnet Sports |
| DIVISION TWO | Churwell Lions | Ossett Common Rovers |
| PREMIER RESERVE DIVISION | Whitkirk Wanderers | Carlton Athletic |
| RESERVE DIVISION | Whitkirk Wanderers A | Magnet Sports |
| PREMIER DIVISION LEAGUE CUP | Sandy Lane | Nestle Rowntrees |
| (sponsored by Briggsports) | | |
| DIVISION ONE | Pudsey | Armley Athletic |
| DIVISION TWO LEAGUE CUP | Churwell Lions | Great Preston |
| PREM RES DIVISION LEAGUE CUP | Knaresborough Town | Carlton Athletic |
| RESERVE DIVISION LEAGUE CUP | Whitkirk Wanderers A | Dewsbury Moor Athletic |
| FRED WINTERBURN TEAM TROPHY | Hartshead Senior | |
| GEORGE COPE MEMORIAL REFEREE AWARD | Richard J Hirtsch | |

## FINAL LEAGUE TABLES 1998-99

### PREMIER DIVISION

| | P | W | D | L | F | A | Pts |
|---|---|---|---|---|---|---|---|
| Nestle Rowntrees | 28 | 20 | 5 | 3 | 90 | 38 | 65 |
| Carlton Athletic | 28 | 18 | 4 | 6 | 73 | 34 | 58 |
| Beeston St Anthonys | 28 | 17 | 7 | 4 | 71 | 36 | 58 |
| Whitkirk Wanderers | 28 | 16 | 5 | 7 | 77 | 45 | 53 |
| Rothwell Athletic | 28 | 15 | 7 | 6 | 62 | 38 | 52 |
| Knaresborough Town | 28 | 14 | 4 | 10 | 65 | 58 | 46 |
| Wakefield | 28 | 12 | 4 | 12 | 52 | 48 | 40 |
| Aberford Albion | 28 | 11 | 4 | 13 | 53 | 64 | 37 |
| Horbury Town | 28 | 10 | 4 | 14 | 66 | 66 | 34 |
| Sandy Lane | 28 | 8 | 10 | 10 | 48 | 51 | 34 |
| Horsforth St Margaret's | 28 | 7 | 10 | 11 | 40 | 51 | 31 |
| Bardsey | 28 | 5 | 8 | 15 | 33 | 74 | 23 |
| York Railway Institute | 28 | 6 | 3 | 19 | 49 | 91 | 21 |
| Nostell Miners Welfare | 28 | 4 | 6 | 18 | 34 | 70 | 18 |
| Barwick | 28 | 4 | 5 | 19 | 40 | 89 | 17 |

### DIVISION ONE

| | P | W | D | L | F | A | Pts |
|---|---|---|---|---|---|---|---|
| Wetherby Athletic | 26 | 16 | 6 | 4 | 65 | 29 | 54 |
| Magnet Sports | 26 | 17 | 2 | 7 | 66 | 36 | 53 |
| Pudsey | 26 | 16 | 4 | 6 | 61 | 37 | 52 |
| Selby RSSC | 26 | 17 | 1 | 8 | 60 | 47 | 52 |
| Mount St Mary's | 26 | 15 | 4 | 7 | 56 | 35 | 49 |
| Pontefract Labour | 26 | 14 | 2 | 10 | 62 | 41 | 44 |
| Armley Athletic | 26 | 11 | 6 | 9 | 56 | 34 | 39 |
| Woodhouse Hill WMC | 26 | 9 | 4 | 13 | 50 | 50 | 31 |
| Featherstone Colliery | 26 | 10 | 1 | 15 | 44 | 62 | 31 |
| Garforth WMC | 26 | 7 | 5 | 14 | 50 | 64 | 26 |
| Robin Hood Athletic | 26 | 7 | 4 | 15 | 31 | 55 | 25 |
| Rothwell Stones | 26 | 7 | 4 | 15 | 34 | 69 | 25 |
| Sherburn White Rose | 26 | 5 | 6 | 15 | 28 | 74 | 21 |
| Willowfield Celtic | 26 | 6 | 1 | 19 | 42 | 72 | 19 |

## PREMIER DIVISION RESULTS CHART 1998-99

| # | Team | 1 | 2 | 3 | 4 | 5 | 6 | 7 | 8 | 9 | 10 | 11 | 12 | 13 | 14 | 15 | 16 |
|---|---|---|---|---|---|---|---|---|---|---|---|---|---|---|---|---|---|
| 1 | Aberford Albion | X | 2-5 | 1-4 | 1-2 | 1-5 | 0-4 | 3-2 | 6-3 | 1-4 | 2-1 | 1-1 | 1-1 | | 4-0 | 1-3 | 4-3 |
| 2 | Bardsey | 1-2 | X | 4-2 | 0-2 | 1-2 | 1-2 | 1-1 | 0-0 | 0-2 | 1-1 | 1-1 | 1-1 | | 1-4 | 0-6 | 0-5 |
| 3 | Barwick | 2-8 | 4-2 | X | 0-6 | 0-4 | 1-2 | 2-4 | 1-3 | 0-1 | 3-3 | 2-3 | 0-1 | | 2-1 | 1-1 | 2-2 |
| 4 | Beeston St Anthony's | 5-1 | 1-1 | 4-2 | X | 3-1 | 3-0 | 2-3 | 4-3 | 1-1 | 3-0 | 2-3 | 2-1 | | 2-2 | 3-0 | 8-0 |
| 5 | Carlton Athletic | 3-1 | 4-1 | 3-3 | 1-1 | X | 3-0 | 2-0 | 6-1 | 1-4 | 4-0 | 2-0 | 4-2 | | 4-2 | 1-1 | 0-1 |
| 6 | Horbury Town | 5-2 | 1-1 | 2-0 | 2-3 | 1-3 | X | 1-2 | 5-1 | 4-5 | 2-4 | 1-1 | 3-3 | | 1-1 | 0-3 | 4-3 |
| 7 | Horsforth St Margarets | 2-1 | 0-0 | 1-1 | 1-3 | 1-2 | 5-1 | X | 2-2 | 1-3 | 0-0 | 0-0 | 0-2 | | 1-2 | 0-4 | 6-2 |
| 8 | Knaresborough Town | 0-1 | 2-1 | 4-1 | 1-3 | 2-0 | 4-3 | 0-0 | X | 5-0 | 2-1 | 1-1 | 2-0 | | 2-1 | 2-3 | 6-0 |
| 9 | Nestle Rowntrees | 1-3 | 7-0 | 8-1 | 8-1 | 1-0 | 4-1 | 3-3 | 5-1 | X | 3-3 | 5-2 | 2-1 | | 5-0 | 5-2 | 3-0 |
| 10 | Nostell Miners Welf | 0-3 | 0-1 | 4-1 | 1-0 | 0-5 | 1-6 | 1-1 | 2-5 | 2-2 | X | 0-3 | 3-2 | | 2-3 | 1-4 | 0-2 |
| 11 | Rothwell Athletic | 2-0 | 1-3 | 4-0 | 1-1 | 1-2 | 3-2 | 5-1 | 1-2 | 3-1 | 1-0 | X | 2-2 | | 2-1 | 0-1 | 4-2 |
| 12 | Sandy Lane | 2-2 | 5-1 | 4-1 | 1-1 | 2-2 | 3-2 | 1-1 | 2-4 | 0-0 | 2-1 | 1-4 | X | | 2-1 | 3-1 | 1-2 |
| 13 | Swillington MW | | | | | | | | | | | | | | | | |
| 14 | Wakefield | 3-1 | 3-0 | 1-0 | 0-1 | 3-1 | 1-3 | 4-0 | 4-1 | 1-2 | 2-1 | 0-3 | 3-0 | | X | 1-1 | 3-3 |
| 15 | Whitkirk Wanderers | 1-1 | 10-1 | 8-3 | 1-1 | 1-4 | 2-1 | 3-0 | 3-2 | 0-2 | 3-0 | 1-6 | 2-0 | | 0-3 | X | 8-0 |
| 16 | York RI | * | 3-4 | 0-1 | 0-3 | 0-4 | 3-7 | 0-2 | 2-4 | 1-3 | 4-2 | 3-4 | 2-2 | | 3-2 | 3-4 | X |

* York RI v Aberford Albion not played - 3 points awarded to Aberford Albion

Swillington MW resigned from the League - playing record expunged

# WEST RIDING COUNTY AMATEUR FOOTBALL LEAGUE

**President:** D H Humpleby Esq
**Secretary:** Mr S Mitchell
24 Burnsall Road, Liversedge, West Yorkshire WF15 6QF
Tel: 01924 404684

For the second season running the championship of the Premier Division was not decided until the final games of the season. Hemsworth Miners Welfare won their final game at Tyersal 4-1 to go level with Storthes Hall, but stay in second place on goal difference. Storthes Hall, who lost the championship last season to local Huddersfield rivals Marsden, when they lost and Marsden managed a 0-0 draw at Hemsworth, knew that a draw or if they lost, without losing by a landslide at home to Marsden they would clinch their first ever championship. They lost 3-0.

In Division One Altofts, who were relegated in 1998-99, made a great bid to return to the top flight at the first attempt, but failed on goal difference, behind Littletown who regained their Premier Division status after a seven year absence. Bay Athletic from Huddersfield in only their third season in the league clinched the top spot winning 2-1 at Dudley Hill Athletic, scoring in the final minute of the final game.

Storthes Hall won the West Riding County FA Challenge Cup, beating West Yorkshire League rivals Aberford Albion 3-1, whilst Hemsworth Miners Welfare lost in their Sheffield & Hallamshire Junior Cup Final to Dinnington Social by 4-3.

As the League enters the new millennium it is hoped that the top three Divisions, Premier, One and Two, will consist of first teams only with reserves sides in Divisions Three and Four.

*Philip W Rhodes, Results & Publicity Secretary*

## ROLL OF HONOUR 1998-99

| | Champions | Runners Up | Cup Winners |
|---|---|---|---|
| PREMIER DIVISION | Storthes Hall | Hemsworth M.W. | Brighouse Town |
| DIVISION ONE | Bay Athletic | Littletown | Ventus/Yeadon Celtic |
| DIVISION TWO | Lower Hopton | Heckmondwike Town | Lower Hopton |
| DIVISION THREE | Trinity Athletic | Dynamoes | Hunsworth |
| DIVISION FOUR (Reserves) | Hemsworth M.W. | Salt Old Boys | Hemsworth M.W. |

## FINAL LEAGUE TABLES 1998-99

### PREMIER DIVISION

| | P | W | D | L | F | A | Pts | GD |
|---|---|---|---|---|---|---|---|---|
| Storthes Hall | 26 | 20 | 0 | 6 | 73 | 27 | 40 | 46 |
| Hemsworth M.W. | 26 | 18 | 4 | 4 | 68 | 28 | 40 | 40 |
| Phoenix | 26 | 15 | 3 | 8 | 73 | 30 | 31* | 43 |
| Brighouse Town | 26 | 12 | 7 | 7 | 47 | 34 | 31 | 13 |
| Campion | 26 | 13 | 4 | 9 | 70 | 51 | 30 | 19 |
| Field | 26 | 11 | 7 | 8 | 57 | 46 | 29 | 11 |
| Ovenden West R | 26 | 12 | 4 | 10 | 49 | 44 | 28 | 5 |
| Tyersal | 26 | 11 | 4 | 11 | 54 | 70 | 26 | -16 |
| Marsden | 26 | 10 | 5 | 11 | 36 | 32 | 25 | 4 |
| Wibsey | 26 | 7 | 6 | 13 | 37 | 51 | 20 | -14 |
| Crag Road Utd | 26 | 8 | 4 | 14 | 33 | 58 | 20 | -25 |
| Golcar Utd | 26 | 6 | 6 | 14 | 35 | 51 | 18 | -16 |
| Halifax Irish | 26 | 8 | 2 | 16 | 43 | 86 | 18 | -43 |
| Pontefract Boro | 26 | 2 | 2 | 22 | 28 | 95 | 6 | -67 |

### DIVISION ONE

| | P | W | D | L | F | A | PT | GD |
|---|---|---|---|---|---|---|---|---|
| Bay Athletic | 30 | 20 | 5 | 5 | 74 | 44 | 45 | 30 |
| Littletown | 30 | 19 | 6 | 5 | 80 | 37 | 44 | 43 |
| Altofts | 30 | 18 | 8 | 4 | 70 | 33 | 44 | 37 |
| Hall Green Utd | 30 | 14 | 9 | 7 | 73 | 53 | 37 | 20 |
| Eastmoor | 30 | 12 | 10 | 8 | 72 | 56 | 34 | 16 |
| Overthorpe | 30 | 12 | 7 | 11 | 65 | 52 | 31 | 13 |
| Dudley Hill Athletic | 30 | 10 | 11 | 9 | 50 | 50 | 31 | 0 |
| Ardsley Celtic | 30 | 8 | 14 | 8 | 45 | 40 | 30 | 5 |
| Rawdon old Boys | 30 | 10 | 10 | 10 | 59 | 61 | 30 | -2 |
| Otley Town | 30 | 10 | 9 | 11 | 46 | 41 | 29 | 5 |
| Salt Old Boys | 30 | 8 | 9 | 13 | 46 | 59 | 25 | -13 |
| Ventus/Yeadon C | 30 | 8 | 8 | 14 | 51 | 81 | 24 | -30 |
| Pudsey Liberal | 30 | 8 | 5 | 17 | 57 | 83 | 21 | -26 |
| Farnley W.M.C. | 30 | 8 | 4 | 18 | 53 | 67 | 20 | -14 |
| Greetland | 30 | 7 | 5 | 18 | 42 | 83 | 19 | -41 |
| Salts | 30 | 5 | 6 | 19 | 31 | 74 | 16 | -43 |

# NORTH EASTERN FINAL LEAGUE TABLES 1998-99

## BARNSLEY & DISTRICT FOOTBALL ASSOCIATION
### PREMIER DIVISION

|                    | P  | W  | D | L  | F  | A  | Pts |
|--------------------|----|----|---|----|----|----|-----|
| Lundwood Lane End  | 22 | 17 | 2 | 3  | 79 | 26 | 53  |
| Thurnscoe Butchers* | 22 | 14 | 5 | 3  | 51 | 22 | 44  |
| Athersley Rec Res. | 22 | 13 | 4 | 5  | 57 | 26 | 43  |
| Dodworth Miners Welf | 21 | 11 | 6 | 4 | 47 | 38 | 39  |
| Silkstone Lions    | 22 | 11 | 3 | 8  | 55 | 49 | 36  |
| Kingstone WMC      | 22 | 11 | 1 | 10 | 64 | 68 | 34  |
| Houghton Main      | 22 | 9  | 5 | 8  | 47 | 33 | 32  |
| The Longcar        | 22 | 8  | 5 | 9  | 42 | 45 | 29  |
| Ashfield WMC       | 21 | 6  | 3 | 12 | 52 | 66 | 21  |
| Darfield Cross Keys | 22 | 3 | 6 | 13 | 23 | 50 | 15  |
| Squires            | 22 | 3  | 3 | 16 | 36 | 68 | 12  |
| New Lodge WMC      | 22 | 3  | 3 | 16 | 32 | 91 | 12  |

## CRAVEN & DISTRICT LEAGUE
### SKIPTON BUILDING SOCIETY PREMIER DIVISION

|                    | P  | W  | D | L  | F  | A  | Pts |
|--------------------|----|----|---|----|----|----|-----|
| Silsden            | 22 | 19 | 3 | 0  | 72 | 17 | 41  |
| Oxenhope Recreation | 22 | 16 | 2 | 4 | 79 | 35 | 34  |
| Skipton Bulldogs   | 22 | 13 | 5 | 4  | 64 | 38 | 31  |
| Crosshills         | 22 | 14 | 3 | 5  | 54 | 30 | 31  |
| Embsay             | 22 | 10 | 5 | 7  | 58 | 32 | 25  |
| Keighley           | 22 | 11 | 2 | 9  | 50 | 49 | 24  |
| Hawer              | 22 | 7  | 5 | 10 | 47 | 52 | 19  |
| Rimington          | 22 | 6  | 6 | 10 | 50 | 56 | 18  |
| Cononley Sports    | 22 | 5  | 2 | 15 | 31 | 61 | 12  |
| Colne Cricket Club | 22 | 5  | 2 | 15 | 33 | 88 | 12  |
| Addingham          | 22 | 4  | 3 | 15 | 30 | 58 | 11  |
| Cowling            | 22 | 2  | 2 | 18 | 26 | 78 | 6   |

## EAST RIDING COUNTY LEAGUE
### PREMIER DIVISION

|                    | P  | W  | D  | L  | F  | A  | Pts |
|--------------------|----|----|----|----|----|----|-----|
| Reckitts           | 22 | 18 | 3  | 1  | 54 | 17 | 39  |
| Bridlington Town   | 22 | 15 | 3  | 4  | 65 | 29 | 33  |
| Chisholms          | 22 | 12 | 5  | 5  | 65 | 35 | 29  |
| Sculcoates Amateurs | 22 | 9 | 11 | 2  | 41 | 27 | 29  |
| Hall Road Rangers Res | 22 | 11 | 6 | 5 | 59 | 36 | 28 |
| North Cave         | 22 | 10 | 6  | 6  | 59 | 42 | 26  |
| Walkington Wanderers | 22 | 7 | 4 | 11 | 42 | 49 | 18  |
| Filey Town         | 22 | 6  | 5  | 11 | 37 | 47 | 17  |
| Westella Willerby  | 22 | 7  | 2  | 13 | 44 | 65 | 16  |
| Beverley O G       | 22 | 3  | 6  | 13 | 28 | 62 | 12  |
| Full Measure       | 22 | 2  | 7  | 13 | 22 | 62 | 11  |
| Holme Rovers       | 22 | 2  | 2  | 18 | 30 | 75 | 6   |

## YORKSHIRE OLD BOYS LEAGUE
### SENIOR A DIVISION

|                    | P  | W  | D | L  | F  | A  | Pts |
|--------------------|----|----|---|----|----|----|-----|
| Leeds University Union | 20 | 15 | 4 | 1 | 47 | 15 | 49 |
| Leeds Medics       | 20 | 12 | 3 | 5  | 51 | 17 | 39  |
| Roundhegians       | 20 | 11 | 5 | 4  | 46 | 32 | 38  |
| Matthew Murray FP  | 20 | 10 | 5 | 5  | 51 | 34 | 35  |
| Yorkshire Bank     | 20 | 8  | 5 | 7  | 46 | 36 | 29  |
| Wakefield City     | 20 | 8  | 4 | 8  | 43 | 47 | 28  |
| Old Modernians     | 20 | 7  | 3 | 10 | 27 | 43 | 24  |
| Old Centralians    | 20 | 6  | 2 | 12 | 31 | 45 | 20  |
| Old Batelians      | 20 | 5  | 4 | 11 | 42 | 71 | 19  |
| Almondburians      | 20 | 4  | 3 | 13 | 27 | 45 | 15  |
| Ealandians         | 20 | 3  | 4 | 13 | 28 | 54 | 13  |

## SOUTH YORKSHIRE AMATEUR LEAGUE
### PREMIER DIVISION

|                    | P  | W  | D | L  | F  | A  | Pts |
|--------------------|----|----|---|----|----|----|-----|
| Hillsborough       | 20 | 12 | 6 | 2  | 67 | 27 | 42  |
| Hollinsend Amateurs | 20 | 12 | 6 | 2 | 54 | 30 | 42  |
| Elm Tree           | 20 | 13 | 3 | 4  | 45 | 31 | 42  |
| Sheffield Medics   | 20 | 10 | 3 | 7  | 67 | 41 | 33  |
| Burncross          | 20 | 8  | 6 | 6  | 32 | 28 | 30  |
| Davy               | 20 | 9  | 3 | 8  | 46 | 52 | 30  |
| Bridge Inn         | 20 | 8  | 4 | 8  | 52 | 44 | 28  |
| SWDCS              | 20 | 8  | 2 | 10 | 45 | 44 | 26  |
| Gate 13            | 20 | 5  | 7 | 8  | 35 | 55 | 22  |
| Sheffield Centralians Rs | 20 | 2 | 3 | 15 | 17 | 57 | 9 |
| Phoenix Res.       | 20 | 0  | 3 | 17 | 23 | 74 | 3   |

## SPEN VALLEY LEAGUE
### PREMIER DIVISION

|                    | P  | W  | D | L  | F   | A  | Pts |
|--------------------|----|----|---|----|-----|----|-----|
| Low Side W.M.C     | 18 | 16 | 1 | 1  | 101 | 24 | 49  |
| SavileTown Youth   | 18 | 13 | 3 | 2  | 66  | 23 | 42  |
| Bulls Head Walkers | 18 | 13 | 2 | 3  | 73  | 29 | 41  |
| Fountain Roberttown | 18 | 9 | 2 | 7 | 67  | 46 | 29  |
| Barclays A         | 18 | 9  | 1 | 8  | 53  | 46 | 28  |
| Lord Nelson        | 18 | 8  | 1 | 9  | 49  | 51 | 25  |
| Airedale Celtic    | 18 | 6  | 1 | 11 | 33  | 70 | 19  |
| Thirsty Man        | 18 | 4  | 1 | 13 | 30  | 74 | 10  |
| Soothill Shooters  | 18 | 2  | 2 | 14 | 19  | 90 | 8   |
| Overthorpe S.V.    | 18 | 1  | 4 | 13 | 28  | 66 | 7   |

## SELBY & DISTRICT INVITATION FOOTBALL LEAGUE
### FIRST DIVISION

|                    | P  | W  | D | L  | F  | A  | Pts |
|--------------------|----|----|---|----|----|----|-----|
| Kellingley Welfare | 18 | 16 | 2 | 0  | 69 | 17 | 50  |
| South Milford      | 18 | 13 | 3 | 2  | 90 | 29 | 42  |
| Britannia Lock Lane | 18 | 10 | 2 | 6 | 38 | 32 | 32  |
| Hensall Athletic   | 18 | 9  | 0 | 9  | 45 | 78 | 27  |
| Fairburn           | 18 | 7  | 3 | 8  | 46 | 55 | 24  |
| Fox Inn            | 18 | 7  | 1 | 10 | 47 | 48 | 22  |
| Kippax Welfare     | 18 | 6  | 2 | 10 | 38 | 43 | 20  |
| Normanton Comrades | 18 | 5  | 4 | 9  | 32 | 44 | 19  |
| Riccall Colliery   | 18 | 5  | 1 | 12 | 34 | 51 | 16  |
| Drax PS            | 18 | 2  | 2 | 14 | 30 | 71 | 8   |

## ROTHERHAM LEAGUE
### PREMIER DIVISION

|                    | P  | W  | D | L  | F  | A  | Pts |
|--------------------|----|----|---|----|----|----|-----|
| Grove Social       | 16 | 12 | 3 | 1  | 61 | 15 | 27  |
| Oaktree 95         | 16 | 12 | 0 | 4  | 67 | 34 | 24  |
| Maltby Sheppey     | 16 | 9  | 2 | 5  | 47 | 46 | 20  |
| Rotherham Town     | 16 | 8  | 3 | 5  | 50 | 37 | 19  |
| Horse & Jockey     | 16 | 7  | 1 | 8  | 46 | 36 | 15  |
| Swinton Cafe Sports | 16 | 7 | 1 | 8 | 50 | 30 | 13  |
| Silverwood CW      | 16 | 6  | 1 | 9  | 46 | 55 | 13  |
| Corner Pocket      | 16 | 2  | 1 | 13 | 23 | 86 | 5   |
| Brinsworth WMC     | 16 | 1  | 2 | 13 | 17 | 68 | 4   |

* points deducted

# NORTH EASTERN FINAL LEAGUE TABLES 1998-99

## DONCASTER & DISTRICT SENIOR FOOTBALL LEAGUE
### PREMIER DIVISION

| | P | W | D | L | F | A | Pts |
|---|---|---|---|---|---|---|---|
| Sutton Rovers | 22 | 15 | 4 | 3 | 70 | 24 | 49 |
| Hemsworth St Patrick | 22 | 16 | 0 | 6 | 66 | 45 | 48 |
| Carcroft Village WMC | 21 | 12 | 4 | 5 | 54 | 38 | 40 |
| Ackworth United | 22 | 12 | 3 | 7 | 62 | 36 | 39 |
| Upton & Harewood | 22 | 9 | 7 | 6 | 48 | 33 | 34 |
| Gateway Inn | 22 | 10 | 2 | 10 | 49 | 50 | 32 |
| Askern Welfare Res. | 22 | 8 | 6 | 8 | 37 | 39 | 30 |
| Edlington WMC | 22 | 6 | 7 | 9 | 34 | 58 | 25 |
| Eden Grove | 21 | 7 | 2 | 12 | 34 | 41 | 23 |
| South Kirkby Colliery R. | 22 | 5 | 6 | 11 | 41 | 52 | 21 |
| Stainforth Central | 22 | 5 | 4 | 13 | 38 | 61 | 19 |
| Scawthorpe Social | 22 | 1 | 5 | 16 | 25 | 81 | 8 |
| ngs Lane Highfield MW w/d | | | | | | | |

*Top: Durham City celebrate promotion*
*Photo: John Lindsey*

*Bottom: Paul O'Connor, Bedlington Terriers' keeper did his bit to keep a clean sheet in both semi final matches of the FA Vase against Thame*
*Photo: Peter Barnes*

## DRIFFIELD & DISTRICT A F LEAGUE
### PREMIER DIVISION

| | P | W | D | L | F | A | Pts |
|---|---|---|---|---|---|---|---|
| Nafferton | 18 | 15 | 2 | 1 | 78 | 22 | 32 |
| Hilderthorpe | 18 | 14 | 1 | 3 | 69 | 18 | 29 |
| Bridlington S C Res. | 18 | 9 | 5 | 4 | 44 | 29 | 23 |
| H. & Cranswick United | 18 | 8 | 2 | 8 | 50 | 43 | 18 |
| Bridlington Rovers | 18 | 6 | 4 | 8 | 27 | 41 | 16 |
| Pack Horse | 17 | 7 | 1 | 9 | 37 | 52 | 15 |
| Beaconsfield | 18 | 5 | 3 | 10 | 38 | 65 | 13 |
| Crown | 18 | 4 | 3 | 11 | 32 | 54 | 11 |
| H. & Cranswick Sra | 17 | 4 | 3 | 10 | 20 | 38 | 10 |
| Flamborough | 18 | 4 | 2 | 12 | 21 | 54 | 10 |

## KEIGHLEY SUNDAY ALLIANCE
### PREMIER DIVISION

| | P | W | D | L | F | A | Pts |
|---|---|---|---|---|---|---|---|
| Craven Athletic | 14 | 14 | 0 | 0 | 75 | 21 | 42 |
| Stanbury | 14 | 10 | 2 | 2 | 65 | 30 | 32 |
| Granby Phoenix | 14 | 7 | 2 | 5 | 43 | 29 | 23 |
| Skipton After Dark | 13 | 6 | 2 | 5 | 36 | 34 | 20 |
| Bingley White Horse | 14 | 6 | 1 | 7 | 45 | 58 | 19 |
| Royal Oak | 12 | 3 | 1 | 8 | 33 | 53 | 10 |
| Keighley Juniors Res | 14 | 2 | 1 | 11 | 19 | 61 | 7 |
| Lord Rodney | 13 | 1 | 1 | 11 | 18 | 48 | 4 |

# BARROW

Match Secretary; Neil McDonald
Birchfield, 6A Salthouse Rd., Barrow-in-
Furness, Cumbria Tel: 01229 828227 (H)
0403 499482 (M)

Press Officer: Phil Yelland
83 camus Drive, Edinburgh EH10 6QY
Tel: 0131 445 1010 (H)
0131 476 8131 (B)

> We apologise to Barrow supporters for the positioning of their Club's pages in the book, but as you all know very late decisions were made regarding their league for the Season 1999-2000.

## FACT FILE

Founded: 1901
Nickname: Bluebirds
Sponsors: Chas Kendall - Bookmakers
Club Colours: All white with blue trim
Change Colours: Yellow/blue/blue
Midweek matchday: Tuesday
Barrow Soccer Hotline: 0930 555 820
Programme: Pages: 44    Price: £1.40
Editorial Team:  Darren Gardner, Phil Yelland, & Russell Dodd
Local Press: North West Evening Mail, Barrow & West Cumberland Advertiser
Local Radio: BBC Radio Furness, BBC Radio Cumbria, Red Rose Radio, Bay Radio
1989-99
Top Scorer: Andy Mutch
Captain: Greg Challender

**GROUND:**    Holker Street Stadium, Wilkie Road, Barrow-in-Furness, CumbriaLA14 5UW
Tel: 01229 820346

**Directions:** M6 to junction 36, A590 to Barrow, enter Barrow on Park Road and after about 2 miles turn left into Wilkie Rd - ground on right.  B.R.1/4 mile

**Capacity:** 4,500        **Seated:** 1000        **Covered Terracing:** 1,200

**Clubhouse:** Barrow Sports & Leisure centre next to ground.
Open matchdays and Functions only. Snack bars on ground

**Club Shop:** Situated on the ground.

**PREVIOUS**    **Leagues:** Lancs Comb 01-21; Football League 21-72; Northern Premier 72-79, 83-84,86-89, 92-98; GM Vauxhall Conference 79-83, 84-86, 89-92, 98-99    **Grounds:** The Strawberry & Little Park, Roose    **Names:**None

**RECORDS**    **Attendance:** 16,854 v Swansea Town, FA Cup 3rd Rd. 1954
**Career Appearances:** Colin Cowperthwaite 704        **Career Goalscorer:** Colin Cowperthwaite 282 (Dec '77-Dec '92).
**Defeat:** 1-10 v Hartlepool Utd, Football Lge Div 4, 1959    **Win:** 12-0 v Cleator, FA Cup 1920.
**Transfer Fee Paid:** £9,000 for Andy Whittaker (Ashton Utd, July 94).
**Transfer Fee Received:** £40,000 for Kenny Lowe (Barnet, Jan 91)

**BEST SEASON**    **FA Trophy:** Winners 1989-90, Semi-Final 87-88
**FA Cup:** Third Round Proper 9 times including once as a non-League club 90-91, 0-1 v Bolton Wanderers (A)

**HONOURS**    F.A. Trophy Winners 89-90, Northern Premier League 97-98, 88-89, 83-84; Lge Cup R-up 87-88, Lge Shield 84-85 R-up 89-90 98-99; Bob Lord Trophy R-up 90-91, Cumbrian Cup 82-8383-84 (R-up 84-85), Lancs Floodlit Cup R-up 86-87, Lancs Sen Cup 54-55 (R-up 51-52 65-66 66-67 69-70), Lancs Challenge Trophy 80-81 (R-up 81-82 84-85), Lancs Comb 20-21, R-up 13-14, Div 2 R-up 04-05 10-11.

Players progressing:        I McDonald, N McDonald, J Laisby, B Diamond, F Gamble, B Knowles, G Skivington, P Byron, L Edwards, K Lowe, M Dobie, T Rigby, N Doherty.

## MANAGER - KENNY LOWE

Date of Appointment            August 1999
Date of Birth                1961
Place of Birth                Sedgefield

PREVIOUS CLUBS
As manager                Gateshead
As player        Hartlepool Utd., Billingham T., Gateshead,
Spearswood Dalmatic (W. Aust.), Morecambe,
Barrow, Barnet, Birmingham C.,
Stoke C., Darlington

HONOURS
As manager                None
as player            England Semi-Pro
N.P.L. 88-89, FA Trophy 89-90, GMV Conference 90-91

# BARROW - MATCH FACTS - 1998-99 SEASON

| No | Date | Venue | Comp | Opponents | Att | Result | Score | Goalscorers |
|---|---|---|---|---|---|---|---|---|
| 1 | 08/08 | H | NPLS | Altrincham | 770 | L | 1-2 | O'Keeffe 85 |
| 2 | 15/08 | H | NC | Stevenage Borough | 2096 | L | 0-1 | |
| 3 | 18/08 | A | NC | Morecambe | 3193 | L | 2-3 | Morton 78, Marginson 81 |
| 4 | 22/08 | A | NC | Rushden & Diamonds | 2259 | L | 0-4 | |
| 5 | 25/08 | H | NC | Doncaster Rovers | 2050 | D | 2-2 | Sutherland 14[og], Coates 87 |
| 6 | 29/08 | H | NC | Telford United | 1604 | D | 1-1 | Kielty 41 |
| 7 | 31/08 | A | NC | Cheltenham Town | 2005 | L | 1-4 | Morton 6 |
| 8 | 05/09 | A | NC | Woking | 1917 | W | 3-2 | Danzey 61[og], Foster 72, Mutch 73 |
| 9 | 08/09 | H | NC | Morecambe | 2073 | W | 2-1 | Mutch 64, Morton 65 |
| 10 | 12/09 | H | NC | Hereford United | 1775 | L | 0-1 | |
| 11 | 15/09 | A | NC | Leek Town | 426 | L | 1-3 | Mutch 28 |
| 12 | 19/09 | A | NC | Dover Athletic | 1117 | D | 1-1 | Mutch 25 |
| 13 | 26/09 | H | NC | Kettering Town | 1443 | D | 0-0 | |
| 14 | 03/10 | A | NC | Kingstonian | 1281 | L | 1-5 | Seagraves 48 |
| 15 | 06/10 | H | Endsl. 1 | Leek Town | 591 | W | 2-1 | O'Keeffe 32, Mutch 73 |
| 16 | 10/10 | A | NC | Welling United | 700 | D | 1-1 | O'Keeffe 75 |
| 17 | 17/10 | A | FA C Q3 | Gateshead | 386 | L | 1-2 | O'Keeffe 88 |
| 18 | 24/10 | A | NC | Hayes | 578 | L | 0-1 | |
| 19 | 07/11 | H | NC | Dover Athletic | 1290 | W | 1-0 | Mutch 74 |
| 20 | 17/11 | A | NC | Doncaster Rovers | 2617 | L | 1-2 | Coates 80 |
| 21 | 21/11 | A | FA T 2 | Hucknall Town | 515 | L | 1-2 | Coates 70 |
| 22 | 28/11 | H | NC | Hednesford Town | 1232 | L | 0-2 | |
| 23 | 01/12 | A | Endsl. 2 | Morecambe | 567 | L | 0-2 | |
| 24 | 05/12 | A | NC | Leek Town | 1047 | W | 2-1 | Mutch 2 50 |
| 25 | 12/12 | A | NC | Kettering Town | 1817 | L | 0-2 | |
| 26 | 15/12 | H | NC | Southport | 1191 | D | 0-0 | |
| 27 | 19/12 | H | NC | Forest Green Rovers | 1176 | W | 2-1 | Coates 53, McCauley 60 |
| 28 | 26/12 | A | NC | Southport | 1426 | W | 4-0 | Coates 53, Foster 57 90, Marginson 82 |
| 29 | 28/12 | H | NC | Northwich Victoria | 2015 | L | 0-1 | |
| 30 | 05/01 | A | L ATS 2 | Southport | 305 | L | 0-2 | |
| 31 | 09/01 | H | NC | Rushden & Diamonds | 2003 | L | 0-2 | |
| 32 | 16/01 | H | NC | Welling United | 1401 | W | 2-1 | Mutch 43, Coates 79 |
| 33 | 23/01 | A | NC | Yeovil Town | 2588 | L | 0-1 | |
| 34 | 30/01 | H | NC | Kingstonian | 1730 | L | 0-1 | |
| 35 | 13/02 | H | NC | Hayes | 1518 | L | 0-1 | |
| 36 | 20/02 | H | NC | Yeovil Town | 1202 | W | 2-0 | Hayward 46, Dawson 57 |
| 37 | 27/02 | A | NC | Telford United | 749 | D | 1-1 | Jones 15 |
| 38 | 06/03 | H | NC | Cheltenham Town | 1773 | D | 1-1 | Dawson 33 |
| 39 | 13/03 | A | NC | Farnborough Town | 758 | D | 2-2 | Johnston 38, Hayward 57 |
| 40 | 20/03 | A | NC | Hereford United | 1521 | L | 0-3 | |
| 41 | 27/03 | H | NC | Kidderminster Harriers | 1738 | L | 0-4 | |
| 42 | 03/04 | H | NC | Farnborough Town | 1530 | W | 1-0 | Johnston 88[p] |
| 43 | 05/04 | A | NC | Northwich Victoria | 1107 | L | 0-1 | |
| 44 | 10/04 | A | NC | Hednesford Town | 794 | L | 0-1 | |
| 45 | 14/04 | A | NC | Forest Green Rovers | 404 | D | 1-1 | Foster 1 |
| 46 | 17/04 | A | NC | Stevenage Borough | 1701 | W | 2-1 | Dawson 64, Foster 80 |
| 47 | 24/04 | H | NC | Woking | 2176 | L | 1-2 | Foster 43 |
| 48 | 01/05 | A | NC | Kidderminster Harriers | 1877 | W | 2-1 | Hayward 12, Foster 60 |

## PLAYING SQUAD 1999-2000:

GOALKEEPERS:

John Boyle, Craig Davies (Telford United), John O'Toole (Northwich Victoria), Jason Wharton (Netherfield Kendal), DEFENDERS: Greg Challender (Winsford United), Wayne Dowell (Accrington Stanley), Kyle Hatton (Morecambe), Kyle Hayton (Morecambe), Andrew Hill (Vickers Sports Club), Richard Johnson (Crooklands Casuals), Paul Jones (Tranmere Rovers), Rob Leitch (Crooklands Casuals), Neil Mcalinden (Barrow Celtic), Graham Shaw, Gareth West (Burnley - trial), Jay Wheeler (Dalton United)
MIDFIELDERS: Dave Barrow (Dalton United), Neil Doherty (Kidderminster Harriers), Mark Ingham, Brian Langhorn (Glaxo), Gary Lewis (Atherton Collieries), Chris Orr (Dalton United), Lee O'keefe (Workington), Lee Prior (Rhyl), Mark Smith, Brian Southworth (Sligo Rovers), Andy Sweatenham (Rochdale)
FORWARDS: Colin Carr-Laughton (Burnley), Ian Foster (Hereford United), Mark Grugel (Everton), Gareth Hamlet (Halifax Town), Warwick Pickering (Heathwaite)

# SOUTHERN
# LEAGUE

# PYRAMID
# SECTION

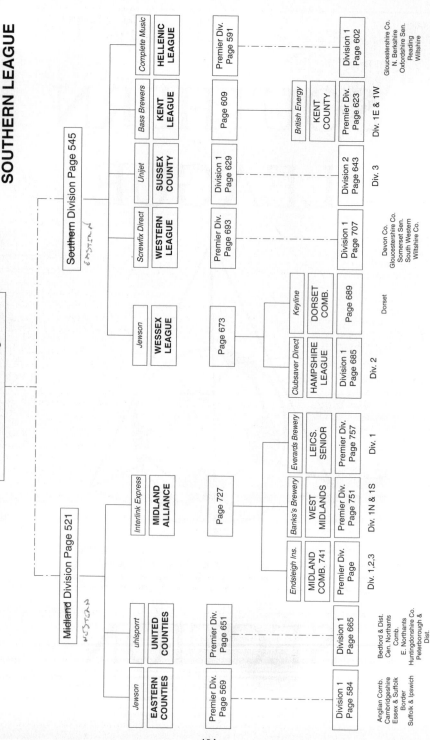

# Dr. Martens
# SOUTHERN LEAGUE

Premier Division Page 472

Midland Division Page 521

Southern Division Page 545

**Jewson**
EASTERN COUNTIES

**uhlsport**
UNITED COUNTIES

**Interlink Express**
MIDLAND ALLIANCE

**Jewson**
WESSEX LEAGUE

**Screwfix Direct**
WESTERN LEAGUE

**Unijet**
SUSSEX COUNTY

**Bass Brewers**
KENT LEAGUE

**Complete Music**
HELLENIC LEAGUE

Premier Div. Page 569

Premier Div. Page 651

Page 727

Page 673

Premier Div. Page 693

Division 1 Page 629

Page 609

Premier Div. Page 591

Division 1 Page 584

Division 1 Page 665

**Endsleigh Ins.**
MIDLAND COMB. 741
Premier Div. Page

**Banks's Brewery**
WEST MIDLANDS
Premier Div. Page 751

**Everards Brewery**
LEICS. SENIOR
Premier Div. Page 757

**Clubsaver Direct**
HAMPSHIRE LEAGUE
Division 1 Page 685

**Keyline**
DORSET COMB.
Page 689

Division 1 Page 707

Division 2 Page 643

**British Energy**
KENT COUNTY
Premier Div. Page 623

Division 1 Page 602

Div. 1,2,3

Div. 1N & 1S

Div. 1

Div. 2

Dorset

Div. 3

Div. 1E & 1W

Anglian Comb.
Cambridgeshire
Essex & Suffolk
Border
Suffolk & Ipswich

Bedford & Dist.
Cen. Northants
Comb.
E. Northants
Huntingdonshire Co.
Peterborough &
Dist.

Devon Co.
Gloucestershire Co.
Somerset Sen.
South Western
Wiltshire Co.

Gloucestershire Co.
N. Berkshire
Oxfordshire Sen.
Reading
Wiltshire

464

# Dr MARTENS LEAGUE

**President:** G E Templeman   **Chairman:** D S R Gillard

**Secretary:** D J Strudwick

PO Box 90, Worcester WR3 8RX

Tel: 01905 757509

Wet, Wet, Wet. The most enduring element of the 1998-99 season was surely the weather; or, more specifically, the rain. Front after front has dropped an unwelcome load almost every day since October. There has been enough rain this season to dampen the spirits of even the finest shower of Fixtures Secretaries, all of whom, in the words of an appropriately named pop group, must have been "Wishing I was lucky" and hoping for "A little help from my friends".

The coldest elements of a regular winter may have been avoided, but Britain's climate dealt its share of "Sweet little mysteries" and, with every famous waterway in the country bursting its banks, it was truly a case of "Hold back the river". Wet, Wet, Wet.

The Pretenders abound at the start of every season, and why not? With every club high on optimism, the campaign kicked off on a hot August afternoon. Could last year's runner-up, Merthyr Tydfil, go one better? Had Burton Albion brewed the right cocktail? Could it be Dorchester's year or would it be an albatross of a season for the Magpies? Would Ilkeston Town prove 'simply red' was best? Or would this year's Champion club come from one of the big cities or conurbations? That's just the Premier Division.

In the Regional Divisions, could Newport AFC, Stafford Rangers or Chelmsford City regain their previous status? Could Ashford Town, Sittingbourne or St Leonards bounce back to the Premier Division immediately after being relegated? Maybe the joint force of Waterlooville and Havant Town would prove irresistible, or perhaps one of the new faces would come good.

As much as I dislike the term, this season's Premier Division very quickly became a 'one horse race'. Nuneaton Borough moved 'earth, wind and fire' to take the top flight by storm. Leading from start to finish, Borough were eight points clear by the end of October, seventeen points ahead at the turn of the year and 23 points to the good at the finishing line. After spending seven of the previous ten seasons in the Midland Division, Nuneaton's transformation was complete. Such was Borough's dominance of the table, the gap between nearest challengers Boston United and Ilkeston Town was four points greater than the space between these two clubs and the dreaded relegation zone!

Although Nuneaton became Queen (or King) of the Premier Division four weeks before the end of the campaign, there was plenty of competition in the 'Boyzone'. As many as eight clubs had a realistic chance of finishing runners-up during the final month. Halesowen Town, Hastings Town, Tamworth and Worcester City appeared late on the scene to challenge the more consistent first quartet of hopefuls, Bath City, Boston United, Gloucester City and Ilkeston Town. Results on the final day determined that Boston and Ilkeston would finish level on 67 points, ahead of Bath, Hastings and Gloucester. Boston led the pack on goal difference to repeat the runners-up spot earned last year in the Northern Premier League.

This year's 'rolling stones' are Bromsgrove Rovers, Gresley Rovers and Cambridge City, who all lose their Premier Division place on playing performance. it is worth dwelling for one moment on the fact that two seasons ago Bromsgrove Rovers were in the Football Conference and Gresley Rovers were the Champions of the Dr Martens League. Despite Nuneaton's strength this year, competition in the Southern Football League is alive, kicking and extremely fierce.

This year's 'Spice Girls' in the Regional Divisions turned out to be Clevedon Town, Newport AFC, Havant & Waterlooville and Margate.

Clevedon led the Midland Division table for most of the season. And, like the other Divisional Champions, they lost only six of their 42 League matches. The Avon club had fortunately built a sufficient cushion for themselves to absorb losing three and drawing two of their final six games. Their shaky form on the run-in certainly scared their

## DR MARTENS LEAGUE CLUBCALL
## 09068 12 11 51
Calls cost 60p per minute

supporters which, by the way, include a corps of drums. Premier Division eardrums had better prepare for Clevedon's 'Band on the Run'.

Clevedon's hiccups also gave Newport AFC hope. Newport's form at Spytty Road was almost unblemished. They became the only club in the League not to lose a game on home soil. But, as if to belie the club's nickname, the Exiles were not so comfortable away. Nine games were lost and only eight were won. Is this where the title was lost? Champions Clevedon won sixteen matches 'on the road'!

Behind the leading two, again, there were a number of challengers. Redditch United showed last season's improvement was no blip on the horizon. Hinckley United built further on the foundations laid by the merger of Athletic and Town. Stafford Rangers posted a warning notice for next year. Whilst their neighbours at Bilston, whose Manager Ian Painter had left for Stafford in the close season, demonstrated the 'stepping out' under Joe Jackson was okay.

When it's diagnosed that two clubs should merge, there may always be a bitter pill or two to swallow, if a long established club loses something of its identity. But the prescription joining Havant Town and Waterlooville proved to be a potent medicine. From the second week of the season the newly constituted club was never out of the top two in the Southern Division. Losing only six matches all season (equally divided between home and away) a tremendous pace was maintained over the 42 game programme. The charge for honours, however, demanded the momentum was sustained. Margate, who lost only seven games, matched H & W point for points and frequently swapped places with their rivals at the top.

Havant secured the Championship in the final midweek of the season, winning game no. 40 (5-1) against their Hampshire colleagues Andover. To be certain of second place Margate had to win at Brackley. The 4-1 victory was enough to ensure the promotion place above Folkestone Invicta, who did all they could on the final day by winning at fourth placed Newport IOW. It was a formidable victory that cemented a fine first season back in the Southern Football League.

Although, at the end of the day, no other club seriously challenged the leaders, intermittent good form shown by Newport IoW, Chelmsford City, Raunds Town, Ashford Town and Baldock Town illustrated the Division had strength in depth. I am sure these clubs will be challenging seriously next season.

The prize guys in the League Cup were Sutton Coldfield Town. Triumphs over Burton Albion and Boston United demonstrated Sutton's appearance in the Final was no fluke. A 2-1 aggregate win over another Premier Division side, Cambridge City, in the Final Tie showed the Royals were emerging from their 'blue period'.

As for Cambridge City, progress in the League Cup should have provided the confidence required to reverse their slide down the League table. It did not, and their Final appearance was, perhaps, cold comfort in an otherwise disappointing season.

For many years now, the League has awarded a monetary prize for the top scoring club, or clubs. This year's £500 bonus is shared between Folkestone Invicta, Newport AFC and Stafford Rangers. Congratulations.

For the past two years the League has encouraged Fair Play by awarding a further £500 for the club incurring fewest disciplinary points. This year's 'Righteous Brothers' are Yate Town. Congratulations.

Dr Martens League success in national cup competitions was not as good as in recent crusades. A school report may suggest "could do better". That is not a criticism but a view I hope will be shared by those clubs who did not achieve the eminence for which they may have budgeted.

In the FA Cup, this year's 'Pretty Things' were Burton Albion, Gresley Rovers, Salisbury City, Tamworth and Worcester City. Regrettably, each failed to make Round Two, but the ugliness of that statistic will be tempered by the £6,000 each club will receive from the FA Cup 'Replay' Fund.

Overall, it could be said, the FA Trophy provided even less chance for prosperity. When six Dr Martens League clubs reached the last 32 of the competition, the League appeared to be on 'Air Wair'. But Hinckley United, Redditch United, Weston-super-Mare, Weymouth and Worcester City all lost at this Fourth Round stage, leaving only Boston United to attend the 'tea party'.

The Pilgrims enjoyed an excellent Fifth Round win over the eventual Northern Premier League Champions, Altrincham, before losing in the Sixth Round to St Albans.

So, as dusk falls on another season, it will not be long before dawn breaks on a new term. The Dr Martens League, therefore, issues a traditional welcome to next year's intake of Freshmen - Burnham, Rocester, Spalding United and Tiverton Town. These are the 'M People' who are all 'moving on up' from the Feeder Leagues. Welcome to the Dr Martens League.

All, no doubt, will hope to make 'roxy' music in their own time, but meanwhile "hails" also mean farewells. This year's 'Moody Blues' (metaphorically speaking only!), who are leaving the Competition, are Andover, Bloxwich Town and Brackley Town.

As I write, we welcome Welling United into the Premier Division by way of relegation from the Football Conference. We anticipated Welling's arrival back into the Southern League at the end of the 1986/87 season. Events at Nuneaton, however, conspired in Welling's favour. Nuneaton Borough FC was eventually 'relegated' from eighteenth place; Welling United FC, in 20th spot, was reprieved. By a strange twist of fate, will Nuneaton swap places with Welling again, under different circumstances, or will the 'Queen of Spades' currently being held by Barrow AFC come up trumps for Welling United? Only time will tell.

Football is all about clubs and players. Of that, there is no doubt. It is said, though, a game could not take place without a referee. The complement of match officials on the Dr Martens League has again enjoyed a marvellous season. Following three promotions to the National List of Referees last year, Richard Beeby and Trevor Parkes have been elevated for next year. Brian Curson was also granted an interview but, sadly, was not selected. Better luck next time, Brian.

After six promotions to the National List of Assistants last season, Bernard Baker, Stephen Bratt, Gary Evetts and John Singh have received the call this year.

Eight Dr Martens League Referees have been promoted tot he Panel List of Referees. That is more than any other League in the County. And there have been no removals from the List in this department.

Phil Sharp was an Assistant Referee on the FA Cup Final. Trevor Parkes assisted the Referee at the FA Trophy Final. The position of Dr Martens League Match Officials at the sharp end of the Football Pyramid, and amongst the upper level of Contributory Leagues, has been recognised and commended.

The above results are due in no small degree to Laurence Jones, Steve Tincknell and Ray Upton, the Chairman, Secretary and Treasurer of the League's Match Officials Association, and Jim Hill, the Assessors' guru. Congratulations, gentlemen. Well done, and thanks, to all the Assessors for their valuable advice. (After each has given seven years fine service, Laurence and Ray retire from their administrative positions later this year. Many thanks for your help.) But 1999/2000 is another season, and the League's strengths in this arena will have to be demonstrated all over again.

The above reflects activities on the field. Of course, just as much happens off the field enabling the above business to take place. With another season still to go on the sponsorship agreement with Dr Martens, the League's Management Committee was delighted when negotiations were completed and Max & Stephen Griggs' Company announced a further four year deal. "Thank you" seems inadequate, any more may sound patronising. But nevertheless, thank you R. Griggs & Co. Thank you, too, Andrew Borge for your cordial liaison.

Thanks, too, ICIS. Although some arrangements have not borne all the promised fruit, from both directions, scores of clubs have benefited from your generosity.

For the next three years it's balls to all clubs from James Gilbert. A tremendous offer from the world's largest supplier of rugby balls will see each member club take delivery of 25 Match (foot) Balls per season. On top of which Rod Webb's Company threw in ten extra balls for the season just ended.

Vandanel has agreed to join the League's group of 'blue chip' sponsors next season by underwriting the cost of Bench Kit for the next three years.

We thank all our sponsors and hope their association with our pedigree competition is enjoyable and mutually beneficial.

The Management Committee. What can I say about the Management Committee, or Board of Directors, as they became on 1 April? (Is there something significant about that date?) Your job is arduous and burdensome. It is no picnic. Its degree of difficulty may best be measured by the number of nominees prepared to take your place each year. On behalf of the clubs, thank you, gentlemen. Thank you, Rod Laight, for your interest to come on board. May the best men win the election at the AGM.

The Board is led by Doug Gillard. Doug seems to have an insatiable appetite for work. Just when I thought he may 'quieten down' following retirement from his business, he responded by saying he now had more time for football! But Doug is lucky. He has two outstanding lieutenants. Mrs Pat Gillard's devotion and support for Doug exceeds anyone's expectations. Because of Pat's commitment to Doug, the League benefits immeasurably. Thanks, Pat.

The League's No. 2 is Keith Allen. Keith has given more than just time to the Competition. Like so many, but almost certainly more than most, Keith has given tangible effort that can be measured in more than pounds and pence. Well done, Keith. And thank you, everyone.

Thanks to everyone who has made a helpful and productive contribution to the League's affairs. I am grateful for the welcome I receive wherever and whenever I visit. My waistline (or lack of one) is testimony to your hospitality. I am sorry I cannot get to call on every club during a season, but the more I am absent from Mission Control, the less work is completed.

I will, however, endeavour to continue to develop myself and the League's services. It has been a difficult year after relocating to a new area. (Moving house is bad enough, especially with all my junk, but house and Office!). I have not been able to call upon the amount of assistance I could when living in my 'home' county. Clare and Paul are missed, and I thank them for their help until June of last year.

The geography of the Office, like that of my new home, is becoming more familiar each day. I believe it's getting better, if not easier. That, largely, is thanks to my jewel of a partner, Janet. The memories I wrote about last year are being made. Remember New York, and in the meantime, your considerable help on the football front, and your comfort around Nursery Cottage, is not being overlooked. Thanks, Rudgie. But never forget, my love of football is a disease. Ask John Maggs!

# PREMIER DIVISION FINAL LEAGUE TABLE 1998-99

| | | P | HOME | | | | | AWAY | | | | | Pts | LEADING SCORERS BY CLUB |
|---|---|---|---|---|---|---|---|---|---|---|---|---|---|---|
| | | | W | D | L | F | A | W | D | L | F | A | | *(these include all goals as reported in the league bulletin)* |
| 1 | Nuneaton Borough | 42 | 16 | 3 | 2 | 52 | 15 | 11 | 6 | 4 | 39 | 18 | 90 | Thomas 17, Williams 15, Wilkin 11 |
| 2 | Boston United | 42 | 12 | 5 | 4 | 42 | 21 | 5 | 11 | 5 | 27 | 30 | 67 | Carmichael 20, Watts 13, Stringfellow, Charles 10 |
| 3 | Ilkeston Town | 42 | 9 | 7 | 5 | 42 | 28 | 9 | 6 | 6 | 30 | 31 | 67 | Moore 14, Knapper 11, Robinson 10 |
| 4 | Bath City | 42 | 12 | 3 | 6 | 41 | 16 | 6 | 8 | 7 | 29 | 26 | 65 | Paul 29, White 13, Colbourne 12 |
| 5 | Hastings Town | 42 | 10 | 4 | 7 | 26 | 23 | 8 | 7 | 6 | 31 | 26 | 65 | McRobert 11, White 11, Smith, Simmons 9 |
| 6 | Gloucester City | 42 | 10 | 5 | 6 | 30 | 22 | 8 | 6 | 7 | 27 | 30 | 65 | Mings 17, Hemmings 10, five others on 8 |
| 7 | Worcester City | 42 | 10 | 5 | 6 | 39 | 30 | 8 | 4 | 9 | 19 | 24 | 63 | Owen 24, Bowen 20, Chenoweth 10 |
| 8 | Halesowen Town | 42 | 11 | 6 | 4 | 47 | 27 | 6 | 5 | 10 | 25 | 33 | 62 | Pearce 31, Burch, Francis 9 |
| 9 | Tamworth | 42 | 10 | 5 | 6 | 37 | 30 | 9 | 0 | 12 | 25 | 37 | 62 | Haughton 17, Hallam 15, Shaw 13 |
| 10 | King's Lynn | 42 | 9 | 8 | 4 | 33 | 20 | 8 | 2 | 11 | 20 | 26 | 61 | Turner 14, Wilson 8, Puttnam 7 |
| 11 | Crawley Town | 42 | 11 | 7 | 3 | 34 | 22 | 6 | 3 | 12 | 23 | 36 | 61 | Abbey 31, Ullathorne 17, Warden 16 |
| 12 | Salisbury City | 42 | 9 | 7 | 5 | 26 | 23 | 7 | 5 | 9 | 30 | 38 | 60 | Sales 19, Randall 15, Harbut 7 |
| 13 | Burton Albion | 42 | 7 | 2 | 12 | 29 | 27 | 10 | 5 | 6 | 29 | 25 | 58 | Garner, Holmes 14, Marsden 7, Stride 6 |
| 14 | Weymouth | 42 | 9 | 6 | 6 | 33 | 26 | 5 | 8 | 8 | 23 | 29 | 56 | Laws 24, Adcock 10, Robinson 9 |
| 15 | Merthyr Tydfil | 42 | 9 | 5 | 7 | 31 | 20 | 6 | 3 | 12 | 21 | 42 | 53 | Griffith 12, Shepherd 11, Chapple 6 |
| 16 | Atherstone United | 42 | 7 | 8 | 6 | 30 | 26 | 5 | 6 | 10 | 17 | 26 | 50 | Green 10, White 9, Aubrey 5 |
| 17 | Grantham Town | 42 | 8 | 3 | 10 | 32 | 28 | 6 | 5 | 10 | 19 | 30 | 50 | Jackson 7, Gilbert 6, Taylor, Speed, Bowman 5 |
| 18 | Dorchester Town | 42 | 9 | 6 | 6 | 29 | 19 | 2 | 9 | 10 | 20 | 44 | 48 | O'Hagan 20, Shepherd 12, Murray 5 |
| 19 | Rothwell Town | 42 | 11 | 4 | 6 | 32 | 23 | 2 | 5 | 14 | 15 | 44 | 48 | Marshall, Moore 10, Jowett 8 |
| 20 | Cambridge City | 42 | 7 | 7 | 7 | 24 | 22 | 4 | 5 | 12 | 23 | 46 | 45 | Kimomya 13, Brown 9, Owen 6 |
| 21 | Gresley Rovers | 42 | 7 | 4 | 10 | 27 | 30 | 5 | 4 | 12 | 22 | 43 | 44 | Pitt 15, Rowland 13, Simpson 6 |
| 22 | Bromsgrove Rovers | 42 | 7 | 5 | 9 | 22 | 30 | 1 | 2 | 18 | 16 | 54 | 30 | Payne 14, Ball 5, Bennett 4 |

# PREMIER DIVISION RESULTS CHART 1998-99

plus Attendance/Fixture Chart

| | | 1 | 2 | 3 | 4 | 5 | 6 | 7 | 8 | 9 | 10 | 11 | 12 | 13 | 14 | 15 | 16 | 17 | 18 | 19 | 20 | 21 | 22 |
|---|---|---|---|---|---|---|---|---|---|---|---|---|---|---|---|---|---|---|---|---|---|---|---|
| 1 | Atherstone U | X<br>X | 2-1<br>333 | 0-0<br>203 | 5-1<br>332 | 2-2<br>502 | 0-1<br>253 | 2-1<br>310 | 3-1<br>260 | 1-2<br>278 | 1-1<br>244 | 2-1<br>285 | 0-2<br>391 | 1-1<br>213 | 3-3<br>401 | 1-2<br>311 | 2-1<br>216 | 0-2<br>2043 | 2-2<br>258 | 2-0<br>211 | 0-1<br>829 | 0-0<br>225 | 1-1<br>402 |
| 2 | Bath City | 3-1<br>647 | X<br>X | 8-0<br>390 | 3-0<br>802 | 2-0<br>716 | 1-0<br>654 | 2-0<br>888 | 0-1<br>631 | 1-2<br>1027 | 1-1<br>864 | 3-0<br>857 | 0-0<br>1456 | 0-2<br>592 | 1-2<br>735 | 2-0<br>955 | 3-0<br>775 | 1-3<br>1285 | 2-0<br>557 | 3-5<br>716 | 3-0<br>1181 | 2-1<br>790 | 0-0<br>486 |
| 3 | Boston Utd | 0-0<br>1022 | 3-2<br>909 | X<br>X | 2-2<br>822 | 4-0<br>1006 | 2-2<br>2005 | 3-1<br>1230 | 5-1<br>747 | 1-0<br>907 | 3-0<br>1925 | 4-1<br>1026 | 2-0<br>671 | 1-1<br>874 | 0-1<br>616 | 0-1<br>1436 | 0-3<br>737 | 2-3<br>1159 | 0-0<br>984 | 3-1<br>782 | 2-0<br>553 | 2-1<br>1100 | 3-1<br>1023 |
| 4 | Bromsgrove | 0-0<br>485 | 1-3<br>580 | 1-1<br>524 | X<br>X | 0-0<br>466 | 2-1<br>396 | 1-0<br>458 | 1-2<br>508 | 0-1<br>634 | 4-2<br>561 | 0-0<br>851 | 2-5<br>890 | 2-1<br>409 | 0-2<br>524 | 1-0<br>591 | 0-1<br>515 | 0-4<br>608 | 3-0<br>641 | 0-2<br>348 | 2-1<br>841 | 2-2<br>333 | 0-2<br>878 |
| 5 | Burton Albion | 0-3<br>960 | 0-1<br>741 | 0-2<br>1230 | 2-1<br>712 | X<br>X | 4-1<br>628 | 1-2<br>770 | 7-0<br>671 | 5-3<br>742 | 0-1<br>839 | 1-0<br>2103 | 0-1<br>620 | 3-1<br>660 | 1-2<br>1088 | 0-1<br>703 | 0-1<br>645 | 1-1<br>1059 | 0-0<br>576 | 1-2<br>690 | 2-1<br>920 | 1-2<br>865 | 0-1<br>952 |
| 6 | Cambridge | 3-1<br>216 | 1-1<br>178 | 1-4<br>304 | 3-1<br>217 | 0-0<br>294 | X<br>X | 0-0<br>271 | 0-0<br>284 | 1-1<br>359 | 1-0<br>325 | 1-2<br>268 | 2-0<br>307 | 0-1<br>254 | 0-1<br>274 | 2-1<br>539 | 1-2<br>287 | 1-1<br>546 | 2-2<br>268 | 1-3<br>275 | 0-1<br>338 | 1-0<br>201 | 3-0<br>258 |
| 7 | Crawley Tn | 3-0<br>577 | 0-2<br>727 | 2-2<br>854 | 4-1<br>877 | 1-1<br>730 | 1-1<br>1271 | X<br>X | 1-1<br>517 | 2-1<br>911 | 2-0<br>865 | 2-0<br>435 | 1-1<br>438 | 3-1<br>1074 | 2-1<br>1759 | 3-1<br>907 | 0-2<br>848 | 0-3<br>443 | 1-0<br>675 | 1-1<br>503 | 1-0<br>835 | 2-2<br>767 | 2-1<br>643 |
| 8 | Dorchester | 2-1<br>541 | 1-1<br>808 | 0-0<br>630 | 3-0<br>558 | 2-1<br>472 | 1-1<br>548 | 1-2<br>433 | X<br>X | 0-0<br>668 | 3-2<br>552 | 1-0<br>802 | 2-0<br>431 | 1-2<br>508 | 0-1<br>539 | 2-1<br>503 | 1-1<br>595 | 0-1<br>802 | 3-1<br>520 | 4-0<br>571 | 0-1<br>560 | 1-1<br>4159 | 1-2<br>514 |
| 9 | Gloucester | 0-0<br>563 | 2-1<br>704 | 2-2<br>510 | 4-3<br>463 | 0-1<br>617 | 3-1<br>536 | 2-0<br>584 | 4-1<br>606 | X<br>X | 0-1<br>593 | 0-0<br>531 | 2-0<br>535 | 2-3<br>394 | 1-1<br>703 | 2-1<br>610 | 2-1<br>576 | 1-0<br>1010 | 2-1<br>442 | 1-2<br>448 | 0-1<br>702 | 0-0<br>516 | 0-2<br>668 |
| 10 | Grantham T | 1-1<br>462 | 0-1<br>948 | 1-3<br>978 | 4-1<br>915 | 2-3<br>697 | 0-1<br>300 | 1-2<br>626 | 1-1<br>381 | 0-1<br>522 | X<br>X | 3-1<br>369 | 0-0<br>590 | 1-2<br>294 | 3-1<br>856 | 0-1<br>667 | 5-3<br>688 | 2-0<br>1170 | 3-0<br>511 | 2-1<br>730 | 1-2<br>430 | 2-0<br>507 | 0-3<br>478 |
| 11 | Gresley Rvrs | 2-1<br>573 | 1-2<br>547 | 1-0<br>583 | 1-3<br>435 | 0-2<br>1998 | 3-0<br>550 | 1-1<br>503 | 2-0<br>502 | 2-3<br>512 | 0-1<br>517 | X<br>X | 2-0<br>570 | 0-0<br>432 | 1-3<br>720 | 2-1<br>413 | 0-0<br>505 | 0-3<br>1490 | 1-3<br>419 | 4-1<br>571 | 2-3<br>684 | 1-2<br>560 | 1-1<br>490 |
| 12 | Halesowen | 3-1<br>683 | 2-2<br>750 | 1-1<br>670 | 1-0<br>808 | 1-3<br>902 | 2-1<br>609 | 3-2<br>698 | 3-1<br>503 | 0-1<br>743 | 5-1<br>661 | 3-4<br>543 | X<br>X | 3-3<br>742 | 4-1<br>454 | 0-1<br>601 | 2-0<br>685 | 2-0<br>1521 | 4-0<br>587 | 3-3<br>537 | 3-0<br>831 | 2-2<br>689 | 0-0<br>704 |
| 13 | Hastings Tn | 0-0<br>371 | 2-2<br>288 | 1-0<br>398 | 2-0<br>367 | 1-4<br>224 | 2-0<br>463 | 3-0<br>415 | 1-0<br>513 | 0-0<br>620 | 1-3<br>417 | 1-2<br>355 | 2-0<br>555 | X<br>X | 3-0<br>485 | 1-0<br>308 | 0-2<br>462 | 0-4<br>710 | 1-1<br>445 | 3-2<br>376 | 1-2<br>487 | 0-1<br>366 | 1-0<br>410 |
| 14 | Ilkeston Town | 1-2<br>569 | 0-0<br>748 | 1-3<br>828 | 2-1<br>568 | 1-2<br>1155 | 0-0<br>450 | 3-1<br>632 | 5-2<br>523 | 4-3<br>639 | 1-1<br>667 | 4-1<br>678 | 2-2<br>588 | 3-3<br>446 | X<br>X | 0-0<br>555 | 2-0<br>483 | 0-1<br>1338 | 3-0<br>610 | 3-0<br>483 | 3-5<br>543 | 1-1<br>644 | 3-0<br>648 |
| 15 | King's Lynn | 0-0<br>574 | 1-0<br>650 | 1-2<br>915 | 0-0<br>621 | 2-0<br>750 | 0-3<br>541 | 2-0<br>672 | 1-1<br>485 | 2-0<br>561 | 1-1<br>793 | 4-0<br>475 | 1-1<br>732 | 0-0<br>659 | 1-1<br>888 | X<br>X | 3-0<br>664 | 2-4<br>1039 | 2-0<br>867 | 3-3<br>652 | 4-2<br>486 | 1-2<br>592 | 2-0<br>663 |
| 16 | Merthyr Tyd | 2-0<br>500 | 0-0<br>506 | 2-2<br>602 | 2-0<br>484 | 0-2<br>657 | 3-3<br>539 | 3-1<br>540 | 1-1<br>447 | 0-1<br>343 | 1-0<br>521 | 1-2<br>650 | 1-0<br>343 | 1-0<br>477 | 1-2<br>446 | 0-1<br>555 | X<br>X | 2-1<br>582 | 4-1<br>384 | 0-1<br>431 | 6-0<br>370 | 1-1<br>426 | 0-1<br>496 |
| 17 | Nuneaton | 1-0<br>2242 | 1-1<br>2018 | 1-1<br>1440 | 6-0<br>1533 | 4-1<br>2030 | 4-0<br>1515 | 2-1<br>1409 | 0-0<br>1330 | 2-0<br>1538 | 2-0<br>1919 | 3-1<br>2945 | 4-3<br>1230 | 1-0<br>1211 | 1-3<br>1638 | 4-0<br>1564 | 6-1<br>1228 | X<br>X | 2-0<br>2007 | 0-1<br>1404 | 2-0<br>2099 | 4-2<br>1227 | 2-0<br>1724 |
| 18 | Rothwell Tn | 2-0<br>241 | 3-2<br>248 | 1-1<br>239 | 2-0<br>210 | 1-4<br>351 | 3-1<br>243 | 1-1<br>287 | 1-1<br>343 | 0-1<br>239 | 0-1<br>210 | 2-0<br>253 | 2-1<br>241 | 1-3<br>223 | 3-1<br>323 | 0-2<br>255 | 4-0<br>288 | 1-1<br>574 | X<br>X | 1-0<br>175 | 2-1<br>349 | 1-0<br>261 | 1-2<br>214 |
| 19 | Salisbury C | 0-2<br>360 | 3-2<br>682 | 0-0<br>521 | 1-0<br>494 | 0-2<br>560 | 4-1<br>308 | 0-2<br>279 | 3-3<br>367 | 1-1<br>667 | 1-0<br>419 | 2-2<br>352 | 1-2<br>771 | 1-0<br>462 | 0-0<br>337 | 2-2<br>449 | 1-0<br>763 | 1-1<br>1050 | 0-2<br>363 | X<br>X | 2-1<br>421 | 1-0<br>932 | 2-0<br>317 |
| 20 | Tamworth | 2-1<br>905 | 1-1<br>462 | 4-2<br>501 | 1-0<br>522 | 0-1<br>717 | 6-1<br>473 | 3-1<br>387 | 1-0<br>482 | 1-1<br>512 | 1-1<br>529 | 0-1<br>594 | 3-1<br>603 | 1-5<br>451 | 2-2<br>476 | 0-2<br>585 | 4-2<br>587 | 1-1<br>1404 | 3-2<br>397 | 2-1<br>519 | X<br>X | 1-3<br>591 | 0-1<br>599 |
| 21 | Weymouth | 0-1<br>727 | 2-1<br>1350 | 1-1<br>807 | 3-1<br>1066 | 0-0<br>927 | 1-2<br>913 | 1-3<br>634 | 2-1<br>2921 | 5-3<br>505 | 1-0<br>1041 | 3-1<br>657 | 1-2<br>961 | 1-2<br>503 | 2-2<br>721 | 1-0<br>885 | 0-0<br>1042 | 1-1<br>1350 | 5-0<br>930 | 1-1<br>951 | 0-3<br>894 | X<br>X | 2-1<br>934 |
| 22 | Worcester | 1-2<br>1043 | 0-3<br>602 | 1-0<br>690 | 3-1<br>1270 | 2-0<br>864 | 4-2<br>907 | 1-2<br>757 | 2-2<br>894 | 2-2<br>1045 | 1-2<br>1012 | 3-3<br>789 | 3-4<br>1403 | 0-0<br>574 | 2-0<br>1007 | 3-2<br>682 | 6-1<br>812 | 0-4<br>1355 | 1-0<br>721 | 0-0<br>703 | 1-0<br>1112 | 3-0<br>816 | X<br>X |

# DR MARTENS LEAGUE CUP 1998-99

## FIRST ROUND

| | | | | |
|---|---|---|---|---|
| Cambridge City | 4,4 | v | 3,1 | Brackley Town |
| Dartford | 1,1 | v | 1,5 | Tonbridge Angels |
| Shepshed Dynamo | 5,0 | v | 1,1 | Paget Rangers |
| Raunds Town | 3,1 | v | 1,4 | Baldock Town |
| Margate | 3,0 | v | 3,2 | Folkestone Invicta |
| Ashford Town | 2,2 | v | 3,1 | Hastings Town |
| St Leonards | 2,2 | v | 2,0 | Fisher Athletic |
| Erith & Belvedere | 0,0 | v | 1,5 | Crawley Town |
| Newport AFC | 4,1 | v | 2,1 | Cinderford Town |
| Weston S Mare | 3,2 | v | 2,2 | Yate Town |
| Havant & Water'vle | 2,1 | v | 3,1 | Weymouth |
| Bashley | 1,2 | v | 1,2 | Salisbury City |
| Merthyr Tydfil | 2,3 | v | 3,4 | Bath City |
| Clevedon Town | 1,2 | v | 0,4 | Witney Town |
| Dorchester Town | 3,0 | v | 1,0 | Fleet Town |
| Andover | 1,1 | v | 2,5 | Newport IoW |
| Sutton Coldfield T | 2,2 | v | 0,0 | Hinckley United |
| Racing Club War'k | 2,3 | v | 3,1 | Stafford Rangers |
| Tamworth | 4,4 | v | 0,1 | Gresley Rovers |
| VS Rugby | 0,1 | v | 1,1 | Bedworth United |
| Moor Green | 1,2 | v | 4,2 | Burton Albion |
| Atherstone United | 3,2 | v | 1,1 | Nuneaton Borough |
| Halesowen Town | 2,1 | v | 1,0 | Bromsgrove Rovers |
| Worcester City | 1,1 | v | 3,1 | Bilston Town |
| Bloxwich Town | 1,2 | v | 3,4 | Stourbridge |
| Gloucester City | 3,1 | v | 1,0 | Cirencester Town |
| Blakenall | 0,2 | v | 4,2 | Solihull Borough |
| Evesham United | 1,1 | v | 2,4 | Redditch United |
| Rothwell Town | 3,1 | v | 0,0 | Chelmsford City |
| Grantham Town | 0,4 | v | 1,0 | Ilkeston Town |
| Boston United | 1,5 | v | 2,0 | Kings Lynn |
| Corby Town | 0,1 | v | 3,0 | Stamford AFC |

## SECOND ROUND

| | | | | |
|---|---|---|---|---|
| Cambridge City | 2 | v | 0 | Tonbridge Angels |
| Shepshed Dynamo | 4 | v | 2 | Baldock Town |
| Folkestone Invicta | 2 | v | 1 | Hastings Town |
| St Leonards | 3 | v | 2 | Crawley Town |
| Newport AFC | 2 | v | 0 | Weston S Mare |

| | | | | |
|---|---|---|---|---|
| Weymouth | 1,1 | v | 1,3 | Bashley |
| Bath City | 0,1 | v | 0,3 | Witney Town |
| Dorchester Town | 4 | v | 2 | Newport IoW |
| Sutton Coldfield T | 3 | v | 0 | Racing Club War'k |
| Tamworth | 1,1 | v | 5,1 | Bedworth United |
| Burton Albion | 2,1 | v | 1,1 | Atherstone United |
| Halesowen Town | 0 | v | 2 | Bilston Town |
| Stourbridge | 2 | v | 0 | Gloucester City |
| Solihull Borough | 2 | v | 1 | Redditch United |
| Rothwell Town | 1,0 | v | 0,0 | Grantham Town |
| Boston United | 1 | v | 0 | Stamford AFC |

## THIRD ROUND

| | | | | |
|---|---|---|---|---|
| Cambridge City | 4 | v | 2 | Shepshed Dynamo |
| Folkestone Invicta | 2 | v | 3 | St Leonards |
| Newport AFC | 0 | v | 2 | Bashley |
| Witney Town | 1 | v | 2 | Dorchester Town |
| Sutton Coldfield T | 2 | v | 1 | Bedworth United |
| Burton Albion | 1,0 | v | 1,0 | Bilston Town |
| Stourbridge | 2 | v | 1 | Solihull Borough |
| Rothwell Town | 1 | v | 3 | Boston United |

## FOURTH ROUND

| | | | | |
|---|---|---|---|---|
| Cambridge City | 0,1 | v | 0,1 | St Leonards |
| (Cambridge won on away goals rule) | | | | |
| Bashley | 0 | v | 3 | Dorchester Town |
| Sutton Coldfield T | 1 | v | 0 | Burton Albion |
| Stourbridge | 0 | v | 2 | Boston United |

## SEMI-FINALS

| | | | | |
|---|---|---|---|---|
| Cambridge City | 3,1 | v | 0,3 | Dorchester Town |
| Sutton Coldfield T | 1,2 | v | 0,2 | Boston United |

## FINAL

| | | | | |
|---|---|---|---|---|
| Cambridge City | 0,1 | v | 2,0 | Sutton Coldfield T |

# STAR DR MARTENS STRIKERS

*Top left: Steve Tate (Havant & Waterlooville FC)   Photo: Andrew Chitty*
*Top right: David Laws (Weymouth)   Photo: Andrew Chitty*
*Bottom left: Martin Paul (Bath City)*
*Bottom left: Mark Turner (Kings Lynn)*

# ATHERSTONE UNITED

## CLUB OFFICIALS

Chairman: **Ku Akeredolu**
President: **C Culwick**
Secretary: **Neil Dykes**

18 Greendale Close, Atherstone,
Warwickshire CV9 1PR Tel: 01827 714326
Commercial Manager: **T Jago**

## FOOTBALL MANAGEMENT TEAM

Manager: Ron Bradbury 01203 382548
Asst Manager: R Stockley
Physio: S Welch

### FACT FILE

Formed: 1979
Nickname: The Adders
Club Sponsors: T.B.A.
Colours: Red & white stripes/red/red
Change colours: Yellow & blue/blue/blue
Midweek home matchday: Monday 7.30pm
Reserve's Lge: Midland Comb. Reserve Div.
1998-99
Captain: Mark Albrighton
P.o.Y.: Mark Albrighton & Dale Belford
Top scorer: Paul White

**GROUND**    Sheepy Road, Atherstone, Warwickshire. CV9 1HG
Tel: 01827 717829

**Directions:** Half mile north of town centre on B4116 Twycross/Ashby road.

Capacity: 3,500    Cover: 1,000    Seats: 373    Floodlights: Yes

**Clubhouse:** Open during normal licensing hours, all usual facilities.
Club Shop: Programmes, magazines, souvenirs etc. Contact: Sreve Clark 01827 712812

Pages: 28    Price: £1
Editor: Brian Stephenson 01827 715067
Local Press: Tamworth Herald, Evening News,
Atherstone Herald, Coventry Telegraph.
Local Radio: Mercia Sound, CWR

**PREVIOUS**    **Leagues:** West Midlands 1979-87

**CLUB RECORDS**    **Attendance:** 2,873 v V.S. Rugby, F.A. Cup 1st Round Proper 1987-88
**Win:** 12-2 vTipton Town (H), West Midlands (Regional) League Premier Division 86-87
**Defeat:** 1-7 v Rushden & Diamonds, Beazer League Premier Division 94-95
**Goalscorer:** Alan Bourton    **Appearances:** Lee Spencer
**Fee Paid:** £4,500 toGloucester City for Gary Bradder, 1989
**Fee Received:** £40,000 for Andy Rammellfrom Manchester United, September 1989

**HONOURS**    Southern Lge Midland Div 88-89; West Midlands Lge 81-82 86-87 (Lge Cup 81-82,Premier Div Cup 86-87, Div 2 Cup (Res.)
86-87); Walsall Senior Cup 83-84; Midland Combination Reserve Division 87-88; Birmingham Senior Cup R-up 89-90

**BEST SEASON**    **FA Cup:** 2nd Rd Proper 1990-91, 0-1 v Crewe Alexandra (A)
**FA Trophy:** 1st Round 88-89 91-92.

Players progressing: Andy Rammell (Manchester United)

*Steve Prindiville (Nuneaton) just manages to head clear against Atherstone. Photo: Keith Clayton*

# ATHERSTONE UNITED - MATCH FACTS - 1998-99 SEASON

| No | Date | Venue | Comp | Opponents | Att | Result | Score | Goalscorers |
|---|---|---|---|---|---|---|---|---|
| 1 | 22/08 | A | DMP | Merthyr Tydfil | 500 | L | 0-2 | |
| 2 | 24/08 | H | DMP | Ilkeston Town | 401 | D | 3 - 3 | White 9 11, Green 17 |
| 3 | 29/08 | H | DMP | Cambridge City | 253 | L | 0-1 | |
| 4 | 31/08 | A | DMP | Worcester City | 1043 | W | 2-1 | Green 35, Wright 89 |
| 5 | 05/09 | H | DMP | Dorchester Town | 260 | W | 3-1 | White 33 73, Middleton 40 |
| 6 | 09/09 | A | DMP | Salisbury City | 360 | W | 2-0 | Barrett 19, Green 88 |
| 7 | 12/09 | H | DMP | Rothwell Town | 258 | D | 2-2 | White 60, Hart 83 |
| 8 | 15/09 | H | DMP | Ilkeston Town | 569 | W | 2-1 | Martin 48 69 |
| 9 | 19/09 | H | DMP | Bath City | 333 | W | 2-1 | White 63, Middleton 77[p] |
| 10 | 21/09 | H | DMP | Worcester City | 402 | D | 1-1 | White 74 |
| 11 | 26/09 | A | DMP | Halesowen Town | 683 | L | 1-3 | Middleton 90[p] |
| 12 | 03/10 | H | FA C Q2 | **Nuneaton Borough** | **2029** | D | **0-0** | |
| 13 | 06/10 | A | FA C Q2 r | **Nuneaton Borough** | **3019** | L | **0-3** | |
| 14 | 10/10 | A | DMP | Gloucester City | 563 | D | 0-0 | |
| 15 | 24/10 | H | DMP | Merthyr Tydfil | 216 | W | 2-1 | Green 3, Wright 78 |
| 16 | 04/11 | H | M Inv 2 | **Cheslyn Hay** | **31** | W | **2-1** | **Green 10 29** |
| 17 | 07/11 | A | DMP | Burton Albion | 960 | W | 3-0 | Marsden 61[og], Kelly 63, White 80 |
| 18 | 09/11 | H | DM C 1(1) | **Nuneaton Borough** | **531** | W | **2-1** | **Niblett 47, Wright 81** |
| 19 | 14/11 | A | DMP | Grantham Town | 462 | D | 1-1 | Kelly 37 |
| 20 | 21/11 | H | FA T 2 | **Southport** | **502** | D | **0-0** | |
| 21 | 24/11 | A | FA T 2 r | **Southport** | **741** | L | **1 - 2** | **Blair 49** |
| 22 | 28/11 | A | DMP | Cambridge City | 216 | L | 1-3 | Green 5 |
| 23 | 05/12 | H | DMP | Hastings Town | 213 | D | 1-1 | Landon 12 |
| 24 | 07/12 | H | BSC 2 | **Paget Rangers** | **91** | D | **1-1** | **Middleton 60** |
| 25 | 15/12 | A | DM 1(2) | **Nuneaton Borough** | **558** | W | **3-1** | **Middleton 65[p], Kelly 77, Landon 90** |
| 26 | 19/12 | H | DMP | Weymouth | 225 | D | 0-0 | |
| 27 | 22/12 | A | BSC 2 r | **Paget Rangers** | **37** | L | **1 - 2** | **Martin 45** |
| 28 | 26/12 | A | DMP | Nuneaton Borough | 2242 | L | 0-1 | |
| 29 | 28/12 | H | DMP | Tamworth | 829 | L | 0-1 | |
| 30 | 01/01 | H | DMP | Bromsgrove Rovers | 332 | W | 5 - 1 | Green 24, White 53, Olner 65, Bennett 86, Albrighton 90 |
| 31 | 02/01 | A | DMP | Hastings Town | 371 | D | 0-0 | |
| 32 | 09/01 | H | DMP | Gloucester City | 278 | L | 1 - 2 | Hart 71 |
| 33 | 20/01 | H | DM C 2 | **Burton Albion** | **191** | D | **1-1** | **Kelly 21** |
| 34 | 30/01 | A | DMP | Boston United | 1022 | D | 0-0 | |
| 35 | 02/02 | A | DM C 2 r | **Burton Albion** | **332** | L | **1 - 2** | **Smith 77[p]** |
| 36 | 06/02 | H | DMP | Crawley Town | 310 | W | 2-1 | Mackie 1[og], Albrighton 10 |
| 37 | 13/02 | A | DMP | Bromsgrove Rovers | 485 | D | 0-0 | |
| 38 | 15/02 | H | DMP | Gresley Rovers | 285 | W | 2-1 | Aubrey 65, Green 85 |
| 39 | 20/02 | H | DMP | Burton Albion | 502 | D | 2-2 | Olner 35, Aubrey 86 |
| 40 | 27/02 | A | DMP | Gresley Rovers | 573 | L | 1 - 2 | Abury 53 |
| 41 | 09/03 | A | M Inv 3 | **Oldbury United** | **41** | W | **2-1** | **Aubrey 30, Mountford 70[og]** |
| 42 | 13/03 | H | DMP | King's Lynn | 311 | L | 1 - 2 | Middleton 45 |
| 43 | 15/03 | H | DMP | Salisbury City | 211 | W | 2-0 | Olner 88, Green 90 |
| 44 | 20/03 | A | DMP | Bath City | 647 | L | 1-3 | Albrighton 38 |
| 45 | 22/03 | H | M Inv QF | **Wednesfield** | **124** | W | **2-1** | **Aubry 67, Redgate 82** |
| 46 | 27/03 | A | DMP | Weymouth | 727 | W | 1 - 0 | Albrighton 47 |
| 47 | 03/04 | H | DMP | Nuneaton Borough | 2043 | L | L | 0-2 |
| 48 | 05/04 | A | DMP | Tamworth | 905 | L | 1 - 2 | Ball 58 |
| 49 | 10/04 | A | DMP | Dorchester Town | 541 | L | 1 - 2 | Ball 45 |
| 50 | 13/04 | A | DMP | King's Lynn | 574 | D | 0-0 | |
| 51 | 17/04 | H | DMP | Grantham Town | 244 | D | 1-1 | Stanborough 17 |
| 52 | 20/04 | A | DMP | Rothwell Town | 241 | L | L | 0-2 |
| 53 | 22/04 | H | M Inv SF | **Bridgnorth Town** | **104** | W | **1 - 0** | **Olner 87** |
| 54 | 24/04 | A | DMP | Crawley Town | 577 | L | 0-3 | |
| 55 | 26/04 | H | DMP | Boston United | 203 | D | 0-0 | |
| 56 | 01/05 | A | DMP | Halesowen Town | 391 | L | L | 0-2 |
| 57 | 03/05 | H | M Inv F | **Bandon** | **220** | W | **2-1** | **White 22, Middleton 36**   (at Oldbury United) |

**PLAYING SQUAD 1999-2000:**

GOALKEEPERS: Dale Belford (Hinckley United), Steve Mokler (Gloucester City)

DEFENDERS: Mark Adams (Bedworth United), Darren Ball (Ilkeston Town), Martyn Rowntree (Rocester), Boyd Young

MIDFIELDERS: Richard Barratt, Kevin Elvin (Nuneaton Borough), Leon Kelly, Craig Knight (Atherstone United), Lee Middleton (Cambridge United), Jonathon Mills (Cambridge United), Marc Orton (Gresley Rovers), Luke Vincent (Nuneaton Borough), Ray Woods (Worcester City)

FORWARDS: Stuart Aubrey (Polesworth North Warwick), Leon Kerin (Massey-Ferguson), Paul White (Nuneaton Borough)

# BATH CITY

## CLUB OFFICIALS

Chairman: **Stephen Hall**
Directors: J Turner, KLoach,
G.Todd,P.Weaver,M.Hughes.

Secretary: **Jason Turner,** c/o the club,
01225 423087 (B) & 0378 430488 (M)

Commercial Director: **G.Todd**
Safety Officer: **J Watt**
Press Officer: **P.Bodin**

## FOOTBALL MANAGEMENT TEAM
Manager: Paul Bodin
Assistant Mnaager: Steve White
Physios:Terry Hardwell & Dave Monks

## FACT FILE

Founded: 1889
Nickname: Stripes & The City
Midweek home matchday: Tuesday
Colours: Black & white stripes/black/b & w
Change: All yellow
Youth League: South West Co,
Somerset Youth Floodlit
Ladies Team: Yes
1998-99 Captain: Colin Towler
Top scorer: Martin Paul
P.o.Y.: Mike Davis

OFFICIAL MATCHDAY PROGRAMME
Season 1998-99     Issue 25 £1.30

Today's Visitors:

Pages: 40 Price £1.30

Editor: Chris Stillman
Tel: 01761 433528

## GROUND
Twerton Park, Twerton, Bath Avon BA2 1DB.
Tel: 01225 423087/313518 Fax: 01225481391
**Directions:** Twerton Park is situated on the A4/A36 Lower Bristol Road - on theBristol side of Bath City Centre (Approx 2.5 miles). The area is serviced by J18 on the M4. From the centre of Bath the bus route is No.5 - Twerton High Street
Capacity: 8,840      Seated: 1,017      Covered Terracing: 4,800
**Clubhouse:** Several bars open all week and full service with menu on match-days catering for up to 250 people            Club Shop: Contact Mr K Sellick

**PREVIOUS**          **Grounds:** The Belvoir Ground, Lambridge 1889-1932
                     **Leagues:** Southern League, Vauxhall Conference

**CLUB RECORDS**  **Attendance:** 18,020 v Brighton & Hove Albion, FA Cup.
                  **Defeat:** 9-0 Yeovil Town 46-47      **Victory:** 8-0 v Boston united 98-99
                  **Career goalscorer:** Paul Randall.      **Career appearances:** David Mogg (530)
                  **Transfer fee paid:** £15,000 for Nicky Tanner from Bristol City
                  **Transfer fee received:** £80,000 for Jason Dodd from Southampton

**BEST SEASON**   **FA Cup:** 63-64, 93-94      **FA Trophy:** 89-90, 4th Rd

**HONOURS**       Southern League Champions 59-60, 77-78; R-up 29-33, 61-62, 89-90; Southern League Cup 78-79; Somerset Premier Cup 51-52, 52-53, 57-58, 59-60, 65-66, 69-70, 77-78, 80-81, 81-82, 83-84, 84-85, 85-86, 88-89, 89-90, 93-94, 94-95;Anglo-Italian Cup R-up 76-77, 77-78
Players progressing: Alan Skirton (Arsenal),Tony Book (Plymouth A.), Kenny Allen (Bournemouth), Peter Rogers (Exeter C.), R Bourne (Torquay), Dave Wiffil (Manchester C.), Stan Mortensen (Blackpool), Brian Wade (Swindon Town), Jeff Meacham (Bristol R.), Martin Hirst (BristolC.), Paul Bodin (Swindon), Graham Withey (Coventry), Jason Dodd (Southampton),Paul Adcock (Torquay)

Back Row: Martin Paul, Jim Fraser, Stuart James, Rob Wadsworth, Mark Harrington. Middle Row: Steve Tregale (Physio), Colin Towler, Rob Skidmore, Dave Elsey, Mark Hervin, Mike Davis, Graham Colbourne, Nick Brooks, Stewart Naughton (Youth Dev). Front Row: Lee Vickerman, Peter Tisdale, Steve White (Asst Mngr), Paul Bodin (Mngr), Gary Wotton, Gareth Loydon

# BATH CITY - MATCH FACTS - 1998-99 SEASON

| No | Date | Venue | Comp | Opponents | Att | Result | Score | Goalscorers | |
|----|------|-------|------|-----------|-----|--------|-------|-------------|---|
| 1 | 22/08 | H | DMP | King's Lynn | 955 | W | 2-0 | Davis 2, Fraser 86 | |
| 2 | 25/08 | A | DMP | Weymouth | 1350 | L | 1-2 | Bodin 17 | |
| 3 | 29/08 | A | DMP | Crawley Town | 727 | W | 2-0 | Harrington 19, Davis 69 | |
| 4 | 31/08 | H | DMP | Gloucester City | 1027 | L | 1-2 | Bodin 33 | |
| 5 | 05/09 | A | DMP | Tamworth | 462 | D | 1-1 | Paul 14 | |
| 6 | 08/09 | H | DMP | Hastings Town | 592 | L | 0-2 | | |
| 7 | 12/09 | H | DMP | Grantham Town | 948 | W | 1-0 | Paul 90 | |
| 8 | 15/09 | H | DMP | Weymouth | 790 | W | 2-1 | Paul 34, Bodin 78[p] | |
| 9 | 19/09 | A | DMP | Atherstone United | 333 | L | 1-2 | Colbourne 65 | |
| 10 | 22/09 | A | DMP | Gloucester City | 704 | L | 1-2 | Harrington 86 | |
| 11 | 26/09 | H | DMP | Bromsgrove Rovers | 802 | W | 3-0 | Bodin 14[p], Paul 49 54[p] | |
| 12 | 03/10 | H | FA C Q2 | Cirencester Town | 626 | W | 3-1 | Bodin 36[p], Colbourne 49, Paul 86 | |
| 13 | 10/10 | H | DMP | Burton Albion | 716 | W | 2-0 | Paul 39, Bodin 85 | |
| 14 | 13/10 | H | SPC 1 | Backwell United | 308 | W | 3-1 | White 55 77, Colbourne 64 | |
| 15 | 17/10 | A | FA C Q3 | Walton & Hersham | 391 | D | 2-2 | White 73, Paul 77 | |
| 16 | 20/10 | H | FA C Q3 r | Walton & Hersham | 656 | W | 3-0 | Bodin 33, Loydon 62, Paul 80[p] | |
| 17 | 24/10 | A | FA T 1 | Dorchester Town | 522 | W | 2-0 | Davis 23, Loydon 84 | |
| 18 | 03/11 | A | FA C Q4 | Hendon | 357 | L | 0-4 | | |
| 19 | 07/11 | A | DMP | Cambridge City | 654 | W | 1-0 | Paul 37 | |
| 20 | 10/11 | A | DM C 1(1) | Merthyr Tydfil | 225 | W | 3-2 | Giles 44[og], Colbourne 55, White 77 | |
| 21 | 14/11 | A | DMP | Ilkeston Town | 748 | D | 0-0 | | |
| 22 | 17/11 | A | SPC 2 | Bishop Sutton | 183 | W | 4-1 | Fraser 16 65, Paul 21, White 72 | |
| 23 | 21/11 | A | FA T 2 | Rushden & Diamonds | 1989 | L | 0-2 | | |
| 24 | 24/11 | H | DM C 1(2) | Merthyr Tydfil | 398 | W | 4-3 | Richards 10 80, Colbourne 52 90 | |
| 25 | 28/11 | A | DMP | Bromsgrove Rovers | 580 | W | 3-1 | Paul 3 69 76 | |
| 26 | 05/12 | A | DMP | Merthyr Tydfil | 775 | W | 3-0 | Paul 58, Skidmore 63, Fraser 78 | |
| 27 | 07/12 | A | DMP | Worcester City | 602 | W | 3-0 | Fraser 15, Paul 20, Davis 30 | |
| 28 | 12/12 | A | DMP | Halesowen Town | 1456 | D | 0-0 | | |
| 29 | 15/12 | H | DM C 2 | Witney Town | 272 | D | 0-0 | | |
| 30 | 19/12 | A | DMP | Rothwell Town | 248 | l | 2-3 | James 2, White 89 | |
| 31 | 28/12 | A | DMP | Dorchester Town | 808 | D | 1-1 | Colbourne 6 | |
| 32 | 01/01 | A | DMP | Merthyr Tydfil | 506 | D | 0-0 | | |
| 33 | 03/01 | H | DMP | Ilkeston Town | 735 | L | 1-2 | Towler 4 | |
| 34 | 14/01 | A | DM C 2 r | Witney Town | 93 | L | 2-3 | Paul 21, Davis 86 | |
| 35 | 16/01 | A | DMP | Gresley Rovers | 857 | W | 3-0 | White 12, Paul 63 74 | |
| 36 | 23/01 | H | DMP | Crawley Town | 888 | W | 2-0 | Paul 18, Fraser 64 | |
| 37 | 30/01 | A | DMP | Nuneaton Borough | 2018 | D | 1-1 | White 40 | |
| 38 | 06/02 | H | DMP | Grantham Town | 864 | D | 1-1 | Fraser 42 | |
| 39 | 09/02 | A | SPC QF | Brislington | 155 | D | 2-2 | Davis 16, Colbourne 34 | 3 2 |
| 40 | 13/02 | A | DMP | Burton Albion | 741 | W | 1-0 | White 42 | |
| 41 | 16/02 | H | DMP | Salisbury City | 716 | L | 3-5 | Colbourne 60 85, Davis 82 | |
| 42 | 20/02 | A | DMP | Nuneaton Borough | 1285 | L | 1-3 | Bodin 88 | |
| 43 | 02/03 | H | SPC SF | Clevedon Town | 347 | D | 0-0 | (3-4 pens) | |
| 44 | 16/03 | H | DMP | Worcester City | 486 | D | 0-0 | | |
| 45 | 20/03 | H | DMP | Atherstone United | 647 | W | 3-1 | Walker 43 81, Davis 83 | |
| 46 | 23/03 | A | DMP | King's Lynn | 650 | L | 0-1 | | |
| 47 | 27/03 | A | DMP | Halesowen Town | 621 | D | 2-2 | Richards 26, Fraser 64 | |
| 48 | 30/03 | A | DMP | Hastings Town | 288 | D | 2-2 | Colbourne 1, Davis 90 | |
| 49 | 03/04 | A | DMP | Salisbury City | 682 | L | 2-3 | White 4 24 | |
| 50 | 05/04 | H | DMP | Dorchester Town | 631 | L | 0-1 | | |
| 51 | 10/04 | H | DMP | Rothwell Town | 557 | W | 2-0 | Paul 4[p] 15[p] | |
| 52 | 17/04 | A | DMP | Boston United | 909 | L | 2-3 | Harrington 14, Paul 21 | |
| 53 | 20/04 | H | DMP | Boston United | 390 | W | 8-0 | Davis 10, Bodin 12, Harrington 22, Paul 34[p] 39 57, Colbourne 60, White79 | |
| 54 | 22/04 | A | DMP | Cambridge City | 178 | D | 1-1 | Paul 53[p] | |
| 55 | 24/04 | H | DMP | Tamworth | 1181 | W | 3-0 | Paul 31 70, Davis 65 | |
| 56 | 01/05 | A | DMP | Gresley Rovers | 547 | W | 2-1 | Paul 3[p] 24 | |

## PLAYING SQUAD 1999-2000:

GOALKEEPERS: Elliott Jackson (Oxford United), Mark Teasdale (Trowbridge Town), Alan Churchward (Caine Town/Highworth/Hungerford - cover)

DEFENDERS: Paul Bodin (Swindon Town), Mark Clode (Swansea City), Lee Collier (Yeovil Town/Larkhall Athletic), David Elsey (Mangotsfield United - dual reg.), Jon Holloway (Gloucester City), Kevin Lloyd (Ex-Hereford United/Cardiff City), Fidel Richards, Rob Skidmore (Forest Green Rovers), Peter Tisdale (Welton Rovers), Graham Colbourne (Paulton Rovers), Stuart James (Weymouth), Scott Walker (Exeter City)

FORWARDS: Mike Davis (Bristol Rovers), Jimmy Fraser (Worcester City), Martin Paul (Bristol Rovers), Colin Towler (Yate Town), Steve White (Cardiff City)

# BOSTON UNITED

**CLUB OFFICIALS**
Chairman: **S.Burgess**
President: **Mr A E Bell**
Vice-Chairman: **P.Malkinson**

Gen. Manager/Secretary/Comm. Manager:
**John Blackwell,**
14-16 Spain Place, Boston,
Lincs PE26 6HN  Tel: 01205 364406 (office**)**

**FOOTBALL MANAGEMENT TEAM**

Manager: Steve Evans
Asst Manager: Reevor Quow

**FACT FILE**
Founded: 1934
Nickname: The Pilgrims
Sponsors: Wards Brewery
Colours: Amber/black/amber
Change colours: Blue & Green
Midweek matchday: Wednesday
Newsline: 0898 121 539
Reserve League: Lincolnshire League
98-99 Captain: Martin Hardy
P.o.Y.: Martin Hardy
Top scorer: Matt Carmichael

**GROUND**
York Street, Boston, Lincs
Tel: 01205 364406 office, 365524/5 matchday no., 354063 fax
**Directions:** A1 to A17 Sleaford-Boston, over rail crossing, bear right at Eaglepub to lights over Haven Bridge, thru lights opposite New Store, right intoYork Street. Ground just off town centre
Capacity: 8,771          Cover: 8,771          Seats: 1,826          Floodlights: Yes
**Clubhouse:** (01205 362967) Open every day except Tuesday. Live entertainmentSaturday, pool, darts, dominoes, Sunday football teams
Club Shop: At club office (as secretary's address, above) not ground. Metal Badges: 2 types

Pages: 44
Price: £1
Editor: Secretary

**PREVIOUS**        **Leagues:** Midland 21-58 62-64; Southern 58-61; Central Alliance 61-62; UnitedCounties 65-66; West Midlands (Regional) 66-68; Northern Premier 68-79, 93-98; Alliance Premier (Conference) 79-93
**Names:** Boston Town; Boston Swifts.        **Grounds:** None

**CLUB RECORDS**    **Attendance:** 10,086 v Corby Tn, floodlit inauguration 1955
**Scorer:** Chris Cook (181)        **Appearances:** Billy Howells, 500+
**Win:** 14-0 v Spilsby Tn, Grace Swan Cup, 92-93
**Fee Paid:** £14,000 for Micky Nuttell (Wycombe Wanderers)        **Fee Received:** £25,000 for Gary Jones (Southend Utd 93)

**BEST SEASON**    **FA Trophy:** Runners-up 84-85        **FA Cup:** Third Round replay 73-74, 1-6 V Derby County (H), after 0-0
League clubs defeated: Derby 55-56, Southport 70-71, Hartlepool 71-72, Crewe82-83

**HONOURS**        Northern Prem Lg 72-73 73-74 76-77 77-78 (R-up 71-72 95-96), Lg Cup 73-74 75-76(R-up 77-78), Challenge Shield 73-74 74-75 76-77 77-78; Lincs Snr Cup (12); E Anglian Cup 60-61; Central All 61-62 (Lg Cup 61-62); Utd Counties Lg 65-66 (Lg Cup 65-66);W Mids (Reg) Lg 66-67 67-68, Eastern Professional F'loodlit Cup 71-72 (R-up 76-77); Non-League Champion of Champions Cup 72-73 73-74 76-77 77-78; Midland Lg R-up 55-56. Dr.Martens Premier Runners -Up 98-99.

Players progressing: Jim Smith (Colchester), Steve Thompson(Lincoln), Brendon Phillips (Mansfield), Gordon Simmonite (Blackpool), SimonGarner (Blackburm), John Froggatt & Bobby Svarc (Colchester), David Gilbert, Neil Grayson, Jamie Pascoe, Robbie Curtis, Dean Trott (Northampton), Tim Dalton(Bradford C.), Gary Jones (Southend)

*Lucky for Boston United that this Gainsborough corner goes over, look how many players need the loo!*
*Photo: Bill Wheatcroft*

476

# BOSTON UNITED - MATCH FACTS - 1998-99 SEASON

| No | Date | Venue | Comp | Opponents | Att | Result | Score | Goalscorers |
|---|---|---|---|---|---|---|---|---|
| 1 | 25/07 | H | L SC QF | Grimsby Town | 416 | L | 0-1 | |
| 2 | 22/08 | A | DMP | Dorchester Town | 630 | D | 0-0 | |
| 3 | 26/08 | H | DMP | Rothwell Town | 984 | D | 0-0 | |
| 4 | 29/08 | H | DMP | Nuneaton Borough | 1159 | L | 2-3 | Watts 29, Bailey 81 |
| 5 | 31/08 | A | DMP | Ilkeston Town | 828 | W | 3-1 | Charles 44 82[p], Munton 85 |
| 6 | 05/09 | H | DMP | Bromsgrove Rovers | 822 | D | 2-2 | Charles 54[p], Watts 86 |
| 7 | 08/09 | A | DMP | Halesowen Town | 670 | D | 1-1 | Stanhope 76 |
| 8 | 12/09 | H | DMP | Salisbury City | 782 | W | 3-1 | Stanhope 2, Charles 37, Lovell 73[og] |
| 9 | 15/09 | A | DMP | Rothwell Town | 239 | D | 1-1 | Charles 47[p] |
| 10 | 19/09 | H | DMP | Merthyr Tydfil | 737 | L | 0-3 | |
| 11 | 26/09 | A | DMP | Gresley Rovers | 583 | L | 0-1 | |
| 12 | 30/09 | H | DMP | Ilkeston Town | 616 | L | 0-1 | |
| 13 | 03/10 | A | FA C Q2 | Congleton Town | 231 | L | 0-1 | |
| 14 | 10/10 | A | DMP | Weymouth | 807 | D | 1-1 | Hardy 18 |
| 15 | 17/10 | H | DMP | Dorchester Town | 747 | W | 5-1 | Munton 24, Stanhope 48, Stringfellow 59, Carmichael 69, Watts 87 |
| 16 | 21/10 | H | MC | Derby County | 630 | W | 3-1 | Carmichael, Stringfellow, Carbonari[og] |
| 17 | 27/10 | A | FA T 1 | Stocksbridge Park Steels | 221 | D | 1-1 | Carmichael 10 |
| 18 | 29/10 | H | FA T 1 r | Stocksbridge Park Steels | 527 | W | 1-0 | Carmichael 75 |
| 19 | 31/10 | H | DMP | Hastings Town | 874 | D | 1-1 | Carmichael 65 |
| 20 | 04/11 | H | DMP | Halesowen Town | 671 | W | 2-0 | Charles 51[p], Stringfellow 73 |
| 21 | 07/11 | A | DMP | Nuneaton Borough | 1440 | D | 1-1 | Stanhope 31 |
| 22 | 11/11 | H | DM C 1(1) | King's Lynn | 507 | W | 5-0 | Carmichael 37 46 78, Watts 35 56 |
| 23 | 14/11 | A | DMP | Cambridge City | 304 | W | 4-1 | Carmichael 12, Stanhope 14, Venables 64, Horseman 80 |
| 24 | 21/11 | H | FA T 2 | Worksop Town | 1018 | D | 1-1 | Carmichael 49 |
| 25 | 24/11 | A | FA T 2 r | Worksop Town | 668 | W | 4-0 | Stringfellow 36, Watts 62, Hardy 64, Munton 90 |
| 26 | 28/11 | A | DMP | Tamworth | 501 | L | 2-4 | Watts 3 64 |
| 27 | 05/12 | H | DMP | Burton Albion | 1006 | W | 4-0 | Stanhope 1 49, Carmichael 63, Childs 76[p] |
| 28 | 12/12 | A | DMP | Bromsgrove Rovers | 524 | D | 1-1 | Curtis 32 |
| 29 | 15/12 | A | DM C 1(2) | King's Lynn | 221 | L | 1-2 | Carmichael 16 |
| 30 | 19/12 | H | DMP | Gloucester City | 907 | W | 1-0 | Carmichael 75 |
| 31 | 26/12 | A | DMP | King's Lynn | 915 | W | 2-1 | Hardy 32[p], Spearing 37[og] |
| 32 | 28/12 | H | DMP | Grantham Town | 1925 | W | 3-0 | Andrews 39[og], Curtis 47, Watts 68 |
| 33 | 01/01 | H | DMP | Cambridge City | 2005 | D | 2-2 | Carmichael 19, Stringfellow 22 |
| 34 | 03/01 | A | DMP | Burton Albion | 1230 | W | 2-0 | Childs 3, Watts 90 |
| 35 | 09/01 | A | DMP | Hastings Town | 398 | L | 0-1 | |
| 36 | 13/01 | H | DM C 2 | Stamford | 304 | W | 1-0 | Childs 78 |
| 37 | 16/01 | A | FA T 3 | Gainsborough Trinity | 1647 | W | 4-1 | Mason 32, Stringfellow 47, Venables 78, Costello 89 |
| 38 | 23/01 | A | DMP | Gloucester City | 510 | D | 2-2 | Charles 24, Venables 62 |
| 39 | 30/01 | H | DMP | Atherstone United | 1022 | D | 0-0 | |
| 40 | 06/02 | H | FA T 4 | Redditch United | 1426 | W | 2-0 | Venables 9, Carmichael 88 |
| 41 | 13/02 | A | DMP | Crawley Town | 854 | D | 2-2 | Carmichael 7, Charles 82 |
| 42 | 16/02 | A | DM C 3 | Rothwell Town | 87 | W | 3-1 | Watts 11, Carmichael 49, Hardy 55 |
| 43 | 20/02 | H | DMP | Gresley Rovers | 1026 | W | 4-1 | Carmichael 17 52, Stringfellow 33, Rawle 43 |
| 44 | 23/02 | H | DM C QF | Stourbridge | 221 | W | 2-0 | Charles 14, Stanhope 69 |
| 45 | 27/02 | H | FA T 5 | Altrincham | 2575 | W | 2-0 | Watts 19 72 |
| 46 | 13/03 | H | DMP | Crawley Town | 1230 | W | 3-1 | Charles 32, Hardy 63, Rawle 79 |
| 47 | 20/03 | H | DMP | Weymouth | 1100 | W | 2-1 | Childs 6, Rawle 80 |
| 48 | 24/03 | H | DM C SF(1) | Sutton Coldfield Town | 516 | D | 2-2 | Walters 14, Mason 33[p] |
| 49 | 27/03 | A | FA T QF | St Albans City | 2723 | L | 1-2 | Watts 23 |
| 50 | 29/03 | A | DMP | Worcester City | 690 | L | 0-1 | |
| 51 | 31/03 | A | DM C SF(2) | Sutton Coldfield Town | 275 | L | 0-1 | |
| 52 | 03/04 | H | DMP | King's Lynn | 1436 | W | 3-1 | Featherstone 52, Carmichael 73, Mason 85 |
| 53 | 05/04 | H | DMP | Grantham Town | 978 | D | 0-0 | |
| 54 | 10/04 | A | DMP | Salisbury City | 521 | W | 2-0 | Stringfellow 49, Featherstone 63 |
| 55 | 14/04 | H | DMP | Tamworth | 553 | W | 3-2 | Curtis 52, Watts 54, Stanhope 60 |
| 56 | 17/04 | H | DMP | Bath City | 909 | L | 0-8 | |
| 57 | 20/04 | A | DMP | Bath City | 390 | D | 2-2 | Featherstone 51 84 |
| 58 | 24/04 | A | DMP | Merthyr Tydfil | 602 | D | 0-0 | |
| 59 | 26/04 | A | DMP | Atherstone United | 203 | D | 0-0 | |
| 60 | 01/05 | H | DMP | Worcester City | 1023 | W | 3-1 | Curtis 12, Stringfellow 22, Childs 69 |

## PLAYING SQUAD 1999-2000:

GOALKEEPERS: Paul Bastock (Kettering Town), Matt Dickins (Altrincham), Nick Maddison

DEFENDERS: Jason Burnham (Worcester City), Joby Gowshall (Lincoln City), Colin Hoyle (King's Lynn), Glenn Maddison, Danny Seager, Andy Taylor (Crawley Town), Paul Wilson (Aylesbury United)

MIDFIELDERS: Steve Appleby (Bourne Town), Steve Chambers (Mansfield Town), Gary Childs (Wisbech Town), Gareth Jelleyman (Peterborough United), Mike Melson, Ross Nicholls, Gary Porter (Scarborough), Trevor Quow (Stamford), Mark Rawle (Rushden & Diamonds), David Rennie (Peterborough United), Andrew STanhope (King's Lynn), Ian STringfellow (King's Lynn), Leigh Taylor (Wyberton)

FORWARDS: Peter Costello (Hong Kong), Andy Kimomya (Nuneaton Borough), Micky Nuttell (King's Lynn), Kevin Slinn (Raunds Town), Joe Vaughan

# BURTON ALBION

## CLUB OFFICIALS

Chairman: **C B Robinson** 01283 813943(H)
Vice Chairman:
Secretary: **Tony A Kirkland**, 40 Hurst Drive,
Stretton, Burton-on-Trent DE13 0ED
01283 536510 (H). 0374 102485 (Mobile)
Commercial Man: **Peter Alcock**
Press Officer: **David Twigg** (01283 562013)

### FOOTBALL MANAGEMENT TEAM
Manager: Nigel Clough
Assistant Manager: Gary Crosby
Physio: Matt Brown

### FACT FILE

Formed: 1950
Nickname: Brewers
Sponsors: B.I. Industries
Colours: Yellow with black trim
Change colours: Sky blue, black trim
Midweek matchday: Tuesday

**GROUND** Eton Park, Princess Way, Burton-on-Trent DE14 2RU Tel: 01283 565938
**Directions:** From south M42 - A38 (Lichfield), follow signs forBurton, take 2nd turn for Burton
(A5121), right at island - ground on left: From M6 north - jct 15 and follow A50 for Stoke and
Uttoxeter, follow A50 signs to Burton, continue under bypass, left into Shakespeare Rd after
canal bridge (opp. Navigation Inn), ground at end. From M6 North, leave at Jct 15. Follow A50
Stoke & Uttoxeter. Leave for A38 South to Burton & Lichfield at Toyota Factory. Leave Burton
North A5121 past Pirelli Factory to Island .Turn right ground is on left.
Capacity: 4,500        Cover: 2,500        Seats: 400        Floodlights: Yes
**Clubhouse:** `The Football Tavern' - open normal pub hours. Full hot & cold menu.
Steward: T.B.A.                Club Shop: Yes

Pages: 48 Price: £1
Editor: David Twigg (01283 562013)
Local Press: Burton Daily Mail (01283 43311)
Local Radio: Radio Derby

**PREVIOUS**      **Leagues:** West Midlands 1950-58; Southern 58-79; Northern Premier 79-8;
**Ground:** Wellington Street 50-57

**CLUB RECORDS**  **Attendance:** 5,860 v Weymouth, Southern Lg Cup Final 2nd leg, 1964
(22,500 v Leicester City, F.A. Cup 3rd Rd 1984 - played at Derby County F.C.)
**Goalscorer:** Ritchie Barker, 157.          **Appearances:** Phil Annable, 567
**Fee Paid:** £21,000 to for R Jones and J Pearson (Kidderminster)
**Fee Received:** £60,000 for Darren Carr (C Palace 89)

**BEST SEASON**  **FA Trophy:** R-up 86-87 (SF 74-75)        **FA Cup:** 3rd Rd Prop 55-56, 84-85. 1st Rd 9 times

**HONOURS**      Sth Lg Cup 63-64 96-97 (R-up 88-89), Div 1 (Nth) R-up 71-72 73-74; Nth Prem Lg Chall Cup 82-83 (R-up 86-87), Presidents
Cup R-up 85-86 (SF 86-87); BirminghamSnr Cup 53-54 70-71 (R-up 86-87); FA Trophy R-up 86-87; GMAC Cup SF 86-87;
Bass Charity Vase 81-82 85-86, Challenge Cup 84-85; Wt Mids Lg R-up 53-54; Staffs Sen Cup 55-56

Players progressing: L Green & T Parry & S Aston (Hartlepool65/66), G Hunter (Lincoln 65), D Jones (Newport 68), R Barker & J Bourne & TBailey
(Derby 67/69/70), M Pollock & S Buckley (Luton 74), P Ward (Brighton75), Tony Moore (Sheffield Utd 79), C Swan & G Clayton (Doncaster 80 &
86), RJobson (Watford 82), P Haycock (Rotherham 86), A Kamara (Scarborough 87), PGroves (Leicester City 88), S Cotterill & J Gayle (Wimbledon
89), D Carr(Crystal Pal. 89), D Smith & D Roberts (Wolves 90 & 92)

*Back Row (L-R): Wayne Sutton, Mark Jones, Andy Garner, Nick Goodwin, Craig Smith.   Middle Row: Anton Thomas,
Michael Allsop, Mark Blount, Aarron Webster, Allan Davies, Darren Stride, David Holmes.   Front Row: Danny George, Neil
Glasser, Pat Lyons, Nigel Clough, Gary Crosby, Jamie March, Terry Henshaw, Dale Anderson   Photo: M Bannister*

# BURTON ALBION - MATCH FACTS - 1998-99 SEASON

| No | Date | Venue | Comp | Opponents | Att | Result | Score | Goalscorers |
|----|------|-------|------|-----------|-----|--------|-------|-------------|
| 1 | 30/07 | H | BV Gp 2 | Stoke City | n/k | L | 0-2 | |
| 2 | 03/08 | H | BV Gp 2 | Leicester City | n/k | W | 3-1 | Lyons 25, Smith, Holmes |
| 3 | 22/08 | A | DMP | Rothwell Town | 351 | W | 4-1 | Blount 3, Holmes 60, Smith 75 85 |
| 4 | 25/08 | H | DMP | Worcester City | 952 | L | 0-1 | |
| 5 | 29/08 | H | DMP | Merthyr Tydfil | 645 | L | 0-1 | |
| 6 | 31/08 | A | DMP | Halesowen Town | 902 | W | 3-1 | Garner 39 64, C Smith 82 |
| 7 | 05/09 | H | DMP | Cambridge City | 628 | W | 4-1 | Garner 10 47, Spooner 66, Cotter 73 |
| 8 | 08/09 | A | DMP | Nuneaton Borough | 2030 | L | 1-4 | Garner 42 |
| 9 | 12/09 | H | DMP | Bromsgrove Rovers | 712 | W | 2-1 | Cotter 86, Davidson 90 |
| 10 | 14/09 | A | DMP | Worcester City | 864 | L | 0-2 | |
| 11 | 19/09 | A | DMP | Crawley Town | 730 | D | 1-1 | Garner 53 |
| 12 | 22/09 | H | DMP | Halesowen Town | 620 | L | 0-1 | |
| 13 | 26/09 | H | DMP | Gloucester City | 742 | W | 5-3 | Holmes 25 71 90, Garner 50[p], Davis 74 |
| 14 | 03/10 | A | FA C Q2 | Rocester | 423 | W | 1-0 | Holmes 33 |
| 15 | 10/10 | A | DMP | Bath City | 716 | L | 0-2 | |
| 16 | 17/10 | H | FA C Q3 | Nuneaton Borough | 1894 | W | 2-1 | Holmes 41, Smith 54 |
| 17 | 20/10 | H | BSC 1 | Stratford Town | 153 | D | 0-0 | |
| 18 | 24/10 | H | FA T 1 | Grantham Town | 588 | D | 0-0 | |
| 19 | 27/10 | A | FA T 1 r | Grantham Town | 570 | W | 3-0 | Grocutt 21, Smith 31, Blount 74 |
| 20 | 31/10 | A | FA C Q4 | Morpeth Town | 534 | W | 1-0 | Holmes 24 |
| 21 | 03/11 | H | DMP | Nuneaton Borough | 1059 | D | 1-1 | Holmes 73 |
| 22 | 04/11 | A | BSC 1 r | Stratford Town | 50 | W | 2-1 | Bradshaw 9, Francis 37 |
| 23 | 07/11 | H | DMP | Atherstone United | 960 | L | 0-3 | |
| 24 | 10/11 | A | DM C 1(1) | Moor Green | 164 | D | 2-2 | Ejiofor 32 42 |
| 25 | 14/11 | A | FA C 1 | Kingstonian | 1505 | L | 0-1 | |
| 26 | 17/11 | H | DM C 1(2) | Moor Green | 261 | W | 4-1 | Ejiofor 28 70, Sutton 37 75 |
| 27 | 21/11 | H | FA T 2 | Bamber Bridge | 676 | W | 5-0 | Spooner 50 65, Stride 54, C Smith 73, Holmes 90 |
| 28 | 28/11 | H | DMP | Grantham Town | 839 | L | 0-1 | |
| 29 | 01/12 | H | B SC 2 | Kings Norton Town | 116 | L | 1-4 | Francis 31 |
| 30 | 05/12 | A | DMP | Boston United | 1006 | L | 0-4 | |
| 31 | 12/12 | H | DMP | Rothwell Town | 576 | D | 0-0 | |
| 32 | 19/12 | A | DMP | Tamworth | 717 | W | 1-0 | Marsden 15 |
| 33 | 26/12 | H | DMP | Gresley Rovers | 2103 | W | 1-0 | Grocutt 63 |
| 34 | 28/12 | A | DMP | Ilkeston Town | 1155 | W | 2-1 | Lyons 7, Holmes 44 |
| 35 | 01/01 | A | DMP | Gresley Rovers | 1998 | W | 2-0 | Smith 12, Webster 76 |
| 36 | 03/01 | H | DMP | Boston United | 1230 | L | 0-2 | |
| 37 | 09/01 | H | DMP | Weymouth | 865 | L | 1-2 | Stride 59 |
| 38 | 20/01 | A | DM C 2 | Atherstone United | 191 | D | 1-1 | Stride 37 |
| 39 | 23/01 | H | DMP | King's Lynn | 703 | L | 0-1 | |
| 40 | 25/01 | A | FA T 3 | Altrincham | 825 | L | 0-1 | |
| 41 | 30/01 | A | DMP | Grantham Town | 697 | W | 3-2 | Garner 15 51, Marsden 71 |
| 42 | 02/02 | H | DM C 2 r | Atherstone United | 332 | W | 2-1 | Marsden 5 6 |
| 43 | 06/02 | H | DMP | Salisbury City | 690 | L | 1-2 | Clough 8 |
| 44 | 13/02 | H | DMP | Bath City | 741 | L | 0-1 | |
| 45 | 15/02 | H | DM C 3 | Bilston Town | 179 | D | 0-0 | |
| 46 | 20/02 | A | DMP | Atherstone United | 502 | D | 2-2 | Marsden 9 37 |
| 47 | 23/02 | A | DMP | Hastings Town | 224 | W | 4-1 | Lyons 33 37, Blount 39, Garner 67 |
| 48 | 27/02 | A | DMP | Weymouth | 927 | D | 0-0 | |
| 49 | 02/03 | A | DM C 3 r | Bilston Town | 119 | D | 1-1 | Mason 55        (won on away goals) |
| 50 | 09/03 | A | DMP | Dorchester Town | 472 | L | 1-2 | Marsden 88 |
| 51 | 13/03 | H | DMP | Hastings Town | 660 | W | 3-1 | Holmes 35, Starbuck 68, Stride 75 |
| 52 | 16/03 | A | DM C QF | Sutton Coldfield Town | 197 | L | 0-1 | |
| 53 | 20/03 | A | DMP | Gloucester City | 617 | W | 1-0 | Holmes 87 |
| 54 | 27/03 | A | DMP | King's Lynn | 750 | L | 0-2 | |
| 55 | 30/03 | A | DMP | Cambridge City | 294 | D | 0-0 | |
| 56 | 03/04 | A | DMP | Merthyr Tydfil | 657 | W | 2-0 | Anderson 24, Garner 34[p] |
| 57 | 05/04 | H | DMP | Ilkeston Town | 1088 | L | 1-2 | Pitt 74 |
| 58 | 10/04 | A | DMP | Bromsgrove Rovers | 466 | D | 0-0 | |
| 59 | 17/04 | H | DMP | Dorchester Town | 671 | W | 7-0 | Garner 10 78, Anderson 26 69, Clough 32, Henshaw 48, Holmes 87 |
| 60 | 24/04 | A | DMP | Salisbury City | 560 | W | 2-0 | Garner 66[p], Holmes 72 |
| 61 | 27/04 | H | DMP | Tamworth | 920 | W | 2-1 | Stride 60 90 |
| 62 | 01/05 | H | DMP | Crawley Town | 770 | L | 1-2 | Blount 5 |

## PLAYING SQUAD 1999-2000:

GOALKEEPERS: Nick Goodwin (Gresley Rovers)
DEFENDERS: Mark Blount (Gresley Rovers), Alan Davies (Manchester City), Danny George (Doncaster Rovers), Terence Henshaw (Notts County), Jamie March (Nuneaton Borough), Richard Smith
MIDFIELDERS: Craig Dean (Atherstone United), Neil Glasser (Grantham Town), Pat Lyons (Derby County), Darren Stride
FORWARDS: Nigel Clough (Manchester City), Gary Crosby (Lincoln United), Daniel Davidson, Emeka Ejiofor, Andy Garner (Gresley Rovers), David Holmes (Gloucester City), Craig Smith (Derby County), Malcolm Solomon (Boldmere St Michaels - dual), Phil Starbuck (Cambridge City), Anton Thomas (Nuneaton Borough)

# CAMBRIDGE CITY

## CLUB OFFICIALS

Chairman: **Dennis Rolph**
President: **Sir Neil Westbrook**, CBE MA FRICS
Secretary: **Stuart Hamilton**
55 Crowhill, Godmanchester,
Huntingdon, Cambs
Tel: 01480 382675
Press Officer: Secretary

## FOOTBALL MANAGEMENT TEAM

Manager: Chris Tovey
Asst Manager: Tom Finney
Physios: J.Tanis and Karen White

**FACT FILE**

Formed: 1908
Nickname: Lilywhites
Sponsors: Lancer UK
Colours: White & black halves/black/white &
black hoops
Change colours: Green & Yellow
halves,green,green& yellow hoops
Midweek matchday: Monday
Reserves' League: Eastern Counties

*City Review*
The Official Programme of
**Cambridge City Football Club**
1998/99 Season
Dr Martens

The FA Cup Sponsored by AXA
2nd Qualifying Round
City v Glossop North End
Saturday 3rd October 1998
Kick off 3pm
THE F.A. CUP
Vol No 2    Main Club Sponsors
Issue No 6    LANCER    £1.00

Pages: 28 Price: £1.00
Editor: David Crane (01223 233057)

Local Press: Cambridge Evening News
Local Radio: BBC Radio Cambridge

**GROUND**        City Ground, Milton Road, Cambridge CB4 1UY Tel: 01223 357973

**Directions:**        50 yards on left from start of  A1309, Cambridge to Ely Rd.
        30 mins walk from Cambridge BR
Capacity: 5,000        Cover: 1,400        Seats:423        Floodlights: Yes
**Clubhouse:** 11am-11pm Mon-Sat, 12-3 & 7pm-10.30 Sun. Bingo, Dances, Pool, Darts
**Club Shop:** Sells programmes, club history, badges, scarves, pennants, replica shirts etc.
Contact Neil Harvey (01223 235991)

**PREVIOUS**        **Leagues:** Bury & Dist. 08-13 19-20, East Anglian 08-10, Southern Olympian 11-14, Southern Amateur 1913-35,
        Spartan 35-50, Athenian 50-58        **Name:** Cambridge Town 1908-51
**CLUB RECORDS**        **Attendance:** 12,058 v Leytonstone, FA Amateur Cup 1st Rd, 1949-50
        **Scorer:** Gary Grogan **Appearances:** Mal Keenan
        **Fee Paid:** £8,000 for Paul Coe (Rushden & Diamonds)        **Fee Received:** £100,000 from Millwall for Neil Harris 1998
**BEST SEASON**        **FA Amateur Cup:** Semi Final 27-28        **FA Trophy:** 2nd Rd. 86-87 87-88
        **FA Cup:** 1st Rd; v Ashford 66, v Swindon 46, v Walthamstow Ave. 48, v Hereford 93
**HONOURS**        Southern Lg 62-63 (R-up 70-71, Southern Div 85-86, Div 1 R-up 69-70, Champ Cup62-63; E Anglian Cup (9); Eastern Prof
        Floodlit Lg 65-66 72-73, Cambs Prof Cup(6); Cambs Invitation Cup (7); Spartan Lg 47-48 48-49 (R-up 49-50); EasternDiv
        Champs 45-46); Southern Amat Lg 20-21 27-28 28-29 30-31 31-32; Bury & Dist.Lg (4); E Anglian Lg (6); AFA Snr Cup 30-31
        46-47 47-48(shared) 48-49 49-50;AFA Invitation Cup 50-51; Hunts Prem Cup 62-63 64-65; Suffolk Sen Cup 09-10;
        Addenbrookes Hosp Cup 87-88; The Munns Youth Cup 82-83 83-84 84-85; ChilternYouth Lge Cup R-up 75-76; South Mids Lg
        Youth Trophy 82-83; Robinson Cup 87-8889-90; Jim Digney 89-90; Essex & Herts Youth Lg 89-90 Southern Lg Cup R-up 98-9
Players progressing: K Wright (West Ham 46), A Gallego(Norwich 47), A Stokes (Watford 61), D Weddle (Middlesbrough 61), D Hicksen(Bury 62), B
Harvey (Blackpool 62), R Whitehead (Darlington 62), G Cummins(Hull 62), R Pearce (Peterborough 63), A Banks (Exeter 63), T Carroll (Ipswich66),
Dominic Genovese (Peterborough 88), Roy Jones (Swindon), Winston Dubose(Oldham), K Wilkin (Northampton Tn 91), S Flack (Cardiff City 95), D
Hedcock(Sheffield Wed 96), Neil Harris (Millwall 1998)

*Main stand, Cambridge City FC, Milton Road*

# CAMBRIDGE CITY - MATCH FACTS - 1998-99 SEASON

| No | Date | Venue | Comp | Opponents | Att | Result | Score | Goalscorers |
|----|------|-------|------|-----------|-----|--------|-------|-------------|
| | 22/08 | H | DMP | Gloucester City | 359 | D | 1-1 | Harriott 5 |
| | 25/08 | A | DMP | Hastings Town | 463 | L | 0-2 | |
| | 29/08 | A | DMP | Atherstone United | 253 | W | 1-0 | Reeder 80 |
| | 31/08 | H | DMP | King's Lynn | 539 | W | 2-1 | Kimomya 53, Norfolk 60 |
| | 05/09 | A | DMP | Burton Albion | 628 | L | 1-4 | Kimomya 44 |
| | 08/09 | H | DMP | Grantham Town | 325 | W | 1-0 | Venables 44 |
| | 12/09 | A | DMP | Weymouth | 913 | W | 2-1 | Kiwomya 4 87[p] |
| | 15/09 | H | DMP | Hastings Town | 254 | L | 0-1 | |
| | 19/09 | H | DMP | Halesowen Town | 307 | W | 2-0 | Robbins 15, Cambridge 60 |
| | 22/09 | A | DMP | King's Lynn | 541 | W | 3-0 | Kimomya 33 50, Cambridge 70 |
| | 26/09 | A | DMP | Salisbury City | 308 | L | 1-4 | Brown 10 |
| | 03/10 | H | FA C Q2 | Glossop North End | 265 | D | 1-1 | Kimomya 48 |
| | 06/10 | A | FA C Q2 r | Glossop North End | 231 | D | 1-1 | Starbuck 23 (4-5 pens) |
| | 10/10 | H | DMP | Gresley Rovers | 268 | L | 1-2 | Robbins 45 |
| | 17/10 | A | DMP | Merthyr Tydfil | 539 | D | 3-3 | Kimomya 11, Saddington 19, King 45 |
| | 24/10 | A | FA T 1 | Harrow Borough | 200 | L | 2-4 | Robbins 14 25 |
| | 31/10 | H | DMP | Ilkeston Town | 274 | L | 0-1 | |
| | 03/11 | A | DMP | Grantham Town | 300 | W | 1-0 | Starbuck 43 |
| | 07/11 | A | DMP | Bath City | 654 | L | 0-1 | |
| | 10/11 | H | DM C 1(1) | Brackley Town | 102 | W | 4-3 | Brown 37 44 86, Owen 65 |
| | 14/11 | H | DMP | Boston United | 304 | L | 1-4 | Brown 67 |
| | 25/11 | A | DM C 1(2) | Brackley Town | 74 | W | 4-1 | Kimomya 2 36, Owen 17, Brown 60 |
| | 28/11 | H | DMP | Atherstone United | 216 | W | 3-1 | Galliers 10, Sweet 57, Brown 65 |
| | 05/12 | A | DMP | Ilkeston Town | 450 | D | 0-0 | |
| | 12/12 | A | DMP | Gloucester City | 536 | L | 1-3 | Holden 74 |
| | 15/12 | A | DM C 2 | Tonbridge Angels | 224 | W | 2-0 | Kiwomya 42, Brown 87 |
| | 19/12 | H | DMP | Nuneaton Borough | 546 | D | 1-1 | Kimomya 65[p] |
| | 28/12 | H | DMP | Crawley Town | 1271 | D | 1-1 | Brown 81 |
| | 01/01 | A | DMP | Boston United | 2005 | D | 2-2 | Owen 65, Kiwomya 76 |
| | 02/01 | H | DMP | Salisbury City | 275 | L | 1-3 | Starbuck 70 |
| | 09/01 | A | DMP | Tamworth | 473 | L | 1-6 | Leete 34 |
| | 16/01 | H | DMP | Dorchester Town | 284 | D | 0-0 | |
| | 23/01 | H | DMP | Worcester City | 258 | W | 3-0 | Galliers 18, Reeder 25, Owen 55 |
| | 06/02 | H | DMP | Rothwell Town | 268 | D | 2-2 | Reeder 70, Spring 75 |
| | 13/02 | A | DMP | Nuneaton Borough | 1515 | L | 0-4 | |
| | 20/02 | H | DMP | Tamworth | 338 | L | 0-1 | |
| | 23/02 | A | DM C 3 | Shepshed Dynamo | 131 | W | 4-2 | Galliers 14 54, Holden 45, Owen 73 |
| | 27/02 | A | DMP | Dorchester Town | 548 | D | 1-1 | Wilde 78 |
| | 09/03 | H | DM C QF | St Leonards | 145 | D | 0-0 | |
| | 13/03 | A | DMP | Rothwell Town | 243 | L | 1-3 | Campbell 68 |
| | 16/03 | A | DM C QF r | St Leonards | 151 | D | 1-1 | Tovey 43 (won on away goals) |
| | 20/03 | A | DMP | Bromsgrove Rovers | 396 | L | 1-2 | Spring 62 |
| | 23/03 | A | DM C SF(1) | Dorchester Town | 229 | W | 3-0 | Leete 32, Adams 65, Ellis 87 |
| | 28/03 | H | DM C SF(2) | Dorchester Town | 287 | L | 1-3 | Leete 32 |
| | 30/03 | H | DMP | Burton Albion | 294 | D | 0-0 | |
| | 03/04 | H | DMP | Gresley Rovers | 550 | L | 0-3 | |
| | 05/04 | H | DMP | Crawley Town | 271 | D | 0-0 | |
| | 10/04 | A | DMP | Halesowen Town | 609 | L | 1-2 | Mahorn 20[p] |
| | 13/04 | H | DM C F(1) | Sutton Coldfield Town | 222 | D | 0-0 | |
| | 17/04 | H | DMP | Merthyr Tydfil | 287 | L | 1-2 | Owen 80[p] |
| | 20/04 | H | DMP | Weymouth | 201 | W | 1-0 | Newby 83 |
| | 22/04 | H | DMP | Bath City | 178 | D | 1-1 | Thompson 58 |
| | 24/04 | A | DMP | Worcester City | 907 | L | 2-4 | Cogger 31, Leete 49 |
| | 27/04 | A | DM C F(2) | Sutton Coldfield Town | 817 | L | 1-2 | Newby 9 |
| | 01/05 | H | DMP | Bromsgrove Rovers | 217 | W | 3-1 | Leete 4, Newby 14 64 |

## PLAYING SQUAD 1999-2000:

GOALKEEPERS: Martin Davies (Dover Athletic)

DEFENDERS: Jason Carter (Diss Town), Neil Coburn, Steve Gawthrop (Mildenhall Town), David Hercock (Stamford), Steve Holden (Stevenage Borough), Brian Linighan (Bury), James Saddington (Chelmsford City)

MIDFIELDERS: Mark Adams (Sudbury Town), Adie Cambridge (Histon), Gary Crick, Wayne Goddard (Chelmsford City), Andrew Kirkup (Nuneaton Borough), Keith Lockhart (Sudbury Town), Andy Pincher (Chelmsford City), Mark Reeder, Chris Tovey (Chelmsford City), Adam Wilde (Cambridge City)

FORWARDS: Daniel Brailsford, Paul Byatt (Great Shelford), Ian Cambridge (Chelmsford City), Neil Cogger (Haverhill Rovers), Ben Galliers, Paul Mahorn (Cambridge United), Mark McCammon (Cambridge United), Keith Newby (Cambridge United), Steve Rutter (Erith & Belvedere)

# CLEVEDON TOWN

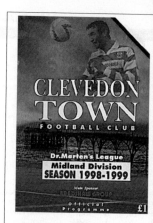

## CLUB OFFICIALS

President:
Chairman: **John Croft**

Secretary: **Mike Williams**
34 Robinia Walk, Whitchurch,
Bristol BS14 0SH
Tel: 01275 833835

### FOOTBALL MANAGEMENT TEAM
Manager: Steve Fey
Asst. Manager:
Coach: Jeff Meacham
Physio: T Banks

### FACT FILE

Formed: 1880
Nickname: The Seasiders
Sponsors:
Colours: Blue & white stripes/blue/blue
Change colours: All yellow or all green
Midweek Matches: Tuesday
Reserves' League:
97-98 - Captain: Steve Lester
P.o.Y.: I Harvey
Top scorer: M Rawlins (27)

Pages: 40 Price: 80p
Editor: Steve Small Tel: 01275 875612 (H)
Local Radio: Radio Bristol
Local Press: South Avon Mercury

## GROUND

Hand Stadium, Davis Lane, Clevedon
Tel: 01275 341919 (ground)    01275 341641 (office)

**Directions:** M5 Jct 20 - follow signs for Clevedon Town Sports Complex; first left into Central Way (at island just after motorway), 1st left at mini-r'bout into Kenn Rd, 2nd left Davis Lane; ground half mile on right. Or from Bristol(B3130) left into Court Lane (opposite Clevedon Court), turn right after 1mile, ground on left. Nearest BR station: Nailsea & Backwell. Buses from Bristol

Capacity: 3,650          Seats: 300          Cover: 1,600          Floodlights: Yes
**Clubhouse:** Open every day and evening. Separate function suite & lounge bar.Hot food available. Matchday refreshment bar within ground sells confectionary, teas & hot food
**Club Shop:** Sells all types of souvenirs, programmes and replica kit. Exchanges welcome. Contact J Anderson

**PREVIOUS**      **Leagues:** Weston & District, Somerset Senior, Bristol Charity, Bristol &District, Bristol Suburban, Western 74-93
**Grounds:** Dial Hill ('til early 1890's); Teignmouth Road ('til 1991)
**Names:** Clevedon FC, Ashtonians (clubs merged in 1974)

**CLUB RECORDS**  **Attendance:** 1,295 v Tiverton Town, Western Lge Prem. Div. 17/4/93
(At Teignmouth Road: 2,300 v Billingham Synthonia, FA Amateur Cup, 52-53)
**Win:** 18-0 v Dawlish Town (H), Western League Premier Division 24/4/93
**Defeat:** 13-3 v Yate YMCA (A), Bristol Comb 67-68

**BEST SEASON**   **FA Cup:** 3rd Qual. Rd 2nd replay 92-93 v Newport AFC, 2-4 after two 1-1
**FA Amateur Cup:** 3rd Round Proper, 52-53
**FA Vase:** 6th Round 87-88, v Sudbury Town (A)
**FA Trophy:** 2nd Round 98-99

**HONOURS**       Western League 92-93 (R-up 91-92, League Cup R-up 92-93), Bristol Charity League,
Somerset Senior Cup 01-02 04-05 28-29 76-77, Somerset Snr League Div 1(Res.) 92-93

*Back Row (L-R): Phil Hucker (Coach), Rob Claridge, Steve Peters, Lee Jefferies, Paul Milsom, David Mogg, Steve Weaver, Shaun Andrews, Matt Rawlings, Tony Cook, Marco Micciche, Steve Bobbins (Trainer)*
*Front Row: Mark Badman, Danny Haines, Ian Harvey (captain), Jeff Meacham (Asst Mngr), Steve Fey (Manager),*

# CLEVEDON TOWN - MATCH FACTS - 1998-99 SEASON

| No | Date | Venue | Comp | Opponents | Att | Result | Score | Goalscorers |
|---|---|---|---|---|---|---|---|---|
| 1 | 22/08 | H | DM M | Stamford | 269 | D | 2-2 | Milsom 43, Reeves 62 |
| 2 | 25/08 | A | DM M | Evesham United | 121 | W | 1-0 | Milsom 30 |
| 3 | 29/08 | H | DM M | Wisbech Town | 289 | L | L | 0-2 |
| 4 | 31/08 | H | DM M | Bloxwich Town | 224 | W | 4-1 | Cook 29, Ford 44, Rawlins 73 88[p] |
| 5 | 05/09 | A | DM M | Bedworth United | 185 | W | 1-0 | Cook 61 |
| 6 | 12/09 | A | DM M | Shepshed Dynamo | 153 | W | 1-0 | Jefferies 14 |
| 7 | 15/09 | H | DM M | EVESHAM United | 229 | D | 1-1 | Jefferies 51 |
| 8 | 19/09 | H | FA C Q1 | **Cinderford Town** | **275** | D | **1-1** | **Reeves 66** |
| 9 | 22/09 | A | FA C Q1 r | **Cinderford Town** | **256** | D | **0-0** | **(4-5 pens)** |
| 10 | 26/09 | A | DM M | Hinckley United | 211 | W | 2-0 | Rawlins 4, Jefferies 60 |
| 11 | 29/09 | A | DM M | Bloxwich Town | 50 | W | 4-1 | Cook 40 89, Sweeney 80, Rawlins 87 |
| 12 | 10/10 | A | DM M | Stafford Rangers | 304 | W | 2-0 | Cook 19 77[p] |
| 13 | 17/10 | H | DM M | VS Rugby | 300 | W | 5-1 | Cook 9[p] 85, Milsom 54, McLoughlin 57, Jefferies 78 |
| 14 | 31/10 | H | DM M | Shepshed Dynamo | 288 | W | 2-1 | Andrews 36, Ford 53 |
| 15 | 04/11 | A | DM M | Newport AFC | 631 | D | 1-1 | Ford 62 |
| 16 | 07/11 | A | DM M | Blakenall | 85 | W | 5-2 | Cook 18 24 81, McLoughlin 44, Jefferies 61 |
| 17 | 10/11 | H | DM C 1(1) | **Witney Town** | **191** | **W** | **1-0** | **Rawlins 56** |
| 18 | 14/11 | H | DM M | Bedworth United | 331 | L | 3-4 | McLoughlin 27, Cook 43 54 |
| 19 | 17/11 | H | SPC 2 | **Weston-Super-Mare** | **258** | **W** | **2-0** | **Sweeney 31, Rawlins 80** |
| 20 | 21/11 | A | FA T 2 | **Maidenhead United** | **208** | L | **0-1** | |
| 21 | 24/11 | A | DM C 1(2) | **Witney Town** | **94** | L | **2-4** | **Sweeney 43, Rawlins 80** |
| 22 | 28/11 | H | DM M | Bilston Town | 306 | W | 3-0 | Cook 59, Lester 61, Ford 79 |
| 23 | 05/12 | A | DM M | Wisbech Town | 460 | W | 2-0 | Cook 77, Rawlins 87 |
| 24 | 12/12 | A | DM M | Redditch United | 254 | W | 1-0 | Andrews 49 |
| 25 | 19/12 | H | DM M | Racing Club Warwick | 331 | W | 2-0 | Cook 70, Reeves 77 |
| 26 | 26/12 | A | DM M | Weston-super-Mare | 348 | W | 3-1 | Lester 47, Andrews 63, Cook 79 |
| 27 | 28/12 | H | DM M | Cinderford Town | 413 | W | 2-0 | Andrews 75, Cook 89 |
| 28 | 01/01 | H | DM M | Redditch United | 585 | W | 3-0 | Cook 22, Wring 39, Rawlins 82 |
| 29 | 02/01 | A | DM M | Stafford Rangers | 857 | D | 0-0 | |
| 30 | 09/01 | H | DM M | Sutton Coldfield Town | 409 | W | 2-0 | Hier 41[og], Rawlins 88 |
| 31 | 23/01 | A | DM M | Stamford | 147 | W | 3-1 | Cook 44, Haines 50, McLoughlin 64 |
| 32 | 26/01 | H | SWB | **Clevedon United** | **424** | **W** | **6-1** | **Milsom 29 47, Lester 50, McLoughlin 57, Meacham 74, Shorland 89** |
| 33 | 30/01 | A | DM M | Sutton Coldfield Town | 242 | L | 1-3 | Cook 89 |
| 34 | 09/02 | H | SPC QF | **Mangotsfield United** | **183** | **W** | **2-1** | **Cook 28, Lester 31** |
| 35 | 13/02 | A | DM M | Stourbridge | 178 | W | 2-1 | Jefferies 61, Cook 85 |
| 36 | 20/02 | H | DM M | Solihull Borough | 354 | W | 2-0 | McLoughlin 21, Cook 67 |
| 37 | 23/02 | H | DM M | Newport AFC | 1006 | W | 2-1 | Rawlins 21, Andrews 39 |
| 38 | 02/03 | A | SPC SF | **Bath City** | **347** | D | **0-0** | **(4-3 pens)** |
| 39 | 06/03 | A | DM M | Bilston Town | 216 | W | 1-0 | Andrews 79 |
| 40 | 09/03 | A | DM M | Moor Green | 136 | W | 3-2 | Andrews 33, Lester 45, Jefferies 47 |
| 41 | 13/03 | H | DM M | Stourbridge | 455 | D | 0-0 | |
| 42 | 20/03 | A | DM M | Racing Club Warwick | 113 | W | 3-0 | Cook 27[p] 79, Peters 45 |
| 43 | 27/03 | H | DM M | Moor Green | 301 | D | 1-1 | Rawlins 28 |
| 44 | 03/04 | H | DM M | Weston-Super-Mare | 594 | W | 2-0 | Cook 22, McLoughlin 50 |
| 45 | 05/04 | A | DM M | Cinderford Town | 293 | W | 4-1 | Milsom 8, Cook 17 50, Rawlins 23 |
| 46 | 10/04 | A | DM M | Solihull Borough | 133 | L | 0-2 | |
| 47 | 13/04 | H | DM M | Hinckley United | 142 | L | 0-1 | |
| 48 | 17/04 | H | DM M | Blakenall | 482 | L | 1-2 | McLoughlin 45 |
| 49 | 21/04 | A | DM M | Paget Rangers | 86 | W | 3-0 | McLoughlin 9 38, Jefferies 28 |
| 50 | 24/04 | A | DM M | VS Rugby | 215 | D | 2-2 | Milsom 29, Cook 89 |
| 51 | 01/05 | H | DM M | Paget Rangers | 733 | D | 1-1 | Cook 68 |
| 52 | 04/05 | H | SPC F | **Taunton Town** | **801** | D | **3-3** | **Cook 51[p], Ford 84, McLoughlin 103 (5-4 pens) (at Yeovil Town)** |

## PLAYING SQUAD 1999-2000:

**GOALKEEPERS:** Richard Fey (Patchway/Bristol MF/ Old Georgians - cover), Chris Joseph (Cadbury Heath - cover), Steve Weaver

**DEFENDERS:** Danny Haines (Bristol City), Iain Harvey (Swindon Town), Lee Jefferies (Trowbridge Town), Steve Peters (Cinderford Town), Gary Rice (Dorchester Town), Jimmy Wring (Newport AFC)

**MIDFIELDERS:** Mark Badman (Bristol City), Richard Ford (Nottingham Forest), Steve Lester, Paul McLoughlin (Forest Green Rovers), Marco Micciche (Bath City), Neil Reeves (Trowbridge Town), Jim Rollo (Forest Green Rovers), John Shorland (Patchway Town), David Sweeney (Westbury United)

**FORWARDS:** Tony Cook (Weymouth), Robert Claridge (Bristol Rovers), Paul Milsom (Trowbridge Town), Matt Rawlins (Mangotsfield United)

# CRAWLEY TOWN

### CLUB OFFICIALS

Chairman: **John Maggs**
President: **Ken Symons**

Secretary: **Dave Haining**
20 Irving Walk, Tilgate, Crawley RH10 5BQ
Tel: 01293 535683
Commercial Manager: **Gary Clark**

### FOOTBALL MANAGEMENT TEAM
Football TeamManager: **Cliff Cant**
Asst Man: **John Broughton**
Physio: **Richard Massimo**

### FACT FILE

Formed: 1896
Nickname: The Reds
Sponsors: Cruiseway
Colours: All red
Change colours:All white
Midweek matchday: Tuesday
Reserves' League: Suburban

**GROUND**        Broadfield Stadium, Brighton Road, Crawley RH11 9RX Tel: 01293 410000

**Directions:**        M23 exit 11, 2nd exit off roundabout, A23, towards Crawley.
Turn left at next r/about into ground

Capacity: 4,800        Cover: 4,200        Seats: 1,080        Floodlights: Yes

**Clubhouse:** Weekdays 11-3 & 6-11, Sat & B. Hols 11-11, Sun noon-10.30. Snacks available
**Club Shop:** Sells programmes, metal badges, hats, scarves, mugs, replica kits

**PREVIOUS**        **Leagues:** Sussex County 1951-56; Metropolitan 56-63        **Grounds:** Malthouse Farm 1896-1914 38-40; Victoria Hall + Rectory
Fields 18-38;Yetmans Field 45-49, Town Mead 49-53 54-97, Ilfield Rec Grd 53-54

**CLUB RECORDS**  **Attendance:** 4,104 v Barnet, FA Cup 2nd Rd 4/12/93
**Goalscorer:** Phil Basey 108 (68-72)                **Appearances:** John Maggs 652 (63-73 75-79)
**Win:** 10-0 v Chichester United, Sussex Co. Lge Div 2 17/12/55
**Defeat:** 0-10 v Arundel (A), Sussex County Lge 9/2/52
**Fee Paid:** £5,000 for David Thompson (Wokingham, May 92)
**Fee Received:** £50,000 for Craig Whitington (Scarborough 93)

**BEST SEASON**  **FA Trophy:** 3rd Rd 98-99
**FA Cup:** 3rd Rd Proper 91-92, 0-5 v Brighton & HA (A)        League Clubs defeated: Northampton Town 91-92

**HONOURS**        Sussex Snr Cup (2) 89-91 (R-up 58-59 95-96); Sussex I'mediate Cup 26-27; Sussex Prof. Cup 69-70; Southern Lg S Div.R-Up
83-84; Merit Cup 70-71;Sussex Floodlit Cup (3) 90-93; Sussex Lg Div 2 R-up 55-56; Gilbert RiceF'lit Cup 79-80 83-84; Southern
Co's Comb. Floodlit Cup 85-86; Met Lg Chal. Cup 58-59; Mid-Sussex Snr 02-03; Montgomery Cup 25-26 Sussex Floodlit Cup 98-99

Players progressing: Ray Keeley, Graham Brown (Mansfield68), Andy Ansah (Brentford 87), Craig Whitington (Scarborough 93)

*Back Row: Richard Massimo (Physio), Dave Stevens, Phil Barber, Simon Ullathorne, John Mackie, Adrian Blake, Jon Warden, Brian Owen (Coach), Mark Hawthorne, Sean McEntagart, Tony Sweet, Justin Gregory, Denver Birmingham*

# CRAWLEY TOWN - MATCH FACTS - 1998-99 SEASON

| No | Date | Venue | Comp | Opponents | Att | Result | Score | Goalscorers |
|----|------|-------|------|-----------|-----|--------|-------|-------------|
|  | 22/08 | A | DMP | Halesowen Town | 698 | L | 2-3 | McEntaggart 4, Warden 51 |
|  | 25/08 | H | DMP | Salisbury City | 835 | D | 1-1 | Ullathorne 41 |
|  | 29/08 | H | DMP | Bath City | 727 | L | 0-2 |  |
|  | 31/08 | A | DMP | Rothwell Town | 287 | D | 1-1 | Gregory 31 |
|  | 05/09 | H | DMP | Nuneaton Borough | 675 | L | 0-3 |  |
|  | 08/09 | A | DMP | Dorchester Town | 433 | W | 2-1 | Payne 48, Barber 79 |
|  | 12/09 | H | DMP | Worcester City | 643 | W | 2-1 | Abbey 69, Warden 79 |
|  | 16/09 | A | DMP | Salisbury City | 279 | W | 2-0 | Ullathorne 10, Abbey 76 |
|  | 19/09 | H | DMP | Burton Albion | 730 | D | 1-1 | Abbey 65 |
| 0 | 22/09 | H | DMP | Rothwell Town | 503 | W | 1-0 | Abbey 64 |
| 1 | 26/09 | A | DMP | Grantham Town | 626 | W | 2-1 | Abbey 60, Gregory 69 |
| 2 | 29/09 | H | SFC 2 | **East Preston** | n/k | W | 4-0 | **Abbey(2), Walden, Hawthorne** |
| 3 | 03/10 | H | FA C Q2 | **Canterbury City** | 906 | W | 5-0 | **McEntaggart 13, Viegas 16 67, Barber 17, Abbey 69** |
| 4 | 10/10 | H | DMP | King's Lynn | 848 | W | 3-1 | Gregory 10, Viegas 45, Warden 90 |
| 5 | 13/10 | H | SFC 3 | **Horsham YMCA** | 305 | W | 3-0 | **Abbey 29, Ullathorne 40 42** |
| 6 | 17/10 | H | FA C Q3 | **Billericay Town** | 1321 | W | 1-0 | **Warden 90** |
| 7 | 03/11 | H | FA C Q4 | **Slough Town** | 1874 | D | 0-0 |  |
| 8 | 07/11 | A | DMP | Merthyr Tydfil | 540 | L | 1-3 | Warden 59 |
| 9 | 09/11 | A | FA C Q4 r | **Slough Town** | 881 | L | 2-3 | **Abbey 36, Ullathorne 43** |
| 0 | 11/11 | A | DM C 1(1) | **Erith & Belvedere** | 71 | W | 1-0 | **Warden 29** |
| 1 | 14/11 | H | DMP | Gloucester City | 911 | W | 2-1 | Abbey 12, McEwan 86 |
| 2 | 16/11 | A | FA T 1 | **Leatherhead** | 335 | W | 2-1 | **Taylor 51, Abbey 82** |
| 3 | 21/11 | H | FA T 2 | **Sittingbourne** | 677 | D | 2-2 | **McEntaggart 18, Payne 65[p]** |
| 4 | 24/11 | H | FA T 2 r | **Sittingbourne** | 248 | W | 5-1 | **Payne 51[p], Abbey 53 65, Hawthorne 73, Ullathorne 77** |
| 5 | 28/11 | A | DMP | Worcester City | 757 | W | 2-1 | Ullathorne 29, Abbey 60 |
| 6 | 01/12 | H | SSC 2 | **Shoreham** | 238 | W | 3-0 | **Abbey 31 49, Lutwyche 79** |
| 7 | 05/12 | H | DMP | Tamworth | 767 | W | 1-0 | Warden 63 |
| 8 | 08/12 | H | DM C 1(2) | **Erith & Belvedere** | 217 | W | 5-0 | **Ullathorne 39 83[p], Abbey 57, Warden 69 76** |
| 9 | 12/12 | A | DMP | Nuneaton Borough | 1409 | L | 1-2 | Taylor 44 |
| 0 | 16/12 | A | DM C 2 | **St Leonards** | 233 | L | 2-3 | **Abbey 16 45** |
| 1 | 19/12 | H | DMP | Bromsgrove Rovers | 877 | W | 4-1 | Barber 62, Abbey 69[p] 76, Ullathorne 83 |
| 2 | 22/12 | H | SFC QF | **Sidley United** | 305 | W | 8-5 | **Veigas 10, Abbey 20 37 55, Warden 83 107, Ullathorne 98, Hawthorne 106** |
| 3 | 28/12 | H | DMP | Cambridge City | 1271 | D | 1-1 | Hawthorne 90 |
| 4 | 01/01 | H | DMP | Hastings Town | 1759 | W | 3-1 | Abbey 23 63, McEwan 40 |
| 5 | 09/01 | H | DMP | Halesowen Town | 1074 | D | 1-1 | Ullathorne 59 |
| 6 | 16/01 | H | FA T 3 | **Chesham United** | 1138 | L | 2-3 | **Mackie 32, Warden 61** |
| 7 | 23/01 | A | DMP | Bath City | 888 | L | 0-2 |  |
| 8 | 26/01 | H | SC 3 | **Ringmer** | 183 | W | 3-0 | **McEntaggart 40, Warden 55 57** |
| 9 | 30/01 | H | DMP | Ilkeston Town | 907 | W | 2-1 | Abbey 69 84 |
| 0 | 06/02 | A | DMP | Atherstone United | 310 | L | 1-2 | Abbey 80 |
| 1 | 09/02 | A | SSC QF | **Whitehawk** | 110 | W | 2-1 | **Abbey 47, Taylor 50** |
| 2 | 13/02 | H | DMP | Boston United | 854 | D | 2-2 | McEntaggart 42, Ullathorne 45 |
| 3 | 16/02 | H | DMP | Weymouth | 634 | W | 3-1 | Mackie 56, Hawthorne 67, Powell 88[og] |
| 4 | 20/02 | A | DMP | Gloucester City | 584 | L | 0-2 |  |
| 5 | 23/02 | H | DMP | Dorchester Town | 517 | D | 1-1 | Thompson 65 |
| 6 | 27/02 | A | DMP | Ilkeston Town | 632 | L | 1-3 | Warden 37 |
| 7 | 03/03 | H | SSC SF | **Worthing** | 281 | L | 0-2 | (at Horsham) |
| 8 | 06/03 | H | DMP | Grantham Town | 865 | W | 2-0 | Mackie 3, Ullathorne 76 |
| 9 | 09/03 | A | SFC SF(1) | **Horsham** | 418 | W | 1-0 | **McEwen 52** |
| 0 | 13/03 | A | DMP | Boston United | 1230 | L | 1-3 | Ullathorne 31[p] |
| 1 | 20/03 | A | DMP | Gresley Rovers | 503 | D | 1-1 | McEntaggart 36 |
| 2 | 23/03 | H | SFC SF(2) | **Horsham** | 612 | W | 3-1 | **Abbey 17[p], Ullathorne 39 41** |
| 3 | 27/03 | H | DMP | Merthyr Tydfil | 443 | L | 0-2 |  |
| 4 | 30/03 | A | DMP | Bromsgrove Rovers | 458 | L | 0-1 |  |
| 5 | 03/04 | H | DMP | Weymouth | 602 | D | 2-2 | McEwen 37, Abbey 45 |
| 6 | 05/04 | A | DMP | Cambridge City | 271 | D | 0-0 |  |
| 7 | 10/04 | H | DMP | Gresley Rovers | 438 | W | 2-0 | Payne 31, Ullathorne 51 |
| 8 | 13/04 | H | SFC F | **Saltdean United** | 452 | W | 2-0 | **Hawthorne 12, McEwen 83** (at Lancing) |
| 9 | 17/04 | A | DMP | King's Lynn | 672 | L | L | 0-2 |
| 0 | 20/04 | A | DMP | Tamworth | 387 | L | 1-3 | Johnson 55 |
| 1 | 24/04 | H | DMP | Atherstone United | 577 | W | 3-0 | Ullathorne 38, Taylor 85 90 |
| 2 | 27/04 | A | DMP | Hastings Town | 415 | L | 0-3 |  |
| 3 | 01/05 | A | DMP | Burton Albion | 770 | W | 2-1 | Abbey 9, McEntaggart 22 |

**PLAYING SQUAD 1999-2000:**

GOALKEEPERS: Adrian Blake (Carshalton Athletic), Paul Hart (Erith & Belvedere), Michael Riach
DEFENDERS: Glenn Geddes (Burgess Hill Town), Ian Payne (Vancouver), Tony Sweet
MIDFIELDERS: Ryan Andrews (Broadbridge Heath), Phil Barber (Dover Athletic), Denver Birmingham (Erith & Belvedere), Justin Gregory (Hastings Town), Vivian Jeffrey (Carshalton Athletic), Rod McAree (Chesham United)
FORWARDS: Ben Abbey (Maidenhead United), Dave McEwan (Crawley Town), Simon Ullathorne (Cambridge City)

# DORCHESTER TOWN

**CLUB OFFICIALS**
Chairman: **C E Clark**
President:
Vice Chairman: **K Miller**
Comm Mgr: **Keith Kellaway** (01305 262451)
Secretary: **David Martin**
7 Old Brickfields, Broadmayne,Dorset
Tel:01305 853400
General Manager: Keith Kellaway

**FOOTBALL MANAGEMENT TEAM**

Manager: Stuart Morgan
Physio: Geoff Dine

**FACT FILE**

Formed: 1880
Nickname: The Magpies
Sponsors:Contract Motoring Services
Colours: Black & white stripes/black/black
Change colours: All red
Midweek games: Tuesdays (7.45)
Newsline (Magpies Hotline): 0839 664412
Reserves' League: Dorset Comb

**GROUND**  Avenue Stadium, Weymouth Avenue, Dorchester DT1 2RY Tel: 01305 262451

**Directions:** Situated at the junction of the town bypass (A35) and the Weymouth road (A354)
Nearest station: Dorchester South
Capacity: 7,210          Cover: 4,000          Seats: 710          Floodlights: Yes

Pages: 32 Price:£1.00
Editor: Melvin Cross( 01305 848365)

**Clubhouse:** Dorchester Lounge Club - access via main entrance to stadium.
Cold food and snacks
**Club Shop:** Sells replica shirts, badges, mugs, etc

Local Press: Dorset Evening Echo,
Western Gazette, Western Daily Press
Local Radio: Two Counties Radio, Wessex FM

**PREVIOUS**  **Leagues:** Dorset; Western 1947-72
**Grounds:** Council Recreation Ground, Weymouth Avenue 1880-1929; The Avenue Ground, Weymouth Avenue 29-90

**CLUB RECORDS** **Attendance:** 4,000 v Chelsea, official ground opening 1990. Competitive: 4, 159 v Weymouth, Southern Lge Prem Div , 99
**Goalscorer:** Dennis Cheney 61 (in one season)          **Appearances:** Derek (Dinkie) Curtis 458 50-66
**Win:** 7-0 v Canterbury (A), Southern Lge Southern Div 86-87
**Defeat:** 0-13 v Welton Rovers Western Lge 66
**Fee Paid:** £12,000 for Chris Townsend (Gloucester City, 1990)
**Fee Received:** £35,000 for Trevor Senior (Portsmouth, 1981)

**BEST SEASON** **FA Trophy:** 3rd Rd replay 71-72, 96-97
**FA Cup:** 2nd Rd Replay 81-82, 1-2 v A.F.C. Bournemouth after 1-1.  2nd Rd 54-55 57-58; 1st Rd 7 times

**HONOURS**  Southern Lg 85-85, R-up 79-80 (Div 1 Sth R-up 77-78), Lg Cup 86-87 (R-up 91-92); Western Lg 54-55 (R-up 60-61, Div 2 R-up 49-50), Lge Cup 54-54; Dorset Snr Cup 50-51 60-61 67-68 68-69 71-72 93-94 94-95; Dorset Lg 37-38

Players progressing: Len Drake (Bristol Rovers 57), David Noake (Luton 59), Mike Turner (Swindon 61), Trevor Senior (Portsmouth 81), David Wes (Liverpool 83), Mike Squire (Torquay 84), Jeremy Judd (Torquay 84),Tony White(Bournem'th 85), Graham Roberts (Spurs, Chelsea, Rangers, England) who progressed via Weymouth. Darren Garner (Rotherham U, 95), Craig Taylor(Swindon),Syfyan Ghazghazi(Club African De Tunis 98)

*Back Row (L-R): Mark Morris, Danny O'Hagan, Stuart Morgan (Manager), Julian Alsford, Roy O'Brien, Rob Murra Middle Row: Bryan Baysfield (Asst Manager), Dave Wright, Owen Pickard, Martyn Sullivan, James Dungey, Kevi Maloy, Chris Higgs, Dave Lovell, Neil Coates, Geoff Dine (physio). Front Row: Andy Harris, Ryan Cross, Ma*

# DORCHESTER TOWN - MATCH FACTS - 1998-99 SEASON

| No | Date | Venue | Comp | Opponents | Att | Result | Score | Goalscorers |
|----|------|-------|------|-----------|-----|--------|-------|-------------|
| | 22/08 | H | DMP | Boston United | 630 | D | 0-0 | |
| | 25/08 | A | DMP | Gloucester City | 606 | L | 1-4 | Ghazghazi 64 |
| | 29/08 | A | DMP | Gresley Rovers | 502 | L | L | 0-2 |
| | 31/08 | H | DMP | Hastings Town | 508 | L | 1-2 | O'Hagan 84 |
| | 02/09 | H | SMT | **Derby County** | n/k | D | 0-0 | |
| | 05/09 | A | DMP | Atherstone United | 260 | L | 1-3 | Ghazghazi 70 |
| | 08/09 | A | DMP | Crawley Town | 433 | L | 1-2 | O'Hagan 88 |
| | 12/09 | A | DMP | Tamworth | 482 | L | 0-1 | |
| | 19/09 | H | DMP | Grantham Town | 552 | W | 3-2 | Middleton 10 71, O'Hagan 82 |
| 0 | 22/09 | A | DMP | Hastings Town | 531 | L | 0-1 | |
| 1 | 26/09 | H | DMP | Ilkeston Town | 539 | L | 0-1 | |
| 2 | 30/09 | A | DMP | Salisbury City | 367 | D | 3-3 | Sullivan 50 55, Middleton 76 |
| 3 | 03/10 | H | FA C Q2 | **Salisbury City** | 616 | **L** | 0-3 | |
| 4 | 10/10 | A | DMP | Nuneaton Borough | 1330 | D | 0-0 | |
| 5 | 17/10 | A | DMP | Boston United | 747 | L | 1-5 | O'Hagan 84 |
| 6 | 24/10 | H | FA T 1 | Bath City | 522 | L | L | 0-2 |
| 7 | 07/11 | H | DMP | Worcester City | 514 | L | 1-2 | Shepherd 66 |
| 8 | 10/11 | H | DM C 1(1) | **Fleet Town** | 159 | W | 3-1 | **Murray 46 87, Shepherd 50** |
| 9 | 21/11 | H | DMP | Halesowen Town | 431 | W | 2-0 | Shepherd 23 72 |
| 0 | 24/11 | A | DM C 1(2) | **Fleet Town** | 32 | D | 0-0 | |
| 1 | 28/11 | A | DMP | King's Lynn | 485 | D | 1-1 | Shepherd 8 |
| 2 | 05/12 | H | DMP | Salisbury City | 571 | W | 4-0 | Sullivan 49 52, Shepherd 67, Cross 88 |
| 3 | 12/12 | A | DMP | Merthyr Tydfil | 447 | D | 1-1 | O'Hagan 79[og] |
| 4 | 15/12 | H | DM C 2 | **Newport IoW** | 151 | W | 4-2 | **Shepherd 22, Ghazghazi 30, O'Hagan 69, Hards 76 [og]** |
| 5 | 19/12 | H | DMP | King's Lynn | 503 | W | 2-1 | O'Hagan 38, Shepherd 81 |
| 6 | 28/12 | H | DMP | Bath City | 808 | D | 1-1 | O'Hagan 34 |
| 7 | 01/01 | H | DMP | Weymouth | 4159 | D | 1-1 | Murray 1 |
| 8 | 02/01 | A | DMP | Bromsgrove Rovers | 508 | W | 2-1 | Lovell 9, Shepherd 10 |
| 9 | 09/01 | H | DMP | Rothwell Town | 520 | W | 3-1 | O'Hagan 48 76, Shepherd 74 |
| 0 | 16/01 | A | DMP | Cambridge City | 284 | D | 0-0 | |
| 1 | 30/01 | A | DMP | Worcester City | 894 | D | 2-2 | Murray 54, O'Hagan 75 |
| 2 | 02/02 | A | DM C 3 | **Witney Town** | 103 | W | 2-1 | **Medlin 69, Coates 85** |
| 3 | 06/02 | H | DMP | Nuneaton Borough | 802 | L | 0-1 | |
| 4 | 13/02 | A | DMP | Ilkeston Town | 523 | L | 2-5 | Groves 87, Lovell 89 |
| 5 | 16/02 | A | DM C QF | **Bashley** | 267 | W | 3-0 | **Harris 32, O'Hagan 48, Alexander 68** |
| 6 | 20/02 | H | DMP | Bromsgrove Rovers | 558 | W | 3-0 | Alexander 53, O'Hagan 66, Murray 78 |
| 7 | 23/02 | A | DMP | Crawley Town | 517 | D | 1-1 | Shepherd 45 |
| 8 | 27/02 | A | DMP | Cambridge City | 548 | D | 1-1 | Sullivan 71 |
| 9 | 06/03 | A | DMP | Halesowen Town | 503 | L | 1-3 | Shepherd 70 |
| 0 | 09/03 | H | DMP | Burton Albion | 472 | W | 2-1 | Alexander 40[p], Sullivan 72 |
| 1 | 13/03 | H | DMP | Merthyr Tydfil | 595 | D | 1-1 | O'Hagan 84 |
| 2 | 20/03 | H | DMP | Tamworth | 560 | L | 0-1 | |
| 3 | 23/03 | H | DMC SF(1) | **Cambridge City** | 229 | **L** | 0-3 | |
| 4 | 27/03 | A | DMP | Grantham Town | 381 | D | 1-1 | O'Hagan 21[p] |
| 5 | 28/03 | A | DMC SF(2) | **Cambridge City** | 287 | W | 3-1 | **Rice 52, O'Hagan 69[p] 89[p]** |
| 6 | 30/03 | A | DMP | Weymouth | 2921 | L | 1-2 | Cooper 40 |
| 7 | 03/04 | H | DMP | Gloucester City | 668 | D | 0-0 | |
| 8 | 05/04 | A | DMP | Bath City | 631 | W | 1-0 | Lovell 50 |
| 9 | 10/04 | H | DMP | Atherstone United | 541 | W | 2-1 | Harris 88, Coates 89 |
| 0 | 17/04 | H | DMP | Burton Albion | 671 | L | 0-7 | |
| 1 | 24/04 | H | DMP | Gresley Rovers | 802 | W | 1-0 | O'Brien 57 |
| 2 | 01/05 | A | DMP | Rothwell Town | 343 | D | 1-1 | Middleton 82 |

## PLAYING SQUAD 1999-2000:

GOALKEEPERS: Gavin Davies (Portland United), James Dungey (Plymouth Argyle/Bodmin Town), Simon Harvey, Chris Higgs (Lyme Regis/Exeter City), Kevin Maloy (Cheltenham Town)

DEFENDERS: Julian Alsford (Chester City), Ryan Cross (Sligo Rovers), Chris Ferrett (Salisbury City), Andy Harris (Bridport), David McGhee (Porthleven), Mark Morris (Hastings Town), Roy O'Brien (AFC Bournemouth), Martyn Sullivan (Torrington)

MIDFIELDERS: Neil Coates (Yeovil Town), Simon Cooper (Gloucester City), John Cross (Cardiff City), Dave Lovell, Geoff McLean (Yeovil Town), Rob Murray (Richmond Kickers), William Stringer (Bridport), David Wright (Portsmouth - trial)

FORWARDS: Sufyan Ghazghazi (Africain de Tunis), Matthew Groves (Portsmouth), Keith Middleton (Hamworthy United), Danny O'Hagan (Weston-super-Mare), Owen Pickard (Yeovil Town), Paul Roast (Allendale)

# GLOUCESTER CITY

## CLUB OFFICIALS

Chairman: **Rob Thomas**
President: **R F Etheridge**
Vice-Chairman: **Peter Barnes**
Chief Executive: **Rob Thomas**

Secretary: **Jason Mills** 25 Hewlett Road,
Cheltenham, Gloucestershire GL52 6AD
Tel & FAX: 01242 700496 (M): 0468 750590

Press Officer: **Rob Thomas** (01452 305051)
General Manager: **Mike Bullingham**
01452 421400

## FACT FILE

Formed: 1889
Nickname: The Tigers
Sponsors: Hartland Renault
Colours: Yellow & black/yellow/yellow
Change colours: Red & white/white/red
Midweek games: Tuesday
98-99- Captain: Chris Burns
P.o.Y.: Gary Kemp
Top scorer: Adie Mings

### FOOTBALL MANAGEMENT TEAM
Manager: Brian Hughes
Assistant & Reserve Team Manager:
Steve Fergusson
Physio: Adrian Tandy

**GROUND** Meadow Park, Sudmeadow Road, Hempsted, Gloucester GL2 6HS
Tel: 01452 421400
**Directions:** From North: A40 then then A4301 towards City Centre & Historic Docks, right into Severn Road over swingbridge, right into Llanthony Road/Hempsted Lane, 2nd right into Sudmeadow Road, ground 50yds on left
Capacity: 5,000        Cover: 3,000        Seats: 560        Floodlights: Yes
**Clubhouse:** Meadow Park Sports & Social Club at entrance to ground. Normal licensing hours. H & C food available. **Club Shop:** Yes

Pages: 44 Price: £1
Editor: Mike Dunstan Tel: 01242 250087

Local Press: Gloucester Citizen,
Western Daily Press
Local Radio: Severn Sound,
BBC Radio Gloucestershire

**PREVIOUS** **Leagues:** Bristol & Dist. (now Western) 1893-96, Gloucester & Dist. 97-1907, NorthGlos. 07-10, Glos. North Senior 20-34, Birmingham Comb. 1935-39
**Grounds:** Longlevens 1935-65, Horton Road 65-86        **Name:** Gloucester Y.M.C.A

**CLUB RECORDS** **Attendance:** 4,000 v Dagenham & Redbridge, FA Trophy S-F 2nd Leg, 12.4.97
**Win:** 10-0 v Sudbury Town (H), FA Cup 3rd Rd Q., 17.10.98        **Defeat:** 1-12 v Gillingham 9.11.46
**Goalscorer:** Reg Weaver, 250        **Appearances:** Stan Myers & Frank Tredgett in 1950s
**Fee Paid:** £25,000 for S Fergusson (Worcester City), and D Holmes (Gresley R.)
**Fee Received:** £25,000 Ian Hedges (AFC Bournemouth, 1990)

**BEST SEASON** FA Cup: 2nd Rd 89-90        FA Trophy: Semi-Final 1996-97

**HONOURS** Southern Lg R-up 90-91 (Lg Cup 55-56 (R-up 81-82), Midland Div 88-89), Glos NthSen Lg 33-34, Glos Sen. Cup 37-38 49-58 65-66 68-69 70-71 74-75 78-79 79-80 81-82 82-83 83-84 90-91 92-93, Sen Amat Cup (Nth) 31-32)

Players progressing: Numerous including William Teague (61) & Rod Thomas (64)to Swindon, John Layton (Hereford 74), Ian Main (Exeter 78), Mike Bruton(Newport 79), Mel Gwinnett (Bradford C. 84), Steve Talboys (Wimbledon 91)

*Wayne Fairclough (Red 3), brings down Gloucester's Andy mainwaring and concedes a free kick just outside the penalty area. Photo: Bill Wheatcroft*

## GLOUCESTER CITY - MATCH FACTS - 1998-99 SEASON

| No | Date | Venue | Comp | Opponents | Att | Result | Score | Goalscorers |
|----|------|-------|------|-----------|-----|--------|-------|-------------|
| 1 | 22/08 | A | DMP | Cambridge City | 359 | D | 1-1 | Mainwaring 77 |
| 2 | 25/08 | H | DMP | Dorchester Town | 606 | W | 4-1 | Burns 5, Hemmings 43, Wyatt 51, Mings 73 |
| 3 | 29/08 | H | DMP | Ilkeston Town | 703 | D | 1-1 | Fergusson 88[p] |
| 4 | 31/08 | A | DMP | Bath City | 1027 | W | 2-1 | Wyatt 16, Fergusson 51[p] |
| 5 | 05/09 | A | DMP | King's Lynn | 561 | L | 0-2 | |
| 6 | 08/09 | H | DMP | Weymouth | 516 | D | 0-0 | |
| 7 | 12/09 | H | DMP | Nuneaton Borough | 1010 | W | 1-0 | Tucker 11 |
| 8 | 19/09 | A | DMP | Hastings Town | 620 | D | 0-0 | |
| 9 | 22/09 | H | DMP | Bath City | 704 | W | 2-1 | Fergusson 11[p], Holloway 55 |
| 10 | 26/09 | A | DMP | Burton Albion | 742 | L | 3-5 | Keeling 5, Mings 59 63 |
| 11 | 29/09 | A | DMP | Bromsgrove Rovers | 634 | W | 1-0 | Kemp 89 |
| 12 | 03/10 | H | FA C Q2 | **Paulton Rovers** | **507** | W | **2-1** | **Keeling 27, Bennett 88** |
| 13 | 06/10 | A | GSC | **Cirencester Town** | **140** | W | **3-1** | **Bennett 16, Webb 98 118** |
| 14 | 10/10 | H | DMP | Atherstone United | 563 | D | 0-0 | |
| 15 | 17/10 | H | FA C Q3 | **Sudbury Town** | **621** | D | **0-0** | **Bennett, Burns(2), Hemmings, Callinan, Mings(3), Kemp, Hoskins** |
| 16 | 24/10 | A | FA T 1 | **Chertsey Town** | **246** | W | **5-0** | **Hemmings 40 54 59, Mings 44 47** |
| 17 | 31/10 | A | FA C Q4 | **Kidderminster Harriers** | **1690** | L | **1-2** | **Webb 63** |
| 18 | 07/11 | H | DMP | Tamworth | 702 | L | 0-1 | |
| 19 | 10/11 | H | DM C 1(1) | **Cirencester Town** | **188** | W | **1-0** | **Blackler 25[og]** |
| 20 | 14/11 | A | DMP | Crawley Town | 911 | L | 1-2 | Hemmings 20 |
| 21 | 21/11 | H | FA T 2 | **Kingstonian** | **652** | L | **1-2** | **Tucker 41** |
| 22 | 24/11 | A | DM C 1(2) | **Cirencester Town** | **125** | W | **3-1** | **Kemp 16, Wyatt 72, Hoskins 74** |
| 23 | 28/11 | A | DMP | Gresley Rovers | 512 | W | 3-2 | Hemmings 2, Burns 45, Mings 70 |
| 24 | 05/12 | H | DMP | Bromsgrove Rovers | 463 | W | 4-3 | Wyatt 48 82, Ashley 64[og], Hemmings 90 |
| 25 | 07/12 | A | DMP | Weymouth | 505 | L | 3-5 | Wyatt 39, Burns 51, Kemp 60 |
| 26 | 12/12 | H | DMP | Cambridge City | 536 | W | 3-1 | Kemp 12 72, Mings 28 |
| 27 | 16/12 | A | DM C 2 | **Stourbridge** | **111** | L | **0-2** | |
| 28 | 19/12 | A | DMP | Boston United | 907 | L | 0-1 | |
| 29 | 28/12 | A | DMP | Worcester City | 1045 | D | 2-2 | Holloway 11[p], Mainwaring 85 |
| 30 | 01/01 | H | DMP | Salisbury City | 667 | D | 1-1 | Mainwaring 66 |
| 31 | 02/01 | H | DMP | Rothwell Town | 442 | W | 2-0 | Mings 65 88 |
| 32 | 09/01 | A | DMP | Atherstone United | 278 | W | 2-1 | Mainwaring 3 39 |
| 33 | 16/01 | H | DMP | Grantham Town | 593 | L | 0-1 | |
| 34 | 23/01 | H | DMP | Boston United | 510 | D | 2-2 | Mings 73 87 |
| 35 | 26/01 | A | DMP | Merthyr Tydfil | 343 | W | 1-0 | Kemp 78 |
| 36 | 30/01 | A | DMP | Halesowen Town | 743 | W | 1-0 | Holloway 42[p] |
| 37 | 06/02 | H | DMP | Gresley Rovers | 531 | D | 0-0 | |
| 38 | 13/02 | A | DMP | Grantham Town | 522 | W | 1-0 | Callinan 60 |
| 39 | 16/02 | A | GSC SF | **Forest Green Rovers** | **501** | W | **4-2** | **Mainwaring 23, Holloway 82[p] 118[p], Mings 100** |
| 40 | 20/02 | H | DMP | Crawley Town | 584 | W | 2-0 | Tucker 53, Mainwaring 81 |
| 41 | 27/02 | H | DMP | King's Lynn | 610 | W | 2-1 | Kemp 21, Mings 78 |
| 42 | 06/03 | A | DMP | Rothwell Town | 239 | W | 1-0 | Holloway 68[p] |
| 43 | 09/03 | H | DMP | Merthyr Tydfil | 576 | W | 2-1 | Burns 45, Mings 65 |
| 44 | 13/03 | A | DMP | Tamworth | 512 | D | 1-1 | G Thorne 26 |
| 45 | 20/03 | H | DMP | Burton Albion | 617 | L | 0-1 | |
| 46 | 27/03 | H | DMP | Hastings Town | 394 | L | 2-3 | Burns 17, Holloway 78 |
| 47 | 03/04 | A | DMP | Dorchester Town | 668 | D | 0-0 | |
| 48 | 05/04 | H | DMP | Worcester City | 668 | L | 0-2 | |
| 49 | 10/04 | A | DMP | Nuneaton Borough | 1538 | L | 0-2 | |
| 50 | 17/04 | H | DMP | Halesowen Town | 535 | W | 2-0 | Hemmings 41, Wyatt 81 |
| 51 | 24/04 | A | DMP | Ilkeston Town | 639 | L | 3-4 | Mainwaring 48, Callinan 50 89 |
| 52 | 01/05 | H | DMP | Salisbury City | 448 | L | 1-2 | Hemmings 86 |
| 53 | 04/05 | H | GSC F | **Cheltenham Town** | **950** | L | **0-3** | |

**PLAYING SQUAD 1999-2000:**

GOALKEEPERS: Ryan Gannaway (Cheltenham Town), Mark Hervin (Bath City), Ben Lambert

DEFENDERS: Tommy Callinan (Dorchester Town), Matthew Coupe (Forest Green Rovers), Steve Fergusson (Worcester City), Gary Kemp (Almondsbury Picksons), Nigel Niblett (Kidderminster Harriers), Gary Thorne (Swindon Town), Wayne Thorne (Swindon Town), Jamie Vittles (Bideford)

MIDFIELDERS: Paul Chenoweth (Worcester City), Brendan Hackett (Burton Albion), Steve Jenkins, Andy Tucker (Cheltenham Town), Dave Webb (Trowbridge Town), Nathan Wigg (Forest Green Rovers)

FORWARDS: Dominic Barclay (Macclesfield Town), Steve Bennett (Swindon Town), Gary Cook (Hereford United - trial), Darren Keeling (Yeovil Town), David Nichols, Tom Rutter, Jamie Smith (Gloucester City), Jimmy Smith (Cheltenham Town), Mike Wyatt (Bath City)

# GRANTHAM TOWN

## CLUB OFFICIALS

Chairman: **Barry Palmer**
President: **Mr.Michael Bird**

Secretary: **Mr Pat Nixon**
72 Huntingtower Road, Grantham,
Lincs NG31 7AU
Tel: 01476 564408

**FOOTBALL MANAGEMENT TEAM**
Manager: Dave `Gilbert
Asst Mgr:Matt Carmichael
Physio: Nigel Marshall

**FACT FILE**

Formed: 1874
Nickname: Gingerbreads
Sponsors: Crystal Motors
Colours: Black & white stripes/black/black
Change: Blue/blue, black/blue or black
Midweek matchday: Tuesday
Reserves' League: Lincolnshire
98-99 - Captain: Simon Dakin
P.o.Y.: Dave Gilbert
Top scorer:Dave Gilbert

**GROUND** South Kesteven Sports Stadium, Trent Road, Grantham, Lincs Tel: 01476 562011

**Directions:** Midway between A1 and A52 on edge of Earlesfield Industrial Estate; from A1
take A607 to Earlsfield Ind. Est and continue into Trent Rd

Capacity: 7,500          Cover: 1,950          Seats: 750          Floodlights: Yes

**Clubhouse:** (01476 593506) Open evenings and weekends. Bar, darts, pool etc. Frequent live
entertainment. Available for functions
**Club Shop:** Programmes and a wide range of souvenirs. Contact club number.

Rrogramme: 38 pages £1.50
Local Press: Grantham Journal, Nottingham
Evening Post, Melton & GranthamTrader,
Grantham Citizen, Lincolnshire Echo
Local Radio: Radio Lincolnshire, Lincs FM

**PREVIOUS**     **Leagues:** Mid Amat All, Central All. 11-25 59-61, Midland Co's 25-59 61-72,Southern Lge 72-79, Northern Prem. 79-85
                 **Names:** Grantham FC, pre-80. Grounds: London Rd up to 90

**CLUB RECORDS** **Attendance:** 3,695 v Southport. F.A.Trophy Quarter Final 97-98
                 **Win:** 13-0 vRufford Colliery (H), FA Cup Preliminary Rd 15/9/34          **Career Goalscorer:** Jack McCartney 416
                 **Defeat:** 0-16 v Notts County Rovers (A), Midland Amateur All. 22/10/1892          **Career Appearances:** Chris Gardiner 664
                 **Transfer fee paid:** £1,000 for Gary Jones (Doncaster Rovers, 1989)
                 **Transfer fee received:** £20,000 for Gary Crosby (Notts Forest 87)

**BEST SEASON** **FA Cup:** 3rd Rd 1883-84 86-87 1973-74. Comp Proper on 23 occasions
                **FA Trophy:** Quarter Final 1971-72, 97-98
**HONOURS**     Southern Lg R-up 73-74 (Div 1 Nth 72-73 78-79, Merit Cup 72-73), Southern Lg Mid Div Champions 97-98. Midland Co's Lg(3)
                63-64 70-72 (R-up 37-38 64-65 69-70, Lg Cup 68-69 70-71), Midland Amtr Lg10-11 (Lg Cup R-up 10-11), Central All. 24-25
                (Southern Div R-up 59-60), LincsSnr Cup 1884-851936-37 (R-up(5) 34-36 39-40 45-47), Lincs Co. `A' Cup(3) 53-54 60-62 (R-
                up 49-50 52-53 57-58), Lincs Co. Snr Cup 71-72 82-83 (R-up 80-81)

Players progressing: E Morris (Halifax 50), P Thompson/R Cooke (Peterborough 64/80), J Rayner (Notts County 64), D Dall (Scunthorpe 79),
N Jarvis/H Wood (Scunthorpe 80), D White (Bristol Rvrs 86), T Curran (Grimsby 87), G Crosby (Nottm Forest 87),
A Kennedy (Wrexham 87), R Wilson (Lincoln 87)

*Grantham Town FC.   Photo: Bill Wheatcroft*

## GRANTHAM TOWN - MATCH FACTS - 1998-99 SEASON

| No | Date | Venue | Comp | Opponents | Att | Result | Score | Goalscorers |
|---|---|---|---|---|---|---|---|---|
| | 22/08 | A | DMP | Worcester City | 1012 | W | 2-1 | Pell 54, Glasser 81 |
| | 25/08 | H | DMP | Bromsgrove Rovers | 915 | W | 4-1 | Jackson 11, Speed 15, Gilbert 26[p], Twynham 75 |
| | 29/08 | H | DMP | Salisbury City | 730 | W | 2-1 | Jackson 29, Gilbert 78[p] |
| | 31/08 | A | DMP | Nuneaton Borough | 1919 | L | 0-2 | |
| | 05/09 | H | DMP | Merthyr Tydfil | 688 | W | 5-3 | Taylor 6, Jackson 15 75, Gilbert 80[p], Bowman 89 |
| | 08/09 | A | DMP | Cambridge City | 325 | L | 0-1 | |
| | 12/09 | H | DMP | Bath City | 948 | L | 0-1 | |
| | 15/09 | A | DMP | Bromsgrove Rovers | 561 | L | 2-4 | Nwadike 27, Bowman 46 |
| | 19/09 | A | DMP | Dorchester Town | 552 | L | 2-3 | Wilton 28, Gilbert 60[p] |
| | 22/09 | H | DMP | Nuneaton Borough | 1170 | W | 2-0 | Jackson 9 23 |
| | 26/09 | H | DMP | Crawley Town | 626 | L | 1-2 | Taylor 26[p] |
| | 03/10 | H | FA C Q2 | **West Midlands Police** | 572 | W | 4-0 | Taylor 15 70, Twynham 60, Gwyther 90 |
| | 10/10 | A | DMP | Halesowen Town | 661 | L | 1-5 | Taylor 30 |
| | 17/10 | A | FA C Q3 | **Glossop North End** | 471 | W | 3-2 | Taylor 50, Speed 67, Archer 76 |
| | 24/10 | A | FA T 1 | **Burton Albion** | 588 | D | 0-0 | |
| | 27/10 | H | FA T 1 r | **Burton Albion** | 570 | L | 0-3 | |
| | 31/10 | A | FA C Q4 | **Tamworth** | 805 | L | 1-2 | Twynham 23 |
| | 03/11 | H | DMP | Cambridge City | 300 | L | 0-1 | |
| | 07/11 | H | DMP | Salisbury City | 419 | L | 0-1 | |
| | 10/11 | H | DM C 1(1) | **Ilkeston Town** | 354 | W | 4-0 | Speed 14, Gilbert 45, Pell 63, Taylor 66 |
| | 14/11 | H | DMP | Atherstone United | 462 | D | 1-1 | Jackson 48 |
| | 28/11 | A | DMP | Burton Albion | 839 | W | 1-0 | Pell 57 |
| | 01/12 | A | DM C 1(2) | **Ilkeston Town** | 195 | L | 0-1 | |
| | 05/12 | H | DMP | Weymouth | 507 | W | 2-0 | Speed 39, Pell 90 |
| | 19/12 | A | DMP | Gresley Rovers | 517 | W | 1-0 | Bowman 50 |
| | 22/12 | H | DM C 2 | **Rothwell Town** | 429 | D | 0-0 | |
| | 26/12 | H | DMP | Ilkeston Town | 856 | W | 3-1 | Henderson 61 69, Bowman 85 |
| | 28/12 | A | DMP | Boston United | 1925 | L | 0-3 | |
| | 02/01 | H | DMP | Halesowen Town | 590 | D | 0-0 | |
| | 09/01 | H | DMP | Worcester City | 478 | L | 0-3 | |
| | 16/01 | A | DMP | Gloucester City | 593 | W | 1-0 | Gilbert 71[p] |
| | 19/01 | A | DM C 2 r | **Rothwell Town** | 124 | L | 0-1 | |
| | 23/01 | A | DMP | Hastings Town | 417 | W | 3-1 | Gilbert 23[p], Myall 89[og], Bowman 90 |
| | 30/01 | H | DMP | Burton Albion | 697 | L | 2-3 | Cleaver 8, Gwyther 60 |
| | 06/02 | A | DMP | Bath City | 864 | D | 1-1 | Gwyther 80 |
| | 13/02 | H | DMP | Gloucester City | 522 | L | 0-1 | |
| | 20/02 | A | DMP | King's Lynn | 793 | D | 1-1 | Cleaver 73 |
| | 23/02 | H | DMP | Gresley Rovers | 369 | W | 3-1 | Quayle 3, Cleaver 18, Nwadike 49 |
| | 27/02 | H | DMP | Rothwell Town | 511 | W | 3-0 | Andrews 20, Quayle 89 90 |
| | 06/03 | A | DMP | Crawley Town | 865 | L | 0-2 | |
| | 16/03 | A | DMP | Rothwell Town | 210 | W | 1-0 | Cleaver 46 |
| | 20/03 | A | DMP | Merthyr Tydfil | 521 | L | 0-1 | |
| | 27/03 | H | DMP | Dorchester Town | 381 | D | 1-1 | Dakin 16 |
| | 30/03 | A | DMP | Tamworth | 529 | D | 1-1 | Nwadike 88 |
| | 03/04 | A | DMP | Ilkeston Town | 667 | D | 1-1 | Gilbert 49 |
| | 05/04 | H | DMP | Boston United | 978 | L | 1-3 | Speed 62 |
| | 10/04 | H | DMP | Tamworth | 430 | L | 1-2 | Martin 69 |
| | 13/04 | H | DMP | Hastings Town | 294 | L | 1-2 | Martin 8 |
| | 17/04 | A | DMP | Atherstone United | 244 | D | 1-1 | Goodwin 34 |
| | 24/04 | H | DMP | King's Lynn | 667 | L | 0-1 | |
| | 01/05 | A | DMP | Weymouth | 1041 | L | 0-1 | |

**PLAYING SQUAD 1999-2000:**

GOALKEEPERS: Gary Germaine (Leek Town), Ryan Moulds (Boston Town - dual reg.)

DEFENDERS: John Andrews (Grantham Town), Craig Gaunt (Singapore), Jim Neal (Gainsborough Trinity), Emeka Nwadike, Adrian Speed

MIDFIELDERS: Dwayne Beckett (Doncaster Rovers), Darren Bogan (Arnold Town), Wayne Bullimore (Scarborough), Dave Gilbert, Darren Gwyther, Robert McKenzie (Rotherham United), Nick Reeson (Lincoln City), Benjamin Sweet (Cambridge City)

FORWARDS: Matt Carmichael (Boston United), Neil Featherstone (Boston United), Dave Taylor (Stamford), Carl Ranter (Kingstonian/Bridgnorth Town), Paul Watts (Grantham Town), Tim Wilkes (Telford United)

# HALESOWEN TOWN

**CLUB OFFICIALS**
Chairman: **Ron Moseley**
President: **Laurence Wood**
Vice Chairman: **Nigel Pitt**
Secretary: **Stewart Tildesley**
83 Bloomfield Street, Halesowen B63 3RF
Tel: 0121 5508443
Commercial Manager: **Nigel Pitt**
Press Officer: **Paul Floud** (0121 550 8999)

**FOOTBALL MANAGEMENT TEAM**
Manager: John Chambers
A sst Manager: Alan Moore
Physio: Jeff Jones

**FACT FILE**
Formed: 1873
Nickname: Yeltz
Sponsors: Hamer Ford
Newsline: 0930 555818
Colours: White with black & yellow trim
Change colours: All Blue & White trim
Midweek home matchday:Tuesday
Reserve's League: None
98-99- Captain: Phillip Wood
P.o.Y.: Paul Birch
Top scorer: Steven Piearce (31)

**GROUND**      The Grove, Old Hawne Lane, Halesowen, West Midlands B63 3TB
FAX No: 0121 602 0123   Tel No: 0121 550 2179
**Directions:**   M5 jct 3, A456 (signed Kidderminster) to 1st island turn right (signed A459 Dudley), left at next island (signed A458 Stourbridge), at next island take 3rd left into Grammar School Lane, then Old Hawne Lane - ground 400 yds on left
Capacity: 5,000          Cover: 1,420          Seats: 420          Floodlights: Yes
**Clubhouse:** (0121 602 2210) 12-2.30 & 7-11 (10.30 Sun) pm daily. Cold snacks served.
**Club Shop:** Sells replica strips, T-shirts, waterproof tops, coats, scarves, programmes, badges etc

Pages: 44  Price: £1.20p  Editor: R Pepper
Local Press: Sports Argus, Express & Star, Birmingham Mail, Halesowen News, Stourbridge & Halesowen Chronicle
Local Radio: BBC West Midlands, B.R.M.B., Beacon

**PREVIOUS**      **Leagues:** West Mids 1892-1905 06-11 46-86, Birmingham Comb. 11-39

**CLUB RECORDS** **Attendance:** 5,000 v Hendon F.A. Cup 1st Rd Proper 1954, (18,234 v Southall,1986 FA Vase Final at Wembley)
**Goalscorer:** Paul Joinson 369          **Appearances:** Paul Joinson 608
**Win:** 13-1 v Coventry Amateurs, Birmingham Senior Cup, 1956
**Defeat:** 0-8 v Bilston, West Midlands League, 7/4/62
**Fee Paid:** £7,250 for Stuart Evans (Gresley 1996)
**Fee Received:** £40,000 for Jim Rodwell (Rushden & Diamonds 96)

**BEST SEASON** **FA Vase:** Winners 84-85, 85-86 R-up 82-83      **FA Trophy:** 3rd Round Proper 94-95
**FA Cup:** 1st Rd 9 times: 54-55 then each season from 84-85 to 91-92

**HONOURS**      Southern Lg Premier Div R-up 96, Southern Lg Midland Div 89-90, W Mids Lg(5) 46-47 82-85 85-86 (R-up 64-65, Lg Cup 82-83 84-85),B'ham Snr Cup 83-84,97-98 (R-up 51-52 67-68), Staffs Snr Cup 88-89 (R-up 83-84), FA Vase (2) 84-86 (R-up 82-3) Worcs Snr Cup 51-52 61-62 (R-up 87-88), Midland Comb. Res Div 89-90

Players progressing: Arthur Proudler (Aston Villa), Cyril Spiers (Aston Villa), Billy Morris (Wolves), Dean Spink (Aston Villa), Stuart Cash (Nottm Forest), Andrew Pearce, Tim Clarke & Sean Flynn (Coventry), DeanStokes (Port Vale), Frank Bennett (Southampton), Julian Alsop (Bristol Rovers)

*Back Row (L-R): N Chambers (Manager), J Jones (Physio), R Collins, N Harvey, R Elmes, D McDonnell, J Owen, W Lloyd, P Wood, N Smith, S Piearce, E Wright, G Blackwell (Physio)*
*Front Row: R Robinson-Little (kit boy), A Bradley, M Hollis, S Skidmore, R Crisp, M Peters, I Reed, P Birch, A Cooper, M Gardiner.*

# HALESOWEN TOWN - MATCH FACTS - 1998-99 SEASON

| No | Date | Venue | Comp | Opponents | Att | Result | Score | Goalscorers |
|---|---|---|---|---|---|---|---|---|
| 1 | 01/08 | H | ABT | Hednesford Town | n/k | D | 0-0 | |
| 2 | 22/08 | H | DMP | Crawley Town | 698 | W | 3-2 | Harding 28, Piearce 44, Birch 81 |
| 3 | 25/08 | A | DMP | Gresley Rovers | 570 | L | 0-2 | |
| 4 | 29/08 | A | DMP | King's Lynn | 732 | D | 1-1 | Reed 68 |
| 5 | 31/08 | H | DMP | Burton Albion | 902 | L | 1-3 | Piearce 31 |
| 6 | 05/09 | A | DMP | Weymouth | 961 | W | 2-1 | Piearce 41, Cooper 71 |
| 7 | 08/09 | H | DMP | Boston United | 670 | D | 1-1 | Francis 61 |
| 8 | 12/09 | A | DMP | Hastings Town | 555 | L | 0-2 | |
| 9 | 15/09 | H | DMP | Gresley Rovers | 543 | L | 3-4 | Birch 25, Peters 41, Reed 62 |
| 10 | 19/09 | A | DMP | Cambridge City | 307 | L | 0-2 | |
| 11 | 22/09 | A | DMP | Burton Albion | 620 | W | 1-0 | Gardiner 19 |
| 12 | 26/09 | H | DMP | Atherstone United | 683 | W | 3-1 | Crisp 67[p], Francis 68, Peters 81 |
| 13 | 03/10 | H | FA C Q2 | **Eastwood Town** | **604** | D | **2-2** | **Gardiner 59, Piearce 86** |
| 14 | 07/10 | A | FA C Q2 r | **Eastwood Town** | **322** | W | **1-0** | **Bradley 80** |
| 15 | 10/10 | H | DMP | Grantham Town | 661 | W | 5-1 | Reed 22, Bradley 28, Francis 53 79, Black 86 |
| 16 | 13/10 | A | WSC 1 | **Moor Green** | **209** | L | **1-2** | **Reed 57** |
| 17 | 17/10 | H | FA C Q3 | **Gresley Rovers** | **652** | L | **1-2** | **Bradley 55** |
| 18 | 24/10 | H | FA T 1 | **Guiseley** | **324** | L | **0-2** | |
| 19 | 31/10 | A | DMP | Rothwell Town | 241 | L | 1-2 | Francis 5 |
| 20 | 04/11 | A | DMP | Boston United | 671 | L | 0-2 | |
| 21 | 07/11 | H | DMP | King's Lynn | 601 | L | 0-1 | |
| 22 | 10/11 | H | DM C 1(1) | **Bromsgrove Rovers** | **403** | W | **1-0** | **Birch 90** |
| 23 | 14/11 | H | DMP | Merthyr Tydfil | 685 | W | 2-0 | Francis 56, Piearce 71 |
| 24 | 21/11 | A | DMP | Dorchester Town | 431 | L | 0-2 | |
| 25 | 28/11 | A | DMP | Nuneaton Borough | 1230 | L | 3-4 | Birch 6, Francis 44 89 |
| 26 | 01/12 | A | BSC 2 | **Willenhall Town** | **203** | W | **2-0** | **Piearce 11 52** |
| 27 | 05/12 | H | DMP | Worcester City | 704 | D | 0-0 | |
| 28 | 09/12 | A | DM C 1(2) | **Bromsgrove Rovers** | **132** | W | **2-1** | **Francis 9, Piearce 13** |
| 29 | 12/12 | A | DMP | Bath City | 1456 | D | 0-0 | |
| 30 | 19/12 | H | DMP | Salisbury City | 537 | D | 3-3 | Piearce 68, Wright 72, Crisp 89[p] |
| 31 | 22/12 | H | DM C 2 | **Bilston Town** | **209** | L | **0-2** | |
| 32 | 26/12 | A | DMP | Tamworth | 603 | L | 1-3 | Reed 31 |
| 33 | 28/12 | H | DMP | Bromsgrove Rovers | 808 | W | 1-0 | Wright 88 |
| 34 | 01/01 | H | DMP | Nuneaton Borough | 1521 | W | 2-0 | Birch 14, Wright 90 |
| 35 | 02/01 | A | DMP | Grantham Town | 590 | D | 0-0 | |
| 36 | 09/01 | A | DMP | Crawley Town | 1074 | D | 1-1 | Crisp 49 |
| 37 | 12/01 | H | BSC 3 | **Wolverhampton Wanderers** | **454** | L | **1-2** | **Reed 52** |
| 38 | 30/01 | H | DMP | Gloucester City | 743 | L | 0-1 | |
| 39 | 06/02 | A | DMP | Merthyr Tydfil | 343 | L | 0-1 | |
| 40 | 13/02 | H | DMP | Rothwell Town | 587 | W | 4-0 | Birch 22 67, Piearce 75 78 |
| 41 | 20/02 | A | DMP | Salisbury City | 771 | W | 2-1 | Piearce 8 26 |
| 42 | 27/02 | A | DMP | Worcester City | 1403 | W | 4-3 | Piearce 53 75 82, Burch 61 |
| 43 | 06/03 | H | DMP | Dorchester Town | 503 | W | 3-1 | Piearce 57 76, Reed 67 |
| 44 | 13/03 | H | DMP | Weymouth | 689 | D | 2-2 | Elmes 45, Cooper 85 |
| 45 | 20/03 | A | DMP | Ilkeston Town | 588 | D | 2-2 | Lloyd 26, Elmes 51 |
| 46 | 27/03 | H | DMP | Bath City | 621 | D | 2-2 | Elmes 43, Piearce 88 |
| 47 | 03/04 | H | DMP | Tamworth | 831 | W | 3-0 | Piearce 2 49 86 |
| 48 | 05/04 | A | DMP | Bromsgrove Rovers | 890 | W | 5-2 | Jackson 11[og], Piearce 14 55 82, Wright 20 |
| 49 | 10/04 | H | DMP | Cambridge City | 609 | W | 2-1 | Gardiner 29, Crisp 82 |
| 50 | 13/04 | H | DMP | Ilkeston Town | 454 | W | 4-1 | Elmes 31, Piearce 41, Birch 73, Bradley 88 |
| 51 | 17/04 | A | DMP | Gloucester City | 535 | L | 0-2 | |
| 52 | 24/04 | H | DMP | Hastings Town | 742 | D | 3-3 | Piearce 42 75 90 |
| 53 | 01/05 | A | DMP | Atherstone United | 391 | W | 2-0 | Elmes 59, Piearce 78 |

## PLAYING SQUAD 1999-2000:

GOALKEEPERS: Paul Beswick, Chris Bolton, Matt Sidaway (Dudley Town - cover)

DEFENDES: Ashley Brown (Gresley Rovers), Ross Collins, Matt Gardiner, Jason Owen (Stafford Rangers), Paul Wood

MIDFIELDERS: Paul Birch (Exeter City), Anthony Briscoe (Shrewsbury Town), Robbie Dennison (Hereford United), Paul Harding (Worcester City), Matthew Hollis, Mark Peters (Bromsgrove Rovers), Darren Wright (Stafford Rangers)

FORWARDS: Nathan Harvey, Gary Piggott (Stafford Rangers), Lynden Rowland (Gresley Rovers), Clinton Thomas (Kidderminster Harriers), Evran Wright (Worcester City)

# HAVANT & WATERLOOVILLE

### CLUB OFFICIALS
Chairman:T.B.A.
President: **Arthur Saitch, Maurie Hibberd**
Vice Chairman: **Derek Pope**
Directors: Trevor Brock, Ray Jones, John Carter, Peter Dermott, Sandy Peters,
Secretary: **Trevor Brock**, 2 Betula Close, Waterlooville, Hampshire. PO7 8EJ
Tel: 01705 267276

### FACT FILE
Formed: 1998    Nickname: Magnets
Sponsors: TBA
Colours: White & yellow & navy/navy/navy
Change colours: Green
Midweek matchday: Tuesday
Reserves' League: None
98-99 - Top Scorer: Steve Tate (32)
P. of Y.: Simon Elley
Captain: Simon Elley

**HAVANT & WATERLOOVILLE**
*Football Club*

Official Match Day Programme Price £1.00

Saturday 1st May 1999
Dr. Martens League
Southern Division
**ST. LEONARDS**

| | |
|---|---|
| **FOOTBALL MANAGEMENT TEAM** | Manager: Billy Gilbert<br>Asst Manager: Mick Jenkins<br>Physio: Phil Ashwell |

**GROUND**    West Leigh Park, Martin Road, West Leigh, Havant PO9 5TH Tel: 01705 787822

**Directions:** Take B2149 to Havant off the A27 (B2149 Petersfield Rd if coming out of Havant). 2nd turning off dual carriageway into Bartons Road then 1st right into Martins Road. 1 mile from Havant BR station

Capacity: 6,000    Cover: 1,500    Seats: 290    Floodlights: Yes
**Clubhouse:** Open every day, lunchtime and evening. 2 bars, function suites. Hot & cold food available    Club Shop: Sells various souvenirs & progs

Pages: 32 Price: £1
Editor: Adrian Gardiner
Local Press: News (Portsmouth)
Local Radio: Ocean Sound, Radio Solent

**PREVIOUS**    (Havant) **Leagues:** Portsmouth 58-71; Hants 71-86; Wessex 86-91. **Names:** LeighPark; Havant & Leigh Park; Havant **Grounds:** Front Lawn 1958-83    *(Waterlooville)* **Leagues:** Waterlooville & District, Portsmouth 38-53, Hants1953-71.
**Grounds:** Convent Ground 10-30, Rowlands Avenue Recreation Ground 30-63, Jubliee Park 63-98
**CLUB RECORDS**    (Havant) **Attendance:** 3,500 v Wisbech Town, FA Vase QF 85-86
**Win:** 10-0 three times; v Sholing Sports (H), FA Vase 4th Rd 85-86, v PortsmouthRoyal Navy (H), Wessex League 90-91; v Poole Town, Southern Lge SouthernDiv. 94-95.    **Defeat:** 1-7 v Camberley Town (H), FA Vase 3rd Rd 88-89
**CareerGoalsscorer:** Unknown    **Career Appearances:** Tony Plumbley
**Transfer fee paid:** £5,750 for John Wilson (Bashley, 90)    **Received:** £7,000 for Steve Tate (Waterlooville, 1993)
*(Waterlooville)* **Transfer fee paid:** £6,000 for Steve Tate (Havant Town, 93)    **Received:** £6,000 for Dave Boyce (Gravesend & Northfleet, 93)
**BEST SEASON**    (Havant) **FA Cup:** 4thd Qual Rd 98-93 (lost on penalties at Hayes)). **FA Vase:** Qtr Final85-86
*(Waterlooville)*    **FA Trophy:** 3rd Rd 98-99 (lost 0-1 at Worcester City)    **FA Amateur Cup:** 1st Rd 59-60
**FA Cup:** 1st Rd 2nd replay 83-84, 0-2 v Northampton T. (A) after two 1-1 draws
**HONOURS**    (Havant): FA Sunday Cup 68-69, Wessex Lg 90-91 (R-up 88-89), Hampshire Lg Div 372-73 (Div 4 71-72), Hampshire Senior Cup Winners 93-94,94-95 R-up 91-92 Hants.Intermediate Cup, Hampshire Junior Cup, Russell Cotes Cup 91-92, PortsmouthSenior Cup 83-84 84-85 91-92, Gosport War Memorial Cup 74-75 91-92 92-93 94-95, Southern Counties Floodlit Cup R-up 91-92, Hampshire Floodlit Cup 85-86,Portsmouth Lg *(Waterlooville)*: Southern Lg Div 1 Sth 71-72 (Lg Cup 86-87, R-up 82-83), HantsLg R-up 69-70 (Div 2 59-60 64-65, Div 3 (East) R-up 53-54), Hants Snr Cup 69-7072-73 84-85 (R-up 75-76 90-91), Russell Cotes Cup 88-89, Portsmouth Lg 49-5050-51 51-52 (Div 2 46-47, Div 3 38-39), Portsmouth Snr Cup 68-69, PortsmouthVictory Cup 59-60 69-70
**Players progressing**    (Havant); Bobby Tambling (Chelsea)    *(Waterlooville)*; Phil Figgins (Portsmouth 73), Paul Hardyman (Portsmouth 83), Guy Whittingham (Portsmouth via Yeovil Town 88), Paul Moody (Southampton 91)

*Havant & Waterlooville FC pictured with the Dr Martens Southern Division Championship Shield*

*Photo: Andrew Chitty*

494

## HAVANT & WATERLOOVILLE - MATCH FACTS - 1998-99 SEASON

| No | Date | Venue | Comp | Opponents | Att | Result | Score | Goalscorers |
|----|------|-------|------|-----------|-----|--------|-------|-------------|
| 1 | 22/08 | A | DM S | Chelmsford City | 421 | W | 2-0 | Tate 46[p], Lovell 82 |
| 2 | 25/08 | H | DM S | Newport IoW | 549 | W | 3-0 | Lovell 18 75, Tate 58 |
| 3 | 29/08 | H | DM S | Folkestone Invicta | 229 | W | 3-1 | Tate 30 88, Ansty 89 |
| 4 | 31/08 | A | DM S | Tonbridge Angels | 424 | D | 0-0 | |
| 5 | 05/09 | H | DM S | Raunds Town | 322 | W | 3-1 | Tate 12, Elley 44, Anstey 76 |
| 6 | 08/09 | A | DM S | Andover | 193 | W | 4-0 | Tate 56, Lovell 65, Anstey 82, Wakefield 87 |
| 7 | 12/09 | H | DM S | Baldock Town | 297 | W | 2-0 | Wakefield 26, Lovell 30 |
| 8 | 15/09 | A | DM S | Newport IoW | 352 | W | 1-0 | Lovell 18 |
| 9 | 19/09 | H | FA C Q1 | Hassocks | 260 | W | 1-0 | Wakefield 70 |
| 10 | 26/09 | A | DM S | Erith & Belvedere | 142 | L | 0-2 | |
| 11 | 29/09 | H | DM S | Tonbridge Angels | 242 | D | 2-2 | Wood 22 40 |
| 12 | 03/10 | H | FA C Q2 | Hampton | 310 | W | 5-1 | Wood 12 72, Tate 42, Anstey 62, Wakefield 82 |
| 13 | 06/10 | A | SCCFC 1 | Littlehampton Town | 62 | W | 6-1 | Anstey 12 20 36, Tate 32 62, Wakefield 65 |
| 14 | 10/10 | H | DM S | Ashford Town | 332 | W | 2-0 | Wood 9, Anstey 23 |
| 15 | 17/10 | H | FA C Q3 | Witham Town | 302 | D | 0-0 | |
| 16 | 20/10 | A | FA C Q3 r | Witham Town | 180 | W | 4-0 | Wood 38 65 77, Wakefield 89 |
| 17 | 27/10 | H | HSC 2 | Fareham Town | 118 | W | 5-0 | Tate 15[p] 28 65, Lush 25, Price 68 |
| 18 | 07/11 | H | DM S | Sittingbourne | 333 | L | 0-1 | |
| 19 | 09/11 | H | FA C Q4 | Hayes | 956 | D | 2-2 | Wakefield 18, Watts 71[og] |
| 20 | 11/11 | A | FA C Q4 r | Hayes | 623 | D | 1-1 | Milkins 62                          (3-4 pens) |
| 21 | 17/11 | H | DM C 1(1) | Weymouth | 137 | L | 2-3 | Ansty 4, Price 9 |
| 22 | 21/11 | A | FA T 2 | Margate | 409 | W | 3-1 | Wakefield 15 89, Tate 86 |
| 23 | 24/11 | A | DM C 1(2) | Weymouth | 473 | D | 1-1 | O'Rourke 22 |
| 24 | 28/11 | H | DM S | Fisher Athletic | 341 | W | 2-0 | Jones 5, Lovell 89 |
| 25 | 01/12 | H | HSC 3 | Hamble Assc | 81 | W | 5-0 | Anstey 24, Lovell 49 62 89, Wakefield 73 |
| 26 | 05/12 | A | DM S | Corby Town | 102 | W | 2-0 | Tate 4, Anstey 83 |
| 27 | 12/12 | A | DM S | Baldock Town | 145 | W | 5-0 | Tate 7 26, Milkins 34, Wood 74, Wakefield 84 |
| 28 | 15/12 | H | HRCC 2 | Fleetlands | n/a | | | (withdrew) |
| 29 | 19/12 | H | DM S | Cirencester Town | 289 | W | 3-0 | Tate 21, Milkins 47, Lovell 83 |
| 30 | 28/12 | A | DM S | Bashley | 356 | D | 2-2 | Tate 87 90 |
| 31 | 01/01 | A | DM S | Yate Town | 238 | L | 0-2 | |
| 32 | 09/01 | H | DM S | Brackley Town | 299 | W | 3-1 | Tate 52 90[p], Lovell 60 |
| 33 | 23/01 | A | DM S | Fisher Athletic | 192 | W | 3-2 | Tate 25, Lovell 68, Wood 73 |
| 34 | 28/01 | H | FA T 3 | Worcester City | 254 | L | 0-1 | |
| 35 | 03/02 | A | HSC QF | Cowes Sports | 148 | W | 5-0 | Jones 9, Wakefield 15, Tate 22, Wood 36, Gilbert 81 |
| 36 | 06/02 | H | DM S | Folkestone Invicta | 528 | W | 1-0 | Wakefield 36 |
| 37 | 13/02 | A | DM S | St Leonards | 311 | W | 4-0 | Price 52, Jones 64, Wood 75 90 |
| 38 | 16/02 | H | DM S | Fleet Town | 255 | W | 2-0 | Wakefield 47, Wood 57 |
| 39 | 20/02 | H | DM S | Margate | 701 | W | 1-0 | Tate 89 |
| 40 | 23/02 | A | DM S | Brackley Town | 102 | W | 2-0 | Tate 66, Lovell 82 |
| 41 | 27/02 | A | DM S | Sittingbourne | 391 | W | 1-0 | Wood 43 |
| 42 | 06/03 | A | DM S | Dartford | 201 | W | 2-0 | Wakefield 23, Lovell 88 |
| 43 | 09/03 | H | HSC SF(1) | Aldershot Town | 728 | L | 0-3 | |
| 44 | 13/03 | A | DM S | Corby Town | 255 | D | 0-0 | |
| 45 | 16/03 | A | DM S | Witney Town | 168 | D | 1-1 | Wood 22 |
| 46 | 20/03 | A | DM S | Cirencester Town | 158 | W | 3-1 | Tate 48, Hambley 70, Lovell 82 |
| 47 | 23/03 | A | DM S | Ashford Town | 357 | W | 3-0 | Wood 10 39, Lovell 50 |
| 48 | 27/03 | H | DM S | Yate Town | 284 | W | 2-0 | Tate 16, Hambley 86 |
| 49 | 30/03 | A | HSC SF(2) | Aldershot Town | 1342 | D | 1-1 | Lovell 87 |
| 50 | 02/04 | H | DM S | Fleet Town | 260 | W | 6-4 | Lovell 13 57, Woods 15, Tate 20 48 83 |
| 51 | 05/04 | H | DM S | Bashley | 420 | W | 3-0 | Wood 45 50, Hambley 53 |
| 52 | 10/04 | A | DM S | Margate | 810 | L | 0-2 | |
| 53 | 13/04 | H | DM S | Chelmsford City | 336 | L | 0-3 | |
| 54 | 17/04 | H | DM S | Erith & Belvedere | 357 | L | 0-2 | |
| 55 | 24/04 | A | DM S | Raunds Town | 134 | D | 1-1 | Wood 45 |
| 56 | 25/04 | H | DM S | Witney Town | 389 | W | 3-1 | Elley 9 78, Ritchie 41[p] |
| 57 | 27/04 | H | DM S | Andover | 594 | W | 5-1 | Wood 7 41 67 85, Lovell 64 |
| 58 | 29/04 | H | DM S | Dartford | 240 | D | 1-1 | Wakefield 23 |
| 59 | 01/05 | H | DM S | St Leonards | 426 | W | 2-1 | Milkins 20, Tate 81 |

## PLAYING SQUAD 1999-2000:

GOALKEEPERS: Mark Brown (Waterlooville)

DEFENDERS: Aaron Cook (Swansea City), Liam Daish (ex-Coventry City), Simon Elley, Gary McDonald (Portsmouth), Miles Rutherford (Worthing)

MIDFIELDERS: Craig Anstey, Paul Curran (Andover), Tim Hambley (Fisher Athletic), Calvin Hore (Sidlesham - dual reg.), Matt Jones (BAT Sports), Paul Masters, Dave Milkins (Waterlooville), Ben Price (Porthsmouth), Stuart Ritchie (Newport IoW)

FORWARDS: Wayne Eastman (Portsmouth), Steve Tate (Waterlooville), James Taylor (Bashley), Dave Wakefield (Portsmouth), Paul Wood (Andover), Nick Wyatt (Newport IoW)

# ILKESTON TOWN

## CLUB OFFICIALS
Chairman: **Paul Millership**
President: **Robert Lindsay**
Secretary: **David N Harwood**
14 Abingdon Gardens, Chilwell,
Nottingham.NG9 5BJ
Tel No: 0115 925 9163
Commercial Management:
Midland Sports Promotions

### FOOTBALL MANAGEMENT TEAM

Manager / Coach: Keith Alexander
Asst Manager: Gary Simpson

### FACT FILE

Re Formed: 1945
Nickname: The Robins
Sponsors: Ron Brooks Ilkeston Toyota
Colours: Red/black/red
Change colours: All purple
Midweek matchday: Tuesday
Reserves' League: Midland Comb

**GROUND**     New Manor Ground, Awsworth Rd, Ilkeston Tel: 115 932 4094

**Directions:** M42 to M1 junc 23A, continue on M1 to junc 26, exit left onto A610 towards Ripley, take 1st exit signed Awsworth and Ilkeston (A6096), follow bypass signed Ilkeston A6096. Turn right after 1/2 mile signed Cotmanhay. Ground 200 yards on left
Capacity: 3,500          Seats: 270          Cover: 1,100          Floodlights: Yes

**Clubhouse:** Open Wed-Fri 7-11pm, Sat-Sun noon-3 & 7-11pm, and Mon or Tue if there is a match. Snacks behind bar. Large tea bar open matchdays 2-5pm (6.30-9pm for night games)
**Club Shop:** Sells wide range of souvenirs & programmes + `Team Talk'.
Contact Manager (0115 9305 622) or club secretary

Programme:
Pages: 32          Price: £1
Editors: Mic Capill, J Shiels, D Payne

**PREVIOUS**     **Leagues:** Midland 1894-1902 25-58 61-71; Notts & Derby Senior 1945-47; CentralAlliance 47-61; Midland Counties 1961-71 73-82; Southern League 1971-73; Northern Co.East 1982-86; Central Midlands 86-90; West Midlands (Regional) 90-94.
**Ground:** Manor Ground, Manor Rd (1945-92)

**CLUB RECORDS**     **Attendance:** 2,504 v Boston United FA Cup 1st Rd 15/11/97
**Win:** 14-2 v Codnor M.W 46-47: 13-0 v Swanwick OB 46-47
**Defeat:** 1-11 v Grantham T. 47-48: 0-10 v VS Rugby 85-86
**Career Goalscorer:** Jackie Ward 141. **Career Appearances:** Terry Swincoe 377
**Season Goalscorer:** Barry Jepson 62, 1952-53
**Transfer fee paid:** £7,500 Justin O'Reilly (Southport 1998)
**Transfer fee received:** £25,000 for Francis Green (Peterborough Utd)

**BEST SEASON**     **FA Cup:** 2nd Rd 1-1, 1-2 v Scunthorpe Utd 97-98          **FA Vase:** 4th Round 88-89 1-2 v Tamworth
**FA Trophy:** 3rd Round 82-83 1-5 v Enfield, 94-95 2-2, 1-2 v Kidderminster H

**HONOURS**     Southern Lge, Midland Div 94-95, (R-up 97-98); West Mids (Regional) Lg 93-94, Lg Cup 93-94, Div 1 91-92, Lg Cup 91-92; Central Mids Lg Cup 87-88; Midland Lg 67-68 (R-up 1898-99); Midland Co Lg 67-68; Central Alliance 51-52 52-53 53-54 54-55 (R-up 47-48 55-56)

*John Knapper, Ilkeston Town, scores from the spot against Gresley Rovers. Photo: Keith Clayton*

# ILKESTON TOWN - MATCH FACTS - 1998-99 SEASON

| No | Date | Venue | Comp | Opponents | Att | Result | Score | Goalscorers |
|----|------|-------|------|-----------|-----|--------|-------|-------------|
| 1 | 22/08 | H | DMP | Weymouth | 644 | D | 1-1 | Ball 21 |
| 2 | 24/08 | A | DMP | Atherstone United | 401 | D | 3-3 | Ball 27, Knapper 32[p] 54[p] |
| 3 | 29/08 | A | DMP | Gloucester City | 703 | D | 1-1 | Knapper 48[p] |
| 4 | 31/08 | H | DMP | Boston United | 828 | L | 1-3 | Wright 74 |
| 5 | 05/09 | A | DMP | Hastings Town | 485 | L | 0-3 | |
| 6 | 08/09 | H | DMP | Tamworth | 548 | L | 3-5 | Robinson 28, Thompson 68, Simpson 78 |
| 7 | 12/09 | A | DMP | Gresley Rovers | 720 | W | 3-1 | Robinson 5, Knapper 50[p], Middleton 63 |
| 8 | 15/09 | H | DMP | Atherstone United | 569 | L | 1-2 | Robinson 17 |
| 9 | 19/09 | H | DMP | Salisbury City | 483 | W | 3-0 | Simpson 51, Eshelby 82, Ball 87 |
| 10 | 22/09 | H | DM C P(1) | Wisbech Town | 353 | W | 4-1 | Wright 44, Eshelby 48, Alsop 73, Weaver 74 |
| 11 | 26/09 | A | DMP | Dorchester Town | 539 | W | 1-0 | Robinson 36 |
| 12 | 30/09 | A | DMP | Boston United | 616 | W | 1-0 | Knapper 16[p] |
| 13 | 03/10 | H | FA C Q2 | Moor Green | 521 | W | 2-0 | Robinson 12, Fairclough 44 |
| 14 | 07/10 | A | DM C P(2) | Wisbech Town | 300 | D | 3-3 | Moore 25 63, Alsop 81 |
| 15 | 10/10 | H | DMP | Worcester City | 648 | W | 3-0 | Robinson 2, Knapper 16[p], Ludlum 77 |
| 16 | 17/10 | H | FA C Q3 | King's Lynn | 793 | L | 1-2 | Ball 63 |
| 17 | 24/10 | A | FA T 1 | Blakenall | 258 | L | 0-2 | |
| 18 | 31/10 | A | DMP | Cambridge City | 274 | W | 1-0 | Weaver 45 |
| 19 | 03/11 | A | DMP | Tamworth | 476 | D | 2-2 | Helliwell 19, Ball 20 |
| 20 | 07/11 | H | DMP | Rothwell Town | 610 | W | 3-0 | Ludlum 33, Robinson 44[p] 46 |
| 21 | 10/11 | A | DM C 1(1) | Grantham Town | 354 | L | 0-4 | |
| 22 | 14/11 | H | DMP | Bath City | 748 | D | 0-0 | |
| 23 | 21/11 | H | DMP | King's Lynn | 555 | D | 0-0 | |
| 24 | 28/11 | A | DMP | Salisbury City | 337 | D | 0-0 | |
| 25 | 01/12 | H | DM C 1(2) | Grantham Town | 195 | W | 1-0 | Moore 37 |
| 26 | 05/12 | H | DMP | Cambridge City | 450 | D | 0-0 | |
| 27 | 12/12 | A | DMP | Weymouth | 721 | D | 2-2 | Moore 10, Eshelby 84 |
| 28 | 19/12 | H | DMP | Merthyr Tydfil | 483 | W | 2-0 | Robinson 38, Moore 77 |
| 29 | 26/12 | A | DMP | Grantham Town | 856 | L | 1-3 | Knapper 7[p] |
| 30 | 28/12 | H | DMP | Burton Albion | 1155 | L | 1-2 | Ball 66 |
| 31 | 03/01 | A | DMP | Bath City | 735 | W | 2-1 | Clifford 15, Weaver 78 |
| 32 | 09/01 | H | DMP | Nuneaton Borough | 1338 | L | 0-1 | |
| 33 | 23/01 | H | DMP | Gresley Rovers | 678 | W | 4-1 | Knapper 9[p], Moore 18, O'Reilly 59, Allsop 87 |
| 34 | 30/01 | A | DMP | Crawley Town | 907 | L | 1-2 | Moore 64 |
| 35 | 02/02 | A | DSC 3 | Buxton | 96 | W | 2-1 | Fearon 33, O'Reilly 82 |
| 36 | 06/02 | A | DMP | Bromsgrove Rovers | 524 | W | 2-0 | Moore 29, O'Reilly 41 |
| 37 | 13/02 | H | DMP | Dorchester Town | 523 | W | 5-2 | Helliwell 18, O'Reilly 27 82, Ludlum 44, Alsop 88 |
| 38 | 20/02 | A | DMP | Worcester City | 1007 | L | 0-2 | |
| 39 | 23/02 | H | DSC QF | Alfreton Town | 270 | W | 3-1 | Eshelby 2, Clifford 51, Robinson 86 |
| 40 | 27/02 | H | DMP | Crawley Town | 632 | W | 3-1 | Knapper 58[p], Moore 61, O'Reilly 75 |
| 41 | 06/03 | A | DMP | Merthyr Tydfil | 446 | W | 2-1 | Wright 28, Helliwell 64 |
| 42 | 13/03 | H | DMP | Bromsgrove Rovers | 568 | W | 2-1 | O'Reilly 38, Knapper 53 |
| 43 | 20/03 | H | DMP | Halesowen Town | 588 | D | 2-2 | O'Reilly 40, Alsop 85 |
| 44 | 27/03 | A | DMP | Nuneaton Borough | 1638 | W | 3-1 | Moore 11, O'Reilly 20, Allsop 82 |
| 45 | 30/03 | H | DSC SF | Gresley Rovers | 489 | W | 1-0 | Ludlum 58 |
| 46 | 03/04 | H | DMP | Grantham Town | 667 | D | 1-1 | Fearon 35 |
| 47 | 05/04 | A | DMP | Burton Albion | 1088 | W | 2-1 | Knapper 37, Moore 47 |
| 48 | 10/04 | H | DMP | Hastings Town | 446 | D | 3-3 | Allsop 17, Helliwell 61, Moore 68 |
| 49 | 13/04 | A | DMP | Halesowen Town | 454 | L | 1-4 | Moore 22 |
| 50 | 17/04 | A | DMP | Rothwell Town | 323 | L | 1-3 | Wright 52 |
| 51 | 24/04 | H | DMP | Gloucester City | 639 | W | 4-3 | Middleton 47, Eshelby 54 78, Weaver 60 |
| 52 | 01/05 | A | DMP | King's Lynn | 888 | D | 1-1 | O'Reilly 12 |

## PLAYING SQUAD 1999-2000:

GOALKEEPERS: James Baker (Heanor Town), Damian Beattie (Notts County), Scott Finders
DEFENDERS: Charlie Bishop (Northampton Town), Wayne Fairclough (Grantham Town), Dean Fearon, Mark McKevitt (Mansfield Town), Simon Weaver, James Whitehead, Dale Wright
MIDFIELDERS: Tony Dennis (Gainsborough Trinity), Paul Raynor (Kettering Town), Ian Robinson, Tony Simpson (Gresley Rovers)
FORWARDS: Kevin Allsop, Martin Chauntrey (Mansfield Town), Ian Helliwell (Burnley), Chris Hurst (Emley), Wayne Manners (Dunkirk), Justin O'Reilly (Southport), George Vitali, Devon White (Shrewsbury Town)

# KING'S LYNN

## CLUB OFFICIALS

Chairman: **John Scales**
President: **Jim Chandler**

Secretary: **Martin Davis**
158 Lynn Road, Wisbech,
Cambs PE13 3EB
Tel: 01945 583567 (H & B)

## FOOTBALL MANAGEMENT TEAM

Manager:Gary Mills
Asst Man: Darren Gee
Physio: Dave Edgeley

### FACT FILE

Formed: 1879
Nickname: The Linnets
Sponsors: Eastern Group
Colours: Royal Blue with gold trim/Blue/Blue
& Gold hoops
Change colours: All red
Midweek home matchday: Tuesday
Reserves League: U.C.L. Res Div 1
98-99 - Captain: Colin Hoyle
P.o.Y.: Dave Puttnam
Top scorer: Mark Turner (12)

## GROUND

The Walks Stadium, Tennyson Road, King's Lynn PE30 5PB
Tel: 01553 760060

**Directions:** At mini r-about arriving from A10/A47 take Vancouver Avenue. Ground on left after a half mile. Quarter mile from King's Lynn (BR), half mile from bus station

Capacity: 8,200        Cover: 5,000        Seats: 1,200        Floodlights: Yes

**Clubhouse:** Normal licensing hours, with extension on matchdays
**Club Shop:** Sells metal badges and other merchandise

Official Sponsors 1998/99
K.O. 7.45pm
OFFICIAL MATCH PROGRAMME 1998/99
De Martens Premier Division
KING'S LYNN FOOTBALL CLUB
The Walks Stadium, Tennyson Road, King's Lynn, Norfolk PE30 5PB
£1.50

Pages: 24  Price: £1.20
Editor: Secretary
Local Press: Lynn News & Advertiser,
Eastern Daily Press
Local Radio: KLFM

**PREVIOUS**     **Leagues:** Norfolk & Suffolk; Eastern Co.s 35-39 48-54; UCL 46-48; Midland Co.s54-58; NPL 80-83
**Name:** Lynn Town  Ground: None

**CLUB RECORDS**  **Attendance:** 12,937 v Exeter, FA Cup 1st Rd 50-51
**Win:** 17-0 v Beccles 29/30        **Defeat:** 0-11 v Aston Villa FA Cup 1905/6
**Career Appearances:** Mick Wright 1,152 (British Record)
**Career Goalscorer:** Malcolm Lindsay 321
**Transfer Fee Paid:** Shaun Keeble Wisbech 98-99        **Transfer Fee Received:** Mark Paul , Southampton.98-99

**BEST SEASON**   **FA Cup:** 3rd Rd 61-62 (0-4 at Everton). Competition Proper on 14 occasions; 05-06 37-38 49-50 51-52 58-63 64-65 68-69
71-72 73-74 84-85. Rd 2 97-98        League clubs defeated: Aldershot 59-60, Coventry 61-62, Halifax 68-69
**FA Trophy:** 2nd Rd 78-79        **FA Vase:** 5th Rd 94-95 (0-2 at Diss Town        **FA Amateur Cup:** R-up 1900-01

**HONOURS**       FA Amateur Cup R-up 1900-01, Southern Lg R-up 84-85 (Div 1 R-up 63-64), NPLPresidents Cup 82-83, Eastern Co's Lg 53-54
(R-up 49-50 52-53 (Lg Cup 53-54),Norfolk & Suffolk Lg(8)(R-up(6)), E Anglian Lg R-up(2), Norfolk Snr Cup(19)(R-up(20),
Norfolk Invitation Cup 94-95, Norfolk Premier Cup 68-69(jt) 73-74, EastAnglian Cup(4)(R-up(3), Eastern Prof Floodlit Lg 68-69,
Southern Lg Midland R-up 95-96

Players progressing: N Rowe (Derby 1949), B Taylor & P Ward (Bradford P. A. 54& 55), T Reynolds (Darlington 54), G Reed (Sunderland 55), P
McCall (Bristol C55), J Neal (Swindon 57), T Dryburgh (Oldham 57), J Hunter (Barrow 59), JStevens (Swindon), G Catleugh (Watford), George
Walters (Chesterfield 64), P McNamee (Notts County 1966), W Biggins (Burnley), Jackie Gallagher (Peterborough 80), Andy Higgins (Rochdale 83),
Neil Horwood (Grimsby 86),Darren Rolph (Barnsley 87), Mark Howard (Stockport 88), Andy Hunt, MalcolmLindsay

Back Row: M Turner, C
Clark, P Fitzpatrick, D
Roberts, G Fuff, M
Nuttell, C Hoyle (c)
Middle Row: R Simper
(kit), D Puttnam, D
Robinson, P Ramsey, C
Martini, J Palmer, S
McGinty, L Cotteril, D
Edgeley (Physio)
Front Row: S Keeble, D
Gee, G Mills (P/Man), T
Spearing (P/Coach), J
Goss
Photo: Lynn News/Citizen
Newspapers

498

# KING'S LYNN - MATCH FACTS - 1998-99 SEASON

| No | Date | Venue | Comp | Opponents | Att | Result | Score | Goalscorers |
|----|------|-------|------|-----------|-----|--------|-------|-------------|
| | 29/07 | A | KC | **Wisbech Town** | 590 | L | 0-4 | |
| | 22/08 | A | DMP | Bath City | 955 | L | 0-2 | |
| | 25/08 | H | DMP | Nuneaton Borough | 1039 | L | 2-4 | Cotterill 20 37 |
| | 29/08 | H | DMP | Halesowen Town | 732 | D | 1-1 | Hilton 10 |
| | 31/08 | A | DMP | Cambridge City | 539 | L | 1-2 | Stringfellow 57 |
| | 05/09 | H | DMP | Gloucester City | 561 | W | 2-0 | Gibson 65, Sterling 89 |
| | 08/09 | A | DMP | Bromsgrove Rovers | 591 | L | 0-1 | |
| | 12/09 | H | DMP | Merthyr Tydfil | 664 | W | 3-0 | Nuttell 34, Hardy 37, Delicata 87 |
| | 15/09 | A | DMP | Nuneaton Borough | 1564 | L | 0-4 | |
| 0 | 19/09 | H | DMP | Weymouth | 598 | L | 1-2 | Nuttell 41[p] |
| 1 | 22/09 | H | DMP | Cambridge City | 541 | L | 0-3 | |
| 2 | 26/09 | A | DMP | Worcester City | 682 | L | 2-3 | Nuttell 21, Roberts 45 |
| 3 | 03/10 | A | FA C Q2 | **Bromsgrove Rovers** | 807 | D | 1-1 | **Cotterill 18** |
| 4 | 06/10 | H | FA C Q2 r | **Bromsgrove Rovers** | 715 | W | 2-1 | **Nuttell 16 100** |
| 5 | 10/10 | A | DMP | Crawley Town | 848 | L | 1-3 | Fuff 50 |
| 6 | 17/10 | A | FA C Q3 | **Ilkeston Town** | 793 | W | 2-1 | **Mitchell 24, Bishop 74[og]** |
| 7 | 31/10 | H | FA C Q4 | **West Auckland Town** | 1314 | L | 0-1 | |
| 8 | 02/11 | A | FA T 1 | **Weymouth** | 497 | L | 0-1 | |
| 9 | 07/11 | A | DMP | Halesowen Town | 601 | W | 1-0 | Wilson 26 |
| 0 | 11/11 | A | DM C 1(1) | **Boston United** | 507 | L | 0-5 | |
| 1 | 14/11 | A | DMP | Weymouth | 885 | L | 0-1 | |
| 2 | 21/11 | A | DMP | Ilkeston Town | 555 | D | 0-0 | |
| 3 | 28/11 | H | DMP | Dorchester Town | 485 | D | 1-1 | Wilson 43 |
| 4 | 05/12 | A | DMP | Gresley Rovers | 413 | L | 1-2 | Puttnam 26 |
| 5 | 12/12 | H | DMP | Tamworth | 486 | W | 4-2 | Turner 50, Puttnam 75, Robinson 85, Palmer 90 |
| 6 | 15/12 | H | DM C 1(2) | **Boston United** | 221 | W | 2-1 | **Gowshall 55[og], Cotterill 65** |
| 7 | 19/12 | A | DMP | Dorchester Town | 503 | L | 1-2 | Wilson 59 |
| 8 | 26/12 | H | DMP | Boston United | 915 | L | 1-2 | Turner 71 |
| 9 | 03/01 | H | DMP | Gresley Rovers | 475 | W | 4-0 | Allen 7, Turner 21 40 75 |
| 0 | 16/01 | A | DMP | Salisbury City | 449 | D | 2-2 | Turner 26, Robinson 51 |
| 1 | 23/01 | A | DMP | Burton Albion | 703 | W | 1-0 | Puttnam 90 |
| 2 | 30/01 | H | DMP | Hastings Town | 659 | D | 0-0 | |
| 3 | 06/02 | A | DMP | Tamworth | 585 | W | 2-0 | Wilson 77, Puttnam 88 |
| 4 | 13/02 | H | DMP | Worcester City | 663 | W | 2-0 | Turner 35 45 |
| 5 | 20/02 | H | DMP | Grantham Town | 793 | D | 1-1 | Puttnam 31 |
| 6 | 23/02 | A | DMP | Rothwell Town | 255 | W | 2-0 | Wilson 38, McGinty 85 |
| 7 | 27/02 | A | DMP | Gloucester City | 610 | L | 1-2 | Wilson 8[p] |
| 8 | 06/03 | H | DMP | Salisbury City | 652 | D | 3-3 | Fuff 20, Mills 35, Wilson 89 |
| 9 | 13/03 | A | DMP | Atherstone United | 311 | W | 2-1 | Robinson 5, Wilson 90[p] |
| 0 | 16/03 | H | DMP | Bromsgrove Rovers | 621 | D | 0-0 | |
| 1 | 20/03 | A | DMP | Hastings Town | 308 | L | 0-1 | |
| 2 | 23/03 | H | DMP | Bath City | 650 | W | 1-0 | Puttnam 31 |
| 3 | 27/03 | H | DMP | Burton Albion | 750 | W | 2-0 | Turner 33, Puttnam 63 |
| 4 | 03/04 | A | DMP | Boston United | 1436 | W | 1-0 | Turner 79 |
| 5 | 05/04 | H | DMP | Rothwell Town | 867 | W | 2-0 | Turner 52, Keeble 83 |
| 6 | 10/04 | A | DMP | Merthyr Tydfil | 555 | W | 1-0 | Robinson 84 |
| 7 | 13/04 | H | DMP | Atherstone United | 574 | D | 0-0 | |
| 8 | 17/04 | H | DMP | Crawley Town | 672 | W | 2-0 | Nuttell 70, McGinty 88 |
| 9 | 24/04 | A | DMP | Grantham Town | 667 | W | 1-0 | Turner 68 |
| 0 | 01/05 | H | DMP | Ilkeston Town | 888 | D | 1-1 | Turner 32 |

## PLAYING SQUAD 1999-2000:

**GOALKEEPERS:** Chuck Moussaddik (Connecticut Wolves), Duncan Roberts (Mansfield Town)

**DEFENDERS:** Craig Clark (Stamford), Paul Fitzpatrick (Gresley Rovers), Glenn Fuff (Rushden & Diamonds), Gary Mills (Gresley Rovers), Steven Nottingham (Stamford), Paul Ramsey (Grantham Town), Tony Spearing (Peterborough United)

**MIDFIELDERS:** Shaun Frowhawk, Jeremy Goss (ex-Norwich City), Mark Harbottle (Hinckley United), Tony Marsden (Gresley Rovers), Stephen McGinty (Blakenall), Dave Robinson (Grantham Town), Mark Turner (Telford United)

**FORWARDS:** Shaun Keeble (Wisbech Town), John Palmer (Boots Athletic), Dave Puttnam (Gresley Rovers), Worrell Sterling (Spalding United), Lee Wilson (Solihull Borough)

# MARGATE

## CLUB OFFICIALS
Chairman: **Steve Wrightson**
President: **Gordon Wallace**
Vice Chairman: **Richard Piper**
Press Officer: Chairman
Secretary: **K E Tomlinson**
65 Nash Road, Margate CT9 4BT
Tel: 01843 291040
Commercial Manager: **Michael Knight**

### FOOTBALL MANAGEMENT TEAM
Manager: Chris Kinnear
As.Manager: Kevin Raine
Physio: John Griffin

## FACT FILE
Formed: 1896
Nickname: The Gate
Sponsors: Link Music Limited
Newsline: 0891 800 665
Colours: Blue & white/blue & white
Change colours: Maroon/white
Midweek matchday: Tuesday
Reserves' League: Kent Lg. Div 2

98-99 Captain; Tony Dixon
P.o.Y.: Billy Edwards
Top Scorer: Paul Sykes

**GROUND**          Hartsdown Park, Hartsdown Road, Margate CT9 5QZ Tel: 01843 221769

**Directions:**      A28 into Margate, turn right opposite Dog & Duck P.H. into Hartsdown Road,
proceed over crossroads and ground is on left. Ten mins walk from Margate (BR)

Capacity: 6,000          Cover: 3 sides      Seats: 400          Floodlights: Yes
**Clubhouse:** Flexible hours, private functions, matchday facilities.
Steward: Pam & Mark Weatherly
**Club Shop:** Contact Paul Turner 01843 293056

Pages: 44 Price: 80p
Editor: Steve Ball
Local Press: Isle of Thanet Gazette, Thanet
Times, Thanet Extra
Local Radio: Radio Kent, Invicta Radio

**PREVIOUS**          **Leagues:** Kent 11-23 24-28 29-33 37-38 46-59; Southern 33-37
**Grounds:** Margate College; Dreamland, Northdown Rd; Garlinge          **Name:** Thanet Utd 1981-89

**CLUB RECORDS** **Attendance:** 14,500 v Spurs, FA Cup 3rd Rd 73
**Win:** 8-0 v Tunbridge Wells (H) 66-67 & v Chatham Town (H) 87-88   **Career Goalscorer:** Dennis Randall 66 (season 66-67)
**Defeat:** 11-0 v AFC Bournemouth (A), FAC 1st Rd. 20.11.71     **CareerAppearances:** Bob Harrop
**Transfer fee paid:** £5,000 for Steve Cuggy (Dover Ath93)
**Transfer fee received:** Undisclosed for Martin Buglione (St Johnstone 92-93)

**BEST SEASON** **FA Trophy:** Third Round replay 78-79.          **FA Cup:** 3rd Rd 72-73 (0-6 to Spurs), 36-37 (1-3 at Blackpool)
League clubs defeated: Gillingham 29-30, Q. P.R., Crystal Palace 35-36, Bournemouth & Boscombe Ath. 61-62, Swansea 72-73

**HONOURS**          Southern Lg 35-36 (Lg Cp 67-68 (R-up 61-62 74-75), Div 1 62-63 (R-up 66-67), Div 1 Sth 77-78, East Div R-up 33-34,
Merit Cup 66-67 77-78, Midweek Sect. 36-37),
Kent Lg (4), (R-up 5, Div 2 4, Lg Cp 4), Kent Snr Cup (4), Kent Snr Shield(8), Kent F'lit Cp 62-63 66-67 75-76

Players progressing:          Over 40 including J Yeomanson (West Ham 47), D Bing/GWright (West Ham 51), T Bing (Spurs 56),
S Foster (C Palace 61), J Fraser(Watford 62), R Walker (Bournemouth 65), K Bracewell (Bury 66),
T Jenkins/RFlannigan (Reading 69-70), M Blyth (Millwall 78), M Buglione (St Johnstone 92)

*Margate's Phil*
*Collins (Blue) gets in*
*a shot before David*
*Henham of St*
*Leonards can get in*
*a challenge.*
*Photo: Alan Coomes*

# MARGATE - MATCH FACTS - 1998-99 SEASON

| No | Date | Venue | Comp | Opponents | Att | Result | Score | Goalscorers |
|----|------|-------|------|-----------|-----|--------|-------|-------------|
| 1 | 09/08 | A | DML S | **Forest Green Rovers** | 375 | L | 1-1 | O'Connell 89 (L 0-2 pens) |
| 2 | 22/08 | H | DM S | Andover | 294 | W | 4-1 | Planck 76 85 88, Takalobighashi 83 |
| 3 | 25/08 | A | DM S | Fisher Athletic | 156 | W | 1-0 | Planck 55 |
| 4 | 29/08 | A | DM S | Raunds Town | 88 | D | 2-2 | Sykes 31, Dixon 45 |
| 5 | 31/08 | H | DM S | Ashford Town | 545 | D | 1-1 | Spiller 67 |
| 6 | 05/09 | A | FA C P | **Ashford Town** | 515 | D | 1-1 | Dixon 75 |
| 7 | 08/09 | H | FA C P r | **Ashford Town** | 486 | L | 1-2 | **Takalobighashi 107** |
| 8 | 12/09 | H | DM S | Corby Town | 95 | L | 1-3 | Sykes 42 |
| 9 | 15/09 | H | DM S | Fisher Athletic | 166 | W | 2-1 | Dixon 52, Planck 66 |
| 10 | 26/09 | A | DM S | Tonbridge Angels | 409 | W | 3-0 | Munday 15, Spiller 44, Sykes 55 |
| 11 | 29/09 | A | DM S | Ashford Town | 582 | W | 2-1 | Planck 9, Munday 90 |
| 12 | 03/10 | H | DM S | Baldock Town | 275 | W | 3-0 | Spiller 1 40, Sykes 2 |
| 13 | 10/10 | H | DM S | Witney Town | 265 | D | 0-0 | |
| 14 | 13/10 | H | DM S | Erith & Belvedere | 220 | D | 1-1 | Dixon 61 |
| 15 | 17/10 | A | DM S | Cirencester Town | 90 | W | 2-0 | Sykes 44, Collins 57 |
| 16 | 24/10 | H | DM S | Raunds Town | 194 | L | 0-2 | |
| 17 | 07/11 | H | DM S | Yate Town | 308 | W | 3-0 | O'Connell 60, Martin 70, Sykes 81 |
| 18 | 10/11 | H | DM C 1(1) | **Folkestone Invicta** | 308 | D | 3-3 | Spiller 47, Dixon 53, Sykes 73 |
| 19 | 14/11 | A | DM S | Chelmsford City | 438 | W | 3-2 | Spiller 3, Sykes 55 88 |
| 20 | 21/11 | H | FA T 2 | **Havant & Waterlooville** | 409 | L | 1-3 | **Sykes 65** |
| 21 | 28/11 | H | DM S | Corby Town | 266 | W | 6-0 | Dixon 6, Munday 8 17, Pilkington 53, Collins 70 80 |
| 22 | 01/12 | A | DM C 1(2) | **Folkestone Invicta** | 368 | L | 0-2 | |
| 23 | 05/12 | A | DM S | Andover | 74 | W | 3-1 | Sykes 17, Spiller 29 85 |
| 24 | 12/12 | H | DM S | Bashley | 318 | W | 5-0 | Sykes 30 44 74, Collins 85, Munday 89 |
| 25 | 19/12 | A | DM S | St Leonards | 352 | W | 6-1 | Pilkington 27 80, Sykes 44 65, Munday 85, Collins 87 |
| 26 | 26/12 | H | DM S | Sittingbourne | 602 | W | 2-1 | Sykes 45 90[p] |
| 27 | 01/01 | A | DM S | Dartford | 429 | D | 0-0 | |
| 28 | 09/01 | H | DM S | Tonbridge Angels | 337 | W | 2-0 | Sykes 33 44 |
| 29 | 23/01 | H | DM S | Dartford | 433 | D | 2-2 | Lamb 8, Munday 16 |
| 30 | 26/01 | H | KSC QF | **Ashford Town** | 175 | W | 2-1 | **Sykes 37, Collins 93** |
| 31 | 30/01 | H | DM S | Cirencester Town | 365 | W | 2-0 | Dixon 3, Spiller 26 |
| 32 | 06/02 | A | DM S | Yate Town | 97 | W | 1-0 | Saunders 15 |
| 33 | 13/02 | H | DM S | Chelmsford City | 514 | D | 2-2 | Saunders 20, Sykes 25 |
| 34 | 20/02 | A | DM S | Havant & Waterlooville | 701 | L | 0-1 | |
| 35 | 27/02 | H | DM S | Brackley Town | 407 | W | 2-0 | Saunders 44, Spiller 68 |
| 36 | 06/03 | H | DM S | Fleet Town | 68 | W | 2-1 | Pilkington 1, Planck 90 |
| 37 | 13/03 | A | DM S | Bashley | 242 | L | 1-2 | Munday 88 |
| 38 | 20/03 | A | DM S | Erith & Belvedere | 195 | W | 2-0 | Collins 12, Saunders 28 |
| 39 | 23/03 | H | KSC SF | **Welling United** | 273 | L | 2-3 | **Spiller 55, O'Connell 89** |
| 40 | 27/03 | H | DM S | St Leonards | 336 | W | 2-1 | Collins 54, Dixon 65 |
| 41 | 30/03 | H | DM S | Newport IOW | 261 | W | 1-0 | Sykes 86 |
| 42 | 03/04 | A | DM S | Sittingbourne | 519 | W | 4-0 | Saunders 35, Spiller 39, Martin 51[p], Planck 84 |
| 43 | 05/04 | H | DM S | Folkestone Invicta | 915 | W | 1-0 | Dixon 12 |
| 44 | 10/04 | H | DM S | Havant & Waterlooville | 810 | W | 2-0 | Martin 6, Saunders 70 |
| 45 | 13/04 | H | DM S | Fleet Town | 360 | L | 1-2 | Planck 20 |
| 46 | 17/04 | A | DM S | Witney Town | 122 | D | 1-1 | Munday 64 |
| 47 | 20/04 | A | DM S | Baldock Town | 194 | W | 1-0 | Spiller 2 |
| 48 | 24/04 | H | DM S | Newport IoW | 730 | L | 1-2 | Dixon 70 |
| 49 | 27/04 | A | DM S | Folkestone Invicta | 1257 | L | 0-2 | |
| 50 | 01/05 | A | DM S | Brackley Town | 224 | W | 4-0 | Munday 8, Planck 24, Saunders 70, Johnson 86[og] |

## PLAYING SQUAD 1999-2000:

GOALKEEPERS: Kevin Readings (Dover Athletic), Lee Turner (Gravesend & Northfleet)
DEFENDERS: Tony Dixon (Dover Athletic), Bill Edwards (Fisher Athletic), Elliott Martin, Jason Moore (Dover Athletic/Deal Town), Iain O'Connell (Dover Athletic), Malcolm Pointer, Graham Porter (Ashford Town)
MIDFIELDERS: Gary Blackford (Dagenham & Redbridge), Paul Lamb (Gravesend & Northfleet), Mark Munday (Gravesend & Northfleet), Paul O'Brien (Ashford Town), Jay Saunders (Gravesend & Northfleet), Lee Williams (Gillingham)
FORWARDS: Phil Collins (Dartford), Tommy Planck (Sittingbourne), Paul Sykes (Welling United), Mohammad Takalogighashi, John Utterson

# MERTHYR TYDFIL

### CLUB OFFICIALS
Joint Presidents:
**The Archbishop of Cardiff**,
His Grace John Aloysious Ward,
**The Lord Bishop of Llandaff**,
The Right Rev. Roy Davies
Chairman: **Lyn Mitchell**
Managing Director: **Owen Edwards**
Football Se/Press Off. **Anthony Hughes**
Commercial Manager: **Kelly Jenkins**

### FOOTBALL MANAGEMENT TEAM

Manager: **Roger Gibbins**
As.Man/ Physio: **Terry Moore**

### FACT FILE
Formed: 19445
Nickname: The Martyrs
Sponsors :Hoover PLC
Colours: White & black/black/black
Change colours: All amber
Midweek home matchday: Tuesday
Reserves' League: None

98-99 - Top scorer: Cohen Griffiths
Captain: Gareth Abrahams
P.o.Y.: Adrian Needs

Pages: 32          Price: £1.00
Editor: Anthony Hughes
Tel: 01685 359921
Local Press:
Local Radio:

**GROUND**          Penndarren Park, Merthyr Tydfil, Mid Glamorgan  Tel: 01685 384102
**Directions:** (South) A470 Express Way to Merthyr through Town Centre to Pontmorlais (traffic lights) turn left then first right, first right at Catholic Church and right again into Park Terrace to ground. (North) Heads of theValley road to Town Centre, to Pontmorlais (traffic lights) turn right, then as above
Capacity: 10,000          Seats: 1,500          Cover: 5,000          Floodlights: Yes
**Clubhouse:** Open Mon. to Sun. 6.30 - 11.00pm. 2 club cafes open on matchdays for hot food
**Club Shop:**          Sells replica kits, club souvenirs & programmes.
          Contact Mel Jenkins01443 692336

**PREVIOUS**          **Leagues:** Southern League  46 -89 (Southern League 46-59, 1st Division 59-61, 64-71, !st Div. North 72-79, Premier Div. 61-64, 71-72, 88-89, Midland Div. 79-88), G M Conference 89-95.
          **Names:** None                    **Grounds:** None

**CLUB RECORDS**  **Attendance:** 21,000 v Reading FA Cup 2nd Rnd 1949/50
          **Win:** 11-0                    **Defeat:** 9-2
          **Transfer fee paid:** £10,000 to Cardiff City for Robbie James 1992
          **Transfer fee received:** £12,000 for Ray Pratt from Exeter City 1981

**BEST SEASON**  **Welsh FA Cup:** Winners 48-49 50-51 86-87
          **FA Trophy:** 3rd Rd v Northwich Vic 95-96          **FA Cup:** 2nd Round on six occasions. League clubs defeated: Bristol Rovers

**HONOURS**          Welsh FA Cup 48-49, 50-51, 86-87; Southern League 47-48, 49-50, 50-51, 51-52, 53-54; Southern League (Midland) 87-88; Southern League (Premier) 88-89;Southern League Cup 47-48, 50-51

Players Progressing : Syd Howarth (Aston Villa), Cyril Beech, Gilbert Beech,Bill Hullet, Ken Tucker (Cardiff City), Nick Deacy (Hereford United), GordonDavies (Fulham), Ray Pratt (Exeter City), Peter Jones, Paul Giles (Newport County)

*Back Row (L-R): Colin Loss, Tony Rees (now Ebbw Vale), Dean Clarke, Ian French, Neil O'Brien, Gary Wager, Shaun Chapple, David Barnhouse, Anthony Rivett, Chris Summers, Colin Addison. Front: Anthony Jenkins, Ian Mitchell, Cohen Griffiths, Gareth Abraham, Roger Gibbins, Roy Jordan, Terry Green, Darren Poretta*

## MERTHYR TYDFIL - MATCH FACTS - 1998-99 SEASON

| No | Date | Venue | Comp | Opponents | Att | Result | Score | Goalscorers |
|---|---|---|---|---|---|---|---|---|
| 1 | 05/06 | A | SNC SF | **Hamrun Spartans** | n/k | W | 2-0 | |
| 2 | 06/06 | A | SNC F | **Sliema Wanderers** | n/k | D | 1-1 | Evans 85 (3-5 pens) |
| 3 | 22/08 | H | DMP | Atherstone United | 500 | W | 2-0 | Lima 67, Griffiths 80 |
| 4 | 25/08 | A | DMP | Tamworth | 587 | L | 2-4 | Evans 17, Griffith 79 |
| 5 | 29/08 | A | DMP | Burton Albion | 645 | W | 1-0 | Shepherd 84 |
| 6 | 31/08 | H | DMP | Gresley Rovers | 650 | L | 1-2 | Griffith 90 |
| 7 | 05/09 | A | DMP | Grantham Town | 688 | L | 3-5 | Abraham 11 56, Williams 43 |
| 8 | 08/09 | H | DMP | Worcester City | 496 | L | 0-1 | |
| 9 | 12/09 | A | DMP | King's Lynn | 664 | L | 0-3 | |
| 10 | 15/09 | H | DMP | Tamworth | 370 | W | 6-0 | Shepherd 20 48, Chapple 23[p] 37, Griffith 38, Lima 69 |
| 11 | 19/09 | A | DMP | Boston United | 737 | W | 3-0 | Phillips 26, Chapple 63, Lima 88 |
| 12 | 22/09 | A | DMP | Gresley Rovers | 505 | D | 0-0 | |
| 13 | 26/09 | H | DMP | Hastings Town | 477 | W | 1-0 | Harris 77 |
| 14 | 03/10 | H | FA C Q2 | **Weymouth** | 507 | L | 0-2 | |
| 15 | 05/10 | A | FAW P A | **Cardiff City** | 1161 | D | 2-2 | **Chiverton 6, Griffith 72** |
| 16 | 10/10 | H | DMP | Bromsgrove Rovers | 484 | W | 2-0 | Griffith 8, Chapple 53 |
| 17 | 13/10 | H | FAW P A | **Bangor City** | 378 | W | 2-1 | **Chiverton 60, Chapple 85** |
| 18 | 17/10 | H | DMP | Cambridge City | 539 | D | 3-3 | Griffith 44 80, Chapple 65 |
| 19 | 24/10 | A | DMP | Atherstone United | 216 | L | 1-2 | Griffith 22 |
| 20 | 07/11 | H | DMP | Crawley Town | 540 | W | 3-1 | Shepherd 25 56, Griffith 34 |
| 21 | 10/11 | H | DM C 1(1) | **Bath City** | 225 | L | 2-3 | **Lima 4, Ramasut 25** |
| 22 | 14/11 | A | DMP | Halesowen Town | 685 | L | 0-2 | |
| 23 | 17/11 | H | FAW P A | **Cardiff City** | 945 | D | 0-0 | |
| 24 | 21/11 | H | FA T 2 | **Basingstoke Town** | 481 | L | 0-2 | |
| 25 | 24/11 | A | DM C 1(2) | **Bath City** | 398 | L | 3-4 | **Griffith 43 87, Porretta 74** |
| 26 | 28/11 | H | DMP | Rothwell Town | 384 | W | 4-1 | Shepherd 43 77, Chapple 44[p], Griffith 52 |
| 27 | 01/12 | A | FAW P A | **Bangor City** | 150 | D | 0-0 | |
| 28 | 05/12 | H | DMP | Bath City | 775 | L | 0-3 | |
| 29 | 08/12 | A | FAW P A | **Rhyl** | 151 | D | 1-1 | **Shepherd 69** |
| 30 | 12/12 | H | DMP | Dorchester Town | 447 | D | 1-1 | Martin 27 |
| 31 | 15/12 | H | FAW P A | **Rhyl** | 200 | W | 2-1 | **Griffith 6, Curtis 8[og]** |
| 32 | 19/12 | A | DMP | Ilkeston Town | 483 | L | 0-2 | |
| 33 | 28/12 | H | DMP | Weymouth | 426 | D | 1-1 | Martin 37 |
| 34 | 01/01 | H | DMP | Bath City | 506 | D | 0-0 | |
| 35 | 03/01 | A | DMP | Nuneaton Borough | 1228 | L | 1-6 | |
| 36 | 09/01 | H | DMP | Salisbury City | 431 | L | 0-1 | |
| 37 | 23/01 | A | DMP | Bromsgrove Rovers | 515 | W | 1-0 | Griffith 30 |
| 38 | 26/01 | H | DMP | Gloucester City | 343 | L | 0-1 | |
| 39 | 06/02 | H | DMP | Halesowen Town | 343 | W | 1-0 | Griffith 88 |
| 40 | 13/02 | A | DMP | Salisbury City | 763 | L | 0-1 | |
| 41 | 15/02 | A | DMP | Worcester City | 812 | L | 1-6 | Richards 42 |
| 42 | 20/02 | A | DMP | Rothwell Town | 228 | L | 0-4 | |
| 43 | 27/02 | H | DMP | Nuneaton Borough | 582 | W | 2-1 | Evans 17, Shepherd 86 |
| 44 | 06/03 | H | DMP | Ilkeston Town | 446 | L | 1-2 | Griffith 2 |
| 45 | 09/03 | A | DMP | Gloucester City | 576 | L | 1-2 | Williams 75 |
| 46 | 13/03 | A | DMP | Dorchester Town | 595 | D | 1-1 | Shepherd 13 |
| 47 | 16/03 | A | FAW P QF | **Barry Town** | n/k | L | 0-1 | |
| 48 | 20/03 | H | DMP | Grantham Town | 521 | W | 1-0 | Abraham 8 |
| 49 | 27/03 | A | DMP | Crawley Town | 443 | W | 2-0 | Richards 55, Shepherd 64 |
| 50 | 03/04 | H | DMP | Burton Albion | 657 | L | 0-2 | |
| 51 | 05/04 | A | DMP | Weymouth | 1042 | D | 0-0 | |
| 52 | 10/04 | H | DMP | King's Lynn | 555 | L | 0-1 | |
| 53 | 17/04 | A | DMP | Cambridge City | 287 | W | 2-1 | Chiverton 8, Williams 55 |
| 54 | 24/04 | H | DMP | Boston United | 602 | D | 2-2 | Richards 7, Abraham 55 |
| 55 | 01/05 | A | DMP | Hastings Town | 462 | W | 2-0 | French 38 90 |

## PLAYING SQUAD 1999-2000:

GOALKEEPERS: Neil Thomas
DEFENDERS: Ian Benbow, Ben Brewer (Blackburn Rovers), Ryan Durham (Hereford United), Roger Gibbins (Weston-super-Mare), Ben Graham, Robert King
MIDFIELDERS: Danny Carter (Barry Town), Paul Giles (Ebbw Vale), Andy Power (Weston-super-Mare), Thomas Ramasut (Cardiff City), Mark Williams (Ebbw Vale)
FORWARDS: Eston Chiverton (Ebbw Vale), Cohen Griffith (Ebbw Vale), Anthony Jenkins (Merthyr Tydfil), Ian Mitchell (Cwmbran Town), Gary Shepherd (Ton Pentre)

# NEWPORT COUNTY A.F.C.

## CLUB OFFICIALS

Chairman: **John Williams**
President: **Brian Toms** MBE

Secretary: **Mike Everett**
43 Downing Street, Newport. NP9 0JL
Tel: 01633 669572
Community Director: **Martin Greenham**
Tel: 01633 663110
Football in the Community Off: **Glyn Jones**

### FOOTBALL MANAGEMENT TEAM
Manager: Tim Harris
Asst Manager: Chris Hyde
Physio: Tony Gilbert
Trainer: David Williams

**FACT FILE**
Formed: 1989
Nickname: The Exiles
Sponsors: Acorn Recruitment
Colours: Amber shirts and black shorts
Change colours:All white
Midweek matchday: Wednesday
Youth League: South West Counties Youth

98-99 Captain: Grantley Dicks
Top scorer: Karl Bayliss (31)
P.o.Y.: Bradley Thomas
Players P.o.Y.: Dean Clarke

Pages: 42      Price: £1.20
Editor: Ray Taylor (01443 237545)
Local Press: South Wales Argus, South Wales Echo
Local Radio: Red Dragon

**Club Headquarters:** The King, 76 Somerton Road, Newport. NP9 0JX
Fax: 01633 271771 Tel: 01633 662262

**GROUND** Newport Stadium, Spytty Park, Langland Way, Newport, Gwent.
FAX 01633 669572   Tel: 01633 671800

**Directions:** From Severn Bridge on M4 take 1st exit signed Newport (jct 24), 1st left at r'bout follow signs for industrial area, left at r'bout after 2 1/2miles, over 2 r'bouts, next left for ground. Ample free parking available at ground
Capacity: 3,300          Cover: 1,236      Seats: 1,236      Floodlights: Yes
**Clubhouse:** Small bar at ground with hot and cold scacks also available.
**Club Shop:** Open matchdays, sells a wide selection of souvenirs & programmes

**PREVIOUS**  **Leagues:** Hellenic 89-90  **Grounds:** London Road, Moreton-in-Marsh 89-90; Somerton Park, Newport 90-92; Gloucester City FC 92-94 (exile period due to dispute with FAW re League of Wales)
**Names:** Newport AFC were formed after the demise of Newport County in1988-89, name change 1999.

**CLUB RECORDS  Attendance:** 2,475 v Redditch United, Beazer (Midland) 24.8.94
**Win:** 9-0 v Pontllottyn Blast Furnace (A), Welsh Cup First Round 1/9/90
**Defeat:** 1-6 v Stafford Rangers (A) BHL 6/1/96
**Career Goalscorer:** Chris Lilygreen 93    **Career Appearances:** Mark Price 275 (222 Lg + 53 cup)
**Transfer fee paid:** £3,700 for Mark Williams from Merthyr Tydfil **Transfer fee received:** £1,000 from RedditchU for Paul Burton
**BEST SEASON  FA Cup:** 4th Qualifying Rd 92-93      **FA Trophy:** 2nd Rd Proper 95-96          **FA Vase:** N/A
**HONOURS** Hellenic Lge Prem Div 89-90 (Lge Cup 89-90); Gloucs Sen Cup Winners 93-94;Southern Lg. Mid Div Champions 94-95, R-up 98-99 Merit Cup Jnt Win 94-95, 98-99 Gwent FA Sen. Cup Winners 96-97, 97-98, 98-99

*Back Row (L-R): Andy Fisher, Karl Bayliss, Danny Hill, Craig Lima, Jason Donovan, Dean Clark Front Row: Grantley Dicks (captain), Gary Marshall, Carl Dale, Darren Robison, Bradley Thomas Photo: Roger Turner*

# NEWPORT A.F.C. - MATCH FACTS - 1998-99 SEASON

| No | Date | Venue | Comp | Opponents | Att | Result | Score | Goalscorers |
|----|------|-------|------|-----------|-----|--------|-------|-------------|
| 1 | 22/08 | H | DM M | Sutton Coldfield Town | 587 | W | 4-0 | Bayliss 31 33 73, Brown 82 |
| 2 | 25/08 | A | DM M | Redditch United | 345 | D | 1-1 | Brown 90 |
| 3 | 27/08 | A | GSC 1 | **Chepstow Town** | 150 | W | 4-0 | **Chesters 11, Brown 15, Flynn 26, Donovan 77** |
| 4 | 29/08 | H | DM M | Stamford | 270 | L | 1-3 | Bayliss 34 |
| 5 | 31/08 | H | DM M | Stourbridge | 591 | W | 4-2 | Brazil 6, Thomas 53, Dicks 74, Evans 79 |
| 6 | 05/09 | H | FA C P | **Weston-Super-Mare** | 568 | D | 0-0 | |
| 7 | 08/09 | A | FA C P r | **Weston-super-Mare** | 334 | L | 0-1 | |
| 8 | 12/09 | A | DM M | Paget Rangers | 323 | W | 1-0 | Bayliss 25 |
| 9 | 16/09 | H | DM M | Redditch United | 418 | D | 1-1 | Brown 65 |
| 10 | 19/09 | H | DM M | VS Rugby | 599 | W | 3-2 | Bayliss 13, Brown 28, Evans 90 |
| 11 | 26/09 | A | DM M | Stafford Rangers | 558 | L | 0-1 | |
| 12 | 29/09 | A | DM M | Stourbridge | 380 | W | 4-3 | Bayliss 40 80[p], Brown 44 78 |
| 13 | 03/10 | H | DM M | Hinckley United | 669 | W | 1-0 | Robison 76 |
| 14 | 10/10 | A | DM M | Solihull Borough | 251 | L | 1-3 | Bayliss 19 |
| 15 | 17/10 | H | DM M | Bilston Town | 537 | W | 5-0 | Bayliss 6 59, Brown 12, Tapp 52, Preedy 77 |
| 16 | 28/10 | H | FA T 1 | **Heybridge Swifts** | 325 | L | 2-4 | **Bayliss 25[p] 40** |
| 17 | 31/10 | A | DM M | Evesham United | 227 | W | 2-0 | Hill 3, Bayliss 76 |
| 18 | 04/11 | H | DM M | Clevedon Town | 631 | D | 1-1 | Bayliss 16 |
| 19 | 07/11 | H | DM M | Racing Club Warwick | 634 | W | 2-1 | Robison 58, Hill 86 |
| 20 | 11/11 | H | DM C 1(1) | **Cinderford Town** | 264 | W | 4-2 | **Brown 2, Evans 7, Flynn 43, Hill 78** |
| 21 | 14/11 | A | DM M | Bloxwich Town | 140 | W | 6-0 | Thomas 4 65, Brown 26 43, Clark 28, Bayliss 45 |
| 22 | 24/11 | A | DM C 1(2) | **Cinderford Town** | 178 | D | 1-1 | **Hopkins 80** |
| 23 | 28/11 | A | DM M | Hinckley United | 316 | D | 0-0 | |
| 24 | 02/12 | H | GSC SF | **Fields Park Pontllanfraith** | 113 | W | 2-0 | **Robison 59, Thomas 64** |
| 25 | 05/12 | A | DM M | Moor Green | 273 | L | 1-4 | Bayliss 66 |
| 26 | 12/12 | H | DM M | Bloxwich Town | 605 | W | 4-0 | Swallow 11[og], Bayliss 24, David Hunt 35, Flynn 89 |
| 27 | 16/12 | H | DM C 2 | **Weston-Super-Mare** | 232 | W | 2-0 | **Marshall 30, Tapp 67** |
| 28 | 19/12 | A | DM M | Bedworth United | 279 | W | 1-0 | Flynn 74 |
| 29 | 28/12 | H | DM M | Weston-Super-Mare | 769 | W | 2-1 | French 48, Bayliss 90 |
| 30 | 01/01 | H | DM M | Evesham United | 944 | W | 3-0 | Clark 41, Light 44, French 80 |
| 31 | 02/01 | A | DM M | Sutton Coldfield Town | 311 | L | 0-1 | |
| 32 | 09/01 | H | DM M | Shepshed Dynamo | 767 | D | 1-1 | Bayliss 55 |
| 33 | 16/01 | H | DM M | Bilston Town | 302 | L | 2-5 | L Brown 70, Donovan 75 |
| 34 | 23/01 | H | DM M | Wisbech Town | 624 | W | 4-1 | Lima 19, Bayliss 38, Flynn 54, French 64 |
| 35 | 27/01 | H | DM C 3 | **Bashley** | 273 | L | 0-2 | |
| 36 | 30/01 | A | DM M | VS Rugby | 300 | W | 2-1 | Donovan 35, Clark 39 |
| 37 | 06/02 | H | DM M | Stafford Rangers | 659 | W | 3-1 | Donovan 20, Thomas 36, Bayliss 79 |
| 38 | 15/02 | H | GSC F | **Caerleon** | 420 | W | 4-0 | **Tapp 14 15 24, French 72** |
| 39 | 20/02 | H | DM M | Bedworth United | 665 | W | 1-0 | French 3 |
| 40 | 23/02 | A | DM M | Clevedon Town | 1006 | L | 1-2 | Bayliss 85[p] |
| 41 | 27/02 | A | DM M | Racing Club Warwick | 280 | D | 0-0 | |
| 42 | 06/03 | A | DM M | Stamford | 628 | W | 2-1 | Hill 4 22 |
| 43 | 10/03 | H | DM M | Paget Rangers | 514 | W | 2-1 | Thomas 20, Marshall 30 |
| 44 | 20/03 | H | DM M | Blakenall | 720 | W | 3-0 | Marshall 16, Dale 53, Brown 84 |
| 45 | 27/03 | A | DM M | Shepshed Dynamo | 310 | L | 1-3 | Bayliss 48 |
| 46 | 03/04 | H | DM M | Cinderford Town | 839 | W | 4-1 | Bayliss 12 26 90[p], Robinson 64 |
| 47 | 05/04 | A | DM M | Weston-super-Mare | 576 | L | 0-2 | |
| 48 | 10/04 | A | DM M | Wisbech Town | 409 | W | 3-0 | Bayliss 37[p], Dale 45, Marshall 90 |
| 49 | 15/04 | A | DM M | Cinderford Town | 497 | W | 5-2 | Bayliss 2[p] 33 74, Hill 54, Thomas 57 |
| 50 | 17/04 | H | DM M | Solihull Borough | 1094 | W | 4-1 | Dale 38, Bayliss 62, Thomas 73, Brown 76 |
| 51 | 24/04 | A | DM M | Blakenall | 231 | D | 3-3 | Brown 5, Dale 32[p] 50 |
| 52 | 01/05 | H | DM M | Moor Green | 1015 | W | 3-2 | Hunt 47, Marshall 62, Tapp 75 |

**PLAYING SQUAD 1999-2000:**

GOALKEEPERS: Andrew Fisher (Havant Town), Pat Mountain (Gloucester City/Yeovil Town), Jon Roberts (Inter Cable Tel)

DEFENDERS: Robbie Chesters, Grantley Dicks (Forest Green Rovers), Jason Donovan (Ebbw Vale), Mike Flynn, Danny Hunt (Swindon Town), David Hunt (Cardiff City), Craig Lima (Merthyr Tydfil), Glenn Willis

MIDFIELDERS: Lee Brown (Fields Park Pontllanfraith), Dean Clarke (Merthyr Tydfil), Leigh Hall (Hereford United), Danny Hill (Cinderford Town), Anthony Hopkins (UIW Cardiff), Darren Robison (Trowbridge Town), Gary Smart (Forest Green Rovers), Andrew Smith (Hereford United)

FORWARDS: Karl Bayliss (Forest Green Rovers), Carl Dale (Yeovil Town), Roy Jordan (Pegasus Juniors), Andy Mainwaring (Gloucester City), Steve Tapp (Cinderford Town)

# ROTHWELL TOWN

### CLUB OFFICIALS
Chairman: **Stuart Andrews**
Vice-Chairman: **Keith Johnson**
President: **Ken Cheney**
Secretary: **Roger Barratt**
18 Norton St., Rothwell, Northants NN14 2DE
Tel: 01536 507744
Press Officer/Comm Mgr: **Peter Bradley**
Tel: 01536 710925

### FOOTBALL MANAGEMENT TEAM
Manager: Jack Murray
Physio: Graham Simmonds
Asst Manager: Graham Simmonds
Coach: Kim Davies

### FACT FILE

Founded: 1895
Nickname: The Bones
Sponsors: Forester Health
Colours: Blue, black + white trim/black/black
Change Colours: Red, black & white trim,
black/black
Midweek matchday: Tuesday
Newsline: 0930 555 829
Reserves' League: Utd Counties Res Div

**GROUND**                    Cecil Street, Rothwell, Northants NN14 2EZ Tel: 01536 710694
**Directions:** A14/A6 to Rothwell. At town centre r'about turn into BridgeStreet (right if north-bound, left if southbound), take 3rd left into Tresham Street, ground is at top on left.
3 miles from Kettering (BR); Rothwell is served by Kettering to Market Harborough buses
Capacity: 3,500        Seats: 264        Cover: 1,264        Floodlights: Yes
**Clubhouse:** Rowellian Social Club, open every evening and weekend lunchtimes. Crisps and rolls available on matchdays (hot food and drinks available in ground). `Top of the Town Ballroom', lounge seats 200
**Club Shop:** Sells various souvenirs incl. metal badges.

Pages: 48 Price: 90p
Media Relations Officer: Mark Southon
Tel: 01162 774877

Local Press: Northants Evening Telegraph,
Chronicle & Echo, Herald & Post
Local Radio: BBC Radio Northants, KCBC

**PREVIOUS**        **Leagues:** Northants 1896-1911 21-33, Kettering Amateur 11-21 33-48, Leics.Senior 48-50, United Counties 50-56 61-94, Central Alliance 56-61        **Grounds:** Harrington Rd, Castle Hill        **Name:** Rothwell Town Swifts

**CLUB RECORDS**  **Attendance:** 2,508 v Irthlingborough Diamonds, United Counties League 1971
**Win:** 17-0 v Stamford, FA Cup Preliminary Round replay 1927
**Defeat:** 1-10 v Coalville Town, Leicestershire Sen Lge 1949
**Transfer fee paid:** Undisclosed for Andy Wright (Aylesbury 1992)
**Transfer fee received:** Undisclosed for Matty Watts (Charlton 1990)

**BEST SEASON**  **FA Cup:** Third Qualifying Round 98-99
**FA Trophy:** Second Round Proper 94-95        **FA Vase:** Fifth Round 92-93 (1-2 v Bridlington Town)

**HONOURS**        Northants Lg1899-1900 (R-up 1895-96 96-97 97-98), Northants Snr Cup 1899-1900 23-24 59-60 88-89 95-96 (R-up 24-25 71-72 87-88), United Counties Lg 92-93 94-95 (R-up 69-70 70-71 87-88 89-90 90-91), KO Cup 55-56 70-71 71-72 91-92 92-93 (R-up 77-78 79-80 82-83), Div 2 52-53 53-54, Div 2 Cup 52-53 53-54, Benevolent Cup 92-93 94-95 (R-up 89-90 90-91), Southern League Mid Div R-up 96-97

Players progressing: Lee Glover (Nottingham Forest) 1987, Matty Watts (CharltonAth.) 1990

*Back Row (L-R): Wayne Spencer, Paul Wagstaff, Ben Lord, Andy Bullimore, Danny Finlay, John Parsons, Glyn Davies, Steve Coates, Ricky Marshall, Derek Brown, Graham Simmonds*
*Centre: Dougie Keast, Gary Pick, Andy Kirkup, Manager Jack Murray, Chairman Stuart Andrews, General Manager Jim Conde, Richard Preston, Simon Dunlop, Richard Jowett. Front: Andy Tiday, Andy Evans, Andre Marsh.*

# ROTHWELL TOWN - MATCH FACTS - 1998-99 SEASON

| No | Date | Venue | Comp | Opponents | Att | Result | Score | Goalscorers |
|---|---|---|---|---|---|---|---|---|
| 1 | 22/08 | H | DMP | Burton Albion | 351 | L | 1-4 | Marshall 43 |
| 2 | 26/08 | A | DMP | Boston United | 984 | D | 0-0 | |
| 3 | 29/08 | A | DMP | Hastings Town | 445 | D | 1-1 | Tiday 34 |
| 4 | 31/08 | H | DMP | Crawley Town | 287 | D | 1-1 | Bullimore 78[p] |
| 5 | 05/09 | A | DMP | Worcester City | 721 | L | 0-1 | |
| 6 | 08/09 | H | DMP | Gresley Rovers | 253 | W | 2-0 | Marshall 44 45 |
| 7 | 12/09 | A | DMP | Atherstone United | 258 | D | 2-2 | Foley 2, Jowett 58 |
| 8 | 15/09 | H | DMP | Boston United | 239 | D | 1-1 | Davis 78 |
| 9 | 19/09 | A | DMP | Bromsgrove Rovers | 641 | L | 0-3 | |
| 10 | 22/09 | A | DMP | Crawley Town | 503 | L | 0-1 | |
| 11 | 26/09 | H | DMP | Weymouth | 261 | W | 1-0 | Meads 4 |
| 12 | 03/10 | A | FA C Q2 | Stapenhill | 105 | W | 4-0 | Marshall 9, Jowett 46 52 66 |
| 13 | 10/10 | H | DMP | Salisbury City | 175 | W | 1-0 | Heffernan 85 |
| 14 | 17/10 | A | FA C Q3 | Raunds Town | 241 | D | 2-2 | Marshall 12, Jowett 88 |
| 15 | 20/10 | H | FA C Q3 r | Raunds Town | 300 | L | 0-1 | |
| 16 | 31/10 | H | DMP | Halesowen Town | 241 | W | 2-1 | Spencer 75, Heffernan 85 |
| 17 | 07/11 | A | DMP | Ilkeston Town | 610 | L | 0-3 | |
| 18 | 10/11 | H | DM C 1(1) | Chelmsford City | 102 | W | 1-0 | Coates 48 |
| 19 | 14/11 | H | DMP | Bromsgrove Rovers | 210 | W | 2-0 | Bullimore 48[p], Jowett 88 |
| 20 | 21/11 | A | FA T 2 | Hendon | 202 | D | 1-1 | Heffernan 64 |
| 21 | 23/11 | A | DM C 1(2) | Chelmsford City | 167 | W | 3-0 | Marshall 4 24, Jowett 90 |
| 22 | 28/11 | A | DMP | Merthyr Tydfil | 384 | L | 1-4 | Heffernan 36 |
| 23 | 01/12 | H | NSC QF | Rushden & Diamonds | 253 | L | 0-1 | |
| 24 | 05/12 | H | DMP | Nuneaton Borough | 574 | D | 1-1 | Wagstaffe 50 |
| 25 | 12/12 | H | DMP | Burton Albion | 576 | D | 0-0 | |
| 26 | 14/12 | H | FA T 2 r | Hendon | 186 | L | 1-2 | Heffernan 59 |
| 27 | 19/12 | H | DMP | Bath City | 248 | W | 3-2 | Jowett 10, Dunlop 13, Marshall 49 |
| 28 | 22/12 | A | DM C 2 | Grantham Town | 429 | D | 0-0 | |
| 29 | 02/01 | A | DMP | Gloucester City | 442 | L | 1-2 | Marshall 34[p] |
| 30 | 09/01 | A | DMP | Dorchester Town | 520 | L | 1-3 | Meads 43 |
| 31 | 16/01 | H | DMP | Tamworth | 349 | W | 2-1 | Moore 28 50 |
| 32 | 19/01 | H | DM C 2 r | Grantham Town | 124 | W | 1-0 | Moore 53 |
| 33 | 30/01 | A | DMP | Weymouth | 930 | L | 0-5 | |
| 34 | 06/02 | A | DMP | Cambridge City | 268 | D | 2-2 | Marshall 40, Moore 65 |
| 35 | 13/02 | A | DMP | Halesowen Town | 587 | L | 0-4 | |
| 36 | 16/02 | H | DM C 3 | Boston United | 87 | L | 1-3 | Foley 70 |
| 37 | 20/02 | H | DMP | Merthyr Tydfil | 228 | W | 4-0 | Bullimore 23, Spencer 26, Moore 30 68 |
| 38 | 23/02 | H | DMP | King's Lynn | 255 | L | 0-2 | |
| 39 | 27/02 | A | DMP | Grantham Town | 511 | L | 0-3 | |
| 40 | 06/03 | H | DMP | Gloucester City | 239 | L | 0-1 | |
| 41 | 13/03 | H | DMP | Cambridge City | 243 | W | 3-1 | Lord 33, Bullimore 65 82 |
| 42 | 16/03 | H | DMP | Grantham Town | 210 | L | 0-1 | |
| 43 | 23/03 | A | DMP | Tamworth | 397 | L | 2-3 | Foley 31, McDonald 38 |
| 44 | 27/03 | A | DMP | Salisbury City | 363 | W | 2-0 | Wilkes 6, Moore 39 |
| 45 | 03/04 | H | DMP | Hastings Town | 223 | L | 1-3 | Moore 43 |
| 46 | 05/04 | A | DMP | King's Lynn | 867 | L | 0-2 | |
| 47 | 10/04 | A | DMP | Bath City | 557 | L | 0-2 | |
| 48 | 13/04 | A | DMP | Gresley Rovers | 419 | W | 3-1 | McDonald 1, Moore 37, Davies 52 |
| 49 | 17/04 | H | DMP | Ilkeston Town | 323 | W | 3-1 | Foley 5 61, Moore 45 |
| 50 | 20/04 | H | DMP | Atherstone United | 241 | W | 2-0 | Moore 43, Jowett 74 |
| 51 | 24/04 | A | DMP | Nuneaton Borough | 2007 | L | 0-2 | |
| 52 | 28/04 | H | DMP | Worcester City | 214 | L | 1-2 | Moore 7 |
| 53 | 01/05 | H | DMP | Dorchester Town | 343 | D | 1-1 | Preston 15 |

## PLAYING SQUAD 1999-2000:

GOALKEEPERS: John Hughes (Wisbech Town), John Parsons (Sutton Coldfield Town)
DEFENDERS: Derek Brown (Nuneaton Borough), Andy Bullimore (Grantham Town), Glyn Davies (Nuneaton Borough)
MIDFIELDERS: Simon Dunlop (Raunds Town), Les Hornby (Hinckley United), Ben Lord (Higham Town), Kevin McDonald (Corby Town), Gary Pick (Shepshed Dynamo)
FORWARDS: Richard Jowatt (Nuneaton Borough), Scott Machin (VS Rugby), Wayne Spencer (Corby Town), Paul Wagstaff (VS Rugby)

# SALISBURY CITY

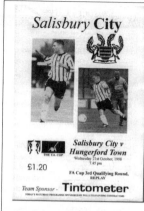

**Salisbury City**

Salisbury City v
**Hungerford Town**
Wednesday 21st October, 1998
7.45 pm
£1.20
FA Cup 3rd Qualifying Round,
REPLAY

Team Sponsor - **Tintometer**

**CLUB OFFICIALS**
Chairman: **P R McEnhill**
Vice-Chairmam: **T.B.A.**
Secretary: **Sean Gallagher**
1 Tempest Road, Beamont Park, Amesbury,
Wilts SP47UE Tel: 01980 626855 (H & Fax)
Press Officer: **David Macey**
Tel: **01264 773765**
Youth Dev. Off.: **Simon Pickett**
Commercial Manager: **Geoff Butler**

**FACT FILE**
Formed: 1947
Nickname: The Whites
Sponsors: R.T.Rogers
Colours: White/black/white
Change colours: yellow/blue/yellow
Midweek matchday: Tuesday
Reserve Team's League: None
Club Line: 'City Line' 0930 555 864
1998-99
Captain: Ian Chalk
Top scorer: Paul Sales

**FOOTBALL MANAGEMENT TEAM**
Manager: Geoff Butler
Reserve Team Manager: Brian O'Donnell
Fitness Therapist: Dawn Cornforth
Youth Managers: Symon Pickett& Terry Hall

**GROUND** The Raymond McEnhill Stadium, Partridge Way, Old Sarum, Salisbury SP4 6PU
Tel:01722 333988/326454, Fax 01722 323100
**Directions:** The Stadium is situated off the main A345 (Salisbury - Amesbury) road on the
northern edge of the city some two miles from the City centre. Continue on this road, turn right
onto A338 signed Old Sarum Business Park, Partridge Way & ground on left
Capacity: 4,000          Cover: 3,062          Seats: 462          Floodlights: Yes
**Clubhouse:** On ground, open matchdays only. Hot & cold snacks available
**Club Shop:** Sells replica shirts, memorabilia, programmes, scarves, metal badges, souvenirs.
Contact Commercial Office (01722 326454)

Pages: 48 Price: £1.20
Editor: Kevin Gover
Local Press: Salisbury Journal, Evening Echo
& Sports Echo, Western DailyPress
Local Radio: Wiltshire Sound, Spire F.M

**PREVIOUS**     **Leagues:** Western 47-68   **Name:** Salisbury FC, 47-92
**Ground:** Hudson Field 47-48, Victoria Park 48-97

**CLUB RECORDS**   **Attendance:** 8,902 v Weymouth, Western League 48
**Win:** 9-0 v Westbury United (H), FA Cup 1st Qual. Rd 72
**Career Goalscorer:** Royston Watts 180 (59-65)          **Defeat:** 0-7 v Minehead, Southern League 1975
**Transfer fee paid:** £5,750 for Peter Loveridge (Dorchester Town, 90)          **Career Appearances:** Barry Fitch 713 (63-75)
**Transfer fee received:** £16,000 for Ian Thompson (AFC Bournemouth, 83)

**BEST SEASON**   **FA Trophy:** 2nd Rd 96-97 (lost to Dorchester Town)
**FA Amateur Cup:** 2nd Rd 49-50 (lost to Hendon)          **FA Cup:** 2nd Rd 59-60 (lost to Newport County)

**HONOURS**       Southern Lg Southern Div Champ 94-95, R-up 85-86 92-93; Western Lg 57-58 60-61,R-up 58-59 59-60 61-62 66-67 67-68;
Hants Senior Cup 61-62 63-64; Wilts Premier Shield 56-57 59-60 61-62 66-67 67-68 70-71 77-78 78-79 95-96 98-99

Players progressing: Eric Fountain (Southampton 48), Cyril Smith (Arsenal 48),Tony Alexander (Fulham 65), John Evans (Stockport County 67), Graham
Moxon (Exeter 75), Eric Welch (Chesterfield 76), Ian Thompson (Bournemouth 83),Trevor Wood (Port Vale 88), Denny Mundee (Bournemouth 88),
Matthew Carmichael (Lincoln 90), Shaun Brookes (Barnet 91), Andrew Dungey (Exeter C. 97), Andrew Sargent (Plymouth A. 97)

*FA Cup action from the Raymond McEnhill stadium as Salisbury take on the Hull City defence.   Photo: M Wray*

# SALISBURY CITY - MATCH FACTS - 1998-99 SEASON

| No | Date | Venue | Comp | Opponents | Att | Result | Score | Goalscorers |
|---|---|---|---|---|---|---|---|---|
| | 22/08 | H | DMP | Tamworth | 421 | W | 2-1 | Sales 37, Housley 88 |
| | 25/08 | A | DMP | Crawley Town | 835 | D | 1-1 | Randall 47[p] |
| | 29/08 | A | DMP | Grantham Town | 730 | L | 1-2 | Randall 8 |
| | 31/08 | H | DMP | Weymouth | 932 | W | 1-0 | Housley 86 |
| | 05/09 | A | DMP | Gresley Rovers | 571 | L | 1-4 | Randall 44[p] |
| | 09/09 | H | DMP | Atherstone United | 360 | L | L | 0-2 |
| | 12/09 | A | DMP | Boston United | 782 | L | 1-3 | Randall 45 |
| | 16/09 | H | DMP | Crawley Town | 279 | L | 0-2 | |
| | 19/09 | A | DMP | Ilkeston Town | 483 | L | 0-3 | |
| 0 | 22/09 | A | DMP | Weymouth | 951 | D | 1-1 | Randall 9 |
| 1 | 26/09 | H | DMP | Cambridge City | 308 | W | 4-1 | Randall 17 80, Holmes 73, Ferrett 82 |
| 2 | 30/09 | H | DMP | Dorchester Town | 367 | D | 3-3 | Randall 14, Sales 30, Harbut 82 |
| 3 | 03/10 | A | FA C Q2 | Dorchester Town | 616 | W | 3-0 | Emms 19, Randall 55, Ferrett 80 |
| 4 | 10/10 | A | DMP | Rothwell Town | 175 | L | 0-1 | |
| 5 | 17/10 | A | FA C Q3 | Hungerford Town | 386 | D | 1-1 | Rofe 81 |
| 6 | 21/10 | H | FA C Q3 r | Hungerford Town | 421 | W | 3-2 | Sales 45 90, Harbut 55 |
| 7 | 24/10 | H | FA T 1 | Carshalton Athletic | 335 | W | 2-1 | Ferrett 4, Sales 35 |
| 8 | 03/11 | A | FA C Q4 | Carshalton Athletic | 277 | W | 6-0 | Housley 17 45 88, Harbut 57, Randall 62, Sales 83 |
| 9 | 07/11 | H | DMP | Grantham Town | 419 | W | 1-0 | Randall 11 |
| 0 | 10/11 | A | DM C 1(1) | Bashley | 215 | D | 1-1 | Sales 59 |
| 1 | 14/11 | H | FA C 1 | Hull City | 2570 | L | 0-2 | |
| 2 | 21/11 | A | FA T 2 | Woking | 1640 | L | 1-2 | Bright 62 |
| 3 | 25/11 | H | DM C 1(2) | Bashley | 253 | D | 2-2 | Randall 30, Sales 45 |
| 4 | 28/11 | H | DMP | Ilkeston Town | 337 | D | 0-0 | |
| 5 | 05/12 | A | DMP | Dorchester Town | 571 | L | 0-4 | |
| 6 | 12/12 | H | DMP | Worcester City | 317 | W | 2-0 | Bowers 53, Bright 62 |
| 7 | 19/12 | A | DMP | Halesowen Town | 537 | D | 3-3 | Hayter 26, Sales 37, Bright 65 |
| 8 | 28/12 | H | DMP | Hastings Town | 462 | W | 1-0 | Randall 50 |
| 9 | 01/01 | H | DMP | Gloucester City | 667 | D | 1-1 | Sales 13 |
| 0 | 02/01 | A | DMP | Cambridge City | 275 | W | 3-1 | Randall 25[p], Emms 60, Sales 82 |
| 1 | 06/01 | H | WPS QF | Warminster Town | 108 | W | 9-0 | Sales 19 27 48 59, Chalk 44 64, Hayter 61 87, Bowers 63 |
| 2 | 09/01 | A | DMP | Merthyr Tydfil | 431 | W | 1-0 | Hayter 45 |
| 3 | 16/01 | H | DMP | King's Lynn | 449 | D | 2-2 | Sales 8, Harbut 62 |
| 4 | 23/01 | A | DMP | Nuneaton Borough | 1404 | W | 1-0 | Hayter 63 |
| 5 | 30/01 | H | DMP | Bromsgrove Rovers | 494 | W | 1-0 | Hayter 30 |
| 6 | 06/02 | A | DMP | Burton Albion | 690 | W | 2-1 | Sales 19, Bright 61 |
| 7 | 13/02 | H | DMP | Merthyr Tydfil | 763 | W | 1-0 | Harbut 25 |
| 8 | 16/02 | A | DMP | Bath City | 716 | W | 5-3 | Sales 14, Randall 28, Bowers 32 68, Harbut 78 |
| 9 | 20/02 | H | DMP | Halesowen Town | 771 | L | 1-2 | Sales 51 |
| 0 | 27/02 | A | DMP | Bromsgrove Rovers | 348 | W | 2-0 | Rofe 88, Sales 90 |
| 1 | 06/03 | A | DMP | King's Lynn | 652 | D | 3-3 | Winter 21, Chalk 59, Sales 78 |
| 2 | 08/03 | A | DMP | Worcester City | 703 | D | 0-0 | |
| 3 | 13/03 | H | DMP | Nuneaton Borough | 1050 | D | 1-1 | Housley 34 |
| 4 | 15/03 | A | DMP | Atherstone United | 211 | L | 0-2 | |
| 5 | 23/03 | A | WPS SF | Highworth Town | 107 | W | 2-1 | Bowers 37, Emms 84 |
| 6 | 27/03 | H | DMP | Rothwell Town | 363 | L | 0-2 | |
| 7 | 03/04 | H | DMP | Bath City | 682 | W | 3-2 | Chalk 62 69, Fearon 82 |
| 8 | 05/04 | A | DMP | Hastings Town | 376 | L | 2-3 | Chalk 77, Braybrook 79 |
| 9 | 10/04 | A | DMP | Boston United | 521 | D | 0-0 | |
| 0 | 17/04 | A | DMP | Tamworth | 519 | L | 1-2 | Housley 35 |
| 1 | 24/04 | H | DMP | Burton Albion | 560 | L | 0-2 | |
| 2 | 28/04 | A | DMP | Gresley Rovers | 352 | D | 2-2 | Harbut 23, Fearon 51 |
| 3 | 01/05 | A | DMP | Gloucester City | 448 | W | 2-1 | Bowers 14, Randall 42 |
| 4 | 13/05 | A | WPS F | Swindon Supermarine | n/k | W | 2-1 | Curtis 43, Fearon 67  (at Swindon Town) |

## PLAYING SQUAD 1999-2000:

GOALKEEPERS: Paul Myers (Weymouth)

DEFENDERS: Mark Boulton (Weymouth), Darren Curtis (Fulham), Lee Dyson (Ards), Roger Emms, Ian Howell (Bashley), Matt Jackson, Andy Jones, Darren Lush (Havant & Waterlooville)

FORWARDS: Tyrone Bowers (Fareham Town), Robbie Harbut (Bashley), Danny Rofe, Ian Savage (Hampton & Richmond Borough), Kevin Braybrook (Yeovil Town), Ian Chalk, James Hayter (AFC Bournemouth), Neil Housley (Weymouth), Kevin James (Southampton), Paul Sales (Bashley), Martin Shepherd (Dorchester Town)

# TAMWORTH

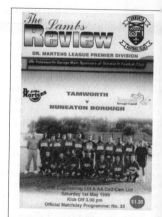

**CLUB OFFICIALS**
Chairman: **Bob Andrews**
Vice Chairman: **Tony Reeves**
President: **Len Gendle**
Secretary: **Rod A Hadley**, 38 Godolphin,
Riverside, Tamworth B79 7UF
Tel: 01827 66786 & Fax
Press Officer: **Mark Maybury**
Commercial Manager: **Steve Shaw**

**FOOTBALL MANAGEMENT TEAM**
Manager: Paul Hendrie
Asst Man.: Andy Dwyer
Physio: Peter Denham

**FACT FILE**

Formed: 1933
Sponsors: Nissan - Polesworth Garage
Nickname: Lambs or Town
Colours: Red/red/black
Change colours: All blue
Midweek home matchday: Tuesday
Reserves' League: Midland Comb. Res Div
98-99 Captain: Willie Batchelor
P.o.Y.: Rob Warner
Top scorer: Warren Haughton

Pages: 28 Price: £1
Editor: Brian & Theresa Whitehouse
Local Press: Tamworth Herald,
Tamworth Times
Local Radio:Centre FM,Extra Gold/Radio WM

**GROUND**  The Lamb Ground, Kettlebrook, Tamworth, Staffs B77 1AA
Tel: 01827 65798 FAX: 0182765798
**Directions:**  Follow the signs for Town Centre/Snowdome, then for Kettlebrook.
The entrance to the ground & car parks is in Kettlebrook Road, 50yards
from the traffic island by the railway viaduct (B5000)
Capacity: 3,410    Cover: 1,191  Seats: 402  Floodlights: Yes
**Clubhouse:** Club on ground - open matchdays, training nights and tote night only
**Clubshop:** Yes, fully stocked

**PREVIOUS**  **Leagues:** Birmingham Combination 33-54, West Midlands (initially Birmingham Lg) 54-72 84-88, Southern 72-79 83-84,
Northern Premier 79-83    **Grounds:** Jolly Sailor Ground 33-34

**CLUB RECORDS**  **Attendance:** 4,920 v Atherstone Tn, Birm Comb 48    **Career Goalscorer:** Graham Jessop 195
**Win:** 14-4 v Holbrook Institute (H), Bass Vase 34 **Season Goalscorer:** Percy Vials 64 (36-37)
**Defeat:** 0-11 v Solihull (A), Birmingham Comb. 40    **Career Appearances:** Dave Seedhouse 869
**Transfer Fee paid:** £5,000 for Steve Cartwright (Colchester Utd, 88)
**Transfer Fee  received:** £7,500 for Martin Myers (Telford Utd, 90)

**BEST SEASON**  FA Cup: 2nd Rd 69-70 (0-6 at Gillingham)    **FA Trophy:** Quarter Final    **FA Vase:** Winners 88-89

**HONOURS**  FA Vase 88-89, West Mids Lg 63-64 65-66 71-72 87-88 (R-up(2) 67-69, Div 2 55-56, Lg Cup(5) 64-66 71-72 85-86 87-88 (R-up
70-71)), Birmingham Snr Cup 60-61 65-66 68-69 (R-up 36-37 63-64), Staffs Snr Cup 58-59 63-64 65-66 (R-up 55-56 66-67 70-
71), Midland F'lit Cup R-up 71-72 72-73, Camkin Cup 71-72 (R-up 70-71)

Players progressing: P Hilton (WBA 49), A Godridge (Swansea 50), W Ealing (Doncaster), Higgins (Fulham), P Weir (Cardiff), S Fox (Wrexham), S
Cartwright (Colchester 88), S Ryder (Walsall), D Williams (Brentford)

*Back Row: Andy Dyce (Asst Mngr) triallist, Dennsi Mulholland, Leon Mitchell, Tim Steele, Jon Howard, Martin
Ruddock, Tony Rowe, Michael Grey, Darren Shaw, Ian Bennett, James Wood, Paul Hendrie (Manager)
Front Row: Jon Price, David Foy, Warren Haughton, Gary Smith, Rob Warner, Mick Colley, Paul Hallon.   Photo: PB*

# TAMWORTH - MATCH FACTS - 1998-99 SEASON

| No | Date | Venue | Comp | Opponents | Att | Result | Score | Goalscorers |
|---|---|---|---|---|---|---|---|---|
| | 22/08 | A | DMP | Salisbury City | 421 | L | 1-2 | Haughton 90 |
| | 25/08 | H | DMP | Merthyr Tydfil | 587 | W | 4-2 | Shaw 8 55, Dixon 14, Gray 65 |
| | 29/08 | H | DMP | Worcester City | 599 | L | 0-1 | |
| | 31/08 | A | DMP | Bromsgrove Rovers | 841 | L | 1-2 | Warner 85 |
| | 05/09 | H | DMP | Bath City | 462 | D | 1-1 | Smith 69 |
| | 08/09 | A | DMP | Ilkeston Town | 548 | W | 5-3 | Dixon 36, Smith 42 51 60, Yates 52 |
| | 12/09 | H | DMP | Dorchester Town | 482 | W | 1-0 | Wood 86 |
| | 15/09 | A | DMP | Merthyr Tydfil | 370 | L | 0-6 | |
| | 19/09 | H | DMP | Gresley Rovers | 594 | L | 0-1 | |
| 0 | 22/09 | H | DMP | Bromsgrove Rovers | 522 | W | 1-0 | Shaw 15 |
| 1 | 26/09 | A | DMP | Nuneaton Borough | 2099 | L | 0-2 | |
| 2 | 03/10 | A | FA C Q2 | **Leek CSOB** | **247** | W | **3-2** | **Shaw 18, Batchelor 53, Haughton 75** |
| 3 | 10/10 | A | DMP | Hastings Town | 487 | W | 2-1 | Yates 4, Shaw 84 |
| 4 | 17/10 | A | FA C Q3 | **Brigg Town** | **401** | W | **2-0** | **Haughton 19, Yates 52** |
| 5 | 31/10 | H | FA C Q4 | **Grantham Town** | **805** | W | **2-1** | **Haughton 74, Shaw 85** |
| 6 | 03/11 | H | DMP | Ilkeston Town | 476 | D | 2-2 | Haughton 16 67 |
| 7 | 07/11 | A | DMP | Gloucester City | 702 | W | 1-0 | Yates 45 |
| 8 | 14/11 | H | FA C 1 | **Exeter City** | **2485** | D | **2-2** | **Shaw 28, Smith 52** |
| 9 | 17/11 | H | DM C 1(1) | **Gresley Rovers** | **326** | W | **4-1** | **Crawford 26, Shaw 68 89, Wood 88** |
| 0 | 21/11 | H | FA T 2 | **Stalybridge Celtic** | **611** | L | **1-3** | **Haughton 68** |
| 1 | 24/11 | A | FA C 1 r | **Exeter City** | **3152** | L | **1-4** | **Haughton 75** |
| 2 | 28/11 | H | DMP | Boston United | 501 | W | 4-2 | Howard 10, Haughton 28, Shaw 75, Smith 80 |
| 3 | 01/12 | H | BSC 2 | **Bedworth United** | **220** | W | **2-0** | **Warner 11, Haughton 32** |
| 4 | 05/12 | A | DMP | Crawley Town | 767 | L | 0-1 | |
| 5 | 12/12 | A | DMP | King's Lynn | 486 | L | 2-4 | Moore 18, Haughton 24 |
| 6 | 19/12 | H | DMP | Burton Albion | 717 | L | 0-1 | |
| 7 | 22/12 | A | DM C 1(2) | **Gresley Rovers** | **178** | W | **4-0** | **Hallam 41, Moore 57, Wood 74 81** |
| 8 | 26/12 | A | DMP | Halesowen Town | 603 | W | 3-1 | Shaw 21, Hallam 28 82 |
| 9 | 28/12 | A | DMP | Atherstone United | 829 | W | 1-0 | Haughton 45 |
| 0 | 01/01 | A | DMP | Worcester City | 1112 | L | 0-1 | |
| 1 | 09/01 | H | DMP | Cambridge City | 473 | W | 6-1 | Hallam 16 40 59 78, Shaw 80 87 |
| 2 | 16/01 | A | DMP | Rothwell Town | 349 | L | 1-2 | Batchelor 1 |
| 3 | 23/01 | H | DMP | Weymouth | 591 | L | 1-3 | Batchelor 28 |
| 4 | 30/01 | A | DMP | Gresley Rovers | 684 | W | 3-2 | Smith 35 74, Warner 46 |
| 5 | 02/02 | H | BSC 3 | **Kings Norton Town** | **281** | W | **4-1** | **Pippard 43[og], Howard 44, Haughton 59 90[p]** |
| 6 | 06/02 | H | DMP | King's Lynn | 585 | L | 0-2 | |
| 7 | 11/02 | A | DM C 2 | **Bedworth United** | **124** | D | **1-1** | **Haughton 13** |
| 8 | 13/02 | A | DMP | Weymouth | 894 | W | 3-0 | Haughton 11 46 84 |
| 9 | 16/02 | H | DM C 2 r | **Bedworth United** | **296** | L | **1-5** | **Sanders 25[og]** |
| 0 | 20/02 | A | DMP | Cambridge City | 338 | W | 1-0 | Hallam 61 |
| 1 | 23/02 | H | BSC QF | **Birmingham City** | **872** | L | **0-4** | |
| 2 | 27/02 | H | DMP | Hastings Town | 451 | L | 1-5 | Ball 71[og] |
| 3 | 09/03 | H | SSC 2 | **Stoke City** | **143** | L | **0-6** | |
| 4 | 13/03 | H | DMP | Gloucester City | 512 | D | 1-1 | Hallam 7 |
| 5 | 20/03 | A | DMP | Dorchester Town | 560 | W | 1-0 | Warner 84 |
| 6 | 23/03 | H | DMP | Rothwell Town | 397 | W | 3-2 | Shaw 10, Haughton 81, Hallam 90 |
| 7 | 30/03 | H | DMP | Grantham Town | 529 | D | 1-1 | Smith 73 |
| 8 | 03/04 | A | DMP | Halesowen Town | 831 | L | 0-3 | |
| 9 | 05/04 | H | DMP | Atherstone United | 905 | W | 2-1 | Hallam 73[p], Grocutt 83 |
| 0 | 10/04 | H | DMP | Grantham Town | 430 | W | 2-1 | Colley 10, Briggs 11 |
| 1 | 14/04 | A | DMP | Boston United | 553 | L | 0-2 | |
| 2 | 17/04 | H | DMP | Salisbury City | 519 | W | 2-1 | Hallam 12 51 |
| 3 | 20/04 | H | DMP | Crawley Town | 387 | W | 3-1 | Hallam 58 60, Gray 80 |
| 4 | 24/04 | A | DMP | Bath City | 1181 | L | 0-3 | |
| 5 | 27/04 | A | DMP | Burton Albion | 920 | L | 1-2 | Cheatham 20[og] |
| 6 | 01/05 | H | DMP | Nuneaton Borough | 1404 | D | 1-1 | Briggs 64 |

**PLAYING SQUAD 1999-2000:**

GOALKEEPERS: Darren Acton (Kidderminster Harriers), Harvey Willetts (Blakenall)

DEFENDERS: Willie Batchelor (Barry Town), Matthew Briggs (University of Memphis), Richard Clark (Evesham United), Ian Cooksey (Evesham United), Michael Crawford, Paul Hatton (Hednesford Town), Jon Howard (Wolverhampton Wanderers), Robbie Mutchell (Kettering Town), Rob Warner (Hereford United)

MIDFIELDERS: Neil Burden (Kings Norton Town), Nick Colley (Telford United), Dave Foy (Stafford Rangers), Darren Grocutt (Burton Albion), Warren Haughton, Mark Wolsey (Kidderminster Harriers)

FORWARDS: Micky Cotter (Burton Albion), Julian Dunkley (Rushden & Diamonds), Mark Hallam (Forest Green Rovers), Gary Smith (Worcester City), Tim Steele (Exeter City), Gary Swift, Bruce Whitehead (Long Melford)

# WEYMOUTH

## CLUB OFFICIALS

Chairman: **Peter Shaw**
Vice Chairman: **Mike Archer**

Secretary: **Terry Northover**
2 Stoke Rd, Weymouth, Dorset DT4 9JF
Tel: 01305 771480

### FOOTBALL MANAGEMENT TEAM
Manager: Fred Davies
Asst Manager:
Physio: Bob Lucas

### FACT FILE

Formed: 1890
Nickname: The Terras
Sponsors: Park Engineering
Colours: Claret & sky/claret & sky
Change colours: White with terra cotta trim
Midweek matchday: Tuesday
Reserves' League: Wessex Comb
98-99 - Captain: Alex Browne
P.o.Y: John Waldock
Top scorer: David Laws (28)

Pages: 36 Price: £1
Editor: Ian White (01305 826913
Local Press: Dorset Evening Echo
Local Radio: Wessex FM

**GROUND**  Wessex Stadium, Radipole Lane, Weymouth, Dorset DT4 9XJ Tel: 01305 785558

**Directions:** Arriving from Dorchester on A354, turn right following signs to Granby Industrial
Estate at Safeway r'bout - ground on right as you enter estate
Capacity: 10,000          Cover: All sides     Seats: 800     Floodlights: Yes

**Clubhouse:** Matchdays & functions. Hot & cold food available
**Club Shop:** Matchdays only. Progs & souvenirs.
During week contact Amanda (01305 815752)

**PREVIOUS**  **Leagues:** Dorset Lge, Western 1907-23 28-49, Southern 23-28 49-79, Alliance Premier 79-89
**Ground:** Recreation Ground (until 1987)

**CLUB RECORDS**  **Attendance:** 4,995 v Manchester Utd, ground opening, 21/10/87
**Career Goalscorer:** W Farmer, Haynes. 275     **Career Appearances:** Tony Hobson 1,076
**Transfer fee paid:** £15,000 for Shaun Teale (Northwich)   **Transfer fee received:** £100,000 for Peter Guthrie (Spurs, 1988)

**BEST SEASON**  **FA Cup:** Fourth Round 61-62, 0-2 v Preston N.E. (A). 1st rd on 29 occasions
League clubs defeated: Merthyr Town 24-25, Aldershot 49-50, Shrewsbury T. 56-57,Newport County 61-62, Cardiff C. 82-83
**FA Amateur Cup:** First Round 1900                **FA Trophy:** Fourth Round replay 1976-77

**HONOURS**  All Prem Lg R-up 79-80 (Lg Cup 81-82); Prem Inter Lg Cup R-up 87-88 (QF 90-91);Sth Lg 64-65 65-66 (R-up 54-55 77-78), Lg
Cup 72-73 (R-up 5), Sthn Div R-up 91-92; Wstn Lg 22-23, Div 2 33-34 36-37, (R-up 35-36 47-48); Dorset Sen. Cup (26);Mark
Frowde Cup (12)

Players progressing: A Smith (Accrington 61), G Bond/T Spratt/A Donnelly/M Cave(Torquay 61/65/67/68), P Leggett (Swindon 62), R Fog
(Aldershot 63), B Hutchinson (Lincoln 65), A Wool (Reading 71), A Beer (Exeter 74), B Iles(Chelsea 78), G Roberts (Spurs 80), T Gulliver/R Hill/
Townsend/P Morrell/JSmeulders (Bournemouth 66/67/79/83/84), T Agana (Watford), A Townsend/D Hughes(Southampton), S Claridge (C Palace
B McGorry/S Teale (Bournemouth), T Pounder/R Evans (Bristol Rvrs), R Pethick (Portsmouth 93)

*Back Row (L-R): Andy Mason, David Laws, Lee Bradford, Mark Boulton, Paul Myers, Mark Gammon, Ian Hutchinson,
Steve Richardson*
*Front Row: Tommy Killick, John Waldock, Richard Spiller, Alex Browne (capt), Craig Mansell, Mark Robinson, Matthew
Hale. Photo: Andrew Chitty*

# WEYMOUTH - MATCH FACTS - 1998-99 SEASON

| No | Date | Venue | Comp | Opponents | Att | Result | Score | Goalscorers |
|---|---|---|---|---|---|---|---|---|
| 1 | 25/07 | H | BLT. | Bristol City | n/k | L | 2-5 | Laws 17, Hutchinson 60 |
| 2 | 22/08 | A | DMP | Ilkeston Town | 644 | D | 1-1 | Laws 6[p] |
| 3 | 25/08 | H | DMP | Bath City | 1350 | W | 2-1 | S Browne 44, Mason 75 |
| 4 | 29/08 | H | DMP | Bromsgrove Rovers | 1066 | W | 3-1 | Laws 8 75, Robinson 12 |
| 5 | 31/08 | A | DMP | Salisbury City | 932 | L | 0-1 | |
| 6 | 05/09 | H | DMP | Halesowen Town | 961 | L | 1-2 | Birkby 23 |
| 7 | 08/09 | A | DMP | Gloucester City | 516 | D | 0-0 | |
| 8 | 12/09 | H | DMP | Cambridge City | 913 | L | 1-2 | Birkby 24 |
| 9 | 15/09 | A | DMP | Bath City | 790 | L | 1-2 | Gammon 67 |
| 10 | 19/09 | A | DMP | King's Lynn | 598 | W | 2-1 | Mansell 18, Laws 68 |
| 11 | 22/09 | H | DMP | Salisbury City | 951 | D | 1-1 | Robinson 81 |
| 12 | 26/09 | A | DMP | Rothwell Town | 261 | L | 0-1 | |
| 13 | 03/10 | A | FA C Q2 | Merthyr Tydfil | 507 | W | 2-0 | Gammon 79, Robinson 90 |
| 14 | 10/10 | H | DMP | Boston United | 807 | D | 1-1 | Laws 83 |
| 15 | 17/10 | A | FA C Q3 | Welling United | 602 | L | 2-3 | Adcock 55, Laws 82 |
| 16 | 31/10 | A | DMP | Nuneaton Borough | 1227 | L | 2-4 | Laws 80[p], Boulton 88 |
| 17 | 02/11 | H | FA T 1 | King's Lynn | 497 | W | 1-0 | Laws 2 |
| 18 | 07/11 | A | DMP | Gresley Rovers | 560 | W | 2-1 | Laws 62, Hutchinson 76 |
| 19 | 14/11 | H | DMP | King's Lynn | 885 | W | 1-0 | Heath 84 |
| 20 | 17/11 | A | DM C 1(1) | Havant & Waterlooville | 137 | W | 3-2 | Robinson 44, Adcock 74 84 |
| 21 | 21/11 | H | FA T 2 | Braintree Town | 774 | W | 2-1 | Robinson 23, Wellman 89 |
| 22 | 24/11 | H | DM C 1(2) | Havant & Waterlooville | 473 | D | 1-1 | Adcock 21 |
| 23 | 28/11 | H | DMP | Hastings Town | 803 | L | 1-2 | Laws 24[p] |
| 24 | 01/12 | H | DSC 3 | Poole Town | 322 | W | 1-0 | Adcock 39 |
| 25 | 05/12 | A | DMP | Grantham Town | 507 | L | 0-2 | |
| 26 | 07/12 | H | DMP | Gloucester City | 505 | W | 5-3 | Adcock 7 72, Robinson 17, Powell 19, Hutchinson 35 |
| 27 | 12/12 | H | DMP | Ilkeston Town | 721 | D | 2-2 | Laws 40, Robinson 60 |
| 28 | 15/12 | A | DM C 2 | Bashley | 180 | D | 1-1 | Laws 62 |
| 29 | 19/12 | A | DMP | Atherstone United | 225 | D | 0-0 | |
| 30 | 21/12 | H | DM C 2 r | Bashley | 436 | L | 1-3 | Adcock 79 |
| 31 | 28/12 | A | DMP | Merthyr Tydfil | 426 | D | 1-1 | Laws 27 |
| 32 | 01/01 | A | DMP | Dorchester Town | 4159 | D | 1-1 | Richardson 64 |
| 33 | 02/01 | H | DMP | Worcester City | 934 | W | 2-1 | Laws 32 65 |
| 34 | 05/01 | H | DSC QF | Bridport | 365 | W | 1-0 | Boulton 48 |
| 35 | 09/01 | A | DMP | Burton Albion | 865 | W | 2-1 | Mansell 45, Hutchinson 78 |
| 36 | 16/01 | H | FA T 3 | Sutton United | 1060 | W | 1-0 | Laws 54 |
| 37 | 23/01 | A | DMP | Tamworth | 591 | W | 3-1 | Robinson 11, Laws 61 86 |
| 38 | 30/01 | H | DMP | Rothwell Town | 930 | W | 5-0 | Laws 21 82, Mansell 45 55, Robinson 64 |
| 39 | 06/02 | H | FA T 4 | Forest Green Rovers | 1415 | L | 1-2 | Mason 88 |
| 40 | 13/02 | H | DMP | Tamworth | 894 | L | 0-3 | |
| 41 | 16/02 | H | DMP | Crawley Town | 634 | L | 1-3 | Laws 39 |
| 42 | 20/02 | A | DMP | Hastings Town | 366 | W | 1-0 | Mansell 6 |
| 43 | 27/02 | H | DMP | Burton Albion | 927 | D | 0-0 | |
| 44 | 06/03 | A | DSC SF | Hamworthy Engineering | 250 | W | 4-1 | Brown 43 69, Gammon 73, Adcock 90 |
| 45 | 07/03 | H | DMP | Gresley Rovers | 657 | W | 3-1 | Browne 25, Adcock 39, Laws 51 |
| 46 | 13/03 | H | DMP | Halesowen Town | 689 | D | 2-2 | Mansell 17, Laws 64 |
| 47 | 20/03 | A | DMP | Boston United | 1100 | L | 1-2 | Mansell 87 |
| 48 | 27/03 | H | DMP | Atherstone United | 727 | L | 0-1 | |
| 49 | 30/03 | H | DMP | Dorchester Town | 2921 | W | 2-1 | Laws 14[p] 25 |
| 50 | 03/04 | A | DMP | Crawley Town | 602 | D | 2-2 | Laws 4, Browne 17 |
| 51 | 05/04 | H | DMP | Merthyr Tydfil | 1042 | D | 0-0 | |
| 52 | 10/04 | A | DMP | Worcester City | 816 | L | 0-3 | |
| 53 | 14/04 | A | DSC F | Wimborne Town | 452 | W | 4-1 | Gammon 28 65 69[p], Browne 49 (at Dorchester T) |
| 54 | 17/04 | H | DMP | Nuneaton Borough | 1350 | D | 1-1 | Robinson 50 |
| 55 | 20/04 | A | DMP | Cambridge City | 201 | L | 0-1 | |
| 56 | 24/04 | A | DMP | Bromsgrove Rovers | 333 | D | 2-2 | Laws 60 70 |
| 57 | 01/05 | H | DMP | Grantham Town | 1041 | W | 1-0 | Brown 40 |

## PLAYING SQUAD 1999-2000:

GOALKEEPERS: Dan Claxton (Dorchester United), Scott Cooksey (on loan from Shrewsbury)

DEFENDERS: Lee Bradford (Dorchester Town), Alex Browne, Simon Browne (Salisbury City), Darren Powell (Bashley), Matthew Hale (Bristol City), Matt Hare (Sligo Rovers), Ian Hutchinson (Halifax Town), Craig Mansell (Hereford United), Andrew Mason (Thame United), Micky Preston (Torquay United), Mark Robinson (Gravesend & Northfleet), Andy Turrell, John Waldock (Weymouth)

FORWARDS: Paul Adcock (Gloucester City), Richard Ball (Bromsgrove Rovers), Chris Evans (Bridport), Mark Gammon (Truro City), Stuart Heath, David Laws (Bishop Auckland)

# WORCESTER CITY

## CLUB OFFICIALS

Chairman: **Dr Michael Sorensen**
Vice Chairman: **Laurie Brown**

Secretary: **Steve Bond**
4 Ferry Close, Worcester, Worcs WR2 5PQ
Tel: 01905 423120/25427

## FOOTBALL MANAGEMENT TEAM

Manager:Graham Allner
Assistant Manager: Paul Davies
Physio: Archie Richards

## GROUND

**Directions:** M5 jct 6 (Worcester North), follow signs to Worcester, right at first lights, St Georges Lane is 3rd left. 1 mile from Foregate Street (BR)station
Capacity: 3,443          Cover: 2,000          Seats: 1,223          Floodlights: Yes

**Clubhouse:** Open every evening and Saturday and Sunday daytime. Cold snacks available
**Club Shop:** Sells programmes and souvenirs. Contact Sarah Bushell c/o club

FACT FILE
Formed: 1902
Nickname: The City
Sponsors: Banks's
Newsline: 0930 555 810
Colours: Blue & white/blue/white
Change colours: All yellow
Midweek matchday: Monday
Reserve Lge: Central Conference
1998-99
Captain: Chris Greenman
P.o.Y: Carl Heeley
Top Scorer: Mark Owen

St George's Lane, Barbourne, Worcester WR1 1QT
Tel: 01905 23003 Fax: 26668

Pages: 36          Price: £1.20
Editor: Julian Pugh (01905 723234)
Local Press: Berrows Journal,
Worcester Evening News
Local Radio: Radio Wyvern,
BBC Hereford & Worcester

WORCESTER CITY
V
ROTHWELL TOWN
SATURDAY 5TH SEPTEMBER 1998
KICK OFF 3.00PM

**PREVIOUS**          **Leagues:** West Mids (Birmingham) 1902-38, Southern 38-79, Alliance Premier 79-85
                     **Names:** Berwick Rangers     **Grounds:** Severn Terrace, Thorneloe, Flagge Meadow

**CLUB RECORDS**     **Attendance:** 17,042 v Sheff Utd (lost 0-2), FA Cup 4th Rd 24/1/59
                     **Win:** 18-1 v Bilston, Birmingham League 21/11/31          **Defeat:** 0-10 v Wellington, Birmingham League 29/8/20
                     **Career Goalscorer:** John Inglis 189 (1970-77)     **Career Appearances:** Bobby McEwan 596 (1959-75)
                     **Transfer fee paid:** £8,500 for Jim Williams (Telford United, 1981)
                     **Transfer fee received:** £27,000 for John Barton (Everton, 1979)

**BEST SEASON**      **FA Cup:** 4th Rd 58-59. 1st Rd (12)
                     **FA Trophy:** QF 69-70 73-74 80-81 81-82          **Welsh Cup:** Semi-Final 78-79

**HONOURS**          Southern Lg 78-79, Div 1 67-68, Div 1 Nth 76-77, Lg Cup R-up 45-46 59-60, Chal.Cup 39-40, Champs Cup 78-79; West Mids
                     (B'ham) Lg(4) 13-14 24-25 28-30 (R-up (3) 31-34); Worcs Snr Cup (26) 07-14 28-30 32-33 45-46(jt) 48-49 55-59 60-61 62-63
                     64-65 69-70 77-78 79-80 81-82 83-84 87-88 96-97; B'ham Snr Cup 75-76; Staffs Snr Cup 76-77; Inter Lg Champs Cup 78-79

Players progressing: A Awford (Portsmouth 91), P King/K Ball (Cardiff C.60/65), JWilliams/M Gayle (Walsall 79/91), J Fairbrother (Peterborough 65),
DTennant (Lincoln 66), R Davies (Derby 71), N Merrick (Bournemouth 74), J Barton(Everton 79), A Preece (Wrexham 90), D Lyttle (Swansea 92)

*Worcester City's Jon Purdie (9) and Paul Davies in action against Bromsgrove Rovers.     Photo: Tim O'Grady*

## WORCESTER CITY - MATCH FACTS - 1998-99 SEASON

| No | Date | Venue | Comp | Opponents | Att | Result | Score | Goalscorers |
|----|------|-------|------|-----------|-----|--------|-------|-------------|
| 1 | 08/08 | H | PC | Hereford United | 890 | D | 1-1 | Bowen 42 |
| 2 | 22/08 | H | DMP | Grantham Town | 1012 | L | 1-2 | Burnham 73[p] |
| 3 | 25/08 | A | DMP | Burton Albion | 952 | W | 1-0 | Woods 13 |
| 4 | 29/08 | A | DMP | Tamworth | 599 | W | 1-0 | Wright 81 |
| 5 | 31/08 | H | DMP | Atherstone United | 1043 | L | 1-2 | Bowen 88 |
| 6 | 05/09 | H | DMP | Rothwell Town | 721 | W | 1-0 | Owen 45 |
| 7 | 08/09 | A | DMP | Merthyr Tydfil | 496 | W | 1-0 | Chenoweth 68 |
| 8 | 12/09 | A | DMP | Crawley Town | 643 | L | 1-2 | Wright 90 |
| 9 | 14/09 | H | DMP | Burton Albion | 864 | W | 2-0 | Cotterill 19, Owen 22 |
| 10 | 19/09 | H | DMP | Nuneaton Borough | 1355 | L | 0-4 | |
| 11 | 21/09 | A | DMP | Atherstone United | 402 | D | 1-1 | Bowen 64 |
| 12 | 26/09 | H | DMP | King's Lynn | 682 | W | 3-2 | Burnham 62[p], Chenoweth 68, Bowen 78 |
| 13 | 03/10 | A | FA C Q2 | Mangotsfield United | 344 | W | 1-0 | Chenoweth 2 |
| 14 | 10/10 | A | DMP | Ilkeston Town | 648 | L | 0-3 | |
| 15 | 17/10 | H | FA C Q3 | Falmouth Town | 931 | W | 3-1 | Bowen 3, Richards 22, Griffiths 46 |
| 16 | 19/10 | H | BSC 1 | Dudley Town | 181 | W | 3-1 | Griffiths 15, Burnham 41[p], Bowen 77 |
| 17 | 24/10 | H | FA T 1 | Billericay Town | 441 | W | 2-1 | Richards 38, Bowen 64 |
| 18 | 03/11 | H | FA C Q4 | Langney Sports | 1012 | W | 7-0 | Bowen 23 68, Griffiths 55 65, Chenoweth 66 82, Owen 85 |
| 19 | 07/11 | A | DMP | Dorchester Town | 514 | W | 2-1 | Chenoweth 9, Bowen 77 |
| 20 | 09/11 | H | DM C 1(1) | Bilston Town | 736 | D | 1-1 | Wells 74 |
| 21 | 14/11 | A | FA C 1 | Torquay United | 3023 | L | 0-1 | |
| 22 | 21/11 | A | FA T 2 | Fisher Athletic | 204 | D | 1-1 | Griffiths 12 |
| 23 | 23/11 | H | FA T 2 r | Fisher Athletic | 531 | W | 5-1 | Wright 24 48 58, Woods 56, Cottrill 73 |
| 24 | 28/11 | A | DMP | Crawley Town | 757 | L | 1-2 | Cottrill 19 |
| 25 | 30/11 | H | B SC 2 | WalsalL | 273 | W | 1-0 | Cottrill 32 |
| 26 | 02/12 | A | DM C 1(2) | Bilston Town | 43 | L | 1-3 | Wright 60 |
| 27 | 05/12 | A | DMP | Halesowen Town | 704 | D | 0-0 | |
| 28 | 07/12 | H | DMP | Bath City | 602 | L | 0-3 | |
| 29 | 12/12 | A | DMP | Salisbury City | 317 | L | 0-2 | |
| 30 | 19/12 | H | DMP | Hastings Town | 574 | D | 0-0 | |
| 31 | 26/12 | A | DMP | Bromsgrove Rovers | 878 | W | 2-0 | Owen 34 85 |
| 32 | 28/12 | H | DMP | Gloucester City | 1045 | D | 2-2 | Owen 1 38 |
| 33 | 01/01 | H | DMP | Tamworth | 1112 | W | 1-0 | Cottrill 58 |
| 34 | 02/01 | A | DMP | Weymouth | 934 | L | 1-2 | Cottrill 11 |
| 35 | 09/01 | A | DMP | Grantham Town | 478 | W | 3-0 | Owen 10 69 69 |
| 36 | 23/01 | A | DMP | Cambridge City | 258 | L | 0-3 | |
| 37 | 28/01 | A | FA T 3 | Havant & Waterlooville | 254 | W | 1-0 | Owen 43 |
| 38 | 30/01 | H | DMP | Dorchester Town | 894 | D | 2-2 | Bowen 19, Cottrill 62 |
| 39 | 01/02 | A | B SC 3 | West Bromwich Albion | 413 | W | 2-0 | Chenoweth 1, Greenman 83[p] |
| 40 | 06/02 | A | FA T 4 | Northwich Victoria | 1109 | L | 0-1 | |
| 41 | 08/02 | A | W SC QF | Redditch United | 95 | W | 4-2 | Bowen 28, Davis 34 42 87 |
| 42 | 13/02 | A | DMP | King's Lynn | 663 | L | 0-2 | |
| 43 | 15/02 | H | DMP | Merthyr Tydfil | 812 | W | 6-1 | Owen 5 25 52, Purdie 29 35, Green 75[p] |
| 44 | 20/02 | H | DMP | Ilkeston Town | 1007 | W | 2-0 | Owen 44, Lutz 77 |
| 45 | 22/02 | H | B SC QF | Solihull Borough | 326 | W | 5-2 | Owen 3 72, Bowen 40, Lutz 60, Burnham 66 |
| 46 | 27/02 | A | DMP | Halesowen Town | 1403 | L | 3-4 | Owen 5 58, Davis 37 |
| 47 | 06/03 | A | DMP | Hastings Town | 410 | L | 0-1 | |
| 48 | 08/03 | H | DMP | Salisbury City | 703 | D | 0-0 | |
| 49 | 13/03 | H | DMP | Gresley Rovers | 789 | D | 3-3 | Chenoweth 61 65, Bowen 71 |
| 50 | 16/03 | A | DMP | Bath City | 486 | D | 0-0 | |
| 51 | 20/03 | A | DMP | Nuneaton Borough | 1724 | L | L | 0-2 |
| 52 | 22/03 | H | W SC SF | Stourbridge | 341 | W | 2-1 | Greenman 55[p], Bowen 82 |
| 53 | 29/03 | H | DMP | Boston United | 690 | W | 1-0 | Cottrill 38 |
| 54 | 03/04 | H | DMP | Bromsgrove Rovers | 1270 | W | 3-1 | Davis 75 82, Bowen 85 |
| 55 | 05/04 | A | DMP | Gloucester City | 668 | W | 2-0 | Bowen 12 89 |
| 56 | 07/04 | H | B SC SF | Birmingham City | 380 | L | 1-3 | Owen 15 |
| 57 | 10/04 | H | DMP | Weymouth | 816 | W | 3-0 | Purdie 1, Bowen 17, Chenoweth 37 |
| 58 | 17/04 | A | DMP | Gresley Rovers | 490 | D | 1-1 | Sandeman 68 |
| 59 | 19/04 | H | W SC F(1) | Kidderminster Harriers | 1019 | W | 3-2 | Bowen 28, Sandeman 42, Owen 83 |
| 60 | 24/04 | H | DMP | Cambridge City | 907 | W | 4-2 | Owen 34 58, Bowen 45[p], Carter 71[og] |
| 61 | 27/04 | A | W SC F(2) | Kidderminster Harriers | 1176 | L | L | 0-2 |
| 62 | 28/04 | A | DMP | Rothwell Town | 214 | W | 2-1 | Owen 46 70 |
| 63 | 01/05 | A | DMP | Boston United | 1023 | L | 1-3 | Bowen 86 |

## PLAYING SQUAD 1999-2000:

GOALKEEPERS: Darren Steadman (Kidderminster Harriers), Danny Watson (Bridgnorth Town)

DEFENDERS: Paul Bloomfield (ex-Cheltenham Town), Graham Brown (Kidderminster Harriers), Marc Burrow, Chris Greenman (Peterborough United), Carl Heeley (Sutton Coldfield Town), Steve Hillman, Dave Richards (Walsall)

MIDFIELDERS: Ian Cottrill (Nuneaton Borough), Andy Ellis (Woking), Richard Gardner (Bromsgrove Rovers), Nathan Jukes (Dorchester Town), Keith Knight (Cheltenham Town), Steve Lutz (Pershore Town), Jon Narbett (Kidderminster Harriers), Shaun Rouse (Trowbridge Town), Bradley Sandeman (Kettering Town)

FORWARDS: Sam Bowen (Merthyr Tydfil), Paul Davies (Hednesford Town), Michael Griffiths (Worcester City), Jon Purdie (Kidderminster Harriers), Kevin Willetts (Kidderminster Harriers)

# NON-LEAGUE NEWSDESK

## FOR RESULTS, TABLES AND NEWS FROM THE NON-LEAGUE PYRAMID

Now entering its fifth full season, Non-League Newsdesk has become firmly established as the number one magazine for up-to-date news and statistics from the Pyramid world.

Founded in 1995 by former Non-League Club Directory editor James Wright, Non-League Newsdesk will in 1999-2000 celebrate its 200th edition. The magazine is delivered to subscribers every midweek (usually Wednesday) carrying all the previous week's results, together with current tables, from around FIFTY leagues.

For many of the more senior competitions, full match details (such as goalscorers and attendances) are supplied. County and League Cup competitions are also extensively featured, as are the FA Umbro Trophy and FA Carlsberg Vase, and the involvement of the non-League clubs in the AXA sponsored FA Cup.

But Non-League Newsdesk is not just a statistical work. Each week the magazine carries up-to-date news stories and listings of managerial changes and transfers.

The magazine is therefore particularly popular with -
       * Clubs, who find much of the information extremely useful for matchday
       programmes and in checking on forthcoming opponents, particularly those from
outside their own league.
       * Statisticians, who see the weekly stats as the most extensive, accurate and
       up-to-date available.
       * Groundhoppers, who find it invaluable in picking their games.
       * The more general non-League enthusiast who likes to keep abreast of the
       most current news.
If you would like to see a free sample copy from 1998-99, please send an SAE to James Wright at the address below.

Leagues featured in Non-League Newsdesk include: Nationwide Conference, UniBond, Ryman, Dr Martens, First NW Trains NWCL, SGL West Lancs, Manchester, Carlsberg West Cheshire, Green Contract Services Mid-Cheshire, Arnott Insurance Northern, Northern Co's (East), Redferns Central Midlands, Powerleague Notts Alliance, West Yorkshire, Deejays Lincs, Everards Leics, Vaux Wearside, JPL Wade Northern Alliance, Herts, A Quote Insurance Reading, Courage Combined Co's, Cherry Red Chiltonian, Minerva SSML, Essex Senior, Essex Intermediate, Kent Blaxill Essex & Suffolk Border, Interlink Alliance, Endsleigh Midland Comb, Banks's West Mids, Springbank Vending Midland, Complete Music Hellenic, Glos. County, Somerset Senior, Screwfix Western, Jewson SW, Jolly's Cornwall Combination, Cornish Guardian East Cornwall, Westward Developments Devon, Jewson Wessex, Keyline Dorset Comb., Dorset Co., Hampshire, Unijet Sussex, Bass Kent, British Energy Kent Co., Jewson ECL, Lovewell Blake Anglian Combination, McGinty's Suffolk & Ipswich, Uhlsport UCL, Optimum Interiors Capital and Central Conference, League of Wales, CC Sports Welsh League, Cymru Alliance.

JAMES WRIGHT, 13 NORTHFIELD AVENUE, TAUNTON, SOMERSET TA1 1XF
TEL/FAX: 01823 327720  MOBILE: 0421 004219  E-MAIL:NLNEWSDESK@ZETNET.CO.UK

## Subscription Rates

Non-League Newsdesk costs just 80p per week plus first class postage (26p). It is produced every Monday during the season except the week between Christmas and New Year. The table below shows how much a subscription will cost from your chosen starting date.

| FROM | to Xmas | Full season |
|---|---|---|
| Aug 9th | £21.20 | £42.40 |
| Aug 16th | £20.14 | £41.34 |
| Aug 23rd | £19.08 | £40.28 |
| Aug 30th | £18.02 | £39.22 |
| Sept 6th | £16.96 | £38.16 |
| Sept 13th | £15.90 | £37.10 |
| Sept 20th | £14.84 | £36.04 |
| Sept 27th | £13.78 | £34.98 |
| Oct 4th | £12.72 | £33.92 |
| Oct 11th | £11.66 | £32.86 |
| Oct 18th | £10.60 | £31.80 |
| Oct 25th | £9.54 | £30.74 |
| Nov 1st | £8.48 | £29.68 |
| Nov 8th | £7.42 | £28.62 |
| Nov 15th | £6.36 | £27.56 |
| Nov 22nd | £5.30 | £26.50 |
| Nov 29th | £4.24 | £25.44 |
| Dec 5th | £3.18 | £24.38 |
| Dec 12th | £2.12 | £23.32 |
| Dec 19th | £1.06 | £22.26 |
| Jan 3rd | n/a | £21.20 |
| Jan 10th | n/a | £20.14 |
| Jan 17th | n/a | £19.08 |
| Jan 24th | n/a | £18.02 |
| Jan 31st | n/a | £16.96 |
| Feb 7th | n/a | £15.90 |
| Feb 14th | n/a | £14.84 |
| Feb 21st | n/a | £13.78 |
| Feb 28th | n/a | £12.72 |
| Mar 7th | n/a | £11.66 |
| Mar 14th | n/a | £10.60 |
| Mar 21st | n/a | £9.54 |
| Mar 28th | n/a | £8.48 |
| April 4th | n/a | £7.42 |
| April 11th | n/a | £6.36 |
| April 18th | n/a | £5.30 |
| April 25th | n/a | £4.24 |
| May 2nd | n/a | £3.18 |
| May 9th | n/a | £2.12 |
| End of season issue | | £1.06 |

## TO ORDER
Simply send your:
Name, Address, Tel. No., When you want your subscription to start and whether it is Until Christmas or until the End of the season

Please send cheque or postal order payable to Non-League Newsdesk to the address opposite

516

# BROMSGROVE ROVERS - MATCH FACTS - 1998-99 SEASON

| No | Date | Venue | Comp | Opponents | Att | Result | Score | Goalscorers |
|----|------|-------|------|-----------|-----|--------|-------|-------------|
| | 22/08 | H | DMP | Gresley Rovers | 851 | D | 0-0 | |
| | 25/08 | A | DMP | Grantham Town | 915 | L | 1-4 | Ashley 67[p] |
| | 29/08 | A | DMP | Weymouth | 1066 | L | 1-3 | Amos 61 |
| | 31/08 | A | DMP | Tamworth | 841 | W | 2-1 | Payne 36 89 |
| | 05/09 | H | DMP | Boston United | 822 | D | 2-2 | Ulfig 5, Bennett 64 |
| | 08/09 | A | DMP | King's Lynn | 591 | W | 1-0 | Ulfig 38 |
| | 12/09 | H | DMP | Burton Albion | 712 | L | 1-2 | Payne 64 |
| | 15/09 | A | DMP | Grantham Town | 561 | W | 4-2 | Payne 6 12, Cooksey 76, Robinson 88 |
| | 19/09 | H | DMP | Rothwell Town | 641 | W | 3-0 | Payne 5 32, Moore 89 |
| 0 | 22/09 | A | DMP | Tamworth | 522 | L | 0-1 | |
| 1 | 26/09 | A | DMP | Bath City | 802 | L | 0-3 | |
| 2 | 29/09 | H | DMP | Gloucester City | 634 | L | 0-1 | |
| 3 | 03/10 | H | FA C Q2 | King's Lynn | 807 | D | 1-1 | Bennett 34 |
| 4 | 06/10 | A | FA C Q2 r | King's Lynn | 715 | L | 1-2 | Moore 74 |
| 5 | 10/10 | A | DMP | Merthyr Tydfil | 484 | L | 0-2 | |
| 6 | 24/10 | H | DMP | Nuneaton Borough | 608 | L | 0-4 | |
| 7 | 07/11 | H | DMP | Hastings Town | 409 | W | 2-1 | Cooper 26, Ashley 37[p] |
| 8 | 10/11 | A | DM C 1(1) | Halesowen Town | 403 | L | 0-1 | |
| 9 | 14/11 | A | DMP | Rothwell Town | 210 | L | 0-2 | |
| 20 | 21/11 | H | FA T 2 | Hednesford Town | 721 | L | 1-2 | Payne 44 |
| 21 | 28/11 | H | DMP | Bath City | 580 | L | 1-3 | Sutton 84 |
| 22 | 05/12 | A | DMP | Gloucester City | 463 | L | 3-4 | Payne 30 88, Bennett 67 |
| 23 | 09/12 | H | DM C 1(2) | Halesowen Town | 132 | L | 1-2 | Moore 85 |
| 24 | 12/12 | H | DMP | Boston United | 524 | D | 1-1 | Payne 86 |
| 25 | 19/12 | A | DMP | Crawley Town | 877 | L | 1-4 | Winstone 59 |
| 26 | 26/12 | H | DMP | Worcester City | 878 | L | 0-2 | |
| 27 | 28/12 | A | DMP | Halesowen Town | 808 | L | 0-1 | |
| 28 | 01/01 | A | DMP | Atherstone United | 332 | L | 1-5 | Sutton 10 |
| 29 | 02/01 | H | DMP | Dorchester Town | 508 | L | 1-2 | Payne 42 |
| 30 | 09/01 | A | DMP | Gresley Rovers | 435 | W | 3-1 | Payne 55 77, Bennett 64 |
| 31 | 12/01 | H | W SC QF | Moor Green | 211 | D | 2-2 | Munday 5, Payne 78 |
| 32 | 23/01 | H | DMP | Merthyr Tydfil | 515 | L | 0-1 | |
| 33 | 30/01 | A | DMP | Salisbury City | 494 | L | 0-1 | |
| 34 | 02/02 | A | W SC QF r | Moor Green | 127 | W | 3-2 | Ashley 78, Petty 82, Bowater 85 |
| 35 | 06/02 | H | DMP | Ilkeston Town | 524 | L | 0-2 | |
| 36 | 13/02 | H | DMP | Atherstone United | 485 | D | 0-0 | |
| 37 | 20/02 | A | DMP | Dorchester Town | 558 | L | 0-3 | |
| 38 | 27/02 | H | DMP | Salisbury City | 348 | L | 0-2 | |
| 39 | 06/03 | A | DMP | Nuneaton Borough | 1533 | L | 0-6 | |
| 40 | 13/03 | A | DMP | Ilkeston Town | 568 | L | 1-2 | Gardner 46 |
| 41 | 16/03 | A | DMP | King's Lynn | 621 | D | 0-0 | |
| 42 | 20/03 | H | DMP | Cambridge City | 396 | W | 2-1 | Winstone 2, T Davies 50 |
| 43 | 30/03 | H | DMP | Crawley Town | 458 | W | 1-0 | Gardner 16[p] |
| 44 | 03/04 | A | DMP | Worcester City | 1270 | L | 1-3 | Ball 57 |
| 45 | 05/04 | H | DMP | Halesowen Town | 890 | L | 2-5 | Winstone 24, Ball 54 |
| 46 | 10/04 | H | DMP | Burton Albion | 466 | D | 0-0 | |
| 47 | 14/04 | A | WSC SF | Kidderminster Harriers | 515 | L | 1-6 | Ball 76 |
| 48 | 17/04 | A | DMP | Hastings Town | 367 | L | 0-2 | |
| 49 | 24/04 | H | DMP | Weymouth | 333 | D | 2-2 | Ball 34 80 |
| 50 | 01/05 | A | DMP | Cambridge City | 217 | L | 1-3 | Cooper 17 |

# GRESLEY ROVERS - MATCH FACTS - 1998-99 SEASON

| No | Date | Venue | Comp | Opponents | Att | Result | Score | Goalscorers |
|----|------|-------|------|-----------|-----|--------|-------|-------------|
| 1 | 31/07 | H | BV Gp 1 | Notts County | n/k | L | 1-3 | |
| 2 | 04/08 | H | BV Gp 1 | West Bromwich Albion | n/k | W | 1-0 | |
| 3 | 22/08 | A | DMP | Bromsgrove Rovers | 851 | D | 0-0 | |
| 4 | 25/08 | H | DMP | Halesowen Town | 570 | W | 2-0 | Rowland, Lonergan 71 |
| 5 | 29/08 | H | DMP | Dorchester Town | 502 | W | 2-0 | Rowland 3, Pitt 48 |
| 6 | 31/08 | A | DMP | Merthyr Tydfil | 650 | W | 2-1 | Fowkes 13, Rowland 22 |
| 7 | 05/09 | H | DMP | Salisbury City | 571 | W | 4-1 | Pitt 11 86[p], Simpson 30 61 |
| 8 | 08/09 | A | DMP | Rothwell Town | 253 | L | 0-2 | |
| 9 | 12/09 | H | DMP | Ilkeston Town | 720 | L | 1-3 | Orton 60 |
| 10 | 15/09 | A | DMP | Halesowen Town | 543 | W | 4-3 | Pitt 4 11 64, Rowland 26 |
| 11 | 19/09 | A | DMP | Tamworth | 594 | W | 1-0 | Simpson 90 |
| 12 | 22/09 | H | DMP | Merthyr Tydfil | 505 | D | 0-0 | |
| 13 | 26/09 | H | DMP | Boston United | 583 | W | 1-0 | Pitt 24 |
| 14 | 03/10 | A | FA C Q2 | Shepshed Dynamo | 428 | W | 2-1 | Pitt 1[p] 10[p] |
| 15 | 10/10 | A | DMP | Cambridge City | 268 | W | 2-1 | Pitt 22, Fowkes 83 |
| 16 | 17/10 | A | FA C Q3 | Halesowen Town | 652 | W | 2-1 | Fitzpatrick 75, Pitt 87 |
| 17 | 31/10 | A | FA C Q4 | Frickley Athletic | 530 | D | 0-0 | |
| 18 | 05/11 | H | FA C Q4 r | Frickley Athletic | 621 | W | 2-1 | Simpson 60, Stratford 70[og] |
| 19 | 07/11 | A | DMP | Weymouth | 560 | L | 1-2 | Fitzpatrick 37 |
| 20 | 09/11 | H | FA T 1 | Stamford | 322 | W | 1-0 | Rowland 49 |
| 21 | 14/11 | A | FA C 1 | Walsall | 4274 | L | 0-1 | |
| 22 | 17/11 | A | DM C 1(1) | Tamworth | 326 | L | 1-4 | Sandar 34 |
| 23 | 21/11 | A | FA T 2 | Hinckley United | 397 | L | 0-2 | |
| 24 | 28/11 | H | DMP | Gloucester City | 512 | L | 2-3 | Rowland 57 84 |
| 25 | 05/12 | H | DMP | King's Lynn | 413 | W | 2-1 | Brown 60 77 |
| 26 | 12/12 | A | DMP | Hastings Town | 355 | W | 2-1 | Rowland 20, Pitt 71[p] |
| 27 | 19/12 | H | DMP | Grantham Town | 517 | L | 0-1 | |
| 28 | 22/12 | H | DM C 1(2) | Tamworth | 178 | L | 0-4 | |
| 29 | 26/12 | A | DMP | Burton Albion | 2103 | L | 0-1 | |
| 30 | 28/12 | H | DMP | Nuneaton Borough | 1490 | L | 0-3 | |
| 31 | 01/01 | H | DMP | Burton Albion | 1998 | L | 0-2 | |
| 32 | 03/01 | A | DMP | King's Lynn | 475 | L | 0-4 | |
| 33 | 09/01 | H | DMP | Bromsgrove Rovers | 435 | L | 1-3 | Pitt 50 |
| 34 | 16/01 | A | DMP | Bath City | 857 | L | 0-3 | |
| 35 | 19/01 | A | DSC 3 | Stapenhill | 150 | W | 3-2 | Fitzpatrick 1[p], Smith 25, Rowland 30 |
| 36 | 23/01 | A | DMP | Ilkeston Town | 678 | L | 1-4 | Smith 52 |
| 37 | 30/01 | H | DMP | Tamworth | 684 | L | 2-3 | Simpson 31, Orton 45 |
| 38 | 06/02 | A | DMP | Gloucester City | 531 | D | 0-0 | |
| 39 | 13/02 | H | DMP | Hastings Town | 432 | D | 0-0 | |
| 40 | 15/02 | A | DMP | Atherstone United | 285 | L | 1-2 | Pitt 27 |
| 41 | 20/02 | A | DMP | Boston United | 1026 | L | 1-4 | Fowkes 73 |
| 42 | 23/02 | A | DMP | Grantham Town | 369 | L | 1-3 | Rowlands 89 |
| 43 | 27/02 | H | DMP | Atherstone United | 573 | W | 2-1 | Rowland 27, Carvell 73 |
| 44 | 07/03 | A | DMP | Weymouth | 657 | L | 1-3 | Payne 79 |
| 45 | 13/03 | A | DMP | Worcester City | 789 | D | 3-3 | Simpson 26, Carvell 35, Payne 37 |
| 46 | 16/03 | H | DSC QF | Sandiacre Town | 191 | W | 1-0 | Grant 78 |
| 47 | 20/03 | H | DMP | Crawley Town | 503 | D | 1-1 | Kearns 21 |
| 48 | 30/03 | A | DSC SF | Ilkeston Town | 489 | L | 0-1 | |
| 49 | 03/04 | H | DMP | Cambridge City | 550 | W | 3-0 | Orton 48 59, Fowkes 52 |
| 50 | 05/04 | A | DMP | Nuneaton Borough | 2945 | L | 1-3 | Rowland 90 |
| 51 | 10/04 | A | DMP | Crawley Town | 438 | L | 0-2 | |
| 52 | 13/04 | H | DMP | Rothwell Town | 419 | L | 1-3 | Rowland 44 |
| 53 | 17/04 | H | DMP | Worcester City | 490 | D | 1-1 | Rowland 33 |
| 54 | 24/04 | A | DMP | Dorchester Town | 802 | L | 0-1 | |
| 55 | 28/04 | A | DMP | Salisbury City | 352 | D | 2-2 | Orton 6, Broadhurst 60 |
| 56 | 01/05 | H | DMP | Bath City | 547 | L | 1-2 | Pitt 52[p] |

518

# HASTINGS TOWN - MATCH FACTS - 1998-99 SEASON

| o | Date | Venue | Comp | Opponents | Att | Result | Score | Goalscorers |
|---|------|-------|------|-----------|-----|--------|-------|-------------|
| | 22/08 | A | DMP | Nuneaton Borough | 1211 | L | 0-1 | |
| | 25/08 | H | DMP | Cambridge City | 463 | W | 2-0 | Fox 20 87 |
| | 29/08 | H | DMP | Rothwell Town | 445 | D | 1-1 | White 90[p] |
| | 31/08 | A | DMP | Dorchester Town | 508 | W | 2-1 | McRobert 29 64 |
| | 05/09 | H | DMP | Ilkeston Town | 485 | W | 3-0 | Romasz 2, Fox 72 86 |
| | 08/09 | A | DMP | Bath City | 592 | W | 2-0 | McRobert 4, Romasz 20 |
| | 12/09 | H | DMP | Halesowen Town | 555 | W | 2-0 | Beard 72, McRobert 90 |
| | 15/09 | A | DMP | Cambridge City | 254 | W | 1-0 | McRobert 22 |
| | 19/09 | H | DMP | Gloucester City | 620 | D | 0-0 | |
| | 22/09 | H | DMP | Dorchester Town | 531 | W | 1-0 | Morris 72 |
| | 26/09 | A | DMP | Merthyr Tydfil | 477 | L | 0-1 | |
| | 03/10 | A | FA C Q2 | Newmarket Town | 320 | D | 1-1 | Fox 82 |
| | 06/10 | H | FA C Q2 r | Newmarket Town | 538 | W | 2-1 | McRobert 4 104 |
| | 10/10 | H | DMP | Tamworth | 487 | L | 1-2 | Beard 12 |
| | 17/10 | H | FA C Q3 | Yeovil Town | 1156 | L | 0-3 | |
| | 31/10 | A | DMP | Boston United | 874 | D | 1-1 | Yates 13 |
| | 02/11 | H | FA T 1 | Chelmsford City | 298 | D | 2-2 | Jones 81, McRobert 83 |
| | 05/11 | A | FA T 1 r | Chelmsford City | 264 | W | 1-0 | Simmonds 50 |
| | 07/11 | A | DMP | Bromsgrove Rovers | 409 | L | 1-2 | Myall 28 |
| | 10/11 | A | DMC1(1) | Ashford Town | 437 | W | 3-2 | McRobert 6 55, Sargent 71 |
| | 14/11 | H | DMP | Nuneaton Borough | 710 | L | 0-4 | |
| | 21/11 | A | FA T 2 | Ashford Town | 531 | W | 2-0 | McRobert 68 89[p] |
| | 24/11 | H | DMC1(2) | Ashford Town | 213 | L | 1-2 | White 64 (won on away goals rule) |
| | 28/11 | A | DMP | Weymouth | 803 | W | 2-1 | Yates 62 79 |
| | 01/12 | A | SSC 2 | Broadbridge Heath | 140 | W | 5-0 | Morris 14 83, Simmons 28, Smith 42, Mintram 89 |
| | 05/12 | A | DMP | Atherstone United | 213 | D | 1-1 | Yates 26 |
| | 12/12 | H | DMP | Gresley Rovers | 355 | L | 1-2 | McRobert 48 |
| | 19/12 | A | DMP | Worcester City | 574 | D | 0-0 | |
| | 22/12 | A | DM C 2 | Folkestone Invicta | 267 | L | 1-2 | White 37 |
| | 28/12 | A | DMP | Salisbury City | 462 | L | 0-1 | |
| | 01/01 | A | DMP | Crawley Town | 1759 | L | 1-3 | Playford 68 |
| | 02/01 | A | DMP | Atherstone United | 371 | D | 0-0 | |
| | 09/01 | H | DMP | Boston United | 398 | W | 1-0 | Playford 89 |
| | 23/01 | H | DMP | Grantham Town | 417 | L | 1-3 | Jones 16 |
| | 25/01 | H | FA 3 | St Albans City | 380 | L | 0-3 | |
| | 30/01 | A | DMP | King's Lynn | 659 | D | 0-0 | |
| | 02/02 | H | SSC 3 | Portfield | 98 | W | 4-0 | Bourne 5, Yates 35, White 65[p], Jones 76 |
| | 13/02 | A | DMP | Gresley Rovers | 432 | D | 0-0 | |
| | 17/02 | A | SSC QF | Burgess Hill Town | 168 | W | 1-0 | Playford 60 |
| | 20/02 | H | DMP | Weymouth | 366 | L | 0-1 | |
| | 23/02 | H | DMP | Burton Albion | 224 | L | 1-4 | Playford 57 |
| | 27/02 | A | DMP | Tamworth | 451 | W | 5-1 | Smith 9 19, Howard 46[og], Myall 81, Sargeant 88 |
| | 06/03 | H | DMP | Worcester City | 410 | W | 1-0 | Sargent 38 |
| | 13/03 | A | DMP | Burton Albion | 660 | L | 1-3 | Myall 16 |
| | 17/03 | H | SSC SF | Horsham | 180 | W | 2-1 | Yates 8, White 50 (at Lancing) |
| | 20/03 | H | DMP | King's Lynn | 308 | W | 1-0 | Myall 15 |
| | 27/03 | A | DMP | Gloucester City | 394 | W | 3-2 | Sargent 61, White 66[p], Simmonds 75 |
| | 30/03 | H | DMP | Bath City | 288 | D | 2-2 | White 63[p], Simmonds 68 |
| | 03/04 | A | DMP | Rothwell Town | 223 | W | 3-1 | Simmonds 25, Smith 26, Myall 83 |
| | 05/04 | H | DMP | Salisbury City | 376 | W | 3-2 | White 2, Simmonds 16, Smith 37 |
| | 10/04 | A | DMP | Ilkeston Town | 446 | D | 3-3 | Myall 20, Simmonds 38, White 45 |
| | 13/04 | A | DMP | Grantham Town | 294 | W | 2-1 | Smith 52, Simmonds 87 |
| | 17/04 | H | DMP | Bromsgrove Rovers | 367 | W | 2-0 | Tuppenny 12, Smith 71 |
| | 24/04 | A | DMP | Halesowen Town | 742 | D | 3-3 | Tuppeney 62[p], Jones 63, Myall 76 |
| | 27/04 | H | DMP | Crawley Town | 415 | W | 3-0 | Smith 12 19, White 72 |
| | 01/05 | H | DMP | Merthyr Tydfil | 462 | L | 0-2 | |
| | 03/05 | H | SSC F | Worthing | n/k | L | 0-3 | (at Crawley Town) |

Keith Clayton
Photo: Garry Letts

# MIDLAND DIVISION FINAL LEAGUE TABLE 1998-99

| | P | W | D | L | F | A | Pts |
|---|---|---|---|---|---|---|---|
| Clevedon Town | 42 | 28 | 8 | 6 | 83 | 35 | 92 |
| Newport AFC | 42 | 26 | 7 | 9 | 92 | 51 | 85 |
| Redditch United -3 | 42 | 22 | 12 | 8 | 81 | 45 | 75 |
| Hinckley United | 42 | 20 | 12 | 10 | 58 | 40 | 72 |
| Stafford Rangers | 42 | 21 | 8 | 13 | 92 | 60 | 71 |
| Bilston Town | 42 | 20 | 11 | 11 | 79 | 69 | 71 |
| Solihull Borough | 42 | 19 | 12 | 11 | 76 | 53 | 69 |
| Moor Green | 42 | 20 | 7 | 15 | 71 | 61 | 67 |
| Blakenall | 42 | 17 | 14 | 11 | 65 | 54 | 65 |
| Shepshed Dynamo | 42 | 17 | 12 | 13 | 62 | 54 | 63 |
| Sutton Coldfield Town | 42 | 17 | 8 | 17 | 46 | 57 | 59 |
| Stourbridge | 42 | 16 | 10 | 16 | 60 | 55 | 58 |
| Evesham United | 42 | 16 | 9 | 17 | 63 | 63 | 57 |
| Wisbech Town | 42 | 16 | 9 | 17 | 59 | 66 | 57 |
| Weston-super-Mare | 42 | 15 | 10 | 17 | 59 | 56 | 55 |
| Bedworth United | 42 | 15 | 9 | 18 | 63 | 52 | 54 |
| Cinderford Town | 42 | 13 | 8 | 21 | 61 | 74 | 47 |
| Stamford | 42 | 13 | 7 | 22 | 60 | 75 | 46 |
| Paget Rangers | 42 | 11 | 12 | 19 | 49 | 58 | 45 |
| VS Rugby | 42 | 12 | 9 | 21 | 53 | 74 | 45 |
| Racing Club Warwick | 42 | 5 | 8 | 29 | 38 | 93 | 23 |
| Bloxwich Town | 42 | 1 | 2 | 39 | 26 | 151 | 5 |

# MIDLAND DIVISION RESULTS CHART 1998-99

| | | 1 | 2 | 3 | 4 | 5 | 6 | 7 | 8 | 9 | 10 | 11 | 12 | 13 | 14 | 15 | 16 | 17 | 18 | 19 | 20 | 21 | 22 |
|---|---|---|---|---|---|---|---|---|---|---|---|---|---|---|---|---|---|---|---|---|---|---|---|
| 1 | Bedworth U | X | 1-1 | 0-1 | 5-1 | 1-0 | 0-1 | 2-1 | 1-2 | 2-0 | 0-1 | 1-1 | 0-0 | 1-1 | 0-1 | 1-2 | 0-2 | 3-1 | 0-1 | 1-2 | 2-0 | 1-1 | 0-2 |
| 2 | Bilston Tn | 1-1 | X | 2-2 | 5-2 | 4-2 | 0-1 | 2-2 | 2-1 | 3-2 | 5-2 | 1-1 | 1-0 | 0-0 | 3-2 | 3-1 | 1-2 | 1-1 | 1-0 | 2-1 | 2-4 | 0-3 | 3-1 |
| 3 | Blakenall | 2-0 | 1-1 | X | 2-0 | 1-0 | 2-5 | 0-1 | 3-0 | 0-2 | 3-3 | 1-0 | 1-0 | 3-3 | 1-1 | 2-1 | 2-1 | 1-4 | 1-1 | 1-1 | 3-0 | 1-1 | 1-1 |
| 4 | Bloxwich T | 0-5 | 1-6 | 0-2 | X | 1-4 | 1-4 | 0-4 | 0-3 | 1-5 | 0-6 | 1-2 | 1-4 | 0-5 | 1-2 | 2-6 | 1-6 | 2-5 | 0-2 | 0-2 | 1-1 | 0-1 | 1-3 |
| 5 | Cinderford | 1-4 | 1-2 | 2-2 | 6-1 | X | 1-4 | 3-2 | 0-0 | 2-3 | 2-5 | 0-1 | 1-2 | 1-2 | 0-1 | 2-3 | 1-1 | 2-1 | 0-1 | 1-2 | 2-1 | 2-3 | |
| 6 | Clevedon T | 3-4 | 3-0 | 1-2 | 4-1 | 2-0 | X | 1-1 | 0-1 | 1-1 | 2-1 | 1-1 | 2-0 | 3-0 | 2-1 | 2-0 | 2-0 | 2-2 | 0-0 | 2-0 | 5-1 | 2-0 | 0-2 |
| 7 | Evesham U | 2-1 | 1-2 | 0-2 | 8-0 | 1-2 | 0-1 | X | 2-2 | 1-0 | 0-2 | 0-1 | 0-0 | 1-1 | 0-0 | 1-1 | 3-2 | 1-0 | 0-5 | 2-0 | 3-1 | 0-4 | 5-1 |
| 8 | Hinckley U | 0-0 | 1-2 | 0-2 | 2-0 | 0-0 | 0-2 | 0-1 | X | 5-1 | 0-0 | 2-1 | 3-0 | 1-1 | 3-0 | 4-1 | 1-0 | 1-2 | 0-3 | 1-0 | 1-1 | 1-1 | 0-0 |
| 9 | Moor Green | 1-2 | 1-3 | 2-1 | 0-1 | 1-2 | 2-3 | 2-1 | 1-1 | X | 4-1 | 2-1 | 3-1 | 0-3 | 2-0 | 0-0 | 4-2 | 3-2 | 3-1 | 2-1 | 0-1 | 1-2 | 1-1 |
| 10 | Newport | 1-0 | 5-0 | 3-0 | 4-0 | 4-1 | 1-1 | 3-0 | 1-0 | 3-2 | X | 2-1 | 2-1 | 1-1 | 1-1 | 4-1 | 3-1 | 2-1 | 4-2 | 4-0 | 3-2 | 2-1 | 4-1 |
| 11 | Paget Rgrs | 2-2 | 0-2 | 3-3 | 6-0 | 0-0 | 0-3 | 1-2 | 0-1 | 0-1 | 0-1 | X | 2-1 | 3-1 | 0-1 | 0-5 | 0-2 | 1-2 | 1-0 | 2-3 | 2-5 | 2-2 | 0-2 |
| 12 | RC Warw'k | 1-3 | 1-2 | 2-2 | 2-0 | 1-2 | 0-3 | 0-4 | 0-2 | 1-3 | 0-0 | 2-1 | X | 1-3 | 2-3 | 0-3 | 1-4 | 1-1 | 3-1 | 1-1 | 2-2 | 0-4 | 0-3 |
| 13 | Redditch U | 2-1 | 1-0 | 0-3 | 3-2 | 4-1 | 0-1 | 3-0 | 6-0 | 3-0 | 1-1 | 1-1 | 1-1 | X | 1-4 | 1-0 | 3-1 | 2-0 | 0-1 | 3-0 | 1-0 | 0-0 | 3-0 |
| 14 | Shepshed | 2-0 | 2-1 | 0-0 | 1-0 | 1-1 | 0-1 | 2-2 | 2-3 | 2-2 | 3-1 | 0-0 | 2-1 | 3-5 | X | 4-1 | 0-0 | 5-1 | 0-3 | 0-2 | 1-0 | 0-2 | 2-2 |
| 15 | Solihull B | 1-0 | 1-1 | 5-3 | 7-0 | 1-2 | 2-0 | 3-0 | 1-3 | 2-3 | 3-1 | 1-0 | 3-2 | 1-1 | 1-1 | X | 3-1 | 2-1 | 1-1 | 2-0 | 0-0 | 3-0 | 1-0 |
| 16 | Stafford R | 1-2 | 6-3 | 3-2 | 4-0 | 2-2 | 0-0 | 7-3 | 0-2 | 1-2 | 1-0 | 1-1 | 6-1 | 1-0 | 1-2 | 1-1 | X | 5-1 | 3-1 | 1-1 | 3-0 | 3-1 | 5-0 |
| 17 | Stamford | 1-2 | 2-2 | 1-0 | 1-0 | 1-2 | 1-3 | 0-1 | 1-4 | 1-0 | 3-1 | 1-2 | 4-1 | 1-4 | 0-3 | 2-2 | 3-0 | X | 3-0 | 0-1 | 2-1 | 1-2 | 4-2 |
| 18 | Stourbridge | 2-6 | 1-0 | 2-2 | 2-0 | 0-0 | 1-2 | 1-0 | 0-1 | 0-2 | 3-4 | 1-1 | 4-1 | 3-3 | 0-2 | 1-0 | 1-1 | 1-0 | X | 1-0 | 0-3 | 0-1 | 1-0 |
| 19 | Sutton C'fd | 1-0 | 0-1 | 1-0 | 3-1 | 1-4 | 3-1 | 1-1 | 0-3 | 2-2 | 1-0 | 1-2 | 1-0 | 2-1 | 1-0 | 1-1 | 1-1 | 3-1 | 0-3 | X | 0-2 | 0-1 | 1-0 |
| 20 | VS Rugby | 4-4 | 3-3 | 0-1 | 2-0 | 2-3 | 2-2 | 0-2 | 1-1 | 0-2 | 1-2 | 2-1 | 3-1 | 2-1 | 1-0 | 3-3 | 2-3 | 2-1 | 0-2 | 0-1 | X | 1-0 | 0-1 |
| 21 | W.S.Mare | 0-3 | 4-2 | 0-3 | 3-3 | 1-2 | 1-3 | 2-1 | 1-1 | 0-2 | 2-0 | 0-1 | 2-0 | 0-1 | 2-2 | 1-1 | 2-3 | 3-0 | 0-0 | 4-2 | 2-0 | X | 1-2 |
| 22 | Wisbech T | 2-1 | 2-3 | 1-0 | 3-0 | 2-0 | 0-2 | 2-3 | 0-1 | 1-1 | 0-3 | 1-1 | 4-0 | 0-3 | 3-2 | 0-1 | 0-2 | 0-0 | 3-3 | 1-1 | 3-1 | 2-1 | X |

*Eric Marsh and Andrew Chitty*
*Photo: Graham Cotterill*

# BEDWORTH UNITED

## CLUB OFFICIALS

Chairman: **Peter Randle**
Vice Chairman:

Secretary: **Graham J Bloxham**
43 Mount Pleasant Road, Bedworth,
Warwicks CV12 8EX

Press Officer: **Jamie Home**

**FOOTBALL MANAGEMENT TEAM**
Manager: Billy Hollywood
Asst Mgr: Mark Harrison
Club Doctor: Philip Earl
Physio: John Roberts

### FACT FILE

Formed: 1896
Nickname: Greenbacks
Sponsors: Bedworth Telegraph
Colours: Green & white/white/white
Change colours: Yellow & green
Midweek matchday: Tuesday
Reserves: Midland Comb Res Lg.
Youth League: Midland Floodlit Youth

**THE GREENBACKS**
BEDWORTH UNITED FOOTBALL CLUB - OFFICIAL PROGRAMME

v. CINDERFORD TOWN
Saturday, May 1st 1999 - K.O. 3.00pm
(Dr. Martens League)

£1

BEDWORTH EVENING TELEGRAPH & BEDWORTH ECHO

**GROUND** The Oval, Miners Welfare Park, Coventry Road, Bedworth CV12 8NN
Tel: 01203 314302

rections: M6 jct 3, into Bedworth on B4113 Coventry to Bedworth road, ground200yds past
st Bedworth Leisure Centre on this road. Coaches should park atthis Leisure Centre. Buses
m Coventry and Nuneaton pass ground

apacity: 7,000    Cover: 300    Seats: 300    Floodlights: Yes
ubhouse: Social club open every day 7.30-11pm & w/e noon-3pm. Hot and cold bar food
ub Shop: Selling a wide range of souvenirs & programmes.
Contact : Ron Kemp   01203 318014

Pages: 18    Price: £1
Editor: Ron Kemp:( 01203 318014)
Local Press: Heartland Evening News, Weekly
Tribune, Bedworth Echo,
Coventry Evening Telegraph
Local Radio: Mercia Sound, BBC CWR

**EVIOUS**    **Leagues:** Birmingham Comb. 47-54; West Mids (at first Birmingham) Lg 54-72
**Name:** Bedworth Town 47-68    **Ground:** British Queen Ground 11-39

**UB RECORDS**   **Attendance:** 5,127 v Nuneaton Borough, Southern Lg Midland Division 23/2/82
**Win:** 11-0    **Defeat:** 1-10
**Career Goalscorer:** Peter Spacey (1949-69)    **Career Appearances:** Peter Spacey
**Transfer fee paid:** £1,750 for Colin Taylor (Hinckley Town, 1991-92)
**Transfer fee received:** £30,000 for Richard Landon (Plymouth Argyle, January 1994)

**ST SEASON**   **FA Trophy:** Second Round 80-81
**FA Cup:** 4th Qualifying Rd 1983/89/90

**NOURS**    Birmingham Comb.(2) 48-50, Birmingham Snr Cup(3) 78-79 80-82, Midland Floodlit Cup 81-82 92-93

ayers progressing: Phil Huffer (Derby County 1953), Geoff Coleman(Northampton Town 1955), Ian Hathaway (Mansfield Town 1989), Richard
ndon(Plymouth Argyle 1994)

ack Row: Billy Hollywood (Manager), Paul Bedder, Christy McKenzie, Steve Brown, Guy Sanders, Craig Glover,
mon Black, Tom Lenton, Lee Darlison, Jamie Bunch, Mark Harrison (Asst Manager), Philip Earl (Club Doctor)
ont Row: Chris Goodman, John Halford, Jai Stanley, Anthony Robinson, Paul Corsden, Paul O'Brien, Robbie Beard

# BILSTON TOWN

## CLUB OFFICIALS
Chairman: **Morris Baker**
Vice-Chairman: **A K Hickman**
President: **Dennis Turner MP**
Press Officer: **A Owen**
Secretary: **Jeff Calloway**
4 Mervyn Rd, Bradley, Bilston,
West Midlands WV14 8DF
Tel: 01902 681660

## FOOTBALL MANAGEMENT TEAM
Manager: Joe Jackson
Asst Manager: Tom Stokes
Coach: T.B.A.
Physio: Jon King

**FACT FILE**

Formed: 1895
Nickname: Steelmen or Boro
Sponsors: Stowlawn Ltd and Second City
Colours: Orange/white/white
Change colours: White/black/orange
Midweek matchday: Tuesday
Reserves' League: No reserve team
Youth Team:West Midland (Regional)
League Youth Division

**THE STEELMEN** *Review*

1997/98 Season
OFFICIAL PROGRAMME

Dr Martens

BILSTON TOWN FOOTBALL CLUB
QUEEN STREET, BILSTON

80p

**GROUND**    Queen Street, Bilston WV14 7EX Tel: 01902 491498
**Directions:** M6 junction 10, A454 towards Wolverhampton then pick up A563 towards Bilston and turn left into Beckett Street after a little over a mile,ground at bottom. 3 miles from Wolverhampton (BR), bus 45 from bus station passes ground. Buses 78 and 79 from Birmingham stop within quarter of a mile of ground
**Capacity:** 4,000      **Cover:** 350      **Seats:** 350      **Floodlights:** Yes
**Clubhouse:** Open evenings & weekend lunchtimes (normal pub hours). Usual club activities
**Club Shop:** Sells a range of souvenirs and programmes.
    Contact Paul Calloway, 4 Mervyn Rd, Bradley, Bilston, West Mids WV14 8DF

Pages: 24 Price: 70p
Editor: Secretary (01902 491799)
Local Press: Expess & Star, Evening Mail
Local Radio: Radio West Mids, WABC,
Beacon, BRMB

**PREVIOUS**    **Leagues:** Birmingham Comb. 07-21 48-54, (Birmingham) West Mids 21-32 54-85
    **Names:** Bilston Utd 1895-1932, Bilston**Ground:** Prouds Lane 1895-1921

**CLUB RECORDS  Attendance:** 7,500 v Wolverhampton Wanderers, floodlight opening 1953
    Competitive: 7,000 v Halifax Town, F.A. Cup First Round 1968
    **Win:** 12-2 v Tipton Town          **Defeat:** 0-8 v Merthyr Tydfil
    **Career Goalscorer:** Ron McDermott 78      **Career Appearances:**  Unknown
    **Transfer fee paid: Transfer fee received:** From Southend United for Ron Poutney, 1975

**BEST SEASON    FA Trophy:** 2nd Round 70-71, 74-75          **FA Vase:** Quarter Finals 92-93
    **FA Cup:** 2nd Rd replay 72-73  (0-1 at Barnet after 1-1 draw). Also 1st Rd 68-69. League clubs defeated: None

**HONOURS**    West Mids Lg 60-61 72-73 (R-up 22-23 70-71 73-74 74-75 75-76 84-85, Lg Cup 72-73 (R-up 65-66), Div 2 56-57),
    Birmingham Senior Cup 1895-96  Wednesbury Charity Cup 1981-81 81-82 82-83 84-85 (R-up 83-84)

Players progressing: R Ellows (Birmingham), James Fletcher (Birmingham 1950),Stan Crowther (A Villa 1955), Ron Pountney (Southend 1975),
    K Price(Gillingham), Campbell Chapman (Wolves 1984) Joe Jackson (Wolves), Mike Turner (Barnsley  1999)

*Bilston Town. Photo: David Linney*

# BLAKENALL

**CLUB OFFICIALS**
Chairman: **P Langston**
Vice Chairman: **D Cotterill**
President: **J Bridgett**
Secretary: **David Birch**, 64 Wimperis Way,
Great Barr, Birmingham B43 7DF
Tel: 0121 360 3574
Commercial Manager: **Jeff Husted**
(01922 400600)
Press Officer: **Russell Brown**
(0836 383874 Mobile)

**FOOTBALL MANAGEMENT TEAM**
Managers : Mick Folland & Paul Knox
Coach: JimSkidmore

**FACT FILE**

Founded: 1946
Nickname: Nall
Sponsor: Castlemore Securities
Colours: Blue white trim/blue/blue white trim
Change: Red & Black/black/black & white
Midweek Matchday: Tuesday

1998-99 - Captain: Darren Simkin
P.o.Y.: Darren Simkin
Top scorer: Les Palmer (24)

Pages: 52 Price: 80p
Editor: Russell Brown Tel: 0836 383874

Local Press: Express & Star, Walsall
Chronicle, Walsall Advertiser, Walsall
Observer, Sunday Mercury, Sports Argus
Local Radio: BBC West Midlands,
BRMB, Beacon Radio

**GROUND** Red Lion Ground, Somerfield Rd, Leamore, Walsall, West Mids  Tel: 01922 405835

**Directions:** M6 jct 10, follow signs for Walsall centre. At 1st lights turn left (about 200yds from Motorway junction) into Bloxwich Lane. Keep following this lane to the `T' junction and turn right into Leamore Lane, at this islandturn left into Somerfield Road. Ground approx. 400yds on right
Nearest Railway Station: Bloxwich North, (5 minutes walk from ground)
Capacity: 2,500     Seats: 250     Cover: 250     Floodlights: Yes
**Clubhouse:** Open 7-11 (Mon-Sun), 1-11 (Sat). Food available matchdays     Club Shop: No

**PREVIOUS**     **Leagues:** Bloxwich Comb.; Staffs County; Midland Comb. 60-79; W Midlands Reg Lge79-95; Midland All 95-97
**Names:** None

**CLUB RECORDS** **Attendance:** 1,550 v Halesowen Town 85-86
**Win:** 11-0 v Bilston United 26/4/95
**Defeat:** 0-7 v Macclesfield Town (Staffs Sen Cup) 31/1/95
**Fee Received**: £10,000 for Darren Simkin (Wolverhampton Wanderers, 1992)

**BEST SEASON**     FA Trophy: 2nd Rd 98-99          FA Vase: 2nd Rd Proper 91-92

**HONOURS**     Midland Football Alliance  96-97, R-up 95-96; Industrial Rewinds Lge Cup 95-96; Midland Invitation Triangular Cup 94-95, R-up 97-98; West Midlands Reg Prem Div88-89, R-up 94-95, Prem Div Lge Cup 94-95; Walsall Sen Cup 63-64 74-75 75-76 76-77 80-81 88-89 95-96 97-98 98-99; Midland Comb 76-77

Players progressing: Darren Simkin (Wolverhampton Wanderers)

*Back Row: Mick Folland (Joint Manager), Steve Hooper (Physio), Mick Williams, Darren Smith (c), John Muir, Matt Lowe, Tommy Byrne, Ricky Marshall, Steve Hillman, Mark Simms, Danny Rochester, Jim Skidmore (Coach), Paul Knox (Joint Manager)*
*Front Row: Mark Swann, Chris Smith, Les Palmer, Jack Skidmore (Mascot), Lee Harper, Ian Bennett, Robert Plant*

# BROMSGROVE ROVERS

## CLUB OFFICIALS

Chairman: **Keith McMaster**

President: **Charles W Poole**

Secretary: **Eddie Million**

c/o Bromsgrove Rovers FC

Commercial Manager: **Rebecca O'Neill**

### FOOTBALL MANAGEMENT TEAM

Manager: Brian Kenning

Trainer: Stewart Pinfold

Physio: Paul Sunners

### FACT FILE

Formed: 1885

Sponsors: All Saints Masterfit (Bromsgrove).

Nickname: Rovers or Greens

Colours: Green & white stripes/black/green.

Change colours: All red.

Midweek matchday: Tuesday

Reserves' league: Central Conference.

Newsline: 0891 88 44 96.

Pages: 40 Price: £1.20
Editors:
Brian Perry 0121 628 6009
Alan Saunders 01527 833838

**GROUND**  Victoria Ground, Birmingham Road, Bromsgrove, Worcs, B61 0DR

Tel: 01527 876949

**Directions:** Ground is situated on the north side of Bromsgrove on the Birmingham Road, off the A38 Bromsgrove by pass. The M5 and M42 join the A38 to the north of the town making it easy to get to the ground without having to go into town. The 144 Midland Red bus runs from New Street Station Birmingham and passes the ground.

Capacity: 4,893    Seated: 394    Covered Terracing: 1,344

**Clubhouse:** Victoria Club (01527 878260) - Serves hot & cold food. Big screen TV, pool table & darts. Open matchdays and week-day evenings.

**Club Shop:** Selling replica clothing & souvenirs. Contact Doug Bratt (01527 874997).

**PREVIOUS**   **Leagues:** Birmingham Lge 1898-08, Birmingham Combination 1908-53, Birmingham 53-65, West Midlands 65-72, Southern League - Northern Div. 73-79, Midland Div.79-1986, Premier Div. 86-92, GMVC 92-97
**Grounds:** Old Station Road 1885-87, Recreation Ground 87-88, Churchfields 88-97, Well Lane 1897-1910.

**CLUB RECORDS**   **Attendance:** 7,389 v Worcester City - 1957
**Win:** 11-0 - v Hinckley Ath. 1970, v Halesowen Town `A' 1939    **Defeat:** 0-12 v Aston Villa `A' 1939
**Career goalscorer:** Chris Hanks 238, 1983-84    **Career appearances:** Shaun O'Meara 763, 1975-94
**Fee paid:** £3,000 for Recky Carter (Solihull B.) 93-94    **Fee received:** Undisclosed for Scott Cooksey (Peterborough) Dec. 93

**HONOURS**   Vauxhall Conference R-up 92-93, Lge Cup 94-95 95-96; Bob Lord Trophy 94-95; Spalding Cup 95/96; Southern Lge Prem 91-92, R-up 86-87, Cup 92-93, R-up 86-87, Midland Div 85-86, Merit Cup 85-86, Cup 85-86, R-up 73-74 87-88; Bill Dellow Cup 85-86; Worcester Sen Cup (8), R-up (10); Birmingham Sen Cup 46-47, R-up 47-48 88-89; W Mid Lge R-up 67-70, Cup 67-68 70-71; Birminham Lge 59-60, R-up 04-05 56-57 60-61; Birmingham Comb 46-47, R-up 49-50 50-51; Hereford Charity Chall Cup 46-47, R-up 47-48.

Players progressing: M McKenna (Northampton 46),R Hartle (Bolton 52), A McLean (Bury 53), A Smith (A.Villa 54), M Deakin (C Palace 54), B Puster (Leicester 58), Tom Smith (Sheff Utd 1978), Malcolm Goodman (Halifax 1979), Steve Smith (Walsall 1980), Gary Hackett (Shrewsbury 1983), Bill McGarry, Martyn O'Connor (C Palace 1992), Scott Cooksey (Peterborough 1993), Steve Taylor (Crystal Palace 1995).

*Bath City's Steve White shoots v Bromsgrove Rovers. Photo: Bob Chester*

# CINDERFORD TOWN

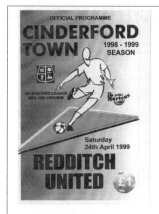

OFFICIAL PROGRAMME

**CINDERFORD TOWN**

1998 - 1999 SEASON

UHLSPORTS LEAGUE MIDLAND DIVISION

Saturday 24th April 1999

**REDDITCH UNITED**

£1

## CLUB OFFICIALS

Chairman: **Ashley Saunders**
President: **S Watkins**
Vice Chairman: **Ray Reed**

Secretary: **Chris Warren**
9c Tusculum Way, Mitcheldean,
Glos GL17 0HZ
01594543065 (H) 01594 542421 x 2360 (B)

Press Officer: **Keith Aston**

## FOOTBALL MANAGEMENT TEAM

Manager: John Murphy (01242 574882)
Asst. Manager: Geoff Medcroft
Physio: Keith Marfell

### FACT FILE

Formed: 1922
Nickname: Town
Sponsors: K.W.Bell
Club colours: White & Black
Change colours: All Red
Midweek matchday: Tuesday
Reserves' League: No reserve team
98-99- Captain:Wayne Hatswell
Top Scorer: Jody Bevan
P.o.Y.: Darren McCluskey

**GROUND** The Causeway, Hilldene, Cinderford, Glos. Tel: 01594 827147 or 822039

Directions: From Gloucester take A40 to Ross-on-Wye, then A48 - Chepstow. In 8miles turn right at Elton garage onto A4151 signed Cinderford, thru Littledean, up steep hill, right at crossroads, second left into Latimer Rd. Ground 5 minswalk from town centre

Capacity: 2,500 Cover: 1,000 Seats: 250 Floodlights: Yes

Pages: 50 Price: 80p
Editor: Mike Bradley
Tel: 01594 824566

Clubhouse: Open every day. 2 bars, kitchen, 2 skittle alleys, darts, dancehall,committee room
Club Shop: Souvenirs, club badges (£¨3.00), ties, mugs , scarves and pennants Programme exchanges welcome - contact secretary for shop and programmes.

**PREVIOUS** Leagues: Glos Northern Snr 22-39 60-62, Western 46-59, Warwickshire Comb 63-64,West Midlands 65-69, Gloucestershire County 70-73 85-89, Midland Comb. 74-84,Hellenic 90-95
Names: None Grounds: Mousel Lane, Royal Oak

**CLUB RECORDS** Attendance: 4,850 v Minehead, Western League, 1955-56
Win: 13-0 v Cam Mills 38-39 Defeat: 0-10 v Sutton Coldfield 78-79
Career Appearances: Russell Bowles 528 Career Goalscorer: Unknown

**BEST SEASON** FA Cup: 2nd Rd v Gravesend 95-96 FA Trophy: 2nd Qual Rd
FA Vase: 2nd Rd 91-92 FA Amateur Cup: 3rd Qual Rd 52

**HONOURS** Hellenic Lg Premier Champions 94-95, Premier Lg.Cup 94-95, Floodlit Cup 93-94,Div 1 90-91; Glos Northern Snr Lg Div 1 38-39 60-61, R-up (6); Nth Glos Lg Div1 38-39 60-61; Glos Snr Amtr Cup (Nth) (6), R-up (3); Western Lg Div 2 56-57; Warwickshire Comb. 63-64; W Mids Lg Prem Div Cup 68-69; Glos Jnr Cup (Nth) 80-81; Midland Comb. 81-82; Glos Co. Lg R-up 69-70 71-72 73-74; Glos FA Trophy R-up 92-93; Hungerford Cup 94-95

Back Row: Paul Donnelly, Andy Hoskins, Jody Bevan, John Rendall, Will Steadman, Wayne Hatswell, Adie Harris
Front Row: Martin Thompson, Steve Powell, Brian Kayll, Scott Medcroft
Photo: Roger Turner

# CIRENCESTER TOWN

## CLUB OFFICIALS

Chairman: **Stephen Abbley**
17 Dianmer Close, Hook, Swindon. SN4 8ER.
Tel: 01743853293 (H) 01793 884900 (B)
Secretary: **Jim Saunders**
35 Chesterton Park, Cirencester, Glos. GL7 1XS
Tel: 01258 659002 (H)
Commercial Manager: **Margaret Marsh**
Press Officer: **Jim Saunders**

## FOOTBALL MANAGEMENT TEAM

Manager: Ray Baverstock 01242 260619
Coach: Mark Boyland
Physio: Steve Slaughter

**FACT FILE**

Founded: 1889
Nickname: Ciren
Sponsors: P.H.H./Cheltenham Windows
Colours: Red & black/ black/ red
Change colours: Blue/ black/ blue
Midweek Matchday: Tuesday
Reserves' League: Cirencester & District

**GROUND**     The Stadium, Smithsfield, Chesterton Lane, Cirencester Tel: 01285 645783

**Directions:** Follow signs on by-pass to Bristol & West. At the roundabout where the Sports Centre is situated, follow the road `up the hill' and take the first left and then immediately right. Situated 3 miles from Kemble (BR)

Capacity: 3,000          Seats: 236          Cover: 500          Floodlights: Yes

**Clubhouse:** Open Tuesday - Friday evenings & Saturday. Snacks are available onmatchdays.
Club Shop: None

Pages: Yes          Price: £1
Editor: Margaret Marsh Tel. 01258 645783

Local Press: Standard, Western Daily Press
Local Radio: BBC Radio Gloucester,
Severn Sound

**PREVIOUS**     **Leagues:** Hellenic League  Names: None.  Grounds: None

**CLUB RECORDS  Attendance:** 2,600 v Fareham 1969
**Win:** Unknown  **Defeat:** Unknown
**Career Goalscorer:** Unknown  **Career Appearances:** Unknown
**Transfer fee paid:** None  **Transfer fee received:** None

**BEST SEASON     FA Trophy:** 1st Qual. Round 1996-97 (1st season in comp.)
**FA Vase:** Never past the 1st Round          **FA Cup:** 3rd Preliminary Round, 1996-97

**HONOURS**     Gloucestershire Senior Amateur Cup 89-90; Hellenic League Div One Challenge Cup 90-91; Hellenic League Prem Div 95-96, League Cup 95-96; Gloucestershire County Cup 95-96

Players progressing: None

*Corby Town v Cirencester Town. Photo: Peter Barnes*

# EVESHAM UNITED

## FACT FILE

## CLUB OFFICIALS

Chairman: **Jim Cockerton**
Vice Chairman: **Steve Lane**
President: **M E H Davis**
Treasurer: **Dave Wright**
Secretary/Press Officer: **Mike J Peplow**
68 Woodstock Rd, St Johns,
Worcester WR2 5NF
Tel: 01905 425993

**FOOTBALL MANAGEMENT TEAM**

Manager: Mick Brennan
Asst Manager: Mark Chambers
Physio: Lee O'Neill

Nickname: The Robins
Sponsors; B anks's
Colours: Red & white/white/white
Change Colours: All blue
Formed: 1945
Midweek matches: Tuesday
Reserves' League: No reserve team
98-99 - Captain: Paul West
P.o.Y: Paul West
Top Scorer: Matt Coppin

**GROUND**   Common Road, Evesham, Worcestershire WR11 4PU
Tel: 01386 442303

**Directions:** From Evesham High Street turn into Oat St, and join one-way system, turn right between Willmotts factory called Conduit Hill into Common Rd, ground 200yds down on right just before railway bridge. 5 minutes walk from Evesham BR station
Capacity: 2,000          Seats: 350          Cover: 600          Floodlights: Yes

**Clubhouse:** Open matchdays and training nights.
Cold food available in club, and hot food from tea hut on matchdays

Club Shop: Contact John Hawkins c/o the club

Programme:
Pages: 36 Price: £1
Editor: Mike Peplow (01905 425993)
Local Press: Evesham Journal,
Worcester Evening News, Gloucester Echo
Local Radio: Radio Wyvern,
BBC Hereford & Worcester

**PREVIOUS**   **Leagues:** Worcester, Birmingham Combination, Midland Combination 51-55 65-92, West Midlands Regional 55-62
**Name:** Evesham Town
**Ground:** The Crown Meadow (pre-1968)

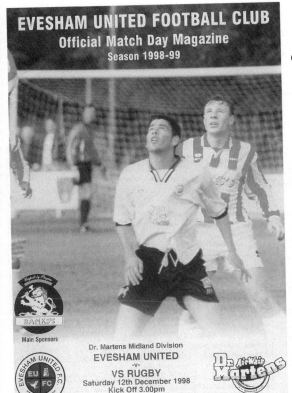

EVESHAM UNITED FOOTBALL CLUB
Official Match Day Magazine
Season 1998-99

Main Sponsors

Dr. Martens Midland Division
EVESHAM UNITED
-v-
VS RUGBY
Saturday 12th December 1998
Kick Off 3.00pm

**CLUB RECORDS**   **Attendance:** 2,338 v West Bromwich A., friendly 18/7/92
**Win:** 11-3 v West Heath United
**Defeat:** 7-2 v Tamworth
**Career Goalscorer:** Sid Brain
**Career Appearances:** Rob Candy
**Transfer fee paid:** £1,500; to Hayes for Colin Day, 1992
**Transfer fee received:** £5,000 for Simon Brain (to Cheltenham Town)

**BEST SEASON**   **FA Vase:** Quarter Finals 1991-92
**FA Amateur Cup:** Runners-up 1923-24
**FA Trophy:** 3rd Qual Rd 96-97
**FA Cup:** 2nd Qual Rd 96-97

**HONOURS**   FA Amateur Cup R-up 23-24, Worcestershire Snr Urn(2) 76-78 (R-up 90-91), Midland Comb.(6) 52-53 54-55 65-66 67-69 91-92 (Chal. Cup 53-54 87-88 91-92 (R-up(5) 54-55 71-72 83-84 88-90)), Worcestershire Comb. 52-53 54-55; B'gham Combination R-up 30-31, Evesham Hosp. Cup 89-90, Tony Allden Mem. Cup 1973 19881992

Players progressing:   Billy Tucker, Gary Stevens (Cardiff 77), Kevin Rose(Lincoln 78), Andy Preece (Northampton 86), Simon Brain (Hereford, via Cheltenham Town), Billy Turley (Northampton Tn)

529

# GRESLEY ROVERS

**CLUB OFFICIALS**
Chairman: **Peter Hall**
President: **Gordon Duggins**
Vice Chairman: **Dennis Everitt**
Secretary / Press Officer: **Neil Betteridge**,
34 Thorpe Downs Road, Church Gresley,
Swadlincote, Derbys DE11 7PG
Tel: 01283 226229
Commercial Manage: **Terry Brumpton**

**FACT FILE**
Formed: 1882
Nickname: The Moatmen
Sponsors: Dunn Group
Colours: Red & white/red/red
Change colours: Sky blue & navy/navysky
Midweek matchday: Tuesday
Reserves' League: Midland Comb (Res. Div.)

**FOOTBALL MANAGEMENT TEAM**

Manager/Coach:Brian Kenning
Asst Manager: Steve Spooner
Physio: Mel Mole

98-99 Captain:Richard Wardle
P.o.Y.: Stuart Ford
Top scorer: Ian Pitt & Lynden Rowland

**GROUND**  Moat Ground, Moat Street, Church Gresley, Swadlincote, Derbys DE11 9RE
Tel: 01283 216315

**Directions:** To A444 via either the A5, A38, A5121 or M42 , Junction 11. On reaching A444
head for Castle Gresley. Take exit at large island to Church Gresley,at next island 2nd exit
(Church St), then 2nd left (School St) then 1st left into Moat St.  5 miles Burton-on-Trent (BR).
Buses from Swadlincote and Burton

Capacity: 2,000        Cover: 1,200        Seats: 400        Floodlights: Yes
**Clubhouse:** Inside ground, open Mon, Tues & Thurs eves & matchdays
Club Shop: Sells merchandise, programmes, metal badges etc.
Contact KathSouthern (01283 221898)

Pages: 36        Price: £1.00
Editor: Terry Brumpton (01543 279249)
Local Press: Derby Evening Telegraph, Burton
Mail, Burton Trader, SwadlincoteTimes
Local Radio: BBC Radio Derby & Cente F.M.

**PREVIOUS**    **Leagues:** Burton Lge 1892-95 97-01 09-10 43-45, Derbyshire Sen 1895-97 02-03,Leics Sen 1890-91 98-99 08-09 10-12 15-16
35-42 45-49, Notts 01-02, Midland 03-06, Central All 11-15 19-25 49-53 59-67, Birmingham Comb 25-33 53-54, Birmingham
(now West Mids) 54-59 75-92, Central Comb 33-35, East Mids 67-75

**Grounds:** Mushroom Lane, Albert Village 1882-95, Church Str., Church, Gresley.1895-1909
**CLUB RECORDS**   **Attendance:** 3,950 v Burton Albion, Birmingham (now West Mids) Lg Division One,57-58
**Win:** 23-0 v Holy Cross Priory, Leics Jun Cup 1889-90      **Defeat:** 1-15 v Burton Crusaders, 1886-87
**Career Goalscorer:** Gordon Duggins 306      **Career Appearances:** Dennis King 579
**Transfer fee received:** £30,000 for Justin O'Reilly (Port Vale 1996)
**Transfer fee paid:** £2,500 for David Robinson (Ilkeston Town 97)
**BEST SEASON**    **FA Vase:** Runners-up 90-91, (SF 92-93)      **FA Trophy:** Qtr Finals 95-96

**HONOURS**
FA Cup: 1st Rd Proper: 30-31 (1-3 at York City), 94-95 (1-7 at Crewe Alex.)    League clubs defeated: None
Southern Lge Champ 96-97; FA Vase R-up 90-91; West Mids Lg 90-91 91-92 (R-up 85-86 88-89); Lg Cup 88-89 R-Up. 86-87 91-
92; Southern Lg Mid Div R-up 92-93; Derbys Snr Cup (7), (R-Up (2); Leics Snr Cup 1898-99 46-47 (R-Up 1899-90 45-46); Leics
Sen Lg 00-01 46-47 47-48 R-Up (7); Coalville Charity Cup 46-47; Derby Senior Cup (S) (2) R-Up 00-01; Bass Vase (6); Cent All
64-65 66-67 R-Up(3) (Lg Cup 52-53); East Mids Reg Lg (2) R-Up (2); Dr.Martens (S Lge) Cup Fin 93-94
Players progressing: Phil Gee (Derby County 85), Mark Blount (Sheffield Utd 94), Colin Loss (Bristol City 94), Justin O'Reilly (Port Vale 96)

Back Row: Neil Kitching, Steve Coates, Stuart Ford, Ian Wright, Paul Wardle, Ian Bluck.  Middle: Dennis Everitt (vice chairman), Ernie Talbot (kit
manager), Harry Southern (social club steward), Stan Crockett (director),Liam walshe, Les Williams, Richard Wardle (capt.), Paul Dowell, Neil
Broadhurst, Wayne Thornbill, Peter Hall (chairman), Neil Betteridge (secretary), Barrie Morton (commercial director). Front: Melvyn Mole (physio),
Andy Murtin, Graeme Fowkes, Mick Dandar, Brian Kenning (manager), Mack Peters, Chris Bradshaw, Dave Evans, Steve Spooner (asst. man.)

# HINCKLEY UNITED

## CLUB OFFICIALS

Chairman: **Kevin Downes**
Vice Chairman: **Rob Mayne**
Secretary: **Stuart Millidge**
25 Elizabeth Rd, Hinckley, Leics. LE10 OQY
Tel: 01455 449935
Press Officer: **Andy Gibbs** (01455 233483)

### FOOTBALL MANAGEMENT TEAM
Manager:Dean Thomas Ass Man: Mark
O'Kane, Coach: Paul Bancroft
Physio: Julie Hayton

### FACT FILE
Formed: 1997
Colours: Red & blue/blue/red
Change colours: Amber & black/black/amber
Midweek matchday: Tuesday
Reserves' League: Mid Comb Res Div

98-99 - Top scorer:
P.o.Y.: Wayne Starkey
Captain: Morton Titterton

Programme:
Pages: 44 Price: £1
Editor: Steve
Local Radio: Fosse Radio
Local Press: Heartland Evening Echo,
Hinckley Times, Leicester Mercury,
Coventry Evening Telegraph

**GROUND** Middlefield Lane, Hinckley, Leics. LE10 0RB 01455 613553/615012
**Directions:** From M69 junction 1 take A5 north to Dodwells Island, then A47(sign Leicester).
At 3rd r/about turn right (Stoke Road) then first right(Tudor Road), until crossroads. Turn left
(Middlefield Lane), ground at end oflane on left
Capacity: 5,000       Cover: 1,000       Seats: 320       Floodlights: Yes
**Clubhouse:** Social club with lounge, games room and concert hall
Club Shop: Sells programmes, books, vidoes, badges, mugs Hinckley Town Records &
Hinckley Athletic Records

**PREVIOUS**     **Names:** Hinckley Athletic (1889) & Hinckley Town (prev. Westfield Rovers 58-66) merged in 1997
**Grounds:** Westfield Playing Field 58-60; Coventry Rd Rec Grd 60-68; Leicester Rd68-97
**Leagues:** Town: S Leicester & Nuneaton Amat, Leics Snr 72-86, Central Mids 86-88, West Mids 88-90
*Athletic: Leics. & Northants; Leics. Sen.; Birmingham Comb. 14-39 47-54; West Midlands (Regional) 54-59 64-94; Southern 63-64*

**CLUB RECORDS**   **Attendance:** Town: 2,000 v Real Sociedad 86. *Athletic: 5,410 v Nuneaton Boro 49*
**Win:** Town; 10-0 v Kettering Tn Res, Central Mid Lge B.E. Webbe Cup
**Defeat:** Town: 0-10 v Barry Town, Southern Lge Mid Div
**Career Goalscorer:** Town: Paul Purser. *Athletic: M Hodgkins*     **Career Appearances:** *Athletic: Steve Markham 455 86-96*
**Fee paid:** Town: £1,600 for John Lane (V.S. Rugby)     **Fee received:** Town: £1,750 for Colin Taylor (Bedworth Utd)

**BEST SEASON**   **FA Vase:** Town: 3rd Rd 85-86. Athletic: 5th Rd 89-90 93-94     **FA Trophy:** *United: 4th Rd 2-3 v Yeovil Town 98-99*
**FA Cup:** Town: 4th Qual Rd v Welling 88-89. *Athletic: 2nd Rd v Queens Park Rangers 54-55*

**HONOURS**     Town: West Midlands (Regional) Lg 89-90, Central Midlands Lg 86-87 (R-up 87-88, B E Webbe Cup R-up 86-87 87-88, Gerry
Mills Cup R-up 87-88), Leics Senior Lg R-up 83-84 (Div 2 72-73, Div 2 Cup 72-73), Leics.Chall. Cup 89-90 (R-up 90-91 93-94),
Leics Senior Cup (Jelson Holmes) R-up 87-88, Leics Senior Cup 88-89, Midland Floodlit Cup 88-89 (R-up 91-92 93-94).
*Athletic: Leics Snr Cup 1899-1900 00-01 09-10 82-83, Leics Snr Lg 1896-97 97-98 99-1900 08-09 09-10 13-14, Birmingham
Comb. 23-24 26-27 (R-up 22-23), West Mids (Reg.) Lg R-up 82-83,Birmingham Snr Cup 54-55 (jt with Brush Sports), Leics
Challenge Cup 57-58 58-5959-60 60-61 61-62 67-68*
Players progressing: *Athletic: John Allen (Port Vale), Keith Scott (Swindon via Wycombe W.), Gary Pick (Hereford), Mike Love (Wigan)*

*Steve Thompson, Yeovil midfielder, shows superb control skills, though tightly marked, in the closely contested 4th
Round FA Trophy tie against Hinckley United. Photo: Ken Gregory*

# MOOR GREEN

**CLUB OFFICIALS**
Chairman: **Ian Childs**
Vice-Chairman: **John Bassford**

Secretary: **Nigel Collins**, 7 The Morelands,
West Heath, Birmingham B31 3HA
Tel: 0121243 3661 (H), 0121 475 0240 (B)
Press Officer: **Peter Clynes**
(0121 745 3262)
Commercial Man.: Commercial Dept.
Tel: 0121 777 8961

**FOOTBALL MANAGEMENT TEAM**
Manager: Bob Faulkner
Physio: Steve Shipway
Coach: Doug Griffiths/Kim Casey

**FACT FILE**
Formed: 1901
Nickname: The Moors
Sponsors: Bradstocks Insurance
Colours: Light/dark blue halves/navy/light blue
Change colours: Jade & lime/jade
Midweek matchday: Tuesday
Reserve League: No reserve team

**GROUND**  `The Moorlands', Sherwood Rd., Hall Green. B28 OEX. Tel: 0121 624 2727

**Directions:**  Off Highfield Rd, which is off A34 (B'ham to Stratford)
Hall Green & Yardley (BR) half mile
**Capacity:**  3,250          Cover: 1,200          Seats: 250          Floodlights: Yes
**Clubhouse:**  Two bars, dance floor. Open nightly & weekend lunch
**Club Shop:**  Selling scarves, mugs, stickers, programmes etc

Programme:
Pages: 52 Price: £1
Editor: Michael Mulryan (0121 608 7078)
Local Press: Solihull News, Solihull Times,
Birmingham Post & Mail, Express &Star
Local Radio: Radio WM, BRMB

**PREVIOUS**  **Leagues:** (friendlies only 1901-21) Birmingham & Dist. A.F.A. 1908-36; Central Amateur 36-39; Birmingham Comb 45-54;
West Mids 54-65; Midland Comb 65-83
**Grounds:** Moor Green Lane 1901-02; numerous 02-22; Windermere Road 1910-30

**CLUB RECORDS**  **Attendance:** 5,000 v Romford, FA Amtr Cup 51
**Career Goalscorer:** Phil Davies 221          **Career Appearances:** Michael Hawkins 800
**Transfer fee paid:** £1,000 for Adrian O'Dowd (Alvechurch)
**Transfer fee received:** £90,000 for Ian Taylor (Port Vale)

**BEST SEASON**  **FA Cup:** 1st Rd Proper 79-80 (lost 2-3 Stafford Rgs)
**FA Trophy:** 1st Rd Prop 90-91, 0-3 v Burton Albion; 96-97, 3-5 v AshtonUnited

**HONOURS**  Southern Lg Mid Div R-up 87-88, Mids Comb 80-81 (R-up(4) 74-76 79-80 82-83, Div 185-86, Presidents Cup(2) 66-68 78-79),
Mids Comb Chall Cup 80-81 (R-up 69-7082-83), Lord Mayor of B'ham Charity Cup 90-91, Mids F'lit Cup(2) 90-92, Tony Allden
Tphy 81- 82, B'ham Snr Cup 57-58, Worcs Snr Cup R-up 86-87, B'ham Jnr Cup66-67, Worcs Jnr Cup 85-86, Solihull Charity
Cup 85-86, Smedley Crook Mem.Cup 87-88, Cent Amat Lg 36-37 37-38 38-39, Verviers (Belg) Tphy 32-33 36-37,AFA Chall
Cup 38-39, AFA Snr Cup 26-27 35-36, Mids F'lit Yth Lg Cup R-up 87-88,B'ham County Yth Lg Cup R-up 83-84

Players progressing: H Smith/R Jefferies (Aston Villa 47/50), F Pidcock(Walsall 53), P Woodward/B Mack (W B Abion 54), S Cooper (Birmingham
City 83),K Barnes (Manchester City), P Brogan (Mansfield Town), I Taylor (Pt Vale 92), S Talbot (Pt Vale 94), D Busst (Coventry 92)

*Left: Stourbridge v Moor Green. Photo: M Wray*

# PAGET RANGERS

## CLUB OFFICIALS

Joint Chairmen:
**R R Ruddick & D J Culling**

Secretary: **Derek Culling**
Tel: 0121 378 5459
Press Officer: **Chris Inman**
Commercial Manager: Chairmen

### FOOTBALL MANAGEMENT TEAM
Manager/Physio: Eddie Caulfield
Asst Manager: Paul Edwards
Coach: Chris Sharpe
Physio: D J Culling

### FACT FILE
Formed: 1938
Nickname: The 'Bears'
Sponsors:INA Bearing Co. Ltd.
Colours: Gold/black/gold
Change colours: All red
Midweek matchday: Tuesday
Reserves' League: No reserve team

98-99 - Top scorer: T Burroughs
P.o.Y. & Players P.o.Y: Gary Knight
Captain: Chris Keogh

**GROUND**    Vale Stadium, Farnborough Rd., Castle Vale, Birmingham B35 7BE
Tel: 0121 747 6969  Fax: 0121 747 6862  Press/Matchdays: 0121 749 7707

**Directions:** M6 North to Junct. 5. Turn right onto A452. Turn right at 1st r'about into Tangmere Drive. Fork right into Farnborough Rd. 800 yds turn right signed Fort centre. M6 South to Spaghetti junction. Take signs for Tyburn Rd (A38) Turn right onto A452. Turn left opposite Jaguar factory then as above (Tangmere Drive)

Capacity: 5000          Cover: 200          Seats: 280          Floodlights: Yes 257 Lux
**Clubhouse:** 'Spitfire Club'. Open daily. Capacity 150. Servery from kitchen to ground.
No club shop - metal badges, ties etc avail. from committee.

Pages: 24    Price: £1
Editor: R R Ruddick 0121 747 6969
Local Press: Sutton Coldfield News,
Sutton Observer
Local Radio: Radio WM, BRMB
Vale FM 106.2

**PREVIOUS**    **Leagues:** Birmingham Suburban; Central Amateur; Midland Combination 50-81;Southern 87-88; West Midlands (Regional) 88-94; Interlink Midland Alliance 94-95, Southern League 95-
**Grounds:** Pype Hayes Park 38-46; Springfield Road, Walmley 46-93, Ground Share Sutton Coldfield Town >98.

**CLUB RECORDS** **Attendance:** 2,000 v Aston Villa, F'light opening 1971
**Win:** 24-1 v Evesham Town 1949
**Career Appearances:** Gary Williams 618
**Transfer fee paid:** No transfer fee paid for any player

**Defeat:** 1-6 v Gloucester 87/Halesowen Town 87/Moor Green 88
**Career Goalscorer:** Albert Broadhead
**Transfer fee received:** John Gittens (Southampton) £15,000

**BEST SEASON** **FA Cup:** Third Qual Round 94-95
**FA Vase:** Fourth Rd 88-89, 0-1 v Wisbech     **FA Trophy:** 2nd Round 98-99, 0-2 v Accrington Stanley
**HONOURS**    West Mids Lg R-up 91-92 (Lg Cup 91-92); Midland Comb.(6) 59-61 69-71 82-83 85-86 (R-up 77-78, Lg Cup 59-60 66-67, Div 1 Cup 70-71, Div 3 82-83(res)); B'hamJnr Cup 51-52; Walsall Snr Cup 85-86; Midland Alliance 94-95; Lord Mayor of Birmingham Charity Cup 94-95; Staffs Sen Cup R-up 94-95

Players progressing: John Gittens (Southampton), Gary Bull (Southampton), Lloyd Harrison (Torquay)

Back Row (L-R): Dave Wallace (Trnr), Chris Sharp (Coach), Rasheed Anifowose, Adam Whitehouse, Stuart Clark, Chris Keogh (C), Gary Price, Gary Knight, Sean Small, John Hunt, Paul Edwards (Asst Mgr), Eddie Caulfield (Mgr) Front Row: Stuart Randall, Mark Beddowes, Richard Brown, Trevor Burroughs, Kevin Casson, Mickey Nicholls, Andy Biddle, Joshua Brown (Mascot)

# RACING CLUB WARWICK

**CLUB OFFICIALS**

Chairman: **Pat Murphy**

Secretary: **Robin Lamb**
Tel: 01926 774255

**FOOTBALL MANAGEMENT**

Manager:Steve Sykes

**FACT FILE**

Formed: 1919
Nickname: Racers
Colours: Gold & black/black/black
Change colours: Red&white/red/red
Midweek matchday: Wednesday
Youth's League: Mid F/Lit Yth Lge

98-99 - Captain: R.Burke
P.o.Y.: Richard Anstiss
Top scorer: Jason Percival

**GROUND**

Townsend Meadow, Hampton Road, Warwick CV34 6JP
Tel: 01926 495786
**Directions:** On the B4095 Warwick to Redditch road (via Henley in Arden) next to owners' & trainers' car park of Warwick Racecourse. From M40 jct 15 (1 1/2 miles) take A429 into Warwick, left into Shakespeare Ave., straight over island, right at T-junction into Hampton Rd, ground 300yds on left. 2 milesfrom Warwick BR station
Capacity: 1,000          Cover: 200          Seats: 250          Floodlights: Yes
**Clubhouse:** 01926 495786 Open every evening & Sat &Sun lunchtimes
**Club Shop:** Scarves, mugs, badges, programmes - contact Robin Lamb, 01926 774255

**PREVIOUS**    **Leagues:** Birmingham & West Mids All., Warwickshire Comb., West Midlands (Regional) 67-72, Midland Comb. 72-89
**Names**: Saltisford Rovers 1919-68, Warwick Saltisford 68-70          **Grounds:** Coventry Road

**CLUB RECORDS**    **Attendance:** 1,000 v Halesowen Town, FA Cup 1987
**Transfer fee paid:** £1,000 for Dave Whetton (Bedworth United)          **Win:** 9-1 v Knowle
**Transfer fee  received:** £2,000 for Ian Gorrie (Atherstone Utd)          **Defeat:** 0-6 v Tamworth
**Career Goalscorer:** Steve Edgington 200          **Career Appearances:** Steve Cooper 600

**BEST SEASON**    **FA Vase:** 4th Round 77-78          **FA Cup:** 3rd Qual Rd 92-93          **FA Trophy:**

**HONOURS**    Midland Combination 87-88 (R-up 88-89); Warwick Lg 33-34 34-35 35-36; Birmingham & West Mids Alliance 48-49; Birmingham & Dist Alliance Senior Cup 49-50; Leamington & Dist Lg 37-38 45-46 46-47 47-48; Leamington Hospital Cup 37-38 46-47; Warwick Cinderella Cup 35-36 36-37 37-38 38-39 46-47; T G John Cup 36-37; Leamington Junior Cup 38-39 46-47

Players progressing: None

*Back Row: P Garnel (Asst Mgr), R Ellison, S Clarke, A McGil, K Francis, R Anstiss, J Woodley, R Higgs, R Sheedy, N McFarlane, M Bewell (Manager)*
*Front Row: A Smith, L John, R Burke (Captain), B Agar, P Eden, K Shirly*

# REDDITCH UNITED

## CLUB OFFICIALS

Chairman: **Rod Laight**
President: **Major Jim Gillespie**
Secretary: **M A Langfield**
73 Other Rd., Redditch, Worcs B98 8DP
Tel: 01527 67945
Commercial Manager: **Dave Roberts**
Press Off: **R Newbold** Tel: 01527 458852

### FOOTBALL MANAGEMENT TEAM
Manager: Rob Smith
Asst Manager:Jan Mulders
Coach: Mark Dearlove
Physio: John Kane

**FACT FILE**

Formed: 1900
Nickname: The Reds
Colours: All red
Change colours: All royal blue
Midweek matchday: Tuesday
Reserves' League: Midland Comb. Res Div

1998-99
P. o. Y.: Neil Manton
Captain: Paul Molloy

Football Club
Season 1998-1999

Members of:
The Dr. Martens Southern Football League

Official Programme £1.00

Main Sponsor: Protex (Fasteners) Ltd.

**GROUND** Valley Stadium, Bromsgrove Road, Redditch B97 4RN
Tel: 01527 67450

Directions: Access 7 on town centre ring-road takes you into Bromsgrove Road (via Unicorn Hill) - ground entrance 400yds past traffic lights on right.Arriving from Bromsgrove take first exit off dual carriageway. Ground 400 ydsfrom Redditch BR station and town centre
Capacity: 9,500          Cover: 2,000          Seats: 400          Floodlights: Yes
Clubhouse: Large clubroom and lounge boardroom. Open matchdays and for private hire.
Food available on matchdays; hot dogs, burgers, chips etc          Club Shop: No

Pages: 48 Price: £1.00
Editor: Roger Newbold Tel: 01527 458852

Local Press: Redditch Indicator, Redditch Advertiser, Birmingham Evening Mail, Redditch Standard
Local Radio: BBC Hereford & Worcester

**PREVIOUS** **Leagues:** Birmingham Comb. 05-21 29-39 46-53, West Midlands 21-29 53-72, Southern 72-79, Alliance Premier (Conf) 79-80
**Name:** Redditch Town          **Ground:** HDA Spts Ground, Millsborough Rd

**CLUB RECORDS** **Attendance:** 5,500 v Bromsgrove, league match 54-55
**Transfer fee paid:** £3,000 for Paul Joinson                                        **Win:**
**Transfer fee received:** £42,000 for David Farrell (Aston Villa, 1991)          **Defeat:**
**Career Appearances:**                                                            **Career Goalscorer:**

**BEST SEASON** **FA Cup:** 1st Rd replay 71-72, 0-4 v Peterborough U (A) after 1-1 draw. Also 1st Rd 71-72
**FA Trophy:** 1st Round 1978-79

**HONOURS** Southern Lg Div 1 Nth 75-76 (Midland Div R-up 85-86) S.Lg Cup R-up 97-98 West Mids (B'ham) Lg Southern Sect. 54-55, Birmingham Comb. 13-14 32-33 52-53 (R-up 06-07 14-15 51-52), Staffs Snr Cup 90-91, Birmingham Snr Cup 24-25 31-32 38-39 76-77, Worcs Snr Cup 894-95 1930-31 74-75 76-77 (R-up 1888-89 1929-30 52-53 73-74), Worcs Jnr Cup 90-91

Players progressing: Hugh Evans (Birmingham 1947), Trevor Lewes (Coventry1957), David Gilbert (Chesterfield 1960), Mike Tuohy (Southend Utd 1979), NeilSmith (Liverpool), David Farrell (Aston Villa 1992)

*Back Row: James Burke, Kerry Giddings, Matt Pugh, Jan Mulders (Asst Plyr/Mngr), Dave Adey, Nigel Laker, Ross Knight, Simon Marsh, Mark Smith, John Kane (Physio)*
*Front Row: Rob Smith (Plyr/Mngr), Paul Burton, Mark Dearlove (Plyr/Coach), Meil Manton, Adam Nichols, Jamie Hart, Craig Gillett*

# ROCESTER

## CLUB OFFICIALS

Chairman: **A.Hawksworth**

Secretary: **Gilbert Egerton**
23 Eaton Rd, Rocester, Uttoxeter,
Staffs ST145LL.
Tel: 01889 590101

## FOOTBALL MANAGEMENT TEAM

Manager: Terry Greeg
Asst Mgr: Karl Wilcox/Mark Bromley
Reserves' Mgr: Alf Hawksworth

### FACT FILE

Founded: 1876
Nickname: Romans
Sponsors: Stenson Bubble
Colours: Amber/black/black
Change colours: All blue
Reserves' Lge: North Staffs (North)
Midweek matchday: Tuesday

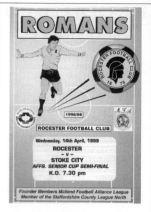

**GROUND**    The Rivers Field, Mill Street, Rocester, Uttoxeter, Staffs Tel: 01889 590463

**Directions:** From A50 r'bout adjoining Little Chef at Uttoxeter take B5030 to Rocester & Alton Towers, right into Rocester village after 3miles over narrow bridge, in village centre bear right at sharp left-hand bend into Mill St., ground 500yds on left just past former cotton mill.

32 pages    50p
Editor: Ian Cruddas  (01889 564173).

Capacity: 4,000        Seats: 230        Cover: 500        Floodlights: Yes

**Clubhouse:** On matchdays (normal licensing hours).  Hot drinks & snacks.
**Club Shop:** Yes

**PREVIOUS**    **Leagues:** Ashbourne; Leek & Moorland; Cheadle & Dist; Uttoxeter Amateur; Stafford 53-57; Staffordshire County North 57-84; Staffordshire Senior 84-87; West Midlands 87-94; Midland alliance 94-99.
**Ground:** Mill Street, Rocester (early 1900s-1987)

**BEST SEASON**    **FA Cup:** 3rd Qual. Round 97-98, 1-2 v Bromsgrove Rovers (A)    **FA Vase:** 5th Round 86-87, 1-3 v Garforth Town (H) aet.

**RECORDS**    **Attendance:** 1,026 v Halesowen T., FA Vase 4th Rd Jan.'87 (at Leek Town)
**Goalscorer:** Mick Collins        **Appearances:** Peter Swanwick.
**Fee Paid:** £1,000 for Paul Ede from Burton Albion, Sept.1989.
**Fee Received:** £12,000 for Mark Sale from Birmingham City 1994
**Win:** 14-0 (twice)        **Defeat:** 0-9

**HONOURS**    West Mids Lg R-up 89-90 (Div 1 87-88, Div 1 Cup 87-88), Staffs Senior Lg (2) 85-87, Staffordshire FA Vase 85-86 87-88; Midland Alliance 98-99

Players progressing: Bert Carpenter (Manchester Utd), Joe Carpenter (Brighton), George Shepherd (Derby), Mark Sale (Birmingham, Torquay),Tony Hemmings (Wycombe via Northwich)

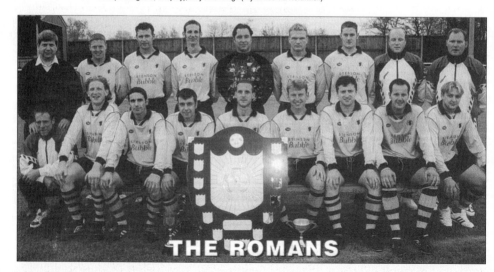

# SHEPSHED DYNAMO

## CLUB OFFICIALS

Chairman: **Michael Voce**
President / Vice Chairman: TBA

Secretary: **Peter Bull**
17 Welland Rd, Barrow-on-Soar,
Leicestershire LE12 8NA
Tel: 01509 413338
Press Officer: **Maurice Brindley**
Tel: 01509 267922
Commercial Manager: **T.B.A.**

### FACT FILE

Re-formed: 1994
Nickname: T.B.A.
Sponsors: T.B.A.
Colours: Black & white/black/black
Change colours: Blue/blue/blue
Midweek matchday: Tuesday
Reserves' League: Midland Comb.

### FOOTBALL MANAGEMENT TEAM

Manager: John Hanna
Assistant Manager: David Williams
Physio: Adrian Hannah

98-99 - Top scorer:Carl Smaller
P. o Y. & Captain: Pat Clarke

**GROUND**　The Dovecote, Butthole Lane, Shepshed, Leicestershire
Tel: 01509 650992

**Directions:** M1 junction 23, A512 towards Ashby, right at first lights, right atgarage in Forest Street, right into Butthole Lane opposite Black Swan. Fivemiles from Loughborough (BR)

Capacity: 5,000　　Cover: 1,500　　Seats: 209　　Floodlights: Yes

Pages: 40　Price: £1.00
Editor: Peter Bull Tel: c/o Club

Local Press: Loughborough Echo,
Leicester Mercury, Coalville Times
Local Radio :Radio Leicester, Oak FM

**Clubhouse:** Takes 120 in main room, 50 in others
**Club Shop:**Yes (Steve Straw & Alan Gibson)

**PREVIOUS**　**Leagues:** Leicestershire Senior 07-16 19-27 46-50 51-81, Midland Counties 81-82, Northern Counties (East) 82-83, Southern 83-88, Northern Premier 88-93, Midland Combination 93-94,Midland Alliance 94-96
**Names:** Shepshed Albion 1890-1975 91-94, Shepshed Charterhouse 75-91
**Grounds:** Ashby Road (pre-1897), Little Haw Farm
**CLUB RECORDS** **Attendance:** 2,500 v Leicester C. (friendly) 96-97
**Win:** 10-0 v Bloxwixh T. (H), Mid. Comb. 93-94　　**Defeat:** 0-7 v Hyde Utd. (A)  NPL 90-91
**Career Goalscorer:** Jeff Lissaman 104 (81-86)　　**Career Appearances:** Austin Straker 300
**Transfer fee paid:** £2,000 for Doug Newton (Charterhouse)
**Transfer fee received:** £10,000 for John Deakin  from Birmingham City (Charterhouse)
**BEST SEASON**　**FA Vase:** Semi-Finalists 78-79　　　　**FA Trophy:** 3rd Rd Replay v Emley 98-99
**FA Cup:** 1st Rd 82-83, 1-5 v  Preston North End (A), 96-97 v Carlisle United (a) 0-6
**HONOURS**　Southern Lge Midland Div. R-up 83-84, N.C.E. Lge 82-83 (League Cup 82-83), Midland Counties Lge 81-82 (League Cup 81-82), Leicestershire Senior Lge 10-11 20-21 78-79 79-80 80-81 (R-up 21-22, Div 2 53-54 65-66 77-78, Div 2 Cup 77-78), Leicestershire Senior Cup (7), Loughborough Charity Cup 92-93 Interlink Midland Alliance Winners 95-96

Players progressing:  Neil Grewcock (Burnley 84), Gordon Tucker (Huddersfield 87), Devon White (Bristol R. 87), John Deakin (Birmingham City)

# SOLIHULL BOROUGH

### CLUB OFFICIALS
Chairman: **John Hewitson**
President: **Joe McGorian**
Vice Chairman: **Trevor Stevens**
Commercial Man.: **Roger Lucas**
Secretary: **John A France**, 22 Swallows
Meadow, Shirley, Solihull B90 4QB
Tel: 0121733 6584
Press Officer: **Richard Crawshaw**
Tel: 01564 702746

### FOOTBALL MANAGEMENT TEAM
Manager: Paul Dyson
Reserve Manager: Chris Conway
Coach: Paul Holleran
Physio: Dave Smith

### FACT FILE
Formed: 1951
Nickname: Boro
Sponsors: Carling Black Label
Colours: Red/white/red
Change colours: Yellow/black/yellow
Midweek matchday: Wednesday
Reserve's League: Midland Combination
Reserve Division
98-99 Captain: Paul Brogan
P.o.Y.: Andy Penny
Top scorer:J Dowling

**GROUND**
Ground Share at Redditch Utd
Valley Stadium, Bromsgrove Road, Redditch B97 4RN Tel: 01527 67450
**Directions:** Access 7 on town centre ring-road takes you into Bromsgrove Road (via Unicorn
Hill) - ground entrance 400yds past traffic lights on right. Arriving from Bromsgrove take first
exit off dual carriageway. Ground 400 yds from Redditch BR station and town centre
Capacity: 9,500          Cover: 2,000          Seats: 400          Floodlights: Yes
**Clubhouse:** Large clubroom and lounge boardroom. Open matchdays and for private hire.
Food available on matchdays; hot dogs, burgers, chips etc          **Club Shop:** Yes

Pages: 52 Price: £1
Editors: Donna Matthews
0121 682 5783
Local Press: Solihull Times, Solihull News,
Sunday Mercury, Sports Argus
Local Radio: Radio WM, BRMB

**PREVIOUS**          **Leagues:** Mercian; Midland Combination 69-91
**Name:** Lincoln FC          **Grounds:** Widney Stadium, Solihull 65-88

**CLUB RECORDS**   **Attendance:** 2,135 v Darlington FA Cup 1st Rd replay. At previous ground: 400 vMoor Green, Midland Comb . Div . 2 , 1971
**Win:** 9-1 v Alfreton Town FA Trophy 1st Rd 97-98
**Defeat:** 1-7 v VS Rugby (A), Birmingham Senior Cup
**Career Goalscorer:** Joe Dowling          **Career Appearances:** Darrel Houghton
**Transfer fee paid:** £15,000 for Recky Carter, from Kettering Town
**Transfer fee received:** £30,000 for Andy Williams (to Coventry)

**BEST SEASON**   **FA Cup:** 1st Rd 97-98; 1-1,3-3 (2-4pen) v Darlington
**FA Vase:** 5th Rd 74-75          **FA Trophy:** 1st Rd Prop 97-98

**HONOURS**          Southern Lg Midland Div 91-92; Midland Comb. R-up 90-91, Chall Cup R-up 74-75 90-91, Presidents Cup R-up 69-70; Lord
Mayor of Birmingham Charity Cup 91-92 92-93 94-95 96-97; Worcs Sen. Cup R-up 92-93 96-97 97-98; Birmingham Sen. Cup
94-95

Players Progressing:          Kevin Ashley (Birmingham C.), Andy Williams (Coventry C.), Geoff Scott (Leicester C.), Danny Conway (Leicester C.),

# STAFFORD RANGERS

## CLUB OFFICIALS

Chairman: **C.S.Went**
Vice-Chairmam: **R.E.Tonge**

Secretary: **Peter Wall**
c/o Stafford Rangers F
Tel: 01785 602430
Press Officer: **Chris Godwin**

## FOOTBALL MANAGEMENT TEAM
Manager: I Painter
Physio: B. Whittaker
Coach: A King

## GROUND

**Directions:** From M6 junction 14, A34 (Stone) to roundabout, straight over into Beaconside, take third right into Common Road, ground one mile ahead. From Town Centre, follow signs for B5066 (Sandon) turn left by new housing estate. Two miles from railway station

Capacity: 6,000      Cover: 3,000      Seats: 426      Floodlights: Yes

Clubhouse: Yes - Open every day. Food available
Club Shop: Two shops, one old programmes and one souvenirs run by Jim & IreneDalglish

### FACT FILE

Formed: 1876
Nickname: The Boro
Colours: Black & White stripes/black/black
Change :Maroon & azure/maroon/maroon
Midweek matchday: Tuesday
Reserves' League: No reserve team

98-99- Captain: D Emerson
P.o.Y.: A .Eccleston
Top scorer:R.Mitchell

Marston Road Stafford ST16 3BX
Tel: 01785 602430  Fax : 01785 602431

Pages: 40 Price: £1.00
Editor: Peter Wall Tel. 01785 602430
Local Press: Staffordshire Newsletter, Express & Star, Evening Sentinel
Local Radio: Radio Stoke, Beacon Radio, Signal Radio

---

**PREVIOUS**  **Leagues:** Shropshire 1891-93, Birm 1893-96, 21-40, N Staffs 1896-1900, Cheshire 00-01, Birm Comb 00-12, 46-52, Cheshire Co. 52-69, N.P.L. 69-79, 83-85, Alliance Prem 79-83, GMVC 85-95
**Grounds:** Lammascotes, Stone Rd, Newtown, Doxey (until 1896)

**CLUB RECORDS**  **Attendance:** 8,536 v Rotherham Utd FA Cup 3rd Rd 75
**Win:** 11-0 v Dudley Town FA Cup 6.9.58      **Defeat:** 0-12 v Burton Town Birmingham Lge 13.12.30
**Career Goalscorer:** M Cullerton 176      **Career Appearances:** Jim Sargent
**Transfer fee paid:** £13,000 for S Butterworth from VS Rugby 90
**Transfer fee received:** £100,000 for Stan Collymore from Crystal Palace 1990

**BEST SEASON**  **FA Trophy:** Winners 1971-72 & 78-79. R-up 75-76
**FA Cup:** 4th Rd 74-75, 1-2 v Peterborough Utd. (H)      League clubs defeated: Halifax, Stockport, Rotherham

**HONOURS**  Birm Comb Champ 12-13; Birm Lge Champ 25-26; N.P.L. Champ 71-72, 84-85, Champ Shield 84-85; FA Trophy 71-72, 78-79, R-up 75-76; Bob Lord Trophy 85-86; Wednesday Charity Cup 20-21; Mid F/light Cup 70-71; Jim Thompson Shield 86-87; Staffs Sen Cup 54-55 56-57 62-63 71-72 77-78 86-87 91-92

Players progressing:  M Aleksic (Plymouth), J Arnold (Blackburn), R Williams/MCullerton/T Bailey (Port Vale), K Barnes (Man City), A Lee (Tranmere), ECameron (Exeter), W Blunt (Wolves), G Bullock (Barnsley), K Mottershead(Doncaster), McIlvenny (WBA), S Collymore (C Palace), P Devlin (Notts Co.),R Price (Birmingham C.)

*Back Row(L-R): Ken Jones, Steve Owens, Delwyn Humphreys, Richard Mitchell, Jon Williams, Pay Hayward, Jason Owen, Farrell Kilbane, Darren Boughey, Tony Eccleston, Archie King*
*Front Row: Micky Gynn, Neil Cartwright, Jason Smith, Ian Painter, Craig Love, Gary Piggott, Darren Wright, Phil Tongue*
*Photo: Marshall's Sports Service (Birmingham)*

# STOURBRIDGE

## CLUB OFFICIALS

Chairman: **Larry Homer**
Vice Chairman: **Roy Cooper**
Secretary/Press Officer: **Hugh Clark**
10 Burnt Oak Drive, Stourbridge,
W. Mids DY8 1HL
Tel: 01384 392975

### FOOTBALL MANAGEMENT TEAM
Manager: Mick Guest
Assistant Manager;Martin Thomas
Coach: Kelvin Sukkivan
Physio: Steve Ball

### FACT FILE
Formed: 1876
Nickname: The Glassboys
Sponsors: Carlsberg
Colours: Red & white stripes
Change colours: Yellow & blue
Midweek matchday: Tues
Reserves' League: Midland Comb
98-99 - Captain: L.Yates
Top scorer: P.Hunter (16)
Supporters P.o.Y.: Scott Colcombe
Players P.o.Y.: Adam Bastable

**GROUND** War Memorial Athletic Ground, High St., Amblecote, Stourbridge DY8 4HN
Tel: 01384 394040
**Directions:** Take A491, signposted Wolverhampton, from Stourbridge ring-road -ground
300yds on left immediately beyond traffic lights and opposite `RoyalOak' pub. Buses 311, 313
from Dudley, and 256 from Wolverhampton, pass ground. 1 mile from Stourbridge Town (BR)
Capacity: 2,000          Cover: 1,250          Seats: 250          Floodlights: Yes
**Clubhouse:** Open every evening from 8pm and Sunday lunchtimes
Club Shop: Programmes & souvenirs. Contact Nigel Gregg

Pages: 28          Price: £1
Editors: Hugh Clark & Nigel Gregg

Local Press: Stourbridge News & County
Express, Express & Star, Dudley EveningMail
Local Radio: Radio West Wids, B.R.M.B.,
Beacon

**PREVIOUS          Leagues:** West Midlands (previously Birmingham) 1892-1939 54-71, BirminghamCombination 45-53
**Grounds:** None          **Name:** Stourbridge Standard
**CLUB RECORDS Attendance:** 5,726 v Cardiff City, Welsh Cup final 1st leg 74 (post war); 14,000v W.B.A. Res 1901-02 Birm Lge (pre war)
**Career Goalscorer:** Ron Page 269          **Career Appearances:** Ron Page 427
**Transfer fee received:** £20,000 for Tony Cunningham (Lincoln C 79)
**Transfer fee paid:**
**BEST SEASON     FA Cup:** 4th Qual Rd: v Arnold 67-68, v V.S. Rugby  84-85 & 85-86 v Southport 98-99
**FA Trophy:** Qtr Final 70-71
**HONOURS**          Welsh Cup R-up 73-74; Southern Lg Midland Div 90-91 (Lg Cup 92-93), Div 1 North73-74, Merit Cup 73-74; West Mids (prev.
Birmingham) Lg 23-24 (R-up 4); Birmingham Comb. R-up 51-52; Birmingham Snr Cup 49-50 45-46 75-76 (R-up 3);Worcs Snr
Cup 9, (R-up 12); Herefordshire Snr Cup 54-55; Camkin Cup R-up 69-70; Camkin Presidents Cup 70-71; Albion Shield 43-44;
Keys Cup 37-38 62-63, Worcs Comb. R-up 27-28; Worcester Jnr Cup R-up 27-28; Tillotson Cup R-up 39-40, Brierley Hill Lg R-
up 44-45 (Lg Cup R-up 44-45); Brierley Hill Yth Lg Coronation Cup 56-57
Players progressing:          P Clark (Stockport Co. 65), K Ball (Walsall 72), P Freeman (W B A 68), C Bates/R Haywood (Shrewsbury T. 74),
L Lawrence (Shrewsbury T. 75), S Cooper (Torquay 78), T Cunningham (Lincoln 79), M Gwinnet (Peterborough 81)

*Right: Nicky Law (Stourbridge) heads clear under pressure from Nick Kirk (Sutton Coldfield). Photo: Keith Clayton*

# SUTTON COLDFIELD TOWN

## CLUB OFFICIALS

Chairman: **Kevin Holt**
Secretary: **Fred Rought**
25 Lebanon Grove, Chase Terrace,
Burntwood, Staffs. WS7 8BE
Tel: 01543 685029
Press Officer: **Brian Turner**
Commercial Manager: **Peter Young**

**FOOTBALL MANAGEMENT TEAM**
Manager: Gary Bradder
Asst Man: Alan Hampton
Physio: Reg Brassington

## FACT FILE

Formed: 1897
Nickname: Royals
Colours: Blue & white/blue/blue & white
Change colours: Red & black/red/red &
black
Midweek matchday: Tuesday
Reserves' League: No reserve team

Programm
Pages: 20   Price: 80p
Editor: Peter Young Tel.
Local Press: Sutton Coldfield News,
Sutton Observer
Local Radio: BRMB, Radio WM

**GROUND**              Central Ground, Coles Lane, Sutton Coldfield B72 1NL
                        Tel: 0121 354 2997 or 0121 355 5475

**Directions:** A5127 into Sutton, right at Odeon cinema (Holland Rd), then first right into Coles
Lane - ground 150 yds on left. 10 mins walk from SuttonColdfield (BR), bus 104 from
Birmingham

**Capacity:** 4,500      Cover: 500      Seats: 200      Floodlights: Yes
**Clubhouse:**      Brick built lounge & concert room, fully carpeted and extensively decorated
                    Open daily, food available
**Club Shop:**      Selling metal badges, scarves, hats, pens, rosettes, progs
                    Contact Paul Vanes (0121 770 9835)

**PREVIOUS**      **Leagues:** Central Birmingham, Walsall Sen., Staffs Co., BirminghamComb. 50-54, West Mids (Regional) 54-65 79-82,
                  Midlands Comb. 65-79      **Name:** Sutton Coldfield FC 1879-1921
                  **Grounds:** Meadow Plat 1879-89/ Coles Lane (site of current ambulance station) 90-1919

**CLUB RECORDS  Attendance:** 2,029 v Doncaster Rovers, F.A. Cup 80-81 (Receipts £2,727)
                  **Career Goalscorer:** Eddie Hewitt 288      **Career Appearances:** Eddie Hewitt 465
                  **Fee paid:** £1,500 twice in 1991, for Lance Morrison (Gloucester) & Micky Clarke(Burton A.)
                  **Fee received:** £25,000 for Barry Cowdrill (WBA 1979)

**BEST SEASON     FA Cup:** 1st Rd 80-81, 0-1 v Doncaster R (H), 92-93, 1-2 v BoltonWanderers (A)
                  **FA Trophy:** 1st Round replay 1989-90      **FA Amateur Cup:** 2nd Round 1970-71

**HONOURS**       Southern Lg Midland Div R-up 82-83, West Mids Lg 79-80 (Lg Cup 80-81 81-82), Midland Comb.(2) 77-79 (R-up(2) 69-71, Lg
                  Cup 69-70), Walsall Senior Lg 46-47, Walsall Sen. Cup(3) 77-80 (R-up 80-81), Staffs Sen. Cup R-up 89-90, Lord Mayor of
                  Birmingham Charity Cup 95-96, R-up 93-94, Worcs Sen. Cup SF 88-89, Walsall Challenge Cup R-up 46-47 47-48, Sutton
                  Charity Cup 46-47 65-66 71-72 86-87 89-90 90-91, Express & Star Cup 44-45

**Players progressing:**   Arthur Corbett (Walsall 49), Paul Cooper (Manchester C.), Noel Blake (Leeds), Steve Cooper (Barnsley),
                  Peter Latchford (WBA), Mark Smith (Wolves), John Barton (Everton), Barry Cowdrill (WBA 79),Colin Dryhurst (Halifax 79),
                  Dale Belford (Notts Co. 87), Ellis Laight (Torquay 92)

*Mark Holt (Sutton Coldfield) lets fly at the Stourbridge goal. Photo: Keith Clayton*

541

# TIVERTON TOWN

## CLUB OFFICIALS

President: **Dan McCauley**
Chairman: **Dave Wright**
Vice-Chairman: **Pete Buxton**

Secretary: **Ramsay Findlay**
35 Park Road, Tiverton, Devon EX16 6AY
Tel: 01884 256341

## FOOTBALL MANAGEMENT TEAM

Manager: Martyn Rogers
Asst Manager: Martin Grimshaw
Physio: Alan Morgan

**FACT FILE**
Formed: 1920
Nickname: Tivvy
Colours: All Yellow
Change colours: All white
Midweek matches: Wednesday
Reserves' League: none
1998-99
Top Goalscorer: Phil Everett
P. of Y.: Mickey Fallon
Captain: Neil Saunders

**GROUND**    Ladysmead, Bolham Road, Tiverton, Devon EX16 8SG
Tel: 01884 252397

**Directions:** M5 Jct 27, west towards Tiverton on A361, continue to end of dual carriageway and turn left at r'about; ground entrance 300yds on right alongside BP petrol station

Capacity: 3,500    Seats: 300    Cover: 1,200    Floodlights: Yes

Pages: 56    Price: £1.00 (with colour)
Editor/ Press Officer: John Fournier
Tel No: 01884 32904

**Clubhouse:** Lunctimes, evenings. All day Sat during season. 3 bars. Food(burgers, chips etc)
**Club Shop:** Yes

**HONOURS**    FA Vase 97-98 98-99; Western Lg 93-94 94-95 96-97 97-98 (R-up 92-93 95-96 98-99);
Les Phillips Cup 92-93 94-95 95-96 96-97 97-98; Amateur Trophy 77-78 78-79, Div 1 R-up 88-89;
Devon St Lukes Cup 90-91 91-92 92-93 94-95 96-97 (R-up 89-90); Devon & Exeter Lg 51-52 66-67 70-71 84-85;
Devon Snr Cup 55-56 65-66; East Devon Snr Cup 35-36 37-38 52-53 55-56 60-61 62-63 66-67;
North Devon Charity Cup 72-73 86-87

**PREVIOUS**    **League:** Devon & Exeter; Western League    **Ground:** The Elms, Blundell Road 1920-39

**BEST SEASON**    **FA Vase:** Winners 97-98 98-99, R-up 92-93
**FA Cup:** 1st Rnd 90-91 91-92 94-95 97-98

**RECORD**    **Attendance:** 3,000 v Leyton Orient, FA Cup First Round Proper 1994-95
**Career Goalscorer:** Kevin Smith 303 - Phil Everett at start of 99-00 season has 301

Players progressing: Jason Smith (Coventry City 93 &Swansea City 98), Mark Saunders (Plymouth Argyle 95)

# WESTON-super-MARE

### CLUB OFFICIALS
President: **D A Usher**

Chairman: **Paul T Bliss**

Secretary/Press Officer: **Keith Refault**

c/o Weston Super Mare FC
Tel: 01934 635665

### FOOTBALL MANAGEMENT TEAM

Coach: John Relish
Assistant Coach: Graham Withey
Physio: Dave Lukins

### FACT FILE

Formed: 1899
Nickname: Seagulls
Sponsors: Firstgroup
Colours: White/blue/blue
Change colours: All yellow
Midweek matches: Tuesday
Reserves' League: Somerset Senior
98-99- Captain: Andy Llewellyn
P.o.Y.:Alan Bird
Top scorer: Justin Pritchard (15)

WESTON-SUPER-MARE
FOOTBALL CLUB
WOODSPRING PARK, WINTERSTOKE ROAD, TEL: (01934) 621618

ANNUAL REVIEW
SEASON
1998 - 1999

WESTON-SUPER-MARE          £1

**FirstGroup** 🌀          Dr. Marten's LEAGUE
MIDLAND DIVISION
1998-1999

**GROUND**      Woodspring Park, Winterstoke Road, Weston-super-Mare BS23 2YG
Tel: 01934 6355665 or 621618

Directions: M5 Jct 21. A370 along dual carriageway to 4th roundabout. First left and immediately right at small roundabout, club on right. FromSouth: M5 Jct 22, follow Weston signs for approx 7 miles, right at first r'bout(by Hospital), left at next r'bout, ground 1 mile on left. Twenty minsutes walk fromWeston-super-Mare (BR)
Capacity: 2,000      Seats: 250      Cover: 1,000      Floodlights: Yes
Clubhouse: Mon-Fri 7-11pm, Sat 12-11pm, Sun 12-3 & 7-11pm.
2 skittle alleys, 2bars. Bar meals and hot meals everyday
Club Shop: Selling a wide range of souvenirs & programmes.Contact Alan White at the club.9

Pages: 32      Price: £1
Editor: Secretary Tel. 01934 635665
Local Press: Bristol Evening Post,
Western Daily Press
Local Radio: Somerset Sound, Radio Bristol

**PREVIOUS**      League: Western 1900-92 ( Not continuous)          Name: Borough of Weston-super-Mare
Grounds: The Great Ground, Locking Road 48-55, Langford Road 55-83

**CLUB RECORDS**  Attendance: 2,623 v Woking, FA Cup First Round Proper replay 23/11/93
At Langford Road: 2,500 v Bridgwater Town, FA Cup First Round Proper replay 1961-62
**Win:** 11-0 v Paulton Rovers                          **Defeat:** 1-12 v Yeovil Town Reserves
**Career Goalscorer:** Matthew Lazenby, 180          **Career Appearances:** Harry Thomas, 740
**Transfer fee received:** £20,000 Stuart Jones fromSheffield Wednesday 98  **Transfer fee paid:** None

**BEST SEASON**  FA Cup: 1st Rd Proper replay 61-62, 0-1 v Bridgwater Town after 0-0; 94-95, 0-1 v Woking (A) after 2-2
FA Trophy: 14th Round 98-99          FA Vase: Have not entered

**HONOURS**      Somerset Snr Cup 23-24 26-27; Western Lg Champions 91-92 (R-up 76-77), Lg Cup 76-77 (R-up 89-90), Merit Cup 76-77 77-
78; Somerset Snr Lg (Reserves) Div 1 87-88 (R-up 90-91), Div 2 R-up 85-86, Div 3 84-85

Players progressing: Shaun Rouse (Carlisle United 94), Ian Maine, John Palmer(Bristol City),Wayne Brown(Chester City 97), Stuart Jones (Sheffield Wed 98), Ryan Souter (Bury 99)

Back Row: John Relish (Coach), James Hoyt, Ian Juryeff, Mark Price, Alan Bird, Dave Mogg, Deion Vernon, Ian Haslett, Andy Power, Dave Lukins (Physio), Gareth Lukins (Kit Manager)
Front Row: Paul Terry, Leigh White, Craig Dann, Andy Llewellyn (Captain), Ryan Souter, Dave Bell

# YATE TOWN

## CLUB OFFICIALS

Acting Chairman: **D.A.Phillips**
President: **R Hewetson**

Secretary: **Terry Tansley**
1 Tyning Close, Yate, Avon. BS37 5PN
Tel: 01454 324305
Press Officer/Commercial Man:T.B.A.

**FOOTBALL MANAGEMENT TEAM**

Manager: Martin Durnell
Asst Manager/Coach: Danny Iddles
Physio:Sam Durant

### FACT FILE

Formed: 1946
Nickname: The Bluebells
Sponsors: T.B.A.
Colours: White/navy/navy
Change colours: All Red
Midweek matchday: Tuesday
Reserve Team's League: Bristol Suburban
1998-99
Top scorer:Paul Metheringham
P. of Y.: Simon Bean & Adie Taverner
Captain: Danny Iddles

**GROUND**        Lodge Road, Yate, Bristol BS37 7LE Tel: 01454 228103

**Directions:** M4 jct 18, A46 towards Stroud, then A432 to Yate. Turn right at top of railway bridge into North Road, first left past traffic lights. Five miles from Bristol Parkway BR main line station, half mile from Yate BR station. Buses 329, X68 and 328

Capacity: 2,000        Cover: 236        Seats: 236        Floodlights: Yes

**Clubhouse:** Open every night & weekend lunchtimes. Skittles, darts, pool, live entertainment
**Club Shop:** Selling programmes & usual souvenirs. Contact: Secretary

Pages: 40  Price: £1
Editor: Terry Tansley c/o Club
Local Press: Bristol Evening Post, Western Daily Press, North Avon Gazette
Local Radio: GWR, Radio Bristol

**PREVIOUS**        **Leagues:** Gloucestershire County 68-83, Hellenic 83-89
                **Name:** Yate YMCA 1946-70        **Grounds:** Yate Aerodrome 50-54, Newmans Field 54-60, Sunnyside Lane 60-84

**CLUB RECORDS** **Attendance:** 2,000 for Bristol Rovers v Bristol Rovers Past, Vaughan Jones testimonial 90
                **Win:** 13-3 v Clevedon, Bristol Premier Comb 67-68        **Defeat:**
                **CareerGoalscorer:** Kevin Thaws        **Career Appearances:** Gary Hewlett
                **Transfer fee paid:** None        **Transfer fee received:** £15,000 for Mike Davis (Bristol Rovers 93)

**BEST SEASON**    **FA Vase:** Fifth Round 1991-92        **FA Cup:**                    **FA Trophy:**

**HONOURS**        Hellenic Lg(2) 87-89 (Div 1 R-up 84-85, Lg Skol Cup R-up 87-88), Glos Chal.Tphy 88-89 (R-up 78-79), Glos Snr Amtr Cup Sth 77-78 91-92(res) 92-93(res),Glos Snr Chal. Cup (Nth) R-up 89-90 92-93 94-95, Stroud Charity Cup R-up 74-75 81-82 84-85 (Sect. A Winners(6) 76-78 79-80 82-83 87-89), Berkeley Hosp. Prem.Cup(3) 73-75 80-81, S.W. Co's Sutton Vase 85-86 Dr.Martens Fairplay award 98-99

Players progressing:Richard Thompson (Newport Co.), Phil Purnell (Bristol R.), Darren Tilley (York C.), Steve Winter (Walsall), Mike Davis (Bristol R. 93)

*Yate goalie Simon Bean smothers the ball from a Tonbridge attack. Photo: Alan Coomes*

# SOUTHERN DIVISION FINAL LEAGUE TABLE 1998-99

|  | P | W | D | L | F | A | Pts |
|---|---|---|---|---|---|---|---|
| Havant & Waterlooville | 42 | 29 | 7 | 6 | 85 | 32 | 94 |
| Margate | 42 | 27 | 8 | 7 | 84 | 33 | 89 |
| Folkestone Invicta | 42 | 26 | 8 | 8 | 92 | 47 | 86 |
| Newport IOW | 42 | 23 | 7 | 12 | 68 | 40 | 76 |
| Chelmsford City | 42 | 20 | 12 | 10 | 91 | 51 | 72 |
| Raunds Town | 42 | 19 | 13 | 10 | 87 | 50 | 70 |
| Ashford Town | 42 | 17 | 12 | 13 | 59 | 54 | 63 |
| Baldock Town | 42 | 17 | 9 | 16 | 60 | 59 | 60 |
| Fisher Athletic | 42 | 16 | 11 | 15 | 58 | 54 | 59 |
| Bashley | 42 | 17 | 7 | 18 | 74 | 77 | 58 |
| Witney Town | 42 | 15 | 12 | 15 | 56 | 48 | 57 |
| Cirencester Town | 42 | 16 | 8 | 18 | 61 | 66 | 56 |
| Sittingbourne | 42 | 12 | 18 | 12 | 53 | 56 | 54 |
| Dartford | 42 | 14 | 10 | 18 | 48 | 53 | 52 |
| Erith & Belvedere | 42 | 15 | 7 | 20 | 48 | 64 | 52 |
| Tonbridge Angels | 42 | 12 | 15 | 15 | 48 | 59 | 51 |
| St Leonards | 42 | 14 | 8 | 20 | 57 | 72 | 50 |
| Fleet Town | 42 | 12 | 11 | 19 | 54 | 72 | 47 |
| Corby Town | 42 | 10 | 10 | 22 | 48 | 73 | 40 |
| Yate Town | 42 | 10 | 7 | 25 | 37 | 79 | 37 |
| Andover | 42 | 6 | 10 | 26 | 50 | 115 | 28 |
| Brackley Town | 42 | 6 | 8 | 28 | 41 | 105 | 26 |

# SOUTHERN DIVISION RESULTS CHART 1998-99

|  |  | 1 | 2 | 3 | 4 | 5 | 6 | 7 | 8 | 9 | 10 | 11 | 12 | 13 | 14 | 15 | 16 | 17 | 18 | 19 | 20 | 21 | 22 |
|---|---|---|---|---|---|---|---|---|---|---|---|---|---|---|---|---|---|---|---|---|---|---|---|
| 1 | Andover | X | 1-5 | 2-2 | 1-1 | 3-2 | 1-3 | 0-2 | 1-2 | 1-0 | 3-1 | 2-5 | 0-0 | 0-4 | 0-4 | 1-3 | 0-2 | 1-2 | 2-2 | 1-3 | 2-2 | 3-1 | 1-1 |
| 2 | Ashford T | 1-1 | X | 2-1 | 1-3 | 4-1 | 2-1 | 2-1 | 4-1 | 0-3 | 2-0 | 1-1 | 3-1 | 0-2 | 0-3 | 1-2 | 1-0 | 1-0 | 0-0 | 3-0 | 0-2 | 3-1 | 0-0 |
| 3 | Baldock T | 2-2 | 3-0 | X | 3-1 | 1-2 | 1-1 | 1-1 | 2-0 | 3-2 | 2-1 | 2-0 | 3-1 | 0-3 | 0-5 | 0-1 | 0-2 | 3-1 | 4-1 | 0-2 | 1-2 | 1-0 | 5-0 |
| 4 | Bashley | 3-1 | 3-3 | 1-5 | X | 3-1 | 1-4 | 4-2 | 2-0 | 1-0 | 1-3 | 0-1 | 2-0 | 4-1 | 2-2 | 2-1 | 1-3 | 5-2 | 2-1 | 5-6 | 2-3 | 2-1 |  |
| 5 | Brackley T | 1-0 | 1-2 | 0-1 | 2-1 | X | 1-5 | 1-3 | 2-2 | 0-0 | 1-1 | 2-0 | 1-1 | 2-0 | 0-4 | 1-4 | 1-1 | 1-4 | 2-1 | 0-2 | 0-4 | 3-0 |  |
| 6 | Chelmsford | 4-0 | 3-0 | 3-0 | 0-1 | 6-1 | X | 2-2 | 3-0 | 3-0 | 2-0 | 3-3 | 0-0 | 2-1 | 0-2 | 2-3 | 4-3 | 3-2 | 1-1 | 1-1 | 3-0 | 2-2 | 5-3 |
| 7 | Cirencester | 1-4 | 1-3 | 1-1 | 1-1 | 2-1 | 3-1 | X | 2-0 | 2-0 | 0-2 | 2-1 | 3-5 | 0-1 | 1-3 | 0-2 | 3-0 | 2-1 | 2-0 | 3-0 | 1-1 | 1-1 | 1-1 |
| 8 | Corby Tn | 4-0 | 2-0 | 1-3 | 0-3 | 3-0 | 2-1 | 1-1 | X | 1-2 | 1-3 | 1-0 | 1-1 | 1-3 | 0-2 | 3-1 | 5-1 | 0-0 | 0-0 | 1-4 | 0-1 | 2-2 | 5-1 |
| 9 | Dartford | 3-1 | 0-0 | 1-2 | 2-1 | 6-1 | 1-0 | 4-1 | 2-0 | X | 2-0 | 2-0 | 1-3 | 3-4 | 0-2 | 0-0 | 0-2 | 0-1 | 1-1 | 0-0 | 1-1 | 0-0 | 1-0 |
| 10 | Erith & B | 0-1 | 2-1 | 0-0 | 0-3 | 3-2 | 0-2 | 0-1 | 0-2 | 2-0 | X | 1-2 | 1-1 | 1-1 | 2-0 | 0-2 | 0-3 | 3-1 | 2-2 | 3-1 | 0-0 | 0-1 | 0-2 |
| 11 | Fisher A L | 2-0 | 0-1 | 1-2 | 2-1 | 2-0 | 1-0 | 4-1 | 2-1 | 2-1 | 4-1 | X | 3-3 | 1-1 | 2-3 | 0-1 | 0-0 | 1-2 | 0-0 | 1-0 | 1-0 | 1-3 | 2-1 |
| 12 | Fleet Tn | 3-3 | 3-3 | 4-0 | 0-0 | 3-0 | 0-2 | 0-4 | 3-1 | 2-1 | 2-1 | 2-1 | X | 0-1 | 4-6 | 1-2 | 0-1 | 2-4 | 0-2 | 1-2 | 0-1 | 2-0 | 1-0 |
| 13 | Folkestone | 6-2 | 2-1 | 4-0 | 2-1 | 4-0 | 3-2 | 3-2 | 4-1 | 1-2 | 2-1 | 0-0 | 4-0 | X | 0-1 | 2-0 | 3-2 | 3-2 | 2-2 | 0-2 | 1-1 | 2-1 | 3-2 |
| 14 | Havant & W | 5-1 | 2-0 | 2-0 | 3-0 | 3-1 | 0-3 | 3-0 | 0-0 | 1-1 | 0-2 | 2-0 | 2-0 | 3-1 | X | 1-0 | 3-0 | 3-1 | 0-1 | 2-1 | 2-2 | 3-1 | 2-0 |
| 15 | Margate | 4-1 | 1-1 | 3-0 | 5-0 | 2-0 | 2-2 | 2-0 | 6-0 | 2-2 | 1-1 | 2-1 | 1-2 | 1-0 | 2-02 | X | 1-2 | 0-2 | 2-1 | 2-1 | 2-0 | 0-0 | 3-0 |
| 16 | Newport | 2-0 | 1-1 | 0-1 | 4-0 | 2-0 | 1-1 | 2-1 | 3-0 | 1-0 | 1-3 | 2-0 | 1-1 | 2-1 | 0-1 | 0-1 | X | 2-0 | 3-0 | 2-2 | 3-0 | 2-0 | 4-0 |
| 17 | Raunds Tn | 10-0 | 1-1 | 1-1 | 1-1 | 4-2 | 3-3 | 1-0 | 3-1 | 7-0 | 7-1 | 2-2 | 4-0 | 2-2 | 1-1 | 2-2 | 2-0 | X | 1-1 | 3-2 | 0-0 | 0-0 | 3-0 |
| 18 | Sittingb'ne | 4-1 | 0-0 | 3-3 | 1-0 | 0-0 | 1-1 | 3-0 | 1-0 | 2-1 | 0-1 | 2-2 | 0-2 | 0-3 | 0-1 | 0-4 | 1-0 | 0-1 | X | 0-0 | 5-1 | 1-1 | 2-2 |
| 19 | St Leonards | 3-1 | 1-2 | 1-0 | 1-2 | 3-3 | 0-4 | 1-2 | 1-1 | 1-0 | 1-3 | 1-1 | 2-0 | 0-3 | 0-4 | 1-6 | 2-2 | 0-2 | 1-2 | X | 1-0 | 2-1 | 4-1 |
| 20 | Tonbridge | 4-1 | 2-2 | 1-3 | 3-3 | 1-0 | 1-1 | 1-3 | 0-0 | 0-1 | 4-0 | 1-3 | 1-0 | 1-1 | 0-0 | 0-3 | 0-0 | 2-1 | 2-2 | 1-4 | X | 0-2 | 0-1 |
| 21 | Witney T | 4-2 | 0-2 | 1-0 | 2-0 | 8-1 | 1-0 | 2-1 | 2-1 | 0-1 | 0-2 | 1-1 | 3-1 | 1-2 | 1-1 | 1-1 | 0-1 | 0-1 | 3-0 | 1-2 | 1-0 | X | 0-0 |
| 22 | Yate Tn | 1-2 | 1-0 | 3-1 | 2-1 | 2-1 | 1-2 | 0-1 | 1-1 | 1-1 | 0-1 | 1-2 | 1-3 | 0-4 | 2-0 | 0-1 | 0-4 | 0-3 | 3-1 | 2-1 | 0-0 |  | X |

*Peter Barnes*
*Photo: Garry Letts*

# ASHFORD TOWN

### CLUB OFFICIALS
Chairman: **Ernie Warren**
President: **Ashley M Batt**
Secretary/Press Officer: **A Lancaste**r
128 Kingsnorth Rd, Ashford, Kent TN23
2HY Tel: 01233 621325
Vice Chairman: **Peter Barton**
Commercial Director:
**Ernie Warron** Tel: 01233 634125

### FOOTBALL MANAGEMENT TEAM
Manager: Nigel Donn
Asst Manager: None
Coach: Nicky Sparks
Physio: George Sargeant

### FACT FILE
Formed: 1930
Nickname: Nuts & Bolts
Colours: All Green
Change colours: All White
Midweek home matchday: Tuesday
Reserves ' League: No Reserve team

**GROUND**   The Homelands, Ashford Road, Kingsnorth, Ashford, Kent TN26 1NJ
Tel: 01233 611838
Directions: M20 jct 10, follow A2070 signs towards Brenzett & Lydd airport, dual carriageway
to junction of old A2070, ground 1 mile on left thro' village of Kingsnorth. 4 miles south of Ashford
Capacity: 3,200        Cover: 1,250     Seats: 500       Floodlights: Yes
Clubhouse: Open matchdays and for special functions. Licensed bar, function room. Limited
food - sandwiches & simple snacks.
Club Shop: Sells old progs, pennants, scarves, badges etc. Contact Alan Bird(01233 662680)

Pages: 32 Price: £1.00
Editor: Elaine Orsbourne
Local Press: Kentish Express
Local Radio: Radio Kent, Invicta Radio

**PREVIOUS**       **Names:** Ashford United, Ashford Railway, Ashford F.C.
**Leagues:** Kent 30-59.  Ground: Essella Park, Essella Rd 30-87

**CLUB RECORDS** **Attendance:** 6,525 (at Essella Park, previous ground), v Crystal Palace, FA Cup 1st Rd 1959.
3,363 (at current ground), v Fulham FA Cup 1st Round 1994.
**Goalscorer:** Dave Arter 197. **Appearances:** Peter McRobert 765
**Win:** 10-1 v Bury Town, February 1964. **Defeat:** 0-8 v Crawley Town, November1964
**Fee Paid:** £7,000 for J Ross & D Arter (Sittingbourne, March 94)
**Fee Received:** £25,000 for Jeff Ross & Dave Arter (Hythe Tn, 90). Individually: £20,000 for Lee McRobert (Sittingbourne, 93)

**BEST SEASON** **FA Trophy:** Semi Final 72-73, 96-97 2nd Rd
**FA Cup:** 2nd Rd 61-62, 0-3 v QPR (H), 66-67, 0-5 v Swindon (A). 1st Rd 7 times.     League clubs defeated: None.
**HONOURS**       FA Trophy SF 72-73; Southern Lg Southern Div R-up 86-87 95-96; Kent Lg 48-49(R-up 31-32), Lg Cup 38-39; Kent Senior Cup
58-59 62-63 92-93 95-96
Players progressing: Ollie Norris (Rochdale 61), HowardMoore (Coventry 66), Tony Godden (WBA 75), Lee McRobert (Millwall 94)

*Folkestone's Steve Lawrence (stripes) outjumps Ashford's Tristian Hodges but puts his header over. Photo:Alan Coomes*

# BALDOCK TOWN

**CLUB OFFICIALS**
Joint Chairmen:
**Mike Watson-Challis** & **Ray Childerstone**
Secretary: **Cyril T Hammond**
2 Elmwood Court, High Street.,
Baldock, Herts SG7 6AY
01462 894253(H) 01462 895449(B)
General Manager: **B Williams**
Press Officer: **David Hammond**
Tel: 01462 892797

**FOOTBALL MANAGEMENT TEAM**

Team Manager: Robbie O'Keefe
Physio: Fred Day

**FACT FILE**

Formed: 1889

Nickname: Reds

Colours: All red

Change colours: All white

Midweek home matchday: Wednesday

Reserve Team's League: No reserve team

**GROUND** Norton Road, Baldock, Herts SG7 5AU Tel: 01462 895449
Directions: Off A1(M) at Letchworth/Baldock sign, left to 3rd island, A505 toBaldock, Norton Road is left off A505, left past Orange Tree pub, ground on right after railway bridge. From North or East turn left into town, Hitchin Street, right into Norton then proceed as above. From Baldock station (KingsCross to Royston line) - left down Ickneild Way and right into Norton Road
Capacity: 3,000 Cover: 1,250 Seats: 250
Clubhouse: Members' bar and separate function room. Food available

BALDOCK TOWN FOOTBALL CLUB
1996 - 1997 SEASON

B T F C

REDS REVIEW

SIC VOS · NON · VOBIS

F.A. CUP (SPONSORED BY LITTLEWOODS)
2nd QUALIFYING ROUND REPLAY
**BALDOCK TOWN**
VERSUS
**STEVENAGE BOROUGH**
WEDNESDAY 2nd OCTOBER 1996
KICK OFF 7.30pm

MEMBERS OF:
HERTFORDSHIRE F.A.
Dr. MARTENS LEAGUE
ASSOCIATE MEMBER OF THE F.A.

OFFICIAL MATCHDAY PROGRAMME £1.00

Pages: 48 Price: £1
Editor: TBA
Local Press: Comet, Gazette
Local Radio: Radio Bedfordshire, Chiltern

**PREVIOUS** **Ground:** Bakers Close (until 1982)
**Leagues:** South Midlands 25-39 47-54 63-83, Parthenon 54-59, London 59-63,United Counties 83-87

**CLUB RECORDS** **Attendance:** 1,588 v Stevenage Boro. FA Cup 2nd Prelim 96-97
**Goalscorer:** Unknown. **Appearances:** Keith (Paddy) Stanton 550
**Fee Paid:** £2,000: for Colin Hull (Bishop's Stortford) & for Glen Russell(Braintree 1993)
**Fee Received:** £30,000 for Kevin Phillips (Watford F.C.)

**BEST SEASON** **FA Vase:** 5th Round 83-84 **FA Trophy:** 2nd Qual. Round 90-91
**FA Cup:** 4th Qual. Round replay 91-92, 0-1 v Halesowen Town (A) after 1-1

**HONOURS** United Counties Lg R-up 83-84 86-87, South Mids Lg 27-28 65-66 67-68 69-70 (R-up 53-54 82-83, Lg Cup 65-66 69-70, Div 1 49-50, Reserve Div 1 66-67), HertsCharity Cup 91-92 94-95, Herts Charity Shield 57-58 69-70, Wallspan Floodlit Cup 85-86, Hinchingbrooke Cup 86-87, TSI Floodlit Cup 88-89, Woolwich E.B.S.Cup 83-84, Herts Intermediate Cup 86-87. Southern Lge R-up 94-95. Southern LgeCup Dr Martens 95-96

Players progressing: Ian Dowie (Luton), Alan Stewart (Portsmouth), Kevan Phillips (Watford)

*Back Row (L-R): Gary Roberts (Asst. Mgr), Glen Russell, John Shanks, Gary Simpson, Adam Wheeler, Simon Catmur, Toma Johansen, Paul De Luca, Mark Goddard (Physio)*
*Front Row: Steve Cook (Asst. Mgr), Dak Lee, Barry Dellar, Danny Power, Ricky Dear, Ray Kilby, Gary Walker*
*Photo: G Whittington*

# BASHLEY

## CLUB OFFICIALS
Chairman: **G.Parsons**
President: **K.D.Taylorl**
Vice Chairman: **Frank Whitman**
Secretary: **Ray Murphy,** Flat 10, Richmond
Court, 122 Richmond Park
Road,Bournemouth, Dorset BH8 8TH
Commercial Manager: **Mary Whitman**
Press Officer: **Terry Collett**

## FOOTBALL MANAGEMENT TEAM

Manager: Jimmy Case
Asst Manager/Coach: Barry Blankley
Physio: Chris Lovegrove

### FACT FILE

Formed: 1947
Nickname: The Bash
Sponsors: T.B.A.
Colours: Yellow & black
Change colours: Blue & white
Midweek matchday: Tuesday
Reserves' League: Wessex Comb
98-99 Captain: Dave Morris

Pages: 36 Price: £1
Editor:
Local Press: Bournemouth Echo, Southern
Pink, New Milton Advertiser
Local Radio: 2CR,Solent, Ocean Sound

**GROUND**        Recreation Ground, Bashley, Hampshire BH25 5RY. Tel: 01425 620280

**Directions:** A35 Lyndhurst towards Christchurch, turn left down B3058 towardsNew Milton, ground on left in Bashley village. Half hour walk from New Milton(BR) station

Capacity: 4,250        Cover: 1,200        Seats: 200        Floodlights: Yes

**Clubhouse:** Usual licensing hours. Snacks available
Club Shop: Open matchdays

**PREVIOUS**        **Leagues:** Bournemouth 50-83; Hants 83-86; Wessex 86-89

**CLUB RECORDS Attendance:** 3,500 v Emley, F.A. Vase S.F. 1st Leg 87-88
**Win:** 21-1 v Co-operative (A), Bournemouth Lge, 64        **Defeat:** 2-20 v Air Speed(A), Bournemouth Lge, 57
**Career Goalscorer:** Colin Cummings        **Career Appearances:** John Bone
**Transfer fee paid:** £7,500 for J Stagg from Andover        **Transfer fee received:** £7,500 for Darren Powell from Weymouth 95

**BEST SEASON**        **FA Cup:** 2nd Rd Proper 1994-95, 0-1 v Swansea City
**FA Vase:** Semi Final 87-88, Qtr Final 88-89  FA Trophy: 2nd Round 91-92

**HONOURS**        Southern Lg Southern Division 89-90 (Lg Cup SF 89-90), Wessex Lg 86-87 87-88 88-89, Hants Lg Div 3 84-85,
Hants Lg Combination 88-89, Russell Cotes Cup 88-89 90-91 92-93

Players Progressing : Wayne Brown (Bristol City, 1994), David Billington Peterborough 1996), Ryan Young (Plymouth 1997), Dean Higgins (Torquay 1998), Danny Smith (Bournemouith 1998), Craig Davies (Cardiff City 1998), Tony Wallis (Cardiff City 1999).

*Taylor's sliding effort for Bashley is blocked by the Viking Sports' defence with Jamie Laidlaw close up in support.*
*Photo: D Nicholson*

# BURNHAM

## CLUB OFFICIALS

Chairman: **Malcolm Higton**
Vice Chairman: **M A Beavis**
Press Officer: **Secretary**
Secretary: **Alan King**
41 Underwood Road, High Wycombe,
Bucks HP13 6YD (01494523920)

**FOOTBALL MANAGEMENT TEAM**
Manager: Shane Chandler
Coach: John Griffith
Physio: Mark Green

## FACT FILE

Founded:
Sponsors: Caflon International
Colours: Blue & white/blue/white
Change colours: Yellow/yellow/black
Midweek matchday: Tuesday
Reserve Team's Lge: Suburban

97-98 - Captain: Paul Brett
P.o.Y.: Jamie Furmage
Top Scorer: Shane Small (14)

Programme:
30 pages      Editor: Cliff Sparkes
Local Press: Slough Observer, South Bucks
Express, Maidenhead Advertiser,
Buckingham Advertiser
Local Radio: Star FM,
BBC Thames Valley, 210 FM

**Ground:** The Gore, Wymers Wood Road, Burnham, Slough SL1 8JG
Tel: 01628 602467/602697
**Directions:** North west of village centre, 2 miles from Burnham BR station, 2miles from M4 junction 7, 5 miles from M40 junction 2, 100yds north of Gorecrossroads - fork right into Wymers Wood Rd and ground is immediately on right
Capacity: 2,500      Cover: 250      Seats: 250      Floodlights: Yes      Club Shop: Yes
**Clubhouse:** Open every evening and w/e lunch. Darts and pool, two bars, usual matchday food

**HONOURS** Athenian Lg R-up(2) 78-80, Hellenic Lg 75-76 98-99 (Div 1 R-up 72-73, Lg Cup 75-76 98-99, Div 1 Cup 71-72), London Spartan Lg 84-85 (Lg Cup 84-85), Reading Comb. Lg Cup 70-71 (All Champions Cup 70-71), Wycombe Comb. R-up (4) 65-67 68-70

**PREVIOUS**   **Leagues:** Sth Bucks & East Berks; Maidenhead Intermediate; Windsor,Slough & Dist; Gt Western Comb. 48-64; Wycombe Comb. 64-70; Reading Comb. 70-71; Hellenic 71-77; Athenian 77-84; London Spartan 84-85; Southern 85-95; Hellenic 95-99
**Name:** Burnham & Hillingdon 1985-87      **Ground:** Baldwin Meadow (until 20's)

**BEST SEASON**   **FA Cup:** 3rd Qualifying Rd   **FA Vase:** Semi-Final 82-83, Q-F 77-78.
**FA Trophy:** Third Qualifying Rd replay 89-90

**RECORD**   **Attendance:** 2,380 v Halesowen Town, FA Vase 2/4/83
**Scorer:** Fraser Hughes 65, 69-70      **Win:** 18-0 v High Duty Alloys, 70-71
**Defeat:** 1-10 v Ernest Turners Sports, 63-64

Players progressing: D Hancock (Reading), R Rafferty (Grimsby Town), D Payne(Barnet)

*Back Row (L-R): Mark O'Sullivan, Marcus Richardson, Paul Sampson, Mike Tomlinson, Reuben Howell, David Dyson, Steve Lockhart, Simon Pentland, Mark Green (Physio)*
*Front Row: Shane Small, Steve Bunce, Matty Potter, Jamie Furmage, Leigh Elliot, Paul O'Sullivan*

# CHELMSFORD CITY

## CLUB OFFICIALS

Chairman: **Peter Stroud**
Tel: 01245 471917(H) 0385 990233(M)

Secretary: **David Selby**
34 Paddock Drive,Chelmsford CM1 6SS
Tel 01245 464922

## FOOTBALL MANAGEMENT TEAM

Manager: Roy McDonough
Asst Manager: Paul Roberts

**FACT FILE**

Formed: 1938
Nickname: City
Sponsors: QM Ashfelt
Colours: Claret, white trim/claret/claret
Change colours: Sky blue/navy/sky blue
Midweek matches : Monday
Reserves' League:
98-99 Captain: Brett Girling
Top Scorer: Ian Cambridge
P.o.Y: Ian Cambridge

**GROUND**  Ground Share with Billericay Town
New Lodge, Blunts Wall Road, Billericay CM12 9SA Tel: 01277 652188

Directions: From Shenfield (A129) right at 1st lights then 2nd right. FromBasildon (A129) over 1st lights in town, then left at next lights and 2nd right. Half mile from Billericay (GER) station (London Liverpool St. - Southend line). Ground 5 mins walk from buses 222, 251, 357, 255, 551 Capacity: 3,500        Seats: 424        Cover: 600        Floodlights: Yes

Clubhouse: Open eves 8-11pm (except Mon),1pm-11pm Sat & w/e lunch noon-2.30pm.
Club Shop: Sells progs, badges, scarves, mugs etc. Contact Helen Williams via club

Pages 44  Price; £1.40
Editor: Trevor Smith (01245 353052)

Local Press: Essex Chronicle,
Chelmsford Weekly News,
East Anglian Daily Times, Evening Gazette
Local Radio: Essex Radio/Breeze AM,
BBC Essex

**PREVIOUS**  Leagues: None        **Grounds:** New Whittle Street 38-97
Name: None (Brentwood Town were incorporated in 1970)
**CLUB RECORDS**  Attendance: 16,807 v Colchester, Southern League 10/9/49
Goalscorer: Tony Butcher, 287 (1957-71)        **Appearances:** Derek Tiffin, 550 (1950-63)
Win: 10-3 v Billericay Town (H), Essex Senior Cup, 4/1/93
Defeat: 2-10 v Barking (A), FA Trophy, 11/11/78
Fee Paid: £10,000 for Tony Rogers (Dover Athletic, 1992)        **Fee Received:** £50,000 for David Morrison (Peterborough 94)
**BEST SEASON**  FA Cup: 4th Rd, 1938-39 (v Birmingham City). 1st Rd 25 times
FA Trophy: Semi-final 69-70 v Telford Utd
**HONOURS**  Southern Lg 45-46 67-68 71-72 (R-up 48-49 60-61 63-64 65-66); Southern Div 88-89, R-up 97-98, Lg Cup 45-46 59-60 (R-up  60-61); Merit Cup 71-72; Southern Lg War-Time (East) 39-40); Essex Prof Cup 5; Essex Snr Cup 85-86 88-89 92-93; Non-League Champs Chall Cup 71-72; E Anglian Cup 48-49; Eastern Co's Lg(3) 46-49(Lg Cup 59-60); Eastern F'lit Comp 6, (Cup 72-73 74-75); Metropolitan Lg 67-68, Lg Prof Cup 67-68, Autumn Shield 70-71; Essex Snr Lg Cup 84-85; Harry Fisher Mem. Tphy 88-89

Players progressing: G Merton (Watford 48), G Adams (Orient 49), W O'Neill(Burnley 49), B Farley/S McClellan/L Dicker/P Collins (Spurs 49/49/51/68), O Hold (Everton 50), R Marden (Arsenal 50), C McCormack (Barnsley 50), D Sexton(Luton 51), W Bellet & R Mason & A Nicholas (Orient 61 & 63 & 65), R Gladwin(Norwich 66), B King (Millwall 67), J O'Mara (Bradford City 74), N Spink (Aston77), M Dziadulewicz (Wimbledon 79), M Cawston (Southend 84), P Coleman (Exeter84), J Keeley & A Owers (Brighton 86 & 87), I Brown (Bristol C 93), D Morrison (Peterborough 94)

*Chelmsford's Brett Girling and Fisher's Anthony Turner tangle for the ball*
*Photo: Alan Coomes*

# CORBY TOWN

**CLUB OFFICIALS**
Chairman: **James Kane**
President: **H Hatterley**
Secretary: **GordonKyle**, 15 Oslo
Gardens,Corby, Northants NN18 9DS
(01536 743781)

**FOOTBALL MANAGEMENT TEAM**

Manager:Peter Dowsinh
Coach: Lee Adam
Physio: Ian Lochhead

**FACT FILE**

Formed: 1948
Nickname: The Steelmen
Sponsor: British Steel
Colours: Blacjk& white stripes.black,black
Change colours: White& Red,white,white
Midweek matchday: Wednesday
Reserves' League: United Counties Res Div
98-99 - Top Scorer:A.Evans
P. of Y.: K.Fox
Captain: D.Keast

**GROUND** Rockingham Triangle Stadium, Rockingham Road, Corby NN17 2AE
Tel: 01536 406640

**Directions:** On northern outskirts of town at junction of A6003 and A6116,opposite entrance to Rockingham Castle grounds. One and a half miles from Corby (BR)

Capacity: 3,000     Cover: 1,150     Seats: 960     Floodlights: Yes

**Clubhouse:** VP Lounge open matchdays and during the week
**Club Shop:** Sells badges, programmes etc. Contact C Woolmer Tel: 01536 260900

Pages: 32 Price: £1
Editor: D.Tilley
Local Press: Northampton Evening Telegraph
Local Radio: BBC Radio Northampton,
Hereward, KCBC

**PREVIOUS** Leagues: United Counties 35-52, Midland 52-58

**CLUB RECORDS** Attendance: 2,240 v Watford, pre-season friendly 86-87
At Old Ground; 10,239 v Peterborough Utd, FA Cup 3rd Qual. Rd 52-53
**Win:** 14-0 v Gainsborough Trinity, 56-57       **Defeat:** 0-10 v Paget Rangers, 95-96
**Career Goalscorer:** David Hofbauer 141 (84-95)   **Career Appearances:** Derek Walker600 (78-92)
**Transfer fee paid:** £2,700 for Elwyn Roberts (Barnet, 81)   **Transfer fee received:** £20,000 for Matt Murphy (Oxford U. 93)

**BEST SEASON** FA Cup: 3rd Rd 65-66 (lost to Plymouth). 1st Rd on five occasions; 54-55 63-6667-68
League clubs defeated: Luton Town 65-66       **FA Trophy:** 3rd Rd, 1986-87

**HONOURS** UCL 50-51 51-52 (R-up 37-38), Midland Lg R-up 52-53, Southern Lg Midland Div R-up 90-91 (Merit Cup 63-64 90-91),
Northants Snr Cup 6; Maunsell Cup  83-84, Daventry Charity Cup 94-95, Midland Floodlit Cup 74-75, Evans Halshaw F'lit Cup
91-92, Anglia Floodlit Trophy 68-69 72-73, Chelmsford Invitation Cup 63-64 64-65 65-66 (joint), Kettering & Dist Samaritan Cup
60-61(joint) 68-69, Wellingborough Charity Cup 50-51, Desborough Nursing Cup 48-49 50-51 (joint), Bob Cumning
Cup 6

Players progressing:      A McCabe (Chesterfield 55), L Chalmers (Leicester C. 56), K Brown (Nottm Forest 56), P Kearns (Aldershot 62),
N Dean (Southampton 63), H Curran (Millwall 64), D McNeil/A McGowan/G Reilly (Northampton69/75/76), P Chard (Peterborough 79), T Morley

*Back Row: David Hollis, Kevin Fox, Tyrone Mintus, Oswald Mintus, Rich Tuffey, Scott Munton, Glyn Horner*
*Front Row: Simon Reilly, Jimmy Simpson (now St Neots), Andy Coleman, Danny Pouttney, Gavin Cox, Danum*
*Russell, Darran Stephens (now Rothwell Town).   Photo: David Tilley*

# DARTFORD

## CLUB OFFICIALS
Chairman: **David Skinner**
Vice-Chairman: **Norman Grimes**
Secretary: **Andy Clark**
57 Shenley Road, Dartford, Kent DA1 1YF
Tel.01322 221582
Commercial Man.: TBA
Press Officer: Secretary

## FOOTBALL MANAGEMENT TEAM
Manager: Gary Julians
Coach:Asst-Manager: Bob Glozier
Physio: Peter Lucia-Hennis/Terry Skelton

## FACT FILE
Formed: 1888
Nickname: The Darts
Colours: White & black/black/black
Change colours: Red/white/red
Midweek home matchday: Monday
Reserves' League: Winstonlead Kent Div 1

**GROUND**     Purfleet FC, Thurrock Hotel, Ship Lane, Grays, Essex Tel: 01708 868901

Directions: M25 North; through Dartford Tunnel 1st exit, at roundabout take Ship Lane exit
(sign Purfleet FC), ground 100 yards on right beside Thurrock Hotel

Capacity: 4,500          Cover: 1,000          Seats: 300          Floodlights: Yes

Programme:
Pages: 40 Price: £1
Editor: Mike Brett-Smith Tel: 01322 277243
Local Press: Dartford Times, Kent Today
Local Radio: Radio Kent, Millennium Radio

Clubhouse:
Club Shop: Open matchdays. Mail Order: Norman Grimes 01474 815236

**PREVIOUS**
**Leagues:** Kent 1894-96, 97-98, 99-1902, 09-14, 21-26, 93-96; Southern Lg 1896-98, 99-1900, 26-81, 82-84, 86-92; GMVC 81-82, 84-86
**Grounds:** The Brent/Westgate House, Potters Meadow, Engleys Meadow, Summers Meadow, Watling St, Cray Wanderers, Erith & Belverdere

**CLUB RECORDS** Attendance: 11,004 v Leyton Orient FA Cup 48
Career Appearances: Steve Robinson 653
Win: 11-1 v Faversham Tn Kent Snr Cup 65          **Defeat:** 0-10 v Guildford City SouthernLge 46
Transfer fee paid: £6,000 for John Bartley (Chelmsford 88) **Received:** £25,000 forAndy Hessenthaler (Redbridge Forest)

**BEST SEASON**   **FA Trophy:** Runners-up 74          **FA Vase:** 2nd Qual Rd 95/96
FA Cup: 3rd Rd Prop 35-36 & 36-37          League clubs defeated: Cardiff (1935), Exeter(1961), Aldershot (1968)

**HONOURS**   Southern Lg 1930-31, 31-32, 73-74, 83-84, R-up 87-88, 88-89, Eastern Div 30-31,31-32, Southern Div 80-81, Southern Lg Div
2 1896-97, Lg Cup 76-77, 87-88, 88-89, Championship Shield 83-84, 87-88, 88-89; Kent Lg 1995-96, Lg Cup 24-25,Kent Snr
Cup 29-30, 34-35, 38-39, 69-70, Snr Trophy 95-96, Inter Lg Chall 1974;FA Trophy R-up 1974

**Players progressing:**   Idris Hopkins (Brentford 32), Fred Dall(West Ham 36), Riley Cullum/Fred Alexander/Ted Croker (Charlton 47/48/48)
Frank Coombs (Bristol C 49), James Kelly (Gillingham 51), Tom Ritchie (Grimsby 58), Dave Underwood (Watford 60),
Derek Hales (Luton 72), Andy Hessenthaler (Watfordvia Redbridge F)

*Dartford skipper Paul Sawyer in acrobatic action.   Photo: K Gillard*

# ERITH & BELVEDERE

**CLUB OFFICIALS**
Chairman: **John McFadden**
President: **L O'Connell**
Vice Chairman: **Peter Bird**
Secretary: Miss **Kellie Discipline**
108 Chastilion Road, Dartford, Kent DA1
3LG Tel: -01322 275766
Press Off./Commecial Man.: Martin Tarrant
Tel: 01322 275766

**FOOTBALL MANAGEMENT TEAM**

Manager: Mike Acland 01322 225594
Asst Manager / Coach: Dave Hough
Physio: Rob Couldwell

**FACT FILE**

Formed: 1922
Nickname: Deres
Colours: Blue & white/blue/white
Change colours: All red
Midweek home matchday::Wednesday
Reserves' League: None
98-99 - Captain: Paul Roberts
P.o.Y.: Aaron Barnett
Top scorer: Dave Fisher

NUFARM UK LTD
SPONSORS OF
ERITH & BELVEDERE F.C

**GROUND** Park View Rd Ground, Welling, Kent DA16 1SY Tel: 0181 301 1196
**Directions:** As for Welling United F.C.:M25,then A2 towards London.Take Welling turn-off,
ground one mile. By rail to Welling stationBR (BR) ground 3/4 mile.
Capacity: 1,500    Cover: 1,000    Seats: 500    Floodlights: Yes
**Club Shop:** Sells programmes, badges and pens
**Clubhouse:** Licensed social club open matchdays and weekends. Cold snacks available.
Separate canteen provides hot food on matchdays

Pages: 30 Price: £1.00p
Editor: Mike Tarrant Tel: 01322 275766
Local Press: Kentish Times, Kentish
Independent
Local Radio: Radio Kent, Radio Mellenium

**PREVIOUS**          **Leagues:** Kent 22-29 31-39 78-82, London 29-31, Corinthian 45-63, Athenian 63-78
**Names:** Belvedere & District FC (Formed 1918, restructured 1922)

**CLUB RECORDS**   **Attendance:** 5,573 v Crook Colliery Welfare Amt Cup 3rd Rd 1949
**Win:** 14-2 v Royal Marines, Kent Lge 18/11/33. (16-2 v RAF Friendly 4/9/41)   **Defeat:** 0-15 v Ashford, Kent Lge 28/4/37
**Career Appearances:** Dennis Crawford 504, 56-71    **Career Goalscorer:** Colin Johnson284, 61-71

**BEST SEASON**    **FA Amateur Cup:** Runners-up 1923-24, 37-38   **FA Trophy:** Third Qualifying Round second replay 89-90
**FA Vase:** Third Round 76-77    **FA Cup:** 4th Qual Rd 1924-25 (Equiv to 1st Rd Prop). League clubs defeated: None

**HONOURS**          FA Amat Cup R-up 23-24 37-38; Athenian Lge Div 1 R-up 70-71 (Lge Cup 73-74), Memorial Shield 67-68; Corinthian Lge R-up
62-63, (Lge Cup 47-48 48-49 49-50); Kent Lge 81-82, (Lge Cup R-up 81-82); London Sen Cup 44-45 (R-up 38-39); KentAmat
Cup 6, (R-up 4); Kent F/lit Lge R-up 67-68; Kent Interm Cup R-up 90-91; Kent Jun Cup 67-68; Kent County Yth Lge 90-91;
Kent Yth Cup 87-88. Bromley Hosp Cup 38-39; Essex & Herts Border Comb Cup 73-74.

Players progressing:       John Coshall (West Ham 28), Fred Ford 36/ Cyril Hammond 46/ KeithPeacock 62 (Charlton),
Tommy Ord (Chelsea 72), Sean Devine (Barnet 95)

*Erith's P Bates and
Margate's M Munday
Photo: K Eillard*

# FISHER ATHLETIC (LONDON)

## CLUB OFFICIALS

Chairman: **Chris Georgiou**
Vice Chairman: **Dave Wilding**
Secretary: **John Leyden** c/o Club
General Manager: **Cheryl Stepton**

### FOOTBALL MANAGEMENT TEAM
Manager: Alan Walker
Coach: Chris Hiscock
Physio: Joe Miller

### FACT FILE

Formed: 1908
Nickname: The Fish
Sponsors: Greene King
Colours: Black & white stripes/white/white
Change colours: Blue/white/white
Midweek matchday: Tuesday
Reserves' League: Suburban Premier
98-99 - Captain: Ricky Pearson
P.o.Y.: Steve Aris
Top scorer: Bryn Charles

**GROUND**               The Surrey Docks Stadium, Salter Road, London SE16 1LQ
                         Tel: 0171 231 5144 Fax: 0171 2520060

Directions:    8 minutes walk from Rotherhithe (tube).
               2 miles from London Bridge (main line). Buses 188, P11, P14

Capacity: 5,300        Cover: 4,283      Seats: 400      Floodlights: Yes

                       Clubhouse: None                   Club Shop: None

Pages: 40        Price: £1
Editor: Cheryl Stepton
Local Press: Southwark News,
South London Press
Local Radio: Capital & Capital Gold

**PREVIOUS**      **Leagues:** Parthenon, West Kent, Kent Amateur, London Spartan 76-82, Southern 82-87, GMV Conference 87-91
                  **Names:** Fisher Athletic 08-93, Fisher`93 93-96      **Ground:** London Road, Mitcham

**CLUB RECORDS**  **Attendance:** 4,283 v Barnet, GMV Conference 4/5/91
                  **Win:** 7-0 v Lewes Sept 95, FA Cup              **Defeat:** 0-6 v Salisbury, 21/8/93
                  **Career Goalscorer:** Paul Shinners 205          **Career Appearances:** Dennis Sharp 720
                  **Transfer fee paid:** £2,000 for Bryn Charles (Fleet Town)
                  **Transfer fee received:** £45,000 for Paul Gorman (Charlton 1991)

**BEST SEASON**   **FA Cup:** 1st Rd 84-85 (0-1 at home to Bristol City), 88-89 (0-4 at BristolRovers)
                  **FA Trophy:** Third Round replay 87-88  **FA Vase:** Second Round replay 82-83      **FA Amateur Cup:**

**HONOURS**       Southern Lg 86-87 (R-up 83-84, Southern Div 82-83, Lg Cp 84-85, Championship Cup 87-88, Merit Cup), London Spartan Lg
                  80-81 81-82 (R-up 78-79, Senior Div77-78, Div 2 R-up 76-77), Parthenon Lg 61-62 (Lg Cup 63-64 65-66), Kent AmateurLg 73-
                  74 74-75 (R-up 72-73), London Senior Cup 84-85 87-88 88-89, LondonIntermediate Cup 59-60 (R-up 75-76), Kent Senior Cp
                  83-84, Kent Senior Trophy 81-82 82-83, Surrey Intermediate Cup 61-62

Players progressing:      John Bumstead (Chelsea), Trevor Aylott (Bournemouth), Paul Shinners (Orient 84), Dave Regis (Notts Co. - via Barnet),
                          Paul Gorman(Charlton 91), Sean Devine (Barnet via Okonia Nicossia), George Barry (LeytonOrient),
                          Dean Martin (West Ham Utd), Jason Lee (Charlton), Ken Charlery (Barnet), Steve Watts (Leyton Orient)

Fisher Athletic (London) FC 1998-99 Squad:
Back Row: Tubbsy (Kit Man), Steve Watts, Simon Dyer, Bryn Charles, Lee Osborne, Mark McAllister, Matt Middleton, Neville Gordon, Tim Hambley,
Brian Lee, Bob Davies.  Front Row: Steve aris, Jimmy Jones, Paul Manning, Bradley Gamble, Daniel Fletcher, Darren Amos, Phil O'Neil.

# FLEET TOWN

### CLUB OFFICIALS
Chairman: **Jason Grenham**
President: **Les Hocking**
Vice Chairman: **Colin Sturgess**
Secretary: **Dave Grenham**
149 Aldershot Road, Church Crookham,
Fleet, Hants GU130JS
Tel. 01252 623021 (H)

### FOOTBALL MANAGEMENT TEAM
Manager: Trevor Norris
Assistant Manager: Jess Bone
Coach: Clive Talentire
Physio: Steve Hyde

### FACT FILE
Founded: 1890
Formed: 1947
Nickname: The Blues
Sponsors: Hart Dist Council
Colours: Navy & sky/sky/navy & sky
Change: Yellow & red/yellow & red/yellow
Midweek Matches: Tuesday
Reserves' League: Suburban

**GROUND**    Calthorpe Park, Crookham Road, Fleet, Hants Tel: 01252 623804

**Directions:**    Leave the M3 at Junction 4A. Follow signs to Fleet via A3013.
At 5th roundabout (a T-junction), turn left over railway bridge.
Carry on past `Oatsheaf' pub on the right - ground is 1/4 mile further on right.

Capacity: 2,000        Seats: 200        Cover: 250        Floodlights: Yes
**Clubhouse:** Yes. Hot & cold food served
**Club Shop:** Yes

Programme:
Pages: 20 Price: 50p
Editor: Steve Beagley

**PREVIOUS**    **Leagues:** Hampsire 61-77, Athenian, Combined Co's, Chiltonian, Wessex 89-95
**Names:** None        **Grounds:** None

**CLUB RECORDS**    **Win:** 7-0
**Transfer fee paid:** £1,500 to Farnborough, 1991
**Career Goalscorer:** John Smith
**Career Appearances:** Steve Hodge  / Paul Dear

**HONOURS**    Wessex Lg 93-94, Lg Cup R-up 92-93, Hants Lg Div 2 R-up 61-62 (Div 1 R-up 60-61), Aldershot Snr Cup 92-93,
Simpsonair Challenge Shield 1993, Hants Yth LgDiv 3 92-93.

*Back Row (L-R): Ricky Jones, Lee Raby, Ben Davey, John Williams, Mark Frampton, Tommy Taylor, Gavin Smith,*
*John Murphy, Trevor Norris (Manager), Dylan Pearson, Jesse Bone (Assistant Manager)*
*Front Row: Steve Hyde (Physio), Andy Darnton, Alex Booker, Koo Dumbuya, Adam Galvin*
*Photo: Gordon Whittington*

# FOLKESTONE INVICTA

## CLUB OFFICIALS

Chairman: **Tommy Guiver**
President: **Bill Hewson**
Secretary: **Neil Pilcher**
25 Pavilion Rd, Folkestone, Kent. CT19 5RW
Tel: 01303 245066

## FOOTBALL MANAGEMENT TEAM

Manager: Neil Cugley
Asst Manager: Dave Williams
Physio: Frank Clarke

**GROUND**   The New Pavilion, Cheriton Road, Folkestine, Kent CT20 5JU
Tel: 01303 257461

**Directions:** On the A20 behind Safeway foodstore, midway between Folkestone Central & West BR stations

Capacity: 6,500    Seats: 900    Cover: 3,500    Floodlights: Yes

**Clubhouse:** Yes, Stripes Club & Invicta Club
**Club Shop:** Yes

### FACT FILE

Founded: 1936

Sponsors: Eurotunnel(Le Shuttle)
Colours: Amber & black stripes/black/amber
Change Colours: Blue & green
stripes/blue/blue
Midweek matchday: Tuesday
Reserve's League: Winstonlead Kent Div 2

Pages: 60 Price: £1
Editor: Neil Pitcher Tel: 01303 245066
Local Press: Folkestone Herald
Local Radio: Neptune Radio, Radio Light

**PREVIOUS**   **Ground:** South Rd, Hythe (pre-1991). Kent County Lg matches were played on council pitches
**Leagues:** Kent County (pre-1991-98)    **Name:**

**CLUB RECORDS** **Attendance:** 2,332 v West Ham Utd Friendly Nov 96
**Ground Record:** 7,881 Folkestone Town v Margate, Kent Snr.Cup 1958
**Win:** 9-0 v Crockenhill WHL Div 1    **Defeat:** 0-7 v Crockenhill WHL Div 1

**BEST SEASON**   **FA Vase:** Last sixteen 97-98
**FA Cup:** 2nd Qual Rd 95-96    Leagues Clubs Defeated: None

**HONOURS**   (since joining Winstonlead Kent League) Kent Lge R-up 97-98, Kent Senior Trophy R-Up  93-94, 94-95

*Folkestone's Paul Chambers (stripes) sees his shot his the post against Ashford. Photo: Alan Coomes*

# HASTINGS TOWN

## CLUB OFFICIALS

Chairman: T.B.A.
President: David Harding
Vice Chairman: T.B.A.
Secretary / Press Officer: R A Cosens
22 Baldslow Road, Hastings TN34 2EZ
01424 427867 (H) 01424 444635 (B)

**FOOTBALL MANAGEMENT TEAM**
Team Managers: Terry & Dean White
Asst Manager:
Physio: Ray Tuppen

### FACT FILE
Formed: 1894
Nickname: The Town
Sponsors: Alsford Timber
Colours: All white
Change colours: Red/black
Midweek matchday: Tuesday
Reserves' League: Winstonlead Kent Div 2
Newsline: 0930 555 879
98-99 - Captain: Mat Ball
P.o.Y.: Steve Smith
Top scorer: Lee McRobert (13)

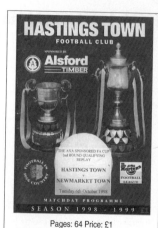

Pages: 64 Price: £1
Editor: David Bealey Tel: (01797 253310)
Local Press: Hastings Observer & News,
Evening Argus
Local Radio: Radio Sussex,
Southern Sound, Arrow FM

**GROUND**      The Pilot Field, Elphinstone Road, Hastings TN34 2AX Tel: 01424 444635

**Directions:** From A21 turn left at 1st mini-r'bout into St Helens Rd, left after 1 mile into St Helens Park Rd, this leads into Downs Rd, at end of Downs Rd (T-junction) turn left, ground 200yds on right. From town centre take Queens Road (A2101). Right at roundabout into Elphinstone Road - ground 1 mile on right.
1 1/2 miles from Hastings BR station - infrequent bus service fromtown centre to ground

Capacity: 4,050          Cover: 1,750          Seats: 800          Floodlights: Yes

**Clubhouse:** Open matchdays, Tues, Thurs & Fri eves from 7pm, and Sundays from 12 noon
**Club Shop:** Sells replica kits, scarves, programmes, pens, key-rings, badges etc

**PREVIOUS**   **Leagues:** South Eastern 04-05, Southern 05-10, Sussex County 21-27 52-85,Southern Amateur 27-46, Corinthian 46-48
**Name:** Hastings & St Leonards Amateurs          **Ground:** Bulverhythe Rec Gd (pre 76)

**CLUB RECORDS** **Attendance:** 4,888 v Notts Forest, friendly 23/6/96. Competitive: 1,774 v DoverAthletic, Southern Lge Prem. Div. 12/4/93
**Goalscorer:** (Season) Stafford Browne (29)
**Transfer Fee Paid:** £8,000 for Nicky Dent from Ashford          **Received:** £50,000 for Paul Smith from Notts Forest

**BEST SEASON** **FA Cup:** 4th Qual. Rd 85-86, 2-3 v Farnborough Town (A)          **FA Trophy: 3rd Rd 1998-99**
**FA Amateur Cup:** 3rd Rd. 38-39          **FA Vase:** 5th Rd. rep. 90-91

**HONOURS**   Southern Lg Cup 94-95, Southern Div 91-92, Div 2 R-up 08-09, Div 2(B) 09-10; Sussex Co Lg R-up 21-22 25-26,
Lg Cup 80-81, Div 2 79-80 (R-up 59-60), Div 2Cup 79-80; Sussex Sen Cup 35-36 37-38 95-96 97-98; AFA Snr Cup 37-38;
Gilbert Rice F/lit Cup 89-90

Players progressing: Peter Heritage (Gillingham), Paul Smith (Nottm Forest)

*Hastings Town. Photo: Roger Turner*

# NEWPORT I.W.

**CLUB OFFICIALS**
Chairman: **Bill Manuel**
Vice Chairman: TBA
President: **W H J Bunday**
Commercial Manager: **Ian Buckman**
Secretary/Press Off.: Chris Cheverton
60 St Davids Road, East Cowes,
Isle ofWight PO32 6EF
Tel: 01983 281789

**FOOTBALL MANAGEMENT TEAM**
Manager: Tony Mount
Physio: Chris Cheverton

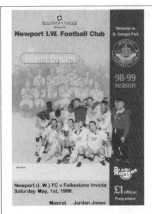

Newport I.W. Football Club

**FACT FILE**
Formed: 1888 Nickname: The Port
Colours: Gold & royal blue trim/gold/gold &
royal trim
Change colours: White with purple trim
Midweek matchday: Tuesday
Reserves' League: Isle of Wight League
98-99 - Captain: John Price
P.o.Y.: Gary Green

**GROUND**St George's Park, St George's Way, Newport, Isle of Wight PO30 2QH
Tel: 01983 525027

**Directions:** Roads from all ferry ports lead to Coppins Bridge R-about at eastern extremity of town. Take Sandown/Ventnor exit, proceed to small r-about, St George's way is first exit (straight on), ground immediately visible on left. Five minute walk from Newport bus station; along Church Litten (past old ground), turn left then right at r-about
Capacity: 5,000          Cover: 1,000          Seats: 300          Floodlights: Yes
**Club Shop:** Sells souvenirs & programmes. Contact Roger Sanders at ground
**Clubhouse:** Open normal licensing hours. 2 bars, full range of hot and cold bar snacks. Buffet inside ground

Newport (I. W.) FC v Folkestone Invicta
Saturday May, 1st, 1999.
Mascot   Jordan Jones

Pages: 28 Price: £1
Editor: Mark Major (01983 525027)
Local Press: Portsmouth Evening News,
I.O.W. County Press,
Southampton Evening Echo
Local Radio: Solent, Isle of Wight Radio,
Power FM

**PREVIOUS**   **Leagues:** Isle of Wight 1896-1928; Hants 28-86; Wessex 86-90
**Ground:** Church Litten (previously Well's Field) 1888-1988

**CLUB RECORDS** **Attendance:** 2,217 FA Cup 1st Rd Nov 1994 v Aylesbury U., (6,000 v Watford, FACup 1st Rd 56-57, at Church Litten)
**Win:** 14-1, v Thornycroft Athletic (H),Hampshire Lge Div. One, 22.12.45
**Defeat:** 2-10, v Basingstoke Town (H),Hampshire Lge Div. One, 12.10.68
**Career Goalscorer:** Eddie Walder          **Career**Appearances: Jeff Austin 540 (69-87)
**Fee paid:** £3,000 for Stuart Ritchie(Bashley, May 1991)          **Fee received**: £2,250 for Mick Jenkins (Havant, March1992)

**BEST SEASON**   **FA Trophy:** 3rd Rd 98-99          **FA Vase:** Fifth Round 91-92, 93-94
**FA Cup:** 2nd Rd 35-36 45-46. 1st Rd another 8 times- 45-46 52-55 56-59 94-95 95-96
League clubs defeated: Clapton Orient 45-46

**HONOURS**   Wessex Lg R-up 89-90, Comb. 91-92 (res.); Hants Lg (11), R-up (7), Div 2 R-up 70-71, Hants Snr Cup (8); Russell Cotes Cup (3); Pickford Cup (4); Isle of Wight Snr (Gold) Cup (33); Hants F'lit Cup 76-77 77-78; Isle of Wight Lg (4) 07-10 23-24; Hants I'mediate Cup 31-32 96-97; Hants Comb. Cup 38-39

Players progressing: Gary Rowatt (Cambridge City, Everton)

# RAUNDS TOWN

**CLUB OFFICIALS**
Chairman: **George Hagan**
President: **Mahen Perera**
Secretary **Mrs Carol Warcup**
9 Warwick Close,Raunds,Northants
Tel:01933 626516
Commercial Manager: **Ralph Maloney**
Tel: 01933 622036

**FOOTBALL MANAGEMENT TEAM**

Manager: Keith Burt
Asst Manager: Glen Burdett

**FACT FILE**
Formed: 1946
Nickname: Shopmates
Sponsors: T.B.A.
Colours: Red & black
Change Colours: Yellow
Midweek matchday: Tuesday
Reserves' League: UCL Reserve Div. One
98-99 - Top Scorer: Kevin Slinn(30)
P. of Y.: Darren Watts
Captain: Andy Peaks

**Raunds Town F.C.**

**GROUND**

Kiln Park, London Road, Raunds, Northants NN9 6EQ
Tel: 01933 623351, Matchdays 01933 460941

**Directions:** Take Raunds turning at roundabout on A45 and ground is first left
Nearest station; Wellingborough. Bus services local

Capacity: 3,000     Seats: 250     Cover: 600     Floodlights: Yes

**Clubhouse:** On ground, open every day
**Club Shop:** Open matchdays, selling shirts, books programmes, contact Malc York, c/o club

Pages: Varies Price: £1.00
Editor: Malc York 01933 311586
Local Press: Northants Evening Telegraph,
Wellingborough Post, Chronicle &Echo
Local Radio: Northants Radio, KCBC,
Connect F.M

**PREVIOUS**    **Leagues:** Rushden & District, Central Northants Combination, United CountiesLeague Prem Div
**Grounds:** Greenhouse Field (until 1948), The Berristers (1948-91)

**CLUB RECORDS** **Attendance:** 1,500 v Crystal Palace, ground opening 23/7/91
**Win:** 9-0 v Potton 95, 11-2 v Brackley 93          **Defeat:** 0-6 v Baldock 83, vBuckingham 84-85
**Career Goalscorer:** Shaun Keeble 208          **Career Appearances:** Martin Lewis 355 (+29subs)
**Transfer fee paid:** £1,000 to Gloucester City for David Johnson 97          **Transfer fee received:** None

**BEST SEASON**    **FA Cup:** 4th Qual Rd, 98-99 (0-2v Enfield),
**FA Vase:** Semi-final v Arlesey Tn 94-5
**FA Trophy:** 3rd Rd v Weston-super-Mare 98-99 ( 2-2, 0-1)

**HONOURS**    UCL Prem Champions 95-96, UCL Div 1 82-83 (R-up 91-92), KO Cup 90-91, (R-up 83-84 93-94), Res Div 1 88-89 95-96 (R-up 86-87 87-88 89-90 90-91 91-92), Reserve KO Cup 84-85 88-89 93-94; Northants Snr Cup 90-91; Hunts Premier Cup R-up 92-93; Daventry Charity Cup R-up 83-84; Northants Jnr Cup 82-83 91-92 (res) 92-93 (res)

Players progressing:    Greg Downs (Norwich)

*Raunds' Kevin Slinn fires home the equaliser in their 1-1 draw with Baldock Town on Easter Monday.*
*Photo: Gordon Whittington*

# SITTINGBOURNE

## CLUB OFFICIALS

Chairman: **Barry Bright**

President: **E H Bennett**

Secretary: **Mrs M Bratton**
c/o Sittingbourne F.C.

Commercial Manager: **Barry Bright**

### FOOTBALL MANAGEMENT TEAM
Manager: Alan Walker

Coach: Paul Haylock

Physio: Kevin Manser

### FACT FILE

Formed: 1881

Nickname: Brickies

Sponsors: Medway Galvanising.

Colours: Red & black stripes/black/red

Change colours: All yellow

Midweek matchday: Wednesday

Newsline: 0891 333 027

Reserves' league: Winstonlead Kent

Pages: 28 Price: £1
Editor: William Rickson c/o the club
Local Press: East Kent Gazette, Kent Today,
Kent Messenger Extra, Sittingbourne& Sheppy
Adscene.
Local Radio: Invicta Supergold, BBC Radio
Kent, Invicta FM

**GROUND**　　　　Central Park, Eurolink, Sittingbourne, Kent ME10 3SB
Tel: 01795 435077 Fax: 01474 814501

Directions: Through Sittingbourne on main A2, club signposted clearly and regularly from both
east and west. 1 mile from Sittingbourne BR station.

Capacity: 8,000　　　　Cover: 3,300　　　Seats: 2,000　　　Floodlights: 420 lux

Clubhouse: The Cabin (Club's Tel No.)

Club Shop: Sells a wide selection of souvenirs etc. Open matchdays or contact Ann Morrison
(01795 664436) or Clive Phillips (01795 477108)

**PREVIOUS**　　　**Leagues:** Kent 1894-1905 09-27 30-39 46-59 68-91, South Eastern 05-09, Southern 27-30 59-67
**Grounds:** SittingbourneRec. Ground 1881-90, Gore Court Cricket Ground 90-92, The Bull Ground1892-1990
**Names:** Sittingbourne United 1881-86

**CLUB RECORDS** **Attendance:** 5,951 v Tottenham Hotspur, friendly 26/1/93
**Transfer fee paid:** £20,000 to Ashford Town for Lee McRobert, 1993.
**Transfer fee received:** £210,000 from Millwall for Neil Emblen and Michael Harle, 1993

**BEST SEASON**　　**FA Cup:** 2nd Rd 25-26 (0-7 at Swindon Town), 28-29 (1-2 at Walsall), plus 1st Rd26-27 30-31 62-63
**FA Trophy:**　　　　　　　　　　　　**FA Vase:**

**HONOURS**　　Southern Lg Southern Div 92-93 95-96; Kent Lg 1897-98 1902-03 57-58 58-59 75-76 83-84 90-91 (Lg Cup 25-26 58-59 73-74
80-81, Div 2 Cup 54-55 57-58 83-84 86-8787-88); Kent Senior Cup 01-02 28-29 29-30 57-58; Kent Senior Shield 25-26 27-28
53-54; Kent Senior Trophy 89-90; Thames & Medway Cup 55-56 58-59; Thames & Medway Comb 02-03 07-08 11-12 24-25
25-26; Chatham Charity Cup 03-04 19-20;" Kent Midweek Lg(res) 91-92 (Lg Cup 90-91).

Players progressing: Jason Lillis (Walsall 93), Neil Emblen & Michael Harle 93, Steve Forbes 94, Lee McRobert 95 (Millwall)
Jimmy Case (Brighton 93), Lee Harper (Arsenal 94).

*Back Row (L-R):*
*Danny Bovis, Paul*
*Daley, Ricky*
*Pearson, Robert*
*Owen, Roy Clarke,*
*Neil Miller*
*Front Row:*
*Stewart Boniface,*
*Damien Hodge,*
*Kenny Pavey, Ben*
*Taylor, Ian Mawson*

# SPALDING UNITED

## CLUB OFFICIALS

Chairman: **Mick Clare**
President: **John Chappell**
Press Officer: **Ray Tucker**
Secretary: **Nigel Clare**, 11 Scoldhall Lane,
Surfleet, Spalding Lins PE11 4BJ Tel/FAX:
01775 680570

## FOOTBALL MANAGEMENT TEAM

Manager: Alan Day
Asst Manager: Glenn Beech
Physio: Alan Todd

**FACT FILE**

Founded: 1921
Nickname: Tulips
Sponsors: Edmondson Ford
Colours: Tangerine & black/black/tangerine
Change: All Blue
Midweek matchday: Tuesday
Reserve League: Utd Counties Res Div
1998-99
Top Goalscore: Gavin Dolby 39

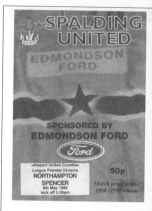

36 pages, 50p
Editor: Bernard Holmes

Local Press : Lincs Free Press, Spalding
Guardian, Peterborough EveningTelegraph

**GROUND**  Sir Halley Stewart Field, Winfrey Avenue, Spalding Tel: 01775 713328

**Directions:** Town centre off A16, adjacent to bus station. 250 yds from Spalding(BR) station

Capacity: 7,000   Seats: 350      Cover: 2,500     Floodlights: Yes

**Clubhouse:** Open matchdays, and events      Club Shop: Yes

**HONOURS**   Utd Counties Lg 54-55 74-75 87-88 98-99 R-up 50-51 51-52 52-53 72-73 75-76 96-97;
KO Cup 54-55 94-95; Northern Co's East Lg 83-84; Lincs Snr Cup 52-53; Hinchingbroke Cup: 98-99
Lincs Snr `A' Cup 87-88, 98-99 R-up 97-98; Snr `B' Cup 50-51; Evans Halshaw F'lit Cup 89-90

**PREVIOUS**   **Leagues:** Peterborough; Utd Co's 31-55 68-78 86-88 91-99; Eastern Co's 55-60; Central Alliance 60-61; Midland Co's 61-68;
Northern Co's East 82-86; Southern 88-91

**BEST SEASON**   **FA Cup:** 1st Round 57-58, 1-3 v Durham City (A), 64-65, 3-5 v Newport Co. (A)
**FA Trophy:** 2nd Qual. Rd 69-70 70-71 71-72 74-75 76-77 81-82
**FA Vase:** Quarter-Finals 89-90, 1-3 v Guiseley

**RECORD**   **Attendance:** 6,972 v Peterborough, FA Cup 1952

Players progressing: Carl Shutt (Sheffield Wed.)

*Back Row (L-R): Alan Mitchell (Physio), Simon Mead, Craig Wilson, Nick Keeble, Martin Rowbottom, Alan Todd (Physio), Mick Lonergan, Adie Barkess, Darren Munton, Alan Day (Manager)*
*Front Row: Dominic Revill, Ian Williams, Darren Cundy, Lee Wilkinson, Gavin Dolby, Kevin Cross, Glen Beech, Nick Robinson, Dave Frecklington. Absent from photo: Pau Langford (injured)*

# ST. LEONARDS

## CLUB OFFICIALS

Chairman: **John Cornelius**
Patron: **Leon Shepherdson**
President: **Mrs K Shepperdson**
Vice-Chairman: **Michael James**
Secretary: **Peter High**
1A Upper Maze Hill, St Leonards-on-Sea,
East Sussex TN38 0LA Tel: 01424 431482
Commercial Manager: **John Huggett**
Tel: 01424 434755 or 0802 920416

### FOOTBALL MANAGEMENT TEAM
Manager: Andy Thomson
Coach: Liam Barham

### FACT FILE
Formed: 1971
Nickname: Saints or Blues
Sponsors:Stamco Timber
Clubcall Line: T.B.A.
Colours: Blue/white/blue
Change colours: White/navy/white
Midweek Matchday: Wednesday
Reserves' League: Kent Midweek
98-99 Captain: Keith Miles
Top Scorer: Keith Miles
P.o.Y.: Adam Flanagan

**GROUND**
The Firs, Elphinstone Rd, Hastings, East Sussex
Tel: 01424 434755 Matchday Office 01424 716362

**Directions:** From M25 & London approach Hastings on the A21. immediately afterthe junct with the A28 on the northern borough boundary, turn right into Junction Rd. At T junct with B2093 turn right onto The Ridge. After 2 miles turn right, opposite the cemetary, into Elphinstone Rd, grd 600yards down hill on left. Nearest station; Ore (Connex South East), 1 mile uphill (no bus or taxi). Hastings (Connex South East) 1.5 miles. Bus service from town centre to ground

Pages: 60 Price: £1
Editor: Peter High (01424 431482)
Local Press: Hastings Observer, Evening Argus
Local Radio: Arrow FM, BBC Southern Counties Radio, Southern FM

Capacity: 3,768 (Day), 3,015 (Even)    Seats: 251    Cover: 1,000    Floodlights: Yes

**Clubhouse:** Licensed bar open normal pubhours. Hot food matchdays. Hot food from tea bar
**Club Shop:** Yes, selling leisure & sports wear, souvenirs & publications, open matchdays

**PREVIOUS**    **Leagues:** Eastbourne & Hastings 71-82, Southern Counties Comb 82-88, Sussex County 88-96
**Grounds:** Council pitches 71-73, Pannel Lane, Pett 73-93    **Names:** Stamco (71-96), St Leonards Stamcroft 96-98

**CLUB RECORDS**    **Attendance:** 1,798 v Tiverton Town, FA Vase 4th Rd. 15/1/95
At old ground: 527v Hastings Town, Sussex Senior Cup 2nd Rd 5/12/92
**Win:** 10-1 v Portfield(H), Sussex County League Div One 4/12/93    **Defeat:** 1-6 v Hailsham Town(A) League Cup 23/9/92.
**Career appearances:** Wayne Farrier (290 92-97)    **Career Goalscorer:** Keith Miles (122 1995-99)
**Transfer fee paid:** None    **Transfer fee received:** £8,000 for Jon Magee (Margate)

**BEST SEASON:**    **FA Cup:** 3rd Qual Rd 96-97 97-98    **FA Vase:** 5th Rd 94-95    **FA Trophy:** 3rd Rd 96-97

**HONOURS**    Sussex Sen Cup 96-97; Sussex RUR Charity Cup R-up 94-95; Hastings Snr Cup 89-90 95-96 96-97, R-up 92-93 97-98; Dr Martens Lge Southern Div R-up 96-97, Merit Cup 96-97; Sussex County Div 1 R-up 94-95 95-96, Div 2 R-up 92-93, Cup R-up 89-90 90-91, Div Three R-up 88-89, Cup R-up 88-89 Kent Midweek Lg.Cup Winners 98-99

**Player progressing:** Sasha Ilic (Charlton Ath 97)

*Back Row: Rob Greig, Jason Bourne, Paul Ruddy, Matt Aseh, Liam Barham, Steve Norman, Barry Gartell, Lee Wood, Clive Gartell, Andy Thomson, Keith Miles, Lloyd Bigg    Front Row: David Henham, Sam Taylor, Adam Flanagan, Richard Divine, Gavin Ramsden, Roy Godden, Richard Stonham, Daniel Small*

# STAMFORD

**FACT FILE**
Founded: 1896
Nickname: Daniels
Sponsors: Newflame
Colours: Red & white
Change Colours: Blue & white
Midweek matchday: Tuesday
Reserves League: UCL Res Div 2
98-99 - Captain: Richard Bailey
P.o.Y.: Richard Bailey
Top Scorer: Nathan Bailey

**GROUND** New Flame Stadium, Kettering Road,Wothorpe Road, Stamford, Lincs
Tel: 01780 763079 (Ckubhouse) 01780 766027 (Pressbox)

Pages :52  Price:£1,00
Editor: Andrew Eason Tel:
Local Newspapers: Stamford Mercury,
Peterborough Evening Telegraph,
Herald &Post
Local Radio:Rutland Radio,LincsFM
Radio Lincolnshire & Radio Cambridgeshire

**Directions:** Off A43 Kettering Rd, 1 mile east of A1. 200 yds from station
**Capacity:** 5,000    Seats: 250    Cover: 1,250    Floodlights: Yes
**Clubhouse:** Open matchdays, Sunday lunchtimes & evenings (bingo).
Food available matchdays - hot and cold
**Club Shop:** Wide range of Lge + non-Lge progs & club souvenirs.
Contact Dave Salisbury (01780 752377)

**PREVIOUS** **Leagues:** Peterborough; Northants (UCL) 08-55; Central Alliance 55-61; Midland Co's 61-72; UCL 72-98
**Grounds:** None    **Names:** None

**CLUB RECORDS** **Attendance:** 4,200 v Kettering, FA Cup 3rd Qual Rd 53
**Win:** 13-0 v Peterborough Reserves, Utd Co's Lge 29-30    **Defeat:** 0-17 v Rothwell,FA Cup 27-28
**Appearances:** Dick Kwiatkowski    **Goalscorer:** Bert Knighten

**BEST SEASON** **FA Cup:** 73-74 4th qual. Round
**FA Vase:** Winners 79-80, R-up 75-76 83-84    **FA Trophy:** 98-99 (1st season) 1st Round

**HONOURS** FA Vase 79-80 (R-up 75-76 83-84); Utd Co's Lg 75-76 77-78 79-80 80-81 81-82 96-97 97-98 (KO Cup 51-52 75-76 79-80 81-82 85-86); Northants Lg 11-12; Lincs Snr`A' Cup 78-79 82-83 97-98; Lincs Snr `B' Cup 51-52 53-54; William Scarber Mem. Cup 70-71 82-83 85-86 88-89 93-94 94-95; Stamford Chal. Cup 89-90; Lincs Jnr Cup 48-49 Hinchbrooke Cup 1906-07, 07-08, 97-98

Players progressing: A Birchenall (Chelsea), R Chester(Aston Villa), T Tye (Chelsea), G Fell (Brighton), C Chapman (Wolves),
S Collins (Peterborough), K Alexander (Grimsby), A Tillson (Grimsby), B Stubbs (Notts Co.), D Genovese (Peterborough)

*The Stamford squad pic-
tured outside their Weston
Super Mare hotel prior to
the Sunday DML Midland
fixture with their hosts
which took place in April.
Top (L-R):
Dave Venables, Andy
Chapman
Danny Clifton, Jon
Harrison, Russell Best,
Andy Furnell
Simon Ward, David Staff,
Andy Lodge, Richard Bailey
Front Row: Pete Foskett
(physio), Dennis Rhule,
Sammy Dale, David Norris,
Nathan Bailey, Ricky
Hailstone, Robbie Blowers,
Billy Jeffrey (Manager)
Photo: Andrew Eason*

# TONBRIDGE ANGELS

## CLUB OFFICIALS

Chairman: **Colin Fry**
Vice Chairman: **Maurice Brown**
Secretary: **Ken Jarrett**
8 Faraday Ride, Tonbridge, Kent TN10 4RL
Tel: 01732 351856
Press Officer:T.B.A.
Commercial Manager:Phil Emblen

## FOOTBALL MANAGEMENT TEAM

Manager:Colin Blewden
Physio: Peter Battell/Chris Dunk

### FACT FILE

Founded: 1948
Nickname: The Angels
Sponsors: Tonbridge Coachworks
Colours: Royal Blue with white trim
Change Colours: All yellow
Midweek matchday: Tuesday
Reserves League: Suburban

98-99 P.o.Y. Uan Gibb
Captain: Alan Tutton

50th Anniversary Season

**TONBRIDGE ANGELS FOOTBALL CLUB**

MEMBERS OF
Dr. MARTENS SOUTHERN LEAGUE SOUTHERN DIVISION
SUBURBAN FOOTBALL LEAGUE

AFFILIATED TO THE KENT COUNTY FOOTBALL ASSOCIATION

MAIN SPONSORS OF TONBRIDGE ANGELS FOOTBALL CLUB

**TONBRIDGE COACHWORKS**

| | |
|---|---|
| **GROUND** | Longmead Stadium, Darenth Avenue, Tonbridge, Kent TN10 3JW |
| | Tel: 01732 352417 |
| **Directions:** | From Tonbridge BR station, through High Street, north up Shipbourne Rd |
| | (A227 Gravesend road) to 2nd mini-r'bout ('The Pinnacles' pub), left into |
| | Darenth Avenue, ground at bottom of Avenue, far side of car park |
| **Capacity:** | 5,000        Seats: 202        Cover: 400        Floodlights: Yes |
| **Clubhouse:** | Open Mon-Sat evenings and Sunday lunchtimes. |
| | Hot food on matchdays from burger bar |
| **Club Shop:** | Yes, progs, replica kits etc, contact Lorraine Parks (01732 350865) |

Pages: 38 Price: £1
Editor:Mayrice Brown c/o Club
Local Press: Kent Messenger, Courier,
Sevenoaks Leader
Local Radio: Invicta, Radio Kent, K,F.M.

**PREVIOUS**    **Leagues:** Southern 48-89, Kent 89-93
**Ground:** The Angel 48-80                    **Names:** TonbridgeAngels, Tonbridge F.C., Tonbridge A.F.C

**CLUB RECORDS** **Attendance:** 1,463 v Yeovil Town, FA Cup 4th Qualifying Round 26/10/91.
At theAngel Ground: 8,236 v Aldershot, FA Cup 1st Round 1951
**Win:** 11-1 v WorthingFA Cup 1951        **Defeat:** 2-11 v Folkstone, Kent Sen Cup 1949
**Career Goalscorer:** Unknown            **Career Appearances:** Mark Gillham, 520 to date
**Transfer fee paid:**                    **Transfer fee received:** £7,500 for Paul Emblen (Charlton Ath 97)

**BEST SEASON** **FA Cup:** First Round (proper) 50-51 51-52 52-53 67-68 72-73
**FA Trophy:**                            **FA Vase:**

**HONOURS**    Kent League 94-95 (League Cup (2)), Southern League Cup Runners-up (2) (SF(1)), Kent Senior Cup 64-65 74-75 (Runners-up (2)), Kent Senior Shield 51-5255-56 57-58 58-59 63-64

Players progressing: R Saunders, M McMcDonald, T Burns, I Seymour, G Moseley, TMorgan, Neil Emblen, Paul Emblen.

*Back Row (L-R): Dave Bourne, Colin Blewden, Joe Radford, Alan Tutton, Andy Garrett, Clint Gooding*
*Front Row: Wayne Balmer, Danny Tingley, Steve Lovell, Ian Gibbs, Andy Kearns, Mark Freeman. Photo: Neil Ingrams*

# V. S. RUGBY

## CLUB OFFICIALS
Chairman: **Brian Melvin**
Commercial Manager: **Jihn Hillier**
Secretary: **Doug Wilkins**,
298 Rocky Lane, Great Barr,
Birmingham B42 1NQ
Tel: 0121 681 1544 (H & Fax)
Press Officer: **Alun Turner**
**Tel:** 01788 567181

## FOOTBALL MANAGEMENT TEAM
Manager:Martin Sockett
Asst Manager: Martin Smith
Physio: Bob Gardner

### FACT FILE
Formed: 1956Nickname: The Valley
Sponsors: Rugby Telegraph & Jaymann
Finance
Colours: Navy & sky/navy/sky
Change colours: All White
Midweek matchday: Wednesday
Club Newsline: 0891 10 19 99
Reserves' League: No reserve team
98-99 - Top scorer:Ashley Warner
P. o Y. & Captain: Kieran Sullivan

**GROUND**        Butlin Road, Rugby, Warks CV21 3ST Tel: 01788 543692

Directions: The ground is situated off Clifton (B5414) on the north side ofRugby. 1 mile walk
from the station

Capacity: 6,000        Cover: 1,000        Seats: 240        Floodlights: Yes

Clubhouse: Open every night and weekend lunchtimes. Entertainment Saturday nights.
        Excellent facilities include Long Alley Skittles, darts and pool
Club Shop: Yes

Pages: 36 Price: £1
Editor: Terry Coley Tel: 0121 240 4521
Local Press: Rugby Advertiser, Coventry
Evening Telegraph, Rugby Observer
Local Radio: Mercia Sound, CWR

**PREVIOUS**        **Name:** Valley Sports, Valley Sports Rugby
        **Leagues:** Rugby & District 1956-63, Coventry & Partnership, North Warks 63-69, United Counties 69-75, West Midlands 75-83

**CLUB RECORDS**   **Attendance:** 3,961 v Northampton FA Cup 1984
        **Win:** 10-0 v Ilkeston Tn FA Trophy 4/9/85        **Defeat:** 1-11 v Ilkeston Town (A) 18.4.98
        **Career Goalscorer:** Danny Conway, 124        **Career Appearances:** Danny Conway, 374
        **Transfer fee paid:** £3,500 R Smith, I Crawley, G Bradder **Transfer fee received:** £15,000 T Angus (Northampton)

**BEST SEASON**    **FA Cup:** 2nd round 87-88, plus 1st Rd 84-85 85-86 86-87 94-95 League clubs defeated: None
        **FA Trophy:**                **FA Vase:** Winners 82-83

**HONOURS**        Southern Lg Midland Div 86-87 (R-up 94-95, Lg Cup 89-90), FA Vase 82-83,Mid Floodlit Cup 84-85 89-90 98 (R-up 86-87),
        Birmingham Snr Cup 88-89 91-92, Utd Co's Lg Div 3 Cup 69-70.
        All-time record FA Trophy win: 10-0 away to IlkestonTown, Preliminary Rd 85-86

Players progressing:        S Storer (Birmingham 1985), S Bicknell (Leicester), S Norris (Scarborough), T Angus (Northampton Town),
        Ashley Walker (Peterborough), Ian King (Stoke City)

*Back in the days of sucess: VS Rugby pressure the Aylesbury defence, part of the record league crowd at Butlin*

# WISBECH TOWN

**WISBECH TOWN FOOTBALL CLUB**

SEASON 1998-99

OFFICIAL PROGRAMME : £1

## CLUB OFFICIALS

Chairman: **Alf Bishop**
Vice Chairman: **Merlin Saddleton**
President: **J W A Chilvers**
Secretary: **John Petch**
34 Walton Rd, Wisbech, Cambs PE13 3EN
Tel: 01945 584333 &Fax)
Press Officer: **R Green**

## FOOTBALL MANAGEMENT TEAM

Manager: Darren Bloodworth
Coach: Alex Irvine
Physio: P Ward

### FACT FILE

Founded: 1920
Nickname: Fenmen
Newsline: 0930 555 865
Colours: All red
Change colours: Blue& white,blue,blue
Midweek Matchday: Tuesday

98-99- Captain: Dan Ashworth
P.o.Y.:Dan Ashworth
Top scorer:Jeremy Illingworth

**GROUND**    Fenland Park, Lerowe Road, Wisbech, Cambs Tel: 01945 584176

Directions: Follow A47 bypass to the West Walton turn off roundabout where there is a Little Chef, turn left for Wisbech, Lerowe Road is first left after 30mph sign. Entering town from north along A1101 cross Freedom Bridge, atroundabout go straight over sign Walsoken/West Walton

Capacity: 3,800        Seats: 284        Cover: 1,000        Floodlights: Yes

Clubhouse: Open every day. Matchday food & drink - Tea, coffee, cold drinks, confectionary, burgers, hotdogs, soup, sandwiches, rolls

Pages: 40 Price: £1
Editor: Gordon Smith Tel: 01945 581767
Local Press: Fenland Citizen,
Wisbech Standard
Local Radio: Radio Cambridgeshire

**PREVIOUS**    **Leagues:** Peterborough; Utd Co's 35-50; Eastern Co's 50-52 70-97; Midland 52-58;Southern 58-70
**Grounds:** Wisbech Park 20-21; Waisoken Rectory 21-22; Harecroft Rd 22-47

**CLUB RECORDS**    **Attendance:** 8,004 v Peterborough United, Midland League 25/8/57
**Goalscorer:** Bert Titmarsh 246 (31-37)**Appearances:** Jamie Brighty (731)
**Win:** 18-1 v Rushden 45-46        **Defeat:** 1-10 v Brighton FA Cup 65-66
**Fee Paid:** £500        **Fee Received:** £4,000

**BEST SEASON**    **FA Cup:** 2nd Rd 57-58, 97-98        League clubs defeated: Colchester
**FA Trophy:** 3rd Qual Rd        **FA Vase:** Semi-Finals 84-85, 85-86

**HONOURS**    Southern Lg Div 1 61-62; Utd Co's Lg (4) 46-48 49-50 61-62 (res) (R-up 48-49, Lg Cup 35-36 (R-up 46-47); Midland Lg R-up 57-58; Eastern Co's Lg 71-72 76-7790-91 (R-up 70-71 73-74 83-84 92-93 96-97), Lg Cup 50-51 70-71 71-72 (R-up 73-74 76-77 86-87); Cambs Invit Cup(8) 52-53 55-56 57-58 74-76 81-83 91-92; E Anglian Cup 87-88 (R-up 40-41 48-49); Peterborough Lg 24-25 27-28 28-29 31-3232-33; Peterborough Snr Cup 32-33 76-77 89-90 97-98

Players progressing: BryanHarvey/Terry Marshall (Newcastle), Jackie Callagher (Peterboro), Paul Scott (Blackpool), Peter Dobson (Ipswich)

*Back Row (L-R): Joe Green, Alex Irvine, Matthew Heaton, Jason Bowler, Warren Ward, Lee Bray, Shaun Keeble, Pau Agnew, Andy Moore, Ian Williams. Front: Phil Ward, Tom Watson, Gary Childs, Phil Marshall, Peter Munns, Kevin Topliss, Chris Dear.*

# WITNEY TOWN

## CLUB OFFICIALS

Chairman: **Brian Constable**
President: **Sir Peter Parker**
Vice-Chairman: Vacant
Press Officer: **Kieran Bushnell**
Tel: 01993 703622
Secretary: **Adrian Bircher**
13 Colwell Drive, Witney, Oxon. OX8 7NJ
Tel: 01993 200913 Mobile: 041 007 3207
Commercial Man/ PRO: **Dermot Gallagher**

### FOOTBALL MANAGEMENT TEAM
Manager: Andy Lyne
Asst Manager : Gary Ackling
Coach: Peter Bridgewater/Paul Holden
Physio: Paul Sunners

**FACT FILE**

Formed: 1885
Nickname: The Blanketmen
Colours: All Yellow
Change colours: Green/white/green
Midweek matchday: Tuesday
Reserves' League: None
Newsline: 0930 555 901

Pages: 40 Price: £1
Editor s : A Bircher & K Bushnell
Tel: 01993 200913
Local Press: Witney Gazette, West Oxon
Standard, Oxford Mail & Oxford Times
Local Radio: Thames Valley FM, Fox (FM)

**GROUND** Marriott Stadium, Downs Rd, Witney, Oxon OX8 7LY. Tel: 01993 702549
**Directions:** From West on A40; take B4047 at island past Burford, follow signs for Witney West & N.W. Industrial Est., thru Minster Lovell to West Witney, right into Downs Rd, ground on right.
From the East on A40, 2nd turn off to Witney and follow signs for South & S.W. Industrial Est., right at r'bout to traffic lights, left and proceed to r'bout, straight over, signs to West Witney Industrial Est., left at lights onto B4047, left into Downs Rd, ground on right. Nearest BR station is Oxford 12 miles away
**Capacity:** 3,500 Cover: 2,000 Seats: 280 Floodlights: Yes
**Club Shop:** Selling programmes and souvenirs. Contact secretary
**Clubhouse:** Members bar open seven days a week 6.30-11pm. Open all day Saturday. Hot food on matchdays

**PREVIOUS** **Leagues:** Reading & Dist., Oxfordshire Senior, Hellenic 53-73
**Name:** Witney F.C. **Ground:** Marriotts Close, Welch Way (pre-1992)

**CLUB RECORDS** **Attendance:** 3,167 v Chelsea 16/11/98 Stand Opening. Competitive: 734 vWealdstone 8/10/92
**Career Goalscorer:** Kenny Clarke 145 **Career Appearances:** Kevin Alder 402 (+6 sub)
**Transfer fee paid:** £3,000 for Steve Jenkins(Cheltenham Town)
**Transfer fee received:** £5,000 for John Bailey (WorcesterCity)

**BEST SEASON** **FA Trophy:** Second Rd 78-79 **FA Amateur Cup:** Second Rd replay - 3 times, 66-67,71-72, 72-73
**FA Cup:** 1st Rd 71-72, 0-3 v Romford (H)

**HONOURS** Southern Lg Div 1 Nth 77-78; Hellenic Lg (8) 54-55 57-58 64-67 70-73 (R-up 53-54 67-68 69-70), Lg Cup (6), Prem Div Benevolent Cup 59-60 63-64; Oxon Snr Lg(5); Oxon Snr Cup (12)

Players progressing: Herbert Smith, Frank Clack (Birmingham City), Arthur Hall(Bristol Rovers 1959), David Moss (Swindon 1969), Jack Newman

*Back Row (L-R): Gary Ackling (Asst Mngr), Justin Merritt, Gary Murphy, Tate Hulbert, Kenny Clarke, Andy Martin, Paul Holden. Front Row: Kevin Alder, Jamie Walters, Steve Ovens, Jason Caffel, Chris Organ, Geoff Neville, Shaun Wimble. Photo: Andrew Chitty*

# JEWSON EASTERN COUNTIES LEAGUE

**Feeder to:** Dr Martens League
**Founded** 1935

**Hon. Patron:** Derek Needham    **President:** Roger Pauley

**Secretary:** Colin Lamb, 3 Land Close, Clacton-on-Sea, Essex CO16 8UJ
Tel: 01255 436398

## FINAL LEAGUE TABLES 1998-99

### PREMIER DIVISION

| | P | W | D | L | F | A | Pts |
|---|---|---|---|---|---|---|---|
| Wroxham | 42 | 27 | 10 | 5 | 88 | 38 | 91 |
| Fakenham Town | 42 | 25 | 10 | 7 | 96 | 50 | 85 |
| Great Yarmouth Tn | 42 | 23 | 9 | 10 | 69 | 36 | 78 |
| Histon | 42 | 19 | 17 | 6 | 80 | 53 | 74 |
| Lowestoft Town | 42 | 19 | 12 | 11 | 78 | 53 | 69 |
| Felixstowe Pt & Tn | 42 | 20 | 9 | 13 | 78 | 56 | 69 |
| Soham Tn Rngrs | 42 | 19 | 12 | 11 | 77 | 73 | 69 |
| Newmarket Town | 42 | 19 | 11 | 12 | 68 | 55 | 68 |
| Sudbury Town | 42 | 20 | 8 | 14 | 75 | 67 | 68 |
| Sudbury Wndrs | 42 | 17 | 8 | 17 | 72 | 62 | 59 |
| Bury Town | 42 | 15 | 14 | 13 | 47 | 46 | 59 |
| Diss Town | 42 | 14 | 15 | 13 | 54 | 59 | 57 |
| Maldon Town | 42 | 16 | 8 | 18 | 69 | 69 | 56 |
| Halstead Town | 42 | 14 | 11 | 17 | 59 | 71 | 53 |
| Warboys Town | 42 | 14 | 10 | 18 | 70 | 86 | 52 |
| Stowmarket Tn | 42 | 12 | 11 | 19 | 59 | 72 | 47 |
| Gorleston | 42 | 12 | 10 | 20 | 52 | 78 | 46 |
| Harwich & Parkeston | 42 | 9 | 14 | 19 | 42 | 62 | 41 |
| Woodbridge Town | 42 | 9 | 11 | 22 | 50 | 73 | 38 |
| Watton United | 42 | 9 | 10 | 23 | 53 | 83 | 37 |
| Ipswich Wanderers | 42 | 5 | 13 | 24 | 49 | 82 | 28 |
| Ely City | 42 | 3 | 11 | 28 | 39 | 100 | 20 |

### FIRST DIVISION

| | P | W | D | L | F | A | Pts |
|---|---|---|---|---|---|---|---|
| Clacton Town | 34 | 22 | 9 | 3 | 93 | 26 | 75 |
| Mildenhall Town | 34 | 21 | 8 | 5 | 79 | 26 | 71 |
| Downham Town | 34 | 21 | 4 | 9 | 65 | 47 | 67 |
| Tiptree United | 34 | 20 | 5 | 9 | 76 | 47 | 65 |
| Needham Market | 34 | 18 | 7 | 9 | 76 | 43 | 61 |
| Swaffham Town | 34 | 18 | 7 | 9 | 56 | 35 | 61 |
| Dereham Town | 34 | 17 | 7 | 10 | 62 | 41 | 58 |
| Chatteris Town | 34 | 16 | 6 | 12 | 51 | 51 | 54 |
| Cornard United | 34 | 14 | 11 | 9 | 49 | 42 | 53 |
| Whitton United | 34 | 13 | 9 | 12 | 52 | 57 | 48 |
| Stanway Rovers | 34 | 11 | 10 | 13 | 43 | 48 | 43 |
| Haverhill Rovers | 34 | 9 | 11 | 14 | 38 | 54 | 38 |
| Norwich United | 34 | 10 | 6 | 18 | 38 | 59 | 36 |
| Brightlingsea Utd | 34 | 7 | 11 | 16 | 53 | 68 | 32 |
| March Town Utd | 34 | 8 | 6 | 20 | 43 | 71 | 30 |
| Hadleigh United | 34 | 7 | 3 | 24 | 34 | 78 | 24 |
| Somersham Town | 34 | 5 | 8 | 21 | 33 | 86 | 23 |
| Thetford Town | 34 | 3 | 4 | 27 | 32 | 94 | 13 |

## LEADING GOALSCORERS 1998-99

### PREMIER DIVISION

| | | |
|---|---|---|
| 36 | Gary Setchell | Fakenham Town |
| 33 | Stuart Roach | Great Yarmouth Town |
| 27 | Brian Devereux | Sudbury Wanderers |
| 25 | Sam Banya | Felixstowe Town |
| 23 | Thomas Noble | Maldon Town |
| 23 | Neil Kennedy | Newmarket Town |
| 22 | Simon Parker | Stowmarket Town |

### FIRST DIVISION

| | | |
|---|---|---|
| 31 | Kris Lee | Tiptree United |
| 29 | Terence Warwick | Tiptree United |
| 27 | Kevin Leggett | Downham Town |
| 23 | Glen Hepburn | Clacton Town |
| | Gavin Crane | Whitton United |
| 20 | Ian Bennett | Clacton Town |

## FIRST DIVISION KNOCK OUT CUP 1998-99

Clacton Town  v  Dereham Town  4-0

# PREVIOUS SEASONS' LEADING GOALSCORERS

## PREMIER DIVISION

| | | | |
|---|---|---|---|
| 1998-99 | 36 | Gary Setchall | Fakenham Town |
| 1997-98 | 37 | Stuart Roach | Great Yarmouth Town |
| | | Neil Kennedy | Histon |
| 1996-97 | 41 | Peter Munns | Wisbech Town |
| 1995-96 | 32 | Paul Smith | Diss and Harwich & Parkeston |
| 1994-95 | 42 | Paul Smith | Harwich & Parkeston |
| 1993-94 | 34 | Scott Snowling | Wroxham |
| 1992-93 | 50 | Matthew Metcalfe | Wroxham |
| 1991-92 | 37 | Jon Rigby | Wroxham |
| 1990-91 | 25 | Steve Parnell | Halstead Town |

## DIVISION ONE

| | | | |
|---|---|---|---|
| 1998-99 | 31 | Kris Lee | Tiptree United |
| 1997-98 | 27 | Scott Witney | Maldon Town |
| 1996-97 | 30 | Glen Driver | Needham Market |
| 1995-96 | 24 | Ray Edwards | Ipswich Wanderers |
| 1994-95 | 30 | Ricky Martin | Downham Town |
| 1993-94 | 25 | Paul Keys | Hadleigh United |
| | | Steve McKenna | Bury Town Reserves |
| 1992-93 | 32 | Adrian Bullett | Soham Town Rangers |
| 1991-92 | 25 | Brendan Doe | Somersham Town |
| | | Matthew Metcalfe | Diss Town |

## CLUBS TO HAVE COMPLETED THE DOUBLE
### OF LEAGUE CHAMPIONSHIP AND LEAGUE CUP
### IN THE SAME SEASON

| | | | |
|---|---|---|---|
| 1936-36 | Harwich & Parkeston | 1977-78 | Lowestoft Town |
| | (Joint Champions) | 1981-82 | Tiptree United |
| 1951-52 | Gillingham Reserves | 1986-87 | Sudbury Town |
| 1953-54 | King's Lynn | 1988-89 | Sudbury Town |
| 1963-64 | Bury Town | 1989-90 | Sudbury Town |
| 1965-66 | Lowestoft Town | 1992-93 | Wroxham |
| 1966-67 | Lowestoft Town | 1995-96 | Halstead Town |
| 1971-72 | Wisbech Town | | |

## CLUBS TO HAVE PROGRESSED TO THE BEAZER HOMES (SOUTHERN) LEAGUE

Season left

| | |
|---|---|
| 1935-36 | Ipswich Town |
| 1936-37 | Chelmsford |
| 1951-52 | Wisbech Town (Joined Southern League 1958) |
| 1953-54 | King's Lynn |
| 1957-58 | Cambridge United and Clacton Town (returned 1964) |
| 1963-64 | Bury Town (returned 1976) |
| 1986-87 | Bury Town (returned 1997) |
| 1989-90 | Sudbury Town (returned 1997) |
| 1990-91 | Braintree Town |
| 1996-97 | Wisbech Town |

# LEAGUE CHAMPIONSHIP PAST RECORDS

## PREMIER DIVISION

| | | |
|---|---|---|
| 1980-81 | Gorleston | Sudbury Town |
| 1981-82 | Tiptree United | Sudbury Town |
| 1982-83 | Saffron Walden Town | Gorleston |
| 1983-84 | Braintree Town | Wisbech Town |
| 1984-85 | Braintree Town | Sudbury Town |
| 1985-86 | Sudbury Town | Colchester United Reserves |
| 1986-87 | Sudbury Town | Braintree Town |
| 1987-88 | March Town United | Braintree Town |
| 1988-89 | Sudbury Town | Braintree Town |
| 1989-90 | Sudbury Town | Thetford Town |
| 1990-91 | Wisbech Town | Braintree Town |
| 1991-92 | Wroxham | Stowmarket Town |
| 1992-93 | Wroxham | Wisbech Town |
| 1993-94 | Wroxham | Halstead Town |
| 1994-95 | Halstead Town | Wroxham |
| 1995-96 | Halstead Town | Diss Town |
| 1996-97 | Wroxham | Wisbech Town |
| 1997-98 | Wroxham | Ely City |
| 1998-99 | Wroxham | Fakenham Town |

## FIRST DIVISION

| | | |
|---|---|---|
| 1990-91 | Norwich United | Brightlingsea United |
| 1991-92 | Diss Town | Fakenham Town |
| 1992-93 | Sudbury Wanderers | Soham Town Rangers |
| 1993-94 | Hadleigh United | Woodbridge Town |
| 1994-95 | Clacton Town | Sudbury Town Reserves |
| 1995-96 | Gorleston | Warboys Town |
| 1996-97 | Ely City | Histon |
| 1997-98 | Ipswich Wanderers | Maldon Town |
| 1998-99 | Clacton Town | Mildenhall Town |

# BURY TOWN

**Secretary:** Mrs Wendy Turner, 64 Winthrop Rd., Bury-St-Edmunds, Suffolk. IP333UF
Tel: 01284 753688
**Ground:** Ram Meadow, Cotton Lane, Bury St Edmunds, Suffolk IP33 1XP Tel: 01284 754721
**Directions:** Leave A14 at sign to Central Bury St Edmunds, follow signs to town centre at exit r'bout,
at next r'bout 1st exit into Northgate St, left at `T' junct (lights) into Mustow St, left immediately into
Cotton Lane - grd 350 yds on right, through `Pay & Display' car park. 10 mins from station
Capacity: 3,500    Cover: 1,500    Seats: 300    Floodlights: Yes
**Clubhouse:** Members'/Public Bars open at matchdays    **Club Shop:** Yes

**HONOURS**    Eastern Counties Lg 63-64, R-up 37-38, Lg Cup 61-62 63-64; MetropolitanLg
65-66, R-up 67-68 70-71, Lg Cup 67-68, Professional Cup 65-66;
Suffolk Premier Cup (9); Suffolk Senior Cup 36-37 37-38 38-39 44-45 84-85
**PREVIOUS**    **Leagues:** Norfolk & Suffolk; Essex & Suffolk Border; Eastern Co's 35-64 76-87;
Metropolitan 64-71    **Names:** Bury St Edmunds 1895-1902; Bury Utd 02-06
**BEST SEASON**    **FA Cup:** 1st Rd replay 68-69, 0-3 v AFC Bournemouth (A) after 0-0
**FA Vase:** Qtr Finals 88-89    **FA Trophy:** 2nd Rd 70-71
**CLUB RECORDS Attendance:** 2,500 v Enfield, FA Cup 3rd Qual. Rd 1986
**Goalscorer:** Doug Tooley 58    **Appearances:** Doug Tooley
Fee Paid: £1,500 for Mel Springett (Chelmsford 1990)
Fee Received: £5,500 forSimon Milton (Ipswich)

**FACT FILE**
Formed: 1872
Nickname: The Blues
Sponsors: T.B.A.
Colours: All blue
Change colours: All red
Midweek matchday: Tuesday
Programme: 40 pages 80p
Editor: Mrs Wendy Turner

1998-99
Captain & P.o.Y.: R.Cornish
Top scorer: K.Layne

**CLUB PERSONNEL**
Chairman: Colin Hurley
Vice Chairman: Russel Ward
President: Cyril Elsey

Manager: Keith Vince
Asst Manager: Keith Vince
Physio: Darren Gibbs

# CLACTON TOWN

**Secretary:** Mrs Sandra Harris, 57 Coopers Lane, Clacton-on-Sea, Essex CO15 2BY
Tel: 01255 476133 email: secretary@clacton-town.com
**Ground:** The Rush Green Bowl, Rushgreen Road, Clacton-on-Sea, Essex CO16 7BQ
Tel/Fax: 01255 432590 email: supporters@clacton-town.com
**Directions:** A133 to Clacton, at r'bout right into St Johns Rd, 4th left CloesLane, 3rd right
Rushgreen Rd, ground approximately half mile on right. From B1027 take main Jaywick turn
off (Jaywick Lane), then 2nd left after about half a mile into Rushgreen Rd. Ground 400 yds.
2 miles from Clacton (BR), buses 3, 5or 5a to Coopers Lane/Rushgreen Rd
Capacity: 3,000    Seats: 200    Cover: Yes    Floodlights: Yes    Club Shop: Yes
Clubhouse: Licensed club. Open 7-11pm Mon-Fri, Wed-Fri lunchtimes & all day Sat & Sun.
Hot & cold food available at all times.

**HONOURS**    Southern Lg Div 1 59-60; Eastern Co's Lg R-up 36-37 53-54 64-65 74-75
(Lg Cup 73-74), Div 1 98-99 (Lg Cup 98-99); Eastern F/lit Cup 95-96;
East Anglian Cup 53-54; WorthingtonEvans Cup 56-57 67-68 74-75.
**PREVIOUS**    **Leagues:** Eastern Co's 35-37 38-58; Southern 58-64
**Grounds:** Clacton Stadium, Old Road 06-87; Gainsford Av (temp)
**RECORD**    **Attendance:** 3,505 v Romford, FA Cup 1st Qual. Rd 1952 (at Old Road)
**BEST SEASON    FA Vase:** 4th Round 74-75    **FA Cup:** 1st Rd, 1-3 v Southend U. (H) 60-61
Players progressing: Vivian Woodward (Spurs), Mick Everitt (Arsenal), Christian McLean (Bristol R.)

**FACT FILE**
Founded: 1892
Nickname: Seasiders
Colours: White/royal blue/royal blue
Change colours: yellow/yellow/royal blue
Midweek Matches: Tuesday
Programme: 40 pages, £1
Editor: Larry Warren (01255 475182)
Local P ress: Clacton Gazette
web Site: http://www.clacton-town.com

**CLUB PERSONNEL**
Owner: Jeff Dewing
Chairman: Stewart Nicholson
General Manager: Colin Harris
Commercial Manager: Michelle Stanley
Tel: 0802 755469

Team Manager: Steve Dowman

# DISS TOWN

**Secretary:** Richard Upson, Bamburgh House, Brewers Green Lane, Diss, NorfolkIP22 3QP
Tel: 01379 642923 (H) 01603 427231 (B) 0836 718729 (M)

**Ground:** Brewers Green Lane, Diss Tel: 01379 651223

**Directions:** Just off B1066 Diss-Thetford road, near Roydon School. 1 1/2 miles from Diss (BR)
Capacity: 2,500Seats: 280Cover: YesFloodlights: Yes
**Club Shop:** Yes, incl. pennants
**Clubhouse:** Open evenings (except Sunday), Sat/Sun lunchtimes, and matchdays

**HONOURS**    FA Vase 94-95; Eastern Co's Lg Div 1 91-92, Anglian Comb. 76-77 78-79(R-
up 74-75, Div 1 67-68 73-74, Lg Cup 67-68 79-80 81-82), Norfolk &
up 74-75, Div 1 67-68 73-74, Lg Cup 67-68 79-80 81-82), Norfolk & Suffolk
Lg R-up 55-56 (Applegate Cup 56-57 57-58(joint)(R-up 55-56)), Norfolk Snr
Cup 74-75 95-96, Norfolk Jnr Cup 1891-92, Jewson Prem Lge R-up 95-96
**PREVIOUS**    **Leagues:** Norwich & District; Norfolk & Suffolk 35-64; AnglianComb. 64-82
**Ground:** Roydon Road 1886-1982
**BEST SEASON    FA Vase:** Winners 94-95, QF 91-92

**RECORDS**    **Attendance:** 1,731 v Atherton LR, FA Vase SF 1st leg 19/3/94

Players progressing A Thurlow (Man City), M Cawston (Norwich), T Whymark(Ipswich),
C Stafford, P Gibbs (Colchester)

**FACT FILE**
Founded: 1888
Nickname: Tangerines
Sponsors: Apple Garages
Colours: Tangerine/navy/tangerine
Change colours: Sky blue/navy/navy
Midweek Matches: Tuesday
Reserve's League: Anglian Combination
Programme: 16 pages, 50p
Editor: Gary Enderby (01953 455979)
1998-99
Captain: Sean Trail
Top Scorer: Coren Hardy
Player of the Year: Darren Scoulding

**CLUB PERSONNEL**
Chairman: Des Tebble
President: Ken Ball
Treasurer: Noel Mullenger
Manager: Paul Chick
Asst Manager: Donnie Pye
Physio: Peter Etheridge

# FAKENHAM TOWN

**Secretary:** Eddie Linnell, 40 Warren Avenue, Fakenham, Norfolk NR21 8NP  Tel: 01328 855445

**Ground:** Clipbush Lane, Fakenham NR21 9QX  Tel/Fax: 01328 856222

**Directions:** Corner of A148 & Clipbush Lane
Capacity: 3,000    Seats: 264    Cover: 500    Floodlights: Yes
**Clubhouse:** Bar, TV. Refreshments available Tel: 01328 855859
Club Shop: Yes

| | |
|---|---|
| HONOURS | Norfolk Snr Cup 70-71 72-73 73-74 91-92 93-94 94-95;,98-99 Eastern Co's Premier Division R-up: 98-99,  Lg Div1, R-up 91-92; Anglian Comb. Cup 78-79 |
| PREVIOUS | **Leagues:** N Norfolk 1884-1910; Norwich & Dist 10-35; Norfolk & Suffolk 35-64; Anglian Comb 64-87 |
| | **Grounds:** Hempton Green 1884-89; Star Meadow 89-1907; Barons Hall Lawn 1907-96 |
| BEST SEASON | **FA Vase:** 98-99 3rd Rd          **FA Cup:** |
| RECORD | **Gate:** 1,000 v Norwich City, floodlight inauguration |

Players progressing Nolan Keeley (Scunthorpe)

### FACT FILE

Founded: 1884
Nickname: Ghosts
Sponsors:English Garages
Colours: Amber & black/black/amber
Change colours: Red & B lack,red,red
Midweek Matchday: Tuesday
Reserves' League: Anglian Comb
Programme: 32 pages, 50p
Editor: John Cushion
Tel: 01328 862548
Local Press : Dereham & Fakenham Times

### CLUB PERSONNEL

Chairman: Tony Fisher
President: G Middleditch
Press Officer: J Cushion
Commercial Manager: T.Vertigan
Manager: Ian Jones

---

# FELIXSTOWE PORT & TOWN

| | |
|---|---|
| **Secretary:** | Steve Page, 11A Lonsdale Close, Ipswich, Suffolk IP4 4HB Tel: 01473 712613 (H) |
| **Ground:** | Dellwood Avenue, Felixstowe IP11 9HT   Tel: 01394 282917 |
| **Directions:** | A45 to Felixstowe. Turn right at 3rd r'bout then 1st left - ground100 yds on left. 5 mins from Felixstowe (BR) and town centre |
| | Capacity: 2,000   Seats: 200         Cover: 200        Floodlights: Yes |
| **Clubhouse:** | Bar, snack bar, TV, darts, pool table. Snacks available |
| **Club Shop:** | Yes including enamel badges & pennants. |
| HONOURS | Suffolk Senior Cup 66-67 74-75 |
| PREVIOUS | **Leagues:** Essex & Suffolk Border; Ipswich & Dist |
| BEST SEASON | **FA Vase:**             **FA Cup:** |
| RECORD | **Attendance:** 1,500 v Ipswich Town, floodlight inauguration 25/1/91 |

### FACT FILE

Founded: 1890
Nickname: Seasiders
Colours: White/blue/gold
Change: Navy blue/navy blue/white
Midweek Matches: Wednesday
Programme: 16 pages, 30p
Editor: Phil Griffiths
Tel: 01394 277156
Local Press: East Anglia Daily Times

### CLUB PERSONNEL

Chairman: Dave Ashford
Fixture Sec: Mike Gosling (01394 279758)
Manager: Scott Clarke
01473 278025 (H)

---

# GORLESTON

**Secretary:** Mrs Pam Lattermore, 7 Station Road, Pulham St Mary, Diss, Norfolk IP21 4QT
     Tel: 01379 608905 (H/Fax)  0411 470858 (M)

**Ground:** Emerald Park, Woodfarm Lane, Gorleston, Great Yarmouth  Tel: 01493 602802

**Directions:** On Magdalen Estate - follow signs to Crematorium, turn left and follow road to ground. Five and a half miles from Great Yarmouth Vauxhall (BR)
Capacity: 5,000    Seats: 250       Cover: 4,000     Floodlights: Yes
**Clubhouse:** Bar, colour TV, pool table, darts, snacks. Matchday Tea, coffee,cold drinks, burgers, hotdogs, rolls       **Club Shop:** Yes

| | |
|---|---|
| HONOURS | Eastern Co's Lg 52-53 72-73 79-80 80-81; Lge Cup 55-56; Norfolk Snr Cup x 13, R-up x 25; Anglian Comb. 68-69, Norfolk & Suffolk Lg x 7; E Anglian Cup (3);Jewson Lge Div 1 95-96 |
| PREVIOUS | **Leagues:** Gt Yarmouth & Dist; Norfolk & Suffolk; Anglian Comb |
| BEST SEASON | **FA Cup:** 1st Rd. 51-52, 57-58        **FA Vase:** |
| RECORD | **Attendance:** 4,473 v Orient, FA Cup 1st Rd 29/11/51 |

### FACT FILE

Founded: 1884
Nickname: Greens
Colours: Green & White
Change colours: All white
Midweek Matchday: Tuesday
Programme: 56/60 pages 50p
Editor: Secretary

### CLUB PERSONNEL

Chairman & President: Jimmy Jones

Managers: Dale Gordon & Robert Fleck

Players progressing: J Joblins (Norwich), M Bailey (Wolves), D Stringer(Norwich), R Carter (Aston Villa), D Carter (Man City), A Brown (Charlton), S Morgan (Cambridge), P Gibbs (Colchester)

# GREAT YARMOUTH TOWN

**Secretary:** Brian Smith, The Bungalow, Humberstone Farm, Cobholm, Great Yarmouth, Norfolk
JR31 0AZ. Tel & Fax: 01493 656099
**Ground:** Wellesey Recreation Ground, Wellesey Road (01493 842936)

**Directions:** Just off Marine Parade, 200yds north of Britannia Pier.1/2 m from Vauxhall BR(BR)
**Capacity:** 3,600 **Seats:** 500 **Cover:** 2,100 **Floodlights:** Yes **Club Shop:** Yes

**Clubhouse:** (01493 843373). Committee Room, TV, darts, pool. Hot & cold food
**HONOURS** Eastern Co's Lg 68-69 (R-up 56-57 67-68 77-78 78-79), Lg Cup 37-38 74-
75 80-81; East Anglian Cup(3); Norfolk Senior Cup x 12, R-up 22;
Norfolk Premier Cupx 2 jt; Norfolk & Suffolk Lg 13-14 26-27 27-28;
Anglian Comb. Cup 65-66(res); E Anglian Lg 56-57(res)

**PREVIOUS** **Leagues:** Norfolk & Suffolk

**BEST SEASON** **FA Cup:** 2nd Rd 52-53, 1st Rd 47-48 **FA Vase:** Semi-Final 82-83
**RECORD** **Attendance:** 8,944 v Crystal Palace, FA Cup 1st Rd 52-53
**Appearances:** John `Jilly' Perkins 499 (1897-1923)
**Scorer:** Gordon South 298 (1927-47) **Win:** 14-0, 2.2.10

Players progressing: R Hollis (Norwich), M Blyth & N Keeley (Scunthorpe), S Davy (West Ham),

### FACT FILE

Founded: 1897
Nickname: Bloaters
Colours: Amber & black stripes/black/black
Change colours: All red
Midweek Matches: Tuesday
Programme: 40 pages, 80p
Editor: Gerry Brown (014493 663171)

98-99 Captain: Mark Vincent
Top Scorer: Stewart Roach
P.o.Y.: Greg Downs

### CLUB PERSONNEL

Chairman: Arthur Fiske

Manager: Paul Tong

---

# HALSTEAD TOWN

**Secretary:** Stephen Webber, 12 Ravens Ave, Halstead, Essex CO9 1NZ
Tel: 01787 476959 (H) 01284 767278 (B)

**Ground:** Rosemary Lane, Broton Ind Est, Halstead, Essex CO9 2HR Tel: 01787 472082

**Directions:** A131 Chelmsford to Braintree - follow signs to Halstead. In Halstead, 1st left
after Police Station, then 1st right, and first left to ground
**Capacity:** 2,000 **Seats:** 312 **Cover:** 400 **Floodlights:** Yes

**Clubhouse:** Open evenings and matchdays

**HONOURS** Eastern Co's Lg 94-95 95-96, R-up 93-94 (Div 1 R-up 89-90), Cup 95-96;
Essex Senior Trophy 94-95 96-97; Knight Floodlit Cup R-up 90-91; Essex
&Suffolk Border Lg 57-59 77-78 94-95(res), (R-up 49-50 54-55 60-61), Div
1(res)94-95); Essex Snr Lg Cup R-up 79-80; Essex Jnr Cup 01-02 46-47 (R-
up 00-01)

**PREVIOUS** **Leagues:** Nth Essex; Halstead & Dist.; Haverhill; Essex & Suffolk Border;
Essex Snr 80-88 **Grounds:** Three Gates 1879-1948, Coggeshall Pieces,
Ravens Meadow, King George Playing Field

**BEST SEASON** **FA Cup:** **FA Vase:**
**RECORD** **Attendance:** 4,000 v Walthamstow Avenue, Essex Senior Cup 1949
Players progressing Steve Allen (Wimbledon Physio)

### FACT FILE

Founded: 1879
Colours: White/black/black
Change colours: All red
Midweek Matches: Tuesday
Programme: 50p
Editor: Paul Downes
Tel: 01787 477320 (H)
Local Press : Halstead Gazette

### CLUB PERSONNEL

Chairman: Mick Coe
Vice-Chairman:Richard Gugacz
President: Mr E J R McDowell
Fixture sec.: Andy Mizon
Tel: 01787 473898 (H) 01206 894096 (B)
Manager: Terry Benson
Physio: B Dunster

---

# HARWICH & PARKESTON

**Secretary:** Andy Schooler, 21 The Vineway, Harwich, Essex CO12 4AX
01255 504590 (H) 01255 509700 (B) 01255 509718 (Bus. Fax)

**Ground:** Royal Oak, Main Road, Dovercourt, Harwich CO12 4AA Tel: 01255 503649

**Directions:** On main road into Dovercourt. 600 yds from Dovercourt (BR)

**Capacity:** 5,000 **Seats:** 350 **Cover:** 1,000 **Floodlights:** Yes
**Clubhouse :** Open every day. Dances, bingo, darts, pool, function room **Club Shop:** Yes

**HONOURS** FA Amateur Cup R-up 1898-99 52-53; Eastern Counties Lg 35-36 (jnt) (Lg
Cup 35-36 36-37 96-97); Essex County Lg 37-38; Athenian Lg Div 1R-up 65-
66 (Div 2 64-65, Lg Cup 64-65); Essex Sen. Cup 1898-99 36-37; Essex Sen.
Trophy 89-90; AFA Senior Cup 35-36 36-37; Worthington Evans Cup 80-81

**PREVIOUS** **Leagues:** Eastern Co's 35-37 38-64; Essex County 37-38; Athenian 64-73
83-84; Isthmian 73-83 **Ground:** Phoenix Field, Seafront

**BEST SEASON** **FA Vase:** Q-F 90-91 **FA Cup:**
**FA Amateur Cup:** R-up 1898-99, 52-53

**RECORD** **Attendance:** 5,649 v Romford, FA Amat Cup 4th Rd 1938
Players progressing: I Gillespie (C Palace), G Waites, K Sanderson, I Brown(Bristol City 91)

### FACT FILE

Founded: 1875
Nickname: Shrimpers
Colours: White & black/black/black
Change colours: Mauve & white/white/mauve
Midweek Matches: Tuesday
Reserve Lge: Essex & Suffolk Border Lge
Prem. Div
Programme: 28 pages, 50p
Editor: Carl Allen
01255 552510

### CLUB PERSONNEL

Chairman: Graham Firth
President: P.Revell
Press Officer: Carl Allan
Manager: Phil Boyland

**GREAT YARMOUTH TOWN**

Back Row: Paul Tong (manager), Stewart Roach, Richie Ervin, Martin Woolsey, Mark Vincent, Nick Banham, Jon White, Danny Holmes, Ian George, Scott McIntosh, Paul Bunce.
Front Row: Mark Armes, Dale Cooper, Greg Downs, Rupert Eglington, Craig Lewis, Craig Cutajar, Neil Prior, Zac Colman

**DISS TOWN**

Back Row: Sean Trail (captain), David Nurse, Tom Casey, Darren Scoulding, Stuart Jopling, Andrew Key, Mark Phillips.
Front Row: Peter Grant, Jason Fletcher, Roger Aldis, Daniel Connelly, Leighton Miller, Philip Bugg, David Bloomfield.
Photo: Malcolm Dixon

# HISTON

**FACT FILE**

**Secretary:** Gareth Baldwin, 5 Caxton Lane, Foxton, Cambridge CB2 6SR Tel: 01223 872989

**Ground:** Bridge Road, Impington, Cambridge (01223 232301 & Fax: 237373)

**Directions:** Leave A14 northern Cambridge bypass on B1049 (signposted Histon and Cottenham). Ground half a mile on right. 5 miles from Cambridge (BR). Bus No.104

**Capacity:** 4,500    **Seats:** 250    **Cover:** 800    **Floodlights:** Yes

**Clubhouse:** Bar/lounge open Tues-Sun eves, Sun lunch and matchdays.Snacks available

**HONOURS**    Eastern Co's Lg Div 1 R-up 96-97, Cup 90-91; Cambridge Invitation Cup77-78 79-80 96-97 (R-up 50-51 52-53 53-54); Spartan Lg Div 1 (East) 50-51; Cambs Chall Cup; Cambs Lg Section; Kershaw Prem Lge R-up 97-98, Sen Lge A 96-97, Cup 96-97; Auto Trader Lge & Cup (U18) 96-97 Kershaw Champions Co Cup (U18) 98-99, Colts League (U17) Champions 98-99

**PREVIOUS**    **Leagues:** Cambridgeshire 04-48; Spartan 48-60; Delphian 60-63; Athenian63-65
**Name:** Histon Institute 04-51

**BEST SEASON**    **FA Cup:** 4th Q 89-90    **FA Vase:** 4th Rd 96-97, 97-98

**RECORD**    **Attendance:** 2,400 v K. Lynn, FA Cup

Founded:  1904
Colours:  Red and black/black/black
Change colours: All blue & white
Midweek Matches: Tuesday
Programme: 16 pages, 80p
Editor: Lisa Whybrow
Local Press : Cambridge Evening News
Local Radio: Q103
BBC Radio Cambridgeshire

**CLUB PERSONNEL**

Chairman:  Gareth Baldwin
President:  G P Muncey
Manager:  Steve Fallon

---

# IPSWICH WANDERERS

**FACT FILE**

**Secretary:**    Martin Head, 246 Sidelate Lane, Ipswich, Suffolk. IP4 3DH Tel: 01473 273811

**Ground:**    Humberdoucey Lane, Ipswich, Suffolk Tel: 01473 728581

**Directions:**    Take Woodbridge Road out of Ipswich,then left fork into Playford Road.Take first left into Humberdoucy Lane Ground 300yds on right
**Capacity:** 2,000    **Seats:** 50    **Cover:** Yes    **Floodlights:** Yes

**Clubhouse:**    Bar,Tea, coffee, cold drinks, confectionary, burgers, hotdogs,sandwiches, rolls

**HONOURS**    Eastern Lge Div 1 97-98

**BEST SEASON**    **FA Cup:**    **FA Vase:**

**PREVIOUS**    **Leagues:** Little David SundayNames: Loadwell Ipswich

**RECORD**    **Attendance:** 335 v Woodbridge, ECL Div 1 4/4/94

Founded: 1983
Nickname: Wanderers
Sponsors: Car Glass & Trim
Colours: Royal & white/blue/blue & white
Change colours: Red & black/black/red & black
Midweek Matches: Tuesday
Programme: Yes
Editor: Alan Haste (01473 711877)
Local Press: East Anglian Daily Times, Evening Star

**CLUB PERSONNEL**

Chairman: A.Haste
President: P.Emmerson
Manager:Colwyn Rowe

---

# LOWESTOFT TOWN

**FACT FILE**

**Secretary:** Terry Lynes, 133 Raglan Street, Lowestoft, Suffolk NR33 2JUTel: 01502 564034

**Ground:**    Crown Meadow, Love Rd, Lowestoft Tel: 01502 573818
**Directions:**    Just off A12, 10 mins from Lowestoft (BR)
**Capacity:** 3,000    **Seats:** 466    **Cover:** 500    **Floodlights:** Yes

**Clubhouse:** Pub hours, Snacks available    Club Shop: Yes (incl metal badges)

**HONOURS**    Eastern Co's Lg(8) 35-36(jnt) 37-38 62-63 64-65 67-68 69-71 77-78, Lg Cup(7) 38-39 54-55 65-67 68-69 75-76 83-84; Norf. & Suffolk Lg(8) 1897-99 1900-04 28-29 30-31; Suffolk Prem. Cup(5) 66-67 71-72 74-75 78-80; Suffolk Snr Cup(10) 02-03 22-24 25-26 31-32 35-36 46-49 55-56; E Anglian Cup(10); Anglian Comb. (Res.) 77-78 79-80 (Lg Cup 76-77); E Anglian Lg (Res.) 57-58 63-64

**PREVIOUS**    **League:** Norfolk & Suffolk 1897-1935

**BEST SEASON**    **FA Cup:** 1st Rd 26-27 38-39 66-67, 67-68, 77-78

**RECORDS**    **Attendance:** 5,000 v Watford, FA Cup 1st Rd 67
**Goalscorer:** M Tooley 383    **Appearances:** C Peck 629
**Win:** 19-0 v Thetford Town (H), Eastern Counties League

Players progressing: Eddie Spearitt (Ipswich 1965), Nigel Cassidy (Norwich1967), Richard Money Scunthorpe 1973), Graham Franklin (Southend 1977)

Founded: 1885
Nickname: Blues
Sponsors: Odebrecht Oil & Gas
Colours: Royal/white/royal
Change colours: All red
Midweek Matches: Tuesday
Reserves' Lge: Anglian Combination
Programme: 20 pages,70p
Editor: Rachel Harrod

**CLUB PERSONNEL**

Chairman: Shaun Cole
President: Roy Harper
Manager: Michael Chapman

# MALDON TOWN

## FACT FILE

**Secretary:** Phil Robinson, 9 Lyndhurst Drive, Bicknacre, Essex CN3 4XL
Tel No: 01245 222633 (H) & 01206 653498 (W)

**Ground:** Wallace Binder Ground, Park Drive, Maldon CM9 5XX (01621 853762)

Capacity: 2,500    Seats: Yes    Cover: Yes    Floodlights: Yes

**HONOURS** Essex Snr Lg 84-85 (Sportsmanship Award 87-88,88-89,94-95, Reserve Shield 93-94), Reserve Cup:94-95, Essex & Suffolk Border Lg 55-56 (Cup 64-65),Essex Intermediate Cup 51-52, Tolleshunt D'Arcy Cup 93-94

**PREVIOUS** **Leagues:** Eastern Counties, Essex & Suffolk Border
**Ground:** Fambridge Road (pre-1994)

**BEST SEASON** **FA Cup:**          **FA Vase:**

**RECORDS** **Attendance:**

Founded: 1946
Colours: Blue & white hoops/blue/blue & white
Change colours: Red & black hoops/black/red
Midweek Matchday: Tuesday
Programme: Yes
Editor: Alan Drewer
96-97 - Captain: Simon Arnold
P.o.Y.: Alex Fiddes
Top Scorer: Scott Witney

**CLUB PERSONNEL**

Chairman: Bob Large
Manager: Ben Embery

---

# MILDENHALL TOWN

## FACT FILE

**Secretary:** Brian Hensby, 14 Sanderling Close, Mildenhall, Suffolk IP28 7LE
Tel: 01638 715772

**Ground:** Recreation Way, Mildenhall, Suffolk (01638 713449)

**Directions:** Next to swimming pool/car, quarter of a mile from town centre

Capacity: 2,000    Seats: None

**Clubhouse:** Open matchdays & functions. Light refreshments available

**HONOURS** Suffolk Junior Cup 1899-1900

**PREVIOUS** **Leagues:** Bury & District; Cambs Lg 2B, 1B & Premier

**RECORD** **Attendance:** 350 v Norwich City, friendly 22/7/89

Founded: 1890
Nickname: Town or Yellows
Colours: Amber/black/black
Change colours: All white
Midweek Matchday: Tuesday
Programme: Free with admission
Editor: F Marshall
Local Press : Bury Free Press,
Newmarket Journal,
Cambridge Evening News

**CLUB PERSONNEL**

Chairman: Brian Brigden
Fixture Secretary: Colin Marchant
Tel: 01842 812123

Manager: Steve O'Donoghue

---

# NEWMARKET TOWN

**Fixture Secretary:** John Olive,9 Tom Jennings Close, Newmarket, Suffolk CB8 0DU

**Ground:** Cricketfield Road, off New Cheveley Road, Newmarket (01638 663637)

**Directions:** 400 yds Newmarket (BR) - turn right into Green Rd, right at cross roads New Cheveley Rd, ground at top on left
Capacity: 1,750    Seats: 144          Cover: 150          Floodlights: Yes

**Clubhouse:** Matchdays only. Refreshments available

**HONOURS** Suffolk Snr Cup 34-35 93-94; Cambs Invitation Cup 58-59; Cambs Chall. Cup 21-22 26-27; Cambs Snr Lg, 19-20; Ipswich Snr Lg 30-31 31-32 32-33 33-34; Peterborough Lg 57-58; Suffolk Premier Cup 93-94 94-95 96-97

**PREVIOUS** **League:** Bury Snr; Ipswich Snr; Essex & Suffolk Border; Utd Co's 34-37; Eastern Co's 37-52

**BEST SEASON** **FA Cup:** 4th Qual. Rd 92-93, 0-2 v Hayes (H)
**FA Vase:** 4th Round 91-92

**RECORD** **Attendance:** 2,701 v Abbey Utd (now Cambridge Utd),
FA Cup 1st Qual.Rd 1/10/49

Players progressing: Mick Lambert (Ipswich), M Wright (Northampton), G Tweed(Coventry), R Fuller (Charlton), Colin Vowden (Camb.Utd.)

## FACT FILE

Founded: 1877
Nickname: Jockeys
Colours: Yellow & navy/navy/navy
Change Colours: All Red
Midweek Matches: Tuesday
Programme: 50p
Editor: Tony Pringle (01638 669438)

**CLUB PERSONNEL**

Chairman: Alf Collen
President: M J Nicholas

Manager: John Wright

# SOHAM TOWN RANGERS

| | |
|---|---|
| Secretary: | Mrs Wendy Gammon, 32 Broad Piece, Soham, Cambs CB7 5EL |
| | Tel: 01353 722139 |
| Ground: | Julius Martins Lane, Soham, Cambs |
| | Tel: 01353 720732 |
| Directions: | A142between Newmarket and Ely |
| | Capacity: 2,000   Seats: 200        Cover: 1,500        Floodlights: Yes |
| Clubhouse: | General bar, Stud Bar, Lounge Bar        **Club Shop:** Yes |

**HONOURS**       Eastern Co's Lg Div 1 R-up 92-93; P'boro. Lg(3)

**PREVIOUS**      **Leagues:** Peterborough & Dist
                 **Ground:** Soham Rangers: Brook Street 1919-47
                 **Names:** Soham Town and Soham Rangers merged in 1947

**BEST SEASON**   **FA Cup:**                      **FA Vase:**

**RECORD**        **Attendance:** 3,000 v Pegasus, FA Amateur Cup 1963

### FACT FILE
Founded: 1947
Nickname: Town or Rangers
Sponsors: C.J.Murfelt
Colours: Green & white/white/white
Change colours: Blue/black/black
Midweek Matchday: Tuesday
Reserves ' League: Cambs Prem. B
Programme: 50p  Editor : Graham Eley
Local Press : Ely Standard, Newmarket
Journal, Cambridge Evening News
1998-99
P.o.Y.: S.Coopere
Top Scorer: N.Docking

### CLUB PERSONNEL
Chairman: M Robinson
President: J Mann
Manager: R Goodjohn
Coach: Mick Drury

---

# STOWMARKET TOWN

| | |
|---|---|
| Secretary: | Colin Davies, 15 Winchester Close, Stowmarket, Tel: 01449 615632 |
| Ground: | Green Meadows Stadium, Bury Road, Stowmarket Tel: 01449 612533 |
| Directions: | About 800 yds from Stowmarket BR station - turn right at 1st lights and head |
| out of town over r'bout into Bury Road - ground on right | |
| Capacity: 2,000 | Seats: 200        Cover: 450        Floodlights: Yes |
| Clubhouse: | Bar open 6.30pm onwards Mon-Fri, weekends 12.0pm onwards. |
| | Matchday food available        Club Shop: Yes, incl. metal badges. |

**HONOURS**       Eastern Co's Lg R-up 91-92, Suffolk Premier Cup(4), Suffolk Snr Cup(10)
                 Suffolk Jnr Cup

**PREVIOUS**      **Leagues:** Ipswich & Dist.; Essex & Suffolk Border 25-52
                 **Grounds:** The Cricket Meadow, 1883-1984
                 **Names:** Stowupland Corinthians; Stowmarket Corinthians; Stowmarket FC

**BEST SEASON**   **FA Cup: 2nd Q Rd 1992**          **FA Vase: 4th Rd 1983-84**

**RECORD**        **Attendance:** 1,200 v Ipswich Town, friendly July 1994
                 At Cricket Meadow: 3,800 v Romford, FA Amtr Cup 1st Rd 15/12/51

Players progressing: Craig Oldfield (Colchester), Les Tibbott, Ted Phillips & Brian Klug (Ipswich)

### FACT FILE
Founded: 1883
Nickname: Stow
Colours: Gold/black/black
Change colours: All Red
Midweek Matches: Wednesday
Reserves' Lge: Essex & Suffolk Border
Programme: 20 pages, 50p
Editor: John Gillingham (01449 674507)
Local Press: East Anglian, Bury Free Press
98-99 - Captain: Steve Gayfer
P.o.Y.: Matthew Platt
Top Scorer: Simon Parker

### CLUB PERSONNEL
Chairman: Derek Barnard
President: John Bultitude
Fixture Sec: Christine Gillingham
Tel: 01449 674507
Manager: Mel Aldis
Ass.Manager/Coach: Dave King
Physio: John Chandler

---

# AFC SUDBURY

| | |
|---|---|
| Ground: | Kingsmarsh Stadium, Brundon Lane, Sudbury, Suffolk CO10 1WQ (01787 376213) |
| Directions: | From Sudbury centre follow Halstead/Chelmsford signs for about 1mile. 1st right |
| | after railway bridge at foot of steep hill, and 1st right after sharp left hand bend |
| Capacity: | 2,500        Seats: 200        Cover: 150        Floodlights: Yes |
| Clubhouse: | Matchdays/ training nights |

**HONOURS**   WANDERERS - Eastern Co's Lg Div 1 92-93, Ess. & Suff. Border Lg(2) 89-91
             (R-up 88-89), Suffolk Snr Cup 90-91

**TOWN**      Southern Lge - Lge Cup 93-94, R-up 96-97, Championship 93-94, Southern Div
             R-up 93-94; Eastern Counties Lg x 7, R-up x 6, Lg Cup x 6, Suffolk Prem.Cup x 13,
             R-up x 7, Suffolk Sen. Cup; E. Anglian Cup 85-86 91-92, R-up 83-84 95-96; Essex
             & Suffolk Border Lg x 5; E.S.B.L. Cup 49-50, R-Up 46-47; Eastern F'lit Group 93-94 94-95

**PREVIOUS**  **Names:** Sudbury Town (1885) & Sudbury Wanderers (1958) merged 1999
             **Leagues:** Town- Essex & Suffolk Border. Wanderers- Suffolk & Ipswich;
             Essex & Suffolk Border; Eastern Co 55-90; Southern 91-97

**BEST SEASON** **FA Vase:** Quarter Final 97-98, 0-2 v Tow Law Town (A), after 1-1
**WANDERERS**   **FA Cup:** 4th Qual Rd., 95-96, 1-4 v Hayes (A), 21.10.95

**TOWN**        **FA Vase:** Runners-up 88-89        **FA Trophy:** 3rd Rd.Proper 95-96
               **FA Cup:** 2nd Rd Proper 96-97, 1-3 v Brentford. Played at Colchester Utd. F.C.

### FACT FILE
Founded: 1999
Colours: Yellow/blue/yellow
Change Colours: All Red
Midweek Matchday: Tuesday
Programme: 48 pages £1
Editor: Darren Witt
Tel: 01787 374654
Local Press : Suffolk Free Press,
East Anglian Daily Times

### CLUB PERSONNEL
Joint Chairman: Nick F Smith & Phil Turner

**Secretary:** David Webb
6 Melford Road, Sudbury, Suffolk CO10 1LS
Tel: 01787 372352 (H)  01787 886000 x6223 (B)

Manager: Keith Martin & Paul Grimsey

DISS TOWN: Back Row (L-R): Sean Trail (captain), David Nurse, Tom Casey, Darren Scoulding, Stuart Jopling, Andrew Key, Mark Phillips. Front Row: Peter Grant, Jason Fletcher, Roger Aldis, Daniel Connelley, Leighton Miller, Philip Bugg, David Bloomfield. Photo: Malcolm Dixon

GREAT YARMOUTH TOWN: Back Row (L-R): Paul Tong (manager), Stewart Roach, Richie Fruin, Martin Woolsey, Mark Vincent, Nick Banham, Jon White, Danny Holmes, Ian George, Scott McIntosh, Paul Bunce. Front Row: Mark Armes, Dale Cooper, Greg Downs, Rupert Eglington, Craig Lewis, Craig Cutasar, Neil Prior, Zac Colman

WROXHAM FC                                                                 Photo: Andrew Chitty

# WARBOYS TOWN

## FACT FILE

**Secretary:** Scott Rendle, 12 CRabbapple Green, Orton Wistow, Peterborough PE2 6YR
Tel No: 01733234904

**Ground:** Sports Field, Forge Way, off High Street, Warboys, Cambs Tel: 01487 823483

**Directions:** Access through Forge Way, half way along south side of High Street
**Capacity:** 2,000   Seats: 50   Cover: 200   Floodlights: Yes

**Clubhouse:** Bar, lounge, function hall. Open every evening & Sunday lunchtime
Entertainment, drinks & snacks

**HONOURS** Utd Co's Lg Div 2 R-up 54-55, P'boro Lg R-up(2) 59-60 61-62, P'boro SnrCup
63-64, Hunts Snr Cup 26-27 28-29 31-32 32-33,94-95. (R-up 92-93), Hunts
Scott Gatty Cup 30-31. Reserves: Hunts Benevolent Cup 57-58, Hunts Junior
Cup 24-25 27-28 52-53, Hunts Lower Junior Cup 75-76 77-78.

**PREVIOUS Leagues:** Peterborough & Dist 46-48 56-88; Utd Co's 50-56; Huntingdonshire 48-50

**RECORD** **Attendance:** 500 v Ramsey Town, Hunts Senior Cup Semi Final

Players progressing: Alex Chamberlain (Ipswich)

Founded: 1885
Nickname: Witches
Colours: Red & white/black/red
Change colours: White/maroon/maroon
Midweek Matches: Tuesday
Programme: 12 pages, 40p
Editor: Martin England
Local Press : Hunts Post (01480 411481)

### CLUB PERSONNEL

Chairman: Geoff Tuffs
Manager: Ian Benjamin

---

# WATTON UNITED

## FACT FILE

**Secretary:** Rick Neave, The New House, Drury Lane, Carbrooke, Thetford, Norfolk
Tel Nos: 01953 882554 (H) 01362 820020 (W) 0467 345201 (M)

**Ground:** Watton Sports Centre, Dereham Road, Watton, Norfolk Tel: 01953 881281

**Directions:** On A1075 towards Dereham about half a mile from junction with B1108
**Capacity:** 2,000   Seats: 50   Cover: 150   Floodlights: Yes

**Clubhouse:** Drinks, sweets & snacks   Club Shop: No

**HONOURS** Anglian Combination 66-67 67-68 85-86 (Lg Cup 66-67 69-70)

**PREVIOUS Leagues:** East Anglian; Anglian Combination

**RECORD** **Gate:** 1,200 v Norwich City, floodlight inauguration 1985

Players progressing: Chris Watts (Norwich), Robert Taylor (Leyton Orient)

Founded: 1888
Nickname: Brecklanders
Sponsors: Style Windows
Colours: White& green/black/black
Change colours: Green/black/green
Midweek Matchday: Tuesday
Reserve's League: Anglian Combination
Programme: 25p
Editor: Secretary

### CLUB PERSONNEL

Chairman: Dick Jessup
Vice-Chairman: Phil Scott
President: Malcolm Warner
Fixture Sec: Nigel Tilford (01953 881441)
Manager: Rick Neave
Physio: M Kay

---

# WOODBRIDGE TOWN

**Secretary:** Eric Smy, 25 Queens Avenue, Woodbridge, Suffolk IP12 4AQ Tel: 01394 384213

**Ground:** Notcutts Park, Seckford Hall Road, Woodbridge, Suffolk Tel: 01394 385308

**Directions:** Turning into Woodbridge off last r'bout from Lowestoft, or 1st r'bout from Ipswich.
Take 1st turning left and 1st left again. Drive to ground at end of road on left
**Capacity:** 3,000   Seats: 50   Cover: 200   Floodlights: Yes

**Clubhouse:** Visitors bar, lounge bar, function hall.Matchday Tea, coffee, cold drinks, hotdogs,
soup, burgers, sandwiches, rolls. Also cooked meals after match

**HONOURS** Suffolk Sen Cup(4), Jun Cup (4); Eastern Co Lg Cup 93-94 97-98, Lge Div 1
R-up 93-94; Ipswich Sen Lge (2)

**PREVIOUS Leagues:** Suffolk & Ipswich Ground: Kingston PF

**BEST SEASON** **FA Cup:**   **FA Vase:** 6th Round 98-99

**RECORD** **Attendance:** 3,000 v Arsenal, floodlight opener 2/10/90

## FACT FILE
Founded: 1885
Nickname: The Woodpeckers
Sponsors: Brafe Engineering Ltd.
Colours: Black & white/black/black
Change colours: All blue
Midweek Matchday: Tuesday
Reserves League: Essex & Suffolk Border
Programme: Free with entry
Editor: D Crowley
Local Press : East Anglian Daily Times
98-99- Captain: Carl David
Top Scorer: Simon Gray 10
P.O.Y.: Dean Garnham

### CLUB PERSONNEL
Chairman: Keith Dixon
President:Andrew Dalby
Football Sec: John Bennett, (01394 385973)
Commercial Manager: David Leech
Manager: David Hubbick

# WROXHAM

**Secretary** : Chris Green, 24 Keys Drive, Wroxham, Norfolk NR12 8SS
Tel: 01603 783936 (H)  01603 683675 (B)
**Ground:** Trafford Park, Skinners Lane, Wroxham, Norfolk Tel: 01603 783538

**Directions:** Arriving from Norwich turn left at former Castle PH and keep left to ground. One and a half miles from Wroxham + Hoveton (BR). Buses 722, 724 and 717

Capacity: 2,500    Seats: 50    Cover: 250    Floodlights: Yes

**Clubhouse:** Bar, pool, darts etc. Drinks, hot & cold food    Club Shop: No

**HONOURS**      Eastern Co's Lg 91-92 92-93 93-94 96-97 97-98, 98-99, R-Up 94-95, (Lg Cup 92-93,R-up 90-91), Div 1 88-89; Norfolk Snr Cup 92-93 96-97 97-98; Anglian Comb(6) (LgCup(7); Reserves completed the double in 94-95

**PREVIOUS**     **Leagues:** Norwich City; East Anglian; Norwich & Dist.; Anglian Comb. 64-88
**Grounds:** Norwich Road; The Avenue; Keys Hill (all pre-1947)

**BEST SEASON**   **FA Vase:** 4th Round 97-98, 98-99
**RECORDS**      **Attendance:** 1,011 v Wisbech Town, E. Counties Lge Prem. Div. 16/3/93
**Goalscorer:** Matthew Metcalf. **Appearances:** Stu Larter
**Win:** 15-2 v Thetford Town (H), E. Counties Lge Prem. Div. 17/1/92
**Defeat:** 1-24 v Blofield (A), Norwich & District League, early 1960s
Players progressing: Matthew Metcalf (Brentford) 93, Paul Warne (Wigan Athletic) 97

## FACT FILE

Founded: 1892
Nickname: Yachtsmen
Colours: Royal & white/blue/blue
Change colours: Red & black/black/red & black
Midweek Matchday: Tuesday
Reserves ' League: Anglian Comb Prem Div
Programme: 20 pages
Editor: Matt Carpenter
Local Press : North Norfolk
Eastern Football (Norwich 628311)
Web-site:www.wroxhamfc.demon.co.uk

### CLUB PERSONNEL

Chairman: Tom Jarrett
President: L King
Press Officer: Secretary
Manager: Bruce Cunningham
Asst Manager: Marty Hubble

FA Cup heroes Ford United on the attack against Newmarket Town in the Vase 3rd Round.  Photo: Dennis Nicholson

# BRIGHTLINGSEA UNITED

**Secretary:** H J Beere, 108 Regent Road, Brightlingsea, Essex CO7 0NZ (01206303122)

**Ground:** North Road, Brightlingsea, Essex (01206 304199)
**Directions:** B1027 Colchester - Clacton, B1029 from Thorrington Cross - followChurch Road into town, left into Spring Road, left into Church Road. Neareststation; Colchester then bus 78 to Brighlingsea
Capacity: 2,000    Seats: 50    Cover: 250    Floodlights: Yes    Club Shop: Yes
**Clubhouse:** Open matchdays & every evening except Sunday. Matchday tea, coffee,& snacks

**HONOURS**    Essex Snr Lg 88-89 89-90 (Harry Fisher Mem. Tphy 89-90 (R-up 88-89), Lg Cup R-up 78-79), Eastern Co's Lg Div 1 R-up 90-91, Essex & Suffolk Border LgPrem. Div Cup 71-72, Harwich Charity Cup 87-88, Worthington Evans Cup 76-77 77-78 78-79
**PREVIOUS**    **Leagues:** Tendring Hundred, Essex & Suffolk Border, Essex Senior 1972-90
**RECORD**    **Gate:** 1,200 v Colchester, friendly 68-69

### FACT FILE
Founded: 1887
Nickname: Oystermen
Colours: Red & white,red,red
Change colours: Yellow & Navy, navy,navy
Midweek Matches: Tuesday
Programme: 24 pages, 30p
Editor: Kim Lay (01206 305797)
Local Press: Essex County Standard, Evening Gazette

### CLUB PERSONNEL
Chairman: Graham Steady
Manager:Gary Harvey

---

# CAMBRIDGE CITY RESERVES

**Secretary:**    Stuart Hamilton, 55 Crowhill, Godmanchester, Huntingdon, Cambs
Tel: 01480 382675

**Ground:**    City Ground, Milton Road, Cambridge CB4 1UY Tel: 01223 357973
**Directions:**    50 yards on left from start of A1309, Cambridge to Ely Rd.
30 minswalk from Cambridge BR
Capacity: 5,000    Cover: 1,400    Seats:423    Floodlights: Yes

**Clubhouse:** 11am-11pm Mon-Sat, 12-3 & 7pm-10.30 Sun. Bingo, Dances, Pool, Darts

**Club Shop:** Sells programmes, club history, badges, scarves, pennants, replica shirts etc.
Contact Neil Harvey (01223 235991)

### FACT FILE
Colours: White & black halves/black/white & black hoops
Change colours: Green & Yellow halves,green,green& yellow hoops
Midweek matchday: Monday
Programme Editor: Secretary

### CLUB PERSONNEL
Chairman: Dennis Rolph
Fixtures Sec.: Andy Dewey
50 Doggett Rd., Cherry Hinton, Cambridge
01223 245694 (H) 01223 555410 (Bus. Fax)
Manager:Jeremy George
Tel; 01954 782484

---

# CHATTERIS TOWN

**Secretary:** Jimmy Gill, 3 West End Close, Chatteris, Cambs PE16 6HW (01354693690)

**Ground:** West Street, Chatteris (01354 692139)
**Directions:** Entering Chatteris on A141 from Huntingdon turn right into West Street after by-pass roundabout. From A142(Isle of Ely way) turnleft at 2nd roundabout.50yds right to West St.
Capacity: 2,000Seats: 250Cover: 400Floodlights: Yes
**Clubhouse:** Bar & tea bar. Matchday drinks & snacks available
Club Shop: no but pennants are available

**HONOURS**    Eastern Counties Lg Cup 67-68, Peterborough Premier Lg(3)
**PREVIOUS**    **League:** Peterborough    **Ground:** First Drove
**RECORD**    **Gate:** 2,000 v March Town Utd, League 5/5/88
Players progressing: Andy Rogers (Reading), Dave Gregory (Plymouth)

### FACT FILE

Founded: 1920
Nickname: Lillies
Colours: White/blue/white
Change colours: Red & black/black/black
Midweek Matches: Wednesday
Programme: 16 pages, 50p

### CLUB PERSONNEL

Chairman: Geoff Allen
President: R.W.Salisbury
Manager: Steven  Taylor

---

# CORNARD UNITED
**Secretary:** Chris Symes, 22 Greenacres, Mile End, Colchester, Essex CO4 (01206851489)
**Ground:** Blackhouse Lane Sportsfield, Great Cornard, Suffolk (01787 376719)
**Directions:** Left off r'bout on A134 coming from Ipswich/Colchester intoSudbury, follow signs for Country Park - ground is immediately opposite along Blackhouse Lane
Capacity: 2,000    Seats: 250    Cover: 500    Floodlights: Yes    Club Shop: No
**Clubhouse:** Open matchdays & Sunday lunchtimes. Matchday Tea, coffee, colddrinks, & snacks
**HONOURS**    Eastern Co's Lg Div 1 89-90 (Lg Cup R-up 92-93), Essex & Suffolk BorderLg 88-89 (Lg Cup 88-89), Suffolk Snr Cup 89-90, Suffolk Jnr Cup R-up 84-85
**PREVIOUS**    **Leagues:** Sudbury S/day 64-65; Bury St Edmunds & Dist 65-72; Colchester71-78; Essex Suffolk Bord 78-89. Grounds: Cornard Rec 64-71; Great CornardUpper School 71-85
**RECORDS**    **Appearances:** Malcolm Fisher. Goalscorer : Andy Smiles
    **Attendance:** 330 v Sudbury Town, Eastern Floodlit League 4/2/92
    **Win:** 18-2 v St Peters House, Colchester Lge 14/9/72
    **Defeat:** 4-10 v Finningham, Bury Lge 7/2/68

### FACT FILE
Founded: 1964    Nickname: Ards
SponsorsGetech
AColours: Blue & white/white/blue
Change colours: Red
Midweek Matches: Tuesday
Reserve League: Essex & Suffolk Border
Programme: 16 pages    Editor: Secretary
Local Press : Suffolk Free Press

### CLUB PERSONNEL
Chairman: Chris Symes
Vice-Chairman: Mike Ford
President: Jim McLaughlin
Manager: Chris Symes
Asst Man.: Jason Stalker    Physio: Mike Ford

# DEREHAM TOWN
FACT FILE

Secretary: Ian Conway, 17 Dale Raod, Dereham, Norfolk NR19 2DD
Tel: 01362 695382 (H)  01362 690460 (B)

Ground: Aldiss Park, Norwich Road, Dereham, Norfolk NR20 3AL
Tel/Fax: 01362 690460

Colours: Black & white/black/black
Change colours: Red & white/white/white
Midweek matchday; Tuesday
Programme editor: Barnes Print
Tel: 01362 860781 Fax: 01362 860977

CLUB PERSONNEL

Chairman: Tim Warner
Tel: 01362 692419 (H)
Fixtures Sec: David West
Tel: 01362 693006 (H) 01362 692433 (B)
Managers: David Seaton & Paul Jarvis

# DOWNHAM TOWN
FACT FILE

Secretary: F.Thorne, 6 Maple Rd., Downham Market, Norfolk, PE38 9PY. (01366382563)

Ground: Memorial Field, Lynn Road, Downham Market, Norfolk (01366 388424)

Directions: One and a quarter miles from Downham Market (BR) - continue to townclock, turn left and ground is three quarters of a mile down Lynn Road
Capacity: 1,000    Seats: None    Cover: Yes    Floodlights: Yes
Clubhouse: Open matchdays, refreshments & snacks available

HONOURSP'boro Lg(5) 62-63 73-74 78-79 86-88, Norfolk Senior Cup 63-64 65-66 (R-up(3) 66-69)

PREVIOUS Leagues: Peterborough

RECORD Attendance: 292 v Diss Town, Jewson League Division One 1991/92

Founded: 1881
Nickname: Town
Colours: Red & white/red/red
Change colours: Sky/Navy/sky
Midweek Matches: Tuesday
Programme: Yes, with entry
Editor: Chairman

CLUB PERSONNEL
Chairman: John Fysh
President: T G Barker
Manager: Steve Tyres

# ELY CITY
FACT FILE

Secretary: Pam Jordan, 3 Marroway Lane, Witchford, Ely, Cambs.CB6 2HU (01353 662353)

Ground: Unwin Sports Ground, Downham Road (01353 662035)
Directions: A10 Ely by-pass turn off for Downham. 3 miles (approx) from Ely(BR)
Capacity: 1,500    Seats: 150    Cover: 350    Floodlights: Yes
Clubhouse: Open matchdays, refreshments available
Club Shop: Metal Badges: Yes

HONOURS      Cambs Snr Cup 47-48, Eastern Co's Lg R-up 69-70 (Lg Cup 79-80)
PREVIOUS      Leagues: Peterborough; Central Alliance 58-60
BEST SEASON   FA Cup: 1st Rd 56-56 (2-6 v Torquay)
RECORD        Gate: 260 v Soham, Eastern Co's Lg Div 1, 12/4/93
              At old ground: 4,260 v Torquay, FA Cup 56-57

Founded: 1885
Nickname: Robins
Colours: All red
Change colours: Jade/black/jade
Midweek Matches: Tuesday
Programme: 20p
Editor: Secretary
Local Press: Ely Standard (01353 667831)

CLUB PERSONNEL

Chairman: Brian Jordan
Manager: Steven Taylor

# HADLEIGH UNITED
FACT FILE

Secretary: Peter Hutchings, 3 Mowlands, Capel St Mary, Ipswich. IP9 2XB Tel: 01473 311093
Ground: Millfield, Tinkers Lane, Duke Street, Hadleigh, Suffolk Tel: 01473 822165
Directions: Turn off A12 approx halfway between Ipswich & Colchester. Take B1070& follow signs to Hadleigh. Duke Street is off the High Street - turn left by Library
Capacity: 3,000    Seats: 250    Cover: 500    Floodlights: Yes
Clubhouse: Open matchdays,
HONOURS       Ipswich & Dist./Suffolk & Ipswich Lg 53-54 56-57 73-74 76-77 78-79
              (Mick McNeil Lg Cup 76-77 80-81 81-82 86-87)), Suffolk Senior Cup 68-69
              71-72 82-83.Eastern Co.Lg Champions 93-94
PREVIOUS      Leagues: Suffolk & Ipswich (prev. Ipswich & D.)(pre-1991)
              Grounds: Grays Meadow, Ipswich Road
RECORDS       Gate: 518 v Halstead Town, FA Vase Replay 17.1.95  Win: 8-1 v
Chatteris(A) 17/1/95  Defeat: 0-7 v Harwich & Parkston (H) 12/10/96, & Wisbech (H) 26/4/97

Founded: 1892
Nickname: Brettsiders
Sponsors: Lancaster
Colours: White & navy/navy/navy
Change colours: All yellow
Midweek Matches: Tuesday
Reserves' Lge: Essex & Suff. Border
Programme: 12 pages, 50p
Editor: Peter Hutchings (01473 311093)

CLUB PERSONNEL
President: K.Grimsey
Chairman: Dave Petts
Manager: Louis Newman

Dean Folkard nets from five yards to put Needham Market on the way to a 3-1 victory over Jewson newcomer Dereham Town in this first ever meeting between the two sides. Photo: Gordon Whittington

MILDENHALL TOWN FC

Photo: Gordon Whittington

Dean Payne of Sporting Connections presents boots to Gary Hudson, captain of Clacton Town FC First team, flanked by Wendy Dewing (left), and Sporting Connection's Jenny Payne, watched by members of the first team squad

# HAVERHILL ROVERS

**Secretary:** Chris Rice, 23 Ovington Place, Haverhill, Suffolk. CB9 0BA.  Tel: 01440 712396

**Ground:** Hamlet Croft, Haverhill, Suffolk  Tel: 01440 702137

**Directions:** Centre of Haverhill
Capacity: 3,000Seats: 200Cover: 200Floodlights: Yes
**Clubhouse:** Open matchdays and functions. Snacks available

**HONOURS**      Eastern Co's Lg 78-79 (Lg Cup 64-65); E & S Border Lg 62-63 63-64; East
                 Anglian Cup 90-91; Suffolk Sen Cup 96-97
**PREVIOUS**     **League:** Essex & Suffolk Border
**RECORD**       **Attendance:** 1,537 v Warrington Town, FA Vase QF 86-87
Players progressing: R Wilkins (Colchester)

**FACT FILE**
Founded: 1886        Nickname: Rovers
Colours: All red
Change colours: All blue
Midweek Matches: Tuesday
Programme: 24 pages, 40p
Editor: Ray Esdale (01440 704670)
Local Press : Haverhill Echo,Cambridge
Evening News
**CLUB PERSONNEL**
Chairman: Terry McGerty
President: N Haylock
Press Officer: Ray Esdale
Managers: Danny Boyle & Lee Barrett
Physio: Mark Bampton

# MARCH TOWN UNITED

**Secretary:** R S Bennett, 47 Ellingham Ave, March, Cambs PE15 9TE (01354 659901)

**Ground:** GER Sports Ground, Robin Goodfellows Lane, March (01354 653073)

**Directions:** 5 mins from town centre, 10 mins from BR station
Capacity: 4,000    Seats: 500      Cover: 2,000      Floodlights: Yes
**Clubhouse:** On ground, seating 150. Light refreshments available

**HONOURS**      Eastern Co's Lg 87-88 (Lg Cup 60-61), Utd Co's Lg 53-64,  Cambs
                 Invitation Cup 54-55, East Anglian Cup 53-54 (jt withBarking)

**PREVIOUS**     **Leagues:** Peterborough; Isle of Ely; Utd Co's 48-54
                 **Ground:** The Avenue (prior to 1946)

**BEST SEASON**  FA Cup 1st Rd53-54 77-78,

**RECORD**       **Gate:** 7,500 v King's Lynn, FA Cup 1956

**FACT FILE**
Founded: 1885
Nickname: Hares
Club colours: Yellow /blue/yellow
Change colours: Black & white/black/black
Midweek Matches: Tuesday
Programme: 30p
Editor: R Bennett
Local Press : Cambs Times, Fenland
Advertiser, Peterborough Evening Telegraph

**CLUB PERSONNEL**
Chairman: Gary Wesley
President: D Wilkinson

# NEEDHAM MARKET

**Secretary:** D Bloomfield, 33 Quinton Road, Needham Market, Suffolk IP6 8DA
Tel: 01449 720693

**Fixture Secrtary::** G.Coombes Tel No: 01449 741200

**Ground:** Bloomfields, Quinton Road, Needham Market, Suffolk
Tel: 01449 721000

**Directions:** Quinton Road is off Barretts Lane which in turn is off Needham Market High Street
Floodlights: Yes

**FACT FILE**
Founded:
Nickname:
Colours: All Green & White
Change Coloures: White/navy/navy
Midweek Matchday: Tuesday
Programme Editor: Ian Verneau
Tel No: 01473 413957

**CLUB PERSONNEL**
Chairman: A.Sparkes
Managers: Jim Fitzgerald & Wayne Leggett
Fixture Secretary: I Croft (01449 676517)
Managers: G Emmerson & C. Macrow

# NORWICH UNITED

**Secretary:** Nigel Harrowing, 43 Cawston Meadow, Poringland, Norwich NR147SX
Tel No & Fax: 0150-8 494335
**Ground:** Plantation Road, Blofield, Norwich, Norfolk NR13 4PL (01603 716963)
**Directions:** Half a mile from Blofield village - coming from Norwich on Yarmouth Rd turn left in
Blofield at Kings Head pub & follow to Plantation Rd (grd on right after bridge over bypass). 1/2
hour Brundall BR (Norwich-Yarmouth line)
Capacity: 3,000    Seats: 100      Cover: 1,000      Floodlights: Yes
Club Shop: Yes incl. metal badges & pennants    **Clubhouse:** Matchday food & drink: Tea,
                 coffee, cold drinks, hotdogs, burgers, soup, sandwiches, rolls
**HONOURS**      Eastern Co's Lg Div 1 90-91 (R-up 89-89, Lg Cup 91-92), Anglian
                 Combination 88-89
**PREVIOUS**     **Ground:** Gothic Club, Heartsease Lane, Norwich (until end of 90-91)
**RECORD**       **Attendance:** 401 v Wroxham, League match, 2/10/91
                 **Goalscorer:** M Money              **Appearances:** Tim Sayer

**FACT FILE**
Founded: 1903
Nickname: Planters
Colours: Old Gold& black/old gold/ black
Change colours: Red& blue/blue/red
Midweek Matches: Tuesday
Programme: 24 pages, 50p
Editor: Secretary
Local Press : Eastern Counties Newspapers
**CLUB PERSONNEL**
Chairman: John Hilditch
Vice-Chairman: J Cubitt
President: Michael Miles
Manager: Bob Barnett
Physio: Mike Chapman

# SOMERSHAM TOWN

ecretary: Norman Burkett, 6 West Leys, St Ives, Cambs. PE17 4DS (01480 464695)

round: West End Ground, St Ives Road, Somersham, Cambs (01487 843384)

irections: On A604 St Ives to Somersham on right as you enter town
apacity: 1,500    Seats: None    Cover: 200    Floodlights: Yes
lubhouse:    Open Friday, Sat/Sun lunchtimes

ONOURS    Hunts Snr Cup 72-73 94-95, Peterboro Snr Cup 84-85, Hinchingbrooke
Cup53-54, Cambs Lg Premier B Div 94-95 (reserves)
REVIOUS    League: Peterborough & Dist
ECORDS    Attendance: 538 v Norwich City, f/light inauguration 91
Goalscorer & Appearances: Terry Butcher
ocal Press : Hunts Post, Cambs News, Citizen Express, St Ives Weekly

### FACT FILE
Founded: 1893    Nickname: Westenders
Sponsors: Rapidtech (UK) Ltd
Colours: All old gold
Change colours: Sky/maroon/sky
Midweek Matchday: Tuesday
Reserve League: Kershaw Senior A
Programme: 76 pages, 30p
Editor/Press Off.: Dave Hardy 01487 840441

### CLUB PERSONNEL
Chairman: Alan Bailey
Vice-Chairman: Norman Burkett
President: Jack Marjason
Manager: Norman Hudson
Coach: Bob Barnett    Physio: Alan Magnus

# STANWAY ROVERS

ecretary: Alan Brierley, 19 Barley Way, Stanway, Colchester CO3 5YD (01206 521606 + Fax)
round: `Hawthorns', New Farm Road, Stanway, Colchester, Essex (01206 578187)
irections: Take turn off marked Stanway off A12. Turn right and go over flyover to Tollgate
bout, 1st right into Villa Rd, after 25 yards turn left into Church Rd, 200 yards on left into New
arm Rd, ground 400 yards on left.Nearest BR station is Colchester North
apacity: 1,500    Seats: None    Cover: 200    Floodlights: Yes
lubhouse: 6.45-11pm eves, 12-11pm Sats. Rolls, soup, tea, coffee etc available matchdays
lub Shop: Pennants & ties
ONOURS    Essex Intermediate Cup R-up 89-90 90-91, Essex & Suffolk Border Lg R-up
91-92 (Div 1 86-87, Div 2 81-81 85-86), Essex Jnr Cup R-up 74-75
REVIOUS    Leagues: Colchester & E Essex; Essex & Suff. Border (pre-1992)
Ground: Stanway Secondary School, Winstree Road (20 years)
ECORD    Gate: 166 v Sudbury Town FA Vase 4/10/97  Win: 8-1 v Swaffham Town
(H), E. Counties Lge Div. 1 26/3/94    Defeat: 0-10 v Sudbury Townt (A), E.C.L. Cup

### FACT FILE
Founded: 1955    Nickname: Rovers
Sponsors: Collier & Catchpole
Colours: Gold/black/black
Change colours: White/black/black
Midweek matchday: Wednesday
Reserves' Lge: Essex & Suff. Border
Programme: 12 pages, 50p
Editor: Alan Brierleylocal press:
Essex Co. Standard, Evening Gazette
### CLUB PERSONNEL
Chairman: Brian Peachey
President: Richard Deguille
Manager: Phil Bloss
Physio: Stuart Bevis

# SWAFFHAM TOWN

ecretary:Carla Hilton,28 Coronation Grove, Swaffham, NorfolkPE37 7NA
el No: 01760720107 (H) 078999 54223 (W & M)
round: Shoemakers Lane, Swaffham, Norfolk (01760 722700)
Capacity: 2,000    Seats: None    Cover: None    Floodlights: Yes
lubhouse: Open Tuesday, Thursday, Saturday & Sunday lunchtimes & evenings.Drinks,
weets etc

ONOURS    Norfolk Snr Cup(2), Anglian Comb. 89-90 (Div 1 88-89)

REVIOUS    Leagues: Dereham, Anglian Combination

ECORD    Attendance: 250 v Downham Town, Eastern Co's League Cup 3/9/91

### FACT FILE
Founded: 1892
Nickname: Pedlars
Midweek Matchday: Tuesday
Colours: Black & white stripes/black/black
Change: All sky blue
Programme: 36 pages, 30p
Editor: Sue Choppen

### CLUB PERSONNEL
Chairman: Stephen Choppen
President: J Smith
Manager: Robin Sainty

# THETFORD TOWN

ecretary: John Wordley, 4 Claxton Close, Thetford, Norfolk IP24 1BA Tel: 01842 762530

round: Mundford Road, Thetford, Norfolk Tel: 01842 766120

irections: Turn off bypass (A11) at A143 junction - ground 800yds next tosports ground
apacity: 2,000    Seats: 400    Cover: 400    Floodlights: Yes
lubhouse: Bar, teas, refreshments, light meals & snacks
lub Shop: No

ONOURS    Eastern Co's Lg R-up 89-90, Norfolk & Suffolk Lg 54-55, Norfolk SnrSenior
Cup 47-48 90-91
REVIOUS    Leagues: Norfolk & Suffolk    Grounds: None
ECORD    Attendance: 394 v Diss Town, Norfolk Snr Cup 91
layers progressing: Dick Scott (Norwich C.), Kevin Seggie (Leeds U.),Simon Milton (Ipswich T.)
ocal Press: Thetford & Watton Times, Bury Free Press

### FACT FILE
Founded: 1884
Sponsors: Sportscene
Colours: Claret & blue/sky/blue
Change: Yellow & black
Midweek Matches: Wednesday
Reserves League: Anglian Comb
Programme: 50p
Editor: Graham Mills (01480 385425)

### CLUB PERSONNEL
Chairman: Michael Bailey
Vice-Chairman: B Richards
Press Officer: Mick Burgess
Manager: Stuart Williams
Coach: Peter Jones

# TIPTREE UNITED

**Secretary:** John Wisbey, 103 Peace Road, Stanway, Colchester, Essex
Tel Nos: 01206 564222 (H) 0403 585814 (M)
**Ground:** Chapel Road, Tiptree, Essex (01621 815213)

**Directions:** Enter town on B1023 - Chapel Road is left at second crossroads,ground 200yds on left. 3 miles from Kelverdon (BR). Served by Eastern NationalColchester to Maldon bus
Capacity: 2,500Seats: 150Cover: 300Floodlights: Yes
**Clubhouse:** Open daily 7-11pm (all day Fri & Sat) & 12-2.30, 7-10.30 Sun. Large bar, two snooker tables, pool, darts, netball, badminton, pigeon club, bingo. Dance hall seats 180, small hall seats 60.                    Club Shop: No

**HONOURS**     Essex Snr Tphy 80-81, Eastern Co's Lg 81-82 (Lg Cup 81-82 84-85), EssexSnr Lg R-up 75-76 77-78, Harwich Charity Cup(4)

**PREVIOUS**     **Leagues:** Essex & Suffolk Border; Essex Snr 78-84

**RECORD**     **Attendance:** 1,210 v Spurs, floodlight inauguration Dec 1990

### FACT FILE
Founded: 1933  Nickname: Strawberries
Sponsors: S Smith (Transport)
Colours: Red& blackstripes/black/black
Change colours: Yellow/blue/white
Midweek Matchday: Tuesday
Reserves' League: Essex & Herts Comb
Programme: 30 pages, 30p Editor: Secretary
Local Press : Colchester Evening Gazette, Essex County Standard

### CLUB PERSONNEL
Chairman: Peter Newman
President: Len Foakes
Manager: Steve Parnell

# WHITTON UNITED

**Secretary:** David Gould, 7 Karen Close, Ipswich, Suffolk IP1 4LP     Tel: 01473 253838

**Ground:** King George V Playing Field, Old Norwich Road, Ipswich, Suffolk. Tel: 01473 464030

**Directions:** Turn off A14, junction A1156 approx 3 miles west of A12/A14junction
Capacity: 600     Seats: No     Cover: 100     Floodlights: Yes
Club Shop: No
**Clubhouse:** Licensed Bar. Hot & Cold Food available

**HONOURS**     Suffolk Senior Cup 58-59 62-63 92-93; Suffolk & Ipswich Lge 46-47 47-48 65-66 67-68 91-92 92-93, Jewson Fairplay Trophy 96-97, 97-98

**PREVIOUS**     **Leagues:** Suffolk & Ipswich

**RECORD**     **Attendance:** 528 v Ipswich Town 29/11/95
League 244 v Ipswich Wanderers13/1/96

### FACT FILE
Formed: 1926     Nickname: None
Sponsors: Speedyhire
Colours: Green & white/green/green
Change colours: All red
Midweek Matches: Wednesday
Youth's League: U18 Eastern Jun Alliance
Programme: Yes
Editor/ Press Officer:Mark Woodward

### CLUB PERSONNEL
Chairman: John Watkins
President: Russell Woodward
Fixture Sec: Alan Elliott (01473 461931)
Manager: Paul Smythe

Influential midfielder for Wroxham, Darren Gill, sets up another attack.                    Photo: Peter Barnes

CAPEL PLOUGH F.C.

EAST BERGHOLT F.C.

LEISTON ST. MARGARETS F.C.

# NON-LEAGUE NEWSDESK

## FOR RESULTS, TABLES AND NEWS FROM THE NON-LEAGUE PYRAMID

Now entering its fifth full season, Non-League Newsdesk has become firmly established as the number one magazine for up-to-date news and statistics from the Pyramid world.

Founded in 1995 by former Non-League Club Directory editor James Wright, Non-League Newsdesk will in 1999-2000 celebrate its 200th edition. The magazine is delivered to subscribers every midweek (usually Wednesday) carrying all the previous week's results, together with current tables, from around FIFTY leagues.

For many of the more senior competitions, full match details (such as goalscorers and attendances) are supplied. County and League Cup competitions are also extensively featured, as are the FA Umbro Trophy and FA Carlsberg Vase, and the involvement of the non-League clubs in the AXA sponsored FA Cup.

But Non-League Newsdesk is not just a statistical work. Each week the magazine carries up-to-date news stories and listings of managerial changes and transfers.

The magazine is therefore particularly popular with -
* Clubs, who find much of the information extremely useful for matchday programmes and in checking on forthcoming opponents, particularly those from outside their own league.
* Statisticians, who see the weekly stats as the most extensive, accurate and up-to-date available.
* Groundhoppers, who find it invaluable in picking their games.
* The more general non-League enthusiast who likes to keep abreast of the most current news.

If you would like to see a free sample copy from 1998-99, please send an SAE to James Wright at the address below.

Leagues featured in Non-League Newsdesk include: Nationwide Conference, UniBond, Ryman, Dr Martens, First NW Trains NWCL, SGL West Lancs, Manchester, Carlsberg West Cheshire, Green Contract Services Mid-Cheshire, Arnott Insurance Northern, Northern Co's (East), Redferns Central Midlands, Powerleague Notts Alliance, West Yorkshire, Deejays Lincs, Everards Leics, Vaux Wearside, JPL Wade Northern Alliance, Herts, A Quote Insurance Reading, Courage Combined Co's, Cherry Red Chiltonian, Minerva SSML, Essex Senior, Essex Intermediate, Kent Blaxill Essex & Suffolk Border, Interlink Alliance, Endsleigh Midland Comb, Banks's West Mids, Springbank Vending Midland, Complete Music Hellenic, Glos. County, Somerset Senior, Screwfix Western, Jewson SW, Jolly's Cornwall Combination, Cornish Guardian East Cornwall, Westward Developments Devon, Jewson Wessex, Keyline Dorset Comb., Dorset Co., Hampshire, Unijet Sussex, Bass Kent, British Energy Kent Co., Jewson ECL, Lovewell Blake Anglian Combination, McGinty's Suffolk & Ipswich, Uhlsport UCL, Optimum Interiors Capital and Central Conference, League of Wales, CC Sports

JAMES WRIGHT, 13 NORTHFIELD AVENUE, TAUNTON, SOMERSET TA1 1XF
TEL/FAX: 01823 327720  MOBILE: 0421 004219  E-MAIL:NLNEWSDESK@ZETNET.CO.UK

## Subscription Rates

Non-League Newsdesk costs just 80p per week plus first class postage (26p). It is produced every Monday during the season except the week between Christmas and New Year. The table below shows how much a subscription will cost from your chosen starting date.

| FROM | to Xmas | Full season |
|---|---|---|
| Aug 9th | £21.20 | £42.40 |
| Aug 16th | £20.14 | £41.34 |
| Aug 23rd | £19.08 | £40.28 |
| Aug 30th | £18.02 | £39.22 |
| Sept 6th | £16.96 | £38.16 |
| Sept 13th | £15.90 | £37.10 |
| Sept 20th | £14.84 | £36.04 |
| Sept 27th | £13.78 | £34.98 |
| Oct 4th | £12.72 | £33.92 |
| Oct 11th | £11.66 | £32.86 |
| Oct 18th | £10.60 | £31.80 |
| Oct 25th | £9.54 | £30.74 |
| Nov 1st | £8.48 | £29.68 |
| Nov 8th | £7.42 | £28.62 |
| Nov 15th | £6.36 | £27.56 |
| Nov 22nd | £5.30 | £26.50 |
| Nov 29th | £4.24 | £25.44 |
| Dec 5th | £3.18 | £24.38 |
| Dec 12th | £2.12 | £23.32 |
| Dec 19th | £1.06 | £22.26 |
| Jan 3rd | n/a | £21.20 |
| Jan 10th | n/a | £20.14 |
| Jan 17th | n/a | £19.08 |
| Jan 24th | n/a | £18.02 |
| Jan 31st | n/a | £16.96 |
| Feb 7th | n/a | £15.90 |
| Feb 14th | n/a | £14.84 |
| Feb 21st | n/a | £13.78 |
| Feb 28th | n/a | £12.72 |
| Mar 7th | n/a | £11.66 |
| Mar 14th | n/a | £10.60 |
| Mar 21st | n/a | £9.54 |
| Mar 28th | n/a | £8.48 |
| April 4th | n/a | £7.42 |
| April 11th | n/a | £6.36 |
| April 18th | n/a | £5.30 |
| April 25th | n/a | £4.24 |
| May 2nd | n/a | £3.18 |
| May 9th | n/a | £2.12 |
| End of season issue | | £1.06 |

TO ORDER
Simply send your:
Name, Address, Tel. No.,
When you want your subscription to start and whether it is Until Christmas or until the End of the season

Please send cheque or postal order payable to Non-League Newsdesk

590

# COMPLETE MUSIC
# HELLENIC FOOTBALL LEAGUE

## FEEDER TO: DR MARTENS LEAGUE

**President:** Norman Matthews    **Chairman:** Michael Broadley
**General Secretary:** Brian King, 83 Queens Road, Carterton, Oxon OX18 3YF
Tel/Fax: 01993 212738

Four Representative football matches were arranged for the season, but the return fixture from season 1997-98 against the Combined Counties Football League due to be played at Highworth Town FC was postponed due to a waterlogged pitch and a suitable subsequent date was not available. Matches were played against the Dr Martens Southern Football League (0-3 defeat at Paget Rangers), the Chiltonian Football League (0-0 at Sandhurst Town FC) and the North Berks Football League (4-2 win at Wantage Town FC). Once again it was a very good record on the part of manager Mick Woolford, who put together a good squad for each fixture and should be congratulated on his efforts on behalf of the league.

The Premier Division Championship was won by Burnham FC, improving on the previous season's third place. The champions secured the title in their final match of the season after an entertaining final two weeks, which saw Carterton Town as runners up attain their highest ever position in the Premier Division. Both clubs displayed a terrific level of consistency with Burnham losing only four league games, in fact their record after ten games read Won five, Drew one, Lost four, and the next 26 league games saw Burnham win 21 and draw five to shade the championship from Carterton Town by three points. Carterton's record saw them suffer one defeat more than the champions. Highworth Town secured third place some fifteen points behind the champions, but Highworth Town were leading goalscorers with 92 goals (2.56 per game), closely followed by Burnham with 88 (2.44 per game) with Carterton scoring 82 (2.28). Unfortunately neither club was able to be promoted through the pyramid to the Dr Martens Southern Football League due to ground grading requirements.

The Division One title was won by Pegasus Juniors FC, who displayed a tremendous level of consistency throughout the season losing only three of their 32 league fixtures and scoring some 96 goals at an average of three per game.

Success in national cup competitions was somewhat disappointing, with the odd exception. Burnham FC succumbed at the first time of asking in the FA Cup Preliminary Round at the hands of Harpenden Town whose next opponents were Banbury United. Four member clubs competed in the First Qualifying Round with Banbury United emerging victorious, whilst the interest of Didcot Town, EFC Cheltenham and Tuffley Rovers was ended. Banbury United faced Epsom & Ewell in the Second Qualifying Round, and after a home 2-2 draw Banbury emerged victorious in the replay 1-0. On to the Third Qualifying Round and a home tie against the mighty Enfield on 17 October. A crowd of 1028 saw the culmination of Banbury United's interest with a 0-4 defeat, a good cup run which will result in a significant cash sum from FA sponsorship. The FA Vase saw eighteen member clubs entered, and defeats in the Qualifying Rounds for several Hellenic teams occurred, while six clubs featured in the First Round Proper, with Bicester Town, Fairford Town and North Leigh progressing to the Second Round where they were joined by Swindon Supermarine, exempt until that stage. Bicester Town after a valiant effort went out to Thame United after extra time. Swindon Supermarine visited Wiltshire rivals Bemerton Heath and were shown no charity and went out 3-0. These defeats ended the Hellenic League interest in national competitions.

Once again success was gained in the County Cup competitions with Hellenic League clubs fairing very well. Pegasus Juniors FC won the Herefordshire Senior Cup defeating Ross Town FC in an all Hellenic League final. Fairford Town FC secured the Gloucestershire Trophy, with Wootton Bassett Town FC winning the Wiltshire Senior Cup. The Wiltshire Premier Shield saw Swindon Supermarine FC in the final whilst Carterton Town FC were once again the 'bridesmaid' as finalists in the Oxfordshire Senior Cup. Congratulations to all clubs whatever the level of success that was attained during the season.

Season 1998-99 saw the second year of sponsorship from 'Complete Music' and I am pleased to report that agreement has been reached for a third season. Thanks are extended to Iain McNay and Martin Costello of 'Complete Music' for their company's interest and support of the Hellenic Football League. Another successful presentation evening was held at the Marriott Hotel in Swindon, but unfortunately some seventeen member clubs did not attend the function which is not considered to be very respectful to the League's sponsors. 1998-99 saw the adoption of 'Gilbert' footballs for use in all Hellenic League and Cup matches as part of a three year deal. Thanks are expressed to Tim Barnard for his involvement in putting this deal together.

Two meetings of the Southern Football League Joint Liaison Committee have been held during the season and were attended by Chairman Michael Broadley and General Secretary Brian King. This league has been to the fore front in attempting to develop a framework for regionalisation of 'pyramid football' below the Nationwide Conference on a stronger geographical base. The Hellenic Football league have met with representatives of our own Joint Liaison Committee on one occasion this season.

Brian King, General Secretary

# FINAL LEAGUE TABLES 1998-99

## PREMIER DIVISION

| | P | W | D | L | F | A | Pts |
|---|---|---|---|---|---|---|---|
| Burnham | 36 | 26 | 6 | 4 | 88 | 31 | 84 |
| Carterton Town | 36 | 25 | 6 | 5 | 82 | 34 | 81 |
| Highworth Town | 36 | 21 | 6 | 9 | 92 | 47 | 69 |
| Banbury United | 36 | 20 | 9 | 7 | 73 | 33 | 69 |
| North Leigh | 36 | 18 | 11 | 7 | 77 | 44 | 65 |
| Endsleigh | 36 | 17 | 5 | 14 | 60 | 36 | 56 |
| Abingdon United | 36 | 17 | 5 | 14 | 61 | 55 | 56 |
| Tuffley Rovers | 36 | 16 | 6 | 14 | 63 | 55 | 54 |
| Didcot Town | 36 | 16 | 5 | 15 | 58 | 52 | 53 |
| Bicester Town | 36 | 15 | 8 | 13 | 58 | 60 | 53 |
| Cirencester Academy | 36 | 12 | 11 | 13 | 42 | 56 | 47 |
| Hallen | 36 | 10 | 14 | 12 | 45 | 48 | 44 |
| Fairford Town | 36 | 10 | 10 | 16 | 42 | 50 | 40 |
| Swindon Supermarine | 36 | 10 | 9 | 17 | 41 | 59 | 39 |
| Shortwood United | 36 | 9 | 11 | 16 | 37 | 61 | 38 |
| Almondsbury Town | 36 | 8 | 7 | 21 | 47 | 82 | 31 |
| Wantage Town | 36 | 8 | 5 | 23 | 36 | 90 | 29 |
| Kintbury Rangers* | 36 | 8 | 8 | 20 | 48 | 89 | 26 |
| Harrow Hill | 36 | 4 | 2 | 30 | 31 | 99 | 14 |

## DIVISION ONE

| | | | | | | |
|---|---|---|---|---|---|---|
| Pegasus Juniors | 32 | 22 | 7 | 3 | 96 | 47 | 73 |
| Ardley United | 32 | 19 | 5 | 8 | 66 | 46 | 62 |
| Forest Green Rvrs Rs. | 32 | 18 | 6 | 8 | 71 | 40 | 60 |
| Milton United | 32 | 18 | 6 | 8 | 62 | 45 | 60 |
| Wootton Bassett Town | 32 | 17 | 7 | 8 | 64 | 43 | 58 |
| Ross Town | 32 | 15 | 7 | 10 | 57 | 41 | 52 |
| Letcombe | 32 | 13 | 9 | 10 | 56 | 47 | 48 |
| Cheltenham Saracens | 32 | 13 | 5 | 14 | 56 | 61 | 44 |
| Worcester College OB | 32 | 11 | 5 | 16 | 42 | 59 | 38 |
| Kidlington | 32 | 10 | 8 | 14 | 51 | 74 | 38 |
| Purton | 32 | 9 | 9 | 14 | 41 | 62 | 36 |
| Bishops Cleeve | 32 | 9 | 7 | 16 | 55 | 66 | 34 |
| Easington Sports | 32 | 8 | 8 | 16 | 47 | 56 | 32 |
| Cirencester United | 32 | 8 | 7 | 17 | 49 | 55 | 31 |
| Clanfield | 32 | 9 | 4 | 19 | 40 | 71 | 31 |
| Watlington Town | 32 | 7 | 9 | 16 | 49 | 69 | 30 |
| Headington Amateurs | 32 | 6 | 11 | 15 | 44 | 64 | 29 |

*points deducted

## PREMIER DIVISION RESULTS CHART 1998-99

| | | 1 | 2 | 3 | 4 | 5 | 6 | 7 | 8 | 9 | 10 | 11 | 12 | 13 | 14 | 15 | 16 | 17 | 18 | 19 |
|---|---|---|---|---|---|---|---|---|---|---|---|---|---|---|---|---|---|---|---|---|
| 1 | Abingdon Utd | X | 5-0 | 1-2 | 2-1 | 2-2 | 1-5 | 0-2 | 0-1 | 1-2 | 2-1 | 1-0 | 2-1 | 2-3 | 4-2 | 1-3 | 3-0 | 0-2 | 1-0 | 0-0 |
| 2 | Almondsbury T | 0-0 | X | 1-0 | 4-4 | 0-2 | 1-5 | 4-2 | 0-0 | 5-5 | 3-0 | 1-1 | 4-0 | 2-1 | 1-2 | 0-4 | 2-2 | 1-2 | 2-5 | 3-1 |
| 3 | Banbury Utd | 4-0 | 4-0 | X | 3-2 | 2-4 | 1-0 | 2-0 | 1-0 | 2-1 | 0-2 | 1-1 | 2-0 | 3-0 | 6-0 | 2-2 | 1-1 | 1-1 | 5-1 | 1-5 |
| 4 | Bicester Town | 1-2 | 3-1 | 1-1 | X | 2-4 | 0-3 | 3-2 | 0-2 | 1-0 | 1-2 | 1-1 | 2-1 | 3-1 | 2-0 | 0-3 | 0-0 | 1-1 | 5-1 | 2-1 |
| 5 | Burnham | 4-2 | 2-1 | 2-0 | 3-1 | X | 2-0 | 3-0 | 2-0 | 2-3 | 2-0 | 2-1 | 5-0 | 1-0 | 5-2 | 2-2 | 4-1 | 4-0 | 2-0 | 4-0 |
| 6 | Carterton T | 3-0 | 4-2 | 0-0 | 1-2 | 1-1 | X | 3-0 | 3-0 | 2-2 | 3-1 | 2-1 | 3-1 | 2-2 | 2-1 | 2-1 | 2-0 | 3-0 | 2-1 | 6-1 |
| 7 | Cirencester Acad | 1-0 | 1-1 | 2-2 | 0-0 | 1-2 | 1-2 | X | 1-5 | 3-1 | 0-3 | 1-0 | 3-2 | 0-3 | 0-0 | 1-1 | 0-0 | 1-0 | 2-2 | 0-0 |
| 8 | Didcot Town | 0-4 | 3-0 | 0-4 | 1-2 | 0-3 | 0-2 | 4-0 | X | 1-3 | 1-1 | 3-0 | 3-1 | 1-2 | 4-0 | 1-1 | 2-0 | 3-0 | 1-5 | 8-2 |
| 9 | EFC Cheltenham | 1-2 | 2-0 | 0-1 | 1-2 | 0-1 | 2-1 | 1-0 | 2-0 | X | 2-1 | Aw | 3-1 | 3-1 | 3-1 | 3-0 | Aw | 1-0 | 0-1 | Aw |
| 10 | Fairford Town | 1-1 | 2-0 | 0-1 | 0-2 | 1-5 | 0-1 | 0-2 | 2-2 | 1-3 | X | 0-2 | 1-1 | 1-0 | 2-0 | 0-0 | 2-1 | 0-1 | 0-1 | 2-0 |
| 11 | Hallen | 1-1 | 2-0 | 1-1 | 6-2 | 1-1 | 3-3 | 1-1 | 1-0 | 0-0 | 0-0 | X | 3-0 | 2-4 | 1-3 | 3-1 | 1-2 | 0-0 | 1-1 | 1-0 |
| 12 | Harrow Hill | 0-3 | 1-3 | 0-4 | 0-2 | 0-2 | 0-3 | 1-2 | 0-1 | 0-7 | 3-3 | 0-4 | X | 1-3 | 3-4 | 2-3 | 0-1 | 1-0 | 3-1 | 4-0 |
| 13 | Highworth Tn | 4-1 | 3-1 | 2-1 | 4-1 | 1-1 | 1-1 | 4-1 | 2-3 | 1-0 | 2-1 | 5-0 | 6-0 | X | 6-1 | 1-1 | 6-1 | 1-1 | 0-2 | 8-2 |
| 14 | Kintbury Rngrs | 2-6 | 0-1 | 2-2 | 1-1 | 2-1 | 0-2 | 1-1 | 1-1 | 0-3 | 2-5 | 3-0 | 1-2 | 0-2 | X | 0-4 | 1-2 | 3-3 | 1-5 | 3-1 |
| 15 | North Leigh | 2-3 | 2-0 | 0-2 | 2-2 | 2-1 | 2-0 | 2-3 | 2-0 | 2-1 | 2-2 | 2-3 | 6-0 | 1-0 | 1-1 | X | 2-0 | 3-1 | 4-1 | 5-0 |
| 16 | Shortwood Utd | 0-4 | 1-0 | 0-1 | 0-1 | 1-1 | 1-3 | 0-1 | 2-0 | 1-1 | 2-2 | 1-1 | 2-0 | 2-2 | 3-5 | 3-3 | X | 1-2 | 0-1 | 1-1 |
| 17 | Sw. Supermarine | 0-2 | 4-1 | 2-1 | 0-2 | 0-3 | 1-2 | 0-0 | 2-3 | 1-1 | 0-2 | 0-0 | 2-1 | 2-5 | 2-0 | 1-1 | 1-2 | X | 3-1 | 4-1 |
| 18 | Tuffley Rovers | 4-0 | 2-0 | 1-3 | 4-2 | 2-1 | 0-1 | 3-4 | 1-2 | 1-0 | 1-0 | 2-1 | 2-1 | 1-3 | 2-2 | 1-2 | 3-0 | 2-2 | X | 1-1 |
| 19 | Wantage Tn | 0-2 | 4-2 | 3-2 | 2-1 | 0-2 | 2-3 | 0-3 | 0-2 | 0-3 | 1-1 | 3-1 | 3-0 | 1-3 | 0-1 | 1-3 | 2-3 | 1-0 | 2-1 | X |

## LEADING GOALSCORERS 1998-99

### PREMIER DIVISION

| | | |
|---|---|---|
| 30 | Philip Rodney | Carterton Town |
| 28 | Graham Sunners | Highworth Town |
| 27 | Justin Miller | Highworth Town |
| 26 | Marcus Richardson | Burnham |
| 18 | Chris Panter | North Leigh |
| 16 | Steven Bunce | Burnham |
| | Andrew Brown | Abingdon Utd |
| | Peter Hutter | North Leigh |
| 15 | Nathan Holt | Highworth Town |
| 14 | Andrew Marriott | Didcot Town |
| | Michael Tomlinson | Burnham |

### DIVISION ONE

| | | |
|---|---|---|
| 36 | Mark Davis | Pegasus Juniors |
| 29 | Craig Cole | Forest Green Rovers |
| 20 | Roy Jordan | Pegasus Juniors |
| 16 | Steven Tucker | Purton |
| | Daryl Addis | Ross Town |
| 14 | Guy Brain | Ross Town |
| | Kacey Johnstone | Bishops Cleeve |
| | Ben Spiero | Letcombe |
| | Nigel Mott | Milton United |
| | Lee Stoddart | Wootton Bassett Town |

# CHERRY RED RECORDS CUP 1998-99

**FIRST ROUND**

| | | | | | | | |
|---|---|---|---|---|---|---|---|
| Watlington Town | v | Purton | 0-2 | Didcot Town | v | Cirencester United | 8-0 |
| Letcombe | v | Forest Green Rvrs Rs | 2-4 | Headington Amat. | v | Cirencester Acad | 0-2 |

**SECOND ROUND**

| | | | | | | | |
|---|---|---|---|---|---|---|---|
| Banbury United | v | Harrow Hill | 2-0 | Kintbury Rangers | v | Hallen | 1*3 |
| Wootton Bassett T | v | Forest Green Rvrs Rs | 3*4 | Burnham | v | Pegasus Juniors | 2-0 |
| Swindon Supermarine | v | Purton | 3-1 | Milton United | v | EFC Cheltenham | 0-2 |
| Cirencester Academy | v | Ross Town | 3-1 | Easington Sports | v | Shortwood United | 1-0 |
| Tuffley Rovers | v | Cheltenham Saracens | 2-0 | Ardley United | v | Didcot Town | 2-0 |
| Worcester College OB | v | Carterton Town | 2-6 | Fairford Town | v | Clanfield | 3-1 |
| Kidlington | v | Bishops Cleeve | 0-2 | Abingdon United | v | Wantage Town | 1-0 |
| North Leigh | v | Highworth Town | 4-3 | Bicester Town | v | Almondsbury Town | 2-0 |

**THIRD ROUND**

| | | | | | | | |
|---|---|---|---|---|---|---|---|
| Burnham | v | Tuffley Rovers | 3-1 | Carterton Town | v | Bicester Town | 2-4 |
| Forest Green Rvrs Rs | v | Ardley United | 1-2 | Hallen | v | Bishops Cleeve | 3-2 |
| Fairford Town | v | Abingdon United | 1-0 | Easington Sports | v | Swindon S'marine | 0-2 |
| EFC Cheltenham | v | North Leigh | 2*3 | Cirencester Acad | v | Banbury United | 0-1 |

**FOURTH ROUND**

| | | | | | | | |
|---|---|---|---|---|---|---|---|
| Ardley United | v | Fairford Town | 4-2 | Banbury United | v | Hallen | 5-1 |
| Burnham | v | Bicester Town | 6-0 | Swindon S'marine | v | North Leigh | 0-1 |

**SEMI-FINALS**

| | | | | | | | |
|---|---|---|---|---|---|---|---|
| Ardley United | v | North Leigh | 0-4, 1-1 | Banbury United | v | Burnham | 1-2, 1-2 |

**FINAL**

| | | | |
|---|---|---|---|
| Burnham | v | North Leigh | 2-0 |

## RED OAK PRESS SUPPLEMENTARY CUP 1998-99

**FIRST ROUND**

| | | | | | | | |
|---|---|---|---|---|---|---|---|
| Kidlington | v | Wootton Bassett Tn | 1-4 | Almondsbury Town | v | Letcombe | 2-1 |
| Kintbury Rangers | v | Harrow Hill | 3-2 | Shortwood United | v | Milton United | 5-4 |

**SECOND ROUND**

| | | | | | | | |
|---|---|---|---|---|---|---|---|
| Cheltenham Saracens | v | Clanfield | 4-4 ab, 2-0 | Cirencester United | v | Highworth Town | 1-7 |
| Wantage Town | v | Worcester College OB | 3-2 | Ross Town | v | Wootton Bassett Tn | 5-1 |
| Pegasus Juniors | v | Almondsbury Town | 3-0 | Kintbury Rangers | v | Headington Amat | 4-2 |
| Shortwood United | v | Purton | 3-1 | Didcot Town | v | Watlington Town | 3-1 |

**THIRD ROUND**

| | | | | | | | |
|---|---|---|---|---|---|---|---|
| Didcot Town | v | Kintbury Rangers | 4-1 | Shortwood United | v | Ross Town | 3-0 |
| Highworth Town | v | Cheltenham Saracens | 3-1 | Wantage Town | v | Pegasus Juniors | 1-5 |

**SEMI-FINALS**

| | | | | | | | |
|---|---|---|---|---|---|---|---|
| Didcot Town | v | Highworth Town | 0-0, 0-1 | Pegasus Juniors | v | Shortwood Utd | 2-1, 0-2 |

**FINAL**

| | | | |
|---|---|---|---|
| Highworth Town | v | Shortwood United | 2-0 |

## NORMAN MATTHEWS FLOODLIGHT CUP 1998-99

**FIRST ROUND**

| | | | | | | | |
|---|---|---|---|---|---|---|---|
| Wantage Town | v | Burnham | 1-3 | Carterton Town | v | Bicester Town | 4-2 |
| Shortwood United | v | Almondsbury Town | 5-1 | Cirencester Acad | v | EFC Cheltenham | 3-2 |
| Didcot Town | v | Abingdon United | 1-0 | | | | |

**SECOND ROUND**

| | | | | | | | |
|---|---|---|---|---|---|---|---|
| Swindon Supermarine | v | Kintbury Rangers | 1-0 | Forest Green Rvrs R | v | Cirencester Acad | 1-0 |
| Didcot Town | v | Carterton Town | 2-4 | Banbury United | v | Burnham | 1-0 |
| Harrow Hill | v | Hallen | 2-3 | Ross Town | v | Shortwood United | 1-2 |
| Highworth Town | v | North Leigh | 1-2 | Fairford Town | v | Tuffley Rovers | 1-2 |

**THIRD ROUND**

| | | | | | | | |
|---|---|---|---|---|---|---|---|
| Forest Green Rvrs Rs | v | Shortwood United | 2-3 | North Leigh | v | Swindon S'marine | 2-5 |
| Tuffley Rovers | v | Hallen | 5*2 | Banbury United | v | Carterton Town | 0-1 |

**SEMI-FINALS**

| | | | | | | | |
|---|---|---|---|---|---|---|---|
| Carterton Town | v | Swindon S. | 2-0, 0-1 | Shortwood United | v | Tuffley Rovers | 0-4, 1-6 |

**FINAL**

| | | | |
|---|---|---|---|
| Carterton Town | v | Tuffley Rovers | 1-4 |

# ABINGDON UNITED

**Secretary:** Terry Hutchinson, 41 Austin Place, Dunmore Farm Estate, Abingdon,Oxon OX14 1LT
Tel: 01235 559019

**Ground:** Northcourt Road, Abingdon OX14 1PL Tel: 01235 203203
Capacity: 2,000     Seats: 52          Cover: 120          Floodlights: Yes

**Directions:** From north (Oxford) leave A34 at Abingdon north sign and Northcourt Rd is 1st major turning after r'bout. From South, East or West leave Abingdonon A4183 and turn left into Northcourt Rd after 1 mile. 2 miles from Redley (BR)
**Clubhouse:** Two bars, food available. Open normal pub hours every day

| | |
|---|---|
| HONOURS | N Berks Lg 53-54 (Lg Cup R-up 53-54), Charity Shield 52-53; Hellenic Lge - Prem Div R-up 96-97, Div 1 R-up 76-77 81-82, Res. Div 97-98, F/Lit Cup 96-97, Lg Cup R-up 89-90, Div 1 Cup 65-66 81-82 R-up 66-67, Reserve Cup 98-99 R-up 93-94; Berks & Bucks Senior Cup R-up 83-84, Senior Trophy 97-98 R-up 93-94 96-97 |
| PREVIOUS | League: North Berks <br> Grounds: None |
| RECORD | Gate: 1,500 v Oxford Utd 1994 <br> Appearances: D Webb |

**FACT FILE**

Founded: 1946
Nickname: The U's
Colours: All yellow
Change colours: All blue
Midweek matchday: Tuesday
Reserves' Lge: Hellenic Res section
Programme: 30p
Editor: W Fletcher, ACJI (01235 20255)

**CLUB PERSONNEL**
Chairman: Pat Evans
General manager: John Blackmore

Manager: R Hayward
Coach: S Morton
Physio: G Corcoran
Press Officer: W Fletcher (01235 203203)

# ALMONDSBURY TOWN

**Secretary:** Roger Perry, 61 Brookbridge House, Standfast Road, Henbury, Bristol BS10 7HW
Tel No: 0117 9590309

**Ground:** Oakland Park, Almondsbury, Bristol Tel: 01454 612220

**Directions:** Adjacent to M5 junction 16 - follow A38 Thornbury - ground firstleft. 4 miles from Bristol Parkway (BR). County bus services to Thornbury,Stroud and Gloucester
Capacity: 2,000     Seats: None          Cover: No          Floodlights: Yes
**Clubhouse:** 7 days, all sports, refreshments, function room, entertainment,skittles

| | |
|---|---|
| HONOURS | Glos Co. Lg(4) 76-78 79-81 (R-up 75-7681-82), GFA Chal. Tphy 78-79 (R-up 80-81), Avon Prem. Comb. 74-75, Glos SnrAmtr Cup 87-88, Hellenic Lg 83-84 (R-up 82-83, Lg Cup(2) 83-85) |
| PREVIOUS | Leagues: Bristol Weslyan; Bristol Suburban; Bristol Premier Comb.; GlosCo <br> Ground: Almondsbury Rec. (until 1986) |
| BEST SEASON | FA Vase:R-up 78-79, SF 77-78 |
| RECORD | Gate: Hellenic Cup Final replay 89-90 |

**FACT FILE**

Founded: 1897
Nickname: Almonds
Colours: Sky/navy/navy
Change colours: All yellow
Midweek Matchday: Tuesday
Programme: 20 pages 25p

**CLUB PERSONNEL**

Chairman: F David Pick
President: Peter Howarth
Manager: Nick Tanner
Coach: Nigel Hawkins
Physio: Steve Watkins

# BANBURY UNITED

**Secretary:** B Worsley, c/o Sol Systems, Unit 4 Mallorie Hse, Beaumont Rd,Banbury, OX16 7RH
Tel: 01295 265638 (H), 01295 255536 (B)
**Ground:** The Stadium, off Station Rd, Banbury, Oxon (01295 263354)
**Directions:** M40 jct 11, follow signs for Banbury then BR station, turn right down narrow lane before entering station forecourt; eastern end of town
Capacity: 6,500     Seats: 50          Cover: 500          Floodlights: Yes     Club Shop: Yes
**Clubhouse:** Match days & week-ends. Mid-week on hire. Hot food available during after matches

| | |
|---|---|
| HONOURS | Oxon Snr Cup 78-79 87-88 (R-up 6); Birmingham Comb. R-up 47-48; Oxon Prof. Cup 52-53(jt) 70-71(jt) 72-73 77-78 79-80(jt); Hellenic Lg.Cup R-Up 91-92; Birmingham Snr Cup R-Up 48-49 59-60 (S.F.46-47); Oxon Snr Lg. 34-35 39-4047-48 (res); Oxon Hosp. Cup 46-47 (R-up 45-46); Oxon Benev. Cup R-up 77-78 80-8182-83; Daventry Charity Cup 88-90; Smiths Mem. Cup 68-70 (R-up 66-68); Hitchin Centenary Cup 68-69 (R-up 67-68); Leamington Charity Cup 51-52; Warks Comb. R-up 57-58 60-61, Presidents Cup R-up 60-61; Midland Floodlit Cup 67-68; Wallspan Comb. 85-86 |
| PREVIOUS | Leagues: Banbury Jnr 33-34; Oxon Snr 34-35; Birmingham Comb. 35-54; W.Mids 54-66; Southern 66-90          **Name:** Banbury Spencer |
| BEST SEASON | FA Cup: 1st Rd replay 73-74 (Also 1st Rd 47-48 61-62 72-73) <br> FA Trophy: 3rd Rd 70-71 73-74 |
| RECORD | Attendance: 7,160 v Oxford City, FA Cup 3rd Qual.Rd, 30/10/48 |

**FACT FILE**
Founded: 1933     Reformed: 1965
Nickname: Puritans
Club Sponsors: T.B.A.
Colours: Red & gold/red/red
Change colours: White & blue/white/white
Midweek matches: Tuesday
Reserves' Lge: Hellenic Res. section
Programme : 24 pages 60p
Editor: Kevin Hicklin
98-99 Captain: Jon Corbett
P.o.Y.: Ian Bowyer
Top Scorer: Jody McKay (19)
**CLUB PERSONNEL**
Chairman: Paul Saunders
Vice Chairman: Brian Kay
President: David Jesson
Commercial Mgr: Nigel Porter
Press Officer: Barry Worsley
Gen Man: Phil Lines Manager: Kevin Brock
Coach: Brian Robinson
Physio: John Source

# BICESTER TOWN

**Secretary:** Phil Allen, 38 Bassett Avenue, Bicester OX6 7TZ
Tel: 01869 252125 (H)  01869 325922 (B)  01869 369026 (F)

**Ground:** Sports Ground, Oxford Rd, Bicester      Tel: 01869 241036
Capacity:      Seats: 250      Cover: 550      Floodlights: Yes

**Directions:**      From Oxford; past Tescos on outskirts of Bicester - ground on right
From Aylesbury; turn left at first island on outskirts of Bicester ontobypass,
right at next island, pass Tescos & ground on right

**Clubhouse:** One bar

**HONOURS**      Hellenic Lg 60-1 77-78 (Lg Cup 90-91 (R-up 92-93), Div 1 76-77)

**PREVIOUS**      **League:** Oxon Senior
**Name:** Slade Banbury Road (pre-1923)

**RECORD**      **Attendance:** 955 v Portsmouth, floodlight inauguration 1/2/94

### FACT FILE

Founded: 1876
Nickname: Foxhunters
Colours: Red & black/black/black
Change: Green & yellow/green/green
Midweek Matchday: Tuesday
Reserves' league: Hellenic Lge Res. Div.
Programme: With entry
Editor: Secretary

### CLUB PERSONNEL

Chairman: Bill Hammond
Vice Chairman: Ray Honour
President: Michael Kinane
Press Officer: Phil Allen (01869 252125)
Manager/Coach: Barry Grant
Coach: Barry Grant
Physio: Ray Huntley

---

# BRACKLEY TOWN

**Secretary/Press Officer:** Pat Ashby, 7 Riverside, Banbury, Oxon. OX16 8TU
Tel: 01327 262955

**Ground:** St James Park, Churchill Way, Brackley, Northants NN13 7EJ      Tel: 01280 704077

**Directions:**      Churchill Way, east off A43, south end of town
Capacity: 3,500      Cover: 150      Seats: 300      Floodlights: Yes

**Clubhouse:**      Fully licensed. Lounge & main hall. Food available. Open all week.
**Club Shop:** None
**PREVIOUS**      **Leagues:** Banbury & District; North Bucks; Hellenic 77-83; United Counties
83-94; Hellenic 94-97      **Names:** None
**Ground:** Banbury Road, Manor Road, Buckingham Road (up to 1974)
**CLUB RECORDS  Attendance:** 600 v Kettering, Northants Senior Cup 1989
**Fee Received:** £2,000 for Phil Mason from Oxford City 98

**BEST SEASON**      **FA Trophy:** 1st Qual Rd 97-98
**FA Cup:** 2nd Qual Rd 97-98      League clubs defeated: None

**HONOURS**      United Counties R-up 88-89 (Div 1 83-84); Northants Snr Cup R-up 88-89;
Buckingham Charity Cup (3); Hellenic Lg Prem 96-97, Div 1 Cup 82-83.

### FACT FILE

Formed: 1890
Nickname: Saints
Colours: Red & white/black/white
Change colours: Yellow/blue/white
Midweek home matchday: Tuesday
Programme: Pages:      Price: £1
Editor: Geoff Lines Tel: 01295 261017
Local Press: Brackley Advertiser,
Banbury Guardian, Herald & Post
Milton Keynes Citizen.
Local Radio: Fox FM

### CLUB PERSONNEL

Chairman: Mike Bosher
President: Clive Lomax
Press Officer: Secretary
Manager: Terry Muckleberg

---

# CARTERTON TOWN

**Secretary:**      Gordon Maxwell, 14 Humphries Closer,Oxon OX18 3HS
(Acting)      Tel & Fax: 01993 212803

**Ground:**      Kilkenny Lane, Carterton, Oxfordshire (01993 842410)

**Directions:**      Enter Swinbrook Rd which off the Burford-Carterton road, proceedinto Kilkenny
Lane (one track road), ground car park 200yds on left beforesharp corner.
Hourly buses to Carterton from Oxford
Capacity:      1,500      Seats: 50      Cover: 100      Floodlights: Yes
**Clubhouse:**      Lounge & fully licensed bar open every day 7.30-11pm, Sat & Sun noon-2pm,
Sat 4-6pm. Snacks & meals available

**HONOURS**      Oxon Junior Shield 85-86; Oxon Snr Cup R-up 90-91 96-97  98-99 Witney &
Dist.Lg 65-66 (Div 1 84-85 76-77); Hellenic Lg Div 1 89-90 93-94 (Reserve Div
1989-90 (R-up 93-94)); Oxon Intermediate Cup R-up 93-94(res.)

**PREVIOUS**      Leagues: Witney & District

**RECORD**      **Gate:** 600 v Oxford Utd, Oxon Snr Cup 93-94
**Goalscorer:** Phil Rodney

### FACT FILE

Founded: 1922
Reformed: 1946/1983
Colours: Black & white/black/black
Change colours: Yellow/blue
Midweek matches: Tuesday
Programme: 20 pages with admission
Editor: Jenny Maxwell (01993 212803)

### CLUB PERSONNEL

President: G Fox
Chairman: G Maxwell
Match Secretary: Glyn Yates

Manager: Derek Beasley
Physio: Andy Slater
Coach: Phil Rodney

ALMONDSBURY TOWN: Back Row (L-R): Simon Panes (joint manager), Danny Slee, Mark Shore, Chris Mitchell, Rich Martin, Matt Snell, Rob Clarke, Nick Scarrett, Steve Rice, Jamie Dutton, Stuart Evans (Under 18 coach). Front Row: Tom Blyth, Andy Vining, Mark

BANBURY UNITED: Back Row (L-R): Vinnie Halsall (coach), Cliff Cousins, Rhydian Purnell, Andrew Parrott, Mike Kearns, Chris Jackson, Jody McKay, Ian Bowyer, Brian Robinson (Asst mngr). Front Row: Steve Jenkins, Karlton Stratford, Terry Muckleberg, Jon Corbett, Darren Reynolds, Kevin Brook, Les Phillips. Photo: Gordon Whittington

NORTH LEIGH                                                        Photo: Gordon Whittington

# CIRENCESTER FOOTBALL ACADEMY

**FACT FILE**

**Secretary:** Phil Corcoran, 8 Garfield Close, Eldene, Swindon, Wilts. SN3 6BZ.
Tel: 01793 611881 (H) 01793 438012 (B) 01285 643938 (F)

**Ground:** Tetbury Road, Cirencester Tel: 01285 654783

**Directions:** From A419 head towards Cirencester town centre (follow signs for Cirencester Hospital). Turn left at Hospital roundabout, and the ground entrance is on the left at the next roundabout.

**RECORD** **Attendance:** 95 v Cirencester United 1984

1998-99 Top Goalscorer: Jonathon Slattery (10)

Founded:
Nickname: Academy
Colours: Green & white/white/white
Change colours: Red & black/black/black
Midweek Matchday: Wednesday

**CLUB PERSONNEL**

Chairman: Tony Bedwell
Tel: 01793 876101
Press Officer: Kirstine Fraser
Tel: 01793 823046
Manager: Pat Slattery
Coach: John Freeth
Physio: Steve Slattery

# DIDCOT TOWN

**FACT FILE**

**Secretary:** Chris Thomas, 48 Slade Road, Diudcot, Oxfordshire OX11 7AT (01235 811124)

**Ground:** Loop Meadow Stadium
Capacity: 5,000    Seats: 250    Cover: 500    Floodlights: Yes

**Directions:** From Town Centre: Take station road (old ground) and turn right under bridge just before station into Cow Lane. Left by Ladygrove Pub into Tamar Way. Then first left at roundabout. From A34: leave at Milton interchange and take Didcot road for approximately one mile. At roundabout take perimeter road Cross three more roundabouts and turn right at third into Avon Way

**Clubhouse:** Every evening and 12 noon to close at weekends and national holidys.

**HONOURS** Hellenic Lg 53-54,Lg Cup 1965-66 66-67 92-9397-98 Div 1 76-77,Div1 Cup 76-7

**PREVIOUS** **Leagues:** Hellenic 53-54; Metropolitan League 57-63
**RECORD** **Attendance:** 550 v Wycombe Wanderers, 1956 (old ground)

Founded: 1907
Nickname: Railwaymen
Colours: All red & white
Change colours: Blue & yellow stripes
Midweek Matchday: Tuesday
Programme: 50p
Editor:Jon Gardner

**CLUB PERSONNEL**

President:
Chairman: John Bailey
Manager: Bob Pratley
Coach: Phil Caulfield
Physio: Mark Roberts

# FAIRFORD TOWN

**FACT FILE**

**Secretary:** William Beach, 33 Park Cross, Fairford, GL7 4LF Tel: 01285 712136 (H)

**Ground:** Cinder Lane, London Road, Fairford, Cirencester Tel: 01285 712071

**Directions:** Entering Fairford on A417 from Lechlade turn left down Cinder Lane150yds after 40mph sign. From Cirencester on same road, follow thru village andturn right down Cinder Lane 400yds afterRailway Inn.
Buses from Swindon,Lechlade and Cirencester
Capacity: 2,000    Seats: 100    Cover: 150    Floodlights: Yes
**Clubhouse:** Open each evening, weekend lunches & before and after all games
**Club Shop:** No

**HONOURS** Glos Challenge Trophy 79-80 (R-up 82-83); Hellenic Lg R-up 78-79 79-8090-91 94-95, (Premier Div Cup 78-79, Div 1 71-72, Div 1 Cup 71-72); Glos Jnr Cup 62-63; Swindon & Dist Lg 64-65 68-69

**PREVIOUS** **Leagues:** Cirencester & District (pre-1946)/ Swindon & District 46-70
**Grounds:** None

**RECORD** **Attendance:** 1,500 v Swindon Town, friendly July 93
**Goalscorer:** Pat Toomey    **Win:** 9-0 v Moreton T    **Defeat:** 0-9 v Sharpness

Founded: 1891
Nickname: Town
Colours: Red/white/red
Change colours: White/blue/blue
Midweek matchday: Wednesday
Reserves' League: Hellenic Reserve section
Programme: 20 pages with admission
Editor/Press Officer: Chairman

**CLUB PERSONNEL**

Chairman: Michael B Tanner
Tel: 01285 713030
President: B W Wall
Manager: Denzil Brisland
Physio: Chris Tye

# HALLEN

**Secretary:** Jonathon Rogers, 114 Wellington Hill West, Westbury on Trym, Bristol BS9 4QY
Tel: 0117 985 6138 (H)  0117 900 1811 (B)

**Ground:** Hallen Playing Fields, Moorhouse Lane, Hallen, Nr Bristol  Tel: 0117 950 2265

**Directions:** M5 jct 17, A4018 to Henbury r'bout, right, right again at junction,next right to
Station Road, left into Avonmouth Road at r'bout. One mile toHallen, ground first
left, then right into lane to ground

**Capacity:** Unknown          Seats: No          Cover: No
**Clubhouse:** Yes

**HONOURS** Glos County Lg 92-93, Glos Snr Trophy 92-93

**PREVIOUS** **League:** Glos County (pre-1993)
**Names:** Lawrence Weston Athletic (80's), Lawrence Weston Hallen (pre-1991)
**Ground:** Kings Weston (early 1980's)

**RECORD** **Attendance:** 803 v Bristol Rovers 1997

### FACT FILE

Founded: 1949
Colours: Royal Bluek/black/black
Change Colours: Green& black/green/red
Midweek Matchday: Tuesday
Programme: No

### CLUB PERSONNEL

Chairman: Barry Phillips
Tel: 0117 950 1754
President: Ken Naish
Coach: D Bruno
Physio: Tammy Mullan

# HARROW HILL

**Secretary:** Geoff Tuffley, 10a Bilson, Cinderford GL14 2LJ
Tel: 01594 825655 (H)  01594 542421 (B) 07803 378317 (M)

**Match Sec:** Robert Partridge, 20 Littledean Hill Road, Cinderford GL14 2BE
Tel: 01594 825360 (H) 01594 542421 (B)

**Ground:** Larksfield Road, Harrow Hill          Tel: 01594 543873

**Directions:** Take A40 west out of Gloucester, follow A40 for 8 miles then takeA4136 to
Longhope, pass by on the outskirts of Michealdean, up steep hill(Plump Hill),
then second turn on the right signed Harrow Hill. At  phone box onthe left
turn right into Larksfield Road, ground on right at top of hill

**RECORD** **Attendance:** 350 v Cinderford Town 92
1998-99          Top Goalscorer: Carl Woodroffe (8)

### FACT FILE

Founded:
Nickname:  Harry Hill
Colours:  Claret & blue/sky/sky
Change Colours: Purple & green/black/black
Midweek Matchday: Tuesday

### CLUB PERSONNEL

Chairman:  Reg Taylor
President:  Ken Jones

Press Officer: Terry Lark
Tel: 01594 827305 & 827190

Manager: Chris Taylor
Coach:  Richard White
Physio:  Sylvia Durham

# HIGHWORTH TOWN

**Secretary:** Fraser Haines, 222 Windrush, Highworth, Swindon SN6 7EB (01793861109)

**Ground:** Elm Recreation Ground, Highworth. (01793 766263)

**Directions:** Enter on A361 from Swindon, past Simpsons Garage, straight overisland, next sharp
left into Green by Vet's Surgery - ground & car park 60ydson left next to Sports Hall

**Capacity:** 2,000     Seats: 50          Cover: 250          Floodlights: Yes     Club Shop: No

**Clubhouse:** Sat 12-2.30 & 4.30-11pm. Mon to Fri 7-11pm. Rolls & Hot food

**HONOURS** Wilts Snr Cup 63-64 72-73 95-96 97-98(R-up 88-89), Hellenic Div 1 Cup 88-
89,Arthur Shipway Cup 88-89 93-94, Swindon & District Lg 63-64 64-65 65-66 68-69 Hellenic
Supplementary Cup Winners: 98-99, Hellenic Reserve Division Two Winners 98-99

**PREVIOUS** **Leagues:** Wilts; Swindon & Dist

**RECORD** **Attendance:** 1,862 v QPR opening Floodlights
**Scorer:** Kevin Higgs     **Appearances:** Rod Haines
**Win:** 12-0 v Beeches, Arthur Shipway Cup 1992
**Defeat:** 2-8 v Milton United, Hellenic Lge Div. 1, 1987

### FACT FILE

Founded: 1894
Nickname: Worthians
Sponsors: One Stop
Colours: Red & black/black/red
Change colours: Blue/blue/white
Midweek matchday: Wednesday
Reserves Lge: Hellenic Reserve Div
Programme: 16 pages, 60p
Editor: Mike Markham (01793 763462)

### CLUB PERSONNEL

President: Alan Vockins
Chairman: Steven Leppard
Match Secretary: Dave Evans (01793 763548)
Press Officer: Mark Hobbs (01793 721779)
Manager: Gary Goodwin
Coach: Chris Seagraves
Physio: Steve Luker

# MILTON UNITED

**Secretary:** Sue Walker, 122 High Street, Sutton Courtney, Abingdon, OX14 4AX
Tel: 01235 847158 (H)

**Ground:** The Sportsfield, High Street, Milton, Abingdon, Oxon Tel: 01235 832999

**Directions:** Exit A34 at Milton, 10 miles south of Oxford & 12 miles north of Jt 13, M4. Take A4130 towards Wantage, after 100m take 1st left, then 1st right into Milton Hill. Entrance 200m on left.

**Capacity:** Seats: None     Cover: None     Floodlights: No     Club Shop: No
**Clubhouse:** On ground, open matchdays

**HONOURS** Hellenic Lg 90-91 (Div 1 89-90 R-Up.94-95)), Nth Berks Lg(4) 85-86 87-89(R-up 84-85 86-87, Lg Cup(3) 84-86 88-89, Div 2 80-81, Charity Shield(4) 84-86 87-89 (R-up 82-83), Nth Berks War Mem. Cup(3) 83-85 87-88, Berks & Bucks I'mediate Cup 90-91

**RECORD** **Attendance:** 500 v Almondsbury Picksons, Hellenic Lg 90-91
**Goalscorer:** Nigel Mott

### FACT FILE

Founded: 1926
Sponsors: Morlands Brewery
Colours: Sky & claret/claret/sky & claret
Change colours: All white
Midweek matchday: Tuesday
Reserves' League: Hellenic Lge Res sect
Programme Editor / Press Officer:
David Taylor (01235 816376)

### CLUB PERSONNEL

Chairman: Ken Tull
President: John Cannon
Match Secretary: Sid Tindall (01491 835630)
Manager: Keith Stopps
Coach: Paul Biddle    Physio: John Belcher

# NORTH LEIGH

**Secretary:** Peter J Dix, 8 Windmill Close, North Leigh, Nr Witney, Oxon OX8 6RP(01993 881199)

**Ground:** Eynsham Hall Park Sports Ground, North Leigh, nr Witney, Oxon (0993881427)

**Directions:** Ground is situated off A4095 Witney to Woodstock road 3 miles east of Witney. Entrance to ground is 300yds east of Main Park Entrance
**Capacity:** 2,000    Seats: 100    Cover: 200    Floodlights: Yes
**Club Shop:** No
**Clubhouse:** Bar open matches. Snacks available

**HONOURS** Hellenic Lg Div 1 R-up 92-93 (Reserves Cup 93-94), Oxon Jnr Shield 56-5783-84, Oxon Charity Cup 84-85 88-89, Witney & Dist. Lg(13) 50-57 84-90 LgCup(10) 47-48 51-52 53-55 56-57 81-82 85-89), Oxon Yth Cup 93-94 94-95, OxonYth u17 Lg & Cup 93-94. Oxford Sen. Cup R-Up 94-95. Marriott Cup 95-96Oxon Under 16 Youth Cup Winners 98-99, Allied Counties Under 18 Youth (West Div)Winners

**PREVIOUS** **Leagues:** Witney & District 08-89

**CLUB RECORDS** **Attendance:** 200 v Oxford United, Friendly August 1998
**Scorer:** P Coles     **Appearances:** P King

### FACT FILE

Founded: 1908
Nickname: None
Sponsors: Various
Colours: All black & blue
Change colours: All blue
Midweek matches: Wednesday
Programme: 20 pages, £1 with entry
Editor: J Fogg

### CLUB PERSONNEL

President: Mrs Christine Smith
Chairman: Peter King
Vice Chairman: B.Shepperd
Press Officer: Barry Norton (01993 881777)
Match Secretary: Reg Kilfoyle (01993 771852)
Manager: Mark Gee
Asst Manager: David Ebsworth
Physio: Roy Keen

# PEGASUS JUNIORS

**Secretary:** Brian James, 7 Loder Drive, Hereford HR1 1DS
Tel: 01432 274982 (H) 01568 612367 (B)

**Ground:** Essex Arms, Widemarsh St, Hereford.    Tel: 0860 558310

**Directions:** A49 Ross Road over Greyfriars Bridge, Victoria Street to end of Edgar Street, turn right, straight over mini-r/about, ground 50 yards on left
**Capacity:**     Seats: None    Cover: None    Floodlights: No
**Clubhouse:** 48 Stowens Street

**HONOURS** Herefordshire Snr Amtr Cup 71-72, Herefordshire Co. Chal. Cup(5) 81-8384-85 87-88 89-90 (R-up 93-94), Worcs Snr Urn 85-86, Hellenic Lg Div 1 84-85(R-up 93-94, Div 1 Cup R-up 93-94)

**PREVIOUS** **Leagues:** Leisure Centre

**RECORD** **Attendance:** 1,400 v Newport AFC 89-90

### FACT FILE

Founded: 1955
Colours: All red
Change colours: Blue & white/blue/blue
Midweek Matchday: Tuesday
Programme: 50p
Editor: Kevin Bishop (01432 353805)

### CLUB PERSONNEL

President: Mark Ellis
Chairman: Robert W Pasley
Press Officer: Kevin Bishop (01432 353805)
Manager: Mark Williams
Asst. Man.: Mick Williams
Physio: Dave Smith

# SHORTWOOD UNITED

**Secretary:** Mark Webb, 1 The Bungalow, Shortwood, Nailsworth, Stroud, Glos GL60SD
Tel: 01453 833204 (H)  01453 763611 (B)

**Ground:** "Meadow Bank", Shortwood, Nailsworth, Gloucestershire (01453 833936)

**Directions:** In Nailsworth turn into Spring Hill then first left. Continue pastshop and and keep left past "Britannia" (signposted Shortwood) - continue toend for ground. 4 miles from Stroud (BR)
Capacity: 5,000   Seats: 50   Cover: 150   Floodlights: Yes   Club Shop: No
**Clubhouse:** Mon-Sat 7-11pm, Sun 12-2 & 7-10.30pm.. Hot food kitchen on matchdays

**HONOURS**   Glos.Co.Lg 81-82 (R-up 80-81), Glos Tphy 83-84 91-92,94-95,(R-up 79-80), Hellenic Lg 84-85 91-92 (R-up 85-86 89-90 94-95, Div 1 R-up 83-84, Div 1Cup83-84), Prem Lge Cup R-up 95-96, Hungerford Merit Cup, Glos Snr Amtr Cup 85-86(R-up 79-80), Stroud Charity Cup 91-92 92-93 94-95 (R-up 95-96), Stroud Lg 27-28 (Div 2 26-27 64-65(res), Div 3 25-26 49-50(res) 62-63(res)), Glos Northern Snr Lg R-up  67-68 91-92(res)(Div 2 62-63 80-81(res) 90-91(res)), Arthur Shipway Cup 78-79 79-80, Supp'tary Cup R-up 98-99, Glos N. Sen 2 R-up 98-99

**PREVIOUS**   **Leagues:** Stroud; Glos Northern Snr; Glos Co
            **Ground:** Table Land, Wallow Green
**RECORD**   **Attendance:** 1,000 v Forest Green Rovers, FA Vase 5th Rd 81-82
            **Goalscorer:** Peter Grant  **Appearances:** Peter Grant
            **Win:** 11-0  **Defeat:** 0-9  **Fee Received:** Paul Tester (Cheltenham, 80-81)

**FACT FILE**
Founded: 1900
Nickname: The Wood
Sponsors: Automold Ltd
Colours: Red & white,red,black
Change: All white
Midweek matchday: Tuesday
Reserves' League: Glos Northern Snr 1
Programme: 18 pages, 50p
Editor: Kevin Horsfall
98-99 Captain: Jim Russell & Nigel Tovey
P.o.Y.: Terry Stevenson
Top Scorer: Kevin Pride
**CLUB PERSONNEL**
Chairman: Peter Webb
Vice C'men: W Stratford, W Lewis
President: R T Tanner
Press Officer: Ashley Loveridge
Tel: 01453 752494
Manager/Coach: John Evans

# SWINDON SUPERMARINE

**Secretary:**Kathy Aldred,18 Whitworth Rd,Swindon SN23BJ Tel: 01793 524762

**Ground:** Hunts Copse, South Marston, Swindon Tel: 01793 824824

**Directions:**   On A361 Swindon/Highworth road, adjoining South Marston Industrial lEstate. Six  miles from Swindon (BR) - buses in direction of Highworth, Fairford &Lechdale. If lost ask for Honda.
            Capacity: 1,000   Seats: 75   Cover: 120   Floodlights: Yes
**Clubhouse:** Yes

**HONOURS:**   Hellenic League - Premier Div. 97-98, R-up 95-96 98-99; Div. One 85-86, 86-87; Reserve Section 96-97; League Cup 96-97; Floodlit Cup 97-98. Wiltshire Senior Cup 82-83, 86-87, 89-90. Wiltshire Premier Shield 96-97
**PREVIOUS**   **Leagues:** Wiltshire Lge.
            **Names:** Vickers Armstrong 46-81,Supermarine 82-91 (merged 1992) , Penhill Youth Centre 70-84, Swindon Athletic 84-89 (merged)
            **Ground:** Supermarine: Vickers Airfield (until mid-1960s);
                   Swindon Ath.: Merton 70-84; `Southbrook', Pinehurst Road 84-92
**RECORD**   **Attendance:** 264 v Moreton Town 1986

**FACT FILE**
Founded: 1992
Colours: Blue & white/blue/blue
Change colours: Yellow/navy/yellow
Midweek Matchday: Wednesday
Programme: Yes

**CLUB PERSONNEL**
Chairman: Steve Moore
President: Cliff Puffit
Press Officer: Judi Moore(01793 790685)
Manager: Alan Dyton
Coach: Glynn Dubber
Physio: Alan Jennings

# TUFFLEY ROVERS

**Secretary:**   Graham Moody, 50 Giles Cox, Quedgeley, Gloucester GL2 4YL
            Tel: 01452 724083 (H & Fax)  01452 522009 (B)

**Ground:**   Glevum Park, Lower Tuffley Lane, Gloucester Tel: 01452 423402

**Directions:**   Follow Gloucester city ring-rd to traffic lights signed M5 South & Bristol. Turn right signed Hempsted & city centre, after 200yds turn right (McDonalds on corner) into Lower Tuffley Lane, ground 400yds on left
            Capacity:   Seats: 50   Cover: Yes   Floodlights: Yes

**Clubhouse:**   800 yds from ground. Open before & after matches, and normal pub hours at other times. Snacks available.   Club Shop: No

**HONOURS**   Hellenic Lg Div 1 92-93 (Div 1 Cup 92-93, F'lit Cup 98-99), Glos Co. Lge 90-91, Glos SnrAmtr Cup 87-88, Stroud Lg 72-73,94-95, Glos Northern Sen. Lg. Div 1 87-88 98-99 (res) Div2 79-80.

**PREVIOUS**   **Leagues:** Stroud; Glos Northern Senior; Glos County (pre-1991)
            **Grounds:** Stroud Rd, Gloucester; Randwick Park, Tuffley

**RECORD**   **Attendance:** 150 v Cinderford Town 94-95

**FACT FILE**
Founded: 1929
Nickname: Rovers
Club Sponsors: Port security
Colours: Claret & blue/white/claret
Change colours: White/blue/blue
Midweek Matchday: Tuesday
Reserve League: Glos.Northern Senior Lge
Programme: approx 10 pages with entry
Editor: Mrs bev Summers (01452 417660)

**CLUB PERSONNEL**
President:
Chairman: Tony Newport

Manager: Chris Gardner
Coach: Geoff Samuels
Physio: Sean Tracey

# WANTAGE TOWN

**Secretary:** Alan Parker, Little Orchard, Manor Road, Wantage, OX12 8DW
Tel: 01235 763842 (H & Fax)

**Ground:** Alfredian Park, Manor Road, Wantage, Oxon Tel: 01235 764781

**Directions:** Take Hungerford Road from Wantage (A338)
The ground is signposted on right opposite recreation ground
Capacity: 1,500    Seats: 50    Cover: 300    Floodlights: Yes

**Clubhouse:** Mon-Fri 7.30-11pm, Sat noon-2.30, 4-7pm    Club Shop: No

**HONOURS** Hellenic Lg R-up 81-82, Div 1 80-81 (R-up 69-70 87-88 91-92 95-96), Div1 Cup
R-up 91-92; Oxon Snr Cup 82-83; Berks & Bucks Intermediate Cup 54-55;
Swindon & District Lg 07-08 33-34 52-53 55-56

**PREVIOUS** **Leagues:** Swindon & Dist. 1901-12 30-35 47-56; N Berks 12-22 38-40 46-47;
Reading & D. 22-30 35-38
**Ground:** Challow Park (pre-1922)

**RECORD** **Attendance:** 500 v Newport AFC 89
**Win:** 11-1 v Amersham Town (A), Hellenic League 60-61
**Defeat:** 0-14 v Thame United (A), 20/1/62
**Goalscorer:** A Rolls

Players progressing: Roy Burton and Colin Duncan (both Oxford United)

### FACT FILE

Founded: 1892
Nickname: Alfredians
Sponsors: Broadway Motors
Colours: Green & white/green & white/white
Change: Blue & white/blue & white/white
Midweek Matchday: Wednesday
Programme: 28 pages, 50p
Editor: Tony Woodward (01367 241328)

### CLUB PERSONNEL

Chairman: A R Woodward
President: Ernie Smart
Match Secretary: Colin Blunsden
Tel: 01235 768605 (H)
1st Team Manager: Stuart Peace
Reserves' Manager: Fred Bint
Physio: Ian Howard

# ARDLEY UNITED

**Secretary:** Alan Mitchell, 24 Orchard Road,Ardley,Bicester,Oxon OX6 9PW
Tel: 01869 346854(H) 01865 846799(W) 01865 846333(FAX)

**Ground:** Ardley Sports Ground, Oxford Road, Ardley (01869 346429)

**Directions:** M40 junc 10 take A43 towards Middleton Stoney on the right after1/2 mile.
From Oxford take A43 through Weston-on-the-Green & Middleton Stoney on
the left hand side.
Capacity:    Cover:    Seats:           Floodlights

Clubhouse:

**HONOURS** Oxon Snr Lg R-up 92-93 (Pres. Cup R-up 90-91 91-92) Hellenic League Div
One 96-97,97-98 Division One Cup 94-5,95-6,96-7,97-98

**PREVIOUS** **Leagues:** Oxon Snr (pre-1993)

**RECORD** **Attendance:** 74 v Watlington Town

**FACT FILE**
Founded:
Colours: Sky/navy/sky
Change colours: Yellow/black/yellow
Midweek matchday: Tuesday

**CLUB PERSONNEL**
President: Ben Gow
Chairman: Norman Stacey
Match Secretary: Alan Mitchell
Tel: 01869 346854 (H)
Manager: Paul Spittle
Coach: Robert Mason
Physio: Norman Stacey

# BISHOPS CLEEVE

**Secretary:** Phil Tustain, 36 Hardy Road, Bishops Cleeve, Cheltenham GL52 4BN
Tel: 01242 697281 (H)  01242 673333 x 2287 (B)

**Ground:** Kayte Lane, Bishops Cleeve
Floodlights: No

**Directions:** North of Cheltenham on the A534, pass Racecourse then turn right at traffic
lights and then left into Kayte Lane, ground half a mile on the left.
**Clubhouse:** Full facilities, bar, dance area

**HONOURS** Hellenic Lg Cup R-up 90-91

**PREVIOUS** **Leagues:** Cheltenham, Nth Glos
**Grounds:** The Skiller (pre-1913), Village Field (pre-1950)

**RECORD** **Attendance:** 1,000 v Newport AFC

**FACT FILE**
Founded: 1892
Nickname: Skinners
Colours: Green/black/green
Change colours: Blue/white/red
Midweek Matchday: Wednesday

**CLUB PERSONNEL**
President: John Davies
Chairman: David Walker
Press Officer: David Lewis (01386 882274)

Manager: Paul Collicutt
Coach:John Banfield
Physio: Will Pember

# CHELTENHAM SARACENS

**Secretary:** Robert Attwood, 179 Arle Road, Cheltenham GL51 8LJ (01242 515855)

**Ground:** Petersfield Park, Tewkesbury Road, Cheltenham (01242 584134)

**Directions:** 1 mile from Cheltenham centre on A4019 Tewksbury Road (next to B &Q) - 1st left
over railway bridge, 1st left and follow service road
Capacity: 2,000    Seats: None        Cover: 100        Floodlights: No
Club Shop: No
**Clubhouse:** 2 mins away at 16-20 Swindon Rd, Cheltenham

**HONOURS** Glos Snr Cup 91-92 Glos Primary Cup 71-72

**PREVIOUS** **League:** Cheltenham 1964-86

**RECORD** **Attendance:** 120 v Bishops Cleeve, 1.1.95

Players progressing: S Cotterill (Wimbledon) 88, K Knight (Reading) 89

**FACT FILE**
Founded: 1964  Nickname: Saras
Colours: Blue, yellow stripe/blue/blue
Change colours: Black, white stripe/black/black
Midweek Matchday: Wednesday
Reserves League: Hellenic Reserve section
Programme : 20 pages, 50p
Editor: Secretary

**CLUB PERSONNEL**
Chairman: Jim Utteridge
Match Secretary: Terry Coates
Press Officer: Terry Coates (01242 692320)
Manager: Ian Ford
Coach:Gerald Oldham
Physio: Jim Utteridge

# CIRENCESTER UNITED

**Secretary/Press Officer:** Gordon Varley, 95 Vaisey Rd, Cirencester, Glos GL7 2JW
Tel: 01285 657836 (H)  0973 631650 (M) 01367 718259 (B)
**Ground:** Four Acres P.F., Chesterton Lane, Cirencester Tel: 01285 885460
**Directions:** Follow by-pass towards Bristol, under footbridge, first left after Cirencester Town
F.C., ground 200yds on left hand side
Seats: None        Cover: No        Floodlights: No        Club Shop: No
**Clubhouse:** Training nights & matchdays. Rolls & sundries available
**HONOURS** Glos Snr Amtr Cup R-up 86-87 89-90; Cirencester Lg 72-73 74-75 (Div
2(3)71-73 74-75, Lg Cup 74-75, Res. Cup 74-75); Cheltenham Lg 76-77 83-84 (Div 275-76, Lg
Cup 83-84 (R-up 86-87), Snr Charity Cup 86-87); Stroud Charity Cup86-87 (Section A 82-83 83-
84); Arthur Shipway Cup 86-87 (R-up 87-88 92-93);Fairford Hospital Cup R-up(4) 83-85 90-91
92-93; Hellenic Res Div 95-96, Cup96-97
**PREVIOUS** **Leagues:** Cirencester & Dist.(4 yrs); Cheltenham (8 yrs)
**RECORDS** **Scorer:** M Day    **Appearances:** A Smith

**FACT FILE**
Founded: 1970   Nickname: Herd
Colours: Red & black/black/red
Change colours: Green & yellow/green/green
Midweek Matchday: Wednesday
Programme : 40 pages, 50p
Editor: N Warriner (01285 656187)

**CLUB PERSONNEL**
President: A Day
Chairman: Paul King
Press Officer: Jason Huxtable (01285 656010)
Manager: Ivor Probert
Coach: Adie Smith
Physio: Brian Muir

# CLANFIELD

**Secretary:** John Osborne, 70 Lancut Road, Witney, Oxon OX8 5AQ    Tel: 01993 771631

**Ground:** Radcot Road, Clanfield, Oxon    Tel: 01367 810314

**Directions:** Situated on the A4095, 8 miles west of Witney & 4 miles east of Faringdon, at the southern end of Clanfield. Buses from Witney - contact Thames Transit for details

Capacity: 2,000    Seats: No    Cover: 300    Floodlights: No

**Clubhouse:** Every evening & Sat/Sun lunch    Club Shop: No

**HONOURS** Oxon Jnr Shield 32-33, Oxon I'mediate Cup 67-68, Witney & Dist. Lg 66-67 (Div 1 65-66, Div 2 64-65), Hellenic Lg Div 1 69-70 (Premier Div Cup 72-73, Div1 Cup 69-70 85-86), Jim Newman Mem. Tphy 83-84 87-88, Faringdon Thursday Memorial Cup 69-70 71-72

**PREVIOUS** **Leagues:** Nth Berks; Witney & Dist    Player of the Year: Shaun Miller

**RECORD** **Attendance:** 65 v Wooton Bassett Town 1997 Top Goalscorer: D.Hamill(12)

### FACT FILE
Founded: 1890
Nickname: Robins
Sponsors: Smurfitt
Colours: Red & white
Change colours: Yellow & Black/black/black
Reserves' League: Hellenic Lge Res. section
Programme: 8 pages, with admission
Editor: Secretary
**CLUB PERSONNEL**
President: B Wallis
Chairman: J Osborne
Manager: Peter Bridgewater
Asst. Man.Graham Foster
Press Officer&Physio: Trevor Cuss

# EASINGTON SPORTS

**Secretary:** Steven Paynton, 73 Bloxham Road, Banbury ,Oxon. OX169JS(01295 259480)
**Ground:** Addison Rd., Easington Estate, Banbury, Oxon (01295 257006)

**Directions:** From Oxford A423. After passing under flyover on the outskirts ofBanbury take first turning left into Grange Road then third right into AddisonRd. Ground at top on left. One and a half miles from Banbury (BR)

Capacity: 1,000    Seats: 50    Cover: 100    Floodlights: No

Programme: Yes, 25p

**Clubhouse:** Changing rooms, showers, bar facilities and food

**HONOURS** Oxon Snr Cup R-up, Oxon Intermediate League & Cup, Oxon Snr Lg

**PREVIOUS** **Leagues:** Banbury Jnr; Oxon Snr; Warkwick Combination
**Ground:** Bodicote

**RECORD** **Attendance:** 250 v Witney Town 68

### FACT FILE
Founded: 1946
Colours: Red & white/black/red & white
Change colours: All white
Midweek Matchday: Wednesday
Reserves' League: Hellenic Res. section

**CLUB PERSONNEL**
Chairman: Jim Hay
President: Bob Cogbill
Manager/Coach: Jim Hay
Physio: Les Horley
Press Officer: Jim Hay

# HEADINGTON AMATEURS

**Secretary:** Stephen Giles, 60 Glebelands, Headington, Oxon. OX3 7EN(01865 430133)
**Ground:** Barton Rec., Barton Village Road, Barton, Oxon Tel: 01865 60489
**Directions:** From Green Rd r'bout, Headington, (on A40) take Barton/Islip exit(1st exit coming from Witney, last coming from London), turn left into NorthWay, follow road for half mile - ground at bottom of hill on left

Seats: None    Cover: None    Floodlights: No    Club Shop: No

**Clubhouse:** Tues & Thurs 6-11, Sat matchdays 4.45-11. Rolls, chips,burgers, hot dogs, etc

**HONOURS** Oxon Snr League(4) 72-74 75-77 (R-up 71-72 74-75 77-78 81-82 84-85, Div1 68-69, Presidents Cup(2) 72-74 (R-up 71-72 77-78 84-85)), Oxon Charity Cup75-76 (Intermediate Cup 88-89), Hellenic League Div 1 R-up 87-88 (Res. Sect.92-93, Res. Cup 91-92)

**PREVIOUS** **Leagues:** Oxford City Junior 49-66; Oxford Senior 67-88

**RECORDS** **Attendance:** 250 v Newport AFC 91 **Scorer:** Tony Penge **Appearances:** Keith Drackett **Win:** 6-0 v Carterton (H) 91 **Defeat:** 1-8 v Banbury United (A), Feb. 94

### FACT FILE
Founded : 1949    Nickname: A's
Sponsors: Oxford Marquees
Colours: All red
Change: Blue/blue/white
Midweek matchday: Tuesday
Reserves' Lge: Hellenic Res. sect
Programme: 8 pages, £1 with entry
Editor: Stan Hawkswood (01865 65546)

**CLUB PERSONNEL**
President: N Smith
Chairman: Donald Light
Press Officer: Paul Sammons
Manager: B McCrae
Coach/Physio: J Taylor

# KIDLINGTON

**Secretary:** Geoff Tallboys, Weatherdale, Water Eaton Lane, Gosford, Kidlington.OX5 2PP
Tel No: 01865 376221

**Ground:** Yarnton Rd, Kidlington, Oxford Tel: 01865 375628

**Directions:** From Kidlington r'bout (junction of A4260 & A34) A423 north toKidlington; after 1st lights take 2nd left (Yarnton Road), ground is 200yds onthe left
Floodlights: No

**Clubhouse:** Two bars open after matches

**HONOURS** Oxon Snr Lg 53-54 (R-up 47-48), Hellenic Lg Cup 74-75 (R-up 68-69 73-7474-75, Div 1 R-up 63-64 78-79), Oxon Intermediate Cup 52-53 84-85 (R-up 68-69 73-74 74-75), FA Vase 5th last sixteen 76-77

**PREVIOUS** **League:** Oxon Snr 47-54
**RECORD** **Attendance:** 2500 v Showbiz XI 1973

### FACT FILE
Founded: 1920
Colours: Green & black/black/green
Change colours: Red & black/black/red
Midweek Matchday: Wednesday
Programme: 20 pages, 20p
Editor: M A Canning

**CLUB PERSONNEL**
President: Gordon Norridge
Chairman: Peter Walton
Manager: K Grossman
Coach: S Dickens
Physio: M Baker

Tuffley Rovers 2 Harrow Hill 1. Second half action as Tuffley attack following a corner. This one hits the bar. Photo: Martin Wray

Dave Hyatt in the Epsom goal covers this Banbury attack. Photo: Steve Ayre

North Leigh hit the Arundel woodwork on this occasion, but hit the net four times to win 4-1. Photo: Gordon Whittington

# LETCOMBE

**Secretary:** Des Williams, 8 Larkdown, Wantage, Oxon. OX12 8HE
Tel: 01235 764130 (H)  01235 225702 (B)

**Ground:** Bassett Road, Letcombe Regis, Wantage, Oxon Tel: 01235 768685

**Directions:** B4507 Swindon road from Wantage, left for Letcombe Regis, follow road thru Letcombe Regis; ground on right on far side of village

**Seats:** No  **Cover:** No  **Floodlights:** No  **Club Shop:** No
**Clubhouse:** Open evenings except Monday. Rolls & hot food sold

**HONOURS** Chiltonian Lg Div 1 90-91, North Berks Lg 89-90 (Lg Cup 87-88, WarMemorial Cup 89-90, A G Kingham Cup 89-90, Faringdon Memorial Cup 98-99

**PREVIOUS** **Leagues:** North Berks 60-90; Chiltonian 90-93

**RECORDS** **Attendance:** 90 v Courage (Reading) 03.90
**Scorer:** R Taylor  **Appearances:** P Davies

### FACT FILE
Founded: 1960    Nickname: Brooksiders
Sponsors: P.J.Drew & Soro's Pizzas
Colours: Blue& Green
Change colours: Yellow & Blue
Midweek Matchday: Wednesday
Reserves' Lge: Hellenic Res. sect
Programme: £1 with entry
Editor: Russell Stock (01235 762387)
### CLUB PERSONNEL
President: Maurice Ginniff
Chairman: Dennis Stock
Vice-Chairman: G Delacoze
Press Officer: Russell Stock
Manager: Des Williams
Coach: Ian Gordon    Physio: Des Williams

# MIDDLE BARTON

**Secretary:** Julie Reed, 5 Hillside Road, Middle Barton, Oxon OX7 7EY
Tel: 01869 347388

**Ground:** Worton Road, Middle Barton, Oxon. Tel: 01869 347597

**Directions:** Middle Barton village is situated on the B4030, 5 miles east of Enstone. 200 metres passed the Fox PH turn left at cross roads, ground 200 metres on right.

**Clubhouse:** Open every evening

**PREVIOUS** **League:** Oxfordshire Senior League

**HONOURS** Oxfordshire Sen. Lge R-up 98-99

### FACT FILE

Founded: 1952
Midweek Matchday: Wednesday
Colours: Blue & white/blue/blue
Change colours: Yellow/black/black
Programme: Yes, first season

### CLUB PERSONNEL

President: Derrick Jarvis
Chairman: John Marks
Press Officer: Bernie Wiggins (01295 812120)
Manager/Coach: Tim Fowler
Physio: Peter Salt

# OLD WOODSTOCK TOWN

**Secretary:** Ian Baxter, Workplace Systems plc, Precedent Drive, Rooksley, Milton Keynes MK13 8PP    Tel: 01908 251340 (B) 01908 201287 (Fax) 0403 451711 (M)

**Ground:** New Road, Woodstock

**Directions:** A44 from Oxford into centre of Woodstock, turn right opposite The Crown into Hensington Road. After half a mile the road bends to the right, take the first turning right into New Road, ground half-way along on the left.

**HONOURS** Oxfordshire Sen. Lge 98-99

**PREVIOUS** **Leagues:** Oxfordshire Senior League

### FACT FILE

Founded:
Midweek Matchday: Tuesday
Colours: Blue & red/blue/blue & red
Change colours: Green & yellow/green/green & Yellow

### CLUB PERSONNEL
**President: Ian F Lenagan**
Chairman: Ted Saxton
Press Officer: Mick Harris (01865 376018)
Manager: Karl Grossman
Coach: Simon Dickens
Physio: Graham Bowerman

# PURTON

**Secretary:** Nick Webb, 4 Glevum Close, Purton, Swindon, Wilts SN5 9HA
Tel: 01793 770242 (H)  01793 852451 (B)

**Ground:** The Red House, Purton, Tel: 01793 770262 (Saturday afternoons only)

**Directions:** Purton is on B4041 Wootton Bassett to Cricklade Road. Ground nearvillage hall
Capacity      **Seats:**None    **Cover:** None    **Floodlights:** No
**Clubhouse:** Open after matches

**HONOURS** Wiltshire Lg  Div One 48-49 85-86, Div 2 83-84, Div 3 86-87;
Wilts Senior Cup (6) 38-39 48-49 50-51 54-55 87-89, Wilts Yth Cup 77-78 85-86 88-89, Fairford Hosp. Cup (3) 87-89 93-94 Hellenic League Div One 95-96

**RECORD** **Attendance:** 508 v Dorcan 5.5.85

### FACT FILE
Founded: 1923
Nickname: The Reds
Sponsors: The Care Company
Colours: All red
Change colours: White & blue/blue/blue
Midweek Matchday: Wednesday
Programme: 40 pagesp
Editor: Alan Eastwood (01793 729844)
### CLUB PERSONNEL
President: Graham Price
Chairman: Steve Webb
Press Officer: Alan Eastwood
Manager: T.B.A.
Ass. Man.: T.B.A.

# ROSS TOWN

**Secretary:** Tim Barnard, Apsley House, Whitchurch, Ross-on-Wye, HR9 6DJ
Tel: 01600 890722 (H) 01600 891111 (B) 07771 927926 (M)

**Ground:** Cinderford Town FC, Causeway Ground, Hilldene, Cinderford (01594822039)
**Directions:** From Gloucester take A40 to Ross-on-Wye, then A48 - Chepstow. In 10miles turn right at Elton garage onto A4151to Cinderford, thru Littledean, up steep hill, right at crossroads, and left into Latimer Rd.( F.C signposted). Ground 5 mins walkfrom town centre
Capacity: 3,500      Cover: 1,000      Seats: 250      Floodlights: Yes

**HONOURS** Hereford Lge 94-95, Charity Shield 95-96; Hereford FA Charity Bowl 94-95; Worcester & Dist Lge 95-96, Baylis Cup 95-96; Hereford FA County Chall Cup 97-99 R-up 95-96; 98-99 Pershore Hospital Charity Cup R-up 95-96
**PREVIOUS** **Leagues:** Hereford Lg, Worcester & District League.
**RECORD** **Attendance:** 147 v Harrow Hill 26/3/97

**FACT FILE**
Founded:1993
Nickname: Riversiders
Colours: Red & white/black/red
Change colours: Blue/white/blue
Midweek Matchday: Tuesday/Wednesday

**CLUB PERSONNEL**
Patron: Dave Sexton
Chairman: Geoff Jones
Director of Footbal and
Press Officer: Chris Parsons (01989 566712)
Manager: Martin Thomas
Coach: Chris Thomas
Physio: Alan Bridges

# WOOTTON BASSETT TOWN

**Secretary:** Rod Carter, 14 Blackthorn Close, Wootton Bassett, Swindon SN4 7JE 01793 851386
**Ground:** Gerard Buxton Sports Ground, Rylands Way, Wootton Bassett, Swindon 01793 853880
**Directions:** M4 jnct 16 to Wootton Bassett (A3102), left at 2nd r'bout (Prince of Wales pub on right), 2nd left into Longleaze (just after Mobil garage) and Rylands Way is 3rd right by shops, ground 100yds on right. From Calne/Devizes direction proceed thru town centre and turn right into Longleaze after Shell petrol station on right - Rylands Ave. is 3rd left.
Capacity: 4,000      Seats: None      Cover: 350      Floodlights: Due      Club Shop: No
**Clubhouse:** Open every matchday. Matchday refreshments - teas, coffees, soups & light snacks
**HONOURS** Hellenic Lg Div 1 Cup 89-90 93-94, Wilts Lg 87-88 (Div 2 84-85,Subsidiary Cup 78-79), Wilts Snr Cup R-up 02-03 03-04 87-88, Ghia Snr 83-84,Ghia Jnr Cup R-up 88-89, FA Amateur Cup QF 26-27
**PREVIOUS** **Leagues:** Wilts (pre-1988)      **Grounds:** None
**RECORD** **Gate:** 2,103 v Swindon T., friendly 7/91      **Win:** 11-2      **Defeat:** 0-9
**Scorer:** Brian (Toby) Ewing      **Appearances:** Steve Thomas

**FACT FILE**
Founded: 1882
Sponsors: Cathy Moore Recruitment
Colours: Blue & yellow/blue/yellow
Change colours: White, black &
blue/black/black
Midweek matchday: Wednesday
Reserve team's League: Wiltshire
Programme: 12 pages, free
**CLUB PERSONNEL**
Chairman: Paul Harrison
President: Keith Lodge
Press Officer: Rod Carter (see Sec)
Manager/Coach: Dave Warren
Physio: Geoff Hawkins

# WORCESTER COLLEGE OLD BOYS

**Secretary:** R. Oakes, 112 Leiden Road, Headington, Oxford OX3 8QU Tel: 01865 750758

**Ground:** Rover Cowley Sports Ground, Cowley, Oxford  Tel: 01865 775463

**Directions:** Take the ring road to the east of city. Leave at exit sign-posted to Horspath. First right, into Roamn Road, leads to ground entrance on the left..

Capacity: 2,000      Cover: Yes      Seats: Yes      Floodlights: No
**Clubhouse:** Open luchtimes and evenings every day.

**PREVIOUS** **League:** Oxfordshire Senior League
**HONOURS** Oxfordshire Sen Lge 97-98, Oxfordshire Charity Cup 96-97

**FACT FILE**
Founded: 1974
Midweek Matchday: Tuesday
Colours: Blue & black/black/black
Change colours: All maroon

**CLUB PERSONNEL**
Chairman: D Quinton
Manager: Paul Creed

Storrington FC. "That's right boys - you just watch while I get scratched to bits getting the ball back!"

Photo: Graham Cotterill

# NON-LEAGUE NEWSDESK

## FOR RESULTS, TABLES AND NEWS FROM THE NON-LEAGUE PYRAMID

Now entering its fifth full season, Non-League Newsdesk has become firmly established as the number one magazine for up-to-date news and statistics from the Pyramid world.

Founded in 1995 by former Non-League Club Directory editor James Wright, Non-League Newsdesk will in 1999-2000 celebrate its 200th edition. The magazine is delivered to subscribers every midweek (usually Wednesday) carrying all the previous week's results, together with current tables, from around FIFTY leagues.

For many of the more senior competitions, full match details (such as goalscorers and attendances) are supplied. County and League Cup competitions are also extensively featured, as are the FA Umbro Trophy and FA Carlsberg Vase, and the involvement of the non-League clubs in the AXA sponsored FA Cup.

But Non-League Newsdesk is not just a statistical work. Each week the magazine carries up-to-date news stories and listings of managerial changes and transfers.

The magazine is therefore particularly popular with -
* Clubs, who find much of the information extremely useful for matchday programmes and in checking on forthcoming opponents, particularly those from outside their own league.
* Statisticians, who see the weekly stats as the most extensive, accurate and up-to-date available.
* Groundhoppers, who find it invaluable in picking their games.
* The more general non-League enthusiast who likes to keep abreast of the most current news.
If you would like to see a free sample copy from 1998-99, please send an SAE to James Wright at the address below.

Leagues featured in Non-League Newsdesk include: Nationwide Conference, UniBond, Ryman, Dr Martens, First NW Trains NWCL, SGL West Lancs, Manchester, Carlsberg West Cheshire, Green Contract Services Mid-Cheshire, Arnott Insurance Northern, Northern Co's (East), Redferns Central Midlands, Powerleague Notts Alliance, West Yorkshire, Deejays Lincs, Everards Leics, Vaux Wearside, JPL Wade Northern Alliance, Herts, A Quote Insurance Reading, Courage Combined Co's, Cherry Red Chiltonian, Minerva SSML, Essex Senior, Essex Intermediate, Kent Blaxill Essex & Suffolk Border, Interlink Alliance, Endsleigh Midland Comb, Banks's West Mids, Springbank Vending Midland, Complete Music Hellenic, Glos. County, Somerset Senior, Screwfix Western, Jewson SW, Jolly's Cornwall Combination, Cornish Guardian East Cornwall, Westward Developments Devon, Jewson Wessex, Keyline Dorset Comb., Dorset Co., Hampshire, Unijet Sussex, Bass Kent, British Energy Kent Co., Jewson ECL, Lovewell Blake Anglian Combination, McGinty's Suffolk & Ipswich, Uhlsport UCL, Optimum Interiors Capital and Central Conference, League of Wales, CC Sports

¯S WRIGHT, 13 NORTHFIELD AVENUE, TAUNTON, SOMERSET TA1 1XF
01823 327720 MOBILE: 0421 004219 E-MAIL:NLNEWSDESK@ZETNET.CO.UK

**Subscription Rates**

Non-League Newsdesk costs just 80p per week plus first class postage (26p). It . is produced every Monday during the season except the week between Christmas and New Year. The table below shows how much a subscription will cost from your chosen starting date.

| FROM | to Xmas | Full season |
|---|---|---|
| Aug 9th | £21.20 | £42.40 |
| Aug 16th | £20.14 | £41.34 |
| Aug 23rd | £19.08 | £40.28 |
| Aug 30th | £18.02 | £39.22 |
| Sept 6th | £16.96 | £38.16 |
| Sept 13th | £15.90 | £37.10 |
| Sept 20th | £14.84 | £36.04 |
| Sept 27th | £13.78 | £34.98 |
| Oct 4th | £12.72 | £33.92 |
| Oct 11th | £11.66 | £32.86 |
| Oct 18th | £10.60 | £31.80 |
| Oct 25th | £9.54 | £30.74 |
| Nov 1st | £8.48 | £29.68 |
| Nov 8th | £7.42 | £28.62 |
| Nov 15th | £6.36 | £27.56 |
| Nov 22nd | £5.30 | £26.50 |
| Nov 29th | £4.24 | £25.44 |
| Dec 5th | £3.18 | £24.38 |
| Dec 12th | £2.12 | £23.32 |
| Dec 19th | £1.06 | £22.26 |
| Jan 3rd | n/a | £21.20 |
| Jan 10th | n/a | £20.14 |
| Jan 17th | n/a | £19.08 |
| Jan 24th | n/a | £18.02 |
| Jan 31st | n/a | £16.96 |
| Feb 7th | n/a | £15.90 |
| Feb 14th | n/a | £14.84 |
| Feb 21st | n/a | £13.78 |
| Feb 28th | n/a | £12.72 |
| Mar 7th | n/a | £11.66 |
| Mar 14th | n/a | £10.60 |
| Mar 21st | n/a | £9.54 |
| Mar 28th | n/a | £8.48 |
| April 4th | n/a | £7.42 |
| April 11th | n/a | £6.36 |
| April 18th | n/a | £5.30 |
| April 25th | n/a | £4.24 |
| May 2nd | n/a | £3.18 |
| May 9th | n/a | £2.12 |
| End of season issue | | £1.06 |

**TO ORDER**
Simply send your:
Name, Address, Tel. No., When you want your subscription to start and whether it is Until Christmas or until the End of the season

Please send cheque or postal order payable to Non-League Newsdesk

# BASS BREWERS
# KENT LEAGUE
## FEEDER TO: DR MARTENS LEAGUE
**President:** D D Baker   **Chairman:** P C Wager   **Vice Chairman:** E V Ward
**Hon. Secretary:** A R Vinter, The Thatched Barn, Catt's Wood Road, Lower Hardress,
Canterbury CT4 5PG   Tel: 01227 700108

During the 1998-99 campaign in the Kent League we have witnessed some historic events, involving a new Premier Division with all clubs playing under floodlights and, unfortunately, the loss of our sponsorship with Winstonlead Cables, probably the longest running in non-League Football. The sad news came midway through the season, when the business was sold, but they continued to support the League until the end and our sincere thanks are extended to the 'Roberts' family.

Back in August, the traditional Challenge Shield match between League Champions and Cup Winners saw honours even as Herne Bay and Greenwich Borough shared the Trophy after a 1-1 draw. In the coming weeks of the new season, it was to become apparent that Deal Town and Ramsgate had both built up strong squads and would be challenging for the major honours. Deal had secured the services of Tommy Sampson, the man responsible for Herne Bay's great successes over the recent years. During the nineties, the Kent League Championship has been won on the final day and this season was no exception as both forementioned clubs were level on points at the start of play. Deal could only draw, whilst the 'Rams' secured the title with victory at Erith Town. Greenwich Borough acquitted themselves well to finish third whilst Thamesmead Town, who lost only two games and conceded just nineteen goals, were fourth.

The Premier Division Marion Wager Cup Final was contested between Deal Town and VCD Athletic, a match which the 'Cinque Port' side won thanks to a single goal. Ramsgate acclaimed the Plaaya Kent Senior Trophy after defeating Sheppey United 8-7 on penalties after a 2-2 draw. Nationally, the AXA FA Cup saw no real surprises but the FA Carlsberg Vase did produce one interesting encounter as the holders, Tiverton Town, made the long trip to Deal. After a close fought match, the visitors were victorious and went on to lift the Vase for a second successive year.

In Division One, another close finish to the League Championship was seen as Deal Town clinched the Trophy only in the final weeks ahead of Dover Athletic and Margate. Deal also reached the Divisional Cup Final only to lose to Dover and Kent Intermediate Cup Final where they were beaten by Fisher Athletic.

Overall, the season has, again, been exciting. The Golden Boot Award was keenly contested; Dean Bowey won the Premiership Award whilst Nick Arundel of Deal collected the Division One honour. The Manager of the Month Award, sponsored this season by Jacetts, was also well received. Attendances through were down this season compared to previous campaigns. Many clubs experienced a loss through the gate and figures overall were down by some 12 per cent on last year's statistics.

For the future, a new chapter is about to be written within Kent Football as, after many months of talks, we welcome a new sponsor in Bass Brewers. Bass do, of course, sponsor the Carling Premiership and the Worthington Cup and we look forward to a long and happy relationship with them. The 'Bass Brewers Kent Football League' will see us enter into the next Millennium.

*Paul Rivers, Press Officer*

## ROLL OF HONOUR 1998-99

|  | *Champions* | *Runners Up* | *Third Place* |
|---|---|---|---|
| PREMIER DIVISION | Ramsgate | Deal Town | Greenwich Borough |
| DIVISION ONE | Deal Town | Dover Athletic | Margate |
|  | *Winners* | *Runners Up* | *Semi Finalists* |
| PREMIER DIVISION CUP | Deal Town | VCD Athletic | Ramsgate |
|  |  |  | Crockenhill |
| DIVISION ONE CUP | Dover Athletic | Deal Town | Dartford |
|  |  |  | Swanley Furness |
| KENT PLAAYA SENIOR TROPHY | Ramsgate | Sheppey United | Herne Bay |
|  |  |  | Lordswood |
| KENT INTERMEDIATE CUP | Fisher Athletic | Deal Town | Beckenham Town |
|  |  |  | Dover Athletic |
| HIGHEST SCORERS | Premier Division: | Ramsgate | 93 goals |
|  | Division One: | Deal Town | 114 goals |
| GOLDEN BOOT AWARD | Premier Division: | Dean Bowey (Ramsgate) | 31 goals |
|  | Division One: | Nick Arundel (Deal Town) | 26 goals |

# FINAL LEAGUE TABLE 1998-99
## PREMIER DIVISION

| | | P | W | D | L | F | A | W | D | L | F | A | Pts |
|---|---|---|---|---|---|---|---|---|---|---|---|---|---|
| | | | | Home | | | | | | Away | | | |
| 1 | Ramsgate | 36 | 15 | 2 | 1 | 55 | 10 | 11 | 3 | 4 | 38 | 14 | 83 |
| 2 | Deal Town | 36 | 11 | 6 | 1 | 37 | 8 | 13 | 3 | 2 | 41 | 16 | 81 |
| 3 | Greenwich Borough | 36 | 12 | 1 | 5 | 32 | 13 | 12 | 3 | 3 | 32 | 15 | 76 |
| 4 | Thamesmead Town | 36 | 11 | 6 | 1 | 28 | 9 | 9 | 8 | 1 | 29 | 10 | 74 |
| 5 | Crockenhill | 36 | 11 | 4 | 3 | 30 | 15 | 8 | 6 | 4 | 32 | 23 | 66 |
| 6 | Chatham Town | 36 | 10 | 5 | 3 | 34 | 15 | 8 | 6 | 4 | 27 | 25 | 65 |
| 7 | VCD Athletic | 36 | 9 | 5 | 4 | 33 | 22 | 7 | 4 | 7 | 28 | 29 | 57 |
| 8 | Whitstable Town | 36 | 12 | 3 | 3 | 37 | 21 | 3 | 6 | 9 | 23 | 31 | 54 |
| 9 | Beckenham Town | 36 | 5 | 7 | 6 | 23 | 23 | 8 | 4 | 6 | 28 | 24 | 50 |
| 10 | Slade Green | 36 | 6 | 6 | 6 | 31 | 22 | 5 | 5 | 8 | 27 | 27 | 44 |
| 11 | Sheppey United | 36 | 8 | 5 | 5 | 32 | 31 | 3 | 3 | 12 | 18 | 28 | 44 |
| 12 | Herne Bay | 36 | 6 | 4 | 8 | 19 | 23 | 3 | 5 | 10 | 15 | 28 | 36 |
| 13 | Lordswood | 36 | 5 | 8 | 5 | 31 | 33 | 3 | 4 | 11 | 16 | 38 | 36 |
| 14 | Cray Wanderers | 36 | 5 | 6 | 7 | 29 | 26 | 3 | 3 | 12 | 24 | 40 | 35 |
| 15 | Canterbury City | 36 | 6 | 3 | 9 | 18 | 30 | 3 | 5 | 10 | 16 | 43 | 35 |
| 16 | Faversham Town | 36 | 4 | 4 | 10 | 17 | 36 | 5 | 1 | 12 | 24 | 44 | 29 |
| 17 | Erith Town | 36 | 4 | 1 | 13 | 18 | 42 | 4 | 4 | 10 | 15 | 37 | 29 |
| 18 | Hythe United | 36 | 5 | 3 | 10 | 25 | 32 | 2 | 4 | 12 | 13 | 33 | 23 |
| 19 | Tunbridge Wells | 36 | 4 | 3 | 11 | 30 | 51 | 1 | 5 | 12 | 16 | 54 | 23 |

# PREMIER DIVISION RESULTS & ATTENDANCES CHART 1998-99

| | | 1 | 2 | 3 | 4 | 5 | 6 | 7 | 8 | 9 | 10 | 11 | 12 | 13 | 14 | 15 | 16 | 17 | 18 | 19 |
|---|---|---|---|---|---|---|---|---|---|---|---|---|---|---|---|---|---|---|---|---|
| 1 | Beckenham Town | X | 1-2 | 1-2 | 2-0 | 1-1 | 0-3 | 1-1 | 2-2 | 0-1 | 0-1 | 0-0 | 1-1 | 2-0 | 1-0 | 2-2 | 0-4 | 4-0 | 3-3 | 2-0 |
| | | X | 65 | 85 | 140 | 165 | 95 | 145 | 102 | 155 | 125 | 71 | 85 | 125 | 75 | 125 | 165 | 130 | 111 | 102 |
| 2 | Canterbury City | 0-2 | X | 3-3 | 2-1 | 0-1 | 1-3 | 1-2 | 2-1 | 0-1 | 1-1 | 1-0 | 0-4 | 1-3 | 1-4 | 0-0 | 0-2 | 3-2 | 1-0 |
| | | 48 | X | 50 | 24 | 30 | 80 | 70 | 51 | 30 | 53 | 60 | 37 | 98 | 53 | 38 | 42 | 58 | 52 | 125 |
| 3 | Chatham Town | 3-2 | 0-0 | X | 2-1 | 4-1 | 0-2 | 2-0 | 2-0 | 0-2 | 6-1 | 0-0 | 2-2 | 2-0 | 1-1 | 0-0 | 2-0 | 6-1 | 0-2 | 2-0 |
| | | 105 | 92 | X | 126 | 102 | 147 | 146 | 153 | 104 | 142 | 93 | 276 | 278 | 142 | 154 | 113 | 102 | 102 | 148 |
| 4 | Cray Wanderers | 0-0 | 5-0 | 6-1 | X | 2-2 | 1-2 | 0-1 | 0-1 | 2-3 | 3-3 | 0-1 | 1-1 | 0-2 | 1-0 | 1-1 | 0-3 | 5-4 | 2-1 | 0-0 |
| | | 96 | 95 | 121 | X | 58 | 87 | 63 | 53 | 122 | 107 | 96 | 68 | 116 | 68 | 102 | 75 | 90 | 127 | 60 |
| 5 | Crockenhill | 3-1 | 2-1 | 0-0 | 2-1 | X | 0-1 | 1-0 | 6-3 | 2-2 | 2-0 | 3-1 | 1-0 | 0-1 | 2-1 | 1-1 | 1-2 | 3-0 | 1-0 | 0-0 |
| | | 105 | 35 | 74 | 83 | X | 85 | 35 | 98 | 104 | 48 | 72 | 106 | 122 | 58 | 153 | 109 | 114 | 136 | 62 |
| 6 | Deal Town | 1-2 | 2-0 | 1-1 | 5-0 | 0-0 | X | 8-0 | 4-0 | 2-0 | 1-0 | 2-2 | 1-0 | 0-0 | 1-0 | 1-1 | 3-0 | 2-1 | 3-1 |
| | | 151 | 184 | 301 | 156 | 221 | X | 164 | 344 | 242 | 216 | 287 | 168 | 374 | 104 | 215 | 178 | 124 | 238 | 142 |
| 7 | Erith Town | 0-1 | 1-0 | 0-3 | 2-2 | 0-3 | 1-2 | X | 1-3 | 1-2 | 1-0 | 1-0 | 1-3 | 0-1 | 2-5 | 0-4 | 0-3 | 5-1 | 2-3 | 0-6 |
| | | 66 | 45 | 53 | 65 | 30 | 53 | X | 34 | 100 | 80 | 65 | 60 | 243 | 60 | 77 | 40 | 53 | 62 | 84 |
| 8 | Faversham Town | 1-1 | 2-4 | 1-4 | 0-3 | 0-2 | 0-3 | 0-1 | X | 0-2 | 1-1 | 1-0 | 2-1 | 1-4 | 2-1 | 1-0 | 0-3 | 2-2 | 0-1 | 3-3 |
| | | 48 | 52 | 68 | 33 | 43 | 86 | 31 | X | 43 | 62 | 48 | 28 | 79 | 65 | 38 | 26 | 62 | 51 | 141 |
| 9 | Greenwich Boro | 4-0 | 5-1 | 0-0 | 1-2 | 0-1 | 5-1 | 3-0 | 1-0 | X | 2-0 | 2-0 | 1-0 | 0-2 | 1-0 | 1-0 | 0-1 | 4-1 | 0-3 | 2-1 |
| | | 161 | 51 | 34 | 131 | 48 | 75 | 77 | 34 | X | 68 | 36 | 38 | 63 | 26 | 110 | 60 | 68 | 58 | 48 |
| 10 | Herne Bay | 0-0 | 0-0 | 0-1 | 2-0 | 0-2 | 0-3 | 2-0 | 0-1 | 0-3 | X | 2-1 | 1-2 | 2-6 | 1-0 | 3-0 | 0-3 | 5-0 | 0-0 | 1-1 |
| | | 133 | 128 | 100 | 71 | 135 | 234 | 76 | 89 | 51 | X | 100 | 98 | 202 | 90 | 107 | 75 | 96 | 135 | 227 |
| 11 | Hythe United | 1-2 | 2-0 | 1-2 | 1-0 | 1-3 | 1-3 | 2-0 | 2-1 | 0-1 | 1-1 | X | 2-4 | 1-2 | 0-0 | 2-4 | 1-3 | 0-0 | 5-2 | 2-4 |
| | | 74 | 152 | 82 | 52 | 59 | 102 | 62 | 33 | 78 | 68 | X | 68 | 81 | 62 | 42 | 48 | 107 | 71 | 92 |
| 12 | Lordswood | 1-4 | 2-2 | 1-2 | 3-2 | 1-1 | 1-1 | 1-1 | 3-2 | 1-2 | 1-2 | 2-2 | X | 1-1 | 2-1 | 1-3 | 1-1 | 2-2 | 2-1 | 5-3 |
| | | 60 | 55 | 201 | 75 | 55 | 95 | 45 | 75 | 85 | 70 | 52 | X | 125 | 91 | 56 | 45 | 70 | 80 | 105 |
| 13 | Ramsgate | 3-2 | 7-0 | 3-0 | 3-1 | 4-2 | 1-0 | 4-1 | 4-0 | 1-0 | 1-0 | 0-1 | 6-0 | X | 4-1 | 4-0 | 0-0 | 6-1 | 3-0 | 1-1 |
| | | 122 | 86 | 82 | 101 | 87 | 243 | 141 | 115 | 191 | 191 | 77 | 92 | X | 100 | 138 | 140 | 220 | 202 | 107 |
| 14 | Sheppey United | 0-5 | 2-2 | 3-3 | 1-1 | 1-4 | 2-3 | 3-0 | 0-4 | 2-2 | 2-1 | 5-1 | 2-0 | 1-0 | X | 3-1 | 1-2 | 1-0 | 1-1 | 2-1 |
| | | 55 | 84 | 48 | 51 | 101 | 67 | 47 | 85 | 76 | 104 | 56 | 72 | 82 | X | 67 | 51 | 72 | 102 | 78 |
| 15 | Slade Green | 1-2 | 4-1 | 0-2 | 1-1 | 0-0 | 1-5 | 0-1 | 2-1 | 1-2 | 0-0 | 3-1 | 6-1 | 1-2 | 0-1 | X | 1-1 | 1-1 | 2-3 | 5-0 |
| | | 152 | 74 | 57 | 130 | 53 | 77 | 66 | 60 | 92 | 92 | 62 | 110 | 140 | 72 | X | 130 | 82 | 120 | 82 |
| 16 | Thamesmead Town | 1-1 | 5-0 | 2-0 | 2-0 | 1-1 | 0-0 | 3-2 | 0-1 | 1-1 | 2-1 | 1-0 | 1-0 | 1-0 | 3-1 | 2-0 | X | 2-0 | 1-1 | 0-0 |
| | | 58 | 56 | 30 | 53 | 48 | 63 | 39 | 53 | 48 | 39 | 36 | 51 | 79 | 48 | 74 | X | 65 | 76 | 48 |
| 17 | Tunbridge Wells | 3-1 | 1-2 | 0-1 | 5-4 | 2-5 | 0-5 | 2-2 | 7-3 | 0-5 | 1-2 | 5-1 | 2-2 | 0-8 | 0-1 | 0-5 | 1-1 | X | 1-2 | 0-1 |
| | | 102 | 90 | 120 | 105 | 70 | 107 | 92 | 78 | 86 | 72 | 90 | 85 | 81 | 102 | 72 | 115 | X | 78 | 95 |
| 18 | VCD Athletic | 0-2 | 0-0 | 1-1 | 4-0 | 2-1 | 0-2 | 3-3 | 3-0 | 0-2 | 1-0 | 4-2 | 3-0 | 1-4 | 3-2 | 2-2 | 0-0 | 4-0 | X | 2-1 |
| | | 71 | 46 | 69 | 125 | 63 | 51 | 73 | 71 | 81 | 84 | 69 | 46 | 75 | 41 | 95 | 121 | 81 | X | 71 |
| 19 | Whitstable Town | 2-0 | 2-1 | 2-1 | 2-5 | 4-2 | 2-2 | 1-0 | 5-1 | 2-1 | 2- | 1-0 | 4-0 | 1-2 | 2-1 | 2-0 | 1-1 | 1-1 | 1-2 | X |
| | | 106 | 107 | 125 | 117 | 109 | 367 | 90 | 113 | 97 | 326 | 89 | 118 | 168 | 130 | 109 | 95 | 80 | 90 | X |

610

# FINAL LEAGUE TABLE 1998-99
## DIVISION ONE

| | | P | Home W | D | L | F | A | Away W | D | L | F | A | Pts |
|---|---|---|---|---|---|---|---|---|---|---|---|---|---|
| 1 | Deal Town | 36 | 14 | 4 | 0 | 70 | 13 | 14 | 2 | 2 | 44 | 12 | 90 |
| 2 | Dover Athletic | 36 | 13 | 2 | 3 | 60 | 20 | 15 | 0 | 3 | 49 | 13 | 86 |
| 3 | Margate* | 36 | 12 | 5 | 1 | 43 | 9 | 11 | 6 | 1 | 42 | 16 | 82 |
| 4 | Swanley Furness* | 36 | 11 | 3 | 4 | 35 | 22 | 9 | 1 | 8 | 34 | 24 | 67 |
| 5 | Thamesmead Town* | 36 | 9 | 4 | 5 | 44 | 34 | 9 | 5 | 4 | 47 | 31 | 65 |
| 6 | Folkestone Invicta | 36 | 11 | 1 | 6 | 50 | 32 | 8 | 6 | 4 | 48 | 38 | 64 |
| 7 | Ramsgate | 36 | 10 | 4 | 4 | 40 | 25 | 7 | 6 | 5 | 34 | 37 | 61 |
| 8 | Hastings Town | 36 | 9 | 4 | 5 | 27 | 25 | 6 | 5 | 7 | 27 | 42 | 54 |
| 9 | Lordswood | 36 | 8 | 4 | 6 | 35 | 30 | 7 | 2 | 9 | 32 | 39 | 51 |
| 10 | Dartford | 36 | 10 | 4 | 4 | 34 | 25 | 4 | 3 | 11 | 26 | 39 | 49 |
| 11 | Sittingbourne** | 36 | 5 | 5 | 8 | 26 | 31 | 8 | 5 | 5 | 31 | 26 | 46 |
| 12 | Chatham Town | 36 | 5 | 2 | 11 | 30 | 45 | 8 | 2 | 8 | 27 | 34 | 43 |
| 13 | Beckenham Town** | 36 | 7 | 2 | 9 | 30 | 29 | 4 | 6 | 8 | 17 | 20 | 39 |
| 14 | Herne Bay | 36 | 6 | 4 | 8 | 32 | 32 | 4 | 3 | 11 | 21 | 43 | 37 |
| 15 | Canterbury City | 36 | 4 | 3 | 11 | 18 | 44 | 7 | 1 | 10 | 24 | 47 | 37 |
| 16 | Cray Wanderers | 36 | 4 | 4 | 10 | 22 | 37 | 4 | 2 | 12 | 24 | 46 | 30 |
| 17 | Hythe United | 36 | 2 | 2 | 14 | 19 | 45 | 5 | 1 | 12 | 20 | 54 | 24 |
| 18 | Crockenhill | 36 | 2 | 4 | 12 | 25 | 47 | 2 | 6 | 10 | 20 | 47 | 22 |
| 19 | Whitstable Town | 36 | 4 | 2 | 12 | 19 | 35 | 1 | 1 | 16 | 13 | 51 | 18 |

\* Points Awarded    \*\* Points Deducted

## DIVISION ONE RESULTS & ATTENDANCES CHART 1998-99

| | | 1 | 2 | 3 | 4 | 5 | 6 | 7 | 8 | 9 | 10 | 11 | 12 | 13 | 14 | 15 | 16 | 17 | 18 | 19 |
|---|---|---|---|---|---|---|---|---|---|---|---|---|---|---|---|---|---|---|---|---|
| 1 | Beckenham Town | X | 0-4 | 0-1 | 4-1 | 3-0 | 2-1 | 0-1 | 0-1 | 2-3 | 1-3 | 3-0 | 1-2 | 4-2 | 1-1 | 1-3 | 2-0 | 1-2 | 3-3 | 2-1 |
| 2 | Canterbury City | 0-3 | X | 1-2 | 1-3 | 2-2 | 3-2 | 1-4 | 0-1 | 0-4 | 0-5 | 2-0 | 2-0 | 1-2 | 0-4 | 1-1 | 0-5 | 0-5 | 0-0 | 4-1 |
| 3 | Chatham Town | 2-2 | 2-3 | X | 1-3 | 1-1 | 3-2 | 0-3 | 0-2 | 4-2 | 0-2 | 4-0 | 5-1 | 0-1 | 0-3 | 3-5 | 1-3 | 0-5 | 0-5 | 4-2 |
| 4 | Cray Wanderers | 1-2 | 6-1 | 1-4 | X | 1-1 | 2-0 | 0-5 | 0-1 | 2-4 | 1-1 | 0-1 | 1-2 | 1-3 | 2-2 | 1-1 | 2-0 | 0-6 | 0-3 | 1-0 |
| 5 | Crockenhill | 0-0 | 1-1 | 0-2 | 3-0 | X | 1-1 | 0-3 | 3-5 | 2-6 | 1-2 | 4-4 | 1-3 | 1-2 | 0-4 | 1-3 | 1-4 | 0-4 | 2-3 | 4-0 |
| 6 | Dartford | 1-0 | 0-1 | 4-0 | 3-0 | 3-1 | X | 0-3 | 0-3 | 4-4 | 1-1 | 0-0 | 3-1 | 2-0 | 1-4 | 2-1 | 1-1 | 3-2 | 4-2 | 2-1 |
| 7 | Deal Town | 3-0 | 7-0 | 5-1 | 5-1 | 7-0 | 3-3 | X | 1-0 | 2-2 | 6-1 | 1-0 | 6-0 | 4-2 | 0-0 | 5-0 | 1-1 | 3-1 | 7-1 | 4-0 |
| 8 | Dover Athletic | 2-0 | 5-0 | 4-0 | 6-0 | 4-2 | 7-3 | 1-1 | X | 2-3 | 2-1 | 6-1 | 2-2 | 3-0 | 4-0 | 4-0 | 1-4 | 3-0 | 1-3 | 3-0 |
| 9 | Folkestone Invicta | 0-3 | 2-3 | 5-2 | 5-2 | 6-1 | 3-1 | 1-3 | 0-4 | X | 6-0 | 3-1 | 1-2 | 3-2 | 1-2 | 3-1 | 2-2 | 3-1 | 4-2 | 2-0 |
| 10 | Hastings Town | 1-1 | 1-0 | 3-1 | 1-1 | 1-1 | 2-1 | 0-3 | 1-3 | 3-2 | X | 3-1 | 4-0 | 0-2 | 0-4 | 2-3 | 1-0 | 1-0 | 2-1 | 1-1 |
| 11 | Herne Bay | 1-0 | 0-2 | 1-2 | 2-4 | 1-1 | 1-3 | 1-1 | 0-4 | 2-0 | 5-1 | X | 4-1 | 4-2 | 1-3 | 3-3 | 1-2 | 0-1 | 2-2 | 3-1 |
| 12 | Hythe United | 1-3 | 1-2 | 0-2 | 4-2 | 1-2 | 1-2 | 1-3 | 0-4 | 1-1 | 2-3 | 0-3 | X | 2-2 | 0-1 | 1-1 | 5-1 | 1-4 | 3-0 |  |
| 13 | Lordswood | 1-1 | 4-1 | 0-2 | 1-6 | 2-1 | 2-1 | 0-1 | 2-5 | 2-2 | 3-0 | 1-0 | 5-1 | X | 2-2 | 0-1 | 1-1 | 5-1 | 1-4 | 3-0 |
| 14 | Margate | 0-0 | 3-0 | 2-1 | 4-0 | 3-1 | 1-0 | 1-0 | 2-0 | 1-1 | 6-0 | 2-0 | 8-1 | 5-1 | X | 1-1 | 0-2 | 0-0 | 1-1 | 3-0 |
| 15 | Ramsgate | 2-1 | 5-1 | 1-1 | 2-0 | 4-2 | 2-1 | 0-5 | 1-3 | 2-3 | 0-0 | 4-0 | 2-1 | 2-2 | 2-3 | X | 6-0 | 1-0 | 1-1 | 3-1 |
| 16 | Sittingbourne | 2-0 | 2-3 | 1-1 | 0-0 | 4-0 | 0-0 | 1-3 | 1-3 | 1-4 | 1-1 | 2-4 | 3-1 | 1-1 | 1-2 | 2-3 | X | 1-0 | 0-4 | 3-1 |
| 17 | Swanley Furness | 1-0 | 2-1 | 1-0 | 1-0 | 2-3 | 4-1 | 4-1 | 0-3 | 3-1 | 2-0 | 1-1 | 3-0 | 4-2 | 1-1 | 2-3 | 2-2 | X | 0-3 | 2-0 |
| 18 | Thamesmead Town | 1-1 | 4-0 | 4-2 | 1-0 | 1-1 | 2-3 | 1-3 | 2-1 | 2-3 | 3-3 | 6-3 | 3-1 | 2-1 | 0-7 | 3-3 | 3-0 | 0-1 | X | 6-1 |
| 19 | Whitstable Town | 1-0 | 2-1 | 1-3 | 2-1 | 1-0 | 0-1 | 0-1 | 0-6 | 3-3 | 2-3 | 1-2 | 0-1 | 1-3 | 0-1 | 1-1 | 1-2 | 2-3 | 1-3 | X |

## MISCELLANEOUS TRIVIA

| | | | | | |
|---|---|---|---|---|---|
| BEST HOME WIN | Premier Division | 8-0 | Deal Town | v | Erith Town |
| | | 7-0 | Ramsgate | v | Canterbury City |
| | Division One | 7-0 | Deal Town | v | Canterbury City |
| | | 7-0 | Deal Town | v | Crockenhill |
| BEST AWAY WIN | Premier Division | 8-0 | Ramsgate at Tunbridge Wells | | |
| | | 6-0 | Whitstable Town at Erith Town | | |
| | Division One | 7-0 | Margate at Thamesmead Town | | |
| | | 6-0 | Dover Athletic at Whitstable Town | | |
| | | 6-0 | Swanley Furness at Cray Wanderers | | |

| | | |
|---|---|---|
| AVERAGE NUMBER OF GOALS PER GAME | Premier Division | 2.98 per game |
| | Division One | 3.62 per game |

# GOLDEN BOOT AWARD 1998-99

| PREMIER DIVISION | | | DIVISION ONE | | |
|---|---|---|---|---|---|
| Dean Bowey | Ramsgate | 31 Goals | Nick Arundel | Deal Town** | 26 Goals |
| Steve Jones | Chatham Town | 22 Goals | Jon Utterson | Margate | 26 Goals |
| Tunde Utsaja* | Slade Green | 20 Goals | Danny Sweeting | Swanley Furness | 25 Goals |

## PREMIER DIVISION CUP 1998-99

**FIRST ROUND**

| | | | | | | | | |
|---|---|---|---|---|---|---|---|---|
| Chatham Town | v | Greenwich Borough | 4-1 | | Sheppey United | v | Deal Town | 0-3 |
| Thamesmead Town | v | Crockenhill | 0-2 | | | | | |

**SECOND ROUND**

| | | | | | | | | |
|---|---|---|---|---|---|---|---|---|
| Chatham Town | v | Slade Green | 2-0 | | Beckenham Town | v | Deal Town | 2-3 |
| Cray Wanderers | v | Lordswood | 1-0 | | Whitstable Town | v | Ramsgate | 0-2 |
| Herne Bay | v | Tunbridge Wells | 1-0 | | Canterbury City | v | VCD Athletic | 1-3 |
| Erith Town | v | Crockenhill | 0-2 | | Faversham Town | v | Hythe United | 2-1, 1-3 |

**QUARTER-FINAL**

| | | | | | | | | |
|---|---|---|---|---|---|---|---|---|
| Chatham Town | v | Deal Town | 0-2 | | Cray Wanderers | v | Ramsgate | 0-1 |
| Herne Bay | v | VCD Athletic | 1-4 | | Crockenhill | v | Hythe United | 2-0 |

**SEMI-FINAL**

| | | | | | | | | |
|---|---|---|---|---|---|---|---|---|
| Deal Town | v | Ramsgate | 1-0, 2-2 | | VCD Athletic | v | Crockenhill | 0-0, 1-1 |

**FINAL**

| | | | |
|---|---|---|---|
| Deal Town | v | VCD Athletic | 1-0 |

## DIVISION ONE CUP 1998-99

**FIRST ROUND**

| | | | | | | | | |
|---|---|---|---|---|---|---|---|---|
| Margate | v | Hythe United | 1-2 | | Dartford | v | Beckenham Town | 3-2 |
| Herne Bay | v | Cray Wanderers | 0-1 | | | | | |

**SECOND ROUND**

| | | | | | | | | |
|---|---|---|---|---|---|---|---|---|
| Canterbury City | v | Hythe United | 2-5 | | Crockenhill | v | Deal Town | 0-1 |
| Hastings Town | v | Folkestone Invicta | 2-5 | | Thamesmead Town | v | Dartford | 1-2 |
| Swanley Furness | v | Chatham Town | 4-3 | | Whitstable Town | v | Lordswood | 3-3, 2-0 |
| Ramsgate | v | Sittingbourne | 1-1, 0-1 | | Cray Wanderers | v | Dover Athletic | 1-1, 1-2 |

**QUARTER-FINAL**

| | | | | | | | | |
|---|---|---|---|---|---|---|---|---|
| Hythe United | v | Deal Town | 0-10 | | Folkestone Invicta | v | Dartford | 2-3 |
| Swanley Furness | v | Whitstable Town | 4-4, 3-1 | | Sittingbourne | v | Dover Athletic | 0-0 |

**SEMI-FINAL**

| | | | | | | | | |
|---|---|---|---|---|---|---|---|---|
| Deal Town | v | Dartford | 3-2, 0-0 | | Swanley Furness | v | Dover Athletic | 0-0, 1-3 |

**FINAL**

| | | | |
|---|---|---|---|
| Deal Town | v | Dover Athletic | 0-2 |

## KENT INTERMEDIATE CUP 1998-99

**FIRST ROUND**

| | | | | | | | | |
|---|---|---|---|---|---|---|---|---|
| Canterbury City | v | VCD Athletic | 0-1 | | Cray Wanderers | v | Thamesmead Town | 2-4 |
| Gravesend & North. | v | Deal Town | 3-5 | | Ramsgate | v | Folkestone Invicta | 1-2 |
| Chatham Town | v | Erith Town | 2-1 | | Hythe United | v | Crockenhill | 5-2 |
| Knatchbull | v | Tonbridge | 1-4 | | | | | |

**SECOND ROUND**

| | | | | | | | | |
|---|---|---|---|---|---|---|---|---|
| VCD Athletic | v | Thamesmead Town | 0-6 | | Herne Bay | v | Deal Town | 0-5 |
| Folkestone Invicta | v | Dover Athletic | 0-3 | | Chatham Town | v | Whitstable Town | 2-0 |
| Dartford | v | Beckenham T 1-1, 3-3, 2p4 | | | Hythe United | v | Tonbridge | 0-6 |
| Margate | v | Fisher Athletic | 0-1 | | Sittingbourne | v | Lordswood | 1-0 |

**THIRD ROUND**

| | | | | | | | | |
|---|---|---|---|---|---|---|---|---|
| Thamesmead Town | v | Deal Town | 3-3, 0-2 | | Dover Athletic | v | Chatham Town | 2-1 |
| Beckenham Town | v | Tonbridge | 1-0 | | Fisher Athletic | v | Sittingbourne | 0-0, 2-1 |

**SEMI-FINAL**

| | | | | | | | | |
|---|---|---|---|---|---|---|---|---|
| Deal Town | v | Dover Athletic | 4-3 | | Beckenham Town | v | Fisher Athletic | 1-3 |

**FINAL**

| | | | |
|---|---|---|---|
| Deal Town | v | Fisher Athletic | 1-3 |

# BECKENHAM TOWN

**Secretary:** Peter Palmer, 107 Wentworth Rd, West Croydon, Surrey CR0 3HZ
Tel: 0181 689 2134 Mobile 0374 728758

**Ground:** Eden Park Avenue, Beckenham, Kent  Tel: 0181 650 1066

**Directions:** M25, A21 to Bromley then follow signs to Beckenham. Ground 1 mile west of town off A214, 2 mins walk from Eden Park (BR) station - trains from London Bridge. Bus 264

**Capacity:** 4,000  **Seats:** 120  **Cover:** 120  **Floodlights:** Yes

**Clubhouse:** All day opening at weekends. Hot & cold food, teas, etc. Bar & dance area. Pool & fruit machines  Club Shop: Yes

**HONOURS** London Spartan Lg Cup R-up 77-78 78-79, Kent Snr Tphy R-up 81-82 93-94,
Kent Lg Cup R-up 84-85 92-93 (Div 2 Cup R-up 90-91)

**PREVIOUS** **Leagues:** S. E. London Amtr 71-73; Metropolitan 73-75; London Spartan 75-82
**Ground:** Stanhope Grove, Beckenham (60 yrs)

**RECORD** **Gate:** 720 v Berkhamsted F.A.Cup 94-95
**Scorer:** Ricky Bennett  **Appearances:** Lee Fabian

**FACT FILE**
Reformed: 1971
Nickname: Reds
Colours: Red & white/red/white
Change Colours: Yellow/black/black
Midweek matchday: Tuesday
Programme: 8 pages, 50p
Editor: Bob Chilvers (0181 301 2624)

**CLUB PERSONNEL**
Chairman: K.Bell
Vice Chairman: B Hollaway
Manager: Kevin Sugrue
Asst Manager: J Moore

# CANTERBURY CITY

**Secretary:** Keith J Smith, 7 Knight Ave, London Rd Est, Canterbury, Kent CT2 8PZ
Tel: 01227 456116

**Ground:** Kingsmead Stadium, Kingsmead Road, Canterbury CT2 7PH (01227 457245)

**Directions:** A28 out of city centre into Military Road. At 1st r-about turn leftinto Tourtel Rd, proceed to next r-about and head straight over into KingsmeadRd - stadium on right opposite Canterbury swimming pool. Half mile from Canterbury West (BR). Bus service 20 from GRavel Walk in city centre

**Capacity:** 5,000 **Cover:** 200  **Seats:** 200  **Floodlights:** Yes  **Club Shop:** Yes

**Clubhouse:** Lounge bar open on matchdays. Snack bar, burgers, hot-dogs, tea, coffee, etc

**HONOURS** Kent Lg Div 2 Cup 49-50 89-90, Div 1 Cup 49-50; Kent Sen. Cup 53-54; Kent
Sen. Trophy 79-80; Kent I'mediate Cup 73-74; Kent Messenger Trophy 74-75;
Frank Norris Mem. Shield 88-89 89-90; Kent Lge Div 2 Champ Res 90-91

**PREVIOUS** **Leagues:** Kent 47-59; Metropolitan 59-60; Southern 60-94
**Name:** Canterbury Waverley  **Grounds:** Wincheap Grove, Bretts Corner 47-58

**BEST SEASON** **FA Cup:** 1st Rd 64-65, 0-6 v Torquay; 68-69, 0-1 v Swindon

**CLUB RECORDS** **Attendance:** 3,542 v Chelsea, Friendly **Win:** 10-0 v Deal Town (H), Southern
Lge 30/1/65 **Defeat:** 0-9 v Corby Town (A), Southern Lge 16/9/63 **Goalscorer:** Wilf Heathcote 113
(48-51) **Appearances:** John Carragher 627 (60-70) **Fee Paid:** £2,000 for Graham Knight
(Maidstone United) **Fee Recieved:** £2,000 for Dave Wiltshire (Gillingham)

**FACT FILE**
Founded: 1947  Nickname: The City
Sponsors: Gladwish Land Sales
Colours: Green & white/white/green & white
Change: Red & black/black/red
Midweek matchday: Wednesday
Reserve's League: Kent Lge Div 1
Programme: 32 pages, 50p
Editor: Keith Smith (01227 456116)
98-99 Captain: Gary Hake
Top scorer: Mark Pollard (11)
P.o.Y.: Andy Keir
Supporters P.o.Y.: Andy Keir

**CLUB PERSONNEL**
Chairman: Tony Roberts
Vice Chairman: TBA
President: V H Heslop
Comm Manager: Geoff Roberts
Managers: Meirion George/Simon Tutt
Physio: David Chapman-Jones

# CHATHAM TOWN

**Secretary:** Brian Burcombe, 4 Hallwood Close, Parkwood, Rainham, Kent ME8 9NT
Tel: 01634 363419

**Ground:** Maidstone Road Sports Ground, Maidstone Road, Chatham, Kent Tel: 01634 812194

**Directions:** M2, A229 Chatham turn-off, follow signs to Chatham, ground one and a half miles
on right opposite garage. 1 mile from Chatham (BR)

**Capacity:** 5,000  **Seats:** 500  **Cover:** 1,000  **Floodlights:** Yes

**Clubhouse:** Matchdays and functions

**HONOURS** Kent Lg(9) 1894-95 03-05 24-25 26-27 71-72 73-74 76-77 79-80 (R-up 02-03
03-24 25-26 70-71 74-75 80-81, Lg Cup 71-72 76-77 (R-up(3)), Thames & Medway Comb.(5)
1896-97 04-06 19-20 23-24, Kent Snr Cup 1888-89 1904-05 10-11 18-19, Kent Snr Shield 19-20

**PREVIOUS** **Names:** Chatham FC; Medway FC (1970s) **Leagues:** Southern (several
spells); Aetolian 59-64; Metropolitan 64-68;Kent (Sev. spells)
**Ground:** Great Lines, Chatham 1882-90

**BEST SEASON** **FA Cup:** QF 1888-89 (incl 2-0 v Nottm Forest  2-0) **FA Trophy:** 3rd Rd 70-71
**RECORD** **Gate:** 5,000 v Gillingham, 1980

**FACT FILE**
Founded: 1882
Nickname: Chats
Sponsors: Topps Scaffolding
Colours: Red & black/black/black
Change Colours: Yellow & green
Midweek matchday: Tuesday
Programme: 24 pages, 60p
Editor: John Crow

**CLUB PERSONNEL**
Chairman: P Enright
President:
Manager: Steve Hearn
Asst Manager: Dave Bourne

# CRAY WANDERERS

**Secretary:** Mr Kerry Phillips, 15 Watling Street, Bexleyheath, Kent DA6 7QJ(01322 554108)

**Ground:** Bromley F.C. Hayes Lane, Bromley, Kent BR2 9EF (0181 460 5291 or 0181 313 3992)

**Directions:** One mile from Bromley South (BR). Buses 316, 146 and 119 passground. Junction 4 off M25, then A21 towards London

Capacity: 5,000    Cover: 2,500    Seats: 1,300    Floodlights: Yes

**Clubhouse:** Open pub hours (freehouse). Hot & cold food available    Club Shop: Yes

**HONOURS** London Lg(2) 56-58 (Lg Cup 54-55), Aetolian Lg 62-63 (Lg Cup 63-64), GtrLondon Lg 65-66 (Lg Cup(2) 64-66), Metropolitan Lg Cup 70-71 (Amtr Cup(2) 66-68), London Spartan Lg(2) 76-78, Kent Lg 01-02 80-81 (R-up 79-80 90-91, Lg Cup 83-84), Kent Snr Tphy 92-93, Kent Amtr Cup(4) 30-31 62-65

**PREVIOUS** Leagues: Kent 1894-1903 6-7 9-14 34-38; W Kent 03-06 07-09; London 20-34 51-59; Kent Amtr 38-39 46-51; S London All 43-46; Aetolian 59-64; GtrLondon 64-66; Metropolitan 66-71; London Metropolitan 71-75; London Spartan 75-78
**Grounds:** Star Lane; Tothills; Twysden; Fordcroft; Grassmeade, St Mary Cray

**CLUB RECORDS Gate:** 1,523 v Stamford, F.A. Vase QF 79-80
**Goalscorer:** Ken Collishaw, 272    **Appearances:** John Dorey c500, 61-72
**Win:** 15-0 v Sevenoaks, 1894-95    **Defeat:** 1-11 v Bromley, 20-21

**FACT FILE**
Founded: 1860
Nickname: Wands
Sponsors: N.Hillman & Sons
Colours: Amber & black
Change Colours: Purple & white
Midweek matchday: Wednesday
Programme: 24 pages, 50p
Editor/Press Officer: Greg Mann
Tel: 0181 318 9604(H) 0171 500 4496B)

**CLUB PERSONNEL**
Chairman: Gary Hillman
President: Bill Faulkner
Director of Football: FranJk Maloney
1st Team Manager:T.B.A.
Asst.Manager: Alan Hudson
Reserve Team Manager: John Barnes
Coach: Peter Little

---

# DEAL TOWN

**Secretary:** Miss Lynne Fox, 32 Manor Road, Deal, Kent CT14 9BX    Tel: 01304 361163

**Ground:** Charles Sports Ground, St Leonards Road, Deal, Kent    Tel: 01304 375623

**Directions:** A258 through Walmer, left into Cornwell Road, continue intoHamilton Road, veer left into Mill Rd, follow round to right into Manor Road, right into St Leonards Road, ground 100 yards on right. 1 mile from both Walmerand Deal BR stations. Local buses stop near ground

Capacity: 2,000    Seats: 150    Cover: 500    Floodlights: Yes

**Clubhouse:** Matchdays & functions. Bar. Tea bar with hot & cold food    Club Shop: No

**HONOURS** Kent Lg 53-54 (R-up 88-89, Lg Cup 57-58 81-82 (R-up 94-95), Kent Snr Tphy 94-95 R-up 82-83 90-91, Gtr London Lg Cup 67-68, Aetolian LgR-up 59-60

**PREVIOUS** Leagues: Kent 09-59; Aetolian 59-63; Southern 63-66; Gtr London 66-71

**RECORDS** **Gate:** 4,000 v Billy Wright showbiz XI, Feb '61
**Scorer:** Joe Brayne 175
**Appearances:** Alan Barrow 544 (recent times)

Player progressing: Danny Wallace (Southampton)

**FACT FILE**
Founded: 1908    Nickname: Town
Sponsors: Mencare Ltd
Colours: Black & white hoops/white/b & w hoops
Change: Yellow & Blue halves/blue/blue
Midweek matchday: Tuesday
Reserves' Lge: Winstonlead Div 2
Programme: 32 pages, 50p
Editor: Colin Adams (01304 372784)
97-98 - Captain: Colin Gilmore
Top Scorer: Simon Bryant 40
P.o.Y.: Simon Bryant

**CLUB PERSONNEL**
Chairman: Roy Smith
Vice-Chairman: Graham Jones
Fixture Sec: Colin Adams (01304 372784)
Press Officer: Tommy Sampson
Tel: 01622 891784
Manager: Tommy Sampson
Asst Manager: Keith Lissenden

---

# ERITH TOWN

**Secretary:** J R Kelly, 88 Hook Lane, Welling, Kent DA16 2DP
Tel: 0181 303 8977

**Ground:** Shared with Greenwich Borough
Harrow Meadow, Eltham Green Rd, Eltham,London SE9 (0181 850 3098)

**Directions:** South Circular (A205) to Yorkshire Grey pub, ground opposite. 1mile from both Eltham and Kidbrooke BR stations

Capacity: 2,500    Seats: 50    Cover: 50    Floodlights: Yes

**PREVIOUS** **Ground:** Flamingo Park, Sidcup (pre 1994)

**FACT FILE**

Colours: Red & blue/black/black
Change Colours: Yellow/black/black
Midweek matchday: Tuesday

**CLUB PERSONNEL**

Chairman: Phillip Legg

# FAVERSHAM TOWN

**FACT FILE**
Founded: 1901
Nickname: Town
Colours: White/blue/red
Change Colours: Red/white/blue
Midweek matchday: Tuesday
Reserves' League: Kent Lg Div 2
Programme: 16 pages, 40p
Editor: Quiram Aisani

**Secretary:** Reg Parr

**Ground:** New Stadium, Salters Lane, Faversham, Kent (01795 532738)

**Directions:** On A2 (Canterbury road) just west of town
Capacity: 2,000      Seats: 350      Cover: 1,500      Floodlights: Yes

**Clubhouse:** Open matchdays (Sat/Sun/Tues) Wed/Thurs. Snacks sold

**HONOURS** Kent Lg 69-70 70-71 77-78 89-90, R-up 87-88, Lg Cup 70-71 90-91, R-up 82-83,
Kent Snr Tphy 76-77 77-78 (R-up 87-88 88-89),
Kent Amtr Cup 56-57 58-59 71-72 72-73 73-74

**CLUB PERSONNEL**
Chairman: Sal Aisani
President: Cris Aisani
Commercial Mgr: Terry Whitehead
Manager: John Glover
Coach: Bob Mason

**PREVIOUS** **Leagues:** Aetolian 59-64; Metropolitan 64-71; Athenian 71-76
**Grounds:** Ashford Rd 1901-46; Gordon Square 46-58

**RECORD** **Gate:** 1,400 v Sheppey Utd, 1949
**Scorer:** Tony Rudd 43        **Appearances:** Bob Mason
**Win:** 8-0 v Greenwich B., Aug'89      **Defeat:** 0-9 v Sittingbourne, Jan '82

---

# GREENWICH BOROUGH

**FACT FILE**
Founded: 1928
Nickname: Boro
Colours: All Red
Change Colours: All black
Midweek matchday: Tuesday
Programme: 16 pages, 50p
Editor: Keith Harmer

**Secretary:** Ms Denise Richmond, 7 Castlecombe Rd, Mottingham, London SE9 6BA
Tel: 0181 289 8956

**Ground:** Harrow Meadow, Eltham Green Rd, Eltham, London SE9      Tel: 0181 850 5360

**Directions:** South Circular (A205) to McDonalds, grd opposite.
1 mile from both Eltham and Kidbrooke BR stations

Capacity: 2,500      Seats: 5o      Cover: 50Floodlights: Yes
**Clubhouse:** Yes

**HONOURS** London Spartan Lg 79-80 (Lg Cup 82-83), Kent Lg 86-87 87-88 (Lg Cup 84-85
86-87), Kent Snr Tphy 84-85, FA Vase 5th Rd 89-90

**CLUB PERSONNEL**
President: R Moore
Chairman: P Meagan
Manager: Dave Mehmet
Asst Manager: R Dowling

**PREVIOUS** **Leagues:** South London Alliance; Kent Amateur; London Spartan 77-84
**Ground:** Erith & Belvedere F.C. 1992-93
**Name:** London Borough of Greenwich

**RECORD** **Gate:** 2,000 v Charlton, floodlight opening, 1978
**Defeat** : 0-8 v Faversham Town, August 1989

---

# HERNE BAY

**FACT FILE**
Founded: 1886Nickname: The Bay
Colours: Blue & white halves
Change Colours: Red & black halves
Midweek matchday: Tuesday
Reserves' League: Kent Lge Div One
Programme: 36 pages, 70p
Editor/Press Off.: Doug Smith (01227742182)
98-99- Captain: Martin Collins
P.o.Y.: Gareth Williams
Top Scorer: Ian Austin

**Secretary:** L Gladwish, 41 Strangers Lane, Canterbury, Kent CT1 3XJ   Tel: 01227 451529

**Ground:** Winch's Field, Stanley Gardens, Herne Bay, Kent      Tel: 01227 374156

**Directions:** Leave new Thanet Way at Herne Bay/Canterbury exit. Follow signs toHerne
Bay via Canterbury Road. After railway bridge (1/2 mile), take first leftinto
SpencerRoad, then first left into Stanley Gardens, Ground on left

Capacity: 4,000      Seats: 200      Cover: 1,500      Floodlights: Yes
Club Shop: Yes            **Clubhouse:** Open matchdays

**HONOURS** Kent Lg 91-92 94-95 96-97 97-98, (R-up 92-93), Div 2 62-63 63-64, R-up92-
93(res) 94-95(res), Lg Cup 96-97, R-up 78-79 97-98, Div 2 Cup 53-54; Kent
Snr Tphy 78-79, 96-97; Kent Amtr Cup 57-58 (R-up 58-59 63-64 68-69 72-73);
Aetolian LgDiv 2 62-63 63-64 (Lg Cup R-up 62-63), Div 2 Cup 62-63 63-64;
Athenian Lg Div 2 70-71 (Lg Cup 66-67); Kent Amtr Lg Cup 53-54 54-55;
Thames & Medway Comb. CupR-up 61-62; FA Cup 4th Qual. Rd 70-71 86-87.

**CLUB PERSONNEL**
Chairman: J Bathurst
Vice Chairman: W Dordoy
President: J Hodkinson
Manager: Geoff Record
Asst. ManagerSteve Brown
Physio: J.Hodkinson

**PREVIOUS** Leagues: East Kent, Faversham & Dist, Canterbury & Dist, Kent Amateur,
Kent 53-59, Aetolian 59-64, Athenian 64-74      **Ground:** Memorial Park 1886-1953

**RECORDS** **Attendance:** 2,303 v Margate, FA Cup 4th Qual. Rd 70-71
**Win:** 15-1; v Canterbury Gas & Water, Kent Amateur Lge 1952
**Defeat:** 0-11 v RAF Manston, Kent Amateur Lge 1935
**Fee received:** £3,000 for Mark Munday (Gravesend) 1994

FAVERSHAM TOWN                                                    Photo: Martin Alsop

CANTERBURY CITY FC: Back Row (L-R): Simon Tutt (joint manager), Dan Hudd, Matt Tutt, Chris Wood, Mark Rees, Andy Keir, Lee Bosson, Adam Stembridge, Mark Pollard, David Chapman-Jones (club doctor). Front Row: Mick Flockhart, Lee Jones, Gary Hake, Scott Wilson, Trevor Santer, Neil Northcott, Garry Elliott, Meirion George (joint manager). Photo: Courtesy of Canterbury Times

"Who pinched the ball?" Action from Erith Town v Ramsgate              Photo: Gordon Whittington

# HYTHE UNITED (1992)

**Secretary:** Martin R Giles, 21 Wych Elm Way, Hythe, Kent. CT21 6QE
Tel: 01303 265962 (H) 01303 267619 (B)

**Ground:** Reachfields Stadium, Fort Rd, Hythe, Kent.  Tel: 01303 264932 or 238256

**Directions:** On A259 west out of Hythe, turn left after light railway lights (Fort Road), entrance at end
Capacity: 3,000  Seats: 400  Cover: 2,400  Floodlights: Yes

**Clubhouse:** Bar open weekends/matchdays & training nights
**Club Shop:** No

**HONOURS** None as Hythe United

**PREVIOUS** Leagues: Kent County Lge

**RECORD** Attendance: 1,655 v Crystal Palace 97-98

### FACT FILE
Founded: 1992
Sponsor: H V Wooding Ltd
Colours: All Red
Change Colours: All blue
Midweek Matchday: Tuesday
Youth League: Kent Youth
Programme: 50p
Editor: T.B.A.
98-99 - Captain: Andy Laker
Top Scorer: Phil Hancock
P.o.Y.: Phil Hancock

### CLUB PERSONNEL
Chairman: David Clapson
President: Rt Hon Michael Howard QC
Press Officer: M R Giles
Manager: David Linstrem
Physio: Frank Barham

---

# LORDSWOOD

**Secretary:** Steve Lewis, Sunnybrook, Gorsewood Road, Hartley, Longfield, Kent DA3 7DF.
Tel: 01474 708233 (H) 01474 708233 (B) 07775 541573 (M)

**Ground:** Lordswood Sports & Social Club  Tel: 01634 669138
North Dane Way, Walderslade, Chatham, Kent ME5 9XX
**Directions:**

Capacity: 600  Seats: 125  Cover: No  Floodlights: Yes

**Clubhouse:** Yes  **Club Shop:** No

**HONOURS** None

**PREVIOUS** **Leagues:** Kent County Lge

**RECORD** **Attendance:** 386

### FACT FILE
Founded: 1968
Nickname: Lords
Colours: Orange/black/black
Change Colours: All green
Midweek Matchday: Tuesday/Thursday
Reserve or Youth League: Both
Programme: Yes
Editor: D Harman

### CLUB PERSONNEL
Chairman: D Sims
Vice Chairman: D Caulfield
Press Officer: D Harman
Manager: B Zillwood

---

# RAMSGATE

**Secretary/Press Officer:** Steve Lancaster. 66 Park Avenue, Birchington, Kent  Tel: 01843 597703

**Ground:** Southwood Stadium, Prices Avenue, Ramsgate, Kent  Tel: 01843 591662

**Directions:** From London on A229, A253 into Ramsgate - left into Netherhill atr'bout, right into Ashburnham Rd, right into Southwood Rd. 15 mins walk from Ramsgate BR station; walk thru Warre Recreation Ground, along St Lawrence HighStr., left at `White Horse', follow Southwood Rd and turn right into PricesAvenue

**Capacity:** 5,000  Seats: 400  Cover: 600  Floodlights: Yes

**Clubhouse:** Open matchdays & private functions. Two bars, two pool tables,darts. Hot & cold food on matchdays  Club Shop: No

**HONOURS** Kent Lg 49-50 55-56 56-57 (Lg Cup 48-49 92-93 93-94 94-95 ) Kent I'mediate Cup 54-55, Kent Snr Cup 63-64, Thames & Medway Cup 60-61, KentSnr Shield 60-61, Kent Floodlit Tphy 69-70, Kent Snr Tphy(2) 87-89

**PREVIOUS** **Leagues:** Southern 59-75
**Name:** Ramsgate Athletic

**RECORDS** **Gate:** 5,200 v Margate, 56-57
**Scorer:** Mick Williamson
**Win:** 9-1 v Crockenhill, Kent League Cup 22/1/94

### FACT FILE
Founded: 1946
Nickname: Rams
Sponsors: Hoverspeed
Colours: Red & white
Change Colours: White/blue/blue
Midweek matchday: Tuesday
Reserves' League: Kent Lge Div. Two
Programme: 28 pages
Editor: Steve Redford (01843 596138)

### CLUB PERSONNEL
Chairman: R Lawson
Vice Chairman: C Payne
President: Tom Pendry
Commercial Manager: Martin Power
Tel: 01843 597703
Manager/Coach: Lennie Lee
Asst Manager: Dave Bostock
Physio: John Burroughs

WHITSTABLE TOWN                                                    Photo: Eric Marsh

Ramsgate celebrate with the Kent League Championship trophy and the Kent Plaaya Senior Trophy.    Photo: Gordon Whittington

LORDSWOOD FC: Back Row (L-R): Andy Taylor, Steve Clements, Andy Battersby, Ray Broad, Paul Piggott, David Johnson, Damon Verrall, Lee Young. Front Row: Neil Crust, Karl Rolls, Grant Gallacher, Neville Jee, Kevin Parry.    Photo: Alan Coomes

# SHEPPEY UNITED

**Secretary:** Barry H Bundock, Dunedin, 104 Southsea Ave., Minster, Sheerness, Kent ME12 2NH
Tel: 01795 876025 (H)  0374 112834 (Mobile)
**Ground:** Sittingbourne F.C. - Central Park, Eurolink,Sittingbourne, Kent ME10 3SB
Tel: 01795 435077 Fax: 01474 814501
**Directions:** Through Sittingbourne on main A2, club signposted clearly and regularly from both
east and west. 1 mile from Sittingbourne BR station
**Capacity:** 8,000    **Cover:** 3,300    **Seats:** 2,000    **Floodlights:** 420 lux
**HONOURS**   Kent Lg(6) 05-07 27-28 72-73 74-75 78-79 94-95, (R-up 03-04 04-05 77-78
83-84, Lg Cup 75-76 78-79, Div 2(res) 32-33 84-85 (R-up 1894-95 1979-80);Thames &
Medway Comb. 08-09 12-13 22-23 25-26 28-29 55-56; Kent Amtr Cup 45-4651-52;
Kent Snr Shield 77-78; Kent Snr Cup R-up(3); Gtr London Lg 64-65.
**BEST SEASON**    **FA Cup:** 6th Qual. Rd 1919-20
**FA Trophy:** 1st Rd Proper 85-86
**PREVIOUS**    **Leagues:** Southern 1894-1901 84-91; Kent 01-27 32-59 72-84; Aetolian 59-;
Gtr London 64-65; Metropolitan Lg 65-71
**Name:** Sheppey Athletic/Ites
**Ground:** Botany Road, St Georges Avenue, Sheerness (pre-1992)
**RECORD**    **Gate:** 4,000 v Sittingbourne, Kent Senior Trophy 1927 (at Botany Road)
**Players progressing:** E C Harper (England, Blackburn, Spurs, Preston)

**FACT FILE**

Founded: 1890
Nickname: Islanders or Ites
Colours: Red & white/white
Change colours: Blue & white stripes
Midweek matchday: Tuesday
Programme: 20 pages, 50p

**CLUB PERSONNEL**

Chairman: Peter Sharrock
Manager: Wayne Barlow

---

# SLADE GREEN

**Secretary:**    Bruce Smith, 15 Gumping Rd, Orpington, Kent BR5 1RX Tel: 01689 858782
**Ground:**    The Small Glen, Moat Lane, Slade Green, Erith, Kent Tel: 01322 351077
**Directions:**    Off A206 between Erith & Dartford.
400 yards from Slade Green BR station. Buses 89 & B13
**Capacity:** 3,000    **Seats:** 150    **Cover:** 400    **Floodlights:** Yes
**Clubhouse:** Yes; Hall, Directors Lounge & Canteen    **Club Shop:** No
**HONOURS**    Kent Snr Tphy 91-92 (R-up 80-81); Kent Lg Cup 82-83; Kent Amtr Lg 52-53 53-54
60-61 (Lg Cup 60-61); Kent Intermediate Cup 61-62; Kent Benevolent Cup46-47;
West Kent  60-61 65-66; Dartford Lg R-up 48-49 (Lg Cup 47-48 (R-up 46-47)); Erith
Hospitals Cup 46-47 48-49; Gtr London Lg R-up 68-69; Plumstead Challenge Cup
48-49
**PREVIOUS**    Leagues: Dartford 46-52; Kent Amateur 52-62; Greater London 62-70
Name: Slade Green Athletic 46-86
**RECORDS**    **Attendance:** 3,000 v Millwall, friendly 25/7/92
**Goalscorer:** Colin Dwyer    **Appearances:** Colin Dwyer
**Win:** 14-0 v Island Social, Kent Amtr Lge 1953    **Defeat:** 1-9 v Whitstable Greater London 64-65
**Players progressing :** Roy Dwight (Nottm Forest), Alan Clark (Charlton) , Fred Lucas
(Charlton)Tommy Tute (Millwall Jan. 1999)

**FACT FILE**
Founded: 1946    Nickname: The Green
Sponsor: T.B.A.
Colours: All white
Change Colours: Yellow & black
Midweek matchday: Tuesday
Reserve League:
Programme: 44 pages, incl. with admission
Editor: Robert Smith (01322 287982)
98-99 - Captain & P.o.Y.:Martin Driscoll
Top scorer:Tommy Tune

**CLUB PERSONNEL**

Chairman: Brian Smith
President: William Dudley
Press Officer: Robert Smith (01322 287982)
Manager: Srteve Waite
Coach: Micky Orme
Physio: Alan Martin

---

# THAMESMEAD TOWN

**Secretary:** Keith Dunsmore, 67 Temple Close, West Thamesmead SE28 0EW (0181 473 6810)
**Ground:** Bayliss Avenue, Thamesmead, London SE28 8NJ Tel: 0181 311 4211
**Directions:** By road: From Dartford tunnel A2 to London, exit Danson Interchange and follow
signs for Thamesmead and Abbey Wood. From Blackheath tunnel exit on south side and follow
signs to Woolwich, to Plumstead and then to Thamesmead
From Abbey Wood (BR) north east along Harrow Manor Way, into Crossway at 3rd r'bout, Bayliss
Av. is 3rd right (Bexley bus 272 stops in Crossway near Bayliss Av.
**Capacity:** 400    **Seats:** 125    **Cover:** 125    **Floodlights:** Yes    **Club Shop:** No
**Clubhouse:** Mon-Fri 6-11pm, Sat 12-11pm, Sun 12-3 & 7-10.30pm. Double bar,lounge, dance-
floor, children's games room, video machines, hot & cold food.New members Bar
**HONOURS**    Spartan Lg Div 3 79-80 (Lg Cup 84-85 86-87); I'mediate champs 85-86);Kent
I'mediate Cup 83-84 94-95; 4 promotions & 9 trophies (inc London & Kent FA Cups)
in progress thru Spartan I'mediate Divs, 1980-87; Kent Lge Div 2 94-95, Div 2 Cup 94-95
**PREVIOUS**    **Leagues:** London Spartan 80-91
**Ground:** Meridian Sports Ground, Charlton
**RECORDS**    **Attendance:** 400 v Wimbledon, ground opening 1988

**FACT FILE**
Founded: 1970
Nickname: The Mead
Sponsors: Courage Brewery
Colours: Green & black
Change Colour: All red
Midweek matchday: Tuesday
Reserves League: Winstonlead Kent D2
Programmes: Yes. 50p
Editor:

**CLUB PERSONNEL**
Chairman: Peter Andrews
Vice Chairman: John Kelly
President: Albert Panting
Press Officer: Matthew Panting
Manager: Terry Hill
Coach: Paul Blades
Physio: Allen Martin

# TUNBRIDGE WELLS

**Secretary:** P C Wager, 46 Mereworth Rd, Tunbridge Wells, Kent TN4 9PL Tel: 01892 524182

**Ground:** Culverden Stadium, Culverden Down, Tunbridge Wells, Kent TN4 Tel: 01892 520517

**Directions:** Leaving town on main Tonbridge rd (A26), turn left opposite`The Hooden' pub - grd half mile. 1 mile from Tunbridge Wells Central(BR). Served by any Tunbridge Wells-Tonbridge bus - to St Johns

**Capacity:** 3,750  **Seats:** 350  **Cover:** 1,000  **Floodlights:** Yes

**Clubhouse:** Open matchdays and as required  **Club Shop:** Yes

**HONOURS**  Kent Lg 84-85 (R-up 68-69, Lg Cup 74-75 77-78 85-86 87-88) Kent SnrTphy R-up 85-86 91-92

**PREVIOUS**  **Names:** None. predecessors: T . Wells FC 1886-1910 47-50 T. Wells Rgrs 03-09 63-67; T. Wells Utd 51-62
**Grounds:** Down Lane 1906; Combley Park 06-10; Swiss Cottage 06-14;Down Farm 19-39; St Johns 47-50; Eridge Road 50-67

**RECORDS**  **Attendance:** 967 v Maidstone United, FA Cup 1969
**Goalscorer:** John Wingate 151  **Appearances:** Tony Atkins 410
**Win:** 10-0 v Deal (H), May'86
**Defeat:** 1-11 v Deal Town (H), 20/2/93

### FACT FILE
Founded: 1886
Reformed: 1967
Nickname: Wells
Colours: Red/White/Red
Change Colours: Yellow/navy/navy
Midweek Matchday: Tuesday
Reserve League:
Programme: 20 pages, 50p
Editor: Secretary

### CLUB PERSONNEL
Chairman: R.Rogers
Vice Chairman:N.Sales
Manager: M.McKeown

# VICKERS CRAYFORD, DARTFORD ATHLETIC

**Secretary:** Brian Norris 47 Oxenden Wood Road, Chelsfield Park, Orpington, KentBR6 6HP
Tel: 01689 854302

**Ground:** Thamesmead Town FC, Bayliss Avenue, Thamesmead,London SE28 8NJ
Tel: 0181 311 4211 (Temporary Groundshare)
Home Ground ( Pending floodlights) Oakwood,Old Road, Crayford, Kent DA1 4DN
Home clubhouse: Lounge Bar  every day and evening. Plus snack bar on matchdays.

**Directions:** From Abbey Wood (BR) north east along Harrow Manor Way, intoCrossway at 3rd r'bout, Bayliss Av. is 3rd right (Bexley bus 272 stops inCrossway near Bayliss Av. By road: From Dartford tunnel A2 to London, exitDanson Interchange and follow signs for Thamesmead and Abbey Wood. From Blackheath tunnel exit on south side and follow signs to Woolwich, to Plumsteadand then to Thamesmead.

**Capacity:** 400  **Seats:** 125  **Cover:** 125  **Floodlights:** Yes

**PREVIOUS**  **League:** Kent County.  **Grounds:** Flamingo Park, Sidcup (pre 1994);
VCD Sports & Social Club,Old Road, Crayford

**RECORD**  **Victory:** 8-2 v DealTown 7.2.98  **Defeat:** 1-5 v Ramsgate 25.10.97

**HONOURS**  Kent County Cup 61-62, 63-64, 94-95, R-Up: 84-85, 89-90. Kent County Lg Div One 96-97 Kent County Premier 96-97. West Kent Cup 87-88.Kent Lge Cup R-up: 98-99. Kent Intermediate Shield (2) R-up(1), Erith Hosp Cup  x4, R-Up x4

### FACT FILE
Founded: 1916
Nickname: The Vickers
Sponsors: MB Fire Protection
Colours: Green & white/green/green
Change Colours: Blue & white/white/blue
Midweek matchday:  Wednesday
Programme: 40 pages 50p

### CLUB PERSONNEL
Chairman: Michael Bonello
Manager: Martin ford
Assistant Manager: Danny Sulman
Coach: Roy Passey
Physio: Peter Burke

1998-99
Captain: DeanFrost
Top Scorer:Richard Dimmock
Player of the Year: Terry Barry

# WHITSTABLE TOWN

**Secretary:** Mrs L.Gurr, 19 Hillview Road, Whitstable, Kent CT5 4HX
**Ground:** Belmont Road, Belmont, Whitstable, Kent  Tel: 01227 266012

**Directions:** From Thanet Way (A299), left at Tescos r'bout and down MillstroodRd - ground at bottom of road, 400yds from Whitstable (BR) station. Car park atGrimshall Rd entrance

**Capacity:** 2,000  **Cover:** 1,000  **Seats:** 500  **Floodlights:** Yes  **Club Shop:** Yes

**Clubhouse:** Social & recreation purposes, open all matchdays. Bar. Hot food &drinks at tea-bar

**HONOURS**  Kent Lg Div 2 27-28 33-34 49-50 (Lg Cup 79-80 (R-up 89-90 91-92)), KentAmtr Lg East 60-61, Kent Amtr Cup 28-29, Kent Snr Tphy R-up 78-79 89-90 92-93,Gtr London Lg Cup R-up 65-66, Kent Amtr Cup 28-29, Kent Midweek Lg Cup 92-93

**PREVIOUS**  **Leagues:** E. Kent 1897-1909; Kent 09-59; Aetolian 59-60; Kent Amtr 60-62 63-64; S E Anglian 62-63; Gtr London 64-67; Kent Premier 67-68 (also in New Brompton, Thanet & Faversham & Dist. Lges over the years)
**Names:** Whitstable Utd (pre-1886); Whitstable Swifts 93-95; WhitstableTown 95-1905; Whitstable FC 08-66

**RECORDS**  **Gate:** 2,500 v Gravesend & Northfleet, FA Cup 3rd Qual. Rd,19/10/87
**Goalscorer:** Barry Godfrey  **Appearances:** Frank Cox 429 (1950-60)
**Win:** 18-0 v Greenstreet (H), Faversham & Dist. Lge 20-21
**Defeat:** 0-10 v Sittingbourne (A), FA Cup 1st Qual. Rd 62-63

### FACT FILE
Founded: 1885
Nickname: Oystermen, Reds, Natives
Club Sponsors: D & J Tyres
Shirt Sponsor: McDonalds
Colours: Red/white/red
Change colours: Yellow/blue
Midweek matchday: Tuesday
Programme: 48 pages, 50p
Editor/Press Off: Trevor Myhill (01227 277297)
98-99 - Captain: Meirion George
P.o.Y.: Mark Jackson
Top Scorer: Mark Jackson

### CLUB PERSONNEL
Chairman: Joe Brownett
Vice Chairman: Trevor Rapley
President: George Gifford
Manager: Simon Kay/Doug Bosson
Asst Manager: John Crabbe
Physio: Tony Pattenden

Right: Crockenhill's Dean Henry is thwarted by VCD's T Barry and keeper Dave Pike
Photo: K Gillard

Below: VCD Athletic in front of their newly built stand

# BRITISH ENERGY KENT COUNTY FOOTBALL ASSOCIATION LEAGUE

**Founded:** 1922

**President:** W C Manklow    **Chairman:** CTC Windiate
**Secretary:** A E Scott

**Press Officer:** Ms S Puxty, 8 Larch Road, Dartford, Kent DA1 2LE Tel: 01322 288488

In one of the most exciting ends to a season for a long time Knatchbull lifted the Premier Division Championship for the first time in the Club's history. They achieved this in their final game of the season beating Sevenoaks Town 2-1 at Hatch Park to conclude a run of eleven League games without defeat. In fact nearly all of the League's eight divisions went to the wire with either promotion or relegation issues being resolved in the final two weeks of the season.

Kennington won the Division One East title by one point from Sheerness East who were the leading scorers in the entire competition with 90 goals. As the Champions were unable to carry out the necessary work to their ground the Islanders were promoted in their place. Joining them in the Premier Division next season are Maidstone United who were crowned Division One West Champions under the Managership of former 'Stones favourite Jason Lillis. Wittersham, who with just sixteen goals conceded had the best defensive record in the entire Competition, lifted the Division Two East title. The Division Two West champions were St George's (Wrotham) who gained promotion for the second successive year. The Division Three West title went to League newcomers Pembury who together with Mastercolour were promoted. In the Reserve Divisions, VCD Athletic retained the Division One title and Otford United won Division Two.

The League had three clubs competing in the 'Plaaya' Kent Senior Trophy and all three put up tremendous performances against Winstonlead Kent League opposition. Milton Athletic travelled to Erith Town and were finally beaten by the odd goal in five, after leading two nil, with a goal deep into stoppage time. Thames Poly visited Thamesmead Town and forced a replay before bowing out by two goals to one. The performance of the round came from Knatchbull who came away from Canterbury City with a fine victory by four goals to two after extra time. Knatchbull could not repeat the feat in the next round, as they were drawn away again, this time going out to Winstonlead Kent League reigning champions Herne Bay, by two goals to nil. The Kent Intermediate Challenge Shield was won by Premier Division Bearsted who defeated New Romney from Division One East by two goals to one after extra time.

The League's domestic cup competitions saw Sevenoaks Town retain the Inter-Regional Challenge Cup by defeating Rye United 1-0 at Dr Martens League Ashford Town FC's ground. Knatchbull completed a League and Cup double by lifting the Eastern Section Senior (Les Leckie) Cup after defeating Kennington 4-1 on Hythe United's ground in a splendid final. There was a shock in the Western Section Reserve Divisions Cup as Thames Polytechnic beat much fancied VCD Athletic 3-1 at Stonebridge Road, home of Ryman League Gravesend & Northfleet. This was Poly's third consecutive attempt to lift this cup and no one could deny they deserved their success after a hard fought final. The League staged a second final at Stonebridge Road, Northfleet, when Maidstone United crowned a superb season by lifting the West Kent Challenge Shield after defeating gallant Moonshot Athletic 2-1 after extra time in a tense final enjoyed by a vociferous crowd of over four hundred. The last of the League's knock out competitions saw University of Kent Reserves' young side collect the Eastern Junior Cup after overcoming Kennington Reserves 2--0 at Canterbury City's Kingsmead Stadium.

During the season the League's representative team retained 'The Tom Stabler Trophy' when they defeated the Unijet Sussex County League Division Three side by three goals to nil at Three Bridges FC's ground in November.

Tragedy struck Chipstead FC in March when David Dougan, aged just twenty four, was injured whilst playing in a Sevenoaks Charity Cup semi-final against St George's (Wrotham). He was immediately taken to hospital in tunbridge Wells and sadly died two days later in a London hospital. A minute's silence was observed at all matches on 13th March and a thanksgiving service was held five days later at St Marys Church, Riverhead, when over three hundred mourners packed into the church in a very moving service.

Saturday 29th May saw the League celebrating the end of another season with a highly successful Presentation Dinner and Dance at the Jarvis Great Danes Hotel and Country Club, Hollingbourne. Principle guests were Dr Andy Spurr, Station Director of British Energy's Dungeness B Power Station, and Barry Bright, Chairman of the Kent County FA who shared the presentation of the awards to the various winners and runners up. During the evening the League President Bill Manklow received the Football Association's prestigious Long and Meritous Service Award for 50 years service to the game which was presented by Barry Bright, a Director of the Football Association. In addition Long Service Club Awards were presented to Kevin Hunt of Lydd Town, David Homewood of Bromley Green and Keith Daniels of VCD Athletic. Frank Mead of Gravesend lifted the Referee of the Year award and the Most Promising Referee of the Year Award went to Greg Smith of Swanley.

At the League's Annual General Meeting on 21st June four new teams were elected into the Competition. Crockenhill were placed in the Premier Division having resigned from the Winstonlead Kent League. Orpington formerly of the London Intermediate League were placed in Division one West and Sheerness East Reserves and

Wittersham Reserves will play in Division Two East. The highlights of the AGM saw University of Kent Reserves Secretary Irene Simmonds collect the much coveted Fair Play Award and a cheque for £250 from Stuart Crooks, British Energy's Business Support Manager. Other clubs, who received cheques for good disciplinary records, were Wickham Park, Kennington, Wittersham, Belvedere, Sevenoaks Town Reserves and Otford United Reserves, who each received £100 and Otford United, Sheerness East, Smarden, Farnborough Old Boys Guild, Ex Blues Reserves and Oakwood Reserves, who each received £50. Alan Hogg of Westerham received a long service Club award having been unable to attend the dinner. Kevin Hayden of Kennington received the Aford Awards Manager of the year following his Club's first Championship title success since 1990. Press Officer Julie Connan indicated her intention to resign during the season and Sharon Puxty joined the Management Committee as the League's Press Secretary.

The League continues to expand its Newsline activities and well known Radio Kent football commentator Andrew Gidley will be conducting interviews on the newsline this season. Why not ring 09086 800 664 and keep abreast of the League News. The line is in operation 24 hours a day, seven days a week.

Cyril Windiate

# FINAL LEAGUE TABLES 1998-99

## PREMIER DIVISION

|  | P | W | D | L | F | A | Pts |
|---|---|---|---|---|---|---|---|
| Knatchbull | 24 | 14 | 4 | 6 | 58 | 39 | 46 |
| Rye United | 24 | 13 | 6 | 5 | 41 | 29 | 45 |
| Aylesford Paper Mills | 24 | 12 | 4 | 8 | 41 | 32 | 40 |
| Sevenoaks Town | 24 | 12 | 3 | 9 | 56 | 39 | 39 |
| Lydd Town | 24 | 10 | 5 | 9 | 39 | 37 | 35 |
| Greenways | 24 | 10 | 5 | 9 | 40 | 45 | 35 |
| Stansfeld | 24 | 9 | 5 | 10 | 28 | 36 | 32 |
| Snodland | 24 | 9 | 4 | 11 | 56 | 50 | 31 |
| Thames Polytechnic | 24 | 8 | 7 | 9 | 27 | 34 | 31 |
| Bearsted | 24 | 7 | 9 | 8 | 23 | 24 | 30 |
| Milton Athletic | 24 | 7 | 6 | 11 | 35 | 44 | 27 |
| AFC Lewisham | 24 | 6 | 6 | 12 | 32 | 44 | 24 |
| Ex Blues | 24 | 4 | 6 | 14 | 30 | 53 | 18 |

## DIVISION ONE WEST

|  | P | W | D | L | F | A | Pts |
|---|---|---|---|---|---|---|---|
| Maidstone United | 20 | 17 | 2 | 1 | 72 | 29 | 53 |
| Beauwater | 20 | 13 | 1 | 6 | 55 | 34 | 40 |
| Wickham Park | 20 | 12 | 3 | 5 | 54 | 32 | 39 |
| Moonshot Athletic | 20 | 10 | 2 | 8 | 46 | 35 | 32 |
| Westerham | 20 | 9 | 2 | 9 | 35 | 31 | 29 |
| Otford United | 20 | 8 | 4 | 8 | 35 | 26 | 28 |
| Phoenix Sports | 20 | 7 | 7 | 6 | 38 | 35 | 28 |
| Sutton Athletic | 20 | 5 | 3 | 12 | 37 | 53 | 18 |
| Rusthall | 20 | 4 | 6 | 10 | 25 | 49 | 18 |
| AFC Blackheath | 20 | 5 | 3 | 12 | 28 | 64 | 18 |
| Eynsford | 20 | 2 | 3 | 15 | 23 | 60 | 9 |

* points deducted

## DIVISION ONE EAST

|  | P | W | D | L | F | A | Pts |
|---|---|---|---|---|---|---|---|
| Kennington | 26 | 22 | 1 | 3 | 78 | 23 | 67 |
| Sheerness East | 26 | 21 | 3 | 2 | 90 | 20 | 66 |
| New Romney | 26 | 16 | 7 | 3 | 78 | 30 | 55 |
| Bromley Green | 26 | 16 | 4 | 6 | 75 | 58 | 52 |
| University of Kent | 26 | 15 | 5 | 6 | 70 | 30 | 50 |
| Broomfield United | 26 | 14 | 1 | 11 | 63 | 51 | 43 |
| St Margarets | 26 | 8 | 7 | 11 | 56 | 62 | 31 |
| Bishopsbourne | 26 | 9 | 4 | 13 | 51 | 72 | 31 |
| Snowdon CW | 26 | 9 | 4 | 13 | 49 | 70 | 31 |
| Iden | 26 | 8 | 3 | 15 | 55 | 84 | 27 |
| Tenterden St Michales | 26 | 6 | 4 | 16 | 47 | 86 | 22 |
| Norton Sports | 26 | 4 | 8 | 14 | 45 | 58 | 20 |
| Woodnesborough | 26 | 4 | 2 | 20 | 33 | 89 | 14 |
| Rye United Res* | 26 | 2 | 3 | 21 | 39 | 96 | 6 |

# PREMIER DIVISION RESULTS CHART 1998-99

| | | 1 | 2 | 3 | 4 | 5 | 6 | 7 | 8 | 9 | 10 | 11 | 12 | 13 |
|---|---|---|---|---|---|---|---|---|---|---|---|---|---|---|
| 1 | A.F.C.Lewisham | X | 0-2 | 0-0 | 3-2 | 6-1 | 1-3 | 3-0 | 3-1 | 1-3 | 2-6 | 2-2 | 2-2 | 1-0 |
| 2 | Aylesford p mill | 3-2 | X | 1-1 | 1-2 | 4-1 | 4-2 | 2-0 | 0-2 | 0-1 | 1-1 | 2-4 | 1-0 | 3-0 |
| 3 | Bearsted | 0-1 | 0-2 | X | 4-1 | 2-2 | 0-0 | 1-2 | 2-1 | 0-2 | 1-0 | 3-1 | 0-2 | 0-0 |
| 4 | Ex Blues | 2-2 | 0-2 | 0-1 | X | 1-1 | 1-2 | 1-2 | 2-2 | 1-2 | 1-0 | 3-1 | 2-4 | 1-1 |
| 5 | Greenways | 4-1 | 0-2 | 4-2 | 1-1 | X | 2-2 | 2-0 | 3-2 | 2-3 | 4-2 | 2-1 | 1-0 | 3-1 |
| 6 | Knatchbull | 4-2 | 3-0 | 2-0 | 4-0 | 5-1 | X | 3-2 | 2-2 | 4-3 | 2-1 | 6-0 | 0-2 | 1-1 |
| 7 | Lydd Town | 3-0 | 2-1 | 0-0 | 3-1 | 1-0 | 3-1 | X | 5-0 | 2-2 | 1-4 | 0-2 | 1-1 | 0-3 |
| 8 | Milton Athletic | 0-0 | 1-2 | 0-0 | 2-1 | 1-0 | 4-3 | 1-3 | X | 0-0 | 4-2 | 2-2 | 6-1 | 0-1 |
| 9 | Rye United | 0-0 | 2-0 | 0-2 | 1-3 | 4-0 | 1-0 | 2-2 | 2-1 | X | 0-2 | 2-2 | 0-1 | 1-0 |
| 10 | Sevenoaks Town | 2-0 | 4-0 | 2-1 | 3-1 | 3-1 | 6-3 | 3-3 | 2-3 | 1-2 | X | 4-2 | 0-1 | 0-0 |
| 11 | Snodland | 2-0 | 2-2 | 0-2 | 5-0 | 1-4 | 1-2 | 2-1 | 6-0 | 2-4 | 5-2 | X | 3-4 | 7-1 |
| 12 | Stansfeld O & B Club | 1-0 | 1-1 | 0-0 | 3-3 | 0-1 | 0-1 | 2-1 | 1-0 | 1-2 | 0-4 | 0-2 | X | 1-2 |
| 13 | Thames Polytechnic | 1-0 | 1-5 | 1-1 | 3-0 | 0-0 | 2-3 | 0-2 | 1-0 | 2-2 | 1-2 | 2-1 | 3-0 | X |

# INTER-REGIONAL CHALLENGE CUP 1998-99

**FIRST ROUND**

| | | | | | | | |
|---|---|---|---|---|---|---|---|
| Snowdown Coll. Welf | v | Sheerness East | 1-2 | Beauwater | v | Otford United | 2-1 |
| Wickham Park | v | Ex Blues | 2-0 | Thames Polytechnic | v | Rusthall | 2-0 |
| Aylesford Paper Mills | v | Sevenoaks Town | 2-6 | Greenways | v | Eynsford | 4-0 |

**SECOND ROUND**

| | | | | | | | |
|---|---|---|---|---|---|---|---|
| Lydd Town | v | Knatchbull | 4-1 | AC Egerton | v | Wickham Park | WP w/o |
| Woodnesborough | v | Bishopsbourne | 6-3 | Phoenix Sports | v | Sevenoaks Tn | 2*2, 3*4 |
| St Margarets | v | Kennington | 0-3 | Beauwater | v | Snodland | 4*3 |
| Tenterden St M Utd | v | Bromley Green | 3-5 | Sutton Athletic | v | Moonshot Athletic | 2-3 |
| Rye United | v | Sheerness East | 5*3 | AFC Lewisham | v | AFC Blackheath | 12-1 |
| University of Kent | v | New Romney | 4-0 | Westerham | v | Stansfeld O & B C | 3-2 |
| Iden | v | Broomfield United | 0-1 | Greenways | v | Bearsted | 0-1 |
| Milton Athletic | v | Norton Sports | 0-1 | Thames Poly | v | Maidstone United | 1-0 |

**THIRD ROUND**

| | | | | | | | |
|---|---|---|---|---|---|---|---|
| Kennington | v | University of Kent | 3*2 | Wickham Park | v | Thames Poly | 2*2, 2p0 |
| Bromley Green | v | Rye United | 0-5 | Sevenoaks Town | v | Bearsted | 3*2 |
| Broomfield United | v | Norton Sports | 3*2 | Westerham | v | Beauwater | 2-1 |
| Lydd Town | v | Woodnesborough | 11-0 | Moonshot Athletic | v | AFC Lewisham | 0-3 |

**FOURTH ROUND**

| | | | | | | | |
|---|---|---|---|---|---|---|---|
| Westerham | v | Wickham Park | . 1-2 | Sevenoaks Town | v | Kennington | 3-2 |
| AFC Lewisham | v | Lydd Town | 1-0 | Broomfield United | v | Rye United | 0-1 |

**SEMI FINALS**

| | | | | | | | |
|---|---|---|---|---|---|---|---|
| Sevenoaks Town | v | Wickham Park | 2-0 | AFC Lewisham | v | Rye United | 0-1 |

**FINAL**

| | | | | |
|---|---|---|---|---|
| Sevenoaks Town | v | Rye United | 1-0 | at Homelands, Ashford Town FC |

# INTER-REGIONAL CHALLENGE CUP RECENT FINALS

| SEASON | WINNERS | RUNNERS UP |
|---|---|---|
| 1987-88 | New Romney | Otford United |
| 1988-89 | Greenways | Lordswood |
| 1989-90 | Stansfeld Oxford & Bermondsey | Vickers Crayford/Dartford Athletic |
| 1990-91 | Bearsted | Scott Sports & Social |
| 1991-92 | Stansfeld Oxford & Bermondsey | Oakwood |
| 1992-93 | Oakwood | Teynham & Lynsted |
| 1993-94 | Bearsted | Rye United |
| 1994-95 | Vickers Crayford/Dartford Athletic | Teynham & Lynsted |
| 1995-96 | Teynham & Lynstead | Lydd Town |
| 1996-97 | Bearsted | Milton Athletic |
| 1997-98 | Sevenoaks Town | Greenways |
| 1998-99 | Sevenoaks Town | Rye United |

**AYLESFORD PAPER MILLS**
Founded: 1919
Secretary: Mrs Lynda Casey, 41 Cobdown Close, Ditton, Maidstone, Kent ME20 6SZ (01732 849476)
Ground: Cobdown Sports & Social Club, Ditton Corner, Station Road, Aylesford (01622 715552)
Colours: Black & white/black/black
Change Colours: Red & black/white/white

**BEARSTED**
Secretary: Mrs Liz Owen, 21 Copsewood Way, Bearsted, Maidstone, Kent ME15 8PL(01622 737709)
Ground: Honey Lane, Otham, Maidstone. (0860 302086)
Founded: 1895
Colours: White/blue/blue
Change Colours: Yellow/blue/blue

**CROCKENHILL**
Secretary: Mike Floate, Newlands Cottages, Stones Cross Road, Crockenhill, Swanley, Kent BR8 8LX (01322 668275)
Ground: The Wesyted Meadow, Wested, Eynsford Road, Crockenhill, Kent. (01322 662097)
Founded: 1946
Colours: Blue & yellow/navy/navy
Change Colours: Red/black/black

**GREENWAYS**
Founded: 1965
Secretary: William Miller, 14 Cygnet Gardens, Northfleet, Kent DA11 7DN (01474 560913)
Ground: Beauwater Leisure Centre, Nelson Road, Northfleet, (01474 359222)
Colours: All green
Change Colours: Red& black

**KNATCHBULL**
Founded: 1980
Secretary: David Howie, 13 Charminster, Washford Farm, Ashford, Kent TN23 5UH (01233 611207)
Ground: Hatch Park, Off A20, Mersham, Nr Ashford, (01233 503549)
Colours: Claret & sky blue/white/sky blue
Change Colours: White/white/Isky blue

**LYDD TOWN**
Founded: 1885
Secretary: Peter Sisley, The Lobster Pot, Warren Road, Littlestone, New Romney, Kent TN28 8PW (01797 366101)
Ground: The Lindsey Field, Dengemarsh Road, Lydd, Romney Marsh (01797 321904)
Colours: Red/green/green
ChangeColours:Blue&white/blue/blue.

**MAIDSTONE UNITED**
Founded: 1966, reformed 1992
Secretary: James reed, 22 Underwood Close, Maidstone, Kent. ME156SR (01622 206349(H) 01622 777000(W) )
Ground: The Athletic Ground, London Road, Maidstone
Founded: 1992
Colours: Gold/black/black
Change Colours: All blue

**MILTON ATHLETIC**
Founded: 1926
Secretary: Paul Duffin, 18 Hales Road, Tunstall, Sittingbourne, Kent ME10 1SR (01795 471260)
Ground: UK Paper Sports Ground, Gore Court Road, Sittingbourne, Kent (01795 47047)
Colours: Royal blue/royal blue/yellow
Change Colours: Red & white stripes/black/black

**RYE UNITED**
Founded: 1938
Secretary: Robert Dixon, 32 The Maltings, Peasmarsh, nr Rye, East Sussex TN31 6ST (01797 230430)
Ground: Sydney Allnut Pavilion, Rye Football & Cricket Salts, Fish Market Rd., Rye, East Sussex (01797 223855)
Colours: Red & black/black/red
Change colours: Yellow & green/green/green
Previous league: Sussex County

**SEVENOAKS TOWN**
Founded: 1883
Secretary: Edwin Diplock, 23 Holly Bush Lane, Sevenoaks, Kent TN13 3TH (01732 454280)
Ground: Greatness Park, Seal Road, Sevenoaks (01732 741987)
Colours: Azure & black stripes/black/black
Change colours: Navy & scarlet quarters/navy/navy

**SHEERNESS EAST**
Founded: 1932
Secretary: Jonathan Longhurst, 16 Hilda Road, Halfway, Sheerness, Kent ME12 3BN (01795 667758)
Ground: Sheerness East Working Mens Club, 47 Queenborough Rd., Halfway, Sheerness (01795 662049)
Colours: Yellow/royal blue/royal blue
Change colours: All royal blue

**SNODLAND**
Founded: 1940
Secretary: Terry Reevs, 136 Townsend Road, Snodland, Kent ME6 5RN (01634 240076)
Ground: Potyn's Field, Paddlesworth Road, Snodland, Kent. (01634 243961)
Colours: Sky & navy/navy/navy
Change colours: Yellow/red/yellow & red

**STANSFELD OXFORD & BERMONDSEY CLUB**
Founded: 1897
Secretary: Edward Ellis, 40 Tilbrook Road, Kidbrooke, London SE3 9QE (0208 319 0903)
Ground: St James Squash & Leisure Club, 35 Marvels Lane, Grove Park, SE12 (0208 851 3522)
Colours: Yellow/ & blue stripes/blue/blue
Change Colours: All red

**THAMES POLYTECHNIC**
Founded: 1888
Secretary: Mrs Shirley Jarvis, 31 Monkton Road, Welling, Kent DA16 3JU (0208 854 5509)
Ground: Greenwich University Sports Ground, Kidbrooke Lane, Eltham, London SE9 (0208 850 1221)
Colours: Yellow & green/green/yellow & green
Change Colours: All blue
Previous league: Kent

## A.F.C. LEWISHAM
Founded: 1998
Secretary: Miss LIsa Suckoo, 1st Floor Flat,254 Leahurst Rd.,
London SE13 5LT (0208 297 2784)
Ground: Ladywell Arena, Doggett Rd., Catford London SE6 (0208
314 1986)
Colours: Blue & Yellow
Change Colours: Yellow/blue/blue

## BEAUWATER
Founded: 1927
Secretary: Robert Taylor, 254 Sun Lane, Gravesend, Kent DA12
5HG (01474 332208)
Ground: Beauwater Leisure Club, Nelson Road, Northfleet (01474
336456)
Colours: Green& Black
Change Colours: Yellow & navy stripes/navy/navy

## EYNESFORD
Secretary: Mr E Walking, 76 Pollyhaugh, Eynesford, Nr Dartford,
Kent DA4 0HF(01322 863673)
Ground: Harrow Meadow, Rear of Castle Hotel, Bower Lane, off
Eynesford HighStreet
Founded: 1894
Colours: White/black/black
Change Colours: Red/black/black

## FLEETDOWN UNITED
Founded: 1971
Secretary: Brian Wakeman, 670 Princes Road, Dartford, Kent
DA2 6JG (01322 228680)
Ground: Heath Lane, Dartford, Kent (01322 273848)
Colours: Tangerine/black/black
Change colours: Red/white/red

## MOONSHOT ATHLETIC
Founded: 1970
Secretary: Joseph Collymore, 37 Vaughan Williams Close,
Deptford SE8 4AW (0208 691 2543)
Ground: Old Bromley Rd Playing Fields, Old Bromley Rd.,
Downham, Kent (0208 313 9510)
Colours: Blue & white/blue/blue
Change Colours: Yellow/blue/yellow

## ORPINGTON
Founded: 1939
Secretary: Les Hill, 8 Cudham Lane, Orpington, Kent BR6 6BZ
(01689 600932)
Ground: Westcombe Park & Orpington Sports Club, Goddington
Lane, Orpington, Kent. (01689 834902)
Colours: Amber/black/black
Change colours: White/black/black
Previous League: London Intermediate

## OTFORD UNITED
Founded: 1900
Secretary: David Dugay, 13 Monckton Road, Borough Green,
Sevenoaks, Kent TN15 8SD (01732 882621)
Ground: Otford Recreation Ground, High Street, Otford, Kent
(01959 524405)
Colours: Amber & black
Change Colours: Blue/green/blue

## PHOENIX SPORTS
Founded: 1935
Secretary: Martyn Cole, 91 Hurst Road, Northumberland Road,
Erith, Kent DA8 3EW (01322 350750)
Ground: Phoenix Sports Club, Mayplace Road East, Bexleyheath,
Kent DA7 6JT (01322 526159)
Colours: Blue & red
Change Colours: Yellow/black/black

## RUSTHALL
Founded: 1899
Secretary: Michael Mace, 'The Roos', 28 Allan Close, Rusthall,
Tunbridge Wells, Kent TN4 8PL (01892 540634)
Ground: Jockey Farm, Nellington Lane, Rusthall, Tunbridge Wells
Colours: Green & yellow/green/green
Change Colours: Blue/black/black

## St GEORGE'S (Wrotham)
Founded: 1965
Secretary: John Underdown, 1 Mountain Close, West St.,
Wrotham, Sevenoaks, Kent TN15 7BD (01732 886106)
Ground: Old Recreation Ground, Old London Road, Wrotham,
Sevenoaks, Kent.
Colours: All royal blue
Change colours: Red & black stripes/black/black

## SUTTON ATHLETIC
Founded: 1928
Secretary: John Willis, 6 Somerset Road, Dartford, Kent DA1 3DP
(01322 222540)
Ground: The Roaches, Parsonage Lane, Sutton at Hone, Nr
Dartford, Kent (01322 280507)
Colours: Yellow & green/green/green
Change Colours: Red/black/red

## WESTERHAM
Founded: 1888
Secretary: Doug Sayers, 16A The Green, Westerham, Kent TN16
1AX (01959 565520)
Ground: Westerham Sports Assoc., King George V Playing
Fields, Costells Meadow, Westerham. (01959 561106)
Colours: Red/black/black
Change Colours: Green/white/green

## WICKHAM PARK
Founded: 1934
Secretary: Brian Greenin, 145 The Avenue, West Wickham, Kent
BR4 0EF (0208 777 2119)
Ground: Wickham Park Sports & Soc. Club, 228-230 Pickhurst
Rise, West Wickham (0208 7772550)
Colours: Red & blacktrim/black/red
Change Colours: All navy blue

## BISHOPSBOURNE
Founded: 1961
Secretary: Nigel Hayes, Robins Grove, 62 The Street, Kingston, Canterrbury ,Kent.CT4 6JC (01227 830360)
Ground: Canteen Meadow, The Street, Bishopsbourne, Nr Canterbury, Kent
Colours: Royal blue
Change Colours: Red & black

## BROMLEY GREEN
Founded: 1930
Secretary: David Stanley, 48 Bredgar Close, Stanhope, Ashford, Kent TN23 5SQ (01233 661312)
Ground: The Swan Centre, Newtown Road, South Willesborough, Ashford, Kent
Colours: Green & white.
Change Colours: White/green/green

## BROOMFIELD UNITED
Founded: 1925
Secretary: Roger Cork, 12 Coulter Road, Herne Bay, Kent CT6 7RH (01227 742480)
Ground: Bridge Recreation Ground, Patrixbourne Road, Bridge, Nr Canterbury
Colours: Tangerine & black
Change Colours: Black & azure

## IDEN
Founded: 1965
Secretary: Gerard Say, 18 Parkwood, Iden, Rye, East Sussex TN31 7XE (01797 280495)
Ground: Iden Playing Field, Iden, Rye, East Sussex
Colours: Tangerine/black/black
Change Colours: Black & white

## KENNINGTON
Founded: 1888
Secretary: Kevin Hayden, 33 Grosvenor Road, Kennington, Ashford, Kent TN24 9PA (01233 627826)
Ground: Kennington Cricket Club Club, Ulley Road, Kennington, Ashford, Kent
Colours: Yellow & sky blue
Change Colours: All red

## NEW ROMNEY
Founded: 1895
Secretary: Mr Daryl Masters, 44 Fernbank Cres, Folkestone, Kent CT19 5SF (01303 253961)
Ground: The Maud Pavilion, Station Road, New Romney, Kent (01797 364858)
Colours: Yellow & navy/navy/yellow
Change Colours: White & navy blue/navy/navy

## NORTON SPORTS
Founded: 1927
Secretary: Colin Page, 2 Foxgrove, Milton Regis, Sittingbourne, Kent ME10 2DW (01795 426675)
Ground: Norton Park, Provender Lane, Norton, Kent
Colours: Blue & yellow/blue/yellow
Change Colours: Red & black/black/red

## SNOWDOWN COLLIERY WELFARE
Founded: 1927
Secretary: Ernest Travers, 21 Bell Grove, Aylesham, Kent CT3 3AT (01304 842680)
Ground: Spinney Lane, Aylesham, Canterbury CT3 3AF (01304 840278)
Colours: Black & white stripes/black/black
Change Colours: All green
Previous League: Kent

## St MARGARETS
Founded: 1970  Re-formed:1993
Secretary: William Hay, 28 The Freedown, St Margarets at Cliffe, Nr Dover, Kent CT15 6BD (01304 852386)
Ground: The Alexander Field, Kingsdown Road, St Margarets at Cliffe, Nr Dover
Colours: White, red & blue sleeves/blue/red
Change Colours: Dark blue/white/red

## TENTERDEN ST MICHAELS UNITED
Founded: 1889
Secretary: Colin Feaver, 19 Eastgate Road, Tenterden, Kent TN30 7AH (01580 761311)
Ground: Recreation Ground, Recretaion Ground Rd., Tenterden (01580 762703)
Colours: Blue & white stripes/blue/blue
Change Colours: All red

## UNIVERSITY OF KENT
Founded: 1967
Secretary: Mrs Irene Simmonds, Sports Federation, Sports Centre, University of Kent, Canterbury, Kent CT2 7NL (01227 768027 or 01227 827430)
Ground: The Playing Fields, University of Kent, off Giles Lane, Canterbury
Colours: Black & white stripes/black/black
Change Colours: Red & black stripes/black/black

## WITTERSHAM
Founded: 1905
Secretary: Mr Leslie Champion, 4 Woodland View, Wittersham, Tenterden, Kent TN30 7QD (01797 270164)
Ground: Wittersham Sports Club, Poplar Road, Wittersham, Tenterden, Kent.
Colours: White/green/green
Change colours: red & white/black/black

## WOODNESBOROUGH
Founded: 1962
Secretary: Geoffrey Hunt, Hillcross Farm, Eastry, Sandwich, Kent CT13 0NY (01304 611311)
Ground: 'Hillborough', Woodnesborough Road, Eastry, Kent (01304 614721)
Colours: Red/black/black
Change Colours: Green/black/black

# UNIJET SUSSEX COUNTY LEAGUE

## FEEDER TO: BEAZER HOMES LEAGUE

## FOUNDED 1920

President: P H Strange    Chairman: Peter Bentley
Secretary: Peter Wells, 37 Bewley Road, Angmering BN16 4JL    (01903 771146)

## FINAL LEAGUE TABLES 1998-99

### DIVISION ONE

| | P | W | D | L | F | A | W | D | L | F | A | Pts | GD |
|---|---|---|---|---|---|---|---|---|---|---|---|---|---|
| Burgess Hill Town | 38 | 15 | 2 | 2 | 63 | 10 | 13 | 3 | 3 | 43 | 14 | 89 | 82 |
| Saltdean United | 38 | 13 | 5 | 1 | 59 | 19 | 13 | 3 | 3 | 41 | 16 | 86 | 65 |
| Horsham YMCA | 38 | 13 | 4 | 2 | 54 | 22 | 11 | 3 | 5 | 43 | 28 | 79 | 47 |
| Langney Sports | 38 | 10 | 2 | 7 | 33 | 20 | 10 | 4 | 5 | 36 | 23 | 66 | 26 |
| Shoreham | 38 | 10 | 5 | 4 | 46 | 31 | 9 | 3 | 7 | 34 | 26 | 65 | 23 |
| Wick | 38 | 10 | 3 | 6 | 29 | 21 | 8 | 4 | 7 | 36 | 28 | 61 | 16 |
| East Preston | 38 | 7 | 4 | 8 | 39 | 34 | 11 | 2 | 6 | 30 | 23 | 60 | 12 |
| Eastbourne United | 38 | 10 | 4 | 5 | 38 | 23 | 7 | 4 | 8 | 21 | 28 | 59 | 8 |
| Pagham | 38 | 8 | 6 | 5 | 21 | 17 | 8 | 5 | 6 | 21 | 22 | 59 | 3 |
| Eastbourne Town | 38 | 10 | 4 | 5 | 36 | 19 | 4 | 8 | 7 | 25 | 43 | 54 | -1 |
| Redhill | 38 | 9 | 3 | 7 | 40 | 28 | 5 | 8 | 6 | 39 | 32 | 53 | 19 |
| Portfield | 38 | 4 | 9 | 6 | 29 | 32 | 8 | 4 | 7 | 33 | 34 | 49 | -4 |
| Hassocks | 38 | 6 | 4 | 9 | 28 | 25 | 7 | 3 | 9 | 23 | 26 | 46 | 0 |
| Whitehawk | 38 | 4 | 6 | 9 | 25 | 28 | 7 | 4 | 8 | 25 | 33 | 43 | -11 |
| Chichester City | 38 | 7 | 6 | 6 | 26 | 26 | 3 | 5 | 11 | 18 | 40 | 41 | -22 |
| Littlehampton Town | 38 | 6 | 2 | 11 | 23 | 42 | 4 | 5 | 10 | 15 | 45 | 37 | -49 |
| Ringmer | 38 | 4 | 5 | 10 | 13 | 24 | 4 | 6 | 9 | 22 | 40 | 35 | -29 |
| Selsey | 38 | 6 | 4 | 9 | 23 | 34 | 1 | 4 | 14 | 19 | 59 | 29 | -51 |
| Hailsham Town | 38 | 4 | 3 | 12 | 21 | 46 | 3 | 1 | 15 | 19 | 55 | 25 | -61 |
| Broadbridge Heath | 38 | 3 | 3 | 13 | 20 | 54 | 1 | 5 | 13 | 12 | 51 | 20 | -73 |

### DIVISION TWO

| | P | W | D | L | F | A | W | D | L | F | A | Pts | GD |
|---|---|---|---|---|---|---|---|---|---|---|---|---|---|
| Sidley United | 34 | 15 | 2 | 0 | 39 | 10 | 11 | 2 | 4 | 33 | 13 | 82 | 49 |
| Three Bridges | 34 | 11 | 4 | 2 | 43 | 16 | 12 | 0 | 5 | 31 | 19 | 73 | 39 |
| Crawley Down Village | 34 | 11 | 3 | 3 | 33 | 20 | 11 | 4 | 2 | 33 | 15 | 73 | 31 |
| Southwick | 34 | 9 | 4 | 4 | 51 | 18 | 9 | 5 | 3 | 33 | 16 | 63 | 50 |
| Mile Oak | 34 | 12 | 3 | 2 | 34 | 13 | 6 | 5 | 6 | 29 | 36 | 62 | 14 |
| Storrington | 34 | 9 | 4 | 4 | 29 | 10 | 9 | 2 | 6 | 25 | 20 | 60 | 24 |
| Sidlesham | 34 | 10 | 5 | 2 | 43 | 13 | 7 | 1 | 9 | 27 | 25 | 57 | 32 |
| Arundel | 34 | 9 | 4 | 4 | 29 | 20 | 7 | 5 | 5 | 28 | 23 | 57 | 14 |
| Lancing | 34 | 6 | 3 | 8 | 29 | 30 | 4 | 8 | 5 | 21 | 25 | 41 | -5 |
| Lingfield | 34 | 6 | 4 | 7 | 32 | 26 | 4 | 5 | 8 | 22 | 30 | 39 | -2 |
| Shinewater Association | 34 | 7 | 4 | 6 | 28 | 23 | 3 | 5 | 9 | 19 | 35 | 39 | -11 |
| Peacehaven & Telscombe | 34 | 5 | 6 | 6 | 26 | 29 | 3 | 6 | 8 | 24 | 38 | 36 | -17 |
| East Grinstead Town | 34 | 6 | 4 | 7 | 25 | 32 | 4 | 1 | 12 | 25 | 46 | 35 | -28 |
| Worthing United | 34 | 6 | 4 | 7 | 31 | 37 | 2 | 5 | 10 | 17 | 36 | 33 | -25 |
| Oakwood | 34 | 6 | 3 | 8 | 26 | 30 | 4 | 0 | 13 | 11 | 42 | 33 | -35 |
| Withdean | 34 | 4 | 3 | 10 | 20 | 32 | 1 | 9 | 7 | 23 | 53 | 27 | -24 |
| Crowborough Athletic | 34 | 4 | 3 | 10 | 26 | 38 | 3 | 3 | 11 | 19 | 42 | 27 | -35 |
| Newhaven | 34 | 1 | 5 | 11 | 12 | 37 | 1 | 2 | 14 | 14 | 60 | 13 | -71 |

# FINAL LEAGUE TABLE 1998-99

## DIVISION THREE

| | P | W | D | L | F | A | W | D | L | F | A | Pts | GD |
|---|---|---|---|---|---|---|---|---|---|---|---|---|---|
| Oving SC | 30 | 13 | 0 | 2 | 43 | 10 | 11 | 2 | 2 | 29 | 10 | 74 | 52 |
| Westfield | 30 | 13 | 1 | 1 | 42 | 8 | 9 | 3 | 3 | 33 | 18 | 70 | 49 |
| St Francis | 30 | 13 | 2 | 0 | 38 | 12 | 8 | 2 | 5 | 21 | 14 | 67 | 33 |
| Wealden | 30 | 7 | 5 | 3 | 25 | 18 | 7 | 4 | 4 | 21 | 17 | 51 | 11 |
| Uckfield Town | 30 | 8 | 2 | 5 | 35 | 17 | 7 | 1 | 7 | 25 | 26 | 48 | 17 |
| Franklands Village | 30 | 5 | 4 | 6 | 20 | 19 | 6 | 5 | 4 | 27 | 19 | 42 | 9 |
| Ifield | 30 | 5 | 3 | 7 | 34 | 40 | 7 | 1 | 7 | 27 | 38 | 40 | -17 |
| Steyning Town | 30 | 4 | 3 | 8 | 21 | 24 | 7 | 1 | 7 | 28 | 30 | 37 | -5 |
| Hurstpierpoint | 30 | 6 | 3 | 6 | 22 | 22 | 5 | 1 | 9 | 21 | 29 | 37 | -8 |
| Bexhill Town | 30 | 7 | 3 | 5 | 25 | 28 | 4 | 1 | 10 | 18 | 38 | 37 | -23 |
| Ansty Rangers | 30 | 5 | 6 | 4 | 27 | 23 | 4 | 3 | 8 | 25 | 23 | 36 | 6 |
| Forest | 30 | 7 | 2 | 6 | 28 | 29 | 3 | 4 | 8 | 18 | 28 | 36 | -11 |
| Royal & Sun Alliance | 30 | 3 | 4 | 8 | 25 | 40 | 4 | 4 | 7 | 27 | 41 | 29 | -29 |
| Haywards Heath Town | 30 | 5 | 4 | 6 | 19 | 18 | 1 | 4 | 10 | 16 | 35 | 26 | -18 |
| Buxted | 30 | 4 | 2 | 9 | 13 | 21 | 0 | 8 | 7 | 19 | 39 | 22 | -28 |
| Midhurst & Easebourne | 30 | 4 | 2 | 9 | 32 | 39 | 2 | 2 | 11 | 13 | 44 | 22 | -38 |

# DIVISION ONE ATTENDANCES CHART 1998-99

| | | 1 | 2 | 3 | 4 | 5 | 6 | 7 | 8 | 9 | 10 | 11 | 12 | 13 | 14 | 15 | 16 | 17 | 18 | 19 | 20 |
|---|---|---|---|---|---|---|---|---|---|---|---|---|---|---|---|---|---|---|---|---|---|
| 1 | Broadbridge Hth | X | 152 | 66 | 47 | 48 | 47 | 83 | 52 | 93 | 83 | 90 | 43 | 45 | 83 | 57 | 68 | 53 | 46 | 78 | 62 |
| 2 | Burgess Hill Tn | 200 | X | 209 | 199 | 232 | 240 | 172 | 339 | 373 | 266 | 194 | 156 | 296 | 205 | 262 | 426 | 218 | 276 | 126 | 244 |
| 3 | Chichester City | 75 | 145 | X | 115 | 60 | 75 | 60 | 85 | 76 | 85 | 115 | 100 | 140 | 110 | 95 | 100 | 145 | 75 | 70 | 85 |
| 4 | East Preston | 97 | 219 | 52 | X | 110 | 61 | 117 | 87 | 98 | 110 | 135 | 76 | 93 | 125 | 101 | 73 | 72 | 101 | 95 | 139 |
| 5 | Eastbourne Tn | 121 | 110 | 72 | 124 | X | 242 | 220 | 65 | 121 | 264 | 122 | 165 | 124 | 73 | 63 | 53 | 135 | 110 | 82 | 126 |
| 6 | Eastbourne Utd | 110 | 215 | 110 | 161 | 221 | X | 250 | 130 | 139 | 250 | 200 | 65 | 131 | 84 | 100 | 180 | 105 | 150 | 148 | 70 |
| 7 | Hailsham Town | 85 | 148 | 130 | 132 | 145 | 318 | X | 130 | 132 | 347 | 105 | 91 | 109 | 189 | 140 | 120 | 167 | 145 | 145 | 90 |
| 8 | Hassocks | 133 | 307 | 91 | 107 | 95 | 112 | 107 | X | 90 | 94 | 116 | 105 | 107 | 111 | 106 | 155 | 95 | 103 | 124 | 125 |
| 9 | Horsham YMCA | 140 | 133 | 65 | 80 | 27 | 75 | 92 | 85 | X | 85 | 68 | 54 | 40 | 117 | 70 | 80 | 101 | 95 | 65 | 110 |
| 10 | Langney Sports | 138 | 242 | 157 | 204 | 406 | 240 | 334 | 171 | 213 | X | 207 | 202 | 219 | 219 | 251 | 269 | 226 | 234 | 261 | 262 |
| 11 | Littlehampton Tn | 98 | 180 | 130 | 198 | 52 | 61 | 85 | 68 | 89 | 70 | X | 150 | 42 | 56 | 72 | 70 | 52 | 55 | 58 | 185 |
| 12 | Pagham | 77 | 157 | 107 | 101 | 103 | 77 | 120 | 117 | 105 | 142 | 153 | X | 111 | 142 | 110 | 163 | 168 | 137 | 101 | 149 |
| 13 | Portfield | 66 | 109 | 72 | 52 | 31 | 65 | 56 | 52 | 53 | 54 | 82 | 52 | X | 42 | 33 | 45 | 104 | 63 | 66 | 62 |
| 14 | Redhill | 102 | 140 | 89 | 92 | 82 | 90 | 92 | 112 | 81 | 101 | 87 | 93 | 90 | X | 104 | 68 | 102 | 95 | 68 | 83 |
| 15 | Ringmer | 80 | 165 | 82 | 66 | 73 | 72 | 90 | 60 | 86 | 114 | 77 | 67 | 66 | 97 | X | 76 | 67 | 98 | 60 | 90 |
| 16 | Saltdean United | 133 | 676 | 129 | 209 | 143 | 89 | 103 | 116 | 93 | 206 | 103 | 189 | 109 | 89 | 159 | X | 139 | 219 | 251 | 169 |
| 17 | Selsey | 102 | 172 | 181 | 115 | 128 | 88 | 131 | 85 | 112 | 107 | 110 | 130 | 119 | 102 | 81 | 91 | X | 169 | 117 | 107 |
| 18 | Shoreham | 86 | 226 | 87 | 74 | 76 | 81 | 101 | 61 | 114 | 105 | 72 | 65 | 80 | 114 | 114 | 157 | 86 | X | 100 | 111 |
| 19 | Whitehawk | 30 | 150 | 50 | 81 | 65 | 60 | 50 | 95 | 92 | 55 | 65 | 60 | 50 | 75 | 112 | 150 | 40 | 75 | X | 70 |
| 20 | Wick | 67 | 168 | 88 | 155 | 128 | 114 | 106 | 88 | 92 | 110 | 160 | 105 | 98 | 105 | 105 | 128 | 132 | 109 | 89 | X |

# DIVISION ONE MERIT TABLE 1998-99

| | | No of Games | Wins | Wins by 5 Goals+ | Clean Sheets | Clean Games | Cautions | Send Offs | Total |
|---|---|---|---|---|---|---|---|---|---|
| 1 | Horsham YMCA | 38 | 120 | 25 | 55 | 110 | -100 | -20 | 190 |
| 2 | Burgess Hill Tn | 38 | 140 | 35 | 95 | 85 | -150 | -40 | 165 |
| 3 | Hassocks | 38 | 65 | 10 | 60 | 120 | -90 | -20 | 145 |
| 4 | Eastbourne Utd | 38 | 85 | 10 | 35 | 110 | -85 | -20 | 135 |
| 5 | Whitehawk | 38 | 55 | 10 | 40 | 110 | -100 | 0 | 115 |
| 6 | Saltdean Utd | 38 | 130 | 25 | 80 | 80 | -155 | -60 | 100 |
| 7 | Wick | 38 | 90 | 5 | 60 | 95 | -115 | -60 | 75 |
| 8 | Shoreham | 38 | 95 | 20 | 55 | 100 | -140 | -60 | 70 |
| 9 | Littlehampton T. | 38 | 50 | 0 | 40 | 105 | -110 | -20 | 65 |
| 10 | East Preston | 38 | 90 | 20 | 35 | 90 | -155 | -20 | 60 |
| 11 | Redhill | 38 | 70 | 25 | 60 | 75 | -145 | -60 | 25 |
| 12 | Broadbridge Hth | 38 | 20 | 0 | 20 | 100 | -150 | 0 | -10 |
| 13 | Langney Sports | 38 | 100 | 5 | 70 | 70 | -170 | -100 | -25 |
| 14 | Pagham | 38 | 80 | 0 | 70 | 75 | -225 | -40 | -40 |
| 15 | Eastbourne Tn | 38 | 70 | 5 | 40 | 75 | -195 | -65 | -70 |
| 16 | Hailsham Town | 38 | 35 | 5 | 15 | 80 | -155 | -60 | -80 |
| 17 | Ringmer | 38 | 40 | 0 | 45 | 70 | -200 | -40 | -85 |
| 18 | Portfield | 38 | 60 | 10 | 45 | 65 | -225 | -60 | -105 |
| 19 | Selsey | 38 | 35 | 0 | 30 | 35 | -325 | -60 | -285 |
| 20 | Chichester City | 38 | 50 | 5 | 45 | 35 | -265 | -160 | -290 |

**MERIT TABLE POINTS**

5 POINTS for every win

5 POINTS for scoring 5 goals or more

5 POINTS for every game with no goals conceded

5 POINTS for every game with no cautions or send-offs

-5 POINTS for each caution

-20 POINTS for every sending off

# P.G. CUNNINGHAM SPORTSMANSHIP TROPHY 1998-99

**WINNERS:** HORSHAM YMCA

| | | | |
|---|---|---|---|
| Horsham YMCA | 78.68 | Mile Oak | 71.18 |
| Storrington | 76.47 | Hailsham Town | 71.08 |
| Arundel | 75.59 | Southwick | 70.59 |
| Eastbourne United | 75.00 | Shoreham | 70.00 |
| East Grinstead Town | 74.24 | Saltdean United | 69.47 |
| East Preston | 73.78 | Wick | 69.21 |
| Whitehawk | 72.63 | Peacehaven & Telscombe | 68.82 |
| Hassocks | 71.84 | Burgess Hill Town | 68.16 |
| Crawley Down Village | 71.76 | Langney Sports | 68.16 |
| Oakwood | 71.76 | Littlehampton Town | 67.57 |
| Broadbridge Heath | 71.58 | Ringmer | 67.37 |
| Sidley United | 71.21 | Three Bridges | 66.97 |
| Lingfield | 71.18 | Shinewater Association | 66.18 |

| | |
|---|---|
| Withdean | 66.18 |
| Pagham | 65.79 |
| Portfield | 65.68 |
| Worthing United | 65.59 |
| Redhill | 65.53 |
| Chichester City | 65.00 |
| Eastbourne Town | 65.00 |
| Sidlesham | 65.00 |
| Newhaven | 62.35 |
| Crowborough Athletic | 61.52 |
| Selsey | 60.79 |
| Lancing | 55.59 |

# DIVISION THREE SPORTSMANSHIP AWARD 1998-99

**WINNERS:** ROYAL & SUN ALLIANCE

# LEADING GOALSCORERS 1998-99

| | | | |
|---|---|---|---|
| **DIVISION ONE** | PHIL CHURCHILL | HORSHAM YMCA | 30 |
| **DIVISION TWO** | CALVIN HORE | SIDLESHAM | 20 |
| | DERREN WOODS | SOUTHWICK | 20 |
| **DIVISION THREE** | DARROL PARRIS | WESTFIELD | 33 |

## DIVISION ONE

| | | |
|---|---|---|
| Broadbridge Heath | Mark Sharp | 9 |
| Burgess Hill Town | Ashley Carr | 20 |
| | Gavin Geddes | 19 |
| | Dominic Shepherd | 19 |
| | Daren Newman | 13 |
| | Shaun Grice | 10 |
| Chichester City | Anton Romasz | 15 |
| East Preston | Chris Jack | 18 |
| | Justin Thorpe | 12 |
| Eastbourne Town | Gary Brockwell | 13 |
| | Nicholas Barden | 11 |
| | Howard Stevens | 10 |
| Eastbourne United | Stephen Loughton | 20 |
| | John Snelgrove | 19 |
| Hailsham Town | Sydney Harman | 16 |
| Hassocks | Andrew Burt | 7 |
| | David Smith | 7 |
| H'ham YMCA | Phillip Churchill | 30 |
| | Matthew Russell | 26 |
| Langney Sports | Matthew Allen | 17 |
| | Paul Balch | 10 |
| Littlehampton Town | Steve Guille | 11 |
| Pagham | Lee Stevens | 12 |
| Portfield | Christopher Male | 14 |
| Redhill | Nicholas Flint | 27 |
| | (inc 15 for EGT) | |
| | Zac Newman | 19 |
| | Jake Hutchinson | 12 |
| Ringmer | Mark Sheriff | 8 |
| Saltdean United | Leighton Allen | 22 |
| | Carl Southwell | 10 |
| Selsey | Warren Bagnall | 9 |
| Shoreham | Andrew Agutter | 13 |
| | John Byrne | 12 |
| | Paul Arscott | 10 |
| Whitehawk | Lee Sale | 7 |
| Wick | Clinton More | 16 |

## DIVISION TWO

| | | |
|---|---|---|
| Arundel | Mark Lephard | 10 |
| Crawley Down Vlge | Douglas Cashamn | 15 |
| | Mark Aldred | 11 |
| Crowborough Ath. | Sean Muggeridge | 9 |
| Lancing | Paul Dendy | 9 |
| Lingfield | Stephen Crawford | 9 |
| | Stewart Small | 9 |
| Mile Oak | Neil Roberts | 13 |
| | Junior Lamont | 13 |
| Newhaven | Justin Tighe | 5 |
| Oakwood | Daniel Cousins | 10 |
| Peace. & Telscombe | Tobi Hutchinson | 10 |
| Shinewater Assoc. | Graham Holman | 16 |
| Sidlesham | Calvin Hore | 20 |
| | Steven Warnick | 12 |
| Sidley United | Shaun Loft | 10 |
| Southwick | Derren Woods | 20 |
| | Scott Carden | 16 |
| | Richard Hewitt | 10 |
| Storrington | Miles Scerri | 10 |
| Three Bridges | Paul Green | 14 |
| | David Emms | 13 |
| | Robert Collins | 10 |
| Withdean | David Agnew | 8 |
| Worthing United | Gavin Jones | 17 |

## DIVISION THREE

| | | |
|---|---|---|
| Ansty Rangers | Nolan Mortimer | 17 |
| Bexhill Town | Robert Warner | 14 |
| | Stephen Pettitt | 10 |
| Buxted | Stuart Martin | 12 |
| Forest | Duane Read | 9 |
| Franklands Village | Stephen Nicol | 8 |
| Haywards Heath T. | Jason Pennicard | 7 |
| Hurstpierpoint | Daniel Bryan | 13 |
| Ifield | Daniel Kemsley | 19 |
| Midhurst & E'bourne | Martin George | 9 |
| Oving S.C. | James Hasler | 20 |
| | Justin Turnill | 13 |
| Royal & Sun All. | Andrew Taylor | 17 |
| | Richard Latham | 15 |
| St Francis | James Laing | 20 |
| Steyning Town | Shaun Berrett | 7 |
| | Glen Geard | 7 |
| Uckfield Town | Andrew Payne | 15 |
| | Andrew Potter | 11 |
| | Paul Carter | 11 |
| Wealden | Andrew West | 18 |
| | Paul Rider | 14 |
| Westfield | Darrol Parris | 33 |
| | Dominic Scott | 11 |

# JOHN O'HARA SUSSEX COUNTY
## LEAGUE CHALLENGE CUP 1998-99

**FIRST ROUND**

| | | | | | | | | |
|---|---|---|---|---|---|---|---|---|
| Langney Sports | v | Sidley United | 3-0 | | Peacehaven & Tels. | v | Redhill | 1-1, 0-2 |
| Portfield | v | Southwick | 3*4 | | Shinewater Assoc. | v | Eastbourne Utd | 2*3 |
| Wick | v | Arundel | 7-1 | | Withdean | v | Burgess Hill Town | 0-4 |

**SECOND ROUND**

| | | | | | | | | |
|---|---|---|---|---|---|---|---|---|
| Broadbridge Heath | v | Newhaven | 2*3 | | Burgess Hill Town | v | Langney Sports | 2-0 |
| Crawley Down Village | v | Hailsham Town | 2-0 | | Crowborough Ath | v | Hassocks | 0*2 |
| East Grinstead Town | v | Chichester City | 0*1 | | Eastbourne Town | v | Oakwood | 6-0 |
| Lancing | v | Littlehampton Town | 2-6 | | Mile Oak | v | Selsey | 4-5 |
| Saltdean United | v | Lingfield | 3-1 | | Shoreham | v | Horsham YMCA | 2*1 |
| Sidlesham | v | Whitehawk | 1-0 | | Southwick | v | Eastbourne United | 1-2 |
| Storrington | v | Pagham | 0-1 | | Three Bridges | v | Ringmer | 1-0 |
| Wick | v | Redhill | 2-1 | | Worthing United | v | East Preston | 0-2 |

**THIRD ROUND**

| | | | | | | | | |
|---|---|---|---|---|---|---|---|---|
| Chichester City | v | Three Bridges | 7-2 | | Crawley Down V. | v | Eastbourne United | 0-1 |
| East Preston | v | Littlehampton Town | 4-2 | | Newhaven | v | Wick | 0-8 |
| Pagham | v | Burgess Hill Town | 0-1 | | Selsey | v | Saltdean United | 2*3 |
| Shoreham | v | Eastbourne Town | 0-1 | | Sidlesham | v | Hassocks | 2-0 |

**FOURTH ROUND**

| | | | | | | | | |
|---|---|---|---|---|---|---|---|---|
| Burgess Hill Town | v | East Preston | 3-3, 2-1 | | Eastbourne Town | v | Sidlesham | 2-1 |
| Saltdean United | v | Chichester City | 4-0 | | Wick | v | Eastbourne United | 0*1 |

**SEMI-FINAL**

| | | | | | | | | |
|---|---|---|---|---|---|---|---|---|
| Burgess Hill Town | v | Eastbourne Town | 4-1 | | Saltdean United | v | Eastbourne United | 4-1 |

**FINAL**

| | | | |
|---|---|---|---|
| BURGESS HILL T | v | SALTDEAN UNITED | 2-1 |


## DIVISION TWO
## SUSSEX COUNTY LEAGUE CHALLENGE CUP 1998-99

**FINAL**

| | | | |
|---|---|---|---|
| STORRINGTON | 0-2 | SIDLEY UNITED | |


## SUSSEX COUNTY F.A.
## INTERMEDIATE CUP 1998-99

**FINAL**

| | | | |
|---|---|---|---|
| OVING S.C. | 2-4 | HASTINGS T. RES | |


A full seasonal report and many more statistics were presented at the League Gala Presentation Dinner in an excellent booklet.

Please contact the League Secretary for copies

# BURGESS HILL TOWN

**Secretary:** The General Secretary, Burges Hill Town F.C., Leylands Park, Burgess Hill, W.Sussex RH15 8AW    Tel: 0144 242429

**Ground:** Leylands Park, Burgess Hill, West Sussex RH15 8AW Tel: 01444 242429
Capacity: 2,000    Seats: 100    Cover: Yes    Floodlights: Yes

**Directions:** Turn east from A273 London Road into Leylands Road, take 4th left (signposted) Leyland Park. Nearest station Wivelsfield

**Clubhouse:** Bar & social facilities. Tea bar    **Club Shop:** No. Club badges available

**HONOURS** Sussex County Lg 75-76 96-97, 97-98,98-99; Lg Cup 73-74 79-80 97-98  98-99 (R-up 90-91), Div 2 74-75 (Cup 73-73), F/lit Cup 96-97, Res  76-77 77-78 91-92, Res. Sect. East 77-78 82-83 84-85, Res. Cup 82-83 98-99; Yth Sect. West 91-92 East 95-96 96-97 97-98 98-99 North 96-97 97-98; Sussex Fives 80; Mid-Sussex Lg 00-01 03-04 39-4046-47 56-57 (Div 2 03-04 (res), Div 3 20-21 36-37, Div 4 (res) 56-57; Mid Sussex Snr Cup 94-95 96-97; Montgomery Cup 39-40 56-57; Mowatt Cup 45-46; Sussex RUR Charity Cup 91-92; Sussex I'mediate Cup 76-77; Sussex Yth Lge 96-97 97-98, Cup 91-92 97-98

**PREVIOUS** Leagues & Grounds: None

**RECORD** Gate: 854 v Clitheroe, FA Vase 4th Rd (H)

### FACT FILE

Founded: 1882
Nickname: Hillians
Sponsors: Time 24
Colours: Yellow/white/yellow
Change colours: All red
Midweek matchday: Tuesday
Programme: Yes

1998-99
Captain: Daren Newman
Top Scorer: Gavin Geddes
P.o.Y.: Marc Cable

### CLUB PERSONNEL

Chairman: Alan Pook
President: Jack Lake
Manager: Alan Pook

# CHICHESTER CITY

**Company Sec:** John F Hutter    Tel: 01243 785839
28 Stockbrigde Gdns, Donnington, Chichester, W Sussex PO19 2QT

**Ground:** Oaklands Park, Chichester Tel: 01243 785978
Capacity: 2,500    Seats: 50    Cover: 500    Floodlights: Yes

**Directions:** Half mile north of city centre adjacent to Festival Theatre. Turn into Northgate car park from Oaklands Way and entrance is beside Tennis and Squash club. 1 mile from Chichester (BR) - walk north through city centre

**Clubhouse:** Licensed, open matchdays and some evenings. Tea barClub Shop: No

**HONOURS** Sussex Co. Lg(5) 59-61 67-68 72-73 79-80 Invitation Cup 47-48 54-55 56-57 63-64, Div 2 Cup 84-85 87-88 90-91, Sussex Snr Cup 25-26, Sussex RUR Charity Cup 60-61(jt with Brighton & HA) 63-64, Sussex I'mediate Cup 67-68
**PREVIOUS** Leagues: Chichester; West Sussex 1886-1920
Name: Chichester FC (pre-1948)
Grounds: New Park Rec. 1873-81; Priory Park 1881-1956
**CLUB RECORDS** Gate: 2,500 v Dorchester, FA Cup 1960
Scorer: David Green(200+)    Appearances: Dave Kelly (448)

### FACT FILE

Founded: 1873
Sponsors: McDonalds
Nickname: Lilywhites
Colours: White/black/white
Change colours:Blue &Blackstripes,blue,black
Midweek matchday: Tuesday
Programme  Editor: T Wallis
Local Press: Chichester Observer

### CLUB PERSONNEL

Chairman: John Hutter
Match Secretary:Phil Littlejohns
Tel: 01243 528007
Press Officer: T Wallis (01705 464438)
Manager: Adrian Girdler
Chief Coach: Kevin Holston
Physio: NickTaylor
Club Steward: Andy Smith(01243 775455)

# EAST PRESTON

**Secretary:** Keith Freeman, 41 Ambersham Cres., East Preston, West Sussex BN161AJ
Tel: 01903 771158

**Ground:** Roundstone Recreation Ground, East Preston, West Sussex Tel: 01903 776026
Capacity:    Seats: None    Cover: 40Floodlights: Yes

**Directions:** Less than a mile from Angmering (BR) station. A259 from Worthing to Roundstone Hotel (6 miles), turn south over railway crossing, left past Centurion garage, right into Roundstone Drive

**Clubhouse:** Licensed bar open Mon-Fri evenings, Sat noon-11pm, Sun noon-11pm. Kitchen serves light refreshments on matchdays

**HONOURS** Sussex Co. Lg  Div 2 Champions 97-98Div 3 83-84, (R-up 90-91), Div 3 Cup 87-88 (R-up 89-90); West Sussex Lg 77-78 80-81 81-82 82-83 (Malcolm Simmonds Cup 80-81 82-83), Div2 Sth 81-82, Div 3 Sth 79-80, Div 5 Sth 82-83; Chichester Cup 87-88; BorehamTphy 77-78 90-91 (R-up 93-94); Vernon Wentworth Cup 80-81 89-90; Worthing Lg 67-68 (Div 2 68-69 (res), Benev. Tphy 66-67 68-69; Worthing Charity Cup 68-69

**PREVIOUS** Leagues: Worthing; W Sussex

### FACT FILE

Reformed: 1966
Nickname: None
Sponsors: Roundstone Garage
Colours: Black & white/black/black
Change: Red/white/red
Reserve's Lge: Sussex Co. Res. Div (Prem)
Programme: Yes
Editor: Andy Mott (01903 726097)
Local Press: Littlehampton Gazette

### CLUB PERSONNEL

President: Greg Stanley
Chairman: Brian Harwood
Manager: Carl Stabler
Asst Manager: Ian Cole

# EASTBOURNE TOWN

**FACT FILE**

**Secretary:** Viv Greenwood, 167 Seaside, Eastbourne BN22 7MP (01323 416667)

**Ground:** The Saffrons, Compton Place Road, Eastbourne, East Sussex (01323723734)
Capacity: 3,000     Seats: 200     Cover: Yes     Floodlights: Yes

**Directions:** Turn south west off the A22 into Grove Road (opposite BR station), and the ground is 1/4 mile on the right

**Clubhouse:** Fully licensed bar. Board room. Tea bar

**HONOURS** Sussex County Lg. 76-77; Sussex Sen Cup x12 1889-91, 93-95, 98-1901, 02-03, 21-22, 31-35, 52-53; Sussex RUR Charity Cup 32-33, 47-48, 49-50; SouthernAmat. Lge. x2; AFA Sen. Cup 21-22, 24-25, R-up 22-23, 23-24; AFA Invitation Cup69-70, R-up 56-57, 68-69, 70-71

**PREVIOUS** Leagues: Southern Amtr 07-46; Corinthian 60-63; Athenian 63-76

**RECORD** Attendance: 7,378 v Hastings Utd. 1953

Founded: 1882
Nickname: `Bourne'
Sponsor: Eastbourne Car Auctions
Colours: Yellow/blue/blue
Changes: Blue & black/black/black
Programme Editor: Chris Backhurst
Tel: 01323 505062

**CLUB PERSONNEL**

Chairman: Roger Addems
Manager: Pete Cherry

---

# EASTBOURNE UNITED

**FACT FILE**
Founded: 1894

**Secretary:** M Stevens, 21 Brookside Ave, Polegate, BN26 6DL (01323 484644)

**Ground:** The Oval, Channel View Rd, Eastbourne, East Sussex (011323-726989)
Capacity: 3,000     Seats: 160     Cover: 160     Floodlights: Yes

**Directions:** To seafront and turn left. Turn left into Channel View Rd atPrincess Park and ground 1st right. 2 miles from Eastbourne (BR)

**Clubhouse:** Bar, lounge, dancefloor, stage, tea bar, board room     **Club Shop:** No

**HONOURS** Sussex Co. Lg 54-55, Sussex Snr Cup(5) 60-61 62-64 66-67 68-69 (R-up 89-90), Sussex RUR Charity Cup 55-56, Metropolitan Lg Cup 60-61, Athenian Lg Div 2 66-67 (Div 1 R-up 68-69), Sussex I'mediate Cup 65-66 68-69

**PREVIOUS** **Name:** Eastbourne Old Comrades     **Leagues:** Sussex Co. 21-28 35-56; Metropolitan 56-64; Athenian 64-77;Isthmian 77-92     **Ground:** Lynchmere

**RECORD** Attendance: 11,000 at Lynchmere

Players progressing: B Salvage, T Funnell, M French

Nickname: The 'Us'
Colours: White/black/white
Change colours: Blue/black/black
Midweek Matchday: Tuesday
Reserve Lge: Sussex County Res. Div. (East)
Programme: 36 pages
Editor: R.Adcock
Local Press: Eastbourne Gazette + Herald, Evening Argus

**CLUB PERSONNEL**
Chairman: I Botting
Vice-Chairman: B Winter
President: N Mansell
Press Officer: M Stevens
Manager: M French
Asst Manager:
Physio: G Bishop

---

# HASSOCKS

**FACT FILE**
Founded: 1902

**Secretary:** Bob Preston, 65 Oakhall Park, Burgess Hill, West Sussex RH15 0DA
Tel: 01444 245695

**Ground:** The Beacon, Brighton Rd, Hassocks Tel: 01273 846040
Capacity: 1,500     Seats: None     Cover: 100     Floodlights: Yes

**Directions:** Off A273 Pyecombe Road to Burgess Hill, 300yds south of Stonepound cross roads (B2116) to Hurstpierpoint  or Hassocks

**Clubhouse:** Clubroom, bar, kitchen  Club Shop: No

**HONOURS** Sussex County Lg Div 3 91-92, Div 2 R-up 94-95, Res. Sect. East R-up 92-93; Southern Counties Comb. 76-77, Lg Cup R-up 79-80; Brighton Hove & Dist. Lg 71-72; Sussex Intermediate Cup 74-75 (R-up 80-81)

**PREVIOUS** **Leagues:** Mid Sussex; Brighton Hove & Dist.; Southern Co's Comb  **Ground:** Adastra Park, Hassocks (pre-1992)

**RECORD** Attendance: 610 v Burgess Hill Town, Sussex County Lge 96-97

Nickname: The Robins
Sponsors: Icon
Colours: Red/white/red
Change colours: All blue
Midweek Matchday: Tuesday/Wednesday
Programme: 24 pages, 50p
Editor: Dave Knight
Admission: £1.50
Local Press: Mid Sussex Times, Evening Argus

**CLUB PERSONNEL**
President: Maurice Boxall
Chairman: Jim Goodrum
Press Off . : Dave Knight (01273 842023)
Manager: Dave John

# HORSHAM YMCA

**Secretary:** Robin Bishop, 6 Brook Close, Storrington, RH20 3NT
Tel: 01903 746332 (H) 0996 202955 (Mob)

**Ground:** Gorings Mead, Horsham Tel: 01403 252689
Capacity: 800          Seats: 100          Cover: 200          Floodlights: Yes

**Directions:** Approaching Horsham fron the East on A281 Brighton Road, the ground is on left & signposted opposite Gorings Mead

**HONOURS** Sussex Co Lge Div 2 65-66 82-83 R-up 94-95 (Lg Cup 81-82, Invitation Cup66-67 67-68, Div 2 Invit. Cup 59-60 61-62 94-95)

**PREVIOUS** **Leagues:** Horsham & Dist/Brighton & Hove/Mid Sussex
**Grounds:** Lyons Field, Kings Road

**RECORD** **Attendance:** 600 v Horsham FA Cup

**FACT FILE**
Founded: 1898
Nickname: YM's
Sponsors: Principal Copiers
Colours: White/black/red
Change colours: All Red
Midweek Matchday: Tuesday
Local Press: West Sussex County Times

**CLUB PERSONNEL**
Chairman: Robert Knight
Match Secretary: Robin Bishop
Tel: 01903 746332
Manager: John Suter
Asst Mgr:
Physio: Robin Bishop

# LANGNEY SPORTS  EASTBOURNE BOROUGH

**Secretary:** Mrs Myra Stephens, 7b Erica Close, Langney, Eastbourne, East Sussex BN23 6HY
Tel: 01323 766050

**Ground:** Langney Sports Club, Priory Lane, Eastbourne, East Sussex  Tel: 01323 766265
Capacity: 2,500          Seats: None          Cover: 1,000          Floodlights: Yes

**Directions:** A22 to Polegate, A27 to Stone Cross, right onto B32104 to Langney Shopping Centre, then left and first right.
One mile from Pevensey & Westham(BR). Buses from Eastbourne
**Clubhouse:** Every evening & lunchtime with adjoining sports hall, boardroom, matchday tea bar
**Club Shop:** Yes

**HONOURS** Sussex Co. Lg R-up 91-92, Div 2 87-88, Lg Cup 89-90, Div 3 86-87, Div 3 Cup 86-87, 5-aside 1990; Sussex I'mediate Cup 85-86, Eastbourne Chall. Cup 85-86 86-87

**PREVIOUS** **League:** Eastbourne & Hastings
**Grounds:** Princes Park, Wartling Rd, Eastbourne/ Adjacent pitch

**RECORDS** **Attendance:** 1,000+ v Crystal Palace, f'light opener 90-91
**Goalscorer:** Nigel Hole 146          **Appearances:** Steve Dell 386
**Win:** 10-1 v Haywards Heath Town, Sussex County Lg Div. 1 11/4/92
**Defeat:** 0-8, v Sheppey United (A), FA Vase Prel. Rd 9/10/93
v Peacehaven & Telscombe (A), Sussex County Lg Div. 1 9/11/93

**FACT FILE**
Founded: 1966
Nickname: None
Sponsors: Nobo Group Plc
Colours: All red
Change: Sky & navy/navy
Midweek Matchday: Tuesday
Programme: Yes
Editor: Mike Spooner (01323 461003)
Local Press: Eastbourne Gazette & Herald

**CLUB PERSONNEL**
Chairman: Len Smith
President: J Stonestreet
Manager: Steve Richardson
Physio: T.B.A

# LITTLEHAMPTON TOWN

**Secretary:** John Savage, 66 Nelson Road, Worthing. BN12 6EN. (01903 502850)

**Ground:** The Sportsfield, St Flora's Road, Littlehampton (01903 713944)
Capacity: 4,000          Seats: 260          Cover: 260          Floodlights: Yes

**Directions:** 10 minutes walk from Littlehampton station (BR) - turn left alongTerminus Rd, continue through High Street and Church Rd to junction with St Flora's Rd (left)

**Club Shop:** No, but metal badges available
**Clubhouse:** Sportsman (Private Club). Separate board room & tea bar

**HONOURS** Sussex Co. Lg 58-59 (jt with Shoreham) 75-77 84-85 90-91 96-97
Sussex Senior Cup 73-74

**RECORD** **Gate:** 4,000 v Northampton, FA Cup 1st Rd Proper 90-91

**BEST SEASON** **FA Vase** Semi-Final 90-91
**FA Cup:** 1st Round 90-91

**FACT FILE**

Founded: 1894
Nickname: Marigolds
Colours: Gold/black/black
Change: Blue/white/white
Midweek Matches: Tuesday
Programme:
Editor:
Local Press: Littlehampton Gazette

**CLUB PERSONNEL**

President: Ian Cunningham
Chairman: Ian Cunningham
Manager: Carl Stabler

PORTFIELD FC: Back Row (L-R): Shane Davies, Jamie Martinez, Kevin Chambers, Chris Rustell, Mark Pannell, Paul Worsfold, Tony Stephens, Paul Morby. Front Row: Lee Pinhorne, John Edwards, Tim Brown, Paul Cowie, Steve Pinhorne, Glen Bridgman.
Photo: Andrw Chitty

PAGHAM

Photo: Peter Barnes

REDHILL FC: Back Row (L-R): Terry Allen (Asst Mngr), Tony Dugdale (Manager), Nigel Brake, Matt Duffield, david Stares, Steve Muskitt, Paul Otway (captain), Paul Hodge, Jonathan Shopland (kit), Brian Dennis (coach). Front Row: Nicky Flint, Bobby Clements, Graham Thurlbeck, Ian Chatfield, Ian Clements, Mark Clements, Zak Newman, Gary Thornton.
Photo: Andrew Chitty

# PAGHAM

**Secretary:** Alan Seal, 6 Greenlea Ave, Pagham, West Sussex PO21 3LH
Tel: 01243 262944 (H)

**Ground:** Nyetimber Lane, Pagham, West Sussex    Tel: 0243 266112
Capacity:    2,000    Seats: 200    Cover: 200    Floodlights: Yes

**Directions:** Turn off A27 Chichester by-pass (signposted A259 Pagham). Ground invillage of Nyetimber. Three miles from Bognor (BR). Buses 260 & 240

**Clubhouse:** Bar open matchdays and some evenings. Hot food, pool, darts,satellite TV. Tea bar
**Club Shop:** No

**HONOURS** Sussex Co. Lg R-up 80-81 87-88 88-89 92-93 (Div 2 78-79 86-87, Lg Cup88-89, Div 2 Cup 71-72 85-86, Res. Sect. West 80-81, Res Section Cup 77-78 80-81 87-88 88-89 90-91 96-97; Sussex F'lit Cup R-up 88-89; Sussex RUR Charity Cup88-89 (R-up 93-94); West Sussex Lg 65-66 68-69 69-70; Malcolm Simmonds Cup 67-68; Sussex I'mediate Cup 66-67

**PREVIOUS Leagues:** Chichester 1903-50; West Sussex 50-69    **Grounds:** None

**RECORDS Gate:** 1,200 v Bognor, 1971    **Scorer:** Mark Vickers/ R Deluca
**Win:** 10-1 v Seaford Town (A), Sussex County League Division Two, 1970
**Defeat:** 0-7 v Newport IOW (H), FA Amateur Cup, mid-1970s

**FACT FILE**
Founded: 1903
Nickname: Lions
Sponsors: City Saes Centre
Colours: White/black/black
Change colours: Yellow/green
Midweek Matchday: Tuesday
Reserve's League: Sussex Co. Reserve Div
Programme: 12 pages, 50p
Editor: Secretary
Local Press: Bognor Observer

**CLUB PERSONNEL**
Chairman: Graham Peach
Vice-Chairman:
President: A Peirce
Press Officer: Ken Randall (01243 555415)
Comm. Manager: Chairman
Manager/Coach: Graham Peach
Asst Manager: S Booker

# PORTFIELD

**Secretary:** Gary Rustell    Tel: 01243 537978
102 Churchwood Drive, Tangmere, Nr Chichester, West Sussex PO20 6GB

**Ground:** Church Road, Portfield, Chichester, West Sussex PO19 4HN    Tel: 01243 779875
Capacity: 2,000    Seats: 20Cover: 200    Floodlights: Yes

**Directions:** A27 from Arundel to Chichester, take road to signposted city centre then 1st left (Church Rd) after supermarket r'bout. 1 mile from Chichester(BR)

**Clubhouse:** 2 bars, pool, snooker, seating for 100, dance floor, darts, and teabar selling hot & cold food.
**Club Shop:** No, but club badges are available.

**HONOURS** Sussex Co. Lg Div 2 72-73 83-84 91-92 (Div 2 Cup 70-71 72-73, Res Sect Prem Lge 94-95, Cup 91-92), W Sussex Lg 46-47 48-49 (Malcolm Simmonds Cup 46-47), Sussex Jnr Cup 45-46, Benevolent Cup 46-47

**PREVIOUS** **League:** West Sussex

**RECORD** **Attendance:** Unknown

**FACT FILE**
Founded: 1896
Nickname: Field
Sponsors: Swinton
Colours: Amber/black/amber
Change colours: All Blue
Midweek Matchday: Tuesday
Programme: Yes
Editor: Chris Dyke
Admission: £2.00 & £1

**CLUB PERSONNEL**
President: S Kenny
Chairman: Terry Rustell
Manager: Richie Reynolds

# REDHILL

**Secretary:** Neil Hoad, 2b Earlswood Rd, Redhill, Surrey RH1 6HE    Tel: 01737 213847

**Ground:** Kiln Brow, Three Arch Road, Redhill, Surrey    Tel: 01737 762129

**Directions:** On left hand side of A23, two and a half miles south of Redhill
Capacity: 2,000    Seats: 150    Cover: 150    Floodlights: Yes
**Club Shop:** Sells usual range of souvenirs. Contact Spencer Mitchell - 01737 780634
**Clubhouse:** Social club, bar, canteen, board room, club shop, tanoy, toilets

**HONOURS** Athenian Lg 24-25 83-84 (LgCup 69-70 70-71), East & West Surrey Lg. 1902-03, Southern Sub Sen West Lg. 1902-03, Surrey Snr Cup 28-29 65-66, Gilbert Rice F'lit Cup 80-81, Sussex Co. Lg Div 2 Cup 91-92, Southern Co's Comb. Cup 90-91,98-99

**PREVIOUS** **Leagues:** E & W Surrey; Spartan 09-10; Southern Sub; London 21-23; Athenian 23-84; Spartan 84-88
**Grounds:** Memorial Sports Ground, London Road 1894-1986

**BEST SEASON** **FA Amtr Cup:** Semi-Final 25    **FA Cup:** 1st Round 57-58

**RECORDS** **Attendance:** 1,200 v Crystal Palace & All Star XI, Brian Medlicott Testimonial 1989
**Goalscorer:** Steve Turner 119    **Appearances:** Brian Medlicott 766
**Win** : 10-0 v Saltdean United (H), Sussex Co. Lg Div 1 18/4/98
**Defeat** : 1-7 v Peacehaven & Telscombe (H), Sussex County Lg Cup 9/2/93

**FACT FILE**
Founded: 1894
Nickname: Reds/Lobsters
Sponsors: Trident Microsystems Ltd.
Colours: Red & white stripes /red /red
Change colours: White/black
Midweek matchday: Tuesday
Reserve League: Sussex Co.Lg
Programme: 36 pages, 50p
Editor: Michael Stewart
Local Press : Surrey Mirror & The Independent

**CLUB PERSONNEL**
Chairman: Nick Creasey
Vice-Chairman: Alan Thurlbeck
President: Malcolm Chatfield
Press Officer: Peter Cox
Manager: Tony Dugdale
Asst Manager: Terry allen
Coach: Brian Dennis

# RINGMER

**Secretary:** Stuart Bean, 91 Springett Avenue, Ringmer, East Sussex BN8 5QS
Tel: 01273 812878

**Ground:** Caburn Ground, Anchor Field, Ringmer  Tel: 01273 812738
Capacity: 1,000     Seats: 100     Cover: Yes     Floodlights: Yes

**Directions:** From Lewes road turn into Springett Avenue opposite Ringmer village green.
Anchor Field first left. Three miles from Lewes (BR)

**Clubhouse:** 2 bars, function room, boardroom, tea bar
**Club Shop:** Club ties & metal badges

**HONOURS** Sussex Co. Lg 70-71, Div 2 68-69, Invit Cup 66-67; Res. Sect. East 79-80 80-81
(R-up 89-90), Yth Section 87-88, Yth SectionEast 87-88; Sussex Snr Cup 72-73
(R-up 80-81); Sussex Jnr Cup 25-26; Sussex Express Sen Charity Cup 94-95

**PREVIOUS**   **League:** Brighton       **Grounds:** None       **Names:** None

**BEST SEASON**  **FA Cup** 1st Rd Proper 70-71

**RECORD**    **Gate:** 1,200 in FA Cup

### FACT FILE
Founded: 1906
Nickname: The Blues
Colours: Sky & navy/navy/navy
Change colours: All yellow
Midweek Matchday: Tuesday
Programme: Yes
Editor: Martin BUrke (01797 230572)
Admission: £2.50
Local Press: Sussex Express

### CLUB PERSONNEL
President: Sir G Christie
Chairman: Richard Soan
Manager: Gary Allen
Press Officer: Martin Burke(01797 230572)
Match Secretary: John McWhirter (01323 847743)

# SALTDEAN UNITED

**Secretary:** Iain Fielding, 40 Rowan Way, Rottingdean, Brighton BN2 7FP
Tel: 01273 304995

**Ground:** Hill Park, Combe Vale, Saltdean, Brighton       Tel: 01273 309898
Capacity: 2,000     Seats: 50     Cover: Yes     Floodlights: Yes

**Directions:** A259 coast road east from Brighton to Saltdean Lido, left into Arundel Drive
West, and Saltdean Vale to bridle path at beginning of Combe Vale.
Club 200yds along track

**Club Shop:** Metal badges available
**Clubhouse:** Licensed bar, lounge, juke box, video games, board room, tea bar.Pool table

**HONOURS** Sussex Co. Lg Div 3 88-89, Div 2 95-96

**PREVIOUS**   **League:** Brighton Hove & Dist Ground: None

**RECORD**    **Attendance:** 676

### FACT FILE
Founded: 1966
Nickname: Tigers
Sponsors: FDM
Colours: Red & black/black/black
Change colours: Blue & white
Programme: Yes
Editor:Rod Flavell (01273 888977)
Local Press: Brighton Evening Argus & Sussex Express

### CLUB PERSONNEL
Chairman: Rod Flavell
Vice Chairman:Mike Walker
President: Jim Bower
Press Officer: JIain Fielding
Manager: Glenn Burvill
Asst Manager: Glenn Geard
Physio: Keith Gray

# SELSEY

**Secretary:** Danny Glew, 2 Colt Street, Selsey, Chichester W.Sussex PO20 9EU
Tel: 01243 605027

**Ground:** High Street Ground, Selsey, Chichester, West Sussex       Tel: 01243 603420
Capacity: 2,250     Seats: 50     Cover: Yes     Floodlights: Yes

**Directions:** Through Selsey High Street to fire station. Take turning into car park alongside the
station. Entrance is in the far corner. Regular buses from Chichester
**Clubhouse:** Bar, hospitality room, lounge, toilets, kitchen

**HONOURS** Sussex Co. Lg R-up 89-90 (Div 2 63-64 75-76 (R-up 86-87), Div 2 Cup 86-87 (R-
up 84-85), Div 2 Invitation Cup 63-64, Sussex 5-aside 88-89), Sussex SnrCup R-
up 63-64, Sussex I'mediate Cup 58-59, Sussex Jnr Cup(Reserves) 76-77,West
Sussex Lg 54-55 55-56 57-58 58-59 60-61 (Malcolm Simmonds Cup 55-56 56-57
57-58 58-59)

**PREVIOUS**   **Leagues:** Chichester & Dist.; West Sussex

**RECORD**    **Gate:** 750-800 v Chichester or Portfield, 50's

### FACT FILE
Founded: 1903
Nickname: Blues
Sponsors: Windmill Club
Colours: Blue/white/blue
Change colours:All yellow
Midweek Matchday: Tuesday
Programme  Editor: Secretary
Match Secretary: Mandie Glew

### CLUB PERSONNEL
President: Roy Glew
Chairman: Mike Hurst
Press Officer: Mr P Emms
Manager: Mick Marsh

SIDLEY UNITED, winners of the Unijet Division 2 Challenge Cup.

Photo: Roger Turner

Mark Howells, East Preston's keeper makes a superb save to thwart Pagham from scoring.

Photo: Graham Cotterill

Littlehampton 0 Redhill 7. Redhill attack once again at The Sportsfield.

Photo: Martin Wray

# SHOREHAM

**Secretary:** Mrs Anne Harper, 66 Willow Crescent, Worthing. BN13 2SX    Tel: 01903 267672

**Ground:** Middle Road, Shoreham-by-Sea, West Sussex    Tel: 01273 454261
Capacity: 1,500    Seats: 20    Cover: 1 stand    Floodlights: Yes

**Directions:** Half mile from Shoreham-by-Sea (BR) - east across level crossing, up Dolphin Road, ground 150yds on right. Or, A27 to Shoreham. At Southlands Hospital turn left down Hammy Lane, left at end, ground opposite

**Clubhouse:** Seats 70. Bar, pool, darts, tea bar    **Club Shop:** No

**HONOURS** Sussex Co. Lg 51-53 77-78 (R-up 34-35, Div 2 61-62 76-77 84-85 93-94,Div 2 Cup 74-75 82-83, Invitation Cup 57-58), Sussex Snr Cup 01-02 05-06,Sussex F'lit Cup R-up 89-90, Sussex RUR Charity Cup 02-03 05-06, VernonWentworth Cup 86-87

**PREVIOUS** **League:** West Sussex
**Ground:** Buckingham Park (pre-1970)

**RECORD** **Gate:** 1,342 v Wimbledon (f/lt opening 86)

### FACT FILE

Founded: 1892
Nickname: Musselmen
Sponsors: Len German Wholesalers
Colours: Blue/white/blue
Change colours: Red & white
Midweek Matchday: Wednesday
Programme: Yes
Editor: Michael Wenham
Local Press: Shoreham Herald

### CLUB PERSONNEL

President: Alf Bloom
Chairman: John Bell
Manager: John Prees
Press Officer: Michael Wenham
Tel: 01273 596009

# SIDLEY UNITED

**Secretary:** Brian Martin, 30 Mayo Lane, Bexhill on Sea, East Sussex,TN39 5EA

**Ground:** Gullivers Sports Ground, Glovers Lane, Sidley, Bexhill-on-Sea
Tel: 01424 217078
Capacity: 1,500    Seats: None    Cover: 150    Floodlights: Yes

**Directions:** From Brighton on A259 to Bexhill bypass traffic lights, left intoLondon Road, continue into Sidley, right into Glovers Lane and 1st left into North Road. One mile from Bexhill (BR)

**Clubhouse:** Large bar area & function room. Tea bar
**Club Shop:** No, but metal badges are available.

**HONOURS** Sussex Co. Lg Div 2 58-59 64-65 98-99, Div. 2 Cup 98-99, Div 2 Invit. Cup 57-58; Sussex Intermediate Cup 47-48, Sussex Jnr Cup 24-25

**PREVIOUS** **Leagues:** East Sussex; Hastings & District
**Grounds:** None

**RECORD** **Attendance:** 1,300 in 1959

### FACT FILE

Founded: 1906
Nickname: Blues
Sponsors: C,Campbell & R Cheale
Colours: Navy & sky/navy/navy & sky
Change colours: White
Midweek Matchday: Tues/ Weds
Programme: Yes    Editor: Graham Watson
Local Press: Bexhill Observer, Bexhill News

### CLUB PERSONNEL

President: Tibby Adams
Chairman: Mike Gardner
Manager: Dickie Day

# THREE BRIDGES

**Secretary:** Martin Clarke, 18 Mannings Close, Pound Hill, Crawley RH10 3TX
Tel: 01293 883726 (H),   0585 662940 (Mob)

**Ground:** Jubilee Field, Three Bridges, Crawley, West Sussex Tel: 01293 442000
Capacity: 3,500    Seats: None    Cover: 400    Floodlights: Yes

**Directions:** From West Three Bridges station, turn second right into ThreeBridges Road and first left 75 yds down, opposite the Plough Inn
**Clubhouse:** Bar, dance floor, pool, darts    **Club Shop:** No

**HONOURS** Sussex Co. Lg R-up 85-86 87-88 88-89 (Div 2 54-55, Invitation Cup 70-71, Div 2 Invitation Cup 62-63), Sussex RUR Charity Cup 82-83

**PREVIOUS** **League s:** Mid Sussex; Redhill & District
**Grounds:** None

**RECORD** **Attendance:** 2,000 v Horsham, 1948

### FACT FILE

Founded: 1901
Nickname: Bridges
Sponsors: Canon
Colours: Amber & black/black/black
Change colours: Blue & white/blue/white
Midweek Matchday: Tuesday
Programme: Yes
Editor: Andy West (01293 883163)
Local Press: Crawley Observer, Crawley News

### CLUB PERSONNEL

President: Jim Steele
Chairman: Alan Bell
Press Officer: Alf Blackler
Manager: Barry Hunt

# WHITEHAWK

**Secretary:** John Rosenblatt, 25 Arundel Street, Brighton BN2 5TH     Tel: 01273 680322

**Ground:** The Enclosed Ground, East Brighton Park   Tel: 01273 609736
Capacity: 3,000     Seats: None     Cover: 500     Floodlights: Yes

**Directions:** Follow Brighton seafront road towards Newhaven, turn inland (Arundel Road) oppo
site Marina, 3rd right into Roedean Road, 1st left intoWilson Ave. 3 miles from
Brighton (BR); take Newhaven, Eastbourne or Saltdean bus to Marina

**Clubhouse:** Licensed bar, pool, darts. Board room. Tea bar     Club Shop: No

**Honours:** Sussex Co. Lg 61-62 63-64 83-84 (Div 2 67-68 80-81, Lg Cup 82-83 93-94,
Invitation Cup 60-61 69-70, Div 2 Cup 80-81), Sussex Snr Cup 50-51 61-
62,Sussex RUR Charity Cup 54-55 58-59 90-91, Sussex I'mediate Cup 49-50,
Sussex Jnr Cup 48-49 51-52, Brighton Charity Cup 51-52 59-60 61-
62 82-83     87-88 88-89,Worthing Charity Cup 82-83

**PREVIOUS** **League:** Brighton Hove & Dist**Grounds:** None
**Name:** Whitehawk & Manor Farm Old Boys (until 1958)

**BEST SEASON** **FA Vase:** 5th Round 93-94

**RECORDS** **Gate:** 2,100 v Bognor Regis Town, FA Cup 4th Qualifying Rd replay 88-89
**Scorer:** Billy Ford     **Appearances:** Ken Powell 1,103

**FACT FILE**
Founded: 1945
Nickname: Hawks
Sponsors: Brighton Co-operative Society
Colours: All red
Change colours: All blue
Midweek Matchday: Wednesday
Programme: £2 with admission
Editor: Tony Kelly (0273 698203)
Local Press: Evening Argus

**CLUB PERSONNEL**
President: Ron Wiltshire
Chairman/Comm Mgr: Ken Powell
Match Sec: Fred Moore
Manager: Paul Hubbard
Asst Manager: Vic Standen
Coach: Paul Hubbard

# WICK

**Secretary:** Paul Beard, 2 Van Gogh Place, North Bersted, Bognor Regis, W.Sussex PO22 9BG
Tel: 01243 822063

**Ground:** Crabtree Park, Coomes Way, Wick, Littlehampton, W. SussexTel: 01903 713535
Capacity: 2,000     Seats: 50     Cover: 200     Floodlights: Yes

**Directions:** A27 to Crossbush, left at traffic lights signed Littlehampton, after 1 mile cross
level crossing, turn left into Coombes Way next to Locomotive PH - ground at
end. One and a half miles from Littlehampton (BR)

**Clubhouse:** First floor. Capacity 120. Tea bar     Club Shp: No

**HONOURS** Sussex Snr Cup 92-93; Sussex Co. Lg 89-90 93-94, Lg Cup 87-88 96-97 (R-up
93-94 94-95), Div 2 81-82 85-86, Div 2 Cup R-up 81-82; Norman Wingate Tphy88-
89 90-91, Res. Sect West 87-88 90-91 94-95; Sussex 5-aside R-up 85-86;Sussex
RURCharity Cup 89-90 97-98;98-99 Gilbert Rice F'lit Cup R-up 80-81 81-82;
Sussex Jnr Cup 59-60; Brighton Charity Cup 85-86; Sussex F'lit Cup R-Up 94-95

**PREVIOUS** **League:** West Sussex     **Grounds:** Southfields Rec

**RECORD** **Attendance:** 900

**FACT FILE**
Founded: 1892
Nickname: Wickers
Sponsors: Swandean
Colours: Red & black/black/black
Change colours: All white
Midweek Matchdays: Tuesday
Reserve League: Sussex Co. Reserve Div
Programme: Yes
Editor/Press Officer:
Thomas Cairns 01903 501857
Local Press: Littlehampton Gazette

**CLUB PERSONNEL**
Chairman: Norman Cairns
Vice-Chairman: J Burnett
President: B Wadsworth
Manager: Mark Dunk
Asst Manager: T.B.A.

WICK FC: Back Row (L-R): J Thompson (Asst Manager), Jim Quinn (Manager), Robbie Pearce, Mark McCullum, Peter Breeckley, Phil
Read, Stuart Hack, Michael Montague, Stuart Green, Jackie Anderson (Physio), Frank Smith (Asst Physio). Front Row: Cameron
Johnson, John Chalaye, Paul Williams, Stewart McCreadie (captain), Phil Churchill, Owen Hill, Nick Vickers, Martin Ellis. Photo: M Wray

# ARUNDEL

**Secretary:** Doug Feest, 342 Goring Road, Worthing. BN12 4PD    Tel: 01903 249276

**Ground:** Mill Road, Arundel    Tel: 01903 882548

**Directions:** A27 from Worthing to Arundel over railway bridge to roundabout.Second exit into Queen Street to town centre, turn right over bridge. Car parkleading to ground 100yards right

Capacity: 2,200    Seats: 100    Cover: 200    Floodlights: 206 lux

**Clubhouse:** 2 bars, kitchen, toilets, telephone, pool, darts, Sky TV. Normal pubhours. No food

**HONOURS**    Sussex Co. Lg 57-58 58-59 86-87 (Lg Cup 86-87, Div 2 Cup 76-77, Res. Sect.
78-79, Res. Sect. Cup 78-79, Merit Table 80-81,Sussex Fives 1984 1987),
Sussex RUR Charity Cup 68-69 72-73 78-79 79-80, Sussex Jnr Cup 07-08,
West Sussex Lg (Res.) 70-71 (Malcolm Simmonds Cup 70-71)

**PREVIOUS**    **League** : West Sussex 1896-1975    **Grounds:** Castle Park; Station Rd Ground

**RECORD**    Gate: 2,200 v Chichester, League 67-68
    Scorer: Paul J Bennett    Appearances: 537, Paul Bennett (goalkeeper)
    Win : 13-0 v Horsham YMCA (H), Sussex Co. Lge Div 1 21/12/85

### FACT FILE
Founded: 1889
Nickname: Mulletts
Colours: Red & white halves/white/red
Change colours: Jade & black
Midweek matchday: Tuesday
Reserves' Lge: Sussex Co. Res Div (West)
Programme: 8 pages, free Editor: P Wells
Local Press: Arun Herald
98-99 - Captain: Jon Tucker
P.o.Y.: Jon Tucker
### CLUB PERSONNEL
Chairman: M.Peters
Vice Chairman: S Brennan
Manager: Mike Rowland

# BROADBRIDGE HEATH

**Secretary:**    Phil Farrelley

**Ground:**    Broadbridge Heath Sports Centre, Wickhurst Lane, Horsham    Tel: 01403 211311

    Capacity: 1,300    Seats: 300    Cover: 300    Floodlights: Yes

**Directions:**    Alongside A24, Horsham north/south bypass. From the A24 Horsham Bypass, at
    thelarge roundabout/underpass take the Broadbridge Heath Bypass towards
    Guildford and then at the first roundabout turn left into Wickhurst Lane.

**Clubhouse:**    Bar. Kitchen serving meals,

**HONOURS**    None

**PREVIOUS**    **Leagues:** Horsham, West Sussex, Southern Co's Comb

**RECORD**    **Attendance:** 240

### FACT FILE
Founded: 1919
Nickname: Bears
Sponsors: Broadbridge Heath Peugeot
Colours: All royal blue
Change colours: All red
Midweek matches: Tuesday
Programme: Yes
Editor: Andy Crisp(01403 252273)
Admission: £2.50
### CLUB PERSONNEL
Chairman: Keith Soane
President: G W Manketelow
Joint Managers:
Gary Croydon, Martin Gander

# CRAWLEY DOWN VILLAGE

**Secretary:**    Stuart Frier, 30 Squires Close, Crawley Down, Surrey. RH10 4JQ
    Tel: 01342 714507 or 0181 667 2753 (B)

**Ground:**    The Haven Sportsfield, Hophurst Lane, Crawley Down.
    Tel: 01342 717140
    Capacity: 1000    Seats: None    Cover: 50    Floodlights: No

**Directions:**    From B2028, follow signpost for village to War Memorial, turn left into Hophurst
Lane, ground 100 yards on left. From A22, Felbridge, left into Crawley Down    Road,
ground 2 miles uphill on right.

**HONOURS**    Sussex County Lge Div 3 R-Up 95-96
    Sussex Intermediate Chall. Cup R-up 95-96

**PREVIOUS**    **League:** Mid Sussex Football League

### FACT FILE
Colours: All red
Programme:Yes

### CLUB PERSONNEL
Chairman: Brian Suckling
Vice-Chairman: Michael Martin
President: Tony Clements
Manager: Alan Watson & Darren Barker
Match Sec. Bob Rashbrook(01293 411457)
Physio: Mike Green

# EAST GRINSTEAD TOWN

**Secretary:** HWebsite:Bruce Talbot,16 Peverel Road, Ifield, Crawley, West Sussex RH11 0TH

**Ground:** East Court, East Grinstead    Tel: 01342 325885
**Directions:**    A264 Tunbridge Wells road (Moat Road) until mini-r'bout at bottom of
    Blackwell Hollow, turn immediately right by club sign then 1st left, ground
    200yds down lane past rifle club on right.
Capacity: 3,000    Seats: None    Cover: 400    Floodlights: Yes    Club Shop: No
**Clubhouse:** Open 1.30-10.30 matchdays, 6-11 midweek matches. Hot food available.

**HONOURS**    Sussex RUR Charity Cup (R-up 74-75); Sussex Co. Lg Invitation Cup 51-52;
    Sussex Jnr Cup (jt) 07-08; Sussex Youth Cup 86-87; Southern Amtr Lg
    Snr Div 3 31-32; Mid-Sussex Lg x 6, Lg Cup x 7; Brighton Lg x 3, Lg Cup x 3
**PREVIOUS Leagues:** Mid-Sussex 00-15 35-37; Sussex Co. 20-32; Southern Amateur 32-35.
**RECORD**    **Attendance:** 2,006 v Lancing, FA Amateur Cup 8/11/48
    **Appearances:** Guy Hill in 19 seasons - 1977-94

### FACT FILE
Founded: 1890    Nickname: Wasps
Sponsors: Rydon Group.
Colours: Gold/black/black
Change colours: Navy & L/blue
Midweek Matchday: Tuesday.
Reserves Lge: Sussex Co. Reserve Div East
Programme: 36 pages, 50p (Matt Gardner)
Press Off.: Bruce Talbot 01293 543809
Local Press: East Grinstead Observer/East
Grinstead Courier,SportsArgus
### CLUB PERSONNEL
Chairman: Bruce Talbot
President: Colin Dixon
Manager: Bobby Smith
Physio: Gary Bullen

# HAILSHAM TOWN

**Secretary/Press Officer:** Derek York, 59 Anglesey Avenue, Horsebridge, Hailsham BN27 3BQ
Tel: 01323 848024
**Ground:** The Beaconsfield, Western Road, Hailsham, East Sussex      Tel: 01323 840446
**Directions:** A22 to Arlington Road, turn east, then left into South Road - leftinto Diplocks Way until Daltons. Four miles from Polegate (BR - Brighton-Eastbourne line); regular bus service from Eastbourne
**Capacity:** 2,000    **Seats:** None    **Cover:** 300    **Floodlights:** Yes
**Clubhouse:** Hot and cold snacks. Open every evening, matchdays and Sundays, teabar
**HONOURS** Sussex County Lg Div 2 R-up 80-81, Southern Co'sComb. 74-75, Sussex RUR Charity Cup, Sussex I'mediate Cup, Hastings Snr Cup,Sussex Jnr Cup, E Sussex Lg Cup, Hailsham Charity Cup, John O'Hara Cup 95-96

**PREVIOUS    League:** E Sussex, Southern Comb  **BEST SEASON    FA Vase:** 5th Rd 88-89
**RECORD    Gate:** 1,350 v Hungerford, FA Vase Feb '89
**Goalscorer:** H Stevens 51, 95-96    **Appearances:** P Comber 713

**FACT FILE**
Founded: 1885    Nickname: None
Colours: Green & yellow/green/yellow
Change colours: All white
Midweek matchday: Tuesday
Programme: Yes
Editor: Secretary
Admission: ¨2.50
98-99 Captain: P Comber
P.o.Y.: D.Winterton
Top Scorer: P.Spencer (10)
**CLUB PERSONNEL**
President: J Whippy
Chairman: T.B.A.
Manager: Streve Richardson

# LANCING

**Secretary:** J Chisnall, 25 Amberley Court, Freshbrook Road, Lancing, W. Sussex BN15 8DS
Tel: 01903 763048
**Ground:** Culver Road, Lancing, West Sussex Tel: 01903 764398. **Directions:** From A27 turn south at Lancing Manor r'about into Grinstead Lane,3rd turning on right North Farm Rd. Turn left then immed. right into Culver Rd.From railway station take 3rd turning on left heading north.
**Capacity:** 2,400    **Seats:** 350    **Cover:** 350    **Floodlights:** Yes
**Clubhouse:** Open matchdays & training nights. Separate tea bar.    Club Shop: No

**HONOURS** Sussex Co. Lg. R-up 49-50 64-65 (Div 2 57-58 69-70 (R-up 82-83), Div 2 Cup 81-82 92-93, Invitation Cup), Sussex RUR Charity Cup 65-66, Brighton Lg 46-47 47-48, Sussex Intermediate Cup 46-47, Brighton Charity Cup 83-84 84-85 86-87.
**PREVIOUS    League:** Brighton Hove & District    **Name:** Lancing Athletic
**Ground:** Croshaw Rec, Sompting.
**RECORDS    Attendance:** 2,591 v Tooting, FA Amateur Cup 22/11/47 At Culver Road: 2,340v Worthing 25/10/52 **Career Appearances:** Dave Menzies 462 **Goals:** Paul Steele 113

**FACT FILE**
Founded: 1941    Nickname: Yellows
Sponsors: Bacon & Co. Estate Agents
Colours: Yellow/blue/yellow
Change colours: All red
Midweek Matches: Wednesday
Programme: Yes
Editor/Press Off.: Len Ralph (01903 763913)
98-99 Captain: Don Shepherd
Top Scorers: Greg Bradley & Paul Dendy
P.o.Y.: Andy long
**CLUB PERSONNEL**
Chairman: John Brown  President: R G Steele
Match Sec: Mike Peters
Manager: Andy Gander
Physio: Peter Towell

# LINGFIELD

**Secretary:** Ian Tomsett, 8 Orchard Cottage, St. Piers Lane, Lingfield, Surrey RH7 6PN
Tel: 01273 591346

**Ground:** Godstone Road, Lingfield, Surrey.
Tel: 01342 834269

**Directions:** A22, 4 miles north of East Grinstead, to Mormon Temple roundabout, take exit Lingfield (B2028) Newchapel Road for 1 1/2 miles. Left at T junction into Godstone Road (B2029) and ground is 1/2 mile on left.

**FACT FILE**
Colours: Red & yellow/black/yellow

**CLUB PERSONNEL**
Manager: Ali Rennie

# MILE OAK

**Secretary:** Colin Brown, 19 The Crescent, Southwick, West Sussex BN42 4LB
Tel: 01273 591346
**Ground:** Mile Oak Recreation Ground, Graham Avenue, Mile Oak. Tel: 01273 423854

**Directions:** From A27 take Mile Oak Road or Locks Hill & Valley Road to Chalky Road, ground 500yds on right along Graham Avenue which runs up valley fromcentre of Chalky Road
**Capacity:**    **Seats:** None    **Cover:** Yes    **Floodlights:** Yes
**Clubhouse:** Mile Oak Pavillion; Hall and tea bar    **Club Shop:** No

**HONOURS** Sussex Co.Lg.Div 2 Champions, Div 3 R-up 91-92 (Div 2 Cup R-up 92-93), Southern Counties Combination 86-87, Brighton Hove & District Lg 80-81, VernonWentworth Cup 85-86, Sussex Intermediate Cup R-up 88-89
**PREVIOUS    Leagues:** Southern Counties Combination; Brighton Hove & District
**Ground:** Victoria Rec., Portslade
**RECORD    Attendance:** 186

**FACT FILE**
Founded: 1960
Nickname: The Oak
Colours: Tangerine/black/tangerine
Change colours: All white
Midweek Matchday: Tuesday
Programme: Yes
Editor: C Tew (01273 416036)
Admission: £1.50
Local Press: Brighton Evening Argus, Shoreham Herald
**CLUB PERSONNEL**
Chairman: Geoff Kerly
President: D Bean
Manager: Tony Gratwicke

# OAKWOOD

**Secretary:** Gerry Martin, Singlegate, Tinsley Green, Crawley RH10 3NS    Tel: 01293 882400

**Ground:** Tinsley Lane, Three Bridges, Crawley, West Sussex    Tel: 01293 515742

**Directions:** From A23 to Gatwick, take 1st set of lights into Manor Royal, pass next lights, over 'bout to warehouse marked Canon, turn right signposted Oakwood. Last clubhouse down lane. Two miles north of Three Bridges (BR)
　　　　Capacity: 3,000    Seats: 20    Cover: Yes    Floodlights: Yes
**Club Shop:** Yes, incl. metal badges
**Clubhouse:** Large bar area, pool tables, multidart boards. Board room & tea bar

| | |
|---|---|
| **HONOURS** | Sussex Snr Cup R-up 92-93, Sussex Co. Lg Div 2 R-up 89-90 (Div 2 Cup 89-90, Div 3 84-85), Southern Comb. Cup 83-84 |
| **PREVIOUS** | **Leagues:** Crawley & Dist., Southern Co's Comb |
| | **Ground:** Park pitches |
| **RECORD** | **Attendance:** 367    **Appearances:** Peter Brackpool |

**FACT FILE**
Founded: 1966    Nickname: Oaks
Sponsors: Linden Plc
Colours: Red & black/black/black
Change colours: Blue/black/black
Midweek Matchday: Tuesday
Reserves' Lge: Sussex Co. Reserve section
Programme: 24 pages
Editor: Simon Milham (01293 615043)
Local Press: Crawley Observer, Crawley News

**CLUB PERSONNEL**
Chairman: Alf Bridges
Press Officer: Simon Milham
Manager: Bryn Marshall
Physio: Ms S Widy

# OVING

| | |
|---|---|
| **Secretary:** | Peter Hall, St Bruno, Prinsted Lane, Emsworth, Hants PO10 8HR |
| | Tel: 01243 372652 |
| **Ground:** | Highfield Lane, Oving, Nr Chichester, W Sussex. Tel: 01243 778900 |
| **Directions:** | Into Oving past the Gribble Inn, follow road round to housing estate - Highfield Lane (left). Ground sign posted 50 yards on right. |
| | Capacity: 1,000    Cover: 100    Floodlights: No |
| **Clubhouse:** | Oving Social Club. Contact 01243 789395    Metal Badges: Yes |
| **HONOURS** | W. Sussex Lge - Div 5 Cup 81-82, Div 5S 81-82, Div 4 Cup 82-83, Div 4S 82-83, Div 3S84-85. Div 2S 87-88, 91-92, Div 1 94-95, Prem. Div 95-96 96-97; Sussex Jun Cup: 86 91; Chichester char. Cup 90-91; Sussex Co. Inter. Cup R-up 98-99; Sussex Co. Div 3 98-99, Div 3 Cup R-up 98-99 |
| **PREVIOUS** | **Leagues:** West Sussex |
| **CLUB RECORDS** | **Attendance:** 276 v Westfield, Sussex co. Lge Div. 3 8.5.99 |
| **Win:** 10-0 v S B Sports (H) Sussex Co.Inter. Cup 10.10.98    **Defeat:** 0-5 v Lingfield (A) 13.9.97 |

**FACT FILE**
Formed: 1978-79    Nickname: "The Vikings"
Colours: Black & white/white/white
Change colours: Blue/black/black
Reserves' Lge: Sussex Co. - Res. Sect. West
Programme: 32 pages £1
Editor: Simon Jasinski (01243 374239)
98-99Captain: Greg Conway
Top Scorer: Jimmy Hasler (35)
**CLUB PERSONNEL**
Chairman: Dusty Miller
Press off.: Ade Adebayo & Kris Dawson
Manager: Paul Gilbert
Asst. Manager: Adie Miles
Coach: Vijay Korgaokar
Physio: Marc Rowbottom

# PEACEHAVEN & TELSCOMBE

**Secretary:** Mrs Margaret Edwards, 87 Ambleside Ave, Peacehaven, E. Sussex BN107LN
　　　　Tel: 01273 583022
**Ground:** Piddinghoe Avenue, Peacehaven, E. Sussex (01273 582471)    **Directions:** Arriving from Brighton on A259, cross r'bout and Piddinghoe Ave. is next left after 2nd set of lights - ground at end. From Newhaven Piddinghoe Ave. is first right after first set of lights. Three miles from Newhaven(BR). Peacehaven is served by Brighton to Newhaven and Eastbourne buses
　　　　Capacity: 3,000    Seats: None    Cover: 250    Floodlights: Yes
**Clubhouse:** Bar open evenings and weekends, pool darts, hot and cold food available. Tea bar
**HONOURS** Sussex Co. Lg 78-79 81-82 82-83 91-92 92-93 94-95 95-96 (R-up 77-78 80-81 90-91, Lg Cup 91-92 92-93, Div 2 R-up 75-76, Div 2 Cup 75-76, Norman Wingate Tphy 82-83 91-92 92-93, Hayden Tphy 82-83 92-93, Div 2 Invitation Cup69-70, Sussex Snr Cup R-up 81-82 92-93, Sussex RUR Charity Cup 77-78 81-82 92-93 (R-up 80-81 89-90 90-91 94-95 95-96), Brighton Charity Cup 91-92 92-93 93-94, Vernon Wentworth 91-92 92-93
**RECORD Attendance:** 1,420 v Littlehampton, Lge 91 **PREVIOUS Leagues:** Lewes; Brighton
**BEST SEASON FA Cup:** 4th Qual. Rd 90-91    **FA Vase:** 6th Rd (Q-F) 95-96, 5th Rd 92-93

**FACT FILE**
Founded: 1923
Nickname: The Tye
Sponsors: Anchor Garage
Colours: All white
Change colours: All sky
Midweek Matches: Wednesday
Programme: Yes
Editor: Secretary

**CLUB PERSONNEL**
Chairman: Jim Edwards
Match Sec: Fred Parris
Press Officer: Secretary
Manager: Gerry Green

# SHINEWATER ASSOCIATION

| | |
|---|---|
| **Secretary:** | Brian Dowling, 79 Harebeating Drive, Hailsham BN27 1JE |
| | Tel: 01323 442488 |
| **Ground:** | Shinewater Lane, Eastbourne. Tel: 01323 765880 |
| | Capacity: 1,000    Seats: None    Cover: 200    Floodlights: No |
| **Directions:** | A27, take B2104 to Eastbourne. At Stone Cross go under railway bridge, 1st right into Larkspur Drive, 1st left into Milfoil Drive, 3rd left into Shinewater Lane |
| **Clubhouse:** | Match days (01323 765880) |
| **RECORD** | **Attendance:** 302 |

**FACT FILE**
Founded:1990 Club
Sponsors: Halifax Property Services
Colours: Navy & sky/navy/navy
Change Colours: Claret
Programme: Freee with entry
Programme Editor: Brian Dowling
Previous League: East Sussex

**CLUB PERSONNEL**
Chairman: John Pinyoun
Managers: Kenny Rogers & Clive Connell

SOUTHWICK FC: Back Row (L-R): Dr David Gordon (Hon. medical officer Sussex FA and Southwick President), Tony Dineen (physio), Dave Funnell (first team assistant), Kevin Platt, Derren Woods, Lee Taylor, Graham Martin, Richard Carter, Derren Guille, Paul Croft (club coach), Roger Brace (first team manager), Peter Keene (chairman). Front Row: Scott Carden, Ben Cullen, Chris Tomsett, Dean Fuller, Richard Hewitt, Graham Souter, Tyrone Raczkonski, Kieran McCurdy. Photo: Kevin Rolfe

LANCING FC: Back Row (L-R): Steve Phythian (manager), Ian Salisbury, Graham Bull, Neil Richardson, Wayne Whittington, Tony Miles, Richard Whittington, Peter Towell (trainer), Tony Simpson (assistant manager). Front Row: Andy Long, Greg Bradley, Chris Copper, Paul Dendy, Guy Whitehead, Don Shepherd, Guy Ovenden, Brett Court. Photo: Worthing & Lancing Herald

OVING SC: Back Row (L-R): Greg Conway (captain), Guy Russell, Mick Godolphin, Lee Conway, Toby Anderton, John Donoghue, Robin Josephs. Front Row: Alex Stay, Andy Durrant, Justin Turnill, Jimmy Hasler, Steve Appleton, Paul Skinner, Steve Rishman, John Bartholomew. Photo: Simon Jasinski

# SIDLESHAM

| | |
|---|---|
| ecretary: | Pete Turner, 64 Hawthorn Road, Bognor Regis, West Sussex PO21 2DD<br>Tel: 01243 822860 |
| round: | Sidlesham Recreation Ground,Sidlesham.    Tel: 01243 641538 |
| irections: | Signposted Hunston/Selsey B2145 from roundabout travel towardsSelsey<br>for 4 miles, ground on right between houses |

**FACT FILE**

Colours: Green & yellow/green/green

**CLUB PERSONNEL**

Chairman: Roy Parker
Manager: Petyer Cleverley


# SOUTHWICK

**ecretary:** Peter Hallett, 10 Hawkins Close, Shoreham-by-Sea, W. Sussex BN43 6TL 01273 700474
**round:** Old Barn Way, off Manor Hall Way, Southwick, Brighton BN43 4NT Tel: 01273 701010
**irections:** Five minutes walk from either Fishergate or Southwick BR stations.By car A27 from
righton take 1st left after `Southwick' sign to Leisure Centre. Ground adjacent.
apacity: 3,500    Seats: 220        Cover: 1,220    Floodlights: Yes
**lubhouse:** Weekdays 12-3 & 6-11, all day Sat., normal hrs Sunday. Members bar & board-
om with bar. Matchday snacks from tea bar.
**ONOURS** Isthmian Lg Div 2 Sth 85-86, Sus. Co. Lg 25-26 27-28 29-30 47-48 68-69 74-75 (R-
0 x 9, Lg Cup 77-78 ,Div 1 Invit. Cup 65-66, Div 2 R-up 65-66), Combined Co's Lg R-up 84-85,
us.Snr Cup x 10, Sus. RUR Charity Cup (10) 1896-97 08-09 10-11 24-26 27-30 37-38 76-77,
7. Sus. Lg1896-97 97-98 1908-09 10-11, Sus. Jnr Cup 1891-92.
**REVIOUS Leagues:** West Sussex 1896-1920; Sussex County 20-52 54-84; Metropolitan52-
4; Combined Co's 84-85; Isthmian 85-92. **BEST SEASON FA Cup:** 1st Round 74-75, 0-5 v
ournemouth **FA Amtr Cup:** 3rd Rd. 28-29 **FA Vase:** 3rd Rd. 79-80 85-86
**ECORD Attendance:** 3,200 v Showbiz side 1971

**FACT FILE**
Founded: 1882    Nickname: Wickers
Sponsors: Guildcare Nursing Homes
Colours: Red & black stripes/black/red
Change Colours: White/black/white
Midweek matchday: Tuesday
Reserve League: Sussex Co. Res Div
Programme: Yes
Editor/ Press Off.: Paul Symes 01273 594142
**CLUB PERSONNEL**
Chairman: Roy Pollard
Vice-Chairman: Dave Cook
President: Dr D W Gordon.
Manager: John Dedman
Asst Manager: Dennis Nicholl
Coach: Paul Croft


# STORRINGTON

| | |
|---|---|
| ecretary: | Keith Dalmon, 4 End Cottages, Storrington Road, Amberley. BN18 9LX<br>Tel: 01798 831887 |
| round: | Recreation Ground, Storrington. Tel: 01903 745860 |
| irections: | Turn west on A283 (off A24).<br>Ground is opposite the pond to the west of the village. |

**FACT FILE**

Colours: All Blue

**CLUB PERSONNEL**

Manager: Malcolm MacMichael


# WESTFIELD

| | |
|---|---|
| ecretary: | Mrs Jenny Drinkwater, 28 Churchfields, Westfield TN35 4SN<br>Tel: 01424 754032 |
| round: | Parish Field. Westfield Tel: 01424 751011 |
| irections: | Take A21 towards Hastings, left onto A28. Westfield Lane, towards Ashford<br>for 2 miles, pitch on left. |

**FACT FILE**
Colours: Yellow /green/yellow

**CLUB PERSONNEL**
Chairman: Brian Over
Westaways, Main Road, Westfield TN35 4QN
Tel: 01424 754844
Manager: Shaun Hardy

# WITHDEAN

**FACT FILE**

| | |
|---|---|
| **Secretary:** | Simon Pattenden, 3188 Bevendean Crescent, Brighton. BN2 4RD |
| | Tel: 01273 747473 |
| **Ground:** | Withdean Stadium, off Valley Drive, Brighton    Tel: 01273 542100 |
| | Capacity: 10,000    Seats: 6,000    Cover: 1,000    Floodlights: No |
| **Directions:** | Off main London - Brighton road |
| **Clubhouse:** | Pub on ground    **Club Shop:** No |

**HONOURS**   Sussex Co. Lg Div 3 92-93 (Div 3 Cup 91-92)

**PREVIOUS**   **Leagues:** Brighton Hove & District
**Ground:** Council pitch

Founded: 1984
Sponsors: Glynn's Vehicle Contracts
Colours: Green & black/black/black
Change Colours: All white
Programme Editor: Gary Arnold
Local Newspaper: Brighton Evening Argus

**CLUB PERSONNEL**
Chairman: T.B.A.
President: T.B.A.
Manager: Dave Cole

# WORTHING UNITED

| | |
|---|---|
| **Secretary:** | Malcolm Gamlen, 1 Westbourne Ave., Worthing, West Sussex BN14 8DE |
| | Tel: 01903 263655 |
| **Ground:** | The Robert Albon Memorial Grd, Lyons Way, Worthing    Tel: 01903 234466 |
| | Capacity:1,000    Seats: 100    Cover: 500    Floodlights: No |
| **Directions:** | From west past Hill Barn r'about to 2nd set of lights, turn left into Lyons Way. |
| | From east 1st set of lights at end of Sompting bypass right into Lyons Way |
| **Clubhouse:** | Bar (capacity 80), refreshment facilities (tea bar)    Metal badges: Yes |

**HONOURS**   As Wigmore Athletic prior to 1988. Sussex Co. Lg Challenge Cup 74-75
(Invitation Cup 59-60, Div 2 52-53, Div 2 Invitation Cup 59-60, Div 3 89-90,
Reserve Section West 92-93, Sussex Jnr Cup 49-50

**PREVIOUS**   **Names:** Wigmore Athletic (founded 1948) merged with Southdown in 1988
**Grounds:** Harrison Road, Worthing

**RECORD**   **Attendance:**180 v Northwood, FA Vase 3rd Rd 91-92

**FACT FILE**
Founded: 1988
Nickname: None
Sponsors: Tinsley Robor
Colours: Sky & white/navy/white
Change colours: All white
Programme: Yes
Editor: N Woolmer (0903 772698)
Local Newspapers: Worthing Herald

**CLUB PERSONNEL**
President: Ken Higson
Chairman: Len Killpatrick
Press Officer: Brian Woolmer
Manager: Tony Elliot

WORTHING UNITED                                    Photo: Gordon Whittington

## ANSTY RANGERS
Secretary: Tina Darbyshire, 6 Faulkners Way, Burgess Hill. RH15 8SB.
Tel: 01444 233030
Ground: Deaks Lane, Ansty Tel: 01444 454010) Directions: Take A272 forAnsty/Haywards Heath, to Ansty prior to mini r/about turn left into Deaks Lane
Colours: Red & black/black/black

## BEXHILL TOWN
Secretary: Mrs Leigh Quinn, 37 Colebrook Road, Bexhill-on-Sea. TN39 3PX Tel: 01424 214197
Ground: The Polegrove, Brockley Rd, Bexhill-on-Sea, E. Sussex Tel: 01424220732 Directions: At Little Common r'bout take 3rd exit to Cooden Sea Rd, left into Cooden Drive for one and a half miles, Brockley Rd on the right. 3/4 mile from Bexhill Central (BR)
Colours: Green & white/white/white

## BOSHAM
Secretary; Paul Robinson, 3 Rowan Road, Havant PO9 2UX Tel: 01705 473113
Ground: Bosham Recreation Ground Tel: 01243 574011
Directions: From Chichester take the A259 towards Portsmouth. On reaching Bosham turn left at the Swan P.H. roundabout. 1/2 mile to T junction, turn left & car park 50 yds on left.
Colours: Red/white/red

## CROWBOROUGH ATHLETIC
Founded: 1894
Secretary: David Mackellow, 38 Eridge Drive, Crowborough,TN6 2TJ (01892 653122)
Ground: Alderbrook Recreation Ground, Fermor Road, Crowborough (01892 661893). Directions: Turn east off A26 at Crowborough. Cross traffic lights, throughHigh Street, right into Croft Rd, continue into Whitehall Rd and Fermor Rd,Alderbrook is 2nd right after mini-r'bout.
Colours: Blue & white/blue/blue Change colours: All red.
Midweek Matchday: Tuesday

## FOREST
Secretary: Gill Hultquist, 117 Ifield Drive, Ifield. RH11 0EA. Tel: 01293 522846
Ground: Roffey Sports & Social Club, Spooners Rd., Roffey. Tel: 01403 210221) Directions: Spooners Rd. is off the main Crawley road, 100 yds from the `Star'PH, towards Crawley
Colours: Claret/blue/white

## FRANKLANDS VILLAGE
Secretary: Mrs Linsey Worsfold, 151a Franklands Village, Haywards Heath. RH163RF. Tel: 01444 416475)
Ground: Hardy Memorial Playing Field, Franklands Village. Tel: 01444 440138) Directions: A272 (Haywards H. to Uckfield). Left at Princess Royal Hosp.r'about. 2nd left & ground at rear of social club
Colours: All Royal blue

## HAYWARDS HEATH TOWN
Secretary: 43 Sunnywood Drive, Haywards Heath RH16 4PE. Tel: 01444 453754
Ground: Hanbury Park Stadium, Haywards Heath Tel: 01444 412837 Directions: A272 to Haywards Heath town centre. At Sussex round-about, north on B2708 (Hazelgrove Road) take first right into New England Road, 4th right (Allen Road) leads to ground.
Colours: Blue & white stripes/blue/blue

## HURSTPIERPOINT
Secretary: Daniel Cleaveley, 10 St Christophers Road, Hurstpierpoint BN6 9UXTel: 01273 835665)
Ground: Fairfield Rec. Ground, Cuckfield Road. (Tel: 01273 834783) Directions: At Hurstpierpoint crossroads, go north into Cuckfield Road (B2117) for 1km. Ground entrance between houses nos.158 & 160
Colours: Blue & black/black/blue

## IFIELD
Secretary: Robert Anderson, 1 Old Orchards, Church Rd, Worth, Crawley. RH107QA. Tel: 01293 886215)
Ground: Ifield Sports Club, Ifield Green, Rusper Road. Tel: 01293 536569) Directions: From A23 Crawley by-pass going north, left at r'about signedCharlwood. Third left into Ifield Green, first right past Royal Oak (PH) intoRusper Rd
Colours: Red/black/red

## NEWHAVEN
Secretary: Peter Foote, 32 Valley Dene, Newhaven BN9 9NF Tel: 01273 513232
Ground: Fort Road Recreation Ground Tel: 01273 513940
Directions: A259, follow one-way system around town, left at Police Station into South Road, which becomes Fort Road.
Colours: Red & green/red & green/red

## ROYAL & SUN ALLIANCE
Secretary: Steve Jenkins, 33 Owlcastle Close, Horsham RH12 5YA Tel: 01403 256697
Ground: Sunallon Sports Club, North Heath Lane, Horsham Tel: 01403 253814) Directions: Heading into Horsham on Warnham road, turn left at 1st lights, overmini-r/about to North Heath Lane, grd on left
Colours: Yellow/blue/blue

## ST. FRANCIS HOSPITAL
Secretary: Colin Mansbridge, 9 Pinehurst, Burgess Hill. RH15 0DG. Tel: 01444244197)
Ground: St. Francis Hospital, Colwell Lane, Haywards Heath. Tel: 01444 441881) Directions: Enter through main entrance of Princess Royal Hospital on Lewesroad, A272 Haywards Heath. Follow signs to Sports Complex
Colours: Green & white/white/green

## SLEAFORD
Secretary: Barry Chambers, 47 Bramber Road, Seaford BN25 1AT Tel: 01323 491932
Ground; The Crouch, Seaford. Tel: 01323 892221
Directions; A259 to Seaford. At mini r'about by station, turn LEFT (from Newhaven) RIGHT (from Eastbourne). At end of Church St., across junction, then left at end. After 500 m turn left up Ashurst Rd. Bramber Rd. is at the top.
Colours: Red & blue/blue/red

## STEYNING TOWN
Secretary: Gina Barnes, 36 Shooting Fields, Steyning BN44 3RQ Tel: 01903815387)
Ground: The Shooting Field, Steyning Tel: 01903 812228) Directions: EnteringSteyning from west, take 1st left into High St, follow into Shooting Fieldestate, ground is 4th rurn left
Colours: Red /white/red

## UCKFIELD TOWN
Secretary: Craig Rome, Flat 3, 26 Newtown, Uckfield. TN22 5DD. Tel: 01825764171)
Ground: Victoria Pleasure Grounds, Uckfield. Tel: 01825 769400)
Directions: Take Eastbourne road (old A22) south of Uckfield town cen-tre. Entrance toground 1/2 mile on right (just after Police station)
Colours: Red/black/black

## WEALDEN
Secretary: Peter Byford, Chelwood, Possingworth Park, Cross in Hand, Heathfield TN21 0TN Tel: 01435 812231
Ground: Wealden Sports Club Tel: 01825 890905
Directions: Located behind the 'Barley Mow' P.H. on the Old Eastbourne Road, south of Uckfield.
Colours: White & blue/blue/white

# REGIONAL LEAGUE TABLES

## ROBERT GRAY MID-SUSSEX LEAGUE
### PREMIER DIVISION

| | | | | | | | |
|---|---|---|---|---|---|---|---|
| Pease Pottage Village | 22 | 15 | 5 | 2 | 72 | 29 | 50 |
| Lindfield | 22 | 14 | 3 | 8 | 52 | 27 | 45 |
| East Grinstead United | 22 | 11 | 9 | 2 | 48 | 23 | 42 |
| Hurstpierpoint Res. | 22 | 11 | 3 | 8 | 50 | 46 | 36 |
| Cuckfield | 22 | 9 | 5 | 8 | 46 | 41 | 32 |
| Felbridge | 22 | 7 | 6 | 9 | 32 | 37 | 27 |
| St Francis Hospital Res. | 22 | 7 | 5 | 10 | 35 | 43 | 26 |
| Maresfield Village | 22 | 7 | 3 | 12 | 35 | 54 | 24 |
| Wisdom Sports | 22 | 6 | 5 | 11 | 40 | 42 | 23 |
| Plumpton Athletic | 22 | 6 | 5 | 11 | 28 | 48 | 23 |
| Clayton | 22 | 6 | 3 | 13 | 44 | 61 | 21 |
| Nutley | 22 | 4 | 6 | 12 | 31 | 62 | 18 |

## PPP EASTBOURNE & DISTRICT LEAGUE

| | | | | | | | |
|---|---|---|---|---|---|---|---|
| CMP | 16 | 14 | 1 | 1 | 58 | 22 | 43 |
| Langney Sports `A' | 16 | 10 | 3 | 3 | 66 | 22 | 33 |
| Cavendish (Sussex) | 16 | 10 | 1 | 5 | 60 | 30 | 31 |
| Icthus United | 16 | 8 | 3 | 5 | 56 | 40 | 27 |
| Eastbourne Fish'men R | 16 | 7 | 3 | 6 | 43 | 38 | 24 |
| Squires | 16 | 7 | 1 | 8 | 69 | 47 | 22 |
| Buccaneer | 16 | 4 | 1 | 11 | 43 | 65 | 13 |
| Parkfield | 16 | 4 | 1 | 11 | 33 | 60 | 13 |
| Parkfield Res. | 16 | 1 | 0 | 15 | 18 | 122 | 3 |

## BRIGHTON HOVE & DISTRICT LEAGUE
### PREMIER DIVISION

| | | | | | | | |
|---|---|---|---|---|---|---|---|
| Midway | 20 | 17 | 3 | 0 | 58 | 24 | 54 |
| Southern Rangers OB | 20 | 11 | 4 | 5 | 44 | 30 | 37 |
| Montpelier Villa | 20 | 10 | 2 | 8 | 26 | 26 | 32 |
| Old Vandeanians | 20 | 9 | 4 | 7 | 63 | 30 | 31 |
| AFC Falcons | 20 | 7 | 6 | 7 | 39 | 31 | 27 |
| Portslade Athletic | 20 | 8 | 3 | 9 | 49 | 43 | 27 |
| AJC Beaufort | 20 | 7 | 4 | 9 | 36 | 45 | 25 |
| Patcham +3 | 20 | 5 | 5 | 10 | 25 | 35 | 23 |
| Sussex University -3 | 20 | 7 | 4 | 9 | 37 | 50 | 22 |
| Rottingdean Village | 20 | 6 | 4 | 10 | 28 | 55 | 22 |
| Preston Village | 20 | 1 | 5 | 14 | 12 | 42 | 8 |

## CRAWLEY & DISTRICT LEAGUE
### PREMIER DIVISION

| | | | | | | | |
|---|---|---|---|---|---|---|---|
| Thomas Bennett | 22 | 15 | 6 | 1 | 84 | 24 | 51 |
| Thomson Athletic | 22 | 14 | 5 | 3 | 69 | 29 | 47 |
| Edwards Sports | 22 | 14 | 3 | 5 | 57 | 38 | 45 |
| TD Sports | 22 | 13 | 2 | 7 | 40 | 33 | 41 |
| Holland Sports | 22 | 12 | 2 | 8 | 47 | 36 | 38 |
| Horley Town | 22 | 9 | 5 | 8 | 58 | 53 | 32 |
| Longley | 22 | 7 | 3 | 12 | 46 | 50 | 24 |
| Beehive Sports | 22 | 7 | 3 | 12 | 40 | 65 | 24 |
| Ifield Res. | 22 | 6 | 3 | 13 | 56 | 91 | 21 |
| Phoenix (Sussex) | 22 | 6 | 1 | 15 | 44 | 62 | 19 |
| Three Bridges `A' -3 | 22 | 5 | 3 | 14 | 36 | 63 | 15 |
| Bluebird Rangers | 22 | 3 | 6 | 13 | 49 | 82 | 15 |

## COVERS WEST SUSSEX LEAGUE - PREM. DIV.

| | | | | | | | |
|---|---|---|---|---|---|---|---|
| Bosham | 14 | 11 | 1 | 2 | 57 | 22 | 34 |
| Upper Beeding | 14 | 9 | 2 | 3 | 39 | 17 | 29 |
| South Bersted | 14 | 8 | 4 | 2 | 26 | 18 | 28 |
| Henfield | 14 | 7 | 2 | 5 | 41 | 27 | 23 |
| Alfold | 14 | 5 | 3 | 6 | 28 | 28 | 18 |
| Cowfold | 14 | 4 | 3 | 7 | 22 | 33 | 15 |
| Stedham United | 14 | 3 | 1 | 10 | 21 | 43 | 10 |
| Lancing United | 14 | 1 | 0 | 13 | 14 | 60 | 3 |

## HAYWARD BOURNEMOUTH LEAGUE - DIV. ONE

| | | | | | | | |
|---|---|---|---|---|---|---|---|
| Bournemouth Civil Service | 24 | 18 | 5 | 1 | 89 | 19 | 59 |
| Westover Bournemouth | 24 | 18 | 2 | 4 | 86 | 34 | 56 |
| Lansdowne | 24 | 17 | 3 | 4 | 91 | 39 | 54 |
| Hamworthy Eng Res. | 24 | 16 | 3 | 5 | 52 | 24 | 51 |
| Bournemouth Electric | 24 | 15 | 3 | 6 | 67 | 48 | 48 |
| Napoleons | 24 | 10 | 2 | 12 | 58 | 64 | 32 |
| Kinson | 24 | 9 | 4 | 11 | 46 | 51 | 31 |
| Sway | 24 | 7 | 7 | 10 | 41 | 61 | 28 |
| Stourvale | 24 | 8 | 4 | 12 | 44 | 65 | 28 |
| Bisterne United | 24 | 7 | 3 | 14 | 51 | 62 | 24 |
| St Marys | 24 | 5 | 3 | 16 | 47 | 79 | 18 |
| Queens Park Athletic | 24 | 3 | 4 | 17 | 42 | 93 | 13 |
| Bournemouth Sports R. | 24 | 1 | 1 | 22 | 27 | 102 | 4 |

## BREWERS EAST SUSSEX LEAGUE - PREMIER DIV.

| | | | | | | | |
|---|---|---|---|---|---|---|---|
| Seaford Town | 20 | 15 | 3 | 2 | 59 | 27 | 48 |
| Rock-a-Nore | 20 | 11 | 5 | 4 | 37 | 18 | 38 |
| Little Common Albion | 20 | 11 | 4 | 5 | 44 | 29 | 37 |
| Polegate | 20 | 9 | 7 | 4 | 51 | 37 | 34 |
| Sandhurst | 20 | 10 | 4 | 6 | 43 | 30 | 34 |
| Hollington United | 20 | 9 | 2 | 9 | 36 | 29 | 29 |
| Wadhurst United | 20 | 8 | 2 | 10 | 34 | 35 | 26 |
| Willingdon Athletic | 20 | 8 | 2 | 10 | 30 | 37 | 26 |
| Peche Hill Select | 20 | 5 | 3 | 12 | 19 | 34 | 18 |
| Northiam | 20 | 4 | 2 | 14 | 23 | 60 | 14 |
| Icklesham Casuals | 20 | 2 | 2 | 16 | 32 | 72 | 8 |

## FANSTONE SOUTHAMPTON LEAGUE - PREMIER DIV.

| | | | | | | | |
|---|---|---|---|---|---|---|---|
| BTC Southampton | 26 | 23 | 2 | 1 | 97 | 14 | 71 |
| Brendon | 26 | 23 | 2 | 1 | 87 | 17 | 71 |
| Nursling | 26 | 22 | 0 | 4 | 103 | 24 | 66 |
| Swift Sporting | 26 | 14 | 0 | 12 | 51 | 44 | 42 |
| North Baddesley | 26 | 11 | 4 | 11 | 41 | 42 | 37 |
| Ford Sports | 26 | 11 | 4 | 11 | 43 | 52 | 37 |
| Esso Fawley Res. | 26 | 10 | 2 | 14 | 43 | 56 | 32 |
| Old Tauntonians | 26 | 9 | 5 | 12 | 39 | 61 | 32 |
| Locksheath Res. | 26 | 8 | 3 | 15 | 47 | 59 | 27 |
| Bishopstoke Social Res. | 26 | 7 | 6 | 13 | 44 | 62 | 27 |
| Durley | 26 | 7 | 6 | 13 | 27 | 61 | 27 |
| Fair Oak Linden | 26 | 6 | 4 | 16 | 39 | 66 | 22 |
| AFC Solent | 26 | 5 | 4 | 17 | 28 | 89 | 19 |
| Otterbourne Res. | 26 | 2 | 6 | 18 | 23 | 65 | 12 |

## PORTSMOUTH NORTH EAST LEAGUE - DIV. ONE

| | | | | | | | |
|---|---|---|---|---|---|---|---|
| Shearer Arms | 12 | 10 | 2 | 0 | 65 | 13 | 32 |
| George & Dragon | 12 | 8 | 2 | 2 | 33 | 22 | 26 |
| Wheatsheaf (Portsm'th) | 12 | 5 | 1 | 6 | 26 | 36 | 16 |
| Grant Thornton | 12 | 3 | 6 | 3 | 21 | 24 | 15 |
| Kingston Arrows | 12 | 3 | 3 | 6 | 31 | 41 | 12 |
| British Star | 12 | 3 | 1 | 8 | 17 | 39 | 10 |
| Rimer | 12 | 2 | 1 | 9 | 24 | 42 | 7 |

# UNITED COUNTIES LEAGUE
## FEEDER TO: DR MARTENS LEAGUE

**Chairman:** Geoff Paul
**Secretary:** Roger Gamble, 8 Bostock Avenue, Northampton NN1 4LW   Tel: 01604 637766
**Press Officer:** Jeremy Biggs   Tel: 01780 763048

SILVERWARE GALORE FOR SPALDING

The last full season of the second millennium proved a triumph for Spalding United, who end the 1990s with a return to the Dr Martens League after a spectacular promotion winning campaign

Spalding finished fifteen points clear of runners-up Desborough in the Premier Division - the biggest winning margin since three points for a win was introduced - and topped up the trophy tally by winning the Lincolnshire Senior Cup 'A', Hinchingbrooke Cup and the league's Highest Aggregate Goalscoring Trophy. After such a successful campaign it was little surprise that Tulips' boss Alan Day was named Manager of the Year - his second such award nine years after his first accolade won with near neighbours Holbeach.

Spalding made their intentions clear from the outset. On Day One they demolished Potton 9-1, a result that proved a good indicator of the fortunes ahead for each side. Eight more victories followed for the Tulips before a single goal defeat at Desborough on 3 October halted the sequence. A week later a Friday night win for Northampton Spencer over Cogenhoe took the Millers to the top of the table - but within 24 hours Spalding were back on pole and remained there until the start of February.

Desborough posed a real threat and from 26 September to 16 February they were unbeaten in nineteen league games, winning sixteen and drawing three. Ar Tarn's strength was their defence where keeper Des Elliott kept thirteen clean sheets in Desborough's charge to the top. The big two met for the second time at the Halley Stewart field on 20 February. Going to the match, Spalding trailed their visitors by five points with two matches in hand. The Tulips warmed up for the clash by ending third placed Bourne's dozen match unbeaten run with a 5-0 Abbey Lawn success, and they duly disposed of Desborough 2-0 to put themselves in control of the title race.

Seven days later Desborough's title bid suffered a further setback in the shape of a home defeat by Kempston, and, although they briefly headed the table again in March, Spalding were by now firm favourites. Twenty eight points from ten games all but wrapped up the title for the Tulips with five matches to play. From Easter Saturday onwards Spalding collected 21 points from 27 on offer while Desborough's final seven games yielded a mere eight point haul.

While Spalding celebrated Desborough could reflect on their highest finish since 1980, while Cogenhoe, who had kicked off the season with three defeats, recovered well enough to equal their best ever final placing of third, just ahead of local rivals Northampton Spencer, where the emergence of a crop of promising youngsters bodes well for the Millers' future. A strong finish by Stewarts & Lloyds earned them fifth place, one position ahead of the surprise success story of the season Bourne, where canny manager Dave McNish turned the Wakes into a force to be reckoned with.

At the bottom of the table Potton's new manager Martin Humberstone always looked to have a struggle on his hands after the summer break up of the Royals' squad. A season of rebuilding brought the Royals just two wins and once they hit bottom place in mid September there was to be no escape. After the end of the lengthy managerial reign of Mick Emms, Long Buckby had a completely new look under Coventry based chief Ashley Alexander. Unfortunately for Buckby, when he quit in January most of his players followed, leaving replacement Kevin Simmonds to rebuild with youngsters. Simmonds had to wait for his team's first goal, and the season ended without him presiding over a victory. Both Buckby and Potton retain their status due to Spalding's promotion.

After several near misses in the promotion race this time round Bugbrooke made no mistake and go up as champions. Badgers' boss Chris Goodchild brought in several players with Premier experience over the summer and the move paid off as Bugbrooke pipped reigning champions Higham after a titanic struggle for supremacy.

In the first half of the season the Division One race looked wide open with Thrapston, Blisworth, Newport Pagnell, Olney and ON Chenecks all briefly topping the table. In the spring the race came down to just two clubs, with Higham, again inspired by player manager Aidy Mann, the slight favourites going into the Easter programme. The Lankies surprisingly dropped points on Easter Monday in a draw at Irchester and were then beaten at home by a St Ives side without an away win in fourteen months! Higham bounced back with a ten goal spree against Woodford, but Bugbrooke were in no mood to slip this time and they won their last four matches to finish three points clear of Higham.

Rob Clark's exciting young Rothwell Corinthians side finished strongly to claim third slot ahead of Whitworths, the experience Cottingham squad and Northampton Vanaid who boasted sixteen clean sheets in their last 21 games!

Burton Park finished bottom of the Division after Harrowby collected four points from their final two matches to pull clear, just reward for the efforts put in by Nicky Andersen to turn their season round after inheriting a club in disarray after three managers had left in two months!

Rothwell retained the Reserve Division One title while longtime leaders Yarley had to settle for third place after Cogenhoe too overhauled them. A dramatic relegation battle saw Wootton and Eynesbury pay the penalty for poor late season form as long time strugglers Thrapston and Whitworths found their form. Newcomers Kettering were crowned Reserve Division Two champions, while Spalding's second string joined their first team in winning promotion, thanks to a last game winner takes all success at the expense of Ford Sports.

The League Knockout Cup went to Stotfold who shrugged off the summer loss of manager Ian Allinson to rebuild to good effect under replacement Phil Pateman. The Eagles pipped Buckingham 4-3 on aggregate to lift the league's domestic cup, but it was a close run thing. Two opportunist Wes Byrne goals and a stunner from Nathan Buckland gave Stotfold a three goal first leg lead but the Robins fought back at Ford Meadow with Darren Harmon converting two spot kicks in his hat-trick. Justin Griffiths' solitary reply for Stotfold gave them the trophy after a nail biting finale which saw the Eagles' Gary Winn sent off.

Northampton Spencer won the Reserve Knockout Cup beating Burton Park Wanderers 5-1 on aggregate while the pre-season Benevolent Cup saw Stamford beat Higham 6-0.

On a national stage Ford Sports caught the eye reaching the 3rd Qualifying Round of the FA Cup in their debut season. Wins over Felixstowe, Leighton and Aveley earned the Motormen a tie against Ryman Premier pacesetters Sutton United. Fords were just four minutes from a giant killing before losing 3-0 in the replay. A disappointing season for our clubs in the FA Carlsberg Vase saw Spalding our best performers, a 5-2 defeat of Rocester took the Tulips into Round Three where they exited at Northwood in a replay.

On the County Cup front Spalding made amends for the previous Lincolnshire campaign's penalty shootout defeat by Stamford, thrashing Louth 5-1 to lift the Senior Cup 'A'. The Huntingdonshire Senior Cup was won by Yaxley who pipped St Neots on a penalty shootout after a 1-1 stalemate - a fitting way to send outgoing manager Dave Willis out of the Leading Dove exit. In the Northants Junior Cup another shootout was required after a goalless draw between Bugbrooke and Thrapston. Underdogs Thrapston maintained their composure the better to take the trophy for the second time. While the St Neots senior side missed out on county cup glory there was a double dose for the reserves who lifted both Scott-Gatty Cup and Benevolent Cup, beating their St Ives counterparts on each occasion - manager Chris Howell is rewarded by promotion to first team duties next term.

Also worthy of mention are Spalding's Hinchingbrooke Cup Final defeat of Barton Rovers in their first postwar venture into the competition, and a place in the East Anglian Cup final for St Neots who lost 2-0 to surprise finalists Ipswich Wanderers.

The latest graduates from our pyramid system are Deeping Rangers, runners-up in the Peterborough & District League. They join Division One for the millennium season. Congratulations to Cogenhoe and Raunds, respective winners of the Fair Play awards for first team and reserve sides. Cogenhoe become the first club to retain a Fair Play Trophy. Our new club Hospitality Award has been won by Rothwell Corinthians in its inaugural season.

At the end of May the league's three year sponsorship arrangement with uhlsport UK Ltd came to a conclusion. We thank David Spensley and his colleagues for their support over the last three years and their contribution to the league over that time.

Jeremy Biggs, Press Officer

# UNITED COUNTIES CONSTITUTION OF DIVISIONS 1999-2000

## PREMIER DIVISION

| | | |
|---|---|---|
| Blackstone, Boston Town | Bourne Town | Buckingham Town |
| Bugbrooke St Michaels | Cogenhoe United | Desborough Town |
| Eynesbury Rovers | Ford Sports Daventry | Holbeach United |
| Kempston Rovers | Long Buckby | Northampton Spencer |
| Potton United | St Neots Town | Stewarts & Lloyds |
| Corby | Stotfold | Wellingborough Town |
| Wootton Blue Cross | Yaxley | |

## DIVISION ONE

| | | |
|---|---|---|
| Blisworth | Burton Park Wanderers | Cottingham |
| Daventry Town | Deeping Rangers | Harrowby United |
| Higham Town | Irchester United | Newport Pagnell Town |
| Northampton ON Chenecks | Northampton Vanaid, | Olney Town |
| Rothwell Corinthians | St Ives Town | Sharnbrook |
| Thrapston Town | Wellingborough Whitworths | Woodford United |

## FINAL LEAGUE TABLE 1998-99
### PREMIER DIVISION

| | | | Home | | | | | Away | | | | | |
|---|---|---|---|---|---|---|---|---|---|---|---|---|---|
| | | P | W | D | L | F | A | W | D | L | F | A | Pts |
| 1 | Spalding United | 38 | 15 | 2 | 2 | 54 | 14 | 15 | 1 | 3 | 52 | 15 | 93 |
| 2 | Desborough Town | 38 | 13 | 2 | 4 | 45 | 22 | 11 | 4 | 4 | 37 | 19 | 78 |
| 3 | Cogenhoe United | 38 | 13 | 2 | 4 | 44 | 17 | 10 | 3 | 6 | 45 | 30 | 74 |
| 4 | Northampton Spencer | 38 | 11 | 4 | 4 | 38 | 17 | 9 | 2 | 8 | 40 | 29 | 66 |
| 5 | Stewart & Lloyds Corby | 38 | 9 | 3 | 7 | 35 | 29 | 10 | 6 | 3 | 35 | 16 | 66 |
| 6 | Bourne Town | 38 | 9 | 4 | 6 | 34 | 33 | 9 | 5 | 5 | 41 | 36 | 63 |
| 7 | Stotfold | 38 | 7 | 6 | 6 | 32 | 27 | 10 | 5 | 4 | 25 | 16 | 62 |
| 8 | Boston Town | 38 | 11 | 4 | 4 | 40 | 24 | 6 | 6 | 7 | 28 | 20 | 61 |
| 9 | Buckingham Town | 38 | 8 | 6 | 5 | 36 | 23 | 9 | 3 | 7 | 35 | 29 | 60 |
| 10 | Yaxley | 38 | 8 | 3 | 8 | 41 | 34 | 10 | 2 | 7 | 46 | 41 | 59 |
| 11 | Wellingborough Town | 38 | 8 | 3 | 8 | 30 | 27 | 8 | 3 | 8 | 27 | 30 | 54 |
| 12 | Blackstone FC | 38 | 7 | 3 | 9 | 24 | 29 | 9 | 2 | 8 | 35 | 27 | 53 |
| 13 | St Neots Town | 38 | 8 | 3 | 8 | 39 | 36 | 7 | 3 | 9 | 31 | 37 | 51 |
| 14 | Wootton Blue Cross | 38 | 7 | 3 | 9 | 32 | 45 | 6 | 5 | 8 | 22 | 32 | 47 |
| 15 | Holbeach United | 38 | 6 | 5 | 8 | 30 | 35 | 6 | 5 | 8 | 32 | 30 | 46 |
| 16 | Ford Sports Daventry | 38 | 5 | 4 | 10 | 24 | 34 | 7 | 5 | 7 | 26 | 23 | 45 |
| 17 | Kempston Rovers | 38 | 5 | 3 | 11 | 24 | 39 | 5 | 3 | 11 | 22 | 36 | 36 |
| 18 | Eynesbury Rovers | 38 | 1 | 4 | 14 | 13 | 51 | 5 | 3 | 11 | 29 | 49 | 25 |
| 19 | Long Buckby AFC | 38 | 2 | 4 | 13 | 11 | 39 | 1 | 2 | 16 | 15 | 60 | 15 |
| 20 | Potton United | 38 | 1 | 4 | 14 | 10 | 59 | 1 | 4 | 14 | 11 | 61 | 14 |

### DIVISION ONE

| | | | Home | | | | | Away | | | | | |
|---|---|---|---|---|---|---|---|---|---|---|---|---|---|
| | | P | W | D | L | F | A | W | D | L | F | A | Pts |
| 1 | Bugbrooke St Michaels | 34 | 11 | 4 | 2 | 54 | 14 | 13 | 2 | 2 | 50 | 15 | 78 |
| 2 | Higham Town | 34 | 9 | 4 | 4 | 42 | 17 | 14 | 2 | 1 | 59 | 11 | 75 |
| 3 | Rothwell Corinthians | 34 | 12 | 2 | 3 | 51 | 27 | 6 | 8 | 3 | 27 | 25 | 64 |
| 4 | Wellingborough Whit. | 34 | 10 | 2 | 5 | 36 | 15 | 9 | 4 | 4 | 37 | 28 | 63 |
| 5 | Cottingham | 34 | 9 | 4 | 4 | 40 | 22 | 9 | 5 | 3 | 40 | 29 | 63 |
| 6 | Northampton Vanaid | 34 | 8 | 6 | 3 | 25 | 14 | 9 | 4 | 4 | 26 | 12 | 61 |
| 7 | Blisworth | 34 | 10 | 5 | 2 | 40 | 17 | 5 | 5 | 7 | 29 | 36 | 55 |
| 8 | Thrapston Town | 34 | 8 | 3 | 6 | 38 | 29 | 6 | 5 | 6 | 28 | 34 | 50 |
| 9 | Newport Pagnell Town | 34 | 7 | 4 | 6 | 45 | 42 | 7 | 3 | 7 | 33 | 37 | 49 |
| 10 | Daventry Town | 34 | 6 | 2 | 9 | 25 | 24 | 8 | 2 | 7 | 31 | 31 | 46 |
| 11 | Northampton ON Chen. | 34 | 6 | 1 | 10 | 30 | 34 | 7 | 5 | 5 | 22 | 27 | 45 |
| 12 | Olney Town | 34 | 6 | 4 | 7 | 25 | 25 | 5 | 4 | 8 | 31 | 24 | 41 |
| 13 | Woodford United | 34 | 6 | 4 | 7 | 29 | 30 | 4 | 5 | 8 | 27 | 44 | 39 |
| 14 | St Ives Town | 34 | 5 | 7 | 5 | 21 | 26 | 2 | 5 | 10 | 10 | 36 | 33 |
| 15 | Irchester United | 34 | 6 | 2 | 9 | 27 | 41 | 3 | 2 | 12 | 17 | 55 | 31 |
| 16 | Sharnbrook AFC | 34 | 3 | 5 | 9 | 22 | 47 | 2 | 3 | 12 | 13 | 47 | 23 |
| 17 | Harrowby United | 34 | 2 | 3 | 12 | 26 | 50 | 3 | 1 | 13 | 23 | 55 | 19 |
| 18 | Burton Park Wanderers | 34 | 2 | 5 | 10 | 16 | 41 | 1 | 2 | 14 | 12 | 48 | 16 |

## STATISTICS 1998-99

| | PREMIER DIVISION | | DIVISION ONE | |
|---|---|---|---|---|
| Most Consecutive Wins | Desborough | 11 | Bugbrooke, N'ton Vanaid | 8 |
| Most Consecutive Draws | Boston, Stotfold | 4 | Blisworth, St Ives & Sharnbrook | 4 |
| Most Consecutive Defeats | Long Buckby | 12 | Harrowby | 12 |
| Longest Unbeaten Run | Desborough | 19 | Bugbrooke | 14 |
| Longest Run Without a Win | Long Buckby | 24 | Harrowby | 18 |
| Longest Run Scoring | Spalding | 23 | Higham | 22 |
| Longest Run Not Scoring | Long Buckby | 8 | St Ives | 5 |
| Longest Run Conceding | Eynesbury | 26 | Newport Pagnell | 26 |
| Longest Run Not Conceding | Spalding | 5 | ON Chenecks | 6 |

# PREMIER DIVISION RESULTS CHART 1998-99

| | 1 | 2 | 3 | 4 | 5 | 6 | 7 | 8 | 9 | 10 | 11 | 12 | 13 | 14 | 15 | 16 | 17 | 18 | 19 | 20 |
|---|---|---|---|---|---|---|---|---|---|---|---|---|---|---|---|---|---|---|---|---|
| 1 Blackstone FC | X | 0-3 | 1-0 | 1-2 | 1-1 | 0-1 | 1-5 | 2-1 | 0-3 | 1-3 | 4-1 | 1-0 | 3-0 | 5-2 | 0-2 | 0-2 | 0-0 | 3-0 | 0-0 | 1-3 |
| 2 Boston | 2-2 | X | 1-1 | 2-0 | 2-5 | 0-3 | 4-4 | 2-2 | 4-1 | 6-1 | 1-0 | 2-0 | 1-0 | 4-0 | 1-2 | 1-0 | 0-1 | 4-1 | 1-0 | 2-1 |
| 3 Bourne | 2-0 | 1-2 | X | 2-4 | 1-0 | 1-3 | 1-0 | 2-2 | 2-1 | 2-0 | 4-0 | 2-2 | 2-1 | 4-3 | 0-5 | 1-3 | 1-2 | 1-0 | 1-1 | 4-4 |
| 4 Buckingham | 0-1 | 1-1 | 2-2 | X | 1-3 | 1-1 | 4-0 | 0-0 | 2-0 | 2-1 | 2-1 | 1-3 | 5-1 | 4-2 | 0-2 | 0-0 | 2-2 | 2-3 | 3-0 | 4-0 |
| 5 Cogenhoe | 0-3 | 1-0 | 2-3 | 1-0 | X | 1-1 | 6-0 | 1-2 | 4-2 | 1-0 | 5-0 | 0-1 | 1-0 | 1-0 | 4-2 | 1-1 | 4-0 | 2-0 | 2-1 | 7-1 |
| 6 Desborough | 1-0 | 2-2 | 5-2 | 1-3 | 3-4 | X | 1-0 | 2-0 | 3-0 | 1-3 | 3-0 | 3-2 | 1-0 | 4-1 | 1-0 | 1-1 | 2-1 | 4-0 | 2-3 | 5-0 |
| 7 Eynesbury | 1-2 | 1-1 | 1-3 | 0-3 | 0-9 | 0-3 | X | 0-1 | 0-2 | 1-3 | 1-3 | 0-3 | 2-2 | 0-0 | 0-7 | 1-3 | 0-3 | 0-1 | 1-1 | 4-1 |
| 8 Ford Sports | 1-4 | 2-0 | 1-5 | 0-1 | 1-0 | 0-4 | 2-3 | X | 0-0 | 3-0 | 6-2 | 0-2 | 1-1 | 2-2 | 0-3 | 0-2 | 0-1 | 1-1 | 3-0 | 1-3 |
| 9 Holbeach | 1-0 | 0-3 | 1-3 | 3-2 | 1-2 | 0-3 | 2-2 | 0-1 | X | 2-2 | 3-2 | 3-1 | 5-1 | 4-4 | 1-2 | 2-1 | 1-3 | 1-1 | 0-2 | 0-2 |
| 10 Kempston | 4-2 | 1-0 | 3-4 | 1-1 | 0-5 | 2-0 | 4-0 | 1-1 | 1-2 | X | 1-0 | 1-2 | 1-1 | 1-4 | 0-4 | 1-3 | 1-3 | 0-2 | 1-2 | 0-3 |
| 11 Long Buckby | 0-3 | 0-0 | 1-2 | 2-4 | 1-1 | 0-1 | 1-3 | 0-6 | 0-0 | 0-0 | X | 0-7 | 2-0 | 0-1 | 1-3 | 0-3 | 0-1 | 0-1 | 3-0 | 0-3 |
| 12 N Spencer | 1-1 | 2-2 | 1-0 | 3-1 | 3-1 | 1-1 | 5-1 | 0-0 | 2-0 | 1-0 | 2-0 | X | 7-0 | 0-1 | 1-2 | 2-1 | 1-2 | 2-0 | 4-1 | 0-3 |
| 13 Potton | 2-1 | 1-6 | 0-3 | 1-2 | 0-3 | 0-0 | 0-2 | 0-5 | 0-10 | 0-1 | 1-1 | 2-2 | X | 0-2 | 1-6 | 0-2 | 1-1 | 0-5 | 0-1 | 1-6 |
| 14 St Neots | 4-1 | 0-0 | 1-5 | 1-0 | 4-1 | 2-5 | 6-1 | 0-2 | 2-3 | 4-3 | 4-2 | 3-0 | 2-2 | X | 2-0 | 0-0 | 0-1 | 3-4 | 0-2 | 1-4 |
| 15 Spalding | 3-4 | 2-1 | 4-0 | 4-1 | 3-1 | 2-0 | 1-0 | 4-0 | 1-1 | 4-0 | 3-0 | 3-1 | 9-1 | 3-0 | X | 1-2 | 1-0 | 1-0 | 3-0 | 2-2 |
| 16 Stewart & Lloyds | 3-2 | 2-1 | 5-0 | 0-0 | 5-0 | 0-2 | 1-1 | 4-0 | 0-2 | 2-1 | 2-2 | 1-5 | 0-1 | 2-1 | 0-2 | X | 0-4 | 0-1 | 3-2 | 5-2 |
| 17 Stotfold | 0-4 | 1-0 | 0-0 | 2-2 | 2-2 | 1-4 | 1-0 | 1-0 | 2-2 | 1-2 | 7-0 | 1-2 | 3-0 | 0-3 | 0-1 | 1-1 | X | 4-0 | 3-3 | 2-1 |
| 18 Wellingborough | 0-1 | 0-1 | 3-3 | 1-3 | 1-3 | 1-2 | 5-2 | 2-1 | 2-0 | 1-1 | 3-0 | 4-0 | 2-0 | 2-1 | 0-4 | 2-1 | 0-0 | X | 0-1 | 1-3 |
| 19 Wootton | 1-4 | 1-4 | 2-2 | 2-6 | 1-2 | 4-2 | 2-1 | 1-0 | 2-2 | 3-1 | 3-1 | 1-0 | 5-0 | 0-2 | 1-3 | 1-5 | 1-1 | 0-5 | X | 1-4 |
| 20 Yaxley | 1-0 | 2-1 | 2-3 | 2-0 | 0-2 | 3-1 | 2-4 | 1-2 | 3-1 | 1-0 | 5-0 | 1-7 | 9-0 | 1-2 | 2-2 | 1-3 | 1-2 | 2-2 | 2-2 | X |

# DIVISION ONE RESULTS CHART 1998-99

| | 1 | 2 | 3 | 4 | 5 | 6 | 7 | 8 | 9 | 10 | 11 | 12 | 13 | 14 | 15 | 16 | 17 | 18 |
|---|---|---|---|---|---|---|---|---|---|---|---|---|---|---|---|---|---|---|
| 1 Blisworth | X | 0-0 | 2-0 | 2-0 | 1-1 | 5-1 | 3-3 | 5-1 | 2-1 | 1-0 | 0-0 | 3-4 | 1-1 | 2-0 | 2-0 | 2-3 | 3-1 | 6-1 |
| 2 Bugbrooke | 8-0 | X | 7-1 | 1-1 | 5-0 | 3-0 | 0-2 | 11-0 | 4-2 | 2-1 | 1-2 | 2-0 | 1-1 | 1-1 | 0-0 | 2-0 | 4-2 | 2-1 |
| 3 Burton PW | 2-1 | 2-6 | X | 1-2 | 0-5 | 1-5 | 0-4 | 4-0 | 2-4 | 0-0 | 0-0 | 0-5 | 1-1 | 0-2 | 1-3 | 1-1 | 1-2 | 0-0 |
| 4 Cottingham | 3-1 | 0-1 | 2-0 | X | 3-2 | 4-0 | 1-2 | 5-0 | 2-2 | 1-2 | 0-1 | 4-3 | 2-2 | 2-2 | 1-1 | 2-1 | 5-0 | 3-2 |
| 5 Daventry | 0-3 | 2-4 | 1-0 | 0-2 | X | 4-1 | 0-2 | 0-1 | 1-1 | 0-1 | 5-1 | 1-3 | 3-0 | 4-0 | 1-2 | 2-1 | 1-1 | 0-1 |
| 6 Harrowby | 1-1 | 2-5 | 2-2 | 1-2 | 1-2 | X | 1-3 | 0-2 | 4-5 | 0-2 | 2-3 | 1-1 | 0-4 | 3-2 | 4-0 | 0-6 | 1-5 | 3-5 |
| 7 Higham | 2-2 | 2-2 | 5-0 | 1-1 | 1-2 | 2-0 | X | 3-1 | 5-0 | 1-0 | 3-1 | 2-0 | 0-1 | 0-1 | 2-1 | 2-2 | 1-2 | 10-1 |
| 8 Irchester | 2-1 | 1-2 | 4-0 | 2-8 | 1-4 | 5-1 | 1-1 | X | 1-3 | 0-4 | 0-4 | 1-0 | 2-3 | 1-1 | 2-1 | 2-3 | 0-4 | 2-1 |
| 9 Newport Pagnell | 4-4 | 0-4 | 3-2 | 3-3 | 3-4 | 8-1 | 0-7 | 3-2 | X | 0-1 | 0-3 | 3-1 | 3-2 | 3-0 | 6-1 | 2-2 | 1-2 | 3-3 |
| 10 N Vanaid | 2-0 | 1-0 | 2-2 | 1-2 | 0-1 | 5-2 | 1-5 | 2-0 | 3-1 | X | 0-0 | 0-0 | 3-0 | 2-0 | 2-0 | 1-1 | 0-0 | |
| 11 ON Chenecks | 1-2 | 1-3 | 3-0 | 2-4 | 2-0 | 3-4 | 0-5 | 4-2 | 1-2 | 0-3 | X | 1-0 | 1-2 | 0-0 | 5-2 | 0-3 | 5-0 | 1-2 |
| 12 Olney | 2-2 | 0-3 | 1-0 | 5-0 | 2-1 | 2-0 | 0-3 | 1-2 | 1-1 | 1-2 | 1-1 | X | 0-1 | 2-0 | 3-1 | 2-3 | 1-4 | 1-1 |
| 13 Rothwell Corinthains | 3-1 | 0-3 | 4-3 | 4-3 | 3-2 | 3-2 | 3-2 | 4-2 | 1-2 | 1-1 | 4-0 | 2-2 | X | 3-0 | 3-0 | 8-0 | 2-3 | 3-1 |
| 14 St Ives | 0-0 | 0-3 | 1-0 | 1-1 | 1-2 | 2-1 | 1-4 | 3-0 | 1-4 | 1-1 | 3-0 | 0-4 | 2-2 | X | 1-1 | 0-0 | 0-0 | 4-3 |
| 15 Sharnbrook | 1-6 | 1-6 | 0-2 | 1-4 | 2-1 | 1-1 | 0-6 | 2-2 | 3-0 | 0-1 | 2-2 | 0-0 | 0-3 | 3-0 | X | 2-3 | 1-7 | 3-3 |
| 16 Thrapston | 3-1 | 1-3 | 1-0 | 1-2 | 3-3 | 5-2 | 0-4 | 2-1 | 3-1 | 2-2 | 2-3 | 1-0 | 2-2 | 1-0 | 10-0 | X | 1-3 | 3-3 |
| 17 Whitworths | 1-2 | 0-4 | 4-0 | 0-2 | 3-0 | 2-0 | 0-1 | 1-1 | 1-3 | 2-1 | 4-0 | 2-0 | 5-0 | 1-1 | 2-0 | 5-0 | X | 3-0 |
| 18 Woodford | 1-2 | 2-1 | 4-0 | 3-3 | 0-1 | 0-2 | 0-5 | 5-0 | 2-1 | 0-4 | 0-1 | 1-8 | 2-2 | 7-0 | 2-0 | 0-0 | 0-0 | X |

# MANAGER OF THE MONTHS AWARDS 1998-99

| | Premier Division | | Division One | |
|---|---|---|---|---|
| August/September | Alan Day | Spalding | Aidy Mann | Higham |
| October | Neil Rodney | Kempston | Neil McAllister | ON Chenecks |
| November | Elwyn Roberts | Stewarts & Lloyds | Aidy Mann | Higham |
| December | Dave Willis | Yaxley | Chris Goodchild | Bugbrooke |
| January | Brian Knight | Wellingborough | Rob Dunion | Cottingham |
| February | Steve Forbes | Cogenhoe | Nick Verity | Northampton Vanaid |
| March | Phil Pateman | Stotfold | Chris Goodchild | Bugbrooke |
| April/May | Alan Day | Spalding | Rob Clark | Rothwell Corinthians |
| | | | | |
| Manager of the Year | Alan Day | Spalding | | |

# UHLSPORT UNITED COUNTIES LEAGUE KNOCKOUT CUP 1998-99

## PRELIMINARY ROUND

| | | | | | | | |
|---|---|---|---|---|---|---|---|
| Potton | v | Stotfold | 0-1 | Northampton Spenc. | v | Stewarts & Ll. | 1*1, 2-3 |
| Buckingham | v | Newport Pagnell | 2-0 | Wootton | v | Burton PW | 4-0 |
| Boston | v | Wellingborough | 4-1 | ON Chenecks | v | Whitworths | 0*1 |
| Holbeach | v | Yaxley | 1*2 | | | | |

## FIRST ROUND

| | | | | | | | |
|---|---|---|---|---|---|---|---|
| St Ives | v | Woodford | 3-0 | Whitworths | v | Higham | 0-4 |
| Boston | v | Blackstone | 2-1 | Harrowby | v | Spalding | 0-5 |
| Olney | v | Blisworth | 3-0 | Stewarts & Lloyds | v | Ford Sports | 2-3 |
| Cogenhoe | v | Kempston | 2-3 | Buckingham | v | Northampton V. | 1-0 |
| Yaxley | v | Long Buckby | 3-2 | Rothwell Corinthians | v | St Neots | 1-0 |
| Thrapston | v | Stotfold | 0-2 | Wootton | v | Bourne | 2-5 |
| Sharnbrook | v | Cottingham | 1*1, 2-3 | Bugbrooke | v | Desborough | 4-6 |
| Eynesbury | v | Irchester | 3-2 | | | | |

## SECOND ROUND

| | | | | | | | |
|---|---|---|---|---|---|---|---|
| Yaxley | v | Desborough | 3-0 | Olney | v | Kempston | 1-2 |
| Eynesbury | v | Stotfold | 2-4 | Higham | v | Spalding | 0-2 |
| Daventry | v | Rothwell Corinthians | 1-3 | Boston | v | Bourne | 2*2, 3-2 |
| Cottingham | v | Ford Sports | 3-2 | Buckingham | v | St Ives | 3-2 |

## THIRD ROUND

| | | | | | | | |
|---|---|---|---|---|---|---|---|
| Boston | v | Yaxley | 3-1 | Kempston | v | Stotfold | 0-2 |
| Buckingham | v | Spalding | 3-2 | Rothwell Corinthians | v | Ford Sports | 1-3 |

## SEMI-FINALS

| | | | | | | | |
|---|---|---|---|---|---|---|---|
| Boston | v | Buckingham | 1-5 | Ford Sports | v | Stotfold | 2-4 |

## FINAL (1st Leg)

| | | | |
|---|---|---|---|
| Stotfold | v | Buckingham | 3-0 |

## FINAL (2nd Leg)

| | | | |
|---|---|---|---|
| Buckingham | v | Stotfold | 3-1 |

## BENEVOLENT CUP 1998-99
### FINAL

| | | | |
|---|---|---|---|
| Stamford | v | Higham | 6-0 |

# uhlsport UNITED COUNTIES LEAGUE LEADING SCORERS/APPEARANCES 1998-99
## PREMIER DIVISION

| | Most Appearances | | Leading Scorers | |
|---|---|---|---|---|
| Blackstone | Rob Speechley | 38 | Jim Warren | 9 |
| Boston | Lee Rippin | 43 | Dave Scotney | 15 |
| Bourne | Paul Pearson | 40 | Willie Straiton | 28 |
| Buckingham | Darren Harmon | 44 | Darren Harmon | 34 |
| Cogenhoe | Roy Anderson | | Roy Anderson | 18 |
| | Matt Freeman, Rob Powell | 38 | James Westley | 18 |
| Desborough | Jim Hamill | 40* | Shaun McPolin | 19 |
| Eynesbury | Neil King | 34 | Dave Goodall, Jason Meeds | |
| | | | Michael McDonnell | 6 |
| Ford Sports | Paul Creaney | 42* | Peter McBean, Byron Miller | |
| | | | | 10 |
| Holbeach | Steve Barnes | 39* | Matt Stevenson | 11 |
| Kempston | Keith Snaylem | 36 | Darryl Constantine | 9 |
| Long Buckby | Graham Flavell | 39* | Ian Green | 7 |
| Northampton Spencer | Stuart Smeathers | 38 | Scott Coleman | 24 |
| Potton | Danny Billington | 34 | Steve Pocock | 4 |
| St Neots | Gerald Sylvester | 39* | Darren Edey | 14 |
| Spalding | Kevin Cross, Simon Mead | 41* | Gavin Dolby | 28 |
| Stewarts & Lloyds | Steve Farr, Richard Lavin | 40 | Dave Torrance | 22 |
| Stotfold | Roy Boon | 45* | Wes Byrne | 19 |
| Wellingborough | Adam Bell, Stuart Knight | 36 | Ross Crick | 10 |
| Wootton | Steve Kuhne | 38 | Steve Kuhne | 16 |
| Yaxley | Nick Conroy | 42* | Dave Robertson | 18 |

* denotes ever present

# BLACKSTONE

**Secretary:** Ian McGillivry, 20 New Road, Ryhall, Stamford, Lincs PE9 4HL
Tel: 01780 762263 (H), 01733 67474 x 2898 (B)

**Ground:** Lincoln Road, Stamford Tel: 01780 757335

**Directions:** A6121 Stamford to Bourne road, 2nd left past MB works

**Capacity:** 1,000    Seats: 100    Cover: Yes    Floodlights: Yes

**Clubhouse:** Open evenings, lunchtimes & matchdays

**HONOURS** UCL Div 1 R-up 87-88 (Benevolent Cup R-up), Lincs Snr Cup `A' 92-93

**PREVIOUS** **Leagues:** Peterborough Works; Peterborough; Stamford & District
**Names:** Rutland Ironworks; Blackstone (until 1975)

**RECORD** **Gate:** 700 v Glinton
**Win:** 11-0 v Brackley, 22/1/94 (A Dunn 6 goals)
**Scorer** (in one game): A Dunn; 6 v Brackley Town, 22/1/94
Players progressing : Craig Goldsmith (Peterborough), Alan Neilson (Newcastle)

### FACT FILE
Founded: 1920
Nickname: Stones
Sponsors: Ideal Shopfitters
Colours: All yellow & royal blue
Change Colours: All red
Midweek matchday: Tuesday
Programme: 32 pages with entry
Editor: Kevin Boor (01780 754584)
Local Press: Stamford Mercury, Herald & Post, Peterborough Evening Telegraph

### CLUB PERSONNEL
President: Darren Laughton
Chairman: Bill Sewell
Manager: Vince Adams
Press Officer: Kevin Boor
Asst Manager: Trevor Smith

# BOSTON TOWN

**Secretary:** A Crick, Daisy Cottage, Shore Rd, Freiston, Boston, Lincs PE22 0LN
Tel: 01205 760162. (H &Fax)

**Ground:** Tattershall Road, Boston, Lincs Tel: 01205 365470

**Directions:** A52 Grantham-Sleaford ,2nd left into Brotherton Rd.,Argyle St.tobridge,immediately over left into Tattersall road,ground 3/4 mile on left
**Capacity:** 6,000    Seats: 450    Cover: 950    Floodlights: Yes    Club Shop: Yes
**Clubhouse:** Open evenings (except Sunday), matchdays & functions. Bar & Lounge.Darts & pool

**HONOURS** Midland Co's Lg 74-75 78-79 80-81 (Lg Cup 76-77); Lincs Snr `A' Cup (5)73-74 79-82 89-90 (Snr `B' Cup 65-66); Central Mids Lg 88-89; Central All 65-66; Lincs Lg 64-65; Und. Co. Lg.Prem Div 94-95

**PREVIOUS** **Leagues:** Lincs 63-65; Central Alliance 65-66; Eastern Co's 66-68;Midland 68-82; Northern Co's East 82-87; Central Midlands 87-91

**BEST SEASONFA Cup:** 1st Rd Proper 76-77, 1-3 v Barnsley (A)
**FA Trophy:** 2nd Round 79-80, 3-6 v Mossley (A) after 0-0
**FA Vase:** Semi-Finals 94-95, 0-2 (agg) v Taunton Town)

**RECORD** **Attendance:** 2,700 v Boston Utd, FA Cup 3rd Qual. Rd 1970
**Goalscorer** (in a season): Carl Smaller 48, 1994-95
Players progressing: Julian Joachim (Leicester City and Aston Villa) , Neil Mann (Hull City)

### FACT FILE
Founded: 1963
Nickname: Poachers
Sponsors: Tempests of Stickney/Keystone Fabricators
Colours: Blue & white/white/blue
Change: All yellow
Midweek Matchday: Tuesday
Reserves League: None 94-95
Programme: 40 pages, 50p
Editor/ Press Officer: Bob Whitaker
Tel: 01205 368445

### CLUB PERSONNEL
Chairman: Mick Vines
Vice Chairman: J Rose
Treasurer: J Rose
Manager: Bob Don-Duncan
Ass.Manager: Dave Scotney
Physio: Don Mitchell

# BOURNE TOWN

**Secretary:** Roger Atkins, 4 Orchard Close, Bourne, Lincs PE10 9DF Tel: 01778 424882

**Ground:** Abbey Lawn, Abbey Road, Bourne, Lincs Tel: 01778 422292

**Directions:** In market place take A151 Spalding Road, ground 500 yds on right.Public transport from Peterborough, Stamford and Grantham
**Capacity:** 3,000    Seats: 300    Cover: 750    Floodlights: Yes
Club Shop: Contact Sec.
**Clubhouse:** Small, open matchdays and specific events. Food, confectionary available

**HONOURS** Utd Co's Lg 68-69 69-70 71-72 90-91 (KO Cup 69-70, Benevolent Cup 90-91, Res Div 2 94-95), Lincs Snr `A' Cup 71-72 (R-up 92-93), Central Alliance Division 1 South 59-60, Lincs Intermediate Cup 85-86

**PREVIOUS** **Leagues:** Peterborough; UCL 47-56; Central All. 58-61; MidlandCos 61-63
**Ground:** Adjacent to cricket field after WW2 until 1947
**RECORD** **Attendance:** 3,000 v Chelmsford, FA Trophy 1970
**Goalscorer:** David Scotney
Players progress ing:    Peter Grummit (Nottm Forest), Shaun Cunnington (Wrexham), David Palmer (Wrexham)

### FACT FILE
Founded: 1883    Nickname: Wakes
Sponsors: Jaychem
Colours: Maroon & sky/sky/maroon
Change Colours: White & sky/white & sky/sky
Midweek matchday: Tuesday
Reserves' Lge: HSUCL Res Div 1
Programme: 50 pages, 50p
Editor: Melvin Ashton (01778 570976)
Local Press: Stamford Mercury, Lincs Free Press, Peterborough EveningTelegraph, Bourne Local

### CLUB PERSONNEL
Chairman: Jim Ashton
Vice-Chairman:
President: Jim Ashton
Press Officer: Jeff Hodson
Manager: Dave McNish
Physio: Dick Joy

# BUCKINGHAM TOWN

**Secretary:** Brian Maycock, 31 Westfield, Buckingham, Bucks Tel: 01280 815529

**Ground:** Ford Meadow, Ford Street, Buckingham Tel: 01280 816257
Capacity: 4,000    Cover: 420    Seats: 420    Floodlights: Yes

**Directions:** From town centre take Aylesbury (A413) road and turn right at Phillips Garage after 400yds. Public transport: train to Milton Keynes, then bus to Buckingham

**Clubhouse:** Open evenings 6.30-11 (12-11 Sat & Sun) Rolls etc available on matchdays. Bingo, dominoes, darts & pool. Concert room with stage for hire,capacity 150    **Club Shop:** Yes

**HONOURS** Southern Lg Southern Div 90-91, Utd Co's Lg 83-84 85-86 (Div 1 R-up 75-76, Div 2 R-up 74-75, Lg Cup 83-84, Div 2 Cup R-up 74-75), Nth Bucks Lg 24-25 28-29 33-34 35-37 38-39 48-50(2) Aylesbury & Dist. Lg 02-03, Berks & Bucks Snr Cup 83-84, Berks & Bucks Jnr Cup 02-03 48-49 (R-up 38-39 72-73), Berks & Bucks Minor Cup 32-33, Buckingham Snr Charity Cup x11, r-up x 5

**PREVIOUS** **Leagues:** Aylesbury & Dist; Nth Bucks; Hellenic 53-57; Sth Mids 57-74; Utd Co's 74-86; Southern Lge 86-97

**BEST SEASON** **FA Cup:** 1st Round 1984-85    **FA Vase:** Quarter Finals 1990-91 & 92-93

**RECORD** **Attendance:** 2,451 v Orient, FA Cup 1st Rd 84-85
**Fee paid:** £7,000 for Steve Jenkins (Wealdstone, 1992)
**Fee received:** £1,000 for Terry Shrieves (Kettering)

## FACT FILE

Formed: 1883
Nickname: The Robins
Sponsors: Wipac
Colours: All red
Change colours: All white
Midweek Matchday:
Reserves' League: No reserve team
Programme: Yes
Newsline: 0891 884 431
Local Press: Buckingham Advertiser, MK Citizen, Herald & Post
Local Radio: Chiltern Radio, Fox FM (102.6 fm), 3 Counties Radio

## CLUB PERSONNEL

Chairman: Brian Maycock

---

# BUGBROOKE ST MICHAELS

**Secretary:** Roger Geary, 31 Kislingbury Rd, Bugbrooke, Northampton NN7 3QG
Tel: 01604 831678

**Ground:** Birds Close, Gayton Road, Bugbrooke Tel: 01604 830707
Capacity: 2,500    Seats: 120    Cover: Yes    Floodlights: Yes

**Directions:** M1 Jct 16, take A45 Northampton to Daventry road.At Kislingbury, follow signposts to Bugbrooke. Left into Gayton Road on Gayton side of village

**Clubhouse:** Yes - normal licensing hours

**HONOURS** Northants Junior Cup 89-90, Central Northants Comb. 68-69 69-70 70-71 71-72 76-77 85-86, UCL Res Div 2 R-up 94-95 U.C.L. Div One Champions 98-99

**PREVIOUS** **League :** Central Northants Combination 1952-87    **Ground:** School Close

**RECORD** **Attendance:** 1,156    **Scorer:** Vince Thomas    **Appearances:** Jimmy Nord

Players progressing: Kevin Slinn (Watford), Craig Adams (Northampton)

## FACT FILE

Founded: 1929
Nickname: Badgers
Sponsors: Unusual Industries
Club colours: Black & white/black/black
Change colours: Blue & yellow/blue/blue
Reserves' Lge: UCL Res. Div 1
Programme: Eight pages
Editor: Stuart Sutton

## CLUB PERSONNEL

Chairman: Tom Treacy
President: John Curtis
Manager: Chris Goodchild
Asst Manager: Mark Panter
Press Officer: Mark Panter

---

# COGENHOE UNITED

**Secretary:** Sue Wright, 6 Braefield Road, Cogenhoe, Northants NN7 1ND
Tel: 01604 890737 (H), 01604 890277 (B),  Fax: 01604 890641

**Ground:** Compton Park, Brafield Rd, Cogenhoe, Northants (01604 890521)
**Directions:** Turn off A428 at Brafield-on-the-Green, first turn right toCogenhoe or A45 to Billing Aquadrome. Carry on, take second Cogenhoe turn on left

Capacity: 5,000    Seats: 100    Cover: 200    Floodlights: Yes    Club Shop: No
**Clubhouse:** Tues-Fri 7-11, Sat 12-3 & 4-11, Sun 12-3 & 7-10.30 Snacks. Hot food on matchdays

**HONOURS** UCL Div 1 R-up 86-87 (Res. Div 2 88-89), K.O. Cup 96-97; Daventry Charity Cup 91-92 95-96, (R-up 79-80); Central Northants Comb 80-81 82-83 83-84 (R-up 81-82, Prem Div Cup 82-83 (R-up 78-79), Div 1 Cup R-up 77-78, Charity Shield 82-83 83-84)

**PREVIOUS** **League:** Central Northants Combination 1967-84
**Ground:** Cogenhoe Village PF 1967-84

**RECORD** **Gate:** 1,000 v Eastenders XI, Charity match 8/7/90
**Scorer & Appearances:** Tony Smith
**Win:** 22-0 v Ravensthorpe, Cen. Northants Comb. Prem. Div. KO Cup, 79-80
**Defeat:** 0-6 v Yardley United, Central Northants Comb. Div. 1, 76-77
Players progressing : Darren Bazeley (Watford 89), Darren Harmon (Notts Co. 89),Matt Murphy (Oxford Utd 93), Gary Leonard (Northampton 1978)

## FACT FILE

Founded: 1967
Nickname: Cooks
Sponsors: Supertrucking
Colours: All royal
Change: Black & white/white/white
Midweek matchday: Tuesday
Reserves' Lge: UCL Res. Div 1
Programme: 32 pages with Admission
Editor:Sue Wright
Local Press: Chronicle & Echo, Northants Evening Telegraph

## CLUB PERSONNEL

Chairman: Derek Wright
Vice Chairman: Bob Earl
President: Steve Brockwell
Comm. Man.: Robert Jones
Manager: Steve Forbes
Assistant Manager: Dino Cirelli
Physio: Ian Blair

KEMPSTON ROVERS: Back Row (L-R): Neal Rodney (manager), Paul Stansfield, Steve Rigby, Jon Dean, John Amis, Paul Shepherd, Nick Starbrook, Grahame Scott, Stuart Mann, Daryl Constantine, Rodney Griffiths, Gary Salisbury (coach), Len McMain (Physio). Front row: Chris Payne, Jason Quince, Danny Griggs, Matthew Woolgar, Lee Daly, Keith Snaylam. Photo: Gordon Whittington

Midfield dynamo Tuncay Korkmaz leaps to power the ball into the top corner of Kempston's net. Photo: Clive Hillier

BLACKSTONE FC

Photo: Bill Wheatcroft

# DESBOROUGH TOWN

**FACT FILE**
Founded: 1896
Nickname: Ar Tarn
Colours: Blue & white/blue/blue
Change Colours: All red
Previous Leagues: None
Midweek matchday: Tuesday
Programme: 40 pages with entry
Editor:John Lee
Local Press: Evening Telegraph,Northants
Post,Chronicle & Echo,& Harborough Mail

98-99 - Captain: Brian Jeffrey
Top Scorer: Shaun McPolin

**Secretary:** John Lee, 85 Breakleys Road, Desborough, Northants NN14 2PT
Tel: 01536 760002

**Ground:** Waterworks Field, Braybrooke Rd, Desborough Tel: 01536 761350
Capacity: 8,000   Seats: 250   Cover: 500   Floodlights: Yes

**Directions:** Half a mile west of A6 following signs for Braybrooke
**Clubhouse:** Lounge & main hall, 2 bars, games room. Every eve. & w/e lunchtimes
**Club Shop:** No

**HONOURS** Utd Co's (Prev. Northants) Lg 00-01 01-02 06-07 20-21 23-24 24-25 27-28 48-49
66-67 (R-up 02-03 10-11 19-20 22-23 79-80, 98-99), Div 2 10-11, 28-9(Res),R-up
09-10 (Res) 26-27(Res) 51-52(Res), KO Cup 77-78 96-97; Northants Snr Cup10-11
13-14 28-29 51-52; Desborough Charity Cup 97-98,98-99

**PREVIOUS** **Leagues:** None
**RECORD** **Attendance:** 8,000 v Kettering Town
**Win:** 10-1: v Huntingdon Utd (A) 1957 & v Stewarts & Lloyds (A) 1965, both UCL.
**Defeat:** 11-0 v Rushden Town (A) 1934
**Fee received:** £8,000 for Wakeley Gage, from Northampton Town
Players progressing: Wakeley Gage (Northampton), Jon Purdie & Campbell Chapman (Wolves),
Andy Tillson (Grimsby)

**CLUB PERSONNEL**
Chairman:Alan Panter
President: Bryan Walmsley
Press Officer: John Lee
Manager: Derek Maddox
Asst Manager: Dave McHuchinson
Physio: John Wright

# EYNESBURY ROVERS

**Secretary:** Derek Irons, 12 Hadleigh Close, Bedford MK41 8JW. Tel: 01234 268111

**Ground:** Hall Road, Eynesbury, St Neots Tel: 01480 477449
Capacity: 3,000   Seats: 270   Cover: 500   Floodlights: Yes

**Directions:** Approx 2 miles from A1, on South side of St Neots urban area, near Ernulf School

**Clubhouse:** Large bar, capacity 150, committee room   **Club Shop:** Contact Dave Crisp

**HONOURS** UCL Div 1 76-77; Hunts Snr Cup 13-14 46-47 48-51 54-55 56-57 69-70 84-85 90-
93 95-96; Hunts Premier Cup 50-51 90-91 95-96; Hinchingbrooke Cup (7) 46-47
48-52 57-58 66-67; Cambs Invitation Cup 61-62; E Anglian Cup R-up 90-91 91-92;
Hunts Scott Gatty Cup 35-36 56-57 84-85 89-90 (R-up 93-94 res); Hunts Jnr Cup 21-22 26-27

**PREVIOUS** **Leagues:** Sth Mids 34-39; UCL 46-52; Eastern Co's 52-63

**BEST SEASON** **FA Vase:** 2nd Rd 85-86 88-89
**FA Cup:** 4th Qual. Rd 54-55, 1-3 v Camb. Utd (A)

**RECORD** **Gate:** 5,000 v Fulham 1953

Players progressing: Chris Turner (Peterborough), Denis Emery (Peterborough)

**FACT FILE**
Founded: 1897
Nickname: Rovers
Sponsors: Classic Windows
Colours: Royal & white/royal/royal
Change Colours: Yellow/black/yellow
Midweek matchday: Tuesday
Reserves' League: Utd Counties Res. Div. 2
Programme: 28 pages, 50p
Editor: Graham Mills
Local Press: Hunts Citizen, Cambridge
Evening News, St Neots Weekly News

**CLUB PERSONNEL**
Chairman: Brian Abraham
Vice Chairman: Mike Preece
Manager: Peter Schofield

# FORD SPORTS

**FACT FILE**
Founded: 1968
Nickname: Motormen
Sponsors: Ford Sports & Social Club
Colours: Blue/white/blue
Change : Red & black/black/red & black
Midweek matches:
Reserves' Lge: UCL Res Div 2
Programme: 12 pages
Editor: John Hinton

**Secretary:** Mick Fryatt, 2 Mayfield Drive, Daventry, Northants NN11 5QB
Tel Nos: 01327 876789 (H) 01327 305407 (W)

**Ground:** Royal Oak Way South, Daventry, Northants Tel: 01327 709219
Capacity: 1,000   Seats: Yes   Cover: Yes   Floodlights: Yes

**Directions:** Enter Daventry on A45 or A361 and follow signs for Royal Oak Way

**Clubhouse:** Yes

**HONOURS** UCL Div 1 92-93, 95-96, Knockout Cup 97-98, Benevolent Cup R-up 92-93;
Highest Agg. Goalscoring Trophy 92-93; Northants Sen Cup R-up 96-97

**PREVIOUS** **League:** Central Northants Comb

Player progressing: Martin Aldridge (Northampton)

**CLUB PERSONNEL**
Chairman: John Bailham
Managers: Darren Wood
Assistant Manager: Shane Geary
Physio: Dave Bull

# HOLBEACH UNITED

**Secretary:** Paul Beeken, 36 West End, Holbeach, Lincs PE12 7HA Tel: 01406 425355 (H)

**Ground:** Carters Park, Park Road, Holbeach Tel: 01406 424761

Capacity:4,000    Seats: 200    Cover: 450    Floodlights: Yes

**Directions:** Second left at traffic lights in town centre, 220 yds down road on left.
From King's Lynn; sharp right at traffic lights

**Clubhouse:** Large bar, lounge & kitchen, open every night **Club Shop:** No

**HONOURS** Utd Co's Lg 89-90 (KO Cup 64-65 89-90), Benevolent Cup, Evans Halshaw Cup 97-98; Lincs Snr Cup `A' 83-84 84-85 86-87 (Senior Cup `B' 57-58)

**PREVIOUS** **Leagues:** Peterborough; Utd Co's 46-55; Eastern Co's 55-62; Midland Co's62-63

**BEST SEASON** **FA Cup:** 1st Rd Proper 82-83, 0-4 v Wrexham (at Peterborough)
**FA Trophy:** 2nd Qual. Round 69-70 71-72
**FA Vase:** 5th Round 88-89, 2-4 v Wisbech Town

**RECORD** **Gate:** 4,094 v Wisbech 1954

Players progressing: Peter Rawcliffe (Lincoln)

### FACT FILE
Founded: 1929
Nickname: Tigers
Sponsors: West End Garage
Colours: Old gold & black/black/black
Change Colours: White/blue/blue
Midweek matchday: Tuesday
Reserves' Lge: Peterborough
Programme: 44 pages, 50p
Editor: David Ingle
Local Press : Lincs Free Press, Spalding
Guardian, Peterborough Evening Telegraph

### CLUB PERSONNEL
Chairman: Bryan Thompson
President: Francis Bissadike
Manager: Jimmy Jackson
Asst Manager/Physio: Howard Shoebridge

---

# KEMPSTON ROVERS

**Secretary:** Alan Scott, 26 King William Rd, Kempston, Bedford MK42 7AT  Tel: 01234 854875

**Ground:** Hillgrounds Leisure, Hillgrounds Rd, Kempston, Bedford Tel: 01234 852346.
Capacity: 2,000    Seats: 100    Cover: 250    Floodlights: Yes

**Directions:** M1 jct 13, A421 to Kempston, Hillgrounds Rd is off the B531 main Kempston-Bedford road. Entrance to Hillgrounds Road is opposite Sainsburys onthe B531 - ground can be found just over twi miles from Sainsburys entrance.British Rail to Bedford Thameslink/Midland then bus No.103 from Bedford town centre stops outside ground

**Club Shop:** No, but old programmes available from clubhouse
**Clubhouse:** Open 7-11pm Tues - Sun. & w/e lunch 12-3pm. Sky TV, pool, hot pies & pasties.

**HONOURS** United Counties Lge 73-74 (R-up 56-57 59-60), Div 1 57-58 85-86, Div 2 55-56 (R-up 67-68), KO Cup 55-56 57-58 59-60 74-75 76-77. Beds Senior Cup 08-09 37-38 76-77 91-92 (R-up 92-93)

**PREVIOUS** **League:** South Midlands 27-53
**Grounds:** Bedford Rd 1900s-1973; Hillgrounds Road 74-86 (3 grounds in same road!)

**BEST SEASON** **FA Cup:** **FA Vase:**

**RECORD** **Attendance:** Unknown **Scorer:** Doug Jack

Players progressing: Ernie Fenn (WBA), Matthew Woolgar (Luton 1994)

### FACT FILE
Founded: 1884
Nickname: Walnut Boys
Club Sponsors: Audi Vindis Bedford
Colours: Red & white/black/black
Change Colours: All yellow
Midweek matchday: Tuesday
Reserves's Lge: Bedford & Dist
Programme: 24 pages, 40p
Editor: Richard Coop
Local Press: Bedfordshire Times,
Herald & Post, Beds on Sunday

### CLUB PERSONNEL
President: H Gilbert
Chairman: Mark Salsbury
Vice-Chairman: Russell Shreeves
Press Officer : Secretary
Manager:Ken Davidson
Asst Manager: Bobby Roberts
Coach: Mel Fisher

---

# LONG BUCKBY

**Secretary:** Mrs Eileen Buse, 6 Church close, West Haddon, Northants, NN6 7DY
Tel: 01788 510563

**Ground:** Station Rd, Long Buckby Tel: 01327 842682
Capacity: 1,000    Seats: 200    Cover: 200    Floodlights: Yes

**Directions:** On Daventry - Long Buckby road. 400 yds from station (Northampton -Rugby line)

**Clubhouse:** Bar & concert room. Open matchdays

**HONOURS** UCL KO Cup 84-85, UCL Div 2 70-71 71-72, Div 2 KO Cup 71-72, Div 3 69-70; Northants Snr Cup R-up; Daventry Charity Cup 96-97

**PREVIOUS** **Leagues:** Rugby & D.; Central Northants Comb. (pre-1968)
**Name:** Long Buckby Nomads 1936

**BEST SEASON** **FA Vase:** 2nd Rd 85-86
**FA Cup:** 1st Qualifying Rd 92-93

**RECORD** **Gate:** 750 v Kettering, Northants Snr Cup Final 1984

Players progressing: Gary Mills (Nottm Forest), Vince Overson (Burnley),
Des Waldock (Northampton),Steve Norris (Scarborough)

### FACT FILE
Nickname: Bucks
Sponsors: Northampton Elec Dist
Colours: All blue
Change colours: All red
Midweek matchday: Tuesday
Reserves' Lge: HSUCL Res Div 1
Programme: 8 pages
Editor: Rod Pryor
Local Press : Chronicle & Echo,
Daventry Weekly News

### CLUB PERSONNEL
President: Alister Bruce
Chairman: Ted Thresher
Manager: Kevin Simmonds
Assistant Manager: Martin McNulty
Physio: Robert Stafferton

# NORTHAMPTON SPENCER

**Secretary:** Dave Ling, 26 Pritchard Close, Rectory Farm, Northampton NN3 5BW
Tel: 01604 407124

**Ground:** Kingsthorpe Mill, Studland Rd., Northampton NN3 1NF  Tel: 01604 718898
Capacity:  2000    Seats: 100    Cover: 350    Floodlights: Yes

**Directions:** Turn off Kingsthorpe Road at traffic lights into Thornton Rd., 1st right into Studland Rd. and ground is at the end.

**Clubhouse:** Open during normal licensing hours. Lounge and bar.    **Club Shop:** No

**HONOURS:** UCL 91-92, r-up 92-93, 97-98, Div. 1 84-85, KO Cup 88-89 93-94, r-up 87-88 96-97 97-98, Benevolent Cup 91-92; Northants Sen. Cup r-up 90-91 93-94.

**PREVIOUS** **League:** Northampton Town Lge 36-68
**Name:** Spencer School Old Boys
**Grounds:** Dallington Park 36-70, Duston High School 70-72

**BEST SEASON** **FA Cup:** 1st Qual. Rd 93-94, 96-97
**FA Vase:** 4th Round 87-88, 1-2 v Gresley Rovers
**RECORDS** **Attendance:** 800 v Nottm. Forest, dressing room opener 1993

Players progressing: Paul Stratford (Northampton), Wakeley Gage (Northampton)

### FACT FILE
Founded: 1936
Nickname: Millers
Sponsors: Park Lans Windows
Colours: Yellow/green/yellow
Change colours: All red
Midweek matchday: Tuesday
Reserves' League: UCL Res Div 1
Programme: 48 pages 50p
Editor: Andy Goldsmith (01604 412382)

### CLUB PERSONNEL
President: J Sampson
Chairman: Graham Wrighting
Press Off.: Andy Goldsmith (01604 412382)
Manager: Gary Sargent
Asst. Man.: Keith Bowen

# POTTON UNITED

**Secretary:** Derek Inskip, 16 Sheffield Close, Potton, Beds SG19 2NY   Tel: 01767 260355

**Ground:** The Hollow, Biggleswade Road, Potton Tel: 01767 261100
Capacity: 2,000    Seats: 200    Cover: 250    Floodlights: Yes
**Directions:** Outskirts of Potton on Biggleswade Road (B1040). 3 1/2 miles from Sandy (BR).
United Counties buses from Biggleswade
**Clubhouse:** Yes

**HONOURS** Utd Co's Lg 86-87 88-89, KO Cup 72-73, Benevolent Cup 88-89; Beds Snr Cup(5) 47-49 63-64 75-76 77-78 (R-up 94-95 96-97); Wallspan Floodlit Cup 87-88; Hinchingbrooke Cup 51-52 84-85 89-90 90-91 91-92; Hunts Premier Cup 89-90 91-92 94-95(jt) 96-97; Beds I'mediate Cup 43-44; Southern Comb. Cup 92-93; Nth Beds Charity Cup (12); East Anglian Cup 96-97; Jess Pigott Trophy 96-97

**PREVIOUS** **Leagues** : Sth Mids 46-55; Central Alliance 56-61
**Ground:** Recreation Grnd pre-1947

**BEST SEASON** **FA Trophy:** 3rd Qual. Round 71-72 72-73
**FA Vase:** 5th Round 89-90, 1-2 v Billericay Town
**FA Cup:** 3rd Qual. Round 74-75, 1-2 v Bedford Town

**RECORD** **Attendance:** 470 v Hastings Town, FA Vase 1989

### FACT FILE
Founded: 1943
Nickname: Royals
Club Sponsors: T.B.A.
Colours: Blue & white/blue/blue
Change Colours: Red/white/red
Midweek matchday: Tuesday
Reserves' Lge: UCL Res. Div. Two
Programme: 28 pages, 50p
Editor: T.B.A.
Local Press: Biggleswade Chronicle,

### CLUB PERSONNEL
President: Peter Hutchinson
Chairman: Nigel Westhorp
Press Officer: Secretary
Manager: Martin Humberstone
Asst Manager: Jeff Wells

# ST. NEOTS TOWN

**Secretary:** Graham Izzard

**Ground:** Rowley Park, Cambridge Rd, St Neots, Cambs  Tel: 01480 470012
Capacity:  3,000    Seats: No    Cover: 250    Floodlights: Yes
**Directions:** Through the town centre, under the railway bridge, ground is 1st left

**Clubhouse:** Yes

**HONOURS** Hunts Snr Cup(34), UCL 67-68 (KO Cup 67-68 68-69), Metropolitan Lg 49-50(Lg Cup 79-80), South Midlands Lg 32-33, Huntingdonshire Lg 90-91 92-92 93 94-95

**PREVIOUS** **Leagues:** South Midlands 27-36 46-49; United Counties 36-39 51-56 66-69 73-88; Metropolitan 49-51 60-66; Central Alliance 56-60; Eastern Counties 69-73; Huntingdonshire 90-94    **Name:** St Neots & District 1879-1957

**BEST SEASON** **FA Cup:** 1st Rd 66-67, 0-2 v Walsall (A)
**FA Vase:** 3rd Rd 78-78    **FA Trophy:** 2nd Qual. Rd 69-70 72-73

**RECORD** **Attendance:** 2,000 v Wisbech, 1966
Players progressing: Frank Atkins (Cambridge), John Gregory (Aston Villa)
and Matthew Oakey (Southampton)

### FACT FILE
Founded: 1879
Nickname: Saints
Sponsors: TBA
Club colours: Sky & navy/navy/navy
Change colours: All white
Reserves' Lge: UCL Res Div 2
Programme: Yes
Editor: Mike Birch

### CLUB PERSONNEL
Chairman: Bob Page
Press Officer: Neil Holmes (01480 383382)
Manager: Chris Howell

St Neots' Darren Edey beats Eynesbury Rovers keeper Jamie Schofield from the penalty spot in Saints' 6-1 win.
Photo: Gordon Whittington

Handrahan Timbers defender clears Ian Green's (Long Buckby) header off the line - but the well placed linesman gave a goal.
Photo: Keith Clayton

ST NEOTS TOWN FC: Back Row (L-R): Craig Lambert (physio), Barry Cavilla (assistant manager), Russell Douglas, Dean Stockwell, Gerald Sylvester, Mick McCreanor, Howard Phillips, Guy Loveday (manager), Mike Brookes (assistant manager). Front Row: Chris Jones, Simon Johnson, Graham McMillan, Paul Bloss, Mark Oakley, Dean Payne, Frank Atkins, Neil Pope. Photo: Peter Barnes

# STEWARTS & LLOYDS

**Secretary:** Dave Foster, 29 Tettenhall Close, Corby, Northants NN198 9PJ
Tel: 01536 742358

**Ground:** Recreation Ground, Occupation Road, Corby Tel: 01536 401497
Capacity: 1,500 Seats: 100 Cover: 200 Floodlights: Yes

**Directions:** The ground is situated on Occupation Rd at the rear of Stewart & Lloyds Leisure
Club, next to old Corby Town F.C. ground

**Clubhouse:** Licensed bar **Club Shop:** No

**HONOURS** UCL R-up 85-86, Div 1(2) 73-75; UCL KO Cup, Prem 95-96, Div 1 Cup(2)73-
75, Div 2 KO Cup(2) 75-77)

**PREVIOUS** **Leagues:** Kettering Amateur

**BEST SEASON** **FA Cup:** **FA Vase:**

**RECORD** **Goalscorer:** Joey Martin 46 (92-93)

Players progressing : Andy McGowan (Northampton), Willie Graham (Brentford)

### FACT FILE
Formed: 1935
Nickname: None
Sponsor: Weldon
Colours: Yellow/blue/yellow
Change Colours: All red
Midweek matchday: Tuesday
Programme: 12 pages with admission
Editor/Press Officer: Dave Foster

### CLUB PERSONNEL
Chairman: Peter Webb
Vice Chairmen: Gordon Hall, Harry Nelson
Manager: Elwyn Roberts
Asst Manager:Stuart Carmichael
Physio: Roger White

# STOTFOLD

**Secretary:** W Clegg, 12 Common Rd, Stotfold, Hitchin, Herts SG5 4BX Tel: 01462 730421

**Ground:** Roker Park, The Green, Stotfold, Hitchin, Herts Tel: 01462 730765
Capacity: 5,000 Seats: 300 Cover: 300 Floodlights: Yes

**Directions:** A507 from A1, right at lights, right at T-jct.
A507 from Bedford via Shefford, left at lights, right at T-jct

**Clubhouse:** Clubroom, bar, refreshment bar, dressing rooms, physio room

**HONOURS** Utd Co's Lg R-up 93-94, KO Cup Winners 98-99 R-up 91-92, Res Div 1 87-88;
Sth Mids Lg 80-81 (R-up 55-56 57-58 58-59 59-60 63-64 65-66 77-78), Div 1 53-54, Chal. Tphy
81-82; Beds Snr Cup 64-65 93-94; Beds Premier Cup 81-82; 98-99 Beds I'mediate Cup 58-59; Nth
Beds Charity Cup 55-56 56-57 61-62 81-82 87-88 90-91 97-98;Beds Colts Lg 88-89; Southern
Comb Cup 94-95 95-96 96-97; Hinchingbrooke Cup R-up 97-98

**PREVIOUS** **Leagues:** Biggleswade & District/ North Herts/ South Midlands 51-84

**BEST SEASON: FA Cup:** **FA Vase:**

**RECORD** **Attendance:** 1,000 v Letchworth Town, FA Amtr Cup
**Scorer:** Roy Boon **Appearances:** Roy Boon/Dave Chellew

### FACT FILE
Founded: 1904 Reformed: 1945
Nickname: Eagles
Sponsors: Motorola
Colours: Amber/black/black
Change Colours: All Sky blue
Midweek matchday: Tuesday
Reserves' League: UCL Reserve Division One
Programme: 22 pages with entry
Editor: John Talbot
Local Press: Comet, Biggleswade Chronicle

### CLUB PERSONNEL
Chairman: John Talbot
Vice Chairman: Tom Peacock
President: David Chellow
Manager: Phil Pateman
Asst Manager: Dick Newman/Gary Winn
Press Officer: Bill Clegg
Physio: Nobby Kearns

# WELLINGBOROUGH TOWN

**Secretary :** Mick Walden, 5 Fernie Way, Wellingborough, Northants NN8 3LB Tel: 01933 279561

**Ground:** Dog & Duck, London Road, Wellingborough, Northants Tel: 01933 223536
Capacity: 5,000 Seats: 300 Cover: 500 Floodlights: Yes

**Directions:** 200yds off A45 by-pass, by Dog & Duck PH. 1 mile from Wellingborough (BR)

**Clubhouse:** Full facilities. Open evenings & Sat lunchtimes **Club Shop:** No

**HONOURS** Utd Co's Lg 10-11 62-63 64-65, Metropolitan Lge 69-70, Northants Snr Cup
1896-97 1901-02 02-03 33-34 47-48 49-50 81-82, Maunsell Cup 20-21 21-22

**PREVIOUS** **Leagues:** Midland 1895-97 98-1901; Southern 01-05 71-89;
Northants (Utd Co's)19-34 36-56 61-68; Central Alliance 56-61;
Metropolitan 68-70; West Midlands Regional 70-71

**BEST SEASON FA Cup:** 1st Round 28-29, v Bristol Rovers; 65-66, 1-2 v Aldershot Town
**FA Trophy:** 1st Round 71-72, 0-3 v Dartford after 1-1 & 0-0
**FA Vase:** 1sr Rd. 95-96

**RECORD** **Attendance:** 4,013 v Kettering Town
**Goalscorer:** S Hill **Appearances:** P Hayes 165, 1985-89
Players progressing: Phil Neal (Northampton), Fanny Walden (Spurs)

### FACT FILE
Founded: 1867
Nickname: Doughboys
Sponsors: Overstone Park School
Colours: White/blue/white
Change Colours: All red
Midweek matchday: Tuesday
Reserve League: HSUCL Res. Div. Two
Programme: 16 pages 30p
Editor: Secretary

### CLUB PERSONNEL
Chairman: Corville Brown
President:
Press Officer: Secretary
Manager: Brian Knight
Coach: Joe Kiernan
Physio: Tif Felton

# WOOTON BLUE CROSS

**Secretary:** Trevor Templeman, 3 Pollys Yard, Newport Pagnell, Bucks MK16 8YU
Tel: 0958 718482 (H)  01908 613323 (B)

**Ground:** Weston Park, Bedford Road, Wootton Tel: 01234 767662
Capacity:  2,000  Seats: 50  Cover: 250  Floodlights: Yes
**Directions:** Four miles south of Bedford on main road through village at rear of Post Office

**Clubhouse:** Main hall, bar, darts, pool, bingo. Open every evening and w/e lunchtimes
**Club Shop:** No

**HONOURS** Utd Co's Lg Div 2 67-68 69-70 (KO Cup 82-83, Div 2 Cup 64-65), South Midlands Lg 47-48 (R-up 49-50), Beds Sen. Cup 70-71, Hinchinbrooke Cup(5)

**PREVIOUS** **Leagues:** Bedford & District; South Midlands 46-55
**Grounds:** Recreation Ground, Fishers Field, Rose & Crown, Cockfield

**BEST SEASON** **FA Vase:** 3rd Rd 74-75
**FA Cup:** 2nd Qual. Rd 50-51 (3-4 v Hitchin (H))

**RECORD** **Gate:** 838 v Luton, Beds Prem. Cup 1988

Players progressing: Tony Biggs (Arsenal)

**FACT FILE**
Founded: 1887
Nickname: Blue Cross
Sponsors: Vision Blinds
Colours: Blue & white/blue/blue
Change: All yellow
Reserves' League: United Counties Res. Div 1
Midweek matchday: Tuesday
Programme: 24 pages  Editor: Secretary

Local Press : Bedfordshire Times, Bedford Herald, Beds Express, Beds on Sunday

**CLUB PERSONNEL**
President: J Clarke
Chairman: Trevor Templeman
Manager: Steve Kuhne
Assistant Manager: Phil Cavener
Physio: Trevor Templeman
Press Officer: Secretary

# YAXLEY

**Secretary:** Malcolm Larrington, 70 Main Street, Yaxley, Peterborough PE7 3DB
Tel: 01733 243276 (H)

**Ground:** Holme Road, Yaxley Tel: 01733 244928
Capacity:  1,000+  Seats: 150  Cover: Yes  Floodlights: Yes

**Directions:** A1, then A15 at Norman Cross up to traffic lights. Turn right then immediately right again. Follow the road for approx. 1 mile, then turn right into Holme Rd.. The ground is approx. 200 yards on left

**HONOURS** UCL Div 1 96-97, Benevolent Cup 97-98; Hunts Senior Cup ( 5 times Inc 98-99) Peterborough League (2); Peterborough Senior Cup (2); West Anglia League;Scott-Gatty Cup

**PREVIOUS** **Leagues:** Peterborough & District, Huntingdonshire, West Anglia

**FACT FILE**
Founded:
Sponsor: Reads Removals
Colours: All blue
Change colours: All tangerine
Programme: Yes
Editor: Robin Peel

**CLUB PERSONNEL**
President: John Dowse
Chairman: Malcolm Whaley
Vice Chairman: Geoff Heathcote
Manager: Paul Humphries
Asst Manager: Jimmy Watson

Wellingborough Town 0 Wootton Blue Cross 1. A close shave for the visitors' keeper but his side did get the only goal of the game.
Photo: Gordon Whittington

# BLISWORTH

**Secretary:** Peter Edwards, 31 Windmill Ave, Blisworth, Northants NN7 3EQ
Tel: 01604 858171 (H), 0585 369933 (B)

**Ground:** Blisworth Playing Field, Courteenhall Road, Blisworth Tel: 01604 858024
Capacity: 1,000        Seats: None        Cover: None        Floodlights: No

**Directions:** Courteenhall Road off A43

**Clubhouse:** Yes

**HONOURS** Northants Junior Cup 88-99

**PREVIOUS** **League:** Central Northants Combination 1978-87
Player progressing: Dave Johnson (Northampton 83-84)

**FACT FILE**
Founded: 1890
Sponsors: Target Furniture, JB King Plant Hire
Colours: White/black/black & white
Change colours: Black, white & red/black/black
Reserves' Lge: UCL Res. Div. 2
Programme: No

**CLUB PERSONNEL**
Chairman: Pete Edwards President: L Piggott
Manager: Brian Oldham
Asst Man:Gary Edwards, Coach:RichardlLarge
Physio: Elaine Johnson

# BURTON PARK WANDERERS

**Secretary:** David Haynes, 58 Drayton Road, Lowick, Northants NN14 3BG
Tel: 01832 735060 (H), 01933 229777 x 4706 (B)

**Ground:** Latimer Park, Polwell Lane, Burton Latimer Tel: 01536 725841
Capacity: 1,000        Seats: 100        Cover: 150        Floodlights: No

**Directions:** Entering Burton Latimer, turn off A6 Station Rd and right into Powell Lane;
ground on the right

**HONOURS** UCL Div 1 R-up, Benevolent Cup R-up
**PREVIOUS** **League:** Kettering Amateur
**RECORD** **Attendance:** 253 v Rothwell, May 1989
Players progressing : Shaun Wills (Peterborough)

**FACT FILE**
Founded: 1961        Nickname: The Wanderers
Sponsor: Prescott Motors
Colours: All blue
Change Colours: Yellow & green/black/black
Midweek matchday: Tuesday
Prog: 16 pages with entry
Local Press : Northants Evening Telegraph,
Northants Post

**CLUB PERSONNEL**
Chairman: Bernard Lloyd
Vice Chairman: Paul Clarke
Manager: Eddie Lynch
Asst Manager: Jim Prior
Physio: Nicky Mann

# COTTINGHAM

**Secretary:** Lindsay Brownlie, 30 Bancroft Rd, Cottingham, Market Harborough LE168XA
Tel: 01536 771009
**Ground:** Berryfield Rd, Cottingham Tel: 01536 770051
Capacity: 1,000        Seats: None        Cover: Yes        Floodlights: No
**Directions:** One and a half miles from Corby on A427 turn right to Cottingham.At junction of
B670 turn left; Berryfield Road 200 yds on right
**Clubhouse:** Bar & changing rooms

**HONOURS** UCL Div 1 R-up 97-98; Northants Junior Cup

**PREVIOUS** **Leagues:** Market Harborough; Kettering Amateur; East Midlands Alliance

**FACT FILE**
Founded:
Sponsors: B & J Decorators
Colours: Yellow/green/yellow
Change colours: Orange/black/black
Reserves' Lge: UCL Res. Div. 2
Programme: No

**CLUB PERSONNEL**
Chairman: Mike Beadsworth
Vice Chairman: Brian Tilley
Manager: Rob Dunion
Asst Manager: Willie Kelly

# DAVENTRY TOWN

**Secretary:** Miss Joanne Place, 30 The Cherwell, Daventry, Northants NN11 4QJ
Tel: 01327 311844 (H), 01327 300001 (B)
**Ground:** Elderstubbs Farm, Leamington Way, Daventry, Northants Tel: 01327 706286
Capacity:        2,000        Seats: 250        Cover: 250        Floodlights: Yes
**Directions** Adjacent to A45 by-pass at top of Staverton Road Sports Complex
**Clubhouse:** Large bar/kitchen
**HONOURS** UCL Div 1(2) 89-91 (Lg Cup R-up 92-93, Highest Aggregate Cup), Northants
Junior Cup 36-37 60-61 91-92
**PREVIOUS** **Leagues:** Northampton Town (pre-1987)/ Central Northants Combination 87-89
**BEST SEASON** **FA Cup:** Prel. Rd 94-95
**FA Vase:** Preliminary Rd 91-92 94-95
**RECORD** **Attendance:** 350 v Ford Sports 1991

**FACT FILE**
Founded: 1886
Sponsor: Campbell Estate Agents
Colours: Black & white/black/black
Change colours: All red
Midweek Matchday: Tuesday
Reserves League: Central Northants Comb
Programme: 4 Pages Editor: Tony Perry
**CLUB PERSONNEL**
Chairman: Mel Knowles
Vice Chairman: Grant Hughes
President: Paul Webster
Managers: Kevin Flear/Craig Robson
Physio: Tony Jackson
Asst Man.: Robin Humphries, Moz Elliott

# DEEPING RANGERS

**Secretary:** Haydon Whitham, 3 Everingham, Orton Brimbles, Peterborough PE2 5XP
Tel: 01778 344701
**Ground:** Deeping Sports Club, Outgang Road, Market Deeping, Lincs.
Tel: 01778 344701
Capacity: 1,000    Seats: 180    Cover: 180    Floodlights: No
**Directions:** From Deeping town centre take the A15 towards Bourne. Turn right at Towngate Tavern following signs to Industrial Estate & club is 1/4 mile on left.
**Clubhouse:** Bar and lounge. Changing rooms

**HONOURS** Peterborough & Dist. Lge Div 3 67, Div. 2 69, Div. 1 70, Prem. Div. R-up 95-96 98-99; Lincs Sen. Cup 83-84 87-88 88-89
Peterborough FA Senior Cup 91-92 96-97 Minor Cup 67,
**PREVIOUS** **League:** Peterborough & District

### FACT FILE
Founded: 1966
Nickname; Rangers
Colours: Claret & blue
Change colours: White/claret/sky blue
Programme: planned for 99-00

### CLUB PERSONNEL
President: Albert Lawrence
Chairman: Sid Bailey
Match Sec.: Robin Crowson
01778 348287 (H)
Manager: Mel Landin
Asst. Manager: John Hickling

# HARROWBY UNITED

**Secretary:** Michael Kavanagh,218 Queensway, Grantham, Lincs.NG31 9RA(0836 266816-M)

**Ground:** Harrowby Playing Fields, Harrowby Lane, Grantham Tel: 01476 590822
Capacity: 1,500    Seats: 100    Cover: 150    Floodlights: No
**Directions:** From A1 take B6403, go past A52 roundabout, past Ancaster turn and take road to Harrowby. Continue into Grantham, ground on right opposite Cherry Tree PH.
**Clubhouse:** Large bar open normal licensing hours

**HONOURS** Utd Co's Lg Div 1 91-92 (Benev. Cup R-up 91-92), Mids Regional All. 89-90 (Lg Cup 89-90), Lincs Snr `B' Cup(2) 90-92
**PREVIOUS** **Leagues:** Grantham; Lincs; East Mids Regional Alliance (pre-1990)
**BEST SEASON** FA Vase: Preliminary Round 91-92

Players progressing: Richard Liburd (Middlesbrough)

### FACT FILE
Founded: 1949
Nickname: Arrows
Sponsor: Bailey Trailers
Colours: Blue & white/blue/blue
Change colours: Red & white/white/red
Reserves' League: Grantham
Programme: 12 pages  Ed: Pete Salvin

### CLUB PERSONNEL
Chairman: Paul Daglish
Vice Chairman: Robert Wilson
Manager: Micky Anderson
Asst Mgr: Mick Atter
Coach: Tony Cook
Physio: Simon Shaw

# HIGHAM TOWN

**Secretary:** Chris Ruff, 23 Queensway, Higham Ferrers, Northants. NN10 8BU Tel: 01933 358862
**Ground:** Recreation Ground, Vine Hill Drive, Higham Ferrers Tel: 01933 353751
Capacity: 1,000    Seats: Nil    Cover: 100    Floodlights: No
**Directions:** From Kettering 1st right on A6 after junction to St Neots. From Bedford, 3rd left after entering town on A6 from Rushden. Higham is served by London-Bedford-Corby United Counties Coachlines, and their local services Northampton-Raunds and Bedford-Kettering
**Clubhouse:** During season 8.30-11pm Tues, Thurs, Fri, Sat after games & 12-1.30pm Sun. Light refreshments available after Saturday games

**HONOURS** UCL Div 1 97-98, R-up 70-71 71-72 89-90 92-93 93-94 94-95 95-96 98-99;
Northants Lg 21-22 22-23(R-up 23-24 26-27); Northants Snr Cup 21-22 (R-up 30-31 32-33);
Maunsell Premier Cup 22-23 33-34
**PREVIOUS** **Leagues:** Wellingborough 20-21; Northants (now UCL) 21-36; Rushden 46-50
**RECORD** **Attendance:** 5,700 v Chesterfield, FA Cup final qualifying round replay 22-23
**Scorer:** Jon Ogden 157 (Lge)    **Appearances** : Brian Harbour 485

### FACT FILE
Founded: 1895  Reformed: 1920 & 1946
Nickname: Lankies
Sponsors: Higham News
Colours: Sky & navy/navy/navy
Change colours: Black & white/black/black
Midweek matchday:: Tuesday
Reserves' Lge: UCL Reserve Div
Programme: 12 pages with admission
Editor: Secretary
### CLUB PERSONNEL
President: Vijay Patel
Chairman: Richard Williams
Vice Chairman: Brian Kirk
Manager: Adie Mann   Asst Mgr: Matt Carroll
Physio: Keith Bates

# IRCHESTER UNITED

**Secretary:** Glyn Cotter, 26 Denford Way, Wellingborough, Northants NN8 5UB
Tel: 01933 402514

**Ground:** Alfred Street, Irchester (01933 312877)
Capacity: 1,000    Seats: None    Cover:Yes    Floodlights: No

**Directions:** Off Rushden Road to Wollaston Road, next to recreation ground

**Clubhouse:** Yes

**HONOURS** Northants LgDiv 2 30-31 31-32,Northants Jnr.Cup 29-30,33-34,48-49 75-6, Rushden & Dis.t Lg 28-29 29-30,32-33,33-34 36-3746-47 50-51 51-52 56-57
**BEST SEASON** FA Cup: Prel. Rd 34-35
FA Vase: Preliminary Round 77-78
**PREVIOUS** **Leagues:** Rushden & District 1936-69

### FACT FILE
Colours: Blue& Black,black,black
Change colours: Black& White,black,red
Reserves' Lge: UCL Res. Div. 2
Programme: No

### CLUB PERSONNEL
Chairman: Geoff Cotter
Manager: Andy Toon
Physio: Mick Howarth

# NEWPORT PAGNELL TOWN

**Secretary:** John Anderson, 59 Willen Road, Newport Pagnell, Bucks MK16 0DE
Tel: 01908 610440

**Ground:** Willen Road, Newport Pagnell Tel: 01908 611993
Capacity: 2,000      Seats: 100      Cover: 100      Floodlights: Yes

**Directions:** Adjacent to A422 Newport Pagnell by-pass

**Clubhouse:** Open every evening      Club Shop: No

**HONOURS** UCL Div 1 82-83 (R-up 91-92, Div 1 Cup 77-78),
Daventry Charity Cup R-up 93-94

**PREVIOUS** **Leagues:** North Bucks 63-71; South Midlands 71-73

**BEST SEASON** **FA Vase:** 2nd Round 84-85

**FACT FILE**
Founded: 1963
Nickname: Swans
Sponsors: Brian Currie
Colours: White & green/green/green
Change colours: Red/white/green
Midweek Matchday: Tuesday
Reserves League: United Counties
Programme: 56 pages   Editor: Ernie Print

**CLUB PERSONNEL**
Chairman: Gerry Ward
Vice Chairman: Ernie Print
President: Ken Inch
Manager:Jim Diggins

# NORTHAMPTON O.N. CHENECKS

**Secretary:** Ashley Clarkson, 11 Tideswell Close, West Hunsbury, Northampton NN4 9XY
Tel Nos:- 01604 708253 (H) 01234 211521 (W) 07775 940992 (M)
**Ground:** Billing Road, Northampton Tel: 01604 34045

Capacity: 1,350      Seats: Yes      Cover: Yes      Floodlights: No

**Directions:** South ring road, exit A43 Kettering. Turn left at the lights, to the top of hill and

the ground is 200 yds on right
**Clubhouse:** Yes

**HONOURS** UCL Div 1 77-78 79-80, Northants Jnr Cup R-up 93-94

**PREVIOUS** **Leagues:** N'pton Town (pre-1969)

**FACT FILE**
Founded: 1946
Colours: Blue & white/blue/blue
Change colours: All red
Reserves' League: UCL Res Div 1
Midweek Matchday:
Prog.: 16 pages with entry
Editor: Eddie Slinn

**CLUB PERSONNEL**
Chairman: John Wilson
Vice Chairman: Eddie Slinn
President: Claude Hasdell
Manager: Neil McAllister
Asst Manager: Claude Hasdell
Physio: John Goodger

# NORTHAMPTON VANAID

**Secretary:** Tony Loveday, 28 Blueberry Rise, Ecton Brook, North'ton NN3 2AX (01604 406606)

**Ground:** Fernie Fields, Moulton, Northampton Tel: 01604 670366

Capacity: 700      Seats: 100      Cover: Yes      Floodlights: No

**Directions:** R'bout at Lumbertub pub take turn to Moulton, 1st right signposted

**Clubhouse:** Large bar. Hot food/bar meals

**HONOURS** UCL Div 1 93-94, Benevolent Cup R-up 93-94;

Northants Jnr Cup 93-94 96-97 97-98; Northampton Town Lg 88-89 89-90
**PREVIOUS** **League:** Northampton Town (pre-1993)

**RECORD** **Attendance:** 78

**FACT FILE**
Founded: 1968Nickname: Vans
Sponsors: Personnel Assurance,Barretts Club
Colours: All Blue
Change colours: Black & white/black/black
Reserves' League: UCL Res Div 1
Programme Editors: Tony & June Loveday
**CLUB PERSONNEL**
Chairman: Rob Clarke
Vice Chairman: Steve Tebbutt
President: A Blundell
Manager: Nick Verity
Asst Manager: Adam May
Physio: Paul Massey

# OLNEY TOWN

**Secretary:** Andrew Baldwin, 49 Midland Road, Olney, Bucks MK46 4BP
Tel: 01234 711071

**Ground:** East Street, Olney , Bucks. Tel: 01234 712227
Capacity: 2,000      Seats: None      Cover: Yes      Floodlights: No
**Clubhouse:** Yes

**Directions:** Enter Olney on A509 from Wellingborough, 100yds on left enter East St,
the ground is 200 yds on left
**HONOURS** UCL Div 1 72-73, Berks & Bucks I'mediate Cup 92-93

**PREVIOUS** **Leagues:** Nth Bucks, Rushden & Dist

**FACT FILE**
Founded: 1910
Sponsors: Cyclo Sports
Colours: Black & white/black/black
Change colours: Yellow & black/black/black
Programme: 32 pages
Editor: Barry Simons

**CLUB PERSONNEL**
Chairman:Barry Simons
President: Andrew Soul
Manager: John Dower
Asst Manager: Bob Read
Coach: Russell Ward
Physio: Peter Munting

NEWPORT PAGNELL FC: Back Row (L-R): Andy Gibb, Jamie Williams, David Marsh, Anthony Clark, Gareth Handley, Danny Goodwin, Paul Edgeworth, Neil Humphrey, Chris Proctor, Mel Johnston (Physio), Danni Janes (Joint manager). Front Row: Mark Gidman, Ian Halsall, Paul Stokes (captain), Jeff Milne, Danny Norris. Photo: Gordon Whittington

ROTHWELL CORINTHIANS: Back Row (L-R): David Briffa, Tony Fargnoli, Bill Riddle, Greg Smith, Kev Malcolm, Chris Munns, Derek Simmons. Front Row: Scott Stirling, Jamie Wright, Paddy McCann, Neil Barratt, Lane Clark, Colin Tew. Photo: Gordon Whittington

THRAPSTON TOWN: Back Row (L-R): Gary Petts (manager), Simon Tate, Shaun Molloy, Phil Turner, Mark Buckby, Glen Turner, Kevin Jeffries, Barry Carter (assistant manager). Front Row: Tom Thurlow, Rory Petts (mascot), David Peet, Paul Johnson, Dominc Deradi, Rob Stewart, Adam Kirk, Tyrone Wilson, Keith Manson. Photo: Gordon Whittington

# ROTHWELL CORINTHIANS

**Secretary:** Bob Clelland, 5 Drake Close, Rothwell, Northants NN14 6DJ
Tel: 01536 710134

**Ground:** Seargeant's Lawn, Desborough Road, Rothwell, Northants.
Tel: 01536 418688
Capacity: Unknown     Seats: 50          Cover: 200          Floodlights: Yes

**Directions** A6 towards Desborough, on right opposite Greening Road
**Club House:** Yes                    **Club Shop:** No

**HONOURS** East Midlands Alliance (2)
**PREVIOUS** **League** East Midlands Alliance

**FACT FILE**
Founded: 1930's
Nickname: Corinthians
Sponsor: Springfir Estates
Colours: Red,black,black
Change colours: All blue
Programme: Yes
Editor: Brian Johnson

**CLUB PERSONNEL**
Chairman: Brian Johnson
Vice Chairman: May Clelland
President: Terry Smith
Manager: Rob Clark
Physio: Mick Fox

---

# ST. IVES TOWN

**Secretary:** Jim Stocker, 23 Townsend Road, Needingworth, St. Ives, Huntingdon, Cambs
Tel: 01480 492680 (H)  01480 456256 (B)
**Ground:** Westwood Road, St. Ives, Cambs.Tel: 01480 463207
**Directions:** From Huntingdon: A1123 thru Houghton, right at 2nd lighs intoRamsey Rd,
after quarter mile turn right opp. Fire Station into Westwood Road
From A604: Follow Huntingdon signs past 5 r'bouts, left into Ramsey Rd at
lights then follow as above.
Capacity: 5,000          Seats: 130 Cover: 300          Floodlights: Yes
**Clubhouse:** Bar and entertainment room. Normal licensing hours.
**HONOURS** Hunts Snr Cup 00-01 11-12 22-23 25-26 29-30 81-82 86-87 87-88,
Cambs League 22-23 23-24 24-25.
**PREVIOUS** **Leagues:** Cambs; Central Amtr; Hunts; P'boro. & D. (pre-1985).
**Ground:** Meadow Lane
**RECORD** **Gate:** 400 v Saffron Walden Town, FA Vase.

**FACT FILE**
Founded: 1887
Nickname: Saints
Colours: White & black/black/black & white
Change colours: Blue/red/blue
Midweek matchday: Tuesday
Reserves' Lge: UCL Res Div 2
Programme editor: Alastair Robinson
Tel: 01480 460409 (H)

**CLUB PERSONNEL**
Match Sec.: Alistair Robinson
38 High St., Needingworth, Huntingdon,
Cambs. Tel: 01480 460409 (H)

---

# SHARNBROOK A.F.C.

**Secretary:** Roy Boulton, 10 St Mary's Avenue, Rushden, Northants NN10 9EP
Tel: 01933 315890

**Ground:** Lodge Rd, Sharnbrook, Northants. Tel: 01234 781080
Capacity: 1,000          Seats: None          Cover: Yes          Floodlights: No

**Directions:** Second sign to Sharnbrook from Rushden on A6, under railway bridge, right at
T-junction, left past church, right into Lodge Road
**Clubhouse:** Yes

**HONOURS** Bedfordshire Intermediate Cup 73-74
**PREVIOUS** **Leagues:** Bedford & Dist (pre-1968)
Player progressing: Matt Jackson (Luton, Everton & Norwich City)

**FACT FILE**

Sponsor: Lansdown Homes
Colours: Red & Blue Stripes,Blue,Red
Change colours: Yellow,black,yellow
Programme: 12 pages
Editor: Dai Hurst

**CLUB PERSONNEL**

Chairman: Jim Donaldson
President: John Boyles
Manager: Ali Woods
Physio: Jim Donaldson

---

# THRAPSTON TOWN

**Secretary:** Barry Carter, 23 Fletcher Gardens,Thrapston, Kettering, Northants.nn1 4UJ
Tel No: 01832 735879
**Ground:** Chancery Lane, Thrapston, Northants  Tel: 01832 732470
Capacity: 1,000          Seats: Yes          Cover: Yes          Floodlights: No

**Directions:** Chancery Lane off A605 in town centre
**Clubhouse:** Yes

**HONOURS** Northants Junior Cup 87-88, 98-99 Kettering Am Lg 70-71 72-73 73-74 77-78

**PREVIOUS** **League:** Kettering Amateur (pre-1978)

**FACT FILE**
Founded: 1960
Nickname: Venturas
Sponsor: Hobbs Direct Mail
Colours: All blue & yellow
Change colours: White/blue/blue
Programme: Yes     Editor: Dave Overend

**CLUB PERSONNEL**
President: Derek Barber
Chairman: Dave Harris
Vice  Chairman: Barry Carter
Manager: Gary Petts
Asst Manager: Barry Carter
Physio: Nigel Gore

# WELLINGBOROUGH WHITWORTHS

**FACT FILE**
Sponsor: Whitworth Brothers
Colours: All yellow
Change colours: Red & white/red/red
Reserves' Lge: UCL Res Div 2
Programme: No

**Secretary:** Brian Higgins, 1 Knightlands Road, Irthlingborough, Northants. NN9 5SU

Tel: 01933 650031

**Ground:** London Road, Wellingborough, Northants. Tel: 01933 227324

Capacity: 700　　　Seats: None　Cover: Yes　　　Floodlights: No

**Directions:** Off London Road at Dog & Duck public house

**Clubhouse:** Yes

**PREVIOUS** **Leagues:** Rushden & Dist.; E. Mids All. (pre-1985)

**HONOURS** Rushden & District Lg 76-77; Northants Jun Cup 96

**CLUB PERSONNEL**
Chairman: Bob Jarvis
Vice Chairman: Dave Woodley
President: Terry Faulkner
Manager: Phil Harvey
Asst Manager: Mick Garrett
Physio: Andrew King

# WOODFORD UNITED

**FACT FILE**
Founded: 1946
Nickname:
Sponsors: Styleglaze
Colours: All red
Change Colours: All blue
Reserves' League: Northants Comb
Programme: 16 pages
Editor: Francis Peacock (01327 263335)

**Secretary:** Andy Worrall, 30 Townsend, Woodford Halse, Daventry, Northants NN113QL
Tel: 01327 261746

**Ground:** Byfield Road, Woodford Halse, Daventry, Northants. Tel: 01327 263734

Capacity: 3,000　　　Seats: 25　Cover: 150　　　Floodlights: No

**Directions** Off A 361 Daventry to Banbury Rd, on Woodford Road out of Byfield

**Clubhouse:** Yes

**PREVIOUS** Leagues: Central Northants Comb pre 70, UCL 70-78, Northants Comb

**HONOURS** Northants Comb 66 67 90 92 95, KO Cup 66 90 93 95 98;

United Counties Lge Div 2 74, KO Cup 74;

**CLUB PERSONNEL**
Chairman: Bob Justice
Vice-Chairman: R Adams
Manager: Andy McGuire
Assistant Manager: Justin Cullen

Newport press for another goal against Olney.

Photo: Steve Ayre

# SOUTHERN REGIONAL LEAGUE TABLES

## PORTSMOUTH NORTH EAST LEAGUE
### DIVISION ONE

| | | | | | | | |
|---|---|---|---|---|---|---|---|
| Shearer Arms | 12 | 10 | 2 | 0 | 65 | 13 | 32 |
| George & Dragon | 12 | 8 | 2 | 2 | 33 | 22 | 26 |
| Wheatsheaf (Portsm'th) | 12 | 5 | 1 | 6 | 26 | 36 | 16 |
| Grant Thornton | 12 | 3 | 6 | 3 | 21 | 24 | 15 |
| Kingston Arrows | 12 | 3 | 3 | 6 | 31 | 41 | 12 |
| British Star | 12 | 3 | 1 | 8 | 17 | 39 | 10 |
| Rimer | 12 | 2 | 1 | 9 | 24 | 42 | 7 |

## ANDOVER LEAGUE
### DIVISION ONE

| | | | | | | | |
|---|---|---|---|---|---|---|---|
| Kings Somborne | 18 | 14 | 3 | 1 | 82 | 26 | 45 |
| Picket Piece | 18 | 15 | 0 | 3 | 61 | 23 | 45 |
| ABC United Res. | 18 | 10 | 4 | 4 | 60 | 40 | 34 |
| Winchester Labels | 18 | 10 | 3 | 5 | 51 | 50 | 33 |
| Kentsborough | 18 | 7 | 4 | 7 | 66 | 42 | 25 |
| Ludgershall Sports | 18 | 7 | 3 | 8 | 50 | 35 | 24 |
| Inkpen | 18 | 6 | 3 | 9 | 40 | 52 | 21 |
| Southampton Arms | 18 | 4 | 3 | 11 | 18 | 71 | 15 |
| Overwallop Res. | 18 | 2 | 2 | 14 | 27 | 67 | 8 |
| New Street `B' | 18 | 2 | 1 | 15 | 22 | 69 | 7 |

## SKURRAYS WILTSHIRE LEAGUE
### PREMIER DIVISION

| | | | | | | | |
|---|---|---|---|---|---|---|---|
| Shrewton United | 30 | 22 | 6 | 2 | 84 | 25 | 72 |
| Raychem Mowlem | 30 | 21 | 5 | 4 | 117 | 35 | 68 |
| Cricklade Town | 30 | 21 | 4 | 5 | 83 | 29 | 67 |
| Malmesbury Victoria | 30 | 18 | 3 | 9 | 63 | 37 | 57 |
| Biddestone | 30 | 17 | 5 | 8 | 74 | 43 | 56 |
| Devizes Town Res. | 30 | 15 | 5 | 10 | 58 | 35 | 50 |
| Melksham Town Res. | 30 | 14 | 5 | 11 | 51 | 49 | 47 |
| Bradford Town | 30 | 14 | 4 | 12 | 55 | 46 | 46 |
| Bromham | 30 | 12 | 7 | 11 | 43 | 49 | 43 |
| Chippenham Town Res. | 30 | 11 | 8 | 11 | 56 | 62 | 41 |
| Wroughton | 30 | 10 | 5 | 15 | 48 | 60 | 35 |
| Warminster Town Res. | 30 | 7 | 7 | 16 | 25 | 61 | 28 |
| Corsham Town Res. | 30 | 5 | 8 | 17 | 31 | 58 | 23 |
| Purton Res. | 30 | 5 | 2 | 23 | 33 | 110 | 17 |
| Pewsey Vale Res. | 30 | 4 | 4 | 22 | 42 | 102 | 16 |
| Marlborough Town | 30 | 2 | 6 | 22 | 28 | 90 | 12 |

## ALDERSHOT & DISTRICT LEAGUE
### SENIOR DIVISION

| | | | | | | | |
|---|---|---|---|---|---|---|---|
| Keogh | 22 | 18 | 1 | 3 | 98 | 36 | 55 |
| Blackwater | 22 | 17 | 2 | 3 | 89 | 35 | 53 |
| Lindford Royal Exchange | 22 | 15 | 5 | 2 | 69 | 36 | 50 |
| Headley | 22 | 12 | 4 | 6 | 68 | 39 | 40 |
| Hartley Wintney Res. | 22 | 12 | 3 | 7 | 71 | 48 | 39 |
| Yateley Green Res. | 22 | 8 | 5 | 9 | 37 | 49 | 29 |
| Yateley | 22 | 8 | 4 | 10 | 43 | 38 | 28 |
| Farnborough N End R. | 22 | 6 | 2 | 14 | 47 | 88 | 20 |
| FTC | 22 | 5 | 3 | 14 | 29 | 53 | 18 |
| Frimley Town | 22 | 5 | 2 | 15 | 48 | 69 | 17 |
| Alton United | 22 | 5 | 0 | 17 | 46 | 99 | 15 |
| Airborne United | 22 | 4 | 3 | 15 | 35 | 90 | 15 |

## FANSTONE SOUTHAMPTON LEAGUE
### PREMIER DIVISION

| | | | | | | | |
|---|---|---|---|---|---|---|---|
| BTC Southampton | 26 | 23 | 2 | 1 | 97 | 14 | 71 |
| Brendon | 26 | 23 | 2 | 1 | 87 | 17 | 71 |
| Nursling | 26 | 22 | 0 | 4 | 103 | 24 | 66 |
| Swift Sporting | 26 | 14 | 0 | 12 | 51 | 44 | 42 |
| North Baddesley | 26 | 11 | 4 | 11 | 41 | 42 | 37 |
| Ford Sports | 26 | 11 | 4 | 11 | 43 | 52 | 37 |
| Esso Fawley Res. | 26 | 10 | 2 | 14 | 43 | 56 | 32 |
| Old Tauntonians | 26 | 9 | 5 | 12 | 39 | 61 | 32 |
| Locksheath Res. | 26 | 8 | 3 | 15 | 47 | 59 | 27 |
| Bishopstoke Social Res. | 26 | 7 | 6 | 13 | 44 | 62 | 27 |
| Durley | 26 | 7 | 6 | 13 | 27 | 61 | 27 |
| Fair Oak Linden | 26 | 6 | 4 | 16 | 39 | 66 | 22 |
| AFC Solent | 26 | 5 | 4 | 17 | 28 | 89 | 19 |
| Otterbourne Res. | 26 | 2 | 6 | 18 | 23 | 65 | 12 |

THE ISLE OF WIGHT REPRESENTATIVE TEAM: Joe McCormack, Shaun White, Roy Maskell, Andy Watson, Andrew Rayner, Martin Raggett, Jamie Newnham, Adam Barsdell, Darren Plenty, Ashley Wright, Simon Butler, Steve Taylor, Peter Wheeler, Adam Robinson, Mark Pateman, Justin Hughes (manager), John Linington

Farnborough North End at new home Farnborough Gate, near Farnborough North Station

Photo: Eric Marsh

LYMINGTON TOWN of Hampshire League Division 3 at Farnborough North End

Photo: Eric Marsh

POOLE TOWN: Back Row: Paul Ayling (kit), Milan Parodi, Mike McDonnell, Kevin Bush, Gary Grace, Jan Wagenaar, James Wood, John Rowley, Rade 'Tony' Krunic, Dick Thomas (physio), Bill Reid (secretary), Pete Moore (c/o manager). Front Row: Trevor Parker (c/o manager), Mark Smith, Jamie Holland, Danny Adams, Shaun Brooks, Andy Jones, Scott Kelly.

Photo: Andrew Chitty

# JEWSON WESSEX LEAGUE

## FEEDER TO: Dr MARTENS FOOTBALL LEAGUE

### President: Cyril Hurlock

**Chairman:** Alf Peckham    **Vice Chairman:** Norman Cook

**Hon. Secretary:** Tom Linden, 63 Downs Road, South Wonston
Winchester, Hampshire SO21 3EW   (01962 884942)

The League experienced many changes of Officers last season; Cyril Hurlock became President, Norman Cook accepted the duel role of Vice Chairman and temporary Treasurer, until a new Treasurer could be appointed, Bob Rose was appointed to this position in March 1999 and worked with Norman until the end of the season. Malcolm Watts joined the League as Fixtures Secretary, whilst Denis Emery became the Registration Secretary. Other new names were Hamble ASSC (formally Aerostructures S & S), Lymington & New Milton (formerly AFC Lymington), Fareham Town joining the League from the Southern League, Moneyfields promoted from the Hampshire League, the League also welcomed Weymouth Reserves from the Dorset Combination League, New Street Reserves from the Hampshire Combination League, Brockenhurst Reserves from the Bournemouth Senior League and Portsmouth RN Reserves from the Portsmouth Senior League. This season marked the centenary of Brockenhurst FC, a major event for the Club, as their programme states, "Long Live the Badgers".

The 8th August marked the inaugural Jewson Challenge Shield Match between the Champions of our League and Wroxham FC, Champions of the Jewson Eastern League, it was with some particular satisfaction that Lymington & New Milton won the keenly contested match 3-1 on a very hot day in a congested New Forest.

The FA Vase proved to be rewarding for our Clubs. Eastleigh, Fareham Town and AFC Newbury recorded wins in September, whilst Bemerton Heath Harlequins' run started well with a 3-0 win at home to Warminster. Bournemouth went down 4-3 (aet) away to Sandhurst.

We experienced the first of what was to become quite a few problems with floodlighting with Cowes Sports' lights failing against Portsmouth RN. October was somewhat of a nightmare with regard to the weather with almost two weeks of fixtures washed out; more rain at the end of November caused Malcolm Watts further anxiety over fixtures. Bemerton HH continued in the Vase with a home win over Swindon Supermarine, whilst Lymington & New Milton entered the competition with a home win over Wellington Town, with the end of the road for this year coming for Thatcham Town losing at home to Ramsgate. Lymington & New Milton and Bemerton Heath Harlequins continued with their FA Vase success with wins over Hungerford and Ramsgate respectively. At Christmas Thatcham Town headed the First Division whilst Bashley Reserves were top of the Combination Division. In December we were informed of the death of Harry Roffey, Vice President of Christchurch FC.

Bemerton HH lost away to Clitheroe in the Fifth Round of the Vase at the end of January in front of 510 spectators, whilst Lymington & New Milton travelled to Dunston Federation Brewery where they won (aet) in front of 470 spectators. February brought Lymington & New Milton's Vase run to an end at Taunton in front of 1608 spectators; they now faced the task of catching up on a severe backlog of domestic fixtures including County Cups. Apart from the first week in March the weather was much improved and allowed us to "catch up" with the fixtures to some extent. April was a good month for the League, although some domestic cup problems caused matches to be switched, but in the end we were able to complete the season on time, although it was just a little too close for comfort. Christchurch had a very good season, as not only did they finish fifth in the League Table, but their Manager won the Daily Echo Manager of the Month Award on two occasions. Eastleigh also won the same award twice, with different Managers. Wimborne Town may not have won trophies this season, but they had a major role to play, in determining the championship. Cowes Sports had another good season; whilst they did not have a good run in a National Competition, they won the League Cup and finished seventh in the League. Moneyfields found the standard of the League somewhat different in their promotion, but what a season they have had, with a more than creditable eighth place in the First Division, runners up in the Russell Cotes Cup and their Reserves finishing a very close second in the Combination League to a very good Weymouth Reserves team. AFC Totton started the season strongly, and having lost their way a little they finished ninth in the table which is probably the average position held throughout the season, but they finished well winning the Russell Cotes Cup. Gosport Borough hovered in mid table for most of the season, but their Reserves did well in reaching the Combination Cup Final again. Fareham Town found the transition from the Southern league to be quite difficult, but, having been at the wrong end of the table for much of the year, finished a stronger side in thirteenth position. B.A.T. reached fourth place at one stage, hovered in mid table for some time but found points very difficult to come by after January. Whilst East Cowes Vics and Hamble ASSC experienced disappointing and difficult seasons, they both produced outstanding results at times, really upsetting the form book.Whitchurch United spent much of the season looking over their shoulders at the "relegation spot" being battled out by Portsmouth RN and Downton, and they became more involved in the struggle finishing in nineteenth position whilst winning the Hungerford Challenge Cup. Portsmouth RN fought their way out of the relegation spot, leaving Downton to wonder about their future, at this level. A special thanks to AFC Totton and Eastleigh FC for staging our Cup Finals in such a professional manner.

Overall, we have had an excellent season as a League, so whatever your Club or role thank you all for your valuable contribution.

*Tom Linden*

## FIRST DIVISION FINAL LEAGUE TABLE 1998-99

| | P | W | D | L | F | A | W | D | L | F | A | Pts | GD |
|---|---|---|---|---|---|---|---|---|---|---|---|---|---|
| Lymington & New Milton | 38 | 15 | 2 | 2 | 50 | 13 | 12 | 4 | 3 | 42 | 18 | 87 | 61 |
| Thatcham Town | 38 | 15 | 1 | 3 | 58 | 25 | 8 | 8 | 3 | 34 | 21 | 78 | 46 |
| AFC Newbury | 38 | 13 | 3 | 3 | 42 | 20 | 9 | 8 | 2 | 39 | 19 | 77 | 42 |
| Eastleigh | 38 | 10 | 5 | 4 | 29 | 18 | 12 | 3 | 4 | 40 | 25 | 74 | 26 |
| Christchurch | 38 | 12 | 4 | 3 | 41 | 23 | 10 | 3 | 6 | 31 | 30 | 73 | 19 |
| Wimborne Town | 38 | 11 | 7 | 1 | 56 | 17 | 7 | 7 | 5 | 25 | 17 | 68 | 47 |
| Cowes Sports | 38 | 13 | 3 | 3 | 40 | 17 | 6 | 5 | 8 | 37 | 37 | 65 | 23 |
| Moneyfields | 38 | 11 | 2 | 6 | 43 | 27 | 6 | 6 | 7 | 26 | 35 | 59 | 7 |
| AFC Totton | 38 | 7 | 5 | 7 | 31 | 26 | 8 | 5 | 6 | 29 | 24 | 55 | 10 |
| Bemerton Heath Harlequins | 38 | 10 | 2 | 7 | 33 | 21 | 7 | 2 | 10 | 26 | 33 | 55 | 5 |
| Brockenhurst | 38 | 4 | 5 | 10 | 28 | 31 | 10 | 2 | 7 | 24 | 30 | 49 | -9 |
| Bournemouth | 38 | 5 | 6 | 8 | 23 | 33 | 7 | 4 | 8 | 23 | 30 | 46 | -17 |
| Fareham Town | 38 | 7 | 7 | 5 | 28 | 22 | 4 | 5 | 10 | 30 | 45 | 45 | -9 |
| Gosport Borough | 38 | 5 | 7 | 7 | 27 | 28 | 6 | 4 | 9 | 39 | 43 | 44 | -5 |
| B.A.T. | 38 | 4 | 8 | 7 | 27 | 32 | 6 | 5 | 8 | 28 | 33 | 43 | -10 |
| East Cowes Vics | 38 | 8 | 2 | 9 | 32 | 44 | 2 | 2 | 15 | 16 | 59 | 34 | -55 |
| Hamble ASSC | 38 | 3 | 5 | 11 | 25 | 35 | 3 | 4 | 12 | 12 | 33 | 27 | -31 |
| Portsmouth R.N. | 38 | 4 | 5 | 10 | 18 | 31 | 2 | 4 | 13 | 24 | 50 | 27 | -39 |
| Whitchurch United | 38 | 4 | 6 | 9 | 23 | 34 | 1 | 5 | 13 | 13 | 42 | 26 | -40 |
| Downton | 38 | 3 | 4 | 12 | 28 | 53 | 1 | 3 | 15 | 12 | 58 | 19 | -71 |

## FIRST DIVISION RESULTS CHART 1998-99

| | 1 | 2 | 3 | 4 | 5 | 6 | 7 | 8 | 9 | 10 | 11 | 12 | 13 | 14 | 15 | 16 | 17 | 18 | 19 | 20 |
|---|---|---|---|---|---|---|---|---|---|---|---|---|---|---|---|---|---|---|---|---|
| 1 AFC Newbury | X | 0-1 | 2-0 | 3-0 | 1-0 | 4-4 | 3-0 | 4-2 | 6-1 | 2-0 | 1-2 | 5-1 | 2-3 | 1-0 | 2-1 | 3-1 | 1-1 | 1-0 | 1-0 | 0-0 |
| 2 AFC Totton | 0-3 | X | 3-2 | 1-2 | 2-2 | 1-2 | 3-3 | 2-2 | 6-0 | 2-1 | 0-1 | 2-0 | 3-1 | 0-0 | 1-1 | 0-2 | 0-1 | 3-1 | 2-1 | |
| 3 B.A.T. | 2-2 | 2-1 | X | 1-2 | 2-2 | 0-1 | 0-3 | 1-2 | 1-1 | 2-2 | 1-2 | 1-0 | 0-5 | 0-0 | 2-2 | 2-2 | 3-1 | 2-2 | 5-1 | 0-1 |
| 4 Bemerton HH | 1-3 | 2-1 | 1-2 | X | 0-1 | 1-0 | 1-2 | 2-1 | 3-0 | 5-1 | 0-4 | 1-1 | 6-2 | 1-0 | 0-1 | 2-0 | 3-0 | 1-2 | 3-0 | 0-0 |
| 5 Bournemouth | 0-4 | 1-1 | 5-1 | 0-2 | X | 0-1 | 1-1 | 2-4 | 2-2 | 2-0 | 1-1 | 4-2 | 1-1 | 2-0 | 2-0 | 0-2 | 0-4 | 0-5 | 0-0 | 0-2 |
| 6 Brockenhurst | 2-2 | 0-0 | 0-1 | 3-3 | 0-1 | X | 0-1 | 3-5 | 4-1 | 4-0 | 0-1 | 2-3 | 0-1 | 1-3 | 1-2 | 1-1 | 2-1 | 2-2 | 3-0 | 0-3 |
| 7 Christchurch | 2-0 | 2-3 | 0-5 | 2-1 | 1-1 | 1-1 | X | 2-1 | 2-0 | 5-0 | 3-1 | 3-0 | 4-2 | 4-0 | 0-3 | 3-0 | 2-1 | 3-3 | 2-1 | 0-0 |
| 8 Cowes Sports | 0-0 | 3-0 | 2-1 | 3-0 | 5-1 | 3-0 | 0-1 | X | 2-0 | 1-0 | 2-1 | 2-4 | 5-0 | 2-1 | 1-3 | 3-1 | 3-2 | 2-1 | 1-1 | 0-0 |
| 9 Downton | 1-5 | 1-1 | 1-2 | 0-2 | 1-4 | 0-2 | 2-6 | 0-3 | X | 6-3 | 1-4 | 2-2 | 3-3 | 4-0 | 1-7 | 0-2 | 2-2 | 1-2 | 2-1 | 0-2 |
| 10 East Cowes Vics | 2-3 | 2-5 | 3-2 | 2-3 | 3-0 | 1-2 | 2-1 | 1-5 | 2-1 | X | 0-3 | 2-2 | 0-3 | 1-0 | 0-5 | 0-0 | 4-2 | 1-3 | 3-2 | 3-2 |
| 11 Eastleigh | 0-2 | 1-0 | 1-1 | 1-0 | 1-0 | 0-2 | 2-0 | 4-3 | 2-0 | 2-0 | X | 3-0 | 1-1 | 0-0 | 0-3 | 1-3 | 1-1 | 2-1 | 6-0 | 1-1 |
| 12 Fareham Town | 0-0 | 1-4 | 6-1 | 0-2 | 2-1 | 1-2 | 0-2 | 5-0 | 0-0 | 2-1 | 1-1 | X | 2-1 | 1-0 | 3-3 | 1-1 | 2-1 | 0-0 | 1-1 | 2-1 |
| 13 Gosport Borough | 1-1 | 1-3 | 1-1 | 2-1 | 0-1 | 0-1 | 2-1 | 0-0 | 5-3 | 2-0 | 2-3 | 3-3 | X | 1-1 | 1-2 | 1-2 | 3-2 | 1-2 | 0-0 | 1-1 |
| 14 Hamble ASSC | 0-0 | 0-3 | 1-3 | 1-1 | 2-3 | 0-1 | 0-0 | 2-2 | 0-1 | 1-2 | 5-2 | 3-5 | 2-1 | X | 1-1 | 0-2 | 6-0 | 0-4 | 1-2 | 0-2 |
| 15 Lymington & NM | 1-1 | 2-0 | 1-0 | 4-3 | 2-0 | 3-0 | 1-3 | 3-0 | 3-1 | 7-0 | 1-2 | 1-0 | 1-0 | 2-0 | X | 4-0 | 5-0 | 2-2 | 2-0 | 5-1 |
| 16 Moneyfields | 1-3 | 1-2 | 1-3 | 3-1 | 2-1 | 5-0 | 3-0 | 2-0 | 5-0 | 4-1 | 2-4 | 1-1 | 4-3 | 5-0 | 0-3 | X | 3-2 | 0-0 | 1-0 | 0-3 |
| 17 Portsmouth RN | 3-2 | 1-2 | 0-0 | 0-1 | 0-2 | 0-2 | 1-2 | 0-0 | 3-0 | 1-5 | 0-4 | 2-1 | 1-3 | 1-3 | 0-0 | 2-0 | X | 1-2 | 6-0 | 1-1 |
| 18 Thatcham Town | 1-3 | 3-1 | 3-1 | 1-0 | 0-2 | 2-0 | 8-2 | 4-3 | 4-0 | 2-0 | 1-1 | 4-3 | 5-2 | 3-0 | 1-2 | 6-2 | 3-1 | X | 4-1 | 3-1 |
| 19 Whitchurch Utd | 1-4 | 1-1 | 1-1 | 4-1 | 0-0 | 3-1 | 1-2 | 0-4 | 3-1 | 0-0 | 0-2 | 0-1 | 2-1 | 1-3 | 2-3 | 2-3 | 1-1 | 1-1 | X | 0-4 |
| 20 Wimborne Town | 1-1 | 0-0 | 1-1 | 2-1 | 6-1 | 5-2 | 0-1 | 0-0 | 5-0 | 9-0 | 4-1 | 4-1 | 3-3 | 3-1 | 1-0 | 3-3 | 6-0 | 1-1 | 2-0 | X |

## JEWSON WESSEX LEAGUE CUP 1998-99

**FIRST ROUND**

| | | | | | | | |
|---|---|---|---|---|---|---|---|
| Portsmouth RN | v | Bemerton Hth Harl. | 2-4 | B.A.T. | v | AFC Totton | 2-4 |
| Gosport Borough | v | Eastleigh | 1-13 | Whitchurch United | v | AFC Newbury | 2-5 |

**SECOND ROUND** (Aggregate Results)

| | | | | | | | |
|---|---|---|---|---|---|---|---|
| Bournemouth* | v | AFC Newbury | 3-3 | Brockenhurst | v | Lymington & NM | 1-10 |
| Christchurch | v | AFC Totton | 5-2 | Downton | v | Cowes Sports | 2-4 |
| Fareham Town | v | Eastleigh | 3-10 | Hamble ASCC ** | v | East Cowes Vics | 2-2 |
| Moneyfields | v | Bemerton Hth Harl. | 4-2 | Wimborne Town | v | Thatcham Town | 6-2 |

**QUARTER FINAL** (Aggregate Results)

| | | | | | | | |
|---|---|---|---|---|---|---|---|
| Eastleigh | v | Bournemouth | 6-1 | Lymington & NM | v | Wimborne Town | 4-0 |
| Cowes Sports | v | Hamble ASCC | 4-1 | Moneyfields | v | Christchurch | 6-2 |

**SEMI FINAL** (Aggregate Results)

| | | | | | | |
|---|---|---|---|---|---|---|
| Lymington & NM | v | Moneyfields | 4-0 | Cowes Sports* | v | Eastleigh |

**FINAL**

COWES SPORTS v LYMINGTON & NM 0*0 at Eastleigh FC, Cowes Sports won on penalties
* Won on away goals rule ** Won on penalties

# ROLL OF HONOUR 1998-99

| | |
|---|---|
| Champions, Jewson Wessex League | Lymington & New Milton FC |
| Runners Up | Thatcham Town FC |
| Winners, Jewson Wessex League Cup | Cowes Sports FC |
| Runners Up | Lymington & New Milton FC |
| Champions, Combination League | Weymouth FC |
| Runners Up | Moneyfields FC |
| Winners, Combination Cup | Bemerton Heath Harlequins FC |
| Runners Up | Gosport Borough FC |
| Winners, Russell Cotes Cup | AFC Totton |
| Runners Up | Moneyfields FC |
| Winners, Basingstoke Senior Cup | AFC Newbury |
| Winners, Hungerford Challenge Cup | Whitchurch Utd FC |
| Runners Up, Portsmouth Senior Cup | Horndean FC |
| Winners, Best Programmed Award | Brockenhurst FC |
| Winners, Fair Play Award | Bemerton Heath Harlequins FC |

## DAILY ECHO MANAGER OF THE MONTH AWARD

| August | Jackie Stuart | Thatcham Town FC | January | Derek Binns | Lymington & New Milton |
|---|---|---|---|---|---|
| September | Ray Collins | Christchurch FC | February | Derek Holloway | Eastleigh FC |
| October | Roger Sherwood | Eastleigh FC | March | George Wain | Moneyfields FC |
| November | Ray Collins | Christchurch FC | April & May | Jackie Stuart | Thatcham Town FC |
| December | Alex Pike | Wimborne Town FC | | | |

## LEADING GOALSCORERS 1998-99

| FIRST DIVISION | | Lge | Cup | Total | COMBINATION DIVISION | | Lge | Cup | Total |
|---|---|---|---|---|---|---|---|---|---|
| Kevin Marsh | Moneyfields | 24 | 3 | 27 | Jamie Glasson | Bemerton HH | 28 | 4 | 32 |
| Matthew Town | Christchurch | 21 | 2 | 23 | Alex Davis | Brockenhurst | 23 | 6 | 29 |
| Lee Dent | Cowes Sports | 19 | 1 | 20 | Rob Morant | BAT | 22 | 3 | 25 |
| Alan Bundy | Eastleigh | 14 | 6 | 20 | Chris Reader | Weymouth | 23 | 1 | 24 |

Lymington & New Milton who started the season at a new ground with the amalgamation of two clubs but beat the Jewson Eastern Champions, Wroxham, in the Jewson Champions Challenge.
They also went on to win the Jewson Wessex League again and reached the quarter final of the FA Carlsberg Vase
Photo: Andrew Chitty

# A.F.C. NEWBURY

**Secretary:** Keith Simmonds, Foxes Retreat, Worlds End, Beedon, Berks. RG14 1PP
Tel: 01635 247151

**Ground:** Faraday Road, Newbury, Berks.  Tel: 01635 523222

**Directions:** A34 to Robin Hood roundabout, then A4 towards Reading. Right at lights
after 100 yards into Faraday Road. Ground at end of road.

**Previous:** **Names:** Newbury Town

### FACT FILE

Colours: Green & white/white/green & white
Change: Red & white/red/red & white
Midweek Matches: Tuesday

### CLUB PERSONNEL

Chairman:  Steve Hartley Tel: 01488
683783(H) 0118 9304030 (W)

# A.F.C. TOTTON

**Secretary:** Mrs Sheila Benfield, 35 Fishers Road, Totton, Southampton SO40 9HW
Tel: 01703 865421

**GROUND:** Testwood Park, Testwood Place, Totton, Southampton Tel:01703 868981
**Directions:** 5 mins walk from Totton station. Turn off r'bout in Totton centre into Library
Rd, then 1st left & 2nd rd
Capacity: 2,500  Seats: 200   Cover: 250    Floodlights: Yes   Club Shop: No
Clubhouse: Open for matches and training sessions. Burgers, sandwiches, tea,coffee,
biscuits etc available

**HONOURS :** Hampshire League x2

**PREVIOUS :** **League:** Hants 1886-1986
**Name:** Totton FC until merger with Totton Athletic 1979
**Grounds:** Downs Park; Mayfield Park

**RECORD:** **Gate:** 600 v Windsor & Eton, F.A. Cup 4th Qual Rd 82-83

### FACT FILE

Founded:  1886
Nickname:  Stags
Sponsors:  Cap'n Cod
Colours:  All blue
Change colours:  Yellow,navy blue,yellow
Midweek Matches:  Tuesday
Programme:  30 pages 50p

### CLUB PERSONNEL

Chairman:  Bob Devoy
Vice Chairman: P Maiden
President: D Maton
Manager: Ian Robinson
Press Officer: P Chilcott (01703 860453)

# ANDOVER

**Secretary:** Chris Jeremy, 23 Stubbs Court, Artists Way, Andover, Hants SP10 3QR
Tel: 01264 361973
**Ground:** Portway Stadium, West Portway Ind. Estate, Andover SP10 3LF Tel: 01264 333052
**Directions:** From the Andover By-pass A303 follow signs to Portway Ind. estate. On exiting the
A303 turn right at r/about & over bridge, bear off left at next mini r/about and after 150yds turn
right onto estate. Straight on until you enter Hopkinson Way, ground on left 4-500 yds
Capacity: 3,000    Cover: 250    Seats: 250    Floodlights: Yes
Clubhouse: Open matchdays & private function    Club Shop: No    Metal Badges: Yes

**HONOURS**    Wessex Lg R-up 94-95, Western Lg R-up 69-70 70-71; Hants Lg 13-14 24-
25 33-34 44-45 48-49 50-51 61-62 (R-up 42-43), Northern Div 13-14, Div 2 R-up 37-38;
Salisbury & Dist Lg 1894-95 95-96 96-97 99-1900 03-04 07-08 12-13; Hants Sen Cup 48-49 50-
51 55-56 64-65; Russell Cotes Cup 23-24 31-32 37-38 44-45 52-53 58-59 60-61 61-62;
Pickfords Cup 50-51; Hants Interm Cup 59-60 60-61; Hants Junior Cup 19-20 (R-up 1894-95
1910-11 12-13)

**PREVIOUS**    **Leagues:** Salisbury & D.; Hants 1896-98, 1899-1901, 02-62; Southern
1898-99,1971-93 98-99; Western 1962-71; Wessex Lge 93-98

**BEST SEASON**   FA Cup: 1st Rd 62-63, 0-1 v Gillingham
**FA Trophy:** 3rd Qual Rd 69-70, 70-71
**FA Vase:** 4th Rd 94-95, 1-3 v Falmouth Town (A)

### FACT FILE

Founded: 1883
Nickname: The Lions
Colours: Red & black/black/red
Change cols: Black & white/whitek/black
Midweek Matches: Tuesday
Reserve Team's League: None
Programme: 50 pages  50p

### CLUB PERSONNEL

Chairman: Ken Cunningham-Brown
President: R Coleman
Manager: Ken Cunningham-Brown
Asst Manager: Mike Burford
Physio: Chris Burford

# B.A.T. SPORTS

**Secretary:** Mike Geddes,     Tel: 01703 337460 (H), 01703 793420 (W) 0589 614158(M)
39 Pacific Close, Victoria Quay, Ocean Village,Southampton, SO14 3 TX

**Ground:** BAT Sports Ground, Southern Gdns, off Ringwood Road, Totton Tel: 01703 862143

**Directions:** Into centre of Totton, proceed up Ringwood Rd past small r'bout,2nd left into
Southern Gardens. Half mile from Totton (BR), bus X2(Southampton-Bournemouth)

**Capacity:** 3,000     Seats: 150     Cover: 150     Floodlights: Yes

**Clubhouse:** Normal licensing hrs, all day for members' sports facilities. Hot & cold snacks

**BEST SEASON**     **FA Vase:** 2nd Rd 96-97

### FACT FILE
Founded: 1925
Colours: All b lue
Change: Red & black/red/red
Midweek Matches: Tuesday
Programme: 20 pages, 30p

### CLUB PERSONNEL
Chairman: Ray Roberts
Manager: Ray Light & Dave Blandford

---

# BEMERTON HEATH HARLEQUINS

**Secretary:** A J Hardwick, 2 Ashley Rd, Salisbury, Wilts. SP2 7BZ Tel: 01722 333015

**Ground:** Western Way, Bemerton Heath, Salisbury, Wilts Tel: 01722 331925

**Directions:** Turn off A36 Salisbury-Bristol Rd at Skew Bridge (right turn if coming out of
Salisbury), 1st left into Pembroke Rd for half mile, 2nd left along Western Way -
ground quarter mile at end. 40 mins walk from Salisbury(BR) station.
Bus 351 or 352 from city centre stops at junction of Pembroke Rd/Western Way

**Capacity :** 2,000     Seats: 155     Cover: 350     Floodlights: Yes
**Clubhouse:** Yes

**HONOURS**     Wilts Snr Cup 92-93. Wilts Lg(3) as Bemerton Athletic

**PREVIOUS**     **Names:** Bemerton Athletic, Moon FC & Bemerton Boys; all merged in 1989
**Leagues:** Bem. Ath.: Salisbury. & Wilts Comb.
Moon: Salisbury. & Andover Sunday     Bem.Boys: Mid Wilts
**RECORD**     **Attendance:** 1,118 v Aldershot Town FA Cup 1st Qual Rd Aug 94
**Appearances:** Keith Richardson

### FACT FILE
Founded: May 1989
Nickname: Quins
Colours: Black & white/black/black & white
Change colours: Amberwhite/white
Midweek Matches: Tuesday
Programme: 32 pages, 50p

### CLUB PERSONNEL
Chairman: George Parker
President: Peter Say
Manager: Steve Slade
Ass.Manager: Kevin Franklyn
Physio: Andy Nash
Coach: Gary Cross

---

# BOURNEMOUTH

**Secretary:** Mrs Sandra Dominey, 26 Victoria Road, Parkstone, Poole, Dorset BH12 3BB
Tel: 01202 737859 (H) 01202 749584 (B)

**Ground:** Victoria Park, Namu Rd., Winton, Bournemouth, Dorset Tel: 01202 515123

**Directions:** Any bus to Wimborne Road, Winton. 2 miles from Bournemouth Central(BR)

**Capacity:**     3,000     Seats: 250     Cover: 250     Floodlights: Yes

**Clubhouse:** Open daily 7-11pm. Sandwiches & hot snacks available.     Club Shop: No

**HONOURS**     Hants Lg 13-13 21-22, B'mouth Snr Cup 66-67 89-90, Texaco F'lit Cup R-up 91-
92, Hants I'mediate Cup 49-50 69-70, Hants Yth Cup 54-55 57-58 67-68

**PREVIOUS**     **Leagues:** Hampshire  **Ground:** Dene Park 1888-90
**Names:** Bournemouth Rovers 1875-88; Bournemouth Dene Park 1888-90

**RECORD**     **Scorer:** B Head
**Fee Received:** £1,500 for Chike Onourah (Wimborne 93-94)

### FACT FILE
Founded: 1875
Nickname: Poppies
Sponsors: Chapel Carpets
Colours: All red
Change colours: All green
Midweek Matches: Tuesday
Reserves' League: Jewson Wessex Comb
Programme: 58 pages, 50p
Editor: Mark Willis
Local Press: Evening Echo
### CLUB PERSONNEL
Chairman: V C Dominey
Vice Chairman: J B Wood
President: D Nippard
Comm. Manager: Alex Pike
Press Officer: Mark Willis
Manager: Alex Pike
Asst Manager: Nick Jennings
Coach: Chris Weller
Physio: Irvin Brown

Whitchurch's Jason Dinham (left) and Paddy Rasmussen (East Cowes Vics) battle for possession          Photo: Francis Short

AFC NEWBURY: Back Row (L-R): Mick Cumming, Graig Angell, Glen Damen, Simon Wiltshire, Tony Thirlby, Stuart Wylie. Front Row: Neal Butler, Paul Hargood, Richard Sayer, Spencer Annetts, John Stephenson.          Photo: Alan Coomes

MONEYFIELDS: Back Row (L-R): Matthew Lafferty, Paul Brookes, Robbie Stokes, Neil Darnley, Richard Molyneux, Garfield Mitchell, Joe Long, Robert John. Front Row: Callum Cutler, Richard Warwick, Kevin Marsh, Nathan Wall, James Butlin.

# BROCKENHURST

**ecretary:** Paul Christopher, 31 Brookside Road, Bransgore, Christchurch, Dorset BH23 8NA
Tel: 01425 674084 (H)

**round:** Grigg Lane, Brockenhurst, Hants Tel: 01590 623544

**irections:** M27 Junc 1, A337 to Lyndhurst, round one-way system, A337 to Brockenhurst, turn ght at Carey's Manor Hotel into Grigg Lane, ground 200 yds on the right

apacity: 2,000    Seats: 200    Cover: 300    Floodlights: Yes

ubhouse: Every evening plus Tues, Sat & Sun lunchtimes

**ONOURS**    HampshireIntermediate Cup 61-62; Bournemouth Senior Cup 60-61; Hampshire Lg 75-76, R-up 73-74 79-80, Div 2 70-71 R-up 60-61, Div 3 59-60.

**REVIOUS**    **League:** Hampshire Lge 24-26  47-86

**EST SEASON**    **FA Amateur Cup:** 2nd Round 73-74
3-99 - Captain: Danny Husbands    P.o.Y.: Jason Ahmet    Top Scorer: Lee Jennings

### FACT FILE
Founded: 1898        Nickname: The Badgers
Sponsor: Drew Smith Builders
Colours: Blue & white/blue/blue
Change colours: Red & white/red/red
Midweek Matches: Tuesday
Reserves League: Wessex Comb
Programme: 34 pages, 50p,
Editor/Press Officer: Paul Christopher

### CLUB PERSONNEL
Chairman: Colin Rickman
President: Mike Kimber
Vice Chairman: Graham Cobb
Manager: Phil Janes
Asst. Mgr: M Cobb    Res Mgr: G Price
Physio: Alan Butters

# CHRISTCHURCH

**ecretary:** Mrs D Page, 87 The Albany, Manor Road, Bournemouth BH1 3EJ Tel: 01202 551977

**round:** Christchurch Sporting Club, Hurn Bridge, Avon Causeway, ChristchurchTel: 01202 473792

**irections:** A338 from Ringwood, turn off signed Hurn Airport on left. Before Airport use mini undabout & take exit signed Sopley & ground is immed. on the right. 3 miles Christchurch (BR)

Capacity: 2,000    Seats: 215    Cover: 265    Floodlights: Yes

**lubhouse:** Normal pub hours. Cooked food at lunchtimes

**ONOURS**    Hants Jnr Cup 1892-93 1911-12 20-21; Hants Int. Cup 86-87; Pickford Cup 91; Hants Lg Div 2 37-38 47-48 85-86 (Div 3 56-57); B'mouth Snr Cup (5) 56-57 59-60 67-70; B'mouth Page-Croft Cup 94-95

**REVIOUS**    **League:** Hampshire    **Ground:** Barrack Rd Recreation Grd (>1984)

**ECORD**    **Appearances** : John Haynes

ayers progressing: Jody Craddock (Cambridge Utd 93), Dan West (Aston Villa94)

### FACT FILE
Founded: 1885
Nickname: Priory
Sponsors: Franklin Transport
Colours: All royal blue (white trim)
Change colours: All Red
Midweek Matches: Tuesday
Programme: 16 pages, 50p
Editor: Phil Old
98-99 - P.o.Y.: Phil Langdown & Neil Massie

### CLUB PERSONNEL
Chairman: Robin Osborne
Vice Chairmen: Mick Ryan & Derek Nippard
President: Dennis James
Press Officer: Dennis James
Manager: Ray Collins
Physio: Graham Brown

# COWES SPORTS

**ecretary:** W G Murray, 247 Arctic Road, Cowes, Isle of Wight PO31 7PJ Tel: 01983 294445

**round:** Westwood Park, Reynolds Close, off Park Rd, Cowes, Isle of Wight Tel: 01983 293793

**irections:** Take Park Road out of Cowes centre. Reynolds Close is a right turn half mile up hill

apacity: 1395    Seats: Yes    Cover: Stand    Floodlights: Yes

ubhouse: Yes            Club Shop: No

**ONOURS**    Hampshire League 93-94,  Isle of Wight Gold Cup 94-95,Wessex Lg.Cup 98-9

**REVIOUS**    **League:** Hampshire (pre-1994)

**EST SEASON**    **FA Cup:** 4th Qual. Rd replay 57-58, 1-4 v Trowbridge (A) after 2-2
**FA Vase:** 4th Rd97-988

### FACT FILE
Founded:
Colours: Blue & white stripes,black,blue
Change colours:Amber & Black
Midweek Fixtures: Wednesday
Reserves' Lge: I.O.W. Saturday Lg.
Programme Editor: Roger Hendeg

### CLUB PERSONNEL
President: Ada Leigh
Chairman: Ray Sleep
Manager: Derek Ohren

# DOWNTON

**Secretary:** Brian Trent 21 Fison Walk, Bishopdown, Salisbury, Wilts SP1 3JF Tel: 01722 323097

**Ground:** Brian Whitehead Sports Ground, Wick Lane, Downton Tel: 01725 512162

**Directions:** Travel south from Salisbury on A338 for about 7 miles. Turn right intoWick Lane, and the ground is a qtr mile on left

| Capacity: 1600 | Seats: 250 | Cover: Nil | Floodlights: Yes |
|---|---|---|---|

**Clubhouse:** Bar with kitchen facilities     Club Shop: No

**HONOURS**    Wilts Sen Cup 79-80 80-81, (R-up 55-56 91-92 94-95); Wilts Jun Cup 49-50; Bournemouth Sen Lge 60 61 62 64 65 67 68, Sen Lge Cup 61-62 63-64 66-67, Cup 62-63 79-80; Wessex Lge Cup 95-96; Wessex Comb Cup (R-up 95-96); RussellCotes Cup 95-96; Hayward Cup 64-65

**PREVIOUS**     **League:** Bournemouth, Hants (pre-1993)

**FACT FILE**

Founded: 1905
Nickname: The Robins
Sponsor: Lex Vauxhall Salisbury
Colours: Red/white/red
Change colours:Yellow/blue/yellow
Midweek Matchday: Tuesday
Programme: Yes
Editor: James Blake

**CLUB PERSONNEL**

Chairman: James Blake
President: R Tanner
Manager: M Savage
Coach: C Huxford
Physio: T Ship

# EAST COWES VICTORIA ATHLETIC

**Secretary:** Lee Bray, 2 Benton Close, Est Cowes I.O.W. Tel: 01983 298657

**Ground:** Beatrice Avenue Ground, East Cowes, I.O.W. Tel: 01938 297165

**Directions:** From the ferry: 1 mile from town centre on lower main road to Newport or Ryde near Whippingham Church adjacent to Osborne Middle School

| Capacity: 4,000 | Seats: 250 | Cover: 400 | Floodlights: Yes |
|---|---|---|---|

**Clubhouse:** Open most evenings & matchdays. Crisps etc available **Club Shop:** No

**HONOURS**    (as East Cowes Vics pre-'68): Wessex Lg Cup 87-88, IOW Senior Gold Cup 79-80 81-82 82-83 83-84 84-85 85-86 88-89, Hants Lg 85-86 86-87 (Div 2 52-53 82-83, Div 3 63-64 71-72, Div 3 West 47-48), IOW Lg x9, (Div 2 x3, Div 3 x2, Comb. x3), IOW Chal. Cup x13, IOW Mem. Cup x5, Brooklyn Cup 86-87 87-88 89-90 91-92, IOW Charity Cup 23-24 25-26, IOW Centenary Cup 89-90 91-92

**PREVIOUS**    **Names:** E. Cowes Victoria (founded 1888) merged with E. Cowes Athletic in 1968 **Leagues:** (E.C. Vics): I.o.W. 1898-19 21-47; Hants 14-21 47-87

**RECORD**    **Attendance:** 2,000 v Poole Town, FA Cup 1954    **Appearances** : Joe Reed **Win** : 9-0 v Brading Town (A), Hampshire Lg 86-87 **Defeat** : 0-10 v Andover (A), Wessex Lg 94-95

**FACT FILE**

Founded: 1968
Nickname: Vics
Sponsors: Bishops Insurance
Colours: Red & white/black/black
Change colours: Yellow/blue/blue
Midweek Matches: Tuesday
Reserves ' League: I.o.W. Lge
Programme: 40 pages, 50p
Editor: Alan Green (01983 296069)

**CLUB PERSONNEL**

Chairman: George Stanton
Vice-Chairman/Gen Manager: Steve Stay
Manager: Dale Young
Coach: Pete Young
Physios: Mike Reed & Kevin Marsay

# EASTLEIGH

**Secretary:** Miss Andrea Vowles, 28 Franklyn Avenue, Sholing, Southampton, Hants SO19 8AP Tel No: 01703 447802

**Ground:** 'Ten Acres', Stoneham Lane, North Stoneham, Eastleigh SO50 -9HT Tel: 01703 613361

**Directions:** M27, Jct 5, to r'bout - exit marked Stoneham Lane. Carry on to r'bout & come back down Stoneham Lane, turning right opp. Concord Club. Ground 400 yds on left. Southampton Parkway (BR) 3/4 mile. Bus 48 (S'hampton-Winchester) to Stoneham Church stop

Capacity: 4,300    Seats: 175    Cover: 210    Floodlights: Yes    Club Shop: No

Clubhouse: 11-11 Mon-Sat plus Sundays. Extensive function facilities. All catering undertaken

**HONOURS**    Wessex Lg Cup R-up 91-92, Hants Lg Div 2 69-70 (R-up 54-55 60-61 62-63 64-65(Res), Div 3(W) 50-51 53-54 70-71(Res), Comb.(Res) (3) R-up 96-Hants, Comb Cup (Res) 96-7,97-8 Midweek F'lit Cup 78-79, Soton Snr Lg(W) 49-50 (R-up 51-52(Res), Div 1 56- 57) 57- 58(Res)), Russell Cotes R-up 76-77 80-81 89-90,

**PREVIOUS**    **Leagues:** Southampton Jnr & Snr 46-59/ Hants 50-86 **Names:** Swaythling Ath. 46-73; Swaythling 73-80 **Grounds:** Southampton Common 46-47; Walnut Avenue, Swaythling 47-75

**BEST SEASON**    **FA Vase:** 4th Round 82-83,90-91, 94-95

**RECORDS**    **Gate:** 2,500 v Southampton, floodlight opener 30/9/75 **Scorer** : Johnny Williams, 177    **Appearances** : Ian Knight, 611 **Win:** 12-1 v Hythe & Dibden (H) 11/12/48    **Defeat:** 0-11 v Austin Spts (A) 1/1/47

**FACT FILE**

Founded: 1946
Nickname: None
Sponsors: Southern Exhaust Sedrvices
Colours: All blue
Change colours: White/white/white
Midweek matches: Tuesday
Programme: 32 pages with admission
Editor: Richard Vowles & Tommy Whale

**CLUB PERSONNEL**

Chairman: Roger Sherwood
President: Clive Wilson
Manager:Derek Holloway
Asst Manager: Derek Dempsey
Physio: Bert Wyatt

# JEWSON CHAMPIONS SHIELD
### Lymington & New Milton (Champions of Jewson Wessex League) 3
### Wroxham (Champions of Jewson Eastern League) 1

Top left: Wroxham keeper Ryan Lemmon pulls off the ultimate in fingertip saves.
Top right: The Jewson Champions Shield
Bottom left: Graham Kemp (right, Lymington & New Milton) and Mark Crowe (Wroxham) before the kick off to the Jewson Champions Shield.
Bottom right: Lymington's manager Derek Binns receives the winner's cheque from Mike Warner, Jewson Operations Director South.

# FAREHAM TOWN

**Secretary:** Malcolm Harper, 20 Hampton Grove, Catisfield, Fareham, Hants PO15 5NL
Tel: 01329 8413476 (H)  01329 844074 (Fax)  0410 689939 (M)

**Ground:** Cams Alders, Highfield Avenue, Fareham, Hants PO14 1JA Tel: 01329 231151

**Directions:** M27, J11, follow A27 towards Southampton. After passing Fareham station turn left at traffic lights (2nd left) into Redlands Ave.. Turn right at Redlands Inn then left into Highfields Ave.
Capacity: 5,500    Cover: 500    Seats: 450    Floodlights: Yes
**Clubhouse:** Open every evening except Sundays. Food available
**Club Shop:** Sells programmes, scarves & fanzines

| | |
|---|---|
| **HONOURS** | Hants Lg (8) 59-60 62-67 72-73 74-75 (R-up 55-56 60-61 67-68 71-72 76-77 78-79, Div 2 R-up 52-53, Eastern Div 24-25, Div 3 East 49-50), Hants Snr Cup 56-57 62-63 67-68 92-93, Russell Cotes Cup (6) 64-65 72-77, Gosport War Memorial Cup, SW Co's Cup (2), Pickford Cup (2), |
| **PREVIOUS** | **Leagues:** Portsmouth 47-49, Hants 49-79, Southern 79-98 |
| | **Name:** Fareham FC    **Ground:** Bath Lane |
| **BEST SEASON** | **FA Trophy:** Semi Final 86-87    **FA Amateur Cup:** 2nd Rd 63-64 66-67 73-74 |
| **FA Vase:** 1st Rd 98-99 | **FA Cup:** 1st Rd replay 88-89, 2-3 v Torquay U. (H) after 2-2 |
| **RECORDS** | **Attendance:** 2,650 v Wimbledon, FA Cup 1965. |
| | (at Southampton F.C.) 6,035 v Kidderminster H., FAT S-F  2nd leg 86-87 |
| | **Fee received:** £43,000 for David Leworthy (Spurs) |

**FACT FILE**
Formed: 1947
Nickname: The Town
Sponsors: Portsmouth Evening News
Colours: Red/whitered
Change colours: Whiteblack/black
Midweek matchday: Wednesday
Reserves' League: Hampshire Comb
Programme: 36 pages £1
Editor: Ian Tewson Tel. 01329 662624

**CLUB PERSONNEL**
Chairman: Chris Solen 01329 847784 (H)
01329 844111 (B)
Director of Football: John Green
President: Ken Atkins
General Manager: Tony Adams (01705 615931)
Press Officer: M Willis
Manager: Mark Chamberlain (01705 327527)
Physio: James McKay

# GOSPORT BOROUGH

**Secretary:** B V Cosgrave, 2 Cavanna Close, Rowner, Gosport PO13 0PE Tel: 01329314117
**Ground:** Privett Park, Privett Road, Gosport, Hants Tel: 01705 501042 (Office)
**Directions:** M27 Junct 11, A32 Fareham to Gosport. At Brockhurst r-about (about 3 miles) right into Military Rd passing thru H.M.S. Sultan, left into Privett Rd at next r-about, ground 300yds left signed 'Privett Park Enclosure'. 2 miles from Portsmouth Harbour (BR) or Fareham (BR)
Capacity: 4,500    Cover: 500    Seats: 450    Floodlights: Yes    Club Shop: No
**Clubhouse:** Matchdays only - from 1.30 Sat., 6.30 Wed. Refreshment hut sells hot food & drinks
**HONOURS** Wessex Lg Cup 92-93, Southern Lg Div 1 South R-up 84-85, Hants Lg 45-46 76-77 77-78 (Div 3 (Res.) 70-71 75-76), Portsmouth Lg R-up 44-45, HantsSenior Cup 87-88, Russell Cotes Cup R-up 94-95, Hants Intermediate Cup 70-71, Portsmouth Senior Cup 61-62 69-70 70-71 94-95, South West Counties PrattenChallenge Cup 77-78
**BEST SEASON** **FA Trophy:** 1st Rd 88-89    **FA Amateur Cup:** 3rd Rd 47-48 66-67
**FA Vase:** 6th Rd rep 77-78    **FA Cup:** 4th Qual. Rd 80-81 (lost to Windsor & Eton)
**PREVIOUS** **Leagues:** Portsmouth 44-45; Hants 45-78; Southern 78-92
**Name:** Gosport Borough Athletic
**RECORD** **Attendance:** 4,770 v Pegasus, FA Amtr Cup 1951
**Scorer:** Richie Coulbert 192    **Appearances:** Tony Mahoney 764
**Win:** 14-0 v Cunliffe-Owen, Hampshire Lg Div 1 45-46
**Defeat:** 0-9 twice    v Newport, Hants Lg Div 1 47-48.
v Gloucester (A), SouthernLg Prem Div 89-90

**FACT FILE**
Founded: 1944
Nickname: The Boro'
Sponsors: Cars-R-Us
Colours: Yellow/blue/blue
Change colours: All red
Midweek matchday: Tuesday
Reserves ' League: Wessex Combination
Programme: 20 pages, 50p
Editor: Ian Hay (01329 314601)
Local Press: Portsmouth Evening News, Southampton Evening Echo

**CLUB PERSONNEL**
Chairman: JohnHawes
President: W J Adams
Manager: Barry Cook
Coaches: Dave Pitt & Dave Taviner
Physio: Dave Topliss

# HAMBLE AEROSTRUCTURES SPORTS & SOCIAL CLUB

| | |
|---|---|
| **Secretary:** | Richard Phippard, 198 Butts Road, Sholing, Southampton SO19 1BP Tel:01703 438413 |
| **Ground:** | Folland Park, Kings Avenue, Hamble.,Southampton SO31 4NF Tel: 01703 452173 |
| **Directions:** | M27 junction 8, then B3397 to Hamble. Half mile fromHamble (BR); turn right out of station, proceed for one mile then turn right before shops into Kings Avenue. Ground 1000 yards on right in works sports ground. |
| | Capacity: 1000    Seats: 150    Cover: 150    Floodlights: Yes |
| **Clubhouse:** | 300 capacity social club. Cricket & bowls |
| **HONOURS:** | Hampshire Lg Div 3 80-81 (Div 4 79-80), Hampshire Intermediate Cup 79-90, Southampton Senior Cup 84-85 86-87 91-92 |
| | As Hamble AS&SC: Jewson Wessex League Cup 97-98 |
| **PREVIOUS** | **Name:** Folland Sports (pre-1990), Aerostructures SSC 90-97 |
| **RECORD** | **Defeat:** 1-10 v Andover (A), Wessex League 93-94 |

**FACT FILE**
Colours: Maroon & Sky Blue
Change colours: Navy & white
Midweek Matches: Tuesdays & Wednesdays
Reserves ' League: Wessex Comb
Under 18 & Under16: So'ton Youth Lgs

**CLUB PERSONNEL**
President: Alistair Tritten
Chairman: Peter Mence
Assistant Secretary: Matthew Newbold
Treasurer:Barry Morse
SeniorManagers: Nigel Kent &Dick Donohoe

# LYMINGTON & NEW MILTON

**ecretary:** John Osey, 9 Samphire Close, Lymington, Hants SO41 9LR Tel: 01590 676995
**Ground:** Fawcett Fields,Christchurch Rd., New Milton,Hants  BH25 6QF (01425 6281910
**Directions:** M27 Jct 1 follow A337 to Lyndhurst one way system(A35) towards Christchurch. Left
■ Hinton Admiral at Cat & Fiddle.Follow Ringwood road ,then left at A337 roundabout to New
Milton. Ground one mile on left past Chewton Glen Hotel.
**Capacity:** 3,000    Seats: 262    Cover: 262    Floodlights: Yes
**Clubhouse:** Open seven days a week 11.0 am to 11.0 pm. Hot food and functions availab le
**HONOURS** Wessex Lg 92-93 96-97 97-98, 98-99 R-up 91-92 95-96, Wessex  Lg Cup 88-89, R-up
4-95, 98-99 Wessex Comb. 92-93, Hants Snr Cup R-up 89-90, Texaco Cup 91-92, Bournemouth
Snr Cup 92-93, R-up 96-97, Russell Cotes Cup 93-94 94-95, R-up91-92 92-93; Pickford Cup R-up
2-93. Jewson Champions Shield 98-99

**BEST SEASON**    **FA Cup:** 3rd Qual. Rd 92-93, 0-1 v Cheltenham T. (H)
            **FA Vase:** 98-99 Quarter Final, 1-3 v Taunton Town (A)
**PREVIOUS**    **Names:** Lymington Town (until 1988 merger with Wellworthy Ath.),
            AFC Lymington 88-98 (until merger with New Milton Town)
        **Ground:** Ampress Ground (Wellworthy Ath.), until 1988 merger
**RECORD**    **Attendance:** 2,900 v Karen Mills Memorial Day 12.3.95
        **Scorer:** Darren Pitter 197    **Appearances:** Graham Kemp 322
        **Win:** 11-1 v Romsey Town (H), Wessex League 9/11/92
        **Defeat:** 0-8 v Basingstoke Town (A), Hampshire Senior Cup 10/4/90

## FACT FILE

Founded as Lymington & New Milton: 1998
Nickname: Linnets
Sponsors: Sewards
Colours: Red & bluek/blue/red
Change colours: Yellow & green/green/green
Midweek Matches: Tuesday
Reserves ' League: Wessex Comb

Programme: 48 pages, £1.00
Editor/Press Officer: Richard Milbery

## CLUB PERSONNEL

Chairman: Ian Snook
V - Chairmen: Richard Millbery/Bob Philpott
President: Jack Holliday & Ted Goodyer

Manager: Derek Binns
Coach: Alan Farrar

---

# MONEYFIELDS

**Secretary:**    Peter Shires, 242 Grafton Street, Mile End, Portsmouth.
        Tel: 01705 645813(H)  01705 359571 (W) 07957 77921(M)

**Ground:**    Moneyfields Sports Ground, Moneyfields Avenue, Copnor, Portsmouth,Hants.
        Tel: 01705 665260

        Capacity:   1,500    Seats: No    Cover: 100    Floodlights: No

**Directions:**    From Southampton & the west - travel east on M27 onto A27. Take exit marked
        Southsea A2030. (From east take the same exit). Head south along A2030 exit
        and turn right into Tangier Road (4th right). Follow until`Tangiers' PH & take next
        right into Folkestone Road. Carry  on into Martin Rd & club is in front of you.

**Clubhouse:** No        **Club Shop**: No

## FACT FILE

Founded:
Colours: Yellow/blue/blue.
Change:  Green & white/ green/green.
Midweek Fixtures: Wednesday
Programme:
Editor:

## CLUB PERSONNEL

Chairman:David Jupe
Tel: 01705 359571 (H)

---

# PORTSMOUTH ROYAL NAVY

**Secretary:**    Roy Newman  8 Kimpton Close, Lee-on-Solent, Hants PO13 8JY
        Tel: 01705 799198 (H)
**Ground:**    Victory Stadium, USSG Burnaby Road, West Portsmouth.
        Tel: 01705 724235, (Clubhouse 01705 291660)

**Directions:**    From Portsmouth Harbour (BR), turn right onto The Hard, pass underthe rail
        bridge and turn left into Park Road, after approx 200yards take 1st right into
        Burnaby Road. Entrance to ground 100 mtrs on the right

**Capacity:** 1,500    Seats: 500    Cover: 500    Floodlights: Yes    Club Shop: No

**Clubhouse:** Open 1.5hrs before k.o. & 2hrs after game on matchdays or by arrangement only

**HONOURS**    Russell-Cotes Cup 67-68; Basingstoke Lg Div 2; Hants Lge Div 2 67-6877-78 80-81

**PREVIOUS**    **Leagues:** Hampshire 62-86

## FACT FILE
Formed: 1962
Nickname: Sailors
Colours: All blue
Change colours: Red/black/red
Midweek Matches: 1st X1 Mon., Res Tues.
Reserves ' League: Wessex Combination
Programme: 50p    Editor: Roy Newman

1998-99
Captain: Paul Willetts
Top Scorer: Fraser Quirke
P.O.Y.: Pat Mulholland

## CLUB PERSONNEL
Chairman: Dave Bridger
Press Officer: Jim Molloy

Manager: Vince Hall
Physio: A Hylands

# THATCHAM TOWN

**Football Secretary:** Peter Woodage, 5 Elm Grove, Thatcham, Berks. RG18 3DJ
Tel: 01635 861937

**Ground:** Waterside Park, Crookham Rd, Thatcham, Berks Tel: 01635 862016

Capacity: 3,000    Seats: 300    Cover: 300    Floodlights: Yes

**Directions:** M4 junc 13, take A34 to Newbury, then right onto A4 towards London.
InThatcham turn right to the railway station. The ground is on the left
beyond the station -  2 minutes walk.From South A34 to Newbury,take A339 to Basingstoke,left to
Thatcham then left again down Crookham Rd. Ground on right just before station

**Clubhouse:** Open every evening & lunchtimes    **Club Shop:** Yes

**HONOURS** Wessex Lg 95-96,R-up 98-99, Cup 90-91 91-92 94-95 96-97, (R-up twice)

**PREVIOUS** Ground: Station Road 46-52; Lancaster Close 52-92

**BEST SEASON** FA Cup: 4th Qual Rd 96-97

**RECORD** **Attendnace:** 1,400 v Aldershot, FA Vase

**FACT FILE**

Founded: 1895
Sponsors: Panasonic Gsm Mobile Phones
Colours: White with blue pinstripe,blue,blue
Change colours:Red,black,black
Midweek Matches: Tuesday
Programme: 28 pages, 50p
Editor: Dave Ware

**CLUB PERSONNEL**

Chairman: Phil Holdway
President:
General Secretary: John Haines
Press Officer: Phil Holdway (*01635 867803)
Manager: Jackie Stuart
Coach:Neal Baker

---

# WHITCHURCH UNITED

**Secretary:** Dave McGuire, 35 Salcombe Close, Chandlers Ford, Southampton. SO534PJ
Tel: 01703 261637 (H) 0831299230 (W & M)

**Ground:** Longmeadow, Winchester Road, Whitchurch Tel: 01256 892493

**Directions:** From Whitchurch (BR) station; turn left after Railway Inn, follow road to end, turn
right into main road, arriving in town turn left alongWinchester Road. Ground three
quarters of a mile on left

**Capacity:** Seats: 200    Cover: Yes    Floodlights: Yes

**Clubhouse:** Hot food on matchdays. Sports hall with squash courts and indoor bowling green

**PREVIOUS** **Leagues:** Hampshire (pre-1992)

**BEST SEASON** **FA Vase:** Extra-Preliminary Rd 93-94, 1-3 v Peppard (H)

**FACT FILE**

Founded:
Colours:  Red & black/black/black
Change colours:  White/blue/blue.
Midweek Matches:  Tuesday
Programme:  24 pages

**CLUB PERSONNEL**

Chairman:  Phil Dawson Tel: 01256 896777

---

# WIMBORNE TOWN

**Secretary:** Stephen Churchill, 40 Dales Drive, Wimborne, Dorset BH21 2JT
Tel: 01202 889806 (H), 01202 564835 (B), 07957 235334 (Mob)

**Ground:** The Cuthbury, Cowgrove Road, Wimborne, Dorset BH21 4EL Tel: 01202 884821

Capacity: 3,250    Seats: 275    Cover: 150    Floodlights: Yes

**Directions:** Wimborne to Blandford Road, behind Victoria Hospital

**Clubhouse:** Eves 7-11, Sat noon-11, Sun 12-6 Bar & Skittle alley    **Club Shop:** Yes

**HONOURS** FA Vase 91-92; Wessex Lg 91-92 93-94 (R-up 92-93 96-97), Lg Cup 93-94 (R-up 90-
91 95-96); Dorset Lg Div 1 80-81 81-82 (R-up 38-39 72-73), Div 2 31-32 34-35 36-37(R-up 35-36),
Lg Cup R-up (4) 72-74 80-82; Dorset Snr Cup 91-92 96-97, (R-up 80-82 85-86 98-99); Mark
Frowde Cup 92-93 94-95; Dorset Snr Amateur Cup 36-37 63-64;Dorset Jnr Cup 31-32 36-37 (R-
up 13-14 34-35); Dorset Minor Cup 12-13; Dorset Jnr Amateur Cup (3) 34-36 38-39; Bankes
Charity Cup 89-90 94-95 95-96, TexacoF/Light Cup 90-91

**PREVIOUS** **Leagues:** Dorset Lge, Dorset Comb, Western 81-86

**BEST SEASON** FA Vase: Winners 91-92    FA Cup: 1st Rd Proper 82-83

**RECORDS** **Attendance:** 3,250 v Bamberbridge FA Vase Semi-Final 28/3/92
**Goalscorer:** Jason Lovell    **Win** (Wessex Lg): 9-0 v Eastl Cowes Vics 99-99
**Appearances:** Nicky Bridle    **Defeat** (Wessex Lg): 2-6 v Thatcham Town 91-92

**FACT FILE**
Founded: 1878    Nickname: Magpies
Sponsors: Nicolas O'Hara
Colours: Black & white stripes/black/black
Change colours: Yellow/green/yellow
Midweek Matches: Tuesday
Reserve League: Wessex Combination
Programme: 24 pages, 50p
Editor: Secretary
**1998-99** - Captain: Dan West
Top Scorer: Darren Elmes
P.o.Y.: Michael White

**CLUB PERSONNEL**
Chairman: Nicholas O'Hara
President: Brian Maidment
Press Officer: Secretary
Manager: Alex Pike
Asst. Mgr: Mike Buxton
Coach: Alan Smith
Physio: Irvin Brown

# HAMPSHIRE FOOTBALL LEAGUE

Established: 1896

**Chairman:** G Cox

**Secretary:** J Moody, 13 Tadfield Crescent, Romsey, Hampshire SO51 5AN
Tel: 01794 500672

The last season of the Millennium was one of the busiest I can remember and for the League's administrators there was certainly no close season. During the summer and throughout the season we were grappling with the problem of the formation of the Premier Division with meetings and correspondence with the Football Association, the Wessex League Joint Liaison Committee and the Senior Leagues Joint Liaison Committee. Ian Craig must be congratulated on all the work he has put into this project.

Lymington Town were admitted to the league as a new club and they were joined by Amesbury Town and PFC Durrington, both from the Salisbury League, and Wicor Mill from the Portsmouth League. Unfortunately, PFC Durrington resigned before half the season was over and we also lost Netley Central Sports Reserves, after the Club was involved in a series of disciplinary cases brought by the Hampshire Football Association. New Milton FC resigned from the League at the end of the season after completing all their fixtures. The Club, formed in 1898 and disbanded in 1999, were members of the Hampshire League from 1924 to 1936, and 1946 to date. At the time of writing the League could lose two more Clubs, Ordnance Survey and Queens Keep, who have lost their joint ground in Shirley due to the parent company putting it up for sale. We hope they can find League-standard accommodation elsewhere in Southampton. Next season we welcome Micheldever Village FC and we hope they enjoy their stay with us. Sadly there was no promotion and relegation between ourselves and the Jewson Wessex League this season due mainly to our top three Clubs not having the ground grading standards required by that league. All Clubs should note that their grounds must be of a JWL standard by 1st April for any consideration to be given to promotion.

It was very satisfying that two of our four divisions were not decided until the last week of the season and the other two were only won in the previous week. The Division One title seemed to be between Alton Town, Poole Town and New Street for most of the season, but late runs by Colden Common and Blackfield & Langley pressed the top three at the end. Our Division One Trophy was presented on the field of play to Alton Town by Chairman Geoff Cox.

The Division Two crown seemed destined for Petersfield Town until a fantastic late run by Paulsgrove (winning their last ten games) saw them snatch it away. Paulsgrove must be congratulated on their achievement as they had to play at least three games a week during the last few weeks of the season. The Division Two Championship Cup was presented by Vice Chairman Ron Chandler. The Club's backlog of fixtures was due mainly to their cup runs and they capped a brilliant season by making it a League and Cup double by beating Wessex Combination side Horndean Reserves in the Final of the Portsmouth Senior Cup. The sides drew 2-2 in the first game, which couldn't go to extra time because the floodlights at the final venue, Moneyfield Sports, had to be turned off by 10pm!

It looked as if the Division Three Championship would go to one of our new Clubs, Amesbury Town or Lymington Town, but when Clanfield had caught up with their backlog of fixtures, again due to cup commitments, they ran out Champions by a mile. The Championship Trophy was presented by Grounds Officer Ian Craig. The Club made it a very successful season by doubling this up with the Hampshire Intermediate Cup, which they won at Fareham Town FC, defeating BTC from the Southampton Premier League by 3-1.

Colden Common Reserves dominated the Combination Division and they actually clinched the title on their own ground with a splendid 9-1 romp against Petersfield Town Reserves, who not only secured a second season undefeated at home, but notched up their 100th goal of the season. Secretary John Moody presented the Championship Trophy and got soaked in champagne for his troubles!

It was perhaps not surprising that two of our top three in Division One reached the Trophyman League Cup Final, but Poole Town were rather fortunate in reaching their second successive final as they had previously lost to Alton Town by 4-3 in a cracking match at Holt in an earlier round. However, it was subsequently found that Alton had played an ineligible player and Poole were reinstated. A simple administrative error denied Alton Town from going for a League and Cup double. Their plight serves as a warning to all our Clubs whose reserves play in any League other than the Hampshire Combination; make sure you sign any players playing in our Cups on the Hampshire League registration forms. The Final was played at Cams Alders and we thank Fareham Town for their hospitality once again. Poole justified their place in the Final by defeating New Street 1-0 despite playing with 10 men for over an hour due to their goalkeeper being sent off. Poole became the first Club to retain the Cup.

Like the senior final, the Trophyman Combination Cup Final was a close-fought game with Hythe & Dibden Reserves defeating Fleet Spurs Reserves 1-0 at the By-Pass Ground. Hythe, too, justified their win by beating red-hot favourites Colden Common Reserves in the semi-final thus denying the Club the chance of a League and Cup double. Our thanks to Romsey Town FC for hosting this final and Amesbury Town, Lymington Town, Blackfield & Langley and Romsey Town for holding the semi-finals of our Cups. Our thanks also go to Trophyman who once again sponsored our cup competitions and Geoff Cox presented both trophies.

The League's Officers and Committee members were once again involved in nearly 100 meetings of one sort or another throughout the season. A major innovation was the monthly Bulletin, the League Telephone Information Line and our Web Page, and thanks go to Tony Spencer and John Royston-Ford for the tremendous amount of work they have put in on those projects.

John Moody, League Secretary

# FINAL LEAGUE TABLES 1998-99

## DIVISION ONE

| | P | W | D | L | F | A | Pts |
|---|---|---|---|---|---|---|---|
| Alton Town | 36 | 28 | 6 | 2 | 117 | 28 | 90 |
| Poole Town | 36 | 27 | 6 | 3 | 124 | 42 | 87 |
| Colden Common | 36 | 21 | 6 | 9 | 54 | 38 | 69 |
| Blackfield & Langley | 36 | 18 | 3 | 15 | 89 | 81 | 57 |
| New Street | 36 | 17 | 5 | 14 | 83 | 67 | 56 |
| Brading Town | 36 | 15 | 9 | 12 | 66 | 51 | 54 |
| Fleet Spurs | 36 | 15 | 8 | 13 | 73 | 53 | 53 |
| Stockbridge | 36 | 14 | 9 | 13 | 67 | 66 | 51 |
| Fleetlands | 36 | 15 | 6 | 15 | 71 | 78 | 51 |
| Liss Athletic | 36 | 15 | 5 | 16 | 63 | 57 | 50 |
| Locksheath | 36 | 15 | 5 | 16 | 66 | 64 | 50 |
| Mayflower West Wight | 36 | 14 | 7 | 15 | 54 | 61 | 49 |
| Horndean | 36 | 12 | 9 | 15 | 67 | 71 | 45 |
| Pirelli General | 36 | 12 | 7 | 17 | 60 | 66 | 43 |
| Hayling United | 36 | 11 | 6 | 19 | 40 | 60 | 39 |
| Vosper Thornycroft | 36 | 11 | 6 | 19 | 56 | 77 | 39 |
| Winchester City | 36 | 10 | 6 | 20 | 47 | 86 | 36 |
| Bishopstoke Social | 36 | 8 | 5 | 23 | 37 | 106 | 29 |
| Romsey Town | 36 | 5 | 4 | 27 | 40 | 122 | 19 |

## DIVISION TWO

| | P | W | D | L | F | A | Pts |
|---|---|---|---|---|---|---|---|
| Paulsgrove | 34 | 23 | 6 | 5 | 94 | 30 | 75 |
| Petersfield Town | 34 | 20 | 7 | 7 | 76 | 39 | 67 |
| Winchester Castle | 34 | 17 | 7 | 10 | 70 | 51 | 58 |
| Co-op Sports | 34 | 15 | 11 | 8 | 65 | 58 | 56 |
| Esso Fawley | 34 | 16 | 7 | 11 | 60 | 45 | 55 |
| AFC Basingstoke | 34 | 16 | 7 | 11 | 56 | 44 | 55 |
| Yateley Green -2 | 34 | 14 | 8 | 12 | 66 | 64 | 48 |
| Otterbourne | 34 | 13 | 7 | 14 | 75 | 65 | 46 |
| Tadley | 34 | 13 | 7 | 14 | 64 | 64 | 46 |
| Milford & Milton | 34 | 13 | 7 | 14 | 60 | 69 | 46 |
| Hythe & Dibden | 34 | 12 | 9 | 13 | 57 | 61 | 45 |
| AC Delco | 34 | 12 | 8 | 14 | 58 | 58 | 44 |
| Verwood Town | 34 | 12 | 8 | 14 | 54 | 65 | 44 |
| Overton United | 34 | 12 | 7 | 15 | 56 | 67 | 43 |
| Hilsea | 34 | 11 | 6 | 17 | 70 | 75 | 39 |
| Queens Keep | 34 | 9 | 9 | 16 | 54 | 76 | 36 |
| Hamble Club | 34 | 6 | 5 | 23 | 52 | 94 | 23 |
| Netley Central Sports | 34 | 5 | 8 | 21 | 37 | 99 | 23 |

## DIVISION ONE RESULTS CHART 1998-99

| | | 1 | 2 | 3 | 4 | 5 | 6 | 7 | 8 | 9 | 10 | 11 | 12 | 13 | 14 | 15 | 16 | 17 | 18 | 19 |
|---|---|---|---|---|---|---|---|---|---|---|---|---|---|---|---|---|---|---|---|---|
| 1 | Alton Town | X | 1-4 | 1-1 | 5-2 | 4-0 | 4-0 | 4-2 | 3-0 | 1-1 | 7-1 | 8-1 | 0-0 | 5-2 | 3-1 | 7-2 | 1-0 | 6-1 | 4-0 | 8-1 |
| 2 | Bishopstoke Social | 0-5 | X | 1-4 | 2-3 | 0-2 | 3-6 | 0-4 | 1-1 | 3-5 | 1-0 | 0-4 | 1-2 | 1-1 | 1-0 | 1-3 | 1-0 | 1-5 | 0-6 | 3-3 |
| 3 | Blackfield & Langley | 0-5 | 6-0 | X | 1-1 | 1-2 | 4-3 | 2-3 | 1-3 | 5-1 | 1-6 | 5-1 | 4-2 | 2-7 | 3-1 | 1-2 | 2-4 | 4-1 | 3-0 | 1-3 |
| 4 | Brading Town | 3-4 | 0-2 | 0-1 | X | 0-1 | 7-1 | 1-0 | 2-0 | 3-2 | 2-1 | 1-0 | 0-0 | 3-1 | 2-2 | 2-2 | 8-0 | 3-0 | 3-4 | 1-0 |
| 5 | Colden Common | 0-2 | 0-2 | 2-0 | 2-2 | X | 2-1 | 4-0 | 1-0 | 3-1 | 2-1 | 3-1 | 3-0 | 3-3 | 2-1 | 0-2 | 0-0 | 2-0 | 3-2 | 2-0 |
| 6 | Fleetlands | 1-1 | 3-2 | 5-2 | 2-2 | 0-1 | X | 2-1 | 0-3 | 1-1 | 0-0 | 0-2 | 1-3 | 3-0 | 6-1 | 0-6 | 3-0 | 2-1 | 1-4 | 0-0 |
| 7 | Fleet Spurs | 1-1 | 10-0 | 0-1 | 1-1 | 0-1 | 3-1 | X | 1-0 | 3-0 | 1-2 | 3-0 | 1-0 | 2-2 | 2-2 | 1-2 | 4-2 | 3-3 | 4-1 | 2-0 |
| 8 | Hayling United | 1-0 | 0-1 | 3-4 | 2-0 | 1-0 | 1-2 | 2-2 | X | 2-1 | 2-0 | 2-2 | 0-1 | 1-0 | 2-0 | 1-4 | 2-2 | 1-1 | 2-2 | 0-1 |
| 9 | Horndean | 0-2 | 0-4 | 4-0 | 0-4 | 1-2 | 2-3 | 1-1 | 3-1 | X | 1-4 | 5-3 | 2-2 | 2-4 | 1-0 | 0-2 | 5-2 | 3-3 | 6-0 | 1-1 |
| 10 | Liss Athletic | 0-4 | 0-1 | 2-1 | 2-0 | 0-0 | 2-1 | 3-2 | 2-1 | 2-0 | X | 0-2 | 3-1 | 4-1 | 1-3 | 0-3 | 7-1 | 1-1 | 1-1 | 7-1 |
| 11 | Locksheath | 1-2 | 0-0 | 1-2 | 3-1 | 1-0 | 1-2 | 1-1 | 1-0 | 0-0 | 4-2 | X | 2-3 | 1-2 | 3-1 | 2-2 | 3-0 | 3-0 | 1-0 | 4-1 |
| 12 | Mayflower W Wight | 1-2 | 3-1 | 3-3 | 0-1 | 3-1 | 1-2 | 3-2 | 2-1 | 2-3 | 2-1 | 2-0 | X | 4-3 | 2-2 | 1-1 | 1-0 | 0-0 | 3-0 | 1-2 |
| 13 | New Street | 0-1 | 6-0 | 1-2 | 2-1 | 0-0 | 6-3 | 0-1 | 6-0 | 2-3 | 2-1 | 2-1 | 4-1 | X | 1-3 | 2-1 | 4-1 | 2-4 | 0-4 | 3-0 |
| 14 | Pirelli General | 1-2 | 3-0 | 3-1 | 1-0 | 0-2 | 4-5 | 2-0 | 4-0 | 3-3 | 2-0 | 0-3 | 1-2 | 0-1 | X | 0-4 | 6-1 | 1-1 | 1-2 | 2-0 |
| 15 | Poole Town | 1-0 | 8-0 | 4-3 | 5-1 | 2-0 | 2-2 | 3-1 | 5-0 | 1-1 | 0-2 | 4-3 | 4-0 | 3-1 | 3-3 | X | 7-0 | 7-0 | 4-1 | 4-2 |
| 16 | Romsey Town | 0-4 | 3-1 | 3-7 | 1-1 | 3-3 | 0-5 | 1-3 | 0-3 | 1-2 | 0-1 | 0-6 | 3-1 | 1-2 | 5-2 | 0-9 | X | 1-5 | 0-5 | 1-2 |
| 17 | Stockbrige | 0-1 | 3-0 | 2-4 | 1-2 | 2-3 | 2-1 | 4-2 | 3-1 | 1-0 | 2-1 | 3-0 | 3-0 | 1-1 | 2-3 | 2-3 | 2-0 | X | 2-0 | 1-1 |
| 18 | Vosper Thornycroft | 1-1 | 1-1 | 0-2 | 0-0 | 0-2 | 3-0 | 0-4 | 0-1 | 0-4 | 2-2 | 1-4 | 2-1 | 2-4 | 0-1 | 1-5 | 4-0 | 1-3 | X | 4-3 |
| 19 | Winchester City | 1-5 | 2-1 | 1-5 | 0-3 | 2-0 | 1-3 | 1-2 | 2-0 | 0-2 | 2-1 | 6-1 | 2-1 | 2-5 | 0-0 | 1-4 | 0-4 | 2-2 | 1-2 | X |

## TROPHYMAN LEAGUE CUP 1998-99

**QUARTER FINALS**

| Amesbury Town | v | Colden Common | 1*3 | Brading Town | v | Vosper Thorneycroft | 1-2 |
|---|---|---|---|---|---|---|---|
| New Street | v | Fleet Spurs | 7-3 | Poole Town | v | Alton Town | 3-4 |

**SEMI FINALS**

| New Street | v | Colden Common | 3-2 | Poole Town | v | Vosper Thorneycroft | 5-1 |
|---|---|---|---|---|---|---|---|

**FINAL**

| Poole Town | v | New Street | 1-0 | at Fareham Town |
|---|---|---|---|---|

## TROPHYMAN COMBINATION CUP 1998-99

**QUARTER FINALS**

| Clanfield Reserves | v | Fleet Spurs Reserves | 4-5 | Colden Common Rs | v | Paulsgrove Res | 2-1 |
|---|---|---|---|---|---|---|---|
| Hythe & Dibden Res | v | Netley Central Spts Rs | 4*2 | Overton United Rs | v | Pirelli General Res | 3-0 |

**SEMI FINALS**

| Colden Common Res | v | Hythe & Dibden Res | 0-1 | Overton Utd Res | v | Fleet Spurs Res | 0-3 |
|---|---|---|---|---|---|---|---|

**FINAL**

| Hythe & Dibden Res | v | Fleet Spurs Res | 1-0 | at Romsey Town |
|---|---|---|---|---|

## AFC ALDERMASTON
Secretary: G Daw, 58 Portway, Baughurst, Tadley, Hants. RG26 5PE
Tel: 0118 981 1270
Ground: AWRE Aldermaston Recreation Society
Colours: All blue

## AFC BASINGSTOKE
Secretary: T Purnell, 1 Byfleet Avenue, OLd Basing, Basingstoke,
Hants RG24 7HD (01256 23239)
Ground: War Memorial Park, Crossborough Hill, Basingstoke, Hants
Colours: Blue & black/black/black

## ALTON TOWN
Secretary: A J M Hillman, 19a Beechwood Rd, Alton, Hants GU34 1RL
(0142087103)
Ground: Bass Spts Ground, Anstey Rd, Alton (01420 82465)
Colours: Black & red/black/black
Midweek home matchday: Any

## AMESBURY TOWN
Secretary: Peter Taylor, Virginia House, Coldharbour, Amesbury, Wilts.
SP4 7AH  Tel: 01980 623212
Ground: Recreation Ground, Amesbury
Colours: Blue/white/blue

## BLACKFIELD & LANGLEY
Secretary: Ian Hore, 5 Foxhayes Lane, Blackfield, Southampton, Hants
SO45 2QD (01703 893325)
Ground: Gang Warily Rec., Newlands Rd, Blackfield, Southampton,
Hants (01703 893603)
Colours: All Green
Midweek home matchday: Wednesday

## BISHOPS WALTHAM TOWN
Secretary: N Bailey, 46 Clayland Rd., Bishops Waltham, Southampton
SO32 1BH Tel: 01489 894888
Ground: priory Park, Southampton
Colours: Red & black/black/red

## BRADING TOWN
Secretary: Mick Edmondston, Seawinds, Nunwell St., Sandown.I.O.W.
PO36 9DE(01983 404770)
Ground: Vicarage Lane, Brading, Isle of Wight (01983 405217)
Cols: All red

## COLDEN COMMON
Secretary: M.Budden, 44 Orchard Close, Colden Common,
Winchester,Hampshire.SO21 1ST (01962 713813)
Ground: Colden Common Recreation Ground, Main Road, Colden
Common (01962712365)
Colours: Red & white/black/red
Midweek home matchday: Wednesday

## ESSO (FAWLEY)
Secretary: Mr A Haws, 40 Hollybank Rd, Hythe, Southampton, Hants
SO45 5FQ (01703 843402)
Ground: Esso Recreation Club, Long Lane, Holbury, Southampton,
Hant (01705893750)
Colours: White/blue/red

## HAYLING UNITED
Secretary: Mrs S Westfield, 14 Harold Road, Hayling Island, Hants
PO11 9LT (01705 463305)
Ground: Hayling Park, Hayling Island, Hants
Colours: Red & navy/navy/navy
Midweek home matchday: Tuesday

## HORNDEAN
Secretary: Mrs Gladys Berry, 74 Five Heads Road, Horndean PO8 9NZ
(01705 591698)
Ground: Five Heads Park, Five Heads Road, Horndean (01705
591363)
Colours: Black & Red/black/black

## HYTHE & DIBDEN
Secretary: Mr A Moyst, 105 Hobart Drive, Hythe, Southampton, Hants
SO40 6FD (01703 847335)
Ground: Ewart Rec Ground, Jones Lane, Hythe, Southampton (01703
845264 -matchdays only)
Colours: Green/green/yellow

## LISS ATHLETIC
Secretary: W.E.Moseley, 3 Yew Tree Place, Liss, Hants. GU33 7ET
(01730 894631)
Ground: Newman Collard PF, Hill Brow Rd, Liss, Hants (01730
894022)
Colours: All Blue & White
Midweek home matchday: Thursday

## LOCKS HE ATH
Secretary: Michael Harrison, 30 Whitebeam Road, Hedge End,
Southampton, Hants.SO30 OPZ (01489 784470)
Ground: Locksheath Rec, Warsash Rd, Titchfield Common, Eastleigh
(01489600932)
Colours: Red/black/black

## LYMINGTON TOWN
Secretary: D Webb, 21 Keyhaven Rd., Milford on Sea, Hants. SO41
0QW  Tel: 01590 644629
Colours: Red/white/red & white

## NEW STREET
Secretary: Mrs F J Waterman, `Jorin Bay' 2 Pine Walk, Andover, Hants
SP10 3PW(01264 362751)
Ground: Foxcotte Park, Charlton Down, Andover.(01264 358358)
Colours: Green & black/black/green
Midweek home matchday: Tuesday or Wednesday

## PETERSFIELD TOWN
Secretary: M Nicholl, 49 Durford Rd, Petersfield, Hants GU31 4ER
(01730300518)
Ground: Love Lane, Petersfield, Hants (01730 233416)
Colours: Red & Black/Black/Black
Midweek Matches: Wednesday

## PIRELLI GENERAL
Secretary: Miss Bernice Fox 31 Spring Close, Fair Oak, Eastleigh,
Hants SO507BB (01703 693537)
Ground: Jubilee Spts Ground, Chestnut Ave., Eastleigh (01703
612721)
Colours: Blue & white/white/white
Midweek home matchday: Tuesday

## RINGWOOD TOWN
Secretary: Mrs Crewe, 278 Wyndham rd., Bournemoutht BH1 4QT
Tel: 01202 398975
Ground: Long Lane, Ringwood. Tel: 01425 473448
Colours: All red

## ROMSEY TOWN
Secretary: Andy Spreadbury, 13 Tanners Road, North Baddesley
Southampton SO52 9FD (01703 739034)
Ground: The By-Pass Ground, South Front, Romsey (01794 512003)
Colours: Yellow & black/black/black

## STOCKBRIDGE
Secretary: Graham Howard, 1 Moat Cottages, Longstock,Stockbridge, Hants.SO20 6EP (01264 810753)
Ground: The Recreation Ground, High Street, Stockbridge, Hants
Colours: All red

## VOSPER THORNYCROFT
Secretary: Peter Prin, 454 Bursledon Road, Sholing, Southampton, Hants. SO19 8QQ (01703 403829)
Ground: Vosper Thornycroft Spts Ground, Portsmouth Rd, Sholing, Southampton(01489 403829)
Colours: All royal

## WEST WIGHT MAYFLOWER
Secretary: Mr C J Papadatos, 5 Albion Close, Porchester, Fareham, Hants PO16 9EW (01329 510623)
Ground: Clarence Gardens, Southsea (01705 824246 - FAX 01705 727273)
Colours: Blue & black stripes/black/black

## HAMPSHIRE LEAGUE DIVISION ONE

## A.C. DELCO
Secretary: Brian Cook, 17 Hickory Gardens, West End, Southampton.SO30 3RN(01703 613334)
Ground: AC Delco Spts Ground, Stoneham Lane, Eastleigh (01703 613334)
Colours: Royal Blue & white stripes/black/blue
Change: Red & Black stripes/White/Black
Midweek home matchday: Wednesday

## BISHOPSTOKE SOCIAL
Secretary: Tony Boland, 34 Fryern Close, Chandlers Ford, Hants SO50 2LF (01703262763)
Ground: Chicken Hall Lane, Bishopstoke, Eastleigh, Hants (01860 612038)
Colours: Green & Black/Black/Black    Change: All Blue

## CLANFIELD

## CO-OP SPORTS

## FLEETLANDS
Secretary: David Bell, 72 White Hart Lane, Portchester, Hants. PO16 9BQ.(01705321781)
Ground: Lederle Lane, Gosport, Hants (01329 239723)
Colours: Red & black/white/white    Change: All white
Midweek home matchday: Any

## FLEET SPURS
Secretary: C R Filkins, 5 Byron Close, Fleet, Hants GU13 9QD (01252 627385)
Ground: Ancells Farm, Fleet, Hants
Colours: Red & black/black/red
Change: Blue or green or purple/turqu/white

## HILSEA
Secretary: Mr Terry Harwood, 147 Manners Rd, Southsea, Hants PO4 0BD (01705785140)
Ground: Portsmouth Sailing Centre, Eastern Rd, Portsmouth PO3 5LY (01705670119)
Colours: Yellow/blue/white    Change: Blue/blue/white

## ORDNANCE SURVEY

## OTTERBOURNE
Secretary: R J Broom, 249 Passfield Rd, Eastleigh, Hants SO5 5DE (01703328992)
Ground: Oakwood Park, off Oakwood Ave., Otterbourne (01962 714681)
Colours: Red/white/red & white    Change: Blue & white/blue/blue

## OVERTON UNITED
Secretary: Mrs A Wheeler, 3 Lordsfield Gardens, Overton, Hants RG25 2EW (01256771241)
Ground: Recreation Centre, Bridge Street, Overton (01256 770561)
Colours: Blue & white stripes/white/blue
Change: Green & purple/purple/purple
Midweek home matchday: Tuesday or Thursday

## PAULSGROVE
Secretary: S J Cox, 22 Alameda Road, Purbrook, Waterlooville, Hants. PO7 5HD (01705 785110)
Ground: The Grove Club, Marsden Rd (off Allaway Avenue), Paulsgrove, Portsmouth (01705 324102)
Colours: Red & black stripes/black/red
Change: Blue & white/blue/black
Midweek home matchday: Wednesday

## POOLE TOWN
Secretary: Bill Read, 15 Addison Close, Romsey, Hants SO51 7TL (01794 517991)
Ground: Petersham Lane, Gants Common, Holt, Wimborne, Dorset (01258 840379)
Colours: Red & white/red/white
Change Colours: Yellow & black/blue/yellow

## TADLEY TOWN
Secretary: Mike Miller, Meadow View, West Heath, Baughurst, Hants RG26 5LE(01256 850700)
Ground: The Green, Tadley, Hants
Cols: Blue & maroon stripes/maroon/maroon
Change: Yellow/blue/blue

## VERWOOD
Secretary: Mrs J A Fry, 19a Noon Hill Rd, Verwood, Dorset BH31 7DB (01202822826)
Ground: Pottern Park, Pottern Way, Verwood, Dorset
Colours: All red          Change: All blue
Midweek home matchday: Tuesday

## VOSPER THORNEYCROFT

## WINCHESTER CASTLE
Secretary: A J Rutter, 79 South Ham Road, Basingstoke, Hants RG22 6AA (01256842689)
Ground: Hants County Council Spts Ground, Petersfield Rd, Chilcomb, Winchester(01962 866989)
Colours: Red & black/black/red
Change: Blue & white/white/blue

## WINCHESTER CITY
Secretary: Geoffrey Cox, 9 Burnetts Gdns, Horton Heath, Eastleigh, Hants SO57BY (01703 693021)
Ground: Hillier Way, Abbotts Barton, Winchester (01962 863553)
Colours: Red & white/black/red
Change: White/green/green

## YATELEY GREEN
Secretary: Alan Baynes, 7 Borderside, Yateley, Camberley Surrey GU17 7LJ
Ground: Yateley Recreation Ground, Reading Road, Yateley, Camberley, Surrey
Colours: Green/black/black    Change: Red/black/black

---

**DIVISION TWO CLUBS**
AWBRIDGE, BASING ROVERS, BRAISHFIELD, BROUGHTON, COMPTON, FARNBOROUGH NORTH END, HAMBLE CLUB, HADLEIGH, HEDGE END, LAVERSTOKE & FORD, MICHELDEVER VILLAGE, QUEENS KEEP, NETLEY CENTRAL SPORTS, WICOR MILLS

# KEYLINE DORSET COMBINATION LEAGUE

**Founded: 1957**

**President:** M Ewings     **Chairman:** R E Maidment

**Secretary:** Geoff Theobald, 41 South Road, Corfe Mullen
Wimborne, Dorset BH21 3HZ   Tel: 01202 697994

The chase for League Championship honours proved to be a two horse race between Portland United and Parley Sports. Although Parley were twelve points clear at the turn of the year, Portland United were crowned Champions, for the first time since 1971, after winning their last game of the season. Hamworthy Engineering and Dorchester Town Reserves finished the season in third and fourth places respectively.

At the other end of the table, early in the season things looked bleak for Flight Refuelling who lost their first nine games, but recovered well to finish in eighth place. As the season progressed Sherborne Town found themselves in bottom place once again, but they also recovered well to pull away from the relegation zone leaving Shaftesbury FC poised for the drop into the Dorset League, only to be reprieved when last season's Champions, Sturminster Marshall FC, withdrew from the League due to financial problems.

The Combination Cup Final, played at Days Park, Swanage, in front of a crowd of between 400 and 500 people, was contested by Portland United and Parley Sports Football Clubs. The match saw Portland United win by three goals to nil to retain the Cup and complete their first League and Cup double.

The Representative squads under managers David Copeland - Sturminster Marshall FC (Senior and Intermediate) and Alan Elliott - Allendale FC (Under 21) performed well, the Seniors beating Wiltshire League by 1-0 at Warminster, the Intermediates losing 4-0 to the Bournemouth FA at Hurn Bridge and the Under 21s losing the Bournemouth FA by 3-2 also at Hurn Bridge.

Geoff Theobald, Hon Secretary

## FINAL LEAGUE TABLE 1998-99

| | P | W | D | L | F | A | Pts |
|---|---|---|---|---|---|---|---|
| Portland United | 36 | 30 | 3 | 3 | 106 | 25 | 93 |
| Parley Sports | 36 | 29 | 4 | 3 | 115 | 26 | 91 |
| Hamworthy Eng'ring* | 36 | 22 | 4 | 10 | 99 | 47 | 67 |
| Dorchester Town Res. | 36 | 16 | 11 | 9 | 81 | 42 | 59 |
| Bridport Res. | 36 | 16 | 7 | 13 | 56 | 46 | 55 |
| Blandford United* | 36 | 14 | 11 | 11 | 52 | 38 | 52 |
| Sturminster Newton Utd | 36 | 14 | 9 | 13 | 60 | 65 | 51 |
| Flight Refuelling | 36 | 15 | 5 | 16 | 60 | 63 | 50 |
| Bournemouth Sports* | 36 | 14 | 8 | 14 | 79 | 80 | 49 |
| Hamworthy United | 36 | 12 | 9 | 15 | 50 | 61 | 45 |
| Allendale | 36 | 13 | 4 | 19 | 60 | 78 | 43 |
| Gillingham Town* | 36 | 12 | 9 | 15 | 75 | 87 | 42 |
| Westland Sports | 36 | 11 | 8 | 17 | 67 | 79 | 41 |
| Weymouth Sports | 36 | 10 | 8 | 18 | 55 | 109 | 38 |
| Swanage Town & Herston | 36 | 9 | 10 | 17 | 44 | 64 | 37 |
| Sherborne Town | 36 | 10 | 6 | 20 | 35 | 67 | 36 |
| Sturminster Marshall | 36 | 10 | 5 | 21 | 39 | 77 | 35 |
| Wareham Rangers | 36 | 10 | 4 | 22 | 50 | 101 | 34 |
| Shaftesbury * | 36 | 8 | 9 | 19 | 38 | 66 | 30 |

* points deducted

## LEADING GOALSCORERS 1998-99

| | | | | | |
|---|---|---|---|---|---|
| Danny Gibbons | Hamworthy Engineering | 32 | Nick Preston | Portland United | 17 |
| Christian Chambers | Gillingham Town | 26 | Mark Gaskell | Hamworthy United | 17 |
| Paul Spence | Bournemouth Sports | 23 | Mick Greeno | Portland United | 16 |
| Derrent Blenman | Parley Sports | 20 | Stuart Pomeroy | Allendale | 15 |
| Simon Freak | Sturminster Newton | 19 | Keith Middleton | Dorchester Town | 15 |
| Lee Stebbings | Portland United | 19 | Darren Whyton | Portland United | 15 |
| Andy Turrell | Portland United | 19 | Paul Watts | Westland Sports | 14 |
| Paul Honeybun | Flight Refuelling | 18 | Matthew Dyer | Westland Sports | 14 |
| Kerion Wall | Parley Sports | 18 | Martin Hanmer | Blandford United | 14 |
| Dave Lane | Flight Refuelling | 18 | Jason Irvine | Westland Sports | 14 |
| Paul Holmes | Portland United | 17 | Andy Southern | Dorchester Town | 14 |
| Paul Dykes | Hamworthy United | 17 | Andy Hitchcock | Bridport | 14 |

# RESULTS CHART 1998-99

| | 1 | 2 | 3 | 4 | 5 | 6 | 7 | 8 | 9 | 10 | 11 | 12 | 13 | 14 | 15 | 16 | 17 | 18 | 19 |
|---|---|---|---|---|---|---|---|---|---|---|---|---|---|---|---|---|---|---|---|
| 1 Allendale | X | 0-1 | 2-1 | 0-3 | 0-3 | 3-0 | 4-2 | 0-3 | 2-2 | 1-3 | 0-5 | 1-2 | 1-0 | 4-1 | 6-3 | 1-4 | 3-0 | 3-2 | 2-2 |
| 2 Blandford United | 4-2 | X | 1-2 | 0-0 | 1-0 | 1-2 | 3-2 | 0-1 | 2-1 | 1-1 | 0-3 | 2-0 | 2-1 | 0-0 | 0-1 | 0-0 | 5-0 | 2-3 | 0-0 |
| 3 Bournemouth Sports | 2-3 | 3-1 | X | 2-1 | 1-1 | 1-2 | 2-2 | 2-8 | 2-2 | 2-7 | 1-3 | 3-0 | 8-0 | 3-0 | 2-4 | 3-3 | 3-2 | 1-2 | 2-1 |
| 4 Bridport | 1-0 | 1-0 | 2-0 | X | 0-0 | 0-3 | 1-1 | 2-0 | 4-0 | 0-3 | 1-1 | 3-1 | 2-0 | 3-0 | 0-1 | 2-1 | 1-2 | 1-2 | 1-2 |
| 5 Dorchester Town | 2-2 | 1-1 | 2-0 | 2-0 | X | 3-0 | 3-0 | 2-1 | 0-2 | 0-4 | 0-4 | 5-2 | 4-0 | 1-2 | 6-0 | 3-0 | 1-0 | 2-2 | 6-0 |
| 6 Flight Refuelling | 2-0 | 0-6 | 1-1 | 1-3 | 1-1 | X | 5-0 | 0-2 | 0-0 | 3-5 | 1-2 | 2-0 | 3-1 | 0-3 | 2-1 | 2-0 | 2-3 | 3-2 | 8-2 |
| 7 Gillingham Town | 3-3 | 3-0 | 5-2 | 0-2 | 3-3 | 2-4 | X | 2-4 | 2-0 | 1-3 | 1-3 | 5-1 | 3-1 | 0-3 | 0-0 | 1-4 | 4-3 | 2-1 | 2-2 |
| 8 Hamworthy Engineering | 5-1 | 0-2 | 4-1 | 3-2 | 1-2 | 3-1 | 7-1 | X | 2-1 | 1-1 | 1-5 | 3-1 | 5-0 | 0-1 | 5-1 | 2-1 | 2-2 | 3-0 | 8-0 |
| 9 Hamworthy United | 0-2 | 2-1 | 1-2 | 4-2 | 1-1 | 4-1 | 1-1 | 0-2 | X | 0-2 | 0-2 | 3-2 | 3-1 | 5-1 | 1-0 | 0-0 | 1-2 | 0-1 | 0-3 |
| 10 Parley Sports | 4-0 | 0-0 | 6-0 | 3-0 | 4-1 | 2-1 | 6-0 | 3-0 | 2-3 | X | 4-1 | 5-0 | 1-0 | 5-0 | 5-0 | 3-0 | 2-0 | 6-2 | 5-0 |
| 11 Portland United | 6-0 | 2-1 | 2-1 | 0-3 | 1-0 | 5-1 | 4-0 | 5-1 | 7-0 | 0-0 | X | 3-0 | 3-0 | 4-1 | 2-1 | 6-0 | 5-1 | 2-0 | 1-1 |
| 12 Shaftesbury | 2-1 | 1-3 | 1-1 | 0-0 | 1-1 | 0-3 | 3-1 | 1-0 | 4-1 | 0-1 | 0-3 | X | 0-3 | 0-1 | 2-2 | 0-1 | 0-1 | 3-1 | 2-2 |
| 13 Sherborne Town | 2-0 | 0-0 | 2-3 | 0-3 | 2-1 | 2-0 | 1-5 | 0-0 | 0-0 | 1-0 | 0-2 | 0-0 | X | 3-2 | 0-2 | 1-0 | 2-1 | 3-0 | 1-1 |
| 14 Sturminster Marshall | 0-3 | 2-6 | 0-1 | 1-1 | 2-2 | 0-1 | 1-3 | 1-1 | 1-0 | 0-2 | 0-1 | 0-4 | 3-2 | X | 2-4 | 2-1 | 0-2 | 3-1 | 0-1 |
| 15 Sturminster Newton | 2-0 | 1-1 | 1-1 | 2-2 | 0-4 | 0-2 | 3-3 | 1-3 | 1-1 | 4-3 | 3-0 | 1-1 | 0-1 | 4-2 | X | 2-0 | 0-1 | 1-1 | 2-0 |
| 16 Swanage & Herston | 0-2 | 0-0 | 2-2 | 0-1 | 0-0 | 0-0 | 0-5 | 1-0 | 2-2 | 0-1 | 0-5 | 0-1 | 0-0 | 2-0 | 2-5 | X | 5-2 | 2-0 | 7-2 |
| 17 Wareham Rangers | 3-2 | 1-2 | 2-4 | 1-3 | 1-8 | 1-0 | 2-2 | 0-* | 3-6 | 2-3 | 0-3 | 0-0 | 0-3 | 1-2 | 2-1 | 3-0 | X | 2-4 | 1-2 |
| 18 Westland Sports | 3-2 | 1-1 | 2-4 | 6-3 | 3-2 | 3-3 | 1-5 | 2-3 | 0-1 | 1-3 | 2-3 | 1-1 | 3-1 | 2-2 | 1-2 | 2-2 | 6-0 | X | 2-2 |
| 19 Weymouth Sports | 0-4 | 1-2 | 2-* | 4-2 | 1-8 | 1-0 | 1-3 | 2-4 | 1-2 | 1-7 | 0-3 | 3-2 | 4-1 | 4-0 | 1-4 | 3-2 | 3-3 | 0-2 | X |

# COMBINATION LEAGUE CUP 1998-99

## FIRST ROUND

| | | | |
|---|---|---|---|
| Sturminster Marshall | v | Weymouth Sports | 1-2 |
| Westland Sports | v | Wareham Rangers | 4-3 |
| Swanage T & Herst. | v | Bournemouth Sports | 3-0 |

## SECOND ROUND

| | | | |
|---|---|---|---|
| Allendale | v | Portland United | 1-4 |
| Bridport | v | Westland Sports | 2-0 |
| Gillingham Town | v | Sturminster Newton | 1-2 |
| Swanage T & Herston | v | Sherborne Town | 2-0 |
| Blandford United | v | Dorchester Town | 0-3 |
| Flight Refuelling | v | Parley Sports | 0-7 |
| Shaftesbury | v | Hamworthy Eng. | 0-4 |
| Weymouth Sports | v | Hamworthy United | 2-3 |

## THIRD ROUND

| | | | |
|---|---|---|---|
| Bridport | v | Parley Sports | 1-3 |
| Hamworthy United | v | Dorchester Town | 0-2 |
| Hamworthy Eng. | v | Swanage T & Herst | 4-1 |
| Portland United | v | Sturminster Newton | 6-2 |

## SEMI FINALS

| | | | |
|---|---|---|---|
| Parley Sports | v | Hamworthy Eng. | 4-2 |
| Portland United | v | Dorchester Town | 1-0 |

## FINAL

| | | | |
|---|---|---|---|
| PARLEY SPORTS | v | PORTLAND UNITED | 0-3 |

# TREVOR WILLIAMS FAIR PLAY TROPHY 1998-99

| | Cautions | Sent Off | Points |
|---|---|---|---|
| Allendale | 13 | 1 | 16 |
| Weymouth Sports | 17 | 1 | 20 |
| Blandford United | 20 | 1 | 23 |
| Wareham Rangers | 19 | 2 | 25 |
| Dorchester Town | 22 | 3 | 31 |
| Shaftesbury | 31 | - | 31 |
| Bournemouth Sports | 26 | 2 | 32 |
| Gillingham Town | 29 | 3 | 38 |
| Bridport | 27 | 4 | 39 |
| Parley Sports | 33 | 2 | 39 |

# ALLENDALE

**Chairman:** E Case (01202 887920 H, 01258 857191 B)

**Secretary:** Rod Pope, 51 Dalkeith Road, Corfe Mullen Wimborne, BH21 3PQ (01202602922 H, 01929 424601 B)

**Ground:** Redcotts Recreation Ground, School Lane, Wimborne

Colours: White/blue/blue    Change Colours: All red

# BLANDFORD UNITED

**Chairman:** M.Westwood
**Secretary:** Mrs Catherine Johnson, 37 Damory Street,Blandforf Forum, Dorset DT117EU (01258 455899)
**Ground:** Recreation Ground, Park Road, Blandford Forum, Dorset. (HQ Tel: 01258456374)
Cover: No        Clubhouse: No       Programme: Yes
Colours: All Royal Blue
Change colours: Green & white/ green/green & white

# BOURNEMOUTH SPORTS CLUB

**Chairman:** R.Mitchell

**Secretary:**Andy Carr 260 West Way, Broadstone, Poole Bh18 9L101202 871625 (H) 01020 402149 (W)
**Ground:** Chapel Gate, East Parley, Christchurch, Dorset BH23 6BD (01202 581933)
Cover: No        Clubhouse: Yes    Programme: Yes
Colours: Gold/black/gold    Change colours: All red

# BRIDPORT Reserves

**Chairman:** David Fowler
**Secretary:** Keith Morgan, 95 Orchard Crescent, Bridport DT6 5HA 01308 456142 (H)  01308 424 269 (W)
**Ground:** The Beehive, St Mary's Field, Bridport, Dorset (01308 423834)
Colours: Red & black/black/red & black
Change colours:All blue.

# DORCHESTER TOWN Reserves

**Chairman:** C E Clarke
**Secretary:** David Martin,7 Old Brickfields, Broadmayne DT2 8UX 01305 853400 (H) 07971 172795 (M)
**Ground:** The Avenue Stadium, Dorchester. (01305 262451)
Cover: Yes        Floodlights: Yes    Clubhouse: Yes
Programme: Yes
Colours: Black & white stripes/black/black
Change: All red.

# FLIGHT REFUELLING

**Chairman:** A Miles
**Secretary:** Harry W Doyle, 39 Towers Way, Corfe Mullen, Wimborne, BH21 3UA (01202 604640)
**Ground:** Merley Park, Merley, Wimborne, Dorset (01202 885773)
Cover: No        Clubhouse: Yes    Programme: Yes
Colours:Sky blue/navy blue/navyblue.
Change colours:Green & white hoops/white/white.

# GILLINGHAM TOWN

**Chairman:** E Murphy
**Secretary:** David J Ayles, 37 Sylvan Way, Bay Road, Gillingham SP8 4EQ (01747822065)
**Ground:** Hardings Lane, Gillingham (01747 823673)
Cover: Yes
Programme: Yes   Clubhouse: Yes
Colours: Tangerine/black/tangerine
Change colours: Yellow & green/green/green

# HAMWORTHY ENGINEERING

**Chairman:** M,Robson
**Secretary:** Ray Willis ,52 Heckford Road, Poole BH15 2LY (01202 773 290)
**Ground:** Hamworthy Rec. Club, Magna Rd, Canford Magna, Wimborne, Dorset BH21 3AE(01202 881922)
Cover: No        Clubhouse: Yes    Programme: No
Colours: All green.
Change colours: Blue & White stripes/blue/blue.

# HAMWORTHY UNITED

**Chairman:** D.Manuel
**Secretary:** Peter Gallop, 51A Symes Road, Hamworthy, Poole, Dorset BH15 4PR(01202 670792)
**Ground:** The County Ground, Blandford Close, Hamworthy, Poole, Dorset (01202674974)
Cover: Yes            Floodlights: Yes
Programme: Yes            Clubhouse: Yes
Colours: Yellow & Black stripes/black/black.
Change colours: Green & black stripes/black/black

# PARLEY SPORTS

**Chairman:** N.Coombes
**Secretary:** Mrs Pat Coombes,332 Christchurch Road, West Parley, Ferndown. BH22 8SN
**Ground:** Parley Sports Club, Christchurch, West Parley, Bournemouth, Dorset(01202 573345)
Cover: No            Clubhouse: Yes
Colours: Yellow/blue/blue
Change colours: Blue/white/blue.

# PORTLAND UNITED

**Chairman:** P.Laming
**Secretary:**David Naerger, 5 Three Yards Close, Portland Tel Nos: 01305 821553 (H) 01305 768888 (W)
**Ground:** New Grove Corner, Grove Road, Portland (01305 861489)
Cover: Yes        Clubhouse: Yes
Programme: Yes
Colours: All blue    Change colours: White/black/red

# SHAFTESBURY

**Chairman:** A P Humphries
**Secretary:** Ms Sue Crocker, 18 St.Rumbolds Road, Shaftesbury. SP7 8NE (01747 851986)
**Ground:** Cockrams, Coppice Street, Shaftesbury (01747 853990)
Cover: Yes        Floodlights: Yes    Clubhouse: Yes
Colours: Red & white stripes/red/red
Change colours: Yellow/black/black

## SHERBORNE TOWN

**Chairman:** F Henderson
**Secretary:** Mike Mock, 67 Yew TRe Close, Yeovil. BA20 2PB Tel Nos: 01935 426219 (H) 01935 703934 (W)
**Ground:** Raleigh Grove, The Terrace Playing Fields, Sherborne (01935 816110)
Cover: Yes        Clubhouse: Yes        Programme: Yes
Colours: White & black/black/black.
Change colours: Yellow/blue/yellow

## WESTLAND SPORTS

**Chairman:** M Murley
**Secretary:** Alan Fisher, c/o Westlands Sports & Social Club, Westbourne Grove, Yeovil. BA20 2DD (01935 474297 messages)
**Ground:** Westland Sports Ground, Westbourne Close, Yeovil (01935 703810)
Cover: No        Clubhouse: No        Programme: Yes
Colours: Red/Black/Black
C hange colours: Blue/white/red

## STURMINSTER NEWTON UNITED

**Chairman:** A.Stockley
**Secretary:** Richard Frear 44 Green Close, Sturminster Newton DT10 1BL (01258473036)
**Ground:** Barnetts Field, Honeymead Lane, Sturminster Newton, Dorset. (01258471406)
Cover: Yes        Clubhouse: No        Programme: Yes
Colours:Red & Black /blue/blue.
Change colours:Blue & Black/blue/blue.

## WEYMOUTH SPORTS

**Chairman:** A Burt
**Secretary:** Steve Walker, 48 Jestrys Avenue, Weymouth DT3 5NN (01305 813566)
**Ground:** Weymouth College, Cranford Ave., Weymouth, Dorset (01305 208859/208860)
Colours: Blue & amber stripes/blue/blue.
Change: Red/black/red
Prev. Lge: Dorset (champs 1993)

## SWANAGE TOWN & HERSTON

**Chairman:** Leonard Marsh        **President:** Mayor of Swanage
**Fixture Secretary:** Eric Webster, 24 James Day Mead, Ulwell Road, Swanage BH191NQ (01929 423522)
**Ground:** Days Park, off De Moulham Road, Swanage, Dorset (01929 424633)
Cover: Yes                Floodlights: Yes
Clubhouse: Yes            Programme: Yes
Colours: White/black/black    Change colours: All yellow & sky blue

## WINCHAMPTON UNITED

**Chairman:** A Wrixon

**Secretary:** Roger Hibberd, 373 Sopwith Crescent, Merley, Wimborne BH21 1XJ Tel: 01202 889226 (H) 07074 747990 (M)

**Ground:** Critchell Park, Winchampton, Wimborne. Tel: 01258 840986
Colours: Green & yellow/green/yellow
Change Colours: Blue & white/blue/blue

## WAREHAM RANGERS

**Chairman:** G.Hawkes
**Secretary:** Mrs Carol White, 18 Folly Lane, Wareham, Dorset BH20 4HH (01929551765)
**Ground:** Purbeck Sports Centre,Worgret Rd, Wareham, Dorset
Cover: No        Clubhouse: No        Programme: Yes
Colours: Amber & black/black/black
Change colours: All sky blue

NOW IN ITS RECORD 9TH YEAR OF PUBLICATION

# BRITAIN'S MOST POPULAR NATIONAL NON-LEAGUE FOOTBALL MONTHLY

# TEAM TALK

# SCREWFIX DIRECT WESTERN LEAGUE

**President:** Stan Priddle    **Chairman:** R J Webber

**Secretary:** M E Washer, 16 Heathfield Road, Nailsea, Bristol BS19 1EB
Tel: 01275 851314

## FINAL LEAGUE TABLES 1998-99

### PREMIER DIVISION

| | P | W | D | L | F | A | Pts |
|---|---|---|---|---|---|---|---|
| Taunton Town | 38 | 33 | 3 | 2 | 134 | 33 | 102 |
| Tiverton Town | 38 | 29 | 4 | 5 | 118 | 27 | 91 |
| Chippenham Town | 38 | 25 | 7 | 6 | 93 | 41 | 82 |
| Melksham Town | 38 | 20 | 10 | 8 | 73 | 44 | 70 |
| Paulton Rovers | 38 | 18 | 12 | 8 | 70 | 42 | 66 |
| Brislington | 38 | 18 | 10 | 10 | 74 | 44 | 64 |
| Yeovil Town Reserves | 38 | 18 | 4 | 16 | 70 | 66 | 58 |
| Bridport | 38 | 16 | 7 | 15 | 61 | 68 | 55 |
| Bridgwater Town | 38 | 15 | 9 | 14 | 68 | 51 | 54 |
| Backwell United | 38 | 15 | 7 | 16 | 56 | 48 | 52 |
| Mangotsfield United | 38 | 14 | 9 | 15 | 60 | 58 | 51 |
| Barnstaple Town | 38 | 14 | 8 | 16 | 72 | 55 | 50 |
| Bristol Manor Farm | 38 | 15 | 4 | 19 | 61 | 57 | 49 |
| Elmore | 38 | 14 | 6 | 18 | 68 | 82 | 48 |
| Bishop Sutton | 38 | 12 | 7 | 19 | 65 | 81 | 43 |
| Westbury United | 38 | 9 | 8 | 21 | 42 | 103 | 35 |
| Bideford | 38 | 10 | 1 | 27 | 40 | 108 | 31 |
| Odd Down | 38 | 5 | 15 | 18 | 44 | 86 | 30 |
| Keynsham Town | 38 | 6 | 7 | 25 | 33 | 99 | 25 |
| Calne Town | 38 | 3 | 4 | 31 | 34 | 143 | 13 |

### FIRST DIVISION

| | P | W | D | L | F | A | Pts |
|---|---|---|---|---|---|---|---|
| Minehead | 36 | 31 | 4 | 1 | 124 | 25 | 97 |
| Dawlish Town | 36 | 27 | 6 | 3 | 83 | 28 | 87 |
| Street | 36 | 27 | 4 | 5 | 85 | 36 | 85 |
| Devizes | 36 | 20 | 7 | 9 | 79 | 43 | 67 |
| Clyst Rovers | 36 | 21 | 4 | 11 | 76 | 51 | 67 |
| Wellington | 36 | 20 | 6 | 10 | 71 | 42 | 66 |
| Exmouth Town | 36 | 20 | 4 | 12 | 80 | 49 | 64 |
| Pewsey Vale | 36 | 18 | 4 | 14 | 72 | 46 | 58 |
| Corsham | 36 | 15 | 10 | 11 | 47 | 58 | 55 |
| Welton Rovers | 36 | 13 | 7 | 16 | 61 | 58 | 46 |
| Bitton | 36 | 12 | 9 | 15 | 67 | 59 | 45 |
| Larkhall Athletic | 36 | 13 | 5 | 18 | 51 | 65 | 44 |
| Ilfracombe Town | 36 | 12 | 7 | 17 | 61 | 71 | 43 |
| Torrington | 36 | 13 | 0 | 23 | 56 | 79 | 39 |
| Warminster Town | 36 | 9 | 3 | 24 | 40 | 79 | 30 |
| Chard Town | 36 | 9 | 2 | 25 | 49 | 102 | 29 |
| Frome Town | 36 | 7 | 5 | 24 | 44 | 102 | 26 |
| Glastonbury | 36 | 3 | 6 | 27 | 47 | 111 | 15 |
| Heavitree United | 36 | 4 | 3 | 29 | 31 | 120 | 15 |

Taunton Town's players celebrate after winning the Screwfix Direct Premier Division

# PREMIER DIVISION RESULTS CHART 1998-99

| | | 1 | 2 | 3 | 4 | 5 | 6 | 7 | 8 | 9 | 10 | 11 | 12 | 13 | 14 | 15 | 16 | 17 | 18 | 19 | 20 |
|---|---|---|---|---|---|---|---|---|---|---|---|---|---|---|---|---|---|---|---|---|---|
| 1 | Backwell Utd | X | 1-3 | 0-2 | 1-1 | 0-0 | 1-0 | 0-2 | 0-4 | 5-1 | 0-1 | 0-0 | 6-0 | 4-1 | 0-1 | 0-1 | 1-0 | 0-0 | 0-3 | 3-1 | 3-0 |
| 2 | Barnstaple Town | 2-5 | X | 3-0 | 11-4 | 3-0 | 5-1 | 3-1 | 1-0 | 1-1 | 0-1 | 1-1 | 5-0 | 0-1 | 3-1 | 1-1 | 1-1 | 1-2 | 0-2 | 6-1 | 1-2 |
| 3 | Bideford | 1-4 | 1-0 | X | 1-8 | 0-2 | 0-1 | 0-3 | 1-0 | 2-0 | 1-6 | 0-1 | 1-2 | 5-2 | 0-3 | 4-1 | 1-2 | 1-10 | 0-6 | 0-1 | 1-2 |
| 4 | Bishop Sutton | 2-1 | 0-3 | 2-1 | X | 1-2 | 0-1 | 3-3 | 1-2 | 1-1 | 1-1 | 5-2 | 3-1 | 0-2 | 0-1 | 5-3 | 1-2 | 4-2 | 1-2 | 1-2 | 2-3 |
| 5 | Bridgwater Town | 3-0 | 3-1 | 0-2 | 0-3 | X | 4-0 | 2-2 | 2-2 | 8-1 | 1-1 | 0-2 | 1-0 | 4-2 | 0-3 | 1-1 | 3-1 | 0-1 | 0-0 | 6-1 | 1-1 |
| 6 | Bridport | 1-0 | 3-1 | 2-3 | 2-2 | 3-1 | X | 1-1 | 0-6 | 3-0 | 3-3 | 2-2 | 3-1 | 2-2 | 1-3 | 2-2 | 1-2 | 1-0 | 2-1 | 4-1 | 1-4 |
| 7 | Brislington | 1-0 | 3-0 | 5-0 | 1-0 | 3-1 | 1-1 | X | 3-0 | 5-0 | 3-3 | 1-2 | 1-0 | 2-1 | 1-1 | 2-0 | 1-1 | 1-3 | 1-3 | 1-1 | 2-1 |
| 8 | Bristol Manor Fm | 1-2 | 2-1 | 5-2 | 0-0 | 0-3 | 0-1 | 0-2 | X | 3-2 | 1-2 | 4-2 | 2-1 | 4-0 | 0-2 | 3-0 | 1-2 | 0-1 | 1-2 | 1-1 | 2-0 |
| 9 | Calne Town | 1-3 | 1-2 | 1-1 | 4-2 | 0-3 | 0-3 | 0-7 | 1-0 | X | 0-5 | 1-3 | 2-3 | 0-3 | 0-4 | 2-2 | 0-3 | 0-6 | 1-7 | 1-3 | 3-2 |
| 10 | Chippenham Tn | 1-0 | 2-0 | 5-0 | 3-0 | 2-0 | 3-1 | 1-0 | 2-1 | 6-1 | X | 2-0 | 0-0 | 3-0 | 0-0 | 5-1 | 2-1 | 1-3 | 4-3 | 5-0 | 2-1 |
| 11 | Elmore | 0-4 | 2-1 | 3-4 | 0-1 | 3-1 | 1-2 | 3-1 | 0-3 | 3-2 | 2-4 | X | 2-2 | 1-0 | 2-2 | 3-0 | 0-2 | 2-3 | 1-4 | 10-1 | 2-0 |
| 12 | Keynsham Town | 0-1 | 0-0 | 2-0 | 0-2 | 1-4 | 1-6 | 1-4 | 1-1 | 3-2 | 1-5 | 0-6 | X | 0-1 | 0-3 | 2-2 | 0-1 | 0-0 | 0-4 | 1-2 | 2-4 |
| 13 | Mangotsfield Utd | 1-0 | 2-2 | 1-0 | 1-2 | 0-0 | 4-1 | 4-1 | 1-3 | 9-0 | 1-0 | 1-0 | 0-0 | X | 3-3 | 2-2 | 2-4 | 2-3 | 0-1 | 1-2 | 3-2 |
| 14 | Melksham Town | 1-1 | 0-1 | 3-1 | 4-0 | 2-1 | 0-2 | 1-3 | 3-1 | 3-2 | 1-0 | 3-1 | 6-1 | 0-0 | X | 3-0 | 1-1 | 1-3 | 1-1 | 3-0 | 2-4 |
| 15 | Odd Down | 1-1 | 1-0 | 2-0 | 0-0 | 1-4 | 2-3 | 0-0 | 2-1 | 5-3 | 1-1 | 0-2 | 1-2 | 2-3 | 1-1 | X | 1-1 | 1-4 | 0-4 | 0-1 | 2-5 |
| 16 | Paulton Rovers | 3-1 | 2-2 | 8-0 | 4-0 | 1-1 | 2-0 | 1-4 | 1-2 | 5-0 | 1-0 | 5-2 | 1-0 | 1-1 | 0-0 | 1-1 | X | 0-3 | 0-2 | 1-1 | 0-0 |
| 17 | Taunton Town | 4-1 | 1-1 | 4-2 | 3-0 | 3-1 | 4-1 | 1-0 | 3-1 | 7-0 | 4-2 | 10-0 | 8-0 | 3-2 | 6-0 | 4-0 | 4-0 | X | 1-0 | 2-1 | 3-0 |
| 18 | Tiverton Town | 3-5 | 4-0 | 5-0 | 5-1 | 2-0 | 2-0 | 3-1 | 6-0 | 4-0 | 6-1 | 5-0 | 5-2 | 1-0 | 2-0 | 7-1 | 0-0 | 1-2 | X | 6-0 | 2-0 |
| 19 | Westbury Utd | 0-0 | 1-6 | 1-2 | 2-4 | 1-5 | 1-0 | 0-0 | 1-3 | 4-0 | 1-5 | 1-1 | 0-3 | 0-1 | 1-4 | 1-1 | 1-5 | 2-6 | 1-1 | X | 3-2 |
| 20 | Yeovil Town | 1-2 | 1-0 | 2-0 | 4-2 | 1-0 | 2-0 | 2-1 | 2-1 | 4-0 | 1-3 | 4-1 | 1-0 | 0-0 | 1-3 | 2-2 | 1-4 | 3-7 | 0-3 | 2-0 | X |

## TOP GOALSCORERS 1998-99
(League matches only)

| | | |
|---|---|---|
| E Laight | Taunton Town | 42 |
| A Lynch | Taunton Town | 41 |
| J Charlesworth | Minehead (inc 6 for Dawlish) | 36 |
| P Everett | Tiverton | 27 |
| C Griffen | Chippenham Town (now with Swindon) | 27 |
| B Flippance | Pewsey Vale | 25 |
| N Woon | Minehead | 25 |
| G Morgan | Minehead | 24 |
| R Hancox | Dawlish | 23 |
| R Hope | Clyst | 22 |

## HIGHEST LEAGUE ATTENDANCES 1998-99

| | | | | |
|---|---|---|---|---|
| Tiverton Town | v | Taunton Town | 1647 | 27.02.99 |
| Taunton Town | v | Tiverton Town | 1065 | 10.10.98 |
| Elmore | v | Tiverton Town | 1043 | 02.04.99 |
| Chippenham Town | v | Melksham Town | 968 | 02.04.99 |
| Chippenham Town | v | Taunton Town | 731 | 13.02.99 |
| Tiverton Town | v | Calne Town | 670 | 27.03.99 |
| Bridgwater Town | v | Taunton Town | 642 | 28.12.98 |
| Tiverton Town | v | Chippenham Town | 579 | 11.11.98 |
| Tiverton Town | v | Elmore | 572 | 08.05.99 |
| Taunton Town | v | Bridgwater Town | 567 | 05.04.99 |
| Tiverton Town | v | Brislington | 504 | 16.01.99 |

## PREMIER DIVISION ATTENDANCES 1998-99

| | Aggregate | | Average Gate | | Gates over 200 | |
|---|---|---|---|---|---|---|
| | 1998-99 | (1997-98) | 1998-99 | (1997-98) | 1998-99 | (1997-98) |
| Backwell United | 1940 | 2126 | 102.1 | 112 | 1 | 1 |
| Barnstaple Town | 3004 | 2629 | 158.1 | 138 | 2 | 2 |
| Bideford | 1692 | 2022 | 89.05 | 106 | 2 | 2 |
| Bishop Sutton | 1966 | 1283 | 103.5 | 71 | 1 | 1 |
| Bridgwater Town | 4297 | 5244 | 226.15 | 276 | 5 | 14 |
| Bridport | 2861 | 3031 | 150.6 | 160 | 2 | 4 |
| Brislington | 1768 | 1334 | 93.05 | 70 | 1 | - |
| Bristol Manor Farm | 711 | 1307 | 37.42 | 69 | - | - |
| Calne Town | 1803 | 1707 | 94.9 | 90 | - | 1 |
| Chippenham Town | 5314 | 3241 | 279.9 | 171 | 11 | 5 |
| Elmore | 2960 | 2213 | 155.8 | 116 | 2 | 1 |
| Keynsham Town | 2519 | 2009 | 132 | 106 | 4 | 3 |
| Mangotsfield United | 3102 | 2966 | 163.26 | 156 | 6 | 4 |
| Melksham Town | 2674 | 3265 | 140.73 | 172 | 3 | 5 |
| Odd Down | 1043 | 957 | 54.9 | 50 | - | - |
| Paulton Rovers | 3473 | 3266 | 182.8 | 172 | 4 | 5 |
| Taunton Town | 8348 | 6175 | 439.36 | 325 | 19 | 18 |
| Tiverton Town | 9233 | 9108 | 485.94 | 428 | 19 | 19 |
| Westbury United | 1915 | 1924 | 100.8 | 101 | 1 | - |
| Yeovil Town | 2719 | 2550 | 143.1 | 142 | 2 | 3 |

# PAST RECORDS

## WESTERN FOOTBALL LEAGUE CHAMPIONS

| | | | |
|---|---|---|---|
| 1980-81 | Bridgwater Town | 1990-91 | Weston-super-Mare |
| 1981-82 | Bideford | 1991-92 | Clevedon Town |
| 1982-83 | Bideford | 1992-93 | Tiverton Town |
| 1983-84 | Exmouth Town | 1993-94 | Tiverton Town |
| 1984-85 | Saltash United | 1994-95 | Tiverton Town |
| 1985-86 | Exmouth Town | 1995-96 | Taunton Town |
| 1986-87 | Saltash United | 1996-97 | Tiverton Town |
| 1987-88 | Liskeard Athletic | 1997-98 | Tiverton Town |
| 1988-89 | Saltash United | 1998-99 | Taunton Town |
| 1989-90 | Taunton Town | | |

## WESTERN FOOTBALL LEAGUE FIRST DIVISION CHAMPIONS

| | | | |
|---|---|---|---|
| 1980-81 | Chippenham Town | 1990-91 | Minehead |
| 1981-82 | Shepton Mallet | 1991-92 | Westbury United |
| 1982-83 | Bristol Manor Farm | 1992-93 | Odd Down |
| 1983-84 | Bristol City Reserves | 1993-94 | Barnstaple Town |
| 1984-85 | Portway-Bristol | 1994-95 | Brislington |
| 1985-86 | Portway-Bristol | 1995-96 | Bridgwater Town |
| 1986-87 | Swanage Town & Herston | 1996-97 | Melksham Town |
| 1987-88 | Welton Rovers | 1997-98 | Bishop Sutton |
| 1988-89 | Larkhall Athletic | 1998-99 | Minehead |
| 1989-90 | Ottery St Mary | | |

## WESTERN FOOTBALL LEAGUE CHALLENGE CUP WINNERS

| | | | |
|---|---|---|---|
| 1954-55 | Poole Town | 1974-75 | Falmouth Town |
| 1955-56 | Salisbury City | 1975-76 | No competition |
| 1956-57 | Trowbridge Town | 1976-77 | Weston-Super-Mare |
| 1957-58 | Bridgwater Town | 1977-78 | Bridport |
| 1958-59 | Yeovil Town | 1978-79 | No competition |
| 1959-60 | Torquay United | 1979-80 | Frome Town |
| 1960-61 | Exeter City | 1980-81 | Dawlish Town |
| 1961-62 | Bristol City | 1981-82 | Bridgwater Town |
| 1962-65 | No competition | 1982-83 | Frome Town |
| 1965-66 | Glastonbury | 1983-84 | Dawlish Town |
| 1966-70 | No competition | 1984-85 | Bideford |
| 1970-71 | Bridport | 1985-86 | Portway-Bristol |
| 1971-72 | Bideford | 1986-87 | Saltash United |
| 1972-73 | Bridport | 1987-88 | Saltash United |
| 1973-74 | Mangotsfield United | | |

## LES PHILLIPS CHALLENGE CUP WINNERS

| | | | |
|---|---|---|---|
| 1988-89 | Exmouth Town | 1994-95 | Elmore |
| 1989-90 | Plymouth Argyle Reserves | 1995-96 | Tiverton Town |
| 1990-91 | Elmore | 1996-97 | Tiverton Town |
| 1991-92 | Plymouth Argyle Reserves | 1997-98 | Tiverton Town |
| 1992-93 | Tiverton Town | 1998-99 | Yeovil Town Reserves |
| 1993-94 | Tiverton Town | | |

# BARNSTAPLE TOWN

**Secretary:** David Cooke, 51 Walnut Way, Whiddon Valley, Barnstaple, Devon. EX32 7RF
Tel: 01271 326088
**Ground:** Mill Road, Barnstaple, North Devon Tel: 01271 343469
**Directions:** A361 towards Ilfracombe (from M5 Jct 26), in Barnstaple follow A361 Ilfracombe
signs, second left after crossing small bridge is Mill Road
**Capacity:** 5,000    **Seats:** 250    **Cover:** 1,000    **Floodlights:** Yes
**Clubhouse:** Full license. Bar snacks    **Club Shop:** Yes

**HONOURS** Western Lg 52-53 79-80 (R-up 80-81 81-82, Div 1 49-50 94-95, Merit Cup74-75
83-84 84-85, Comb. 92-93), Devon Professional Cup 62-63 64-65 67-68 69-70
71-73 (X2) 74-75 76-81 (X5), Devon Lg, Devon St Lukes Cup 87-88, Devon Snr
Cup 92-93, Devon Youth Cup 48-49 51-52

**PREVIOUS** **Leagues:** Nth Devon, Devon & Exeter, S. Western    **Name:** Pilton Yeo Vale
**Grounds:** Town Wharf (> 1920); Highfield Rd, Newport (> 35), Pilton Pk, Rock Pk

**RECORDS** **Attendance:** 6,200 v Bournemouth, FA Cup 1st Rd, 54    **Appearances:**
**Win:** 12-1 v Tavistock (H), FA Cup 3rd Qual. Rd 1954    Trevor Burnell
**Defeat:** 1-10 v Mangotsfield Utd (A), Western Lge Prem. Div. 90-91

**BEST SEASON** **FA Cup:** 1st Rd replay 51-52    **FA Vase:** 4th Rd 94-95
Players progressing: Len Pickard (Bristol R. 51), John Neale (Exeter72), Barrie Vassallo (Torquay
77), Ian Doyle (Bristol C. 78), Ryan Souter (Swindon 94), Jason Cadie (Reading 94)

**FACT FILE**
Founded: 1906
Nickname: Barum
Sponsors: Apex Sports
Colours: Red/black/white
Change colours: Yellow/white/white
Midweek Matches: Tuesday
Reserve League:
Programme: 50p
Programme Editor: David Priscott
Local Press: N. Devon Journal Herald
98-99 - Captain: Gary Bedler
P.o.Y.: Simon Langmead
Top Scorer: Andy Stevens

**CLUB PERSONNEL**
President: Wilf Harris
Chairman: John Cann
Manager: Mark Jenkins
Asst Manager: Stuart Smith
Physio: Amanda James

# BIDEFORD

**Secretary:** Kevin Tyrrell, 69 Laurel Ave., Bideford, devon EX39 3AZ Tel: 01237 4707747

**Ground:** The Sports Ground, Kingsley Road, Bideford Tel: 01237 474975

**Directions:** A361 for Bideford - ground on right as you enter the town
**Capacity:** 6,000    **Seats:** 120    **Cover:** 1,000    **Floodlights:** Yes
**Clubhouse:** `Robins Nest' - on ground. Open lunchtimes and evenings, snacks and bar menu.
Mgr: Mrs Sue Tyrell

**HONOURS** Western Lg  63-64 70-7171-72 81-82 82-83, Div 1 51-52, Div 3 49-50, Lg Cup 71-
72 84-85; Alan Young Cup 64-65 69-70; Merit Cup 68-69; Subsidiary Cup 71-72;
Devon Snr Cup 79-80; Devon St Lukes Cup 81-82 83-84 85-86 95-96 (R-up 86-87 91-92 94-95)

**PREVIOUS** **Leagues:** Devon & Exeter 47-49; Western 49-72; Southern 72-75
**Name:** Bideford Town    **Ground:** Hansen Ground (1 season)

**BEST SEASON** **FA Cup:** 1st Rd 64-65(replay) 73-74 77-78 81-82. **FA Vase:**

**RECORD** **Gate:** 6,000 v Gloucester C., FA Cup 4th Qual. Rd 60
**Scorer:** Tommy Robinson 259    **Appearances:** Derek May 527
**Win:** 16-0 v Soundwell 50-51    **Defeat:** 0-12 v Paulton 96-97

Players progressing: Shaun Taylor (Swindon Town) Tony Dennis (Cambridge)

**FACT FILE**
Founded: 1949
Nickname: Robins
Colours: All Red
Change colours: All white
Midweek Matchday: Tuewday
Programme: 32 pages, 50p
Editor: Ian Knight

**CLUB PERSONNEL**
President: C Prust
Chairman: Jim McElwee
Manager:Sean Joyce
Reserve Manager: Barry Hooper

# BISHOP SUTTON

**Secretary:** Roy Penney, 53 Ridgway Lane, Whitchurch, Bristol BS14 9PJ Tel: 01275 541392

**Ground:** Lakeview Football Field, Bishop Sutton Tel: 01275 333097

**Directions:**    On A368 at rear of Butchers Arms pub - ground signposted on left entering village
from the West
**Capacity:** 1,500    **Seats:** None    **Cover:** 200    **Floodlights:** No
**Clubhouse:** Open matchdays. Rolls, pies and usual pub food available    **Club Shop:** No

**HONOURS** Somerset Snr Lg R-up 89-90 (Div 1 83-84 (R-up 81-82), Div 2 82-83), Bristol &
Avon Lg 80-81 (Div 2 79-80), Somerset Jnr Cup 80-81, Weston Yth Lg77-78,
Chew Valley KO Cup 83-84, Mid-Somerset Lg(Res) R-up 82-83 (Div 3 81-82)

**PREVIOUS** **Leagues:** Weston & Dist. Yth; Bristol & Avon; Somerset Snr (pre 1991)
**Ground:** Adjacent cricket field

**BEST SEASON** **FA Cup:**    **FA Vase:**

**CLUB RECORDS** **Attendance:** 400 v Bristol City, friendly
**Win:** 15-0 v Glastonbury Res
Players progressing: David Lee (Chelsea), S Williams (Southampton), J French(Bristol R.)

**FACT FILE**
Founded: 1977
Nickname: Bishops
Sponsors: Crown Insulation
Colours: All blue
Change colours: All yellow
Midweek Matches: Tuesday
Youth team's League: Somerset Mid Week
Programme: Yes
Editor: G Williams

**CLUB PERSONNEL**
Chairman: G.Williams
Vice Chairman: Roy Penney
President: Bob Redding
Manager: Chris Mountford
Coach: Chris Stutt
Physio: Vernon Ashton

# BRIDGWATER TOWN '84

**Secretary:** Miss Sally Wright, 37 Kidsbury Rd, Bridgwater, Som. TA6 7AQ Tel: 01278 421189

**Ground:** Fairfax Park, College Way, Bath Road, Bridgwater Tel: 01278 446899 (matchdays and weekday mornings only )

**Directions:** M5 jct 23, follow signs to Glastonbury (A39), turn right for Bridgwater (A39). Look for sign to Bridgwater College via College Way One mile from Bridgwater (BR) station

**Capacity:** 2,000    **Seats:** 150    **Cover:** Yes    **Floodlights:** Yes

**Clubhouse:** On the Ground

**HONOURS** Somerset Senioir Cup 93-94, Somerset Senior Lge 90-91 91-92 , Western Lge Div 1 95-96

**PREVIOUS** **League:** Somerset Snr (pre-1994)**Names:** None
**BEST SEASONFA Cup:** 2nd Q Rd    **FA Vase:** First Round

**RECORDS** **Attendance:** 1,112 v Taunton Town 26.2. 97

**FACT FILE**
Founded: 1984
Nickname: The Robins
Sponsor: TMB Patterns
Colours: Red&white stripes/red/white
Change colours: All blue
Midweek Matchday: Tuesday
Youth Team's League: U18 Floodlight
Programme: Yes
Editors: G ordon Nelson & Mark Hollidge

**CLUB PERSONNEL**
Chairman: Keith Setter
President: Tom Pearce
Press Officer: GordonNelson
Manager: Alan Hooker
Sports Injury Therapist: Dave Callow
L.C.S.P., F.A.Dip.

# BRIDPORT

**Secretary:** Ian Hallett, Brookside, Burstock, Dorset DT8 3LJ (O1308 868795)

**Ground:** The Beehive, St Mary's Field, Bridport, Dorset Tel: 01308 423834

**Directions:** Take West Bay road from town centre, turn right just before Palmers Brewery

**Capacity:** 2,000    Seats: 200    Cover: 400    Floodlights: Yes    Club Shop: No

**Clubhouse:** Yes, open matchdays and for functions. Hot and cold snacks available

**HONOURS** Western Lg Cup 70-71 72-73 77-78 (R-up 76-77, Div 1 R-up 94-95, Merit Cup 69-70 71-72 73-74); Dorset Comb.(3) 85-88 (Lg Cup 86-87 87-88); Dorset Snr Cup(8) 63-64 69-71 75-76 78-81 87-88; Dorset Snr Amtr Cup(6) 48-50 54-55 56-57 70-72; W. Dorset Chal. Bowl 07-08; Perry Str. Lg 22-23; Mark Frowde Cup 76-77 88-89
**PREVIOUS** **Leagues:** Perry Street; Western 61-84; Dorset Combination 84-88 **Grounds:** Pymore (pre 1930s); Crown Field (pre 1953)
**BEST SEASON** **FA Cup:**    FA Vase:5th Round 88-89
**RECORD** **Attendance:** 1,150 v Exeter City, 1981; 3,000 v Chelsea, at Crown, 1950 **Scorer (in a season):** Ellis Hoole 36 **Fee received:** £2,000 for Tommy Henderson **Fee paid:** £1,000 for Steve Crabb

**FACT FILE**
Founded: 1885
Nickname: Bees
Sponsors: ABC Blinds
Colours: Red & black/black/red & black
Change colours: Blue & black/blue/blue
Midweek Matches: Tuesday
Reserves ' League: Dorset Combination
Programme: 40pages, 50p
Editor: Ian Hallett (01308 868795)

**CLUB PERSONNEL**
President: B Williams
Chairman: David Fowler
Manager: Trevor Senior
Asst Manager/Physio: Tony Diaz

# BRISLINGTON

**Secretary:** David Braithwaite, 3 Ashcott,Whitchurch, Bristol BS14 0AG Tel: 01275 542040H 0117 9238469 (W)

**Ground:** Ironmould Lane, Brislington, Bristol Tel: 0117 977 4030
**Directions:** 4 miles out of Bristol on main A4 to Bath - turn left up lane opposite Garden Centre just before dual carriageway (500 yards past Park & Ride on right )

**Capacity:** 2000    Seats: 144    Cover: 1000    Floodlights: Yes

**Clubhouse:** Yes - on ground, open matchdays    **Club Shop:** No

**HONOURS** Somerset Senior Cup 92-93 R-up 93-94; Somerset Senior League, Les Phillips Cup SF 93-94, Premier Cup 95-96

**PREVIOUS** **League:** Somerset Senior (pre-1991)

**BEST SEASON** **FA Vase:** 3rd Rd 89-90, 2-3 v Abingdon T. (A) **FA Cup:**

**RECORD** **Attendance:**

**FACT FILE**
Formed:
Nickname: Bris
Sponsors: Trade Windows
Colours: Red & black/black/black & red
Change colours: Yellow & blue/blue/blue
Midweek matches: Tuesday
Reserves ' League: Somerset Senior
Programme: £1.00
Editor: Laserset (0117 969 5487)

**CLUB PERSONNEL**
President: C Elston
Chairman: Geoff Hobbs
Vice-Chairman: M Richardson
Manager: Tony Ricketts
Asst Manager: Graham Bird
Physio: Dave Gould

# BRISTOL MANOR FARM

**Secretary:** Mike Lawrence, 2 East Parade, Sea Mills, Bristol BS9 2JW
Tel: 0117 968 3349 (H) 0117 968 3571 (W)
**Ground:** `The Creek', Portway, Sea Mills, Bristol BS9 2HS Tel: 0117 968 3571

**Directions:** M5 jct 18 (Avonmouth Bridge), follow A4 for Bristol - U-turn on dual carriageway by Bristol & West sports ground and return for half mile on A4- ground entrance is down narrow lane on left (hidden entrance). Near to Sea Mills station (BR Temple Meads-Severn Beach line)

Capacity: 2,000    Seats: 84      Cover: 350      Floodlights: Yes    Club Shop: No

**Clubhouse:** Open every evening & lunchtime Sat & Sun. Lounge bar, skittle alley, bar meals.

**HONOURS**     Western Lg Div 1 82-83, Glos Tphy 87-88, Glos Amtr Cup 89-90,
Somerset Snr Lg Div 1 (Lg Cup, Div 2)
**PREVIOUS**    **Leagues:** Bristol Suburban 64-69; Somerset Snr 69-77
**Name:** Manor Farm O.B. 1964-68    **Grounds:** None
**BEST SEASON**   **FA Cup:**       **FA Vase:**
**RECORD**      **Attendance:** 500 v Portway, Western Lg 1974
**Goalscorer:** Chris Rex, 222        **Appearances:** Paul Williams, 821
**Win:** 8-2, v Frome (A), 2/9/84        **Defeat:** 1-8, v Exmouth (A), 5/5/86
**Fee paid:** Nil    **Fee received:** £3,000 for Nicky Dent (Yeovil Town, 1989)
Players progressing: Ian Hedges (Newport) 88-89, Gary Smart (Bristol Rovers)

**FACT FILE**
Formed: 1964
Nickname: The Farm
Club Sponsors: Wardle Fencing
Colours: Red/black/red
Change colours: All sky blue
Midweek Matchday: Tuesday
Reserve s' League: Somerset Senior
Programme: 28 pages, 50p
Editor: Steve Price (0117 982 6952)

**CLUB PERSONNEL**
Chairman: Fred Wardle
Vice Chairman: Brian Bartlett
President: Fred Wardle
Manager: Geoff Bryant
Asst Mgr: Barry Fry
Physio: Alan Williams

# CHIPPENHAM TOWN

**Secretary:** Chris Blake, 28 Sadlers Mead, Chippenham, Wilts SN15 3PB Tel: 01249 658212

**Ground:** Hardenhuish Park, Bristol Road, Chippenham Tel: 01249 650400

**Directions:** M4 jct 17, A350 into Chippenham, follow signs for Trowbridge/Bath until r'bout, left onto A420 into town, ground 400yds on left 15 mins walk from railway station on main A420 Bristol Road

Capacity: 4,000    Seats: 100      Cover: 300      Floodlights: Yes

**Clubhouse:** Yes, open matchdays. Food available    **Club Shop:** Yes

**HONOURS**     Western Lg 51-52 (Div 1 80-81, Div 2 52-53(Res)80-81), Wilts Shield,
Wilts Snr Cup, Wilts Snr League
**BEST SEASON**   **FA Cup:** 1st Rd 51-52       **FA Vase:**
**PREVIOUS**    **Leagues:** Hellenic, Wiltshire Senior, Wiltshire Premier
**Grounds:** Westmead, Lowden, Little George Lane, Malmesbury Rd
**RECORD**      **Gate:** 4,800 v Chippenham Utd, Western Lg, 1951
**Goalscorer:** Dave Ferris    **Appearances:** Ian Monnery

**FACT FILE**
Formed: 1873    Nickname: The Bluebirds
Club Sponsors: DL Windows
Steltorfield/Costcutters/Shoestring
Club colours: Blue & white/blue/blue
Change colours: All yellow
Midweek matches: Wednesday
Programme: 32 pages, 50p
Editor/Press Officer: TBA
Local Press: Chippenham News,
Wilts Gazette

**CLUB PERSONNEL**
Chairman: Malcolm Lyus
Vice-Chairman: TBA
President: G W Terrell
Tresurer: Richard Terrell
Commercial Manager: Geoff Snell
Manager: Tommy Saunders
Physio: Steve Lodge

# DAWLISH TOWN

**Secretary:** John Wathen, 35 Lower Drive, Dawlish, Devon. EX7 0AT. Tel: 01626 864403

**Ground:** Playing Fields, Sandy Lane, Exeter Road, Dawlish Tel: 01626 863110

**Directions:** Approx 1 mile from centre of town, off main Exeter road (A379)
Capacity:    2,000    Seats: 200      Cover: 200      Floodlights: Yes
**Clubhouse:** Open nightly, situated in car park opposite ground

**HONOURS**     Western Lg Div 1 R-up 98-99, Lg Cup 80-81 83-84, Devon Premier Cup 69-70
72-73 80-81, Devon Snr Cup 57-58 67-68, Devon St Lukes Cup 82-83 (R-up 81-
82), Carlsberg Cup 96
**BEST SEASON**   **FA Cup:**       **FA Vase:** Quarter Finals 86-87
**PREVIOUS**    **League:** Devon & Exeter    **Ground:** Barley Bank 1875-1900
**RECORD**      **Gate:** 1,500 v Heavitree Utd, Devon Prem. Cup Q-Final
**Defeat:** 0-18 v Clevedon (A), Western Lge Prem. Div. 92-93

**FACT FILE**
Founded: 1889
Colours: Green & white/green/white
Change colours: All blue & white
Midweek matchday: Wednesday
Programme: 34 pages, 30p
Programme Editor: Roy Bolt

**CLUB PERSONNEL**
President: Bob Webster
Chairman: John Wathen
Manager: Tony Bowker

BACKWELL UNITED: Back Row (L-R): Jamie Patch (manager), Mark Sullivan, Marcus Brown, Lee Gould, Dave Wilcox, Paul Turner, Dave Hook, Adam Tudor, Rob Pritchard, Chris Coles, Ben Sheppard. Front Row: Ben Nelki, Craig Patch, Paul Fowler, Steve Phillips, Brett Gready, Ryan King, Benji Tricker.

BARNSTAPLE TOWN: Back Row (L-R): Russell Frayne, Keith Shapland, Rob Calderhead, Rob Gough, Steve Kidd, Ryan Draper, Gary Bedler, Steve Gibson, Darren Hawkins, Roger Bonaparte, Simon Dawe, Kevin Prust. Front Row: Daniel Gulliver, Graham Waters, Dave Cooke (secretary), Paul Mitchell (chairman), Mark Jenkins (manager), Charles Keeble (main sponsor), Andy Rollason, Simon

BIDEFORD: Back Row (L-R): Ian Knight (physio), Stuart Collings, Andy Clark, Ryan Kelly, Carl Armstrong, Jim McElway, Nick Spy, Hector Christie, Dave Downing, Paul Hutchins, John Wright, Mark Knight, Kevin Tyrrell (secretary). Front Row: David Newson, Kevin Darch, John McMullen, Shaun Hadley, Sean Joyce (manager), Richard Gomm, Darren Polhill, Daniel Bell

# ELMORE

**Secretary:** Neville Crocker, c/o Elmore FC Tel: 01884 256634

**Ground:** Horsdon Park, Tiverton, Devon EX16 4DE Tel: 01884 252341

**Directions:** M5 Jct 27, A373 towards Tiverton, leave at 1st sign for Tiverton &Business Park, ground 500yds on right

Capacity: 2,000     Seats: 200          Cover:     Floodlights: Yes

**Clubhouse:** 11am-11pm Mon-Sat. Full canteen service - hot & cold meals & snacks

**Club Shop:** Yes

**HONOURS**     East Devon Snr Cup 72-73 75-76, Western Lge R-up 94-95. Lge Cup 90-91,94-95, Div 1 R-up 90-91, Prem Div Merit Cup R-up 91-92, Div 1 Merit Cup 86-87 89-90 90-91, Devon St Lukes Cup R-up 90-91, Devon Snr Cup 87-88, Devon Intermediate Cup 60-61, Football Express Cup 60-61, Devon & Exeter Lg Div 2A 73-74 86-87(res)(Div 1A 76-77(res)), Devon Yth Cup 77-78.

**PREVIOUS**     **Leagues:** Devon & Exeter 47-74; South Western 74-78     **Grounds:** None

**BEST SEASON     FA Cup:**                    **FA Vase:**
**RECORD**          **Attendance:** 1,713 v Tiverton Town Fri.April 14th 95
                         **Appearances:** P Webber          **Goalscorer:**
                         **Win:** 17-0                              **Defeat:** 2-7

**FACT FILE**

Founded: 1947
Nickname: Eagles
Club Sponsors: Ken White Signs
Colours: Green & white/white/white
Change colours: Red & black/black/black
Midweek matches: Tuesday
Reserve League: None
Programme: 12 pages, 30p
Editor: Richard Tapp(01884 252341)

**CLUB PERSONNEL**

Chairman: Alan J Cockram
Vice Chairman: P.J.Garnsworthy
Manager: Peter Buckingham
Asst Manager: R Moore
Physio: M Crocker

# MANGOTSFIELD UNITED

**Secretary:** Roger Gray, 105 Chiltern Close, Warmley, Bristol BS15 5UW Tel: 0117 961 6523

**Ground:** Cossham Street, Mangotsfield, Bristol BS17 3EW Tel: 0117 956 0119
**Directions:** M4 jct 19, M32 jct 1; A4174 marked Downend, through lights, over double mini-r'bout to Mangotsfield, left by village church onto B4465 signposted Pucklechurch, ground quarter mile on right. From central Bristol take A432 thru Fishponds, Staple Hill, to Mangotsfield and turn right by village church onto B4465. From Bath/Keynsham follow A4175, right at island at Willsbridge onto A431, then rejoin A4175 at next island (Cherry Garden Hill) to Bridge Yate, straight over double mini-r'bout and take 1st left, right into Carsons Rd after 1 mile and follow to Mangotsfield village & turn right by church onto B4465
Capacity: 2,500     Seats: 300     Cover: 800          Floodlights: Yes     Club Shop: Yes
**Clubhouse:** Open 11-11. Snacks - hot food on matchdays. Lounge bar for official functions etc

**HONOURS** Western Lg 90-91, Lg Cup 73-74 r-up 86-87, Div 1 r-up 82-83; Somerset Prem. Cup 87-88, r-up 88-89 95-96; Glos Snr Cup 68-69 75-76; Glos FA Trophy 84-85 86-87 90-91 94-95 96-97; Hungerford Invit. Cup 74-75; Rothmans Nat. Cup r-up 77-78; Hanham Invit. Charity Cup 84-85 85-86;
**BEST SEASON     FA Vase:** Semi Final 95-96          **FA Cup:**
**PREVIOUS**     **Leagues:** Bristol & District 50-67; Avon Premier Combination 67-72
**RECORD**          **Attendance:** 2,386 v Bath City, FA Cup 77-78
Players progress ing: G Megson, S White, G Penrice, P Purnell, N Tanner, M Hooper

**FACT FILE**
Founded: 1950
Nickname: The Field
Sponsors: Goldline
Colours: White/maroon/sky
Change colours: Yellow/navy/yellow
Midweek matchday: Tuesday
Reserve League: Somerset Senior
Programme: 32 pages, 50p
Editor: Bob Smale (0117 9401926)

**CLUB PERSONNEL**
President: A J Hill
Chairman:  Richard Davis
Vice Chairman: P Selway
Press Officer: Secretary
Manager: Nick Tanner
Physio: Ian Weston

# MELKSHAM TOWN

**Secretary:**     David Phillips, 37 Duxford Close, Bowerhill,Melksham,Wlts. SN167 6XNk
                         Tel: 01225 706904

**Ground:**     The Conigre, Melksham (01225 702843)
                    Capacity:3,000     Seats: 150          Cover: 1,500          Floodlights: Yes

**Directions:**     Just off main square in grounds of Melksham House

**Clubhouse:** Inside ground, open every evening & weekend lunchtimes

**HONOURS**     Wilts Lg 03-04 93-94 (R-up 24-25 29-30 59-60 67-68 68-69 71-72), Western Lg Div 1 79-80, 96-97, Wilts Snr Cup 03-04 69-70 77-78 (R-up 57-58 67-68 68-69), Wilts Shield 80-81 81-82 84-85 ,85-86,97-98 (R-up 86-87).

**PREVIOUS**     **Leagues:** Wiltshire 1894-1974 93-94; Western 74-93
                         **Grounds:** Challymead; Old Broughton Road Field

**BEST SEASON     FA Cup:** 2nd Q Rd 57-58          **FA Vase:** 3rd Rd 81-82,98-99
                         **FA Amateur Cup:** 1st Rd 68-69

**RECORD**          **Attendance:** 2,821 v Trowbridge Town, FA Cup 57-58

**FACT FILE**

Founded: 1876
Colours:yellow/black/yellow
Change colours: All white
Midweek Matchday: Tuesday

**CLUB PERSONNEL**

President: H J Goodenough
Chairman: Mike Perrin
Manager: Darren Perrin

BRISLINGTON: Back Row (L-R): Dave Bright, Lee Scading, Richard Ollie, Paul Sainsbury, Paul Anderson, Andy Weeks. Middle Row: Dave Gould, Richard Thomas, Mark Rodger, Ashley Marr, Bradley Haynes, Andy Thacker, Kevin Scott, Jason Ford, Martin Wheeler. Front Row: Steve Back, Mark Branch, Simon Warren, Gary Fisher, Tony Ricketts (manager), Jeff Hazel, Lee Patch, Mark Summers, Steve Jenkins

CHIPPENHAM TOWN: Back Row (L-R): Tony Bennell, Neal Horrock, Steve Twedle, Ian Jones, Ian Harris, Richard Tompkin, Steve Campbell, Darren Hobbs. Middle Row: Mark Cutler, John Woods, Nick Tiley, Mike Godwin, Jeremy Christopher, Steve Perkins, Steve Lodge, Lea James, Gary Lewis, Simon Charity. Front Row: Chris Blake (secretary), Richard Terrell (trainer), Tommy Saunders (manag-

BRIDGWATER TOWN: Back Row (L-R): Jamie Winter, Tim Dyer, Shaun Strange, Matt Francis. Middle Row: Leigh Hurford, Steve Caldwell, Nigel Williams, Julian Stearnes, Pete Copeland, Dave Callow (physio). Front Row: Craig Rice, Jon Bowering, Gareth Morgan, Alan Hooker (manager), Marc Antonelli, Keith Graddon, Danny Milford

# MINEHEAD

**Secretary:** Mike Till, 6 Badger Park, Minehead, Som. TA24 6LL Tel: 01643 706309

**Ground:** The Recreation Ground, Irnham Road, Minehead, Somerset (01643 704989)

**Directions:** Entering town from east on A39 turn right into King Edward Road at Police station, first left into Alexandra Rd and follow signs to car park;ground entrance within. Regular buses to Minehead from Taunton, the nearestrailhead. (Steam train 'holiday route' Taunton to Minehead)

Capacity: 3,500    Seats: 350    Cover: 400    Floodlights: Yes

**Clubhouse:** Yes    **Club Shop:** No

**HONOURS**    Southern Lg R-up 76-77, Div 1 Sth 75-76, Merit Cup 75-76;
Western Lg R-up 66-67 71-72, Div 1 90-91 98-99, Alan Young Cup 67-68 (jt with
Glastonbury),Somerset Premier Cup 60-61 73-74 76-77

**PREVIOUS**    **Leagues:** Somerset Senior; Southern 72-83

**RECORD**    **Attendance:** 3,600 v Exeter City, FA Cup 2nd Rd, 77
**Defeat:** 1-11 v Odd Down (A), Western Lge Prem. Div. 19/3/94
Longest unbeaten run of league games 36, May 1998- May 1999

**BEST SEASON**    FA Cup: 2nd Round 76-77, 1-2 v Portsmouth (A); 77-78, 0-3 v Exeter City (H).
League clubs defeated: Swansea City 1-0 (A) 76-77
**FA Vase:**    **FA Trophy:** Not applicable

**FACT FILE**
Founded: 1889
Colours: Blue & white/blue/blue
Change colours: Yellow/black/black
Midweek Matches: Tuesday
Reserves League: TBA
Programme: Yes
Editor:

**CLUB PERSONNEL**
Chairman: Peter Bate
Tel: 01643 704063

Manager: Chris Porter
Coach: Charlie Kirk

---

# ODD DOWN ATHLETIC

**Secretary:**    Mike Mancini, 36 Caledonian Rd., East Twerton, Bath BA2 3RD
Tel: 01225 423293

**Ground:**    Coombe Hay Lane, Odd Down, Bath Tel: 01225 832491

**Directions:**    On main Bath/Exeter road - leaving Bath turn left into Combe Hay Lane opposite
Lamplighters Pub. 40 mins walk from Bath (BR)

Capacity: 1,000    Seats: 160    Cover: 250    Floodlights: Yes

**Clubhouse:** Yes, open noon-3 & 7-11pm. Hot & cold food available
**Club Shop:** No

**HONOURS**    Western Lg Div 1 92-93, Somerset Snr Cup 91-92

**PREVIOUS**    **Leagues:** Wilts Premier, Bath & District, Somerset Senior

**BEST SEASON**    **FA Cup:**    **FA Vase:**

**RECORD**    **Appearances:** T Mancini & T Ridewood, both 335
**Scorer:** Joe Matano 104
**Win:** 11-1 v Minehead (H), Western Lge Prem. Div. 19/3/94

**FACT FILE**
Founded: 1901
Sponsors: Crest Homes
Colours: All blue
Change :Black & whitestripes/black/lack;
Midweek Matches: Wednesday
Reserves ' League: Somerset Senior
Programme: 12 pages with admission
Editor: Secretary

**CLUB PERSONNEL**
President: P A L Hill
Chairman: N Fenwick
Vice Chairman: Mike Wilkins
Manager: Vic Flip[pance

---

# PAULTON ROVERS

**Secretary:** John Pool, 111 Charlton Park, Midsomer Norton,Bath BA3 4BP Tel: 01761415190

**Ground:** Athletic Ground, Winterfield Road, Paulton Tel: 01761 412907

**Directions:** Leave A39 at Farrington Gurney (approx 15 miles south of Bristol),follow A362 marked Radstock for two miles, left at junction B3355 to Paulton,ground on right. Bus services from Bristol and Bath

Capacity: 5,000    Seats: 138    Cover: 200    Floodlights: Yes

**Club Shop:** Old programmes available - contact Chairman
**Clubhouse:** 3 bars, lounge, skittle alley, dance hall. Capacity 300. Cateringfacilities

**HONOURS**    Western Lg Div 2 R-up 1900-01; Somerset Snr Cup 00-01 02-03 03-04 07-08
08-09 09-10 34-35 67-68 68-69 71-72 72-73 74-75; Somerset Snr Lg 00-01
03-04 04-05 70-71 71-72 72-73 73-74; Somerset F/Lit Youth Lge 96-97

**PREVIOUS**    **Leagues:** Wilts Premier; Somerset Snr
**Grounds:** Chapel Field; Cricket Ground; Recreation Ground 1946-48

**BEST SEASON**    **FA Cup:**    **FA Vase:**

**RECORDS**    **Attendance:** 2,000 v Crewe, FA Cup, 1906-07
**Appearances:** Steve Tovey    **Goalscorer:** D Clark

**FACT FILE**
Founded: 1881
Nickname: Rovers
Sponsors: Barons Property Centre/Bass
Breweries
Colours: White/maroon/maroon
Change colours: Yellow/navy/navy
Midweek matches: Tuesday
Reserves' League: Somerset Snr
Programme: 20 pages, 50p
Editor: D Bissex (01761 412463)
Local Press: Bath Evening Chronicle,
Bristol Evening Post, Western Daily Press

**CLUB PERSONNEL**
President: Mr T Pow
Chairman: David Bissex
Vice Chairman: Mr D Carter
Manager: Alan Pridham
Physio: Mike Brown

MANGOTSFIELD UNITED: Back Row (L-R): Mike Brown (physio), Dave Morrissey, Nick Wilson, Ricky Griffiths, Joe Mogg. Middle Row: Martin Boyle, Leigh Williams, Lee Barlass, Tony Court, Cody Allen, Paul Cichy, Neil Rosslee, Eddie Gregg. Front Row: Gary Davis, Kevin Coles, Andy Black (manager), Nigel Gillard (assistant manager), Noel O'Sullivan, Gary Thomas.

MELKSHAM TOWN: Back Row (L-R): Simon Price, Matty Messenger, Adam Gingell, Wayne Munday, Jerad O'Pray, Ally Hines, Mike Brooks, Darren Chitty, Steve Cripps, Justin Messenger, Kevin Bush, John Scott. Front Row: Frank Coleman, Stuart Irons, David Clayton

HEAVITREE UNITED: Back Row (L-R): David O'Neill, Stephen Taylor, Adam Carpenter, Keith Graham, Phil Howe, Roy Roberts, Karl Hinds, Steve Riley (manager). Front Row: Melvin Ousley, Wayne King, Scott Isaac, Terry Wheatley, Jody Hacksworthy, Adam Gray, Lee Jordan

# TAUNTON TOWN

**Secretary:** The Secretary, c/o the club, Tel: 01823 333833 (H)
**Ground:** Wordsworth Drive, Taunton, Somerset TA1 2HG Tel: 01823 278191
**Directions:** Leave M5 Jct 25, follow signs to town centre, at 2nd set of lights turn left into Wordsworth Drive; ground on left. 25 mins walk from Taunton (BR); turn left out of station and follow road right through town centre bearing left into East Reach. Follow road down and turn right into Wordsworth Drive shortly after Victoria pub
**Capacity:** 4,000   Seats: 250   Cover: 1,000   Floodlights: Yes   Club Shop: Yes
**Clubhouse:** Social club to accommodate 300, full bar facilities, separate bar & hall for private functions
**HONOURS** FA Vase R-up 93-94, Western Lg 68-69 89-90 (R-up 93-94 97-98), Les Phillips Cup R-up 97-98, Alan Young Cup 73-74 75-76 (jt with Falmouth), Charity Chall. Cup 49-50 50-51), Somerset Snr Lg 52-53, Somerset Prem. Cup R-up 82-83 89-90 92-93 98-99
**PREVIOUS    Leagues:** Western 54-77; Southern 77-83   **Grounds:** Several prior to 1953
**BEST SEASON    FA Cup:** 1st Rd Proper 81-82, 1-2 v Swindon T. (A)   **FA Trophy:** 1st Rd Proper 80-81, 1-5 v Hendon at Q.P.R   **FA Vase:** Finalists 93-94, S-F 97-98 98-99, Q-F 96-97.
**RECORDS    Attendance:** 3,284 v Tiverton Town, FA Vase Semi-Final 98-99
**Appearances:** Tony Payne   **Scorer** (in a season) : Reg Oram 67
**Win:** 12-0 v Dawlish Town (A), FA Cup Prel. Rd, 28/8/93
**Defeat:** 0-8 v Cheltenham Town (A), FA Cup 2nd Qual. Rd, 28/9/91
**Players progressing:** Charlie Rutter (Cardiff), Stuart Brace (Southend), Steve Winter (Torquay) Kevin Maloy (Exeter C.)

**FACT FILE**
Formed: 1947
Nickname: Peacocks
Club Sponsors: Taunton Cider Co
Colours: Sky blue & claret/claret/sky blue
Change colours: Yellow/sky blue/yellow
Midweek matches: Wednesday
Reserves ' League: None
Programme: 32 pages, £1
Editor: Les Gill
Newsline: 0930 555 849

**CLUB PERSONNEL**
Chairman: T F Harris
Treasurer: Joan Ellis
Press Officer: Joan Ellis
Manager: Russell Musker
Asst Manager: Derek Fowler
Physio: Barry Wilson

# WESTBURY UNITED

**Secretary:**    Mrs Joy Bown, 23 Leighton Park Road, Westbury, Wilts. BA13 3RX
Tel: 01373 823987

**Ground:**    Meadow Lane, Westbury Tel: 01373 823409

**Directions:**    In town centre, A350, follow signs for BR station, Meadow Lane on right (club signposted). Ten mins walk from railway station (on main London-South West and South Coast-Bristol lines)

Capacity: 3,500   Seats: 150   Cover: 150   Floodlights: Yes

**Clubhouse:** Evenings 7-11pm, Fri, Sat & Sun lunchtimes 12-3pm   Club Shop: Yes

**HONOURS**    Western Lg Div 1 91-92, Wilts Senior Cup 31-32 32-33 47-48 51-52, Wilts Combination, Wilts Lg 34-35 37-38 38-39 49-50 50-51 55-56, Wilts Premier Shield R-up 92-93

**PREVIOUS**    **Leagues:** Wilts Comb.; Wilts Co. (pre-1984)
**Ground:** Redland Lane (pre-1935)

**BEST SEASON    FA Cup:        FA Vase:**

**RECORD Gate:**    4,000 - v Llanelli, FA Cup 1st Rd 37 & v Walthamstow Ave. FA Cup 37

Players progressing: John Atyeo (Bristol City)

**FACT FILE**
Formed: 1921
Nickname: White Horsemen
Colours: Green & white/white/green
Change colours: Sky & navy/blue/blue
Midweek Matches: Tuesday
Reserves' league: Trowbridge Lge
Programme: 16 pages, 30p
Editor: Mike Taylor (01373 826754)

**CLUB PERSONNEL**
Chairman: Phillip Alford
Vice Chairman: Bert Back
President: George Nicholls
Managers: Nigel Tripp & Lee Darby
Physio: Lee Webb

# YEOVIL TOWN RESERVES

**Secretary:**    Jean Cotton, c/o Club.
Tel: 01935 428130 (H) 01935 423662 (B)  Fax: 01935 473956

**Ground:**    Huish Park, Lufton Way, Yeovil Somerset, BA22 8YF.
Tel: 01935 23662    Fax 01935 73956

**Directions:**    Leave A303 at Cartgate roundabout and take A3088 signposted Yeovil.Take first exit at next roundabout and first exit at next roundabout intoLufton Way. Railway station - Yeovil Pen Mill (Bristol/Westbury to Weymouth)2.5 miles from ground. Yeovil Junction (Waterloo to Exeter) 4 miles.
Bus service from both stations on Saturday - matchdays

Capacity: 8,720   Seats: 5,212   Terracing: 3,508   Floodlights: Yes

**Club Shop:**    Open on matchdays selling full range of souvenirs, match programmes etc

**Clubhouse:**    Matchdays hot + cold food available. Meals can be ordered with advance notice. All weather astro turf pitch available for bookings9am-10pm

**HONOURS:** Western League: Champions 58-59, Div. 1 R-up 97-98

**FACT FILE**
Founded: 1895
Nickname: Glovers
Sponsors: Precision Publishing Papers
Colours: Green/white/green
Change colours: Navy & red/navy/navy & red
Midweek matchday: Wednesday
Programme: Yes

**CLUB PERSONNEL**
Chairman: John Fry
President: S N Burfield
Manager: Terry Rowles
Physio: Maurice O'Donnell

**CALNE TOWN:** Back Row (L-R): Graham Learmonth (manager), Marcus Lovesey, Phil Penning, Ben Sammett, Andy Kilgour, Spencer Clifford, Dave Chappell, Simon Hillier, Eddie Stephenson, John Ledgister, Tim Beech, Mark Pounder, Sean Hughes Front Row: Dalyon Gleed, Paul Ranger, Russell Webster, Martin Ford, Mark Neale, Andy Beale, Stuart Greatwood

**EXMOUTH TOWN:** Back Row (L-R): Simon Harris, Richard Uffendell, Russ Wilson (manager), Lee Weatherall, Lee Aston, Lee Annunziata, Shaun Moore, Badder Alfaresi    Front Row: Richie Hope, Dave Roddick, Ian Mortimore, Gary Carpenter, Danny Burwood, Tiv Lowe, James Collins. Mascot: Nathan Carpenter

**MINEHEAD** celebrate winning the First Division

# BITTON

**Secretary:** Michael Hall, 14 Pillingers Road, Kingswood, Bristol BS15 8DE Tel: 0117 960 3627

**Ground:** The Recreation Ground, Bath Road, Bitton, Tel: 0117 932 3222
Capacity: 500    Cover: 80 Seats: 48    Floodlights: No

**Directions:** M4 junc 18. Take A46 towards Bath, at first roundabout take A420 for Wick/
Bridgeyate. On approach to Bridgeyate turn left at mini-r'about onto A4175 and follow
for 2.2 miles, then left for Bath on the A431. The ground is 100 yards on right.
Nearest station: Keynsham Bristol

**Clubhouse:** Weekdays 7.30-11, Sat. all day, Sun 12-3 & 7.30-10.30    Club Shop: No
**HONOURS**    Glos. Jun Cup r-up 90; Avon Prem. Lg r-up 94, 95; Glos Sen amat Cup 95;
Glos Chall Trophy r-up 97; Glos County Lg r-up 97.

**PREVIOUS**    **Leagues:** Avon Premier Comb., Glos County

### FACT FILE
Founded: 1922
Sponsors: ESL Designs & Graphics
Colours: Red & white stripes/black/black
Change colours: All yellow
Midweek Matches: Tuesday 6.30 ko.
Programme: 36 pages    Editor: Paul Cater

### CLUB PERSONNEL
Chairman: David Venables (01275 542335)
Vice Chairman: Steve Webb (0117 967 4114)
President: Roy Ewans
Commercial Man.: Paul Cater (0117 932 5205)
Manager: Andy Black (0117 967 0730)

---

# CALNE TOWN

**Secretary:**    Laurie Drake, 22 Falcon Rd, Calne, Wilts SN11 8PL Tel: 01249 819186
**Ground:**    Bremhill View, Lickhill Rd., North End, Calne Tel: 01249 816716
**Directions:**    From Bristol to Chippenham, on entering town keep left all the way taking slip
road to North End, off main Swindon Road
Capacity: 2,500    Seats: 78    Cover: 250    Floodlights: Yes    Club Shop: No
**Clubhouse:** Mon-Fri 7-11pm, Sat-Sun 12-11pm. Filled rolls, hot food, tea,coffee, sweets etc
**HONOURS**    Western Lg Div 1 R-up 92-93; Wilts Snr Cup 12-13 34-35 84-85 (R-up1894-95
94-95 1911-12 49-50); Wilts Lg 33-34, ('Ghia' Cup 8) 1-81 85-86, Div 279-81,
Div 3 85-86, Div 4 81-82
**PREVIOUS**    **League:** Wilts Co. (pre-1986)    **Ground:** Anchor Road Rec. 1887-1967
**Names:** Calne Town (1886) & Harris Utd merged; Calne & Harris Utd (1921-67)
**RECORD**    **Attendance:** 1,100 v Swindon, Friendly 25/7/1987
**Scorer:** Robbie Lardner    **Appearances:** Gary Swallow, 259
**Win:** 11-1 v Heavitree (H)    **Defeat:** 2-7 v Odd Down (A)

### FACT FILE
Founded: 1887    Nickname: Lilywhites
Sponsors: Calne Engineering
Colours: White/black/black
Change colours: Yellow/blue/yellow
Midweek Matchday: Tuesday
Programme: 20 pages, 50p
Editor: Gordon Field (01249 813926)
98-99 - Captain: Ian Monnery
Top Scorer: Graig Tuck
P.o.Y.: Ian Monnery

### CLUB PERSONNEL
President: Fred Rutty
Chairman: Steve Walker
Manager: Graham Learmont

---

# CHARD TOWN

**Secretary:**    Brian Beer, The Club Office, Chard Town FC.
Tel: 01460 62997 (H), 01460 61402 (Club)
**Ground:**    Town Ground, Zembard Lane, Chard TA20 1JL Tel: 01460 61402
Capacity: 1,500    Seats: 60    Cover: 200    Floodlights: Yes
**Directions:** 150 yards from the town centre, off Combe Street.
8 miles from Crewkerne BR station
**Clubhouse:** Matchdays & most evenings. Snacks served

**HONOURS**    Som. Snr Lg 49-50 53-54 59-60 67-68 69-70 (Lg Cup 61-62 71-72 76-77);
Western Lg Div 1 R-up 83-84 87-88 95-96, (Merit Cup 82-83, Comb. Cup(Res)
91-92 (R-up 92-93)); Som. Snr Cup 52-53 66-67; S W Co's Cup 88-89;
Western Com Lge 96-97, Cup 96-97.

**BEST SEASON**    **FA Cup:** 2nd Qual Rd. 77-78 82-83    **FA Vase:**

**PREVIOUS**    **Leagues:** Somerset Snr 20-24 48-75; Perry Street 25-48 **Grounds:** None

### FACT FILE
Founded: 1920
Nickname: Robins
Colours: Scarlet/black/black
Change colours: White/white/red
Midweek matches: Tuesday
Reserves ' League: None
Programme: 24 pages with entry
Editor: Mike Froom

### CLUB PERSONNEL
Chairman: Brian Beer
Manager: Gerry Pearson
Physio: Richard Butt

---

# CLYST ROVERS

**Secretary:** Bob Chamberlain, Orchard Cottage, Clyst St George, Exeter EX3 0NZ(01392 873498)
**Ground:** Waterslade Park, Clyst Honiton, Devon Tel: 01392 366424
**Directions:** A30 following signs for Exeter Airport. Coming from Exeter take 1st right after airport
turning (ground signposted) up narrow 200yds past Duke of York Pub
Capacity: 3,000    Seats: 130    Cover: 300    Floodlights: Yes
Club Shop: Yes, Programmes, souvenirs etc
**Clubhouse:** Open one and a half hours before kick off and after game. Excellent food available
**HONOURS**    Devon St Lukes Cup R-up 92-93, Western Lg Cup SF 92-93
**PREVIOUS**    **Leagues:** Exeter & District 26-44 51-66; Exeter & District Sunday 67-82;
South Western 81-92    **Grounds:** Fair Oak 1926-44
**RECORD**    **Gate:** 768 v Tiverton, Devon St Lukes final 11/5/93
**Win:** 6-0 v Heavitree United, 1993
**Defeat:** 0-12 v Torpoint Athletic, South Western League, October 1990

### FACT FILE
Founded: 1926    Reformed: 1951
Nickname: Rovers
Sponsors: Vantage Pharmacy, Paignton
Colours: Yellow/black/black
Change colours: All blue
Midweek Matches: Tuesday
Programme: 32 pages, 30p
Editor: Ray Dack (01392 215075)

### CLUB PERSONNEL
President: Mr P W Brown
Chairman: Bob Chamberlain
Vice Chairman: Colin Dadson
Manager: Rob Green
Physio: Bill Wreford

# CORSHAM TOWN

**FACT FILE**
Founded: 1893
Sponsors: Hong Kong House & Addkey Print
Colours: All red
Change colours: Yellow/blue/blue
Midweek matchday: Tuesday

**Secretary:** Richard Taylor, 7 Cresswells, Corsham, Wilts SN13 9NT    Tel: 01249 714406
Internet: www.widcom.demon.co.uk

**Ground:** Southbank Ground, Lacock Road, Corsham, Wilts. SN13 9HS  Tel: 01249 715609
**Directions** From the A4 turn into Corsham at the Hare & Hounds PH roundabout, taking the
Melksham Road, B3353, past the Methuen Arms PH then straight across the next
mini-r'about into Lacock Road. The ground is situated 1/2 mile on right

| Capacity: | Seats: | Cover: | Floodlights: No |
**Clubhouse:** No                     Club Shop: No

**CLUB PERSONNEL**
President:
Chairman: Colin Hudd
Manager: Chris Jeffries

**HONOURS**    Wiltshire Lge. 97-98, Wiltshire FA Sen. Cup 75-76 96-97,
Wiltshire Lge. KO Cup 95-96 96-97
**PREVIOUS**   **League:** Wiltshire Co. Lge

# DEVIZES TOWN

**Secretary:**    Chris Dodd, 69 Broadleas Park, Devizes, Wilts. SN10 5JG. Tel: 01380 726205

**FACT FILE**

**Ground:**    Nursteed Road, Devizes. Tel: 01380 722817

Founded: 1883
Colours: Red & white stripes/black/red
Change colours: All yellow
Midweek Matchday: Tuesday

**Directions:**    Off Nursteed Road (A342 signposted Andover); leaving town ground on right
opposite Eastleigh Rd

Capacity: 2,500    Seats: 130    Cover: 400    Floodlights: Yes

**HONOURS**    Wilts Snr Cup 07-08 49-50 56-57 57-58 58-59 60-61 61-62 62-63 65-66 67-68
70-71 71-72 73-74 78-79

**CLUB PERSONNEL**

**PREVIOUS**    **Leagues:** Wilts Comb.; Wilts Premier
**Name:** Southbroom (until early 1900s)    **Ground:** London Rd (pre 1946)

Chairman:Les Moore
Manager: Brian Newlands

# EXMOUTH TOWN

**FACT FILE**
Formed: 1933
Nickname: `Town' or `Blues'
Colours: Blue & white/blue/blue
Change cols: Red & white/black/red & white
Midweek matchday: Tuesday
Reserves' League: Gt Mills Comb
Programme: 36 pages, 30p
Editor: J.Dibsdall

**Secretary:David Richardson J.P.,**44 Whitchurch Avenue, Exeter. EX2 1NT (01392 430985)
**Ground:** King George V Ground, Southern Road, Exmouth Tel: 01395 263348

**Directions:** On right side of main Exeter to Exmouth road (A376). Half mile from Exmouth (BR)

Capacity: 2,500    Seats: 100    Cover: 250    Floodlights: Yes    Club Shop: Yes
**Clubhouse:** Open every night and weekend lunchtimes. Snacks available

**HONOURS**    Western Lg 83-84 85-86 (R-up 86-87 88-89); Lg Cup 88-89; Div 1 R-up 81-82;
Sportmanship Tphy 86-87 92-93); Devon Premier Cup 70-71 79-80; Devon St
Lukes Cup 84-85 88-89 89-90; Devon Snr Cup 50-51; East Devon Snr Cup
50-51 82-83; Harry Wood Mem. Cup 81-82; Exmouth Chal. Cup [7]

**CLUB PERSONNEL**
President: Brian Bradley
Chairman: Malcolm Hale
Vice Chairman: John Dibsdall
Manager:Russell Wilson
Physio: Julian Bennett

**PREVIOUS**    **League:** Devon & Exeter 1933-73
**BEST SEASON**    **FA Vase:** SF 84-85    **FA Cup:**
**RECORD**    **Gate:** 2,395 v Liverpool XI, friendly in 1987    **Scorer:** Mel Pym, 117
**Appearances:** Keith Sprague, Geoff Weeks 410 (Western Lg)

# FROME TOWN

**FACT FILE**
Founded: 1904    Nickname: Robins
Sponsors: Telewest Communications
Colours: All red
Change colours: Purple/navy/navy
Midweek matchday: Wednesday
Reserves ' League: Somerset Senior
Programme: 24 pages, 50p
Editor: Secretary

**Secretary:** Geoff Norris, 10 Clumber Drive, Frome, Somerset BA11 2LG (01373 464 803)
**Ground:** Badgers Hill, Berkeley Road, Frome Tel: 01373 453643

**Directions:** On the Westbury Road, 1 mile from town centre and Frome BR station
Capacity: 5,000    Seats: 250    Cover: 800    Floodlights: Yes    Club Shop: No
**Clubhouse:** Evenings & weekends. Cold food only

**HONOURS**    Wiltshire Lge 1909-10,1910-11,Western Lg 78-79 (Div 2 19-20, Div 2R-up 54-
55, Lg Cup 79-80 82-83, Merit Cup 82-83, Alan Young Cup 79-80,Subsidiary
Cup 59-60), Somerset Prem Cup 66-67 68-69 82-83, Wilts Prem Lg 62-63,
Western Co's Cup F'lit Cup 83-84, Somerset Snr Cup 32-33 33-34 50-51, Somerset
Snr Lg 06-07 08-09 10-11

**CLUB PERSONNEL**
President: Mr C W M Norton
Chairman: Paul McGuinness
Vice Chairman: Steve Porter, Geoff Norris
Manager: Kingsley John
Physio: Bob Stokes

**PREVIOUS**    **League:** Somerset Senior, Wilts League and Wilts Premier

**BEST SEASON**    **FA Trophy:** 2nd Rd v Boston Utd (a) 0-4, 1984-85
**FA Cup:** 1st Rd Proper v L.Orient 1954-55    **FA Vase:** 2nd Rd v Paulton R (a) 1-2
**RECORD**    **Attendance:** 8,000 v Leyton Orient, F.A.Cup 1st Rd. 58

# ILFRACOMBE TOWN

**Secretary:** Tony Alcock, 2 Worth Road, Ilfracombe, North Devon EX34 9JA Tel: 01271 862686

**Ground:** Marlborough Park, Ilfracombe, Devon Tel: 01271 865939

**Directions:** A361 to Ilfracombe. Turn1st right in town after lights and follow Marlborough Rd to the top, ground on left

**Capacity:** 2,000    **Seats:** 60 **Cover:** 450    Floodlights: Yes    Club Shop: No

**Clubhouse:** Every night 7-11pm and weekend lunchtimes. Hot & cold meals on matchdays

**HONOURS**    E Devon Prem Lg 25-26  28-29  29-30, N Devon Senior Lg, N Devon Prem Lg 66-67 70-71 81-82 82-83, Western Lg Div 2 R-up 52-53, Les Phillips Cup R-up 91

**PREVIOUS**    **Leagues:** North Devon 04-14 20-22 60-84; East Devon Premier 22-31;Exeter & District 32-39 46-49; Western 49-59
**Names:** Ilfracombe FC 02-09; Ilfracombe Utd 09-14; Ilfracombe Comrades 14-20

**RECORDS**    **Attendance:** 3,000 v Bristol City, Ground opening, 2/10/24
**Goalscorer:** Paul Jenkins 77    **Appearances:** Paul Jenkins 428

### FACT FILE
Founded: 1902         Nickname: Bluebirds
Sponsors: Park View
Colours: All Blue
Change colours: Yellow/black
Midweek matchday: Tuesday
Reserves ' League: North Devon
Programme: The Bluebird 8 pages, 40p
Editor: Peter Bidgood (01271 864756)

### CLUB PERSONNEL
Chairman: Phil Hill
Vice-Chairman: Ron Holman
President: Mrs Jo Rose
Manager: Dave Sheehan
Physio: Ernie Cochrane

# KEYNSHAM TOWN

**Secretary:** Iain Anderson, 195 Mount Hill Road, Hanham, Bristol BS15 9SU  Tel: 0117 961 6426

**Ground:** Crown Field, Bristol Road, Keynsham Tel: 0117 986 5876

**Directions:** A4 from Bristol to Bath, ground on left  before entering village opposite Crown Inn. Bus service every 30 mins from Bristol passes ground. 10mins walk from Keynsham BR station

**Capacity:** 2,000    Seats: 120    Cover: 500    Floodlights: Yes

**Clubhouse:** Evenings & before & after games. Sunday lunch. Snacks    Club Shop: No

**HONOURS**    Somerset Lg Div 1 77-78; Somerset Snr Cup 51-52 57-58; GFA Jnr Cup 25-26; Somerset & Avon (South) Premier Cup 79-80 (SF 93-94);

**BEST SEASON**    FA Cup: 4th Qual. Rd    **FA Vase:**

**PREVIOUS**    **Leagues:** Bristol District, Bristol Comb., Bristol Premier, Somerset
**Grounds:** The Hams 1886-1910; Gaston 1910-25; Park Road 25-30; Charlton Rd 30-39

**RECORD**    **Attendance:** 3,000 v Chelsea, f'light opening 88-89.
Competitive:2,160 v Saltash, Amateur Cup, Oct 1952

98-99 - Captain: Stuart Nethercott    Top Scorer: Wayne Norman  P.o.Y.: Mark Brain

### FACT FILE
Founded: 1895         Nickname: K's
Sponsors: Ace Building Services Ltd
Colours: All amber
Change colours: All white
Midweek matchday: Monday
Reserves ' League: Somerset Senior
Programme: 32 pages, 50p
Editor: Mark Brown (0117 969 5487)

### CLUB PERSONNEL
Chairman: Phil Gane
President: Lester Clements
Press Officer: D Brassington
Manager: Paul Hirons
Physio:Dave Souter

# LARKHALL ATHLETIC

**Secretary:**    Mervyn Liles, 9 Eastbourne Ave., Claremont Rd., Bath BA1 6EW (01225319427)

**Ground:**    "Plain Ham", Charlcombe Lane, Larkhall, Bath (01225 334952)

**Directions**    A4 from Bath, 1 mile from city centre turn left into St Saviours Rd. In Larkhall square fork left, and right at junction, road bears into Charlcombe Lane. Ground on right as lane narrows

Capacity: 1,000    Seats: None    Cover: 50 Floodlights: No

**HONOURS**    Somerset Senior Cup 75-76, Somerset Senior Lg,; Western Lg Div 1 88-89 93-94 94-95(Div1 Merit Cup(4) 83-86 87-88(jt with Yeovil Res)

**PREVIOUS**    **League:** Somerset Senior

### FACT FILE
Founded: 1914
Nickname: Larks
Colours: Royal & white/royal & white/royal
Change colours: Red & white/red & white/red
Midweek Matches: Tuesday
Programme: Yes

### CLUB PERSONNEL
President: Tony Rhymes
Chairman: Jim McLay
Tel: 01373 834050
Manager: Paul Rankin

# PEWSEY VALE

**Secretary:** Mrs Barbara Flippance, 17 Slater Rd, Pewsey SN9 5EE Tel: 01672 563665

**Ground:** Recreation Ground, Ball Rd, Pewsey Tel: 01672 562990

**Directions:** On entering Pewsey from A345, at the Market Place proceed to end of High Street and turn right into Ball Rd, entrance to ground on right opposite pub. BR to Pewsey station
Cover: Yes    Floodlights: No

**HONOURS**    Wiltshire County League 92-93

**PREVIOUS**    **League:** Wiltshire County (pre-1993)
**Name:** Pewsey Y.M. (until late 1940s)

### FACT FILE
Colours: All black & white
Change colours: Blue& white/white/white
Midweek matchday: Tuesday

### CLUB PERSONNEL
Chairman: Rob Thompson
Manager: Russell Goodenough

**DEVIZES TOWN:** Back Row (L-R): David Lloyd, Chris Jones, Andy Stone, Nigel Curtiss, Julian Alexander, Tim Wootton, Nick Taylor, David Kilmurray, Phil Fry (physio). Front Row: Darren Walters, Andy Coombs (captain), Paul Thompson, Justin King

**FROME:** Back Row (L-R): Paul Antell, Aaron Blacker, Terry Moore, Keith Ball, Mark Slater, Stuart Luke, Andy Doel. Front Row: Matt Cowler, Jamie Manley, Tim John, Darren James, Paul Bendell, Kingsley John

**ILFRACOMBE TOWN:** Back Row (L-R): Nick Langmead, Lee Cochrane, Steve Burns, Mark Brereton, Kevin Squire, Phil Bell, Luke Fishlock, Marcus Vaughan, Paul Rockey, Steve Hobbs. Front Row: Kevin Pickard, Matthew Brereton, Luck Alcock, Roger Brereton (asst mngr), Shaun Lang (captain), Ross Middleton, Neil Gage

# STREET

**Secretary:** Mark Clarke, 1 Deerswood Gardens, Street, Somerset BA16 9PY Tel: 01458 440695

**Ground:** The Tannery Ground, Middlebrooks, Street, Somerset
Tel: 01458 445987 Matchdays 01458 448227
**Directions:** Sign posted from both ends of A39 & B3151, Station Castle Cary
Capacity: 2,000 Seating: 120 Cover: 25 Floodlights: Yes Club Shop: No

**HONOURS:** Western Lge R-up 52-53

**RECORDS:** Attendance: 4,300 v Yeovil Town FA Cup 17/11/47

**PREVIOUS:** Grounds: Victoria Field, Tunpike Ground

### FACT FILE
Founded: 1880 Nickname The Cobblers
Sponsors C I C A
Colours: Green & white/white/white
Change colours: Red & black/black/black
Midweek home matchday: Tuesday
Programme: 44 pages 50p
Editor: M Clarke

### CLUB PERSONNEL
Chairman: Andrew Walton
Manager: Simon White
Asst Mgr: Simon Culliford
Physios: Dick Pickersgill, Andrew Lee

---

# TORRINGTON

**Secretary:** David Priscott, 6 Highfield Terrace, Bishops Tawton, Barnstaple EX32 0AN
Tel: 01271 328316
**Ground:** Vicarage Field, School Lane, Great Torrington Tel: 01805 622853 **Directions:** In town centre turn left by parish church, right at swimming pool, ground behind swimming pool. Good parking. Red Bus from Bideford & Barnstaple (nearest BR station).Bus stop 300yds from ground
Capacity: 4,000 Seats: 100 Cover: 1,000 Floodlights: Yes Shop: No
**Clubhouse:** Weekdays 7-11pm, Sat 11-11 & Sun 12-3. Light snacks available on matchdays.

**HONOURS** Western Lg R-up 90-91; Merit Cup 91-92 93-94 95-96; South Western Lg Cup 81; Devon St Lukes Cup R-up 95-96 96-97; Devon & Exeter Lg & Cup 73-74; Festivalof Britain Cup 96-97; Les Phillips Cup R-up 91-92; Torridge Cup (13)
**PREVIOUS** Leagues: N Devon; Devon & Exeter; S Western 77-84 Grounds: None
**BEST SEASON FA Vase:** 5th Rd 84-85 FA Cup: 2nd Qual Rd. 81-82
**RECORDS Scorer:** Trevor Watkins, 254 **Appearances:** Mike Gilbert 527

### FACT FILE
Formed: 1908
Nickname: Torrie or Supergreens
Sponsors: R & S Ware
Colours: Green & white
Change cols: Blue & white stripes/white/white
Midweek Matches: Wednesday
Programme: 48 pages, 50p Editor: Secretary

### CLUB PERSONNEL
President: Keith Curtis
Chairman: Winston Martin
Manager: Jeff Evans
Coach: Paul Terry
Physio: Albert Williams

---

# WARMINSTER TOWN

**Secretary:** John Loftus, 34 George St., Warminster, Wilts. BA12 8QB
Tel: 01985 219324 (H), 01985 218516 (B)
**Ground:** Weymouth Street, Warminster, Wilts BA12 9NS, Tel: 01985 217828
**Directions:** Take A350 for Weymouth from lights at centre of town - ground on left at brow of hill
Capacity: 2,000 Seats: 75 Cover: 150 Floodlights: Yes
**Clubhouse:** Yes. Evenings & matchdays Club Shop: No

**HONOURS** Wilts Snr Cup 1900-01 02-03 10-11, R-up 09-10 26-27 32-33 53-54; Wilts Prem. Lg 56-57; Wilts Jnr Cup R-up 21-22 27-28 55-56 58-59; Central Wilts Lg 08-09
**PREVIOUS League:** Wiltshire**Grounds:** None
**RECORD Attendance:** 1,500 for Ladies International, England v Wales, mid-1970s
**BEST SEASON FA Cup:** 2nd Qual. Rd.(x5) **FA Vase:** 2nd Qual Rd
**1998-99** Captain: Mick Byrne P.o.Y.: Tony Brett Top Scorer: Chris Tricker

### FACT FILE
Founded: 1878
Nickname: Red & blacks
Sponsors: The Assam
Colours: Red & black stripes/black/red
Change: All white
Midweek Matchday: Tuesday
Reserve League: Wiltshire
Programme: 50p
Editor: Roger Bowden

### CLUB PERSONNEL
Chairman: Adrian Palmer
Vice-Chairman: Rod Kitley
General Manager: Derek Graham
Manager: Derek Graham

---

# WELLINGTON

**Secretary:** Dave Grabham, 12 Drakes Park, Wellington, SomersetTA21 8TB
Tel: 01823 664946 (H), 01823 355687 (B)
**Ground:** Wellington Playing Field, North Street, Wellington, Somerset Tel: 01823 664810
**Directions:** At town centre traffic lights turn into North St., then first left by Fire Station into the public car park that adjoins the ground
Capacity: 3,000 Seats: None Cover: 200 Floodlights: Yes
**Clubhouse:** Yes **Club Shop:** No

**HONOURS** Western Lg Div 1 R-up 80-81, Merit Cup 91-92, Comb Lge 95-96;Comb Lge KO Cup 95-96 98-99; Somerset Snr Lg Div 1 R-up; Rowbarton & Seward Cup
**PREVIOUS Leagues:** Taunton Saturday, Somerset Senior
**RECORD Attendance:** **Goalscorer:** Ken Jones
**BEST SEASON FA Cup:** 1st Qual Rd. 81-82, 84-85 **FA Vase:** 2nd rd Prop 98-99
**98-99** - Captain: Kevin Bryant P.o.Y.: Stuart Parris Top Scorer: Darren Bryant

### FACT FILE
Founded: 1892
Sponsors: A J Shire & Wadham Fencing
Colours: All tangerine
Change cols: Blue & claret stripes/blue/blue
Midweek Matches: Wednesday
Reserve Lge: Devon & Exeter Sen Div
Programme: Yes Editor: Jeff Brown

### CLUB PERSONNEL
Chairman: Selwyn Aspin
Vice-Chairman: Mike Bull
President: Alan Shire
Manager: Iain Blake
Reserves Manager: Adrian Gladstone Smith
Physio: Ken Pearson

# WELTON ROVERS

**Secretary:** Geoff Baker, 6 Longfellow Road, Westfield, Radstock, Bath BA3 3YZ
Tel: 01761 413742
**Ground:** West Clewes, North Road, Midsomer Norton, Somerset Tel: 01761 412097

**Directions:** A367 Bath to Radstock ō right at lights at foot of hill onto A362,ground on right.

**Capacity:** 2,400    **Seats:** 300        **Cover:** 300        **Floodlights:** Yes    **Club Shop:** No

**Clubhouse:** 7.30-11pm daily, plus Sat matchdays 1.30-2.45pm, Sun 12-2pm

**HONOURS** Western Lg 11-12 64-65 65-66 66-67 73-74, Div 1 59-60 87-88,Amateur Cup 56-57
57-58 58-59 59-60, Alan Young Cup 65-66 66-67 67-68(jt); Somerset Snr Cup 06-07
11-12 12-13 13-14 19-20 24-25 25-26 60-61 61-62 62-63, Som. I'mediate Cup 77-78,
Som. Jnr Cup 06-07(jt) 24-25 30-31, WBC Clares City of Wells Cup 78-79

**PREVIOUS**    **Leagues:** None    **Names:** None    **Grounds:** None

**BEST SEASON**    **FA Cup:**        **FA Vase:**
**RECORD**        **Attendance:** 2,000 v Bromley, FA Amateur Cup 1963

## FACT FILE

Formed: 1887
Nickname: Rovers
Sponsors: Young Bros (Roofing)
Colours: Green & white/green/green
Change colours: All Yellow
Midweek matchday: Monday
Reserve s' League: Somerset Senior
Programme: 12 pages, 25p
Editor: M Brown

## CLUB PERSONNEL

Chairman: Rae James
Manager: Adrian Britton
Asst Manager: Martin Finn
Physio: John Carver

**WELLINGTON:** Back Row (L-R): Iain Blake (Player/manager), Jason Greedy, Steve Jenkins, Simon Towler, Stuart Parris, Kevin Bryant, Matt Burfield, Martin Jenkins. Front Row: Mark Jones, Paul Pocock, Steve Trevelyna, Sean Maunder, Mark Wescott, Chris May, Rob Lowe

**WELTON ROVERS:** Back Row (L-R): Martin Finn (asst mngr), Neil Button, Andy Perrett, Paul Slocombe, Ken Scrivens, Alan Powell, Jon Porter, Phil Shrimpton, Adrian Britton (manager). Front Row: Ian Davis, Mark Evans, Trevor O'Neill, James Gower, Mark Jones, Andy Rowsell, Simon O'Reilly

# JEWSON SOUTH WESTERN FOOTBALL LEAGUE

**President:** Tristan H Scott    **Chairman:** Bob Bell

**Secretary:** Wendy Donohue, 115 Longfield, Falmouth, Cornwall TR11 4SL
Tel/Fax: 01326 316642

This season saw the inclusion of Plymouth Parkway in our ranks bringing the total of teams to seventeen. They, along with Torpoint and Saltash, started very well with the latter two clubs remaining unbeaten in August. Torpoint had notable wins over Falmouth and St Blazey. At the other end of the table Tavistock and Launceston made poor starts. The next two months saw the first qualifying rounds of the FA Cup and Vase, when the most notable result was a 1-0 home win for Falmouth against Vase holders Tiverton in the FA Cup. Whilst St Blazey started what was going to prove a long Cup campaign in an away win at Pershore. The early pacesetters in the JSWL were Truro, Porthleven, Wadebridge and Saltash.

Competition in the League was very even over the next couple of months and in early December Saltash headed the table closely followed by Porthleven and the two surprise teams at that time, Wadebridge and Millbrook. At the bottom of the table things were beginning to look familiar with St Austell, Launceston and Tavistock filling the bottom places. St Blazey were still in the Vase having beaten sides from supposedly higher leagues. Fixtures beginning to become a problem with the extremely wet weather, Cup matches and County calls all taking their toll. Most affected were Falmouth and St Blazey.

The New Year saw the Quarter Finals of the JSWL Cup taking place with Torpoint, Falmouth, Saltash and Porthleven going into the Semi Finals. Tavistock met Vospers Oak Villa and Parkway played Plymouth Civil Service in the Devon Premier Cup; unfortunately both were defeated leaving the JSWL without a representative.

February saw the Quarter Finals of the Charity Cup played when Bodmin, Porthleven, St Blazey and Wadebridge pro-gressed into the Semis. Porthleven had now taken over as League leaders from Saltash with Bodmin and Millbrook still in close contention. In the FA Vase St Blazey met Porthleven in an epic encounter which saw St Blazey win 2-1. They were now our only representatives. Their league fixtures were now seriously behind schedule. In the next round of the Vase they met Dunstan Federation Brewery from the Northern League. They proved a very strong side and swept St Blazey aside.

All the Cup competitions were reaching their closing stages with Porthleven featuring in all three Semi Finals. The Charity Cup saw them paired against St Blazey, whilst the other semi featured Bodmin and Wadebridge. The League Cup saw them playing Saltash, the other Semi was Falmouth against Torpoint. In the Senior Cup Porthleven were to play Bodmin whilst St Blazey were matched against Millbrook. The League now showed Porthleven forging ahead of Millbrook, Saltash and fourth placed St Blazey who were fourteen points behind the leaders. At the bottom an improving Tavistock had moved away from the re-election zone, but St Austell and Launceston were still there now joined by Torpoint who were having a nightmare sea-son, especially at home.

March saw the Senior Cup Semis decided. Bodmin recorded a great win over Porthleven at Truro whilst Millbrook out-fought and out-ran St Blazey to win 2-1 at Bodmin. This ensured there would be a new name on the Cup as, although both sides had featured in finals before, both had lost to Liskeard. The League moved on with Porthleven increasing their lead whilst Falmouth, who had indicated their intention of seeking promotion to the Screwfix League if they finished first or second in the JSWL, and St Blazey played catch up with their fixtures.

April proved a mixed month for Porthleven. In the League Cup they defeated Saltash to reach the Final, whilst in the other Semi Torpoint and Falmouth needed a replay and extra time to separate them with Falmouth winning 3-2. These two matches were amongst the most entertaining I had seen all season. The Senior Cup Final saw Bodmin beat Millbrook 2-1 in what was not a great final. Ricky Cardew won't mind that, however, as this victory saw him complete a full set of all trophies available in the County and JSWL. St Blazey now found themselves having to play sixteen games to the end of the season, whilst runaway leaders Porthleven only needed a few more wins. Porthleven continued to play well but dropped vital points at Parkway, who must have been delighted with their 2-1 win.

May saw St Blazey still winning in the League and also picking up the Charity Cup with a superb display against Wadebridge, winning 4-1. The JSWL Cup final saw Porthleven meet Falmouth at Truro. The match started evenly, then after about fifteen minutes played and in the space of four minutes Luke Hodge of Falmouth scored a brilliant hat trick to win the Cup. Porthleven never recovered from this early set back and Falmouth were deserved winners. Porthleven had now gone out of all Cup competitions despite being in all the Semi-Finals and one Final. In the League Falmouth had fallen away, but St Blazey had won all their games apart from a 0-0 draw at Millbrook. The crunch match was on a Monday night at Porthleven when they only needed a win in their last League match to secure the title for the first time in their history. St Blazey could afford a draw as they still had two games to play after this game.

A large crowd was treated to a magnificent match. Porthleven playing with a strong wind dominated the first half and at half time led 3-0. The second half was a complete contrast. St Blazey threw everything at Porthleven, scored early, saw Gary Penhalligan save a Matt Salmon penalty, then scored a penalty through the same player and finally equalised at 3-3. In a frantic last few minutes there were chances at both ends but the final whistle saw a total contrast in the teams. Porthleven for so long the leaders knew they they could now do nothing to win the League, which depended on the last two matches at Blaize Park. St Blazey got a huge lift from this result and duly beat Falmouth and St Austell to win the title.

Whilst I feel a twinge of disappointment for Porthleven who, despite playing so well throughout the season ended up with nothing, I must congratulate St Blazey who played sixteen matches in just six weeks winning fourteen and drawing two to win the League title and Charity Cup. An amazing achievement.

Another season beckons and there is all to play for.

# JEWSON SOUTH WESTERN LEAGUE ROLE OF HONOUR 1998-99

| | WINNERS | RUNNERS UP | THIRD PLACE | FOURTH PLACE |
|---|---|---|---|---|
| League Championship | St Blazey AFC | Porthleven FC | Truro City FC | Falmouth Town FC |
| League Cup | Falmouth Town | Porthleven | | |
| Ground Trophy | Torpoint | St Blazey | Newquay | Wadebridge |
| Sporting Trophy | Wadebridge | Torpoint | Penzance | |
| Top Referee | Ian McKinnon | | | |

### LEADING GOALSCORERS

| | | | | |
|---|---|---|---|---|
| Mark Rapsey | 33 | Wadebridge Town | Marcus Crocker | 20 | Saltash |
| Charlie Legg | 29 | Porthleven | Justin Harrington | 16 | Porthleven |
| Nigel Thwaites | 23 | Porthleven | Andy Bowker | 14 | Saltash |
| Ian Rowe | 21 | St Blazey | | | |

## FINAL LEAGUE TABLE 1998-99

| | P | W | D | L | F | A | Pts | | P | W | D | L | F | A | Pts |
|---|---|---|---|---|---|---|---|---|---|---|---|---|---|---|---|
| St Blazey | 32 | 23 | 5 | 4 | 69 | 25 | 74 | Holsworthy | 32 | 11 | 8 | 13 | 50 | 56 | 41 |
| Porthleven | 32 | 22 | 7 | 3 | 102 | 36 | 73 | Plymouth Parkway | 32 | 10 | 6 | 16 | 50 | 74 | 36 |
| Truro City | 32 | 18 | 8 | 6 | 65 | 37 | 62 | Liskeard Athletic | 32 | 8 | 9 | 15 | 47 | 62 | 33 |
| Falmouth Town | 32 | 17 | 8 | 7 | 57 | 35 | 59 | Tavistock | 32 | 8 | 8 | 16 | 32 | 47 | 32 |
| Wadebridge Town | 32 | 17 | 6 | 9 | 64 | 34 | 57 | Newquay | 32 | 10 | 2 | 20 | 40 | 64 | 32 |
| Millbrook | 32 | 17 | 5 | 10 | 55 | 32 | 56 | St Austell | 32 | 7 | 5 | 20 | 29 | 67 | 26 |
| Saltash United | 32 | 15 | 7 | 10 | 56 | 45 | 52 | Torpoint Athletic | 32 | 5 | 5 | 22 | 39 | 73 | 20 |
| Bodmin Town | 32 | 15 | 5 | 12 | 65 | 57 | 50 | Launceston | 32 | 4 | 5 | 23 | 33 | 105 | 17 |
| Penzance | 32 | 12 | 7 | 13 | 58 | 62 | 43 | | | | | | | | |

## DIVISION ONE RESULTS CHART 1998-99

| | | 1 | 2 | 3 | 4 | 5 | 6 | 7 | 8 | 9 | 10 | 11 | 12 | 13 | 14 | 15 | 16 | 17 |
|---|---|---|---|---|---|---|---|---|---|---|---|---|---|---|---|---|---|---|
| 1 | Bodmin Town | X | 2-0 | 5-3 | 3-0 | 3-4 | 1-3 | 5-0 | 0-1 | 2-3 | 0-3 | 3-0 | 2-3 | 1-0 | 3-0 | 2-2 | 3-0 | 1-2 |
| 2 | Falmouth Town | 1-0 | X | 0-0 | 4-1 | 2-1 | 2-1 | 3-0 | 1-0 | 2-2 | 0-0 | 4-1 | 1-0 | 1-1 | 2-0 | 1-3 | 0-1 | 0-2 |
| 3 | Holsworthy | 2-2 | 1-1 | X | 4-0 | 2-2 | 1-0 | 1-0 | 1-2 | 3-3 | 1-3 | 3-0 | 0-1 | 5-3 | 2-3 | 2-1 | 1-3 | 3-6 |
| 4 | Launceston | 2-3 | 1-6 | 0-2 | X | 0-2 | 1-4 | 1-0 | 0-3 | 4-3 | 0-8 | 1-3 | 1-4 | 1-4 | 1-0 | 1-2 | 0-3 | 1-1 |
| 5 | Liskeard Ath | 1-1 | 1-3 | 5-0 | 1-1 | X | 1-1 | 2-1 | 0-1 | 0-1 | 2-3 | 0-1 | 1-4 | 2-0 | 0-1 | 3-3 | 0-2 | 0-5 |
| 6 | Millbrook | 2-3 | 1-2 | 1-0 | 3-1 | 4-0 | X | 1-0 | 3-1 | 1-1 | 0-2 | 3-0 | 0-0 | 2-1 | 1-1 | 2-0 | 0-1 | 0-2 |
| 7 | Newquay | 0-2 | 2-2 | 1-0 | 4-0 | 2-3 | 0-3 | X | 0-4 | 1-0 | 1-1 | 2-3 | 0-1 | 1-0 | 4-2 | 3-1 | 0-5 | 0-1 |
| 8 | Penzance | 4-4 | 2-2 | 1-2 | 2-3 | 2-2 | 1-2 | 3-0 | X | 4-1 | 1-3 | 5-2 | 2-1 | 0-1 | 2-2 | 5-1 | 1-6 | 0-3 |
| 9 | Plymouth Parkway | 1-2 | 1-3 | 2-2 | 6-4 | 2-2 | 0-2 | 2-4 | 2-3 | X | 3-2 | 1-2 | 0-2 | 0-1 | 2-1 | 2-1 | 1-0 | 0-4 |
| 10 | Porthleven | 5-1 | 1-2 | 0-1 | 8-3 | 5-1 | 3-1 | 3-2 | 10-0 | 6-0 | X | 3-1 | 3-3 | 6-1 | 1-0 | 1-1 | 2-2 | 1-1 |
| 11 | St Austell | 1-4 | 2-3 | 0-5 | 0-0 | 2-1 | 2-3 | 0-1 | 2-2 | 0-3 | 1-2 | X | 0-1 | 0-3 | 0-0 | 2-0 | 2-4 | 0-3 |
| 12 | St Blazey | 2-2 | 2-1 | 5-0 | 3-1 | 0-0 | 1-0 | 4-1 | 1-1 | 5-0 | 1-4 | 3-0 | X | 3-0 | 3-0 | 2-3 | 2-0 | 2-0 |
| 13 | Saltash Utd | 3-2 | 1-3 | 1-0 | 7-0 | 3-2 | 2-1 | 3-1 | 1-1 | 4-1 | 1-3 | 0-0 | 1-2 | X | 2-0 | 3-2 | 2-3 | 4-2 |
| 14 | Tavistock | 3-0 | 1-0 | 1-1 | 1-1 | 1-3 | 0-3 | 4-2 | 1-0 | 2-3 | 1-2 | 0-0 | 0-1 | 0-0 | X | 1-0 | 1-1 | 2-0 |
| 15 | Torpoint Ath | 2-3 | 1-3 | 0-2 | 3-3 | 1-2 | 1-3 | 1-4 | 0-3 | 0-2 | 3-4 | 0-2 | 1-4 | 1-1 | 0-1 | X | 0-1 | 1-0 |
| 16 | Truro City | 1-3 | 1-1 | 0-0 | 5-0 | 4-2 | 1-1 | 0-3 | 1-0 | 4-1 | 1-1 | 3-0 | 0-2 | 1-1 | 3-2 | 4-2 | X | 2-1 |
| 17 | Wadebridge Town | 4-0 | 2-1 | 4-0 | 3-0 | 1-1 | 0-3 | 3-0 | 4-1 | 1-1 | 0-3 | 4-1 | 0-1 | 1-1 | 1-0 | 1-2 | 2-2 | X |

## JSWL CHALLENGE CUP 1998-99

**PRELIMINARY ROUND**

| Launceston | v | Millbrook | 0-4 |
|---|---|---|---|

**FIRST ROUND**

| Falmouth Town | v | Bodmin Town | 2-0 | Holsworthy | v | Wadebridge Town | 2-3 |
|---|---|---|---|---|---|---|---|
| Newquay | v | Millbrook | 0-1 | Liskeard Athletic | v | Torpoint Athletic | 1-2 |
| Penzance | v | Plymouth Parkway | 2-2, 1-2 | Porthleven | v | St Austell | 3-1 |
| St Blazey | v | Truro City | 2-1 | Tavistock | v | Saltash United | 0-2 |

**QUARTER FINALS**

| Wadebridge Town | v | Saltash United | 1-3 | St Blazey | v | Falmouth Town | 1-4 |
|---|---|---|---|---|---|---|---|
| Plymouth Parkway | v | Torpoint Athletic | 1-2 | Millbrook | v | Porthleven | 2-4 |

**SEMI FINALS**

| Porthleven | v | Saltash United | 3-1 | Falmouth Town | v | Torpoint Athletic | 2*2, 3*2 |
|---|---|---|---|---|---|---|---|

**FINAL**

| Falmouth Town | v | Porthleven | 3-0 | at Truro |
|---|---|---|---|---|

714

# BODMIN TOWN

**Secretary:** David Sandry, 21 Rock Lane, Bodmin PL31 1NR (01208 75248)

**Ground:** Priory Park, Bodmin. Tel: 01208 78165

**Directions:** Just off town centre in large park complex,at rear of town car park

**Capacity:** Cover: Grandstand    Seats: Yes    Floodlights: Yes

**Clubhouse:** Mon-Thu 6.30-11pm (matchdays 6-11), Fri-Sat 12-11pm,
Sun 12-3 & 7-10.30pm,  unless Sky matches are on then 12 -10.30 pm
Bar snacks available most times    Club Shop: No

**Honours:** South Western Lg 90-91 93-94 (R-up 76-77, 92-93, 94-95, Lg Cup 93-94 ,97-98
(R-up 7-78 88-89 94-95,95-96), Cornwall Snr Cup Winners 98-99 R-up 93-94,
Cornwall Charity Cup 86-87 89-90,96-97.Cornish Guardian E.C.P.L.Supplimentary
Cup 91-92 (R-Up. 93-94)-GordonSweet Cup 90-91,92-93,98-99

**FACT FILE**
Founded: 1889    Nickname: Black & Ambers
Sponsors: Gynn Construction
Colours: Yellow & black/black/yellow
Change colours: All white
Midweek Matchday: Wednesday
Reserves' League: East Cornwall Premier
Programme: 64pages, 40p
Programme Editor: Secretary
**CLUB PERSONNEL**
Chairman: C.Hooper
Vice-Chairman: P.Lee
President: A.Gynn
Manager: Ricky Cardew
Asst Manager: Phil Brown
Physio: Jim Brewer

# CALLINGTON TOWN

**Secretary:** Philip Brown, Mount Pleasant Cottage, Harrow barrow, Callington PL17 8JL
Tel: 01822 833851

**Ground:** Callington Community School, Launceston Road, Callington.

Colours: Blue & yellow

# FALMOUTH TOWN

**Secretary:** John E Thompson, 45 Woodland Avenue, Penryn, Cornwall TR10 8PG
Tel No: 01326 372972(H) 01326 372778 (W)

**Ground:** Bickland Park, Bickland Vale, Falmouth, Cornwall  Tel: 01326 375156

**Directions:** Follow A39 to Tregoniggie Industrial Estate - will pass ground on left.
1 1/2 miles from Penmere Halt (BR) on Falmouth-Truro branch line. Bus service from town centre

**Capacity:** 6,000    Seats: 300    Cover: 1,200    Floodlights: Yes    Club Shop: TBA

**Clubhouse:** Mon-Fri 7-11pm, Sat 12-11pm, Sun 12-3 & 7-10.30pm. Meals available

**HONOURS:** Cornish Senior Cup x 10 R-up x 7; Western Lg x 4, Lg Cup 74-75, Alan Young
Cup x 3; South Western Lg x 12 R-up x 4, Lg Cup x 10 R-up x 5; Pratten Cup    73-74,
Cornwall Charity Cup 59-60 94-95,

**BEST SEASON**    **FA Cup:** 1st Round 62-63 & 67-68
**FA Vase:** Quarter Final 86-87    **FA Trophy:** 2nd Round 77-78

**PREVIOUS**    **Leagues:** Cornish Snr 50-51; South Western 51-74; Western 74-83
**RECORDS**    **Gate:** 6,300 v Oxford United, FA Cup 1st Round 3/11/62

**FACT FILE**
Founded: 1949    Nickname: Town
Club Sponsors: Stralfors/ Diadora
Colours: Amber/black
Change colours: Red/white
Midweek Matchday: Tues/Wed
Reserves' League: Cornwall Comb
Programme: 16 pages, 30p
Editor/ Press Off.: Mike Odgers 01209 715766
**CLUB PERSONNEL**
Chairman: Malcolm Newland
Vice Chairman: Paul Ashburn
President: Seb Coe
Manager: David Ball
Asst Man.: Dave Ball    Coach: Keith Barker

# HOLSWORTHY

**Secretary:** Mel Goodenough, Rose Cottage, Horrels Ford,Milton Damerel, Holsworthy
EX22 NU Tel Nos: 01409 261402 (H) 01805 622315 (emergency W)

**Ground:** Upcott Field Tel: 01409 254295
Cover: Yes    Floodlights: No

**Directions:** Leaving town centre on A388 towards Bideford, 100 yards past mini-r'about on left.

**Honours:** Devon Senior Cup 53-54 (Prem. Cup 71-72 78-79), Devon Junior Cup 38-39

**FACT FILE**
Nickname: Magpies
Colours: Black & White/Black/black & white
Change colours:yellow/green/green & yellow
Programme: 28 pages, ¨2 with entry
Editor: Terry Trewin.& Bob Thomson
**CLUB PERSONNEL**
Chairman: Mike Pett
Manager: Peter England
Assistant Manager: Alan Mayes

# LAUNCESTON

**Secretary:** Chris Martin, 3 Tavistock Road, Launceston, Cornwall PL15 9HA
Tel: 01566 776175

**Ground:** Pennygillam, Launceston (0566 773279)

**Directions:** Follow signs to Pennygillam Ind. Est., just off main A30 -ground 400yds on left
Capacity:    Seats: 150    Cover: 150    Floodlights: Yes

**Clubhouse:** Open after every game. Bar meals available.    Club Shop: No

**HONOURS** South Western Lg Winners  94-95, R-up 84-85, S.W Lg.Cup Winners: 95-96
Cornish Snr Cup 1899-1900 00-01 82-83 (R-up 92-93, Charity Cup R-up 88-89)

Founded: 1891    Nickname: Clarets
Colours: Claret & blue/blue/claret
Change colours: Sky/Sky/claret
Midweek matchday: Tues/Wed
Reserves' League: Plymouth & Dist
Programme: Yes
Joint Chairmen:
Keith Ellacott, Alan Bradley
President: Mr.S.Dawe
General Manager: Keith Ellacott
Manager: J.Dent    Physio: G.Hart

# LISKEARD ATHLETIC

**Football Secretary:** Brian Olver, Windrush, Tremeddan Lane, Liskeard, Cornwall PL14 3DS
**Gen. Secretary:** D J Rawlings, Bradwood, Woodgate Rd., Liskeard PL14 6DY
**Ground:** Lux Park, Liskeard, Cornwall (01579 42665) **Directions:** Take Tavistock Road (A390) from town centre, after 1/2 mile turn left on St Cleer Road (follow signs to Lux Park Sports Complex) & ground is 200 yards on left. Half mile from Liskeard BR station
**Capacity:** 2,000 **Seats:** 100 **Cover:** 300 **Floodlights:** Yes **Club Shop:** No
**Clubhouse:** (01579 342665) Normal licensing hours. Hot & cold food available
**HONOURS:** South Western Lg 76-77 78-79 (R-up 75-76 77-78; Lg Cup 76-77 78-79) Western Lg 87-88 (R-up 85-86 89-90, Merit Cup 80-81); Cornwall Snr Cup 04-05 83-84 84-85 85-86 88-89 89-90 93-94 (R-up 70-71 75-76 76-77 78-79 94-95); Cornwall Charity Cup 21-22 79-80, Cornwall Jnr Cup 05-06 13-14 26-27; SWPratten Cup 78-79; E Cornwall Prem RAOB Cup 67-68, Plymouth & Dist. Lg 60-61(Div 1 59-60 (R-up 54-55 73-74), Div 2 76-77(Res)), Victory Cup 60-61, Charity Cup 59-60), E Cornwall Prem. Lg (Res) 84-85 92-93 93-94(Lg.Cup 88-89 93-94)
**PREVIOUS Leagues:** E. Cornwall Prem., Plymouth & Dist., South Western 66-79, Western 79-95
**RECORDS** **Goalscorer:** T Turner 59, 60-61 **Appearances:** Brian Bunney, 500+

**FACT FILE**
Formed: 1889 Nickname: Blues
Sponsors: J P Leisure & Gilbert Outfitters
Colours: Blue & White/blue/blue & white
Change colours: All white
Midweek matchday: Tuesday
Programme: 40 pages, 50p
Editor: K Lobb / D J Rawlings
**CLUB PERSONNEL**
Chairman: Keith Lobb
Vice Chairman: Dave Rawlings
President: R D Burt
Manager: Chris Burchell
Asst Manager: mike
Physio: Eddie Harrison

# MILLBROOK

**Secretary:** Paul May, 20 Cedar Drive, Torpoint, Cornwall PL11 2QQ. Tel No: 01752 812154 (H)
**Ground:** Mill Park, Millbrook, Cornwall (01752 822113)

**Directions:** From Torpoint Ferry - 3 miles to Antony on A374, fork left, after 1 mile turn left again and follow B3247 to Millbrook (3 miles), take road marked 'Town Centre Southdown', right at mini-r'bout after 1/4 mile, ground clearly visible. From Tamar Bridge - follow signs for Torpoint, 2 miles after Polbathic right turning marked Millbrook, 5 miles to Millbrook then proceed as above
**Capacity:** **Seats:** None **Cover:** 200 **Floodlights:** Yes **Club Shop:** No
**Clubhouse:** Weekdays 7-11pm, Sat 11am-11pm, Sun noon-3 & 7.30-10.30. Hot food (chips, burgers etc) available during and after matchdays
**HONOURS:** South Western Lg R-up 81-82, Cornwall Snr Cup R-up 83-84 (Charity Cup 84-85, Jnr Cup 75-76), Plymouth & District Lg 80-81 (Div 1 R-up 76-77)
**PREVIOUS** **Leagues:** Plymouth Comb.(8yrs)/ Plymouth & Dist.(6yrs)
**CLUB RECORDS** **Scorer:** Unknown **Appearances:** John Horne 215

**FACT FILE**
Founded: 1973 Nickname: The Brook
Sponsors: Plymouth Boat Cruises Ltd
Colours: White & Black/white/red
Change colours: Sky/royal blue/royal blue
Midweek matchday: Tuesday
Reserve's League: Plymouth & District
Programme: 20 pages, 10p
Editor: J Weekes (01752 822637)
**CLUB PERSONNEL**
President: Mrs E Weekes
Chairman: Martin Bettridge
Vice Chairman: K Townsend
Press Officer: W Linney
Managers: Paul Stevens & John Hilson
Asst Manager: S Matthews

# NEWQUAY

**Secretary:** John Hawkey, 16 Higher Tower Rd, Newquay, Cornwall.TR7 1QL (01637871884)
**Ground:** Mount Wise, Newquay (01637 872935)
**Directions:** 1/2 mile from Newquay BR, follow 1-way system for 1/2 mile - ground signed on left before the Windsor Hotel
**Capacity:** 4,000 **Seats:** 250 **Cover:** 500 **Floodlights:** Yes **Club Shop:** No
**Clubhouse:** 7-11pm w/days, 12-11pm Sat, 12-10.30 Sun. Hot & cold snacks during matches
**HONOURS:** Cornish Snr Cup 34-35 52-53 54-55 56-57 91-92(R-up(10) 05-07 08-09 25-26 33-34 35-36 57-58 69-70 84-85 87-88), S. Western Lg(7) 58-60 77-78 79-80 81-82 83-84 87-88 (R-up 57-58 85-86 94-95, Lg Cup 55-56 88-89(R-up(4) 56-58 79-81), Cornwall Charity Cup(13) 06-07 08-09 53-56 57-59 62-63 69-70 74-75 76-78 88-89 (R-up(10) 07-08 20-21 56-57 60-61 73-74 75-76 81-82 84-87), W. Cornwall Lg 06-07 (R-up(2) 07-09), Cornish Snr Lg Herald Cup 34-35 (R-up(7) 33-34 35-36 49-51 55-57 58-59)
**PREVIOUS** **Leagues:** West Cornwall; Plymouth & District 21-27; Cornish Senior 31-51
**BEST SEASON** FA Vase: 3rd Round 90-91

**FACT FILE**
Founded: 1890 Nickname: Peppermints
Sponsors: Studs Sports
Colours: Red & white stripes
Change colours: Blue & white
Midweek Matchday: Tuesday
Reserve League: Cornwall Combination
Programme: 24 pages, 50p Editor: J Hawkey
**CLUB PERSONNEL**
Chairman: T Warne
Vice-Chairman: A Kendall
President: J L Parker
Manager/Coach: Dominic Evans
Physio: Ross McOnie

# PENZANCE

**Secretary:** John Mead, 8 Chyanclare, St Clare Street, Penzance TR18 2PG
Tel No: 01736 369066 (H)

**Ground:** Penlee Park - (01736 61964)
**Directions:** Seafront road past harbour, after amusement arcade turn right atr'bout (Alexander Rd), ground second right. Fifteen minutes walk from Penzance(BR); directions as above
**HONOURS** Cornish Snr Cup 1892-93 95-96 97-98 98-99 1903-04 07-08 47-48 60-61 72-73 80-81 (R-up 1896-97 99-1900 00-01 04-05 48-49 49-50 54-55 56-57 74-75),South Western Lg 55-56 56-57 74-75 (Lg Cup R-up 60-61), Cornwall Charity Cup 47-48 48-49 (R-up 21-22 63-64), Cornwall Snr Lg Div 2 57-58 (Div 2 Cup 53-54 54-55), Cornwall Comb. R-up 65-66 (Lg Cup 69-70 (R-up 81-82)), Cornwall Jnr Cup(West) 03-04 04-05 05-06 07-08 09-10
Players progressing: Gerry Gazzard (Brentford), Tony Kellow (Exeter)

**FACT FILE**
Founded: 1888
Nickname: Magpies
Colours: Black & white/black/black
Change colours: All yellow
Reserves' league: Cornwall Comb
**CLUB PERSONNEL**
President: Len Stanbury
Chairman: Jim Dann
Manager:Robbie Stephens
Trainer: Ken Prowse

# PLYMOUTH PARKWAY

Secretary: Stuart Cadmore, 25 Dudley Gardens, Eggbuckland, Plymouth PL6 5PE
Tel: 01752 782661
Ground: The Parkway, Ernesettle Lane, Plymouth. Tel: 01752 363080 (Clubhouse)
Directions: From Tamar Bridge, take 1st exit signed St Budeaux/Ernesettle. Then 1st exit at roundabout, following Ernesettle Ind Est. Ground at bottom of hill on right

**FACT FILE**
Colours: Yellow/royal blue/white
Change colours: Azure blue/black/black
**CLUB PERSONNEL**
Chairman: Mark Rowles
Manager: Gez Baggott

# PORTHLEVEN

Team Secretary: Vidal James, 23 Parc-an -Bans,Camborne, TR14 7RW (01209 710618)

Ground: Gala Parc, Mill Lane, Porthleven (0208 574754)
Directions: From Penzance on A394, B3304 into Porthleven, ground on left immediately before own. From Helston on B3304 ground on right as you exit town. Buses from Helston & Penzance
Capacity: 1,500    Seats: None    Cover: Yes    Floodlights: Yes    Shop: No
Clubhouse: Mon-Fri 7-11pm, Sat 11am-8pm, Sun 11-3 & 7-10.30pm. Full food menu at wek-ends

PREVIOUS        Grounds: Treza Downs; Sunset Farm
                Leagues: West Penwith; Cornwall Snr; South Western 66-77; Cornwall Comb. 77-89
HONOURS Sth Western Lg R-up 72-73, 98-99 Lg Cup R-up 98-99, Cornwall Comb.(6), (Lg
Cup(6), CornwallCharity Cup 70-71, 97-98 Cornwall Snr Cup R-up 68-69, 97-98 George Evely
Cup 64-65 65-66 83-84 86-87, West Penwith Lg, Penzance Hosp. Cup, Penzance Charity Cup

**FACT FILE**
Founded: 1896
Nickname: Fishermen
Colours: Amber/black
Change colours: All blue
Midweek Matchday: Wednesday
Reserves' Lge: Cornwall Comb
Programme: 20p
**CLUB PERSONNEL**
President: Mr P F Johns
Chairman: Mr L.Williams
Vice Chairman: Mr N.Chapman
Comm. Mgr: Mr P.Gardner
Manager: Alan Carey
Coaches:G Torrance &G Bannister

# SALTASH UNITED

Secretary: P J Gammage, 23 Spire Hill Park, Saltash, Cornwall, PL12 4SR    Tel: 01752 844046

Ground: Kimberley Stadium, Callington Road, Saltash, Cornwall Tel: 01752 845746
Directions: First left after crossing Tamar Bridge, through town centre, at top of town fork right at nin- roundabout, ground 400 yds ahead on left.
Capacity: 3,000        Seats: 250        Cover: 250        Floodlights: Yes
Clubhouse: Club attached to stand and caters for dancing and clubactivities.Saphire Lounge aters for wedding receptions,quiz nights and private functions etc
PREVIOUS        Leagues: Cornwall Snr; Sth Western  51-59 62-76; E Cornwall Prem 59-62;
                Western 76-95
HONOURS         Cornwall Snr Lg 49-50 50-51, Western Lg 84-85 86-87 88-89 (R-up 83-84 87-
                88, Lg Cup  86-87 87-88 (R-up 88-89), Div 1 76-77, Merit Cup 79-80 87-88),
                Sth Western Lg 53-54 75-76 (R-up 3), Lg Cup 3, Cornwall Snr Cup 6

**FACT FILE**
Formed: 1945
Nickname: The Ashes
Colours: Scarlet&Black/black/black
Change: All Royal Blue with yellow trim
Midweek Matchday: Wednesday
Programme: 52 pages,50p
Editor: Marian Gammage

**CLUB PERSONNEL**
President: P Skinnard
Chairman: Michael Howard
Manager: Leigh Cooper

# St. AUSTELL

Secretary:    Peter Beard, 24 Alexandra Rd, St Austell, Cornwall PL25 4QP
              Tel: 01726 64138
Ground:       Poltair Park, Poltair Road, St. Austell                Tel: 01726 66099
Directions:   5 mins walk north of St Austell (BR)
              Capacity: 8,000        Seats: 200        Cover: 300        Floodlights: No
Clubhouse:    Mon-Fri 7-10.30 & Sat 12-11pm Food is available
PREVIOUS      Leagues: Rocky Park (1890s)
RECORD        Gate: 15,000 v Penzance, Senior Cup 49
HONOURS       South Western Lg 68-69 (R-up 4), Lg Cup 64-65 71-73 87-88 (R-up 4),
              Cornish Senior Cup(11)

**FACT FILE**
Founded: 1890
Sponsors: Kwik Print
Colours: White/black/black
Change colours: Blue/black/blue
Midweek Matchday: Tuesday
Reserves' League: East Cornwall Prem.
**CLUB PERSONNEL**
Chairman: Glyn Rowett
Asst Chairman: Alan Lucas
Manager: Dave Pearce
Asst Manager: Keith Hosbani

# St. BLAZEY

Secretary: Ken Cocks, 20 North St Tywardreath, Par, Cornwall PL24 2PN Tel: 01726 815187

Ground: St Blaise Park, Station Road, St Blazey Tel: 01726 814110

Directions:    A390 Liskeard-St Austell road, turn into Station Road at lights inSt Blazey village; ground 100 yards on left. One and a half miles from Par (BR)

              Capacity: 3,500    Seats: 200        Cover: 700        Floodlights: Yes
Clubhouse: Mon-Thur 11-3pm & 7-11pm, Fri &Sat 11-11.45pm, Sun 12-3pm & 7-11pm.
              Bar snacks        Club Shop: No

HONOURS        South Western Lg (7), R-up  ( 9), Lg Cup 5, (R-up 5), Cornish Snr Cup ,Cornish
Charity Cup 35-36 56-57 83-84, 98-99 Cornwall Snr Lg Cup (Herald Cup) 35-3648-49

RECORDS        Gate: 6,500 v St Austell, Cornwall Snr Cup 48-49
               Goalscorer: B Tallamy        Appearances: W Isbell

**FACT FILE**
Founded: 1896
Nickname: Saints
Sponsors: Express Joinery
Colours: All Green & black
Change colours: Blue & white/blue/blue
Midweek matchday: Wednesday
Reserve's League: East Cornwall Premier
Programme: 24 pages,50p
Editor: Steve Paynter
**CLUB PERSONNEL**
Chairman: Mr H Cooke
Vice Chairman: Mr A.Putt
Manager: Trevor Mewton
Assistant Manager: Paul Goodwin

# TAVISTOCK AFC

**FACT FILE**
Founded: 1888

**Secretary:** Philip Lowe, 1 Bainbridge Court, Colebrook, Plympton, Plymouth PL7 4HH
Tel: 01752 335273

**Ground:** Langsford Park, Crowndale Rd, Tavistock (01822 614447)

**Directions:** A386 from Plymouth, 2nd left after Ford garage into Crowndale Road and the ground is half mile on left opposite Tavistock College

**Capacity: 2,000    Seats: 200    Cover: 200    Floodlights: Yes    Club Shop: No**

**Clubhouse:** Open all day Saturday and evenings 6.30-10.30 or 11pm. Hot & cold food

**HONOURS** Devon Premier Cup R-up 94-95, Devon Snr Cup 1889-90 1968-69 77-78 81-82, South Western Lg Cup 68-69 (R-up 76-77 83-84), Bedford Cup -numerous times; Devon Charity Cup 78-79, R-up 77-78

**RECORDS   Gate:** 5,000 v Calstock, Bedford Cup final 1952

**Appearances:** A Pethick 1,000+

Players progressing: Peter & Neil Langman (Plymouth A., 51 & 53); Robbie Pethick (Portsmouth); Mike Trebilcock (Plymouth A. 65); Harold Redmond & Danny Sullivan (Crystal Pal. 57 - £100)

Nickname: `Tavy' or `Lambs'
Sponsors: SMC / Applied Automation
Colours: Red & Black/black/black
Change colours: All Blue
Midweek matchday: Tuesday
Reserves' Lge: Plymouth & Dist Comb. (Prem)
Programme: 32 pages, with entry
Editor: Vice Chairman
**CLUB PERSONNEL**
Chairman: David Rowe
Vice Chairman: Eric Pinch (Press Officer)
Manager: Steve Hart
Asst Manager: Gary Tiffany
Physio: Les Mewton

# TORPOINT ATHLETIC

**Secretary:** Vic Grimwood, 43 Henerdon Heights, Plympton PL7 3EY (01752 81344)

**Ground:** Mill Field (01752 812889)

**Directions:** Bear left from Torpoint ferry, ground down hill on left after halfa mile

**Capacity:    Seats: Yes    Cover: Yes    Floodlights: No**
**Clubhouse:** Yes

**PREVIOUS    League:** Plymouth & District League.(Premier)

**BEST SEASON    FA Vase:** 4th Round 93-94, 0-3 v Diss Town (H), eventual winners

**HONOURS**    South Western Lg 64-65 66-67 (Lg Cup R-up 65-66), Cornish Snr Cup 8

**FACT FILE**

Colours: Gold & black stripes/gold/gold
Change colours: Green & White/White/White
Programme: Yes

**CLUB PERSONNEL**

Chairman: Austin Toms
Manager: Phil Cardew

# TRURO CITY

**Secretary:** Ray Rowe, 5 Alverton Gardens, Truro, Cornwall TR1 1JA (01872 270684)

**Ground:** Treyew Road, Truro, Cornwall (01872 278853)

**Capacity: 5,000    Seats: 250    Cover:Yes    Floodlights: Yes**

**Directions:** On A39 by-pass south of city.
10 mins walk from BR station; up hill and left at junction

**HONOURS**    South Western Lg 60-61 69-70 92-93 95-96 97-98, (R-up 54-55 62-63 66-67 67-68 70-71 96-97), Lg Cup 59-60 66-67(jt) 92-93 (R-up 54-55 58-59 67-68 93-94 95-96 97-98); Cornish Snr Cup x13; Cornish Charity Cup x7; Cornish Snr Lg 31-32 32-33; Cornwall Combination 94-95 98-99 League Cup: 1968,78,86,88,99

**FACT FILE**
Formed: 1889
Colours: Red & black/black/black
Change colours: Blue
Midweek Matchday: Tuesday
Programme: Yes

Reserve s' League: Cornwall Combination

**CLUB PERSONNEL**
Chairman: Drew Weir
Manager: Chris webb

# WADEBRIDGE TOWN

**Secretary:** Mike Tregaskes, 10 TRezaise Close, Roche, St Austell Pl26 8HW
Tel Nos: 01726 890782 (H) 01726 890782 (W)

**Ground:** Bodieve Park (0208 812537)

**Seats: Yes    Cover: Ample    Floodlights: No**

**Directions:** At junction of A39 and B3314 to east of Wadebridge

**HONOURS**    South Western Lg R-up 68-69 78-79 79-80 (Lg Cup 5), (R-up 3), CornishSenior Cup 79-80, Cornish Charity Cup 8

**FACT FILE**

Nickname: Bridgers
Colours:All red/white
Change colours: All blue/white
Reserve s' League: East Cornwall Premier

**CLUB PERSONNEL**

Chairman: Dave Herring
Manager: Robbie Black

# WESTERN DEVELOPMENTS
# DEVON COUNTY LEAGUE

**President:** Carl Throgmorton

**Chairman:** David Moore   **Vice Chairman:** Stephen Ware

**Hon. Secretary:** Philip Hiscox

19 Ivy Close, Wonford, Exeter EX2 5LX   (Tel/Fax: 01392 493995)

Another season over with, though in fact the Season at least for a League administrative body never really ends, you just wipe a slate clean and start again!

The 1998-99 season had some notable landmarks by which the League's progress can be seen, and as early as September 12th the League claimed a "first", when Willand Rovers took the field at Truro City in an FA Vase tie, the first time a Devon League club had competed at that level. Ironically whilst our one entry produced one defeat there was some satisfaction come the end of the season when Tiverton Town's match winner in the Wembley final was Scot Rogers - only last season Scot had been farmed out to Cullompton Rangers to get extra first team experience!

By about September another Devon League "old boy", Geoff Breslan who had played the most of the 1996-97 season with Newton Abbot Spurs, was a regular in Exeter City's first team and getting goals and rave reviews, and hopefully in a year or two's time we will be praising brother Gavin who stuck with Teignmouth all season but will start his YTS with Exeter in August.

The League's dominance of the County's Premier Cup continued at pace with three of the semi-finalists, and for the third year running the Cup winners came from the Devon League. This time round it was Cullompton Rangers who went on to emulate Dartmouth by gaining a runners-up spot in the League. The fact that nobody has yet achieved a "double", let alone a "treble" of honours, is further proof of the all round strength of the League.

The League's main honour was also to find a new home, for whilst Willand Rovers have always been a leading side honours had eluded them until this season, a great home record of eighteen wins and one draw proved the foundation for their first title.

There was a new name on the Throgmorton Cup too, when after a close fought final Ottery St Mary edged home 1-0 against previous holders Stoke Gabriel. This was the "Otters"' first playing honour in the Devon League since 1994.

The League's bottom two sides both depart - Teignmouth it has to be said struggled to meet the levels required and finished well adrift at the bottom, whilst Plymouth Command followed up their previous best season with their worst, finishing six points clear of safety. Though they had indicated their withdrawal due to ever increasing services commitments, they would have been relegated anyway as the "pyramid" worked at its best since the League's formation.

For the new season we welcome the Champions of the Devon & Exeter League, Exeter Civil Service; they completed the required work to their Foxhayes home and take their rightful place for the new season. Joining the League from the opposite direction are Heavitree United, one of the oldest clubs in Devon having been founded in 1885. The "Heavies" have ended a 23 year association with the Western League and will be welcomed to the Devon League for the new season.

The League's administration has seen changes during the season as new Chairman David Moore and Vice Chairman Steve Ware took office; they have both contributed to the forward thinking that is rapidly making the League well regarded. The remaining officers, Adrian Codling, Barry Widdicombe and Mike Sampson, have all continued their sterling efforts and have been helped by a more active set of Club Representatives on the LMC.

Philip Hiscox, League Secretary

## FINAL LEAGUE TABLE 1998-99

| | P | W | D | L | F | A | W | D | L | F | A | Pts |
|---|---|---|---|---|---|---|---|---|---|---|---|---|
| Willand Rovers | 38 | 18 | 1 | 0 | 67 | 11 | 10 | 5 | 4 | 34 | 22 | 90 |
| Cullompton Rangers | 38 | 13 | 5 | 1 | 46 | 17 | 13 | 2 | 4 | 38 | 23 | 85 |
| Budleigh Salterton | 38 | 13 | 4 | 2 | 57 | 22 | 12 | 3 | 4 | 58 | 25 | 82 |
| Vospers Oak Villa | 38 | 11 | 4 | 4 | 64 | 26 | 10 | 4 | 5 | 43 | 29 | 71 |
| Ottery St Mary | 38 | 11 | 3 | 5 | 40 | 21 | 9 | 3 | 7 | 31 | 29 | 66 |
| Appledore | 38 | 12 | 2 | 5 | 58 | 33 | 6 | 8 | 5 | 32 | 24 | 64 |
| Stoke Gabriel | 38 | 9 | 7 | 3 | 42 | 24 | 7 | 6 | 6 | 42 | 38 | 61 |
| Dartmouth United | 38 | 12 | 2 | 5 | 43 | 32 | 6 | 5 | 8 | 32 | 34 | 61 |
| Newton Abbot Spurs | 38 | 10 | 4 | 5 | 38 | 29 | 7 | 3 | 9 | 29 | 41 | 58 |
| Buckfastleigh Rangers | 38 | 9 | 5 | 5 | 58 | 27 | 8 | 1 | 10 | 39 | 34 | 57 |
| Crediton United | 38 | 11 | 2 | 6 | 43 | 27 | 7 | 1 | 11 | 24 | 37 | 57 |
| Topsham Town | 38 | 8 | 6 | 5 | 53 | 30 | 6 | 4 | 9 | 29 | 36 | 52 |
| Newton Abbot | 38 | 7 | 5 | 7 | 33 | 32 | 6 | 7 | 6 | 24 | 20 | 51 |
| Newton St Cyres | 38 | 8 | 3 | 8 | 27 | 29 | 6 | 5 | 8 | 35 | 37 | 50 |
| Ivybridge Town | 38 | 9 | 2 | 8 | 41 | 27 | 5 | 1 | 13 | 38 | 66 | 45 |
| Alphington | 38 | 6 | 4 | 9 | 33 | 42 | 4 | 2 | 13 | 28 | 58 | 36 |
| Plymstock United | 38 | 5 | 3 | 11 | 20 | 32 | 1 | 7 | 11 | 21 | 48 | 28 |
| Elburton Villa | 38 | 5 | 4 | 10 | 26 | 42 | 2 | 1 | 16 | 22 | 56 | 26 |
| Plymouth Command | 38 | 3 | 3 | 13 | 21 | 49 | 3 | 2 | 14 | 23 | 60 | 20 |
| Teignmouth | 38 | 2 | 1 | 16 | 23 | 87 | 0 | 0 | 19 | 17 | 116 | 4 |

## RESULTS CHART 1998-99

| | | 1 | 2 | 3 | 4 | 5 | 6 | 7 | 8 | 9 | 10 | 11 | 12 | 13 | 14 | 15 | 16 | 17 | 18 | 19 | 20 |
|---|---|---|---|---|---|---|---|---|---|---|---|---|---|---|---|---|---|---|---|---|---|
| 1 | Alphington | X | 1-1 | 2-1 | 0-2 | 0-3 | 2-4 | 3-2 | 3-1 | 2-3 | 2-2 | 0-4 | 2-1 | 0-2 | 8-1 | 3-4 | 2-5 | 2-0 | 1-1 | 0-5 | 0-0 |
| 2 | Appledore | 5-2 | X | 3-4 | 1-4 | 2-0 | 1-1 | 2-4 | 4-2 | 4-1 | 2-0 | 4-1 | 1-3 | 2-0 | 4-1 | 5-2 | 2-0 | 11-2 | 2-1 | 2-2 | 1-3 |
| 3 | Buckfastleigh Rgrs | 4-3 | 0-2 | X | 2-3 | 4-0 | 1-2 | 3-3 | 5-0 | 2-2 | 3-1 | 1-1 | 1-0 | 1-1 | 5-0 | 2-2 | 2-3 | 13-1 | 3-1 | 1-2 | 5-0 |
| 4 | Budleigh Salterton | 6-0 | 2-2 | 2-0 | X | 6-3 | 3-0 | 4-0 | 4-1 | 7-1 | 1-1 | 0-2 | 2-2 | 3-0 | 2-0 | 1-0 | 4-3 | 5-2 | 0-0 | 3-1 | 2-4 |
| 5 | Crediton United | 3-1 | 1-3 | 3-1 | 2-3 | X | 0-3 | 0-5 | 4-1 | 5-1 | 0-1 | 3-0 | 0-0 | 3-0 | 0-2 | 6-2 | 3-2 | 3-0 | 1-0 | 4-0 | 2-2 |
| 6 | Cullompton Rgrs | 1-0 | 1-0 | 1-0 | 2-2 | 4-0 | X | 1-0 | 3-2 | 1-0 | 1-0 | 1-3 | 2-0 | 2-1 | 5-0 | 1-1 | 2-2 | 9-0 | 5-2 | 2-2 | 2-2 |
| 7 | Dartmouth United | 2-1 | 1-1 | 3-2 | 2-1 | 0-1 | 2-5 | X | 3-0 | 5-2 | 2-0 | 3-2 | 3-4 | 2-4 | 2-1 | 1-1 | 4-2 | 3-1 | 2-1 | 1-3 | 2-0 |
| 8 | Elburton Villa | 1-3 | 3-1 | 0-4 | 1-6 | 0-4 | 0-1 | 2-1 | X | 1-0 | 1-1 | 2-2 | 1-2 | 3-4 | 2-0 | 0-0 | 2-2 | 5-0 | 2-5 | 0-2 | 0-4 |
| 9 | Ivybridge Town | 5-1 | 1-1 | 0-1 | 0-2 | 3-2 | 2-1 | 3-2 | 5-2 | X | 1-2 | 5-0 | 4-2 | 0-1 | 0-3 | 1-0 | 2-2 | 8-0 | 0-2 | 1-2 | 0-1 |
| 10 | Newton Abbot | 2-0 | 2-2 | 1-4 | 1-3 | 3-0 | 1-2 | 2-3 | 2-1 | 1-0 | X | 0-2 | 0-1 | 2-2 | 3-1 | 4-1 | 2-2 | 2-0 | 2-2 | 2-2 | 1-4 |
| 11 | Newton Abbot S | 2-2 | 0-4 | 2-3 | 2-2 | 1-0 | 4-1 | 1-1 | 3-2 | 4-0 | 0-0 | X | 4-1 | 0-2 | 2-5 | 3-1 | 0-2 | 3-1 | 3-0 | 2-1 | 2-1 |
| 12 | Newton St Cyres | 2-2 | 2-1 | 2-1 | 0-2 | 1-2 | 0-2 | 1-2 | 2-1 | 4-0 | 0-0 | 3-0 | X | 0-3 | 3-1 | 2-0 | 2-2 | 3-2 | 0-2 | 0-5 | 0-1 |
| 13 | Ottery St Mary | 0-3 | 3-3 | 6-1 | 5-0 | 1-0 | 1-1 | 2-0 | 1-0 | 1-0 | 3-0 | 3-1 | 0-1 | X | 2-2 | 3-1 | 2-4 | 5-1 | 0-1 | 2-0 | 0-2 |
| 14 | Plymouth Comm. | 0-3 | 1-0 | 1-4 | 1-2 | 0-2 | 1-4 | 0-2 | 2-0 | 2-9 | 0-4 | 2-4 | 2-2 | 0-2 | X | 2-2 | 0-2 | 5-1 | 2-2 | 0-2 | 0-2 |
| 15 | Plymstock United | 1-4 | 1-1 | 0-1 | 0-2 | 1-2 | 0-1 | 1-0 | 0-0 | 2-3 | 0-2 | 1-4 | 2-1 | 0-2 | 1-1 | X | 2-1 | 5-1 | 2-1 | 1-2 | 0-3 |
| 16 | Stoke Gabriel | 3-1 | 2-5 | 1-0 | 0-0 | 2-0 | 0-2 | 1-1 | 3-0 | 4-3 | 1-1 | 1-1 | 1-1 | 2-1 | 8-0 | 2-2 | X | 4-1 | 5-1 | 1-3 | 1-1 |
| 17 | Teignmouth | 2-0 | 0-2 | 1-10 | 0-16 | 2-4 | 1-2 | 2-3 | 2-6 | 2-6 | 0-7 | 0-1 | 0-8 | 0-4 | 3-2 | 1-1 | 1-2 | X | 2-3 | 3-7 | 1-3 |
| 18 | Topsham Town | 9-1 | 1-2 | 1-1 | 1-6 | 3-0 | 1-3 | 2-2 | 1-2 | 2-4 | 2-0 | 5-0 | 2-1 | 2-2 | 3-2 | 4-1 | 0-0 | 12-1 | X | 2-2 | 0-0 |
| 19 | Vospers Oak Villa | 3-0 | 1-1 | 1-0 | 3-2 | 0-0 | 2-3 | 1-1 | 2-1 | 9-1 | 1-2 | 5-1 | 4-4 | 5-0 | 3-1 | 3-0 | 4-5 | 13-1 | 1-2 | X | 3-1 |
| 20 | Willand Rovers | 7-1 | 1-0 | 4-1 | 2-0 | 4-1 | 1-0 | 3-0 | 7-0 | 8-2 | 0-0 | 2-0 | 6-1 | 2-0 | 4-0 | 4-0 | 2-1 | 5-2 | 3-2 | 2-0 | X |

## LEADING GOALSCORERS 1998-99

| | | |
|---|---|---|
| Justin Osborne | Stoke Gabriel | 42 |
| Sean Cornish | Vospers Oak Villa | 37 |
| Kevin Smith | Willand Rovers | 36 |
| Bradley Swiggs | Buckfastleigh | 36 |
| Roger Bonaparte | Vospers Oak Villa | 33 |
| Scot Howarth | Budleigh Salterton | 33 |
| Mark Seatherton | Cullompton | 33 |

## SPORTSMANSHIP AWARD 1998-99

Note: The Award is based on Referees' marks awarded out of 10 for all League games

| Position | Club | Marks | Average |
|---|---|---|---|
| 1 | Ottery St Mary | 310 | 8.15 |
| 2 | Newton St Cyres | 296 | 7.78 |
| 3= | Appledore | 295 | 7.76 |
| 3= | Plymstock United | 295 | 7.76 |

## OTHER LEAGUE AWARDS

| | |
|---|---|
| CHARITY SHIELD | STOKE GABRIEL |
| HOSPITALITY AWARD | CREDITON UNITED |
| PRESS AWARD | NEWTON ST CYRES |
| PROGRAMME AWARD | NEWTON ABBOT SPURS AFC |

## THROGMORTON CUP 1998-99
### FINAL
OTTERY ST MARY   1-0   STOKE GABRIEL

## ALL TIME LEADING GOALSCORERS

| | | |
|---|---|---|
| David Downing | 106 | Appledore |
| Mark Seatherton | 104 | Willand/Cullompton |
| Alan Clarke | 102 | Appledore |
| Justin Osborne | 101 | Stoke Gabriel |

# GLOUCESTER COUNTY LEAGUE

**Chairman:** A C Barrett

**Hon. Secretary:** D J Herbert, 8 Fernhurst Road, St George, Bristol BS5 7TQ

Tel: 0117 951 7696

## FINAL LEAGUE TABLE 1998-99

|  | P | W | D | L | F | A | Pts |
|---|---|---|---|---|---|---|---|
| Cadbury Heath | 34 | 27 | 4 | 3 | 89 | 32 | 85 |
| Highridge United | 34 | 21 | 8 | 5 | 79 | 32 | 71 |
| Winterbourne United | 34 | 20 | 7 | 7 | 69 | 35 | 67 |
| Patchway Town | 34 | 19 | 10 | 5 | 57 | 37 | 67 |
| Dursley Town | 34 | 17 | 7 | 10 | 46 | 31 | 58 |
| DRG | 34 | 15 | 8 | 11 | 59 | 48 | 53 |
| Frampton Athletic | 34 | 14 | 10 | 10 | 57 | 38 | 52 |
| Old Georgians | 34 | 16 | 4 | 14 | 51 | 56 | 52 |
| Broad Plain House OB | 34 | 14 | 7 | 13 | 57 | 47 | 49 |
| Henbury Old Boys | 34 | 13 | 10 | 11 | 51 | 43 | 49 |
| Ellwood | 34 | 10 | 12 | 12 | 28 | 41 | 42 |
| Broadwell Amateurs | 34 | 11 | 8 | 15 | 32 | 47 | 41 |
| Pucklechurch Sports | 34 | 10 | 7 | 17 | 41 | 55 | 37 |
| Brockworth | 34 | 9 | 8 | 17 | 31 | 51 | 35 |
| Viney St Swithins | 34 | 8 | 8 | 18 | 33 | 61 | 32 |
| Tytherington Rocks | 34 | 7 | 10 | 17 | 47 | 63 | 31 |
| Totterdown Pt of Bristol | 34 | 4 | 7 | 23 | 33 | 66 | 19 |
| Wotton Rovers | 34 | 2 | 3 | 29 | 26 | 103 | 9 |

# JOLLY'S CORNWALL COMBINATION

## FINAL LEAGUE TABLE 1998-99

|  | P | W | D | L | F | A | Pts |
|---|---|---|---|---|---|---|---|
| Truro City Res. | 38 | 31 | 3 | 4 | 108 | 36 | 96 |
| Penryn Athletic | 38 | 30 | 5 | 3 | 110 | 29 | 95 |
| Perranwell | 38 | 24 | 5 | 9 | 99 | 42 | 77 |
| RNAS Culdrose | 38 | 23 | 2 | 13 | 70 | 53 | 71 |
| Goonhavern | 38 | 21 | 7 | 10 | 87 | 51 | 70 |
| St Just | 38 | 21 | 5 | 12 | 103 | 61 | 68 |
| Helston Athletic | 38 | 19 | 8 | 11 | 89 | 66 | 65 |
| Falmouth Town Res. | 38 | 19 | 7 | 12 | 94 | 58 | 64 |
| Mullion | 38 | 16 | 11 | 11 | 66 | 60 | 59 |
| St Ives Town (Cornwall) | 38 | 16 | 9 | 13 | 70 | 68 | 57 |
| Porthleven Res. | 38 | 15 | 7 | 16 | 72 | 77 | 52 |
| Wendron CC United | 38 | 14 | 5 | 19 | 75 | 74 | 47 |
| Penzance Res. | 38 | 10 | 15 | 13 | 60 | 79 | 45 |
| Mousehole | 38 | 13 | 5 | 20 | 70 | 92 | 44 |
| Newquay Res. | 38 | 9 | 8 | 21 | 81 | 90 | 35 |
| Troon -3 | 38 | 9 | 8 | 21 | 51 | 87 | 32 |
| Illogan RBL | 38 | 7 | 11 | 20 | 57 | 97 | 32 |
| Marazion Blues | 38 | 8 | 6 | 24 | 47 | 105 | 30 |
| St Agnes | 38 | 8 | 3 | 27 | 51 | 90 | 27 |
| Ludgvan | 38 | 0 | 4 | 34 | 28 | 173 | 4 |

# SOMERSET SENIOR FOOTBALL LEAGUE

**President:** W Crew Esq.

**Hon Treasurer:** D Milverton
6 Northmead Close, Midsomer Norton, Bath BA3 2SG
Tel: 01761 412253

## FINAL LEAGUE TABLES 1998-99

### PREMIER DIVISION

|  | P | W | D | L | F | A | Pts |
|---|---|---|---|---|---|---|---|
| Clevedon United | 34 | 26 | 6 | 2 | 73 | 22 | 84 |
| Fry Club | 34 | 23 | 5 | 6 | 82 | 37 | 74 |
| Timsbury Athletic | 34 | 21 | 6 | 7 | 69 | 42 | 69 |
| Radstock Town | 34 | 17 | 8 | 9 | 54 | 37 | 59 |
| Burnham United | 34 | 17 | 7 | 10 | 72 | 45 | 58 |
| Oldland Abbotonians | 34 | 17 | 7 | 10 | 60 | 48 | 58 |
| Portishead | 34 | 15 | 9 | 10 | 53 | 44 | 54 |
| Shirehampton | 34 | 12 | 11 | 11 | 62 | 49 | 47 |
| Brislington Res. | 34 | 13 | 8 | 13 | 44 | 43 | 47 |
| Nailsea United | 34 | 13 | 5 | 16 | 59 | 57 | 44 |
| Backwell United Res. | 34 | 9 | 14 | 11 | 50 | 51 | 41 |
| Shepton Mallet Town | 34 | 8 | 14 | 12 | 35 | 41 | 38 |
| Bridgwater Town Res. | 34 | 10 | 7 | 17 | 56 | 63 | 37 |
| Robinsons | 34 | 8 | 11 | 15 | 48 | 82 | 35 |
| Westland United | 34 | 8 | 6 | 20 | 44 | 84 | 30 |
| Hengrove Athletic | 34 | 7 | 7 | 20 | 35 | 63 | 28 |
| Imperial | 34 | 6 | 8 | 20 | 35 | 64 | 26 |
| Peasedown Athletic | 34 | 3 | 7 | 24 | 25 | 84 | 16 |

### DIVISION ONE

|  | P | W | D | L | F | A | Pts |
|---|---|---|---|---|---|---|---|
| Mangotsfield United Rs. | 34 | 29 | 2 | 3 | 127 | 27 | 89 |
| Worle | 34 | 28 | 2 | 4 | 127 | 36 | 86 |
| Wells City | 34 | 23 | 4 | 7 | 116 | 33 | 73 |
| Stockwood Green | 34 | 19 | 5 | 10 | 85 | 46 | 62 |
| Watchet Town | 34 | 19 | 4 | 11 | 82 | 54 | 61 |
| Congresbury | 34 | 17 | 6 | 11 | 78 | 55 | 57 |
| Nailsea United Res. | 34 | 15 | 5 | 14 | 54 | 46 | 50 |
| Castle Cary | 34 | 13 | 8 | 13 | 60 | 60 | 47 |
| Cheddar | 34 | 14 | 4 | 16 | 100 | 70 | 46 |
| Saltford | 34 | 14 | 4 | 16 | 69 | 75 | 46 |
| Long Sutton | 34 | 12 | 7 | 15 | 75 | 67 | 43 |
| Odd Down Res. * | 34 | 13 | 2 | 19 | 59 | 92 | 40 |
| Cleeve West Town | 34 | 9 | 9 | 16 | 60 | 75 | 36 |
| Bishop Sutton Res. | 34 | 9 | 7 | 18 | 62 | 73 | 34 |
| Winscombe | 34 | 9 | 5 | 20 | 45 | 71 | 32 |
| Portishead Res. | 34 | 7 | 10 | 17 | 69 | 73 | 31 |
| Ilminster Town | 34 | 7 | 10 | 17 | 63 | 77 | 31 |
| Weston St Johns | 34 | 2 | 0 | 32 | 22 | 323 | 6 |

### DIVISION TWO

|  | P | W | D | L | F | A | Pts |
|---|---|---|---|---|---|---|---|
| Paulton Rovers Res. | 32 | 20 | 5 | 7 | 100 | 40 | 65 |
| Welton Rovers Res. | 32 | 20 | 4 | 8 | 108 | 47 | 64 |
| Clevedon United Res. | 32 | 19 | 6 | 7 | 72 | 49 | 63 |
| Keynsham Town Res. | 32 | 17 | 6 | 9 | 86 | 43 | 57 |
| Burnham United Res. | 32 | 17 | 3 | 12 | 65 | 47 | 54 |
| Larkhall Athletic Res. | 32 | 16 | 6 | 10 | 61 | 48 | 54 |
| Nailsea Town | 32 | 15 | 8 | 9 | 85 | 65 | 53 |
| Clandown* | 32 | 15 | 8 | 9 | 71 | 54 | 52 |
| Blackbrook | 32 | 14 | 6 | 12 | 57 | 54 | 48 |
| Westland United Res. | 32 | 12 | 6 | 14 | 73 | 90 | 42 |
| Peasedown Athletic Rs. | 32 | 12 | 3 | 17 | 63 | 84 | 39 |
| Wrington-Redhill | 32 | 10 | 6 | 16 | 60 | 71 | 36 |
| Frome Town Res. | 32 | 10 | 6 | 16 | 58 | 89 | 36 |
| Churchill Club | 32 | 9 | 5 | 18 | 56 | 88 | 32 |
| Yatton Athletic | 32 | 8 | 5 | 19 | 57 | 90 | 29 |
| Long Ashton* | 32 | 6 | 6 | 20 | 47 | 96 | 23 |
| Glastonbury Res. | 32 | 6 | 3 | 23 | 59 | 123 | 21 |

### DIVISION THREE

|  | P | W | D | L | F | A | Pts |
|---|---|---|---|---|---|---|---|
| Dundry Athletic | 30 | 26 | 4 | 0 | 111 | 24 | 82 |
| Banwell * | 30 | 21 | 3 | 6 | 99 | 43 | 65 |
| Cutters Friday | 30 | 20 | 5 | 5 | 89 | 39 | 65 |
| Wells City Res. | 30 | 19 | 3 | 8 | 102 | 50 | 60 |
| Kewstoke | 30 | 15 | 5 | 10 | 79 | 60 | 50 |
| Frome Collegians | 30 | 13 | 6 | 11 | 53 | 48 | 45 |
| Tunley Athletic | 30 | 12 | 6 | 12 | 58 | 54 | 42 |
| Backwell United `A' | 30 | 13 | 2 | 15 | 78 | 77 | 41 |
| Temple Cloud | 30 | 11 | 5 | 14 | 53 | 67 | 38 |
| Imperial Res.8 | 30 | 13 | 2 | 15 | 53 | 66 | 37 |
| Fry Club Res. | 30 | 9 | 9 | 12 | 56 | 61 | 36 |
| St George E-Gordano* | 30 | 9 | 3 | 18 | 43 | 82 | 29 |
| Clutton | 30 | 9 | 2 | 19 | 57 | 108 | 29 |
| Shepton Mallet Town R* | 30 | 6 | 8 | 16 | 42 | 59 | 25 |
| Cheddar Res. | 30 | 7 | 4 | 19 | 48 | 91 | 25 |
| Hengrove Athletic Res. | 30 | 2 | 3 | 25 | 17 | 109 | 9 |
| * points deducted |  |  |  |  |  |  |  |

# SOUTH WEST LEAGUE TABLES 1998-99

## SOUTH DEVON LEAGUE
### PREMIER DIVISION

| | P | W | D | L | F | A | Pts |
|---|---|---|---|---|---|---|---|
| Newton Abbot '66 | 26 | 23 | 3 | 1 | 111 | 22 | 71 |
| Upton Athletic | 26 | 21 | 2 | 3 | 91 | 32 | 65 |
| Galmpton United | 26 | 14 | 7 | 5 | 61 | 39 | 49 |
| Nortel Paignton | 26 | 14 | 3 | 9 | 60 | 45 | 45 |
| Chudleigh Athletic | 26 | 11 | 5 | 10 | 44 | 30 | 38 |
| Liverton United | 26 | 11 | 4 | 11 | 60 | 62 | 37 |
| Stoke Gabriel Res. | 26 | 11 | 4 | 11 | 60 | 78 | 37 |
| Hele Rovers | 26 | 10 | 5 | 11 | 52 | 49 | 35 |
| Kingskerswell | 26 | 10 | 2 | 14 | 46 | 53 | 32 |
| Brixham Villa | 26 | 9 | 4 | 13 | 51 | 59 | 31 |
| Chagford | 26 | 9 | 1 | 16 | 42 | 54 | 28 |
| Dartington Sports | 26 | 8 | 3 | 15 | 55 | 82 | 27 |
| Newton Abbot Spurs Res. | 26 | 4 | 2 | 20 | 37 | 89 | 14 |
| Dartmouth YMRC -3 | 26 | 4 | 2 | 20 | 27 | 101 | 11 |

## STROUD & DISTRICT LEAGUE
### DIVISION ONE

| | P | W | D | L | F | A | Pts |
|---|---|---|---|---|---|---|---|
| Slimbridge Town | 26 | 18 | 3 | 5 | 70 | 28 | 39 |
| Ramblers | 26 | 12 | 8 | 6 | 61 | 39 | 32 |
| Tuffley Rovers `A' | 26 | 13 | 5 | 8 | 57 | 42 | 31 |
| Tetbury Town | 26 | 13 | 4 | 9 | 49 | 41 | 30 |
| Kings Stanley Res. | 26 | 10 | 6 | 10 | 51 | 52 | 26 |
| Upton St Leonards | 26 | 9 | 8 | 9 | 49 | 55 | 26 |
| Hillesley United | 26 | 11 | 4 | 11 | 53 | 54 | 26 |
| ICI Fibres | 26 | 11 | 2 | 13 | 39 | 45 | 24 |
| Whiteshill United | 26 | 8 | 7 | 11 | 43 | 39 | 23 |
| Leonard Stanley | 26 | 6 | 11 | 9 | 40 | 39 | 23 |
| Charfield | 26 | 9 | 5 | 12 | 32 | 44 | 23 |
| Thornbury Town Res. | 26 | 7 | 7 | 12 | 43 | 55 | 21 |
| Wotton Rovers Res. | 26 | 8 | 5 | 13 | 41 | 57 | 21 |
| Ebley | 26 | 5 | 9 | 12 | 46 | 73 | 19 |

## YEOVIL & DISTRICT LEAGUE
### PREMIER DIVISION

| | P | W | D | L | F | A | Pts |
|---|---|---|---|---|---|---|---|
| Stoke-sub-Hamdon | 22 | 17 | 2 | 3 | 76 | 28 | 53 |
| Normalair Sports | 22 | 16 | 3 | 3 | 70 | 40 | 51 |
| Ash Rovers | 22 | 16 | 2 | 4 | 71 | 25 | 50 |
| Henstridge United | 22 | 14 | 5 | 3 | 69 | 36 | 47 |
| Milborne Port | 22 | 13 | 2 | 7 | 52 | 33 | 41 |
| AFC Camel | 22 | 8 | 3 | 11 | 48 | 65 | 27 |
| Baltonsborough -3 | 22 | 8 | 5 | 9 | 57 | 45 | 26 |
| Ilchester United | 22 | 7 | 4 | 11 | 49 | 61 | 25 |
| Bradford Sports | 22 | 7 | 2 | 13 | 41 | 57 | 23 |
| Masons Arms | 22 | 3 | 3 | 16 | 33 | 75 | 12 |
| Martock United | 22 | 3 | 2 | 17 | 36 | 93 | 11 |
| Wincanton Town | 22 | 2 | 3 | 17 | 34 | 76 | 9 |

## PERRY STREET LEAGUE
### PREMIER DIVISION

| | P | W | D | L | F | A | Pts |
|---|---|---|---|---|---|---|---|
| Crewkerne | 20 | 17 | 2 | 1 | 69 | 13 | 63 |
| Combe St Nicholas | 20 | 15 | 3 | 2 | 74 | 17 | 48 |
| Merriott Rovers | 20 | 15 | 2 | 3 | 74 | 22 | 47 |
| Axminster Town | 20 | 13 | 2 | 5 | 55 | 26 | 41 |
| Lyme Regis | 20 | 12 | 1 | 7 | 50 | 41 | 37 |
| Halstock | 20 | 7 | 3 | 10 | 32 | 44 | 24 |
| Norton-sub-Hamdon | 20 | 7 | 3 | 11 | 36 | 55 | 24 |
| South Petherton | 20 | 4 | 2 | 14 | 34 | 64 | 14 |
| Forton | 20 | 3 | 5 | 12 | 26 | 64 | 14 |
| Chard Athletic | 20 | 1 | 3 | 16 | 24 | 76 | 6 |
| Ilminster Town Res. -3 | 20 | 2 | 2 | 16 | 21 | 73 | 5 |

## BRISTOL & SUBURBAN LEAGUE
### PREMIER DIVISION ONE

| | P | W | D | L | F | A | Pts |
|---|---|---|---|---|---|---|---|
| Bristol Telephones | 30 | 18 | 11 | 1 | 69 | 24 | 47 |
| Avonside Court | 30 | 20 | 5 | 5 | 70 | 30 | 45 |
| P & W United | 30 | 17 | 7 | 6 | 54 | 32 | 41 |
| Cadbury Heath Res. | 30 | 15 | 9 | 6 | 61 | 35 | 39 |
| St Aldhelms | 30 | 16 | 7 | 7 | 69 | 44 | 39 |
| Avonmouth | 30 | 14 | 8 | 8 | 58 | 45 | 36 |
| Yate Town Res. | 30 | 13 | 7 | 10 | 67 | 57 | 33 |
| Exeter United | 30 | 12 | 7 | 11 | 64 | 65 | 31 |
| Ridings High | 30 | 9 | 10 | 11 | 55 | 50 | 27 |
| Glenside Hospital SC | 30 | 10 | 6 | 14 | 54 | 56 | 26 |
| Raysfield | 30 | 9 | 7 | 14 | 51 | 64 | 25 |
| Stoke Gifford United | 30 | 10 | 3 | 17 | 65 | 71 | 23 |
| Broad Plain Hse OB R. | 30 | 7 | 8 | 15 | 42 | 63 | 22 |
| Almondsbury | 30 | 7 | 6 | 17 | 46 | 66 | 20 |
| Almondsbury Town Res. | 30 | 8 | 2 | 20 | 37 | 91 | 18 |
| Old Cothamians | 30 | 1 | 5 | 24 | 28 | 97 | 7 |

## BODMIN TRO. DUCHY LEAGUE
### PREMIER DIVISION

| | P | W | D | L | F | A | Pts |
|---|---|---|---|---|---|---|---|
| Biscovey | 26 | 20 | 1 | 5 | 81 | 27 | 61 |
| Dobwalls | 26 | 20 | 1 | 5 | 85 | 38 | 61 |
| St Stephen | 26 | 18 | 3 | 5 | 70 | 41 | 57 |
| Probus | 26 | 17 | 2 | 7 | 75 | 47 | 53 |
| Boscastle | 26 | 13 | 4 | 9 | 69 | 48 | 43 |
| Lanreath | 26 | 12 | 4 | 10 | 70 | 55 | 40 |
| Delabole United | 26 | 10 | 4 | 12 | 63 | 65 | 34 |
| Fowey United | 26 | 9 | 5 | 12 | 54 | 67 | 32 |
| Nanpean Rovers Res. | 26 | 9 | 4 | 13 | 51 | 53 | 31 |
| St Dominick | 26 | 8 | 5 | 12 | 51 | 75 | 29 |
| Callington Town Res. | 26 | 9 | 2 | 15 | 33 | 68 | 29 |
| Godolphin Atlantic | 26 | 6 | 8 | 14 | 48 | 62 | 26 |
| Newmoor Rovers | 26 | 6 | 5 | 15 | 45 | 67 | 23 |
| Polperro | 26 | 1 | 2 | 23 | 29 | 111 | 5 |

# SOUTH WEST LEAGUE TABLES 1998-99

## DEVON & EXETER LEAGUE
### PREMIER DIVISION

|  | P | W | D | L | F | A | Pts |
|---|---|---|---|---|---|---|---|
| Exeter Civil Service | 26 | 20 | 4 | 2 | 93 | 28 | 64 |
| Buckland Athletic | 26 | 19 | 5 | 2 | 79 | 14 | 62 |
| Pinhoe | 26 | 17 | 2 | 7 | 55 | 40 | 53 |
| University of Exeter | 26 | 12 | 6 | 8 | 59 | 37 | 42 |
| Feniton | 26 | 12 | 5 | 9 | 52 | 61 | 37 |
| Budleigh Salterton Res. | 26 | 9 | 6 | 11 | 41 | 65 | 33 |
| Okehampton Argyle | 26 | 9 | 5 | 12 | 50 | 50 | 32 |
| St Martins | 26 | 9 | 5 | 12 | 42 | 51 | 32 |
| Exmouth Amateurs | 26 | 9 | 5 | 12 | 49 | 70 | 32 |
| Sidmouth Town | 26 | 8 | 4 | 14 | 32 | 65 | 28 |
| Seaton Town | 26 | 8 | 2 | 16 | 41 | 55 | 26 |
| Exeter St Thomas | 26 | 7 | 5 | 14 | 34 | 47 | 25 |
| Dawlish Villa | 26 | 7 | 2 | 17 | 36 | 63 | 23 |
| Witheridge | 26 | 4 | 8 | 14 | 31 | 48 | 20 |

## EAST CORNWALL PREMIER LEAGUE

|  | P | W | D | L | F | A | Pts |
|---|---|---|---|---|---|---|---|
| Callington Town | 34 | 27 | 4 | 3 | 110 | 41 | 85 |
| Liskeard Athletic Res. | 34 | 23 | 4 | 7 | 97 | 50 | 73 |
| Bodmin Town Res. | 34 | 22 | 6 | 6 | 85 | 38 | 72 |
| St Dennis | 34 | 20 | 7 | 7 | 83 | 50 | 67 |
| Wadebridge Town Res. | 34 | 18 | 10 | 6 | 72 | 42 | 64 |
| Camelford | 34 | 19 | 6 | 9 | 86 | 38 | 63 |
| Nanpean Rovers | 34 | 16 | 6 | 12 | 61 | 51 | 54 |
| St Breward | 34 | 14 | 8 | 12 | 64 | 50 | 50 |
| Saltash United Res. | 34 | 13 | 7 | 14 | 63 | 54 | 46 |
| Sticker | 34 | 12 | 7 | 15 | 42 | 81 | 43 |
| Roche | 34 | 12 | 6 | 16 | 72 | 62 | 42 |
| St Cleer | 34 | 11 | 9 | 14 | 60 | 68 | 42 |
| St Blazey Res. | 34 | 11 | 5 | 18 | 51 | 63 | 38 |
| Padstow United | 34 | 11 | 4 | 19 | 48 | 67 | 37 |
| Bude | 34 | 9 | 9 | 16 | 51 | 67 | 36 |
| St Austell Res. | 34 | 5 | 5 | 24 | 28 | 109 | 20 |
| Torpoint Athletic Res. | 34 | 4 | 6 | 24 | 42 | 97 | 18 |
| Foxhole Stars | 34 | 2 | 5 | 27 | 33 | 120 | 11 |

## BNLFM TAUNTON LEAGUE
### DIVISION ONE

|  | P | W | D | L | F | A | Pts |
|---|---|---|---|---|---|---|---|
| Sydenham Rangers | 20 | 15 | 2 | 3 | 73 | 23 | 47 |
| Highbridge Town | 20 | 13 | 3 | 4 | 69 | 37 | 42 |
| Bishops Lydeard | 20 | 10 | 5 | 5 | 54 | 38 | 35 |
| Redgate | 20 | 10 | 4 | 6 | 54 | 41 | 34 |
| Wyvern | 20 | 10 | 3 | 7 | 43 | 36 | 33 |
| Alcombe Rovers | 20 | 7 | 4 | 9 | 46 | 55 | 25 |
| Sturm Sports | 20 | 7 | 3 | 10 | 46 | 56 | 24 |
| Dulverton Town | 20 | 7 | 2 | 11 | 40 | 52 | 23 |
| Middlezoy Rovers | 20 | 6 | 3 | 11 | 37 | 56 | 21 |
| Creech | 20 | 6 | 2 | 12 | 38 | 55 | 20 |
| Porlock | 20 | 2 | 3 | 15 | 42 | 87 | 9 |

## BRISTOL PREMIER COMBINATION
### PREMIER DIVISION

|  | P | W | D | L | F | A | Pts |
|---|---|---|---|---|---|---|---|
| Roman G St George | 26 | 21 | 2 | 3 | 66 | 21 | 65 |
| AXA Sun Life | 26 | 15 | 5 | 6 | 57 | 31 | 50 |
| St Philips Marsh AS | 26 | 13 | 6 | 7 | 67 | 48 | 45 |
| Hallen Res. | 26 | 13 | 6 | 7 | 49 | 37 | 45 |
| Hillfields Old Boys | 26 | 10 | 6 | 10 | 69 | 43 | 36 |
| Bristol 5 Old Boys | 26 | 11 | 3 | 12 | 45 | 43 | 36 |
| Hartcliffe | 26 | 10 | 6 | 10 | 45 | 52 | 36 |
| Longwell Green Sports | 26 | 8 | 10 | 8 | 42 | 29 | 34 |
| Thornbury Town | 26 | 11 | 1 | 14 | 41 | 52 | 34 |
| Nicholas Wanderers | 26 | 7 | 10 | 9 | 36 | 44 | 31 |
| Hanham Athletic | 26 | 8 | 3 | 15 | 32 | 57 | 27 |
| Shaftesbury Crusade | 26 | 6 | 6 | 14 | 33 | 65 | 24 |
| Olveston United | 26 | 6 | 5 | 15 | 35 | 74 | 23 |
| Stapleton | 26 | 5 | 7 | 14 | 40 | 60 | 19 |

## BRISTOL & DISTRICT LEAGUE
### SENIOR DIVISION

|  | P | W | D | L | F | A | Pts |
|---|---|---|---|---|---|---|---|
| Winterbourne United Res. | 28 | 21 | 2 | 5 | 76 | 49 | 65 |
| Patchway Town Res. | 28 | 18 | 3 | 7 | 76 | 40 | 57 |
| Rangeworthy | 28 | 17 | 4 | 7 | 79 | 51 | 55 |
| RMC Wick | 28 | 13 | 6 | 9 | 61 | 55 | 45 |
| Seymour United | 28 | 13 | 5 | 10 | 83 | 64 | 44 |
| Hartcliffe Comm Centre | 28 | 12 | 6 | 10 | 62 | 48 | 42 |
| Hartcliffe Res. | 28 | 11 | 5 | 12 | 56 | 64 | 38 |
| Fishponds Athletic | 27 | 9 | 10 | 9 | 59 | 61 | 37 |
| Frampton Athletic Res. | 28 | 10 | 6 | 12 | 69 | 52 | 36 |
| South Bristol Central | 28 | 10 | 6 | 12 | 73 | 67 | 36 |
| Oldland Abbotonians R. | 28 | 10 | 6 | 12 | 50 | 53 | 36 |
| Roman Glass St G Res. | 28 | 8 | 7 | 13 | 49 | 61 | 31 |
| Nicholas Wanderers Res. | 28 | 9 | 3 | 16 | 48 | 62 | 30 |
| Henbury Old Boys `A' | 28 | 5 | 6 | 17 | 53 | 102 | 21 |
| Stockwood Breakaways | 28 | 4 | 5 | 19 | 30 | 95 | 17 |

## BETA FALMOUTH-HELSTON LEAGUE
### DIVISION ONE

|  | P | W | D | L | F | A | Pts |
|---|---|---|---|---|---|---|---|
| Penryn Athletic Res. | 30 | 29 | 1 | 0 | 104 | 25 | 88 |
| Helston Athletic Res. | 30 | 23 | 1 | 6 | 63 | 30 | 70 |
| Holman SC | 30 | 20 | 6 | 4 | 60 | 20 | 66 |
| Chacewater | 30 | 19 | 6 | 5 | 69 | 33 | 63 |
| Duchy | 30 | 19 | 3 | 8 | 82 | 53 | 60 |
| Perranporth | 30 | 13 | 8 | 9 | 66 | 49 | 47 |
| William IV | 30 | 12 | 2 | 16 | 57 | 52 | 38 |
| Camborne Town | 30 | 10 | 6 | 14 | 66 | 73 | 36 |
| St Day | 30 | 9 | 7 | 14 | 42 | 52 | 34 |
| Troon Res. | 30 | 10 | 4 | 16 | 59 | 74 | 34 |
| Pendeen Rovers | 30 | 9 | 5 | 16 | 50 | 62 | 32 |
| Falmouth Athletic | 30 | 10 | 2 | 18 | 66 | 102 | 32 |
| Mawnan | 30 | 8 | 7 | 15 | 50 | 58 | 31 |
| Rosudgeon-Kennegy | 30 | 8 | 3 | 19 | 44 | 77 | 27 |
| Hayle | 30 | 4 | 7 | 19 | 34 | 73 | 19 |
| Falmouth Town `A' | 30 | 3 | 0 | 27 | 28 | 103 | 9 |

# SOUTH WEST LEAGUE TABLES 1998-99

## BIDEFORD TOOLS NORTH DEVON
### PREMIER DIVISION

|  | P | W | D | L | F | A | Pts |
|---|---|---|---|---|---|---|---|
| Shamwickshire Rovers | 30 | 23 | 5 | 2 | 104 | 36 | 74 |
| Combe Martin | 30 | 24 | 1 | 5 | 112 | 45 | 73 |
| Fremington | 30 | 20 | 5 | 5 | 92 | 41 | 65 |
| Bradworthy United | 30 | 20 | 4 | 6 | 91 | 46 | 64 |
| Morwenstow | 30 | 19 | 5 | 6 | 80 | 43 | 62 |
| Braunton | 30 | 19 | 2 | 9 | 80 | 43 | 59 |
| Dolton Rangers | 30 | 13 | 4 | 13 | 72 | 54 | 43 |
| Ilfracombe Town Res. -3 | 30 | 11 | 5 | 14 | 56 | 59 | 35 |
| Kilkhampton -3 | 30 | 11 | 3 | 16 | 45 | 71 | 33 |
| A'dore & B'ford AAC R | 30 | 9 | 4 | 17 | 65 | 70 | 31 |
| Holsworthy Res. | 30 | 8 | 6 | 16 | 42 | 67 | 30 |
| Georgeham & Croyde | 30 | 8 | 1 | 21 | 35 | 77 | 25 |
| Torrington Admirals | 30 | 7 | 4 | 19 | 52 | 113 | 25 |
| Putford | 30 | 5 | 6 | 19 | 35 | 76 | 21 |
| Barnstaple AAC | 30 | 6 | 3 | 21 | 41 | 98 | 21 |
| South Molton | 30 | 5 | 6 | 19 | 38 | 100 | 21 |

## GLOUCESTER NORTHERN SENIOR LEAGUE
### PREMIER DIVISION

|  | P | W | D | L | F | A | Pts |
|---|---|---|---|---|---|---|---|
| Tuffley Rovers Res. | 30 | 23 | 4 | 3 | 88 | 38 | 73 |
| Hardwicke | 30 | 22 | 4 | 4 | 87 | 37 | 70 |
| Smiths Athletic | 30 | 21 | 4 | 5 | 87 | 40 | 67 |
| Whitminster | 30 | 20 | 3 | 7 | 63 | 37 | 63 |
| Lydney Town | 30 | 19 | 4 | 7 | 68 | 36 | 61 |
| Taverners | 30 | 13 | 3 | 14 | 48 | 50 | 42 |
| Sharpness | 30 | 11 | 5 | 14 | 66 | 53 | 38 |
| Tewkesbury YMCA | 30 | 10 | 8 | 12 | 54 | 54 | 38 |
| Kings Stanley | 30 | 9 | 8 | 13 | 31 | 37 | 35 |
| Crescent United | 30 | 9 | 6 | 15 | 42 | 65 | 33 |
| St Marks CA | 30 | 8 | 7 | 15 | 31 | 63 | 31 |
| Cheltenham Civil Serv. | 30 | 7 | 7 | 16 | 46 | 56 | 28 |
| Brimscombe & Thrupp | 30 | 7 | 6 | 17 | 35 | 73 | 27 |
| Lydbrook Athletic | 30 | 6 | 8 | 16 | 42 | 71 | 26 |
| Longlevens | 30 | 7 | 5 | 18 | 34 | 69 | 26 |
| Eagle Star | 30 | 3 | 8 | 19 | 38 | 81 | 17 |

## CHELTENHAM LEAGUE
### DIVISION ONE

|  | P | W | D | L | F | A | Pts |
|---|---|---|---|---|---|---|---|
| Bourton Rovers | 24 | 18 | 4 | 4 | 69 | 27 | 52 |
| Campden Town -3 | 23 | 17 | 3 | 3 | 84 | 40 | 51 |
| St James | 24 | 15 | 1 | 8 | 67 | 34 | 48 |
| Innsworth | 24 | 15 | 2 | 7 | 47 | 41 | 47 |
| Warden Hill | 24 | 13 | 5 | 6 | 57 | 42 | 44 |
| Rowanfield Athletic -3 | 23 | 14 | 0 | 9 | 60 | 40 | 39 |
| Bredon | 24 | 8 | 5 | 10 | 38 | 47 | 30 |
| Kings | 24 | 7 | 6 | 11 | 34 | 55 | 27 |
| Beeches (Glos.) | 24 | 8 | 2 | 14 | 51 | 65 | 26 |
| Brockworth Res. | 24 | 7 | 4 | 13 | 32 | 49 | 25 |
| Shipton Oliffe | 24 | 7 | 3 | 14 | 33 | 55 | 24 |
| Prestbury Rovers | 24 | 4 | 5 | 15 | 40 | 69 | 17 |
| Northleach Town | 24 | 3 | 1 | 20 | 34 | 82 | 10 |

St Marks CA Res. - withdrawn

## CROCKETTS MID-SOMERSET LEAGUE
### PREMIER DIVISION

|  | P | W | D | L | F | A | Pts |
|---|---|---|---|---|---|---|---|
| Pilton United | 18 | 13 | 2 | 3 | 62 | 22 | 40 |
| Coleford Athletic | 18 | 10 | 4 | 4 | 47 | 30 | 34 |
| Timsbury Athletic R. -1 | 18 | 10 | 5 | 3 | 37 | 21 | 34 |
| Evercreech | 18 | 7 | 2 | 9 | 33 | 48 | 23 |
| Stoke Rovers | 18 | 6 | 4 | 8 | 35 | 37 | 22 |
| Mells & Vobster United | 18 | 5 | 7 | 6 | 41 | 46 | 22 |
| Chew Magna | 18 | 5 | 7 | 6 | 24 | 29 | 22 |
| Littleton Sports | 18 | 5 | 5 | 8 | 24 | 38 | 20 |
| Meadow Rangers | 18 | 4 | 5 | 9 | 33 | 38 | 17 |
| Farmborough | 18 | 2 | 5 | 11 | 20 | 47 | 11 |

## BRISTOL & AVON LEAGUE
### PREMIER DIVISION

|  | P | W | D | L | F | A | Pts |
|---|---|---|---|---|---|---|---|
| Eagle House CA | 20 | 18 | 1 | 1 | 91 | 24 | 55 |
| Bristol Spartak | 20 | 15 | 2 | 3 | 66 | 31 | 47 |
| Filwood Sports | 20 | 14 | 3 | 3 | 73 | 23 | 45 |
| Blaise Inn | 20 | 11 | 3 | 6 | 58 | 22 | 36 |
| CTK Southside Res. | 20 | 9 | 3 | 8 | 37 | 49 | 30 |
| Dundry Athletic Res. | 20 | 8 | 4 | 8 | 46 | 57 | 28 |
| Chipping Sodbury `A' | 20 | 5 | 4 | 11 | 46 | 50 | 19 |
| Fishponds Old Tavern | 20 | 5 | 3 | 12 | 37 | 72 | 18 |
| Crockerne Pill | 20 | 5 | 2 | 13 | 25 | 63 | 17 |
| Nailsea Town Res. | 20 | 3 | 2 | 15 | 35 | 86 | 11 |
| Lockleaze Res. | 20 | 1 | 5 | 14 | 25 | 65 | 8 |

## BRISTOL DOWNS LEAGUE
### DIVISION ONE

|  | P | W | D | L | F | A | Pts |
|---|---|---|---|---|---|---|---|
| Clifton St Vincents | 24 | 19 | 3 | 2 | 72 | 24 | 60 |
| Sneyd Park | 24 | 19 | 1 | 4 | 82 | 25 | 58 |
| Clifton Rockets | 24 | 16 | 3 | 5 | 88 | 37 | 51 |
| Pumphouse | 24 | 12 | 2 | 10 | 58 | 49 | 38 |
| Horse & Groom | 24 | 11 | 5 | 8 | 55 | 55 | 38 |
| The Albion | 24 | 10 | 3 | 11 | 73 | 67 | 33 |
| Compass Athletic | 24 | 9 | 5 | 10 | 47 | 58 | 32 |
| Retainers | 24 | 9 | 5 | 10 | 44 | 56 | 32 |
| Tebby | 24 | 9 | 3 | 12 | 59 | 53 | 30 |
| Durdham Dynamoes | 24 | 8 | 5 | 11 | 38 | 42 | 29 |
| St Judes YC | 24 | 7 | 6 | 11 | 47 | 74 | 27 |
| Coach & Horses | 24 | 2 | 2 | 20 | 25 | 86 | 8 |
| Ceramic Palace | 24 | 1 | 5 | 18 | 24 | 86 | 8 |

# INTERLINK EXPRESS
# MIDLAND FOOTBALL ALLIANCE

**President:** N D Jeynes   **Chairman:** P Fellows
**Secretary:** Bob Thomas   Tel: 01922 710565 (H/fax)
07956 908242 (Mob)   07625 638296 (Pgr)
**Press Officer:** David Coulson
Tel: 01283 516725   Fax: 01283 512392
**Website:** welcome.to./the.mfa

This is the fifth annual report of the Midland Football Alliance since its inception in 1994. The League continues to be indebted to its main sponsors, Interlink Express, whose support gives us the necessary resources not only to administer the League in an effective manner but also to provide member clubs with excellent financial rewards at the end of the season.

The other sponsors to whom we are also extremely grateful are James Gilbert Ltd, who supply each club with twelve match balls per season, Bernard Davis who sponsors the Invitation Cup, Industrial Rewind Services who sponsor the League Cup, Zenith Securities Ltd who sponsor the Hospitality Cup, Joe McGorian who sponsors the annual match between the League Winners and the League Cup Winners, Polymac Services who sponsor the award for the Top Goalscorer, the team with the best Disciplinary Record and the Manager of the Year and Newsline who sponsor the Team of the Month award.

Rocester were League Champions after finishing as runners-up in 1997-98. During the season both Oldbury United and Boldmere St Michaels looked as if they would mount a serious challenge to Rocester for the title, but both fell away to finish third and fourth respectively, sixteen and seventeen points behind the Champions. It was left to Kings Norton Town to sustain a real challenge, and it was only in the last week of the season that Rocester could be confirmed as champions.

The League Cup was keenly contested, the semi-finalists being Bridgnorth Town, Oldbury United, Stapenhill and West Midlands Police. The Final saw Oldbury United defeat West Midlands Police 3-2.

Stapenhill had an excellent victory over Spalding United in one of the early rounds of the FA Cup, and were duly rewarded with being named team of the round by AXA, the sponsors of the FA Cup, and received a commemorative shield.

Generally our clubs had a disappointing year in the FA Vase, with only Oldbury United having a reasonable run, but congratulations go to Kings Norton Town who won the Worcestershire Senior Urn.

The Midland Invitation Cup, sponsored by Mr B Davis, is a competition for clubs in the Midland Football Alliance and its three feeder leagues, together with two invited clubs from the Southern League and Bandon of the West Midlands (Regional) League, and resulted in a 2-1 victory for Atherstone United.

Prior to the start of the season the match for the Joe McGorian Trophy competed for by the previous season's League Runners Up and League Cup winners saw Knypersley Victoria take the trophy after defeating Rocester.

As usual our Referees and Assistant Referees received many prestigious appointments during the season. Kevin Nind and John Holbrook were Assistant Referees for the FA Youth Cup Final, Ray Gould an Assistant Referee for the FA Sunday Cup Final, and Amy Rayner an Assistant Referee for the FA Women's Cup final. Trevor Kettle and Tony Green have been promoted as Panel League Referees, and Gary Chapman and William Ramsay have been appointed to the Football League Assistant Referees list.

This will be my last report as General Secretary of the Midland Football Alliance as I will be resigning following the AGM in June 1999. I wish my successor and the League best wishes for the future.

P G Dagger, General Secretary/Treasurer

## MFA UP TO FULL STRENGTH FOR THE 1999-2000 SEASON

The Interlink Express Midland Football Alliance will consist of 22 clubs for the 1999-2000 season with the arrival of newly promoted Cradley Town from the Bank's West Midlands (Regional) League and Oadby Town from the Leicestershire Senior League. Relegated Bloxwich Town have made a quick return to the MFA after just one season in the Dr Martens Midland Division. Oadby Town have become the first club to be promoted from the Everards Leicestershire Senior League since its elevation into the Non-League Pyramid when it became a feeder league to the Interlink Express Midland Football Alliance.

Once again there has been no relegation from the MFA this season but the League has lost Rocester after they gained promotion to the Dr Martens Midland and West Division. Now that the MFA is up to full strength the relegation issue will come into effect for the 1999-2000 season if any of our three feeder leagues are in a position to promote a club from their respective Premier Divisions.

Midland Football Alliance clubs for the 1999-2000 season are:

| | | | |
|---|---|---|---|
| Barwell | Halesowen Harriers | Pershore Town | Stourport Swifts |
| Bloxwich Town | Kings Norton Town | Rushall Olympic | Stratford Town |
| Boldmere St Michaels | Knypersley Vicoria | Sandwell Borough | Wednesfield |
| Bridgnorth Town | Oadby Town | Shifnal Town | West Midlands Police |
| Chasetown | Oldbury United | Stapenhill | Willenhall Town |

# INTERLINK EXPRESS MIDLAND FOOTBALL ALLIANCE ANNUAL AWARDS 1998-99

### INTERLINK EXPRESS PARCELS LTD
### LEAGUE CHAMPIONSHIP SHIELD
League Champions    Rocester FC
Runners Up    Kings Norton Town

### INDUSTRIAL REWIND SERVICES
### GOLDEN SOVEREIGN LEAGUE CUP
Winners    Oldbury United FC
Runners Up    West Midlands Police FC

### ZENITH SECURITIES LIMITED
### HOSPITALITY CUP
Winners    Halesowen Harriers FC
Runners Up    Knypersley Victoria FC
    West Midlands Police FC

### PAT FELLOWS
### BEST PROGRAMME AWARD
Winners    Willenhall Town FC

### JOE McGORIAN CUP
Winners    Knypersley Victoria FC

### KEVIN KEEGAN
### PLAYER OF THE YEAR AWARD
Winner    Ian Long
    Oldbury United FC

### POLYMAC SERVICES
### GOLDEN BOOT TOP GOALSCORER AWARD
Winner    Andy Lucas
    Barwell FC

### POLYMAC SERVICES
### BEST DISCIPLINARY AWARD
Winners    Rocester FC

### POLYMAC SERVICES
### MANAGER OF THE YEAR AWARD
Winner    Terry Greer
    Rocester FC

### INTERLINK EXPRESS
### MIDLAND INVITATION CUP
Sponsored by Bernard & Irene Davis
Winners    Atherstone United FC
Runners Up    Bandon FC

### JAMES GILBERT LTD SPECIAL PRESENTATION
Signed Gilbert Footballs presented to the finalists of the League Cup and the Midland Invitation Cup
Oldbury United FC    West Midlands Police FC
Atherstone United FC    Bandon FC

League Champions Rocester FC show off their silverware at the Midland Football Alliance Annual Awards Evening - the League Championship Shield, Manager of the Year Award, and the Best Disciplinary Award (the first time a Championship winning side has won this award).
Pictured left to right: Alf Hawksworth (Rocester Chairman), Theresa Chell, Terry Greer (Rocester Manager), Richard Owen, Ian Cruddas, Paul Ede.

# FINAL LEAGUE TABLE 1998-99

|  |  | Home |  |  |  |  | Away |  |  |  |  |  |
|---|---|---|---|---|---|---|---|---|---|---|---|---|
|  | P | W | D | L | F | A | W | D | L | F | A | Pts |
| Rocester | 38 | 16 | 1 | 2 | 49 | 18 | 9 | 6 | 4 | 31 | 18 | 82 |
| Kings Norton Town | 38 | 12 | 1 | 6 | 27 | 16 | 13 | 4 | 2 | 38 | 13 | 80 |
| Oldbury United | 38 | 9 | 6 | 4 | 30 | 15 | 10 | 3 | 6 | 37 | 27 | 66 |
| Boldmere St Michaels | 38 | 11 | 3 | 5 | 34 | 27 | 8 | 5 | 6 | 22 | 22 | 65 |
| Barwell | 38 | 10 | 6 | 3 | 39 | 23 | 7 | 4 | 8 | 30 | 31 | 61 |
| Halesowen Harriers | 38 | 9 | 3 | 7 | 38 | 30 | 8 | 5 | 6 | 27 | 33 | 59 |
| Rushall Olympic | 38 | 6 | 8 | 5 | 30 | 26 | 10 | 2 | 7 | 27 | 18 | 58 |
| Shifnal Town | 38 | 9 | 3 | 7 | 31 | 29 | 7 | 5 | 7 | 28 | 31 | 56 |
| West Midlands Police | 38 | 7 | 6 | 6 | 22 | 22 | 8 | 4 | 7 | 28 | 30 | 55 |
| Chasetown | 38 | 7 | 7 | 5 | 29 | 20 | 5 | 10 | 4 | 19 | 18 | 53 |
| Bridgnorth Town | 38 | 7 | 6 | 6 | 26 | 22 | 7 | 5 | 7 | 18 | 18 | 53 |
| Stourport Swifts | 38 | 7 | 6 | 6 | 31 | 25 | 6 | 5 | 8 | 25 | 25 | 50 |
| Knypersley Victoria | 38 | 8 | 3 | 8 | 29 | 31 | 5 | 5 | 9 | 30 | 30 | 47 |
| Willenhall Town | 38 | 6 | 6 | 7 | 25 | 22 | 7 | 2 | 10 | 26 | 31 | 47 |
| Wednesfield | 38 | 6 | 2 | 11 | 37 | 38 | 6 | 4 | 9 | 26 | 34 | 42 |
| Pelsall Villa | 38 | 5 | 3 | 11 | 21 | 33 | 6 | 4 | 9 | 20 | 34 | 40 |
| Stapenhill | 38 | 6 | 2 | 11 | 24 | 37 | 5 | 3 | 11 | 27 | 45 | 38 |
| Sandwell Borough | 38 | 2 | 6 | 11 | 11 | 30 | 8 | 1 | 10 | 26 | 35 | 37 |
| Pershore Town | 38 | 4 | 6 | 9 | 21 | 32 | 4 | 5 | 10 | 26 | 32 | 35 |
| Stratford Town | 38 | 4 | 3 | 12 | 16 | 38 | 3 | 5 | 11 | 23 | 45 | 29 |

# RESULTS CHART 1998-99

|  |  | 1 | 2 | 3 | 4 | 5 | 6 | 7 | 8 | 9 | 10 | 11 | 12 | 13 | 14 | 15 | 16 | 17 | 18 | 19 | 20 |
|---|---|---|---|---|---|---|---|---|---|---|---|---|---|---|---|---|---|---|---|---|---|
| 1 | Barwell | X | 2-0 | 2-0 | 2-2 | 1-1 | 0-2 | 2-2 | 1-1 | 3-1 | 2-0 | 1-1 | 1-0 | 6-2 | 4-3 | 3-0 | 2-3 | 3-1 | 1-3 | 1-1 | 2-0 |
| 2 | Boldmere St M | 4-3 | X | 2-0 | 0-0 | 2-0 | 1-3 | 2-1 | 0-4 | 0-1 | 2-2 | 0-1 | 2-1 | 2-0 | 2-1 | 2-2 | 3-2 | 6-2 | 2-1 | 2-1 | 0-2 |
| 3 | Bridgnorth Town | 1-3 | 1-1 | X | 0-0 | 0-1 | 2-2 | 1-0 | 0-1 | 2-0 | 2-1 | 0-1 | 1-2 | 2-1 | 0-1 | 2-2 | 2-1 | 3-0 | 2-2 | 0-0 | 5-3 |
| 4 | Chasetown | 4-0 | 0-1 | 0-0 | X | 1-3 | 0-2 | 2-1 | 1-1 | 1-1 | 0-0 | 0-3 | 0-0 | 3-2 | 4-0 | 4-0 | 2-1 | 1-1 | 2-4 | 4-0 | 0-0 |
| 5 | Halesowen Harr. | 4-1 | 2-3 | 0-0 | 2-1 | X | 1-1 | 3-0 | 3-5 | 4-1 | 2-1 | 2-2 | 1-3 | 2-1 | 1-3 | 3-1 | 0-1 | 4-2 | 0-1 | 1-3 | 3-0 |
| 6 | Kings Norton Tn | 1-0 | 0-1 | 2-0 | 2-2 | 0-1 | X | 2-0 | 1-0 | 1-0 | 3-1 | 0-1 | 1-3 | 1-0 | 0-1 | 3-1 | 1-0 | 3-1 | 2-0 | 2-3 |
| 7 | Knypersley Vic. | 0-4 | 1-2 | 1-2 | 1-3 | 3-0 | 1-1 | X | 0-1 | 1-2 | 2-0 | 0-0 | 0-4 | 2-1 | 1-1 | 4-2 | 3-1 | 2-1 | 3-1 | 3-1 | 1-4 |
| 8 | Oldbury United | 1-0 | 5-1 | 2-1 | 1-1 | 2-0 | 0-2 | 1-2 | X | 1-1 | 1-0 | 1-0 | 1-1 | 1-2 | 2-0 | 5-1 | 0-2 | 5-0 | 1-1 | 0-0 | 0-0 |
| 9 | Pelsall Villa | 0-2 | 1-0 | 0-2 | 3-1 | 1-1 | 1-2 | 2-2 | 0-1 | X | 1-2 | 1-6 | 0-2 | 1-2 | 0-2 | 2-3 | 1-1 | 1-0 | 4-1 | 1-3 | 1-0 |
| 10 | Pershore Town | 0-3 | 1-1 | 0-0 | 1-1 | 1-2 | 0-3 | 1-2 | 1-3 | 0-2 | X | 1-2 | 3-2 | 1-3 | 1-1 | 1-0 | 1-2 | 1-1 | 1-1 | 4-3 | 2-0 |
| 11 | Rocester | 2-3 | 2-1 | 2-0 | 1-1 | 6-2 | 1-0 | 1-0 | 3-1 | 4-1 | 3-2 | X | 1-0 | 3-0 | 4-2 | 1-2 | 1-0 | 7-1 | 2-1 | 3-0 | 2-1 |
| 12 | Rushall Olympic | 4-4 | 0-0 | 0-1 | 2-1 | 3-3 | 1-2 | 1-1 | 2-1 | 0-0 | 1-1 | 4-1 | X | 1-1 | 1-1 | 1-3 | 2-3 | 2-0 | 1-0 | 0-1 | 4-2 |
| 13 | Sandwell Boro | 0-0 | 0-1 | 3-0 | 0-1 | 0-0 | 0-3 | 1-1 | 0-2 | 0-1 | 2-0 | 0-3 | 0-2 | X | 0-0 | 1-3 | 1-1 | 1-1 | 2-0 | 0-4 | 0-1 |
| 14 | Shifnal Town | 1-2 | 1-1 | 3-1 | 1-2 | 0-1 | 0-3 | 2-1 | 3-2 | 0-3 | 1-4 | 1-1 | 2-1 | 2-0 | X | 3-0 | 2-2 | 2-3 | 2-1 | 3-0 | 2-1 |
| 15 | Stapenhill | 0-1 | 0-1 | 0-3 | 1-0 | 3-4 | 0-3 | 1-4 | 2-5 | 1-0 | 1-1 | 2-1 | 0-1 | 4-1 | 1-3 | X | 1-0 | 2-2 | 2-3 | 1-3 | 2-1 |
| 16 | Stourport Swifts | 3-0 | 1-1 | 0-0 | 0-1 | 2-0 | 0-3 | 3-3 | 1-1 | 3-0 | 1-0 | 1-0 | 0-1 | 1-2 | 3-3 | 2-2 | X | 1-4 | 4-0 | 1-2 | 4-2 |
| 17 | Stratford Town | 1-0 | 1-4 | 0-4 | 0-0 | 2-5 | 3-1 | 0-3 | 1-2 | 1-3 | 2-1 | 1-1 | 1-0 | 0-1 | 0-2 | 0-3 | 0-3 | X | 0-0 | 2-3 | 1-2 |
| 18 | Wednesfield | 2-2 | 0-2 | 1-3 | 1-2 | 0-1 | 2-4 | 2-1 | 0-3 | 9-1 | 4-1 | 2-4 | 2-3 | 0-1 | 5-1 | 3-1 | 1-0 | 1-4 | X | 2-2 | 0-2 |
| 19 | West Mids Police | 1-0 | 2-0 | 0-0 | 0-0 | 1-1 | 0-0 | 0-5 | 5-2 | 1-1 | 1-2 | 0-2 | 2-0 | 2-4 | 2-0 | 2-1 | 1-1 | 2-0 | 0-1 | X | 0-2 |
| 20 | Willenhall Town | 2-2 | 2-1 | 0-1 | 0-0 | 5-1 | 0-1 | 3-1 | 3-1 | 2-1 | 1-1 | 1-1 | 0-1 | 1-2 | 0-3 | 3-0 | 0-0 | 0-0 | 2-4 | 0-1 | X |

# LEADING GOALSCORERS 1998-99

| | | | | | |
|---|---|---|---|---|---|
| Andy Lucas | Barwell | 32 | Mark Williams | Halesowen Harriers | 14 |
| Scott Eaton | Stapenhill | 20 | Shaun Bradbury | Chasetown | 13 |
| Neil Kitching | Boldmere St Michaels | 20 | Andy Dutton | Knypersley Victoria | 13 |
| Charlie Blakemore | Chasetown | 16 | Mick Ede | Rocester | 13 |
| Mark Clarke | Halesowen Harriers | 16 | Paul James | Knypersley Victoria | 13 |
| Mark Holdcroft | Wednesfield (inc 4 for Rushall) | 15 | Ian Palin | Knypersley Victoria | 13 |
| Carl Tranter | Bridgnorth Town | 15 | Tony Dixon | Pelsall Villa | 12 |
| Jason Treharne | Shifnal Town | 15 | Martin Hallam | Stourport Swifts | 12 |
| Chris Burton | West Midlands Police | 14 | Robbie Wilson | Rushal Olympic | 12 |
| Jonathon Nesbitt | Kings Norton Town | 14 | Andy Wright | Oldbury United | 12 |
| Chris Rawlinson | Rocester | 14 | | | |

## INTERLINK EXPRESS MIDLAND INVITATION CUP 1998-99

**FIRST ROUND**

| | | | | | | |
|---|---|---|---|---|---|---|
| Bilston Com. College | v | Star | 3-2 | Bolehall Swifts | v | Knypersley Victoria | 2-4 |
| Bridgnorth Town | v | Stafford Town | 1-0 | Chasetown | v | Pershore Town | 0*1 |
| Cheslyn Hay | v | Dudley Sports | 6-1 | Downes Sports | v | Cradley Town | 0-1 |
| Ellistown | v | Barrow Town | 1-3 | Feckenham | v | Gornal Athletic | 1-0 |
| Highgate United | v | Continental Star | 0-1 | Halesowen Harriers | v | Darlaston Town | 5-2 |
| Kirby Muxloe | v | Studley BKL | 1-0 | Meir K A | v | Rushall Olympic | 1-2 |
| Oldbury United | v | Birstall United | 2-0 | Pelsall Villa | v | Barwell | 1-3 |
| Rocester | v | Aylestone Park | 3-1 | Sandwell Borough | v | Oadby Town | 2-3 |
| Southam | v | Handrahan Timbers | 3-0 | St Andrews | v | Wednesfield | 1-0 |
| Stourport Swifts | v | Ibstock Welfare | 3-0 | Stratford Town | v | Kings Norton Town | 1-0 |
| Tividale | v | Dudley Town | 3-1 | West Midlands Police | v | Friar Lane OB | 2-0 |
| Willenhall Town | v | Blakenall | 5*4 | | | | |

**SECOND ROUND**

| | | | | | | |
|---|---|---|---|---|---|---|
| Anstey Nomads | v | Stapenhill | 1-0 | Boldmere St Mi. | v | Barwell | 2-4 |
| Bridgnorth Town | v | Stourport Swifts | 3-2 | Cheslyn Hay | v | Atherstone United | 1-2 |
| Cradley Town | v | Pershore Town | 3-0 | Feckenham | v | Stratford Town | 1-0 |
| Kirby Muxloe | v | Continental Star | 4-2 | Lutterworth Town | v | Barrow Town | 1-3 |
| Malvern Town | v | West Midlands Police | 1-3 | Oadby Town | v | Bilston Com. College | 0-3 |
| Rocester | v | Bandon | 0-2 | Rushall Olympic | v | Thringstone United | 1*2 |
| Tividale | v | Oldbury United | 0-2 | Wednesfield | v | Southam United | 2-1 |
| Wolverhampton Cas. | v | Knypersley Victoria | 3-2 | Willenhall Town | v | Halesowen Harriers | 1-2 |

**THIRD ROUND**

| | | | | | | |
|---|---|---|---|---|---|---|
| Barrow Town | v | Bilston Com. College | W-O | Bridgnorth Town | v | Barwell | 5p3 0*0 |
| Feckenham | v | Cradley Town | 0-2 | Halesowen Harriers | v | Anstey Nomads | 2-1 |
| Kirby Muxloe | v | Thringstone United | 5V0 | Oldbury United | v | Atherstone United | 1-2 |
| West Midlands Police | v | Wednesfield (at WMP) | 2*3 | Wolverhampton Cas. | v | Bandon | 0-3 |
| (Result reversed Kirby Ineligible player) | | | | | | |

**FOURTH ROUND**

| | | | | | | |
|---|---|---|---|---|---|---|
| Bridgnorth Town | v | Cradley Town | 2-1 | Thringstone United | v | Barrow Town | 3-1 |
| Atherstone United | v | Wednesfield | 2-1 | Bandon | v | Halesowen Harriers | 1-0 |

**SEMI-FINALS**

| | | | | | | |
|---|---|---|---|---|---|---|
| Atherstone United | v | Bridgnorth Town | 1-0 | Thringstone United | v | Bandon | 2-5 |

**FINAL**

| | | | | |
|---|---|---|---|---|
| ATHERSTONE UTD | v | BANDON | 2-1 | at York Road, Oldbury United FC |

## INDUSTRIAL REWINDS LEAGUE CHALLENGE CUP 1998-99

**FIRST ROUND**

| | | | | | | |
|---|---|---|---|---|---|---|
| Barwell | v | Willenhall Town | 2-1 | Stratford Town | v | Shifnal Town | 2-2, 2-0 |
| Rushall Olympic | v | Kings Norton Town | 0-1 | Pershore Town | v | BridgnorthTown | 0-1 |

**SECOND ROUND**

| | | | | | | |
|---|---|---|---|---|---|---|
| Sandwell Borough | v | Chasetown | 1-0 | Stourport Swifts | v | Knypersley Victoria | |
| Halesowen Harriers | v | Wednesfield | 0-1 | Rocester | v | Kings Norton Town | 3-1 |
| Boldmere St M | v | Bridgnorth | 1-2 | Shifnal Town | v | West Mids Police | 0-1 |
| Stapenhill | v | Barwell | 2-1 | Oldbury United | v | Pelsall Villa | 2-1 |

**QUARTER FINALS**

| | | | | | | |
|---|---|---|---|---|---|---|
| Bridgnorth Town | v | Wednesfield | 3-0 | West Mids Police | v | Rocester | 3-2 |
| Oldbury United | v | Sandwell Borough | 1-0 | Stapenhill | v | Knypersley Victoria | 2-1 |

**SEMI FINALS**

| | | | | | | |
|---|---|---|---|---|---|---|
| West Mids Police | v | Stapenhill | 3-0, 2-2 | Oldbury United | v | Bridgnorth Town | 1-0, 2-1 |

**FINAL**

| | | | | |
|---|---|---|---|---|
| W MIDS POLICE | v | OLDBURY UNITED | 2-3 | at Halesowen Harriers FC. Att: 278 |

# BARWELL

**Secretary:** Mrs Shirley Brown, 101 Eskdale Road, Hinckley, LE10 0NW (01455 446048)

**Ground:** Kirkby Rd, Barwell, Leics (01455 843067).
**Directions:** M42 jct 10 (Tamworth Services), A5 towards Nuneaton. Remain on A5for approx 11 miles, go straight on at traffic lights at the Longshoot Motelthe 400 yards at r/about take 1st exit left sign A47 Earl Shilton, in 3 milesat traffic lights go straight ahead and in 1 mile at r/about take first leftexit sign Barwell in village centre 1/2 mile go straight over mini r/about, 20yards turn right into Kirkby Rd, ground 400 yards on right.
Capacity: 2,500          Seats: 140          Cover: 750          Floodlights: Yes
**Clubhouse:** Evenings & lunchtimes. Snacks available.     **Club Shop:** No

**HONOURS:** Barwell Athletic: Leics Snr Lg Tebbutt Brown Cup 91-92, Leics Sen Cup96-97.

**PREVIOUS** Leagues: Midland Combination 92-94. (Barwell Ath.: Leics Senior.
Hinckley: Central Midlands 86-88)
Names: Barwell Athletic F.C., Hinckley F.C. - amalgamated in 1992.
Ground: Barwell Athletic: None. Hinckley: groundshare at HinckleyAth. pre-'92
**RECORDS** Goalscorer: Andy Lucas
Appearances: Kevin Johnson.

**FACT FILE**
Founded: 1992.
Nickname: Kirkby Roaders
Sponsors: Cleartherm
Colours: All yellow with green trim
Change colours: All blue
Midweek matchday: Tuesday
Programme: 36 pages,70p
Editor: R Backhouse/R Boorman
98-99Captain: Mark Drinkwater
Top Scorer: Andy Lucas
P.o.Y.: Andy Lucas

**CLUB PERSONNEL**
Chairman: David Laing.
Vice Chairman: Ron Borman.
President: Derek Lucas
Press Officer: Merv Nash.
Manager: Paul Purser
Asst Manager: Mark Rosegreen
Physio: Viv Coleman

# BLOXWICH TOWN

**Secretary:** Kevin Edwards, 149 Coalpool Lane, Walsall WS3 1QL Tel: 01922 868608

**Ground:** Abbey Park, Glastonbury Crescent, Bloxwich, Walsall Tel: 01922 477640
**Directions:** A34 Walsall-Bloxwich, then west onto A4124. Ground 2-3 miles on right, sign-posted Mossley Estate
Capacity: 1,000          Seats: 200          Covered: 400          Floodlights: Yes
**Clubhouse:** Yes          **Club Shop:** No

**HONOURS** Midland Alliance 97-98, League Cup R-up 97-98; Bloxwich Comb.(2), Staffs Co. Lg Div 1, Walsall Snr Cup 96-97 R-up 86-87, Invitation Cup 89-90, Midland Comb. Prem. Div. 95-96 R-Up.94-95. Div 1 89-90, Alan Peck Cup x3 Carlsberg Chall. Cup 95-96, Industrial Rewinds Lge Cup R-up 96-97

**PREVIOUS**     **Leagues:** Midland Combination (Prem, Div 1)     **Names:** Bloxwich AFC.

**CLUB RECORDS** Atendance: 252
Win: 8-1 v Alvechurch     Defeat: 9-0 v Shepshed Dynamo
Goalscorer: Mark Holdcroft  Appearances: Stephen Hillman

**BEST SEASON** FA Vase: 3rd Rd Proper 97-98
FA Cup: 97-98 First Season          League Clubs Defeated: None

**FACT FILE**

Founded: 1972
Nickname: Kestrels
Sponsors: Alvin Amario/Rough & Ready
Colours: Blue & white/white/blue
Change Colours: Red & Black/Black/Black
Midweek Matches: Tues/Thurs
Programme: 30 pages 50p
Editor: Phil BradburnTel: 0121 554 7266

**CLUB PERSONNEL**
President: M M Ross
Chairman: Veejay Thaper

Manager: M Folland/P Knox
Coach: Jim Skidmore
Physio: Steve Hooper

# BOLDMERE St. MICHAEL

**Secretary:** Des Green, 4 Blandford Avenue, Castle Bromwich, Birmingham B36 9HX
Tel: 0121 747 8404
**Ground:** Church Road, Boldmere, Sutton Coldfield
Tel: 0121 373 4435 or 0121 384 7531
**Directions:** A38 & A5127 from City towards S. Coldfield, left at Yenton lights onto A452 (Chester Rd), Church Rd is 6th turning on the right.
Nearest station: 400yds from Chester Road (BR).
Capacity: 2,500          Seats: 230          Covered: 400          Floodlights: Yes
**Clubhouse:** Bar & lounge, every evening and four lunchtimes.

**HONOURS:** Birmingham AFA 36-37; Birmingham AFA Snr Cup; Birmingham Jnr Cup, FA Amtr Cup SF 47-48; AFA Snr Cup 47-48; Central Amtr Lg 48-49; Midland Comb 85-86 88-89 89-90, Challenge Cup 77-78 89-90; Tony Allden Mem. Cup 78-79 88-89 91-92; Challenge Trophy 86-87; Sutton Charity Cup 96-97.
**PREVIOUS:**     **Leagues:** West Mids 49-63; Midland Combination 63-94.

Players Progressing: John Barton (Everton, Derby County),Kevin Collins (Shrewsbury), Jack Lane (Birmingham City, Notts Co.), John Lewis(Walsall), Don Moss (Cardiff, C Palace), Harry Parkes (Aston Villa), Wally Soden (Coventry).

**FACT FILE**

Founded: 1883
Nickname: Mikes.
Sponsor: Swift Forwarding
Colours: White/black/black
Change colours: Yellow/green/yellow
Midweek matches: Tuesday
Programme: 32 pages, 90p
Editor: John Smart (0121 350 6356)

**CLUB PERSONNEL**

Manager: Alan Parsons

# BRIDGNORTH TOWN

**Secretary:** Mary Boot, 68 Wellmeadow,Bridgenorth,Shropshire WV15 6DE (01746 764204)
**Ground:** Crown Meadow, Innage Lane, Bridgnorth, Salop WV16 6PZ (01746 762747)
**Directions:** Follow signs for Shrewsbury (A458) over river bridge on by-pass,turn right for town centre at island, right at T junction, 1st left into Victoria Road, right at cross-road, follow road into Innage Lane, ground on left.
**Capacity:** 1,600  **Shop:** Yes  **Seats:** 250  **Cover:** 700  **Floodlights:** Yes
**Clubhouse:** Evenings & weekend lunches,  Dancehall, darts, pool, hot food on matchdays
**Record Fee Recieved:** £10,000 for Delwyn Humphries from Kidderminster Harriers
**Players Progressing:**Roger Davies (Derby county) and Paul Jones ( Wolves via Kidd'ter H)

| | |
|---|---|
| HONOURS: | Midland Comb 79-80 82-83 (R-up 76-77 80-81); Lg Cup 78-79, Tony Allden Mem Cup R-up, Kidderminster & Dist Lge,Shropshire Snr Cup 85-86; Shropshire County Cup 70-71 75-76 76-77 78-79 79-80;Welsh Amt Cup 70-71; Shropshire County Jun Cup 98-99. |
| BEST SEASON: | FA Cup: 3rd Qual Rd 64-65FA Vase: 5th Rd 75-76, 94-95 |
| PREVIOUS | Leagues: Kidderminster & Dist until 68; Midland Comb 68-83; Southern Lge, Midland Div. 83-96    Names: St Leonards Old Boys pre 46 |
| RECORDS | Goalscorer: Roger Davies 157    Appearances: Kevin Harris 426 Attendance: 1,600 v South Shields FA Vase 5th Rd 1976 |

**FACT FILE**
Founded: 1946
Nickname: The Town
Sponsors:
Colours: Blue & white/white/blue
Change colours: All red
Midweek matchday: Tuesday
Programme: 24 pages,60p
Editor: Simon Bromley
Local Press : Shropshire Star, Bridgnorth Journal, Express & Star.. Local Radio: Beacon, BBC Radio Shropshire
Youth League: West Mids Regional Regional
**CLUB PERSONNEL**

Chairman: Simon Bromley
Vice Chairman: Ian Thomas
President: Mike Williams
Manager:Les Bristow
Asst Manager: Paul Blakeley
Physio: Andy Perry

# CHASETOWN

**Secretary:** P E Dixon, c/o Club

**Ground:** The Scholars, Church Street, Chasetown (01543 682222/684609).
**Directions:** Follow Motorways M5, M6 or M42 and follow signs for A5. A5 to White Horse Road/Wharf Lane, left into Highfields Rd (B5011), left into Church Street at top of hill, ground at end just beyond church. Buses 394 or 395 W Mids Travel, 94 Chase Bus,from Walsall, 860 Midland Red from Cannock.
**Seats:** 112**Cover:** 250**Capacity:** 2,000**Floodlights:** Yes
**Clubhouse:** Mon-Fri 7.30-11pm, Sat 11.30am-11pm, Sun 8-10.30pm. Basic snacks.
**Club Shop:** Yes

| | |
|---|---|
| HONOURS | West Mids Lg R-up 90-91 92-93 (Lg Cup 89-90 90-91, Div 1 77-78 (R-up73-74 74-75 75-76 80-81 82-83), Div 1 Cup R-up 80-81 82-83, Div 2 R-up 87-88,Div 2 Cup R-up 86-87); Walsall Snr Cup 90-91 92-93; Staffs Snr Cup R-up 91-92. |
| BEST SEASON | FA Cup:    FA Vase: |
| PREVIOUS | Name: Chase Terrace Old Scholars 54-72  Ground: Burntwood Rec Cte (pre'83) |
| Leagues: | Cannock Yth 54-58; Lichfield & Dist. 58-61; Staffs Co. 61-72; West Mids 72-94. |
| RECORDS | Attendance: 659 v Tamworth, FA Cup 2nd Qual Rd 1/10/88. |
| | Appearances: A Cox 469 (+15)    Win: 14-1 v Hanford (H), Walsall Snr Cup 17/10/92. |
| | Goalscorer: T Dixon 172    Defeat: 1-8 v Telford U Res., West Mids (Reg.) Lge Div 1 |

**FACT FILE**

Founded: 1954.
Nickname: Scholars
Colours: All blue
Change Colours: All Red.
Sponsors: Aynsley Windows
Midweek matchday: Tuesday
Reserves League: West Midlands
Programme: 26 pages, 50p
Editor/Press Officer: Mike Fletcher

**CLUB PERSONNEL**

Chairman: G Rollins
Vice Chairman: B Simpson
President: A Scorey.
Manager: Cliff Painter
Asst Manager: Brian Fox
Physio: E Highfield.

# CRADLEY TOWN

**Secretary:** David Attwood, 4 Birch Coppice, Quarry Bank, Brierley Hill, W Midlands DY5 1AP
Tel: 01384 637430
**Ground:** Beeches View, Beeches View Ave, Cradley, Halesowen, B63 2HB. (01384 569658)

**Directions:** M5 jct 3, take A456, right at 2nd island, left into Rosemary Rdafter Fox Hunt pub, Lansdown Rd, Dunstall Rd, left at T-junction, left again atnext T-junction (Beecher Rd East), 1st left (Abbey Rd), right at end, ground50yds on left. Nearest BR station is Cradley Heath
**Capacity:** 3,000    **Seats:** 200    **Cover:** 1,500    **Floodlights:** Yes
**Clubhouse:** Open matchdays only. Food available    Club Shop: No

| | |
|---|---|
| HONOURS | West Mids Lg Div 1 90-91, Midland Comb. Div 2 72-73 R-up 75-76 77-78, Presidents Cup 74-75 75-76, Invitation Cup 72-73); Metropolitan Lg 70-71, Wednesbury Charity Cup 90-91, Dudley Guest Hosp. Cup 71-72 72-73 75-76 90-91 |
| PREVIOUS | Leagues: Metropolitan; Brierley Hill; Kidderminster; West Mids Amtr; Midland Comb. 71-82; West Midlands 82-99    Name: Albion Haden United |
| RECORDS | Gate: 1,000 v Aston Villa, friendly |
| | Goalscorer: Jim Nugent    Apearances: R J Haywood |
| | Win: 9-1 v Wolverhampton United (H), West Midlands Lge 1990 |
| | Defeat: 0-9 v Paget Rangers (A) Midland Invitation Cup 97 |
| | Transfer fee paid: £1,000 for Darren Marsh (Oldswinford, 1992) |
| | Received: £20,000 for John Williams (Swansea, 1991) |

**FACT FILE**
Founded: 1948
Nickname: Lukes
Sponsors: Allen Homes/Garian Roofing & Cladding
Colours: Red & black/black/black
Change colours: Yellow/blue/blue
Midweek matchday: Tuesday
Reserve's League: West Mids Lge Div One
Programme: Yes

**CLUB PERSONNEL**
President: W Forrest
Chairman: Graham Taylor
Vice Chairman: Peter Cooper
Press Officer: Trevor Thomas (01384 569658)

Manager: Trevor Thomas
Asst Mgr: Anthony Clark
Physio: Derek Cronin

# HALESOWEN HARRIERS

**Secretary:** Mrs Christine Beasley, 43 Hawne Lane, Halesowen, West Midlands B633RN (0121 550 3788 H and 07788 697167 Mobile).
**Ground:** Hayes Park, Park Rd, Colley Gate, Halesowen (01384 896748.
**Directions:** On A458 Birmingham to Stourbridge Rd (B'ham 10 miles, Stourbridge 4miles). M5 Jct 3 (towards Kidderminster), right at 1st island (towards Dudley),turn left at island (towards Stourbridge), straight over next island then 3m to grd left side, 200yds past Park Lane. 1 mile Lye BR
**Capacity:** 4,000      **Seats:** 350      **Cover:** 500      **Floodlights:** Yes
**Clubhouse:** Open every evening. Limited range of hot snacks, but full cold snack kitchen.
**Club Shop:** Yes

**HONOURS**West Mids Lg Div 1 85-86 (Div 2 84-85, Div 2 Cup 84-85), Inter City Bowl 67-68 68-69, Festival Lg(5)(R-up(9)), FA Sunday Cup SF 79-80, Midland Sunday Cup, Birmingham Sunday Cup.
**PREVIOUS**Leagues: Festival (Sunday)/ West Midlands (pre-1994).Grounds: Birmingham parks 61-70/ Halesowen Town FC 70-84 (both whilst in Sunday football).
**RECORDS**Attendance: 750; friendlies v Walsall and Wolves in 1985. Competitive;450 v Lye, Lge 1988. **Win:** 12-1 v Lichfield & v Malvern Town, 1986. **Defeat:** 2-8 v Frickley Athletic (A), F.A. Cup 2nd Qual Rd 26/9/92. **Fee paid:** £750 to Oldswinford for L Booth, 1991.

### FACT FILE

Founded: 1961
Nickname: None
Sponsors:Ludlow Coaches,Bevan Contracts
Colours: White/black/white
Change colours: Yellow/Blue/Yellow
Midweek matchday: Tuesday or Wednesday.
Programme: 28-36 pages
Editor: Rob Shinfield (01384 850819)

### CLUB PERSONNEL

Chairman: Derek Beasley
Tel: 01384 896748(W) and 070803 880510(M)

---

# KINGS NORTON TOWN

**Secretary:** Mike Rowley, 61 Derwent Drive, Priorslee, Telford, Shrops TF2 9QR
Tel: 01952 200020
**Ground:** The Valley Stadium, Bromsgrove Road, Redditch (01527 67450).
**Directions:** Access 7 on town centre ring-road takes you into Bromsgrove Road(via Unicorn Hill) - ground entrance 400yds past traffic lights on right.Arriving from Bromsgrove take first exit off dual carriageway. Ground 400 yds from Redditch BR station and town centre.
**Capacity:** 9,500      **Cover:** 2,000      **Seats:** 400      **Floodlights:** Yes
**Clubhouse:** ???      **Club Shop:** ???

HONOURS     Midland Comb Div 1 95-96, Challenge Vase R-up 93-94, Kings Norton Lg Divs 1 + 2 & Lg Cup, J W Hunt Cup 95-96, Mercian Lg Div 1, Birmingham Works Lg,Birmingham Jnr Cup R-up, Birmingham Vase R-up 95-96.
PREVIOUS     **League:** Midland Comb, Birmingham Works. Richmond Amateurs: Birmingham AFA, pre-1994. **Names:** Richmond Swifts, Swift Personalised Products (found ed 1979)/Richmond Amateurs - clubs merged in 1994. **Grounds:** Shirley TownFC (pre-'92)/ Wythall Park, Silver Street,Wythall (Wythall FC) 92-93/ Alvechurch FC 93-94 (pre-Xmas)/ British Gas Sports Ground, Woodacre Rd, Erdington 93-94, Triplex Sports 94-97
RECORDS     Goalscorer: A Dunkley (21, 93-94).
Win: 6-0 v Burntwood, 93-94Defeat: 0-6 v Archdales, 92-93.

### FACT FILE

Founded: 1994
Nickname: Nomads
Sponsors: Swift Personalised Products
& BGR Financial Consultants.
Colours: White & red/black/red & white
Change colours Green/white/black
Programme: Yes
Midweek matchdays: Tuesday.

### CLUB PERSONNEL

Chairman: M Rowley
Vice-Chairman: S Sanders.
Comm. Manager/Press Officer: Fred Evans
Manager: Pete Dunbavin
Asst Manager:
Coach: Morris Gittens

---

# KNYPERSLEY VICTORIA

**Secretary:** Steve Chawner, 18 John St., Biddulph, Stoke on Trent. ST6 6BB (01782 518998)

**Ground:** Tunstall Road, Knypersley, Stoke-on-Trent, (01782 522737 club).
**Directions:** M6 Jct 15 join A500, 4th exit, pick up A527, follow through Tunstall, Chell, to Biddulph. Ground is situated on A527 just before Biddulph. From M6 jct 18 follow signs to Holmes Chapel then Congleton, A527 to Biddulph,continue thru lights, ground on left.
**Capacity:** 1,200      **Seats:** 200      **Cover:** 200      **Floodlights:** Yes **Club Shop:** Yes
**Clubhouse:** Open from 1pm Saturdays, 7pm weekdays. Hot snacks at tea bar

HONOURS     West Mids Lg Div 1 92-93, Staffs Snr Lg 84-85 (Lg Cup 84-85 85-86), Staffs Co. Lg R-up 79-80, Staffs FA Vase 83-84 86-87, Sentinel Cup 86-87,     Leek & Moorlands Lg 72-73 (Div 2 71-72). Industrial Rewinds Cup 98, Joe McGorian Cup 88.
**BEST SEASON  FA Cup** 3rd Qual Rd 96-97 **FA Vase:**
PREVIOUS     **Leagues:** Leek & Moorlands 69-78; Staffs Co. (North) 78-83; Staffs Sen 83-90; W Midland (Reg) 90-94. **Grounds:** None
RECORDS     **Attendance:** 1,100 v Port Vale, friendly 1989
**Goalscorer:** J Burndred 128          **Appearances:** Terry Stanway 601
**Fee paid:** £1,000 M Biddle (Congleton 93) **Defeat:** 0-9 v Meir KA, Staffs Sen.
**Win:** 10-0 v Clancey Dudley, West Midls (Reg.) Div. 1 90-91

### FACT FILE

Founded: 1969.
Nickname: The Vics.
Sponsors: Potters Packaging
Colours: Claret & sky/claret/claret & sky.
Midweek matchday: Tues/Thurs
Reserve League: Staffs Senior.
Programme: 40 pages 60p.
Editor/ Press Officer: J A Shenton
(01782 517962).

### CLUB PERSONNEL

Chairman: Dave Nixon
Vice Chairman: Alan Farr
President: G Quinn

Manager: Terry Stanway
Coach: Mick Biddle
Physio: T.B.A.

# INTERLINK EXPRESS MIDLANDS FOOTBALL ALLIANCE ANNUAL AWARDS

Top left: The Golden Boot Top Goalscorer Award. Andy Lucas became the league's top goalscorer and also broke the MFA goalscoring record which had stood since the first season of the MFA. Andy scored 32 goals, previous record was 31 goals. Pictured here is Mary Lycett of sponsors Polymac Services presenting the award to Andy Lucas of Barwell FC.

Top right: Polymac Services Manager of the Year Award. Rocester FC manager Terry Greer (right) is seen receiving the award and a magnum of champagne from sponsor Malcolm Lycett of Polymac Services.

Bottom: Kevin Keegan Player of the Year Award. Ian Long (centre) of Oldbury United FC receives the award from John Young (right) of the Football Association. Also pictured (left) Mrs Young.

# OADBY TOWN

**FACT FILE**
Colours: Red/white/black

**Secretary:** Kevin Zupp, 14 Swiftway, Lutterworth, Leics LE17 4PB  Tel: 01455 550358

**Ground:** Invicta Park, Wigston Road, Oadby, Leics LE2 5QG  Tel: 0116 271 5728

**Directions:** Oadby is situated 4 miles south of Leicester on the A6. from Oadby church in the centre of town, follow signposts for Wigston. The ground is 3/4 mile from        t h e church on the left.

Capacity:         Cover: 224        Seating: 224        Floodlights: Yes

**Clubhouse:** Yes

**HONOURS** Leicestershire Senior Lge: 63-64 67-68 68-69 72-73 94-95 96-97 97-98 98-99;
Div. 2 51-52; Lge Cup 77-78 93-94 94-95;
Leics Senior Cup 62-63 63-64 75-76 76-77 80-81

Charity Cups Rolleston 58-59 59-60 68-69 74-75 88-89 93-94 96-97 97-98;
Coalville 60-61 63-64 65-66 69-70; Harborough 83-84 88-89; Oadby 70-71;
Battle of Britain 93-94 94-95 96-97

**PREVIOUS**        **Leagues:** Leicestershire Senior League

**CLUB PERSONNEL**
Chairman: Brian Ford Powell
Vice Chairman: Stuart Blyth
President: Bob Mallet
Vice President: Alan Hussey
General Manager: Stewart Warrington

Manager: Alan Hussey
Asst. Manager: Steve Scott
Physio: Derek Hewitt

---

# OLDBURY UNITED

**Secretary:** Paul Charnock, 27 Pennyhill Lane, West Bromwich, W.Mids B71 3RP
Tel: 0121 588 8369
**Ground:** The Cricketts, York Road, Rowley Regis, Warley, West Midlands (0121 5595564).
**Directions:** M5 jct 2, follow Blackheath & Halesowen signs, first left at lights and fourth right into York Road (turning before motorway flyover), ground200yds on left. One and a half miles from Sandwell & Dudley and Rowley Regis BR stations. Bus 404 from West Bromwich, Oldbury and Blackheath.
Capacity: 3,000        Seats: 300        Cover: 1,000        Floodlights: Yes
**Clubhouse:** Mon-Fri 7.30-11pm, Sat-Sun 12-2.30 (12-11pm Sat matchdays). Snacks available on matchdays.        **Club Shop:** No

**HONOURS** West Mids Lg 92-93, Staffs Snr Cup 87-88, Midland Comb. R-up 78-79(Presidents Cup 72-73(res), Div 3 R-up 82-83(res), Chal. Vase 82-83(res)),Walsall Snr Cup 82-83, B'ham Snr Amtr Cup, Oldbury Lg Div 2 61-62, Worcs Snr Urn 86-87, Sandwell Charity Cup 86-87, Interlink Invitation Cup 96-97. Industrial Rewinds League Cup: 98-99
**PREVIOUS** Leagues: Oldbury 58-62/ Warwick & W Mids All. 62-65/ Worcs (later
Midland)Comb. 65-82/ Southern 82-86.
Names: Queens Colts 58-62/ Whiteheath Utd 62-65.
**RECORDS** Attendance: 2,200 v Walsall Wood, Walsall Snr Cup Final 1982.
Win: 10-1 v Blakenall        Defeat: 1-9 v Moor Green.

**FACT FILE**
Founded: 1958
Nickname: Cricketts,The Blues.
Sponsors: Beswick Paper Group, Oldbury.
Colours: Navy with sky trim/blue/blue
Change colours: All amber
Midweek matchday: Tuesday
Programme: 28 pages, 60p
Editor: Football Secretary.

**CLUB PERSONNEL**

Chairman: Roy Keeling.
Vice Chairman: Ken Harris.
Press Officer: Ian Whitmore
Manager: John Morris
Asst Mgr: Kevin Sweeney
Physio: Paul Millard

---

# PELSALL VILLA

**Secretary:** Gareth J Evans, 72 St Pauls Crescent, Pelsall, Walsall WS3 4ET(01922 693114).
**Ground:** The Bush, Walsall Road, Pelsall, Walsall
Tel: 01922 682018 Club, 01922 692748 Ground
**Directions:** M6 jct 7 marked A34 B'ham. Take A34 towards Walsall to 1st island,turn right (marked Ring Road), cross two islands. At large island at bottom of hill take last exit marked Lichfield, up hill, cross next island to lights.Continue to next set of lights and turn left (B4154 Pelsall). Over railway bridge to Old Bush pub on right (next to Pelsall Cricket & Sports Club).
Capacity: 2,000        Seats: Yes        Cover: 624        Floodlights: Yes  **Club Shop:** Yes
**Clubhouse:** Mon-Fri 7-11pm, Sat noon-11pm, Sun noon-3 & 7-10.30pm. Hot &cold meals.

**HONOURS** West Mids Lg - Prem. Lge 94-95 (R-up 95-96) Div Cup 95-96, Div 1 Cup 88-89 (R-up 89-90, Div 2 Cup R-up 83-84, Walsall Snr Cup R-up 89-90 92-93, Wednesbury Charity Cup 6, (R-up 7), D Stanton Shield(2) 73-75 (R-up 75-76), Sporting Star Cup 76-77 (R-up 61-62), Prem Div Tphy(res)89-90), Rugeley Charity Cup 78-79 (R-up 69-70), Bloxwich Charity Cup(2), Edge Cup 83-84, Ike Cooper Tphy R-up 89-90. Midland Triangle Cup 95-96.
**BEST SEASON** FA Cup: 3rd Qual. Rd 92-93, 2-4 V Gainsborough T. (A).
FA Vase: 5th Rd 92-93, 0-1 v Buckingham T. (A)
**PREVIOUS** League: Staffs County (South) 61-81, West Midlands 82-96 Grounds: None
**RECORDS** Attendance 2,060 v Aston Villa 29.7.98
Goalscorer: Dean Walters 231 Appearances: Neil Coles 538

**FACT FILE**
Reformed: 1961
Nickname: Villians
Sponsor: Metelec
Colours: Red & black/red/red
Change colours: Blue & white/blue/blue
Midweek home matchday: Wednesday
Programme: 68 pages, 60p
Editor: Secretary

**CLUB PERSONNEL**

Chairman: R.New
Vice Chairman: J H Gough
President: B J Hill
Press Officer: B J Hill
Manager: Kevin Gough
Asst Manager: A.Dixon
Physio: R.Pickering

BARWELL FC: Back Row (L-R): Dave Laing (chairman), Matt Willcock, Jason Gotch, Scott Mackay, Ian Monroe, Mark Drinkwater, Keith Morris, Adam Turner, Viv Coleman (physio), Paul Purser (manager). Front Row: Andy Rutherford, Steve Markham, Kev Murray, Mark Rosegreen (assistant manager), Andy Lucas (League's top scorer), Les Williams, Darren Grassby, Scott Clamp.

PELSALL VILLA: Back Row (L-R): Paul Madders, Kevin Hickman, Tony Dixon, Neil Coles, Adrian Horne, Stephan Corbett, Lee Davies, Neil Holmes, Justin Anstey, Richard Pickering. Front Row: Ian Turnbull, Kevin Lee, Paul Baines, Simon Hughes, Graham Slide, Stuart Turnbull. Photo: Marshall's Sports Services (Birmingham)

BLOXWICH: Back Row (L-R): Dave Downing (manager), Roger Fowler, Paul Bates, Craig Skitt, Matthew Cartwright, Scott Turbutt, Scott Hall, Jim Tipper, Steve Howells. Front Row: Brian Lee, Simon Swallow, Jason Paddock, Darren Barnwell, Lee Fields, Simon Roberts, Michael Green. Photo: Marshall's Sports Services (Birmingham)

# PERSHORE TOWN 88

**Match Secretary:** Ian Gill, 2 Sebright Close, Pershore, Worcs WR10 1QF (01386554116 H).

**Ground:** King George V Playing Fields, King Georges Way, Pershore, Worcs (01386556902).
**Directions:** M5 jct 7, A44 to Pershore (8 miles) cross 1st lights in Pershore,at 2nd lights turn left & fold road round into King Georges Way, ground immediately on left.
Capacity: 4,000          Seats: 200          Cover: 200          Floodlights: Yes (148 lux)

**Clubhouse:** Bar open Mon-Fri 7.30-11pm, Fri 3-6pm, Sat noon-11pm, Sun noon-3 & 7-10.30pm. Coffee, tea, soup, hot pies and rolls available during matches.    **Club Shop:** No

| | |
|---|---|
| **HONOURS** | Midland Comb Prem 93-94, Div 2 89-90; Worcs Jnr Cup 90-91, Robert Biggart Cup 90-91 91-92 94-95 96-97 98-99, (R-up 89-90 95-96); Worcs Snr |
| Urn | 95-96, R-up 92-93, Jack Mould Cup 90-91, Alfred Terry Cup 90-91 |
| | Martley Hosp. Cup(`A') 90-91,Pershore Hosp. Cup(Res) 92-93 93-94 94-95, R-up 94-95 97-98; Evesham Hosp.Minor Cup R-up(`A') 94-95. |
| **BEST SEASON** | FA Cup: 4th Qual Rd 94-95, 1-3 v Yeading |
| | FA Vase: 3rd Rd 95-96, 1-2 v Burgess Hill T. |
| **PREVIOUS** | League: Midland Comb 89-90 90-94. |
| **RECORDS** | Atttendance: 1,356 v Yeading, FA Cup 4th Qual. Rd 23/10/93. |
| | Scorer: Simon Judge 124    Appearances: Gary Aldington, 290 |

**FACT FILE**
Founded: 1988.
Nickname: The Town
Colours: Blue & White,blue,blue
Change colours:Red,black, red
Midweek matchday: Tuesday
Reserves' Lge: Banks's W.Mid Lg Div 1 (S)
Programme: 20 pages,60p
Editor: Grahan Hill
98-99- Captain: Mick Lowe
P.o.Y.: Andy Yapp

**CLUB PERSONNEL**
Chairman: Anthony Bradstock
Vice Chairmen: Terry Conway, Bill Jones
Treasurer: Paul Carr
Secretary: Don Roberts
Manager: Keith Ingram
Asst Mgr: Mike Pugh
Coach: Frank Concannon

---

# RUSHALL OLYMPIC

**Secretary:** Peter Athersmith, 46 Blakenall Lane, Leamore, Walsall, W Mids WS31HG
Tel: 01922 712632
**Ground:** Dales Lane, off Daw End Lane, Rushall, Nr Walsall (01922 641021).
**Directions:** From Rushall centre (A461) take B4154 signed Aldridge. Approx. 1mile on right, directly opposite Royal Oak P.H., in Daw End Lane. Grd on right. 2 miles Walsall (BR) station.
Capacity: 2,500    Seats: 200    Cover: 200    Floodlights: Yes    **Club Shop:** No
**Clubhouse:** Bar/lounge, every night 8-11pm, Sat matchdays, Sun noon-2.30pm
**HONOURS** West Mids Lge Div 1 79-80; Walsall Amtr Lge Div 1 55-56, Div 2 52-53, Snr Cup 54-55 55-56, Jabez Cliff Cup 55-56 ; Staffs Co. Lge Div 1 60-61 61-62 62-63          64-65
(Div 2 56-57); Walsall Charity Cup 52-53; Walsall Chal.Cup 54-55 56-57;
Walsall Mem. Charity Cup (x7) 55-62; W Preston Chal. Cup 56-57; Cannock &
Dist. Charity Cup 56-57; Wednesbury Snr Cup 58-59 59-60 60-61; Sporting Star          Cup
59-60 60-61(jt) 64-65 65-66 67-68; J W Edge 62-63 66-67; Walsall Snr          Cup
64-65; Lichfield Charity64-65 66-67; Staffs Yth Cup 81-82.
**BEST SEASON FA Vase:          FA Cup:**
**PREVIOUS    Leagues:** Walsall Amateur 52-55/ Staffs County (South) 56-78/ West
Midlands (Reg) 78-94. **Grounds:** Rowley Place 51-75/ Aston University 76-79.
**RECORDS    Attendance:** 2,000 v Leeds Utd Old Boys, charity match 1982.
**Goalscorer:** Graham Wiggin    **Appearances:** Alan Dawson (400+ apps)

**FACT FILE**

Founded: 1951
Nickname: Pics.
Sponsors: WM Print
Colours: Amber with black trim/black/black
Change colours: White with red trim/red/red
Midweek matchday: Tuesday
Youth League: West Mids (Reg.)
Programme: 36 pages, 50p
Editor/ Press Officer: Darren Stockall
(01922 379153).

**CLUB PERSONNEL**

Chairman: John Burks
Vice Chairman: Trevor Westwood
President: Brian Greenwood.
Manager: John Allen
Asst Manager: Bob Hubble
Physio: Lee Horrocks

---

# SANDWELL BOROUGH

**Secretary:**    Joe Owen, 42 Chartwell Drive, Wolverhampton WV10 8JQ
Tel: 01902 780479 (H)    0121 520 1234 (B)

**Ground:**    Oldbury Stadium, Newbury Lane, Oldbury Tel: 0121 544 4013
**Directions:** Follow A4123 B'ham-Wolverhampton Rd, past island at jnt 2 M5, after half mile turn left into Newbury Lane and stadium is on the right. 2 miles from Sandwell & Dudley (BR).
Capacity: 3,000    Seats: 200    Cover: 200    Floodlights: Yes

**Clubhouse:** Licensed bar overlooking pitch. Open everyday

| | |
|---|---|
| **HONOURS** | Mids Comb Chall Cup R-up 49-50 51-53 67-68 74-75, Chall Tphy R-up 88-89,Pres. Cup 79-80 (R-up 76-77), Div 2 R-up 79-80; B'ham Jnr Cup; Industrial Rewind Lge Cup 94-95. |
| **PREVIOUS** | Leagues: B'ham Suburban; Central Amtr; Worcs (Midlands Comb.) 48-88, 90-94; Southern 88-90. |
| | Ground: Londonderry, Smethwick 18-81 |
| **BEST SEASON** | FA Vase:          FA Cup: |
| **RECORDS** | Attendance: 950 v Halesowen T., FA Cup 1987 |

Players progressing: Andy Micklewright(Bristol R.),Gary Bull (South'ton) Mick Mason(Mack'field)

**FACT FILE**

Founded: 1918.
Nickname: Trees
Colours: All green
Change Colours: Red/white/red
Midweek matches: Tuesday
Programme: 16 pages 60p
Editor: Trevor Hackwood

**CLUB PERSONNEL**

Chairman: Joe Owen
Manager: Dave Downing

# SHIFNAL TOWN

**Secretary:** Glyn Davies, 30 Drayton Road, Shifnal, Shropshire, TF11 8BT (01952460326 H)

**Ground:** Phoenix Park, Coppice Green Lane, Shifnal, Shropshire.

**Directions:** M54 jct 3, A41 towards Newport, 1st left for Shifnal (3 miles), in Shifnal take 1st right, and sharp right again up Coppice Green Lane, ground800yds on left past Idsall School.
**Capacity:** 3,000     **Seats:** 224     **Cover:** 300     **Floodlights:** Yes

**Clubhouse:** Not on ground but in Newport Rd, Shifnal.    Open Mon-Fri 7.30-11pm, Sat 12-2.30 & 7.30-11pm (matchdays 12-11pm), Sun 12-3 & 7.30-10-30
**Club Shop:** No

**HONOURS**    West Mids Lg 80-81 81-82 Div 1 78-79, Shropshire Snr Cup 80-81 90-91 92-93.

**BEST SEASON    FA Cup:** 1982-83     **FA Vase:** 1983-84

**PREVIOUS    Leagues:** Wellington (East Dist.) 64-69; Shropshire County 69-77 85-93; West Midlands 77-85; Midland Combination 94-95.
**Grounds:** Admirals Park 80-85

**RECORDS    Attendance:** 1,002 v Bridgnorth T., FA Vase 3rd Rd 83-84 (Admirals Park)
**Goalscorer:** Steve Kelly 35  **Appearances:** John Powell 268

### FACT FILE
Founded: 1964
Nickname: None.
Sponsors: Associated Cold Stores & Transport Ltd.
Colours: Red & white/black/red & white
Change cols: Blue & white/white/blue & white
Midweek matchday: Tuesday
Reserves' League: West Midlands
Programme: 32 pages, 60p
Editor: J.Wilson (01952 274855).
98-99 Player of the Year: Mick Kiernan

### CLUB PERSONNEL
Chairman: Mr. A.Dodd
Vice Chairman: Mr. R Owen
President: Mr.D.Millward
Press Off: M.Holt (01952 299347)
Manager: Ken Howells
Asst Manager: Martin Mackenzie
Physio: Charlott Lewis

# STAPENHILL

**Secretary:** Peter Begent, 22 Grasmere Close, Stapenhill, Burton-on-Trent DE159DS
Tel: 01283 540583
**Ground:** Edge Hill, Maple Grove, Stapenhill, Burton-on-Trent (01283 562471).
**Directions:** 3 miles from Burton on A444 Measham Rd, turn right (coming from Burton) at Copperhearth Pub Hse into Sycamore Rd, Maple Grove is 5th left. 3miles from Burton-on-Trent (BR) buses 15, 16 from opposite station.
**Capacity:** 2,000     **Seats:** 200     **Covered:** 500     **Floodlights:** Yes
**Clubhouse:** In ground. Pub hours. Matchday tea bar.    **Club Shop:** No

**HONOURS**    Midland Combination R-up 92-93 Div 1 89-90, Challenge Cup 92-93 93-94, Leics Snr Lg 59-60 86-87 88-89 (Tebbutt Brown Cup (2) 87-89), Leics Snr Cup 69-70 86-87, Derby Snr Cup R-up 88-89 91-92.
**BEST SEASON    FA Cup:**                  **FA Vase:**
**PREVIOUS    League:** Leics Snr 58-89/ Midland Combination 89-94.
**Name:** Stapenhill Waterside Community Centre.
**RECORDS    Attendance:** 2,000 v Gresley, Derbys Snr Cup final 88-89.
**Goalscorer:** Brian Beresford 123     **Appearances:** Ian Pearsall 172.
**Win:** 11-0 v Alcester Town (H), Midland Comb. Prem. Div.,1992-93.
**Defeat:** 0-7 v Bridgnorth Town, FA Vase.

### FACT FILE
Founded: 1947
Nickname: Swans
Sponsors: TAG Football Kits
Colours: Red & Green
Change Colours: All blue
Midweek matchday: Tuesday
Programme: 50p
Editor: Secretary
98-99 - Captain: Matthew Freeman
Top Scorer: Scott Eaton
P.O.Y.: Peter Allum

### CLUB PERSONNEL
Chairman: Tony Smith
Vice Chairman: Ken Hulland
President: Fred Sleigh.
Press Officer: Secretary.
Manager: Mick Curry
Asst Manager: John Wayte

# STOURPORT SWIFTS

**Secretary:** John McDonald, 65 Princess Way, Stourport-on-Severn (01299 822088).

**Ground:** Walshes Meadow, Harold Davis Drive, Stourport-on-Severn (01299 825188).
**Directions:** Follow one-way system through Stourport sign posted Sports Centre.Go over River Severn Bridge, turn left into Harold Davies Drive. Ground is at rear of Sports Centre. Nearest rail station is Kidderminster.

**Capacity:** 2,000 **Seats:** 250 **Cover:** 150 **Floodlights:** Yes

**Clubhouse:** Open matchdays. Hot snacks available. Licensed bar.     **Club Shop:** No

**HONOURS**    West Mids Prem Div R-Up 94-95 96-97 97-98, Lg Div 1 R-up 87-88, Prem Div Cup 92-93, Div 2 Cup R-up 82-83; Worcs Snr Urn 92-93 93-94 94-95 97-98 Worcs Infirmary Cup 94-95 95-96 97-98

**BEST SEASON FA Cup         FA Vase**

**PREVIOUS    Leagues:** Kidderminster/ Worcester/ Midland Combination.
**Grounds:** Bewdley Rd; Moor Hall Park; Feathers Farm; Olive Grove; Hawthorns.

**RECORDS    Attendancee:** 4,000 v Birmingham, charity match.
**Goalscorer:** Gary Crowther     **Appearances:** Ian Johnson
**Win:** 10-0     **Defeat:** 1-7

### FACT FILE
Founded: 1882.
Nickname: Swifts
Sponsors: M.I.P. Halesowen
Colours: Yellow & black/black/black
Change colours: All Red
Midweek matchday: Tuesday
Programme: 40 pages,80p
Editor/ Press Officer: Dave Watts (01299 823349)

### CLUB PERSONNEL
Chairman: Chris Reynolds

President: Roy Crowe.
Managers: Rod Brown
Coach: Gary Whild

738

# STRATFORD TOWN

**Secretary:** Leslie Welsh, 10 Ivy Lane, Ettington, Warwicks. CV37 7TD. (01789740952)

**Ground:** Masons Road, off Alcester Road, Stratford-upon-Avon, Warks (01789297479).
**Directions:** Follow the signs for Alcester/Worcester A422 from the town centre.
Masons Road is the 1st right afterthe railway bridge.
400 yards from Stratford-on-Avon (BR)station.
Local buses for West Green Drive.
Capacity: 1,100          Seating/Cover: 200          Floodlights: Yes

**Clubhouse:** Open every night except Sunday          **Club Shop:** No.

**HONOURS** Midland Comb 56-57 86-87; Chal. Cup 86-87 88-89 (R-up 55-56); Chal. Vase 81-82; Jack Mould Tphy 81-82; Tony Allden Mem. Cup 86-87; B'ham Snr Cup62-63.

**BEST SEASON** **FAVase:** **FA Cup:**

**PREVIOUS** **Leagues:** W Mids 57-70/ Mid Com. 70-73 75-94/ Hellenic 70-75.

**RECORDS** **Attendance:** 1,078 v Aston Villa, Birmingham Snr Cup, Oct 1996

Players progressing: Martin Hicks (Charlton '77), Roy Proverbs (Coventry, '56)

### FACT FILE

Founded: 1944
Nickname: The Town
Sponsors: Porters Precision Products
Colours: Tangerine/black/tangerine
Change Colours: White/white/black
Midweek Matchday: Tuesday
Reserves' League: Midland Comb. Res. Div..
Programme: 20 pages, 50p
Editor:

### CLUB PERSONNEL

Chairman: G Cutler
Vice-Chairman: T.B.A.
President: P Chatburn
Commercial Mgr: J Carruthers.
Manager: S Dixon
Physio: N Dixon

# WEDNESFIELD

**Secretary:** Trevor Highfield, 8 Greensway, Wednesfield, Wolverhampton. WV11 1BA
Tel: 01902 733086

**Ground:** Cottage Ground, Amos Lane, Wednesfield, Wolverhampton (01902 735506).
**Directions:** From Wolverhampton on the A4124 Wednesfield Rd. Stay on road right through Wednesfield until island. Leave island at 1st exit (Wood End Rd), left after 200yds into Amos Lane. Ground on right, approx. 400yds along. 3 miles Wolverhampton BR station. Bus 559 to Wood End or 560 to Red Lion.
Capacity: 1,000          Seats: 148          Cover: 250          Floodlights: Yes

**Clubhouse:** Evenings 7-11pm. Food (burgers, chips etc) on 1st team matchdays.
**Club Shop:** No.

**HONOURS** West Mids Lg Div 1 76-77 (R-up 77-78).
**BEST SEASON** **FA Vase:** **FA Cup:**
**PREVIOUS** **League:** Wolverhampton & District Amateur 61-76/West Midlands 77-97.
**Ground:** St Georges PF 61-76          **Name:** Wednesfield Social 61-89.
**RECORDS** **Attendance:** 480 v Burton Albion, FA Cup 1981.

### FACT FILE

Founded: 1961.
Nickname: Cottagers.
Sponsors: Ansells
Colours: Red & white/black/red & white
Change colours: Yellow & blue/blue/blue & yellow
Midweek matchday: Tuesday
Programme: 50p
Editor: TBA

### CLUB PERSONNEL

Chairman: Roger Thomas
Vice Chairman: J Massey
Manager/Coach: Ken Hall
Physio: M Andrews
Commercial Mgr: D Clayton
Press Officer: J Massey (01902 781819).

*WEST MIDLANDS POLICE FC*                    *Photo: Bill Wheatcroft*

# WEST MIDLANDS POLICE

**Secretary:** John Black, 57 Grosvenor Close, Sutton Coldfield, W.Mids. B756RP. 0121 308 7673

**Ground:** Police Sports Ground, `Tally Ho', Pershore Road, Edgbaston, Birmingham B57RN
Tel: 0121 472 2944

**Directions:** 2 miles south west of city on A441 Pershore Road. Ground is on the left 50yds past Priory Road lights (Warks County Cricket Ground).
3 miles from Birmingham New Street (BR) - buses 41, 45 & 47 from city.

**Capacity:** 2,500          **Seats:** 224          **Covered:** 224          **Floodlights:** Yes

**Clubhouse:** Complex of 3 bars including snooker room, ballroom, kitchen.
Hot &cold food. Open all day.          **Club Shop:** No.

**HONOURS**          Mids Comb 90-91 (R-up 94-95, Chal. Cup 74-75 (R-up 85-86)), Tony Allden Mem. Cup 75-76 (R-up 91-92), B'ham Jnr Cup, Worcs Snr Urn 84-85 90-91 91-92 (R-up 81-82 85-86), National Police Cup (12) 61-65 66-67 69-70 73-76 80-81 87-88 91-92 (R-up (7) 67-68 70-72 76-78 88-89 94-95), Aston Villa Cup 60-61 64-65 65-66.

**BEST SEASON**          **FA Vase:** Quarter Final 91-92          **FA Cup:**

**PREVIOUS**          Leagues: B'ham Wednesday 28-38; Mercian 46-53; B'ham Works 53-69; Midland Comb 74-94.

**RECORDS**          **Attendance:** 1,072 v Sudbury Town, FA Vase QF 29/2/92.

## FACT FILE

Founded: 1974
Colours: Red & black stripes/black/black & red
Change Colours: Yellow with blue trim/yellow/yellow
Midweek matchday: Tues/Thurs.
Reserves' League: Midland Combination.
Programme: 16 pages, 50p
Editor: K Horrigan
(0121 626 4020x6100)

## CLUB PERSONNEL

President: Chief Constable E,Crew
Chairman: Asst Chief Constable Anne Summers
Vice Chairman 7 Chief Inspector: M.Rose
Manager: Jim Scott
Commercial Manager: John Black.
Press Officer: Tony Pearson.

# WILLENHALL TOWN

**Secretary:** Malcolm Skitt, 52 Longwood Rise, Willenhall, W. Mids WV12 4AX (01902 632557)

**Ground:** Noose Lane, Willenhall, West Midlands (01902 605132-club, 636586-office).
**Directions:** M6 Jnc 10 follow 'new' Black Country route and then 'Keyway'. On leaving 'Keyway' follow signs to Wolverhampton(A454). At 'Neachells' P H house right into Neachells Lane, and first right again into Watery Lane. At island turn left onto Noose Lane, ground is 200yds on left.

**Capacity:** 5,000          **Seats:** 324          **Cover:** 500          **Floodlights:** Yes

**Clubhouse:** Open Mon-Thurs 12-3 & 7-11pm, Fri-Sat 11am-11pm, Sun 12-2 & 7-10.30pm.
Snacks available.          **Club Shop:** Yes

**HONOURS**          FA Vase R-up 80-81; West Mids Lg 78-79, Div 1 75-76, Prem. Div Cup 79-80, Div 2 Cup 78-79(res); Southern Midland 83-84; Birmingham Snr Cup R-up 82-83; J W Hunt Cup 73-74.

**BEST SEASON**          **FA Vase:** Runners-up 80-81 **FA Cup:**
**PREVIOUS**          **Leagues:** Wolverhampton Amateur/ Staffs County/ West Mids 75-82 91-94/Southern 82-91.

**RECORDS**          Attendance: 3,454 v Crewe Alexandra, FA Cup 1st Rd 1981.
Goalscorer: Gary Matthews          Appearances: Gary Matthews.
Players progressing: Sean O'Driscoll (Fulham ),Joe Jackson (Wolves), Stuart Watkiss (Wolves), Tony Moore (Sheff U), Andy Reece (Bristol R.), Wayne O'Sullivan (Swindon).

## FACT FILE

Founded: 1953
Nickname: Reds
Sponsors: Aspray Transport.
Colours: Red & white/red/red
Change colours: Blue & red
Midweek matchday: Tuesday.
Reserves League: Midland Comb.
Programme: 40 pages, 70p
Editor: Bill Taylor (01902 843435)

## CLUB PERSONNEL

President: Jack Williams
Chairman: David Homer
Vice Chairman: Keith Badger
Manager: Kevin Hadley
Asst Manager: Paul Waddington
Physios: Mike Andrews & Garyt McHale

*WILLENHALL TOWN: Back Row (L-R): Dean Stevens, Mick Andrews, Steve Ingram, Martin Dobson, Dave Chapman, Chris Jones, Dave Butler, Simon Prince, Andy Harnett, Archie Perry, John Chambers. Front Row: Darren Goodhall, Nick Henley, Jason Paddock, Matt French, Steve Cookson, Steve Charlton, Andy Kelly, Paul Casey. Photo: Marshall's Sports Services (Birmingham)*

# ENDSLEIGH INSURANCE
# MIDLAND FOOTBALL COMBINATION
### FEEDER TO: MIDLAND ALLIANCE

**Chairman:** Ian Johnson
**Hon Secretary:** Norman Harvey
115 Millfield Road, Handsworth Wood, Birmingham B20 1ED    Tel: 0121 3574172

Newcomers to the Premier Division Alveston FC lifted the Premier Division title at the first attempt, a stunning achievement, despite having to contend with major fixture congestion due to their successes in cup competitions. They completed a double with a 2-0 win over Coventry Sphinx in the Challenge Cup Final, held at Villa Park. They were also winners of the Smedley Crooke Cup and were runners up in the Birmingham County FA Vase and the Coventry Evening Telegraph Cup. Not surprisingly Steve Sykes was awarded the Manager of the Year for the season. He has since moved on to manage Southern League Racing Warwick. It will be interesting to see how the club cope with his loss.

The runners up battle was much closer, with Cheslyn Hay coming through the pack to win the runners up place.

Division One saw Northfield Town crowned Champions, from Knowle, who also won the Birmingham County FA Vase creating a shock by beating Alveston in the Final.

The Presidents Cup saw Alvis overcome Thimblemill Rec 2-0 in the Final, while Blackheath Electrodrives lifted the JW Hunt Cup beating Brownhills Town at Molineux.

Fairfield Vila reacted the best way to a ground grading relegation by lifting the title, from Brownhills Town. The Challenge Vase Final went to extra time before Handsaker got the better of a spirited Barlestone St Giles side in their first major Combination Final.

MCI Claines were the outstanding side in Division Three, lifting a superb treble of League Championship, a Challenge Urn victory over Bustleholme Reserves and a Worcester Junior Cup victory to boot. Another new club Burman Hi-Ton were comfortable runners up.

The Reserve Division title was won by the strong Burton Albion side for the second successive season. They were chased all the way by local rivals Gresley Rovers Reserves, who gained consolation in the cup competitions, beating Atherstone United Reserves in the Challenge Trophy Final and beating Boldmere St Michaels in the Fazeley Charity Cup.

Sadly our sponsorship deal with Endsleigh Insurance ceased at the end of the season, we would like to thank our friends from Endsleigh for their valued support over the last four seasons. They are not lost to us as they are one of a number of companies showing interest in sponsoring our Challenge Cup competition, which will again be held at Villa Park.

We are however, delighted to announce the the Combination has new sponsors for the Millennium season. The league will now be known as The Rapide Midland Football Combination. Rapide are a nationwide DIY and Car Car product manufacturers and have agreed an improved three year sponsorship deal.

Once again we have a number of new clubs joining us. Coventry Alliance side Nuneaton Griff come into the Premier Division and interestingly enough two sides from the Festival League in Birmingham Sunday football, Brookvale Athletic and Romulus have joined Division One, an interesting development.

Finally Mr Midland Combination Les James has stepped down from the role of treasurer after 42 years of service to the Combination, fortunately he will remain as President so he will still be with us.

# FINAL LEAGUE TABLES 1998-99

## PREMIER DIVISION

| | P | W | D | L | F | A | Pts |
|---|---|---|---|---|---|---|---|
| Alveston | 34 | 21 | 8 | 5 | 74 | 32 | 71 |
| CheslynHay | 34 | 18 | 10 | 6 | 61 | 42 | 64 |
| Southam United | 34 | 16 | 10 | 8 | 70 | 49 | 58 |
| Kings Heath | 34 | 17 | 6 | 11 | 66 | 51 | 57 |
| Massey Fergusons | 34 | 15 | 10 | 9 | 57 | 51 | 55 |
| Meir K.A | 34 | 15 | 9 | 10 | 69 | 47 | 54 |
| Studley B.K.L | 34 | 14 | 11 | 9 | 67 | 43 | 53 |
| G.P.O. Coventry | 34 | 15 | 8 | 11 | 67 | 65 | 53 |
| Handahan Timbers | 34 | 41 | 10 | 10 | 56 | 47 | 52 |

| | P | W | D | L | F | A | Pts |
|---|---|---|---|---|---|---|---|
| Bolehill Swifts | 34 | 13 | 8 | 13 | 58 | 48 | 47 |
| Highate United | 34 | 13 | 7 | 14 | 69 | 59 | 46 |
| Feckenham | 34 | 10 | 14 | 10 | 45 | 42 | 44 |
| Coventry Sphinx | 34 | 12 | 7 | 15 | 53 | 64 | 43 |
| Alvechurch | 34 | 12 | 4 | 18 | 61 | 77 | 40 |
| Continental Star | 34 | 11 | 7 | 16 | 57 | 69 | 37 |
| Kenilworth Town | 34 | 8 | 8 | 18 | 37 | 67 | 32 |
| Coleshill Town | 34 | 6 | 6 | 22 | 46 | 78 | 24 |

## DIVISION ONE

| | P | W | D | L | F | A | PT |
|---|---|---|---|---|---|---|---|
| Northfield Town | 30 | 22 | 2 | 6 | 95 | 32 | 68 |
| Knowle | 30 | 20 | 4 | 6 | 78 | 33 | 64 |
| Blackheath E' Drives | 30 | 19 | 7 | 4 | 83 | 45 | 64 |
| Alvis | 30 | 16 | 3 | 11 | 69 | 66 | 51 |
| Thimblemill R.E.C | 30 | 14 | 5 | 11 | 67 | 43 | 47 |
| Chelmsley Town | 30 | 15 | 2 | 13 | 61 | 58 | 47 |
| Holly Lane | 30 | 13 | 6 | 11 | 59 | 51 | 45 |
| Wellesbourne | 30 | 14 | 2 | 14 | 57 | 55 | 44 |
| Shirley Town | 30 | 12 | 4 | 14 | 50 | 74 | 40 |
| Burntwood | 30 | 10 | 6 | 14 | 70 | 71 | 36 |
| Hamshall | 30 | 9 | 9 | 12 | 52 | 54 | 36 |
| Studley B.K.L. Res | 30 | 10 | 5 | 15 | 49 | 58 | 35 |
| Kings Norton Town Res | 30 | 9 | 3 | 18 | 52 | 82 | 30 |
| Loughborough Athletic | 30 | 10 | 0 | 20 | 38 | 84 | 30 |
| West Mids Fire Service | 30 | 8 | 5 | 17 | 40 | 68 | 29 |
| Colletts Green | 30 | 8 | 5 | 17 | 40 | 68 | 20 |

## DIVISION TWO

| | P | W | D | L | F | A | PT |
|---|---|---|---|---|---|---|---|
| Fairfeld Villa | 30 | 22 | 4 | 4 | 91 | 28 | 70 |
| Brownhills Town | 30 | 22 | 2 | 6 | 99 | 43 | 68 |
| Wyre Forest | 30 | 18 | 6 | 6 | 79 | 36 | 60 |
| County Sports | 30 | 18 | 6 | 6 | 75 | 34 | 60 |
| Mile Oak Rovers | 30 | 19 | 3 | 8 | 75 | 45 | 60 |
| Old Hill Town | 30 | 17 | 3 | 10 | 61 | 44 | 54 |
| Handsaker | 30 | 15 | 6 | 9 | 68 | 39 | 51 |
| Earlswood Town | 30 | 15 | 4 | 11 | 56 | 47 | 49 |
| G.N.P. Sports | 30 | 13 | 2 | 15 | 59 | 73 | 41 |
| West Midlands Police R | 30 | 8 | 12 | 10 | 48 | 50 | 36 |
| Barlestone St Giles | 30 | 10 | 5 | 15 | 53 | 75 | 35 |
| Cadbury Athletic | 30 | 9 | 7 | 14 | 50 | 71 | 34 |
| Kenilworth Wardens | 30 | 8 | 5 | 17 | 40 | 69 | 29 |
| Ledbury Town | 30 | 4 | 2 | 24 | 42 | 100 | 14 |
| Enville Athletic | 30 | 3 | 5 | 22 | 37 | 101 | 14 |
| Wonder Vaults | 30 | 2 | 2 | 26 | 30 | 108 | 8 |

*Alveston celebrate after winning the Challenge Cup to add to the Championship Shield and the Smedley Crooke Cup.*

## PREMIER DIVISION LEADING GOALSCORERS 1998-99

| | | |
|---|---|---|
| Derek Hall | Highgate United | 40 |
| Simon Windsor | Alveston | 30 |
| Andrew Underwood | Feckenham | 25 |
| Terry Ball | Cheslyn Hay | 22 |
| Mark Cartwright | Kings Heath | 21 |
| Chris Partridge | GPT Coventry | 20 |

| | | |
|---|---|---|
| Total amount of goals scored in League and Cup | | 1133 |

| | | |
|---|---|---|
| Best Defence in Division | Alveston | 32 goals |
| Best Attack in Division | Alveston | 74 goals |

## PREMIER DIVISION LEADING GOALSCORERS BY TEAM

| | | |
|---|---|---|
| Alvechurch | Dean Meyrick | 17 |
| Alveston | Simon Windsor | 30 |
| Bolehall Swifts | Paul Casey | 13 |
| Cheslyn Hay | Terry Ball | 22 |
| Coleshill Town | Antony Matthews | 16 |
| Continental Star | Delroy Amory | 9 |
| Coventry Sphinx | Joey Fletcher | 17 |
| Dudley Sports | Clifton Lambert | 6 |
| Feckenham | Andrew Underwood | 25 |
| GPT Coventry | Chris Partridge | 20 |
| Handrahan Timbers | Huw Lewis | 15 |
| Highgate United | Derek Hall | 40 |
| Kenilworth Town | Darren Timms | 7 |
| Kings Heath | Mark Cartwright | 21 |
| Massey Ferguson | Neil Fern | 14 |
| Meir KA | Steve Bott | 19 |
| Southam United | Alister Innes | 14 |
| Studley BKL | Lee Adams & Brian Powell | 12 |

## DIVISION ONE LEADING GOALSCORERS 1998-99

| | | |
|---|---|---|
| Mark Robinson | Knowle | 32 |
| Frank Woodburn | Chelmsley Town | 28 |
| Dean Baker | Holly Lane | 27 |
| Thomas Breen | Blackheath Electro | 24 |

| | | |
|---|---|---|
| Total amount of goals scored in League and Cup | | 1019 |

| | | |
|---|---|---|
| Best Defence in Division | Northfield Town | 32 goals |
| Best Attack in Division | Northfield Town | 95 goals |

## PREMIER DIVISION LEADING GOALSCORERS BY TEAM

| | | |
|---|---|---|
| Alvis | Chris Reid | 22 |
| Blackheath Electrodrive | Thomas Breen | 24 |
| Burntwood | Mathew Worth | 23 |
| Chelmsley Town | Frank Woodburn | 28 |
| Colletts Green | Wayne Elcock | 12 |
| Hams Hall | Paul Arnold | 11 |
| Holly Lane | Dean Baker | 27 |
| Kings Norton Town | Des Hamilton | 9 |
| Knowle | Mark Robinson | 32 |
| Loughborough Athletic | Alan Nicholson | 6 |
| Northfield Town | Michael McKeon & Simon Volrath | 16 |
| Shirley Town | Malcolm Kelly | 11 |
| Studley BKL Reserves | Carl Dainter | 14 |
| Thimblesmill Rec | Kevin Ibrahim | 15 |
| Wellesbourne | Lee Ross | 14 |
| West Midland Fire | Carl Smith | 8 |

Top: Ashley Proctor (Alveston) hits the ball past Luke McCormick (GPT).   Photo: Keith Clayton

Bottom: GPT Coventry line up wearing shirts with new sponsor's name, Marconi.   Photo: Martin Wray

# ALVECHURCH VILLA

**Secretary:** Alan Deakin, 58 Chesterfield Close, Northfield, Birmingham, B31 3TR(0121 411 1745)
**Ground:** Lye Meadow, Redditch Rd, Alvechurch, Worcs (0121 445 2929)
**Directions:** M42 jct 2, follow signs to Redditch, taking dual carriageway. At island turn right (signed Alvechurch) ground approx one mile on right. Ground is actually on Redditch Road, just south of Alvechurch village

| | | | |
|---|---|---|---|
| **Capacity:** 3,000 | **Seats:**100 | **Cover:**Yes | **Floodlights:**Yes |

**Clubhouse:** Evenings and matchdays      **Club shop:** Yes
**HONORS**    Mid Comb Chall Cup R-up 95-96, Smedley Crooke Cup R-up 94-95
**CLUB RECORDS Goalscorer:** Dean Meyrick **Appearances:** Dean Meyrick
**PREVIOUS**    **Leagues:** None
        **Name:** None (predecessors, Alvechurch FC, founded 1929, folded in 1992)

Founded: 1994
Nickname: The Church
Sponsors: Centreprint
Colours: Gold/black/black
Change colours: White,blue,blue
Midweek matchday: Wednesday
Chairman: Andy Roberts
Director of Football: Lee Shaw
Patron: Roy Yardley
Manager: Keith Westwood/Stewart Anderson
98-99 Player of the Year: Simon Redhead

# ALVESTON

**Secretary:** Ken Unitt, 47 Luddington Road, Stratford upon Avon, Warwicks. CV37 9SG
     Tel No: 017898 205698

Colours: All Maroon and Sky Blue
Change Colours: Black& white/white/white.

**Ground:** Home Guard Club, Main Street, Tiddington, Stratford-upon-Avon. Tel: 01789 297718

**Directions:** The ground is on the Stratford-Wellesbourne Road (B4086). From Stratford via B4086 into Tiddington. Home Guard Club is last building on right through Tiddington.
         **Floodlights:** Yes

# BLACKHEATH ELECTRODRIVES

**Secretary/Press Officer:** G.Ellison, 66 Richmond Grove, Wollaston, Stourbridge DY8 4SF
     Tel No; 01384 836112 (H) 0121 698 3362 (W)

Colours: Red& white/red/red
Change Colours: all blue

**Ground:** Electrodrives Sports Ground, Cakemore Road,Rowley Regis, Warley
     Tel: 0121 559 9105 (Social Club)
**Directions:** Ground is on Birmingham to Stourbridge Road (A458) betwwen Lye and Colley Gate.

# BOLEHALL SWIFTS

**Secretary:** Mal Tooley, 7 Ninefoot Lane, Belgrave, Tamworth, Staffs B77 2NA(01827 251973)
**Ground:** Rene Road, Bolehall, Tamworth (01827 62637)
**Directions:** A51 signs south to Bolebridge island, left under railway archesinto Amington Rd, 4th eft into Leedham Ave, fork right into Rene Rd, ground onright by school. From Tamworth BR station walk up Victoria Road for three quarters of a mile and catch No.3 or No.6 mini-bus to Bolehall. Alight at Leedham Avenue or Rene Road and follow as above

| | | | | |
|---|---|---|---|---|
| **Capacity:** 2,000 | **Seats:** 500 | **Cover:** 600 | **Floodlights:** Yes | **Club Shop:** No |

**Clubhouse:** Large Social Club. Open evenings 7-11 & lunchtimes. Snacks available
**HONOURS:** Midland Comb. Div 2 84-85, F/Lit Cup R-up 96-97, Chall. Vase 84-85, Presidents Cup R-up 85-86; Fazeley Char Cup 84-85 (R-up 85-86); Ernie Brown Mem. Cup R-up 89-90 90-91 91-92 92-93 94-95 98-99, Jack Mould Cup R-up 85-86 Tony Allden Nenorial Cup 98-99

Founded: 1953     Nickname: Swifts
Colours: All Green
Change Colours: yellow/black/yellow
Sponsors: Need -A-Skip-Hire Ltd.
Midweek matches: Tuesday
Programme: 24 pages, 70p
Editor: W Gould (01827 64530)
President: mr.L. Fitzpatrick
Chairman: J.Latham
Vice-Chairman: K.Norchi
Manager: Ron Tranter Ass.Man: D.Finney
Coach: J.Capaldi
Physio: D.Crump

# CHESLYN HAY

**Secretary:** J Rogers, 22 John Riley Dr., New Invention, Willenhall WV12 5AS (01922 860064)
**Ground:** Scholars Ground,Chasetown F.C., Church St., Chasetown, Walsall. 01543 682222
**Directions:** M6 Junct 11, A460 to Cannock, A5 to Brownhills, to Whitehouse Rd and Wharf Lane, at junction turn left into Highfield Rd., leading to Church St., ground on left.

| | | | | |
|---|---|---|---|---|
| **Capacity:** 2,000 | **Seats:** 200 | **Cover:** 300 | **Floodlights:** Yes | **Club Shop:** Yes |

**Clubhouse:** Evenings 7-11pm. Food (burgers, chips etc) on 1st team matchdays
**HONOURS:**    Midland Comb. Prem Div. R-up 98-99, Div. 3 R-up 94-95;
          Wolves Cup 86-87 87-88, Staffs. Chall. Cup 96-97; Walsall Chall. Cup 96-97;
          W H Johns Mem. Cup 96-97; J W Hunt Cup R-up 96-97
**CLUB RECORDS Appearances:** Gary Osborne 492
          **Goalscorer:** Ian Morgan 142 (in 113 games)

Founded: 1984
Sponsors: Pro Clean Ind. Services
Colours: Orange/white/black
Change colours: Blue & white stripes/blue/white
Programme: Yes
Editor: F Lowbridge 01543 577743

Chairman: R G Cross 01922 401126
Press Officer: C Cross
Jt. Managers: Carl Oulton & Andy Jones
Physio: M Bailey

# COLESHILL TOWN

**Secretary:** George Phillips,49 Circus Avenue, Chelmsley Wood, B'ham B37 7NG
**Tel No:** 0121 770 9513 (H) 0930 826901
**Ground:** Pack Meadow, Packington Lane, Coleshill Warwks B46 3JQ (01675 46325)
**Directions:** M6 Jct 4 Take A446 (Siugnposted to Lichfield) for 3/4 ,
**Clubhouse:** Bar open 7 nights a week. Bar manager residentmile across dual carriage way
(B4117( sign to Coleshill). Right into Packington Lane after 3/4 mile ground on left after 1/2 mile
**HONOURS:** Mercian Lg 75-76, Walsall Snr Cup 82-83 R-up 83-84, Midland Comb. R-up
83-84, Div 2 69-70 R-up 74-75, Invitation Cup 70, Presidents Cup R-up x2 67-69
**CLUB RECORDS: Attendance:** 1,000
Players progressing: Gary Shaw (Aston Villa)

Founded: 1894
Nickname: Coalmen
Colours: All Blue
Change Colours:All Orange
Midweek matches: Tues/Thurs
Programme: 30p,
Editor: Mavis Gordon

Chairman:
Manager: Martin Sockett

# CONTINENTAL STAR

**Secretary:** Barry Cole,14 Devine Croft, Tipton, West Midlands DY4 8XJ
**Tel No:** 0121 557 0092(H) 0976 313574 (M)
**Ground:** Paget Rangers F.C., Vale Stadium, Farnborough Road, Castle Vale. B 35 5UH.
**Terl No:** 0121 747 6969 Floodlights : Yes
**Directions:** M6 Jct 6 take A38 to Lichfield. Right Tyburn House island on to A452 (Chester
Road). Left into Tangmere Drive at island then right into Farnborough Road. Turn right into Fort
Centre Car Park after half a mile.
Capacity: 3,000          Seats: 50          Cover: 50Floodlights: Yes
**Clubhouse:** Bar open 7 nights a week. Bar manager resident
**HONOURS:**       Midland Comb Div One R-up 96-97; Birmingham Vase

Colours:  Yellow/Blue/Yellow

Manager:  Derek Stevens/ Lincoln Moses

# COVENTRY SPHINX

**Secretary:** Richard McKinnon, 52 Sunbury Road, Stonehouse Estate, Coventry CV3 4DN
**Tel No:** 01203 305789

Colours:
Sky blue & navy/navy/navy
Change Colours:All white

**Ground:** Sphinx Drive, off Siddeley Avenue, Stoke Aldermoor, Coventry
Ground Tel: 01203 451361  Social Club 02476 451361

**Floodlights:** Yes

Manager:  Willie Knibbs

# FECKENHAM

**Secretary:**  M G Hawkes,4 Mill Lane, Redditch B96  6HY
**Tel Nos:** (01527 893341 (H) and 0411 859314 (M)

**Ground:** Evesham United F.C. Common Road, Evesham, Worcs. **Floodlights :** Yes
Ground and Social Club Tel No: 01386 442303

Colours: Green& Yellow/green/yellow
Change Colours: All Yellow

**Directions :** as for Evesham United (Dr Martens League)

**Floodlights:** Yes

# HANDRAHAN TIMBERS

**Secretary:** Robert Hopkins, Junction Rd, Audnam, Stourbridge, W Mids DY8 4JY (01384 838270)
**Ground:** Mile Flat Sports Ground, Mile Flat, Wallheath, Kingswinford, W. Mids (01381 484755)
**Directions:** Find A449 (Penn Road) to Wall Heath then into Enville Road which runs into Mile Flat.
Cover: 200          Seats: 40          Floodlights: No
**Clubhouse:** Teas and refreshments          Club Shop: No
**HONOURS**       Midland Comb. Div 1 R-up 93-94, Birmingham Chall. Vase R-up 93-94,
Wednesbury Charity Cup 91-92, J W Hunt Cup 92-93 R-up 93-94; Invitation Cup 94-95
**PREVIOUS**       Leagues: Staffs County Lg (South) 82-86       **Grounds:** None
**CLUB RECORDS  Goalscorer:** Paul Baker    **Appearances:** Jonathan Pole
           **Win:** 9-0          **Defeat:** 0-6

Founded: 1982
Nickname: Timbers
Sponsors: W J Handrahan & Son
Colours: Red/black/black
Change colours: Sky/navy/navy
Midweek matchday: Wednesday
Programme: All games except outside cups
Chairman: E J Smith
President: W J Handrahan
Manager: Glen Taylor/Nigel Kirkham
Asst Manager: Phillip McNally
Press Officer: E J Smith (01384 295394)

# HIGHGATE UNITED

**Secretary:** G Read, 23 Southam Rd, Hall Green, Birmingham B28 8DQ (0121-777-1786)
**Ground:** The Coppice, Tythe Barn Lane, Shirley, Solihull B90 1PH (0121 7444194)
**Directions:** A34 from City through Shirley, fork right B4102 (Tanworth Lane), half mile then right
into Dickens Heath Rd, then first right & ground on the left. 100yds from Whitlocks End (BR)
Capacity: 5,000    Seats: 250    Covered: 750    Floodlights: Yes
**Clubhouse:** Members Club open Tue to Thur, Sat & Sun. Light refreshments available weekends
**HONOURS** Midland Comb (3) 72-75 (Div 2 66-67 68-69 71-72), Lg Cup (5) 72-74 75-77 84-85
(R-up 78-79 92-93); Presidents Cup 70-71 85-86); Tony Allden Mem. Cup 74-75;
Invit. Cup 68-69 71-72 85-86; West Mids All. 63-64; Birmingham Snr Cup 73-74
**CLUB RECORDS  Attendance:** 4,000 v Enfield, FA Amateur Cup QF 1967
Players progressing: John Gayle (Wimbledon), Keith Leonard (A Villa), Geoff Scott (Leicester C.)

Founded: 1947    Nickname: The Gate
Colours: All red
Change Colours: white/blue/blue
Midweek matches: Tuesday
Programme: 28 pages, 50p
Editor: Terry Bishop (0676 22788)

Chairman: T G Bishop
Treasurer: G Read
Press Officer: N C Sawyer
Manager: Jim Simms
Physio: Richard Flynn

# KENILWORTH TOWN

**Secretary:** Sally McKenzie, Marlborough House, Holly Walk, Leamington Spa CV32 4JA
Tel Nos: 01926 855247 (H) 01926 886632 (W)

**Ground:** Gypsy Lane, off Rouncil Lane, Kenilworth (01926 850851)
Floodlights :Yes

**Directions:** Exit 4 off M6or Exit 6 off M42 Take A452 to Kenilworth follow main road to bottom of
High Street. Take Leek Wootton turn, then first right  into Rouncil Lane. Ground 150 yards on left in
Gypsy Lane.

Colours:  All blue
Change Colours: white/blue/white

# KINGS HEATH

**Secretary:** John Parker,31 Mappleborough Road, Shirlewy, Solihull B90 1AG
Tel No: 0121 430 4920
**Ground:** Alvechurch F.C., Lye Meadow, Redditch Road, Alvechurch B48 7RS (o121 445 29290
**Directions:** A34 from City through Shirley, fork right B4102 (Tanworth Lane), half mile then right
into Dickens Heath Rd, then first right & ground on the left. 100yds from Whitlocks End (BR)
Capacity: 5,000    Seats: 250    Covered: 750    Floodlights: Yes
**HONOURS** Midland Comb. Div 1 R-up 92-93, Div 2 R-up 82-83, Presidents Cup R-up 79-80 81-82
92-93; Birmingham Chall. Vase R-up 86-87; Worcester Sen Urn 96-97,Chall. Cup R-up 96-97
**PREVIOUS**        Names: Horse Shoe FC/ Kings Heath Amateur
                   Ground: Shirley Town (pre-1994)
Player progressing: Geoff Scott (Stoke C.)

Founded: 1964
Nickname: The Kings
Colours: Old gold/black/old gold
Change Colours: white/blue/blue
Midweek Matchday:
Programme: 12 pages
Editor: M Kite

Manager: Clive Seeley

# MARCONI F.C. (formerly G.P.T. (COVENTRY))
**Chairman:** B.Olsen  **Vice-Chairman:** D.Ryan  **Press Officer:** P.Scan;lon

**Secretary:** P Scanlon, 61 Norton Hill, Wyken, Coventry, West Mids CV2 3AX
Tel: 01203 616576
**Ground:** Marconi (Coventry) Sports Ground, Allard Way ,Copsewood, Coventry
Tel: 01203 451157 (Ground & Social Club )        Floodlights: Yes
**Directions:** Near Fire station and Mill Pool Public House.
**Clubhouse:**        12-11 Saturdays 6.00-11.00 weekdays

**HONOURS:**        Midland Comb Div 1 96-97, Presidents Cup 96-97.
                    Only ever winners of Coventry Evening Telegraph Cup (3 years)

Formed: 1923
Sponsors: Marconi
Colours: White with blue trim/white/white
Change colours:  All red
Programme: 16pages Price:
Editor P.Scanlon 75p

Manager: C.Davies
Assistant Manager: J.McGinty
Physio: P.Tovey

# MASSEY-FERGUSON
**Secretary:** Terry Borras, 4 Ashbridge Road, Allesley Park, Coventry CV5 9LA
Tel Nos: 01203 675 745 (H) 01203 691961 (W&Fax) 0802 691064 (M)
**Ground:** Massey-Ferguson Sports Ground, Banner Lane, Tile Hill, Coventry  (01203 694400)
**Directions:** A45 to Meridan turn (B4104). Over two traffic islands, turn rightat 3rd island into
Pickford Grange Lane, continue to Pickford Green Lane, &Hockley Lane, left into Broad Lane,
right into Banner Lane, 3rd entrance right
Seats: 70  Cover: 200        **Clubhouse:** Not on ground
**HONOURS**        Midland Comb. Div 1 94-95, Div 2 93-94, Chall. Vase 93-94, Chall Cup 94-95,
Presidents Cup 94-95; Coventry  Evening Telegraph Cup 95-96
**PREVIOUS**        League: Coventry Alliance (pre-1993)

Colours: Red & Black,Black,Red
Change Colours:Light blue with dark blue trim
Programme: Yes

Chairman: Dave Malintel

Manager: John Halford, Geoff Brassington
Coach: Carl Lascelles
Physio: Joe Doolan

# MEIR K.A.

**Secretary:** Des Raeney, 56 Bridgewood Street, Longton, Stoke -on-Trent ST3 1LN
Tel No: 01782 325624
**Ground:** Stanley Park, Hilderstone Road, Meir Heath, Stoke-on-Trent (01782388465)
**Directions:** M6 jct 14, A34 to Stone, A520 to Rough Close then Meir Heath, turnright (B5066)
ground approx 1 mile on right. 3m Blythe Bridge (BR)
Capacity: 5,000 Seats: 200 Cover: 250 Floodlights: YesClub Shop: No
Clubhouse: open matchdays. Hot food
**HONOURS:**     Staffs Snr Lg 88-89, 90-91; Staffs FA Vase 93-94; Walsall & Dist Sen Cup
    89-90;Mid Comb Prem Lge R-up 96-97; Mid Comb Lge Chall Cup R-up 97-98
**PREVIOUSLeagues:** Staffs Alliance/ Staffs Snr 84-92
**Ground:** Normacot Rec          **Name:** 'The Station'&'Shoulder of Mutton.'

Founded: 1972    Nickname: Kings
Colours: Old gold/black/black
Change colours: Claret & blue/blue/blue
Midweek matchday: Wednesday
Programme: 32 pages 50p
Editor: Kelly Reaney (01782 325624)
President: Peter Bott
Chairman: Des Reaney
Vice Chairman: Graham Lovatt
Manager: Des Reaney Coach: Bernie Bramwell
Press Officer: Mark Allen (01782 304472)
Commercial Mgr: Paul Robinson

# NORTHFIELD TOWN

**Secretary:** Monty Patrick, 38 Pensford Rd, Northfield, Birmingham B31 3AG
    Tel: 0121475 2057

Colours: Yellow/blue/yellow
Change colours: all green

**Ground:** The Cricketts, York Road, Oldbury , Warley B65 0RR
    Tel: 0121559 5564(ground & social club)          Floodlights : Yes

**Directions:** M5 Jct2 to large roundabout (Birchley Island) take 2nd left towards Blackheath
    A4034. At traffic lights turn into Titford L then 3rd right into York Road.
    Ground 200yards on left.

# NUNEATON GRIFF

**Secretary:** Bob Archer, 27 Park Lane, Robinsons End, Nuneaton, Warwicks CV10 8LX
    Tel No: 02476 375593 (H)

Colours: Blue & white/blue/red&blue
Change Colours: All yellow

**Ground:** The Pingles Stadium, Avenue Road, Nuneaton.
    TelNos: Ground 02476 370688  Social Club: 02476 386798

**Directions:** Avenue Road (A4252) leads to Cedar Tree Pub. traffic lights where you turn left into
stadium car park service road which is unsuitable for coachesi

# SOUTHAM UNITED

**Secretary:** R J Hancocks, 18 Warwick Road, Southam, Leamington Spa CV33 0HN
    Tel: 01926 813483
**Ground:** Banbury Road Ground, Southam, Leamington Spa. Tel: 01926 812091
**Directions:** A423 - 12 miles south of coventry on the Banbury side of Southam
Capacity: 2000     Seats: 200     Cover: 250     Floodlights: Yes
**Clubhouse:** Yes, with food available          **Club Shop:** No
**HONOURS**    Midland Comb. Prem. Div. R-up 97-98: Birmingham County Sat. Vase 97-98;
    Coventry Chall. Cup; Coventry City Cup; Coventry & N. Warwicks. Lge Pre. Div.
**RECORD**    **Attendance:** 1,500 v Coventry City, friendly 86-87

Founded: 1905
Sponsors: Mayfair Securities - B&M Coaches
Colours: White & black/black/black
Change colours: red & black/white/white
Midweek Matchday: Tuesday
Programme: 10 pages 50p
Editor: Ian Jowsey
Chairman: D Shanahan
Presss Officer: Ian Jowsey
Manager: Sean McCabrey
Asst. Man.: Paul Whitehead
Physio: Carl Shirley

# STUDLEY B.K.L.

**Secretary:** Mark Sealey, 31 Evenlode Close, Lodge Park, ReddB98 7N (01527 457 949)

**Ground:** B.K.L. Sports & Social Club (The Beehive), Abbeyfields Drive,Studley, Warwiicks.
    Tel Nos`: Ground & Social club: 01527 853817
    Capacity : 1,000     Seats: None     Cover: Yes     Floodlights: No

**HONOURS**    Midland Comb. Div 1 91-92, Chal Cup R-up: 91-92, Presidents Cup R-up: 91-
    92, Div2 Cup 87-88,Smedley Cooke Charity Cup 90-91,91-92, Birmingham Vase: 96-97
**PREVIOUS**    **Leagues:** Redditch & South Warwickshire Sunday Combination 71-87
**RECORD**    **Appearances:** Lee Adams     **Goalscorer:** Kevin Rowlands

Founded: 1971    Nickname: Bees
Sponsors: BKL Fittings
Colours: Sky/navy/navy
Change colours: Yellow /sky blue/sky blue
Programme: 50p    Editor: Gordon Wilkie
Reserve's League:
Chairman: D Robinson
Vice-Chairman: Alec James
Press Officer: Dave Chiswell
Manager: John Adams
Asst Manager: Alan Scarfe & Glen Adams
Physio: Dave Middleton

## ALVIS S.G.L.
**Secretary:** D A Leslie, 9 Stephenson Close, Milverton, Leamington Spa CV32 6BS Tel: 01926 336700
**Ground:** Alvis Sports & Social Club, Green Lane, Finham, Coventry. Tel: 01203 692576
**Colours:** Blue and White/White/Blue

## BROOKVALE ATHLETIC
**Secretary:** Alan Fleming,28 Manor Road, Streetly, W.Mids B74 3NG (012 353 9260)
**Ground:** Sutton Town F.C. Coles Lane, Sutton Coldfield (0121 355 5475)
**Colours:** Blue/yellow/blue

## BROWNHILLS TOWN
**Secretary:** Paul Dixon, 263 Chase Road, Burntwood, Stafafs WS7 0EA (01543 683730)
**Ground:** Holland `Park, The Parade, Brownhills, Walsall(0956535545)
**Colours:** Yellow/blue/blue

## BURNTWOOD
**Secretary:** Mervyn Ellis, 11 Green Meadows, Heath Hayes, Cannock, Staffs WS125YA Tel: 01543 271770
**Ground:** Memorial Institute, Rugeley Road, Burntwood. Tel: 01543 675578
**Colours:** Red and Blue /Blue/Red

## CHELMSLEY TOWN
**Secretary:** Martin Smallwood, 244 Coleshill Heath Road, Marston Green,Birmingham B37 7HH (01926 493098)
**Ground:** The Pavilion, Coleshill Road, Marston Green, West Midlands (0121 7795400)
**Colours:** Sky blue & white stripes/black/black

## COUNTY SPORTS
**Secretary:** Geoff Woodward, 2 Lansdowne Rd., Worcester WR1 1ST Tel: 01905 23341
**Ground:** County Council Sports Ground, Claines Lane, Worcester Tel: 0589 329771
**Colours:** Yellow/blue/blue

## DUDLEY SPORTS
**Secretary:** John Lewis, 6 Hern Rd., Brieley Hill, West Mids DY5 2PW Tel: 01384 895782
**Ground:** High Ercal Avenue, Brierley Hill, West Mids ( 01384 826420)
**Colours:** Red & blue/blue/red Change colours:  All blue

## FAIRFIELD VILLA
**Secretary/Press Officer:** C W Harris, 7 Churchill Road, Catshill, Bromsgrove B610PE Tel: 01527 831049
**Ground:** Recreation Ground, Stourbridge Road (B4091), Fairfield, Bromsgrove Tel: 01527 77049
**Colours:** White/black/black

## HAMS HALL
**General Manager/Press Officer:** Bob Ringrose, 6 Holly Drive, Hurley, Atherstone,Warks CV9 2JY Tel: 0827 872747
**Ground:** Hams Hall Generating Station, Lea Marston, Sutton Coldfield B76 0BG Tel: 0370 936219
**Colours:** White/black/black

## HOLLY LANE '92
**Secretary:** R G Ashton, 19 Grange Road, Erdington, Birmingham B24 0DG Tel: 0121 350 2352
**Ground:** Holly Sports & Social Centre, Holly Lane, Erdington, Birmingham B249LH. tel: 01213 730979
**Colours:** Yellow/green/green

## KINGS NORTON TOWN RESERVES
**Secretary:** Mike Rowley, 61 Derwent Drive, Priorslee, Telford, Shropshire TF2 9QR
**Ground:** The Valley Stadium, Bromsgrove Rd, Redditch

## KNOWLE
**Secretary:** Roger Whittick, 149 Richmond Road, Solihull B92 7RZ Tel No 0121 684 2753
**Ground:** Hampton Rd, Knowle, Solihull , W.Mid B93 0NX (01564 779807)
**Colours:** Red/black/black

## LOUGHBOROUGH ATHLETIC
**Secretary:** John Belton: 51 Farndale Drive, Loughborough, Leics.LE112RG Tel No: 01509 231583 (H) 01509 231583 (W)
**Ground:** The Drome, Derby Road Playing Fields, Derby Road, Loughborough Tel: 01509 610022
**Colours:** All yellow

## MALVERN ATHLETIC (formerly Colletts Green)
**Secretary:** Marg Coldicott, 3 Blagdon Close, St Peters, Worcester Tel: 01905 767386
**Ground:** Victoria Park, Pickersleigh, Malvern Link Tel: 01905 830442
**Colours:** All green with white trim

## MILE OAK ROVERS
**Secretary:** Keith Lycett, 1 Price Avenue, Mile Oak, Tamworth, Staffs. B78 3NL Tel Nos 018267 708735 (H)01827 89614(W)
**Colours:** Navy & Yellow/navy/navy

## ROMULUS
**Secretary:** Roger Evans, 34 Leam Drive, Church Farm, Burntwood, WS7 9JG Tel: 01543 675152
**Ground:** Bolehall Swifts F.C.,Rene Rd, Bolehall, Tamworth B77 3NN Tel: 01827 62637
**Colours:** Red & white/red/red

## SHIRLEY TOWN
**Secretary:** B Fox, 26 Claines Road, Northfield, Birmingham B31 2EE Tel: 0121 475 4465
**Ground:** Shirley Stadium, Tile House Lane, Shirley, Solihull Tel: 0121 744 1560
**Colours:** All maroon

## THIMBLEMILL R.E.C.
**Secretary:** Karl Young, 30 Moorpool Close, Harborne, Birmimgham Tel: 0121 427 2807
**Ground:** Thimblemill Recreation, Thimblemill Road, Smethwick, Warley. Tel: 0121 429 2459
**Colours:** White (blue trim)/white/navy blue

## WELLESBOURNE
**Secretary:** Ted Forster Tel: 01926 494507
**Ground:** The Sports Field, Loxley Close, Wellesbourne Tel: 01789 841878
**Colours:** Blue & white halves/blue/blue

## WEST MIDLANDS FIRE SERVICE
**Secretary:** Mr J Clarke, 51 Stonebury Avenue., Eastern Green, Coventry CV5 7FW Tel: 01203 467997
**Ground:** `The Glades', Lugtrout Lane, Solihull Tel: 0121 705 8602
**Colours:** Red with black pin stripe/Black/Black

---

**DIVISION TWO CLUBS**
ARCHDALE '73, BARLESTONE St GILES, BURMAN HI-TON, CADBURY ATHLETIC, EARLSWOOD TOWN, ENVILLE ATHLETIC, G N P SPORTS, HANDSAKER, KENILWORTH WARDENS, LICHFIELD ENOTS, MCL CLAINES, OLD HILL TOWN, POLESWORTH NORTH WARWICK, WEST MIDLANDS POLICE RESERVES & WYRE FOREST

# MIDLAND FLOODLIT YOUTH LEAGUE

## FINAL LEAGUE TABLES 1998-99

### PREMIER DIVISION

| | P | W | D | L | F | A | Pts |
|---|---|---|---|---|---|---|---|
| Burton Albion | 22 | 14 | 6 | 2 | 56 | 22 | 48 |
| Hinckley United | 22 | 13 | 5 | 4 | 39 | 19 | 44 |
| West Bromwich Alb | 22 | 11 | 6 | 5 | 50 | 30 | 39 |
| Kidderminster Harr. | 22 | 9 | 7 | 6 | 40 | 26 | 34 |
| Quorn | 22 | 9 | 7 | 6 | 35 | 35 | 34 |
| Halesowen Town | 22 | 9 | 6 | 7 | 32 | 29 | 33 |

| | P | W | D | L | F | A | Pts |
|---|---|---|---|---|---|---|---|
| Atherstone United | 22 | 8 | 7 | 7 | 37 | 38 | 31 |
| Bedworth United | 22 | 6 | 7 | 9 | 36 | 43 | 25 |
| Nuneaton Borough | 22 | 6 | 6 | 10 | 27 | 34 | 24 |
| Boldmere St Michaels | 22 | 5 | 6 | 11 | 46 | 62 | 21 |
| Hereford United | 22 | 4 | 6 | 12 | 28 | 45 | 18 |
| Bromsgrove Rovers | 22 | 0 | 7 | 15 | 23 | 66 | 6 |

### NORTHERN DIVISION

| | P | W | D | L | F | A | Pts |
|---|---|---|---|---|---|---|---|
| Walsall Wood | 22 | 15 | 3 | 4 | 54 | 23 | 50 |
| Sutton Coldfield Town | 22 | 15 | 3 | 4 | 59 | 34 | 48 |
| Hednesford Town | 22 | 14 | 2 | 6 | 63 | 30 | 44 |
| Stourbridge | 22 | 11 | 8 | 3 | 40 | 21 | 41 |
| Oadby Town | 22 | 10 | 5 | 7 | 38 | 31 | 35 |
| VS Rugby | 22 | 8 | 5 | 9 | 37 | 45 | 29 |
| Barrow Town | 22 | 7 | 7 | 8 | 50 | 48 | 28 |
| Tamworth | 22 | 8 | 4 | 10 | 40 | 45 | 28 |
| Gresley Rovers | 22 | 6 | 5 | 11 | 34 | 47 | 23 |
| Coleshill Town | 22 | 6 | 3 | 13 | 33 | 55 | 21 |
| Dudley Sports | 22 | 5 | 2 | 15 | 31 | 65 | 17 |
| Shepshed Dynamo | 22 | 2 | 2 | 18 | 20 | 55 | 8 |

### SOUTHERN DIVISION

| | P | W | D | L | F | A | Pts |
|---|---|---|---|---|---|---|---|
| Gloucester City | 22 | 19 | 2 | 1 | 68 | 19 | 59 |
| Worcester City | 22 | 16 | 1 | 5 | 74 | 28 | 49 |
| Redditch United | 22 | 13 | 4 | 5 | 59 | 33 | 43 |
| Racing Club Warwick | 22 | 12 | 4 | 6 | 48 | 28 | 40 |
| Stratford Town | 22 | 12 | 4 | 6 | 54 | 40 | 40 |
| Malvern Town | 22 | 11 | 3 | 8 | 62 | 50 | 36 |
| Kenilworth Town | 22 | 6 | 5 | 11 | 33 | 54 | 23 |
| Evesham United | 22 | 6 | 3 | 13 | 31 | 45 | 21 |
| Pershore Town | 22 | 6 | 3 | 13 | 32 | 59 | 21 |
| Pegasus Juniors | 22 | 6 | 1 | 15 | 34 | 58 | 19 |
| Alvechurch | 22 | 4 | 3 | 15 | 37 | 67 | 15 |
| Ross Town | 22 | 3 | 3 | 16 | 19 | 70 | 12 |

## CUP DETAILS

| | WINNERS | RUNNERS-UP |
|---|---|---|
| LEAGUE CUP | Sutton Coldfield Town | Gloucester City |
| BIRMINGHAM FA YOUTH CUP | Atherstone United | Burton Albion |
| LEICS & RUTLAND FA YOUTH CUP | Hinckley United | |
| STAFFORDSHIRE FA YOUTH CUP | Burton Albion | |
| WORCS FA YOUTH CUP | Worcester City | Stourbridge |

# BANKS'S BREWERY
# WEST MIDLANDS (REGIONAL) LEAGUE

## FEEDER TO: MIDLAND ALLIANCE

**Hon Secretary:** Neil Juggins
14 Badgers Lane, Blackwell, Bromsgrove

---

Having missed out last time round, Kington Town proved themselves the season's outstanding club, with a league and cup double to celebrate. Cradley Town, meanwhile, had to settle for second best in what was, nevertheless, the most successful season in the club's history.

For most of the season Cradley led the way, with Kington trailing some way behind, albeit with games in hand. Newly promoted Smethwick Rangers held second place for several months, but they were always in the position of having played more games than the other top clubs and were not really realistic challengers. A final placing of fifth was still a good achievement for a first campaign in the top flight. Kington trailed Cradley by eighteen points at one stage, but this lead was gradually whittled away and an important win for the Herefordshire club in a head-to-head meeting at the end of March was followed by a loss of form for the Black Country side, which saw them lose five of their last dozen games. Kington, however, were virtually unstoppable, for following defeat at Darlaston in January they put together an eighteen game unbeaten run which ended with defeat in the return fixture at Cradley, by which time the championship was already assured. They accumulated 59 points from their last 22 games to finish twelve points clear at the top. Cradley just held off the challenge of Stafford Town (who picked up 25 points out of the final 30) to win the Keys Cup. Indeed, the top five clubs all recorded their highest ever placings in the WMRL. The campaign finally closed with Kington's 3-1 league cup final win over Cradley at Malvern.

The effects of being denied promotion due to ground grading requirements were felt at Lye Town, the reigning champions suffering a player exodus and spending much of the campaign near the foot of the table. A run of just two defeats in the final twelve games enabled the club to finish with mid-table respectability.

Wolverhampton United endured another miserable campaign. Their only victory of the season came as early as the third game, and the subsequent run of 37 games without a win left them just short of the all-time league record. Attempts to avoid this unwanted record will have to continue in Division One (North) next season, the club having been relegated after three seasons in the top flight which have seen them win just eight league games out of 108. Their single victory was the lowest total ever achieved in a programme of 40 games or more.

In the regionalised Division One Wellington was the most successful club, matching the efforts of Herefordshire neighbours Kington by clinching a league and cup double. In the South section, Leominster Town were amongst the early pace-setters but by the end of November Wellington and newcomers Causeway United had turned it into a two-horse race. Causeway took over at the top just before Xmas, a position they held until the completion of their fixtures on 1st May. Wellington were left with the task of taking four points from three games, which they duly did with a game to spare, and ended a highly successful league campaign with a number of RMRL records: the highest proportion of wins in a season; the highest goals per game ratio; lowest goals against total. Causeway's run of 34 points from their last fourteen games was overshadowed by Wellington's run of 37 from thirteen.

The North section was a much more open affair, although Great Wyrley led the way for three months. Heath Hayes, Lucas and Brereton all held the lead for a period before newcomers Little Drayton took over on February 20th, a position they held until completing their fixtures on 8th May. However, three points deducted for an infringement prior to Xmas proved to be costly and Heath Hayes proceeded to win their three games in hand to clinch the title.

At the bottom end of the two sections three clubs endured particularly miserable campaigns, especially the second half. Corestone failed to win any of the last eighteen games, whilst Walsall Wood reserves, having won 7-1 at Corestone, then took just two points from seventeen subsequent games to finish last. Their total of nine points was the lowest ever recorded at this level, beating their own record set a year earlier! Meanwhile another new club, Borgfeld Celtic, managed just a single point from their last eleven games and also finished bottom.

There was little success from WMRL clubs in the national competitions. Lye Town were the only participants in the F.A. Cup and they exited at the first hurdle, eliminated by Racing Warwick. In the F.A. Vase there were some spectacular scorelines, but little actual progress. Malvern and Tividale were thrashed 0-8 and 0-7 respectively, whilst only Kington made any real progress, recording victories of 8-0, 6-4 and 3-0 before going down 4-5 to Oldbury United in the Second Round.

751

# FINAL LEAGUE TABLES 1998-99
## PREMIER DIVISION

| | P | W | D | L | F | A | Pts |
|---|---|---|---|---|---|---|---|
| Kington Town | 40 | 32 | 3 | 5 | 120 | 39 | 99 |
| Cradley Town | 40 | 28 | 3 | 9 | 98 | 40 | 87 |
| Stafford Town | 40 | 27 | 5 | 8 | 89 | 38 | 86 |
| Wolverhampton Cas'ls | 40 | 24 | 5 | 11 | 99 | 72 | 77 |
| Smethwick Rangers | 40 | 21 | 8 | 11 | 88 | 52 | 71 |
| Darlaston Town | 40 | 21 | 7 | 12 | 81 | 63 | 70 |
| Bandon | 40 | 19 | 7 | 14 | 72 | 53 | 64 |
| Malvern Town | 40 | 16 | 12 | 12 | 76 | 62 | 60 |
| Tipton Town | 40 | 17 | 6 | 17 | 62 | 75 | 57 |
| Bustleholme | 40 | 16 | 7 | 17 | 63 | 71 | 55 |
| Gornal Athletic | 40 | 14 | 11 | 15 | 68 | 65 | 53 |
| Lye Town | 40 | 12 | 15 | 13 | 56 | 54 | 51 |
| Star | 40 | 14 | 8 | 18 | 55 | 63 | 50 |
| Dudley Town | 40 | 11 | 13 | 16 | 52 | 67 | 46 |
| Tividale | 40 | 12 | 9 | 19 | 55 | 69 | 45 |
| Brierley Hill Town | 40 | 11 | 12 | 17 | 57 | 74 | 45 |
| Westfields | 40 | 9 | 15 | 16 | 57 | 69 | 42 |
| Ludlow Town | 40 | 12 | 5 | 23 | 46 | 82 | 41 |
| Ettingshall Holy Trinity | 40 | 10 | 9 | 21 | 62 | 87 | 39 |
| Walsall Wood | 40 | 5 | 7 | 28 | 43 | 99 | 22 |
| Wolverhampton Utd | 40 | 1 | 9 | 30 | 33 | 138 | 12 |

## DIVISION ONE NORTH

| | P | W | D | L | F | A | Pts |
|---|---|---|---|---|---|---|---|
| Heath Hayes | 28 | 19 | 5 | 4 | 75 | 28 | 62 |
| Little Drayton Rangers -3 | 28 | 19 | 6 | 3 | 74 | 24 | 60 |
| Lucas Flight Controls | 28 | 18 | 4 | 6 | 91 | 37 | 58 |
| Great Wyrley | 28 | 17 | 5 | 6 | 75 | 35 | 56 |
| Brereton Social | 28 | 16 | 8 | 4 | 83 | 48 | 56 |
| Newport | 28 | 17 | 5 | 6 | 62 | 40 | 56 |
| Cannock Chase | 28 | 14 | 7 | 7 | 63 | 43 | 49 |
| Sedgley White Lions | 28 | 11 | 7 | 10 | 44 | 38 | 40 |
| Morda United | 28 | 9 | 3 | 16 | 55 | 72 | 30 |
| Shifnal Town Res. | 28 | 9 | 2 | 17 | 42 | 66 | 29 |
| Wolverhampton Cas R | 28 | 8 | 4 | 16 | 53 | 79 | 28 |
| Wyrley Rangers | 28 | 6 | 5 | 17 | 39 | 92 | 23 |
| Wolverhampton Town | 28 | 3 | 7 | 18 | 35 | 71 | 16 |
| Corestone Services | 28 | 2 | 8 | 18 | 37 | 105 | 14 |
| Walsall Wood Res. * | 28 | 2 | 4 | 22 | 25 | 75 | 9 |

## DIVISION ONE SOUTH

| | P | W | D | L | F | A | Pts |
|---|---|---|---|---|---|---|---|
| Wellington (Hereford) | 26 | 22 | 1 | 3 | 115 | 17 | 67 |
| Causeway United | 26 | 21 | 1 | 4 | 75 | 24 | 64 |
| Leominster Town | 26 | 13 | 5 | 8 | 57 | 48 | 44 |
| Bromyard Town | 26 | 13 | 3 | 10 | 43 | 34 | 42 |
| Tividale Res. | 26 | 12 | 4 | 10 | 48 | 49 | 40 |
| Sikh Hunters | 26 | 12 | 3 | 11 | 68 | 70 | 39 |
| Halesowen Harriers Rs | 26 | 11 | 4 | 11 | 59 | 51 | 37 |
| Malvern Town Res. | 26 | 9 | 7 | 10 | 45 | 54 | 34 |
| Cradley Town Res. | 26 | 10 | 2 | 14 | 43 | 50 | 32 |
| Hinton | 26 | 10 | 2 | 14 | 53 | 68 | 32 |
| Pershore Town Res. | 26 | 9 | 4 | 13 | 28 | 50 | 31 |
| Mahal | 26 | 7 | 5 | 14 | 42 | 67 | 26 |
| Lye Town Res. | 26 | 8 | 1 | 17 | 44 | 91 | 25 |
| Borgfeld Celtic | 26 | 3 | 2 | 21 | 36 | 83 | 11 |

* points deducted

## PREMIER DIVISION RESULTS CHART 1998-99

| | 1 | 2 | 3 | 4 | 5 | 6 | 7 | 8 | 9 | 10 | 11 | 12 | 13 | 14 | 15 | 16 | 17 | 18 | 19 | 20 | 21 |
|---|---|---|---|---|---|---|---|---|---|---|---|---|---|---|---|---|---|---|---|---|---|
| 1 Bandon | X | 3-0 | 2-0 | 0-0 | 5-0 | 0-0 | 3-2 | 1-3 | 0-3 | 4-1 | 2-2 | 3-0 | 0-4 | 2-3 | 4-0 | 1-0 | 2-1 | 3-0 | | | |
| 2 Brierley Hill T | 2-2 | X | 2-1 | 0-5 | 0-1 | 2-4 | 2-0 | 2-3 | 0-4 | 2-0 | 3-3 | 4-2 | 2-1 | 0-2 | 0-0 | 1-4 | 1-2 | 1-2 | | | |
| 3 Bustleholme | 0-2 | 2-1 | X | 0-2 | 2-1 | 2-1 | 1-0 | 0-1 | 0-4 | 3-0 | 1-2 | 4-4 | 1-2 | 0-2 | 3-2 | 1-4 | 3-1 | 6-0 | | | |
| 4 Cradley Town | 2-1 | 2-2 | 5-0 | X | 3-1 | 3-0 | 5-1 | 3-0 | 2-1 | 1-0 | 1-1 | 1-2 | 1-0 | 2-1 | 2-0 | 3-2 | 4-1 | 2-1 | | | |
| 5 Darlaston T | 1-2 | 1-1 | 1-1 | 1-2 | X | 0-0 | 2-0 | 2-2 | 2-1 | 6-2 | 4-3 | 3-1 | 6-2 | 2-3 | 3-2 | 3-0 | 1-0 | 5-0 | | | |
| 6 Dudley Town | 2-1 | 2-3 | 2-0 | 0-4 | 0-3 | X | 4-0 | 0-2 | 1-2 | 2-2 | 0-0 | 2-1 | 0-0 | 2-5 | 3-1 | 0-0 | 1-1 | 2-1 | | | |
| 7 Ettingshall H T | 5-1 | 0-0 | 6-0 | 0-4 | 2-2 | 1-1 | X | 1-1 | 1-1 | 2-1 | 1-1 | 1-2 | 3-4 | 1-2 | 2-3 | 2-1 | 2-1 | 5-0 | | | |
| 8 Gornal Athletic | 0-2 | 1-1 | 5-1 | 1-2 | 1-1 | 3-1 | 0-1 | X | 1-1 | 1-1 | 2-1 | 1-1 | 1-2 | 3-4 | 1-2 | 2-3 | 2-1 | 2-1 | 1-0 | 0-0 | |
| 9 Kington Town | 5-2 | 3-0 | 1-2 | 2-0 | 4-0 | 3-0 | 1-1 | 6-0 | X | 2-1 | 3-1 | 3-0 | 2-1 | 2-1 | 2-3 | 8-0 | 3-1 | 4-1 | | | |
| 10 Ludlow Town | 1-0 | 0-3 | 3-0 | 1-0 | 0-3 | 2-1 | 1-0 | 1-5 | 0-5 | X | 4-1 | 1-1 | 1-5 | 0-2 | 0-2 | 3-1 | 1-1 | 2-0 | | | |
| 11 Lye Town | 3-1 | 0-1 | 1-1 | 2-3 | 1-1 | 3-3 | 1-2 | 3-1 | 2-3 | 2-0 | X | 1-3 | 0-0 | 2-1 | 1-0 | 1-1 | 0-1 | 3-1 | | | |
| 12 Malvern Town | 1-0 | 2-2 | 1-2 | 3-1 | 3-0 | 0-0 | 5-2 | 3-0 | 3-1 | 1-2 | 4-0 | X | 3-1 | 0-0 | 0-2 | 2-2 | 1-1 | 2-0 | | | |
| 13 Smethwick R | 1-1 | 0-0 | 3-3 | 2-1 | 7-2 | 1-3 | 3-1 | 1-0 | 1-1 | 6-1 | 1-0 | 4-1 | X | 1-2 | 0-0 | 1-3 | 2-1 | 4-1 | | | |
| 14 Stafford Town | 1-2 | 1-1 | 1-2 | 1-0 | 0-4 | 2-0 | 2-2 | 2-0 | 2-3 | 1-0 | 1-0 | 3-1 | 3-2 | X | 0-0 | 3-0 | 5-0 | 5-1 | | | |
| 15 Star | 2-0 | 0-2 | 0-1 | 2-6 | 3-2 | 3-1 | 1-1 | 2-4 | 0-2 | 1-0 | 1-1 | 1-1 | 1-3 | 0-2 | X | 1-1 | 5-1 | 1-0 | | | |
| 16 Tipton Town | 3-2 | 3-0 | 3-1 | 2-0 | 2-3 | 2-0 | 0-0 | 0-3 | 5-1 | 0-4 | 0-2 | 0-4 | 0-2 | 0-2 | | X | 2-1 | 3-3 | | | |
| 17 Tividale | 1-0 | 3-3 | 2-3 | 3-1 | 0-1 | 1-1 | 3-1 | 2-1 | 1-1 | 0-0 | 0-1 | 0-3 | 3-1 | 2-0 | 1-2 | | X | 3-1 | | | |
| 18 Walsall Wood | 0-3 | 3-1 | 0-0 | 1-5 | 1-2 | 0-1 | 2-1 | 5-1 | 1-3 | 4-1 | 1-3 | 1-3 | 0-2 | 0-2 | 1-2 | 2-3 | 0-1 | X | | | |
| 19 Westfields | 1-1 | 2-0 | 3-2 | 0-1 | 3-0 | 2-2 | 3-3 | 2-2 | 0-3 | 1-0 | 0-0 | 1-6 | 0-2 | 0-2 | 2-1 | 2-3 | 1-0 | 0-0 | X | | |
| 20 Wolv'ton Cas | 1-5 | 3-0 | 2-0 | 1-6 | 1-2 | 4-3 | 4-1 | 3-0 | 1-3 | 2-0 | 0-0 | 4-3 | 1-1 | 0-6 | 2-0 | 6-0 | 0-2 | 4-1 | | X | |
| 21 Wolv'ton Utd | 1-2 | 2-5 | 2-2 | 1-4 | 1-3 | 2-2 | 1-5 | 3-2 | 1-4 | 0-2 | 0-3 | 0-0 | 1-6 | 1-7 | 0-2 | 0-3 | 3-4 | 1-1 | | | X |

## LEAGUE CUPS 1998-99

| | WINNERS | FINALISTS | |
|---|---|---|---|
| PREMIER DIVISION | Kington Town | Cradley Town | 3-1 |
| DIVISION ONE | Wellington | Sedgley White Lions | 2-1 |
| YOUTH DIVISIONS | Tividale | Gornal Athletic | 3-0 |

# BANDON

**Secretary:** Timothy Hebbard, Old Hall Cottage, 4 Wapping Alley, Claverley, Bridgnorth, Shrops WV5 7DS (01746 710633)

**Ground:** Crown Meadow, Innage Lane, Bridgnorth (01746 762747)

**Directions:** Follow signs for Shrewsbury A458, over river bridge on by-pass, At next island turn right (Town Centre). At 'T' junc turn right, 1st left intoVictoria Rd, right at crossroads and follow road into Innage Lane

**FACT FILE**
Founded: 1988
Colours: Blue & white/blue/blue
Change colours: White/blue/white

**CLUB PERSONNEL**
Chairman: Michael Smith

---

# BRIERLEY HILL TOWN

**Secretary:** Bill Hughes, 13 Barnett Close, Kingswinford, West Midlands, DY6 9PW
Tel: 01384 288855
**Ground:** The Dell Sports Stadium, Bryce Rd, Pensnett, Brierley Hill, West Mids (01384 77289)
**Directions:** At lights in Brierley Hill High St turn into Bank St by PoliceStation. Over bridge into Pensnett Rd, ground 3/4 mile on left Paddy's Garage.Entrance 120yds in Bryce Rd
Capacity: 5,000          Seats: 300          Cover: 300          Floodlights: Yes
**Clubhouse:** Open Mon, Wed & Fri. Hot foods & drinks on matchdays

**HONOURS**          West Mids Lg Prem. Div Cup R-up 84-85 (Div 1 80-81 (Div 1 Cup 80-81))
**PREVIOUS**          **Leagues:** Kidderminster (8 seasons); Staffs County (South)(7 seasons);
West Midlands Regional (pre-94)

Founded: 1955
Nickname: Lions
Colours: Blue & white/blue/blue/
Change colours: All Yellow
Midweek matchday: Mon or Wed
Programme: 20 pages, 50p
Editor: Secretary
Chairman: Anthony Purchase
Vice-Chairman: Terry Baker
Manager: Richard Gwinnett
Asst Manager: Steve Scott
Coach: Chris Conway

---

# BUSTLEHOME

**Secretary:** Suzanne Glover, 15 Swann Hill, Hurst Hill, Coseley, WolverhamptonWV14 9UP
Tel: 01902 659380

**Ground:** Darlaston Town FC, Waverley Rd, Darlaston, W Midlands (0121 526 4423)

**Directions:** M6 jct 10, A454 Walsall/Willenhall. Take the A454 towardsWillenhall. Turn left at traffic lights, outside the Lane Arms Public Houseinto Bentley Road North. Follow road down hill, over railway & canal bridges to lights. Cross over lights into Richard Street & along Victoria Road. Take the first right into Slater Street, ground on left
Capacity:          Seats: Yes          Cover: Yes          Floodlights: Yes

**FACT FILE**
Founded: 1975
Colours: Yellow/green/green
Change colours: White/green/green

**CLUB PERSONNEL**
Chairman: Geoff Fellows

---

# DARLASTON TOWN

**Secretary:** Mrs Kath Abley, 42 Addenbrooke Street, Darlaston (0121 531 0487)
**Ground:** City Ground, Waverley Rd, Darlaston (0121 526 4423) **Directions:** M6 Jct 10, A454 towards Willenhall, left at lights outside`Lane Arms' into Bentley Rd North, follow this down hill & over the railway & canal bridges to traffic lights. Cross over the lights into Richards St and along into Victoria Rd, 1st right into Slater St and ground on left but entrance is next left in Waverley Rd
Capacity: 2,000 Seats: Yes Cover: Yes Floodlights: Yes  Club Shop: Yes
**Clubhouse:** Open matchdays. Tues/Wed/Thur evenings & Sunday Lunch. Hot/colddrinks/snacks
**HONOURS** West Mids Lg Div 1 89-90 (R-up 91-92 92-93, Div 1 Cup 89-90), B irmingham Snr Cup 72-73, B'ham Vase 90-91 91-92, B'ham Jnr Lg 07-08, B'hamComb. 10-11 37-38 45-46 (Tillotson Cup 36-37 37-38 38-39 45-46), Keys Cup 11-12), Wednesbury Lg(5) 1896-1901
**PREVIOUS** Leagues:(inc Wedn'bury Lg) pre-1908/ B'gham Comb. 08-11 28-54/ WMids 11-28

Founded: 1874          Nickname: Blues
Sponsors: Rubery owen
Colours: Blue & white stripes/blue/blue
Change colours: All yellow
Midweek matcheday: Tuesday
Prog. Editor: Dave Stevenson (0121 526 2465)
Chairman: John Reeves
Match Sec: Neil Arrowsmith (01902 450612)
Press Officer: 'Scotch Bob'
Manager: Jim McMorran
Assistant Manager: Colin Johnson
Physio: Michelle Cookson

---

# DUDLEY TOWN

**Secretary:**Margaret Turner, 3,Straits Road, Lower Gornal, Dudley, DY3 2UY Tel: 01384 214741
**Ground:** Garden Walk Stadium,Garden Walk Lowere Gornal,DudleyDY3 2NH Tel: 01384 358398
**Directions:** From Dudley take A459, left at Green Dragon Pub, on B4175 take 2nd exit at island, continue to Old Bulls Head, left into Redhall Rd & 2nd left into Garden Walk. From Wolverhampton, use A449 past Wombourne, left at Himley House lights into B4176.Over next lights at Bull St., 2nd left into Central Drtive, then 1st left into Bank Rd and follow this to ground
Capacity: 500          Cover: 1000 Seats: 100 Floodlights: Yes  Club Shop: Yes
**Clubhouse:** Peacocks social club open on matchday . Snacks available from clubhouse
**HONOURS**          Southern Lg Midland Div 84-85, Birmingham Comb 33-34 (R-up 34-35 47-48), Midland (Worcs) Comb 31-32 (R-up 29-30 30-31), West Mids Lg Cp R-up 75-76 (Div2 Cp R-up 80-81), Birmingham Senior Cup 85-86 (R-up 64-65 83-84)

**FACT FILE**
Formed: 1893          Nickname: The Robins
Colours: Red/black/black
Change: Yellow/black or white/black or red
Midweek matchday: Tuesday 7.45pm
Programme: Pages:28 Price:60p
Editor: Paul Hawthorne
Chairman: Nevil Jeynes
Vice Chairman: Alan Guest
President: N D Jeynes
Manager: Ian davis
Asst Manager:Tommy Johnson

# ETTINGSHALL HOLY TRINITY

**Secretary:** Graham Mills, 27 Ashen Close, Sedgley, Dudley, West Mids DY3 3UZ(01902 66222)
**Ground:** Aldersley Stadium, Aldersley Road, Tettenhal, Wolverhampton (01902 751171)
**Directions:** From Wolverhampton take A41 Tettenhall Road, 1.5 miles turn right into Lower Street, then right into Aldersley Road, ground on right
**HONOURS** West Mids Lg Div 1 Cup R-up 85-86 (Div 2 R-up 84-85), Sporting Award 85-86,Staffs Co. Lg R-up 82-83 (Lg Shield 82-83 83-84), Ike Cooper Cup 82-84 83-84,Sporting Club Award 81-82, Wolverhampton & District Amateur Lg 80-81 (Div 1 65-66, Div 2 64-65), Div 1/2 Cup 64-65 65-66, A H Oakley Cup 80-81, J W Hunt Cup 82-83 83-84 (R-up 79-80), Wolverhampton Cup 83-84 (R-up 82-83)
**PREVIOUS** **League:** Wednesbury Church & Chapel (early 1900s), Bilston Youth (1950s),Wolverhampton & District Amateur (1960s), Staffs County (South)

### FACT FILE
Founded: 1920 Nickname: Trins
Club Sponsors: DKB Electric/ John O'Dell
Colours: All Green/white
Change colours: Red & white/red/red
Midweek matchday: Wednesday
Prog. Editor: John Edwards (01785 713458)
Chairman: John O'Dell
President: David Gadd
Manager: Graham Mills
Asst Manager:
Physio: Tony Kiddle

# GORNAL ATHLETIC

**Secretary:** Keith Birch, 24 Dursley Close, Willenhall, West Midlands WV12 4DE(01902 410784)
**Ground:** Garden Walk Stadium, Lower Gornal, Dudley, West Midlands (01384252285)
**Directions:** From Dudley take A459 to Sedgley past the Burton Rd Hospital. 1ston left at the Green Dragon public house on the B4175 (Jews Lane). Follow theroad until you come to the Old Bull's Head, turn left into Rednall Road, 2ndleft to Garden Walk
Capacity: 3,000 Seats: 100 Cover: 500 Floodlights: Yes Club Shop: No
**HONOURS** West Mids Lg Div 1 R-up 83-84 (Div 1 Cup 92-93), Birmingham Vase 91-92
**PREVIOUS** **League:** Midland Comb. 51-63
**Name:** Lower Gornal Ath
**RECORDS** **Transfer fees received:** £1,500 for Gary Bell and for George Andrews both toCardiff City, 1965

### FACT FILE
Founded: 1945 Nickname: Peacocks
Sponsors: Jasper Steels
Colours: Yellow/green/green
Change colours: Blue & black/blue/black
Reserves' Lge: West Mids (Reg.) Lge Res. Div
Chairman: Colin Worth
Commercial Manager: Martin Wedgebury
Manager: John Gwinnell
Coach: Ian Clark/ Ross Hill
Reserves' Manager: Ian Davies

# KINGTON ATHLETIC

**Secretary:** Karen Mayglothing, Wells Cottage, Stanner Road, Kington, HerefordHR5 3NL
Tel: 01544 231151 (H)

**Ground:** Park Road Ground, Mill Street, Kington, Hereford (01544 231007)

**Directions:** Follow signs for kington Town Centre, look for left turn betweenthe Town Clock and the Burton Hotel. Carry on this road for 500 metres, groundon left as road bends

### FACT FILE
Colours: Yellow & black/black/black
Change colours: Maroon & white/maroon/maroon

### CLUB PERSONNEL
Chairman: William Mayglothing

# LUDLOW TOWN

**Secretary:** Mr J Nash, 58 Hucklemarsh Road, Ludlow, Shropshire (01584 874337)
**Ground:** Riddings Park, Riddings Road, Ludlow, Shropshire (01584 875103)
**Directions:** From Kidderminster A4117; straight over r'bout into Henley Rd, 2ndleft into Sandpits Rd, follow road for 1/4 mile until road bears round to theleft into Ridding Rd - grd on right
Capacity: Seats: No Cover: 150Floodlights: YesClubhouse: Yes
**HONOURS** West Mids. Prem Lg.Cup, Finalists 94-95. Div 1 Cup 90-91; Shropshire County Challenge Cup 93-94, 94-95 96-97; Presteigne-Otway Cup 90-91.94-95:
**PREVIOUS** **League:** Kidderminster League 1961-63, Shropshire Co. Lg.: 1963-1978
**BEST SEASON** F.A.Vase: 1st Q Rd. 98-99 ( 1st season) **F.A.Cup:** Never Entered

### FACT FILE
Formed: 1890
Colours: Red & white/black/black
Change colours: Blue & white/white/blue
Midweek Matchdays: Tuesday/Wednesday
Reserve League: Kidderminster
Programme: Yes
Chairman: P.Gwilliam
Vice Chaima: M.Evans,
Manager: Mark Evans
Asst Manager: Bob Bodenham
Physio: Miss J Stretton

# LYE TOWN

**Secretary:** Peter Timmins, Sports Ground, Stourbridge Rd, Lye, Stourbridge, West Midlands (01384 827471 H)
**Ground:** Sports Ground, Stourbridge Road, Lye (01384 422672) **Directions:** On A458 Birmingham-Stourbridge road about 400yds afterlights/crossroads at Lye. From M5 jct 3 take road marked Kidderminster asfaras lights at bottom of Hagley Hill, right at island, 3rd turn off at nextisland,turn off left at crossroads/lights, ground about 400yds on left. Quarter mile from Lye (BR)
Capacity: 5,000 Seats: 200 Cover: 600 Floodlights: Yes **Clubhouse:** Yes (01384 822672)
**HONOURS** West Mids Lg R-up 76-77 78-79 79-80 80-81 (Prem. Div Cup 75-76), Midland Comb.35-36 (R-up 32-33 34-35 37-38), B'ham Snr Cup R-up 80-81
**PREVIOUS** **Leagues:** Midland Combination 31-39
**RECORD** Gate: 6,000 v Brierley Alliance

### FACT FILE
Founded: 1930 Nickname: Flyers
Colours: Blue & white/white/blue
Change Colours: Red/black/red
Programme: 24 pages, 40p
Editor: J.Galloway
Chairman: Roy Pearson
President: Ian Cole
Manager: David Beasley
Coach: Alan Moore
Physio: Harry Hill

# MALVERN TOWN

**Secretary:** Glynne Knapper, 27 Alexandra Lane, Malvern, Worcs WR14 1JF Tel: 01684 574861
**Ground:** Langland Stadium, Langland Avenue, Malvern, Worcs Tel: 01684 574068
**Directions:** From Worcester take A449o Malvern.Turn left at roundabout signposted B4208 to Welland. Left vat traffic lights into Pickersleigh Road. Turn left at Longford Arms pub, into Maddesfield R oad. 2nd left into Langland Ave., ground 100yds on right. 1 mile from Malvern (BR)
Capacity: 4,000      Seats: 140         Cover: 310         Floodlights: Yes
Clubhouse: 2 bars, large dance area, teabar matchdays      Club Shop: No
**HONOURS**        Worcester/ Midland Comb. 55-56 Mid Comb Cup R-up 75-76, WFA Senior Urn Winners (6), WFA Sat Junior Cup Winners (4) Banks's Brewery Premier League Cup R-up 87-88 WFA Nursing Cup Winners 97-98, Robert Biggart Cup Winners 97-98, 98-99
**PREVIOUS League:** Midland Comb. 55-79      **RECORD Gate:** 1,221 v Worcester, FA Cup

**FACT FILE**
Founded: 1947
Sponsors: Clarke Roxburgh
Colours: Claret/white/sky
Change colours: White/black/maroon
Reserves League: Banks's Brewery Div 1 S
Midweek Matchday: Tuesday
Programme: 28pages 50p Editor: Brian Scott
Chairman: Geoff Brewer
President: R H Mann
Manager: Joe Rawle
Assistant Manager: Richard Anson

# SMETHWICK RANGERS

**Secretary:** Mohan S Gill, 11 Middlesmoor, Wilnecote, Tamworth, Staffs B77 4PL (01827 330702)

**Ground:** Bilston United FC Parkfield Stadium, Rooker Ave, Parkfields,Wolverhampton

**Directions:** From Wolverhampton Centre, proceed along A459 to junc Parkfields Rd & Sedgley Rd. Turn left at the main Parkfield traffic lights A4039, sign Ettingshall, travel 500yds, left into Myatt Ave, 1st right into Lawn Rd. Ground on right

**FACT FILE**
Founded: 1972
Colours: Blue & white/blue/blue
Change colours: Red & black/black/black

**CLUB PERSONNEL**
Chairman: Sukbinder Binning

# STAFFORD TOWN

**Secretary:** Dave Rowley, 32 Lodge Rd, Brereton, Rugely, Staffs WS15 1HG Tel: 01889 800779
**Ground:** Stafford Rangers FC, Aston Fields Rd, Stafford  **Directions:** From M6 junction 14, Take 3rd left to Red Hill Roundabout andfollow signs for Aston Fields Ind Est along Beaconside. Aston Fields is signposted 3rd right along Common Road, over railway bridge, ground on right
Capacity: 6,000      Cover: 3,000      Seats: 426         Floodlights: Yes      Club Shop: No
**HONOURS**        WMRL Div 1 93-94, Staffs Snr Lg R-up 91-92, Midland Comb. Div 2 78-79, Staffs Vase 84-85 92-93 (R-up 87-88), Bourne Sports Trophy 84-85, Walsall Sen Cup SF 91-92
**PREVIOUS Leagues:** Staffs County (North) 74-77 82-84; Midland Comb. 77-82; StaffsSen. 84-93
**Names:** Stafford Town 74-90; Stafford MSHD 90-92      **Grounds:** Silkmore Lane 74-77; Burton Manor Spts 77-88; Riverway 88-91; RowleyPark Stad 91-94
**RECORD Win:** 14-0 v Leek CSOB (H), Staffs Senior League 8/10/88

**FACT FILE**
Founded: 1974
Nickname: Reds or Town
Colours: All red
Change colours: Blue/navy/navy
Midweek matches: Mon/Wed
Programme: 28 pages, 50p
Editor: Chris Curtis (01785 605561)
Chairman: Graham Hollingshead
President: T Logan
Press Officer: Chris Curtis
Manager: Alan Somerville

# TIPTON TOWN

**Secretary:** John Cross, 1 Moreton Close, Tipton, West Midlands Dy4 0DG (0121 530 2524)
**Ground:** Tipton Sports Acadamy, Wednesbury Oak Road, Tipton, West Midlands
**Directions:** M6 Jct 9 through Wednesbury taking A461 until right at island signto Tipton. At next island - Ocker Hill - turn full right owards Bilston & Wolverhampton. After 1/3 mile turn left at traffic lights and ground is on left.
**Capacity:** 1000      **Seats:** 200 **Cover:** New covered stand and dressing rooms **Floodlights:**Yes
**Clubhouse:** Open with excellent food available week-ends. 12noon - 7.00 p.m.**Club Shop:** no
**Honours:** West Mid Regional League Dlv One Championship  and League Cup, Wednesbury Senior Charity Cup (5)
**Record Attendance:** Approx 1100 v Wolverhampton Wanderers in a pre season friendly  1.8.88

**FACT FILE**
Founded: 1948
Sponsors: Tipton & Cseley Building Society
Colours: Black & white/black/white
Change colours: All red
Midweek Matchday: Wednesday
Reserves League: Mid Comb Div 3
Programme Editor: Ruth Shinfield
**CLUB PERSONNEL**
Chairman: Harold Charles Hackett
Manager: Phil Marandola

# TIVIDALE

**Secretary:** Paul Boswell, 34 Princes Rd, Tividale, Oldbury, W Mids. B69 2LR Tel: 0121 532 4023
**Ground:** The Beeches, Packwood Rd, Tividale, Warley, W. Midlands B69 1UL tel: 01384 211743
**Directions:** Dudley Port Station to Burnt tree, left towards Birmingham, ground1 mile on right. Or, M5 jct 2, follow Dudley signs A4123, after approx 2 miles turn left into Regent Rd & left again into Elm Terraces, 1st left into Birch Crescent. Packwood Rd is second left - ground at end of cul-de-sac
Capacity: 3,500      Seats: 200         Cover: 1,000         Floodlights: Yes      Club Shop: No
Clubhouse: Mon-Fri 8-11pm, Sat 12-11pm, Sun 12-3 & 8-10.30. Cobs, rolls,sandwiches available
**HONOURS**      West Midlands Lg Div 1 72-73 (Prem. Div Cup 76-77, Div 1 Cup 72-73),
         Wednesbury Charity Cup 76-77
**PREVIOUS    Ground:** City Road   **Leagues:** Handsworth & District 56-60; inactive 60-62; West Mids Alliance 62-66      **RECORD Attendance:** 2,400 v Telford United, FA Cup

Founded: 1954      Nickname: Dales
Sponsors: Midland & North Security Consultants
Colours: Yellow/yellow/blue
Change colours: All Red
Midweek matchday: Tuesday
Programme: 40 pages, 60p   Editor: c/o Club
Newsline: 0891 66 42 52
Chairman: Donald Ashton
President: Lord Peter Archer
Press Officer: T Clark
Manager: Paul Madders
Asst Manager: Ron Blackwood
Physio: John Cotton

# WALSALL WOOD

**Secretary:** John Rousell, 19 Kinver Avenue, Short Heath, Willenhall, W. Midlands, WV12 4LS
Tel: 01902 637711

**Ground:** Oak Park, Lichfield Rd, Walsall Tel: 01543 361084 **Directions:** Off A461 Walsall-Lichfield Rd, 4 miles from Walsall town centre and 100yds south of junction with A4152 Aldridge-Brownhills. If travelling via M6/M5 exit motorway at jct 7 (Post House) and continue on A34 towards Walsall before joining A4148 which connects with the A461. 4 miles from Walsall (BR) station - regular buses pass ground      Capacity: 3,000 Seats: 400 Cover: 400 Floodlights: Yes Clubhouse: Evenings, matchdays and Sunday lunchtimes. Darts, pool. Hot snacks on matchdays
**HONOURS** Midland Comb. 51-52 (R-up 53-54 54-55 57-58 58-59 60-61, Lg Cup 54-55 60-61 (R-up 56-57 58-59)), B'ham Jnr Cup 76-77. Walsall Sportsco: Mids Comb. Lg Cup 79-80

**FACT FILE**

Founded: 1926
Colours: Red/black/red
Change colours: All blue
Chairman: Robert Thomas
Manager: Michael Speake

# WESTFIELDS

**Secretary:& Chief Executive:** Andrew Morris, 17 Fayre Oaks Green, Kings Acre, Hereford HR4 0QT(01432 264711)
**Ground:** Thorn Lighting, Holme Lacy Rd, Rotherwas, Hereford Tel: 01432 268131
**Directions:** Proceed 1.5 mile from Hereford on A49, left in Home Lacy Rd at Broadleys Inn.One mile to Thorn Lighting Rotherwas, ground on the right on Ind. Estate. 2 miles from Hereford (BR)
Capacity: 2,000    Seats: 100    Cover: 150    Floodlights: Yes   Club Shop: Yes
**Clubhouse:** 'Gamecock Inn' Holme Lacey Rd. Hereford (1/2 mile from ground)
**HONOURS** West Mids Lg Div 1 86-87, Div 2 R-up 83-84 (Div 2 Cup 79-80 83-84), Herefordshire Snr Cup 85-86 88-89 91-92 95-96 (Yth Cup 92-93 95-96), Kington Chall. Cup x5; Kington Invit. Cup x4; Presteigne Ottway Cup x4, Worcs Jnr Cup 79-80, Wye Guild Cup x2, Hereford Sunday Lg Prem 75-76 76-77 (Div 1 71-72, Div 2 76-77, Div 3 75-76, Prem Div Cup x2, Div 1 Cup x2, Div 3 Cup 72-73), Smart Brown Cup 67-68, Fair Play Cup 67-68. Dennis Hartland Mem Trophy 95-96, Robert Biggart Trophy 95-

Founded: 1966
Nickname: The Fields
Sponsors: Left Bank Village
Colours: Maroon & sky/sky/sky
Change colours: Sky/white/sky & maroon
Midweek matchday: Tuesday
Programme: Yes    Editor: Andy Morris
Chairman: Alan Dunsford
Vice Chairman: Neil Preece
President: Graham Preece
Manager: Gary Stevens
Coach: Dave Ellis    Physio: Dave Boulton

# WOLVERHAMPTON CASUALS

**Secretary:** Michael Green, 63 St Phillips Avenue, Pennfields Wolverhampton WV67ED
Tel: 01902 333677
**Ground:** Brinsford Lane, Coven Heath, Wolverhampton (01902 783214)
Directions: Onto M54 from M6 North, at Junc 2 turn right (A449 to Stafford).Ground half a mile, turn right into Brinsford Lane. Billbrooke (BR) 2 miles
Seats: 50Cover: 50Capacity: 2,000Floodlights: No
Clubhouse: Bar & snacks, open Tues/Wed/Thurs/Sat/Sun & alternate Mondays
**HONOURS** WMRL Div 1 94-95, R-up (3) 85-88, Div 1 Cup 85-86
**PREVIOUS** Name: Staffs Casuals (pre 81)
Ground: Aldersley Stadium

**FACT FILE**
Founded: 1896
Colours: White & green/green/green
Change colours: Gold/black/gold
Programme: 28pages 30p
Editor: G Smith
**CLUB PERSONNEL**
Chairman: Barry Austin
President: Clive Hammond
Manager: Gary Walters

# CAUSEWAY UNITED

**Secretary:** Frank Webb, 10 Moorfield Drive, halesowen, West Midlands B63 3TG Tel: 0121 550 5219 (H) 0121 550 9916 (B)
**Ground:** Halesowen Town FC, The Grove, Old hawne Lane, Halesowen. Tel: 0121 550 2179
**Directions:** M5, J3, take A456 towards Kidderminster to 1st island 7 turn rt. onto A459 (Dudley). Left at next island onto A458 (Stourbridge). At next island 3rd exit into Old hawne Lane. Ground approx. 400 yds on left. **Colours:** White/blue & red/white

# HEATH HAYES

**Secretary:** John Deans, 280 Hednesford rd., Heath Hayes, Cannock, Staffs. WS12 5DS Tel: 01543 278430 (H) 01543 378181 (B)
**Ground:** Rushall Olympic FC, Dales Lane, Rushall Tel: 01922 641021
**Directions:** From Walsall town centre, take A461 signed Lichfield. After approx. 2 miles turn right at lights into Daw End Lane (B4154). After approx. 1/4 mile & directly opposite Royal Oak PH, turn right into Dales Lane. Ground 50 yds on right.
**Colours:** Blue & white stripes/blue/blue

# LITTLE DRAYTON RANGERS

Secretary: Brian Garratt, 4 Quarry Bank Road, Market Drayton, Shropshire TF9 1DR Tel: 01630 654618 (H)
Ground: Greenfield Sports Club, Greenfield lane, Market Drayton. Tel: 01630 655088
Directions: A41 to Tern Hill island, turn right for Newcastle under Lyme. Over 1st island, and turn right at next island, by Gingerbread PH, towards town centre. After 200 yds turn right, (before going over bridge) into Greenfields Lane. Ground is 150 yds down lane on right.
Colours: Royal blue with pale blue stripes/royal/royal

# STAR

**Secretary:** David Rymer, 6 Callaughton, Much Wenlock, Shropshire TF13 6PT Tel: 01952 727542 (H) 01746 713000 (B)
**Ground:** Lawson Mardon Star, Stourbridge Road, Bridgnorth.
**Colours:** Blue/black/black

# EVERARDS BREWERY
# LEICESTERSHIRE SENIOR FOOTBALL LEAGUE
### Founded 1896

**President:** John M Elsom F.C.A.    **Chairman:** David Jamieson

**Hon Secretary:** Robert J Holmes, 8 Huntsman Close, Markfield, Leics LE67 9XE

Tel: 01530 243093

The League could not have asked for a better climax to the season, with the top two Premier Division teams on level points and everything hanging on the final kick. Oadby won the championship; both teams won, but Birstall United, who were more convincing on the day, had to settle for the runner up trophy through an inferior goal difference.

For a long time it looked as though Holwell Sports would run Oadby close, especially when they defeated the eventual champions in mid-April, but they could not maintain their form and fell away to end fourth just holding off a resurgent St Andrews. Ellistown lifted themselves off the bottom of the table in their last match to leave Friar Lane OB on the bottom rung of the ladder.

Division One was not quite so close with Thurmaston Town, in their first season in the league, hitting the top very early and there they stayed right through the season ending their programme unbeaten and dropping only eight points. After a slow start last year's champions Thurnby Rangers got their act together in their first season back to finish fourth. Harborough Town and North Kilworth battled hard to avoid the wooden spoon but two late wins from North Kilworth kept them off the bottom. Harborough hang on to their league status though with the District League unable to provide a team with the appropriate facilities.

Thurmaston Town became the team of the year by defeating Birstall United, by kicks from the penalty mark in the Beacon Bitter Cup Final at Anstey Nomads.

Birstall though had already been crowned County FA Senior Cup champions, defeating Oadby at Holmes Park, the County FA Headquarters, whilst Oadby reached the final of the Westerby Cup, losing to Leicester City at Filbert Street. Although no side reached the after-Christmas stage of the Vase there were many notable performances against teams of equal or higher status and overall teams won more matches than were lost.

Off the field matters progressed on a number of fronts. Oadby Town became the first club to be promoted to the Midland Football Alliance since the League joined the National League system three years ago. Also the League remains in discussion with the Football Association and the MFA, together with the Midland Combination and West Midlands League to consider non-League football in the Midlands.

The League introduced its own website for the season and this has proved very popular and beneficial in enhancing the League's profile and providing an extra outlet for our sponsors. This will also operate for next season.

The League also saw referee Andy Parson promoted to the Southern League List for next season and seven officials, who have reached the assistant referee list, on the two Contributory Leagues that we serve.

Finally, the League is pleased to announce that they have firmed up a further two-year deal to the end of 2000-01 season with their sponsor, Everards Brewery.

## FINAL LEAGUE TABLES 1998-99

### PREMIER DIVISION

| | P | W | D | L | F | A | PT | GD |
|---|---|---|---|---|---|---|---|---|
| Oadby Town | 34 | 25 | 4 | 5 | 90 | 28 | 79 | 62 |
| Birstall Utd | 34 | 24 | 7 | 3 | 77 | 27 | 79 | 50 |
| Holwell Sports | 34 | 23 | 5 | 6 | 100 | 45 | 74 | 55 |
| Highfield Rgs | 34 | 21 | 3 | 10 | 60 | 39 | 66 | 21 |
| St Andrews | 34 | 18 | 6 | 10 | 87 | 51 | 60 | 36 |
| Quorn | 34 | 14 | 9 | 11 | 79 | 70 | 51 | 9 |
| Kirby Muxloe | 34 | 14 | 8 | 12 | 61 | 54 | 50 | 7 |
| Anstey Nomads | 34 | 14 | 6 | 14 | 57 | 54 | 48 | 3 |
| Thringstone Utd | 34 | 11 | 10 | 13 | 56 | 63 | 43 | -7 |
| Barrow Town | 34 | 12 | 6 | 16 | 48 | 60 | 42 | -12 |
| Cottesmore Ams | 34 | 13 | 3 | 18 | 50 | 72 | 42 | -22 |
| Downes Sports | 34 | 11 | 8 | 15 | 49 | 54 | 41 | -5 |
| Coalville Town | 34 | 10 | 9 | 15 | 53 | 63 | 39 | -10 |
| Ibstock Welfare | 34 | 8 | 11 | 15 | 54 | 60 | 35 | -6 |
| Lutterworth Town | 34 | 8 | 11 | 15 | 44 | 59 | 35 | -15 |
| Aylestone Park OB | 34 | 8 | 6 | 20 | 45 | 90 | 30 | -45 |
| Ellistown | 34 | 3 | 11 | 20 | 24 | 93 | 20 | -69 |
| Friar Lane OB | 34 | 4 | 7 | 23 | 33 | 85 | 19 | -52 |

### DIVISION ONE

| | P | W | D | L | F | A | PT | GD |
|---|---|---|---|---|---|---|---|---|
| Thurmaston Town | 34 | 30 | 4 | 0 | 113 | 21 | 94 | 92 |
| Thurnby Rangers | 34 | 25 | 3 | 6 | 114 | 39 | 78 | 75 |
| Blaby & Whetstone | 34 | 21 | 8 | 5 | 72 | 33 | 71 | 39 |
| Leics YMCA | 34 | 20 | 5 | 9 | 98 | 48 | 65 | 50 |
| Iluncote S&S | 34 | 17 | 7 | 10 | 76 | 53 | 58 | 23 |
| Stoney Stanton | 34 | 17 | 6 | 11 | 66 | 50 | 57 | 16 |
| Fosse Imps | 34 | 16 | 6 | 12 | 83 | 66 | 54 | 17 |
| Anstey Town | 34 | 14 | 5 | 15 | 59 | 58 | 47 | 1 |
| Leics Constab | 34 | 14 | 5 | 15 | 60 | 61 | 47 | -1 |
| Narborough | 34 | 13 | 7 | 14 | 65 | 74 | 46 | -9 |
| Sileby Town | 34 | 13 | 6 | 15 | 58 | 58 | 45 | 0 |
| Bardon Hill | 34 | 13 | 5 | 16 | 69 | 61 | 44 | 8 |
| Loughborough Dyn | 34 | 12 | 6 | 16 | 68 | 75 | 42 | -7 |
| Earl Shilton Alb | 34 | 11 | 5 | 18 | 53 | 76 | 38 | -23 |
| Asfordby Ams | 34 | 8 | 12 | 14 | 63 | 76 | 36 | -13 |
| Saffron Dynamo | 34 | 8 | 5 | 21 | 53 | 76 | 29 | -23 |
| North Kilworth | 34 | 3 | 3 | 28 | 32 | 130 | 12 | -98 |
| Harborough Town | 34 | 1 | 2 | 31 | 21 | 168 | 5 | -147 |

# PREMIER DIVISION RESULTS CHART 1998-99

| | | 1 | 2 | 3 | 4 | 5 | 6 | 7 | 8 | 9 | 10 | 11 | 12 | 13 | 14 | 15 | 16 | 17 | 18 |
|---|---|---|---|---|---|---|---|---|---|---|---|---|---|---|---|---|---|---|---|
| 1 | Anstey Nomads | X | 0-1 | 1-2 | 3-3 | 1-1 | 3-0 | 2-4 | 1-1 | 1-0 | 2-0 | 1-2 | 2-0 | 3-1 | 0-2 | 0-4 | 4-3 | 3-1 | 4-1 |
| 2 | Aylestone | 1-3 | X | 2-0 | 2-2 | 1-0 | 2-4 | 0-1 | 5-1 | 1-2 | 0-2 | 2-5 | 0-2 | 2-2 | 1-1 | 0-6 | 2-1 | 0-7 | 0-0 |
| 3 | Barrow | 1-2 | 3-0 | X | 0-1 | 1-3 | 3-2 | 0-3 | 3-0 | 1-1 | 1-0 | 0-2 | 1-1 | 1-1 | 2-0 | 3-1 | 1-1 | 3-2 | 1-2 |
| 4 | Birstall | 1-0 | 4-1 | 3-0 | X | 1-1 | 3-1 | 2-0 | 5-0 | 2-0 | 3-0 | 1-1 | 4-1 | 0-0 | 5-2 | 1-0 | 1-0 | 3-1 | 2-0 |
| 5 | Coalville | 2-1 | 7-3 | 4-1 | 0-4 | X | 1-2 | 4-3 | 2-1 | 2-2 | 1-2 | 1-1 | 1-1 | 2-3 | 1-0 | 0-2 | 3-3 | 2-1 | 1-2 |
| 6 | Cottesmore | 1-5 | 2-1 | 2-0 | 0-2 | 2-0 | X | 0-2 | 3-1 | 4-0 | 0-1 | 0-2 | 2-0 | 1-3 | 2-2 | 0-2 | 0-2 | 0-5 | 0-3 |
| 7 | Downs | 1-2 | 2-1 | 1-3 | 3-0 | 3-2 | 1-2 | X | 0-0 | 1-1 | 0-3 | 3-3 | 1-0 | 1-0 | 1-2 | 1-4 | 1-2 | 0-1 | 4-4 |
| 8 | Ellistown | 0-0 | 2-4 | 0-4 | 0-5 | 3-1 | 1-4 | 1-1 | X | 2-0 | 0-7 | 0-9 | 0-0 | 1-1 | 1-1 | 0-2 | 1-3 | 2-4 | 0-4 |
| 9 | Friar Lane OB | 0-1 | 1-1 | 3-0 | 0-5 | 1-2 | 1-4 | 0-3 | 0-0 | X | 2-3 | 0-3 | 3-2 | 1-4 | 1-3 | 0-3 | 3-4 | 0-1 | 1-1 |
| 10 | Highfield | 3-2 | 1-2 | 2-0 | 1-1 | 2-1 | 1-0 | 2-1 | 1-1 | 1-0 | X | 2-1 | 3-1 | 3-1 | 2-1 | 1-1 | 0-1 | 1-4 | 2-0 |
| 11 | Holwell | 2-0 | 4-1 | 3-0 | 4-1 | 2-0 | 8-1 | 1-2 | 6-1 | 3-2 | 2-1 | X | 3-0 | 8-1 | 3-1 | 3-0 | 4-2 | 4-2 | 1-0 |
| 12 | Ibstock | 2-4 | 6-2 | 3-2 | 1-2 | 1-1 | 1-2 | 4-1 | 1-1 | 6-0 | 1-4 | 0-1 | X | 3-2 | 0-0 | 2-2 | 2-5 | 2-2 | 3-0 |
| 13 | Kirby | 2-0 | 7-1 | 1-1 | 0-2 | 1-0 | 1-2 | 3-2 | 2-0 | 4-1 | 0-2 | 1-3 | 1-1 | X | 5-1 | 3-1 | 2-1 | 1-1 | 1-1 |
| 14 | Lutterworth | 1-1 | 1-3 | 2-3 | 0-3 | 2-0 | 3-3 | 0-0 | 1-1 | 1-2 | 3-1 | 1-1 | 1-3 | 0-2 | X | 0-4 | 1-1 | 2-0 | 2-2 |
| 15 | Oadby | 2-1 | 4-0 | 3-1 | 3-1 | 5-0 | 1-0 | 2-1 | 5-0 | 3-1 | 2-0 | 3-0 | 1-0 | 2-0 | 1-2 | X | 6-1 | 2-1 | 5-0 |
| 16 | Quorn | 5-2 | 3-3 | 3-0 | 1-1 | 3-4 | 3-3 | 1-1 | 1-2 | 5-2 | 0-2 | 4-5 | 1-1 | 2-1 | 2-1 | 1-4 | X | 2-2 | 4-2 |
| 17 | St Andrews | 2-0 | 2-0 | 4-4 | 0-1 | 1-1 | 5-0 | 2-0 | 5-0 | 7-1 | 1-0 | 5-1 | 3-1 | 3-2 | 2-1 | 3-3 | 2-3 | X | 0-3 |
| 18 | Thringstone | 2-2 | 2-0 | 1-2 | 1-2 | 1-0 | 3-1 | 0-0 | 2-0 | 1-1 | 3-4 | 4-2 | 2-2 | 1-2 | 0-3 | 1-1 | 1-5 | 6-5 | X |

# SENIOR LEAGUE AND SPORTSWORLD CUP LEADING SCORERS 1998-99

## PREMIER DIVISION

| | | |
|---|---|---|
| Phil Marsden | St Andrews | 24 |
| Neal | Cottesmore | 24 |
| Seal | Ellistown | 24 |
| Steve White | Birstall | 22 |
| J Connolly | Birstall | 21 |
| Hunter | Oadby | 20 |
| P Clarke | Downes | 19 |
| Hennigan | Quorn | 18 |
| Keast | Holwell | 18 |
| Warner | St Andrews | 18 |
| Culpin | Thringstone | 17 |

## DIVISION ONE

| | | |
|---|---|---|
| S Kerr | Thurmaston | 39 |
| McManus | Thurnby | 29 |
| A Hollis | Leics. YMCA | 28 |
| Singer | Narborough | 27 |
| S Smith | Fosse Imps | 21 |
| L Nelson | Thurnby | 20 |
| C Warrilow | Thurmaston | 20 |
| Gurney | Blaby & Whetstone | 19 |
| K Glyn-Smith | Leics. YMCA | 18 |
| Coore | Fosse Imps | 17 |
| C McAdam | Anstey Town | 17 |
| Tim Phillips | Loughborough | 17 |

## ANSTEY NOMADS
Colours: Red/white/white
Secretary: Mervyn Miles,66 CharlesDrive, Anstey,Leics.LE7 7BG
Tel No: 0116 236 2909
Ground: Llimah International Park, Cropston Road, Anstey (0116 236 4868)

## AYLESTONE PARK
Colours: Red / black /black
Secretary: Pete Burrows, 27 Cartwight Drive, Oadby, Leicester (0116 2712682)
Ground: Dorset Avenue, Fairfield Estate, Wigston, Leics (0116 277 5307) 40 Seats and Cover for 100. Two tier clubhouse.
Honours: Senior League Runners-up 94-95

## BARROW TOWN
Colours: Red & black/black/red
Secretary: Alan Dawkins, 72 Beaumont Road, Barrow-on-Soar, Loughborough, LeicsLE12 8PJ (01509 413288)
Ground: Riverside Park, Meynell Road, Quorn, Leics (01509 620650) Access via Quorn Lodge Drive & Barrow road. Cover: 50 Seats : No Clubhouse :Yes
Honours: Leics Sen Lg. 92-93 R-up 94-95.Loughborough Charity Cup 68-69,96-97,98-99

## BIRSTALL UNITED
Colours: White/navy/navy
Secretary: Bob Garrard, 58 Halstead Rd, Mountsorrel, Leicester LE12 7HF (0116237 6886)
Ground: Meadow Lane, Birstall (0116 267 1230)

## COALVILLE TOWN
Colours: Black&White/black/black
Secretary: Robert Brooks, 17 Ashland Drive, Coalville, Leics LE67 3NH (01530833269)
Ground: Owen Street Sports Ground, Owen Street, Coalville (01530 833365)

## COTTESMORE AMATEURS
Colours: Green/black/green
Secretary: K Nimmons, 17 Redwing Close, Oakham, Rutland LE15 6DA (01572724582)
Ground: Rogues Park, Main Street, Cottesmore, Rutland (01572 813486) Directions: Rear of Sun Inn. Seating : Yes Cover: Yes Clubhouse : Yes
Honours: Leics. Senior League Cup Winners 1997.

## DOWNES SPORTS
Colours: Tangerine/black/tangerine
Secretary: A. Jacques, 17 Merton Close, Broughton, Astley Leicester Le9 6QP Tel No: 01455 28402 (H) 01455 282028 (W)
Ground: Leicester Rd,Hinckley (01455 615062)
Directions: Off northern perimeter road.

## FRIAR LANE OLD BOYS
Colours: Black & white stripes/black/black
Secretary: Kevin Brooks, 299 Milligan Rd, Leicester LE4 2RJ (0116 224 3854)
Ground: Knighton Lane East, Leicester (0116 283 3629)

## HIGHFIELD RANGERS
Colours: Yellow/blackyellow
Secretary: Maurice Christian, 18 Blanklyn Avenue, Leicester LE5 5FA (0116 2734002)
Ground: 443 Gleneagles Ave., Rushey Mead, Leicester
Tel: 0116 266 0009

## HOLWELL SPORTS
Colours: Green & gold/green/green
Secretary: Mrs Anne Marriott, 24 Church Lane, Croxton Kerrial, Grantham, LincsNG32 1PZ (01476 870658)
Ground: Welby Road, Asfordby Hill, Melton Mowbray, Leics (01664 812663)

## IBSTOCK WELFARE
Colours: Red/black/red
Secretary: R A Wilkinson, 6 Valley Rd, Ibstock, Leicester LE67 6NY (01530 450243) Ground: The Welfare, Leicester Road, Ibstock (01530 260656) Seating : 50 Cover 150 Clubhouse : Yes Honours: Leics Sen Cup Winners 93-94 R-Up 97-98. Leics Sen Lg Div 1 R-Up 90-91. Coalville Ch Cup Winners (3) R-up (4),Loughboro ChCup (4) R-up(2)

## KIRBY MUXLOE S.C.
Colours: Blue/black/black
Secretary: Philip Moloney, 16 Church Lane, Ratby, Leics LE6 0JE (0116 239 2916)
Ground: Ratby Lane, Kirby Muxloe (0116 239 3201)

## LOUGHBOROUGH DYNAMO
Colours: Gold/black/gold
Secretary: Max Hutchinson, 3 Wythburn Close, Loughborough, Leics LE11 3SZ(01509 266092)
Ground: Nanpanton Sport Ground, Loughborough (01509 612144)

## LUTTERWORTH TOWN
Colours: White & blue/blue/blue.
Secretary:Martha Matthews, Silver Leas, Birrewell,Lutterworth,Leics.
Tel No: 01455 552613
Ground: Hall Lane, Bitteswell, Lutterworth, Leics (01455 554046)

## QUORN
Colours: Red/white/red
Secretary: Margaret Berry, 214 BarrowRd.Sileby,Leics.LE12 7LR
Tel: 01509 813259
Ground: Farley Way, Quorn, Leics (01509 620232)

## St ANDREWS SOCIAL CLUB
Colours: Black & white/black/black
Secretary: L Botting, 2 Neston Road, Saffron Lane, Leicester LE2 6RD(0116 224 3961)
Ground: Canal Street, off Aylestone Rd ( next to Big City Tyres)Old Aylestone,Leicester.(01162839298)
Honours: Leics Sen Lg. Premier Champions: 89-90,93-94,95-96

## THRINGSTONE MINERS WELFARE
Colours: Blue , white, red.
Secretary: Peter Hordley,The Willows,9 Main Street, Thringstone,Leics.LE67 8ND
Ground: Homestead Road, Thringstone (01530 223367)

## THURMASTON TOWN
Colours: Black & white stripes, black,black.
Secretary: Kevin Sadler, 81 Woodgreen Road, Leicester LE4 9UD (0116 246 0093)
Ground: Elizabeth Park, Checklands Road, Thurmaston.
Tel No: 0116 260 2519
Honours: Dist. Lg Champs 97-99, Page & Moy Junior Cup Winners 97-98 Leics Div One Champions & Beacon Bitter Cup Winners 98-99

## ANSTEY TOWN
Colours: All blue
Secretary:Colin Hopewell.130 Andrew Road, Anstey, Leicester LE77BB
Tel No:0777 1773418
Ground: Leicester Road, Thurcaston (0116 236 8231)

## ASFORDBY AMATEURS
Colours: All Maroon
Secretary: Stephen Hazeldine,19 Mildmay Close,Melton Mowbray,LeicsLE13 1AH Tel NO:01664 857362
Ground: Hoby Road Sports Ground, Asfordby, Melton Mowbray (01664 434545)

## BARDON HILL
Colours: Red/blue/blue
Secretary: Adrian Bishop, 138 Bradgate Drive, Coalville, Leics LE67 4HG (01530815560)
Ground: Bardon Close, Coalville, Leicester (01530 815569)

## BLABY & WHETSTONE ATHLETIC
Colours: Navy/& white/navy/navy
Secretary: Mrs S C Morris, 10 Winchester Road, Blaby, Leics LE8 3HJ (0116 2773208)
Ground: Blaby & Whetstone Boys Club, Warwick Road, Whetstone (0116 286 4852)

## EARL SHILTON ALBION
Colours: Green & gold/green/green
Secretary: Graham Redshaw,3 Lucas Way,Earl Shilton,Leics.LE9 7GL
Tel No: 01455 847822
Ground: Stoneycroft Park, New Street, Earl Shilton, Leics (01455 844277)

## FOSSE IMPS
Colours: All Red
Secretary: Ivan V Colbourne, 55 Harrowgate Drive, Birstall, Leics LE4 3GQ (0116267 1424)
Ground: Co-op Ground, Birstall Rd, Leicester (0116 267 4059)

## HARBOROUGH TOWN
Colours: Black& white/black/white.
Secretary:JohnChambers,62 Oaklands Drive, Whetstone, Northampton NN3 3JL . Tel No: 01604 412294
Ground:SymingtonsSportsGround
St Mary's Road, Market Har
boroughn,Leics ( Half a mile from town centre and railway styation)

## HUNCOTE SPORTS & SOCIAL
Colours: Yellow & blue/blue/yellow
Secretary: D Russell, 72 Sycamore Way, Littlethorpe, Leics LE9 5HU (0116 2841952)
Ground: Enderby Road, Thurlaston, Leics (01455 888430). Seating: No Cover: No Clubhouse: Yes Directions: 3 miles from exit 21 on M1. Via Enderby on B582. Thurston Lane onto Endersby Road.

## LEICESTER YMCA
Colours: Red & black/black/black
Secretary: Colin Chappell, 132 South Knighton Rd, Leicester, LE2 3LQ (0116 270 27821)
Ground: YMCA Sports Ground, Belvoir Drive, Leicester(0116 244 0740)Directions: M1 Jct21 (M69) onto A563, Soarvalley Way, Aylestone Rd. Left at lights, to city. Belvoir Drive 2nd Right after next lights.Capacity:1,500 Cover 100 Clubhouse: Yes

## LEICESTERSHIRE CONSTABULARY
Colours: Blue&gold/blue/blue.
Secretary: Mick Allard, 8 Evelyn Rd., Braunstone, Leicester LE3 3BA
Tel No: 0116 289 0027
Ground: Police HQ, St Johns, Enderby (0116 248 2198)

## NARBOROUGH & LITTLETHORPE
Colours: Blue/blue/blue&white
Secretary: Mick Dodds, 24 Princess Street, Narborough, Leics LE9 5DH (0116 2867042)
Ground: Ray Hurd Pavilion, Leicester Road, Narborough (Near M1 bridge) (0116275 1855)

## NORTH KILWORTH
Colours: Red/black/red
Secretary: Matthew Bailey, 1Holly Drive,Lutterworth,Leics.LE17 4RG
Tel No: 01455556188
Ground: Rugby Road, North Kilworth, Lutterworth, Leics (01858 880890)

## SAFFRON DYNAMO
Colours: Red/black/black
Secretary: Bob King, 14 Bramley Close, Broughton Astley, Leicester LE9 6QU(01455 284270)
Ground: Cambridge Road, Whetstone, (0116 284 9695) Near County on road from Whetstone to Cosby..
Honours : Many as a Sunday club in last 25 years.

## SILEBY TOWN
Colours: Red & white/black/black
Secretary: Ann Bettles, 6 Jubilee Avenue, Sileby, Leics LE12 7TH (01509 813864)
Ground: Memorial Park, Seagrave Road, Sileby, Leics (01509 816104)

## STONEY STANTON
Colours: Royal Blue/white/royal blue
Secretary:Nigel Bradbury,144 Sketchley ,Burbage,Leics(01455 615305)
Ground: Highfields Farm, Huncote Road, Stoney Stanton,Leics.
Directions: M69 Jct 2 towards Sapcote.1st left toStoney Stanton.Right at mini roundabout and left into Long Street.Follow road out of village Highfield Farm on left.( Clubhouse open but no cover or seats)
Honours: Leics Sen Lg Div 1 R-Up 98

## THURNBY RANGERS
Colours:  Green & white/green/green
Secretary: Pat Darby,69 Kinross Avenue,Thurnby,Lodge Estate, Leics
Tel No: 0116 241 4790
Ground: Dakyn Road, Thurnby Lodge, Leics

# WEST MIDLANDS REGION
# LEAGUE TABLES

## BIRMINGHAM WORKS LEAGUE

| | | | | | | | |
|---|---|---|---|---|---|---|---|
| Birchfield Oaklands | 18 | 16 | 2 | 0 | 66 | 17 | 34 |
| Ansells Star | 18 | 10 | 4 | 4 | 58 | 43 | 24 |
| Westhill Wanderers | 18 | 6 | 9 | 3 | 33 | 21 | 21 |
| Lyndon United | 18 | 8 | 5 | 5 | 39 | 35 | 21 |
| GEC Alsthom | 18 | 6 | 5 | 7 | 41 | 35 | 17 |
| Douglas Kane | 18 | 5 | 6 | 7 | 39 | 39 | 16 |
| Shere Punjab | 18 | 4 | 6 | 8 | 27 | 36 | 14 |
| Olton Ravens | 18 | 2 | 8 | 8 | 28 | 45 | 12 |
| Rubber Plas | 18 | 5 | 1 | 12 | 27 | 35 | 11 |
| Birmingham Eagles | 18 | 3 | 4 | 11 | 29 | 81 | 10 |

## BIRMINGHAM & DISTRICT AFA
## PREMIER DIVISION

| | | | | | | | |
|---|---|---|---|---|---|---|---|
| Smethwick Hall OB | 24 | 12 | 7 | 5 | 36 | 25 | 43 |
| Old Wulfrunians | 24 | 12 | 6 | 6 | 39 | 26 | 42 |
| Britannia Old Boys | 24 | 12 | 5 | 7 | 39 | 35 | 41 |
| Kynoch IMI | 24 | 10 | 7 | 7 | 36 | 32 | 37 |
| Sutton United (Birm.) | 24 | 9 | 8 | 7 | 36 | 26 | 35 |
| Silhill | 24 | 10 | 4 | 10 | 40 | 33 | 34 |
| Wake Green Amateurs | 24 | 10 | 4 | 10 | 56 | 52 | 34 |
| Walsall Phoenix | 24 | 9 | 4 | 11 | 33 | 35 | 31 |
| Handsworth GSOB | 24 | 8 | 6 | 10 | 31 | 40 | 30 |
| Transaction | 24 | 8 | 5 | 11 | 29 | 42 | 29 |
| Barnt Green Old Boys | 24 | 7 | 7 | 10 | 31 | 37 | 28 |
| Village | 24 | 6 | 6 | 12 | 34 | 44 | 24 |
| New Fullbrook | 24 | 6 | 5 | 13 | 28 | 41 | 23 |

## KIDDERMINSTER & DISTRICT LEAGUE
## PREMIER DIVISION

| | | | | | | | |
|---|---|---|---|---|---|---|---|
| Ounsdale | 22 | 17 | 2 | 3 | 57 | 14 | 53 |
| Brinton Chainwire | 22 | 17 | 0 | 5 | 73 | 23 | 51 |
| Ludlow Town Colts | 22 | 14 | 1 | 7 | 46 | 37 | 43 |
| Clee Hill United | 22 | 14 | 1 | 7 | 40 | 41 | 43 |
| Chaddesley Corbett | 22 | 13 | 1 | 8 | 62 | 41 | 40 |
| Kinver | 22 | 9 | 5 | 8 | 45 | 37 | 32 |
| Bewdley Town | 22 | 8 | 5 | 9 | 42 | 41 | 29 |
| Turks Head | 22 | 6 | 5 | 11 | 47 | 51 | 23 |
| Brindley Arms United | 22 | 6 | 3 | 13 | 35 | 61 | 21 |
| Chaddesley Satchmos | 22 | 4 | 4 | 14 | 43 | 64 | 16 |
| Parkdale Rovers | 22 | 5 | 1 | 16 | 24 | 79 | 16 |
| Woofferton | 22 | 3 | 4 | 15 | 23 | 50 | 13 |

Ashwood United - withdrawn

## COVENTRY & DISTRICT LEAGUE
## PREMIER DIVISION

| | | | | | | | |
|---|---|---|---|---|---|---|---|
| Hen Lane Social | 16 | 10 | 4 | 2 | 49 | 22 | 34 |
| Bilton Social | 16 | 9 | 5 | 2 | 45 | 24 | 32 |
| Attleborough Village | 16 | 9 | 2 | 5 | 46 | 31 | 29 |
| Newman Athletic | 16 | 8 | 2 | 6 | 45 | 38 | 26 |
| Hilton | 16 | 8 | 1 | 7 | 43 | 44 | 25 |
| Black Horse Sports | 16 | 7 | 3 | 6 | 41 | 38 | 24 |
| Newdigate Sports | 16 | 6 | 0 | 10 | 47 | 51 | 18 |
| Coventry Dyers | 16 | 2 | 3 | 11 | 40 | 70 | 9 |
| Barlestone | 16 | 2 | 2 | 12 | 23 | 61 | 8 |

## WOLVERHAMPTON COMBINATION
## PREMIER DIVISION

| | | | | | | | |
|---|---|---|---|---|---|---|---|
| IMI Marston | 24 | 19 | 4 | 1 | 69 | 25 | 61 |
| Pilot Dynamo | 24 | 19 | 2 | 3 | 88 | 32 | 59 |
| C E Marshall | 24 | 16 | 3 | 5 | 71 | 44 | 51 |
| Brocton Res. | 24 | 11 | 4 | 9 | 60 | 54 | 37 |
| Great Wyrley Res. | 24 | 9 | 7 | 8 | 41 | 43 | 34 |
| Heath Hayes Res. | 24 | 8 | 5 | 11 | 41 | 58 | 29 |
| Dowty Sports | 24 | 7 | 6 | 11 | 65 | 65 | 27 |
| Whitmore Old Boys | 24 | 8 | 3 | 13 | 42 | 68 | 27 |
| HPC -9 | 24 | 10 | 3 | 11 | 62 | 43 | 24 |
| Red Lion | 24 | 6 | 4 | 14 | 45 | 63 | 22 |
| Chubb Sports | 24 | 6 | 3 | 15 | 38 | 68 | 21 |
| Union Locks | 24 | 4 | 6 | 13 | 46 | 64 | 18 |
| Penkridge Town | 24 | 5 | 3 | 16 | 43 | 65 | 18 |

*Gary Abbott, Aldershot's leading goal scorer, vs Kidderminster*
*Photo: Ian Morsman*

# ISTHMIAN LEAGUE

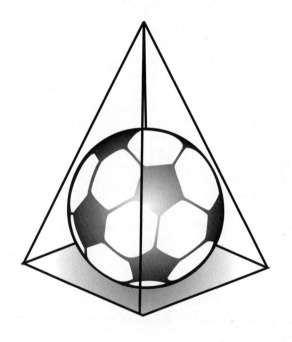

# PYRAMID SECTION

# *Ryman*
# ISTHMIAN LEAGUE

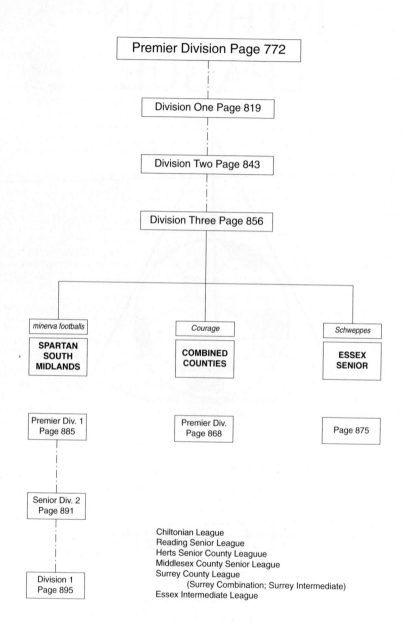

Premier Division Page 772

Division One Page 819

Division Two Page 843

Division Three Page 856

*minerva footballs*

**SPARTAN SOUTH MIDLANDS**

*Courage*

**COMBINED COUNTIES**

*Schweppes*

**ESSEX SENIOR**

Premier Div. 1
Page 885

Premier Div.
Page 868

Page 875

Senior Div. 2
Page 891

Chiltonian League
Reading Senior League
Herts Senior County Leaguue
Middlesex County Senior League
Surrey County League
    (Surrey Combination; Surrey Intermediate)
Essex Intermediate League

Division 1
Page 895

# RYMAN LEAGUE

**Chairman:** A C F Turvey, MCIM, 18 Apple Way, Old Basing, Basingstoke, Hants RG24 7HA
Tel: 01256 461789 (H)   0836 251368 (M)
**Secretary & Treasurer:** N R Robinson FCRArb, 226 Rye Lane, Peckham, London SE15 4NL
Tel: 0181 409 1978 (H)   0171 639 5726 (B)   Fax: 0181 409 1979 (H)   0171 277 6061 (B)
E-mail: nickrob@clara.net

Of the three feeding leagues beneath the Conference it appears that the Ryman League produces most individual high goalscorers and, of course, there are many more clubs, who fancy their chances of promotion and football in the higher sphere.

Last season Aldershot and Aylesbury United held top spot, while hovering in the next three or four places were, at different times, Purfleet, St Albans City, Billericay Town, Enfield and Dagenham & Redbridge. So Sutton United's work was certainly cut out and there were at least fourteen 'six pointers' as so many clubs challenged for that special promotion place.

In the AXA sponsored F.A. Cup, Basingstoke Town now seem to be regulars in the First Round and last season they were beaten at home by Bournemouth. Boreham Wood enjoyed a local 'derby' with Luton Town and Dulwich Hamlet, amidst much excitement, reached the First Round for the first time in 50 years, but lost at home to Southport. Enfield were on First Round duty as usual and did well to take York City to a replay, and neighbours Hendon equalled this feat with two games against Notts County. Graham Roberts was back in the limelight again as he took his club, Slough Town, into battle at Macclesfield and, despite their fluctuating season, the Rebels only went out after a replay and penalties.

Most of these Ryman 'big guns' were accustomed to Cup excitement, but the new structure of the competition may have given a fairer chance to the real minnows and Ryman Division Three clubs Camberley Town and Ford United, who were in their first season with the Isthmians, visited Brentford and Preston North End respectively. What a thrill for all involved and what a credit to the league's strength in depth.

With the excitement of the Cup over it was on with the Umbro Trophy and Carlsberg Vase and once again the League did itself proud by producing semi-finalist in both competitions. St Albans so nearly reached Wembley, holding a two goal lead as half-time edged closer in their second semi-final at Forest Green, and all looked well. But Rovers pulled one back before the break and the home crowd roared them home in a thrilling tie, which was a credit to two of the competition's less fashionable clubs. In their Vase semi-final, Thame United were unlucky to draw Bedlington Terriers who were at their peak and a 0-5 first leg result killed the tie.

In the Premier relegation battle a major change round of personnel at Hampton seemed to have saved the day, but senior members Bishop's Stortford and Bromley have suffered the dreaded drop and Carshalton Athletic were saved by Wealdstone's ineligibility to be promoted.

Three powerful and ambitious clubs, Bedford Town as champions, Harlow Town and Thame United won promotion to Division One and Ford United completed a very satisfying season by finishing Champions of Division Three, going up with Cheshunt and Wingate & Finchley.

In the League Cups, Aldershot Town beat Boreham Wood 2-1 to win the senior competition, Leighton Town beat Windsor & Eton for the Vandanel Trophy and Hendon beat Worthing to claim the Puma Cup.

The representative side was managed by Graham Roberts and held a strong FA XI to a 1-1 draw and a good victory was registered against the Combined Services. The individual and team standards seem as high as ever. So Farnborough Town and Great Wakering Rovers are welcomed to the League and, judging by the busy summer transfer market, half the Premier clubs have ambitions to join the Conference and the majority of smaller clubs are also aiming high.

This is just as it should be, so stand by for a very competitive season in all four divisions.

TW

---

## RYMAN LEAGUE NEWSLINE
# 09066 555 777
Calls cost 60p per minute

# PREMIER DIVISION FINAL LEAGUE TABLE 1998-99

| | | P | HOME | | | | | AWAY | | | | | Pts | LEADING SCORERS BY CLUB |
|---|---|---|---|---|---|---|---|---|---|---|---|---|---|---|
| | | | W | D | L | F | A | W | D | L | F | A | | *(these include all goals as reported in the league bulletin)* |
| 1 | Sutton United | 42 | 14 | 3 | 4 | 48 | 19 | 13 | 4 | 4 | 41 | 20 | 88 | M Watson 29, Akrour 18, Riley 9 |
| 2 | Aylesbury United | 42 | 12 | 3 | 6 | 30 | 18 | 11 | 5 | 5 | 37 | 20 | 77 | Crawshaw 28, Browne 9 King 8 |
| 3 | Dagenham & Redbrige | 42 | 10 | 8 | 3 | 40 | 15 | 10 | 5 | 6 | 31 | 29 | 73 | Cobb 27, Shipp 24, Janney 9 |
| 4 | Purfleet | 42 | 15 | 2 | 4 | 45 | 19 | 7 | 5 | 9 | 26 | 33 | 73 | Georgiou 25, Carthy 10, Coombs 8 |
| 5 | Enfield | 42 | 13 | 4 | 4 | 43 | 22 | 8 | 5 | 8 | 30 | 27 | 72 | Dunwell 23, Darlington 19, Bentley 11 |
| 6 | St Albans City | 42 | 10 | 8 | 3 | 43 | 28 | 7 | 9 | 5 | 28 | 24 | 68 | Clark 40, Howarth 12, Jones 10 |
| 7 | Aldershot Town | 42 | 11 | 4 | 6 | 53 | 21 | 5 | 10 | 6 | 30 | 27 | 62 | Abbott 36, Nartey 22, Fielder, Young 5 |
| 8 | Basingstoke Town | 42 | 10 | 7 | 4 | 32 | 23 | 7 | 3 | 11 | 31 | 30 | 61 | Mancey 28, Xavier 10, Simpson 8 |
| 9 | Harrow Borough | 42 | 10 | 5 | 6 | 43 | 29 | 7 | 4 | 10 | 29 | 37 | 60 | Gavin 18, Lawford 10, Bates, Adolphe, McCormack 8 |
| 10 | Gravesend & Northfleet | 42 | 11 | 2 | 8 | 31 | 23 | 7 | 4 | 10 | 23 | 30 | 60 | Powell 10, Newson 6, Cooper, Bullard, Jackson 5 |
| 11 | Slough Town | 42 | 8 | 6 | 7 | 30 | 25 | 8 | 5 | 8 | 30 | 28 | 59 | Hammatt 15, Deaner, Peirson 7 |
| 12 | Billericay Town | 42 | 9 | 5 | 7 | 28 | 25 | 6 | 8 | 7 | 26 | 31 | 58 | Adekola 19, Portway 8, Gutzmore 7 |
| 13 | Hendon | 42 | 9 | 6 | 6 | 41 | 33 | 7 | 3 | 11 | 29 | 38 | 57 | Whitmarsh 32, Lewis 20, Kelly 6 |
| 14 | Boreham Wood | 42 | 9 | 8 | 4 | 32 | 27 | 5 | 7 | 9 | 27 | 36 | 57 | Samuels 13, Dixon 10, Swan 9 |
| 15 | Chesham United | 42 | 8 | 5 | 8 | 30 | 36 | 7 | 4 | 10 | 28 | 43 | 54 | Lawford 14, Winston 13, Gell, Bushay 5 |
| 16 | Dulwich Hamlet | 42 | 11 | 4 | 6 | 37 | 30 | 3 | 4 | 14 | 16 | 33 | 50 | Stevens 17, Thompson 11, Bartley 10 |
| 17 | Heybridge Swifts | 42 | 8 | 4 | 9 | 28 | 40 | 5 | 5 | 11 | 23 | 45 | 48 | Simpson 11, Wall 7, Lewis 6 |
| 18 | Walton & Hersham | 42 | 8 | 3 | 10 | 31 | 35 | 4 | 4 | 13 | 19 | 42 | 43 | Sayer 12, Ellington 9, Pickett 7 |
| 19 | Hampton | 42 | 6 | 9 | 6 | 24 | 22 | 4 | 3 | 14 | 17 | 49 | 43 | Hippolyte 6, Gallagher 5, Buglione 4 |
| 20 | Carshalton Athletic | 42 | 7 | 5 | 9 | 25 | 31 | 3 | 5 | 13 | 22 | 51 | 40 | Newbury 13, Haynes 9, Smith 8 |
| 21 | Bishops Stortford | 42 | 5 | 4 | 12 | 20 | 41 | 4 | 6 | 11 | 29 | 49 | 37 | Greene 6, Comerford 4, Robbins, Hayes, Benstock 3 |
| 22 | Bromley | 42 | 5 | 7 | 9 | 28 | 32 | 3 | 4 | 14 | 22 | 40 | 35 | Carroll 9, Wordsworth 8, Woolf 5 |

# PREMIER DIVISION RESULTS & ATTENDANCES 1998-99

| | | 1 | 2 | 3 | 4 | 5 | 6 | 7 | 8 | 9 | 10 | 11 | 12 | 13 | 14 | 15 | 16 | 17 | 18 | 19 | 20 | 21 | 22 |
|---|---|---|---|---|---|---|---|---|---|---|---|---|---|---|---|---|---|---|---|---|---|---|---|
| 1 | Aldershot Town | X | 0-1 2008 | 0-1 2272 | 0-1 2075 | 5-0 1723 | 6-0 1964 | 3-0 1687 | 4-0 1927 | 0-0 1207 | 4-3 2601 | 3-1 2270 | 3-1 2025 | 3-0 2371 | 5-0 2304 | 5-2 1694 | 0-2 2018 | 1-1 1966 | 1-1 1376 | 1-1 2106 | 1-2 2048 | 1-2 2796 | 7-2 1450 |
| 2 | Aylesbury United | 0-1 1009 | X | 3-2 865 | 3-0 1121 | 4-2 979 | 0-0 990 | 2-1 693 | 2-0 750 | 0-3 1869 | 0-1 619 | 3-0 430 | 1-2 994 | 2-0 914 | 3-0 506 | 2-0 651 | 1-0 860 | 0-1 301 | 2-1 766 | 0-0 1384 | 0-0 954 | 1-4 2216 | 1-0 743 |
| 3 | Basingstoke Town | 2-1 2810 | 2-1 469 | X | 0-1 709 | 3-1 421 | 1-1 590 | 1-1 530 | 2-1 481 | 4-0 405 | 1-1 723 | 2-1 521 | 1-0 734 | 2-2 355 | 1-0 634 | 2-1 539 | 1-1 873 | 2-2 638 | 3-2 501 | 0-2 687 | 1-2 563 | 1-2 844 | 0-0 463 |
| 4 | Billericay Town | 1-1 1407 | 0-3 674 | 0-0 526 | X | 3-2 625 | 1-0 602 | 2-2 777 | 2-0 568 | 3-0 789 | 1-2 806 | 1-0 619 | 0-1 786 | 0-2 776 | 2-0 615 | 2-2 712 | 2-1 447 | 2-1 710 | 0-1 812 | 1-2 577 | 3-3 651 | 1-2 725 | 1-0 532 |
| 5 | Bishops Stortford | 0-8 715 | 0-3 261 | 0-0 128 | 1-1 257 | X | 2-0 174 | 1-3 174 | 1-2 350 | 5-2 172 | 0-3 246 | 2-1 143 | 1-2 240 | 3-1 274 | 0-2 156 | 0-3 154 | 0-3 174 | 1-3 126 | 0-0 164 | 0-1 236 | 1-1 257 | 1-2 210 | 1-0 209 |
| 6 | Boreham Wood | 1-1 553 | 1-6 425 | 1-1 303 | 0-0 439 | 1-2 309 | X | 0-3 240 | 4-4 338 | 0-0 213 | 0-2 369 | 4-0 255 | 3-2 752 | 3-1 252 | 4-2 228 | 1-0 205 | 2-0 472 | 1-1 202 | 2-1 207 | 1-0 246 | 1-1 450 | 2-0 459 | 0-0 203 |
| 7 | Bromley | 1-1 1239 | 0-1 403 | 1-3 484 | 2-2 399 | 2-4 228 | 2-2 355 | X | 2-3 402 | 0-1 309 | 0-0 458 | 0-3 451 | 2-1 601 | 0-1 661 | 0-0 334 | 3-0 371 | 1-4 337 | 6-1 302 | 2-1 415 | 2-1 299 | 0-1 314 | 1-1 569 | 1-1 317 |
| 8 | Carshalton Athletic | 0-2 1003 | 3-3 346 | 1-0 282 | 3-1 374 | 1-0 283 | 1-1 242 | 1-1 326 | X | 0-1 348 | 0-0 407 | 2-0 376 | 2-1 402 | 1-2 253 | 2-4 292 | 1-2 286 | 1-3 232 | 1-2 304 | 2-1 291 | 0-3 275 | 1-1 348 | 1-0 1807 | 1-3 367 |
| 9 | Chesham United | 0-0 1181 | 1-0 1005 | 0-2 368 | 3-3 533 | 0-1 272 | 2-5 345 | 3-1 171 | 3-0 436 | X | 2-5 424 | 0-0 621 | 2-0 1016 | 3-2 515 | 2-2 317 | 1-4 355 | 0-2 428 | 1-0 316 | 3-3 238 | 1-0 636 | 2-1 337 | 0-3 494 | 1-2 408 |
| 10 | Dagenham & R | 0-1 1059 | 1-0 1006 | 2-0 768 | 1-2 880 | 1-1 629 | 1-1 697 | 3-3 663 | 5-0 520 | 0-0 480 | X | 1-0 599 | 3-3 911 | 0-0 561 | 4-0 440 | 1-0 564 | 6-0 601 | 3-0 727 | 0-1 963 | 3-0 737 | 2-2 705 | 0-0 1100 | 3-1 604 |
| 11 | Dulwich Hamlet | 4-3 1011 | 0-1 528 | 2-0 298 | 2-4 277 | 1-1 306 | 2-0 286 | 2-0 617 | 0-0 284 | 3-2 341 | 1-2 416 | X | 0-1 529 | 1-0 642 | 2-1 220 | 0-2 201 | 3-1 383 | 4-3 276 | 1-2 273 | 2-2 417 | 2-2 297 | 2-1 631 | 3-2 287 |
| 12 | Enfield | 4-0 1026 | 2-3 640 | 3-2 409 | 1-0 428 | 2-1 650 | 1-3 423 | 3-0 557 | 1-0 510 | 2-2 597 | 4-0 726 | 2-1 450 | X | 0-2 556 | 0-0 529 | 5-0 529 | 2-1 750 | 4-1 407 | 1-2 592 | 2-1 558 | 0-0 1011 | 1-1 511 | 3-2 454 |
| 13 | Gravesend & N | 2-1 954 | 1-2 724 | 1-0 563 | 0-0 450 | 4-1 376 | 3-2 370 | 1-2 561 | 3-1 592 | 0-2 492 | 2-0 592 | 0-1 446 | 0-3 483 | X | 3-0 457 | 2-0 375 | 0-1 378 | 3-2 490 | 1-1 358 | 1-2 416 | 0-1 586 | 2-1 536 | 2-0 498 |
| 14 | Hampton | 0-0 1035 | 0-0 264 | 2-1 339 | 0-0 240 | 0-0 226 | 3-3 213 | 2-1 324 | 1-1 222 | 0-1 274 | 1-2 276 | 0-0 239 | 0-2 275 | 1-0 228 | X | 0-0 161 | 3-1 355 | 4-0 363 | 2-3 126 | 2-2 304 | 1-2 332 | 0-3 380 | 2-0 404 |
| 15 | Harrow Borough | 1-0 981 | 1-4 321 | 0-2 293 | 3-3 375 | 2-2 205 | 3-0 227 | 2-0 239 | 8-2 211 | 5-4 326 | 2-1 260 | 3-2 215 | 0-0 401 | 0-1 230 | 4-0 222 | X | 2-2 513 | 2-0 185 | 5-0 207 | 0-2 437 | 0-0 242 | 0-3 255 | 0-1 402 |
| 16 | Hendon | 1-1 922 | 3-3 355 | 2-1 236 | 2-0 227 | 5-3 302 | 0-1 350 | 2-1 307 | 1-1 274 | 2-1 319 | 2-2 308 | 1-1 401 | 2-0 523 | 0-0 315 | 1-2 229 | 1-2 145 | X | 6-1 229 | 1-2 281 | 5-2 330 | 4-3 437 | 0-3 301 | 0-3 315 |
| 17 | Heybridge Swifts | 1-1 302 | 1-1 204 | 3-9 234 | 1-0 666 | 1-2 273 | 2-0 240 | 2-1 181 | 0-2 173 | 0-4 202 | 1-2 345 | 0-2 124 | 2-2 421 | 3-2 268 | 3-0 137 | 2-4 225 | 1-0 177 | X | 0-0 208 | 2-1 291 | 0-3 361 | 2-4 206 | 1-0 260 |
| 18 | Purfleet | 1-1 723 | 0-0 287 | 2-1 184 | 0-2 439 | 3-1 157 | 2-1 134 | 1-0 233 | 4-2 189 | 3-0 132 | 3-0 605 | 2-1 165 | 0-1 503 | 2-1 253 | 4-0 197 | 4-0 149 | 4-0 237 | 2-0 301 | X | 0-4 225 | 1-0 304 | 1-3 276 | 6-1 138 |
| 19 | Slough Town | 2-2 783 | 1-0 890 | 0-1 475 | 1-1 484 | 2-2 768 | 0-3 502 | 2-1 516 | 1-1 509 | 3-1 1060 | 0-1 510 | 1-0 433 | 2-2 737 | 4-0 311 | 3-0 544 | 0-3 432 | 1-1 505 | 0-1 520 | 2-3 590 | X | 1-0 679 | 1-2 585 | 3-0 451 |
| 20 | St Albans City | 1-1 1623 | 2-1 1131 | 4-2 679 | 1-0 826 | 5-1 787 | 1-2 703 | 4-1 373 | 1-0 793 | 2-3 1018 | 2-2 775 | 1-1 346 | 2-1 999 | 0-2 974 | 3-1 668 | 1-1 715 | 4-2 814 | 1-1 439 | 2-0 993 | 3-3 646 | X | 2-2 583 | 1-1 1008 |
| 21 | Sutton United | 5-0 1156 | 1-2 1047 | 1-2 1381 | 4-1 736 | 2-0 732 | 2-1 540 | 2-0 1173 | 3-0 1454 | 2-0 688 | 3-1 959 | 2-0 861 | 1-1 917 | 1-1 833 | 3-2 883 | 2-1 624 | 4-1 682 | 1-1 702 | 2-1 708 | 0-1 842 | 2-3 924 | X | 5-0 611 |
| 22 | Walton & Hersham | 0-4 935 | 0-2 271 | 2-1 213 | 3-4 167 | 2-2 187 | 1-1 220 | 1-0 220 | 3-2 229 | 9-1 207 | 0-1 282 | 3-1 254 | 0-4 321 | 1-3 247 | 0-1 359 | 2-2 227 | 0-3 237 | 0-1 142 | 1-0 159 | 2-0 445 | 1-0 242 | 0-2 585 | X |

# RYMAN LEAGUE CUP 1998-99

## PRELIMINARY ROUND

| | | | | |
|---|---|---|---|---|
| Banstead Athletic | 1 | v | 0 | Witham Town |
| Kingsbury Town | 0 | v | 3 | Leighton Town |
| East Thurrock Utd | 2 | v | 0 | Wokingham Town |
| Bedford Town | 2 | v | 1 | Braintree Town |
| Aveley | 2 | v | 2 | Ford United* |
| (r) Aveley | 0 | v | 2 | Ford United |
| Ware | 0 | v | 0 | Thame United* |
| (r) Ware | 2 | v | 0 | Thame United |
| Bracknell Town | 0 | v | 4 | Tooting & MU |
| Corinthian Casuals | 4 | v | 0 | Horsham* |
| Wealdstone | 4 | v | 1 | Northwood* |
| Hornchurch | 1 | v | 1 | Cheshunt* |
| (r) Hornchurch | 1 | v | 3 | Cheshunt≠ |
| Wingate & Finchley | 1 | v | 2 | Chalfont St Peter |
| Dorking | 2 | v | 3 | Croydon Athletic* |
| Barking | 0 | v | 4 | Harlow Town |
| Hertford Town | 1 | v | 2 | Lewes |
| Abingdon Town | 2 | v | 1 | Epsom & Ewell |
| Hemel H'pstead T | 1 | v | 0 | Edgware Town |
| Camberley Town | 2 | v | 0 | Tring Town |
| Wivenhoe Town | 1 | v | 2 | Windsor & Eton |
| Southall | 0 | v | 1 | Hungerford Town |
| Metropolitan Police | 3 | v | 3 | Tilbury* |
| (r) Metropolitan Plce | 2 | v | 0 | Tilbury* |
| Egham Town≠ | 1 | v | 1 | Clapton |
| Marlow | 5 | v | 2 | Flackwell Heath* |

## ROUND ONE

| | | | | |
|---|---|---|---|---|
| Carshalton Athletic | 4 | v | 3 | Banstead Athletic |
| Leighton Town | 0 | v | 2 | Uxbridge |
| Harrow Borough | 3 | v | 2 | East Thurrock Utd* |
| Bedford Town | 6 | v | 2 | Ford United |
| Bognor Regis Town | 2 | v | 2 | Chesham United* |
| (r) Bognor Regis Tn | 1 | v | 2 | Chesham United |
| Ware | 1 | v | 2 | Dagenham & Red. |
| Heybridge Swifts | 3 | v | 2 | Walton & Hersham |
| Bromley | 3 | v | 0 | Tooting & Mitch. U |
| Purfleet | 4 | v | 2 | Oxford City* |
| Wembley | 1 | v | 1 | Hampton* |
| (r) Wembley | 0 | v | 5 | Hampton |
| Leatherhead | 2 | v | 1 | Corinthian Casuals |
| Aylesbury United | 1 | v | 4 | Leyton Pennant* |
| Wealdstone≠ | 4 | v | 1 | Berkhamsted Town |
| Hornchurch | 0 | v | 3 | Canvey Island |
| Chertsey Town | 3 | v | 2 | Chalfont St Peter |
| Hitchin Town | 0 | v | 1 | Aldershot Town |
| Croydon Athletic | 2 | v | 2 | Harlow Town* |
| (r) Croydon Ath (p) | 1 | v | 1 | Harlow Town* |
| Maidenhead United | 3 | v | 1 | Lewes* |
| Staines Town | 1 | v | 0 | Yeading |
| Abingdon Town | 0 | v | 1 | Slough Town |
| Dulwich Hamlet | 2 | v | 3 | Sutton United |
| Worthing | 0 | v | 1 | Billericay Town |
| Molesey | 1 | v | 2 | Bishop's Stortford |
| Croydon | 2 | v | 4 | Basingstoke Town* |
| Hemel H'pstead T | 0 | v | 1 | Romford |
| Barton Rovers | 2 | v | 1 | Camberley Town |
| Boreham Wood | 2 | v | 0 | Enfield |
| Windsor & Eton | 0 | v | 1 | Hungerford Town |
| Grays Athletic | 1 | v | 3 | Metropolitan Police |
| Clapton | 1 | v | 5 | Marlow |
| St Albans City | 1 | v | 4 | Hendon |
| Whyteleafe | 0 | v | 5 | Gravesend & NF |

## ROUND TWO

| | | | | |
|---|---|---|---|---|
| Carshalton Athletic | 1 | v | 2 | Uxbridge |
| Harrow Borough | 1 | v | 0 | Bedford Town |
| Chesham United | 2 | v | 1 | Dagenham & Red. |
| Heybridge Swifts | 1 | v | 2 | Bromley* |
| Purfleet≠ | 5 | v | 0 | Hampton |
| Leatherhead | 6 | v | 4 | Leyton Pennant |
| Berkhamsted Town | 3 | v | 1 | Canvey Island |
| Chertsey Town | 4 | v | 4 | Aldershot Town* |
| (r) Chertsey Town | 0 | v | 5 | Aldershot Town |
| Croydon Athletic | 0 | v | 2 | Maidenhead United |
| Staines Town | 1 | v | 3 | Slough Town |
| Sutton United | 4 | v | 0 | Billericay Town |
| Bishop's Stortford≠ | 5 | v | 4 | Basingstoke Town* |
| Romford | 1 | v | 2 | Barton Rovers |
| Boreham Wood | 3 | v | 1 | Hungerford Town |
| Metropolitan Police | 3 | v | 4 | Marlow |
| Hendon | 2 | v | 1 | Gravesend & NF |

## ROUND THREE

| | | | | |
|---|---|---|---|---|
| Uxbridge | 1 | v | 0 | Harrow Borough |
| Chesham United | 0 | v | 3 | Bromley |
| Hampton | 2 | v | 5 | Leatherhead |
| Berkhamsted Town | 1 | v | 1 | Aldershot Town* |
| (r) Berkhamsted Tn | 0 | v | 1 | Aldershot Town |
| Maidenhead United | 4 | v | 2 | Slough Town |
| Sutton United | 2 | v | 0 | Basingstoke Town |
| Barton Rovers | 0 | v | 3 | Boreham Wood |
| Marlow | 2 | v | 1 | Hendon |

## ROUND FOUR

| | | | | |
|---|---|---|---|---|
| Uxbridge | 0 | v | 2 | Bromley |
| Leatherhead | 0 | v | 1 | Aldershot Town |
| Maidenhead United | 5 | v | 4 | Sutton United* |
| Boreham Wood | 5 | v | 1 | Marlow |

## SEMI-FINALS

| | | | | |
|---|---|---|---|---|
| (1st) Bromley | 1 | v | 3 | Aldershot Town |
| (2nd) Bromley | 2 | v | 1 | Aldershot Town |
| (1st) Maidenhead U | 2 | v | 3 | Boreham Wood |
| (2nd) Maidenhead U | 0 | v | 1 | Boreham Wood |

## FINAL

| | | | | |
|---|---|---|---|---|
| ALDERSHOT TN | 2 | v | 1 | BOREHAM WOOD |

At Southampton FC

* after extra time     ≠ removed from competition

# PUMA FULL MEMBERS CUP 1998-99

## ROUND ONE

| | | | |
|---|---|---|---|
| Basingstoke Town | 4 | v 1 | Croydon |
| Grays Athletic | 0 | v 1 | Wealdstone |
| Chesham United | 4 | v 1 | Barton Rovers |
| Boreham Wood | 2 | v 0 | Braintree Town |
| Enfield | 2 | v 0 | St Albans City |
| Wembley | 0 | v 2 | Bishop's Stortford |
| Harrow Borough | 1 | v 0 | Leyton Pennant* |
| Romford | 1 | v 0 | Staines Town |
| Leatherhead | 0 | v 1 | Whyteleafe |
| Worthing | 3 | v 1 | Maidenhead Utd |
| Sutton United | 1 | v 3 | Walton & Hersham |
| Slough Town | 1 | v 0 | Bromley |

## ROUND TWO

| | | | |
|---|---|---|---|
| Dulwich Hamlet | 1 | v 0 | Hampton |
| Basingstoke Town | 3 | v 0 | Bognor Regis Town |
| Oxford City | 2 | v 0 | Molesey |
| Yeading | 2 | v 5 | Wealdstone |
| Berkhamsted T (p) | 1 | v 1 | Aylesbury United |
| Chesham United | 2 | v 1 | Dagenham & Red. |
| Boreham Wood | 1 | v 1 | Canvey Island (p) |
| Hendon | 2 | v 1 | Heybridge Swifts |
| Enfield | 1 | v 0 | Bishop's Stortford |
| Purfleet | 2 | v 1 | Billericay Town |
| Uxbridge | 0 | v 2 | Hitchin Town |
| Harrow Borough | 1 | v 3 | Romford |
| Whyteleafe | 2 | v 1 | Gravesend & NF |
| Worthing | 6 | v 0 | Aldershot Town |
| Carshalton Athletic | 2 | v 0 | Chertsey Town |
| Walton & Hersham | 2 | v 0 | Slough Town |

## ROUND THREE

| | | | |
|---|---|---|---|
| Dulwich Hamlet | 3 | v 1 | Basingstoke Town |
| Oxford City | 2 | v 4 | Wealdstone |
| Berkhamsted Town | 0 | v 5 | Chesham United |
| Canvey Island | 0 | v 2 | Hendon |
| Enfield | 0 | v 2 | Purfleet |
| Hitchin Town | 3 | v 1 | Romford |
| Whyteleafe | 0 | v 2 | Worthing |
| Carshalton Athletic | 2 | v 0 | Walton & Hersham |

## ROUND FOUR

| | | | |
|---|---|---|---|
| Dulwich Hamlet | 1 | v 0 | Wealdstone |
| Chesham United | 0 | v 1 | Hendon |
| Purfleet | 2 | v 0 | Hitchin Town |
| Worthing | 3 | v 0 | Carshalton Athletic |

## SEMI-FINALS

| | | | |
|---|---|---|---|
| Dulwich Hamlet | 0 | v 2 | Hendon* |
| Purfleet | 0 | v 1 | Worthing |

## FINAL

| | | | |
|---|---|---|---|
| HENDON | 1 | v 0 | WORTHING |

at Sutton United

---

# VANDANEL TROPHY 1998-99

## ROUND ONE

| | | | |
|---|---|---|---|
| Wingate & Finchley | 1 | v 4 | Leighton Town |
| Tilbury | 1 | v 2 | Northwood* |
| Barking | 3 | v 1 | Ware |
| Windsor & Eton | 1 | v 0 | Flackwell Heath |
| Harlow Town | 1 | v 0 | Ford United |
| Bracknell Town | 1 | v 3 | Thame United |
| Chalfont St Peter | 4 | v 1 | Kingsbury Town |
| Workingham Town | 0 | v 5 | Marlow |
| Dorking | 1 | v 2 | Lewes |
| Egham Town | 1 | v 0 | Hungerford Town |

## ROUND TWO

| | | | |
|---|---|---|---|
| Bedford Town | 1 | v 0 | Cheshunt |
| Leighton Town | 2 | v 1 | Northwood |
| Wivenhoe Town | 3 | v 1 | Witham Town |
| Hornchurch | 1 | v 3 | Barking |
| Tooting & Mitcham U | 4 | v 1 | Horsham |
| Corinthian Casuals | 0 | v 1 | Metropolitan Police |
| Banstead Athletic | 4 | v 2 | Camberley Town |
| Tring Town | 0 | v 2 | Epsom & Ewell |
| East Thurrock Utd | 2 | v 3 | Hertford Town* |
| Hemel H'stead T | 0 | v 2 | Windsor & Eton |
| Harlow Town | 6 | v 0 | Aveley |
| Clapton | 0 | v 2 | Edgware Town |
| Thame United | 3 | v 2 | Chalfont St Peter |
| Southall | 2 | v 0 | Croydon Athletic |
| Marlow | 3 | v 2 | Lewes |
| Abingdon Town | 2 | v 3 | Egham Town |

## ROUND THREE

| | | | |
|---|---|---|---|
| Bedford Town | 1 | v 3 | Leighton Town |
| Wivenhoe Town | 4 | v 1 | Barking |
| Tooting & Mitcham U | 3 | v 1 | Metropolitan Police |
| Banstead Athletic | 1 | v 4 | Epsom & Ewell |
| Hertford Town | 0 | v 2 | Windsor & Eton |
| Harlow Town | 0 | v 1 | Edgware Town |
| Thame United | 1 | v 3 | Southall |
| Marlow | 4 | v 0 | Egham Town |

## ROUND FOUR

| | | | |
|---|---|---|---|
| Leighton Town | 2 | v 1 | Wivenhoe Town |
| Tooting & Mitcham U | 2 | v 1 | Epsom & Ewell |
| Windsor & Eton | 1 | v 4 | Edgware Town |
| Southall | 0 | v 1 | Marlow |

## SEMI-FINALS

| | | | |
|---|---|---|---|
| Leighton Town | 3 | v 2 | Tooting & M Utd* |
| Windsor & Eton | 3 | v 0 | Marlow |

## FINAL

| | | | |
|---|---|---|---|
| LEIGHTON TOWN | 1 | v 0 | WINDSOR & ETON |

at Chesham United FC

---

* after extra time    ≠ removed from competition

* after extra time

This page:
Top: Sutton United with the Ryman Premier Shield
Photo: Gary Letts

Right: Champion Tee shirt, Bedford Town FC.
Photo: Eric Marsh

Below: Aldershot Town, Ryman League Cup winners 1999
Photo: M Sandom

Opposite page:

Top: Wealdstone celebrate promotion to the Ryman Premier Division after their 2-1 victory over Worthing at Woodside Road. Photo: Andrew Chitty

Centre:
Ryman Team v Combined Services
Photo: Ian Morsman

Bottom: Joint Aldershot and Farnborough team for the Rushmoor Cup. Boro won 4-2
Photo: Ian Morsman

# ALDERSHOT TOWN

## CLUB OFFICIALS

Chairman: Karl Prentice
Vice Chairman:John McGinty
Company Secretary: Graham Brookland, c/o
Aldershot Town FC, (0973 172073)
Press Officer: Nick Fryer Tel: 01483 563570

**FOOTBALL MANAGEMENT TEAM**
Manager: George Borg
Asst Man.: Stuart Cash
Physio: Phil Shedden

**GROUND**    Recreation Ground, High Street, Aldershot, Hants GU11 1TW
Tel: 01252 320211 Fax: 01252324347
**Directions:** Ground situated on eastern end of High Street next to large multi-storey B.T.
building. From M3 (jct 4) take A325 to Aldershot. After five milesat r'bout take 1st exit marked
town centre (A323) into Wellington Ave. At Burger King r'bout take 2nd exit into High Street -
ground on left, large carpark adjacent. 5 mins walk from Aldershot (BR)
Capacity: 7,500          Cover: 6,850          Seats: 1,800          Floodlights: Yes
Clubhouse:          matchdays and special functions   Steward: Wally Clarke 01252 338426
Club Shop:          Range of souvenirs, programmes, replica kits.
Open matchdays or contact Janet Guess (01252-528007) for mail order

**PREVIOUS**          **Leagues:** None   **Names:** None   **Grounds:** None

**CLUB RECORDS  Attendance:** 6,870 v Woking (F.A.Cup 4th Q ) 5,9,98.
"Ground record: 19,138 Aldershot FC v CarlisleUnited, FA Cup 4th Rd replay 28/1/70
**Win:** 8-0 v Bishop's Stortford (a) League 5.9.98   **Defeat:** 0-6v Worthing (a) Puma Cup 2.3.99
**Career Goalscorer:** Mark Butler 155. (92-98)   **Career Appearances:** Mark Butler 303. (92-98)
**Transfer Fee Paid:** £11,000 to Billericay Town for Leon Gutzmore (12/98)
**Transfer Fee Received:** £5,000 for Jason Tucker from Enfield 96 and for Lee Endersby from Slough Town (10.98)

**BEST SEASON     FA Cup:** Fourth Qual Rd Replay  98-99          **FA Trophy:** Fourthl Rd 98-99Div 18
**FA Vase:** Quarter Final 93-94

**HONOURS**          Isthmian League Div 1 97-98 92-93; Simpsonair Trophy 92-93; Skol Invitation Trophy 92-93; Hants Senior Cup SF 92-93; 98-
99,Suburban Lge Western Div Champions 94-95; Allied Counties Youth Lge Champions 1994-95; Guradian Insurance Lge Cup  98-99R-up 95-96

*Aldershot Town*                                                                                    *Photo: Ian Morsman*

# ALDERSHOT TOWN - MATCH FACTS - 1998-99 SEASON

| No | Date | Venue | Comp | Opponents | Att | Result | Score | Goalscorers |
|----|------|-------|------|-----------|-----|--------|-------|-------------|
| 1 | 04/08 | A | R C S | Farnborough Town | 1342 | L | 2-4 | Abbott 3[p], Stapleton 10 |
| 2 | 22/08 | A | RL P | Purfleet | 723 | D | 1-1 | Fielder 10 |
| 3 | 25/08 | H | RL P | Hampton | 2304 | W | 5-0 | Abbott(3), Nartey, Sugrue |
| 4 | 29/08 | H | RL P | Gravesend & Northfleet | 2371 | W | 3-0 | Nartey 16, Abbott 38 72 |
| 5 | 01/09 | A | RL P | Chesham United | 1181 | D | 0-0 | |
| 6 | 05/09 | A | RL P | Bishop's Stortford | 715 | W | 8-0 | Endersby 12, Nartey 14 52 56 62 70, Abbott 69 79 |
| 7 | 08/09 | A | RL C 1 | Hitchin Town | 723 | W | 1-0 | Chewins |
| 8 | 12/09 | H | RL P | Dagenham & Redbridge | 2601 | W | 4-3 | Howard 7, Nartey 45, Abbott 58, Sugrue 90 |
| 9 | 15/09 | A | RL P | Bromley | 1239 | D | 1-1 | Abbott 25 |
| 10 | 19/09 | A | RL P | Sutton United | 2796 | L | 1-2 | Abbott 9 |
| 11 | 22/09 | H | RL P | St Albans City | 2048 | L | 1-2 | Champion 31 |
| 12 | 26/09 | A | RL P | Billericay Town | 1407 | D | 1-1 | Chewins 76 |
| 13 | 04/10 | A | FA C Q2 | Bishop's Stortford | 719 | W | 2-0 | Own-Goal, Fielder[p] |
| 14 | 10/10 | A | RL P | Carshalton Athletic | 1003 | W | 2-0 | Hathaway 45, Howard 70 |
| 15 | 13/10 | H | RL P | Hendon | 2018 | L | 0-2 | |
| 16 | 17/10 | A | FA C Q3 | Grays Athletic | 784 | W | 1-0 | John[og] |
| 17 | 31/10 | H | FA C Q4 | Woking | 6870 | D | 0-0 | |
| 18 | 03/11 | A | FA C Q4 r | Woking | 3897 | L | 1-2 | Abbott 37 |
| 19 | 07/11 | H | RL P | Boreham Wood | 1964 | W | 6-0 | Young 33 35 65, Abbott 46 62 82 |
| 20 | 10/11 | H | HSC 2 | Moneyfields | 977 | W | 7-0 | Young 11 16 21 33, Nartey 68 83, Sugrue 84 |
| 21 | 14/11 | A | RL P | Harrow Borough | 981 | L | 0-1 | |
| 22 | 17/11 | H | RL P | Aylesbury United | 2008 | L | 0-1 | |
| 23 | 21/11 | H | FA T 2 | Bromley | 1587 | W | 3-1 | Nartey 70 90, Stapleton 89 |
| 24 | 24/11 | A | RL C 2 | Chertsey Town | 413 | D | 4-4 | Coll, Sugrue, Fielder, Nartey |
| 25 | 28/11 | A | RL P | Enfield | 1026 | L | 0-4 | |
| 26 | 01/12 | H | HSC 3 | Locksheath | 817 | W | 3-0 | Abbott(2), Hathaway |
| 27 | 05/12 | A | RL P | Bromley | 1687 | W | 3-0 | Coll 56, Sharman 71[og], Abbott 82 |
| 28 | 12/12 | A | RL P | Dagenham & Redbridge | 1059 | W | 1-0 | Abbott 64 |
| 29 | 15/12 | H | RL C 2 rep | Chertsey Town | 889 | W | 5-0 | Abbott(2), Young, Philpot, Fielder |
| 30 | 19/12 | H | RL P | Heybridge Swifts | 1966 | D | 1-1 | Young 84 |
| 31 | 28/12 | A | RL P | Basingstoke Town | 2810 | L | 1-2 | Abbott 64 |
| 32 | 02/01 | A | RL P | Dulwich Hamlet | 2270 | W | 3-1 | Fielder 13, Coll 38, Gutzmore 45 |
| 33 | 05/01 | A | RL C 3 | Berkhamsted Town | 375 | D | 3-3 | Hathaway 39 65, Young 63 |
| 34 | 09/01 | A | RL P | Gravesend & Northfleet | 954 | L | 1-2 | Young 20 |
| 35 | 16/01 | H | FA T 3 | Maidenhead United | 2068 | W | 1-0 | Sugrue 37 |
| 36 | 23/01 | A | RL P | Hampton | 1035 | D | 0-0 | |
| 37 | 26/01 | H | RL C 3 rep | Berkhamsted Town | 931 | W | 1-0 | Young 1 |
| 38 | 30/01 | H | HSC QF | Sylvans Sports | 1380 | W | 6-0 | Young 31, Abbott 36 42 62 74, Holsgrove 55 |
| 39 | 02/02 | A | P C 2 | Worthing | 301 | L | 0-6 | |
| 40 | 06/02 | H | FA T 4 | Altrincham | 2754 | L | 1-2 | Nartey 89 |
| 41 | 09/02 | A | RL C QF | Leatherhead | 415 | W | 1-0 | Abbott 8 |
| 42 | 13/02 | H | RL P | Bishop's Stortford | 1723 | W | 5-0 | Nartey 20 24 40 72, Abbott 80 |
| 43 | 16/02 | H | RL P | Walton & Hersham | 1450 | W | 7-2 | Talboys 13, Nartey 27,53,73, Sugrue 46, Abbott 62 67 |
| 44 | 20/02 | A | RL P | Hendon | 922 | D | 1-1 | Nartey 30 |
| 45 | 27/02 | H | RL P | Carshalton Athletic | 1927 | W | 4-0 | Abbott 24, Nartey 46, Hathaway 58, Howard 61 |
| 46 | 06/03 | H | RL P | Billericay Town | 2075 | L | 0-1 | |
| 47 | 09/03 | A | HSC SF(1) | Havant & Waterlooville | 728 | W | 3-0 | Gutzmore 28 31, Talboys 40 |
| 48 | 13/03 | H | RL P | St Albans City | 1623 | D | 1-1 | Abbott 85[p] |
| 49 | 16/03 | H | RL P | Purfleet | 1376 | D | 1-1 | Hathaway 79 |
| 50 | 20/03 | A | RL P | Walton & Hersham | 935 | W | 4-0 | Abbott 6 51, Fielder 16, Gutzmore 63 |
| 51 | 23/03 | A | RL C SF(1) | Bromley | 506 | W | 3-1 | Abbott, Nartey, McGrath |
| 52 | 27/03 | H | RL P | Slough Town | 2106 | D | 1-1 | Abbott 41 |
| 53 | 30/03 | H | HSC SF(2) | Havant & Waterlooville | 1342 | D | 1-1 | Hathaway 38 |
| 54 | 03/04 | A | RL P | Dulwich Hamlet | 1011 | L | 3-4 | Nartey 26, Abbott 85 87 |
| 55 | 05/04 | A | RL P | Basingstoke Town | 2272 | L | 0-1 | |
| 56 | 08/04 | H | RL C SF(2) | Bromley | 1064 | L | 1-2 | Abbott 115 |
| 57 | 10/04 | A | RL P | Boreham Wood | 553 | D | 1-1 | Gutzmore 29 |
| 58 | 13/04 | A | RL P | Slough Town | 783 | D | 2-2 | Abbott 59, Coll 84 |
| 59 | 17/04 | A | RL P | Harrow Borough | 1694 | W | 5-2 | Gutzmore 10, Abbott 24 44 76, Hathaway 57 |
| 60 | 22/04 | A | RL P | Sutton United | 1156 | L | 0-5 | |
| 61 | 24/04 | A | RL P | Aylesbury United | 1009 | W | 1-0 | Abbott 36 |
| 62 | 27/04 | A | RL P | Heybridge Swifts | 302 | D | 1-1 | Fielder 39 |
| 63 | 29/04 | H | RL P | Chesham United | 1207 | D | 0-0 | |
| 64 | 01/05 | H | RL P | Enfield | 2025 | W | 3-1 | Abbott 47 67, McGrath 53 |
| 65 | 03/05 | H | RL C F | Boreham Wood | 1611 | W | 2-1 | Abbott 25 117 (at Slough Town) |
| 66 | 05/05 | H | HSC F | Basingstoke Town | 3143 | W | 1-0 | Abbott 90 (at Southampton) |

## PLAYING SQUAD 1999-2000:

GOALKEEPERS: Luke Garrard (Bracknell T), Mark Russell (Hampton & Richmond Boro), Calvin Sparshatt, Mark Watson
DEFENDERS: Keith Baker, Neil Baker (Farnborough T), Stuart Cash (Enfield), Paul Chambers, Jason Chewins (Basingstoke T), Stuart Harte (Farnborough T), Steve McGrath (Yeovil T), Andy Nunn, Steve Talboys (Sutton Utd), Simon Turner
MIDFIELDERS: Ollie Adedeji (Bromley), Simon Bassey (Carshalton Athletic), Neil Champion (Fareham Town), Colin Fielder (Yeovil Town), Richard Gell (Chesham United), Jesse Hall (Hampton), Ian Hathaway (Colchester United), Stewart Mitchell, Dave Osgood, Darren Robson (Farnborough T), Simon Stapleton (Stevenage Boro), Jimmy Sugrue (Hayes), Russ Watkinson (Kingstonian), Paul Wilson (Barnet)
FORWARDS: Gary Abbott (Slough T), Mark Bentley (Enfield), Sam Cobbett, Owen Coll (Stevenage Boro), Leon Gutzmore (Billericay T), Jon Horsted, Joe Nartey (Chertsey T)

773

# AYLESBURY UNITED

**Welcome to The Stadium, Buckingham Road - home of**
*"THE DUCKS"*

## CLUB OFFICIALS

Chairman: **Bill Carroll**
Vice Chairman: **Roger Payne**

Secretary: **Heather Jan Brunt**
c/o the club.
Press Officer: **Tony Graham**

## FOOTBALL MANAGEMENT TEAM

Manager: Alan Taylor
Assistant Manager: T.B.A.
Physio: T.B.A.

### FACT FILE

Formed: 1897
Nickname: The Ducks
Sponsors: Driftgate Press
Colours: Green & white/green/green
Change colours: Yellow & black, black,black
Midweek home matchday: Tuesday
Reserve Team's League: None
Newsline: 0891 446 824/09066 55 811

1998-99 Captain: Waren Kelly
Top Scorer & P.o.Y.: Gary Crawshaw

**GROUND** The Stadium, Buckingham Road, Aylesbury HP20 2AQ Tel: 01296 436350/436891

**Directions:** On A413 to Buckingham, just off ring road opposite Horse & Jockey PH. Arriving from Buckingham ground is on left - from all other directions follow Buckingham signs and ground on right. Half hour walk from Aylesbury rail and bus stations

| | | | |
|---|---|---|---|
| Capacity 4,000 | Cover: 1000 | Seats: 500 | Floodlights: Yes |
| Clubhouse: | Pub hours, but shut during matches. Bar snacks available | | |
| | Function room available for hire(01296 436891). | | |
| Club Shop: | Sells programmes, magazines, leisurewear, badges etc. | | |
| | Contact DebbieGamage c/o The Club | | |

Pages: 36 Price: £1.50
Editor: Dave Gamage (01296 434006)

Local Press: Bucks Herald, Bucks Advertiser
Local Radio: Three Counties Radio,
Chiltern Radio, Mix 96

**PREVIOUS** **Leagues:** Bucks Contiguous 1897-1903, South Eastern 03-07, Spartan 07-51, Delphian 51-63, Athenian 63-76, Southern 76-88, GMV Conference 88-89
**Grounds:** Printing Works Ground 1897-1935, Sports Stadium, Wendover Rd (ground name changed to The Stadium, Turnfurlong Lane) 35-85, shared grounds 85-86 **Name:** Night School, Printing Works (merged in 1897)

**CLUB RECORDS** **Attendance:** 6,000 v England 1988 (at old ground: 7,500 v Watford, FA Cup 1st Rd1951)
**Career goalscorer:** Cliff Hercules **Career appearances:** Cliff Hercules
**Transfer fee paid:** £15,000 for Glenvile Donegal (Northampton, 1990)
**Transfer fee received:** £35,000 for Glenvile Donegal (Maidstone Utd, 1991)

**BEST SEASON** **FA Trophy:** Quarter-Final replay 80-81 **FA Cup:** 3rd Rd 95. League clubs defeated: Southend Utd 89-90

**HONOURS** Southern Lg 87-88 (Mids Div R-up 84-85, Sth Div R-up 79-80); Athenian Lg Div 2 R-up 67-68; Delphian Lg 53-54 (R-up 52-53, Lg Cup 59-60); Spartan Lg 08-09 (R-up 52-53), West Div 28-29 (R-up 45-46), Div 1 38-39 (R-up 34-35); Berks & Bucks Snr Cup 13-14 85-86 96-97; Isthmian League Cup 94-95, Isthmian Charity Shield 95-96 Isthmian League R-up 98-99

Players progressing: Ray Mabbutt (Bristol Rovers), Phil Barber (Crystal Palace 1986), Jermaine Darlington (Q.P.R. 99)

**Back Row (L-R):** *Mark Rooney, Warren Kelly, Kenrick Roudette, Steve Butler, Lee Harvey, Richard Wilmot, Jason Court, Jason Soloman, Jason Tucker, Jermaine Darlington, Kenny Webster*
**Front :** *Paul Thawley (Physio), Dave Anderson (Astnt Mngr), Richard Harvey, Naseem Bashir, Cliff Hercules, Gary Crawshaw, Bob Dowie (Mngr), Kieran Gallagher, Ian King, Corey Browne, Phil Mason, Peter Lawrence (Coach) Ron Schmidt (Team Astnt)*

## AYLESBURY UNITED - MATCH FACTS - 1998-99 SEASON

| No | Date | Venue | Comp | Opponents | Att | Result | Score | Goalscorers |
|----|------|-------|------|-----------|-----|--------|-------|-------------|
| 1 | 22/08 | H | RL P | Carshalton Athletic | 750 | W | 2-0 | Crawshaw 43 87[p] |
| 2 | 25/08 | A | RL P | Harrow Borough | 321 | W | 4-1 | Brown(3), Rutherford |
| 3 | 29/08 | A | RL P | Enfield | 640 | W | 3-2 | Solomon 12, Browne 89 90 |
| 4 | 01/09 | H | RL P | Boreham Wood | 990 | D | 0-0 | |
| 5 | 05/09 | H | RL P | St Albans City | 954 | D | 0-0 | |
| 6 | 08/09 | H | RL C 1 | **Leyton Pennant** | **243** | L | **1-4** | **Crawshaw** |
| 7 | 12/09 | A | RL P | Slough Town | 890 | L | 0-1 | |
| 8 | 15/09 | H | RL P | Dulwich Hamlet | 430 | W | 3-0 | King 32, Crawshaw 45 61[p] |
| 9 | 19/09 | A | RL P | Heybridge Swifts | 204 | D | 1-1 | Crawshaw 12 |
| 10 | 22/09 | A | RL P | Hendon | 355 | D | 3-3 | Crawshaw 54[p], Solomon 61, Browne 64 |
| 11 | 26/09 | H | RL P | Walton & Hersham | 743 | W | 1-0 | Gallagher 80 |
| 12 | 03/10 | H | FAC Q2 | **Horsham** | **571** | W | **3-1** | **King, Crawshaw(2)** |
| 13 | 10/10 | A | RL P | Bishop's Stortford | 261 | W | 3-0 | Butler 8 80, King 82 |
| 14 | 13/10 | H | RL P | Bromley | 693 | W | 2-1 | King 10, Crawshaw 73 |
| 15 | 17/10 | H | FAC Q3 | **Carshalton Athletic** | **809** | L | **0-1** | |
| 16 | 31/10 | H | RL P | Hampton | 506 | W | 3-0 | Crawshaw 48 80 83 |
| 17 | 07/11 | A | RL P | Sutton United | 1047 | W | 2-1 | Butler 33 48 |
| 18 | 14/11 | H | RL P | Purfleet | 766 | W | 2-1 | Court 35, Rutherford 85 |
| 19 | 17/11 | H | RL P | Aldershot Town | 2008 | W | 1-0 | Solomon 85 |
| 20 | 21/11 | H | FAT 2 | **Harrow Borough** | **655** | D | **1-1** | **Crawshaw** |
| 21 | 24/11 | A | FAT 2 rep | **Harrow Borough** | **306** | W | **3-2** | **Rutherford 35, King 54, Crawshaw 95** |
| 22 | 28/11 | H | RL P | Billericay Town | 1121 | W | 3-0 | Crawshaw 24, Iorfa 69 83 |
| 23 | 05/12 | A | RL P | St Albans City | 1131 | L | 1-2 | Crawshaw 66[p] |
| 24 | 12/12 | H | RL P | Slough Town | 1384 | D | 0-0 | |
| 25 | 28/12 | H | RL P | Chesham United | 1869 | L | 0-3 | |
| 26 | 02/01 | A | RL P | Gravesend & Northfleet | 724 | W | 2-1 | Browne 26, Crawshaw 37 |
| 27 | 23/01 | H | RL P | Harrow Borough | 651 | W | 2-0 | Browne 32, Crawshaw 55 |
| 28 | 25/01 | H | FAT 3 | **Newport IoW** | **468** | W | **2-0** | **Hercules 69, Crawshaw 88** |
| 29 | 30/01 | A | RL P | Boreham Wood | 425 | W | 6-1 | Crawshaw 3,53p,80, King 63, Darlington 65, Butler 90 |
| 30 | 02/02 | A | B&B SC 1 | **Wokingham Town** | **90** | L | **0-1** | |
| 31 | 06/02 | H | FAT 4 | **Whitby Town** | **901** | L | **0-1** | |
| 32 | 13/02 | A | RL P | Dulwich Hamlet | 528 | W | 1-0 | Mahoney-Johnson 38 |
| 33 | 16/02 | H | RL P | Dagenham & Redbridge | 619 | L | 0-1 | |
| 34 | 18/02 | A | P C 2 | **Berkhamsted Town** | **120** | D | **1-1** | **Rooney 90**           (2-4 pens) |
| 35 | 20/02 | A | RL P | Bromley | 403 | W | 1-0 | Harvey 60 |
| 36 | 23/02 | A | RL P | Hampton | 264 | D | 0-0 | |
| 37 | 27/02 | H | RL P | Bishop's Stortford | 979 | W | 4-2 | Crawshaw 4[p] 71, Butler 7 9 |
| 38 | 06/03 | A | RL P | Walton & Hersham | 271 | W | 2-0 | Mead 27, Crawshaw 66 |
| 39 | 09/03 | A | RL P | Carshalton Athletic | 346 | D | 3-3 | Harvey 17, Mason 25, Browne 53 |
| 40 | 13/03 | H | RL P | Hendon | 860 | W | 1-0 | Gallagher 65 |
| 41 | 20/03 | H | RL P | Basingstoke Town | 865 | W | 3-2 | Crawshaw 11 88, Bignall 82 |
| 42 | 23/03 | H | RL P | Enfield | 994 | L | 1-2 | Butler 15 |
| 43 | 28/03 | A | RL P | Dagenham & Redbridge | 1006 | L | 0-1 | |
| 44 | 03/04 | H | RL P | Gravesend & Northfleet | 914 | W | 2-0 | Dolby 45[og], Bignall 61 |
| 45 | 05/04 | A | RL P | Chesham United | 1005 | L | 0-1 | |
| 46 | 10/04 | H | RL P | Sutton United | 2216 | L | 1-4 | Rutherford 59 |
| 47 | 17/04 | A | RL P | Purfleet | 287 | D | 0-0 | |
| 48 | 20/04 | H | RL P | Heybridge Swifts | 301 | L | 0-1 | |
| 49 | 24/04 | A | RL P | Aldershot Town | 1009 | L | 0-1 | |
| 50 | 27/04 | A | RL P | Basingstoke Town | 469 | L | 1-2 | King 17 |
| 51 | 01/05 | A | RL P | Billericay Town | 674 | W | 3-0 | Wilson 22, King 68, Crawshaw 76 |

## PLAYING SQUAD 1999-2000:

GOALKEEPERS: Des Gallagher (Stevenage Borough), Paul O'Reilly (Chesham United), Gary Phillips (Aldershot Town)

DEFENDERS: Paul Benning (Harrow Borough), Robbie Bourne (Purfleet), Iain Duncan (Yeading), Tom Hill, Warren Kelly (Rushden & Diamonds), Mark Newson, Adrian O'Brien, Wayne Stemp (Farnborough Town), Colin Wall (Heybridge Swifts), Stuart Beevor (Stevenage Borough)

MIDFIELDERS: Adam Clarry (London Colney), Bob Dowie (Harrow Borough), Kieran Gallagher, Cliff Hercules (Slough Town), Gary Issott (Totternhoe - dual), Mark Jones, Stacey Joseph (Boreham Wood), Ian King (Telford United), Chris Martin, Phil Mason (Oxford City), Jim Meara, Richard Sharpe, Jason Solomon (Stevenage Borough)

FORWARDS: Mike Bignall (Kidderminster Harriers), Corey Browne (Slough Town), Lee Cook, Gary Crawshaw (Stevenage Borough), Kevin Davies, Russell Douglas (St Neots Town), Joe Gallen, Aiden Kilner (Woking), Neil Selby (Chertsey Town)

# BASINGSTOKE TOWN

## CLUB OFFICIALS
Chairman: **David Knight**
President: **Rafi Pazzak**
Secretary: **Richard Trodd**
5 Lehar Close, Brighton Hill,
Basingstoke RG22 4HT
Tel: 01256 413076
Press Officer: **John Gray**
Commercial Manager: **Chris Richardson**

## FOOTBALL MANAGEMENT TEAM
Manager: Ernie Howe
Asst Manager: Pete Peters
Coach: Steve Richardson
Physio: Mark Randall & Zoe Demster

### FACT FILE
Formed: 1896
Nickname: Stoke
Sponsors: Centerprise International & New Way Nissan
Colours: Blue & gold stripes/blue/blue
Change colours: Red & black stripes/black/black
Midweek home matchday: Tuesday
Reserves' League: Suburban (Prem Div)

1998-99 Captain: Toby Redwood
P.o.Y & Top Scorer: Ian Mancey

VOLUME: 5
ISSUE: 29

BASINGSTOKE TOWN F.C.

OFFICIAL MATCHDAY PROGRAMME - £1
SPONSORED BY DESIGN SERVICES

Pages: 40     Price: £1.20
Editor: Michael Edwards Tel: 01256 410103

Local Press: Basingstoke Gazette (461131)
Local Radio: Radio 210 (01189 413131),
Kestrel Radio (01256 694000)

**GROUND**            Camrose Road, Western Way, Basingstoke RG24 6HW
                      Tel: 01256 325063 or 01256 464353
**Directions:**       Exit 6 off M3 and follow A30 west, ground off Winchester Road.
                      Two miles from bus and rail stations
Capacity: 6,000       Cover: 1,500      Seats: 651      Floodlights: Yes

Clubhouse: Open every day (incl. lunchtime) Steward: Cheryl Fox (01256 464353)
Club Shop: Open daily 10.00-5.00pm, selling programmes, books, scarves, shirts, badges etc.
Contact Chris Richardson, Commercial Manager

**PREVIOUS**      **Leagues:** Hants 1900-40 45-71; Southern 71-87      **Ground:** Castle Field 1896-1947

**CLUB RECORDS**  **Attendance:** 5,085 v Wycombe Wanderers, FA Cup 1st Rd replay 97-98
                  **Win:** 10-0 v Chichester City (H), FA Cup 1st Qualifying Round, September 1976
                  **Defeat:** 0-8 v Aylesbury United, Southern League, April 1979.
                  **Goalscorer:** Paul Coombs 159 (Oct 91 99)      **Appearances:** Billy Coombs
                  **TransferFees - Paid:** £4,750 for Steve Ingham (Gosport Borough)      **Received:** £6,750 for Steve Ingham (Bashley)

**BEST SEASON**   **FA Trophy:** 3rd Rd 98-99, 0-2 v Yeovil T. (H)
                  **FA Cup:** 2nd Rd replay 97-98, 3-4 pens aet 0 -0 v Northampton (H) after 1-1; 2nd Rd 89-90, 2-3 v Torquay U. (H)
                  League clubs defeated: Wycombe Wanderers 97-98

**HONOURS**       Southern Lge Southern Div 85-86; Isthmian League Div 1 R-up 88-89 96-97; Hants League 67-68 69-70 70-71 (R-up 65-66 66-67 68-69), North Div 11-12 19-20); HantsSenior Cup 70-71 89-90 95-96 96-97

Players progressing:      Tony Godfrey (Southampton 58), John Neale (Exeter 72),Mike Doherty (Reading 82), Micky Cheetham (Ipswich 88), Matt Carmichael(Lincoln), Tony Franklin (Exeter), Steve Welsh (Peterborough 90)

*Basingstoke's Tony Cleeve*                                    *Photo: Ian Morsman*

## BASINGSTOKE TOWN - MATCH FACTS - 1998-99 SEASON

| No | Date | Venue | Comp | Opponents | Att | Result | Score | Goalscorers |
|---|---|---|---|---|---|---|---|---|
| 1 | 22/08 | H | RL P | Dulwich Hamlet | 521 | W | 2-1 | Mancey 30, Simpson 69 |
| 2 | 25/08 | A | RL P | Carshalton Athletic | 282 | L | 0-1 | |
| 3 | 29/08 | A | RL P | Heybridge Swifts | 234 | W | 9-3 | Killick 20, Banks 52 76, Emsden 56, Simpson 65 68, Mancey 26, Coombs 83 86 |
| 4 | 01/09 | H | RL P | Enfield | 734 | W | 1-0 | Mancey 80 |
| 5 | 05/09 | H | RL P | Hendon | 873 | D | 1-1 | Mancey 57 |
| 6 | 09/09 | A | RL C 1 | Croydon | 68 | W | 4-2 | Freeman, Own-Goal, Tydeman, Killick |
| 7 | 12/09 | A | RL P | St Albans City | 679 | L | 2-4 | Coombs 72 80 |
| 8 | 15/09 | H | RL P | Harrow Borough | 539 | W | 2-1 | Mancey 87, Mancey 90 |
| 9 | 19/09 | A | RL P | Boreham Wood | 303 | D | 1-1 | Killick 25 |
| 10 | 22/09 | H | RL P | Dagenham & Redbridge | 723 | D | 1-1 | Cleeve 83[p] |
| 11 | 26/09 | A | RL P | Bromley | 484 | W | 3-1 | Hurdle 43, Mancey 59 77 |
| 12 | 03/10 | A | FAC Q2 | Backwell United | 230 | D | 1-1 | Cleeve |
| 13 | 06/10 | H | FAC Q2 r | Backwell United | 547 | W | 1-0 | Mancey 34 |
| 14 | 10/10 | A | RL P | Hampton | 339 | L | 1-2 | Mancey 89 |
| 15 | 13/10 | H | RL P | Billericay Town | 709 | L | 0-1 | |
| 16 | 17/10 | H | FAC Q3 | Chalfont St Peter | 587 | W | 2-0 | Mancey(2) |
| 17 | 20/10 | H | P C 1 | Croydon | 235 | W | 4-1 | |
| 18 | 27/10 | H | HSC 2 | Whitchurch United | 175 | W | 4-0 | Simpson(2), Mancey, Freeman |
| 19 | 03/11 | H | FAC Q4 | Dover Athletic | 1011 | D | 2-2 | Simpson 26, Killick 43 |
| 20 | 07/11 | A | RL P | Purfleet | 184 | L | 1-2 | Coombs 59 |
| 21 | 09/11 | A | FAC Q4 r | Dover Athletic | 1318 | W | 2-1 | Lisk 66, Richardson 83 |
| 22 | 14/11 | A | FAC 1 | AFC Bournemouth | 3830 | L | 1-2 | Mancey 57 |
| 23 | 17/11 | A | RL P | Slough Town | 475 | W | 1-0 | Mancey 65 |
| 24 | 21/11 | A | FAT 2 | Merthyr Tydfil | 481 | W | 2-0 | Redwood 2, Mancey 27 |
| 25 | 23/11 | A | RL C 2 | Bishop's Stortford | 97 | L | 4-5 | Killick(2), Hurdle, Own-Goal |
| 26 | 28/11 | H | RL P | Sutton United | 844 | L | 1-2 | Mancey 90 |
| 27 | 01/12 | H | HSC 3 | Eastleigh | 161 | W | 7-1 | Morley, Xavier(2), Simpson, Mancey(2), Killick |
| 28 | 05/12 | A | RL P | Hendon | 236 | L | 1-2 | Mancey 22 |
| 29 | 12/12 | H | RL P | St Albans City | 563 | L | 1-2 | Mancey 30 |
| 30 | 19/12 | A | RL P | Chesham United | 368 | W | 2-0 | Cleek 45 68 |
| 31 | 22/12 | H | P C 2 | Bognor Regis Town | 301 | W | 3-0 | Mancey(2), Xavier |
| 32 | 28/12 | H | RL P | Aldershot Town | 2810 | W | 2-1 | Simpson 8, Cleeve 63[p] |
| 33 | 09/01 | H | RL P | Heybridge Swifts | 638 | D | 2-2 | Simpson 7, Mancey 45 |
| 34 | 16/01 | H | FAT 3 | Yeovil Town | 1617 | L | 0-2 | |
| 35 | 23/01 | H | RL P | Carshalton Athletic | 481 | W | 2-1 | Mancey 45, Simpson 65 |
| 36 | 30/01 | A | RL P | Dulwich Hamlet | 298 | L | 0-2 | |
| 37 | 02/02 | H | HSC QF | Newport IoW | 236 | W | 2-1 | Thorpe 20, Huxford 53 |
| 38 | 06/02 | H | RL P | Boreham Wood | 590 | D | 1-1 | Wilkinson 16 |
| 39 | 09/02 | A | P C 3 | Dulwich Hamlet | 89 | L | 1-3 | Mancey |
| 40 | 13/02 | A | RL P | Harrow Borough | 293 | W | 2-0 | Xavier 68, Killick 88 |
| 41 | 16/02 | A | RL C 3 | Sutton United | 178 | L | 0-2 | |
| 42 | 20/02 | A | RL P | Billericay Town | 526 | D | 0-0 | |
| 43 | 23/02 | A | RL P | Gravesend & Northfleet | 355 | D | 2-2 | Mancey 38, Xavier 90 |
| 44 | 27/02 | H | RL P | Hampton | 634 | W | 1-0 | Tydeman 54 |
| 45 | 06/03 | H | RL P | Bromley | 530 | D | 1-1 | Beeks 45 |
| 46 | 09/03 | A | RL P | Enfield | 409 | L | 2-3 | Mancey 26, Xavier 36 |
| 47 | 13/03 | A | RL P | Dagenham & Redbridge | 768 | L | 0-2 | |
| 48 | 16/03 | H | HSC SF(1) | Lymington & New Milton | 273 | W | 3-0 | Morley, Mancey(2) |
| 49 | 20/03 | A | RL P | Aylesbury United | 865 | L | 2-3 | Mancey 45, Xavier 74 |
| 50 | 27/03 | H | RL P | Walton & Hersham | 463 | D | 0-0 | |
| 51 | 30/03 | A | HSC SF(2) | Lymington & New Milton | 237 | W | 2-0 | Mancey, Tydeman |
| 52 | 03/04 | H | RL P | Bishop's Stortford | 421 | W | 3-1 | Mancey 44, Sills 87, Xavier 89 |
| 53 | 05/04 | A | RL P | Aldershot Town | 2272 | W | 1-0 | Wilkinson 41 |
| 54 | 10/04 | H | RL P | Purfleet | 501 | W | 3-2 | Mead 1[og], Xavier 65[p], Mancey 88 |
| 55 | 13/04 | A | RL P | Walton & Hersham | 213 | L | 1-2 | Xavier 7 |
| 56 | 15/04 | H | RL P | Chesham United | 405 | W | 4-0 | Mancey 21 85, Xavier 29[p], Harris 38 |
| 57 | 17/04 | A | RL P | Gravesend & Northfleet | 563 | L | 0-1 | |
| 58 | 20/04 | A | RL P | Bishop's Stortford | 128 | D | 0-0 | |
| 59 | 24/04 | H | RL P | Slough Town | 687 | L | 0-2 | |
| 60 | 27/04 | H | RL P | Aylesbury United | 469 | W | 2-1 | Mancey 45 69 |
| 61 | 01/05 | A | RL P | Sutton United | 1381 | W | 2-1 | Xavier 28 35 |
| 62 | 05/05 | A | HSC F | Aldershot Town | 3143 | L | 0-1 | (at Southampton) |

**PLAYING SQUAD 1999-2000:**

GOALKEEPERS: Graham Benstead (Kingstonian), Vince Matassa

DEFENDERS: Paul Hardyman (Slough Town), Mark Lisk (Dorchester Town), Toby Redwood (Dorchester Town), Derek Simpson (Slough Town), Michael Thorp (Slough Town)

MIDFIELDERS: David Asker, Neil Davis (Farnborough Town), Gus Hurdle (Bognor Regis Town), Steve Richardson (Weymouth)

FORWARDS: Alan Carey, Andy Freeman (Reading), Tommy Killick, Craig Luckens, Ian Mancey, Aaron Roberts (Farnham Town), Stuart Willes (BAT Sports), Mark Xavier (Boreham Wood)

# BILLERICAY TOWN

## CLUB OFFICIALS

Chairman: **Rod Moore**
Vice Chairmen: **Jim Hall and John Stacey**
President: **Barry Spall**
Secretary: **Len Dewson,** 14 Graham Close,
Billericay, Essex CM12 0QW (01277622375)
Press Officer: Robert Moore

## FOOTBALL MANAGEMENT TEAM

Manager: Gary Calder, Ass Man:Chris King
Coach: Joe Dunwell
Physio: Dave Lawson

### FACT FILE
Formed: 1880
Nickname: The Town
Sponsors: Tony Thake Distribution
Colours: All royal Blue
Change colours: All yellow
Midweek Matches: Tuesday
Res' Lge: Essex & Herts Border Comb

1998-99 Captain: Chris Moore
P.o.Y.: Dave Root
Top Scorer: David Adekola

**GROUND:**    New Lodge, Blunts Wall Road, Billericay CM12 9SA (01277 652188)
**Directions:** From Shenfield (A129) right at 1st lights then 2nd right. FromBasildon (A129)
over 1st lights in town, then left at next lights and 2nd right. Half mile from Billericay (GER)
(London Liverpool St. - Southend line). 5 mins walk from buses 222, 251, 357, 255, 551
**Capacity:** 3,500    **Seats:** 424    **Cover:** 800    **Floodlights:** Yes
**Clubhouse:** Open every evening 8-11pm (except Monday)(1pm-11pm Sat) and weekend-
lunchtimes noon-2.30pm. Discos, live entertainment
**Club Shop:** Open matchdays for souvenirs, metal badges, old progs, programmesswaps
Nigel Harris (01268 558114)

Pages: 40 Price: £1.20
Editor: Mark Kettley    (01277 636149)
Local Press: Evening Echo, Billericay
Gazette, Billericay Recorder
Local Radio: BBC Radio Essex,
Essex Radio, x FM

**PREVIOUS**    **Leagues:** Romford & Dist. 1890-1914; Mid Essex 18-47; South Essex Comb. 47-66; Essex Olympian 66-71;
Essex Snr 71-77; Athenian 77-79    **Grounds:** Laindon Road (pre-1971).
**CLUB RECORDS  Attendance:** 3,841 v West Ham Utd, Floodlight opener 77. Comp match: 3,193 v Farnborough Tn, FA Vase SF 1st leg 76
**Win:** 11-0 v Stansted (A), Essex Senior League 5/5/76
**Defeat:** 3-10 v Chelmsford City (A), Essex Senior Cup 4/1/93
**Goalscorer:** (career) F Clayden 273, (season) Leon Gutmore 51 (97-98)    **Appearances:** J Pullen 418
**Fees - Paid:** Undisclosed    **Received:** £22,500+ increments for Steve Jones (West Ham, Nov. 1992)
**BEST SEASON    FA Cup:** 1st Rd Proper 97-98    **FA Vase:** Winners - 75-76, 76-77 & 78-79
**FA Trophy:** 1st Rd Prop 93-94,97-98    **FA Amateur Cup:** 3rd Qual Rd 73-74
**HONOURS:**    Essex Snr Lg 72-73 74-75 75-76, R-up 71-2 73-4, Lg Cup 71-74 76-77 (R-up 74-5),Challenge Cup 72-73; Isthmian Lge - Div 2
79-80, Div 1 R-up 80-81, 97-98;Athenian Lg 77-79 (Lg Cup 77-78); East Anglian Cup R-up 79-80 84-5; Essex SnrCup 75-76
(R-up 85-6 93-4 94-5 95-6); Essex Snr Tphy 77-78 79-80; EssexThameside Tphy 86-87 91-92 (R-up 90-1); Essex F'lit Tphy
77-78; Phillips F'lit Tphy 76-77; Rothmans Merit Award 1978
**Players progressing:** D Westwood (QPR) 75, A Hull, D Carter (Peterborough,Orient), D Cass (Orient) 88,
D Ludden (Orient) 92, S Jones (West Ham Utd) 92

*Billericay's goalkeeper Dave Root misses the ball under pressure from Slough's Chris White.   Photo: Alan Coomes*

# BILLERICAY TOWN - MATCH FACTS - 1998-99 SEASON

| No | Date | Venue | Comp | Opponents | Att | Result | Score | Goalscorers |
|----|------|-------|------|-----------|-----|--------|-------|-------------|
| 1 | 22/08 | A | RL P | Bishop's Stortford | 257 | D | 1-1 | Payne 46 |
| 2 | 25/08 | H | RL P | Chesham United | 789 | W | 3-0 | Adekola(2), Gutzmore[p] |
| 3 | 29/08 | H | RL P | Sutton United | 725 | L | 1-2 | Brewer 87 |
| 4 | 31/08 | A | RL P | Purfleet | 439 | W | 2-0 | Adekola 10, Gutzmore 78 |
| 5 | 05/09 | A | RL P | Dagenham & Redbridge | 880 | W | 2-1 | Blackford 78[og], Ridout 80 |
| 6 | 08/09 | A | RL C 1 | **Worthing** | **155** | **W** | **1-0** | **Blaney** |
| 7 | 12/09 | H | RL P | Walton & Hersham | 532 | W | 1-0 | Adekola 86 |
| 8 | 15/09 | A | RL P | Gravesend & Northfleet | 450 | D | 0-0 | |
| 9 | 19/09 | H | RL P | Carshalton Athletic | 568 | W | 2-0 | Gutzmore 53, Adekola 72 |
| 10 | 22/09 | A | RL P | Slough Town | 484 | D | 1-1 | St Hilaire 49 |
| 11 | 26/09 | H | RL P | Aldershot Town | 1407 | D | 1-1 | Adekola 2 |
| 12 | 03/10 | H | FAC Q2 | **Tonbridge Angels** | **503** | **W** | **4-0** | **Adekola 54, Battram 66 85, Ridout 57** |
| 13 | 10/10 | H | RL P | Boreham Wood | 602 | W | 1-0 | Battram 15 |
| 14 | 13/10 | A | RL P | Basingstoke Town | 709 | W | 1-0 | Adekola 10 |
| 15 | 17/10 | A | FAC Q3 | **Crawley Town** | **1321** | **L** | **0-1** | |
| 16 | 20/10 | H | RL P | Hendon | 447 | W | 2-1 | St Hilaire 50, Adekola 89 |
| 17 | 24/10 | A | FAT 1 | **Worcester City** | **441** | **L** | **1-2** | **Adekola 72** |
| 18 | 26/10 | A | RL P | St Albans City | 826 | L | 0-1 | |
| 19 | 03/11 | A | RL C 2 | **Sutton United** | **189** | **L** | **0-4** | |
| 20 | 07/11 | H | RL P | Harrow Borough | 712 | D | 2-2 | Adekola 57, Gutzmore 61 |
| 21 | 21/11 | H | RL P | Hampton | 615 | W | 2-0 | Gutzmore 22[p], Houkes 84 |
| 22 | 28/11 | A | RL P | Aylesbury United | 1121 | L | 0-3 | |
| 23 | 30/11 | A | P C 2 | **Purfleet** | **178** | **L** | **1-2** | **Gutzmore** |
| 24 | 02/12 | A | ESC 3 | **Harlow Town** | **120** | **D** | **1-1** | **Charles** (3-1 pens) |
| 25 | 05/12 | H | RL P | Dagenham & Redbridge | 806 | L | 1-2 | Gutzmore 39[p] |
| 26 | 12/12 | H | RL P | Walton & Hersham | 167 | W | 4-3 | St Hilaire 40 59, Gutzmore 72, Parratt 88 |
| 27 | 19/12 | H | RL P | Dulwich Hamlet | 619 | W | 1-0 | Adekola 37 |
| 28 | 28/12 | A | RL P | Heybridge Swifts | 666 | L | 0-1 | |
| 29 | 02/01 | H | RL P | Bromley | 777 | D | 2-2 | Adekola 58, Nartey 76 |
| 30 | 05/01 | A | ESC 4 | **Romford** | **225** | **L** | **1-3** | **Matthews** |
| 31 | 16/01 | H | RL P | Purfleet | 812 | L | 0-1 | |
| 32 | 23/01 | H | RL P | Chesham United | 533 | D | 3-3 | Nartey 26, Adekola 35 89 |
| 33 | 30/01 | H | RL P | Bishop's Stortford | 625 | W | 3-2 | Adekola 60, Nartey 66, Hooker 88 |
| 34 | 06/02 | A | RL P | Hampton | 240 | D | 0-0 | |
| 35 | 13/02 | H | RL P | Gravesend & Northfleet | 776 | L | 0-2 | |
| 36 | 16/02 | A | RL P | Enfield | 428 | L | 0-1 | |
| 37 | 20/02 | H | RL P | Basingstoke Town | 526 | D | 0-0 | |
| 38 | 27/02 | A | RL P | Boreham Wood | 439 | D | 0-0 | |
| 39 | 06/03 | A | RL P | Aldershot Town | 2075 | W | 1-0 | Adekola 36 |
| 40 | 13/03 | H | RL P | Slough Town | 577 | L | 1-2 | Portway 88 |
| 41 | 16/03 | A | RL P | Dulwich Hamlet | 277 | W | 4-2 | Portway 30 90, Parratt 36[p], Adekola 72 |
| 42 | 20/03 | H | RL P | St Albans City | 651 | D | 3-3 | Adams 16, Parratt 62, Portway 88 |
| 43 | 23/03 | A | RL P | Sutton United | 736 | L | 1-4 | Portway 36 |
| 44 | 27/03 | A | RL P | Hendon | 227 | L | 0-2 | |
| 45 | 03/04 | A | RL P | Bromley | 399 | D | 2-2 | Blaney 79, Portway 89 |
| 46 | 05/04 | H | RL P | Heybridge Swifts | 710 | W | 2-1 | Portway 35, Blaney 55 |
| 47 | 10/04 | A | RL P | Harrow Borough | 375 | D | 3-3 | Adams 38, Portway 41, Parratt 85 |
| 48 | 16/04 | H | RL P | Enfield | 786 | L | 0-1 | |
| 49 | 24/04 | A | RL P | Carshalton Athletic | 374 | L | 1-3 | Parratt 45[p] |
| 50 | 01/05 | H | RL P | Aylesbury United | 674 | L | 0-3 | |

**PLAYING SQUAD 1999-2000:**
GOALKEEPERS: David Root (Kingstonian)
DEFENDERS: Kirk Game (Dagenham & Redbridge), Kevin Jordan (Bishop's Stortford), John Ridout (Bishop's Stortford), Mark Sinfield (Berkhamsted Town), Steve Terry (Enfield)
MIDFIELDERS: Kieran Adams (Barnet), Robbie Gammons (Bishop's Stortford), David Kreyling (Hullbridge Sports), Dean Parratt (Dagenham & Redbridge), Kenrick Roudette (Romford)
FORWARDS: David Adekola (Bishop's Stortford), Simon Bochenski (Hampton), Lennie Dennis (Gravesend & Northfleet), Richard Dunwell (Enfield), Lee Williams (Enfield)

# BOREHAM WOOD

## CLUB OFFICIALS

Chairman: **Paul Moriarty**
President: **W F O'Neill**
Secretary: **Peter Smith**, 26 Briarwood Rd,
Stoneleight, Epson, Surrey KT17 2LY
(0208393 2902 (H) 0411 745987 (W))
Press Officer: **John D Gill** (0181 723 6407)

### FOOTBALL MANAGEMENT TEAM
Manager: Bobby Makin
Asst Manager: Alan Carrington
Coach: Billy Harrigan
Physio: Dave Dickens

**FACT FILE**

Formed: 1948
Nickname: The Wood
Sponsors: L & M Foods / Wansons
Colours: White/black/red
Change colours: Amber & black
Midweek matchday: Tuesday

**GROUND:** Meadow Park, Broughinge Rd, Boreham Wood, Herts WD6 5AL (0181 9535097)

**Directions:** A1 towards London from M25, 1st turn off for Boreham Wood, head fortown cen-
tre, into Brook Rd at r'bout before town centre, Broughinge Rd is 1stleft. 1 mile from Elstree &
Boreham Wood station (Thameslink), then bus 292 or107 to Red Lion (5 minutes walk)
Capacity: 4,502    Cover: 1,568      Seats: 500      Floodlights: Yes
**Clubhouse:** (0181 953 5097). Open during normal licensing hours. Snacks available.
Function room (250) available for hire
**Club Shop:** Sells good selection of souvenirs & programmes.
Contact: Dell Ward 0181 363 7345

Pages: 32 Price: £1
Editor: John Gill
(0181 723 6407)
Local Radio: Chiltern Radio
Local Press: Boreham Wood Times, Watford
Observer, Herts Advertiser

**PREVIOUS**     **Leagues:** Mid Herts 48-52, Parthenon 52-57, Spartan 56-66, Athenian 66-74
              **Ground:** Eldon Avenue 1948-63          **Names:** Boreham Wood Rovers and Royal Retournez, amalgamated in 1948
**CLUB RECORDS** **Attendance:** 2,500 v St Albans, F.A. Amateur Cup 70-71
              **Goalscorer:** Micky Jackson, 208          **Appearances:** Dave Hatchett, 617
              **Transfer Fee Received:** £10,000 from Barnet for Dean Samuels 1996
**BEST SEASON**  **FA Amateur Cup:** 3rd Rd. replay 70-71       **FA Trophy:** Quarter Finals 1995-96. Replay at Chorley 3-4
              **FA Cup:** 2nd Round v Luton Town 1996-97. 1st Rd 77-78, 73-74
**HONOURS:**     Isthmian Lg. Div I 94-95, Isthmian Lg Div 2 76-77 (Yth Cup R-up 80-81), Isthmian Lge. Cup 96-97; Athenian Lg 73-74 (Div 2
              68-69, Div 1 R-up 69-70), Spartan Lg R-up 65-66, Herts Senior Cup 71-72 (R-up 66-67 74-75 79-80 87-88), Herts Junior Cup
              51-52, Parthenon Lg 55-56 (R-up(2) 53-55 56-57, Herts Charity Shield 64-65, Herts Interm Cup 69-70, Herts Charity Cup (5)
              80-81 83-84 85-86 88-90 (R-up 71-72 84-85 86-87 90-91 91-92 92-93), London Senior Cup R-up89-90, London Intermediate
              Cup 70-71, Neale Trophy 69-70, Essex & Herts BorderComb 72-73 (Lg Cup 72-73, Western Div R-up 82-83 89-90), Mithras
              Cup 76-77, Middx Border Lg 81-82 (Lg Cup 79-80), Wallspan Floodlit 86-87

Players progressing:  Colin Franks (Watford & Sheff Utd), Charles Ntamark (Walsall), Dean Samuels (Barnet 96)

*Back Row (L-R): Mark Brown, Alan McCarthy, Bruce Sewell, Martin Taylor, Steve Heffer, Steve Daly, Adam French*
*Front Row: Dominic Grime, Jason Shaw, Shaun Marshall, Steve Saunders, Tony 'Junior' Samuels. Photo: Clive*

# BOREHAM WOOD - MATCH FACTS - 1998-99 SEASON

| No | Date | Venue | Comp | Opponents | Att | Result | Score | Goalscorers |
|---|---|---|---|---|---|---|---|---|
| 1 | 22/08 | A | RL P | Dagenham & Redbridge | 697 | D | 1-1 | Xavier 81 |
| 2 | 25/08 | H | RL P | Bromley | 240 | L | 0-3 | |
| 3 | 29/08 | H | RL P | Walton & Hersham | 203 | D | 0-0 | |
| 4 | 01/09 | A | RL P | Aylesbury United | 990 | D | 0-0 | |
| 5 | 05/09 | A | RL P | Hampton | 213 | D | 3-3 | Heffer 22, Shaw 29, Daly 86 |
| 6 | 08/09 | H | RL C 1 | Enfield | 216 | W | 2-0 | Shaw 80, Dixon 90 |
| 7 | 12/09 | H | RL P | Purfleet | 207 | W | 2-1 | Shaw 71, Dixon 80 |
| 8 | 15/09 | A | RL P | Sutton United | 540 | L | 1-2 | P Shaw 69 |
| 9 | 19/09 | H | RL P | Basingstoke Town | 303 | D | 1-1 | J Shaw 35 |
| 10 | 22/09 | A | RL P | Carshalton Athletic | 242 | D | 1-1 | Heffer 22 |
| 11 | 26/09 | H | RL P | Dulwich Hamlet | 255 | W | 4-0 | J Shaw 22, Dixon 39, Brown 44, Ireland 69 |
| 12 | 03/10 | H | FAC Q2 | Saltdean United | 233 | W | 4-0 | Dixon 3, Xavier 46, Samuels 47, Heffer 56 |
| 13 | 10/10 | A | RL P | Billericay Town | 602 | L | 0-1 | |
| 14 | 13/10 | H | RL P | Heybridge Swifts | 202 | D | 1-1 | Brown 90 |
| 15 | 17/10 | A | FAC Q3 | Royston Town | 239 | W | 2-0 | Xavier 21, McCarthy 77[p] |
| 16 | 20/10 | A | RL P | Enfield | 423 | W | 3-1 | McCarthy 30[p], Samuels 69, Nisbet 75 |
| 17 | 28/10 | A | FAT 1 | Molesey | 102 | W | 2-1 | Samuels, Nisbett |
| 18 | 31/10 | H | FAC Q4 | Sutton United | 541 | W | 1-0 | Dixon 20[p] |
| 19 | 03/11 | H | RL C 2 | Hungerford Town | 68 | W | 3-1 | Dixon, Walker, P Shaw |
| 20 | 07/11 | A | RL P | Aldershot Town | 1964 | L | 0-6 | |
| 21 | 15/11 | H | FAC 1 | Luton Town | 1772 | L | 2-3 | Nisbet 54, Xavier 81 |
| 22 | 17/11 | A | HSC 2 | Ware | 75 | W | 2-0 | Ireland, Dixon |
| 23 | 21/11 | A | FAT 2 | Forest Green Rovers | 432 | L | 1-4 | Samuels 73 |
| 24 | 24/11 | H | P C 1 | Braintree Town | 63 | W | 2-0 | Samuels, Own-Goal |
| 25 | 28/11 | H | RL P | Gravesend & Northfleet | 252 | W | 3-1 | Samuels 13, Brown 77 90 |
| 26 | 01/12 | H | RL P | Harrow Borough | 205 | W | 1-0 | Brown |
| 27 | 05/12 | A | RL P | Purfleet | 134 | L | 1-2 | J Shaw 39 |
| 28 | 12/12 | H | RL P | Hampton | 228 | W | 4-2 | Brown 20, Dixon 24, Samuels 32, Ireland 52 |
| 29 | 19/12 | A | RL P | Slough Town | 502 | W | 3-0 | Brady 5, Dixon 10, Samuels 76 |
| 30 | 21/12 | H | P C 2 | Canvey Island | 77 | D | 1-1 | Collins (0-3 pens) |
| 31 | 28/12 | H | RL P | Bishop's Stortford | 309 | L | 1-2 | P Shaw 55 |
| 32 | 02/01 | A | RL P | Hendon | 350 | W | 1-0 | T Samuels 24 |
| 33 | 09/01 | A | RL P | Walton & Hersham | 220 | D | 1-1 | Samuels 32 |
| 34 | 16/01 | H | RL P | Carshalton Athletic | 338 | D | 4-4 | Heffer 18, Brady 23, Ireland 88, Daly 90 |
| 35 | 23/01 | A | RL P | Bromley | 355 | D | 2-2 | Ireland 12, Heffer 80 |
| 36 | 26/01 | H | HSC QF | Hoddesdon Town | 58 | W | 4-2 | Ireland, Heffer(2), Brady |
| 37 | 30/01 | H | RL P | Aylesbury United | 425 | L | 1-6 | Ireland 37 |
| 38 | 06/02 | A | RL P | Basingstoke Town | 590 | D | 1-1 | Heffer 48 |
| 39 | 13/02 | H | RL P | Sutton United | 459 | W | 2-0 | Shaw 44, Dixon 58 |
| 40 | 15/02 | H | RL P | St Albans City | 703 | W | 2-1 | Vickers 16[og], Samuels 34 |
| 41 | 18/02 | A | RL C 3 | Barton Rovers | 110 | W | 3-0 | Samuels, Brady, Collins |
| 42 | 20/02 | A | RL P | Heybridge Swifts | 240 | L | 0-2 | |
| 43 | 23/02 | H | HSC SF | Potters Bar Town | 90 | W | 3-0 | Samuels, Brady(2) |
| 44 | 27/02 | H | RL P | Billericay Town | 439 | D | 0-0 | |
| 45 | 02/03 | H | RL P | Slough Town | 246 | W | 1-0 | Samuels 27 |
| 46 | 06/03 | H | RL P | Dulwich Hamlet | 286 | L | 0-2 | |
| 47 | 09/03 | H | RL C QF | Marlow | 101 | W | 5-1 | Dixon(2), Ireland, Brown, D Greene |
| 48 | 20/03 | H | RL P | Enfield | 752 | W | 3-2 | Dixon 51, D Grime 66, Brown 77 |
| 49 | 23/03 | A | RL C SF(1) | Maidenhead United | 308 | W | 3-2 | Brown, Samuels, Dixon |
| 50 | 27/03 | A | RL P | Harrow Borough | 227 | L | 0-3 | |
| 51 | 30/03 | H | RL P | Dagenham & Redbridge | 369 | L | 0-2 | |
| 52 | 03/04 | H | RL P | Hendon | 472 | W | 2-0 | Dean 10, Samuels 47 |
| 53 | 05/04 | A | RL P | Bishop's Stortford | 174 | L | 0-2 | |
| 54 | 07/04 | H | RL C SF(2) | Maidenhead United | 102 | W | 1-0 | Dixon 86[p] |
| 55 | 10/04 | H | RL P | Aldershot Town | 553 | D | 1-1 | D Grime 53 |
| 56 | 17/04 | A | RL P | Chesham United | 345 | W | 5-2 | Ireland 31 85, Dean 33 60, Stallard 65[og] |
| 57 | 24/04 | H | RL P | St Albans City | 450 | D | 1-1 | Brady 10 |
| 58 | 27/04 | H | RL P | Chesham United | 213 | D | 0-0 | |
| 59 | 01/05 | A | RL P | Gravesend & Northfleet | 370 | L | 2-3 | D Grime 58, P Shaw 84 |
| 60 | 03/05 | A | RL C F | Aldershot Town | 1611 | L | 1-2 | Samuels 45 (at Slough Town) |
| 61 | 05/05 | H | HSC F | Watford | n/k | W | 3-2 | P Shaw, Prutton, Own-Goal (at Letchworth) |

PLAYING SQUAD 1999-2000:
GOALKEEPERS: Martin Taylor (Bishop's Stortford)
DEFENDERS: Dominic Grime (Hitchin Town), Dave Hatchett (Enfield), Alan McCarthy (Leyton Orient), Gary Nisbit (Collier Row)
MIDFIELDERS: Matt Brady (Barnet), Mark Brown (Luton Town), Paul Moran (Enfield), Andy Prutton (Harrow Borough), Matthew Vier (Stevenage Borough)
FORWARDS: Kerry Dixon (Doncaster Rovers), Shaun Marshall (Enfield), Simon Miller (Barkingside), Anthony Samuels (Leyton Pennant), Paul Shaw (Barkingside)

# CANVEY ISLAND

**FACT FILE**
Formed: 1926
Nickname: Gulls
Sponsors: Kings The Clubs
Colours: Yellow/white/white
Change colours: White/yellow/yellow
Midweek matchday: Tuesday
Reserves' League:
Essex & Herts Border Comb

1998-99 Captain: Steve Tilson
Top scorer & P.o.Y.: Steve Tilson

**CLUB OFFICIALS**
Chairman: **Ray Cross,** 95 Lakeside Path,
Canvey Island, Essex SS8 5PD.
Tel: 01268 684357 (H)
Secretary: **Mrs Frances Roche,** 56 Harvest
Road, Canvey Island SS8 9RP.
Tel: 01268 698586 (H/Fax)
Press Officer: **Tony Roche**
Tel: 01268 698586

**FOOTBALL MANAGEMENT TEAM**
Manager: Jeff King. 01268 511555 (B)
0850 654321 (Mobile)
Asst Manager: Glenn Pennyfather
Physio: Harry Johnson

**GROUND:** Park Lane, Canvey Island, Essex SS8 7PX
Tel: 01268 682991
**Directions:** A130 from A13 or A127 at Sadlers Farm r/about, 1 mile through town centre, 1st
right past old bus garage. Bus 3 or 151 fromBenfleet (BR) to stop after Admiral Jellicoe (PH)
Capacity: 3,108    Seats: 300    Cover: 800    Floodlights: Yes
**Clubhouse:** Open Tues, Thurs & Sats. Full licence. Food avaiable
**Club Shop:** Open matchdays. Selling programmes, badges, shirts etc.
Contact Mrs J Edwards

Programme:
Pages: 32 Price: £1
Editor: Rod Hall (01268 697348)
Local Press: Evening Echo
Local Radio: Essex FM, BBC Essex

**PREVIOUS** **Leagues:** Southend & Dist.; Thurrock & Thameside Comb.; Parthenon; Metropolitan;Gtr London 64-71; Essex Senior
**Grounds:** None                **Names:** None

**CLUB RECORDS** **Attendance:** 3,250 v Brighton & Hove Albion  F.A. Cup 95-96
**Win:** 7-1 v Bedford                                    **Defeat:** 7-0 v Halstead
**Career Appearances:** Steve Price (407)         **Career Goalscorer:** Andy Jones (200)
**Fee received:** £3,000 for Ian Durrant from Grays Athletic
**Fee paid:** £ 5,000 for Chris Duffy to Northwich Victoria

**BEST SEASON** **FA Cup:** 1st Rd v Brighton (2-2) (replay 1-4) 95-96
**FA Vase:** Semi-final v Tiverton 27/3/93         **FA Trophy:** 3rd Rd V Cheltenham Town 98-99

**HONOURS:** Ryman Lge - Div 2 95-96, 97-98,R-up 98-99 Div 3 R-up 94-95; Carlton Trophy  95-96; Essex Sen Lg 86-87 92-93 (Lg Cup 79-
80 92-93),Trophy R-up 93-94; Harry Fisher Mem.Tphy 93-94; Essex Thameside Trophy 93-94; Parthenon Lge Cup 58-59;
Metropolian Lge 67-68 68-69, Cup 67-68 68-69; Thameside 95-96 97-98; Res. Lge 95-96, Cup 95-96, Essex Senior Cup 98-99

Players progressing:  Peter Taylor (Spurs), Gary Heale (Luton T)

*Chertsey's Richard McDonagh just gets in a tackle to stop Steve Parmenter (10) of Canvey getting in a shot.*

# CANVEY ISLAND - MATCH FACTS - 1998-99 SEASON

| No | Date | Venue | Comp | Opponents | Att | Result | Score | Goalscorers |
|----|------|-------|------|-----------|-----|--------|-------|-------------|
| 1 | 22/08 | H | RL 1 | Maidenhead United | 375 | L | 0-4 | |
| 2 | 25/08 | A | RL 1 | Grays Athletic | 307 | W | 1-0 | Porter |
| 3 | 29/08 | A | RL 1 | Wembley | 96 | W | 2-1 | Riley, Jones[p] |
| 4 | 31/08 | H | RL 1 | Staines Town | 210 | W | 2-0 | Tilson(2) |
| 5 | 05/09 | H | FAC P | **Stansted** | 203 | W | 6-1 | **Reilly 8, Brett 19 48, Tilson 63 64[p] 81** |
| 6 | 12/09 | A | RL 1 | Oxford City | 172 | L | 1-2 | Tilson 52 |
| 7 | 15/09 | H | RL 1 | Worthing | 173 | W | 2-0 | Williams, Tilson |
| 8 | 19/09 | H | FAC Q1 | **Histon** | 202 | W | 5-3 | **Jones, Donovan, Tilson, Brazier, Brett** |
| 9 | 22/09 | H | RL 1 | Bognor Regis Town | 225 | W | 2-0 | Williams, Brett |
| 10 | 26/09 | A | RL 1 | Berkhamsted Town | 210 | W | 3-0 | Jones, Tilson[p], Williams |
| 11 | 29/09 | A | RL 1 | Hitchin Town | 274 | L | 0-3 | |
| 12 | 03/10 | A | FAC Q2 | **Wingate & Finchley** | 225 | W | 5-0 | |
| 13 | 06/10 | A | RL C 1 | **Hornchurch** | 120 | W | 3-0 | **Tilson(2), Williams** |
| 14 | 09/10 | H | RL 1 | Romford | 355 | L | 0-2 | |
| 15 | 17/10 | A | FAC Q3 | **Lowestoft Town** | 501 | L | 2-4 | **Reilly, Tilson** |
| 16 | 24/10 | H | FAT 1 | **Wisbech Town** | 350 | W | 1-0 | **Sussex 77** |
| 17 | 27/10 | H | RL 1 | Uxbridge | 219 | W | 1-0 | Porter |
| 18 | 07/11 | A | RL 1 | Wealdstone | 432 | L | 0-3 | |
| 19 | 09/11 | A | EFC 5 | **Ilford** | n/k | W | 2-0 | **O'Shea 22, Ferguson 31** |
| 20 | 14/11 | H | RL 1 | Barton Rovers | 245 | L | 0-2 | |
| 21 | 17/11 | A | RL C 2 | **Berkhamsted Town** | 80 | L | 1-3 | **Hazle** |
| 22 | 21/11 | A | FAT 2 | **Evesham United** | 121 | D | 1-1 | **Hazle 80** |
| 23 | 24/11 | A | FAT 2 rep | **Evesham United** | 153 | W | 5-0 | **Williams 15 56, Britnell 38, Parmenter 43, Walker 79 og** |
| 24 | 28/11 | H | RL 1 | Leyton Pennant | 252 | W | 6-1 | Hazle(3), Cove[og], Reilly, Parmenter |
| 25 | 01/12 | H | ESC 3 | **Barking** | n/k | W | 1-0 | **Tilson 95[p]** |
| 26 | 05/12 | A | RL 1 | Bognor Regis Town | 312 | D | 0-0 | |
| 27 | 12/12 | H | RL 1 | Oxford City | 326 | W | 2-0 | Tilson, Brazier |
| 28 | 19/12 | A | RL 1 | Yeading | 169 | W | 3-1 | Tilson(3) |
| 29 | 21/12 | A | P C 2 | **Boreham Wood** | 77 | D | 1-1 | **Tilson**           **(3-0 pens)** |
| 30 | 28/12 | H | RL 1 | Braintree Town | 730 | W | 2-1 | Tilson(2) |
| 31 | 02/01 | A | RL 1 | Whyteleafe | 208 | D | 5-5 | Williams, Parmenter, Tilson, Brett, Payne |
| 32 | 09/01 | H | RL 1 | Grays Athletic | 440 | W | 2-1 | Parmenter(2) |
| 33 | 16/01 | A | FAT 3 | **Cheltenham Town** | 2045 | L | 1-2 | **Brett 48** |
| 34 | 23/01 | H | RL 1 | Wembley | 360 | W | 3-0 | Tilson, Lindsey, Parmenter |
| 35 | 27/01 | H | ESC 4 | **Chelmsford City** | 152 | W | 4-3 | **Hazle 7 28 80, Porter 67** |
| 36 | 30/01 | A | RL 1 | Staines Town | 238 | W | 3-0 | Brett, Parmenter, Jones |
| 37 | 02/02 | A | RL 1 | Leatherhead | 148 | W | 2-1 | Sussex, Tilson |
| 38 | 06/02 | H | RL 1 | Molesey | 343 | W | 2-1 | James, Brett |
| 39 | 13/02 | A | RL 1 | Worthing | 393 | W | 2-0 | Parmenter, Payne |
| 40 | 20/02 | A | RL 1 | Romford | 385 | L | 0-1 | |
| 41 | 23/02 | H | RL 1 | Yeading | 128 | W | 3-1 | Parmenter, Brett, Jones |
| 42 | 25/02 | H | EFC 5 | **Tilbury** | n/k | L | 1-3 | |
| 43 | 27/02 | H | RL 1 | Croydon | 330 | W | 2-1 | Tilson, Brett |
| 44 | 02/03 | H | ESC QF | **Romford** | 300 | W | 2-1 | **Tilson 76[p], Williams 77** |
| 45 | 04/03 | H | P C 3 | **Hendon** | 129 | L | 0-2 | |
| 46 | 06/03 | A | RL 1 | Hitchin Town | 335 | W | 3-0 | Parmenter, Brett, Williams |
| 47 | 10/03 | A | RL 1 | Molesey | 112 | D | 0-0 | |
| 48 | 13/03 | A | RL 1 | Berkhamsted Town | 155 | W | 3-1 | Sutton, Parmenter, Jones |
| 49 | 16/03 | A | ESC SF | **Clacton Town** | n/k | W | 3-0 | **Parmenter 16, Brett 43 67** |
| 50 | 20/03 | A | RL 1 | Uxbridge | 150 | W | 2-1 | Parmenter, Lindsey |
| 51 | 25/03 | H | EFC 5 | **Ilford** | n/k | W | 2-1 | |
| 52 | 27/03 | H | RL 1 | Leatherhead | 320 | W | 3-0 | Jones(2), Payne |
| 53 | 30/03 | H | E TST 2 | **Leyton Pennant** | n/k | W | 2-0 | **Parmenter 65 90** |
| 54 | 02/04 | H | RL 1 | Whyteleafe | 582 | D | 1-1 | Parmenter |
| 55 | 05/04 | A | RL 1 | Braintree Town | 552 | W | 2-0 | Payne, Williams |
| 56 | 10/04 | H | RL 1 | Wealdstone | 649 | W | 4-2 | Brett, Payne, Tilson, A Jones |
| 57 | 13/04 | A | RL 1 | Chertsey Town | 162 | D | 1-1 | Tilson |
| 58 | 17/04 | A | RL 1 | Barton Rovers | 186 | W | 1-0 | Tilson |
| 59 | 19/04 | H | ETST QF | **Witham Town** | n/k | W | 2-0 | **Parmenter, Jones** |
| 60 | 21/04 | A | RL 1 | Croydon | 81 | L | 0-3 | |
| 61 | 24/04 | H | RL 1 | Chertsey Town | 447 | W | 2-0 | Tilson, Brett |
| 62 | 26/04 | A | ESC F | **Leyton Orient** | 780 | W | 2-1 | **Tilson 1 64**     **(at Southend United)** |
| 63 | 28/04 | A | RL 1 | Maidenhead United | 143 | W | 2-0 | Brett 37, Brazier 40 |
| 64 | 01/05 | A | RL 1 | Leyton Pennant | 120 | D | 1-1 | Lindsay |
| 65 | 06/05 | H | E TST SF | **Southend United** | n/k | L | 0-3 | |

## PLAYING SQUAD 1999-2000:

GOALKEEPERS: Lee Ballard (Chelmsford City), Melvin Capleton (Southend United), Ash Harrison (Dover Athletic), Brian Horne (Farnborough Town), John Keeley (Selsey - dual)

DEFENDERS: Jeff Brazier (Leyton Orient), Garry Britnell (Enfield), Mark Quarrel (local football), Steve Ward (Grays Athletic), Gary Waters

MIDFIELDERS: Mark Barry (Billericay Town), Chris Duffy (Northwich Victoria), Scott Lindsey (Dover Athletic), Steve Parmenter (Billericay Town), Chris Payne (Billericay Town), Steve Tilson (Southend United), Paul Wilson (Southend United)

FORWARDS: Dominic Iofra (Billericay Town), Andy Jones (Billericay Town), Simon Liddle (Dulwich Hamlet), Trevor Paul (Romford)

# CARSHALTON ATHLETIC

## CLUB OFFICIALS

Chairman: **Andy Hay**
Jt-President: **W Stephenson**
Vice Chairman:T.B.A.
Secretary: **Vic Thompson**
11 Poulton Ave, Sutton, Surrey. SM1 3PZ.
Tel: 0181 6446402 (H)
General Manager: **Bob Clifford**
Press Officer: **Roger Fear**
Comm. Man.:Roger Fear

### FOOTBALL MANAGEMENT TEAM
Manager: Gary Bowyer
Coach: Dixon Gill
Physio: Alan McCreeney

## FACT FILE

Formed: 1903
Nickname: Robins
Sponsors: CDL Exhibition Contractors
Colours: White, maroon trim/maroon/white
Change colours: Maroon/white
Midweek matchday: Monday
Reserve League: Suburban
Newsline: 0930 555 877

1998-99
Captain: Matt Elverson
P.o.Y.: Paul Sears
Top Scorer: Richard Newbery

Pages: 20 Price: £1.00p
Editor: Andy Hill (0181 647 6288)

Local Press: Sutton Comet, Sutton Herald
Local Radio: BBc Southern Counties

**GROUND**      War Memorial Sports Ground, Colston Av, Carshalton SM5 2PW
Tel: 0181 642 8658
**Directions:** Turn right out of Carshalton BR Station, and Colston Avenue is first left. Entrance
150 yards on right. London Transport bus 151 from Morden to Wrythe Green Lane
Capacity: 8,000   Cover: 4,500   Seats: 240   Floodlights: Yes
**Clubhouse:** Open every evening and lunchtime. Licenced bar, pool, darts,machines, discos
on Saturday. Separate function hall (bookings taken). Food:sandwiches, rolls, burgers, hot
dogs, teas, coffees and soft drinks. (0181 642 8658)
**Club Shop:** Sells hats, scarves, T-shirts, badges, programmes etc

**PREVIOUS**    **Leagues:** Southern Sub (pre-1911); Surrey Snr 22-23; London 23-46; Corinthian46-56; Athenian 56-73
**Grounds:** Wrythe Recreation Ground 1907-14; Culvers Park 19-20

**CLUB RECORDS  Attendance:** 7,800 v Wimbledon, London Senior Cup
**Career goalscorer:** Jimmy Bolton(242)           **Career appearances:** Jon Warden (504)
**Transfer fee paid:** £5,000 for Junior Haynes 1998    **Transfer fee received:** £15,000 for Curtis Warmington (Enfield)
**Win:** 13-0 v Worthing, Loctite Cup Third Round 28/2/91
**F.A.Trophy :** 3rd Rd 95-96  lodst away at Hyde United (2-3)
**FA Cup:** 2nd Rd 82-83, lost 1-4 at Torquay. - League clubs defeated: None

**HONOURS:**    Isthmian League Div 2 R-up 76-77, Corinthian League 52-53 53-54, Surrey Senior League R-up 22-23, Surrey Senior Cup(3)
Runners-up (5) Surrey Senior Shield 75-76  Runners-up ( 2)), London Challenge Cup  91-92 Isthmian Lg Cup R-up 90-91

Players progressing: Roy Lunnes (Crystal Pal. 60), Les Burns (Charlton 67), Ron Walker (Watford), Nobby Warren (Exeter),Terry Stacey (Plymouth
A.), Frank GeorgelLeyton Orient) ,Tommy Williams (Colchester U), Alan Eagles (Leyton Orient), Derek Razzell (Q.PR),Muray Jones Crystal Pal.)
Gus Caesar (Arsenal), Darren Annon (Brentford) 94, Ian Cox (Crystal Pal.) 94, Carl Asaba (Brentford)

*Carshalton Athletic*

# CARSHALTON ATHLETIC - MATCH FACTS - 1998-99 SEASON

| No | Date | Venue | Comp | Opponents | Att | Result | Score | Goalscorers |
|----|------|-------|------|-----------|-----|--------|-------|-------------|
| 1 | 06/08 | A | T F Cup | Tooting & Mitcham United | n/k | L | 0-1 | |
| 2 | 22/08 | A | RL P | Aylesbury United | 750 | L | 0-2 | |
| 3 | 25/08 | H | RL P | Basingstoke Town | 282 | W | 1-0 | Smith |
| 4 | 29/08 | H | RL P | Bromley | 326 | D | 1-1 | Ajuya 87 |
| 5 | 01/09 | A | RL P | Walton & Hersham | 229 | L | 2-3 | Newbery 62, Smith 90[p] |
| 6 | 05/09 | A | RL P | Purfleet | 189 | L | 2-4 | Robson 58, Newbery 90[p] |
| 7 | 08/09 | H | RL C 1 | Banstead Athletic | 141 | W | 4-3 | Smith(2), M Fowler(2) |
| 8 | 12/09 | H | RL P | Hampton | 292 | L | 2-4 | Newbery 38, Smith 57 |
| 9 | 14/09 | A | RL P | Dagenham & Redbridge | 520 | L | 0-5 | |
| 10 | 19/09 | A | RL P | Billericay Town | 568 | L | 0-2 | |
| 11 | 22/09 | H | RL P | Boreham Wood | 242 | D | 1-1 | Haynes 70 |
| 12 | 26/09 | A | RL P | Heybridge Swifts | 173 | W | 2-0 | Smith 14, J Fowler 25 |
| 13 | 03/10 | A | FAC Q2 | Dorking | 241 | W | 5-0 | Newbery(2), J Fowler, M Fowler, Jones |
| 14 | 10/10 | H | RL P | Aldershot Town | 1003 | L | 0-2 | |
| 15 | 13/10 | A | RL P | Harrow Borough | 211 | L | 2-8 | Smith 19[p], Pitcher 68 |
| 16 | 17/10 | A | FAC Q3 | Aylesbury United | 809 | W | 1-0 | Haynes |
| 17 | 24/10 | A | FAT 1 | Salisbury City | 335 | L | 1-2 | Hynes 58 |
| 18 | 27/10 | H | RL P | Gravesend & Northfleet | 253 | L | 1-2 | Brown 76 |
| 19 | 03/11 | H | FAC Q4 | Salisbury City | 277 | L | 0-6 | |
| 20 | 07/11 | A | RL P | St Albans City | 793 | L | 0-1 | |
| 21 | 10/11 | H | RL C 2 | Uxbridge | 108 | L | 1-2 | Sears |
| 22 | 14/11 | H | RL P | Heybridge Swifts | 304 | L | 1-2 | M Fowler 86 |
| 23 | 28/11 | H | RL P | Bishop's Stortford | 283 | W | 1-0 | Newbery 29 |
| 24 | 01/12 | A | RL P | Dulwich Hamlet | 284 | D | 0-0 | |
| 25 | 05/12 | A | RL P | Hampton | 222 | D | 1-1 | Newbery 3 |
| 26 | 08/12 | H | SSC 1 | Croydon Athletic | 88 | W | 2-0 | Newbery, Gibson |
| 27 | 12/12 | H | RL P | Purfleet | 291 | W | 2-1 | Gorman 36, Sears 52 |
| 28 | 19/12 | A | RL P | Hendon | 274 | D | 1-1 | M Fowler 74 |
| 29 | 22/12 | H | RL P | Enfield | 402 | W | 2-1 | Jones 31, Elverson 64 |
| 30 | 28/12 | H | RL P | Sutton United | 1807 | W | 1-0 | Battams 40 |
| 31 | 02/01 | A | RL P | Chesham United | 436 | L | 0-3 | |
| 32 | 05/01 | H | P C 2 | Chertsey Town | 109 | W | 2-0 | Newbery(2) |
| 33 | 09/01 | A | RL P | Bromley | 402 | W | 3-2 | Newbery 28, Haynes 85, Gray 90[og] |
| 34 | 16/01 | A | RL P | Boreham Wood | 338 | D | 4-4 | Newbery 55 89, Haynes 64 79 |
| 35 | 23/01 | A | RL P | Basingstoke Town | 481 | L | 1-2 | Newbery 13 |
| 36 | 30/01 | H | RL P | Walton & Hersham | 367 | L | 1-3 | Newbery 39 |
| 37 | 06/02 | H | RL P | Gravesend & Northfleet | 592 | L | 1-3 | M Fowler 58 |
| 38 | 09/02 | A | SSC 2 | Whyteleafe | 140 | W | 3-0 | M Fowler(2), Haynes |
| 39 | 13/02 | H | RL P | Dagenham & Redbridge | 407 | D | 0-0 | |
| 40 | 16/02 | H | RL P | Slough Town | 275 | L | 0-3 | |
| 41 | 18/02 | H | P C 3 | Walton & Hersham | 90 | W | 2-0 | Newbery, Haynes |
| 42 | 20/02 | H | RL P | Harrow Borough | 286 | L | 1-2 | Newbery 11 |
| 43 | 23/02 | H | SSC QF | Tooting & Mitcham United | 155 | W | 2-0 | Newbery 53 60 |
| 44 | 27/02 | A | RL P | Aldershot Town | 1927 | L | 0-4 | |
| 45 | 01/03 | A | SSC SF | Kingstonian | 205 | D | 1-1 | Haynes 89 |
| 46 | 09/03 | H | RL P | Aylesbury United | 346 | D | 3-3 | Smith 24 60, Newbery 69 |
| 47 | 15/03 | H | SSC SF r | Kingstonian | 253 | W | 3-2 | Haynes(2), M Fowler |
| 48 | 18/03 | A | P C QF | Worthing | 114 | L | 0-3 | |
| 49 | 20/03 | H | RL P | Dulwich Hamlet | 376 | W | 2-0 | Smith 60, Denys 83 |
| 50 | 27/03 | H | RL P | Enfield | 510 | L | 0-1 | |
| 51 | 03/04 | H | RL P | Chesham United | 348 | L | 0-1 | |
| 52 | 05/04 | A | RL P | Sutton United | 1454 | L | 0-3 | |
| 53 | 13/04 | H | RL P | Hendon | 232 | L | 1-3 | Sears 85 |
| 54 | 17/04 | A | RL P | Slough Town | 509 | D | 1-1 | Denys 87 |
| 55 | 24/04 | H | RL P | Billericay Town | 374 | W | 3-1 | Haynes 17 51, M Fowler 88 |
| 56 | 26/04 | H | RL P | St Albans City | 348 | D | 1-1 | Haynes 20 |
| 57 | 01/05 | A | RL P | Bishop's Stortford | 350 | W | 2-1 | Newbery 79, Hurdle 84 |
| 58 | 03/05 | A | SSC F | Sutton United | 870 | L | 0-3 | (at Metropolitan Police) |

## PLAYING SQUAD 1999-2000:

GOALKEEPERS: Stuart Searle (Woking)

DEFENDERS: Steve Battams (Staines Town), Matt Elverson (Walton & Hersham), Jamie Gibson (Carshalton Athletic), Darren Pitcher

MIDFIELDERS: Lee Akers (Dulwich Hamlet), Gary Bowyer (Tooting & Mitcham United), Matt Edwards (Carshalton Athletic), David Jones (Sutton United)

FORWARDS: Tunde Ajay, Tony Brown (Croydon Athletic), Paul Gorman (Egham Town), Junior Haynes (Sutton United), Richard Newbery (Gravesend & Northfleet)

# CHESHAM UNITED

### CLUB OFFICIALS

President: **Bill Wells**
Chairman: **David Pembroke**
Secretary: **Jim Chambers**
c/o Chesham United FC.
Tel: 01494 774494 (H) 0181327 4016(B)
Commercial Manager: **Brian Lloyd**
Press Officer: **Jim Chambers**

### FOOTBALL MANAGEMENT TEAM
Manager: Lawrie Craker
Assistant Manager: Dave Russell
Physio: Craig Gill

### FACT FILE

Formed: 1886
Nickname: The Generals
Sponsors: MFI
Colours: Blue & orange
Change colours: All Yellow & green
Midweek home matchday: Tuesday
Reserve Team's League: Suburban North
Match information: 0891 884580

**GROUND:** The Meadow, Amy Lane, Amersham Road, Chesham, Bucks. HP5 1NE
Tel: 01494 794244 (ground clubhouse) Fax: 01494 335505

**Directions:** M25 junction 18, A404 to Amersham, A416 to Chesham - go down to r-about at foot of Amersham Hill, then sharp left. 10 mins walk from Chesham station (Metropolitan Line)
Capacity: 5,000    Cover: 2,500    Seats: 284    Floodlights: Yes

**Clubhouse:** Open every evening & matchdays. Bar snacks. Available for hire(business training meetings, weddings etc)
**Club Shop:** Open matchdays                 Metal Badges: Yes

Pages: 52     Price: £1,20
Editors: J & S Chambers
(01494 775490 [H])
Local Radio: Three Counties
Local Press: Bucks Examiner, Bucks Advertiser, Bucks Free Press

**PREVIOUS**    Leagues: Spartan 17-47; Corinthian 47-63; Athenian 63-73

**CLUB RECORDS Attendance:** 5,000 v Cambridge Utd, FA 3rd Rd 5/12/79
**Goalscorer:** John Willis
**Appearances:** Martin Baguley (600+)
**Fee Paid:** Undisclosed (club policy)
**Fee Received:** Undisclosed (club policy)

**BEST SEASON    FA Cup:** 3rd Rd 79-80. 1st Rd 66-67 68-69 76-77 82-83
**FA Amtr Cup:** R-up 67-68
**FA Trophy:** 3rd Rd 92-93 (1-3 v Sutton United [H])

**HONOURS:**    FA Amtr Cup R-up 67-68,
Isthmian Lg 92-93 (Div 1 90-91 96-97), Div 2 Nth 86-87,
Associate Members Cup R-up 90-91, Charity Shield 94-95;
Athenian Lg Div 1 Cup 63-64 68-69;
Corinthian Lg R-up (2) 60-62 (Lg Cup 60-61);
Spartan Lg (4) 21-23 24-25 32-33 (R-up 26-27 29-30 33-34);
Berks & Bucks Snr Cup 21-22 25-26 28-29 33-34 47-48
50-51 64-65 66-67 75-76 92-93 (R-up 94-95)

**Players progressing:**
Bill Shipwright (Watford 53)
Jimmy Strain (Watford 55),
Stewart Scullion (Charlton 65),
John Pyatt (L'pool 67),
Brian Carter (Brentford 68),
Kerry Dixon (Spurs 78),
Tony Currie (Torquay 84)

*Chesham United, venue for the FAXI v Highland League match. Photo: Garry Letts*

## CHESHAM UNITED - MATCH FACTS - 1998-99 SEASON

| No | Date | Venue | Comp | Opponents | Att | Result | Score | Goalscorers |
|----|------|-------|------|-----------|-----|--------|-------|-------------|
| 1 | 22/08 | H | RL P | Enfield | 1016 | W | 2-0 | Winston 44 45 |
| 2 | 25/08 | A | RL P | Billericay Town | 789 | L | 0-3 | |
| 3 | 29/08 | A | RL P | Slough Town | 1060 | L | 1-3 | Hammatt 52 |
| 4 | 01/09 | H | RL P | Aldershot Town | 1181 | D | 0-0 | |
| 5 | 05/09 | H | RL P | Dulwich Hamlet | 621 | D | 0-0 | |
| 6 | 08/09 | A | RL C 1 | **Bognor Regis Town** | 275 | D | 2-2 | **Winston, Argrave** |
| 7 | 12/09 | A | RL P | Heybridge Swifts | 202 | W | 4-0 | Argrave 27 28, Pluckrose 42, Gell 69[p] |
| 8 | 15/09 | H | RL P | Hendon | 428 | L | 0-2 | |
| 9 | 19/09 | A | RL P | St Albans City | 1018 | W | 3-2 | Thompson 9, Winston 16, Francis 20 |
| 10 | 22/09 | A | RL P | Hampton | 274 | W | 1-0 | Engwell 24 |
| 11 | 26/09 | H | RL P | Gravesend & Northfleet | 515 | W | 3-2 | Bushay 15, Gell 51 77 |
| 12 | 29/09 | H | RL C 1 rep | **Bognor Regis Town** | 166 | W | 2-1 | **Argrave, Winston** |
| 13 | 03/10 | A | FAC Q2 | **Bromley** | 422 | L | 1-2 | **Gell** |
| 14 | 10/10 | H | RL P | Dagenham & Redbridge | 424 | L | 2-5 | Bushay 36, Winston 44 |
| 15 | 13/10 | H | RL P | Sutton United | 688 | L | 0-2 | |
| 16 | 21/10 | A | RL P | Bishop's Stortford | 172 | L | 2-5 | Argrave 20, Bushay 71 |
| 17 | 07/11 | H | RL P | Walton & Hersham | 408 | L | 1-2 | Winston 68 |
| 18 | 10/11 | H | P C 1 | **Barton Rovers** | 102 | W | 4-1 | **Winston, Lawford, Denniss, Mitchell** |
| 19 | 17/11 | H | RL P | Purfleet | 238 | D | 3-3 | Flitter 30, Lawford 44 72 |
| 20 | 21/11 | A | FAT 2 | **Yeading** | 190 | D | 3-3 | **Argrave, Thompson, Winston** |
| 21 | 24/11 | H | FAT 2 rep | **Yeading** | 140 | L | 4-0 | **Winston, Bushay(2), Mitchell** |
| 22 | 28/11 | A | RL P | Harrow Borough | 326 | L | 4-5 | Lawford 10, Nabil 15, Winston 45, Brockett 84 |
| 23 | 05/12 | H | RL P | Heybridge Swifts | 316 | W | 1-0 | Winston 70 |
| 24 | 12/12 | A | RL P | Dulwich Hamlet | 341 | L | 2-3 | Winston 48, Mitchell 89 |
| 25 | 19/12 | H | RL P | Basingstoke Town | 368 | L | 0-2 | |
| 26 | 28/12 | A | RL P | Aylesbury United | 1869 | W | 3-0 | Winston 6 46, Lawford 56[p] |
| 27 | 02/01 | H | RL P | Carshalton Athletic | 436 | W | 3-0 | Winston 63, Bashir 83, Nabil 88 |
| 28 | 09/01 | H | RL P | Slough Town | 636 | W | 1-0 | Stephenson 82 |
| 29 | 12/01 | A | B&B SC 1 | **Abingdon Town** | 71 | W | 5-1 | **Bushay(2), Lawford, Totten, Bashir** |
| 30 | 16/01 | A | FAT 3 | **Crawley Town** | 1138 | W | 3-2 | **Winston 18 52 82** |
| 31 | 23/01 | H | RL P | Billericay Town | 533 | D | 3-3 | McAree 23, Thompson 78, Mitchell 87 |
| 32 | 30/01 | A | RL P | Enfield | 597 | D | 2-2 | McAree 16, Hutchins 56 |
| 33 | 02/02 | H | P C 2 | **Dagenham & Redbridge** | 137 | W | 2-1 | **Lawford, Hutchins** |
| 34 | 06/02 | H | FAT 4 | **Hendon** | 521 | L | 0-2 | |
| 35 | 13/02 | A | RL P | Hendon | 319 | L | 1-2 | Lawford 24 |
| 36 | 16/02 | H | B&BSC QF | **Reading** | 156 | W | 2-1 | **Mitchell, Lawford** |
| 37 | 20/02 | H | RL P | Sutton United | 494 | L | 0-3 | |
| 38 | 23/02 | H | RL C 2 | **Dagenham & Redbridge** | 116 | W | 3-1 | **Cork, Lawford, Mitchell** |
| 39 | 06/03 | A | RL P | Gravesend & Northfleet | 492 | W | 2-0 | Lawford 16 71 |
| 40 | 09/03 | H | RL C 3 | **Bromley** | 173 | L | 0-3 | |
| 41 | 11/03 | A | P C 3 | **Berkhamsted Town** | 148 | W | 5-0 | **Gell, Lawford(2), Winston(2)** |
| 42 | 13/03 | H | RL P | Hampton | 317 | D | 2-2 | Lawford 4[p], Thompson 90 |
| 43 | 15/03 | A | B&BSC SF | **Wycombe Wanderers** | 498 | L | 0-4 | |
| 44 | 20/03 | H | RL P | Bishop's Stortford | 272 | L | 0-1 | |
| 45 | 23/03 | H | P C QF | **Hendon** | 147 | L | 0-1 | |
| 46 | 30/03 | H | RL P | St Albans City | 337 | W | 2-1 | Hippolyte 29, Gell 90 |
| 47 | 03/04 | A | RL P | Carshalton Athletic | 348 | W | 1-0 | Lawford 36 |
| 48 | 05/04 | H | RL P | Aylesbury United | 1005 | W | 1-0 | Hutchins 89 |
| 49 | 08/04 | A | RL P | Purfleet | 132 | L | 0-3 | |
| 50 | 10/04 | A | RL P | Walton & Hersham | 207 | L | 1-9 | Lawford 77 |
| 51 | 15/04 | A | RL P | Basingstoke Town | 405 | L | 0-4 | |
| 52 | 17/04 | H | RL P | Boreham Wood | 345 | L | 2-5 | Lawford 10, Hippolyte 35 |
| 53 | 22/04 | H | RL P | Bromley | 171 | W | 3-1 | Lawford 40 42, Mitchell 80 |
| 54 | 24/04 | A | RL P | Bromley | 309 | W | 1-0 | Lawford 10 |
| 55 | 26/04 | A | RL P | Dagenham & Redbridge | 480 | D | 0-0 | |
| 56 | 27/04 | A | RL P | Boreham Wood | 213 | D | 0-0 | |
| 57 | 29/04 | A | RL P | Aldershot Town | 1207 | D | 0-0 | |
| 58 | 01/05 | H | RL P | Harrow Borough | 355 | L | 1-4 | Mitchell 57 |

**PLAYING SQUAD 1999-2000:**
GOALKEEPERS: John Granville, Delroy Preddie (Walton & Hersham), Rob Tenkorang
DEFENDERS: David Everitt (Walton & Hersham), Matt Pearson (Walton & Hersham), Paul Roberts, Dave Stephenson (Hampton)
MIDFIELDERS: Dereck Brown (Welling United), Neil Catlin (Hayes), Alan Dickens, Mark Fiore (Walton & Hersham), Clive Gartell (Sutton United), Jeff Hamlet, Otis Hutchings (Hampton), Paul Kelly (Chertsey Town)
FORWARDS: Chris Boothe (Farnborough Town), Johnson Hippolyte (Hampton), John Lawford (Harrow Borough), Neal Stanley

# DAGENHAM & REDBRIDGE

**THE DAGGER**

**CLUB OFFICIALS**
Chairman: **Dave Andrews**
President: **Harry Hammond**
Secretary: **Derek Almond**,
149 Kings Head Hill, Chingford,
London E4 7JG
Tel: 0181 524 2689
Press Officer: **Dave Simpson**
Tel: 0860 119430

**FOOTBALL MANAGEMENT TEAM**
Manager: Gary Hill
Asst Manager: Terry Harris
Safety Officer: Bill Doig
Physio: John Stannard

**FACT FILE**
Formed: 1992     Nickname: Daggers
Colours: Red/white/ blue
Change colours: All yellow
Midweek matchday: Monday
Res's Lge: Essex & Herts Border Comb.
Match Reports: 0930 555840
Sponsors Main: Compass Plumbing Supplies
Kit: Vandanell
Programme: Recorder Group Newspapers
1998-99 Captain:Jason Broom
Top Scorer: Paul Cobb (28)
P.o.Y.: Lee Matthews

**CHESHAM UNITED**
Monday 12th April 1999 - Kick-Off: 7.45pm
**RYMAN LEAGUE PREMIER DIVISION**

**GROUND:**     Victoria Road, Dagenham RM10 7XL. (0181 592 1549. Fax: 0181593 7227).
**Directions:** On A112 between A12 & A13. Buses 103 & 174, Dagenham East tube station,
turn left and after approximately 500 yards take 5th turning left into Victoria Road.
**Capacity:** 6,000   Seated: 700     Covered: 3,000   Floodlights: Yes
**Clubhouse:** Open 7 days 11am-11pm. Hot & cold food available.
For Functions:Tony Manhood (0181 592 7194) Shop Contact:SteveThompson 0181 5927194
**Club Shop:** Yes, open matchdays,for enquiries on other days contact Steve, above.

Pages: 48     Price: £1.40
Editor: Dave Simpson  Tel: 0860 119430
Local Press: Dagenham Post, Waltham Forest
Guardian, Ilford Recorder
Local Radio: Breeze AM, BBC Radio Essex,
Capital Radio, Active FM.

**PREVIOUS**     **Names:** Ilford FC (1881) & Leytonstone (1886) merged 1979 to form Leytonstone-Ilford. They & Walthamstow Avenue(1900)
merged 1988 to form Redbridge Forest who merged with Dagenham(1949) in 1992 to form Dagenham & Redbridge.
**Grounds:** None       **Leagues:** GMV Conference 92-96.

**CLUB RECORDS  Attendance:** 5,500 v Leyton Orient - FA Cup 1st Rnd - 14.11.92.
**Career goalscorer all competitions:** Danny Shipp 64, Paul Cobb 58  Paul Cavell - 49
**Career appearances (all competitions):** Steve Corner - 251; Jason Broom - 228. Paul Watts -  174
**Win:** 8-1 v Woking (A), GMV Conference 19/4/94, 7-0 v Oxford (H) Rymans Lge1/11/97.
**Defeat:** 0-5 - v Stalybridge Celtic (A), GMV Conference 31/4/94; v Northwich Victoria, GMV Conference 3/9/94 &
v Hyde Utd (H) FA Trophy 2nd Rd.
**Transfer fee paid**  £30,000 to Boston United for Paul Cavell & Paul Richardson -1991.
**Transfer fee received:** £85,000 from Watford for Andy Hessenthaler - 1991

**BEST SEASON**   **FA Cup:** 2nd Rd Proper v Peterborough lost 2-3, 97-98.      **FA Trophy:** R-up 96-97

**HONOURS**     **F.A. Trophy** Runners-up 96-97; Essex Senior 97-98

Players progressing: Juan Mequel DeSouza and Ian Richardson (Birmingham City 94, 95)

*Back Row (L-R): Steve Gracie (Physio), Gary Seymour (Coach), Danny Shipp, Marvin Neufville, Kirk Game, Paul Gothard, Steve*
*Conner, David Culverhouse, Jeff Woolsey, Mark Jamey, Gary Blackford, John Bennett (Manager), Bill Edmans (Kit Manager)*
*Front Row: Lee Matthews, David Pratt, Paul Cobb, Paul Terry, Tolo Mas, Gary Howard, Jason Broom, Tim Cole.*

# DAGENHAM & REDBRIDGE - MATCH FACTS - 1998-99 SEASON

| No | Date | Venue | Comp | Opponents | Att | Result | Score | Goalscorers |
|----|------|-------|------|-----------|-----|--------|-------|-------------|
| 1 | 15/08 | A | R M T | Barking | n/k | L | 2-3 | |
| 2 | 22/08 | H | RL P | Boreham Wood | 697 | D | 1-1 | Shipp 62 |
| 3 | 25/08 | H | RL P | Enfield | 726 | L | 0-4 | |
| 4 | 29/08 | A | RL P | Dulwich Hamlet | 416 | W | 2-1 | Howard 55, Shipp 81 |
| 5 | 31/08 | H | RL P | Heybridge Swifts | 727 | W | 3-0 | Game 11, Goodwin 46, Janney 88 |
| 6 | 05/09 | H | RL P | Billericay Town | 880 | L | 1-2 | Cobb 63[p] |
| 7 | 12/09 | A | RL P | Aldershot Town | 2601 | L | 3-4 | Shipp 14 67, Pratt 19 |
| 8 | 14/09 | H | RL P | Carshalton Athletic | 520 | W | 5-0 | Cobb 22, Shipp 33, Janney 59 63, Cole 90 |
| 9 | 19/09 | A | RL P | Harrow Borough | 260 | L | 1-2 | Cobb 77 |
| 10 | 22/09 | A | RL P | Basingstoke Town | 723 | D | 1-1 | Cobb 41 |
| 11 | 26/09 | H | RL P | Slough Town | 737 | W | 3-0 | Cobb 19 66, Shipp 26 |
| 12 | 03/10 | H | FAC Q2 | Eastbourne Town | 529 | W | 4-0 | Cobb 43, Shipp 53 75, Own-Goal 73 |
| 13 | 10/10 | A | RL P | Chesham United | 424 | W | 5-2 | Pratt 25, Terry 9 75, Shipp 86, Cobb 89 |
| 14 | 12/10 | H | RL P | Walton & Hersham | 604 | W | 3-1 | Cobb 52[p], Shipp 58 86 |
| 15 | 17/10 | H | FAC Q3 | Chipstead | 592 | W | 2-0 | Cobb 60, Cole 85 |
| 16 | 19/10 | H | RL P | Bromley | 663 | D | 3-3 | Goodwin 64, Cobb 66, Janney 68 |
| 17 | 27/10 | H | FAT 1 | Wealdstone | 576 | D | 1-1 | Cobb |
| 18 | 04/11 | H | FAC Q4 | Stevenage Borough | 763 | L | 0-3 | |
| 19 | 07/11 | A | RL P | Bishop's Stortford | 246 | W | 3-0 | Broome 32, Howard 79, Cobb 85 |
| 20 | 09/11 | A | FAT 1 rep | Wealdstone | 404 | W | 5-0 | Cobb 50, Goodwin 72, Shipp 76 87 90 |
| 21 | 17/11 | A | RL P | Hendon | 308 | D | 2-2 | Shipp 24, Game 81 |
| 22 | 21/11 | H | FAT 2 | Barton Rovers | 524 | W | 3-2 | Matthews, Cook[og], Cobb |
| 23 | 24/11 | A | RL C 1 | Ware | 75 | W | 2-1 | Barry, Bird |
| 24 | 28/11 | H | RL P | St Albans City | 705 | D | 2-2 | Bird 60, Broome 90 |
| 25 | 01/12 | A | ESC 3 | Halstead Town | 118 | W | 2-0 | Barry 13, Stevens 71 |
| 26 | 05/12 | A | RL P | Billericay Town | 806 | W | 2-1 | Shipp 38, Game 84 |
| 27 | 12/12 | H | RL P | Aldershot Town | 1059 | L | 0-1 | |
| 28 | 19/12 | A | RL P | Gravesend & Northfleet | 592 | L | 0-2 | |
| 29 | 28/12 | H | RL P | Purfleet | 963 | L | 0-1 | |
| 30 | 02/01 | A | RL P | Sutton United | 959 | L | 1-3 | Cobb 5 |
| 31 | 16/01 | H | FAT 3 | Farnborough Town | 783 | D | 1-1 | Shipp 29 |
| 32 | 23/01 | H | RL P | Enfield | 911 | D | 3-3 | Cobb 50 81, Shipp 84 |
| 33 | 25/01 | A | FAT 3 rep | Farnborough Town | 452 | D | 1-1 | Matthews 120          (4-2 pens) |
| 34 | 27/01 | H | ESC 4 | Bowers United | 161 | W | 4-1 | Shipp 41, Cobb 50, Mas 76, Janney 88 |
| 35 | 30/01 | A | RL P | Heybridge Swifts | 345 | W | 2-1 | Bird 45, Cobb 90[p] |
| 36 | 02/02 | A | P C 2 | Chesham United | 137 | L | 1-2 | Barry |
| 37 | 06/02 | H | FAT 4 | Telford United | 840 | W | 4-0 | Shipp 1 11 38, Pratt 35 |
| 38 | 08/02 | H | ESC QF | Heybridge Swifts | 235 | D | 2-2 | Shipp 13, Broom 104          (4-5 pens) |
| 39 | 13/02 | A | RL P | Carshalton Athletic | 407 | D | 0-0 | |
| 40 | 16/02 | A | RL P | Aylesbury United | 619 | W | 1-0 | Matthews 62 |
| 41 | 20/02 | A | RL P | Walton & Hersham | 282 | W | 1-0 | Cobb 69 |
| 42 | 23/02 | A | RL C 2 | Chesham United | 116 | L | 1-3 | Stevens |
| 43 | 27/02 | H | FAT 5 | St Albans City | 1227 | L | 1-2 | Janney 88 |
| 44 | 03/03 | H | RL P | Hampton | 440 | W | 4-0 | Janney 1 60, Cole 5, Barry 66 |
| 45 | 06/03 | A | RL P | Slough Town | 510 | W | 1-0 | Cobb 84 |
| 46 | 13/03 | H | RL P | Basingstoke Town | 768 | W | 2-0 | Blackford 46, Shipp 49 |
| 47 | 15/03 | H | RL P | Harrow Borough | 564 | W | 1-0 | Pratt 6 |
| 48 | 20/03 | A | RL P | Bromley | 458 | D | 0-0 | |
| 49 | 22/03 | H | RL P | Dulwich Hamlet | 599 | W | 1-0 | Cobb 8 |
| 50 | 28/03 | H | RL P | Aylesbury United | 1006 | W | 1-0 | Cobb 79 |
| 51 | 30/03 | A | RL P | Boreham Wood | 369 | W | 2-0 | Janney 49, Shipp 59 |
| 52 | 03/04 | H | RL P | Sutton United | 1100 | D | 0-0 | |
| 53 | 05/04 | A | RL P | Purfleet | 605 | L | 0-3 | |
| 54 | 10/04 | H | RL P | Bishop's Stortford | 629 | D | 1-1 | Shipp 29 |
| 55 | 17/04 | A | RL P | Hampton | 276 | W | 2-1 | Cobb 11, Janney 52 |
| 56 | 19/04 | H | RL P | Gravesend & Northfleet | 561 | D | 0-0 | |
| 57 | 24/04 | A | RL P | Hendon | 601 | W | 6-0 | Howard 5, Terry 39 44, Woolsey 52, Cobb 57 74 |
| 58 | 26/04 | H | RL P | Chesham United | 480 | D | 0-0 | |
| 59 | 01/05 | A | RL P | St Albans City | 775 | D | 2-2 | Cobb 56, Shipp 65 |
| 60 | 04/05 | H | THT | West Ham United | 1220 | L | 1-7 | |

## PLAYING SQUAD 1999-2000:

GOALKEEPERS: Calvin Hayward, Paul Newell (St Albans City), Perry Sucking (South Africa), Darren Williams (Dulwich Hamlet)

DEFENDERS: Mick Bodley (St Albans City), Tim Cole (Leyton Pennant), Steve Conner (Dartford), Steve Davies (Chelsea), Mark Janney (Tottenham Hotspur), Garry Kimble (Aylesbury United), Bartolome Mas (Billericay Town)

MIDFIELDERS: Greg Allen (Purfleet), Jason Broom (Billericay Town), Steve Heffer (Boreham Wood), Matt Jones (St Albans City)

FORWARDS: Matthew Bird (Leyton Orient), Paul Cobb (Enfield), Nigel Hewes (Heybridge Swifts), Junior McDougald (Brighton & Hove Albion), Narvin Neufville (Ford United), Danny Shipp, Martin St Hilaire (Billericay Town), Paul Terry

# DULWICH HAMLET

## CLUB OFFICIALS

Chairman: **Martin Eede**
President: **Tommy Jover**
Vice Chairman: **Brian Shears**
Secretary:: **Ron McLean**,60 Fawkham
Avenue,New Barn, Kent DA3 7HE Tel: (H)
01474 709495
Press Officer: **John Lawrence**

## FOOTBALL MANAGEMENT TEAM

Manager: Dave Garland
Physio: Danny Keenan

### FACT FILE

Formed: 1893 Nickname: The Hamlet
Sponsors: South London Press
Colours: Navy blue & pink stripes/navy/navy
Change colours: Green & white
stripes/white/white
Midweek matchday: Tuesday
Reserve League: Suburban

1998-99 Captain: Russell Edwards
P.o.Y.: Les Cleveley
Top Scorer: David Stevens(22)

**GROUND:** Champion Hill Stadium, Edgar Kail Way, East Dulwich, London SE22 8BD
Tel: 0171 274 8707
**Directions:** East Dulwich station, 200yds. Denmark Hill station, 10 mins walk. Herne Hill station then bus 37 stops near grd. Buses 40 & 176 from Elephant & Castle, 185 from Victoria
Capacity: 3,000   Cover: 1,000   Seats: 500   Floodlights: Yes
**Clubhouse:** Open 7 days a week, 3 bars. Function rooms and meeting room available for hire. Gymnasium, squash courts (0171 274 8707)
**Club Shop:** Sells programmes, pennants, badges, scarves, baseball caps, replica shirts (by order only). Contact Mishi D Morath at club

Follow the match reports and all the team news everyweek in the
*South London Press*

Pages: 36   Price: £1
Editor: John Lawrence

Local Press: South London Press, Southwark News

**PREVIOUS**   **Leagues:** Camberwell 1894-97; S/thern Sub 1897-1900 01-07; Dulwich 00-01; Spartan 07-08
**Grounds:** Woodwarde Rd 1893-95; College Farm 95-96; Sunray Avenue 96-1902; Freeman's Ground, Champion Hill 02-12; Champion Hill (old ground) 1912-92; Sandy Lane (groundshare with Tooting & Mitcham F.C.) 91-92

**CLUB RECORDS**   **Attendance:** 20,744, Kingstonian v Stockton, FA Am Cup Final 1933  (at refurbished ground): 1,850 v Southport FAC 98-99
**Career Goalscorer:** Edgar Kail 427 (1919-33)                    **Career Appearances:** Reg Merritt 571 (50-66)
**Fee Paid:** T Eames (Wimbledon), G Allen (Carshalton Ath 80)   **Fee Received:** E Nwajiobi (Luton 83)
**Win:** 13-0 v Walton-on-Thames, 37-38         **Defeat:** 1-10 v Hendon, 63-64

**BEST SEASON**   **FA Amateur Cup:** Winners 19-20 31-2 33-4 36-7            **FA Trophy:** Quarter Final 79-80
**FA Cup:** 1st Rd replay 30-31 33-34. 1st Rd on 14 occasions

**HONOURS:**   Isthmian League 19-20 25-26 32-33 48-49, (R-up(7) 21-22 23-24 29-31 33-34 46-47 58-59, Div 1 77-78); London Senior Cup 24-25 38-39 49-50 83-84 (R-up 05-06 07-08 20-21 27-28); Surrey Senior Cup 04-06 08-10 19-20 22-23 24-25 27-28 33-34 36-37 46-47 49-50 57-59 73-75, (R-up 11-12 31-33 37-38 50-51 67-68); London Chal. Cup R-up 91-92; London Charity Cup(12) 10-11(jt) 19-21 22-23 23-24(jt) 25-26 27-29 30-31(jt) 47-48 56-58; Surrey Senior Shield 72-73; Surrey Centen. Shld 77-78; Sth of the Thames Cup (4) 56-60; Southern Comb Cup 73-74

Players progressing: W Bellamy (Spurs), A Solly (Arsenal), L Fishlock/A Gray/APardew (C Palace), J Moseley & E Toser (Millwall), R Dicks (Middlesborough), GJago/J Ryan (Charlton Ath 51/63), G Pearce (Plymouth), R Crisp (Watford 61), ENwajiobi (Luton 83), C Richards & J Glass (Bournemouth), P Coleman (Millwall86), A Perry (Portsmouth 86), N Kelly (Stoke City), C Emberson (Rotherham), CAsaba (Brentford)

*Back Row (L-R): Micky Read (Assistant Manager), John Yems (Coach), Francis Duku, Carl Bartley, Adrian Toppin, Les Cleevely, Luke Anderson, Tony Chin, Russell Edwards, Tony Houghton, Danny Keenan (Physio), Dave Garland (Manager) Front Row: Alan Edwards (Kit Man), Lee Macken, Veli Hakki, Lee Akers, Dean Holness, Dave Stevens, Gary Hewitt, Peter Garland*
*Photo: Bill Wheatcroft*

# DULWICH HAMLET - MATCH FACTS - 1998-99 SEASON

| No | Date | Venue | Comp | Opponents | Att | Result | Score | Goalscorers |
|---|---|---|---|---|---|---|---|---|
| 1 | 22/08 | A | RL P | Basingstoke Town | 521 | L | 1-2 | Thompson 52 |
| 2 | 25/08 | H | RL P | Walton & Hersham | 287 | W | 3-2 | Thompson(2), Holness |
| 3 | 29/08 | H | RL P | Dagenham & Redbridge | 416 | L | 1-2 | Thompson 73 |
| 4 | 01/09 | A | RL P | Hampton | 239 | D | 0-0 | |
| 5 | 05/09 | A | RL P | Chesham United | 621 | D | 0-0 | |
| 6 | 08/09 | H | RL C 1 | Sutton United | 312 | L | 2-3 | Bartley 1, P Garland 55 |
| 7 | 12/09 | H | RL P | Bishop's Stortford | 306 | D | 1-1 | Bartley 58 |
| 8 | 15/09 | A | RL P | Aylesbury United | 430 | L | 0-3 | |
| 9 | 19/09 | H | RL P | Bromley | 617 | W | 2-0 | Thompson 51, McKimm 60 |
| 10 | 22/09 | H | RL P | Harrow Borough | 201 | L | 0-2 | |
| 11 | 26/09 | H | RL P | Boreham Wood | 255 | L | 0-4 | |
| 12 | 03/10 | H | FAC Q2 | Deal Town | 307 | W | 1-0 | Bartley 45 |
| 13 | 09/10 | H | RL P | Sutton United | 631 | W | 2-1 | Thompson 41[p] 66 |
| 14 | 13/10 | A | RL P | Enfield | 450 | L | 1-2 | Thompson 59 |
| 15 | 17/10 | H | FAC Q3 | Purfleet | 308 | D | 2-2 | Thompson 10, P Garland 88 |
| 16 | 19/10 | A | FAC Q3 r | Purfleet | 211 | W | 3-1 | Bartley, Thompson(2) |
| 17 | 24/10 | A | RL P | Gravesend & Northfleet | 446 | W | 1-0 | Bartley 63 |
| 18 | 31/10 | H | FAC Q4 | Newport IoW | 628 | W | 3-2 | Bartley 43, Thompson 50 65 |
| 19 | 03/11 | H | SSC P | Netherne | 73 | W | 3-0 | Gorman(2), Barrett |
| 20 | 07/11 | A | RL P | Hendon | 401 | D | 1-1 | P Garland 88[p] |
| 21 | 14/11 | H | FAC 1 | Southport | 1835 | L | 0-1 | |
| 22 | 21/11 | A | FAT 2 | Cirencester Town | 131 | W | 3-0 | Griggs 7, Bartley 27, Gorman 75 |
| 23 | 24/11 | A | RL P | Heybridge Swifts | 124 | W | 2-0 | Bartley, Garland |
| 24 | 28/11 | H | RL P | Purfleet | 273 | L | 1-2 | Chin 63 |
| 25 | 01/12 | H | RL P | Carshalton Athletic | 284 | D | 0-0 | |
| 26 | 05/12 | A | RL P | Bishop's Stortford | 143 | L | 1-2 | Bartley 36 |
| 27 | 08/12 | A | SSC 1 | Camberley Town | 60 | W | 2-0 | Stevens, Edwards |
| 28 | 12/12 | H | RL P | Chesham United | 341 | W | 3-2 | Stevens 42 52, Bartley 84 |
| 29 | 19/12 | A | RL P | Billericay Town | 619 | L | 0-1 | |
| 30 | 28/12 | H | RL P | Slough Town | 417 | D | 2-2 | Stevens 14, Bartley 18 |
| 31 | 02/01 | A | RL P | Aldershot Town | 2270 | L | 1-3 | Stevens 62 |
| 32 | 05/01 | H | SSC 2 | Walton & Hersham | 142 | L | 0-2 | |
| 33 | 16/01 | H | FAT 3 | Whyteleafe | 492 | L | 1-2 | Bartley 80 |
| 34 | 23/01 | A | RL P | Walton & Hersham | 254 | L | 1-3 | Stevens 45 |
| 35 | 30/01 | H | RL P | Basingstoke Town | 298 | W | 2-0 | Stevens 27 83 |
| 36 | 02/02 | H | P C 2 | Hampton | 114 | W | 1-0 | Stevens |
| 37 | 06/02 | A | RL P | Bromley | 451 | W | 3-0 | Stevens 8 22, Edwards 27 |
| 38 | 09/02 | H | P C 3 | Basingstoke Town | 89 | W | 3-1 | Stevens 38 51, Holness 49 |
| 39 | 13/02 | H | RL P | Aylesbury United | 528 | L | 0-1 | |
| 40 | 16/02 | A | LCC QF | Hampton | 95 | W | 2-1 | Bartley 75 83 |
| 41 | 20/02 | H | RL P | Enfield | 529 | L | 0-1 | |
| 42 | 23/02 | H | RL P | St Albans City | 297 | D | 2-2 | Bartley 10, Stevens 62 |
| 43 | 27/02 | A | RL P | Sutton United | 861 | L | 0-2 | |
| 44 | 06/03 | H | RL P | Boreham Wood | 286 | W | 2-0 | Stevens 20, Barrett 46 |
| 45 | 09/03 | H | P C QF | Wealdstone | 184 | W | 1-0 | Holness 75 |
| 46 | 13/03 | A | RL P | Harrow Borough | 215 | L | 2-3 | Houghton 73, Barrett 80 |
| 47 | 16/03 | H | RL P | Billericay Town | 277 | L | 2-4 | Anderson 67, Stevens 89 |
| 48 | 20/03 | A | RL P | Carshalton Athletic | 376 | L | 0-2 | |
| 49 | 22/03 | A | RL P | Dagenham & Redbridge | 599 | L | 0-1 | |
| 50 | 27/03 | H | RL P | Heybridge Swifts | 276 | W | 4-3 | Stevens 18, P Garland 49[p], Holness 89, Anderson 90 |
| 51 | 30/03 | H | RL P | Hampton | 220 | W | 2-1 | Carroll 6, Stevens 34 |
| 52 | 03/04 | H | RL P | Aldershot Town | 1011 | W | 4-3 | A Garland 16, Stevens 59 66, Harper 90 |
| 53 | 05/04 | A | RL P | Slough Town | 433 | L | 0-1 | |
| 54 | 07/04 | H | P C SF | Hendon | 181 | L | 0-2 | |
| 55 | 10/04 | H | RL P | Hendon | 383 | W | 3-1 | Stevens 30 70, Holness 44 |
| 56 | 22/04 | A | RL P | St Albans City | 346 | D | 1-1 | Harper 85 |
| 57 | 24/04 | H | RL P | Gravesend & Northfleet | 642 | W | 1-0 | P Garland 6 |
| 58 | 28/04 | A | LCC SF | Welling United | n/k | W | 3-1 | P Garland(2), Holness |
| 59 | 01/05 | A | RL P | Purfleet | 165 | L | 1-2 | Carroll 81 |
| 60 | 18/05 | A | LCC F | Uxbridge | 541 | W | 2-1 | Holness 45, Anderson 105 (at Charlton Athletic) |

## PLAYING SQUAD 1999-2000:

GOALKEEPERS: Lee Bray (Wisbech Town), Les Cleevely (Sutton United), Tony Chinn

DEFENDERS: Martin Chester (Enfield), Francis Duku (Crawley Town), Mark Garland, Gary Hewitt (Erith & Belvedere), Tony Houghton (Yeading), Andy Riley (Sutton United), Kevin Smith (Carshalton Athletic)

MIDFIELDERS: Daniel Carroll (Bromley), Peter Garland, Matthew Rush

FORWARDS: Dean Green, Byron Harper (Romford), Dean Holness (Bromley), Curtis Johnson (Walton & Hersham), Richard Sinden, David Stevens (Bromley)

# ENFIELD

## CLUB OFFICIALS

Chairman: **A Lazarou**
President: **R.Prosser**
Secretary: **Roger Reed,**
16 College G/dens, Enfield, Middx EN2 0QF
Tel: 0181 350 4064
Press Officer: **John Jefferson**
Tel 01992 441193

## FOOTBALL MANAGEMENT TEAM
Manager: Jim Chandler
Physio: T.B.A.
Coaches: Eddie Jones/ Peter Hammett

### FACT FILE
Formed: 1893
Nickname: The E's
Sponsors: Enfield Gazette & Advertiser
Newsline: 0930 555845
Colours: All White with blue trim
Change colours: Yellow & Sky
Midweek matchday: Tuesday
Reserve's League: None
Essex & Herts Border Comb
1998-99: Captain & P.o.Y.: Steve Terry
Top Scorer: Steve Darlington (17)

**GROUND:** The Stadium, Southbury Road, Enfield EN1 1YQ  Tel: 0181 292 0665
**Directions:** At junction of A10 & A110.
800 yards from Southbury Road station .Buses from town centre
Capacity: 6,919      Cover: 2,800      Seats: 665      Floodlights: Yes
**Clubhouse:** Sportsmans Lounge, open every  lunch & evening. Snacks. Starlight nightclub, cabaret, dinner & dance
**Club Shop:** Yes, contact Dave Hicks 01992 769156 or Alan Farmer 0181 366 6066

Pages: 48  Price: £1.50
Editor: Scott Reed

Local Press: Enfield Gazette,
Enfield Advertiser, Enfield Independent

**PREVIOUS**       **Leagues:** Tottenham & Dist 1894-95; Nth Middx  96-1903; London 03-13 20-21; Middx 08-12, 19-20; Athenian 12-14 21-39 45-63; Herts & Middx Comb 39-42; Isthmian 63-81; GMV Conference 81-90
                   **Name:** Enfield Spartans 1893-1900   **Grounds:** Baileys Field 1893-96; Tuckers Field 96-1900; Cherry Orchard Lane1900-36
**CLUB RECORDS**   **Attendance:** 10,000 (10/10/62) v Spurs, floodlight opener
                   **Win:** 18-0 v Stevenage FA Cup 2nd Qual 22/10/27 (H)    **Defeat:** 0-12 v Woolwich Polytechnic, London Lge Div 2 27/4/04
                   **Fee Paid:** for Gary Abbott (Barnet)              **Fee Received:** for Paul Furlong (Coventry City)
                   **Scorer:** Tommy Lawrence, 191 1959-1964.          **Appearances:** Steve King 617 (77-89)
**BEST SEASON**    **FA Amateur Cup:** Winners 66-7 69-70 R-up 63-4 71-2   **FA Trophy:** Winners 81-2 87-8
                   **FA Cup:** 4th Rd replay 80-81, 0-3 v Barnsley (at Spurs), Att 35,244, after 1-1.
                   **League clubs beaten:** Wimbledon, Northampton 77-78, Hereford, Port Vale 80-81, Wimbledon 81-82, Exeter 84-85, Orient 88-89, Aldershot 91-92, Cardiff City 94-95, Torquay Utd 94-95
**HONOURS:**       Alliance Premier Lge 82-83 85-86 (R-up 81-82), Lg Cup R-up 81-82; IsthmianLg(8) 67-70 75-78 79-80 94-95 (R-up 64-65 71-72 74-75 80-81 90-92 95-96), LgCup(2) 78-80 (R-up 91-92 94-95); Athenian Lg(2) 61-63 (R-up 34-35); London LgDiv 1 11-12 (R-up 04-05 06-07); Middx Snr Cup 13-14 46-47 61-62 65-66 68-71 77-81 88-89 90-91 97-98, (R-up 10-11 20-21 47-48 51-52 57-60 62-63 66-67 72-73 75-76 84-85); London Snr Cup 34-35 60-61 66-67 71-73 75-76 (R-up 63-64 67-68 70-71); Middx Lg (West) 09-10 (R-up 10-11); European Amtr Cup Winners Cup 69-70
Players progressing: Terry McQuade (Millwall 61), Roger Day (Watford 61), Jeff Harris (Orient 64), Peter Feely (Chelsea 70), Carl Richards & Jon Bailey (B'mouth 80 & 95), Paul Furlong (Coventry 91), Andy  Pape (Barnet 91), GregHeald (Peterborough 94), Lee Marshall (Norwich City 97)

*Back Row (L-R): Dave Lawson (Physio), Lee Williams, Grant Cooper, Mark Bentley, Steve Terry, Andy Hall, Russell Penn, Richard Dunwell, Steve Darlington, Glenn Southgate*
*Front Row: John Deadman, Lee Protheroe, Sammy Cooper, Danny Jones, Gary Caldon, Andy Tomlinson, Darren Annon*
*Photo: Bill Wheatcroft*

# ENFIELD - MATCH FACTS - 1998-99 SEASON

| No | Date | Venue | Comp | Opponents | Att | Result | Score | Goalscorers |
|----|------|-------|------|-----------|-----|--------|-------|-------------|
| 1 | 01/08 | H | APT | Barnet | n/k | L | 2-3 | Dunwell 43 53 |
| 2 | 22/08 | A | RL P | Chesham United | 1016 | L | 0-2 | |
| 3 | 25/08 | H | RL P | Dagenham & Redbridge | 726 | W | 4-0 | Terry, Dunwell(3) |
| 4 | 29/08 | H | RL P | Aylesbury United | 640 | L | 2-3 | Bentley 34, Dunwell 39 |
| 5 | 01/09 | A | RL P | Basingstoke Town | 734 | L | 0-1 | |
| 6 | 05/09 | A | RL P | Bromley | 601 | L | 1-2 | Naylor 43[p] |
| 7 | 08/09 | A | RL C 1 | Boreham Wood | 216 | L | 0-2 | |
| 8 | 12/09 | H | RL P | Gravesend & Northfleet | 556 | L | 0-2 | |
| 9 | 15/09 | A | RL P | Bishop's Stortford | 240 | W | 2-1 | Morgan 32, Richardson 76 |
| 10 | 19/09 | H | RL P | Walton & Hersham | 454 | W | 3-2 | Dunwell 27 35, Penn 43 |
| 11 | 22/09 | H | RL P | Heybridge Swifts | 407 | W | 4-1 | Jones 28, Bentley 37, Penn 47, Naylor 78 |
| 12 | 26/09 | A | RL P | Harrow Borough | 401 | D | 0-0 | |
| 13 | 03/10 | A | FAC Q2 | Croydon | 240 | W | 4-0 | Richardson(2), Penn, Naylor |
| 14 | 09/10 | A | RL P | Hendon | 523 | L | 0-2 | |
| 15 | 13/10 | H | RL P | Dulwich Hamlet | 450 | W | 2-1 | Caldon 2, Bentley 66 |
| 16 | 17/10 | A | FAC Q3 | Banbury United | 1028 | W | 4-0 | Caldon, Darlington, Dunwell, Cooper |
| 17 | 20/10 | H | RL P | Boreham Wood | 423 | L | 1-3 | Bentley 89 |
| 18 | 25/10 | A | FAT 1 | St Leonards | 540 | W | 4-2 | Cooper 14, Naylor 19[p], Darlington 82 89 |
| 19 | 31/10 | H | FAC Q4 | Raunds Town | 443 | W | 2-0 | Richardson 81, Bentley 83 |
| 20 | 07/11 | A | RL P | Slough Town | 737 | D | 2-2 | Terry 90, Bentley 90 |
| 21 | 14/11 | H | FAC 1 | York City | 1634 | D | 2-2 | Dunwell 61, Richardson 66 |
| 22 | 21/11 | A | FAT 2 | Oxford City | 302 | W | 1-0 | Richardson |
| 23 | 24/11 | A | FAC 1 rep | York City | 2131 | L | 1-2 | Dunwell 27 |
| 24 | 28/11 | H | RL P | Aldershot Town | 1026 | W | 4-0 | Bentley 15, Dunwell 27[p], Richardson 72[p] 79 |
| 25 | 01/12 | H | P C 1 | St Albans City | 125 | W | 2-0 | Piper 19[og], Southgate 60 |
| 26 | 05/12 | A | RL P | Gravesend & Northfleet | 483 | W | 3-0 | Deadman 32, Penn 47, Dunwell 78[p] |
| 27 | 12/12 | H | RL P | Bishop's Stortford | 650 | W | 2-1 | Dunwell 18, Richardson 90 |
| 28 | 15/12 | H | P C 2 | Bishop's Stortford | 141 | W | 1-0 | Southgate 30 |
| 29 | 19/12 | A | RL P | Sutton United | 917 | D | 1-1 | Darlington 35 |
| 30 | 22/12 | A | RL P | Carshalton Athletic | 402 | L | 1-2 | Terry 90 |
| 31 | 28/12 | H | RL P | St Albans City | 1011 | D | 0-0 | |
| 32 | 02/01 | A | RL P | Purfleet | 503 | W | 1-0 | Bentley 22 |
| 33 | 05/01 | A | MSC 2 | Hayes | 251 | L | 0-4 | |
| 34 | 18/01 | H | P C 3 | Purfleet | 22 | L | 0-2 | |
| 35 | 23/01 | A | RL P | Dagenham & Redbridge | 911 | D | 3-3 | Darlington 24 59, Penn 66 |
| 36 | 25/01 | A | FAT 3 | Hitchin Town | 519 | D | 3-3 | Darlington, Dunwell[p], Calder |
| 37 | 27/01 | H | FAT 3 rep | Hitchin Town | 302 | L | 0-1 | |
| 38 | 30/01 | H | RL P | Chesham United | 597 | D | 2-2 | Darlington 27, Dunwell 90 |
| 39 | 06/02 | A | RL P | Walton & Hersham | 321 | W | 4-0 | Dunwell 28 45 90, Jones 40 |
| 40 | 13/02 | A | RL P | Bromley | 557 | W | 3-0 | Darlington 9, Deadman 39, Carroll 73[og] |
| 41 | 16/02 | H | RL P | Billericay Town | 428 | W | 1-0 | Deadman 17 |
| 42 | 20/02 | A | RL P | Dulwich Hamlet | 529 | W | 1-0 | Jones 49 |
| 43 | 06/03 | H | RL P | Harrow Borough | 529 | W | 5-0 | Tomlinson 20, Dunwell 21 79, Darlington 52, Jones 76 |
| 44 | 09/03 | H | RL P | Basingstoke Town | 409 | W | 3-2 | Darlington 4 30, Annon 67 |
| 45 | 13/03 | A | RL P | Heybridge Swifts | 421 | D | 2-2 | Cooper 45, Darlington 61 |
| 46 | 16/03 | A | RL P | Hampton | 275 | W | 2-0 | Darlington 41, Bentley 63 |
| 47 | 20/03 | A | RL P | Boreham Wood | 752 | L | 2-3 | Annon 81, G Cooper 90 |
| 48 | 23/03 | A | RL P | Aylesbury United | 994 | W | 2-1 | Terry 24, Darlington 87 |
| 49 | 27/03 | H | RL P | Carshalton Athletic | 510 | W | 1-0 | Morgan 55 |
| 50 | 03/04 | H | RL P | Purfleet | 592 | L | 1-2 | S Darlington 36 |
| 51 | 05/04 | A | RL P | St Albans City | 999 | L | 1-2 | Keen 53[og] |
| 52 | 10/04 | H | RL P | Slough Town | 558 | W | 2-1 | Dunwell 43, Jones 88 |
| 53 | 16/04 | A | RL P | Billericay Town | 786 | W | 1-0 | Darlington 10 |
| 54 | 24/04 | H | RL P | Hampton | 529 | D | 0-0 | |
| 55 | 27/04 | H | RL P | Sutton United | 511 | D | 1-1 | Bentley 45 |
| 56 | 29/04 | H | RL P | Hendon | 750 | W | 2-1 | Bentley 65, Morgan 79 |
| 57 | 01/05 | A | RL P | Aldershot Town | 2025 | L | 1-3 | Darlington 20 |

## PLAYING SQUAD 1999-2000:

GOALKEEPERS: Andy Hall, Jerome John (KIngstonian)

DEFENDERS: Wayne Brown (Kingstonian), Gary Cooper (Kingstonian), Lee Protheroe (Yeading)

MIDFIELDERS: Daneil Alleyne (Grays Athletic), Darren Annon (Kingstonian), Paul Linger (Welling United), Kevin Rattray (Kingstonian), Paul Turner

FORWARDS: James Bunn (Tottenham Hotspur), John Deadman (Purfleet), Alfredo Domingos (Hayes), Richard Dunwell (Billericay Town), Dave Fleming (France)

# FARNBOROUGH TOWN

FACT FILE

Founded: 1967
Nickname: The "Boro"
Club Sponsor: T.B.A.
Club Colours: Yellow & blue
Change colours: Red & black
Midweek matchday: Tuesday
Reserves' League: Suburban (Premier Div.)
Club Newsline: 0898 88 4407
1998-99
Top Goalscorer: Dennis Bailey
P.O.Y.: Barry Miller

**CLUB OFFICIALS**
President: **Charles Mortimer**
Chairman: **Tony Alper**
Vice Chairman: **Hal Carter**
Director: **Michael McCarthy**

Football Secretary: **Vince Williams**
Tel: 01252 522161
Commercial Consultant: **Graham Willis**
Tel: 01924 266393
Press Officer: **David Hughes**
Tel: 01276 28354

**FOOTBALL MANAGEMENT TEAM**
Graham Westley, Dean Coney,
Tommy Mason,
Erskine Smart and Ron Berry
Physio: Ricky Lowe

**GROUND**  John Roberts Ground, Cherrywood Road, Farnborough, Hampshire GU14 8UD
Tel: 01252 541469  Fax: 01252 375613
**Directions:** M3 exit 4, A325 towards Farnborough, right into Prospect Ave. (club signposted),
2nd right into Cherrywood Rd, ground on right. 20-30 min walk fromFarnborough Main,
Farnborough North and Frimley BR stations. Whippet mini-bus route 19 passes ground.
Capacity: 4,900        Seated: 630        Covered Terracing: 1,350
**Clubhouse:** Open during normal pub hours and matchdays. Hot pies, bar meals, crisps etc.
**Club Shop:** Boro' Leisurewear shop - all types of club leisurewear and matchballs (contact
Graham Willis - 01924 266393)
**Supporters Club shop:** Old programmes, scarves, badges etc (contact Paul Doe).

Programme:
Pages: 40            Price: £1.30
Editor: J.D. Printing Services
Other club publications:
"Simon Read's Haircut" (fanzine)
Local Press: Farnborough News
Local Radio: BBC Southern Counties
County Sound

**PREVIOUS**       **Leagues:** Surrey Senior 68-72; Spartan 72-76; Athenian 76-77; Isthmian 77-89; Alliance Premier (Conference) 89-90 91-93 94-
99; Southern 90-91 93-94.                **Grounds:** Queens Road, Farnborough (1969-1976)

**CLUB RECORDS Attendance:** 3,581 v Brentford 22/11/95 (FA Cup).
**Win:** 11-0 v Chertsey Town (H), Spartan League 72-73    **Defeat:** 2-10 v Worplesdon (H), Surrey Senior Lge Div. 1 68-69
**Career Goalscorer:** Simon Read 209, 1986-1994    **Career Appearances:** Brian Broome 529, 1980-1994
**Season Goalscorer:** Simon Read 53, 1988-89.
**Transfer Fee Paid:** £10,000 to Kingstonian for David Harlow December 1994.
**Transfer Fee Received:** £50,000 from Dover Athletic for David Leworthy, August1993

**BEST SEASON    FA Cup:** 3rd Rd Proper replay 91-92, 0-1 v West Ham U. (A) after 1-1
League clubs defeated: Torquay Utd 91-92    **FA Trophy:** Quarter Final 92-93    **FA Vase:** Semi-Final 75-76 76-77

**HONOURS**       Southern Lg 90-91 93-94, Isthmian Lg R-up 88-89 (Div 1 84-85, Div 2 78-79),Athenian Lg Div 2 78-79, Spartan Lg 72-73 73-74
74-75 (Lg Cup 74-75), LondonSpartan Lg 75-76 (Lg Cup 75-76), Hants Snr Cup 74-75 81-82 83-84 85-86 90-91(R-up 93-94)

Players progressing: Dennis Bailey (Crystal Palace), Paul Mortimer (Charlton Athletic), Tommy Jones (Aberdeen), Allan Cockram (Brentford),
Paul Holsgrove (Millwall), Maik Taylor (Barnet), Martin Rowlands (Brentford)

*Back Row (L-R): Cliff Cobb (Physio), Mark Turkington (1st Team Coach), Mike Savage (Coach), Simon Read (1st Team Coach)*
*Middle Row: Ron Manville (Ground/Kit), Andy Taylor, Neil Baker, Jon Underwood, Barry Miller, Stuart MacKenzie, Phil Wingfield,*
*Darren Robson, Wayne Stemp, Justin Day, Ted Shepherd (Scout)*
*Front Row: Chris White, Mark West, Steve Baker, Dennis Bailey, Alan Taylor (Manager), Stuart Harte, David Harlow, Nick Jansen,*
*Keith Rowlands*

# FARNBOROUGH TOWN - MATCH FACTS - 1998-99 SEASON

| No | Date | Venue | Comp | Opponents | Att | Result | Score | Goalscorers |
|----|------|-------|------|-----------|-----|--------|-------|-------------|
| 1 | 04/08 | H | RCS | Aldershot Town | 1342 | W | 4-2 | |
| 2 | 15/08 | A | NC | Leek Town | 527 | L | 0-4 | |
| 3 | 18/08 | H | NC | Forest Green Rovers | 750 | D | 2-2 | West 72, Robson 90 |
| 4 | 22/08 | H | NC | Kettering Town | 635 | L | 1-3 | Bailey 80 |
| 5 | 25/08 | A | NC | Welling United | 648 | D | 0-0 | |
| 6 | 29/08 | A | NC | Hednesford Town | 1100 | D | 0-0 | |
| 7 | 31/08 | H | NC | Dover Athletic | 847 | L | 1-2 | West 30 |
| 8 | 05/09 | H | NC | Leek Town | 578 | W | 2-1 | West 43, Bailey 86 |
| 9 | 12/09 | A | NC | Kidderminster Harriers | 1670 | L | 0-2 | |
| 10 | 15/09 | H | NC | Kingstonian | 759 | W | 4-2 | West 2[p] 43, Harford 58, Bailey 60 |
| 11 | 19/09 | A | NC | Northwich Victoria | 837 | L | 0-3 | |
| 12 | 26/09 | H | NC | Cheltenham Town | 1067 | L | 2-4 | N Baker 37, Mitchell 68 |
| 13 | 28/09 | A | NC | Stevenage Borough | 2379 | L | 1-3 | K Rowlands 44 |
| 14 | 03/10 | A | NC | Doncaster Rovers | 3468 | W | 2-1 | K Rowlands 7, Wye 27 |
| 15 | 06/10 | H | Ends ,1 | Kingstonian | 514 | W | 4-2 | Bailey 23 110[p], N Baker, Rowlands 100 |
| 16 | 10/10 | H | NC | Rushden & Diamonds | 958 | L | 1-2 | Miller 83 |
| 17 | 17/10 | H | FAC Q3 | Heybridge Swifts | 482 | W | 2-0 | |
| 18 | 01/11 | H | FAC Q4 | Yeovil Town | 1396 | L | 1-3 | Day 7 |
| 19 | 04/11 | A | HSC 2 | Portsmouth Royal Navy | 56 | W | 3-0 | |
| 20 | 07/11 | H | NC | Telford United | 613 | W | 3-1 | Bailey 18 67, Underwood 41 |
| 21 | 14/11 | A | NC | Hereford United | 1788 | L | 0-2 | |
| 22 | 21/11 | H | FAT 2 | Dartford | 472 | D | 1-1 | Miller 33 |
| 23 | 25/11 | A | FAT 2 rep | Dartford | 229 | W | 2-1 | Underwood 20, Robinson 59 |
| 24 | 28/11 | H | NC | Southport | 559 | D | 1-1 | Harte 58 |
| 25 | 01/12 | A | HSC 3 | Cowes Sports | 152 | L | 1-2 | |
| 26 | 05/12 | A | NC | Forest Green Rovers | 703 | D | 0-0 | |
| 27 | 12/12 | H | NC | Morecambe | 682 | L | 1-6 | Hughes 82[og] |
| 28 | 19/12 | A | NC | Rushden & Diamonds | 2481 | L | 0-1 | |
| 29 | 22/12 | H | Ends 2 | Rushden & Diamonds | 313 | W | 3-1 | Bailey 44 76 86[p] |
| 30 | 28/12 | A | NC | Yeovil Town | 2924 | L | 3-6 | Low 9 21, Bailey 33 |
| 31 | 02/01 | A | NC | Hayes | 703 | L | 0-1 | |
| 32 | 09/01 | H | NC | Stevenage Borough | 932 | W | 1-0 | Wingfield 79 |
| 33 | 16/01 | A | FAT 3 | Dagenham & Redbridge | 783 | D | 1-1 | Bailey 2 |
| 34 | 23/01 | A | NC | Kingstonian | 1063 | D | 1-1 | Bailey 44[p] |
| 35 | 25/01 | H | FAT 3 rep | Dagenham & Redbridge | 452 | D | 1-1 | West 96 (2-4 pens) |
| 36 | 30/01 | H | NC | Woking | 1507 | W | 2-1 | Bailey 49, West 90 |
| 37 | 06/02 | H | NC | Hayes | 789 | L | 1-5 | West 7 |
| 38 | 09/02 | A | NC | Dover Athletic | 860 | L | 1-2 | Horner 52 |
| 39 | 13/02 | H | NC | Hereford United | 795 | L | 0-4 | |
| 40 | 20/02 | A | NC | Southport | 997 | D | 2-2 | West 33, Bailey 73 |
| 41 | 23/02 | H | Ends QF | Woking | 592 | W | 4-3 | West 47 76, Underwood 66, Bailey 80 |
| 42 | 27/02 | H | NC | Kidderminster Harriers | 733 | L | 2-4 | Bailey 73, Simpson 90 |
| 43 | 06/03 | H | NC | Welling United | 683 | D | 1-1 | Bailey 72[p] |
| 44 | 09/03 | A | NC | Kettering Town | 1389 | L | 1-4 | Bailey 45 |
| 45 | 13/03 | H | NC | Barrow | 758 | D | 2-2 | Bailey 36, N Baker 45 |
| 46 | 16/03 | A | NC | Cheltenham Town | 2265 | D | 0-0 | |
| 47 | 20/03 | H | NC | Northwich Victoria | 552 | L | 1-6 | Boothe 20 |
| 48 | 27/03 | A | NC | Telford United | 662 | L | 1-3 | Wingfield 23 |
| 49 | 03/04 | A | NC | Barrow | 1530 | L | 0-1 | |
| 50 | 05/04 | H | NC | Yeovil Town | 870 | D | 0-0 | |
| 51 | 07/04 | H | Ends SF | Cheltenham Town | 260 | W | 2-0 | Robson 20, Wingfield 52 |
| 52 | 10/04 | A | NC | Woking | 2101 | L | 0-4 | |
| 53 | 17/04 | A | NC | Doncaster Rovers | 893 | W | 1-0 | Robson 65 |
| 54 | 20/04 | H | Ends F(1) | Doncaster Rovers | 643 | L | 0-1 | |
| 55 | 24/04 | H | NC | Hednesford Town | 541 | L | 0-1 | |
| 56 | 01/05 | A | NC | Morecambe | 1136 | L | 0-1 | |
| 57 | 03/05 | A | Ends F(2) | Doncaster Rovers | 7160 | L | 0-3 | |

**PLAYING SQUAD 1999-2000:**

GOALKEEPERS: Martin Hutt (Bracknell Town), Matthew McNally, Dean Beale, Stuart McKenzie (Yeading)
DEFENDERS: Keith Day, Keith Dublin (Southend United), Mark Harper (Sutton United), Mark Hooper (Sutton United), Richard Horner (Wealdstone), Mark Jones, Martin Kuhl (Hong Kong), Tim O'Shea (Instant Dict (Hong Kong)), Bradley Pratt, Lloyd Wye (Kingstonian)
MIDFIELDERS: Steve Baker, Brian Broome, Rob Codnor (Ilkeston Town/Aylesbury United), Scott Corbett (Kingstonian), Lee Endersby (Slough Town), Jimmy Gardiner (Exeter City), Mark Turkington, Michael Warner (Northampton Town), Steve Watson (Sutton United)
FORWARDS: Anday Ansah (Brighton & Hove Albion), Steve Darlington (Enfield), Nick Hooper, Mark West (Slough Town)

# GRAVESEND & NORTHFLEET

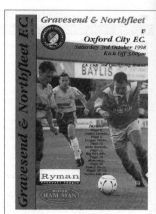

**Gravesend & Northfleet**
v
**Oxford City F.C.**
Saturday 3rd October 1998
Kick Off 3.00pm

## CLUB OFFICIALS

Chairman: **Peter Dean**

Vice Chairman/ Secretary:
**Michael Alan Sears,** c/o club address

Press Officer: **J.Fuggle**
Tel: 01474 533796

## FOOTBALL MANAGEMENT TEAM

Manager: Andy Ford
Physio: Micky Ward

### FACT FILE

Formed: 1946
Nickname: The Fleet
Sponsors: Mister Ham Man
Colours: Red/white/red
Change colours: All blue
Midweek matchday: Monday
Reserves' League: London Suburban Lg

1998-99 Captain: Bruce Sewell
P.o.W.: Craig Wilkins
Top Scorer: Dave Powell

**GROUND:** Stonebridge Road, Northfleet, Kent DA11 9BA Tel: 01474 533796
**Directions:** From A2 take Northfleet/Southfleet exit (B262), follow toNorthfleet then B2175
(Springhead Rd) to junc A226, turn left (The Hill, Northfleet), road becomes Stonebridge Rd,
grd on right at bottom of steep hill after 1 mile - car parking for 400-500. 2 mins from Northfleet
BR station
Capacity: 3,300   Cover: 2,200   Seats: 600   Floodlights: Yes
Clubhouse: Fleet Social Centre. Hot and cold food available at tea bars onmatchdays
Club Shop: Sells progs, hats, scarves, badges etc, & other memorabilia.
Contact John Still or Angela Still

Pages: 32 Price: £1.50
Editor: R.Edwards
Local Press: Gravesend Reporter,
Kent Evening Post, Gravesend Extra,
Leader,The News Shopper
Local Radio: Invicta Radio, Radio Kent,
RTM, Medway FM

**PREVIOUS**   **Leagues:** Kent (Gravesend Utd), Southern 46-79, Alliance Prem. 79-80
**Names:** Gravesend Utd, Northfleet Utd (merged 1946)
**Ground:** Central Avenue (Gravesend Utd) (Northfleet always played at StonebridgeRd)
**CLUB RECORDS Attendance:** 12,036 v Sunderland, FA Cup 4th Rd 12.2.63. 26.081 v Aston Villa FACup 3rd Rd 95-96 at Villa Park
**Goalscorer (career):** Steve Portway 150+ (92-94, 97-present)   **Appearances:** Ken Burrett 537
**Win:** 8-1 v Clacton Tn, Sth Lge 62-63, 7-0 Godalming 95-96 FAC. **Defeat:** 0-9 v Trowbridge Tn, Southern Lge Prem Div 91-92
**Fee Paid:** £8,000 for Richard Newbery (Wokingham 96), £8,000 for Craig Williams(Tonbridge 97)
**Fee Received:** £35,000 for Jimmy Bullard (West Ham 1998)
**BEST SEASON**   **FA Cup:** 4th Rd Replay 1963, 2-5 v Sunderland (A), 1-1 (H)           **FA Trophy:** 3rd Rd 88-89
**HONOURS:** Southern Lg 57-58, Southern Div 94-95, Div 1 Sth 74-75 (R-up 70-71 88-89), Lg Cup 77-78 (R-up 57-58), Champ Cup 77-78;
Kent Sen Cup 48-49 52-53 80-81 (R-up 47-48 76-77 90-91 97-98); Kent Floodlit Cup 69-70 (R-up 72-73); Kent Sen Shield R-
up 47-48 51-52; Kent Interm Cup R-up 87-88; Kent Midweek Lg 95-96, R-up 92-93 93-94 94-95; Kent Youth Lg Cup 82-83 86-
87 96-97; Kent Youth Lg 95-96 96-97; John Ullman Cup 82-83
Players progressing: Several incl. most recently: K Baron (Aldershot 60), R Dwight (Coventry 62), R Cameron (Southend 63),
R McNichol (Carlisle 65), A Humphreys (Mansfield 64), B Thornley (Brentford 65), P Jeavons (Lincoln 66), B Fry (Orient 66),
B Gordine (Sheffield Utd 68), TBaldwin (Brentford 77), L Smelt (Nottm Forest 80), T Warrilow (Torquay 87)

*Gravesend & Northfleet goalkeeper Scott Tarr was kept busy by Sutton United's forwards at The Fleet on a warm*
*sunny March afternoon. Watched by his defenders and Sutton's No 9 he dives to save Sammy Winston's well*
*directed header.*
*Photo: Keith Lodge*

# GRAVESEND & NORTHFLEET - MATCH FACTS - 1998-99 SEASON

| No | Date | Venue | Comp | Opponents | Att | Result | Score | Goalscorers |
|---|---|---|---|---|---|---|---|---|
| 1 | 22/08 | H | RL P | St Albans City | 586 | L | 0-1 | |
| 2 | 25/08 | A | RL P | Hendon | 315 | D | 0-0 | |
| 3 | 29/08 | A | RL P | Aldershot Town | 2371 | L | 0-3 | |
| 4 | 01/09 | H | RL P | Slough Town | 416 | L | 1-2 | Dimmock 75 |
| 5 | 05/09 | H | RL P | Harrow Borough | 375 | W | 2-0 | Bullard 45, Dennis 53 |
| 6 | 08/09 | A | RL C 1 | Whyteleafe | 110 | W | 5-0 | Jackson, Dennis(2), Dean(2) |
| 7 | 12/09 | A | RL P | Enfield | 556 | W | 2-0 | Edwards 51 69 |
| 8 | 15/09 | H | RL P | Billericay Town | 450 | D | 0-0 | |
| 9 | 19/09 | H | RL P | Hampton | 457 | W | 3-0 | Newson 21, Bullard 46, Jackson 65 |
| 10 | 26/09 | A | RL P | Chesham United | 515 | L | 2-3 | Powell 43 65 |
| 11 | 29/09 | H | RL P | Purfleet | 358 | D | 1-1 | Bullard |
| 12 | 03/10 | H | FAC Q2 | Oxford City | 379 | W | 3-1 | Newson, Powell, Jackson |
| 13 | 10/10 | A | RL P | Walton & Hersham | 247 | W | 3-1 | Dimmock 23[p], Powell 42, Jackson 88 |
| 14 | 17/10 | H | FAC Q3 | Dover Athletic | 1058 | D | 0-0 | |
| 15 | 20/10 | A | FAC Q3 r | Dover Athletic | 1034 | L | 2-3 | Bullard 50, Jackson 72[p] |
| 16 | 24/10 | H | RL P | Dulwich Hamlet | 446 | L | 0-1 | |
| 17 | 27/10 | A | RL P | Carshalton Athletic | 253 | W | 2-1 | Daly 1[og], Powell 15 |
| 18 | 31/10 | A | RL P | Harrow Borough | 230 | W | 1-0 | Jackson 35 |
| 19 | 07/11 | A | RL P | Heybridge Swifts | 490 | W | 3-2 | Cranfield 15[og], Newson 52, Dimmock 73 |
| 20 | 21/11 | A | FAT 2 | Newport IoW | 392 | L | 0-1 | |
| 21 | 28/11 | A | RL P | Boreham Wood | 252 | L | 1-3 | Dennis 86 |
| 22 | 01/12 | A | P C 2 | Whyteleafe | 92 | L | 1-2 | Adebowale |
| 23 | 05/12 | H | RL P | Enfield | 483 | L | 0-3 | |
| 24 | 19/12 | H | RL P | Dagenham & Redbridge | 592 | W | 2-0 | Boothe 45, Adebowale 60 |
| 25 | 22/12 | A | RL C 2 | Hendon | 141 | L | 1-2 | Bullard |
| 26 | 28/12 | A | RL P | Bromley | 661 | W | 1-0 | Buglione 85 |
| 27 | 02/01 | H | RL P | Aylesbury United | 724 | L | 1-2 | Bullard 20 |
| 28 | 09/01 | H | RL P | Aldershot Town | 954 | W | 2-1 | Dean 14, Sewell 26 |
| 29 | 19/01 | H | KSC QF | Fisher Athletic | 155 | L | 3-4 | Buglione 40, Bruce 60 85 |
| 30 | 30/01 | A | RL P | St Albans City | 974 | W | 2-0 | Jackson 17, Bullard 38 |
| 31 | 06/02 | A | RL P | Carshalton Athletic | 592 | W | 3-1 | Newson 42, Portway 46 62 |
| 32 | 13/02 | H | RL P | Billericay Town | 776 | W | 2-0 | Powell 30, Sewell 87[p] |
| 33 | 20/02 | A | RL P | Bishop's Stortford | 274 | L | 1-3 | D Edwards 47 |
| 34 | 23/02 | A | RL P | Basingstoke Town | 355 | D | 2-2 | Dean 43 66 |
| 35 | 27/02 | H | RL P | Walton & Hersham | 498 | W | 2-0 | Powell 7, Adebowale 50 |
| 36 | 06/03 | H | RL P | Chesham United | 492 | L | 0-2 | |
| 37 | 09/03 | H | RL P | Hendon | 378 | L | 0-1 | |
| 38 | 13/03 | A | RL P | Purfleet | 253 | L | 1-2 | Booth 75 |
| 39 | 20/03 | A | RL P | Hampton | 228 | L | 0-1 | |
| 40 | 27/03 | H | RL P | Sutton United | 536 | W | 2-1 | Sewell 13, Callinan 44 |
| 41 | 30/03 | H | RL P | Bishop's Stortford | 376 | W | 4-1 | Cooper 19, Newsom 37 62, Dolby 74 |
| 42 | 03/04 | A | RL P | Aylesbury United | 914 | L | 0-2 | |
| 43 | 05/04 | H | RL P | Bromley | 561 | L | 1-2 | Powell 68 |
| 44 | 10/04 | A | RL P | Heybridge Swifts | 268 | L | 2-3 | Cooper 30, Callinan 37 |
| 45 | 13/04 | A | RL P | Sutton United | 833 | D | 1-1 | Powell 85 |
| 46 | 17/04 | H | RL P | Basingstoke Town | 563 | W | 1-0 | Powell 41 |
| 47 | 19/04 | A | RL P | Dagenham & Redbridge | 561 | D | 0-0 | |
| 48 | 24/04 | A | RL P | Dulwich Hamlet | 642 | L | 0-1 | |
| 49 | 27/04 | A | RL P | Slough Town | 311 | L | 0-4 | |
| 50 | 01/05 | H | RL P | Boreham Wood | 370 | W | 3-2 | Cooper 67 68 90 |

## PLAYING SQUAD 1999-2000:

GOALKEEPERS: Mick Desborough, Darren Smith
DEFENDERS: Darren Brodrick (Aldershot Town), Corey Campbell, Tony Dolby (Welling United), Matt Gubbins (Ashford Town), Scott Honeyball (Bishop's Stortford), Bruce Sewell (Boreham Wood), Justin Skinner (Aylesbury United), Dave Walker (Dover Athletic)
MIDFIELDERS: Matt Chaplain (ex-Maidstone United), Ian Gibbs, Jimmy Jackson (Charlton Athletic), Darren Smith (Sittingbourne), Lee Spiller (Margate)
FORWARDS: Paul Booth (Tunbridge Wells), Mark Cooper (Welling United), Danny Edwards (Millwall), Anthony Jones (Leyton Orient), Dave Powell (Sheppey United), Paul Wilson (Ashford Town), Ady Adebowale (Gloucester City)

# HAMPTON & RICHMOND BOROUGH

**CLUB OFFICIALS**
Chairman: **Victor Searle**
President: **Alan Simpson**
Vice Chairman: **Ken Gazzard**
Press Officer: **Les Rance**
Secretary: **Adrian Mann,**
30 Burniston Court, Manor Rd, Wallington,
Surrey SM6 0AD (0181 773 0858)

**FOOTBALL MANAGEMENT TEAM**
Manager: Steve Cordery
Assistant Manager: Tony Coombe
Coach: Paul Shrubb
Physio: Gareth Workman

**FACT FILE**

Formed: 1920
Nickname: Beavers
Sponsors: TBA
Colours: Red & blue halves/white/blue
Change Colours: White/tangerine/white
Midweek Matchday: Tuesday
Reserve Team's League: Suburban
1998-99 - Captain: Steve Cheshire
Top scorer: Johnson Hippolyte
P.o.Y.: Mark Russell

MAIN SPONSOR SEXTON DEMOLITION LTD

Pages: 28   Price: £1.20p
Editor: Les Rance

Local Press: Middx Chronicle, Surrey Comet,
Richmond & Twickenham Times, The Informer

**GROUND:** Beveree Stadium, Beaver Close, off Station Rd, Hampton TW12 2BX
Tel: Office 0181 979 2456(matchdays only) Club: 0181 941 4936 Boardroom: 0181 941 2838
**Directions:** A3 out of London, fork left (signed Staines/Esher/Sandown Pk) onto A243, A309
Staines exit to Hampton Ct at `Scilly Isles' r'bout, left at r'bout after Hampton Court Bridge
onto A308, after 1 mile right into Church St (A311), left after White Hart after 200yds into High
St, Station Rd on right just before junction with A308
Capacity: 3,000   Seats: 300   Cover: 800   Floodlights: Yes
**Clubhouse:** (0181 979 2456). Lounge bar and hall, open on matchdays and training nights.
Hall available for hire. Steward: Steve Penny
**Club Shop:** Sells various souvenirs & prog. Contact Les Rance (0181 287 4682)

**PREVIOUS**     **Leagues:** Kingston & District 21-33; South West Middx 33-59; Surrey Snr 59-64; Spartan 64-71; Athenian 71-73
**Grounds:** Hatherop Rec (until 1959)

**CLUB RECORDS**   **Win:** 11-1 v Eastbourne Utd, Isthmian Lge Div 2 (S), 90-91   **Defeat:** 0-13 v Hounslow Town, Middlesex Senior Cup 62-63
**Goalscorer:** Peter Allen (176) 1964-73   **Appearances:** Tim Hollands (700) 1977-95
**Fees - Paid:** £850 for Andy Gray (Wokingham Town) November 97
**Fees - Received:** £15,000 for Daren Powell(Brentford) August 98
**BEST SEASON**   **FA Cup:** 4th Qual Rd 77-78 (1-2 v Barnet)   **FA Amateur Cup:** 1st Rd Prop 73-74 (2-4 v Leytonstone)
**FA Trophy:** 1st Rd Prop 83-84 (0-2 v Maidstone Utd)
**FA Vase:** 3rd Rd 91-92 (0-1 v Newport IOW), 95-96 (0-1 v Colllier Row)
**HONOURS:** London Snr Cup(2) 86-88; Spartan Lg(4) 64-67 69-70, (R-up 67-68), Lg Cup(4) 64-68 (R-up 2); Surrey Snr Lg 63-64 (Lg Cup
R-up  60-61); Middx Charity Cup 69-70 95-96 97-98,98-99 (R-up 68-69 71-72 89-90 94-95); Middx Snr Cup R-up 71-72 76-77
95-96; Athenian Lg Div 2 R-up 72-73; Southern Comb. Cup 68-69 71-72 76-77 81-82 83-84 85-86 96-97 (R-up 77-78 79-80 97-
98); Isthmian Lge promotion from Div 1 97-98, Div 2 95-96, Div 3 91-92
Players progressing: Andy Rogers (Southampton), Dwight Marshall (Plymouth), Paul Rogers (Sheffield Utd via Sutton Utd),
Derek Bryan (Brentford 97), Darren Powell (Brentford 98)

*Back Row: Gareth Workman (Physio), Dave Stephenson, Ian Savage, Steve Croxford, Mark Russell, Peter Wood, Nick
Burton, Tony Coombe (Assistant Manager)*
*Front Row: Matt Miller, Jason Brown, Steve Cheshire, Johnson Hippolyte, Jamie Beer, Robin Lewis, Warren Drew, Andy Gray*
*Photo: Eric Marsh*

# HAMPTON - MATCH FACTS - 1998-99 SEASON

| No | Date | Venue | Comp | Opponents | Att | Result | Score | Goalscorers |
|----|------|-------|------|-----------|-----|--------|-------|-------------|
| 1 | 01/08 | A | MMCup | Melksham Town | n/k | W | 1-0 | Lewis |
| 2 | 04/08 | H | SNS | Kingstonian | n/k | L | 1-3 | Cooper |
| 3 | 22/08 | H | RL P | Hendon | 355 | W | 3-1 | Hippolyte 57 80, Miller 88 |
| 4 | 25/08 | A | RL P | Aldershot Town | 2304 | L | 0-5 | |
| 5 | 29/08 | A | RL P | St Albans City | 668 | L | 1-3 | Hippolyte 24 |
| 6 | 01/09 | H | RL P | Dulwich Hamlet | 239 | D | 0-0 | |
| 7 | 05/09 | H | RL P | Boreham Wood | 213 | D | 3-3 | Beer 1, Hippolyte 30, Gray 68 |
| 8 | 08/09 | A | RL C 1 | Wembley | 74 | D | 1-1 | Lewis |
| 9 | 12/09 | A | RL P | Carshalton Athletic | 292 | W | 4-2 | Croxford 73, Hippolyte 77 90, Savage 90 |
| 10 | 15/09 | H | RL P | Slough Town | 304 | D | 2-2 | Miller 24, Browne 90 |
| 11 | 19/09 | A | RL P | Gravesend & Northfleet | 457 | L | 0-3 | |
| 12 | 22/09 | H | RL P | Chesham United | 274 | L | 0-1 | |
| 13 | 26/09 | A | RL P | Sutton United | 883 | L | 2-3 | Savage 64[p], Forte 72 |
| 14 | 03/10 | A | FAC Q2 | Havant & Waterlooville | 310 | L | 1-5 | Cheshire 31 |
| 15 | 06/10 | H | RL C 1 r | Wembley | 103 | W | 5-0 | Miller(3), Savage, Stephenson |
| 16 | 10/10 | H | RL P | Basingstoke Town | 339 | W | 2-1 | Hippolyte 32, Savage 70 |
| 17 | 12/10 | A | RL P | Purfleet | 197 | L | 0-4 | |
| 18 | 17/10 | H | RL P | Bishop's Stortford | 226 | D | 0-0 | |
| 19 | 24/10 | A | FAT 1 | Folkestone Invicta | 205 | L | 1-2 | Stephenson 14 |
| 20 | 27/10 | A | LCC 1 | Barking | 75 | W | 3-0 | Hippolyte, James, Miller |
| 21 | 31/10 | A | RL P | Aylesbury United | 506 | L | 0-3 | |
| 22 | 07/11 | H | RL P | Bromley | 324 | W | 2-1 | Barnsby 22, James 58 |
| 23 | 09/11 | A | RL C 2 | Purfleet | 101 | L | 0-5 | |
| 24 | 21/11 | A | RL P | Billericay Town | 615 | L | 0-2 | |
| 25 | 28/11 | A | RL P | Heybridge Swifts | 137 | L | 0-3 | |
| 26 | 30/11 | H | SCC 2 | Raynes Park Vale | 0 | D | 3-3 | (4-2 pens) |
| 27 | 05/12 | H | RL P | Carshalton Athletic | 222 | D | 1-1 | Hippolyte 90 |
| 28 | 12/12 | A | RL P | Boreham Wood | 228 | L | 2-4 | Cheshire 35, Hall 90 |
| 29 | 22/12 | H | RL C 3 | Leatherhead | 106 | L | 2-5 | Croxford, Lewis |
| 30 | 28/12 | A | RL P | Walton & Hersham | 359 | W | 1-0 | Hall 58 |
| 31 | 05/01 | H | MSC 2 | Southall | 95 | W | 3-0 | Savage, Beer, Pittwood |
| 32 | 09/01 | H | RL P | St Albans City | 332 | L | 1-2 | Gallagher 79 |
| 33 | 23/01 | H | RL P | Aldershot Town | 1035 | D | 0-0 | |
| 34 | 30/01 | A | RL P | Hendon | 229 | W | 2-1 | Gallagher 56 66 |
| 35 | 02/02 | A | P C 2 | Dulwich Hamlet | 114 | L | 0-1 | |
| 36 | 06/02 | A | RL P | Billericay Town | 240 | D | 0-0 | |
| 37 | 09/02 | H | MSC QF | Hendon | 108 | L | 0-2 | |
| 38 | 13/02 | A | RL P | Slough Town | 544 | L | 0-3 | |
| 39 | 16/02 | H | LCC QF | Dulwich Hamlet | 95 | L | 1-2 | Beer 19 |
| 40 | 20/02 | H | RL P | Purfleet | 126 | L | 2-3 | Franklin 52 55 |
| 41 | 23/02 | H | RL P | Aylesbury United | 264 | D | 0-0 | |
| 42 | 27/02 | A | RL P | Basingstoke Town | 634 | L | 0-1 | |
| 43 | 03/03 | A | RL P | Dagenham & Redbridge | 440 | L | 0-4 | |
| 44 | 06/03 | H | RL P | Sutton United | 380 | L | 0-3 | |
| 45 | 09/03 | H | RL P | Harrow Borough | 161 | D | 0-0 | |
| 46 | 13/03 | A | RL P | Chesham United | 317 | D | 2-2 | Gallagher 39, Cooper 51 |
| 47 | 16/03 | A | RL P | Enfield | 275 | L | 0-2 | |
| 48 | 20/03 | H | RL P | Gravesend & Northfleet | 228 | W | 1-0 | Barnsby 35 |
| 49 | 23/03 | A | SCC QF | Walton & Hersham | n/k | L | 1-6 | |
| 50 | 27/03 | A | RL P | Bishop's Stortford | 156 | W | 2-0 | Buglione 72 90 |
| 51 | 30/03 | A | RL P | Dulwich Hamlet | 220 | L | 1-2 | Gardner 38 |
| 52 | 03/04 | A | RL P | Harrow Borough | 222 | L | 0-4 | |
| 53 | 05/04 | H | RL P | Walton & Hersham | 404 | W | 2-0 | Reilly 25, Timothy 88 |
| 54 | 10/04 | A | RL P | Bromley | 334 | D | 0-0 | |
| 55 | 13/04 | H | MCC QF | Hanwell Town | 80 | W | 1-0 | Buglione[p] |
| 56 | 17/04 | H | RL P | Dagenham & Redbridge | 276 | L | 1-2 | Gallagher 63 |
| 57 | 24/04 | A | RL P | Enfield | 529 | D | 0-0 | |
| 58 | 27/04 | H | MCC SF | Brook House | 89 | D | 2-2 | Savage, Wood (3-0 pens) |
| 59 | 01/05 | H | RL P | Heybridge Swifts | 363 | W | 4-0 | Gardner 35 81, Buglione 40, Blake 76 |
| 60 | 07/05 | A | MCC F | Southall | 250 | W | 3-0 | Barnsby, Reilly, Gardner (at Yeading) |

**PLAYING SQUAD 1999-2000:**
GOALKEEPERS: Michael Bullen (Chertsey Town)
DEFENDERS: Nick Burton (Aldershot Town), Dudley Gardner (Slough Town), Brian Lee (Fisher Athletic), Danny White (Hemel Hempstead Town)
MIDFIELDERS: Hakan Altinok (Hendon), Erwin Asselman (Hayes), Naseem Bashir (Chesham United), Martin Carter (Chertsey Town), Jason Shaw (Chertsey Town), Richard Vercesi (Ashford Town)
FORWARDS: Martin Buglione (Hayes), Phil Gallagher (Gravesend & Northfleet), Rob Peters (Yeovil Town)

# HARROW BOROUGH

### CLUB OFFICIALS
Chairman: **Jim Ripley**
President: **Jim Rogers**
Secretary/Press Officer: **Peter Rogers,**
21 Ludlow Close, South Harrow, Middx HA2
8SR (0181 248 8003)
Commercial Manager:
**Jim Hayes** c/o the club

### FOOTBALL MANAGEMENT TEAM
Manager: Alan Paris
Asst Manager: Edwin Stein
Physio: Chris Barton

**FACT FILE**

Formed: 1933
Nickname: The Boro
Sponsors: Ranger Plant Hire
Colours: Red, white trim/white/red, white hoops
Change cols: Black & white stripes/black/black
Midweek matchday: Tuesday

1998-99
Captain: Barrie Bates
P.o.Y.: Barrie Bates
Top Scorer: Pat Gavin

**GROUND:** Earlsmead, Carlyon Avenue, South Harrow, Middx HA2 8SS
Tel: 0181 422 5989/5221

**Directions:** Underground to Northolt (Central Line) then 140 bus to Northolt Park BR, 282 bus, to Eastcote Arms or to South Harrow (Piccadilly Line) then 114 or H10 to Kings Rd.Junction. By road leave A40 at Macdonalds roundabout towards Northolt station (A312 north), left at lights, right at next island (Eastcote Arms pub), ground 5th turning on right.
**Capacity:** 3,070 **Cover:** 1,000 **Seats:** 350 **Floodlights:** Yes
**Clubhouse:** Open daily, normal pub hours. Four bars, games room, equipped for all social
events. Hot and coldfood available, buffets by prior request
**Club Shop:** Sells progs, scarves, badges, T-shirts, etc. Contact Tony Trowbridge c/o club

Pages: 32 Price: £1.20p
Editor: Jim Rogers (0181 248 8003)

Local Press: Harrow Observer, Harrow Times

---

**PREVIOUS** **Leagues:** Harrow & Dist 33-4; Spartan 34-40, 45-58; W Middx Comb 40-1; Middx Sen41-45; Delphian 58-63; Athenian 63-75;
**Names:** Roxonian 1933-8; Harrow Town 38-66 **Ground:** Northolt Road 33-4
**CLUB RECORDS Attendance:** 3,000 v Wealdstone, F.A. Cup 1st Qualifying Round 1946
**Scorer:** Dave Pearce, 153 **Appearances:** Steve Emmanuel 522 (1st team only), Les Currell 582, Colin Payne 557
**Fee Paid:** Unspecified to Dagenham for George Duck & Steve Jones, Summer 81
**Fee Received:** £16,000 for Lee Endersby (Enfield 97)
**Win:** 13-0 v Handley Page (A), Middlesex Snr Lg 18/10/41. **Defeat:** 0-8 5 times: Wood Green T. (A) Middx Lge 40,
Met Police (A) Spartan Lg 52, Briggs Spts (A) Spartan Lg 53, Hertford T. (A) Spartan Lge 53, Hendon (A) Middx Snr Cup 65
**BEST SEASON FA Trophy:** Semi final 82-83 **FA Cup:** 2nd Rd 83-84 (1-3 at home to Newport Co)
**HONOURS:** Isthmian Lg 83-84 (Div 1 R-up 78-79); Athenian Lg Div 2 R-up 63-64; Spartan Lg R-up 57-58 (Div 2 West 38-39 (R-up 37-38);
Middx Senior Cup 82-83 92-93; Harrow & Dist. Lg Div 1 R-up 33-34; Middx Charity Cup 79-80 92-93; (R-up 78-79); Middx
Intermediate Cup 55-56; Middx Premier Cup 81-82; Harrow Sen Cup 95 97
Players progressing: M Bottoms (QPR 60), C Hutchings (Chelsea 80), R Holland(Crewe 85), J Kerr (Portsmouth 87), D Howell, A Pape & E Stein
(Barnet), DByrne (Gillingham), R Rosario (Norwich), D Kemp (Crystal Palace), M Doherty(Reading), D Bassett (Wimbledon),
G Borthwick (Bournemouth), B Laryea(Torquay)

*Back Row (L-R): Shanton Towle, Ishmael Dodds, Mark Cooper, Pat Gavin, David Hook, Alan Paris (Player/Manager), Aidan O'Brien, Otis Roberts, Paul Harding, George Goode (Reserve Team Manager), Kenny Webster, Darren Coleman Front Row: Chris Barton (Physio), Andrew Murfin, Sean James, Paul Adolphe, Jon-Barrie Bates (Captain), Frank McCormack, Lee Randall, Nelson Heldt (Reserve Team Assistant), Eddie Stein (Coach)* Photo: Paul Carter

# HARROW BOROUGH - MATCH FACTS - 1998-99 SEASON

| No | Date | Venue | Comp | Opponents | Att | Result | Score | Goalscorers |
|---|---|---|---|---|---|---|---|---|
| 1 | 22/08 | A | RL P | Walton & Hersham | 227 | D | 2-2 | Kumah 31, Gavin 40 |
| 2 | 25/08 | H | RL P | Aylesbury United | 321 | L | 1-4 | N Kumah |
| 3 | 29/08 | H | RL P | Bishop's Stortford | 205 | D | 2-2 | Bates 80, N Kumah 81[p] |
| 4 | 01/09 | A | RL P | Bromley | 371 | L | 0-3 | |
| 5 | 05/09 | A | RL P | Gravesend & Northfleet | 375 | L | 0-2 | |
| 6 | 08/09 | H | RL C 1 | East Thurrock United | 95 | W | 3-2 | Nwaokolo 88, Adolphe 90, Gavin 94 |
| 7 | 12/09 | H | RL P | Sutton United | 255 | L | 0-3 | |
| 8 | 15/09 | A | RL P | Basingstoke Town | 539 | L | 1-2 | Bates 12 |
| 9 | 19/09 | H | RL P | Dagenham & Redbridge | 260 | W | 2-1 | Lawford 29[p], Pratt 62[og] |
| 10 | 22/09 | A | RL P | Dulwich Hamlet | 201 | W | 2-0 | Adolphe 51, Gavin 80 |
| 11 | 26/09 | H | RL P | Enfield | 401 | D | 0-0 | |
| 12 | 03/10 | H | FAC Q2 | Thamesmead Town | 202 | W | 3-0 | O'Brien, Own-Goal, Roberts |
| 13 | 10/10 | A | RL P | Slough Town | 432 | W | 3-0 | Lawford 16 77 83 |
| 14 | 13/10 | H | RL P | Carshalton Athletic | 211 | W | 8-2 | Gavin 9, Adolphe 22, McCormack 51, Lawford 52 71 76 83, Bates 63 |
| 15 | 17/10 | A | FAC Q3 | Langney Sports | 339 | L | 1-4 | Lawford 86 |
| 16 | 20/10 | H | RL P | Heybridge Swifts | 185 | W | 2-0 | Lawford 65, Gavin 80 |
| 17 | 24/10 | H | FAT 1 | Cambridge City | 200 | W | 4-2 | Greaves 48og, McCormack 49, Kumah 71, Walters 90 |
| 18 | 31/10 | H | RL P | Gravesend & Northfleet | 230 | L | 0-1 | |
| 19 | 07/11 | A | RL P | Billericay Town | 712 | D | 2-2 | N Kumah 18 79[p] |
| 20 | 10/11 | H | P C 1 | Leyton Pennant | 104 | W | 1-0 | Lord 100 |
| 21 | 14/11 | H | RL P | Aldershot Town | 981 | W | 1-0 | Bates 24 |
| 22 | 17/11 | H | RL C 2 | Bedford Town | 165 | W | 1-0 | Gavin 45 |
| 23 | 21/11 | A | FAT 2 | Aylesbury United | 655 | D | 1-1 | Roberts |
| 24 | 24/11 | H | FAT 2 rep | Aylesbury United | 306 | L | 2-3 | Toussaint 56, Gavin 80 |
| 25 | 28/11 | H | RL P | Chesham United | 326 | W | 5-4 | Kumah 38, Adolphe 44, Gavin 45 60, McCormack 72 |
| 26 | 01/12 | A | RL P | Boreham Wood | 205 | L | 0-1 | |
| 27 | 05/12 | A | RL P | Sutton United | 624 | L | 1-2 | McCormack 39 |
| 28 | 14/12 | A | RL P | Purfleet | 149 | L | 0-4 | |
| 29 | 19/12 | A | RL P | St Albans City | 715 | D | 1-1 | McCormack 8 |
| 30 | 22/12 | H | P C 2 | Romford | 164 | L | 1-3 | Bates 34 |
| 31 | 28/12 | A | RL P | Hendon | 513 | D | 2-2 | Kumah 28, McCormack 89 |
| 32 | 09/01 | A | RL P | Bishop's Stortford | 154 | W | 3-0 | Bates 31, Gavin 75, Johns 81 |
| 33 | 16/01 | H | RL P | Walton & Hersham | 402 | L | 0-1 | |
| 34 | 23/01 | H | RL P | Aylesbury United | 651 | L | 0-2 | |
| 35 | 30/01 | H | RL P | Bromley | 239 | W | 2-0 | Walker 35, Gavin 53 |
| 36 | 02/02 | A | MSC 2 | Wealdstone | 364 | D | 2-2 | Dodds 80, Gavin 110 |
| 37 | 09/02 | H | MSC 2 rep | Wealdstone | 410 | L | 1-2 | Gavin 80 |
| 38 | 13/02 | H | RL P | Basingstoke Town | 293 | L | 0-2 | |
| 39 | 16/02 | A | RL C 3 | Uxbridge | 91 | L | 0-1 | |
| 40 | 20/02 | A | RL P | Carshalton Athletic | 286 | W | 2-1 | Randall 28, Adolphe 87 |
| 41 | 27/02 | H | RL P | Slough Town | 437 | L | 0-2 | |
| 42 | 06/03 | A | RL P | Enfield | 529 | L | 0-5 | |
| 43 | 09/03 | A | RL P | Hampton | 161 | D | 0-0 | |
| 44 | 13/03 | H | RL P | Dulwich Hamlet | 215 | W | 3-2 | Harding 19, O'Brien 39, Bates 75 |
| 45 | 15/03 | A | RL P | Dagenham & Redbridge | 564 | L | 0-1 | |
| 46 | 20/03 | A | RL P | Heybridge Swifts | 225 | W | 4-2 | Webster 26, Harding 45, Lewis 54[og], Adolphe 81 |
| 47 | 27/03 | H | RL P | Boreham Wood | 227 | W | 3-0 | Adolphe 8, Gavin 58, Harding 63 |
| 48 | 03/04 | H | RL P | Hampton | 222 | W | 4-0 | Adolphe 8, Roberts 60, Mursin 66, Webster 90 |
| 49 | 10/04 | H | RL P | Billericay Town | 375 | D | 3-3 | McCormack 13, Harding 75, Webster 82[p] |
| 50 | 17/04 | A | RL P | Aldershot Town | 1694 | L | 2-5 | Bates 55, Gavin 71 |
| 51 | 22/04 | A | RL P | Hendon | 145 | W | 2-1 | Bates 35, Roberts 87 |
| 52 | 24/04 | H | RL P | Purfleet | 207 | W | 5-0 | Duru 11, McCormack 36, Gusavac 67 68, Gavin 75 |
| 53 | 29/04 | H | RL P | St Albans City | 242 | D | 0-0 | |
| 54 | 01/05 | A | RL P | Chesham United | 355 | W | 4-1 | Bates 50, Gasavao 12 65 80 |

**PLAYING SQUAD 1999-2000:**

GOALKEEPERS: David Hook (Chesham United), Lee Pearce (Staines Town)

DEFENDERS: Paul Adolphe (Dagenham & Redbridge), Darren Coleman (St Albans City), Mark Cooper (Chalfont St Peter), Darren Gorman (Conwy United), Chris Green (Sutton United), David Howell (Harlow Town), Russell Nixon (Dartford), Daniel Nwaokolo (Wokingham Town), Craig O'Connor, Alan Paris (Stevenage Borough), Andy Rose, Kenny Webster (Aylesbury United), Patrick Gavin (Farnborough Town)

MIDFIELDERS: Dwain Clarke, John Hurlock (Chesham United), Johnny Kumah (Kingsbury Town), Dermot Mernagh, John Parsons (local football), Darren Watts (Brackley Town)

FORWARDS: Vladimir Gusavac, Nelson Kumah (Wembley), Damien Markman (Bracknell Town), Otis Roberts (Belgian football), Chris Toussaint (Wembley)

# HENDON

## CLUB OFFICIALS

Chairman: **Ivor Arbiter**

Secretary: **Graham Etchell**, c/o Hendon
FC. Tel: 0181 201 9494 (Club)
Press Officer: Club Secretary

Marketingl Manager: **Jennie Cairns**

## FOOTBALL MANAGEMENT TEAM

Manager: Frank Murphy
Coach: John Johnson
Physio: Caroline Brouwer

### FACT FILE

Formed: 1908
Nickname: Dons or Greens
Sponsors: UK Packaging
Colours: White &Green,green,white & green
Green & white/green/green & white
Midweek matchday: Tuesday
Reserve League: Suburban (Premier))
Club Line: 0930 555 836
1998-99 Captain; Steve Bateman
P.o.Y.:& Top Scorer : Paul Whitmarsh

**GROUND:** Claremont Road, Cricklewood, London NW2 1AE.
Tel: 0181 201 9494 Fax: 0181 905 5966
**Directions:** From Brent Cross station (Northern Line) to the east take firstleft after flyover on North Circular - Claremont Rd is then left at 3rd mni-r'bout. Buses 102, 210, 226 and C11 pass ground
Capacity: 3,029 Cover: 601 Seats: 329 Floodlights: Yes
Clubhouse: (contact Sue Damary 0181 455 9185). Two banqueting suites,conference centre, room hire, restaurant & bars open licensing hours 7 days aweek. Hot & cold food, pool, darts, bingo, members club, satelite TV,entertainments
Club Shop: (Contact Derek Furmedge, 0181 459 2042(H) Sells football souvenirs

**PREVIOUS** **Leagues:** Finchley & Dist. 08-11, Middx 10-11, London 11-14, Athenian 14-63.
**Names:** Christ Church Hampstead to 08, Hampstead Town to 26, Hampstead to 33,Golders Green to 46
**Grounds:** Kensal Rise 08-12; Avenue Ground, Cricklewood Lane 12-26
**CLUB RECORDS** **Attendance:** 9,000 v Northampton, FA Cup 1st Rd 1952
**Goalscorer:** Freddie Evans 176 (1929-35) **Appearances:** Bill Fisher 787 (1940-
**Defeat:** 2-11 v Walthamstow Ave. (A), Athenian Lge 9/11/35 **Win:** 13-1 v Wingate (H), Middx Senior Cup 2/2/57
**Fee Paid:** Paul Whitmarsh (undisclosed) **Fee Received:** £30,000 for Iain Dowie (Luton)
**BEST SEASON** **F.A. Cup:** First Rd 18 times, Second Rd 5 times **F.A.Trophy:** 5th Rd 98-99
**HONOURS:** European Am Champions 72-3; Isthmian Lg 64-5 72-3 (R-up 63-4 65-6 73-4) Lg Cup 76-7 (R-up 86-7), Full Members Cup 94-5 97-8 98-99, Premier Inter-Lge Cup R-up 86-7; Middx Lge 12-3 13-4; Athenian Lg 52-3 55-6 60-1 (R-up 28-9 32-3 47-8 48-9 51-2); London Lg Div 1 R-up 12-13 (Amtr Div 13-4); Finchley & Dist. Lg 10-1; London Snr Cup 63-4 68-9 (R-up 35-6 50-1 54-5 58-9 71-2); Middx Snr Cup (12) (R-up 83-4), Middx Interm 64-5 66-7 72-3, Middx Charity Cup(14); London IntermCup (4) (R-up (2); Suburban Lg 92-3 (R-up 84-5 97-8)
Players progressing: Peter Shearing (West Ham 60), Iain Dowie (Luton 88), PeterAnderson (Luton), Jeff Harris (Orient), Phil Gridelet (Barnsley 90), GerrySoloman (Leyton Orient 91), Junior Hunter & Micah Hyde (both Cambridge 94-95),Simon Clark (Peterborough 94-95)

---

**HENDON**
Official Matchday Programme 1998/99

Thurs. 22nd April 1999 7.30pm

**HARROW BOROUGH**
Ryman
Ryman League Premier £1.20

Pages: 64 Price: £1.50p
Editor: Secretary
Local Press: Hendon Times,
Willesden & Brent Chronicle
Local Radio: Capital, GLR, LBC

*Gary McCann (Hendon) punches clear against Cheltenham.* *Photo: Keith Clayton*

# HENDON - MATCH FACTS - 1998-99 SEASON

| No | Date | Venue | Comp | Opponents | Att | Result | Score | Goalscorers |
|---|---|---|---|---|---|---|---|---|
| 1 | 22/08 | A | RL P | Hampton | 355 | L | 1-3 | Whitmarsh 66 |
| 2 | 25/08 | H | RL P | Gravesend & Northfleet | 315 | D | 0-0 | |
| 3 | 29/08 | H | RL P | Purfleet | 281 | L | 1-2 | Jones 31[og] |
| 4 | 01/09 | A | RL P | Sutton United | 682 | L | 1-4 | Maran 12 |
| 5 | 05/09 | A | RL P | Basingstoke Town | 873 | D | 1-1 | Fitzgerald 78 |
| 6 | 07/09 | A | RL C 1 | St Albans City | 217 | W | 4-1 | Whitmarsh(2), Daly, C Simpson |
| 7 | 12/09 | H | RL P | Bromley | 307 | W | 2-1 | Whitmarsh 57, Maran 82 |
| 8 | 15/09 | A | RL P | Chesham United | 428 | W | 2-0 | Whitmarsh 68 70 |
| 9 | 19/09 | H | RL P | Bishop's Stortford | 302 | W | 5-3 | Whitmarsh 15 49 88, Lewis 37 53 |
| 10 | 22/09 | H | RL P | Aylesbury United | 355 | D | 3-3 | Whitmarsh 1 40, Kelly 27 |
| 11 | 26/09 | A | RL P | St Albans City | 814 | L | 2-4 | Lewis 27, Kelly 40 |
| 12 | 03/10 | H | FAC Q2 | Chelmsford City | 488 | D | 1-1 | Kelly 80 |
| 13 | 05/10 | A | FAC Q2 r | Chelmsford City | 459 | W | 3-2 | Warmington 23, Heald 58, Kelly 68 |
| 14 | 09/10 | H | RL P | Enfield | 523 | W | 2-0 | Whitmarsh 51, Lewis 70[p] |
| 15 | 13/10 | A | RL P | Aldershot Town | 2018 | W | 2-0 | Whitmarsh 36, Lewis 60 |
| 16 | 17/10 | A | FAC Q3 | Harlow Town | 565 | W | 4-2 | Lewis(2), Whitmarsh(2) |
| 17 | 20/10 | A | RL P | Billericay Town | 447 | L | 1-2 | Lewis 55 |
| 18 | 24/10 | H | RL P | Slough Town | 330 | W | 5-2 | Kemp 38[og], Hyatt 45, Lewis 48 81, Whitmarsh 87[p] |
| 19 | 03/11 | H | FAC Q4 | Bath City | 357 | W | 4-0 | Hyatt 14, Whitmarsh 54, Heard 83 90 |
| 20 | 07/11 | A | RL P | Dulwich Hamlet | 401 | D | 1-1 | Fitzgerald 22 |
| 21 | 15/11 | H | FAC 1 | Notts County | 1627 | D | 0-0 | |
| 22 | 17/11 | H | RL P | Dagenham & Redbridge | 308 | D | 2-2 | Whitmarsh 25 60 |
| 23 | 21/11 | H | FAT 2 | Rothwell Town | 202 | D | 1-1 | Hyatt 24 |
| 24 | 26/11 | H | MSC 1 | Hanwell Town | 69 | W | 2-0 | Maran, O'Carroll |
| 25 | 28/11 | A | RL P | Walton & Hersham | 237 | W | 3-0 | Lewis 23 70 83 |
| 26 | 01/12 | A | FAC 1 rep | Notts County | 2230 | L | 0-3 | |
| 27 | 05/12 | H | RL P | Basingstoke Town | 236 | W | 2-1 | Whitmarsh 3, Lewis 26 |
| 28 | 12/12 | H | RL P | Bromley | 337 | W | 4-1 | Kelly 40, Whitmarsh 66 81, Heard 84 |
| 29 | 14/12 | A | FAT 2 rep | Rothwell Town | 186 | W | 2-1 | Lewis 87, Whitmarsh 110 |
| 30 | 19/12 | H | RL P | Carshalton Athletic | 274 | D | 1-1 | Heard 40 |
| 31 | 22/12 | H | RL C 2 | Gravesend & Northfleet | 141 | W | 2-1 | Heard, Whitmarsh |
| 32 | 28/12 | A | RL P | Harrow Borough | 513 | D | 2-2 | Lewis 62 84 |
| 33 | 02/01 | H | RL P | Boreham Wood | 350 | L | 0-1 | |
| 34 | 09/01 | H | RL P | Purfleet | 237 | L | 0-4 | |
| 35 | 16/01 | A | FAT 3 | Worthing | 358 | W | 2-0 | Howard 71, Whitmarsh 90 |
| 36 | 30/01 | H | RL P | Hampton | 229 | L | 1-2 | White 49 |
| 37 | 02/02 | H | MSC 2 | Uxbridge | 92 | W | 2-1 | Witmarsh(2) |
| 38 | 06/02 | A | FAT 4 | Chesham United | 521 | W | 2-0 | Whitmarsh 50, Lewis 65 |
| 39 | 09/02 | A | MSC QF | Hampton | 108 | W | 2-0 | Lewis, Maran |
| 40 | 11/02 | A | RL C 3 | Marlow | 165 | L | 1-2 | Whitmarsh |
| 41 | 13/02 | H | RL P | Chesham United | 319 | W | 2-1 | Whitmarsh 7 61 |
| 42 | 16/02 | H | P C 2 | Heybridge Swifts | 102 | W | 2-1 | Whitmarsh, Maran |
| 43 | 20/02 | H | RL P | Aldershot Town | 922 | D | 1-1 | White 68 |
| 44 | 23/02 | H | LCC 1 | Welling United | 89 | L | 0-3 | |
| 45 | 27/02 | A | FAT 5 | Cheltenham Town | 2514 | L | 0-3 | |
| 46 | 02/03 | H | MSC SF | Wealdstone | 248 | W | 3-0 | Lewis 41 88, Heard 68 |
| 47 | 04/03 | H | P C 3 | Canvey Island | 129 | W | 2-0 | |
| 48 | 06/03 | H | RL P | St Albans City | 437 | W | 4-3 | Lewis 6, Daly 22 90, Clarke 73 |
| 49 | 09/03 | A | RL P | Gravesend & Northfleet | 378 | W | 1-0 | Clarke 74 |
| 50 | 13/03 | A | RL P | Aylesbury United | 860 | L | 0-1 | |
| 51 | 16/03 | H | RL P | Sutton United | 301 | L | 0-3 | |
| 52 | 20/03 | A | RL P | Slough Town | 505 | D | 1-1 | Whitmarsh 65 |
| 53 | 23/03 | H | P C QF | Chesham United | 147 | W | 1-0 | Whitmarsh |
| 54 | 27/03 | H | RL P | Billericay Town | 227 | W | 2-0 | Whitmarsh 57, Fitzgerald 69 |
| 55 | 30/03 | A | RL P | Heybridge Swifts | 177 | L | 0-1 | |
| 56 | 03/04 | A | RL P | Boreham Wood | 472 | L | 0-2 | |
| 57 | 05/04 | H | MSC F | Wembley | 474 | D | 2-2 | Whitmarsh(2)   (4-2 pens) (at Enfield) |
| 58 | 07/04 | A | P C SF | Dulwich Hamlet | 181 | W | 2-0 | Daly, Lewis |
| 59 | 10/04 | A | RL P | Dulwich Hamlet | 383 | L | 1-3 | Kelly 77 |
| 60 | 13/04 | A | RL P | Carshalton Athletic | 232 | W | 3-1 | Whitmarsh 14, Lewis 25, Heald 56 |
| 61 | 17/04 | H | RL P | Heybridge Swifts | 229 | W | 6-1 | Lewis 14 48 54, Whitmarsh 24, Filby 44[og], Clarke |
| 62 | | | | | | | | |
| 63 | 22/04 | H | RL P | Harrow Borough | 145 | L | 1-2 | Lewis 68 |
| 64 | 24/04 | A | RL P | Dagenham & Redbridge | 601 | L | 0-6 | |
| 65 | 27/04 | A | RL P | Bishop's Stortford | 174 | W | 3-0 | Whitmarsh 20 30, Lewis 85   (at St Albans City) |
| 66 | 29/04 | A | RL P | Enfield | 750 | L | 1-2 | Whitmarsh 21 |
| 67 | 01/05 | H | RL P | Walton & Hersham | 315 | L | 0-3 | |
| | 06/05 | A | P C F | Worthing | 331 | W | 1-0 | Maran 20   (at Sutton United) |

## PLAYING SQUAD 1999-2000:

GOALKEEPERS: Neil Gill (Gateshead), Gary McCann  (Dulwich Hamlet)

DEFENDERS: Simon Clarke (Kettering Town), Andy Cox (Hayes), Gary Fitzgerald (Yeading), Matthew Howard (Chesham United), John Simon-White (Watford)

MIDFIELDERS: Jon Daly (St Albans City), Freddie Hyatt (Hayes), Jason McCoy (St Albans City), Marvin Watson (Wembley)

FORWARDS: Jerry Ikazaboah (Bishop's Stortford), Matthew Maran (Ruislip Manor), Karl Simpson (Witney Town), Paul Whitmarsh (Dulwich Hamlet)

# HEYBRIDGE SWIFTS

## CLUB OFFICIALS

Chairman: **Michael Gibson**
President: **Ronnie Locker**
Vice Chairman: **Michael Gibson**
Secretary: **Dennis Fenn,** 31 Saxon Way,
Maldon, Essex CM9 7JN (01621 854798)
Press Officer: **Tim Huxtable**
Treasurer: **Chris Deines**

### FOOTBALL MANAGEMENT TEAM
Manager: Robbie Nihill
Asst Man.: Tony English
Coach: Keith Hull
Physio: Glenn Churchett

### FACT FILE
Formed: 1880
Nickname: Swifts
Sponsors:
Towermaster.Lighting Towers Systems
Colours: Black & white stripes/black/black
Change colours: All Red
Midweek matchday: Tuesday
Reserves' Lge: Essex & Herts Border Comb

**GROUND:** Scraley Road, Heybridge, Maldon, Essex Tel: 01621 852978
**Directions:** Leave Maldon on the main road to Colchester, pass through Heybridge then turn right at the sign to Tolleshunt Major (Scraley Road). The ground on the right. Six miles from nearest station (Witham). By bus via Chelmsfordand Maldon
**Capacity:** 3,000 **Cover:** 1,200 **Seats:** 550 **Floodlights:** Yes
**Clubhouse:** Two bars open every night. Games room, boardroom, kitchen (on matchdays)
**Club Shop:** Open matchdays, selling club sweaters, shirts, scarves, baseball hats, enamel badges, old programmes etc.
Contact Chris Fenn, 40 Drake Avenue,Mayland CM3 6TY (01621 740878)

Pages: 40 Price: £1
Editor: Peter Fen (01621 740878)

Local Press: Maldon & Burnham Standard
Local Radio: BBC Essex, Essex FM,
Chelmer FM

**PREVIOUS Leagues:** Essex & Suffolk Border, North Essex, South Essex, Essex Senior 1971-84

**CLUB RECORDS Attendance:** 2,477 v Woking FA Trophy 97
**Goalscorer:** Julian Lamb 115 (post war), Dave Matthews 112 (Isthmian)
**Appearances:** Hec Askew 500+, Robbie Sach 358 (Isthmian)
**Fee Paid:** None **Fee Received:** £35,000, Simon Royce (Southend Utd)

**BEST SEASON FA Trophy:** Qtr finals v Woking 22/3/97 (lost 0-1)
**FA Cup:** First round 0-2 v Gillingham 11/11/94, 0-3 v Bournemouth 15.11.97 **League clubs defeated:** None

**HONOURS:** Isthmian Lg Div 1 R-up 95-96, Div 2 North 89-90; Essex Senior Lg 81-82 82-83 83-84, Lg Cup 82-83, Trophy 81-82; JT Clarke Cup 82-83; Thorn EMI National Floodlit Competition R-up 82-83; Eastern Floodlit Cup 93-94; East Anglian Cup 93-94 94-95; Essex & Suffolk Border Lge 31-32; Essex Jun Cup 31-32; North Essex Lge 46-47

Players progressing: Simon Royce (Southend United), Peter Cawley & Ben Lewis (Colchester Utd), Alan Hull (Leyton Orient), Jonathan Hunt (Birmingham City), Dominic Naylor (Leyton Orient), Haken Hayrettin (Doncaster Rovers), Derek Payne & Tom Meredith (Peterborough Utd), Ben Barnett, Eddie Stein & Tim Alexander (Barnet), Ashley Vickers (Peterborough United)

*Heybridge keeper Kingsley Banks is well beaten by Bromley's Danny Carroll (far left) as Bromley score the first of six goals on the opening day of the season against Heybridge.* Photo: Alan

# HEYBRIDGE SWIFTS - MATCH FACTS - 1998-99 SEASON

| No | Date | Venue | Comp | Opponents | Att | Result | Score | Goalscorers |
|----|------|-------|------|-----------|-----|--------|-------|-------------|
| 1 | 22/08 | A | RL P | Bromley | 302 | L | 1-6 | Ball 2 |
| 2 | 25/08 | H | RL P | Purfleet | 208 | D | 0-0 | |
| 3 | 29/08 | H | RL P | Basingstoke Town | 234 | L | 3-9 | Raynes 3, W Adcock 15, Ball 26[p] |
| 4 | 31/08 | A | RL P | Dagenham & Redbridge | 727 | L | 0-3 | |
| 5 | 05/09 | A | RL P | Sutton United | 702 | D | 1-1 | Ball 83 |
| 6 | 08/09 | H | RL C 1 | **Walton & Hersham** | **123** | **W** | **3-2** | **Ball, English, Fiddes** |
| 7 | 12/09 | H | RL P | Chesham United | 202 | L | 0-4 | |
| 8 | 15/09 | A | RL P | Walton & Hersham | 142 | W | 1-0 | Rayner 33 |
| 9 | 19/09 | H | RL P | Aylesbury United | 204 | D | 1-1 | English 31 |
| 10 | 22/09 | A | RL P | Enfield | 407 | L | 1-4 | Reeve 84 |
| 11 | 26/09 | H | RL P | Carshalton Athletic | 173 | L | 0-2 | |
| 12 | 03/10 | H | FAC Q2 | **Bashley** | **164** | **W** | **3-1** | **Ball 18[p] 22[p], Devine 55** |
| 13 | 10/10 | A | RL P | St Albans City | 361 | L | 0-3 | |
| 14 | 13/10 | A | RL P | Boreham Wood | 202 | D | 1-1 | Hewes 57 |
| 15 | 17/10 | A | FAC Q3 | **Farnborough Town** | **482** | **L** | **0-2** | |
| 16 | 20/10 | A | RL P | Harrow Borough | 185 | L | 0-2 | |
| 17 | 28/10 | A | FAT 1 | **Newport AFC** | **325** | **W** | **4-2** | **McLean 17, Adcock 19, Fiddles 23, Devine 83** |
| 18 | 03/11 | H | RL C 2 | **Bromley** | **112** | **L** | **1-2** | **Fiddes** |
| 19 | 07/11 | A | RL P | Gravesend & Northfleet | 490 | L | 2-3 | Lewis 10 90 |
| 20 | 14/11 | A | RL P | Carshalton Athletic | 304 | W | 2-1 | Fiddes 12, Wall 35 |
| 21 | 21/11 | H | FAT 2 | **Sutton United** | **319** | **L** | **1-2** | **Hewes** |
| 22 | 24/11 | H | RL P | Dulwich Hamlet | 124 | L | 0-2 | |
| 23 | 28/11 | H | RL P | Hampton | 137 | W | 3-0 | McClean 42, Fiddes 79, Gillespie 84 |
| 24 | 01/12 | A | ESC 3 | **Saffron Walden Town** | **104** | **W** | **6-3** | **Wall(3), Caton, Fiddes, W Adcock** |
| 25 | 05/12 | A | RL P | Chesham United | 316 | L | 0-1 | |
| 26 | 08/12 | H | EFC 7 | **Southend Manor** | **84** | **W** | **7-0** | **Streetley, Heasman(3), Fiddes, Hewes, McClean** |
| 27 | 12/12 | H | RL P | Sutton United | 206 | L | 2-4 | Wall 64[p], Simpson 79 |
| 28 | 19/12 | A | RL P | Aldershot Town | 1966 | D | 1-1 | Streetley 20 |
| 29 | 28/12 | H | RL P | Billericay Town | 666 | W | 1-0 | McClean 64 |
| 30 | 02/01 | A | RL P | Slough Town | 520 | W | 1-0 | Wall 54 |
| 31 | 05/01 | A | ESC 4 | **Braintree Town** | **262** | **W** | **3-0** | **Wall, Heasman(2)** |
| 32 | 09/01 | A | RL P | Basingstoke Town | 638 | D | 2-2 | Heasman 52, Wall 79 |
| 33 | 23/01 | A | RL P | Purfleet | 301 | L | 0-2 | |
| 34 | 30/01 | H | RL P | Dagenham & Redbridge | 345 | L | 1-2 | W Adcock 40 |
| 35 | 08/02 | A | ESC QF | **Dagenham & Redbridge** | **235** | **D** | **2-2** | **Fiddes 57, Heasman 95** (5-4 pens) |
| 36 | 11/02 | A | EFC 7 | **Brightlingsea United** | **35** | **W** | **3-0** | **Mulcahy, Miller(2)** |
| 37 | 13/02 | H | RL P | Walton & Hersham | 260 | W | 1-0 | McClean 3 |
| 38 | 16/02 | A | P C 2 | **Hendon** | **102** | **L** | **1-2** | **Lewis** |
| 39 | 18/02 | A | EFC 7 | **Southend Manor** | **51** | **D** | **4-4** | **Miller 2 52 88, Stevens 45** |
| 40 | 20/02 | H | RL P | Boreham Wood | 240 | W | 2-0 | Simpson 39, Wall 50[p] |
| 41 | 25/02 | H | EFC 7 | **Brightlingsea United** | **53** | **W** | **8-0** | **Lewis, Basefield(2), Simpson(3), Parker, Dominique** |
| 42 | 08/03 | A | RL P | St Albans City | 439 | D | 1-1 | Wall 77 |
| 43 | 13/03 | H | RL P | Enfield | 421 | D | 2-2 | Wall 2[p] 90[p] |
| 44 | 16/03 | H | RL P | Bishop's Stortford | 126 | W | 3-1 | Simpson 31, Lewis 40 51 |
| 45 | 20/03 | H | RL P | Harrow Borough | 225 | L | 2-4 | Simpson 2, Streetley 76 |
| 46 | 23/03 | A | ESC SF | **Leyton Orient** | **n/k** | **D** | **2-2** | **Wall, Heasman** (4-5 pens) |
| 47 | 27/03 | A | RL P | Dulwich Hamlet | 276 | L | 3-4 | Simpson 12 17 55 |
| 48 | 30/03 | H | RL P | Hendon | 177 | W | 1-0 | Fiddes 75 |
| 49 | 03/04 | H | RL P | Slough Town | 291 | W | 2-1 | Gillespie 15, Lewis 82 |
| 50 | 05/04 | A | RL P | Billericay Town | 710 | L | 1-2 | Simpson 83 |
| 51 | 10/04 | H | RL P | Gravesend & Northfleet | 268 | W | 3-2 | T Adcock 14 60, Miyoba 86 |
| 52 | 13/04 | H | RL P | Bromley | 181 | W | 2-1 | Simpson 80, Lewis 90[p] |
| 53 | 17/04 | A | RL P | Hendon | 229 | L | 1-6 | Simpson 26 |
| 54 | 20/04 | A | RL P | Aylesbury United | 301 | W | 1-0 | Simpson 37 |
| 55 | 22/04 | A | EFC QF | **Leyton Pennant** | **78** | **L** | **0-2** | |
| 56 | 24/04 | H | RL P | Bishop's Stortford | 273 | L | 1-2 | T Adcock 79 |
| 57 | 27/04 | A | RL P | Aldershot Town | 302 | D | 1-1 | Simpson 40 |
| 58 | 01/05 | A | RL P | Hampton | 363 | L | 0-4 | |

## PLAYING SQUAD 1999-2000:

**GOALKEEPERS:** Kingsley Banks (Witham Town), John Cheesewright (Braintree Town)

**DEFENDERS:** Mark Cranfield (Braintree Town), Tony English (Colchester United), John Pollard (Bury Town)

**MIDFIELDERS:** Ashley Bond, Adam Gillespie, Graham Mansfield (Dagenham & Redbridge), Nicholas Simpson (Braintree Town)

**FORWARDS:** Tony Adcock (Colchester United), Wayne Adcock (Witham Town), Dean Caldon (Maldon Town), Neal Docking (Chelmsford City), Steve Harding (Burnham Ramblers)

# HITCHIN TOWN

## CLUB OFFICIALS

Chairman: **Terry Barratt**

Secretary: **Roy lizzard,** 2 Bedford Road,
Ickleford, Hitchin,Herts (01462 433171)

Press Officer: **Bary Swain**
Tel: 01462 455096/07977 002954

### FOOTBALL MANAGEMENT TEAM
Manager: Andy Melvin
Physio: Peter Prince
Asst Mgr: Robbie O'Keefe
Coach: Darren Sallon

### FACT FILE
Formed: 1865
Nickname: The Canaries
Sponsors:
Colours: Yellow/green/green
Change colours: white/black/black
Midweek matchday: Tuesday
Clubcall Line: 0930 555 817
Reserves League: Suburban
1998-99 Captain: Mark Burke
P.oY  Daren Bonfield
Top Scorer: Zema Abbey (19)

**GROUND:** Top Field, Fishponds Road, Hitchin SG5 1NU (01462 459028-matchdays only)
**Directions:** On A505 near town centre opposite large green. 1 mile from Hitchin(BR). From
A1(M) Jct 8,A602 towards Bedford into Hitchin.Over two roundabouts thro lights on one way
system.Right at next roundabout for Fishponds Road.
Capacity: 3,800   Cover: 1,250   Seats: 400   Floodlights: Yes
**Clubhouse:** (01462 434483). Members bar, Function Hall (available for hire). Open everyday.
Steward: Eamonn Watson/ Nigel Collins
**Club Shop:** Yes, contact  Medwyn Williams

Pages: 48  Price: £1  Editor:  Barry Swain
Tel:01462 455096 or 01462 433171

Local Press:  Hitchin Gazette/Hitchin Comet,
Herts on Sunday
Local Radio:  Chiltern, Three Counties

**PREVIOUS**   **Leagues:** Spartan 28-39; Hert & Middx 39-45; Athenian 39,45-63
**CLUB RECORDS** **Attendance:** 7,878 v Wycombe Wanderers, FA Amateur Cup 3rd Rd 18/2/56
**Win:** Spartan Lge 29-30 13-0 v Cowley, 13-0 v RAF
**Defeat** (Isthmian Lge): 0-10 v Kingstonian (A) 65-66, v Slough T. (A) 79-80
**Career** (Isthmian Lge) **appearances:** Paul Giggle 950+ 67-88   **Career** (Isthmian Lge) **goals:** Paul Giggle, 129
**Fee paid:** £2,000 for Ray Seeking (Potton United, July 1989)   **Fee received:** Undisclosed
**BEST SEASON** **FA Trophy:** 5th Rd 98-99   **FA Amateur Cup:** Semi Final 60-61, 62-63
**FA Cup:** 2nd Rd on four occasions -
v Swindon 1-3 (A) 76-77, v Boston Utd, 0-1 (A) 73-74, v Wycombe Wand. 0-5 (H) 94-95, v Gillingham 0-3 (A) 95-9
**HONOURS:** Isthmian Lge R-up 68-69Div 1 92-93 R-up 98-99, Spartan Lge 34-35; AFA Sen Cup 30-31; Herts Snr Cup (19-record); London
Sen Cup  69-70 (R-up 72-73); E Anglian Cup 72-73; Herts Charity Cup(16), Herts I'mediate Cup (8); Woolwich Trophy 82-83;
Televised Sport International Cup 88-89 90-91; Southern Comb. Senior Floodlit Cup 90-91
Players progressing: R Smith (Millwall), L Garwood (Spurs 46), C J Walker, WOdell, S Foss, R Stevens, T Clarke, G Goodyear, L Harwood, P
Burridge, RKitchener (Chelsea 54), D Bumstead, M Dixon, D Pacey (Luton 56), M Dixon & BWhitby (Luton 57), K Abiss (Brighton 57), D Hille, G
Ley, R Morton, L Payne (Newcastle), M Small (Brighton), R Nugent (Barnet), Chris McMenamin (Coventry & Peterborough 96)

*Back Row: Darren Salton (Coach), Adam Turner, Carl Williams, Scott Cretton, Zema Abbey, Ian Scott, Darren Bonfield, Jeran
Meah, Marvin Bates, Stuart Kent, Jon Bone, Robbie O'Keefe (Assistant Manager)
Front Row: Mark Burke, Rudi Hall, Tim Allpress, Gary Dixon*

## HITCHIN TOWN - MATCH FACTS - 1998-99 SEASON

| No | Date | Venue | Comp | Opponents | Att | Result | Score | Goalscorers |
|---|---|---|---|---|---|---|---|---|
| 1 | 15/08 | H | HCC | Cheshunt | 201 | W | 1-0 | A Turner |
| 2 | 22/08 | H | RL 1 | Grays Athletic | 241 | W | 4-0 | Fenton(2), Abbey, Gillard |
| 3 | 25/08 | A | RL 1 | Wembley | 105 | W | 1-0 | L Parker |
| 4 | 29/08 | A | RL 1 | Molesey | 133 | D | 0-0 | |
| 5 | 31/08 | H | RL 1 | Worthing | 317 | W | 5-0 | Williams, Parker, Abbey, Fenton[p], Atkinson |
| 6 | 08/09 | H | RL C 1 | Aldershot Town | 723 | L | 0-1 | |
| 7 | 12/09 | A | RL 1 | Bognor Regis Town | 311 | L | 1-6 | Abbey |
| 8 | 15/09 | H | RL 1 | Braintree Town | 261 | W | 1-0 | Salton |
| 9 | 19/09 | A | FAC Q1 | Witham Town | 146 | L | 0-1 | |
| 10 | 26/09 | A | RL 1 | Leatherhead | 227 | D | 1-1 | Parker |
| 11 | 29/09 | H | RL 1 | Canvey Island | 274 | W | 3-0 | Bates, Dixon, Parker |
| 12 | 06/10 | A | RL 1 | Staines Town | 230 | D | 1-1 | Cretton |
| 13 | 10/10 | A | RL 1 | Uxbridge | 175 | W | 2-1 | Parker, Dixon |
| 14 | 13/10 | H | RL 1 | Maidenhead United | 330 | D | 2-2 | Evans[og], Bates |
| 15 | 17/10 | H | RL 1 | Oxford City | 303 | D | 3-3 | Parkin, Tanner, Abbey |
| 16 | 20/10 | H | HSC 1 | St Albans City | 202 | L | 3-4 | Abbey(2), Dixon |
| 17 | 31/10 | H | RL 1 | Wealdstone | 354 | W | 3-1 | Allpress, C Williams, Meah |
| 18 | 07/11 | A | RL 1 | Croydon | 69 | W | 4-1 | Dixon, C Williams, Abbey, Meah |
| 19 | 14/11 | H | RL 1 | Leyton Pennant | 367 | W | 1-0 | Abbey |
| 20 | 21/11 | A | FAT 2 | Hereford United | 1382 | D | 1-1 | A Turner 77 |
| 21 | 28/11 | A | RL 1 | Chertsey Town | 221 | W | 3-1 | Cretton, Parker, Bates |
| 22 | 30/11 | H | FAT 2 rep | Hereford United | 447 | W | 2-1 | Cretton, Dixon 71 |
| 23 | 05/12 | A | RL 1 | Braintree Town | 312 | L | 0-2 | |
| 24 | 12/12 | H | RL 1 | Bognor Regis Town | 417 | W | 4-0 | Abbey(2), Dixon(2) |
| 25 | 15/12 | A | P C 2 | Uxbridge | 55 | W | 2-0 | Hall, Cretton |
| 26 | 28/12 | H | RL 1 | Barton Rovers | 609 | D | 1-1 | Hall |
| 27 | 09/01 | H | RL 1 | Wembley | 328 | W | 3-0 | Parker, Abbey, Norris[og] |
| 28 | 23/01 | H | RL 1 | Molesey | 274 | W | 1-0 | Allpress |
| 29 | 25/01 | H | FAT 3 | Enfield | 519 | D | 3-3 | Parker(2), Dixon |
| 30 | 27/01 | A | FAT 3 rep | Enfield | 302 | W | 1-0 | Parker 18 |
| 31 | 30/01 | A | RL 1 | Worthing | 203 | D | 1-1 | Fenton |
| 32 | 02/02 | H | P C 3 | Romford | 173 | W | 3-1 | Kent, Bates, Burke |
| 33 | 06/02 | H | FAT 4 | Weston-Super-Mare | 549 | W | 2-1 | Abbey 30 76 |
| 34 | 13/02 | A | RL 1 | Maidenhead United | 229 | L | 0-1 | |
| 35 | 16/02 | A | RL 1 | Yeading | 115 | D | 1-1 | Hall |
| 36 | 20/02 | H | RL 1 | Uxbridge | 365 | W | 2-1 | Bates, Hall |
| 37 | 23/02 | A | RL 1 | Berkhamsted Town | 167 | W | 2-1 | Abbey, Parker |
| 38 | 27/02 | H | FAT 5 | Forest Green Rovers | 963 | L | 1-2 | Parker 33 |
| 39 | 06/03 | A | RL 1 | Canvey Island | 335 | L | 0-3 | |
| 40 | 09/03 | H | P C QF | Purfleet | 102 | L | 0-2 | |
| 41 | 13/03 | H | RL 1 | Leatherhead | 318 | W | 2-1 | Abbey, Parker |
| 42 | 16/03 | A | RL 1 | Grays Athletic | 194 | L | 0-1 | |
| 43 | 20/03 | H | RL 1 | Berkhamsted Town | 312 | W | 1-0 | Parker |
| 44 | 22/03 | H | RL 1 | Whyteleafe | 243 | W | 3-2 | Allpress, Williams, Abbey |
| 45 | 27/03 | A | RL 1 | Oxford City | 152 | W | 2-1 | Bates, Hall |
| 46 | 30/03 | H | RL 1 | Staines Town | 322 | W | 1-0 | Scott |
| 47 | 03/04 | A | RL 1 | Romford | 381 | D | 0-0 | |
| 48 | 05/04 | H | RL 1 | Barton Rovers | 427 | D | 0-0 | |
| 49 | 10/04 | H | RL 1 | Croydon | 319 | L | 0-1 | |
| 50 | 17/04 | A | RL 1 | Leyton Pennant | 126 | W | 4-0 | Abbey, Nixon, Williams, Bone |
| 51 | 24/04 | H | RL 1 | Yeading | 456 | W | 2-1 | Scott, Williams |
| 52 | 26/04 | A | RL 1 | Romford | 103 | W | 3-0 | Dixon, Abbey, Hall |
| 53 | 28/04 | A | RL 1 | Wealdstone | 403 | L | 1-2 | Abbey |
| 54 | 29/04 | A | RL 1 | Whyteleafe | 108 | W | 3-0 | Bates(2), Parker |
| 55 | 01/05 | A | RL 1 | Chertsey Town | 188 | W | 3-1 | Scott, Dixon, Parker |

**PLAYING SQUAD 1999-2000:**

GOALKEEPERS: Darren Bonfield (Wealdstone), Simon Coggin, Andrew Palfreyman (Hitchin Town), James Robinson, Richard Wilmot (Aylesbury United)

DEFENDERS: Mark Burke (Arlesey Town - dual), Scott Cretton (Stevenage Borough), James Dilnut (Stevanage Borough), Ken Gillard (Chesham United), Nick Grime (Stevenage Borough), Steve Miller (America)

MIDFIELDERS: Darren Fenton (Stevenage Borough), Rudi Hall (Enfield), Jason Huntly (Brache Sparta), Jeran Meah (Stevenage Borough), Ian Scott (St Albans City), Adam Turner (Arlesey Town - dual), Sam Turner (Luton Town), Carl Williams (Fulham)

FORWARDS: Zema Abbey (Arlesey Town), Marvin Bates (Molesey), Phil Dean (Boreham Wood/Welwyn Garden City), Gary Dixon (Stevenage Borough), Matthew Kearney (Stevenage Borough), Adam Parker (Stevenage Borough)

# PURFLEET THURROCK FC

OFFICIAL PROGRAMME - PRICE £1

**PURFLEET FC**
**1997 -98**

MAIN SPONSOR
T. & P. LEAD ROOFING LTD

PURFLEET V KINGSTONIAN

PROGRAMME SPONSOR          TEAM SPONSOR
T & P LEAD ROOFING LTD    SCANTRUCK LTD

RYMAN LEAGUE PREMIER DIVISION
Saturday 2nd May 1998 kick off 3.00pm

MEMBERS OF THE ICIS
FOOTBALL LEAGUE

**CLUB OFFICIALS**
Chairman: **Grant Beglan**
V/Chairman/Chief Executive: **Tommy Smith**
Secretary: **Tony Perkins** 48 Saltash Road,
Hainault, Essex IG6 2NL
(0181 500 3092)
Match Secretary/Press Officer:
**Norman Posner**
Comm Mger: **Tony Joy** (01375 392906)

**FOOTBALL MANAGEMENT TEAM**
Manager: Colin McBride
Asst Manager: David Crown
Coach: George Cook
Physio: Bob Johnson

**FACT FILE**

Founded: 1985
Nickname: Fleet
Colours: Green & yellow/green/green & yellow
Change colours: All white
Midweek home matchday: Monday
Reserve's League: None

**GROUND:** Thurrock Hotel, Ship Lane, Grays, Essex
Tel: 01708 868901 Fax: 01708 866703
**Directions:** M25 or A13 to Dartford tunnel r'bout. Ground is fifty yards on right down Ship Lane. Nearest station is Purfleet, two miles from ground
Capacity: 4,500    Cover: 1,000    Seats: 300    Floodlights: Yes
**Clubhouse:** 10am-11pm every day. Snooker, squash, weights room, aerobics, a-lacarte restaurant, steam room. Three Bars. 56 Bedroom Hotel. Steward: Tommy South
**Club Shop:** Selling programmes & magazines. Contact Tommy South (01708 868901)

Pages: 44 Price: £1
Editor: Norman Posner (01708 458301 H)

Local Press: Romford, Thurrock Recorder, Thurrock Gazette
Local Radio: Essex Radio, BBC Radio Essex

**PREVIOUS**    League: Essex Senior 85-89.    **Grounds:** None

**CLUB RECORDS Attendance:** 1,578 v West Ham United, friendly 1997
**Goalscorer:** Paul Cobb, 101.    **Appearances:** John Rees, 286
**Win:** 10-0 v Stansted (H) 86-87, v East Ham Utd (A) 87-88 (both Essex SeniorLeague)
**Defeat:** 0-6 v St Leonards Stamco (A), FA Trophy 96-97. 0-6 v Sutton United (H)Isthmian Lge 97-98

**BEST SEASON**    **FA Cup:** Fourth Qual Rd 95-96 (lost 1-3 away to Rushden & D)
**FA Trophy:** Second Rd Prop 95-96 (lost 1-2 away to Macclesfield Tn)

**HONOURS:** Isthmian Lg Div 2 91-92 (Div 1 R-up 93-94), Div 2 Nth R-up 88-89, Associate Members Tphy 91-92; Essex Snr Lg 87-88 (Lg Cup (2) 86-88, R-up 97-98), Stanford Charity Cup 87-88 (R-up 85-86); Essex Thames-Side Trophy 94-95; Loctite Trophy 91-92; Essex Bus Houses Sen L/Cup 93-94; F Budden Trophy 94-95; Essex & HertsBorder Comb R-up 94-95

Players progressing to Football League: Paul Cobb & Lee Williams (Leyton O.)

*Purfleet goalkeeper Steve Mead makes a brave save from Billericay's Leon Gutzmore.*    *Photo: Alan Coomes*

808

# PURFLEET - MATCH FACTS - 1998-99 SEASON

| No | Date | Venue | Comp | Opponents | Att | Result | Score | Goalscorers |
|----|------|-------|------|-----------|-----|--------|-------|-------------|
| 1 | 22/08 | H | RL P | Aldershot Town | 723 | D | 1-1 | Hayes 8 |
| 2 | 25/08 | A | RL P | Heybridge Swifts | 208 | D | 0-0 | |
| 3 | 29/08 | A | RL P | Hendon | 281 | W | 2-1 | Carthy 44, Marshall 45 |
| 4 | 31/08 | H | RL P | Billericay Town | 439 | L | 0-2 | |
| 5 | 05/09 | H | RL P | Carshalton Athletic | 189 | W | 4-2 | Georgiou 9, McFarlane 26, Garvey 28, Cross 84[p] |
| 6 | 07/09 | H | RL C 1 | **Oxford City** | **105** | **W** | **4-2** | **McFarlane, Garvey, Georgiou, Lawrence** |
| 7 | 12/09 | A | RL P | Boreham Wood | 207 | L | 1-2 | Georgiou 9 |
| 8 | 14/09 | H | RL P | St Albans City | 304 | W | 1-0 | Georgiou 52 |
| 9 | 19/09 | A | RL P | Slough Town | 590 | W | 3-2 | Carthy 41, Cross 47, Lawrence 59 |
| 10 | 26/09 | H | RL P | Bishop's Stortford | 157 | W | 3-1 | Garvey 6, Carthy 18, Odegbami 70 |
| 11 | 29/09 | A | RL P | Gravesend & Northfleet | 358 | D | 1-1 | Cross |
| 12 | 03/10 | A | FAC Q2 | **Clapton** | **77** | **W** | **1-0** | **Georgiou** |
| 13 | 09/10 | A | RL P | Bromley | 415 | L | 1-2 | Lawrence 85 |
| 14 | 12/10 | H | RL P | Hampton | 197 | W | 4-0 | Georgiou 24 61 85, Odegbami 90 |
| 15 | 17/10 | A | FAC Q3 | **Dulwich Hamlet** | **308** | **D** | **2-2** | **Georgiou 19 37** |
| 16 | 19/10 | H | FAC Q3 r | **Dulwich Hamlet** | **211** | **L** | **1-3** | **Georgiou 1** |
| 17 | 27/10 | A | FAT 1 | **Leyton Pennant** | **78** | **L** | **3-4** | **Macklin(3)** |
| 18 | 07/11 | H | RL P | Basingstoke Town | 184 | W | 2-1 | Carthy 34, Macklin 37 |
| 19 | 09/11 | H | RL C 2 | **Hampton** | **101** | **W** | **5-0** | **Georgiou(3), Crown(2)** |
| 20 | 14/11 | A | RL P | Aylesbury United | 766 | L | 1-2 | Carthy 6 |
| 21 | 17/11 | A | RL P | Chesham United | 238 | D | 3-3 | Georgiou 35 50 89 |
| 22 | 21/11 | A | RL P | Walton & Hersham | 159 | L | 0-1 | |
| 23 | 23/11 | H | ESC 3 | **Burnham Ramblers** | **75** | **W** | **4-2** | **McFarlane(2), Marshall, Carthy** |
| 24 | 28/11 | A | RL P | Dulwich Hamlet | 273 | W | 2-1 | Coombs 61, Lawrence 88 |
| 25 | 30/11 | H | P C 2 | **Billericay Town** | **178** | **W** | **2-1** | **Georgiou, Southon** |
| 26 | 05/12 | H | RL P | Boreham Wood | 134 | W | 2-1 | Coombes 19, Georgiou 54 |
| 27 | 12/12 | A | RL P | Carshalton Athletic | 291 | L | 1-2 | Obiero 90 |
| 28 | 14/12 | H | RL P | Harrow Borough | 149 | W | 4-0 | Southon 26, Georgiou 52, Odegbami 79, Obiero 90 |
| 29 | 19/12 | H | RL P | Walton & Hersham | 138 | W | 6-1 | Berry 24, Carthey 37, Smart 55og, Cross 62p, Obiero 67, Georgiou 82 |
| 30 | 21/12 | H | RL P | Sutton United | 276 | L | 1-3 | Coombs |
| 31 | 28/12 | A | RL P | Dagenham & Redbridge | 963 | W | 1-0 | Georgiou 21 |
| 32 | 02/01 | H | RL P | Enfield | 503 | L | 0-1 | |
| 33 | 05/01 | A | ESC 4 | **Grays Athletic** | **n/k** | **W** | **3-0** | **Garvey, Obiero(2)** |
| 34 | 09/01 | H | RL P | Hendon | 237 | W | 4-0 | Coombs 17 78, Georgiou 70, Macklin 75 |
| 35 | 16/01 | A | RL P | Billericay Town | 812 | W | 1-0 | Sinfield 83[og] |
| 36 | 18/01 | A | P C 3 | **Enfield** | **22** | **W** | **2-0** | **Obiero 51, Georgiou 57** |
| 37 | 23/01 | H | RL P | Heybridge Swifts | 301 | W | 2-0 | Berry 25, Carthy 86 |
| 38 | 06/02 | H | RL P | Slough Town | 225 | L | 0-4 | |
| 39 | 09/02 | A | ESC QF | **Leyton Orient** | **180** | **L** | **0-1** | |
| 40 | 13/02 | A | RL P | St Albans City | 993 | L | 0-2 | |
| 41 | 15/02 | H | E TST 2 | **Hornchurch** | **107** | **W** | **5-0** | **Lawrence, Garvey, Coombs, Obiero** |
| 42 | 20/02 | A | RL P | Hampton | 126 | W | 3-2 | Coombs 7 34, Carthy 12 |
| 43 | 27/02 | H | RL P | Bromley | 233 | W | 1-0 | Coombs 45 |
| 44 | 06/03 | A | RL P | Bishop's Stortford | 164 | D | 0-0 | |
| 45 | 09/03 | A | P C QF | **Hitchin Town** | **102** | **W** | **2-0** | **Nesling, Obiero** |
| 46 | 13/03 | H | RL P | Gravesend & Northfleet | 253 | W | 2-1 | Chaplin 26[og], Georgiou 79 |
| 47 | 16/03 | A | RL P | Aldershot Town | 1376 | D | 1-1 | Georgiou 52 |
| 48 | 20/03 | A | RL P | Sutton United | 708 | L | 1-2 | Carthy 63 |
| 49 | 29/03 | H | P C SF | **Worthing** | **144** | **L** | **0-1** | |
| 50 | 03/04 | A | RL P | Enfield | 592 | W | 2-1 | Georgiou 62, J McFarlane 86 |
| 51 | 05/04 | H | RL P | Dagenham & Redbridge | 605 | W | 3-0 | Carthy 14, Georgiou 28 32 |
| 52 | 08/04 | H | RL P | Chesham United | 132 | W | 3-0 | Odegbami 32, McFarlane 83, Keeling 85 |
| 53 | 10/04 | A | RL P | Basingstoke Town | 501 | L | 2-3 | Southon 38, Georgiou 42 |
| 54 | 15/04 | H | ETST QF | **Tilbury** | **102** | **W** | **2-0** | **Georgiou, Crown** |
| 55 | 17/04 | H | RL P | Aylesbury United | 287 | D | 0-0 | |
| 56 | 24/04 | A | RL P | Harrow Borough | 207 | L | 0-5 | |
| 57 | 01/05 | H | RL P | Dulwich Hamlet | 165 | W | 2-1 | Georgiou 27, Macklin 65 |

## PLAYING SQUAD 1999-2000:

GOALKEEPERS: Steve Mead (Concord Rangers)
DEFENDERS: Gary Ansell (Canvey Island), Justin Channing (Slough Town), Tony Jones (Concord Rangers), John Purdie (Billericay Town), Jamie Southon (Chelmsford City)
MIDFIELDERS: Martin Carthy (Erith & Belvedere), Robbie Garvey (Enfield), Gary Howard (Dagenham & Redbridge), Paul Taylor (Southen United), Scott Williams (Eton Manor)
FORWARDS: Greg Berry (Millwall), David Carter (Concord Rangers), Paul Coombs (Basingstoke Town), George Georgiou, Martyn Lawrence (Concord Rangers), Tony Macklin (Concord Rangers), Aggrey Obiero (local football), Declan Perkins (Dagenham & Redbridge)

# St ALBANS CITY

## CLUB OFFICIALS

Chairman: **Lee Harding**
President: **Cllr Malcolm MacMillan**
Vice Chairman: **Gary Elliott**
Secretary: **Steve Eames** c/o Club
Safety Officer: **Rex Winn** 0966 175124 (M)
Comm. Man: **Roberta Rolland**

### FOOTBALL MANAGEMENT TEAM

Manager: Bob Dowie
Consultant Physio: Jude Monteath

### FACT FILE

Formed: 1908
Nickname: The Saints
Colours: Yellow with blue trim/blue/whitel
Change colours: Sky Blue with red trim
Midweek home matchday: Monday
Newsline: 0930 555822
Internet: http://www.andyzad.demon.co.uk
E-Mail: andy@andyzad.demon.co.uk
1998-99: Captain: Kevin Mudd
P.O.Y.: Ashley Vickers
Top Scorer: Steve Clark

BOB DOWIE
TAKES OVER

Saturday 1 May '99

Pages: 32    Price: £1.50
Published by Queensway Publishing

**GROUND:** Clarence Park, York Rd, St Albans, Herts AL1 4PL Tel: 01727 866819
**Directions:** Left out of St Albans station - Clarence Pk 200yds ahead acrossHatfield Rd. M25, jct 21 to Noke Hotel island, straight on thru Chiswell Green towards St Albans, straight over 2 mini-r'bouts and one larger island, thru 2sets of lights and right at island at far end of city centre (St Peters St.) into Hatfield Rd, over mini-r'bout, left at 2nd lights into Clarence Rd, ground on left
**Capacity:** 6,000    Cover: 1,900    Seats: 904    Floodlights: Yes
**Clubhouse:** Open matchdays and available for functions. Manager: Ray McCord (01727 837956). Tea bar within ground serves hot food
**Club Shop:** Club merchandise & League & non-League progs,magazines, videos etc
Managers: Lee Woods and Rob Fenn c/o club

Local Press: St Albans & District Observer,
Herts Advertiser
Local Radio: BBC Three Counties,
Chiltern Radio, Oasis

**PREVIOUS** **Leagues:** Herts County 08-10; Spartan 08-20; Athenian 20-23

**CLUB RECORDS** **Attendance:** 9,757 v Ferryhill Ath., FA Amtr Cup QF 27/2/26
**Appearances:** Phil Wood 900 (62-85) **Goalscorer:** W H (Billy) Minter 356 (top scorer for 12 consecutive seasons 1920-32)
**Win:** 14-0 v Aylesbury United (H) Spartan Lge 19/10/12    **Defeat:** 0-11 v Wimbledon (H), Isthmian Lge 9/11/46.
**Fee Paid:** £6,000 for Paul Turner (Yeovil Town Aug 97)    **Fee Received:** £92,750 for Dean Austin (Southend 90/Spurs 92)

**BEST SEASON** **FA Amateur Cup:** Semi final 22-23 24-25 25-26 69-70.    **FA Trophy:** Semi-Final 1998-99 1-2 & 2-3 v Forest Green Rovers
**FA Cup:** 2nd Rd replay 68-69 (1-3 at Walsall after 1-1 draw), 80-81 (1-4 atTorquay after 1-1 draw), 96-97 (9-2 at Bristol City)

**HONOURS:** Isthmian Lg 23-24 26-27 27-28 (R-up 54-55 92-93), Div 1 85-86, Div 2 R-up 83-84, Lg Cup R-up 89-90, Res. Sect. R-up 48-49 60-61 61-62; Athenian Lg 20-21 21-22 (R-up 22-23); Spartan Lg 11-12 (R-up 12-13, East Div 09-10); Herts Co. Lg 09-10 (West    Div 08-09, Aubrey Cup(res) 61-62); London Snr Cup 70-71 (R-up 69-70); AFA Snr Cup 33-34 (R-up 30-31 32-33 34-35); E Anglian Cup 92-93; Herts SnrCup(12) (R-up 10), Herts Snr Tphy 86-87, Herts Charity Cup(25) (R-up(18);Mithras Cup 64-65 71-72 (R-up 76-77); Wycombe F'lit Cup(2) 68-70; St AlbansHosp Cup 45-46; Hitchin Centenary Cup 70-71 (R-up 71-72); Victory Cup 25-26 27-28, Liege Cup 26-27; Billy Minter Invit. Cup (3) 90-93

Players progressing: A Grimsdell (Spurs 11), G Edmonds (Watford 14), R Burke(Man Utd 46), J Meadows (Watford 51), M Rose (Charlton 63), J Kinnear (Spurs 65), J Mitchell (Fulham 72), A Cockram (Brentford 88), D Austin (Southend 90),T Kelly (Stoke 90), M Danzey (Cambridge 92), D Williams (Brentford 93),

*Back Row (L-R): Andy Polston, Paul Turner, Rob Haworth, Mark Keen, Ashley Vickers, Matt Jones*
*Front Row: Lenny Piper, Tom Meredith, Justin Gentle, John Pollard, Dominic Gentle, Mark Kane    Photo: Eric Marsh*

810

# ST ALBANS CITY - MATCH FACTS - 1998-99 SEASON

| No | Date | Venue | Comp | Opponents | Att | Result | Score | Goalscorers |
|----|------|-------|------|-----------|-----|--------|-------|-------------|
| 1 | 06/08 | A | HCC QF | Berkhamsted Town | 130 | W | 6-2 | Jones(2), Cobb, Blaney, Trebble(2) |
| 2 | 22/08 | A | RL P | Gravesend & Northfleet | 586 | W | 1-0 | Clark 17 |
| 3 | 24/08 | H | RL P | Sutton United | 583 | D | 2-2 | Pollard, Clark |
| 4 | 29/08 | H | RL P | Hampton | 668 | W | 3-1 | Kane 51, Clark 55 87 |
| 5 | 01/09 | A | RL P | Bishop's Stortford | 257 | D | 1-1 | D Gentle 19 |
| 6 | 05/09 | A | RL P | Aylesbury United | 954 | D | 0-0 | |
| 7 | 07/09 | H | RL C 1 | Hendon | 217 | L | 1-4 | Own-Goal |
| 8 | 12/09 | H | RL P | Basingstoke Town | 679 | W | 4-2 | Clark 28 90, Jones 45 52 |
| 9 | 14/09 | A | RL P | Purfleet | 304 | L | 0-1 | |
| 10 | 19/09 | H | RL P | Chesham United | 1018 | L | 2-3 | Pollard 29, Jones 32 |
| 11 | 22/09 | H | RL P | Aldershot Town | 2048 | W | 2-1 | Piper 29 72 |
| 12 | 26/09 | H | RL P | Hendon | 814 | W | 4-2 | Clark 18 56, Keen 72, Meredith 90 |
| 13 | 03/10 | A | FAC Q2 | Romford | 427 | W | 2-1 | Piper, Jones |
| 14 | 10/10 | A | RL P | Heybridge Swifts | 361 | W | 3-0 | Clark 45[p], Jones 65, Evans 88 |
| 15 | 12/10 | H | RL P | Slough Town | 646 | D | 3-3 | Haworth 1, Trebble 6, Clark 52[p] |
| 16 | 17/10 | H | FAC Q3 | Basildon United | 533 | W | 3-0 | Haworth 18 21, Gentle 77 |
| 17 | 20/10 | A | HSC 1 | Hitchin Town | 202 | W | 4-3 | Clark(2), Piper, Jones |
| 18 | 26/10 | H | RL P | Billericay Town | 826 | W | 1-0 | Clark 7 |
| 19 | 31/10 | H | FAC Q4 | Kingstonian | 861 | D | 1-1 | Keen 81 |
| 20 | 03/11 | A | FAC Q4 r | Kingstonian | 845 | D | 1-1 | Clark 9 |
| 21 | 07/11 | A | RL P | Carshalton Athletic | 793 | W | 1-0 | Clark 84 |
| 22 | 16/11 | H | HSC 2 | Bishop's Stortford | 148 | W | 3-0 | Clark, Haworth, J Gentle |
| 23 | 21/11 | A | FAT 2 | Leyton Pennant | 301 | W | 3-0 | Haworth, Clark, McLean[og] |
| 24 | 28/11 | A | RL P | Dagenham & Redbridge | 705 | D | 2-2 | Clark 12 26[p] |
| 25 | 01/12 | A | P C 1 | Enfield | 125 | L | 0-2 | |
| 26 | 05/12 | H | RL P | Aylesbury United | 1131 | W | 2-1 | Haworth 51, Clark 61[p] |
| 27 | 12/12 | A | RL P | Basingstoke Town | 563 | W | 2-1 | Clark 36 84 |
| 28 | 19/12 | H | RL P | Harrow Borough | 715 | D | 1-1 | D Gentle 90 |
| 29 | 26/12 | H | RL P | Bishop's Stortford | 787 | W | 5-1 | Clark 5 33, D Gentle 17, Keen 20, Haworth 60 |
| 30 | 28/12 | A | RL P | Enfield | 1011 | D | 0-0 | |
| 31 | 02/01 | H | RL P | Walton & Hersham | 1008 | D | 1-1 | Haworth 64 |
| 32 | 05/01 | A | HCC SF | Ware | 131 | W | 2-1 | Clark 29 47 |
| 33 | 09/01 | A | RL P | Hampton | 332 | W | 2-1 | Clark 7[p], Piper 14 |
| 34 | 23/01 | A | RL P | Sutton United | 924 | W | 3-2 | D Gentle 24, Clark 44[p], Haworth 82 |
| 35 | 25/01 | H | FAT 3 | Hastings Town | 380 | W | 3-0 | Turner 1, Clark 38, Gentle 39 |
| 36 | 30/01 | H | RL P | Gravesend & Northfleet | 974 | L | 0-2 | |
| 37 | 02/02 | H | HSC QF | London Colney | 346 | L | 1-3 | D Gentle |
| 38 | 06/02 | A | FAT 4 | Ashton United | 443 | D | 2-2 | Gentle 45, Haworth 90 |
| 39 | 08/02 | H | FAT 4 rep | Ashton United | 390 | W | 2-1 | Clark 28 89 |
| 40 | 13/02 | H | RL P | Purfleet | 993 | W | 2-0 | Jones 60, Reinelt 80 |
| 41 | 15/02 | H | RL P | Boreham Wood | 703 | L | 1-2 | Jones 90 |
| 42 | 20/02 | A | RL P | Slough Town | 679 | L | 0-1 | |
| 43 | 23/02 | A | RL P | Dulwich Hamlet | 297 | D | 2-2 | Reinelt 24, Haworth 89 |
| 44 | 27/02 | A | FAT 5 | Dagenham & Redbridge | 1227 | W | 2-1 | Mudd 29, D Gentle 67 |
| 45 | 06/03 | A | RL P | Hendon | 437 | L | 3-4 | Haworth 33, Clark 85 87 |
| 46 | 08/03 | H | RL P | Heybridge Swifts | 439 | D | 1-1 | Vickers 56 |
| 47 | 13/03 | H | RL P | Aldershot Town | 1623 | D | 1-1 | Meredith 12 |
| 48 | 20/03 | H | RL P | Billericay Town | 651 | D | 3-3 | Haworth 1 66, Piper 39 |
| 49 | 27/03 | H | FAT QF | Boston United | 2723 | W | 2-1 | Vickers 33, Meredith 88 |
| 50 | 30/03 | H | RL P | Chesham United | 337 | L | 1-2 | Keen 77 |
| 51 | 03/04 | A | RL P | Walton & Hersham | 242 | L | 0-1 | |
| 52 | 05/04 | H | RL P | Enfield | 999 | W | 2-1 | Clark 75 82 |
| 53 | 10/04 | H | FAT SF(1) | Forest Green Rovers | 2120 | D | 1-1 | Risley 21 |
| 54 | 18/04 | H | FAT SF(2) | Forest Green Rovers | 3002 | L | 2-3 | Kilgour 2[og], Clark 42 |
| 55 | 20/04 | H | RL P | Bromley | 373 | W | 4-1 | Harney 10[og], D Gentle 45, Piper 49, Reinelt 57 |
| 56 | 22/04 | H | RL P | Dulwich Hamlet | 346 | D | 1-1 | Clark 76[p] |
| 57 | 24/04 | A | RL P | Boreham Wood | 450 | D | 1-1 | Clark 90 |
| 58 | 26/04 | A | RL P | Carshalton Athletic | 348 | D | 1-1 | Clark 49 |
| 59 | 27/04 | A | RL P | Bromley | 314 | W | 1-0 | Kane 12 |
| 60 | 29/04 | A | RL P | Harrow Borough | 242 | D | 0-0 | |
| 61 | 01/05 | H | RL P | Dagenham & Redbridge | 775 | D | 2-2 | Clark 5, Turner 9[p] |

4 5

## PLAYING SQUAD 1999-2000:

GOALKEEPERS: Ron Fearon (Boreham Wood/Barkingside), Andy Lomas (Aylesbury United), Tony Roberts (Millwall)

DEFENDERS: Tim Allpress (Hitchin Town), Steve Butler (Aylesbury United), Jimmy Carstairs (Ex-Enfield), Lee Harvey (Aylesbury United), Stuart James (Harrow Borough), Mark Keen (Heybridge Swifts), Tom Meredith (Bury Town), Mark Rooney (Aylesbury United), Ashley Vickers (Peterborough United)

MIDFIELDERS: Steve Heard (Hendon), Mark Kane (Heybridge Swifts), Francis McCormack (Harrow Borough), Chris McMenamin (Hitchin Town), Lenny Piper (Welling United), David Pratt (Dagenham & Redbridge)

FORWARDS: Dominic Gentle (Purfleet), Martin Randall (Hayes), Ian Rutherford (Aylesbury United), Scott Witney (St

# SLOUGH TOWN

## CLUB OFFICIALS

Chief Executive:**Roy Merryweather**
Tel: 01753 554833 Fax 01753 533949
Chairman: **Jonathon Freese**
Sec / Press Officer: **Roy Merryweather** Tel:
01753 523358 (B)
Address - c/o the club

### FOOTBALL MANAGEMENT TEAM
Manager: Graham Roberts
Asst Manager: Steve B rowne
Physio: Kevin McGoldrick

### FACT FILE

Formed: 1890
Nickname: The Rebels
Sponsor: The Cable Corporation
Colours: Amber/navy blue/amber
Change colours: All white
Midweek home matchday: Tuesdays

**GROUND:** Wexham Park Stadium, Wexham Road, Slough, Berkshire. SL2 5QR.
Tel: 01753 55483 Fax: 01753 533949
**Directions:** From North : M25 J16 East London M40 J1 - South A412 through Iver Heath to
George Green. 2nd set lights turn right by George PH, George Green.Church Lane 1 mile to
end, then small roundabout, turn left, ground 1/4 mile onright
Capacity: 5,000 Cover: 1,890 Seats: 450 Floodlights: Yes
Clubhouse: Rebels bar & Lounge bar open weekdays 7pm-11pm, weekends, lunchtimes,
evenings. Banqueting hall for all types of functions
Club Shop: Contact: Graham Gowland 01252 873620

Pages: 36 Price: £1.50
Editor: Committee

Local Press: Slough Observer Slough Express
Local Radio: Thames Valley FM, Star FM

**PREVIOUS** **Leagues:** Southern Alliance 1892-93; Berks & Bucks 1901-05; Gt Western Suburban1906-19; Spartan 1920-39; Herts &
Middx 1940-45; Corinthian 1946-63; Athenian1963-73; Isthmian 1973-90, 94-95; Alliance Prem. (GMVC) 90-94
**Grounds:** Dolphin Playing Fields & Stadium, Chalvey Rd Sports Grd, YorkRd Maidenhead 1920, Centre Sports Ground 36-42

**CLUB RECORDS Attendance:** 8,000 - Schoolboys u15 Final Slough v Liverpool - 1976
**Win:** 17-0 v Railway Clearing House - 1921-22 **Defeat:** 1-11 v Chesham Town 1909/10
**Transfer fee paid:** £18,000 for Colin Fielder from Farnborough - 1991 **Career appearances:** Terry Reardon 458 - 64/81
**Received:** £22,000 from Wycombe Wanderers for Steve Thompson **Career goalscorer:** Terry Norris 84 - 25/26

**BEST SEASON** **FA Cup:** 2nd Round Proper, 79-80 (Yeovil T), 82-83 (Bishop's Stortford), 85-86 (Leyton O.), 86-87 (Swansea C.).
League clubs defeated: Millwall, 1-0 (H) Jan. 1983
**FA Trophy:** Semi-Final 1976-77, 2-6(agg) v Dagenham; 97-98, 1-2(agg) v Southport

**HONOURS:** FA Amateur Cup R-up 72-73; Great Western Suburban League R-up 19-20: Spartan League R-up 20-21 21-22 31-32 32-33
38-39; Herts & Middx League R-up 43-44; Corinthian League 50-51 (R-up 45-46 46-47 57-58); Athenian League 67-68 71-72
72-73 (R-up 68-69, Div 1 64-65, Memorial Shield 64-65 71-72 72-73); Isthmian League 80-81 89-90 R-up 94-95, (Div 2 R-up
73-74), Lge Shield 80-81 89-90 (R-up 94-95); Berks & Bucks Sen Cup(9) 02-03 19-20 23-24 35-36 54-55 70-72 76-77 80-81

Players progress ing: Bill McConnell, Peter Angell, Dennis Edwards, RalphMiller, John Delaney, Paul Barron, Dave Kemp, Roy Davies,
Mickey Droy, EricYoung, Alan Paris, Tony Dennis, Lloyd Owusu (Brentford 98)

*Slough Town on the attack against Sutton United at Wexham Park*

## SLOUGH TOWN - MATCH FACTS - 1998-99 SEASON

| No | Date | Venue | Comp | Opponents | Att | Result | Score | Goalscorers | |
|----|------|-------|------|-----------|-----|--------|-------|-------------|---|
| 1 | 22/08 | A | RL P | Sutton United | 842 | W | 1-0 | Riley 25[og] | |
| 2 | 25/08 | H | RL P | Bishop's Stortford | 768 | D | 2-2 | Fiore, McVie | |
| 3 | 29/08 | H | RL P | Chesham United | 1060 | W | 3-1 | Bicknell 28, Thorpe 39, Fiore 89 | |
| 4 | 01/09 | A | RL P | Gravesend & Northfleet | 416 | W | 2-1 | Roach 35, Hughes 60 | |
| 5 | 05/09 | A | RL P | Walton & Hersham | 445 | L | 0-2 | | |
| 6 | 08/09 | A | RL C 1 | Abingdon Town | 93 | W | 1-0 | Denton | |
| 7 | 12/09 | H | RL P | Aylesbury United | 890 | W | 1-0 | Denton 78 | |
| 8 | 15/09 | H | RL P | Hampton | 304 | D | 2-2 | Roach 24, McVie 54 | |
| 9 | 19/09 | H | RL P | Purfleet | 590 | L | 2-3 | King 27, Channing 76 | |
| 10 | 22/09 | H | RL P | Billericay Town | 484 | D | 1-1 | Pearson 90 | |
| 11 | 26/09 | A | RL P | Dagenham & Redbridge | 737 | L | 0-3 | | |
| 12 | 03/10 | H | FAC Q2 | Fleet Town | 465 | D | 1-1 | McVie 33 | |
| 13 | 06/10 | A | FAC Q2 r | Fleet Town | 236 | W | 2-0 | Lines 5[p], Deaner 9 | |
| 14 | 10/10 | H | RL P | Harrow Borough | 432 | L | 0-3 | | |
| 15 | 12/10 | A | RL P | St Albans City | 646 | D | 3-3 | McVie 56, Hammatt 78, Bicknell 90 | |
| 16 | 17/10 | H | FAC Q3 | Halstead Town | 540 | W | 3-1 | Pearson, Channing, Hammatt | |
| 17 | 24/10 | A | RL P | Hendon | 330 | L | 2-5 | Hughes 8, Pierson 58 | |
| 18 | 27/10 | H | P C 1 | Bromley | 220 | W | 1-0 | Fiore | |
| 19 | 03/11 | A | FAC Q4 | Crawley Town | 1874 | D | 0-0 | | |
| 20 | 07/11 | H | RL P | Enfield | 737 | D | 2-2 | Hammatt 51, Deaner 90 | |
| 21 | 09/11 | H | FAC Q4 r | Crawley Town | 881 | W | 3-2 | Deaner 39 55, Hammett 90 | |
| 22 | 14/11 | A | FAC 1 | Macclesfield Town | 2104 | D | 2-2 | Pierson 24, Deaner 38 | |
| 23 | 17/11 | H | RL P | Basingstoke Town | 475 | L | 0-1 | | |
| 24 | 21/11 | A | FAT 2 | Baldock Town | 392 | W | 3-1 | Pierson 31 86, Hammatt 39 | |
| 25 | 24/11 | H | FAC 1 rep | Macclesfield Town | 2010 | D | 1-1 | Hughes 16 | 8 9 |
| 26 | 28/11 | A | RL P | Bromley | 299 | L | 1-2 | Pearson 9 | |
| 27 | 01/12 | A | RL C 2 | Staines Town | 229 | W | 3-1 | Pierson(2), Own-Goal | |
| 28 | 05/12 | H | RL P | Walton & Hersham | 451 | W | 3-0 | Seymour 62, Hammatt 74, Endersby 89 | |
| 29 | 08/12 | H | B&BSC Q2 | Burnham | 303 | L | 1-3 | Fiore | |
| 30 | 12/12 | A | RL P | Aylesbury United | 1384 | D | 0-0 | | |
| 31 | 19/12 | A | RL P | Boreham Wood | 502 | L | 0-3 | | |
| 32 | 22/12 | A | P C 2 | Walton & Hersham | 134 | L | 0-2 | | |
| 33 | 28/12 | A | RL P | Dulwich Hamlet | 417 | D | 2-2 | Hammatt 38 67 | |
| 34 | 02/01 | H | RL P | Heybridge Swifts | 520 | L | 0-1 | | |
| 35 | 09/01 | H | RL P | Chesham United | 636 | L | 0-1 | | |
| 36 | 23/01 | A | RL P | Bishop's Stortford | 236 | W | 1-0 | Engwell 6 | |
| 37 | 25/01 | H | FAT 3 | Rushden & Diamonds | 729 | L | 1-2 | Fiore | |
| 38 | 30/01 | H | RL P | Sutton United | 585 | L | 1-2 | Hammatt 85 | |
| 39 | 06/02 | A | RL P | Purfleet | 225 | W | 4-0 | Deaner 12, Hall 20, Hammatt 26, Kemp 33 | |
| 40 | 13/02 | A | RL P | Hampton | 544 | W | 3-0 | Hammatt 58, Archer 63, Deaner 70 | |
| 41 | 16/02 | A | RL P | Carshalton Athletic | 275 | W | 3-0 | Fiore 43, Barrowcliff 83, Hammatt 86 | |
| 42 | 20/02 | H | RL P | St Albans City | 679 | W | 1-0 | Hammatt 21 | |
| 43 | 23/02 | A | RL C 3 | Maidenhead United | 484 | L | 2-4 | Own-Goal, Line[p] | |
| 44 | 27/02 | A | RL P | Harrow Borough | 437 | W | 2-0 | Hammatt 6, Barrowcliff 84 | |
| 45 | 02/03 | A | RL P | Boreham Wood | 246 | L | 0-1 | | |
| 46 | 06/03 | H | RL P | Dagenham & Redbridge | 510 | L | 0-1 | | |
| 47 | 13/03 | A | RL P | Billericay Town | 577 | W | 2-1 | Quail 37, Hall 58 | |
| 48 | 20/03 | H | RL P | Hendon | 505 | D | 1-1 | Quail 45 | |
| 49 | 27/03 | A | RL P | Aldershot Town | 2106 | D | 1-1 | Archer 37[p] | |
| 50 | 03/04 | H | RL P | Heybridge Swifts | 291 | L | 1-2 | Hall 14 | |
| 51 | 05/04 | H | RL P | Dulwich Hamlet | 433 | W | 1-0 | Archer 90 | |
| 52 | 10/04 | A | RL P | Enfield | 558 | L | 1-2 | Hall 75 | |
| 53 | 13/04 | H | RL P | Aldershot Town | 783 | D | 2-2 | Hall 8, Engwell 53 | |
| 54 | 17/04 | H | RL P | Carshalton Athletic | 509 | D | 1-1 | Hammatt 45 | |
| 55 | 24/04 | A | RL P | Basingstoke Town | 687 | W | 2-0 | Samuels 44, Endersby 90 | |
| 56 | 27/04 | H | RL P | Gravesend & Northfleet | 311 | W | 4-0 | Browne 23, Pye 42, Hammatt 89, Denton 90 | |
| 57 | 01/05 | H | RL P | Bromley | 516 | W | 2-1 | Hammatt 33, Quail 58 | |

**PLAYING SQUAD 1999-2000:**
GOALKEEPERS: Danny Honey (Yeading), Paul Wilkerson (Watford
DEFENDERS: Matthew Bicknell (Reading), Steve Daly (Boreham Wood), Micky Engwell (Chesham United), Al-James Hannigan (Yeovil Town), Graham Roberts (Chesham United), David Timothy (Woking), Chris White (Farnborough Town)
MIDFIELDERS: Steve Browne (Chesham United), Eddie Denton (Aylesbury United), Mark Hall (Hayes), Mark Hawthorne (Crawley Town), Graham Kemp (Yeovil Town), Youness Nabil (Chesham United), Mark Pye (Hendon)
FORWARDS: Lee Archer (Rushden & Diamonds), Andrew Deaner (Yeading), Brian Hammatt (Chesham United), Dean Samuels (Stevenage Borough)

# WALTON & HERSHAM

## CLUB OFFICIALS

Chairman: **A.Payne**
President: TBA
Secretary: **Mark Massingham,** 7b Sidney
Rd., Walton-on-Thames, Surrey. KT12 2NP
Tel: 01932 885814
Press Officer: **Mervyn Rees**
Tel: 01932 245756

## FOOTBALL MANAGEMENT TEAM

Manager: Paul Holden
Asst Manager: Mark Hill
Physio: Stuart Smith

### FACT FILE
Formed: 1896
Nickname: Swans
Sponsors: T.B.A
Colours: White with red band/white/red
Change colours: Yellow/Blue/yellow
Midweek home matchday: Tuesday
Reserve Team's League: Suburban

1998-99 Captain: Alan Dowson
P.o.Y.: Chris Whelan
Top Scorer: Andy Sayer

STOMPOND LANE
HOME OF THE SWANS

WALTON & HERSHAM F.C.
OFFICIAL MATCH DAY PROGRAMME

Ryman

Ryman Premier Division
Walton & Hersham F.C.
v
Chesham United F.C.
Saturday 10th April
Kick off 3.00 p.m.
Sponsored by
The Supporters Club
£1.20

THE RYMAN FOOTBALL LEAGUE

Pages: 36 Price: £1.20
Editor: Mark Massingham Tel: 01932 885814

Local Press: Surrey Herald, Surrey Comet
Local Radio: County Sound,
BBC Southern Counties

**GROUND:**   Sports Ground, Stompond Lane, Walton-on-Thames Tel: 01932 245263 (club)

**Directions:** From North: Over Walton Bridge & along New Zealand Ave., down 1-way street and up A244 Hersham Rd - grd 2nd right. From Esher: Down Lammas Lane then Esher Rd, straight over 1st r'bout, 4th exit at next r'bout (WestGrove) 2nd left at end of Hersham Rd and Stompond Lane 1/2 mile on left.Ten min walk Walton-on-Thames (BR). Bus 218 passes grd

**Capacity:** 6,500   **Cover:** 2,500   **Seats:** 500   **Floodlights:** Yes
**Clubhouse:** (01932 245263). Open most nights. TV, darts, pool, refreshments on matchdays
**Club Shop:** Open matchdays. Contact Richard Old, c/o the club

**PREVIOUS**    **Leagues:** Surrey Senior; Corinthian 45-50; Athenian 50-71

**CLUB RECORDS**   **Attendance:** 6,500 v Brighton, FA Cup First Round 73-74
**Scorer:** Reg Sentance 220 in 11 seasons   **Appearances:** Terry Keen 449 in 11 seasons
**Win:** 10-0 v Clevedon, FA Amateur Cup 1960   **Defeat:** 11-3 v Kingstonian Surrey Sen Shield 58
**Transfer fee paid:** £6,000   **Transfer fee received:** £150,000 for Nathan Ellington 99

**BEST SEASON**   **FA Trophy:** 1st Round 91-92, 94-95   **FA Amateur Cup:** Winners 72-73, (SF 51-52, 52-53)
**FA Cup:** 2nd Rd 72-73 (v Margate), 73-74 (v Hereford). League clubs defeated: Exeter 72-73, Brighton 73-74

**HONOURS:**   Isthmian Lg R-up 72-73, Barassi Cup 73-74; Athenian Lg 68-69 (R-up 50-51 69-70 70-71, Lg Cup 69-70); Corinthian Lg 46-49 (R-up 49-50), Premier Midweek F'litLg 67-69 70-71 (R-up 71-72); Surrey Snr Cup 47-48 50-51 60-61 61-62 70-71 72-73(R-up 46-47 51-52 59-60 69-70 71-72 73-74); London Snr Cup R-up 73-74; SouthernComb. Cup 82-83 88-89 91-92; Surrey Comb. Cup 49-50 91-92; John Livey Memorial Trophy 91-92

Players progressing:  Andy McCulloch (QPR 1970), Mick Heath (Brentford 1971),Paul Priddy (Brentford 1972), Richard Teale (Q.P.R. 1973), SteveParsons (Wimbledon 1977), Stuart Massey (Crystal Palace), Ross Davidson(Sheffield Utd), Nathan Ellington (Bristol Rovers)

*Back Row (L-R): Ross Pickett, Barry Lake, Steve Moss, Delroy Preddie, Matt Pearson, Matt Elverson*
*Front Row: Andy Sayer, Nathan Ellington, Erskine Smart, Gary Holloway, Alan Dowson.      Photo: Andrew Chitty*

# WALTON & HERSHAM - MATCH FACTS - 1998-99 SEASON

| No | Date | Venue | Comp | Opponents | Att | Result | Score | Goalscorers |
|---|---|---|---|---|---|---|---|---|
| 1 | 22/08 | H | RL P | Harrow Borough | 227 | D | 2-2 | Sayer 11, Elverson 80 |
| 2 | 25/08 | A | RL P | Dulwich Hamlet | 287 | L | 2-3 | Sayer(2) |
| 3 | 29/08 | A | RL P | Boreham Wood | 203 | D | 0-0 | |
| 4 | 01/09 | H | RL P | Carshalton Athletic | 229 | W | 3-2 | Johnson 48, Pickett 74[p], Holloway 87 |
| 5 | 05/09 | H | RL P | Slough Town | 445 | W | 2-0 | Pickett 45, Sayer 47 |
| 6 | 08/09 | A | RL C 1 | **Heybridge Swifts** | 123 | **L** | **2-3** | **M Pearson, Rake** |
| 7 | 12/09 | A | RL P | Billericay Town | 532 | L | 0-1 | |
| 8 | 15/09 | H | RL P | Heybridge Swifts | 142 | L | 0-1 | |
| 9 | 19/09 | A | RL P | Enfield | 454 | L | 2-3 | Johnson 50, Everitt 80 |
| 10 | 22/09 | H | RL P | Bromley | 220 | W | 1-0 | Ellington 71 |
| 11 | 26/09 | A | RL P | Aylesbury United | 743 | L | 0-1 | |
| 12 | 03/10 | A | FAC Q2 | **Ash United** | 324 | **W** | **5-1** | **Johnson, Own-Goal, Pickett(2), Sayer** |
| 13 | 10/10 | H | RL P | Gravesend & Northfleet | 247 | L | 1-3 | Pickett 13 |
| 14 | 12/10 | A | RL P | Dagenham & Redbridge | 604 | L | 1-3 | Sayer 72 |
| 15 | 17/10 | H | FAC Q3 | **Bath City** | 391 | D | **2-2** | **Sayer 21, Johnson 37** |
| 16 | 20/10 | A | FAC Q3 r | **Bath City** | 656 | **L** | **0-3** | |
| 17 | 27/10 | H | FAT 1 | **Weston-super-Mare** | 131 | D | **2-2** | **Ellington 67, Sayer 81** |
| 18 | 05/11 | A | FAT 1 rep | **Weston-super-Mare** | 100 | **L** | **0-2** | |
| 19 | 07/11 | A | RL P | Chesham United | 408 | W | 2-1 | Ellington 75, Sayer 80 |
| 20 | 14/11 | H | RL P | Bishop's Stortford | 187 | D | 2-2 | Everitt 65, Whelan 90 |
| 21 | 17/11 | A | P C 1 | **Sutton United** | 246 | **W** | **3-1** | **Ellington(2), Johnson** |
| 22 | 21/11 | H | RL P | Purfleet | 159 | W | 1-0 | Holloway 83 |
| 23 | 28/11 | H | RL P | Hendon | 237 | L | 0-3 | |
| 24 | 05/12 | A | RL P | Slough Town | 451 | L | 0-3 | |
| 25 | 08/12 | H | SSC 1 | **Merstham** | 65 | **L** | **0-0** | |
| 26 | 12/12 | H | RL P | Billericay Town | 167 | L | 3-4 | Pickett 13, Ellington 51, Sayer 85 |
| 27 | 15/12 | A | SSC 1 rep | **Merstham** | 0 | **W** | **6-0** | **Williams(2), Sayer(2), Pickett(2)** |
| 28 | 19/12 | A | RL P | Purfleet | 138 | L | 1-6 | Sayer 85 |
| 29 | 22/12 | H | P C 2 | **Slough Town** | 134 | **W** | **2-0** | **Sayer(2)** |
| 30 | 28/12 | H | RL P | Hampton | 359 | L | 0-1 | |
| 31 | 02/01 | A | RL P | St Albans City | 1008 | D | 1-1 | Ellington 45 |
| 32 | 05/01 | A | SSC 2 | **Dulwich Hamlet** | 142 | **W** | **2-0** | **Sayer, Ellington** |
| 33 | 09/01 | H | RL P | Boreham Wood | 220 | D | 1-1 | Moss 51 |
| 34 | 16/01 | H | RL P | Harrow Borough | 402 | W | 1-0 | Ellington 23 |
| 35 | 23/01 | H | RL P | Dulwich Hamlet | 254 | W | 3-1 | Ellington 57 69, Canonville 86 |
| 36 | 30/01 | A | RL P | Carshalton Athletic | 367 | W | 3-1 | Ellington 6 22, Holloway 17 |
| 37 | 02/02 | A | SSC QF | **Woking** | 495 | **L** | **0-3** | |
| 38 | 06/02 | H | RL P | Enfield | 321 | L | 0-4 | |
| 39 | 09/02 | H | SCC 1 | **Staines Town** | 60 | **W** | **1-0** | **Sayer** |
| 40 | 13/02 | A | RL P | Heybridge Swifts | 260 | L | 0-1 | |
| 41 | 16/02 | A | RL P | Aldershot Town | 1450 | L | 2-7 | Canoville 9, Sayer 37[p] |
| 42 | 18/02 | A | P C 3 | **Carshalton Athletic** | 90 | **L** | **0-2** | |
| 43 | 20/02 | H | RL P | Dagenham & Redbridge | 282 | L | 0-1 | |
| 44 | 23/02 | A | RL P | Sutton United | 611 | L | 0-5 | |
| 45 | 27/02 | A | RL P | Gravesend & Northfleet | 498 | L | 0-2 | |
| 46 | 06/03 | H | RL P | Aylesbury United | 271 | L | 0-2 | |
| 47 | 09/03 | A | SCC 2 | **Chipstead** | n/k | **W** | **3-1** | **Callaghan, Driscoll, Zammitt** |
| 48 | 13/03 | H | RL P | Bromley | 317 | D | 1-1 | Whelan 5 |
| 49 | 20/03 | H | RL P | Aldershot Town | 935 | L | 0-4 | |
| 50 | 23/03 | H | SCC QF | **Hampton** | n/k | **W** | **6-1** | **Dowling(2), Whelan, Fiore, Driscoll, Blackman** |
| 51 | 27/03 | A | RL P | Basingstoke Town | 463 | D | 0-0 | |
| 52 | 03/04 | H | RL P | St Albans City | 242 | W | 1-0 | Holloway 42 |
| 53 | 05/04 | A | RL P | Hampton | 404 | L | 0-2 | |
| 54 | 10/04 | H | RL P | Chesham United | 207 | W | 9-1 | Dowling, Whelan, Bartley(3), Harkness(2), Pickett, Lewis 33[og] |
| 55 | 13/04 | H | RL P | Basingstoke Town | 213 | W | 2-1 | Walker 6, Bartley 85 |
| 56 | 17/04 | A | RL P | Bishop's Stortford | 209 | L | 0-1 | |
| 57 | 24/04 | H | RL P | Sutton United | 585 | L | 0-2 | |
| 58 | 27/04 | H | SCC SF | **Ashford Town (Middx)** | n/k | **W** | **3-1** | **Bartley(3)** |
| 59 | 01/05 | A | RL P | Hendon | 315 | W | 3-0 | Fitzgerald 19[og], Bartley 45, Driscoll 90 |
| 60 | 03/05 | A | SCC F | **Chertsey Town** | n/k | **L** | **2-4** | **Bartley(2)** |

## PLAYING SQUAD 1999-2000:

GOALKEEPERS: John Gregory (Northwood), Darren Smith (Gravesend & Northfleet)

DEFENDERS: Trevor Baron (Woking), Andy Clement (Staines Town), Lewis Craker (Molesey), Alan Dowson (Gateshead), John Humphrey (Egham Town), Robert Marshall (Harrow Borough), Gary Powell (Camberley Town), Chris Whelan (Bangor City), Tom Williams

MIDFIELDERS: Garfield Blackman (Slough Town), Stuart Davidson, Gary Holloway, Jeremy Jones (Molesey), Jamie Pearson, Barry Rake (Slough Town), Simon Ray (Whyteleafe)

FORWARDS: Carl Bartley (Dulwich Hamlet), Ross Pickett (Yeading), Andy Sayer (Enfield), Clive Zammitt

## BISHOP'S STORTFORD - MATCH FACTS - 1998-99 SEASON

| No | Date | Venue | Comp | Opponents | Att | Result | Score | Goalscorers |
|----|------|-------|------|-----------|-----|--------|-------|-------------|
| 1 | 22/08 | H | RLP | Billericay Town | 257 | D | 1-1 | Neufville 6 |
| 2 | 25/08 | A | RLP | Slough Town | 768 | D | 2-2 | Clifford, Greene |
| 3 | 29/08 | A | RLP | Harrow Borough | 205 | D | 2-2 | Greene 48, Forbes 85 |
| 4 | 01/09 | H | RLP | St Albans City | 257 | D | 1-1 | Ikazabou 7 |
| 5 | 05/09 | H | RLP | Aldershot Town | 715 | L | 0-8 | |
| 6 | 09/09 | A | RL C1 | Molesey | 66 | W | 2-1 | Cooper(2) |
| 7 | 12/09 | A | RLP | Dulwich Hamlet | 306 | D | 1-1 | Clark 89 |
| 8 | 15/09 | H | RLP | Enfield | 240 | L | 1-2 | Clifford 55 |
| 9 | 19/09 | A | RLP | Hendon | 302 | L | 3-5 | Conroy 17, McCarthy 71 83 |
| 10 | 22/09 | H | RLP | Sutton United | 210 | L | 1-2 | Ikazaboh 80 |
| 11 | 26/09 | A | RLP | Purfleet | 157 | L | 1-3 | Flain 45 |
| 12 | 04/10 | H | FA C Q2 | Aldershot Town | 719 | L | 0-2 | |
| 13 | 10/10 | H | RLP | Aylesbury United | 261 | L | 0-3 | |
| 14 | 13/10 | A | HSC 1 | Harpenden Town | 68 | W | 3-0 | Cooper(2), Gammons |
| 15 | 17/10 | A | RLP | Hampton | 226 | D | 0-0 | |
| 16 | 21/10 | H | RLP | Chesham United | 1725 | W | 2-0 | Ikazaboh 16, Cooksey 26, Norfolk 60, Ball 87, Gell 88[og] |
| 17 | 27/10 | A | FA T 1 | Whyteleafe | 95 | L | 1-3 | McCarthy |
| 18 | 31/10 | A | RLP | Bromley | 228 | W | 4-2 | Robbins 40, Ashdjian 43, Greene 48 64 |
| 19 | 07/11 | H | RLP | Dagenham & Redbridge | 246 | L | 0-3 | |
| 20 | 10/11 | A | PC 1 | Wembley | 57 | W | 2-0 | Greene, Tucker |
| 21 | 14/11 | A | RLP | Walton & Hersham | 187 | D | 2-2 | Greene 60, Robbins 90 |
| 22 | 16/11 | A | HSC 2 | St Albans City | 148 | L | 0-3 | |
| 23 | 23/11 | H | RLC 2 | Basingstoke Town | 97 | W | 5-4 | Greene(2), Cooksey(2), Gough(at D'ham & Redbridge) (Bishop's Stortford expelled) |
| 24 | 28/11 | A | RLP | Carshalton Athletic | 283 | L | 0-1 | |
| 25 | 05/12 | H | RLP | Dulwich Hamlet | 143 | W | 2-1 | Tucker 29 83 |
| 26 | 12/12 | A | RLP | Enfield | 650 | L | 1-2 | Greene 70 |
| 27 | 15/12 | A | PC 2 | Enfield | 141 | L | 0-1 | |
| 28 | 19/12 | H | RLP | Bromley | 174 | L | 1-3 | Honeyball 26 |
| 29 | 26/12 | A | RLP | St Albans City | 787 | L | 1-5 | Cooper 70 |
| 30 | 28/12 | A | RLP | Boreham Wood | 309 | W | 2-1 | Greene 53, Comerford 75 |
| 31 | 09/01 | H | RLP | Harrow Borough | 154 | L | 0-3 | |
| 32 | 23/01 | H | RLP | Slough Town | 236 | L | 0-1 | |
| 33 | 30/01 | A | RLP | Billericay Town | 625 | L | 2-3 | Robbins 48, Comerford 75 |
| 34 | 13/02 | A | RLP | Aldershot Town | 1723 | | 0-5 | |
| 35 | 20/02 | H | RLP | Gravesend & Northfleet | 274 | W | 3-1 | Whitney 37, M Cooper 70, W Cooper 79 |
| 36 | 27/02 | A | RLP | Aylesbury United | 979 | L | 2-4 | Whitney 2, M Cooper 43 |
| 37 | 06/03 | H | RLP | Purfleet | 164 | D | 0-0 | |
| 38 | 13/03 | A | RLP | Sutton United | 732 | L | 0-2 | |
| 39 | 16/03 | H | RLP | Heybridge Swifts | 126 | L | 1-3 | Whitney 70 |
| 40 | 20/03 | A | RLP | Chesham United | 272 | W | 1-0 | Hayes 68 |
| 41 | 27/03 | H | RLP | Hampton | 156 | L | 0-2 | |
| 42 | 30/03 | A | RLP | Gravesend & Northfleet | 376 | L | 1-4 | Hayes 60 |
| 43 | 03/04 | A | RLP | Basingstoke Town | 421 | L | 1-3 | Benstock 12 |
| 44 | 05/04 | H | RLP | Boreham Wood | 174 | W | 2-0 | Williams 12, Comerford 69 |
| 45 | 10/04 | A | RLP | Dagenham & Redbridge | 629 | D | 1-1 | Benstock 26 |
| 46 | 17/04 | H | RLP | Walton & Hersham | 209 | W | 1-0 | Winger 84 |
| 47 | 20/04 | H | RLP | Basingstoke Town | 128 | D | 0-0 | |
| 48 | 24/04 | A | RLP | Heybridge Swifts | 273 | W | 2-1 | Fannan 72, Comerford 77 |
| 49 | 27/04 | H | RLP | Hendon | 174 | L | 0-3 | |
| 50 | 01/05 | H | RLP | Carshalton Athletic | 350 | L | 1-2 | Hayes 29[p] |

# BROMLEY - MATCH FACTS - 1998-99 SEASON

| No | Date | Venue | Comp | Opponents | Att | Result | Score | Goalscorers |
|---|---|---|---|---|---|---|---|---|
| 1 | 22/08 | H | RLP | Heybridge Swifts | 302 | W | 6-1 | Carroll 9 32 64, Alan 20[p], SteveAns 56, Kyte 61 |
| 2 | 25/08 | A | RLP | Boreham Wood | 240 | W | 3-0 | Carroll, Zahhna-Oni, Stevens |
| 3 | 29/08 | A | RLP | Carshalton Athletic | 326 | D | 1-1 | Stephens 66 |
| 4 | 01/09 | H | RLP | Harrow Borough | 371 | W | 3-0 | Woolf 37, Carroll 46, Kyle 57 |
| 5 | 05/09 | H | RLP | Enfield | 601 | W | 2-1 | Gray 5, Zahhna-Oni 85 |
| 6 | 08/09 | H | RL C 1 | Tooting & Mitcham United | 298 | W | 3-0 | Dennington, Sharman, Stevens |
| 7 | 12/09 | A | RLP | Hendon | 307 | L | 1-2 | Wordsworth 90[p] |
| 8 | 15/09 | H | RLP | Aldershot Town | 1239 | D | 1-1 | Allen 72 |
| 9 | 19/09 | H | RLP | Dulwich Hamlet | 617 | L | 0-2 | |
| 10 | 22/09 | A | RLP | Walton & Hersham | 220 | L | 0-1 | |
| 11 | 26/09 | H | RLP | Basingstoke Town | 484 | L | 1-3 | Allen 73 |
| 12 | 03/10 | H | FA C Q2 | Chesham United | 422 | W | 2-1 | Woolfe, Rawlings |
| 13 | 09/10 | H | RLP | Purfleet | 415 | W | 2-1 | Woolf 10, Adedeji 14 |
| 14 | 13/10 | A | RLP | Aylesbury United | 693 | L | 1-2 | Zahana-Oni 68 |
| 15 | 17/10 | A | FA C Q3 | Hayes | 629 | L | 0-1 | |
| 16 | 19/10 | A | RLP | Dagenham & Redbridge | 663 | D | 3-3 | Carroll 45, Kyte46, Rawlings 54 |
| 17 | 27/10 | A | PC 1 | Slough Town | 220 | L | 0-1 | |
| 18 | 31/10 | H | RLP | Bishop's Stortford | 228 | L | 2-4 | Adedeji 11, Carroll 62 |
| 19 | 03/11 | A | RL C 2 | Heybridge Swifts | 112 | W | 2-1 | Wordsworth(2) |
| 20 | 07/11 | A | RLP | Hampton | 324 | L | 1-2 | Woolf 37 |
| 21 | 14/11 | H | RLP | Sutton United | 569 | D | 1-1 | Wordsworth 22 |
| 22 | 17/11 | H | KSC 1 | Fisher Athletic | 266 | L | 2-3 | Carroll 28, Wordsworth 44 |
| 23 | 21/11 | A | FA T 2 | Aldershot Town | 1587 | L | 1-3 | Sharman 31 |
| 24 | 28/11 | H | RLP | Slough Town | 299 | W | 2-1 | Francis 65[p], Loveday 71 |
| 25 | 05/12 | A | RLP | Aldershot Town | 1687 | L | 0-3 | |
| 26 | 12/12 | H | RLP | Hendon | 337 | L | 1-4 | Woolf 88 |
| 27 | 19/12 | A | RLP | Bishop's Stortford | 174 | W | 3-1 | Wordsworth 12 61, Carroll 25 |
| 28 | 28/12 | H | RLP | Gravesend & Northfleet | 661 | L | 0-1 | |
| 29 | 02/01 | A | RLP | Billericay Town | 777 | D | 2-2 | Rawlings 19, Carroll56 |
| 30 | 09/01 | H | RLP | Carshalton Athletic | 402 | L | 2-3 | Adedeji 43, Wordsworth 72 |
| 31 | 23/01 | H | RLP | Boreham Wood | 355 | D | 2-2 | Wordsworth 39, Kyte 53 |
| 32 | 30/01 | A | RLP | Harrow Borough | 239 | L | 0-2 | |
| 33 | 02/02 | H | L CC 1 | Metropolitan Police | 159 | W | 5-0 | Sharman, White, Carroll(3) |
| 34 | 06/02 | H | RLP | Dulwich Hamlet | 451 | L | 0-3 | |
| 35 | 13/02 | A | RLP | Enfield | 557 | L | 0-3 | |
| 36 | 20/02 | H | RLP | Aylesbury United | 403 | L | 0-1 | |
| 37 | 27/02 | A | RLP | Purfleet | 233 | L | 0-1 | |
| 38 | 06/03 | A | RLP | Basingstoke Town | 530 | L | 1-1 | White 79 |
| 39 | 09/03 | A | RL C 3 | Chesham United | 173 | W | 3-0 | Howells, Wordsworth, Francis |
| 40 | 13/03 | A | RLP | Walton & Hersham | 317 | D | 1-1 | Gray 13 |
| 41 | 16/03 | A | RL C QF | Uxbridge | 103 | W | 2-0 | Sharman, Wordsworth |
| 42 | 20/03 | H | RLP | Dagenham & Redbridge | 458 | D | 0-0 | |
| 43 | 23/03 | H | RL C SF(1) | Aldershot Town | 506 | L | 1-3 | Gray |
| 44 | 30/03 | A | LCC QF | Welling United | n/k | L | 0-2 | |
| 45 | 03/04 | H | RLP | Billericay Town | 399 | D | 2-2 | Wordsworth 45[p], Francis 64 |
| 46 | 05/04 | H | RLP | Gravesend & Northfleet | 561 | W | 2-1 | Smith 70[og], Simpson 83 |
| 47 | 08/04 | A | RL C SF(2) | Aldershot Town | 1064 | W | 2-1 | Harney 36, Woolf 90 |
| 48 | 10/04 | H | RLP | Hampton | 334 | D | 0-0 | |
| 49 | 13/04 | A | RLP | Heybridge Swifts | 181 | L | 1-2 | Sharman 87 |
| 50 | 17/04 | A | RLP | Sutton United | 1173 | L | 0-2 | |
| 51 | 20/04 | A | RLP | St Albans City | 373 | L | 1-4 | Sharman 4 |
| 52 | 22/04 | A | RLP | Chesham United | 171 | L | 1-3 | White 45 |
| 53 | 24/04 | H | RLP | Chesham United | 309 | L | 0-1 | |
| 54 | 27/04 | A | RLP | St Albans City | 314 | L | 0-1 | |
| 55 | 01/05 | A | RLP | Slough Town | 516 | L | 1-2 | Wordsworth 70 |

*Ryman League top scorer Jeff Wood (Ford United) with his side's Division Three Championship trophy*
*Photo: Francis Short*

## DIVISION ONE FINAL LEAGUE TABLE 1998-99

| | | P | W | D | L | F | A | W | D | L | F | A | Pts |
|---|---|---|---|---|---|---|---|---|---|---|---|---|---|
| 1 | Canvey Island | 42 | 17 | 1 | 3 | 45 | 17 | 11 | 5 | 5 | 31 | 24 | 90 |
| 2 | Hitchin Town | 42 | 16 | 4 | 1 | 45 | 14 | 9 | 6 | 6 | 30 | 24 | 85 |
| 3 | Wealdstone | 42 | 14 | 4 | 3 | 43 | 22 | 12 | 2 | 7 | 32 | 26 | 84 |
| 4 | Braintree Town | 42 | 9 | 5 | 7 | 41 | 25 | 11 | 5 | 5 | 33 | 23 | 70 |
| 5 | Bognor Regis Town | 42 | 11 | 3 | 7 | 37 | 19 | 9 | 5 | 7 | 26 | 25 | 68 |
| 6 | Grays Athletic | 42 | 12 | 3 | 6 | 32 | 17 | 7 | 8 | 6 | 24 | 25 | 68 |
| 7 | Oxford City | 42 | 9 | 7 | 5 | 35 | 27 | 7 | 7 | 7 | 23 | 24 | 62 |
| 8 | Croydon | 42 | 10 | 5 | 6 | 30 | 25 | 6 | 8 | 7 | 23 | 28 | 61 |
| 9 | Chertsey Town | 42 | 7 | 8 | 6 | 27 | 29 | 7 | 8 | 6 | 30 | 28 | 58 |
| 10 | Romford | 42 | 7 | 6 | 8 | 28 | 33 | 7 | 9 | 5 | 30 | 30 | 57 |
| 11 | Maidenhead United | 42 | 3 | 7 | 11 | 13 | 28 | 10 | 8 | 3 | 37 | 18 | 54 |
| 12 | Worthing | 42 | 5 | 8 | 8 | 24 | 26 | 8 | 5 | 8 | 23 | 35 | 52 |
| 13 | Leyton Pennant | 42 | 6 | 7 | 8 | 30 | 32 | 7 | 5 | 9 | 32 | 38 | 51 |
| 14 | Uxbridge | 42 | 5 | 7 | 9 | 29 | 27 | 8 | 4 | 9 | 25 | 24 | 50 |
| 15 | Barton Rovers | 42 | 6 | 8 | 7 | 15 | 18 | 5 | 7 | 9 | 28 | 31 | 48 |
| 16 | Yeading | 42 | 6 | 6 | 9 | 27 | 23 | 6 | 4 | 11 | 24 | 32 | 46 |
| 17 | Leatherhead | 42 | 10 | 4 | 7 | 35 | 23 | 2 | 5 | 14 | 13 | 36 | 45 |
| 18 | Whyteleafe | 42 | 9 | 3 | 9 | 34 | 34 | 4 | 3 | 14 | 17 | 38 | 45 |
| 19 | Staines Town | 42 | 6 | 10 | 5 | 18 | 19 | 4 | 5 | 12 | 15 | 37 | 45 |
| 20 | Molesey | 42 | 3 | 11 | 7 | 12 | 30 | 5 | 9 | 7 | 23 | 22 | 44 |
| 21 | Wembley | 42 | 6 | 4 | 11 | 20 | 32 | 4 | 6 | 11 | 16 | 39 | 40 |
| 22 | Berkhamsted Town | 42 | 6 | 5 | 10 | 31 | 37 | 4 | 2 | 15 | 22 | 44 | 37 |

## RESULTS CHART 1998-99

| HOME TEAM | | 1 | 2 | 3 | 4 | 5 | 6 | 7 | 8 | 9 | 10 | 11 | 12 | 13 | 14 | 15 | 16 | 17 | 18 | 19 | 20 | 21 | 22 |
|---|---|---|---|---|---|---|---|---|---|---|---|---|---|---|---|---|---|---|---|---|---|---|---|
| 1 | Barton Rovers | X | 2-0 | 0-2 | 1-3 | 0-1 | 1-1 | 2-0 | 0-1 | 0-0 | 0-0 | 0-2 | 1-1 | 2-1 | 0-0 | 1-1 | 0-0 | 1-0 | 0-3 | 0-1 | 2-0 | 0-0 | 2-1 |
| 2 | Berkhamsted | 2-1 | X | 1-2 | 0-2 | 1-3 | 3-3 | 2-2 | 1-4 | 1-2 | 3-2 | 2-0 | 0-3 | 0-1 | 0-2 | 3-3 | 5-0 | 0-0 | 4-1 | 1-1 | 2-1 | 0-1 | 0-3 |
| 3 | Bognor Regis T | 1-0 | 1-3 | X | 4-0 | 0-0 | 3-1 | 1-2 | 0-1 | 6-1 | 3-0 | 0-1 | 3-1 | 0-0 | 0-1 | 1-1 | 1-0 | 2-0 | 2-0 | 4-1 | 3-1 | 1-2 | 1-3 |
| 4 | Braintree Town | 1-1 | 6-0 | 2-3 | X | 0-2 | 1-2 | 3-2 | 1-1 | 2-0 | 0-0 | 8-2 | 2-2 | 0-0 | 1-2 | 1-3 | 3-0 | 2-4 | 1-0 | 0-1 | 2-0 | 4-0 | 1-0 |
| 5 | Canvey Island | 0-2 | 3-0 | 2-0 | 2-1 | X | 2-0 | 2-1 | 2-1 | 3-0 | 3-0 | 6-1 | 0-4 | 2-1 | 2-0 | 0-2 | 2-0 | 1-0 | 4-2 | 3-0 | 1-1 | 2-0 | 3-1 |
| 6 | Chertsey Town | 2-1 | 0-4 | 3-1 | 0-3 | 1-1 | X | 2-0 | 2-2 | 1-3 | 1-0 | 1-1 | 2-2 | 0-2 | 0-1 | 2-2 | 1-1 | 2-1 | 0-1 | 1-1 | 2-0 | 2-2 | 2-0 |
| 7 | Croydon | 1-0 | 2-0 | 2-1 | 0-0 | 3-0 | 1-4 | X | 2-0 | 1-4 | 2-0 | 2-1 | 0-0 | 2-4 | 2-0 | 1-1 | 2-0 | 2-2 | 2-3 | 0-0 | 0-2 | 1-2 | 2-1 |
| 8 | Grays Athletic | 2-2 | 1-0 | 1-3 | 1-1 | 0-1 | 1-0 | 4-0 | X | 1-0 | 4-0 | 2-3 | 0-2 | 1-0 | 1-0 | 0-1 | 1-2 | 1-0 | 1-1 | 4-1 | 2-0 | 1-0 | 3-0 |
| 9 | Hitchin Town | 1-1 | 1-0 | 4-0 | 1-0 | 3-0 | 3-1 | 0-1 | 4-0 | X | 2-1 | 1-0 | 2-2 | 1-0 | 3-3 | 0-0 | 1-0 | 2-1 | 3-1 | 3-0 | 3-2 | 5-0 | 2-1 |
| 10 | Leatherhead | 4-2 | 2-0 | 1-0 | 0-1 | 1-2 | 1-2 | 7-3 | 1-1 | 1-1 | X | 1-0 | 0-1 | 0-3 | 2-2 | 4-1 | 0-1 | 2-0 | 0-1 | 1-1 | 4-1 | 1-0 | 2-0 |
| 11 | Leyton Pennant | 3-0 | 1-2 | 1-2 | 0-3 | 1-1 | 1-1 | 1-1 | 1-1 | 0-4 | 2-1 | X | 3-1 | 2-2 | 2-1 | 2-2 | 4-1 | 2-3 | 1-2 | 0-0 | 0-1 | 1-2 | 2-1 |
| 12 | Maidenhead | 0-2 | 2-1 | 0-0 | 0-2 | 0-2 | 0-0 | 0-0 | 2-3 | 1-0 | 1-3 | 1-2 | X | 1-1 | 2-2 | 0-2 | 2-1 | 0-2 | 0-2 | 0-1 | 1-1 | 0-0 | 0-1 |
| 13 | Molesey | 0-6 | 0-3 | 0-0 | 2-1 | 0-0 | 0-0 | 0-0 | 1-1 | 0-0 | 1-0 | 1-4 | 0-4 | X | 0-0 | 0-1 | 1-1 | 0-4 | 2-0 | 0-0 | 0-0 | 3-4 | 1-1 |
| 14 | Oxford City | 2-0 | 2-1 | 2-2 | 3-0 | 2-1 | 0-0 | 0-2 | 0-0 | 1-2 | 3-2 | 3-2 | 0-1 | 2-1 | X | 2-2 | 2-2 | 1-3 | 3-1 | 3-1 | 0-1 | 2-2 | 2-2 |
| 15 | Romford | 2-2 | 2-2 | 0-1 | 0-1 | 1-0 | 0-1 | 1-1 | 2-2 | 0-3 | 4-1 | 3-2 | 0-3 | 0-0 | 1-0 | X | 1-0 | 0-0 | 0-4 | 3-4 | 3-1 | 2-1 | 3-4 |
| 16 | Staines Town | 0-0 | 2-0 | 1-1 | 1-1 | 0-3 | 1-3 | 2-1 | 1-0 | 1-1 | 0-0 | 1-1 | 1-1 | 1-0 | 0-0 | 1-2 | X | 0-1 | 2-2 | 2-1 | 1-0 | 0-1 | 0-0 |
| 17 | Uxbridge | 1-0 | 1-1 | 1-3 | 1-2 | 1-2 | 4-2 | 0-0 | 0-1 | 1-2 | 0-0 | 2-2 | 1-1 | 0-0 | 0-3 | 2-3 | 2-2 | X | 0-1 | 4-0 | 5-0 | 1-2 | 2-0 |
| 18 | Wealdstone | 5-2 | 5-2 | 2-0 | 2-2 | 3-0 | 2-2 | 0-1 | 1-2 | 2-1 | 1-1 | 1-0 | 0-3 | 2-2 | 2-0 | 1-0 | 3-1 | 2-1 | X | 1-0 | 2-1 | 4-1 | 2-0 |
| 19 | Wembley | 1-1 | 1-0 | 0-2 | 0-3 | 1-2 | 0-3 | 1-5 | 0-1 | 0-1 | 1-0 | 1-4 | 0-0 | 1-1 | 4-1 | 2-0 | 2-0 | 1-2 | 0-2 | X | 2-1 | 1-2 | 1-1 |
| 20 | Whyteleafe | 3-4 | 4-1 | 1-1 | 2-3 | 5-5 | 2-1 | 0-1 | 1-0 | 0-3 | 1-0 | 0-2 | 3-2 | 1-3 | 0-1 | 2-1 | 3-0 | 3-0 | 0-2 | 1-0 | X | 1-1 | 1-3 |
| 21 | Worthing | 0-0 | 3-2 | 1-0 | 2-2 | 0-2 | 1-1 | 0-0 | 2-1 | 1-1 | 0-1 | 1-1 | 0-1 | 1-1 | 2-4 | 3-0 | 0-1 | 0-0 | 1-2 | 5-3 | 1-2 | X | 0-1 |
| 22 | Yeading | 0-1 | 3-0 | 0-2 | 1-2 | 1-3 | 1-2 | 0-0 | 1-1 | 1-1 | 4-1 | 1-1 | 0-2 | 3-0 | 0-0 | 2-2 | 1-2 | 0-1 | 0-1 | 3-0 | 2-1 | 3-0 | X |

*Wealdstone, the then Southern League club were the first double winners of the Vauxhall Conference and FA Trophy. Brian Hall, their inspirational manager sadly died earlier this year but will be remembered and respected for a lifetime contributing to the game as coach, manager and talent scout.*

# BARTON ROVERS

**CLUB OFFICIALS**
Chairman: **John Milton**
President: **P Howarth**
Vice Chairman: **Ken Burr**
Secretary: **Owen Clark,** 108 Manor Road,
Barton-le-Clay, Bedford MK45 4NS
Tel: 01582 882398
Press Officer: **Nick Rhodes**
Tel: 01582 881865

**FOOTBALL MANAGEMENT TEAM**
Manager: Ian Allinson
Asst Manager: Ian Donnelly
Physio: Mick Clark

**FACT FILE**

Formed: 1898
Nickname: Rovers
Sponsors: SRC Contractors
Colours: All royal blue
Change colours: All yellow
Midweek Matchday: Tuesday
Reserves' League: None

1998-99 Captain: Danny Turner
P.o.Y. Tony McNally
Top Scorer: Carl Drew

Pages: 64 Price: £1
Editor: Nick Rhodes (01582 881865)
Local Press: Luton News, Herald,
Beds on Sunday
Local Radio: Radio Chiltern, Radio Beds
Three Counties Radio

**GROUND** Sharpenhoe Road, Barton-le-Clay, Bedford MK45 4SD (01582 707772)
**Directions:** M1 Jct 12, from London exit turn right, take 2nd right throughHarlington and
Sharpenhoe. Ground on right entering village. Four and a half miles from Harlington (BR), 6
miles from Luton (BR), good bus service fromLuton
Capacity: 4,000 Seats: 160 Cover: 1,120 Floodlights: Yes
Clubhouse: Noon-3pm weekends (no football), noon-11pm (matchdays), 7-11pmweekdays.
Real ale, hot & cold snacks, pool, darts, gaming machines
Club Shop: Yes

**PREVIOUS** **Leagues:** Luton & Dist. 47-54; Sth Midlands 54-79
**Grounds:** Church Pitch 1898-1912; Barton Cutting 1912; Sharpenhoe Rd 12-33;Faldo Rd 33-38; Barton Rec. 46-75

**CLUB RECORDS** **Attendance:** 1,900 v Nuneaton, FA Cup 4th Qual. Rd 1976
**Win:** 17-1 v Flitwick Athletic (H), S Midlands Lge Div 1 55-56
**Defeat:** 1-11 v Leighton United (H), S Midlands Lge Prem Div 62-63
**Scorer:** Richard Camp 152, 1989-98    **Appearances:** Bill Goodyear 478, 1982-98
**Fees - Paid:** £1,000 for B Baldry (Hitchin Town, 1980)    **Received:** £1,000 for BBaldry (Bishop's Stortford, 1981)

**BEST SEASON** **FA Cup:** 1st Round 1980-81, 0-2 v Torquay United (A)
**FA Vase:** Runners-up 77-78 (SF 76-77 81-82, QF 75-76 78-79)    **FA Trophy:** 2nd Rd 98-99

**HONOURS:** Sth Mids Lg(8) 70-73 74-79 (R-up 67-68), Div 1 64-65 (R-up 55-56), Div 2 54-55,Lg Shield 57-58 60-61 68-69, Chal. Tphy 71-
72 74-75 77-78 78-79; Beds Snr Cup(7), R-up (5); Beds Premier Cup 95-96, R-up 81-82 83-84 88-89, Beds Intermediate Cup
53-54; Luton & Dist. Lg Div 3 47-48; North BedsCharity Cup 72-73 74-75 76-77 77-78 79-80 80-81 (R-up 70-71); Isthmian Lg
Associate Members Tphy R-up 92-93; Isthmian Div 2 R-Up 94-95, South Midlands Floodlight Cup 98-99

Players progressing: Kevin Blackwell (Huddersfield T.)

*Back Row (L-R): O Clark (Secretary), I Allinson (Manager), B Gillham, M Clark (Physio), M Young, S Hudspith (Coach), G
Crook, D Cook, M Phillips, A McNally, I Donnelly (Asst. Manager), J Thomas
Front Row: S Hunt, C Drew, R Wilcox, K Coughlin, D Turner (Captain), S Turner, P Seaman, R Fisher.*

# BEDFORD TOWN

## CLUB OFFICIALS
Chairman: **Paul Brown**

Vice Chairman: **Nic Meaney**

President: **Allen J Sturgess**

Secretary: **Barry Stephenson**

9 Aspen Ave., Bedford, Beds MK41 8BX
Tel: 01234342276

### FOOTBALL MANAGEMENT TEAM
Joint Managers:Tony Luff & Jason Reed
Physio: Mick Dilley

### FACT FILE
Founded: 1908    Reformed: 1989
Nickname: Eagles
Sponsors: Allen Sturges Travel
Colours: Blue, white trim/blue/blue
Change Colours: Yellow & black
Midweek Matchday: Tuesday
Reserves' League: Chiltonian

98-99 - Captain: Tony Joyce
Top Scorer:Paul Covington
P.o.Y.: Tony Joyce

Ryman
Football League

Ryman League Division Two
BEDFORD TOWN
v
Hertford Town
Tues 23 March 1999, 7.45pm Kick Off

**Main Club Sponsor**

**Allen Sturges Travel**

Pages: 40  Price: £1
Editor: Adrian Brown(01234 359855)

Local Press:Beds Times, Beds on Sunday
Local Radio: Chiltern Radio,Three Counties

**GROUND**          The New Eyrie, Meadow Lane, Cardington, Bedford MK44 3SB
Fax: 01234 831990 Tel: 01234 838448
**Directions:** BR station Bedford Midland 3miles from ground. Bus station 5 miles walk from station.Service 171 & 172 stop outside ground(Canvins stop). Trains from London Thameslink run every half hour to Bedford.By road: north up M1 to jct 13 onto A421 (right), follow on to bypass at Sandy exit.A603 to Sandy, ground on left just before layby.
Capacity: 3,000    Seats: 150       Cover: 500        Floodlights: Yes
**Clubhouse:** Natchdays bar snacks
**Club Shop:** Good range of merchandise incl. programmes.  Mick Spavins ( 01234 402822)

**PREVIOUS**      **Leagues:** South Midlands 91-94 (predecessors: Utd Co's 08-39; Southern 46-82)
**Grounds:** Allen Park, Queens Park, Bedford (park pitch) 1991-93
(predecessors: London Rd; Gasworks; Queens Pk; The Eyrie, Raleigh Street)

**CLUB RECORDS  Attendance:** 3,000 v Peterborough Utd, ground opening 6/8/93.
At Allen Park, 1,227 v Bedford Utd, South Midlands Lge Div. One, 26/12/91
(predecessors: 18,407 v Everton, FA Cup 4th Round 12/2/66)
**Career scorer:** Jason Reed        **Career appearances:** Jason Reed
**Win:** 9-0 v Ickleford, and Caddington            **Defeat:** 1-5 v Toddington

**BEST SEASON    FA Cup:** 2nd Q 98-99            **FA Vase:** 5th Round 1998-99, 1-2 v Tiverton Town (H)

**HONOURS:**      Isthmian League Div. 2 98-99; South Midlands Lg 94-95 (Div 1 92-93, F'lit Cup 94-95); Hinchingbrook Cup 94-95 94-95; Beds Sen Cup 94-95.  (Predecessors: Southern Lg 58-59 (Div 1 69-70), Utd Co's Lg 30-31 32-33 33-34 (R-up  7 Times) Vandanal Cup 97-8 Beds Prem , Beds Premier Cup  97-98 **FA Cup** 4th Rd 63-64 65-66. **FA Trophy** Semi-Final 74-75.
Players progressing: Bill Garner (Southend 69), Nicky Platnaeur (Bristol Rovers 77). Ray Bailey/Derek Bellotti/Billy Brown/Bert Carberry/PeterHall/Dave Quirke/Bobby Fold (Gillingham 56-67), Phil Driver (Wimbledon 78), Joe Dubois (Grimsby T 53), Ted Duggan (Luton T 56), Harry Duke (Noprwich C 46),John Fahy (Oxford U 64), Ken Flint (Spurs 47), Joe Hooley (Accrington 61), Joe Kirkup (Reading 55), Graham Moxon (Exeter C 75), Bela Olah (Northampton 58),Gary Sergeant (Peterborough U 77), Neil Townsend (Southend U 73)

*Back Row (L-R): Ashley Hilton, Will Cooper, Gary Williams, Paul Daniels, Danny Nicholls, Paul Sherlock, James Heeps, Paul Covington, Gavin Jaggard, Eddie Lawley, Gavin Covington, Mick Dilley (Physio)*
*Front: Luigi Rocco, Steve Searle, Jason Reed (Joint Mngr), Tony Joyce (Cptn), Tony Luff (Joint Mngr), Ian Evason, Chris Tubbs*

# BISHOPS STORTFORD

### CLUB OFFICIALS
Chairman: **John Goodwin**
President: **B W A Bayford**
Vice-Chairman: **Mick Hooker**
Gen Manager: **John Radford**
Secretary: **Martin Stone**
15 Saxon Drive, Witham, Essex CM8 2HL
01376 510162 (H) 0171 653 4858 (B)
Press Officer: **Martin Stone**

### FOOTBALL MANAGEMENT TEAM
Team Manager: Steve Wheeler
Coach: Martin Hayes
Physio: George Eastman

### FACT FILE

Formed: 1874
Nickname: Blues or Bishops
Colours: White & blue stripes/blue/blue
Change colours: Yellow/white/yellow
Midweek matchday: Tuesday
Reserves' Lge: Essex & Herts Border Comb

Pages: 72  Price: £1.50
Editor: Roy Kemp 01279 300647

Local Press: B.Stortford Citizen,
Herts & Essex Observer, Herald
Local Radio: BBC Essex, Essex FM,
Breeze AM, TEN17

**GROUND** Woodside, Dunmow Road, Bishop 's Stortford (01279 656538)
**Directions:** M11 jct 8, A1250 towards town centre, left at first roundabout. Woodside is first
on right opposite Golf Club. Entrance is between industrial units on right. By rail: British Rail:
W. Anglia Line (London, Liverpool Str.-Cambridge)
Capacity: 4,000    Cover: 700    Seats: 298    Floodlights: Yes
Clubhouse: Open lunchtimes,evenings and matchdays.Function room(seating 250) available
for hire available for hire.
Club Shop: Full stock inc. scarves, badges and other souvenirs. Massive stock of proromes
and books etc. Contact Gareth Stephens via club.

**PREVIOUS**    **Leagues:** East Herts 1896-97, 02-06, 19-21; Stansted & Dist. Lg 06-19; HertsCounty 21-25 27-29;
Herts & Essex Border 25-27; Spartan 29-51; Delphian 51-63;Athenian 63-73
**CLUB RECORDS**    **Attendance:** 6,000 v Peterborough Utd, FA Cup 2nd Rd 1972 & v Middlesbrough FACup 3rd Rd replay, 1983
**Win:** 11-0: Nettleswell & Butntmill, Herts Jun Cup 2nd Rd 1911   **Defeat:** 0-13 v Cheshunt (H), Herts Sen. Cup 1st Rd 9/1/26
**Fee Paid:** £1,500 for Phil Hopkins (Walthamstow Ave., 84)    **Fee Received:** £10,000 for Carl Hoddle (Leyton O., 89)
**Scorer:** (Since 29) Jimmy Badcock 123    **Appearances:** Phil Hopkins 543
**BEST SEASON**    **FA Amateur Cup:** Winners 73-74    **FA Trophy:** Winners 80-81
**FA Cup:** 3rd Rd rep. 82-83 (above) - League clubs beaten: Reading 82-83
**HONOURS**    Isthmian Lg Div 1 80-1 94-5 (Lg Cup 88-9, Full Mem. Cup 90-1), Prem. Inter Lg Cup 89-90; Athenian Lg 69-70 (R-up 66-7, Div
1 65-6, Div 2 R-up 64-5); Delphian Lg 54-5; London Snr Cup 73-4; Herts Snr Cup 58-9 59-0 63-4 70-1 72-3 73-4 75-686-7; E
Anglian Cup 81-2; Herts Charity Cup 62-3 65-6 73-4 81-2 82-3 84-5 87-896-7; Herts Charity Shield 54-5; Herts I'mediate Cup
(res) 94-95; Eastern F'lit Cup 84-5; Essex F'lit Cup 67-8; Essex & Herts Border Comb 81-2 88-9 R-up (2) 92-4; Fred Budden
Tphy R-up 78-9 90-1 92-3
Players progressing: P Phelan (Southend 61), M Hollow (Orient 62), P Phillips(Luton 69), T Baker (Colchester 86), T Sorrell (Maidstone,
Colchester, Barnet 88), C Hoddle (Leyton O., Barnet 89), T English (Colchester 89), L Fortune-West (Gillingham 95), L Braithwaite (Exeter City 96)

*Back Row (L-R): Dave Mallet (coach), Lee Norfolk, Simon Gough, Will Cooper, Jason Tucker, Gavin King, Paul Clark, Danny
Foot, Jermaine Wynter, Paul Mahorn, Mickey Stevens (Physio)
Front Row: Matthew Waldron, Ernie Cooksey, Dave Greene, Terry Back (Manager), Terry Robbins (Asst. Manager), Tony
Comerford, Nicky Winger, John Ashdjian*

# BOGNOR REGIS TOWN

## CLUB OFFICIALS

Chairman: **Jack Pearce**
President: **S Rowlands**
Secretary: **Brian Pitchford**, c/o The Club.
01243 587421 (H)
Press Officer: **Paul Edwards**
Comm. Manager: **Maurice Warner**
Gen. Manager: **Jack Pearce**

### FOOTBALL MANAGEMENT TEAM
Manager: Jack Pearce
Asst Manager: Neil Hider
Physio: Steve Robinson/Clair Eastland

### FACT FILE

Founded: 1883
Nickname: The Rocks
Sponsors: Butlins South Coast World
Colours: White (green trim)/green/white
Change colours: Blue/white/red
Midweek home matchday: Tuesday
Reserves ' League: None

BOGNOR REGIS TOWN FOOTBALL CLUB

The Rocks

Ryman

MATCH DAY PROGRAMME

MAIN SPONSORS

OUR VISITORS TODAY:
**WITNEY TOWN FC**
Saturday 21st Nov. 1998 K.O. 3.00pm
TODAY'S MATCH SPONSORS
Atlas Products
Unit F1/F2 Ash Grove Ind Park
Bognor Regis
Tel: 01243 830324

**COMPETITIVE CLEANING**
Cleaning throughout the South
FA Umbro Trophy Round 2
Programme no.11 Price £1

### GROUND
Nyewood Lane, Bognor Regis PO21 2TY
Tel: 01243 822325
**Directions:** West along sea front from pier, past Aldwick shopping centre then turn right into Nyewood Lane
Capacity: 6,000    Cover: 3,800    Seats: 243    Floodlights: Yes
**Clubhouse:** Open every night, matchdays and Sunday lunchtimes. Hot food available
**Club Shop:** Selling programmes and normal club items

Pages: 36  Price: £1
Editor: Maurice Warner Tel: 01243 822325
Local Press: Bognor Regis Journal & Guardian, Bognor Observer, Brighton Argus, Portsmouth News
Local Radio: Radio Sussex, Ocean Sound, Radio Solent, Southern Sound, SpiritFM

**PREVIOUS CLUB RECORDS**
**Leagues:** W Sussex Lge 1896-1926; Brighton, Hove & District Lge 26-27; Sussex County Lge 27-72; Southern Lge 72-81
**Attendance:** 3,642 v Swansea FA Cup 1st Rd replay, '84
**Goalscorer:** Kevin Clements (206)    **Appearances:** Mick Pullen, 967 (20 seasons)
**Transfer Fee Paid:** £2,200 Guy Rutherford 95-96
**Fee Received:** £10,500 for John Crumplin & Geoff Cooper (Brighton & Hove Alb, 87) & Simon Rodger (C Palace 89)

**BEST SEASON**
**FA Amateur Cup:** 1st Round 71-72    **F A Trophy:** 3rd Round 95-96
**F A Cup:** 2nd Rd on four occasions -    League clubs beaten: Swansea 84-85, Exeter 88-89
84-85 2-6 v Reading (A), 85-86 1-6 v Gillingham (A), 88-89 0-1 v Cambridge (H), 95-96 0-4 v Peterborough (A)

**HONOURS:**
Isthmian Lg Div 1 R-up 81-82, (Lg Cup 86-87); Southern Lg R-up 80-81 (Lg Cup R-up 80-81), Merit Cup 80-81; Sussex Lg 48-49 71-72 (R-up 38-39 51-52), Div 2 70-71, Invitation Cup 40-41 49-50 62-63 71-72; Brighton Lg R-up 26-27; W Sussex Lg (5) 20-25 (R-up 1896-97, 25-26), Jnr Lg 10-11 13-14; Southern Co's Comb 78-79; Sussex Snr Cup(9) 54-56 79-84 86-87 94-95 (R-up 51-52 58-59 84-85); Sussex Prof. Cup 73-74, Sussex RUR Cup 71-72; Sussex I'mediate Cup 52-53, Littlehampton Hosp. Cup 29-30 33-34; Bognor Charity Cup(8) 28-29 30-31 32-33 37-38 47-48 58-59 71-73; Gosport War Mem. Cup (2) 81-83 (R-up 86-87); Snr Midweek F'lit Cup R-up 74-75

Players progressing: E Randall (Chelsea 50), J Standing (Brighton 61), A Woon (Brentford 72), J Crumplin & G Cooper (Brighton 87), Simon Rodger (C Palace 89)

*Bognor Regis Town v Witney Town: the Protagonists queue up for the delivery of another Witney corner.    Photo: Kevin*

# BRAINTREE TOWN

### CLUB OFFICIALS
Chairman: **George Rosling**
Vice Chairman: **Ivan Kibble**
President: **Ron Webb**
Secretary: **T A Woodley**, 19a Bailey Bridge Rd., Braintree, Essex CM7 5TT
(01376 326234)
Press Officer: **Ron Webb** (01376 325338)

### FOOTBALL MANAGEMENT TEAM
Manager: Richie Powling
Assistant Manager Chris Whyte
Physio: T.B.A.

### FACT FILE
Founded: 1898
Nickname: The Iron
Sponsors: T.B.A.
Colours:Amber with navy stripe/navy/amber
Change colours: White/navy
Midweek matches: Tuesday
Reserves' Lg: Essex/Herts Border Comb

1998-99 Captain: Nicky Smith
P.o.Y.: Russell Tanner
Top Goalscorer: Gary Bennett (24)

Pages: 40 Price: £1
Editor: Len Llewellyn (01277 363103 T-Fax)
Local Radio: BBC Essex (103.5 fm),
Essex Radio (102.6 fm)

**GROUND** **C**ressing Road Stadium, Clockhouse Way, Braintree, Essex (01376 345617)
**Directions:** From Braintree by-pass, turn into Braintree at the McDonalds r'bout, follow signs for East Braintree Ind. Est. on B1018 - floodlights on left 3 miles into town just past. Orange Tree Pub. Entrance next left in Clockhouse Way, then left again. 1 mile from Braintree & Bocking (BR). Bus 353 from Witham or town centre Town centre 20 mins walk
**Capacity:** 4,000    Cover 1,500    Seats 250    Floodlights:Yes
**Clubhouse:** Open evenings 7-30-11, Sun 12-3, Sat matchday 12.00- 11.00 Full bar facilities
**Club shop:** Contact Jon Weaver 01376 347920 (75 year History of Braintree £15.99)

**PREVIOUS    Leagues:** North Essex 1898-1925; Essex & Suffolk Border 25-28 55-64; Spartan 28-35; Eastern Co's 35-37 38-39 52-55 70-91; Essex Co. 37-38; London 45-52; GtrLondon 64-66; Metropolitan 66-70; Southern 91-96
**Names:** Manor Works 1898-1921; Crittall Ath. 21-68; Braintree & Crittall Ath. 68-81; Braintree FC 81-82
**Grounds:** The Fair Field 1898-1903; Spaldings Meadow, Panfield Lane 03-23

**CLUB RECORDS Attendance:** 4,000 v Spurs, charity challenge match, May 1952
**Career Goalscorer:** Chris Guy 211, 63-90.            **Seasonal Record Scorer:** Gary Bennett 57, 97-98
**Career Appearances:** Paul Young 524, 66-77            **Fee Paid:** £2,000 for Shane Bailey (Sudbury Town)
**Fee Received:** £10,000 Matt Metcalf (Brentford 93) & John Cheesewright(Colchester 93)
**Win:** 15-3 v Hopes (Birmingham Friendly 39), 12-0 v Thetford Tn ( Eastern Lge 35-36)
**Defeat:** 0-14 v Chelmsford City A (Nth Essex Lge 23)

**BEST SEASON** FA Cup: 4th Qual. Rd 69-70 85-86 94-95 97-98
**HONOURS:**    Isthmian Lge Div 2 R-up 97-98, Div 3 R-up 96-97; Guardian Insurance Cup R-up 96-97; Eastern Counties Lg 36-37 83-84 84-85 (R-up 86-87 87-88 88-89 90-91), Lg Cup 87-88 (R-up 35-36 74-75); Essex County Lg R-up 37-38; London Lg (East) R-up 45-46, Lg Cup 47-48(jt) 48-49 51-52 (R-up 49-50); Metropolitan Lg Cup 69-70; Essex Elizabethan Tphy R-up 68-69; E. Anglian Cup 46-47 68-69 95-96; Essex Sen.Tphy 86-87 (R-up 90-91); Essex & Suffolk Border Lg 59-60 84-85 (Lg Cup 59-60); Nth Essex Lg 05-06 10-11 11-12; Essex Sen Cup 95-96 R-up 96-97; Essex Jnr Cup R-up 04-05 05-06 22-23; RAFA Cup 56-57; Gtr Lon. Ben. Cup 65-66; Worthington Evans Cup (3) R-up (4); Eastern F'lit Cup 85-86 96-97 (R-up 94-95 97-98); Anglian F'lit Lg 69-70; Jan Havanaar Inter. Tour. 94-95 (R-up 92-93)
Players progressing: J Dick (West Ham 53), S Wright (Wrexham 83), J Cheesewright (Birmingham C. 91), G Bennett, M Metcalf (Brentford 93), R Reinhelt (Gillingham 93), M de Souza (Birmingham C.), G Culling (Colchester U94)

*Back Row (L-R): Tony Hall (Manager), Phil Boyland (Asst. Manager), Gary Collins, Paul Knights, Lee Hunter, Lee Wilson, Paul Catley, John Bishop, Paul Betson, Trevor Gunn, Simon Milton, Shane Bailey, Tony Last (Physio)*
*Front Row: John Taylor, Ian Gedney, Nicky Simpson, Jack Harrod (Mascot), Russell Tanner, Gary Bennett, Nicky Smith, Alan Vincent*
*Photo: John Weaver*

# BROMLEY

### CLUB OFFICIALS

Chairman: **Glyn Beverly**

Secretary: **Kerry Phillips**
15 Watling Street, Bexleyheath,
Kent. DA6 7QJ
Tel: 01322 554108/529682, Fax 550543)

### FOOTBALL MANAGEMENT TEAM

Manager: Dave Edwards
Coach: T.B.A.
Physio: T.B.A.

### GROUND

**FACT FILE**
Formed: 1892
Nickname: The Lilywhites
Youth League: Southern Youth
Colours: White/black/black
Change colours: All red
Midweek home matchday: Tuesday
Reserve's League: None
Newsline: 0930 555 838

1998-99 Captain: Frank Coles
P.o.Y. Oli Adedeji
Top Scorer: Danny Carroll

Hayes Lane, Bromley, Kent BR2 9EF
Tel: 0181 460 5291 or 0181 313 3992

**Directions**: One mile from Bromley South (BR). Buses 316, 146 and 119 pass ground.
Junction 4 off M25, then A21 towards London
Capacity: 5,000    Cover: 2,500    Seats: 1,300    Floodlights: Yes
**Clubhouse**: Open matchdays. Food available
**Club Shop**: Yes. contact Jim Brown

**BROMLEY FOOTBALL CLUB**
RYMAN FOOTBALL LEAGUE – PREMIER DIVISION
1998-99
OFFICIAL MATCHDAY PROGRAMME
PRICE £1.20

**Ryman**

MAIN SPONSOR: THORNE MARKETING

Pages: 32  Price: £1.20
Editor: John Self (0181 402 2391)

Local Press: Bromley Times
Local Radio: Radio Kent,
Bromley Local Radio

---

**PREVIOUS**  **Leagues:** South London - 1894; Southern 94-96; London 96-98 99-1901; West Kent 01-04; Southern Suburban 04-07; Kent 1898-99, 11-14; Spartan 07-08; Isthmian 08-11; Athenian 19-52
**Grounds:** White Hart Field Cricket Ground, Widmore Rd (pre-1904); Plaistow Cricket Field 1904-37; Hayes Lane 06-37
**RECORDS**  **Attendance:** 12,000 v Nigeria, 1950
**Goalscorer:** George Brown 570 (1938-61)  **Appearances:** George Brown
**Win:** 12-1 v Chertsey FA Cup 75  **Defeat:** 1-11 v Cray Wands 33
**Fee Paid:** Unknown  **Fee Received:** £50,000 for Jon Goodman (from Millwall 90)
**BEST SEASON**  **FA Amateur Cup:** Winners 10-11, 37-38, 48-49
**FA Trophy:** Second Round 91-92  **FA Cup:** 2nd Rd replay v Scarborough 37-38, Lincoln 38-39, Watford 45-46
**HONOURS:**  Isthmian League(4) 08-10 53-54 60-61 (R-up 52-53 55-56 87-88), Div 1 R-up 79-80 5-86 90-91, Prince Phillip 5-a-side Cup 1979; Athenian League 22-23 48-49 50-51 (R-up 35-36); London League Div 2 1896-97; Spartan League 07-08; London Snr Cup 09-10 45-46 50-51; Kent Senior Cup 49-50 76-77 91-92 96-97; Kent AmateurCup (12) 07-08 31-32 35-37 38-39 46-47 48-49 50-51 52-53 53-55 59-60; LondonChallenge Cup 1995-96.
Players progressing:  Roy Merryfield (Chelsea), Stan Charlton (Arsenal 52), RonHeckman (Orient 55), John Gregory (West Ham 51), Bill Lloyd (Millwall 56), Brian Kinsey (Charlton 56), Harold Hobbs (Charlton & England), Matt Carmichael (Lincoln 90), Leslie Locke (QPR 56), Jon Goodman (Millwall 90), Dean Wordsworth (Crystal Palace 97), Landry Zahana-ONI (Luton Town 98)

*Back Row (L-R): George Wakeling (Manager), James Gardner, Ollie Adedeji, Kevin Allen, Keith Sharman, Dave Wietecha, Dean Wordsworth, Danny Carroll, David Gray, Ian Rawlings, Lahdry Zahha-Oni, John Kane (Coach)*
*Front Row: Tony Russell, Shane Samways, Marcel Dennis, Dave Stevens, Dean Francis, Ashley Kenton, John De Palma (Physio)*
*Photo: Kerry Phillips*

# CHERTSEY TOWN

## CLUB OFFICIALS

Chairman: **Nick Keel**
President: **Cllr Chris Norman**
Vice Chairman: **Sav Ramayon**
Press Officer/Secretary: **Chris Gay**
23 Richmond Close, Frimley,
Camberley,Surrey GU16 5NR
Tel: 01276 20745

## FOOTBALL MANAGEMENT TEAM
Manager: Colin Payne
Asst Manager: Roger Goodhind
Coach: Steve Stairs
Physio: Dave Rushmer

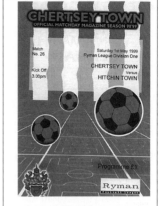

**FACT FILE**

Formed: 1890
Nickname: Curfews
Sponsors: TBA
Colours: Blue & white stripes/white/white
Change colours: All red
Midweek Matchday: Tuesday

1998-99 Captain: Fergus Moore
P.o.Y.: Keith Cooper
Top Scorer: Neil Selley

**GROUND**      Alwyns Lane, Chertsey, Surrey KT16 9DW Tel: 01932 561774

**Directions:** Alwyns Lane is off Windsor Street at north end of shopping centre.
10 mins walk from Chertsey (BR). London Country bus
Capacity: 3,000          Seats: 250          Cover: 1000          Floodlights: Yes

**Clubhouse:** Open weekday evenings and weekend lunchtimes
**Club Shop:** Open matchdays, selling club & football souvenirs. Contact SteveMaughan

Pages: 36 Price: £1
Editor: Chris Gay (01276 20745)
Local Press: Surrey Herald
Local Radio: BBC Southern Counties,
County Sound

**PREVIOUS**      **Leagues:** West Surrey (pre-1899); Surrey Jnr 1899-1920; Surrey Intermediate 20-46; Surrey Snr 46-63; Metropolitan 63-66;
Gtr London 66-67; Spartan 67-75;London Spartan 75-76; Athenian 76-84; Isthmian 84-85; Combined Counties 85-86.
**Grounds:** The Grange (pre-World War 1), The Hollows (pre-1929)

**CLUB RECORDS**   **Attendance:** 2,150 v Aldershot, Isthmian Lge Div. 2 4/12/93
**Goalscorer:** Alan Brown 54, 1962-63
**Win:** 10-1 v Clapton (H), Isthmian Lge Div. 3, 91-92      **Defeat:** 1-12 v Bromley (H), FA Cup Preliminary Rd, 82-83
**Transfer fee received:** £67,500. Paid: Nil

**BEST SEASON**   **FA Vase:** Quarter Final 87-88 91-92      **FA Cup:** 3rd Qual. Rd 92-93, 1-3 v Kingstonian (H)
**FA Trophy:** 2nd Qual Rd 95-96      **FA Amateur Cup:** 3rd Qual Rd 61-62

**HONOURS**      Isthmian Lge Cup 94-95 (Associate Members Trophy 94-95), Div 2 R-up 94-95, Div3 R-up 91-92; Surrey Snr Lge 59-60 61-62
62-63 (Lge Cup 59-60 61-62); CombinedCo's Lge R-up 85-86 (Concours Tphy 85-86); Surrey Snr Cup R-up 85-86;
SpartanLge & Lge Cup R-up 74-75

Players progressing: Rachid Harkouk (Crystal Palace), Peter Cawley (Wimbledon1987), Lee Charles (Q.P.R. 1995)

*Back Row: Steve Stairs, Roger Goodhind, Tony Lynch, Warren Bayliss, Colin Payne, Richard Evans, Graham Benstead, Kiron*
*Philpot, Carl Fergus Moore, Junior Harvey, Dave Rushmer (Physio)*
*Front: Rob Peters, Martin Carter, Neal Bartlett, Keith Cooper, Niel Selby, Jason Shaw, Richard McDonagh.  Photo: Andrew Chitty*

# CROYDON

## CLUB OFFICIALS

Chairman: **Ken Jarvie**
Secretary: **Mrs Jacqueline Jarvie**
2 Spa Close, London SE25 6DS
Tel: 0181 653 7250(H), 0181 654 8555 (B)
Press Officer: **Russell Chandler**
26 Dartnell Rd, Croydon, Surrey. CR0 6JA
Tel: 0181 406 4573 (H) 0181 654 8555 (B)
Match Secretary: **Gordon Tennant**

## FOOTBALL MANAGEMENT TEAM

Manager: Ken Jarvie
Coach: John Finch
Physio: Ian Fairs

## FACT FILE

Formed: 1953
Sponsors:Bass Brewers
Colours: Sky & navy quarters/navy &
sky/navy & sky
Change colours: All red
Midweek home matchday: Wednesday
Reserve Team's League: Suburban
1998-99 Captain: Ali Reeve
P.o.Y.: Ben JUdge Top Scorer: Jason Brown

**GROUND**     Croydon Sports Arena, Albert Road, South Norwood. London. SE25 4QL
                                             Tel: 0181 6543462/8555
**Directions:** Train to East Croydon or Norwood Junction, then bus 12 to eitherBelmont or
Dundee Road. Walk down either - ground at bottom. 5 mins walk fromWoodside (BR)
**Capacity:** 8,000          Cover: 450        Seats: 450        Floodlights: Yes
**Clubhouse:** Open every evening and lunchtime, holds 250, snacks available
               Dancing, discos, bingo. Lounge bar available for private hire
**Club Shop:** Yes

Programme:
Pages: 28 Price: £1.00
Editor: Russell Chandler (0181 406 4573 H)

Local Press: Croydon - Advertiser,
Midweek Post, Times, Guardian

**PREVIOUS**     **Leagues:** Surrey Senior 53-63; Spartan 63-64; Athenian 64-74
                 **Name:** Croydon Amateurs 1953-74

**CLUB RECORDS** **Attendance:** 1,450 v Wycombe, FA Cup 4th Qualifying Rd 1975
                 **Career appearances:** Alec Jackson (400+)
                 **Transfer fee paid:** Steve Brown
                 **Transfer fee received:** Peter Evans (to Sutton Utd)

**BEST SEASON**  **FA Cup:** 2nd Round replay 79-80, 2-3 v Millwall after 1-1
                 **FA Trophy:** 2nd Round 81-82, 82-83
                 **FA Amateur Cup:** 3rd round 71-72

**HONOURS**      Isthmian Lg Div 2 R-up 75-76 95-96, Surrey Snr Cup 81-82 (R-up 76-77), Surrey Prem Cup 86-87, Spartan Lg 63-64,
                 Athenian Lg R-up 71-72 (Div 2 65-66 (R-up 70-71)), Surrey Snr Lg R-up 56-57 60-61 62-63 (Lg Cup 60-61, Charity Cup 53-54
                 62-63, Res Section 57-58), London Senior Cup R-up 78-79, Suburban Lg South 86-87(Lg Cup(2)), Southern Yth Lg 85-86 (Lg
                 Cup 85-86 87-88), Berger Yth Cup 78-79, Southern Youth League Cup  96-97

Players progressing: Alan Barnett (Plymouth
1955), Peter Bonetti (Chelsea), Leroy Ambrose
(Charlton 1979), Steve Milton (Fulham - via
Whyteleafe), Murray Jones (Crystal Pal. - via
Carshalton)

*Croydon's Jason Brown (11) and
Ryan Rummery combine to keep out
Worthing's Mark Burt
Photo: Alan Coomes*

# GRAYS ATHLETIC

## CLUB OFFICIALS

Chairman: **Frank Harris**
Secretary: **Jeff Saxton**
216 Thundersley Park Road,
South Benfleet, Essex SS71HP
Tel: 01268 756964
Press Officer: **Gordon Norman**
Tel: 014024 51733

## FOOTBALL MANAGEMENT TEAM
Manager: Chris Snowsill
Asst Man.:Lee Malcolm
Physio: David Guthrie

### FACT FILE

Formed: 1890
Nickname: The Blues
Sponsors: Harris Commercials
Colours: Royal & white
Change colours: Red/white
Midweek matchday: Tuesday

1998-99 Captain: Steve Mosely
P.o.Y.:Steve Mosely
Top Scorer: Vinny John

**Grays Athletic Football Club**

The Ryman Football League
Division One
Season 1998/99

**Ryman**
football league

Main sponsors:
Roehlig & Co (UK) Ltd
Harris Group of Companies
Coutts Advertising

**GROUND**    Recreation Ground, Bridge Road, Grays RM17 6BZ (01375 391649)
**Directions:** Seven minutes walk from Grays station - turn right round one way system, right into Clarence Road, and at end into Bridge Road. Bus No. 370. By road - A13 towards Southend from London, take Grays exit and follow signs to town centre, keep left on one-way system, continue up hill for about 1/2 mile, turn right into Bridge Road, ground 1/2 mile on right
Capacity: 4,500        Cover: 1,200        Seats: 300        Floodlights: Yes
**Clubhouse:** Bar, pool, darts, bar snacks available. Indoor sports hall.
Stewardess: Sue Riley (01375 377753)
**Club Shop:** Sells `The First Hundred Years', sweaters, T-shirts, replica shirts, scarves, ties, etc.
Contact Bill Grove  01375 391649

Pages: 48 Price: £1
Editor: Jeremy Mason (01375 400188)

Local Press: Thurrock Gazette
Local Radio: BBC Essex, Radio Essex

**PREVIOUS**    **Leagues:** Athenian 12-14, 58-83; London 14-24, 26-39; Kent 24-26; Corinthian 45-58

**CLUB RECORDS** **Attendance:** 9,500 v Chelmsford City, FA Cup 4th Qual. Round 1959
**Win:** 12-0 v Tooting (H) London Lge 24/2/23    **Defeat:** 0-12 v Enfield (A) Athenian Lge 20/4/63
**Goalscorer:** Harry Brand 269 (1944-52)    **Appearances:** Phil Sammons, 673. 1982-97
**Fee Paid:** For Ian Durant (Canvey Island 85)
**Fee Received:** Undisclosed for Tony Witter (C. Palace), Dwight Marshall(Plymouth 1991) and Matthew Lawrence(Wycombe W)

**BEST SEASON**    **FA Cup:** 1st Rd 51-52 88-89        **FA Trophy:** 3rd Rd 92-93    **FA Amateur Cup:** 3rd Rd 63-64

**HONOURS**    Isthmian Div 1 R-up 87-88 (Div 2 Sth 84-85, Lg Cup 91-92); Athenian Lg R-up 82-83, Res. Sect. R-up 58-59 (Cup R-up 59-60); Corinthian Lg 45-46 (R-up 51-52 54-55 56-57), Lg Cup(2) 45-47, Mem. Shield(4) ; Essex Snr Cup 4 (R-up 6); Essex SenTr 98-99; East Anglian Cup 44-45 (R-up 43-44 54-55); Essex Thameside Tphy x6 (R-up 7); Essex Elizabeth Tphy 76-77 (R-up 65-66); Claridge Tphy 87-88 88-89; Mithras Cup 79-80; Essex Int Cup(3) 56-57 58-60 (Jun Cup 19-20 (R-up 58-59); Essex & Herts Border Comb. East 87-88 (Ancillary Cup 78-79, Comb Cup 82-83); Fred Budden Tphy 86-87; Hornchurch Charity Cup 78-79 86-87; Neale Tphy 50-51; Ford Rate Tphy 83-84 85-86 87-88 (R-up 84-85 86-87); Stan Veness Mem. Tphy (8) 87-96

Players progressing: J Jordan (Spurs 47), R Kemp (Reading 49), B Silkman & TBanfield (Orient), G O'Reilly (Spurs), W Entwhistle (Bury 83), M Welch(Wimbledon 84), T Witter (C Palace 90), D Marshall (Plymouth 91), M Lawrence(Wycombe W. 96-97)

*Back Row (L-R): Jamie Wallace, Rikky Hazle, Paul Schneider, Ian Brooks, Ray Taylor, Vinny John (Captain), Danny Snowsill, Robbie McCarthy*
*Front: Steve Dickinson, Danny Hayzelden, Steve Mosely (Coach), Graham Daly, Danny Pridige, Lee Double*

# HARLOW TOWN

### CLUB OFFICIALS

Chairman: **Jeff Bothwell**
Press Officer: **Gavin McWilliams**
Tel: 01279 441894
Secretary: **Graeme Auger**
58 Braziers Quay, South St, Bishops
Stortford, Herts CM23 3YW
Tel: 020 7890 4195 (H)   01279 465998 (W)

**FOOTBALL MANAGEMENT TEAM**
Manager: Eddie McCluskey
Asst. Manager: Fred Donnelly
Physio: Malcolm Roddy

**FACT FILE**
Founded: 1879
Nickname: Hawks
Sponsors: BritSec Int. Ltd
Colours: Red & white/white/white
Change: White & yellow/yellow/yellow
Midweek matches: Wednesday
Reserves' Lge: Essex & Herts Border Comb

96-97 - Captain: Dennis Greene
P.O.Y.: Neil Moore
Top Scorer: Dennis Greene

SEASON 1998-99
**TAUNTON TOWN**
F.A.Carlsberg Vase
Fourth Round
Saturday 9th January 1999.
kick off 3.00 pm.
Official Programme £1

32 pages 70p
Editor: Phil Tuson (01279 416743)
Local Press: Harlow Citizen, Harlow Star,
Harlow Herald & Post
Local Radio: Essex Radio, BBC Essex, Ten 17

**GROUND**
Harlow Sports Centre, Hammarskjold Rd, Harlow CM20 2JF
Tel: 01279 445319

**Directions:** Near town centre, 10 mins walk from Harlow (BR) station
**Capacity:** 10,000      Cover: 500      Seats: 400      Floodlights: Yes
**Club Shop:** Yes
**Clubhouse:** Open daily 11-11 (10.30 Sundays). Hot & cold food available

**PREVIOUS**   **Leagues:** East Herts (pre-1932); Spartan 32-39 46-54; London 54-61; Delphian 61-63; Athenian 63-73;
Isthmian 73-92; inactive 92-93   **Grounds:** Marigolds 1919-22; Green Man Field 22-60

**CLUB RECORDS**   **A ttendance:** 9,723 v Leicester, FA Cup 3rd Rd replay 8/1/80
**Goalscorer:** Jeff Wood (45 in 88-89)   **Appearances:** Norman Gladwin 646 (1949-70)
**Win:** 12-0 v Hertford Ath. (H), E. Herts Lge 5/10/29   **Defeat:** 0-11 v Ware (A), Spartan Lge Div. One (East) 6/3/48

**BEST SEASON**   **FA Amateur Cup:** 2nd Rd 72-73      **FA Trophy:** 2nd Rd(2) 80-82      **FA Vase:** 3rd Rd 88-89
**FA Cup:** 4th Rd 79-80 (lost 3-4 at Watford). Also 1st Rd 80-81 81-82
League clubs defeated: Southend, Leicester 79-80

**HONOURS**   Isthmian Lg Div 1 78-79 (R-up 82-83, Div 2 Nth 88-89, Yth Cup 77-78), Ath'n LgDiv 1 71-72, E Angl. Cup 89-90, Knight F'lit
Cup R-up 87-88, Essex Snr Cup 78-79, Essex F'lit Competition R-up 71-72, London Lg Chal. Cup 59-60, Spartan LgCup 52-
53, Epping Hosp. Cup (3) 46-49, Essex & Herts Border Comb Cup 75-76, Fred Budden Trophy 88-89 89-90,
Chelmsford Yth Lg 86-87 (Lg Cup 86-87 87-88))

Players progressing: Jeff Wood (Charlton 75), Neil Prosser (B'mouth 80)

*Harlow midfielder Roy Parkyn: "That's the hop, skip and jump bit, but what am I supposed to do with this ball stuck on the end of my foot?!"*

# LEATHERHEAD

### CLUB OFFICIALS
Chairman: **David Zackheim**
President: **Gerald Darby**
General Manager: **Keith Wenham** (at club)
Secretary: **Gerald Darby**
Ranmore, Harriots Lane, Ashtead,
Surrey, KT21 2QG
Press Office/Comm. Director: **Keith Wenham**

### FOOTBALL MANAGEMENT TEAM
Manager: Tommy Warrilow
Asst. Manager: Gary Richards
Youth Team Manager: Alex Inglethorpe
Physio: Steve Young

### FACT FILE
Founded: 1946
Nickname: Tanners
Sponsors: The Beer Seller
Colours: Green and White
Change colours: Blue & white
Midweek Matchday: Tuesday

**GROUND** Fetcham Grove, Guildford Rd, Leatherhead, Surrey KT22 9AS
Tel: 01372 360151, Fax: 01372 362705
**Directions:** M25 jct 9 to Leatherhead; follow signs to Leisure Centre, ground adjacent. Half
mile from Leatherhead (BR)
London Country Buses 479 and 408 - ground opposite bus garage
Capacity: 3,400          Seats: 200          Cover: 445          Floodlights: Yes
**Clubhouse:** (01372 360151) Bar open 12-11pm matchdays. Full catering.
**Club Shop:** Yes. 01372 362705

Programme:
Pages: 24 Price: £1
Edito: Robert Wooldridge (0181 669 3824)
Local Press: Leatherhead Advertiser,
Surrey Advertiser
Local Radio: County Sound

**PREVIOUS**    **Leagues:** Surrey Snr 46-50; Metropolitan 50-51; Delphian 51-58; Corinthian 58-63; Athenian 63-72
**Names:** None          **Grounds:** None

**CLUB RECORDS**    **Attendance:** 5,500 v Wimbledon, 1976
**Win:** 13-1 v Leyland Motors 46-47 Surrey Sen Lge          **Defeat:** 1-11 v Sutton United
**Career goalscorer:** Steve Lunn 96-97 (46)          **Career appearances:** P Caswell
**Fee paid:** £1,500 to Croydon (B Salkeld)          **Fee received:** £1,500 from Croydon (B Salkeld)

**BEST SEASON**    **FA Amateur Cup:** Semi finalists 70-71 73-74          **FA Trophy:** Runners-up 77-78
**F A Cup:** 4th Round 74-75, 2-3 v Leicester C.(A). Also 2nd Rd 75-76 76-77 78-79,1st Rd 77-78 80-81
League clubs defeated: Colchester, Brighton 74-75, Cambridge Utd 75-76,Northampton 76-77

**HONOURS**    FA Trophy R-up 77-78; Isthmian Lg Cup 77-78; Corinthian Lg 62-63; Athenian Lg Div 1 63-64;
Surrey Snr Cup 68-69 (R-up 64-65 66-67 74-75 78-79); Surrey Snr Lg 46-47 47-48 48-49 49-50(Lg Cup 49-50),
Snr Shield 68-69, Charity Cup 46-47 49-50); E. Surrey Charity Cup 68-69 (R-up 67-68); London Snr Cup R-up 74-75 77-78;
Surrey Inter Cup 89-90; Southern Comb. Cup 89-90

Players progressing: Chris Kelly (Millwall), B Friend (Fulham), L Harwood (Port Vale), John Humphrey (Millwall)

*Ray Arnott of Leatherhead (Green & White) beats Michael Murphy of Windsor & Eton to the ball.*    Photo: Tim Edwards

# LEYTON PENNANT

## CLUB OFFICIALS

Chairman: **Dave Crabb**
Vice-Chairman: **Dave Salmon**
President: **George Cross**
Secretary: **Andy Perkins**, 4 Chestnut Drive,
Wanstead, London E11 2TA,
Tel: 0181 530 4551
Web site: www.btinternet.com/~andy.perkins
Gen. Manager: **Kevin Moran**
Press Officer: **Andy Perkins**

### FOOTBALL MANAGEMENT TEAM

Team Manager/Coach:Lindon Lynch
Physio: Christie Keene

**FACT FILE**

Formed: 1868
Nickname: Lilywhites
Sponsors: Kay Sports
Colours: White/navy/navy
Change colours: All navy
Midweek home matchday: Tuesday
Reserves' Lge: Essex & Herts Border Comb

1998-99 Caotain: Paul Salmon
P.o.Y.: Billy Read
Top Scorer: Billy Read

**1998 - 1999**
**S E A S O N**
Official Match Day Programme

**£1**

**GROUND**    Wadham Lodge Sports Ground, Kitchener Rd, Walthamstow, London. E17 4JP
Tel: 0181 527 2444

**Directions:**    North Circular Road to Crooked Billet,turn into Chingford Road,then into Brookscroft Road, first on left. Walthamstow Central (Victoria Line tube) one mile away, then buses W21 or 256

Capacity: 2,000        Cover: 600        Seats: 200        Floodlights: Yes

**Clubhouse:** (0181 527 2444). Open 11-11 Mon-Sat, 12-3 & 7-10.30 Sun. No hot food.
Hot snacks from tea bar on matchdays

**Club Shop:** Sells programmes, pennants, scarves, badges etc. Contact Ian Ansell c/o the club

Pages: 32 Price: £1
Editor: John Stacey (0181 527 8116)
Local Press: Waltham Forest Guardian,
Hackney Gazette
Local Radio: LBC

**PREVIOUS**    **Name:** Leyton FC, Leyton Wingate (75-92), Walthamstow Pennant (64-92)
**Leagues:** Leyton & Dist. Alliance, South Essex, Southern 05-11, London 20-26, Athenian 27-82, Spartan (Walthamstow Pennant)
**Grounds:** Brisbane Rd (Home of Leyton Orient), Hare & Hounds Leabridge Road
**CLUB RECORDS**    **Attendance:** 676 v Aldershot, Isthmian Lge 10/2/96
(100,000 saw Leyton v Walthamstow Ave., FA Amateur Cup final at Wembley, April 26th 1952)
**Win:** 10-2 v Horsham 1982                **Defeat:** 1-11 v Barnet 1946
**Transfer fee paid:** £200 for Dwight Marshall (Hampton)    **Transfer fee received:** £6,000 for T Williams (Redbridge Forest)
**Career goalscorer:** Steve Lane 118        **Career appearances:** Steve Hamberger 387
**BEST SEASON**    **FA Amateur Cup:** Winners 26-27 27-28, R-up x6    **FA Vase:** Sixth Rd 83-84
**FA Cup:** 3rd Rd 09-10 League clubs defeated: None    **FA Trophy:** 3rd Rd 86-87
**HONOURS**    Isthmian Lg Div 1 R-up 86-87 (Div 2 North 84-85); Essex Snr Tphy R-up 84-85; National Floodlight Cup 84-85; London Sen.
Cup 03-04 (R-up 33-3437-38 45-46); London Charity Cup 34-35 36-37 R-up (4) London Lg 23-24 24-25 25-26 (R-up 26-27), Lg Cup 56-57; Athenian
Lg 28-29 65-6666-67 76-77 81-82 ,R-up (3), Div 2 Cup R-up 69-70; LondonChall. Cup R-up 09-10 27-28 95-96; East Anglian Cup R-up 45-46 72-73;
Essex Thameside Trophy 64-65 66-67 81-2 (R-up 63-64); Leyton & Dist. All 1892-93 94-95; Eastern Floodlight Comp 97-98
Players progressing: C Buchan (Sunderland 10), Casey (Chelsea 52), K Facey (Orient 52), M Costello (Aldershot 56), D Clark (Orient 61)
D Marshall (Luton)

*Leyton Pennant FC - Winners Eastern Floodlight Competition 1998-99*

# MAIDENHEAD UNITED

## FACT FILE

Formed: 1870
Nickname: Magpies
Sponsors: Trademark Windows
Colours: Black & white stripes/black/black
Change colours: Red/white/white
Midweek matchday: Tuesday
Reserve League: Suburban
Local Press: Maidenhead Advertiser,
Reading Evening Post, Slough Observer
Local Radio: 2-Ten FM, Star FM,
Thames Valley FM

**CLUB OFFICIALS**

Chairman: **Roger Coombs**
Vice Chairman: **Jon Swan**

Secretary: **Ken Chandler**
c/o Maidenhead United

Press Off .: **Jon Swan** (01628 473411)

**FOOTBALL MANAGEMENT TEAM**
Manager: Alan Devonshire
Asst. Mgr./Coach: Carl Taylor
Physio: Jon Urry

**GROUND**    York Road, Maidenhead, Berks SL6 1SQ Tel: 01628 624739/636314

**Directions:** From Maidenhead BR station proceed eastwards down Bell St - grd 300yds.
Ground in Town Centre five minutes from M4
Capacity: 3,500        Cover: 1,200      Seats: 400        Floodlights: Yes
Clubhouse: Open evenings & matchdays. Some hot food
Club Shop: Wide range of programmes and club souvenirs.
Contact Mark Smith (01753 854674)

**PROGRAMME**
Pages: 36 Price: £1
Editor: J Swan/R Jackson
Tel: 01344 723750

**PREVIOUS**    **Leagues:** Southern 1894-1902; West Berks 02-04; Grt West Sub 04-22; Spartan 22-39; Grt West Comb 39-45;
Corinthian 45-63; Athenian 63-73
**Names:** Maidenhead FC, Maidenhead Norfolkians. **Grounds:** None
**CLUB RECORDS** **Attendance:** 7,920 v Southall, FA Amat Cup Q/F 7/3/36        **Season's goalscorer:** Jack Palethorpe 66, 1929-30
**Career appearances:** Bert Randall 532, 1950-64        **Career goalscorer:** George Copas 270, 1924-35
**Win:** 14-1 v Buckingham Town (H), FA Amat. Cup 6/9/52        **Defeat:** 0-14 v Chesham United (A), Spartan Lge 31/3/23
**Transfer fee paid:** Undisclosed        **Transfer fee received:** £5,000 from Norwich for Alan Cordice, 79
**BEST SEASON**    **FA Cup:** Qtr Finals 1873-74 74-75 75-76        **F A Trophy:** 3rd Qual Rd        **FA Amateur Cup:** Semi Final 35-36
**HONOURS**    Isthmian Lg Div 2 Sth R-up 90-91, Full Members Cup 96-97; Spartan Lg x3 R-upx2; Corinthian Lg 57-58 60-61 61-62 R-up 58-
59 59-60, Mem. Shield 56-57 61-62,R-up x4, Neale Cup 48-49 57-58 60-61; Gt Western Suburban Lg 19-20 R-up 20-21;
**Berks**    & Bucks Snr Cup x17, Berks & Bucks Benev. Cup x6 R-up x2; Mithras Cup R-up x4; Southern Comb. Cup R-up 81-82; Sub
Lge West 97-98; Allied Counties Champ 97-98
Players progressing: A Cordice (Norwich 79), P Priddy (Brentford 72), D Kemp (Plymouth), L Sanchez (Reading),
E Kelsey, J Palethorpe (Reading 30), B Laryea(Torquay), R Davies (Torquay)

L-R Back Row: D Harrison, M Banton, J Pritchard, M Bolger, T Cook, T Roffey, L Evans, V Pratt, P Terry, C Prempeh.
Front Row: S Brown, G Mernagh, T Houston, M Creighton, A Robertson, O Ulasi, A Eaton, B Connor.        Photo: Eric Marsh

# OXFORD CITY

## CLUB OFFICIALS

Chairman: **M Woodley**
President:
Vice Chairman: **R Holt**

Press Officer/Secretary: **John Shepperd**
20 Howe Close, Wheatley, Oxford OX33 1SS
Tel: 01865 872181 (& Fax)

### FOOTBALL MANAGEMENT TEAM
Manager: Paul Lee
Asst Manager:
Physio: C.Perkins

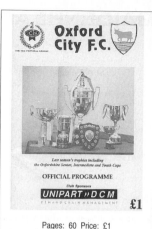

**FACT FILE**

Formed: 1882
Nickname: City
Sponsors: Unipart D.C.M
Colours: Blue & white hoops/blue/blue
Change colours: yellow,black,black
Midweek Matchday: Tuesday
Reserve's League: Suburban Lge Prem Div
1998-99 Captain Andy Walllbridge
Top Scorer: Ian Concannon
P.o.Y.: Julian Dark

*Last season's trophies including*
*the Oxfordshire Senior, Intermediate and Youth Cups*

**OFFICIAL PROGRAMME**

*Club Sponsors*

**UNIPART ▷ D C M**
DEMAND CHAIN MANAGEMENT

**£1**

Pages: 60  Price: £1
Editor: Laurie Simmons
Local Press: Oxford Mail
Local Radio: Thames Valley FM, Fox FM

**GROUND**  Court Place Farm, Marsh Lane, Marston, Oxford. OX3 0NQ.
Tel: 01865 744493.01865 742394 (Clubhouse)

**Directions:** From London M40/A40, ring-road to North, take 1st slip road, follow signs to John Radcliffe hospital and Court Place Farm Stadium, ground on left after leaving flyover. From the north same ring-road.
Capacity: 3,000  Seats: 300  Cover: 400  Floodlights: Yes
Clubhouse: Open matchdays, most refreshments available
Club Shop: Yes, open matchdays, selling souvenirs. Contact Paul Cotterell

**PREVIOUS**   **Leagues:** Isthmian 07-88; South Midlands 90-93
**Grounds:** The White House 1882-1988; Cuttleslowe Pk 90-91; Pressed Steel,Romanway 91-93

**CLUB RECORDS**  **Attendance:** 9,500 v Leytonstone, FA Amateur Cup 50
**Win:** 9-0 v Harlow Town, Isthmian League 9/10/76
**Defeat:** 0-8 v Wycombe Wanderers, Isthmian League - date unknown
**Scorer:** John Woodley  **Appearances:** John Woodley
**Fee Paid:** £3,000 for S Adams (Woking)  **Fee Received:** £17,500 for Howard Forinton (Yeovil T. 1.97)

**BEST SEASON**  **FA Amateur Cup:** Winners 05-06 Runners-up 02-03 12-13  **FA Vase:** Runners-up 94-95
**FA Cup:** Second Round 69-70, 1-5 v Swansea City (H)  **FA Trophy:** 1st Rd Prop 96 v Merthyr Tydfil

**HONOURS**  FA Amateur Cup 05-06 (R-up 02-03 12-13); F.A.Vase R-up 94-95; Isthmian Lg R-up 34-35 45-46, Div 1 95-96 R-up 77-78
South MidlandsLg 92-93; Oxon Senior Cup - 27 times

Players progressing: A Blakeman (Brentford 46), C Holton (Arsenal 50), K Savin(Derby 50), R Adams (Blackpool 48), A Jeffries (Brentford 49), P James (Luton49), D Gordon/E Wilcox (WBA 47/48), V Mobley (Sheffield Wed 63), J Varney (Hull50), P Lee (Hereford 73), H Poole (Port Vale 55), G Parker (Luton 81), M Keown(Arsenal 84), D Meeson (Wolves 52)

Back Row: Paul Lee (manager), Kelvin Alexis (asst. man.), Danny Sewell, Nigel Emsden, Andy Cooper, Andy Wallbridge, Justin Lee, Andy Smith, Matt Hayward, Matty Whitehead, Mark Jones, Chris Perkins (physio). Front Row: Dwaine Strong, Julian Dark, Ian Concannon, Chris Ferdinand, Matty Gooderick, Danny Wise, Gary Smart, Chris Fontaine.
Photo: Tony Bailey

# ROMFORD

## CLUB OFFICIALS

Life President: **Ron Walker**
Chairman: **Mark Corr**

Vice-Chairman: **Steve Gardener**
Secretary:**Derek Robinson**Tel: 01708
726893
Press Officer: **Steve Gardener**
Ken Horne **John Barrington**

### FOOTBALL MANAGEMENT TEAM

Team Manager: Alan Levitt
Physios: Don Calder & Alan Hyde

### FACT FILE
Reformed: 1992
Nickname: The Boro
Sponsors: TBA
Colours: Blue & old gold/blue/blue
Change colours: Red & black/black/black
Midweek home matchday: Tuesday (7.45)
Reserves' League: Essex & Herts Border Prem
Club Call: 0930 555 841
1998-99: Captain & P.o.Y.: Kevin Marsden
Top Scorer: Trevor Paul ( 23)

Pages: 40 Price: £1.20
Editor: David RobinsonTel: 01708 726893
Local Press: Romford Recorder
Local Radio:Active FM

**GROUND** `Sungate', Collier Row Road, Collier Row, Romford, Essex. Tel: 01708 722766

**Directions:** Take the A12 from London as far as the Moby Dick junction. Turn left and then right at the 1st roundabout into Collier Row Road. The ground entrance is signposted 200 yards on the right. Nearest station is Romford (BR). From directly outside the station the London bus 247 passes within 50 yards of the ground

Capacity: 2,500     Cover: 300     Seats: 175     Floodlights: Yes

**Clubhouse:** Open seven days a week 11am - 11pm
**Club Shop:** Open matchdays, selling replica shirts, programmes etc.
Contact Barry Quantrill 01708 705755

**PREVIOUS**     **Names:** Romford FC, formed 1876, folded in the Great War. Reformed 1929 until78. Restarted 1992 & in 96 merged with Collier Row - both names being used for that season only. Name changed to Romford 1997
**Leagues:** Essex Senior 92-96     **Grounds:** Hornchurch 92-95, Ford United 95-96

**CLUB RECORDS Attendance:** 820 v Leatherhead (IL2) 15/4/97
**Career Goalscorer:** Micky Ross 57     **Season goalscorer:** Vinny John 45 (97-98)
**Career Appearances:** Danny Benstock 197
**Win:** 9-0 v Hullbridge (H) ESL 21/10/95     **Defeat:** 1-7 v St Albans (A) EAC 29/10/96
**Transfer fee paid:** £1,500 for Wade Falana (Braintree) June 97 **Transfer fee received:** £4,000 for Vinny John from Grays Ath.

**BEST SEASON**     **FA Cup:** 4th Qual Rd 97-98 v Bromsgrove Rovers (A)
**FA Vase:** 5th Rd 96-97 v Bedlington Terriers 2-1
**FA Trophy:** 2nd Round v Worthing 98-99

**HONOURS**     Essex Senior Lge Champ 95-96, Lge Cup 95-96; Isthmian Div 2 Champ 96-97; East Anglian Cup 97-98

L-R - Back Row: George Eastman (physio), Richie Blake, Gavin Axcell, Kevin Marsden, Lee Smith, Stuart Horne, Ross Risley, John Ray, Billy Hudson, Danny Swaile, John Goodwin (Chairman). Front Row: Carl Fannon, Trevor Paul, Danny Benstock, Steve Wheeler (manager), Bradley Quinton,Chris Magloire, John Doyle. Mascot Jordan Roberts.

# STAINES TOWN

## CLUB OFFICIALS

Chairman: **Alan Boon**
President: **Nigel Iggulden**
Vice Chairman: **Ken Williams**
Secretary: **Steve Parsons**
3 Birch Green, Staines, Middx TW18 4HA Tel: 01784 450420
Commercial Mgr: **Ken Williams**
Press Officer: **Stuart Moore** (01784 421118)

### FOOTBALL MANAGEMENT TEAM

Manager: Ken Ballardr
Asst Manager: Danny Pipe
Physio: Mick Minter/Jug Stephen

### FACT FILE

Formed: 1892
Nickname: The Swans
Sponsors: Courage
Colours: Old gold (blue trim)/royal/royal
Change colours: All white
Midweek matchday: Tuesday
Reserve league: Suburban (since 72)

1998-99
Capt: Mark Fleming
P.o.Y: Mark Costello
Top Scorer: Mark Butler (14)

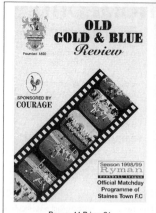

**OLD GOLD & BLUE** *Review*

Founded 1892

SPONSORED BY
**COURAGE**

Season 1998/99
**Ryman**
Football League
Official Matchday
Programme of
Staines Town F.C

**GROUND** Wheatsheaf Park, Wheatsheafe Lane, Staines, Middlesex TW18 2PD (01784 455988)
**Directions:** M25 Jct13 to A30 Staines by-pass to Crooked Billet roundabout. Take town centre exit(A308) and left into South St, at iron bridge. Pass bus staion and bear left into Laleham Rd. Wheatsheafe Lane is 1km on right Buses 481,570,and 573 pass Wheatsheaf Lane.
**Capacity:** 2,500 **Cover:** 850 **Seats:** 250 **Floodlights:** Yes **Food:** Rolls and snacks available
**Club HQ** & Clubhouse: Staines Town FC, Wheatsheaf Lane, Staines (01784 455988).
Fully furnished clubhouse & function hall, open 7-11 matchdays and every evening.s
Rolls and other snacks available Club Shop: Souvenirs available from
Harry Trim, 23 Grosvenor Rd, Staines, Middx TW18 2RN

Pages: 44 Price: £1
Editor: Sec. & Stuart Moore (01784 421118)
Local Press: Staines & Ashford News, Middx Chronicle, Informer, Staines Gaurdian
Local Radio: County Sound, GLR, Capital, Star FM, Radio Wey.

**PREVIOUS** **Leagues:** W London All (pre-1900), W London, W Middx (pre-1905), Gt Western Suburban 05-13 20-24, Gt Western Comb, Munitions Lg (World War 1), London Works(World War 1), Hounslow & Dist 19-20, Spartan 24-35 58-71, Middx Sen 43-52; Parthenon 52-53, Hellenic 53-58, Athenian 71-73
**Names:** Staines Albany and St Peters Institute (merged) in 1895, Staines 05-18, Staines Lagonda 18-25, Staines Vale (2nd World War)
**Grounds:** Edgell Rd (St Peters Inst); The Lammas, Shortwood Common, Mill Mead(Hammonds/Wicks/Pursers Farm); Shepperton Road (to 51); Wheatsheaf Lane (51-96) ,Alwyns Lane Chertsey (1996-8)
**CLUB RECORDS** **Attendance:** 2,750 v Banco di Roma (Barassi Cup) 1975 (70,000 saw 1st leg in Rome)
**Goalscorer:** Alan Gregory 122 **Appearances:** Dickie Watmore 840
**Win:** 14-0 v Croydon (A), Isthmian League Div. 1 19/3/94 **Defeat:** 1-18 v Wycombe Wanderers (A), G West Sub Lge 1909
**Fee Paid:** For R Teale (Slough 81) **Fee Received:** For Scott Taylor (Millwall 95-96)
**BEST SEASON** **FA Amateur Cup:** 3rd Rd 23-24 **FA Trophy:** 2nd Rd 2nd Replay 76-77
**FA Cup:** 1st Rd 84-85, 0-2 v Burton Alb (A) & 1879-80 & 80-81 (as St Peters Institute)
**HONOURS** Isthmian Lg Div 1 74-75 88-89 (Div 2 74-75); Athenian Lg Div 2 71-72 (Div 1 R-up 72-73); Spartan Lg 59-60 (R-up 70-71), Lg Cup 68-69 (R-up 60-61 70-71); Hellenic Lg R-up 55-56 (Lg Cup R-up 53-54 55-56); Gt Western Suburban Lg Div 1 R-up 11-12 22-24 (Div 2 (Middx) 20-21); W London All Div 1 1899-1900; W London Lg Div 1 00-01; W Middx Lg 04-05 (R-up 03-04); London Snr Cup R-up 76-77 80-81; Middx Snr Cup(7), (R-up 09-10 32-33 79-80), Snr Charity Cup 94-95; Barassi Cup76; Southern Comb. Chall. Cup 64-65 66-67 68-69 94-95 96-97,(R-up 67-68 94-95);W Middx Cup 23-24; Staines Cottage Hosp Cup 24-25; Merthyr Middx Charity Shield 90-91,(R-up 94-95); El Canuelo Trophy 92-93 94-95 94-95; Carlsberg Cup 94-95; Melksham Middx Charity Shield 96-97

Pictured before the friendly at Walton & Hersham Aug. 98. L-R Back Row: Chris Wainwright (then manager0 Tommy Williams, Joe O'Shea, Matthew Lovett, Mark Costello, Ken Jefferd, Gavin Harrison, Stuart Udal, Chris Davey (youth manager). Front Row: Mark Fleming, Kelly Phillips, Chris Kerr, Lloyd Wye, Steve Ellis, Mark Butler, Justin Mitchell.

# THAME UNITED

## CLUB OFFICIALS

Chairman: **Jim Tite**
Vice Chairman: **Mike Dyer**
Secretary: **Sally Turner**
c/o Thame United.

**FOOTBALL MANAGEMENT TEAM**
Joint Managers: Andy Sinnott
and Alan Thorne

**FACT FILE**
Founded: 1883
Sponsors:White Horse Turf Limited
Nickname: United
Colours: Red & black hoops/black/red & black hoops
Change colours: Green & white
Midweek Matchday: Tuesday
Reserves' League: Suburban
98-99 - Top Scorer: Liam Herbert
P.o.Y.: Martin Brown
Captain: Martin Brown

**GROUND:** Windmill Road, Thame, Oxon OX9 2DR (01844 213017)
**Directions:** Into Nelson Street from Market Square. 3 miles from Haddenham &Thame Parkway (BR). Nearest bus stop at Town Hall (half mile away)
Capacity: 2,500          Seats: 230          Cover: 400          Floodlights: Yes
**Clubhouse:** Open every evening and weekend lunch times
Banqueting facilities for 200 (weddings, dinners, dances etc)
**Club Shop:** No -

Pages: 24 Price: £1
Editor: Sally Turner (c/o Club)
Local Press: Oxford Mail, Thame Gazette, Bucks Free Press
Local Radio: Radio Oxford, Fox FM, Mix 96

**PREVIOUS**   **Leagues:** Oxon Senior; Hellenic 1959-87; South Midlands 1987-91
**Name:** Thame FC                               **Ground:** None

**CLUB RECORDS**   **Attendance:** 1,035 v Aldershot, Isthmian Div 2 4/4/94
**Win:** 9-0 v Bracknell, 31/10/92          **Defeat:** 2-11 v Hungerford, FA Cup Prelim. Rd 1984
**Career Goalscorer:** Not known          **Career Appearances:** Steve Mayhew
**Transfer Fee received:**                     **Fee paid:**

**BEST SEASON**   **FA Cup:** Third Qualifying Round 91-92, 0-4 v Salisbury   **FA Amateur Cup:** if applicable
**FA Vase:** Semi Final 1998/99

**HONOURS**   Isthmian Lg Div 2 94-95, Div 2 R-up 98-99 Div 3 R-up 92-93; Hellenic Lg 61-62 69-70, Premier Div Cup (4); Sth Mids Lg 90-91; Oxon Snr Cup 1894-95 05-06 08-09 09-10 75-76 80-81 92-93; Oxon Interm Cup 76-77 78-79 91-92; Oxon Charity Cup
Players progressing to the Football League: None

Pictured at Woodbridge Town before their 6th Round FA Carlsberg Vase match          Photo: Eric Marsh

# UXBRIDGE

## CLUB OFFICIALS
Chairman: **Alan Holloway**
Vice-Chairman: **Tom Barnard**
Joint Presidents: **Tom Barnard & Alan Odell**
Secretary: **Roger Stevens**
9 Bourne Ave, Hillingdon, Middx UB8 3AR
Tel: 01895 236879
Res & Youth Sec: **Bob Clayton**
Tel: 01895 857001
Press Officer: **Andy Peart** Tel: 01895 443094
Commercial Manager: **Trevor Birch**
Tel: 0181 813 7291

## FACT FILE
Formed: 1871
Nickname: The Reds
Sponsor: Dagenham Motors
Colours: Red/white/red
Change: Sky & navy blueOr White and black
Midweek matchday: Tuesday
Reserves' League: Suburban (Prem Div)
1998-99
Captain: Mark Gill
P.o.Y.:Stuart Bamford
Top Scorer: Michael Fredriksen (20)

## FOOTBALL MANAGEMENT TEAM
Manager: George Talbot
Coach: Mike Nicks          Physio: Ernie Kempster/Stuart Everley
Res Mgr: Andy Everley      Youth Mgr: Derek Marshall

**GROUND**    Honeycroft, Horton Road, West Drayton, Middx UB7 8HX Tel: 01895 443557
**Directions:** From West Drayton (BR) turn right then 1st right (Horton Road).Ground 1 mile on left. From Uxbridge (LT) take 222 or U3 bus to West Draytonstation, then follow as above. By road, ground 1 mile north of M4 jct 4 takingroad to Uxbridge and leaving by first junction and turning left into Horton Rd- ground 500yds on right
Capacity: 3,770        Cover: 760        Seats: 339        Floodlights: Yes
Club Shop: Good selection of souvenirs & programmes. Contact Averill Hinde
Clubhouse:Open every evening and weekend/bank holiday lunchtimes. (01895 443557)
Hot & cold snacks available on matchdays
Large clubhouse with bar and function room availablefor hire.

FOOTBALL CLUB
MATCHDAY PROGRAMME 1998-99

RYMAN FOOTBALL LEAGUE
DIVISION ONE
Saturday 24th April 1999
Kick Off 3.00pm
**BRAINTREE TOWN**
Programme £1.00

Pages: 48-56 Price: £1.00
Editor: A Peart (01895 443094) & Roy Green (01895 254784)
Local Press: Uxbridge Gazette & Leader, Uxbridge Recorder
Local Radio: Capital, G L R, Star FM

**PREVIOUS**    Leagues: Southern 1894-99; Gt Western Suburban 1906-19, 20-23; Athenian 1919-20, 24-37, 63-82; Spartan 37-38; London 38-46; Gt Western Comb. 39-45;Corinthian 46-63
Name: Uxbridge Town 23-45                                    Grounds: RAF Stadium 23-48, Cleveland Rd 48-78
**CLUB RECORDS** Attendance: 1,000 v Arsenal, floodlight opening 1981
Career Scorer: Phil Duff, 153                                Career Appearances: Roger Nicholls, 1054
**BEST SEASON**    FA Trophy: 2nd Rd.1998-99                FA Vase: 4th Rd 83-84
FA Cup: 2nd Rd 1873-74. Also 1st Rd 1883-84 84-85 85-86    FA Amateur Cup: Runners-up 1897-98
**HONOURS**    FA Amateur Cup R-up 1897-98; London Chall. Cup 93-94 96-97 98-99, R-up 97-98; IsthLge Div 2 S. R-up 84-85; Athenian Lge Cup R-up 81-82, Res. Sect. 69-70, Res. Cup R-up 68-69; Corinthian Lge 59-60 (R-up 48-49), Lge Mem. Shield 50-51 52-53; Middx Sen.Cup 1893-94 95-96 1950-51, R-up 97-98; Middx Sen. Charity Cup 07-08 12-13 35-36 81-82 (R-up 69-70 82-83 85-86); Middx PremCup 95-96; Allied Counties Yth Lge [East] 92-93 (Lge Cup R-up 86-87), Lge Shield 88-89 92-93, R-up 97-98; AC Delco Cup R-up 85-86; Suburban Lge North Div  95-96 97-98, R-up 96-97; Middx Sen Yth Cup 96-97
Players progressing:  William Hill (QPR 51), Lee Stapleton (Fulham 52), Gary Churchouse (Charlton A.), Tony Witter (QPR), Guy Butters (Spurs), Michael Meaker (QPR)

L-R  **Back Row:** George Talbot (manager), Mark Weedon, Phil Granville, Mark Gill, Stuart Bamford, Sean Dawson, Kevin McCormack, Jamie Cleary, Mick Nicks (coach), Ernie Kempster (physio).   **Front Row:** Paul Mills, Nicky Ryder, Michael Fredriksen, Chris Moore, Craig O'Connor, Micky Perry, Gavin Bamford.                                                                            Photo: Peter Barnes

# WEALDSTONE

## CLUB OFFICIALS
Chairman: **Paul Rumens**
Vice Chairman: **Nick Dugard**
Secretary: **Roger Slater** ,c/o 31 Jersey Avenue,Stanmore,Middlesex HA7 2JG
Tel: 0181 552 3595
Commercial Director: **Howard Lambert**
Press Officer: **Graham Sharpe**

## FOOTBALL MANAGEMENT TEAM
Manager: Gordon Bartlett
Asst Mgr: Leo Morris
Physio: Alan Wharton

## FACT FILE
Formed: 1899
Nickname: The Stones
Sponsors: Albro Windows
Colours: Blue & white quarters
Change colours: Yellow
Midweek matches: Tuesday
Reserves' League: None
1998-99
Captain: Chris Walton
P.o.Y: Dominic Sterling
Top Scorer: Carl Holmes (23)

---

**GROUND:** (Sharing with Edgware Town FC) White Lion Ground, High Street, Edgware HA8 5AQ. Tel: 0181 952 6799 ( Mobile Number Match days only : 0421 852488)
**Directions:** Turn left out of Edgware tube station (Northern Line), turn left at crossroads and grd 300yds on right in Edgware High Street just after end of dual carriageway. Buses 32, 142 204, 251, 288, 292, 303 pas ground
Clubhouse: Yes, normal licensing hours          Club Shop: Yes

Pages: 36  Price: £1.30
Editor: Roy Couch (0181 907 4421)

Local Press: Harrow Observer, Harrow Times
Local Radio: Capital, G.L.R., L..B.C.

---

**PREVIOUS**      **Leagues:** Willesden & Dist. 1899-1906 08-13; London 1911-22; Middx 13-22;Spartan 22-28; Athenian 28-64; Isthmian 64-71; Southern 71-79 81-82,88-95; GMVConference 79-81 82-88
**Grounds:** College Farm 03-10; Belmont Rd 10-22; Lower Mead Stad 22-91; Vicarage Rd (Watford FC) 91-93; The Warren (Yeading F.C.) 93-95

**CLUB RECORDS  Attendance:** 13,504 v Leytonstone FA Amateur Cup Fourth Round replay 5/3/49
          **Goalscorer:** George Duck, 251          **Appearances:** Charlie Townsend, 514
          **Win:** 22-0 v The 12th London Regiment (The Rangers)(H), FA Amateur Cup 13/10/23
          **Defeat:** 0-14 v Edgware Town (A), London Senior Cup 9/12/44
**Fees Paid:** £15,000 for David Gipp (Barnet, 90)      **Received:** £25,000 for Stuart Pearce (Coventry City 83); for Sean Norman (Chesham, 1989)

**BEST SEASON     FA Amateur Cup:** Winners 1965-66          **FA Trophy:** Winners 1984-85
       **FA Cup:** Third Round 77-78, 0-4 v Q.P.R. (A). 1st Rd on 13 occasions. League clubs defeated: Hereford Utd and Reading, 77-78
**HONOURS:**      FA Trophy 84-85; FA Amateur Cup 65-66; GMV Conference 84-85; Isthmian Lge - Div3 96-97; Southern Lg Southern Div 81-82, Div 1 South 73-74, Lg Cup 81-82;Athenian Lg 51-52 (R-up 52-53 58-59 60-61); Spartan Lg R-up 22-23; London LgDiv 2 12-13 (R-up 11-12); London Snr Cup 61-62(joint) (R-up 39-40  51-52 60-61); Middx Snr Cup (11); Middx Senior Charity Cup (11); Capital League 84-85 86-87

Players progressing: Stuart Pearce (Coventry City 83), Vinnie Jones(Wimbledon 86), Danny Bailey (Exeter 89),   Phil White (Orient 53), Tom McGhee & John Ashworth (Portsmouth 54 & 62), Charlie Sells (Exeter City 62), Eddie Dilsworth (LincolnCity 67), Colin Franks (Watford 69)

L-R **Back Row:** Alan Wharton (physio), Mick Swaysland, Paul Sharp (goalkeeper coach), Frank O'Brien (coach), Paul Benning, Phil Dicker, Brian Jones, Noel Imber, Dominic Sterling, Lee Walker, Steve Bircham, Chrsi James, Richard Dobson, Ian Waugh.
**Front Row:** Leo Morris, (asst. anager), Gordon Bartlett (manager), Rocky Baptiste, Gerry Brennan, Paul Lamb, Carl Holmes, Paul McKay, Chris Walton, Eddie Boxford, Graham Smith (kit man.)
Photo: James Smith

# WHYTELEAFE

## CLUB OFFICIALS

Chairman: **Paul Owens**
President: **A F Lidbury**

Secretary: **Ian Robertson**
253 Godstone Road, Whyteleafe,
Surrey. CR3 0BD
Tel: 01883 622096 (H&B)
Press Officer: **Peter Stimpson**
Tel: 01883 348310 (H)
Commercial Manager: T Dounce
Tel: 01883 343450

### FOOTBALL MANAGEMENT TEAM

Manager: Lee Richardson
Assistant Man.: B Donnelly
Coach: Mark Coote
Physio: John Knapton

### FACT FILE

Formed: 1946
Nickname: Leafe
Sponsors: Sunday Sport
Colours: Green & white/white/white
Change colours: Yellow & black/black/black
Midweek matchday: Tuesday
Reserve Team's League: Suburban
Local Press: Croydon Advertiser
Local Radio: Mercury

**GROUND**                    15 Church Road, Whyteleafe, Surrey CR3 0AR
                Tel: 0181 660 5491 (Ground) 0181645 0422 (Boardroom)
**Directions:**      Five minutes walk from Whyteleafe (BR) - turn right from station, and left
                into Church Road
Capacity: 5,000          Cover: 600          Seats: 200          Floodlights: Yes

### PROGRAMME
Pages: 36 Price: 70p
Editor: Warren Filmer (0181 660 3255)

**Clubhouse:** Open every lunchtime & evening. Hot & cold food, pool, darts, gaming machines
Clubshop: No

**PREVIOUS**      **Leagues**: Caterham & Edenbridge, Croydon, Thornton Heath & Dist., SurreyIntermediate (East) 54-58, Surrey Senior 58-75,
                Spartan 75-81, Athenian 81-84
                **Names:** None        **Grounds:** None

**CLUB RECORDS  Attendance:** 780
                **Transfer fee paid:** £1,000 for Gary Bowyer (Carshalton)**Transfer fee received:** £25,000 for Steve Milton

**BEST SEASON      FA Vase:** 5th Rd 80-81 85-86
                **FA Trophy:** 3rd Qualifying Rd 89-90          **FA Cup:** Third Qual. Round replay, 1-2 v Wokingham T. (H) after 1-1

**HONOURS**      Isthmian Lge Div 2 South R-up 88-89; Surrey Senior Lge 68-69 (Lge Cup R-up 68-69, Lge Charity Cup 71-72, Res Sect 62-63
        (Chall. Cup 62-63 (R-up 59-60); Surrey Sen. Cup 68-69 (R-up 87-88); Surrey Prem. Cup R-up 84-85; E. Surrey Charity Cup 79-80 (R-up
76-77 77-78); Thornton Heath & Dist Lge 51-52(Lge Cup 51-52) Div 4 R-up 51-52; Edenbridge Charity Cup 51-52; Caterham & Purley Hospital
Cup 51-52; Surrey County Interm Lge East Sect 1 55-56; Surrey Jun. Cup R-up 51-52; Caterham & Edenbridge Lge Div 3 51-52;
Borough of Croydon Charity Cup 56-57; Southern Yth Lge 89-90 (R-up 88-89), Lge Cup 88-89 89-90; Southern Counties M'week F'lit Cup 95-96

Players progressing:  Steve Milton (Fulham)

Photo: Andrew Chitty

840

# WORTHING

## CLUB OFFICIALS

Chairman: **Beau Reynolds**
President: **Morty Hollis**
Vice Chairman: **Ray Smith**

Secretary/Press Off.: **Paul Damper**
19 Fletcher Road, Worthing,
West Sussex BN14 8EX
Tel: 01903 210290

## FOOTBALL MANAGEMENT TEAM
Manager: Brian Donnelly
Assistant Manager:Jason Rutherford
Physio: Alan Robertson

**FACT FILE**
Formed: 1886
Nickname: The Rebels
Sponsors: TK Technology
Colours: Red, with white trim/red/red
Change colours: Blue with white
trim/blue/blue
Midweek matches: Tuesday
1998-99
Captain: Mark Burt
P.o.Y: Mark Knee
Top Scorer: Marc Rice

Pages: 48 Price: £1
Editor: Neil Wycherley
Local Press: Evening Argus, Worthing Herald
Local Radio: Southern FM,
Southern Counties Radio

**GROUND**            Woodside Road, Worthing, West Sussex BN14 7HQ (01903 239575)

**Directions:** Follow A24 to town, at end of Broadwater Rd having gone over railway bridge,
1st right into Teville Rd, right into South Farm RD, 2nd left into Pavilion Rd,
Woodside Rd is first right. Half a mile fromWorthing (BR)
Capacity: 4,500          Seats: 450          Cover: 1,000          Floodlights: Yes
**Clubhouse:** Open 2 hrs before kick-off & closes 11pm. Hot & cold food available
Shop: Sells a good range of souvenirs & programmes. Open matchdays

**PREVIOUS**          **Leagues:** West Sussex Sen 1896-04, 05-14, 19-20; Brighton, Hove & Dist 19-20; Sussex County 20-40, 45-48;
Corinthian 48-63; Athenian 63-77          **Names:** None          **Grounds:** Homefield Park, Beach House Park
**CLUB RECORDS** **Attendance:** 4,500 v Depot Battalion Royal Engineers, FA Amtr Cup 07-08
**Transfer fee paid:** Undisclosed fee for Steve Guille (Bognor Regis Tn 89)
**Transfer fee received:** £7,500 for Tim Read (Woking, 1990)
**Win:** 25-0 v Littlehampton (H) West Sussex Lge 1911-12 **Defeat:** 0-14 v Southwick (A), Sussex County Lge 1946-47
**Career Goalscorer:** Mick Edmonds 275          **Career Appearances:** Geoff Raynsford
**BEST SEASON**     **FA Vase:** 5th Rd 78-79          **FA Trophy:** 4th rd Replay 85-86          **FA Amateur Cup:** Quarter-Final replay 07-08
**FA Cup:** 2nd Rd 82-83, 0-4 v Oxford Utd; 1st Rd 36-37, 94-95 (1-3 v AFC Bournemouth)
**HONOURS**          Isthmian Lg R-up(2) 83-85 (Div 1 82-83, Div 2 81-82 92-93);Isth Full members Cup 98-99, Athenian Lg Div 1 R-up 63-64, Div 2
R-up 71-72, Lg Cup R-up 72-73, Mem. Shield R-up 63-64; Sussex Co. Lg(8) 20-22 26-27 28-29
30-31 33-34 38-40; W Sussex Lg (7); Brighton Char. Cup(9) 29-31 34-35 62-63 69-7173-74(jt) 80-82; Worthing Char. Cup (10); AFA Invit. Cup 63-
64 68-69 73-74 75-76 (Snr Cup R-up 36-37 46-47 48-49); Corinth. Lg Mem. Shield R-up 49-50 (NealeTphy 58-59); Roy Hayden Mem. Tphy 75(jt),
77 78; Don Morecraft Tphy 72 73 76 8182; Sussex F'lit Cup(3) 88-90 97-98; Sussex I'mediate Cup 34-35 64-65; BrightonChal. Shield 29-30 31-32
Players progressing: Ken Suttle (Chelsea 48), Alan Arnell & Fred Perry (Liverpool 54), Craig Whitington (Scarborough, via Crawley Town) 93,
Darren Freeman (Gillingham), Paul Musselwhite (Scunthorpe), Trevor Wood (Port Vale), Richard Tiltman (Brighton)

**L-R  Back Row:** Sammy Donnelly (manager), Alan Robertson (physio), Simon Funnell, Lee Cox, Ben Carrington, Mark Burt, Phil Reid,
Damian Webber, Paul Kennett, Brendan Devery, Danny Smith. **Front Row:** Miles Rutherford, Lee Weston, Tony Holden, Justin Simmons,
Mark Knee, Chris Troak, Simon Robinson, Marc Rice.                                   Photo: Andrew Chitty

# YEADING

## CLUB OFFICIALS

Chairman: **Philip Spurden**
President: **Mr R Carter**
Vice Chairman: **Steve Perryman**
Secretary: **Colin Stupack**
24 Nower Hill,Pinner,Middlesex HA5 5QS
Tel: 0181 868 9311
Press Officer: **Tim Fuell** (l0709 121 4576)

### FOOTBALL MANAGEMENT TEAM
Manager: Jon Turnersst M
Assistants Paul Sweales & Jon Denton
Physios: Eddie Cole &  Denis Collins

**FACT FILE**

Formed: 1965
Nickname: The Ding
Sponsors: T.B.A.
Colours: Red & black stripes/black/black
Change colours: yellow/blue/white
Midweek matchday: Tuesday
Reserve League: Suburban Lge
Youth League: Harrow

FOOTBALL CLUB
*At The Warren*

Ryman
football league

Ryman League
Division One
Season 1998/99 £1

Pages: 32 Price: £1
Editor: Tim Fuell

Local Newspapers: Hayes Gazette

**GROUND** The Warren,Beaconsfield Rd.Hayes,Middx.( 0181 848 7362/7369.Fx:0181 561 1063)
**Directions:** 2 miles from Hayes (BR) - take Uxbridge Road and turn right towards Southall,
right into Springfield Rd and then left into Beaconsfield Rd. Bus 207 stops 1/2 mile from ground
Capacity: 3,500          Cover: 1,000          Seats: 250          Floodlights: Yes
Clubhouse: Open normal pub hours.' The Warren' Conference & Banquetting  suite available
for hire .(Social Secretary: William Gritt)
Club Shop: Planned          Metal Badges: Yes
Well stocked football bookshop at internet site: http://welcome.to/yeadingfc

**PREVIOUS**          **Leagues:** Hayes & District Yth; Uxbridge; S W Middx 1967-74; Middx 74-84;Spartan 1984-87
**CLUB RECORDS** **Attendance:** 3,000; v Hythe Town, FA Vase SF 1990; v Tottenham Hotspur,friendly
                       **Career Goalscorer:** Dave Burt 327          **Career Appearances:** Norman Frape
                       **Fee Paid:** Unknown          **Fee Received:** £45,000 for Andrew Impey (QPR)
**BEST SEASON**     **FA Cup:** Furst Round Proper (93-94 & 94-95)
                       **FA Vase:** Winners 89-90
                       **F.A.Trophy:** 2ndRd (97-98 & 98-99)
**HONOURS**          FA Vase 89-90; Isthmian League Div 2 Sth 89-90 (Div 1 R-up 91-92); SpartanLeague 86-87 (R-up 85-86, Senior Div R-up 84-
                       85, League Cup 85-86 86-87); Middlesex Snr League (6) 71-73 74-76 81-82 83-84 (R-up 73-74 74-75 78-79, LeagueCup (6)
                       72-73 75-76 79-83); South West Middlesex League (2) 69-71; Middlesex SnrCup 89-90 91-92, Middlesex Prem. Cup 80-81,
                       Middlesex I'mediate Cup (5) 70-7274-76 77-78, Middlesex Jnr Cup (4) 68-69 70-72 74-75; Uxbridge League 66-67; Middlesex
                       Border League Cup 86-87 (AJA Cup 86-87); Suburban League Nth 87-88; Allied Counties Yth League 89-90 (Lge Cup 89-90)
Players progressing: Andrew Impey (Leicester City) and Lee Charles (Q.P.R.viaChertsey Town)

Photo: Andrew Chitty

## DIVISION TWO FINAL LEAGUE TABLE 1998-99

| | | P | W | D | L | F | A | GD | Pts |
|---|---|---|---|---|---|---|---|---|---|
| 1 | Bedford Town | 42 | 29 | 7 | 6 | 89 | 31 | 58 | 94 |
| 2 | Harlow Town | 42 | 27 | 8 | 7 | 100 | 47 | 53 | 89 |
| 3 | Thame United | 42 | 26 | 8 | 8 | 89 | 50 | 39 | 86 |
| 4 | Hemel Hempstead Town | 42 | 21 | 12 | 9 | 90 | 50 | 40 | 75 |
| 5 | Windsor & Eton | 42 | 22 | 6 | 14 | 84 | 55 | 29 | 72 |
| 6 | Banstead Athletic | 42 | 21 | 8 | 13 | 83 | 62 | 21 | 71 |
| 7 | Northwood | 42 | 20 | 7 | 15 | 67 | 68 | -1 | 67 |
| 8 | Tooting & Mitcham United | 42 | 19 | 9 | 14 | 63 | 62 | 1 | 66 |
| 9 | Chalfont St Peter | 42 | 16 | 12 | 14 | 70 | 71 | -1 | 60 |
| 10 | Metropolitan Police | 42 | 17 | 8 | 17 | 61 | 58 | 3 | 59 |
| 11 | Leighton Town | 42 | 16 | 10 | 16 | 60 | 64 | -4 | 58 |
| 12 | Horsham | 42 | 17 | 6 | 19 | 74 | 67 | 7 | 57 |
| 13 | Marlow | 42 | 16 | 9 | 17 | 72 | 68 | 4 | 57 |
| 14 | Edgware Town | 42 | 14 | 10 | 18 | 65 | 68 | -3 | 52 |
| 15 | Witham Town | 42 | 12 | 15 | 15 | 64 | 64 | 0 | 51 |
| 16 | Hungerford Town | 42 | 13 | 12 | 17 | 59 | 61 | -2 | 51 |
| 17 | Wivenhoe Town | 42 | 14 | 8 | 20 | 71 | 83 | -12 | 50 |
| 18 | Wokingham Town | 42 | 14 | 4 | 24 | 44 | 79 | -35 | 46 |
| 19 | Barking | 42 | 10 | 11 | 21 | 50 | 75 | -25 | 41 |
| 20 | Hertford Town | 42 | 11 | 2 | 29 | 44 | 96 | -52 | 35 |
| 21 | Bracknell Town | 42 | 7 | 10 | 25 | 48 | 92 | -44 | 31 |
| 22 | Abingdon Town | 42 | 6 | 6 | 30 | 48 | 124 | -76 | 24 |

## RESULTS CHART 1998-99

| HOME TEAM | 1 | 2 | 3 | 4 | 5 | 6 | 7 | 8 | 9 | 10 | 11 | 12 | 13 | 14 | 15 | 16 | 17 | 18 | 19 | 20 | 21 | 22 |
|---|---|---|---|---|---|---|---|---|---|---|---|---|---|---|---|---|---|---|---|---|---|---|
| 1 Abingdon Town | X | 1-2 | 0-0 | 0-3 | 0-1 | 2-2 | 0-2 | 3-2 | 2-5 | 4-1 | 3-2 | 0-4 | 2-2 | 0-4 | 2-4 | 1-4 | 2-6 | 0-2 | 1-6 | 2-3 | 2-4 | 1-1 |
| 2 Banstead Ath | 4-1 | X | 1-0 | 3-1 | 3-1 | 5-1 | 1-1 | 2-2 | 0-4 | 5-1 | 4-4 | 1-1 | 0-1 | 4-1 | 2-0 | 2-0 | 1-3 | 1-1 | 1-0 | 0-1 | 4-1 | 1-3 |
| 3 Barking | 4-2 | 2-2 | X | 1-1 | 0-2 | 2-0 | 1-0 | 0-0 | 0-3 | 4-0 | 3-2 | 1-0 | 2-3 | 0-3 | 0-1 | 0-1 | 1-1 | 4-3 | 1-0 | 2-2 | 1-2 | 1-2 |
| 4 Bedford Town | 1-0 | 1-1 | 1-1 | X | 2-1 | 3-0 | 2-1 | 5-0 | 2-2 | 5-0 | 2-0 | 2-0 | 0-1 | 2-1 | 1-0 | 6-0 | 4-0 | 2-0 | 3-0 | 1-0 | 0-0 | 4-1 |
| 5 Bracknell Tn | 0-5 | 3-0 | 4-0 | 1-2 | X | 4-4 | 0-4 | 1-4 | 1-1 | 3-1 | 0-1 | 3-2 | 2-3 | 0-1 | 1-1 | 0-2 | 1-2 | 0-0 | 0-1 | 1-5 | 1-4 | 1-2 |
| 6 Chalfont St P | 6-2 | 0-2 | 3-1 | 1-2 | 3-2 | X | 2-4 | 1-4 | 0-0 | 4-1 | 1-1 | 0-0 | 3-1 | 0-0 | 2-0 | 2-3 | 0-2 | 0-0 | 3-2 | 1-0 | 5-2 | 3-0 |
| 7 Edgware Tn | 2-1 | 2-5 | 4-1 | 0-1 | 4-0 | 1-1 | X | 0-3 | 1-1 | 4-0 | 0-2 | 2-2 | 1-1 | 0-2 | 1-1 | 0-4 | 0-1 | 1-2 | 2-2 | 2-2 | 1-2 | 3-0 |
| 8 Harlow Town | 3-1 | 2-1 | 1-0 | 3-0 | 7-1 | 2-0 | 6-1 | X | 1-3 | 2-1 | 3-1 | 0-0 | 1-4 | 6-1 | 3-0 | 3-0 | 5-1 | 7-0 | 1-1 | 4-0 | 3-0 | 1-1 |
| 9 Hemel H'stead | 3-0 | 0-1 | 3-0 | 2-1 | 2-2 | 4-1 | 2-1 | 6-0 | X | 3-1 | 3-0 | 2-1 | 2-1 | 3-1 | 4-1 | 1-1 | 0-0 | 4-5 | 1-3 | 2-2 | 1-2 | 1-2 |
| 10 Hertford Town | 3-2 | 6-2 | 3-2 | 0-2 | 1-0 | 0-2 | 0-1 | 0-2 | 1-4 | X | 0-1 | 0-3 | 2-1 | 1-0 | 0-1 | 1-3 | 0-0 | 0-1 | 2-1 | 0-3 | 3-1 | 0-1 |
| 11 Horsham | 3-1 | 2-3 | 2-0 | 0-2 | 1-0 | 0-1 | 0-1 | 2-1 | 1-5 | 1-2 | X | 2-3 | 2-0 | 6-2 | 3-0 | 1-3 | 4-2 | 3-0 | 3-0 | 3-1 | 1-3 | 7-0 |
| 12 Hungerford T | 2-0 | 3-2 | 1-1 | 1-4 | 0-0 | 1-2 | 4-1 | 0-4 | 4-2 | 7-2 | 3-1 | X | 1-1 | 0-0 | 0-2 | 1-1 | 1-0 | 2-1 | 0-1 | 0-1 | 1-2 | 1-0 |
| 13 Leighton Tn | 3-0 | 2-0 | 5-3 | 1-4 | 2-0 | 2-2 | 1-2 | 1-1 | 2-0 | 0-0 | 2-2 | 1-0 | X | 4-2 | 0-2 | 0-1 | 0-5 | 1-2 | 1-1 | 3-2 | 1-4 | 2-1 |
| 14 Marlow | 9-1 | 1-0 | 2-2 | 0-2 | 2-2 | 0-2 | 4-2 | 1-1 | 2-3 | 2-1 | 0-0 | 3-1 | 0-0 | X | 4-3 | 2-0 | 4-2 | 1-2 | 2-2 | 1-3 | 1-2 | 2-1 |
| 15 Met Police | 0-1 | 0-5 | 4-0 | 2-4 | 7-1 | 1-1 | 1-2 | 1-1 | 1-1 | 2-0 | 2-0 | 1-0 | 1-0 | 1-0 | X | 2-1 | 0-2 | 0-2 | 0-1 | 3-3 | 5-2 | 3-0 |
| 16 Northwood | 5-0 | 0-2 | 2-1 | 1-1 | 2-1 | 2-2 | 2-1 | 1-2 | 1-1 | 2-3 | 0-3 | 3-1 | 1-1 | 3-1 | 0-3 | X | 0-2 | 4-2 | 0-7 | 2-0 | 4-1 | 4-1 |
| 17 Thame Utd | 4-0 | 3-3 | 1-0 | 1-2 | 3-0 | 4-0 | 2-2 | 3-0 | 1-0 | 2-0 | 2-2 | 3-3 | 2-1 | 0-2 | 2-1 | 2-0 | X | 0-2 | 4-1 | 5-3 | 4-1 | 2-1 |
| 18 Tooting & M | 4-0 | 0-1 | 3-1 | 1-5 | 1-1 | 1-1 | 2-1 | 0-2 | 2-2 | 3-1 | 1-1 | 4-0 | 1-0 | 0-2 | 1-0 | 0-1 | 1-2 | X | 1-6 | 1-1 | 2-1 | 4-0 |
| 19 Windsor & Eton | 6-0 | 4-0 | 1-2 | 2-1 | 5-2 | 1-2 | 3-0 | 0-1 | 1-0 | 4-1 | 0-2 | 1-0 | 2-1 | 2-1 | 2-0 | 4-1 | 1-1 | 2-1 | X | 2-1 | 1-4 | 2-0 |
| 20 Witham Town | 2-2 | 1-0 | 1-1 | 0-0 | 0-2 | 4-0 | 1-4 | 1-2 | 0-2 | 1-3 | 2-0 | 1-1 | 4-1 | 1-1 | 2-2 | 0-0 | 0-1 | 1-1 | 1-1 | X | 3-1 | 4-2 |
| 21 Wivenhoe Tn | 0-0 | 1-3 | 1-1 | 0-2 | 2-2 | 1-5 | 0-3 | 1-2 | 0-0 | 3-1 | 4-1 | 2-2 | 1-2 | 3-1 | 1-1 | 1-2 | 1-3 | 0-1 | 2-3 | 1-1 | X | 7-1 |
| 22 Wokingham T | 0-1 | 0-3 | 2-3 | 2-0 | 0-0 | 0-3 | 0-0 | 1-2 | 1-2 | 2-1 | 2-1 | 1-2 | 0-1 | 0-3 | 0-1 | 3-0 | 0-3 | 0-2 | 1-0 | 1-0 | 2-0 | X |

# BANSTEAD ATHLETIC

**FACT FILE**

**GROUND**
**Address:** Merland Rise, Tadworth, Surrey KT20 5JG (01737 350982)

**Directions:** Follow signs to Tattenham Corner (Epsom racecourse), then to Banstead Sports Centre. Ground adjacent to swimming pool. Half a mile fromTattenham Corner (BR) Bus 420 from Sutton stops outside ground. Also buses 406 & 727 from Epsom

**Capacity:** 3,500 **Seats:** 250 **Cover:** 800 **Floodlights:** Yes
**Clubhouse:** All week 11am-11pm. 2 bars, real ale, bar snacks
Club Shop: Yes

**HONOURS:** Surrey Snr Lg(6) 50-54 56-57 64-65, R-up(5) 49-50 54-56 57-59, Lg Cup 57-58, Charity Cup 52-53 58-59; London Spartan Lg R-up 77-78 (Lg Cup(2) 65-67);Surrey Prem. Cup R-up 91-92, 95-96; Surrey Snr Shield 55-56; Gilbert Rice F'lit Cup 81-82 86-87 (R-up(4) 82-86); Athenian Lg Cup(2) 80-82 (R-up 82-83 (SF 79-80); Surrey Int. Lg(2) 47-49, Cup 46-47 54-55; E. Surrey Charity Cup (4) 59-6066-67 76-78, R-up 79-80, I'mediate Sect. 75-76 (R-up 76-77), Jnr Sect. 81-82;Southern Comb. Cup R-up 69-70; Suburban Lg R-up 86-87; Carlton T.V. Trophy R-Up 95-96

**PREVIOUS** **Leagues:** Surrey Int., Surrey Snr 49-65, Spartan 65-75, London Spartan 75-79, Athenian 79-84

**CLUB RECORDS** **Attendance:** 1,400 v Leytonstone, FA Amateur 1953
**Win:** 11-0 **Defeat:** 0-11
**Career goalscorer:** Harry Clark **Career appearances:** Dennis Wall
**Transfer fee received:** None **Transfer fee paid:** None

**BEST SEASON** **FA Cup:** 3rd Qual.Rd. 86-87. FA Vase: Semi - finals 96-97

Players progressing : W Chesney & B Robinson (Crystal Palace)

Founded: 1944
Nickname: A's
Sponsors: PDM Marketing
Colours: Amber/black/black
Change colours: Red & white
Programme : Pages: 38 Price: 80p
Editor: Colin Darby (0181 643 5437)
Midweek Matchday: Tuesday

98-99 - Captain: kristian Sorensen
Jt P.O.Y.: Keith Ward/David Taylor
Top scorer: Warin Burton

**CLUB PERSONNEL**

**Secretary:** Gordon Taylor
116 Kingston Avenue, North Cheam, Surrey SM3 9UF
TEL: 0181 641 2957

Chairman: Terry Molloy
President: E C Winser MBE
Press Officer: Colin Darby
Manager: Chick botley
Coach: Steve Tutt/Robin Lewis
Physio: Paul Bishop

# BARKING

**FACT FILE**

**GROUND Address:** Mayesbrook Park, Lodge Avenue, Dagenham RM8 2JR (0181 5956900).
**Directions:** Off A13 on A1153 (Lodge Ave), and groud 1 mile on left. Bus 162 from Barking station. Nearest tube Becontree.
**Capacity:** 2,500 **Cover:** 600 **Seats:** 200 **Floodlights:** Yes
Clubhouse: 2 large bars, open daily 11am-11pm (Sundays Noon-11pm). Hot & cold food and drinks. Club Shop: No

**PREVIOUS** **Grounds:** Eastbury Field, Vicage Field (until 1973)
**Names:** Barking Rovers, Barking Institute, Barking Woodville,Barking Town.
**Leagues:** London 1896-98 09-23, South Essex 1898-21, Leyton & Dist 1899-1900,Athenian 23-52

**CLUB RECORDS** **Attendance:** (At Mayesbrook) 1,972 v Aldershot FA Cup 2nd Rd 78
**Win:** 14-0 v Sheppey Utd Mithras Cup 69-70 **Defeat:** 0-8 v Marlow.
**Fee received:** £6,000 for Alan Hull (Orient) **Fee paid:** None over £1,000
**Goal scorer:** Neville Fox 241 (65-73) **Appearances:** Bob Makin 566

**BEST SEASON** **FA Vase:** 96-97 **FA Amateur Cup:** Runners-up 26-27
**FA Cup:** 2nd Rd rep. 81-82 1-3v Gillingham (A) after 1-1. Also 2nd Rd 78-79 79-80 83-84, and 1st Rd 26-27 28-29 78-80. - League clubs defeated: Oxford Utd 79-80.

**HONOURS** FA Amateur Cup R-up 26-27; Isthmian Lg 78-79 (Lg Cup R-up 76-77); Athenian Lg 34-35 (R-up 24-25); London Lg 20-21 (Div 1 (A) 09-10); South Essex Lg Div 1 1898-99,R-up (2), Div 2 (4); London Senior Cup (4), R-up (3); Essex Senior Cup (7), R-up (3); Dylon Shield 79-80; Eastern Floodlit R-up (3); Essex Elizabethean 66-67, R-up (2); Essex Thameside (4), R-up (4); London Charity Cup61-62 R-up 21-22; London Intermediate Cup 85-86; East Anglian Cup 37-38 53-54;Mithras Cup (3), R-up (2); Premier Midweek (2).

Players progressing: 21 players since 1908 - 1956; Peter Carey (Orient 57), Lawrie Abrahams (Charlton 77), Kevin Hitchcock (Nottm Forest83), Dennis Bailey (Fulham 86), Alan Hull (Orient 87)

Founded: 1880
Nickname: The Blues
Sponsors: Capital Coin Ltd
Colours: Blue & white
Change colours: Red & white
Midweek matchday: Tuesday
Reserves' League: None
PROGRAMME
Pages: 16 Price: 80p
Editor: Roger Chilvers
97-98 Captain:
P.o.Y.: Marc Baker
Top Scorer: Micky Waite

**CLUB PERSONNEL**

**Secretary:** Roger Chilvers
50 Harrow Rd, Barking, Essex IG11 7RA
Tel:0181 5915313

Chairman: John Edgeworth
Vice-Chairman: Paul Lovell
President: Terry Lovell
Press Officer: Derek Pedder
Tel: 0181 529 2483
Manager: Arthur Wenborn
Asst Manager . TBA
Physio: TBA

# BERKHAMSTED TOWN

**FACT FILE**
Formed: 1895
Nickname: Lilywhites
Sponsors: C D Wright Elect Wholesalers
Colours: White/black/black
Change Colours: Red/blue
Midweek Matchday: Tuesday
Reserves' Lge: Suburban Lleague
PROGRAMME
Pages: 64       Price: £1
Editor: Adrian Marson (01923 893320)

**GROUND**
Address:Broadwater, Lower Kings Road, Berkhamsted, Herts HP4 2AA Tel: 01442 862815

**Directions:** Adjacent to Berkhamsted station (Euston-Birmingham line). A41 toBerkhamsted town centre traffic lights, left into Lower Kings Road

Capacity: 2,500      Seats: 170        Cover: 350       Floodlights: Yes
**Clubhouse:** Open 7 days a week. Pool & darts
**Club Shop:** Contact Lee Whybrow

Local Press: Berkhamsted Herald, Berkhamsted Gazette
Local Radio: Chiltern Radio, Mix '96', Three Counties Radio

**PREVIOUS**      **Leagues:** W Herts& Herts Co. 1895-1922; Spartan 22-51, 66-75; Delphian 51-63; Athenian 63-66,83-84; London Spartan 75-83
**Grounds:** Sunnyside Enclosure 1895-1919, Sports Ground 1919-83

**CLUB RECORDS Attendance:** 1,163 v Barnet, FA Cup 3rd Qual. Rd 1987
**Career appearances:** Ray Jeffrey (612)

**CLUB PERSONNEL**
Secretary: Keith Bayliss
56 St Edmunds, Berkhamsted, Herts.
tel: 01442 384937

**BEST SEASON**   **FA Cup:** 3rd Qual Rd v Barnet 87-88, v Slough 91-92, v Chesham U. 92-93
**FA Vase:** 4th Rd v Collier Row 84-85
**FA Trophy:** 1st Rd v Kidderminster Harriers 97-98

Chairman: Brian McCarthy
President: Dennis Wright
Press Off.: Bob Sear (01442 864547 H & B)
Match Sec: Lee Whybrow

**HONOURS**     Herts Senior Cup 52-53; London Spartan Lge 79-80 (Div 2 26-27); Herts Charity Shield 50-51(jt) 73-74 79-80 84-85 90-91; Herts Senior County Lge Aubrey Cup 52-53; St Marys Cup(13); Apsley Senior Charity Cup (9); Southern Comb 84-85(F/lit Cup 84-85)

Players progressing: Frank Broome, Maurice Cook, Keith Ryan(Wycombe)

Manager: Mick Foster
Coach: Mark Pearson
Physio: Chris Hewitt

1998-99 -       Captain:  Paul Lowe        Top scorers: Rory Bray, Terry Nightingale - 13
P.o.Y.: Neil Webb

# CHALFONT ST PETER

**GROUND**
Address: The Playing Fields, Amersham Road, Chalfont St Peter SL9 7BQ Tel: 01753 885797

**FACT FILE**
Founded: 1926
Nickname: Saints
Colours: Red, green trim/green/green & red
Change colours: Yellow/black/black
Midweek matchday: Tuesday
Reserves' League:
PROGRAMME
Pages: 30  Price: 50p   Editor: Mal Keenan
Local Press: Bucks Advertiser, Bucks Examiner, Bucks Free Press, Wycombe Midweek
Local Radio: Chiltern Radio

**Directions:** A413 from Uxbridge (London) to Chalfont. Turn left 100 yds after2nd major roundabout (between Ambulance station and Community Centre. Two miles from Gerrards Cross (BR), regular buses from Slough & Uxbridge

Capacity: 4,500      Cover: 120        Seats: 220        Floodlights: Yes     Club Shop: Yes

Clubhouse: Open every evening, Saturday afternoons and Sunday lunchtimes

**PREVIOUS**      **Leagues:** Great Western Combination 1948-58; Parthenon 58-59; London 60-62;Spartan 62-75; London Spartan 75-76; Athenian 76-84

**BEST SEASON**   **FA Trophy:** 3rd Qual Rd 89-90 91-92
**FA Vase:** 4th Rd 87-88
**FA Cup:** 3rd Qual Rd85-86 (wins over Banbury, King's Lynn and Barking)

**CLUB PERSONNEL**
Secretary: Dave Ward
3 Greenfield End, Chalfont St Perters, Bucks SL9 0DW  ((01494 482208 (H)  0378 144475 -W))
Chairman: Peter Manson
Press Officer: Nick Simon
Manager:Sean West
Physio:

**HONOURS**     Isthmian Lg Div 2 87-88; Athenian Lg R-up 83-84 (Lg Cup 76-77 82-83); London Spartan Lg Div 2 75-76; Berks & Bucks Intermediate Cup 52-53; Berks &Bucks Benevolent Cup 64-65

**CLUB RECORDS Attendance:** 2,550 v Watford, benefit match 85
**Career Goalscorer:** Unknown **Career Appearances:** Colin Davies
**Transfer Fee Paid:** £750 to Chertsey (Steve Church, March 1989)

Players progressing to Football League: Paul Barrowcliff (Brentford), Dean Hooper (Swindon)

# CHESHUNT

**GROUND Address:** The Stadium, Theobalds Lane, Cheshunt, Herts . Tel: 01992 626752

**Directions:** M25 to junction 25, A10 north towards Hertford, next roundaboutthird exit to next roundabout, turn left proceed under railway bridge, turnleft, ground approx 400 yards on right. 400yds from Theobalds Grove BR station,Buses 310, 242, 311 & 363 to Theobalds Grove station

Seats: 285    Cover: 600    Capacity: 2,500    Floodlights: Yes
Clubhouse: Yes    Club Shop: No

**HONOURS:**
Athenian Lg 75-76 (R-up 73-74), Div 1 67-68, Div 2 R-up 65-66, Lg Cup74-75 75-76; Spartan Lg 62-63, Lg Cup 63-64 92-93, (R-up 89-90); London Lg 49-50 (R-up 56-57), Div 1 47-48 48-49 (R-up 46-47), Div 1 Cup 46-47, Lg Cup R-up58-59, Park Royal Cup 46-47; Isthmian Lg Div 2 R-up 81-82 (Div 3 R-up 94-95);Herts Snr Cup 23-24 (R-up 48-49 49-50 68-69 69-70 71-72 73-74); Herts CharityCup 00-01 05-06 (R-up 70-71 74-75 80-81); Herts Charity Shield 46-47 65-66 (52-53 53-54 54-55 63-64 64-65); Herts Snr Centenary Tphy 91-92; East Anglian Cup74-75 (R-up 75-76); Mithras Floodlit Cup 69-70 (R-up 75-76); London Charity Cup73-74; Roy Bailey Tphy 90-91 94-95 97-98

**PREVIOUS:**    **Leagues:** Athenian 19-20 21-31 64-77; London 20-21 24-25 46-51 55-59; Delphian51-55; Aetolian 59-62; Spartan 62-64; Isthmian 77-87
**Name:** None    **Ground:** None

**RECORDS:**    Attendance: 7,000 v Bromley, London Senior Cup 1947

**BEST SEASON:**    **FA Vase:** Quarter Final 81-82
**FA Cup:** 4th Qual. Rd(4)

Players progressing: Ian Dowie, Ruben Abgula, SteveSedgeley, Lee Hodges, Paul Marquis, Steve Terry, Neil Prosser, Mario Walsh

**FACT FILE**
Founded: 1946
Nickname: Ambers
Sponsors: None
Colours: Gold & black
Change colours: All blue
Midweek matchday: Tuesday
Reserves' Lge: Essex & Herts Border Comb
Programme: Pages: 28  Price: £1
Editor: Keith Hughes (01992 627195)

**CLUB PERSONNEL**

Mr Keith Hughes, 28 Peace Close, Rosedale, Cheshunt, Herts EN7 5EQ

Chairman: Georgius Savva
Vice Chairman: Paul Cully
President: Paul Philips
Press Officer: Neil Harrison

Manager: Tom Loizou
Asst Manager: Kevin O'Dell
Physio: Lou Dedman

# EDGWARE TOWN

**GROUND**
**Address:** White Lion Ground, High Street, Edgware HA8 5AQ. Tel: 0181 9526799

**Directions:** Turn left out of Edgware tube station (Northern Line), turn left again at crossroads and ground 300yds on right in Edgware High Street behindWhite Lion pub. Buses 32, 288 142

Capacity: 5,000    Seats: 220    Cover: 1,500    Floodlights: Yes    Club Shop: No

**Clubhouse:** Open nightly and Fri, Sat, Sun lunchtimes.
Hot & cold food matchdays, cold food lunchtimes

**HONOURS:**    Isthmian Lg Div 3 91-92; London Spartan Lg 87-88 89-90 (Lg Cup 87-88); Corinthian Lg R-up 53-54, Memorial Shield 52-53 61-62; Athenian Lge R-up 81-82;Middx Snr Lg 40-41 41-42 42-43 43-44 44-45, Cup 47-48 (R-up 73-74 94-95);London Snr Cup R-up 47-48; Middx Border Lg Cup 79-80; Suburban Lg Div R-up 89-90

**PREVIOUS**    **Leagues:** Corinthian 46-63; Athenian 64-84; London Spartan 84-90
**Names:** Edgware F.C.    **Grounds:** None

**CLUB RECORDS**    Attendance: 8,500 v Wealdstone, FA Cup 1948
**Career Appearances:** John Mangan
**Career Goalscorer:** Steve Newing

**BEST SEASON**    FA Vase: 5th Round, 1991-92
FA Cup:

Players progressing: Brian Stein (Luton), Dave Beasant (Wimbledon), Scott McGleish (Charlton 94)

**FACT FILE**

Founded: 1939
Nickname: Wares
Colours: Green & white Qtrs
Change colours: All yellow
Midweek Matchday: Tuesday
Reserve League: Suburban
Sponsor: Philiam Construction

Programme: Pages: 16  Price: 50p
Editor: Paul Gregory (0181 959 2535)

**CLUB PERSONNEL**

**Secretary:** Barry Boreham, 28 St Brides Ave., Edgware, Middx HA8 6BS
Tel: (0181 9521685)

Chairman: Michael Flynn
President: Mr V Deritis
Patron: Russell Grant

Manager: Jim McGleish
Asst Manager:
Physio: Sarah Gow

# FORD UNITED

**GROUND:** Ford Sports & Soc. Club, Rush Green Rd., Romford. Tel: 01708 745678

**Directions:** On the A124 (Rush Green road) on left going towards Hornchurch. 2 miles from Romford (BR). Buses 173, 175 87, 106, 23

Seats: 354         Cover: Yes         Capacity: 3,000         Floodlights: Yes

Clubhouse: 4 bars, 2 dance halls, tea bar. ??Opening hours & is food available??

Club Shop: No

**HONOURS:** London Snr Cup 55-56 56-57 94-95 97-98; Essex Snr Lge 91-92 96-97,(R-up 94-95),Trophy 90-91 91-92, Cup 39-40 49-50 50-51 51-52 85-86, R-up Spartan Lg 49-50 50-51 55-56 56-57 57-58; London Lg 36-37 38-39; Essex Elizabethan 59-60 60-61 70-71; Gtr London Lg 70-71; Sportsmanship Award 77-78 79-80 80-81; Essex& Herts Border Comb.(res) 94-95 (Lg Cup 94-95); Isthmian League Div 3 98-99

**RECORDS:** **Attendance:** 58,000 Briggs Sports v Bishop Auckland, at St James Park, Newcastle, FA Amateur Cup

**Appearances:** Roger Bond

**Goalscorer:**

**Win:**          **Defeat:**

**PREVIOUS:** **Leagues:** Spartan, Aetolian, Metropolitan, Essex Senior

**Names:**         **Grounds:**

**BEST SEASON:** **FA Vase:** 98-99, 5th Round, 1-2 v Bedlington Terriers (H)

**FA Amateur Cup:** Semi-Final 53-54

**FA Cup:**

Players progressing: Les Allen (Spurs), Mick Flanagan (QPR, Charlton, Crystal Palace), Jim Stannard (Fulham, Southend, Millwall), Nicky Hammond (Arsenal,Swindon), Laurie Abrahams (Charlton), Doug Barton (Reading, Newport)

**FACT FILE**

Nickname: Motormen

Sponsor: Sky Sports

Colours: All blue

Change: All red

Reserves' League: Essex & Herts Border Comb

Programme: Yes

Editor: Michael Ewen (01708 724178 H)

**CLUB PERSONNEL**

**Secretary:** Colin Mynott, 11 Rantree Fold, Basildon, Essex SS16 5TG

(01268 452965 H, 01268 404624 B)

Vice-Chairman: George Adams

President: Paddy Byrne

Manager: Denis Elliott

# HEMEL HEMPSTEAD TOWN

**Ground:** Vauxhall Ground, Adeyfield Rd, Hemel Hempstead HP2 4HW Tel: 01442 259777

**Directions:** Euston to Hemel Hempstead Station. H2 or H3 bus to Windmill Rd,Longlands

Capacity: 3,000         Seats: 175         Cover: Yes         Floodlights: Yes

**Clubhouse:** Tel: 01442 259777. Open 7-11pm weekdays, 12-11pm w/ends & Bank Hols. Tea bar open matchdays

**Club Shop:** No

**HONOURS** Ryman Lge Div 3 98-99; Herts Snr Cup 05-06 07-08 08-09 25-26 61-62 65-66 91-92, Herts Charity Cup/Shield 25-26 34-35 51-52 76-77 83-84 (R-up 90-91), Spartan Lg 33-34, Herts Intermediate Cup 54-55 65-66 83-84, West Herts St Mary Cup 70-71 75-76 82-83 85-86 90-91 91-92 93-94, Athenian Lg Div 1 R-up 64-65  (Res Cup 65-66), Delphian Lg (res) 54-55 (Res Cup 54-55 61-62)

**PREVIOUS** **Leagues:** Spartan 22-52; Delphian 52-63; Athenian 63-77

**Names:** Apsley 1885-1947; Hemel Hempstead Town (merged with Hemel Hempstead Utd in1947)         **Grounds:** Crabtree Lane (til '71)

**CLUB RECORDS** **Attendance:** 2,000 v Watford 1985

(at Crabtree Lane: 3,500 v Tooting, FA AmtrCup 1st Rd 1962)

**Goalscorer:** Dai Price         **Appearances:** John Wallace, 1012

**BEST SEASON** **FA Cup:** Never past Qualifying Rounds

**FA Vase:** 4th Rd 98-99 v Taunton Town

**FACT FILE**

Founded: 1885

Nickname: Hemel

Sponsors: Barling

Colours: All red with white trim

Change colours: Green/white trim

Midweek Matches: Tuesday

Programme: 48 pages, 80p

Editor/Press Off.: Marc Willmore

Local Press: Hemel Gazette, Herald

Local Radio: Beds Radio, Chiltern, Three Counties Radio

**CLUB PERSONNEL**

**Secretary:** Leo Glynn

4 Little Catherells, Gadebridge, Hemel Hempstead, Herts HP1 3QB

Chairman: Dale Boggins

President:

Vice President: Dave Lloyd

Manager: Neil Price

Asst Manager: Roy Butler

Physio: Zoey

**BERKHAMSTED TOWN** - (L-R) **Back Row:** Mick Foster, Rory Brady, Steve Boad, Pete Clifford, Nick Webb, John Richardson, Mark Swales, Paul Love. **Front Row:** David Bayliss (mascot), Stuart Gallagher, Andy Mullins, Dean Chapman, Paul Campbell, Wes Foley, Darren Green, Chris Hewett.
Photo: Clive Butchins

**MOLESEY**- (L-R) **Back Row:** Dave Swindlehurst (club coach), Dave Tilbury, Asa Head, Sean Finnan, James Wastell, Paul Gower, Adam Gray, Ray Best (manager), Rachel Hales (physio), Steve Tebb.
**Front Row:** Simon Mitchell, Geoff Taylor, Lyndon Buckwell, Neil Musgrove, Eben Allen, Grant Hutchinson.
Photo: Andrew Chitty

**WITHAM TOWN**
Photo: Andrew Chitty

# HORSHAM

**GROUND:** Queen Street, Horsham RH13 5AD (01403 252310)

**Directions:** From the station turn left into North Street. Pass the Arts Centreto the traffic lights and turn left. At the next set of lights (200 yards) turn left again into East Street. East Street becomes Queen Street after the IronBridge and the ground lies opposite Queens Head public house

Capacity: 4,500 Seats: 300 Cover: 3,000 Floodlights: Yes
**Clubhouse:** Matchdays only. Hot and cold snacks. Dancehall
**Club Shop:** Yes

**HONOURS** Sussex Snr Cup 33-34 38-39 49-50 53-54 71-72 73-74 75-76; Sussex RUR Cup (13); Sussex Floodlight Cup 77-78; Sussex County Lg (7), R-up (4), Lg Cup 45-46 46-47; Metropolitan Lg 51-52; Athenian Lg Div 1 72-73, Div 2 69-70 72-73; West Sussex Sen Lge (4); ICIS Div 3 95-96

**CLUB RECORDS Attendance:** 8,000 v Swindon, FA Cup 1st Rd, November 1966
**Victory:** 16-1 v Southwick Susussex Co Lg 1945-46
**Defeat:** 1-11 v Worthing Sussex Sen Cup 1913-14
**BEST SEASON FA Cup:** 1st Rd 47-48 (lost 1-9 at Notts County), 66-67 (lost 0-3 v Swindon)
**F.A. Trophy:** 1st Rd Proper Replay 76-77 **F.A.Vase:** 4th Rd Replay 85-86
**PREVIOUS Leagues:** W Sussex Sen; Sussex County 26-51; Metropolitan 51-57; Corinthian 57-63; Athenian 63-73
**Grounds:** Horsham Park, Hurst Park, Springfield Park
Players progressing: Jamie Ndah (Barnet), Darren Freeman (Fulham)

**1998-99 Captain:** Ochea Ikpa **P.o.Y.:** Lee Preston **Top scorer:** Germain Amanuel(20)

### FACT FILE
Founded: 1885
Nickname: Hornets
Club Sponsors: Sunley Homes
Colours: Yellow & green/yellow/yellow
Change colours: All white
Midweek Matches: Tuesday
Reserves' League: Suburban

Programme: 40 pages, £1
Editor: Jeff Barrett (01403 267730)
Local Press: West Sussex County Times:
Market Square, Horsham (01403 253371)

### CLUB PERSONNEL

**Secretary:** Jef Barrett, 3Bunting Close, Horsham, West Sussex RH13 5PA.
Tel No 01403 267730

Chairman: Frank King
Vice Chairman: Jeff Barratt
President: Geoff Holtom
Press Officer: Jeff Barratt (01403 267627)

Manager: Russell Mason
Asst Mgr/Coach: Peter Shaw
Physio: Geoff Brittain

# HUNGERFORD TOWN

**GROUND**
**Address:** Town Ground, Bulpit Lane, Hungerford RG17 0AY
Tel: 01488 682939 (club) 01488 684597 (boardroom) 01488 684597 (Fax)

**Directions:** M4 jct 14 to A4, right and left at Bear Hotel, through town centre on A338, left into Priory Rd, second left into Bulpit Lane, over crossroads, ground on left. 3/4 mile from Hungerford BR station

Capacity: 3,000 Seats: 172 Cover: 200 Floodlights: Yes Club Shop: Yes

**Clubhouse:** Open every evening and lunchtimes including Sunday. 2 bars,dancehall, boardroom/committee room, darts, pool, fruit machines. Hot & coldsnacks. Steward: Terry Tracey (01488 682939)

**HONOURS:** Berks & Bucks Snr Cup 81-82 (R-up 75-76 76-77); Hellenic Lg Div 1 70-71, PremDiv Cup 77-78, Div 1 Cup 70-71, Benevolent Cup 60-61; Hungerford Cup 96-97, Isthmian Lge Representatives in Anglo-Italian Tournament 81.

**PREVIOUS Leagues:** Newbury & D.; Swindon & D.; Hellenic 58-78
**Names:** None **Grounds:** None

**CLUB RECORDS Attendance:** 1,684 v Sudbury Town, FA Vase SF 1st leg 88-89
(20,000 v Modena inItaly 1981)
**Scorer:** Ian Farr (268) **Appearances:** Dean Bailey (approx 400)
**Transfer Fee Paid:** £4,000 for Joe Scott (Yeovil Town)
**Received:** £3,800 for Joe Scott (Barnstaple Town)

**BEST SEASON FA Cup:** 1st Rd 79-80, 1-3 v Slough T. (A)
**FA Vase:** Semi-Final 77-78 79-80 88-89

Players progressing to Football League: Steve Hetzke (Reading, Blackpool,Sunderland), Bruce Walker (Swindon, Blackpool), Des McMahon (Reading), BrianMundee (Bournemouth, Northampton), Darren Anderson

### FACT FILE
Founded: 1886
Nickname: Crusaders
Club Sponsors: Kerridge Insurance
Colours: White/blue/white
Change colours: All red
Midweek Matchday: Tuesday
Reserves' League: Suburban (Premier)
Programme: 24 pages, 50p
Editor:Martyn Leach (01488 683682)
Local Press: Newbury Weekly News,
Newbury Evening Post
Local Radio: Berkshire Radio, Radio 210
98-99 - Captain: Andy Wollen
P.o.Y.: Martyn Churchward
Top scorer: Simon Sly (20)

### CLUB PERSONNEL

Chairman: Alan Holland
Vice Chairman: Ron Tarry
President: Sir Seton Wills
Press Officer: Ron Tarry (01488 682539)
Manager: Don Rogers
Asst Manager: Colin Moyle
Physio: Gerald Smith

Secretary: Ken Holmes
35 Queens Court, St Johns Road, Newbury
Berkshire RG147PX
Tel: 01635 523632

# LEIGHTON TOWN

**GROUND:**
**Address:** Bell Close, Lake Street, Leighton Buzzard, Beds Tel: 01525 373311

**Directions:** From bypass (A505) take A4146 (Billington Rd) towards Leighton Buzzard, straight overfirst roundabout then straight over mini-r'bout & 1st left into car park - ground behindCamden Motors just before town centre. Half mile from Leighton Buzzard (BR)station. Buses from Luton, Aylesbury and Milton Keynes

Capacity: 2,800    Seats: 155    Cover: 300    Floodlights: Yes    Club Shop: Yes

Clubhouse: Normal licensing hours.
Snack/refreshment bar on matchdays - full range of hot snacks & drinks

**HONOURS** Isthmian Lge Div 3 R-up 95-96; Sth Midlands Lg 66-67 91-92, Lg Cup 90-91, O'Brien Tphy 90-91, Reserve Div 1 87-88 91-92 94-95, Res Div 2 76-77, ResChallenge Cup 93-94 94-95; Beds Snr Cup 26-27 67-68 68-69 69-70 92-93; BucksCharity Cup 94-95;98-99 Spartan Lg Div 2 23-24 27-28;
Leighton & District Lg, Beds Intermediate Cup (res) 90-91; Beds Yth Cup 91-92 92-93,94-95 94-95; Chiltern Youth Lg94-95, Lg Cup 93-94; East Anglian Yth.Cup 94-95; Assoc Mem Cup 96-97.98-99

**PREVIOUS** **Leagues:** Leighton & District; South Midlands 22-24 26-29 46-54 55-56 76-92;Spartan 22-53 67-74; United Counties 74-76
**Name:** Leighton United    **Ground:** None

**CLUB RECORDS** **Attendance:** 1,522 v Aldershot T., Isthmian Lg Div 3, 30/1/93
**Win:** 7-2    **Defeat:** 1-6

**BEST SEASON** **FA Cup:** Third Qual. Round 70-71, 1-2 v St Albans City (A)

## FACT FILE
Founded: 1885
Nickname: Reds
Sponsors: Camden Motors
Colours: Red & white
Change colours: All blue
Midweek Matchday: Tuesday
Reserve's League: Suburban
Programme: 50p
Editor: David Friend(01525 375931)
Local Press: Leighton Buzzard Observer, The Herald, The Citizen
Local Radio: Three Counties Radio, Radio Chiltern, Mix 96
98-99 - Captain: Paul Firth
P.o.Y.: Ken Hollis
Top scorer: Jon Pedder

### CLUB PERSONNEL
**Secretary:** Alec Irvine
12 Rowley Furrows, Linslade, Leighton Buzzard, Beds LU77SH
Tel: 01525 376475

Chairman: Iain S McGregor
President: Bill Harrison
Press Officer: Iain S McGregor
Tel: 01525 370142

Manager: Guy Kefford
Physio: Mel Roberts

# MARLOW

**GROUND:**
**Address:** Alfred Davis Memorial Ground, Oak Tree Road, Marlow SL7 3ED (01628 483970)

**Directions:** A404 to Marlow (from M4 or M40), then A4155 towards town centre.Turn right into Maple Rise (by ESSO garage), ground in road opposite (Oak TreeRd). 1/2 mile from Marlow (BR). 1/4 mile from Chapel Street bus stops

Capacity: 3,000    Cover: 600    Seats: 250    Floodlights: Yes
Clubhouse: Open matchdays & most evenings. Snack bar open matchdays
Club Shop: Sells programmes, badges, ties, pens, videos etc

**HONOURS:** Isthmian Lg Div 1 87-88, Div 2 South R-up 86-87, Lg Cup 92-93; SpartanLg Div 1 37-38 (Div 2 West 29-30); Berks & Bucks Sen Cup (11)

**PREVIOUS:** **Leagues:** Reading & Dist.; Spartan 1908-10 28-65; Great Western Suburban;Athenian 65-84
**Name:** Great Marlow
**Grounds:** Crown Ground 1870-1919); Star Meadow 19-24

**CLUB RECORDS:** **Attendance:** 3,000 v Oxford United, FA Cup 1st Rd 1994. (Ground - 8,000 SloughT. v Wycombe W., Berks & Bucks Snr Cup Final, 1972)
**Goalscorer:** Kevin Stone 31
**Appearances:** Mick McKeown 500+
**Fees - Paid:** £5,000 for Richard Evans (Sutton Utd. 94)
**Received:** £8,000 for David Lay from Slought Town 94

**BEST SEASON:** **FA Cup:** Semi-Finals 1882; 3rd Rd 94-95 (0-2 v Swindon) 92-93 (1-5 v Tottenham); 1st Rd on    19 times -1871-85 86-88 92-93 1991-92 94-95
**FA Trophy:** 1st Rd 1987-88, 91-92
**FA Vase:** 5th Rd replay 74-75

Players progressing: Leo Markham (Watford 1972), NaseemBashir (Reading)

## FACT FILE
Formed: 1870
Nickname: The Blues
Sponsors: The Marlow Building Company
Colours: Royal, white trim/royal/royal
Change colours: Orange & black
Midweek matchday: Tuesday
Reserves' League: Suburban Premier
Programme: Pages: 40 Price: £1
Editor: Terry Staines
Local Press: Bucks Free Press, Maidenhead Advertiser, Evening Post
Local Radio: Eleven 70, Radio 210, Thames Valley Radio
Information Line ( normal call rates) : 01932 710215
98-99 - Captain: Grant Goodall
P.o.Y.: Jim Bradley
Top scorer: Robert Gibson (30)

### CLUB PERSONNEL
Secretary; Paul Burdell, 69 Wycombe Rd., Marlow. (01628 483722)
Chairman: Terry Staines
President:
Vice-Chairman:

Press Off./Comm. Man.: Terry Staines
Manager: Graham Pritchard
Coach: Derek Sweetman
Physio: Mark Skoyles

# METROPOLITAN POLICE

**GROUND:**
Metropolitan Police Sports Ground, Imber Court, East Molesey (0181 3987358)
**Directions:** From London: A3 then A309 to Scilly Isles r'bout, right into Hampton Court Way, left
at 1st r'bout into Ember Court Rd - ground faces in 300yds. From M25 jct 10: A3 towards
London for 1 mile, A307 through Cobham, left immediately after Sandown Park into Station Rd -
ground 1 mile on left. Half mile from either Thames Ditton or Esher BR stations

Capacity: 3,000     Seats: 297     Cover: 1,800     Floodlights: Yes     Club Shop: No
**Clubhouse:** (0181 398 1267). Four bars, dancehall, cafeteria open 9am-11pm. Hot & cold food

**HONOURS:**     Isthmian Lg Div 2 R-up 77-78 87-88; Spartan Lg 28-29 29-30 36-37
                 38-39 45-46 53-54 54-55, (R-up 47-48), Lg Cup 59-60 (R-up 57-58);
                 Middx Snr Cup 27-28;Surrey Snr Cup 32-33, Charity Shield 38-39;
                 Metropolitan Lg Cup 68-69 (Amtr Cup 68-69 69-70); London Snr Cup R-
                 up 34-35 40-41; Herts & Middx Comb. 39-40;Diadora Lg Carlsberg
                 Trophy  94-95

**PREVIOUS:**    **Leagues:** Spartan 28-60; Metropolitan 60-71; Southern 71-78
                 **Grounds:** None
                 **Name:** None

**CLUB RECORDS:**  **Attendance:** 4,500 v Kingstonian, FA Cup 1934
                   **Goal Scorer:** Mario Russo
                   **Appearances:** Pat Robert
                   **Win:** 10-1 v Tilbury 1995
                   **Defeat:** 1-11 v Wimbledon, 1956

**BEST SEASON**   **FA Cup:** 1st Rd - 32-33, 0-9 v Northampton T. (A);
                  84-85, 0-3 v Dartford (H);  94-95, 0-3 v Crawley T. (H)

**FACT FILE**
Founded: 1919
Nickname: Blues
Club Sponsors: McDonalds
Colours: All blue
Change colours: Black & White stripes
Midweek Matches: Tuesday
Reserves' League: Suburban

Programme: 10 pages, 50p
Editor/ Press Officer:
Cliff Travis (01932 782215)

Local Press: Surrey Comet, Surrey Herald
Local Radio: County Sounds

**CLUB PERSONNEL**

Secretary: Tony Brooking,
15 Westmoreland Ave, Hornchurch, Essex.
RM112EJ. Tel: (01708 450715)

Chairman: Des Flanders QPM
Vice Chairman:Dave Smith
President: Sir Paul Condon QPM

Manager: Mel Thomas
Physio: Dick Pierce
1998-99 Captain: Adam Wickens
Player of the Year; Dave Newman
Top Scorer: Mark Scott

---

# MOLESEY

**GROUND**     **Address:** 412 Walton Road, West Molesey, Surrey KT8 0JG
               Tel: 0181 941 7989 (Boardroom)    0181 979 4823 (Clubhouse)

               **Directions:** A3 from London to Hook, thenA309 to Marquis of Granby pub, right
               to Hampton Court station, turn left forWest Molesey, ground one mile on left

               Capacity: 4,000     Cover: 600     Seats: 400     Floodlights: Yes
               Clubhouse: Open every evening and weekend lunchtimes
               2 bars, discos, live artists, darts, bingo, pool. Steward: TBA
               Club Shop: Contact John Chambers

**PREVIOUS**    **Name:** Molesey St Pauls 1950-53.    **Grounds:** None
                **Leagues:** Surrey Intermediate 53-56; Surrey Snr 56-59; Spartan 59-72; Athenian72-77

**CLUB RECORDS**  **Attendance:** 1,255 v Sutton United, Surrey Senior Cup Semi-Final 1966
                  **CareerGoalscorer:** Michael Rose, 139
                  **Career Appearances:** Frank Hanley, 453
                  **Transfer fee paid:** £500 for Chris Vidal (Leatherhead 88)
                  **Transfer fee received:** £5,000 for Chris Vidal (Hythe Town 89)

**BEST SEASON**  **FA Vase:** 6th Rd 81-82.   **FA Trophy:** 1st Rd replay 90-91
                 **FA Cup:** First Round Proper 94-95, 0-4 v Bath City (H)

**HONOURS**      Isthmian Lg Div 1 R-up 92-93 (Div 2 South R-up 89-90, Lg Cup R-up 92-93),
                 Surrey Senior Lg 57-58, (Lg Charity Cup 56-57), Spartan Lg R-up 59-60 (Lg
                 Cup 61-62 (R-up 63-64)), Surrey Senior Shield R-up 74-75,
                 Southern Combination Cup 90-91 94-95

Players progressing: John Finch (Fulham), Cyrille Regis (WBA, Coventry &England)

1998-99 -       Captain: Paul Gover   P.o.Y.: Lewis Craker   Top Scorer: Sean Finnan (23)

**FACT FILE**
Formed: 1950
Nickname: The Moles
Colours: White/black/black
Change colours: Yellow/royal
Midweek home matchday: Tuesday
Reserve Team's League: Suburban
Youth Team: Southern Yth Lge

Programme - Pages: 44 Price: £1
Editor: Simon Carthew
c/o the club
Local Press: Surrey Comet, Surrey Herald,
Molesey News
Local Radio: Thames 107.8 FM
Hospital Radio, County Sound, Three
Counties, Star FM.

**CLUB PERSONNEL**

Secretary/Press Officer:
Ben O'Connor (c/o the club)

Chairman: Norman Clark
President: Fred Maynard

Manager: Dave Swindlehurst
Coach: Peter Burdett
Reserve Manager: Dave Wellar

# NORTHWOOD

**GROUND:**
**Address:** Northwood Park, Chestnut Avenue, Northwood (01923 827148)
**Directions:** A404 (Pinner-Rickmansworth) - Chestnut Ave. on left by large grey iron railway bridge. Third of a mile from Northwood Hills station (Metropolitan Line) - turn right out of station to r'bout, left into Pinner Road, left into Chestnut Avenue after 300yds. Buses 282 and H11 to Northwood Hills
Capacity: 2,250    Seats: 150    Cover: 400    Floodlights: Yes
Club Shop: No
**Clubhouse:** Weekends and most evenings from 6pm. Bar. Hot and cold food. Pool, juke-box

**HONOURS:** Isthmian Lg Associate Members Cup 92-93; London Spartan Lg 91-92 (R-up 89-90), Lg Cup 89-90 91-92; Hellenic Lg Div 1 78-79 (Prem Div Cup R-up 81-82); Middx Lg 77-78 (R-up 72-73 76-77), Div 1 R-up 71-72, Challenge Cup 74-75 76-77 77-78; Middx Snr Charity Cup R-up 93-94; Middx Snr Cup SF 91-92 92-93 98-99; Jnr Cup 46-47 47-48 48-49; Harrow & Wembley Lg (9); Middlesex Premier Cup 94-95.

**PREVIOUS:** **Leagues:** Harrow & Wembley 32-69; Middlesex 69-78; Hellenic 79-84; London Spartan 84-92
**Names:** Northwood Town
**Grounds:** None

**CLUB RECORDS: Attendance:** 1,642 v Chelsea Friendly July 1997
**Goal Scorer:** Martin Ellis
**Career Appearances:** Norman Heslop

**BEST SEASON:** **FA Cup:** 2nd Qual Rd 94-95
**FA Vase:** Qtr finals 96-97

Players progressing: Gavin Maguire, Derek Payne (Barnet), Warren Patmore (Cambridge)

**FACT FILE**
Founded: 1902
Nickname: Woods
Sponsors: IFS Freight Forwarding
Colours: All red
Change colours: All yellow
Midweek Matches: Tuesday
Reserve League: Suburban
Programme: 52 pages 80p
Editor: A Evans (02088 566 2880)
Local Press: Ruislip & Northwood Gazette, Watford Observer
97-98 - Captain: Chris Gell
P.o.Y: Dave Sargent
Top Scorer: Keith Boreham

**CLUB PERSONNEL**
**Secretary:** Steve Williams, 35 Evelyn Drive, Hatch End, Pinner, Middx HA5 4RL
Tel: (02088 428 1533 - H & fax)

Chairman: Andy Johnson
Vice Chairman: Geoff Foster
President: Lothar Hahn
Press Off: M Russell (01923 827690)

Manager: Tony Choules
Physio: George Price

# TOOTING & MITCHAM

**GROUND:**
**Address:** Sandy Lane, Mitcham, Surrey CR4 2HD Tel: 0181 648 3248
**Directions:** Tooting (BR) quarter mile.
Sandy Lane is off Streatham Road near the Swan Hotel
Capacity: 8,000    Cover: 1,990    Seats: 1,990    Floodlights: Yes
Clubhouse: Open every evening and weekend lunchtimes. Wide variety of food available
Club Shop: Sells souvenirs & confectionary

**HONOURS:** Isthmian League 57-58 59-60 (Full Members Cup 92-93); Athenian League 49-50 54-55; London Challenge Cup R-up 59-60; Surrey Senior Cup 37-38 43-44 44-45 52-53 59-60 75-76 76-77 77-78; London Senior Cup 42-43 48-49 58-59 59-60 (R-up 43-44 44-45); South Thames Cup 69-70; Surrey Senior Shield 51-52 60-61 61-62 65-66

**PREVIOUS:** **Leagues:** London 32-37, Athenian 37-56    **Ground:** None    **Name:** None

**CLUB RECORDS: Attendance:** 17,500 v QPR, FA Cup 2nd Rd 56-57
**Goalscorer:** Alan Ives 92 (1972-78)    **Appearances:** Danny Godwin 470
**Win:** 11-0 v Welton Rovers, FA Amateur Cup 62-63
**Defeat:** 1-8 v Kingstonian, Surrey Snr Cup 66-67
v Redbridge Forest (H), LoctiteCup 3rd Rd 19/2/91
**Fee Paid:** £9,000 for Dave Flint (Enfield)
**Fee Received:** £10,000 for Herbie Smith (Luton)

**BEST SEASON:** **FA Trophy:** 2nd Qualifying Rd Replay 71-72 81-82
**FA Amateur Cup:** 1st Rd replay 22-23    **FA Vase:**
**FA Cup:** 4th Rd 75-76, 1-3 v Bradford C. (A)
3rd Rd 58-59; 2nd Rd 56-57 76-77;1st Rd 5 other occasions
League clubs defeated: Bournemouth & Boscombe Ath, Northampton 58-59, Swindon 75-76

Players progressing: Trevor Owen (Orient 58), Dave Bumpstead (Millwall 58), Paddy Hasty (Aldersot 58), Walter Pearson(Aldershot ), Richie Ward & Alex Stepney (Millwall 62 & 63), Vic Akers(Watford 75), Paul Priddy (Wimbledon 78), Carlton Fairweather & Brian Gayle(Wimbledon 84)

**FACT FILE**
Formed: 1932
Nickname: Terrors
Sponsors: Claremont Coaches
Colours: Black & white stripes/black/white
Change colours: All red
Midweek matchday: Tuesday
Reserve League: Suburban

Local Press: Mitcham News, South London Press, South London Guardian
Local Radio: Capital
Programme: Pages: 24   Price: 80p
Editor: Jim Silvey

**CLUB PERSONNEL**

**Secretary:** Les Roberts, 91 Fernlea Road, Mitcham, Surrey CR4 2HG (01816 465275)

Chairman: John Buffoni
President: Cliff Bilham
Vice Chairman: Alan Simpson

Commercial Manager: John Pollard
Press Officer: Jim Silvey 0181 640 5678 (H)

Manager: James Bolton
Coach: Peter Shaw
Physio: Danny Keenan

# WEMBLEY

**GROUND**  **Address:** Vale Farm, Watford Road, Sudbury, Wembley HA0 4UR
Tel: 0181 908 8169
**Directions:** Sudbury Town station (Underground) 400 yds, or 10 mins walk
from North Wembley (BR) station. Buses 18, 92, 245 & 182
Capacity: 2,000    Cover: 350    Seats: 350    Floodlights: Yes
Clubhouse: Open every night & weekend lunchtimes.
Hot food on matchdays (0181 904 8169).    Club Shop: No

**PREVIOUS**  **Leagues:** Middx 46-49; Spartan 49-51; Delphian 51-56; Corinthian 56-63;
Athenian 63-75

**CLUB RECORDS**  **Attendance:** 2,654 v Wealdstone, FA Amateur Cup 52-53
**Career goalscorer:** Bill Handrahan 105 (1946-52)
**Career appearances:** Spud Murphy 505 (78-88)
**Win:** 11-1 v Hermes, London Senior Cup 1963
**Defeat:** 0-16 v Chelsea, London Challenge Cup 59-60
**Transfer Fee paid:** Nil
**Fee received:** £10,000 for Gary Roberts (Brentford, 1981)

**BEST SEASON**  **FA Trophy:** 1st Round proper 91-92
**FA Amateur Cup:** 2nd Round 66-67, 68-69
**FA Cup:** 1st Round Proper 1980-81,  0-3 v Enfield (A)

**HONOURS**  Middx Sen Cup 83-84 86-87 (R-up 55-56 68-69 78-79  87-88 91-92 92-93
98-99);Middx Lge 47-48 (Lge Cup 46-47), Middx Charity Cup 67-68 (jnt) 80-
81(jnt) 82-83 86-87  94-95,(R-up 83-84 87-88 96-97); Middx Invitation Cup
56-57; Athenian Lge R-up 74-75 (Div 1 R-up 67-68); Corinthian Lge Mem
Shield R- up 58-59; Delphian Lge R-up 55-56; Spartan Lge Div 1 West 50-
51 (Dunkel Trophy 50-51 jnt); London Sen Cup R-up 55-56; Hitachi Cup SF
83-84; Suburban Lge North 85-86, Lge Cup 84-85 (R-up 83-84)

Players progressing: Keith Cassells (Watford 1977), MikeO'Donague (Southampton 1979), A
McGonigle (Olympiakos), Gary Roberts (Brentford1980), Richard Cadette (Orient 1984)

**FACT FILE**
Formed: 1946
Nickname: The Lions
Sponsors: G & B Builders
Colours: Red & white/red/red
Change colours: All gold
Midweek matchday: Tuesday
Reserves' League: Suburban

Programme - Pages: 28  Price: £1
Editor: Richard Markiewicz
(0181 902 0541 - before 9pm)
Local Press: Wembley & Harrow Observer
Local Radio: Capital, G.L.R
98-99 - Captain: Ian Bates
P.O.Y. & Top Scorer: Davis Haule

**CLUB PERSONNEL**

**Secretary:** Mrs Jean Gumm, 14 Woodfield
Avenue, North Wembley, Middx HA0
3NR(0181 908 3353)

Chairman: Brian Gumm
President: Eric Stringer
Vice Chairman:
Press Officer: Richard Markiewicz
(0181 902 0541 before 9pm)
Commercial Manager: Nick Bennett

Manager: Erol Dyer
Asst. Manager: Roger Linton

# WINDSOR & ETON

**GROUND**
**Address:** Stag Meadow, St Leonards Road, Windsor, Berkshire SL4 3DR (01753860656)
**Directions:** A332 from M4 junct 6. Left at r'bout (B3173), left into St LeonardsRd at lights on T-
junction, ground 500 yards on right on B3022 opposite Stag &Hounds PH. 1 mile from town
centre - pass available to St Leonards Rd. BR toWindsor Central station (from) Slough or
Windsor Riverside (change at Stainesfrom Waterloo)
Capacity: 4,500    Cover: 650    Seats: 400    Floodlights: Yes
Clubhouse: Yes    Club Shop: Yes

**HONOURS**  Isthmian Lg Div 1 83-84 (Div 2 R-up 82-83), Athenian Lg 79-80 80-81 (Lg Cup
79-80 (R-up 78-79 80-81), Div 2 Cup 63-64 (R-up 68-69)), Spartan Lg R-up 36-37
37-38 (Div 1 30-31), Metropolitan Lg R-up 53-54 (Lg Amtr Cup 51-52 52-53, Lg
Cup 52-53 (R-up 53-54 54-55)), Gt Western Suburban Lg R-up 21-22, Berks &
Bucks SnrCup(11) 10-11 36-38 40-45 61-62 87-89 (R-up 07-08 24-25 26-27 38-39
46-47 62-63), Berks & Bucks Benev. Cup 35-36 37-38 46-47 62-63 (R-up 38-39
47-48 49-50)

**PREVIOUS**  **Leagues:** Southern 1895-96; West Berks; Great Western Suburban 1907-22;
Athenian 22-29 63-81; Spartan 29-32; Great Western Comb; Corinthian 45-50;
Metropolitan 50-60; Delphian 60-63    **Ground:** Ballon Meadow 1892-1912

**CLUB RECORDS**  **Attendance:** 8,500 (Charity match)  Appearances: Kevin Mitchell
**Fee Paid:** £9,000 for Keith White (Slough Town)
**Fee Received:** £45,000 for Michael Banton & Michael Barnes (Barnet)

**BEST SEASON**  **FA Amateur Cup:** 4th Rd 21-22  FA Vase: Semi-Final 80-81 (QF 79-80)
**FA Cup:** 2nd Rd replay 83-84. 1st Rd 7 times 25-26 80-81 82-86 91-92.
League clubs defeated: None    **FA Trophy:** 3rd Rd 88-89

Players progressing: Reg Dare (Southampton 1949), Steve Adams (Charlton 1979), Dave
Barnett (Colchester 1988), Vic Woodley (Chelsea & England), Billy Coward (QPR, Walsall), Ken
Groves (Preston), Dave Regis (Notts County)

**FACT FILE**
Founded: 1892
Nickname: Royalists
Sponsors: Murex Welding Products
Colours: All red with green trim
Change colours: White/black/black
Midweek matches: Tuesday
Reserves' League: Suburban (North)
Programme: 28 pages  Editor: Eric Richford

Local Press: Windsor & Eton Express,
Windsor & East Berks Observer,
Evening Post

**CLUB PERSONNEL**

**Secretary:** Steve Rowland,
91 Duke Street, Windsor, Berks SL4 1SJ
Tel: 01753 774528 (H, emergency only)

Chairman: Peter Simpson/Kevin Stott
President: Sir David Hill-Wood, Bt
Press Officer: Secretary

Manager: Allan Davies
Asst Manager: Alan Rowe
Physio: Des Hunt

# WINGATE & FINCHLEY

**GROUND:**

The Abrahams Stadium, Summers Lane, Finchley, London N12 0PD.( 0181 446 2217)

**Directions:** North Circular (A406) to jct with High Road Finchley (A1000), go north and Summers Lane is 200 yds on rt - parking 80 cars. Tube to East Finchley (Northern Line) and then 263 bus to Summers Lane towards North Finchley

Capacity: 8,500    Seats: 500         Cover: 500         Floodlights: Yes
Clubhouse: Open during matches. Also tea-bar selling most refreshments
Club Shop: No

**HONOURS:** Isthmian League Div. 3 R-up 98-99, London Senior Cup Winners 94-95
Ryman Div 3 R-up 98-99

**CLUB RECORDS: Attendance:** 9,555 - Finchley v Bishop Auckland, F.A. Amat Cup QF 49-50
**Career Goalscorer:** Marc Morris 578
**Career Appearances:** Marc Morris 587(1975-93)
**Win:** 9-0, Wingate v Sarratt, Herts Co. Lge Div. 1, 20/4/85
**Defeat:** 0-5, Wingate v Tudor Corinthians, Herts Co. Lge Div. 1, 13/4/85

**BEST SEASON    FA Vase:** 74-75 Quarter Final (Wingate)
**FA Amateur Cup:** Semi-Final (Finchley)

**PREVIOUS:    Names:** Wingate (founded 46), Finchley (founded late 1800s) merged in 91
**Leagues:** (as Wingate & Finchley) South Mids 89-95
**Honours -** Finchley: London Snr Cup, London Charity Cup, Athenian Lg 53-54 (R-up 63-64 65-66), London Lg 36-37 (R-up 35-36, Div 2 06-07(jt with Enfield),Lg Cup 34-35, Park Royal Cup 37-38) Wingate: Middx Lg(2)(R-up(1), Lg Cup), London Lg R-up(2)(Lg Cup(1)), Middx SnrCup SF, Athenian Lg Div 2 69-70, Herts Co. Lg Div 1 84-85 (Aubrey Cup 85-86),Herts I'mediate Cup 84-85, Herts Snr Tphy 86-87, Sth Mids Lg Div 1 R-up 89-90(Lg Cup SF 89-90), Barnet Yth Lg 75-76, Pete Morrison Cup 82-83 83-84 (R-up 79-80 84-85), Hendon & Dist. Int. Div 79-80. Win & Fin: London Sen Cup 79-80

## FACT FILE

Founded: 1991
Nickname: Blues
Colours: Blue/white/blue
Change Colours: All yellow
Midweek matches: Tuesday
Reserve's Lge: Sub Lge U18
Programme: 32pages, £1.00
Editor: Peter Rebak (0181 371 6000)

1998-99
P.o.Y. Ben Strevens:
Top Scorer: Ben Strevens

**CLUB PERSONNEL**

**Secretary:** Richard Cooper, c/o Club
Tel: 0181 446 2217 Fax 0181 343 8194

Chairman:  Peter Rebak
Vice Chairman:
President: Kenneth Aston
Press Off.: Harvey Ackerrman
(Tel No: 0181 349 0160)

Manager: Martin Burt
Coach: Colin Pates
Physio: Jim Connolly

# WITHAM TOWN

**GROUND:**
**Address:**    Spa Road, Witham, Essex CM8 1UN
Tel: 01376 511198 (lounge) 500146 (reception) 520996 (boardroom)

**Directions:**    From Witham BR (network S.E.) station; through pub car park and follow road to Faulkbourne, at  main r'bout turn left and ground is on the right. By road: Off A12 at Witham sign, left at 1st lights (Spinks Lane), right at end of road, follow road under railway bridge - ground 100yds on left

**Capacity:**    2,500    Seats: 150         Cover: 300         Floodlights: Yes
**Clubhouse:**    Open every night and weekend lunctimes.
Hot bar snacks. Steward: Richard Green
Club Shop: No

**HONOURS:**    Essex Snr Lg 70-71 85-86 (R-up 84-85 86-87), Tphy 85-86 (R-up 88-89);
Essex Thameside Trophy R-up 95-96; Loctite Tphy SF 90-91

**PREVIOUS:**    **Leagues:** Mid Essex; Essex & Suffolk Border; Essex Senior 71-87
**Ground:** The Park    **Names:** None

**CLUB RECORDS Attendance:** 800 v Billericay Town, Essex Senior League, May 1976
**Win:** 7-0 v Banstead 27/9/94    **Defeat:** 0-9 v Collier Row 21/10/95
**Goalscorer:** Colin Mitchell    **Appearances:** Keith Dent (16 years)
**Fee received:** for Steve Tilson (Southend)

**BEST SEASON: FA Vase:** 5th Round, 85-86
**FA Cup:** 2nd Qual. Rd 87-88 (v Gravesend), 88-89 (v B. Stortford), 89-90 (v Dartford)

Players progressing to Football League: Steve Tilson (Southend)

98-99 -    Captain: Justin Pearce  P.o.Y.: Kevin Jopson  Top scorer: Lee Guiver

## FACT FILE
Founded:  1947
Nickname:  Town
Colours:  Red & black stripes/white/white
Change colours:  Blue & white
Midweek Matchday:  Tuesday
Reserve's League:
Essex & Herts Border Comb
Programme:  24 pages, 60p
Editor:  Nigel Dudley
Local Press:  Witham & Braintree Times,
Essex Chronicle, East Anglian DailyTimes,
Evening Gazette
Local Radio:  BBC Essex, Essex Radio,
Chelmer Radio

**CLUB PERSONNEL**

**Secretary:** Jim Claydon, 58 Silver Street,
Silver End, Witham, Essex CM8 3QG
01376 584086 H, 01376 583241 x426 B

Chairman:  Reg Wright
Vice Chairman:
President:  B Olley
Press Officer:  G Vale (01376 513861)

Manager:  George Young
Asst Mgr:  Pat Garrett
Physio:  John Barwick

# WIVENHOE TOWN

**GROUND:** Broad Lane Ground, Elmstead Road, Wivenhoe CO7 7HA Tel: 01206 823416
**Directions:** Coming out of Colchester towards Clacton take first turning (right) towards
Wivenhoe, 1st left and ground clearly visible on right at cross-roads. 1 mile from Wivenhoe (BR)
Capacity: 3,000     Cover: 1,300     Seats: 250     Floodlights: Yes
Clubhouse: (01206 825380) Open normal pub hours     Club Shop: A full range of souvenirs etc

**PREVIOUS:     Leagues:** Brighlingsea & District 1927-50; Colchester & East Essex 50-71;
Essex & Suffolk Border 71-79; Essex Senior 79-86     **Name:** Wivenhoe Rangers
**Grounds:** Spion Kop; Broomfield; Claude Watcham's Meadow; Vine Farm;
Spion Kop; Broomfield; King George V Playing Fields; Essex University

**CLUB RECORD     Attendance:** 1,912 v Runcorn, FA Trophy 1st Rd, Feb 1990
**Transfer fee received:** £5,875 for Bobby Mayes (Redbridge Forest)
**Win:** 18-0 v Nayland.     **Defeat:** 0-8 v Carshalton A. (H), Isthmian Lg 28/8/93
**Career goalscorer:** Paul Harrison, 258 in 350 games
**Career appearances:** Keith Bain, 536

**BEST SEASON     FA Cup:** 4th Qual Rd 89-90 2-3 v Halesowen Tn (A), 94-95 1-2 v Enfield (H)
**FA Trophy:** 2nd Rd replay 89-90     **FA Vase:** 5th Rd 82-83;

**HONOURS**     Isthmian Lg Div 1 89-90 (Div 2 Nth 87-88); Essex Snr Lg R-up 79-80 81-82 85-
86(Harry Fisher Tphy 83-84 85-86); Essex & Suffolk Border Lg 78-79, Div 1 72-73,Div 2 71-72, Lg
Cup R-up(2); Colchester & East Essex Lg 52-53 55-56 (R-up 70-71), Div 1 59-60 69-70, Div 2 R-
up 68-69, Lg KO Cup 51-52 52-53 54-55 55-56 (R-up 59-60), Challenge Cup 52-53); Brighlingsea
& Dist Lg Div 1 35-36 36-37 47-48(R-up 37-38), Lg KO Cup 36-37 37-38 47-48, Challenge Cup 36-
37; Essex Snr Tphy87-88 Essex Jnr Cup R-up 55-56 78-79; Amos Charity Cup(7) (R-up 72-73);
StokesCup(3); Wivenhoe Charity Cup (4), (R-up [4]); Cristal Monopole Cup (5), (R-up 2); Sidney
James Mem. Tphy 69-70 (R-up 72-73), Tolleshunt D'Arcy Mem. Cup(3)(R-up 2); Walton & District
Charity Cup 73-74 78-79; Coggeshall Brotherhood Cup80-81; Brantham Charity Cup R-up 82-83;
Worthington Evans Cup 81-82 (R-up 80-8185-86); Harwich Snr Cup R-up 84-85; Woodbridge Chal.
Cup 91-92; Mat FowlerShield 92-93 94-95

Players progressing: Robert Reinelt (Gillingham) 1993

## FACT FILE

Formed: 1925
Nickname: The Dragons
Colours: Royal blue/yellow
Change colours: Red/black
Reserves' League: Essex & Suffolk Border
Midweek matchday: Tuesday
Programme: 36 pages 80p
Editor: P Reeve
Local Press: East Anglian Daily Times,
Colchester Evening Gazette
Local Radio: BBC Radio Essex,
Radio Orwell

### CLUB PERSONNEL

Secretary/Press Officer: Mike Boyle,
15 Daniell Drive, Colchester, Essex
(01206 573223)

Chairman: T.B.A
Vice Chairman: Dave Whymark
President: Harry Welsh

Manager: Steve Dowman
Asst Manager: Steve Pitt
Physio: Barry Wreford

# WOKINGHAM TOWN

**GROUND**
**Address:** c/o Windsor & Eton FC, Stag Meadow, St Leonards Road, Windsor, Berks SL4 3DR
Tel: 01753 860656
**Directions:** A332 from M4 junct 6. Left at r'bout (B3173), left into St Leonards Rd at lights on
T-junction, ground 500 yards on right on B3022 opposite Stag & Hounds PH.
1 mile from town centre - pass available to St Leonards Rd.
BR to Windsor Central station (from) Slough or
Windsor Riverside (change at Staines from Waterloo)
Capacity: 4,500     Cover: 650     Seats: 400     Floodlights: Yes
**Clubhouse:** Yes     Club Shop: No

**HONOURS**     Isthmian Lg R-up 89-90 (Div 1 81-82, Full Members Cup R-up 94-95), Berks &
Bucks Snr Cup 68-69 82-83 84-85 95-96, Berks & Bucks I'mediate Cup 52-53

**PREVIOUS     Leagues:** Reading & Dist.; Great Western Comb 07-54; Metropolitan 54-57;
Delphian 57-59; Corinthian 59-63; Athenian 63-73.
**Grounds:** Oxford Road 1875-1883; Wellington Road 83-96; Langborough Rd
96-1906, Finchampstead Road 06-99

**CLUB RECORDS     Attendance:** 3,473 v Norton Woodseats, FA Amateur Cup 57-58
**Career Goalscorer:** Terry Brown 91
**Career Appearances:** Dave Cox, 533
**Fee paid:** £5,000 for Fred Hyatt (Burnham, 1990)
**Fee received:** £25,000 for Mark Harris (C Palace 88)

**BEST SEASON     FA Trophy:** Semi finals 87-88     **FA Amateur Cup:** 4th Rd 57-58
**FA Cup:** 1st Rd replay 82-83, 0-3 v Cardiff (A) after 1-1
League clubs defeated: None

Players progressing: Ian Kirkwood (Reading 53), John Harley (Hartlepool 76), Kirk Corbin
(Cambridge 78), Phil Alexander (Norwich 81), DougHatcher (Aldershot 83), Steven Butler &
George Torrance (Brentford 84), MarkHarris (C Palace 88), Gary Smart (Oxford 88), Darren
Barnard (Chelsea 90), PaulHolsgrove (Luton Town 91), Darron Wilkinson (Brighton) 92

## FACT FILE

Formed: 1875
Sponsors: Trademark Windows
Nickname: The Town
Colours: Amber & black/black/black
Change colours: Blue & white/blue/blue
Midweek matchday: Tuesday
Programme: Pages: 32 Price: £1
Editor: Mrs Anne Gale
Local Press: Wokingham Times,
Wokingham News, Reading Evening Post
Local Radio: 210 FM
98-99 - Captain: Simon Turner
P.O.Y.: Simon Turner
Top scorer: Dave Puckett (11)

### CLUB PERSONNEL

**Secretary:** John Aulsberry, 8 Paice Green,
Wokingham RG40 1YN (01189 790441)

Chairman: Richard Brown
President: G Gale
Vice Chairman:
Commercial Manager:

Managers: Steve Mellor
Physio: Melanie Garratt

# DIVISION THREE FINAL LEAGUE TABLE 1998-99

| | | P | W | D | L | F | A | GD | Pts |
|---|---|---|---|---|---|---|---|---|---|
| 1 | Ford United | 38 | 27 | 5 | 6 | 110 | 42 | 68 | 86 |
| 2 | Wingate & Finchley | 38 | 25 | 5 | 8 | 79 | 38 | 41 | 80 |
| 3 | Cheshunt | 38 | 23 | 10 | 5 | 70 | 41 | 29 | 79 |
| 4 | Lewes | 38 | 25 | 3 | 10 | 86 | 45 | 41 | 78 |
| 5 | Epsom & Ewell | 38 | 19 | 5 | 14 | 61 | 51 | 10 | 62 |
| 6 | Ware | 38 | 19 | 4 | 15 | 79 | 60 | 19 | 61 |
| 7 | Tilbury | 38 | 17 | 8 | 13 | 74 | 52 | 22 | 59 |
| 8 | Croydon | 38 | 16 | 10 | 12 | 82 | 59 | 23 | 58 |
| 9 | East Thurrock | 38 | 15 | 13 | 10 | 74 | 56 | 18 | 58 |
| 10 | Egham Town | 38 | 16 | 8 | 14 | 65 | 58 | 7 | 56 |
| 11 | Corinthian Casuals | 38 | 16 | 7 | 15 | 70 | 71 | -1 | 55 |
| 12 | Southall | 38 | 14 | 9 | 15 | 68 | 66 | 2 | 51 |
| 13 | Camberley Town | 38 | 14 | 8 | 16 | 66 | 77 | -11 | 50 |
| 14 | Aveley | 38 | 12 | 7 | 19 | 50 | 67 | -17 | 43 |
| 15 | Flackwell Heath | 38 | 11 | 9 | 18 | 59 | 70 | -11 | 42 |
| 16 | Hornchurch | 38 | 10 | 9 | 19 | 48 | 73 | -25 | 39 |
| 17 | Clapton | 38 | 11 | 6 | 21 | 48 | 89 | -41 | 39 |
| 18 | Dorking | 38 | 8 | 7 | 23 | 52 | 98 | -46 | 31 |
| 19 | Kingsbury Town | 38 | 6 | 3 | 29 | 40 | 98 | -58 | 21 |
| 20 | Tring Town | 38 | 5 | 6 | 27 | 38 | 108 | -70 | 21 |

# RESULTS CHART 1998-99

| HOME TEAM | 1 | 2 | 3 | 4 | 5 | 6 | 7 | 8 | 9 | 10 | 11 | 12 | 13 | 14 | 15 | 16 | 17 | 18 | 19 | 20 |
|---|---|---|---|---|---|---|---|---|---|---|---|---|---|---|---|---|---|---|---|---|
| 1 Aveley | X | 0-1 | 2-1 | 2-4 | 2-3 | 0-1 | 2-1 | 2-0 | 1-0 | 1-1 | 0-0 | 1-1 | 2-0 | 1-0 | 0-2 | 1-2 | 0-1 | 3-3 | 1-3 | 2-3 |
| 2 Camberley Town | 4-2 | X | 1-3 | 2-2 | 2-3 | 3-0 | 4-2 | 2-3 | 9-0 | 2-1 | 2-1 | 1-0 | 1-0 | 1-1 | 1-2 | 3-3 | 1-6 | 3-0 | 2-1 | 1-2 |
| 3 Cheshunt | 3-1 | 6-2 | X | 2-0 | 2-2 | 4-2 | 3-0 | 3-3 | 2-1 | 1-1 | 2-0 | 0-0 | 1-0 | 2-1 | 2-0 | 2-0 | 3-1 | 3-0 | 2-1 | 2-2 |
| 4 Clapton | 2-0 | 0-1 | 0-0 | X | 0-1 | 2-1 | 1-2 | 1-0 | 0-3 | 0-4 | 2-1 | 1-9 | 2-3 | 4-1 | 0-2 | 0-4 | 3-1 | 5-2 | 0-4 | 0-4 |
| 5 Corinthian Casuals | 5-1 | 1-4 | 3-0 | 4-2 | X | 4-4 | 0-1 | 1-1 | 1-4 | 3-0 | 2-1 | 2-3 | 5-1 | 2-1 | 3-3 | 2-2 | 3-4 | 2-0 | 0-5 | 0-1 |
| 6 Croydon Athletic | 0-0 | 2-1 | 2-2 | 4-2 | 3-1 | X | 2-3 | 0-2 | 0-1 | 2-3 | 2-2 | 6-2 | 2-1 | 5-1 | 1-0 | 5-1 | 1-3 | 9-1 | 2-2 | 0-1 |
| 7 Dorking | 1-1 | 3-0 | 0-1 | 0-3 | 0-2 | 1-5 | X | 1-1 | 0-4 | 2-2 | 2-4 | 2-7 | 1-3 | 0-1 | 1-5 | 0-5 | 1-1 | 3-0 | 2-5 | 2-1 |
| 8 East Thurrock | 3-0 | 1-1 | 0-1 | 1-1 | 1-0 | 0-0 | 2-2 | X | 2-2 | 2-4 | 4-1 | 1-1 | 2-3 | 4-0 | 0-1 | 2-2 | 3-2 | 6-0 | 4-1 | 2-0 |
| 9 Egham Town | 0-1 | 2-0 | 1-2 | 2-2 | 1-0 | 1-1 | 1-1 | 1-1 | X | 0-2 | 3-0 | 2-3 | 2-2 | 2-0 | 1-2 | 1-1 | 0-4 | 7-2 | 3-1 | 1-2 |
| 10 Epsom & Ewell | 1-0 | 1-1 | 0-0 | 3-0 | 1-2 | 2-0 | 2-1 | 1-2 | 1-0 | X | 4-2 | 0-5 | 2-0 | 4-0 | 1-0 | 1-2 | 0-5 | 3-0 | 1-2 | 0-2 |
| 11 Flackwell Heath | 3-4 | 6-0 | 2-0 | 1-1 | 0-1 | 1-1 | 4-2 | 3-2 | 0-1 | 1-6 | X | 1-2 | 0-0 | 4-2 | 2-0 | 1-1 | 0-3 | 4-0 | 2-1 | 0-4 |
| 12 Ford United | 4-2 | 5-0 | 7-0 | 1-0 | 4-1 | 4-1 | 2-1 | 4-2 | 3-0 | 1-2 | 2-0 | X | 1-1 | 3-0 | 2-0 | 5-1 | 1-1 | 5-1 | 2-0 | 2-3 |
| 13 Hornchurch | 1-4 | 1-0 | 1-4 | 1-3 | 1-1 | 1-4 | 3-0 | 0-2 | 1-5 | 3-0 | 1-1 | 1-4 | X | 2-1 | 1-3 | 3-1 | 2-2 | 3-2 | 1-1 | 0-2 |
| 14 Kingsbury Town | 5-2 | 2-2 | 1-2 | 1-2 | 1-2 | 1-0 | 4-2 | 0-4 | 1-4 | 2-3 | 1-1 | 1-4 | 2-0 | X | 1-2 | 1-4 | 1-3 | 1-2 | 0-3 | 1-6 |
| 15 Lewes | 4-1 | 6-2 | 3-2 | 9-0 | 2-0 | 1-1 | 6-1 | 3-3 | 4-1 | 0-1 | 1-0 | 3-0 | 2-1 | 2-0 | X | 2-1 | 3-0 | 3-1 | 1-0 | 1-2 |
| 16 Southall | 0-1 | 2-0 | 0-2 | 1-1 | 6-2 | 2-3 | 4-4 | 1-2 | 1-2 | 0-1 | 1-4 | 0-3 | 0-0 | 2-1 | 5-0 | X | 3-1 | 3-1 | 2-1 | 1-1 |
| 17 Tilbury | 0-1 | 1-1 | 0-1 | 3-1 | 2-0 | 2-2 | 0-1 | 1-2 | 1-1 | 2-1 | 1-1 | 0-1 | 4-3 | 2-0 | 0-1 | 4-1 | X | 2-1 | 3-1 | 0-1 |
| 18 Tring Town | 0-3 | 1-1 | 1-1 | 1-0 | 3-3 | 1-5 | 1-3 | 4-0 | 2-1 | 2-1 | 1-3 | 1-3 | 0-0 | 1-2 | 2-4 | 0-2 | 0-4 | X | 0-0 | 0-4 |
| 19 Ware | 4-3 | 2-4 | 0-3 | 3-1 | 0-2 | 0-2 | 4-2 | 4-2 | 2-3 | 2-0 | 2-0 | 0-2 | 4-1 | 5-1 | 2-1 | 3-0 | 3-3 | 1-0 | X | 3-2 |
| 20 Wingate & Finchley | 0-0 | 3-0 | 0-0 | 5-0 | 2-1 | 0-1 | 2-1 | 2-2 | 0-1 | 1-0 | 6-2 | 3-2 | 0-2 | 4-0 | 3-2 | 0-1 | 3-1 | 2-1 | 0-3 | X |

856

# ABINGDON TOWN

**Secretary:** Ted Quail, 107 Park Lane, Thatcham, Newbury, Berks RG18 3BZ (01635868967)
**GROUND** Address: Culham Road, Abingdon OX14 3BT (01235 521684)
**Directions:** On A415 road to Dorchester-on-Thames half a mile south of town centre. Nearest rail station is Culham. Main line: Didcot Parkway or Oxford. Bus service from Didcot & London
Capacity: 3,000     Cover: 1,771     Seats: 271     Floodlights: Yes
**Clubhouse:** (01235 521684). 7.30-11pm. 6pm matchdays. 12.30-2.30, 4-11 Sat. Hot food on matchdays. Pool, darts, jukebox, canteen
**Club Shop:** Selling programmes, magazines, scarves. Metal Badges: £2
**HONOURS**     Berks & Bucks Sen Cup 58-59 (R-up 88-89 92-93); Isthmian League Div 2 (Sth) 90-91 (Assoc. Mem. Tphy R-up 90-91); London Spartan Lg 88-89 Hellenic Lge(4) 56-57 58-60 86-87, R-up(3) 70-72 87-88,Lg Cup 57-58 70-71 81-82 (R-up 83-84 86-87), Div 1 75-76, Div 1 Cup 75-76,Res. Div(3) 69-71 86-87, Res. Div Cup 70-71 85-86, Res. Div Suppl. Cup 74-75;Oxford & Dist. Lg (3) 1898-1901; Reading & Dist. Lg 47-48; Berks & Bucks Jnr Cup 06-07; Abingdon Centenary Cup 58-59; Joan Lee Mem. Cup 69-70 70-71 86-87
**PREVIOUS     Leagues:** Oxford & Dist.; West Berks; Reading Temperance; North Berks; Reading & Dist. 1927-50; Spartan 50-53; Hellenic 53-88; London Spartan 88-89
**RECORDS     Attendance:** 1,400 v Oxford City, FA Cup September 1960
**BEST SEASON FA Vase:** Fifth Round, replay, 199-90. **FA Cup:** 4th Qual. Rd 60-61 0-2 v Hitchin, 89-90 1-3 v Slough(H), 92-93 1-2 v Merthyr T.(A) after 0-0

## FACT FILE
Formed: 1870     Nickname: The Abbotts
Sponsors: Morlands
Colours: Yellow & green/green/yellow
Change colours: Black & white
Programme: Pages: 40 Price:£1.00
Editor: Rick Gray (01235 527345)
Midweek Matchday: Wednesday
Reserves ' League: Suburban (West)
Local Press: Oxford Mail, Oxford Times,
Abingdon Herald, South Oxon Guardian

### CLUB PERSONNEL
Chairman: Phil Evans
President: Dr Tim Reynolds
Vice Chairman: Craig Norcliffe
Press Officer: Simon Element (01235 202164)
Manager: Bob Raynor
Asst Manager:T.B.A.
Physio:T.B.A.
Coach: T.B.A.

# AVELEY

**Secretary:** Alan Suttling, 50 Harvey, Grays, Essex RM16 2TX (01375 400741)
**GROUND:** `Mill Field', Mill Road, Aveley, Essex RM15 4TR (01708 865940)
**Directions:** London - Southend A13, turn into Sandy Lane at Aveley.
     Rainham or Purfleet BR stations then bus No. 723 to the ground
     Capacity: 4,000   Cover: 400     Seats: 400     Floodlights: Yes
**Clubhouse:** Normal pub hours. Bar snacks and hot food available    Club Shop: No
**HONOURS:**     Isthmian Lg Div 2 (North) R-up 89-90, Lg (AC Delco) Cup 89-90; London Lg 51-5254-55 (R-up 55-56, Lg Cup 53-54); Delphian Lg R-up 57-58 (Lg Cup 61-62);Athenian Lg 70-71 (Div 2 R-up 68-69); Essex Junior Cup 47-48 48-49; Essex Thameside Trophy 79-80 R-up 97-98; Hornchurch Charity Cup 81-82 (R-up 83-84); East Anglian Cup 88-89, R-up 97-98
**PREVIOUS** Leagues: Thurrock Com 46-49; London 49-57; Delphian 57-63; Athenian 63-73
**RECORDS     Attendance:** 3,741 v Slough T., FA Amateur Cup 27.2.71
     **Goalscorer**: Jotty Wilks, 214     **Appearances:** Ken Riley, 422
     **Win:** 11-1 v Histon, 24/8/63
     **Defeat:** v Orient, Essex Thameside Trophy, 11/4/85
**BEST SEASON     FA Cup:** 1st Rd 70-71, 0-1 v Yeovil    League clubs defeated: None
     **FA Amateur Cup** QF 70-71          **FA Trophy** 3rd Qual Rd replay 74-75
     **FA Vase** 3rd Rd 89-90
1998-99: Captain: Terry Beck     P.o.Y.: C Emmanuel     Top Scorer: C Emmanuel

## FACT FILE
Founded: 1927
Sponsors: Dagenham Motors
Colours: Royal blue/white/royal blue
Change: Red & white/red/red
Midweek matches: Tuesday
Reserves' Lge: Essex & Herts Border Comb
Programme: 30 pages   Price: £1
Editor: Terry King
Local Press: Thurrock Gazette
Recorder
Local Radio: Radio Essex, Essex Radio

### CLUB PERSONNEL
Chairman: David Patient
President: Ken Clay
Press Officer: Terry King
Manager: Craig Johnson
Asst Mgr/Coach: Paul Armstrong
Physio: Phil Hunter

# BRACKNELL TOWN

**Ground:** Larges Lane, Bracknell RG12 9AN. Tel: 01344 412305 (club), 01344 300933 (office)
**Directions:** Off A329 just before Met Office r'bout by Bracknell College, ground 200 yards. From Bracknell (BR)/bus station - right out of station, follow pathover bridge, left down steps and follow cycle path ahead, after 300yds follow curve over footbridge, right and follow lane to end, left and ground on leftafter bend
Capacity: 2,500     Seats: 190     Cover: 400     Floodlights: Yes
Clubhouse: Members' bar open 11am-11pm Mon-Sat, 12-3 & 7-10.30pm Sun.
Club Shop: Yes, selling metal badges, programmes, scarves, club sweaters, club ties

**PREVIOUS     Leagues:** Great Western Comb.; Surrey Snr 63-70; London Spartan 70-75
     **Grounds:** None          **Names:** None
**CLUB RECORDS  Attendance:** 2,500 v Newquay, FA Amateur Cup 1971
     **Career Goalscorer:** Richard Whitty   **Career Appearances:** James Woodcock
**BEST SEASON     FA Cup:** 4th Qual Rd - 88, 1-2 v Cheltenham T., 96, 1-3 v Burton A
**HONOURS:**     Isthmian Lg Div 3 93-94; Berks & Bucks Snr Cup R-up; Spartan Lg 74-75, (Lg Cup 81-82 82-83); Surrey Snr Lg 68-69 (Lg Cup 68-69 69-70)
Players progressing: Willie Graham (Brentford)
98-99 - Captain: M Parker   P.o.Y: Dave Prior   Top Scorer: Dave Prior

## FACT FILE
Founded: 1896          Nickname: Robins
Reserve's League: Suburban (west)
Colours: Red & white stripes/red/red
Change colours: Blue & white stripes/blue/blue
Midweek Matchday: Tuesday
Programme: Pages: 32 Price: £1.00
Editor/Press Off.: Robert Scully 01344 640721

### CLUB PERSONNEL
Secretary: Cliff McFaden
15 Goodways Drive, Bracknell,
Berks RG12 9AU Tel: 01344 640349

Chairman: Dave Mihell
Vice Chairman:
President: Jack Quinton

Manager:
Asst Manager:
Physio:

# CAMBERLEY TOWN

**FACT FILE**

Founded: 1896
Nickname: Krooners, Reds or Town
Colours: Red & white/red/red & white
Change colours: L & D Blue strips
Midweek Matches: Tuesday
Reserve's League: Suburban
Programme: 24 pages, £1
Local Press: Camberley News
Bracknell News

**Secretary:** David Clifford 63 Unglewood Ave, Camberley, Surrey. GU15 1RS
Tel & Fax: 01276 20732
**Ground:** Krooner Park, Krooner Road, off Frimley Rd, Camberley, Surrey GU15 2QP
Tel: 01276 65392 **Directions:** M3 Jct 4, follow signs to Frimley, then B3411 towards
Camberley, ground on left opp. `The Standard' pub
Capacity: 3,000 Seats: 195 Cover: 280 Floodlights: Yes Club Shop: Yes
Clubhouse: Open matchdays & 2 evenings. Food available from burger bar matchdays

**HONOURS:** Isthmian Lg Div 2 R-up 78-79; Surrey Snr Lg 30-31 31-32 32-33 (R-up 46-47
61-62), Lg Charity Cup 37-38 51-52 (R-up 31-32 36-37 54-55 72-73); Surrey Snr Cup 78-
79 (R-up 35-36); W. Surrey Lg 13-14 (R-up 12-13); Ascot & Dist Lg 03-04; Surrey Jnr
Charity Cup R-up 08-09; Surrey Jnr Cup 1897-98 1909-10 (R-up 07-08); Aldershot Snr Lg
12-13 (Lg Charity Cup R-up 21-22); Southern Comb. Cup 80-81 (R-up 78-79 85-86 87-
88); Aldershot Sen Cup 96-97 97-98

**PREVIOUS Leagues:** Ascot & District; West Surrey; Aldershot Snr;
Surrey Snr 22-73 Spartan 73-75; Athenian 75-77 82-84; Isthmian 77-82
**CLUB RECORDS Attendance:** 3,500 v Crystal Pal. friendly 14.10.74
Competitive: 2,066 v Aldershot T., Isthmian Lge Div. 3, 10.11.92
**BEST SEASON FA Vase:** Quarter Final 85-86, 98-99 v Woodbridge
**FA Cup:** 1st Rd Prop 98-99 v Brentwood 4th Qual. 32-33 33-34 97-98

**CLUB PERSONNEL**
Chairman: Ian Waldren
Press Officer: Andy Vaughan
Manager: Eric Howard
Asst Manager:
Coach:
Physio: Ken Weaver

# CLAPTON

**Secretary:** Steven Walters,10 Buttfield Close,Dagenham Village,Essex.RM10 8TJ
Tel: 0181 596 0424
**Ground:** The Old Spotted Dog, Upton Lane, Forest Gate, London E7 9NP
Tel: 0181 472 0822
**Directions:** BR to Forest Gate, tube to Plaistow (District Line). Official entrance in
Upton Lane. Docklands Light Railway to Prince Regent then 325 bus to ground
Capacity: 2,000 Seats: 100 Cover: 180 Floodlights: Yes Club Shop: Yes
Clubhouse: Most eves & match day. Light snacks available. To hire please contact club
**HONOURS:** FA Amateur Cup: 06-07 08-09 14-15 23-24 24-25 (R-up 04-05);
Isthmian Lg 10-11 22-23 (R-up 05-06 07-08 09-10 24-25), Div 2 82-
83; Essex Thames-side Tphy( 2); A.F.A.Invitation Cup ( 2); London
Snr Cup (2); London Charity Cup; Essex Snr Cup (4);Middlx Snr
Cup; Essex Sen Trophy; First English team to play on the continent,
beating a Belgian Select XI over Easter 1890
**PREVIOUS Leagues:** Southern 1894-96 (founder members); London 1896-97
**CLUB RECORDS Attendance:** 12,000 v Tottenham Hotspur, FA Cup 1898-99
**BEST SEASON FA Cup:** 3rd Rd Proper 25-26 (lost 2-3 to Swindon at Upton Park)
League clubs defeated Norwich City 25-26.
**FA Amateur Cup:** 06-07 08-09 14-15 23-24 24-25 (R-up 04-05);

**FACT FILE**
Founded: 1878
Nickname: Tons
Sponsors: Mullalley Const
Colours: Red & white stripes/black/black
Change colours: All blue
Midweek Matchday: Tuesday
Reserves' Lge: Essex/Herts Border Com
Programme: 12-16 pages 60p
Editor: Secretary

**CLUB PERSONNEL**
Chairman: Ken Harris
President:
Press Officer: Secretary
Manager: Lyndon Lynch
Coach: Jeff Davis Physio: Tony Blackwell

# CORINTHIAN CASUALS

**FACT FILE**

**Secretary:** Brian Wakefield, 5 Martingales Close, Richmond, Surrey Tel: 0181 940 9208
**Ground:** King George's Field, Hook Rise South, Tolworth, Surrey KT6 7NA
Tel: 0181 397 3368
**Directions:** A3 to Tolworth r'bout (The Toby Jug). Hook Rise is slip road immediately
after the Toby Jug pub. Turn left under railway bridge after a 1/4mile - grd on right. Half
mile from Tolworth (BR); turn left, continue to Toby Jug, then as above. K2 Hoppa bus
from Kingston passes ground
Capacity: 1,700 Seats: 126 Cover: 500 Floodlights: Yes Club Shop: Yes
Clubhouse: Evenings, matchdays, Sunday lunchtimes. Darts, pool, hot & coldsnacks on
matchdays
**HONOURS** FA Amateur Cup R-up 55-56 (SF 56-57), London Spartan Lg R-up 92-
93 (Lg Cup R-up 91-92); Combined Counties Lg R-up 96-97
**PREVIOUS Leagues:** Isthmian 39-84, Spartan 84-96; Combined Counties 96-97
**BEST SEASON FA Cup:** 1st Rd replay 85-86 **FA Vase:**
**FA Amateur Cup:** Runners-up 55-56
**Career Records: Goals** Cliff West 215 **Appearances** Bruce Martin 420
Players progressing: Peter Phillips (Luton Town),
Andy Gray, Tony Finnegan, Alan Pardew to Crystal Palace

Founded: 1939
Sponsors: T.B.A.
Colours: Chocalte & Pink/sky/sky
Change colours: White/navy/white
Midweek Matchday: Tuesday
Reserves' League: Suburban
Programme: 24-48 pages, £1
Editor: Rob Cavallini

**CLUB PERSONNEL**
Chairman: David Harrison
President: Jimmy Hill
Team Manager: Trevor Waller
Press Officer: Rob Cavallini (0181 404
2763)
Match Secretary:
Gerry Young, (0181 330 6643 H)

# CROYDON ATHLETIC

**Secretary:** Dean Fisher, 153 Chipstead Valley Road, Coulsdon, Surry CR5 3BQ
Tel: 0181 407 3292 (H & Fax), 0171 221 7292 (B)

**Ground:** Mayfields, off Mayfield Road, Thornton Heath, Surrey CR7 6DN (0181-664-8343)

**Directions:** Follow A23 from London & continue on A23 into Thornton Road. After roundabout take !st on right into Silverleigh Road, left fork into Trafford Road which continues into Mayfield Road. To end and turn left and follow narrow road to ground. 1 mile from Norbury (BR). Buses 109, 154

Capacity: 3,000    Seats: 163    Cover: 300    Floodlights: Yes
Clubhouse: Open every evening & weekends    Club Shop: Yes

**HONOURS:** London Spartan Lg winners 94-95, R-up 88-89 93-94, R-up 88-89); London Snr Cup R-up 91-92; Southern Youth Lg 92-93; Bearman Harber MemTrophy 87-88; Wirral Prog 86-87 96-97; Umbro Fair Play Winners 97-98

**PREVIOUS Leagues:** None

**RECORDS    Attendance:** 550    **Goalscorer:** Graham Edginton
**Appearances:** Graham Edginton/ Paul Gall/Leon Maxwell

**BEST SEASON    FA Vase:** 3rd Rd 94-95    **FA Cup:** 2nd Qual. Rd 94-95

Players progressing to Football League: Jamie Ndah (Torquay Utd)

### FACT FILE

Founded: 1990    Sponsors: T.C.S. Media
Colours: Maroon & white/maroon/maroon
Change colours: Yellow/royal/royal/royal
Midweek matches: Tuesday
Reserve League: Suburban (S)
Programme: 52 pages, £1
Editor: Secretary
98-99 - P.o.Y.: John Fowler
Top Scorer: Simon Mitchell

### CLUB PERSONNEL

Chairman: Keith Tuckey
V Chairman/ Press Officer: Clive Thompson
Manager: Haydon Bird
Asst Man.: Peter Thomas
1st Team Coach: Leon Maxwell
Managers Asst: Dave Finch
Physio: Mick Reed

---

# DORKING

**Secretary:** Ray Collins,11 Richmond Way, Fetcham, Surrey KT22 9NP (01372 453867)
**Ground:** Meadowbank, Mill Lane, Dorking, Surrey RH4 1DX (01306 884112)
**Directions:** Mill Lane is off Dorking High St. next to Woolworths and Marks &Spencers opposite the White Horse pub. Fork right in Mill Lane past theMalthouse pub. 1/2 mile from both Dorking and Deepdene (BR) stations
Capacity: 3,600    Cover: 800    Seats: 200    Floodlights: Yes    Club Shop: Yes
Clubhouse: All week &Sun. 4-11 p.m. Sats 12-11pm Hot & cold food on matchdays

**HONOURS** Isthmian Lge Div 2 Sth 88-89, (Full Members Cup R-up 92-93); Surrey Sen Cup R-up 1885-86 1989-90; Surrey Senior Shield (2), R-up (3); Surrey Sen Lge (4), R-up (2), Lge Cup (3); Lge Charity Cup (4), R-up (5); Gilbert Rice F'lit Cup 87-88 (R-up 89-90); Surrey I'mediate Cup 56-57 (R-up 54-55); Southern Comb.Challenge Cup 92-93

**PREVIOUS Leagues:** Surrey Senior 22-56 77-78; Corinthian 56-63; Athenian 63-74 78-80;Southern 74-77Ground: Prixham Lane (until 1953)

**CLUB RECORDS Attendance:** 4,500 v Folkestone Town, FA Cup 1st Qual. Rd 1955 and v Plymouth argyle 1st Rd F.A.Cup 92-93

**BEST SEASON FA Cup:** 1st Round Proper 92-93, 2-3 v Plymouth A. (H) **FA Vase:** 3rd Rd (3) 83-84 86-88 **FA Trophy:** 2nd Rd 91-92

**1998-99 Captain:** Nick Torpey    **P.o.Y.:** Stephen Gillet    **Top Scorer:** Stuart White

### FACT FILE

Formed: 1880    Nickname: The Chicks
Colours: Green & white hoops/green/green
Change colours: All navy blue
Midweek matches: Tuesday
Reserve League: Suburban
Programme: 48 pages £1 Editor: Paul Mason
Press: Dorking Advertiser, Surrey Mirror
Surrey Advertiser
Local Radio: County Sound, Radio Surrey,
Radio Mercury

### CLUB PERSONNEL

Chairman: Jack Collins
President: Ingram Whittingham
Vice-Chairman: Ray Collins
Co. Sec.: Martin Collins
Press Officer: Bryan Bletso
Manager: Ian Dawes
Asst Manager: Chick Banes
Physio: Bennie Fishlock

---

# EAST THURROCK UNITED

**Secretary:** Malcolm Harris, 14 Colne Valley, Upminster, Essex RM14 1QA (01708228818)

**Ground:** Rookery Hill, Corringham, Essex (01375 644166-club)

**Directions:** A13 London-Southend, take 1014 at Stanford-le-Hope for two and ahalf miles - ground on left. Two miles from Stanford-le-Hope and Basildon BR stations

Seats: 160    Cover: 360    Capacity: 3,000    Floodlights: Yes    Club Shop: No
Clubhouse: Open all day seven days a week. Hot and cold snacks

**HONOURS:** Metropolitan Lg Div 2 72-73, Essex Snr Lg R-up 88-89 (Lg Cup 88-89 91-92, Harry Fisher Mem. Tphy 83-84 90-91, Sportsmanship Award 81-82 86-87 89-89), Essex SnrTphy R-up 91-92 95-96, Fred Budden Tphy R-up 89-90, Essex & Herts Border Comb.89-90 (Lg Cup 89-90)

**PREVIOUS Leagues:** Sth Essex Comb.; Gtr London; Metropolitan 72-75; London Spartan 75-79;Essex Snr 79-92

**CLUB RECORDS Attendance:** 947 v Trevor Brooking XI, May 1987. Competitive: 845 v Bashley, FA Vase 1989    **Goalscorer:** Graham Stewart 102 **Appearances:** Glen Case 600+    **Win:** 7-0 v Coggeshall (H) 1984

**BEST SEASON    FA Cup:** 3rd Qual 93-94    **FA Vase:** 5th Rd 84-85

### FACT FILE

Founded: 1969    Nickname: Rocks
Colours: Amber/black/black
Change: Blue/white/white
Midweek Matchday: Tuesday
Reserves' Lge: Essex/Herts Border Com
Programme: 24 pages, 50p
Editor: Tony Smith (01375 892888)
Local Press: Thurrock Gazette/ Thurrock
Recorder
Local Radio: BBC Essex

### CLUB PERSONNEL

Chairman: Harry Caine
Vice Chairman: T.B.A.
President: Alan Gower
Press Officer: Secretary
Manager: Lee Patterson
Physio: T.B.A.

# EGHAM TOWN

**Club Administrator:** Alison Thompson, 138A Thorpe Lea Rd, Egham, Surrey. TW20 8BL
Tel: 01784 463562
**GROUND:** Runnymeade Stadium, Tempest Road, Egham, Surrey TW20 8HX (01784 435226)
**Directions:** M25 jct 13, follow signs to Egham, under M25 at r'bout, left to end, left at mini-r'bout, over railway crossing, left to end (Pooley Green Rd), right, Tempest Rd 2nd right.
Bus 41 43 441 from Staines to Pooley Green Rd. 30 mins Egham or Staines (BR)
**Capacity:** 5,635 **Seats:** 335 **Cover:** 1,120 **Floodlights:** Yes **Club Shop:** No
**Clubhouse:** (01784 435226) 7-11pm daily & weekend lunchtimes. Function hall

**HONOURS** Isthmian Lg Assoc Members Tphy R-up 91-92; Spartan Lg 71-72 (Lg Cup R-up 67-68); Athenian Lg R-up 75-76 (Div 2 74-75); Surrey Snr Cup R-up 91-92, Surrey Snr Lg 22-23, Lg Charity Cup 22-23 (R-up 26-27 34-35); Surrey Intermediate Lg20-21, Charity Cup 19-20 20-21 (R-up 26-27); North West Surrey Charity Cup 20-21; Egham Twinning Tournament 67-68 71-72 74-75 75-76 76-77 80-81; SouthernComb. Floodlit Cup 77-78 (R-up 83-84)
**RECORD** **Attendance:** 1,400 v Wycombe Wanderers, FA Cup 2ndQual Rd 72
**Scorer:** Mark Butler 50 (91-92) Career record scorer as well
**Appearances:** Dave Jones 850+ **Win:** 10-1 v Camberley, 81-82
**PREVIOUS** **Leagues:** Hounslow & District 1896-1914; Surrey Intermediate 19-22; Surrey Senior 22-28 65-67; Spartan 29-33 67-74; Parthenon 64-65; Athenian 74-77
**BEST SEASON FA Cup:** 4th Qual Rd 90-91, 0-2 v Telford Utd (A)

### FACT FILE

Founded: 1877    Nickname: Sarnies/Town
Colours: All old gold with royal piping
Change colours: Blue & yellow/white/white
Midweek Matches: Tuesday
Reserves' League: Suburban
Programme: 40 pages, £1
Editor: A lisonThompson (01784 463562 H)
Local Press: Herald & News
Local Radio: County Sound

### CLUB PERSONNEL

Chairman: Patrick Bennett
Vice Chairman: Peter Barnes
President: Peter Barnes
Press Officer: Steve Kell
(01784 449368)
Managers: Kevin Hinge
Physio: Alan Maynard

# EPSOM & EWELL

**Secretary:** D Wilson, 33 Delaporte Close, Epsom, Surrey KT17 4AF (01372 729817)
**GROUND:** Share with Banstead A. Merland Rise, Tadworth, Surrey KT20 5JG(01737 350982)
**Directions:** Follow signs to Tattenham Corner (Epsom racecourse), then toBanstead Sports Centre. Ground adjacent to swimming pool. Half a mile fromTattenham Corner (BR). Bus 420 from Sutton stops outside ground. Also buses 406& 727 from Epsom
**Capacity:** 3,500 **Seats:** 250 **Cover:** 800 **Floodlights:** Yes **Club Shop:** No
**Clubhouse:** Normal licensing hours, food available
**HONOURS** FA Vase R-up 74-75; London Lg 27-28, R-up (5); Corinthian Lg Memorial Shield 59-60 (R-up 51-52 56-57); Athenian Lg Div 2 R-up 75-76 (Lg Cup R-up 76-77, Div2 Cup R-up 67-68); Isthmian Lg Div 2 77-78 (Div 1 R-up 83-84), Vanranel Ass Members Trophy R-up 97-98; Surrey Snr Lg 25-26 26-27 74-75 (R-up 73-74), Lg Cup73-74 74-75, Charity Cup 26-27 (R-up 73-74), Surrey Snr Cup 80-81 (R-up 3); Surrey Snr Shield 32-33 54-55; Surrey Intermediate Cup 29-30,Charity Cup 57-58; Southern Comb. Cup 79-80 (R-up 82-83 92-93)
**PREVIOUS Leagues:** Surrey Snr 24-27 73-75; London 27-49; Corinthian 49-63; Athenian 63-73 75-77
**CLUB RECORDS Attendance:** 5,000 v Kingstonian, F.A. Cup 2nd Qual. Rd, 15/10/49
**BEST SEASON FA Cup:** 1st Rd 33-34, **FA Vase:** R-up 74-75 **FA Trophy:** 2nd Rd 81-82
**Players progressing:** Matt Elliott (Leicester), Chris Powell(Derby), Paul Harding (Notts County, Birmingham), Murray Jones (Grimsby), Alan Pardew (Charlton), Mick Leonard (Chesterfield)

### FACT FILE

Founded: 1917    Nickname: E's
Colours: Royal & white
Change: All yellow
Midweek Matches: Tuesday
Reserves' League: Suburban
Programme: 28/32 pages, 50p
Editor: Stella Lamont (01737 356245)
98-99 - Captain:Graham Morris
Top Scorer:Joad Tame (21)
P.o.Y.: James Hall
Record Goalscorer: Tommy Tuite

### CLUB PERSONNEL

Chairman: Peter Atkins
Vice Chairman: Stella Lamont
Press Officer: Sec
Manager: Adrian Hill
Coach: John Wood
Physio: John Wood

# FLACKWELL HEATH

**Secretary:** Mrs Christine Hobbs, 23 Southfield Rd., Flackwell Heath, Bucks. HP10 9BT
Tel: 01628 521051
**GROUND:** Wilks Park, Heath End Rd, Flackwell Heath, High Wycombe. HP10 9EA
Tel: 01628 523892
**Directions:** M40 jct 3 Wycombe East, follow signs for F/Heath left up Treadbury Hill & right at top of hill at roundabout. Wilks park 800yds on right, grd at rear of Magpie (PH). Bus 301 either from bus station or High Street near bottom of Crendon Street which comes from BR station. Ask for Oakland Way
**Capacity:** 2,000 **Seats:** 150 **Cover:** Yes **Floodlights:** Yes **Club Shop:** No
**Clubhouse:** Open every night 6.30-11pm & before & after matches. Hot food in tea bar

**HONOURS:** Gt Western Combination 57-58 62-63; Hellenic Lg Div 1 R-up 76-77; Berks & Bucks Snr Cup SF 85-86
**PREVIOUS:** **Leagues:** Wycombe & District; Gt Western Comb.; Hellenic 76-82; Athenian 82-84
**RECORDS:** **Attendance:** 4,500 v Oxford U., charity game 1986 (competitive: 700 v Aldershot Town, 27/10/92)
**Goalscorer:** Tony Wood **Appearances:** Ben Richards
**Win:** 6-0 v Clapton & v Petersfield (both away) **Defeat:** 0-7 v Aveley (H)
**BEST SEASON:** FA Cup: 2nd Qual. Rd replay 90-91, 0-3 v Grays A (A) after 2-2

### FACT FILE

Founded: 1907
Colours: Red/black
Change colours: Yellow/black/black
Midweek Matches: Monday
Reserves' League: Suburban
Programme: 18 pages £1

### CLUB PERSONNEL

Chairman: T Glynn
Vice Chairman: M Baker
President: Ken Crook

# GREAT WAKERING ROVERS

**Ground:** Burroughs Park, Little Wakering Hall Lane, Gt Wakering, Southend-on-Sea SS3 0HQ
(01702 217812)
**Directions:** 4a bus from Shoeburyness (BR), 4a or 4b from Southend - alight at British Legion
in Gt Wakering alongside which runs Little Wakering Hall Lane. A127 past Southend signposted
Gt Wakering. In Gt Wakering, half mile past large Esso garage along High Street is Little
Wakering Hall Lane, ground 250 yds along on left
**Capacity:** 2,100    **Cover:** 300    **Seats:** 150    **Floodlights:** Yes   **Club Shop:** No
**Clubhouse:** Every eve., Sat 11-11, Sun 12-3 & 7.30-10.30. Hot meals, snacks etc matchdays only

**HONOURS**   Essex I'mediate Cup 91-92, Essex I'mediate Lg Div 2 91-92 (Div 3 90-91,Lg Cup
91-92), Southend Charity Shield 90-91 91-92, Essex Snr Lg. 94-95, Lg Res.
Section 94-95 (Wirral Programme Essex Sen. Lg. Award 92-93 94-95)
**PREVIOUS**   **Leagues:** Southend & Dist. 19-81, Southend All. 81-89, Essex I'mediate 89-92
**Ground:** Gt Wakering Rec
**BEST SEASON**   **FA Cup:** 2nd Qual 98-99        **FA Vase:** 5th Round 97-98
**RECORDS**   **Attendance:** 659 v Potters Bar FA Vase 5th Rd 7-2-98
**Win** (in Senior Football): 9-0 v Stansted 27/12/93
**Defeat** (in Senior Football): 1-7 v Bowers Utd, Essex Snr Lge 1-4-98
Players progressing: Les Stubbs (Southend, Chelsea) 1947, Jackie Bridge(Southend Utd)
1948, Kevin Maddocks (Maidstone Utd)

**FACT FILE**
Founded: 1919        Nickname: Rovers
Sponsors: Fox Surveillance
Colours: Green & white stripes/white/green
Change Cols: Yellow & blue stripes/blue/blue
Midweek Matchday: Tuesday
Reserves' Lge: Essex & Herts Border Comb
Programme: 24-32 pages, 50p
Editor: Keith Perryman 01245 354084

**CLUB PERSONNEL**

**Secretary:** Roger Sampson
37 Lee Lotts, Gt Wakering,
Southend SS3 0HA. 01702 218794 (H)

Chairman: Fred Smith
Vice-Chairman: Barry Beadle
President: Eddie Ellis
Manager: Eddie Nash
Physio: Cleave Taylor
Press Officer: Nobby Johnson (01702 297840)

# HERTFORD TOWN

**Ground:** Hertingfordbury Park, West Street, Hertford Tel: 01992 583716

**Directions:** Rail to Hertford Nth (from Moorgate) or Hertford East (LiverpoolStr.); both 15
mins walk. Green Line bus to town centre then 10 mins walk.
By road; off bypass heading east, turn off at Ford garage
**Capacity:** 6,500    **Seats:** 200    **Cover:** 1,500    **Floodlights:** Yes
**Club Shop:** Souvenirs from Graham Showell, 5 Beehive Lane, Welwyn Garden City AL7 4BB
**Clubhouse:** Yes        **Sponsors:** Atlantic Tiger Corporation
**HONOURS**   Herts Char. Cup 72-73, Herts Snr Cup 66-67, Hertford Char. Shd 19-20 20-21
35-36 49-50 55-56 59-60, Eastern Co's Lg Cup 72-73, East Anglian Cup 62-63
69-70, Southern Co's Comb. F-lit Cup 94-95, Mithras Cup SF 85-86,Ryman
Div 3 R-up 97-98
**PREVIOUS**   **Leagues:** Herts Co.; Spartan 21-47 48-59; Delphian 59-63; Athenian 63-72;
Eastern Co's 72-73        **Names:** None      **Grounds:** None
**BEST SEASON**   **FA Cup:** 4th Qual. Rd. 73-74 (lost 1-2 at Hillingdon Borough)

**CLUB RECORDS  Gate:** 5,000 v Kingstonian, F.A. Amateur Cup 2nd Rd 55-56
**Appearances:** Robbie Burns
Players progressing to Football League: G Mazzon (Aldershot), J.Hooker (Brentford)

**FACT FILE**
Founded: 1908        Nickname: The Blues
Colours: Blue & yellow/blue/blue
Change colours: Orange & Black
Midweek Matches: Tuesday
Reserves' Lge: Essex & Herts Border Comb
Programme: 28 pages, 40p
Editor: Martin Climpson:(01992 589972)
Local Newspapers: Hertfordshire Mercury

**CLUB PERSONNEL**

**Secretary:** Stephen Hedley,
29 Upper field Road,Wewyn Garden City,
Herts AL7 3LP( 01707 333712)
President: John Hedley
Chairman: Mike Schulze
Vice Chairman: David Thomas
Press Off.: Graham Showell
Comm. Mgr: Peter Slade
Manager: David Marett
Physio: Ray Price

# HORNCHURCH

**Secretary:** Ted Harris, 13 Claremont Gdns, Upminster, Essex  RM14 1DW (01708 227891)

**GROUND:** The Stadium, Bridge Avenue, Upminster, Essex RM14 2LX (01708 220080)
**Directions:** Fenchurch Street to Upminster (BR) then 10 mins walk. Or tube toUpminster
Bridge (LT), right outside station, 2nd right into Bridge Ave. ground 150yds on right. By road
Bridge Avenue is off A124 between Hornchurch and Upminster. Buses 248, 348, 370, 373
from Hornchurch or Upminster BR stations
**Capacity:** 3,000    **Seats:** 300    **Cover:** 350    **Floodlights:** Yes   **Club Shop:** Yes,
**Clubhouse:** Mon-Fri 7.30-11, Sat 12-11, Sun 12-3. Cafeteria open matchdays
**Club Shop:** Yes, selling programmes, handbooks, scarves, hats, souvenirs etc.
Contact Ron Quantock, 120 The Avenue, Hornchurch, Essex RM12 4JC (01708455529)
**HONOURS:**   Athenian Lg 66-67, Romford Lg(2), Essex Snr Trophy R-up 86-87,
Essex Jnr Cup  Essex Thameside Tphy 84-85,  Isthmian Yth Cup,
CarlsbergTrophy R-up 93-94
**PREVIOUS:**   **Leagues:** Romford 25-38; Spartan 38-52; Delphian 52-59; Athenian 59-75
**Names:** Hornchurch & Upminster (Upminster FC pre-1950s) merged with
UpminsterWanderers in 1961
**RECORDS:**   **Attendance:**  3,000 v Chelmsford, FA Cup 66-67
**BEST SEASON:**   **FA Cup:** 4th Qual Rd 66-67, lost 0-4 at home to Chelmsford City
**F.A. Vase:** 5th Rd 74-75

**FACT FILE**

Founded: 1923      Nickname: Urchins
Sponsors: Premier Snacks
Colours: Red & white/red/red
Change colours: Purple & yellow
Midweek Matches: Tuesday
Reserve Lge: Essex & Herts Border Comb
Programme: 16-20 pages with admission
Editor/Press Off.: Rob Monger 01268 490847
Local Press: Romford Recorder
Local Radio: Essex Radio

**CLUB PERSONNEL**

Chairman: Brian Davie
Vice Chairman: K Nicholls
Manager: Dave Cox
Physio: D Edkins

**CAMBERLEY TOWN**

Photo: Eric Marsh

**CLAPTON**

Photo: Roger Turner

**FORD UNITED** celebrate with the Ryman Division 3 Trophy

Photo: Francis Short

# KINGSBURY TOWN

**Secretary:** David Thomas, 9 Hillview Gardens, Kingsbury, NW9 0DE
**GROUND:** Silver Jubilee Park, Townsend Lane, Kingsbury, London NW9 7NE (0181 2051645)
**Directions:** Underground to Kingsbury, cross road and take bus 183 to TownsendLane (2 miles) - ground in far left-hand corner of Silver Jubilee Park
**Capacity:** 2,500   Seats: 165   Cover: 400   Floodlights: Yes   Club Shop: Yes
**Clubhouse:** Mon-Fri 7-11, Sat 12-11, Sun 12-2.30 & 7-10.30. Food on matchdays
**HONOURS:** Isthmian Lg Div 2 Nth R-up 85-86; Spartan Lg Cup R-up 59-60 64-65; Parthenon Lg 51-52 (Prem Charity Cup 52-53 53-54; Snr Charity Cup 53-54); Middx Snr Cup R-up 88-89; Middx Charity Cup 85-86 (R-up 88-89); Middx Lg Charity Cup ( 3) 44-47; Willesden & Dist. Lg R-up 30-31 (Div 2 34-35)
**PREVIOUS:** **Leagues:** Hellenic 27-30 (as Davis Sports); Willesden & District 30-43; MiddxSnr 44-47; Parthenon 47-59; Spartan 59-76 78-81; Athenian 76-78 81-84
**RECORDS:** **Attendance:** 1 ,300 v Wealdstone, FA Amateur Cup 1971
**BEST SEASON:** **FA Vase:** 4th Rd 74-75
**FA Cup:** 3rd Qual. Rd. 87-88, 0-1 v Leytonstone-Ilford (H)

## FACT FILE

Founded: 1927      Nickname: Kings
Sponsors: VPA Entertainment Technology
Colours: Royal/white/royal
Change colours: Yellow/navy/yellow
Midweek Matches: Tuesday
Reserves' League: Suburban
Programme: 16-20 pages, 50p
Editor: Allan Davies
Local Press: Harrow Observer, Willesden Chronicle, Allsport Weekly, Edgware &Finchley Times

### CLUB PERSONNEL

Chairman: Allan J Davies
Press Officer: Allan Davies (01895 443761)
Manager: Peter Blain
Physio: Margaret Romer

# LEWES

**Secretary:** Steve Kitchener, 8 Malling Down, Lewes, E Sussex BN7 2BN (01273 475228)
**GROUND:** The Dripping Pan, Mountfield Road, Lewes BN7 1XN (01273 472100)
**Directions:** Two minute walk from Lewes (BR) - turn left out of station and left into Mountfield Road. Ground 100 yards on right
**Capacity:** 2,600   Cover: 400   Seats: 400   Floodlights: Yes   Club Shop: Yes
**Clubhouse:** (01273 472100). Bar, tea bar, pool.
**HONOURS:** Isthmian Lg Div 2 R-up 79-80 91-92; Ath'n Lg Div 1 69-70 (Div 2 67-68); Sussex Co. Lg 64-65 (R-up 24-25 33-34 58-59 63-64, Lg Cup 39-40); Mid Sussex Lg 10-11 13-14; Sussex Snr Cup 64-65 70-71 84-85 (R-up 79-80 82-83 87-88); Sussex Royal Ulster Rifles Charity Cup(3) 61-63 64-65; Gilbert Rice F'lit Cup 82-83 88-89; Neale Tphy 68-69; Sussex F'lit Cup 76-77 (SF 83-84); Southern Counties Comb Div1 80-81
**PREVIOUS:** **Leagues:** Mid Sussex 1886-1920; Sussex Co 20-65; Athenian 65-77
**RECORDS:** **Attendance:** 2,500 v Newhaven, Sussex County Lg 26/12/47
**BEST SEASON:** **FA Cup:** 4th Qual. Rd, lost to Harwich & Parkeston
**FA Trophy:** 1st Rd 82-83   **FA Amateur Cup:** 2nd Rd 67-68
**FA Vase:** 1st Rd 79-80

## FACT FILE

Founded: 1885      Nickname: Rooks
Colours: Red & Black stripes/black/red
Change colours: Yellow/green
Midweek matches: Tuesday
Reserves' League: Sussex Co. Res. Sect
Programme: 32 pages, £1  Editor: Martin Burke
Local Press: Evening Argus, Sussex Express
Local Radio: Southern F.M.,B.B.C. Southern Counties

### CLUB PERSONNEL

President: G Lucking
Chairman: S White
Manager: Jimmy Quinn
Asst Man.:

# SOUTHALL

**Secretary:** Keith Chamberlin, 4 Shelley Avenue, Greenford, Middx UB68 8RU Tel; (0181 575 6023)
**Ground:** Ground share with Yeading FC, The Warren, Beaconsfield Rd, Hayes Middx .
Directions: Two miles from Hayes (BR) take Uxbridge Rd and turn right towards Southall, right into Springfield Rd, then left into Beaconsfield Rd. Bus 207 stops half mile from ground.
**Capacity:** 3,500   Cover: 1,500   Seats: 250   Floodlights: Yes
**Clubhouse:** Normal pub hours. Hot snacks available on matchdays      Club Shop: No
**HONOURS:** FA Amtr Cup R-up 24-25, FA Vase R-up 85-86, Isthmian Lg Div 2 R-up 74-75, Gt Western Suburban Lg 12-13, Athenian Lg 26-27 (R-up 54-55), Middx Snr Cup(12)07-08 10-11 11-12 12-13 22-23 23-24 24-25 26-27 36-37 44-45 53-54 54-55, MiddxCharity Cup 10-11 11-12 13-14 22-24(jt with Botwell Mission) 27-28 36-37 51-52 68-69 83-84, London Snr Cup SF 35-36 84-85
**PREVIOUS:** **Leagues**: Southern 1896-1905; Gt Western Suburban; Herts & Middx; Athenian 19-73
**RECORDS:** **Attendance:** 17,000 v Watford, FA Cup 3rd Rd 1935
**BEST SEASON:** **FA Cup:** 3rd Round 35-36, 1-4 v Watford (H) Also 1st Rd 25-26 27-28 28-29 36-37 55-56.   **FA Vase:** Runners-up 85-86
**FA Amateur Cup:** Runners-up 24-25 (SF 25-26, 52-53)

## FACT FILE

Founded: 1871   Nickname: Fowlers
Colours: Red & white stripes/white/rwhite
Change: Yellow & black
Midweek Matchday: Wednesday
Res' Lge: Middx County
Programme: 6 pages, 50p
Editor: Steve Hawkins
Local Press:
Ealing Gazette, Allsports Weekly
Local Radio: Capital
98-99 - Captain: Steve Whitehead
P.o.Y.: Lee Holman
Top Scorer: Danny Yeoman

### CLUB PERSONNEL

Chairman: TBA
Manager: Keith Chamberlin
Assistant Manager: Steve Hawkins
Physio: Keith Chamberlin

# TILBURY

**Secretary:** Shaun McCann c/o The Club (H) 01268 459327 (M) 0788 0548724
**GROUND:** Chadfields, St Chad's Rd, Tilbury, Essex RM18 8NL ( Tel: 01375 843093).
**Directions:** BR from Fenchurch Street to Tilbury Town then bus 384 or 385 By road: M25(jct 30 or 31) - A13 Southend bound, Tilbury Docks turn off after 4 miles,Chadwell St Mary turn off (left) after another 1 1/2 miles, left againafter 400 metres, right at r'bout (signed Tilbury), right into St Chad's Rdafter half mile, 1st right into Chadfields for ground
Capacity: 4,000   Seats: 350   Cover: 1,000   Floodlights: Yes   Club Shop: No
Clubhouse: Open evening, all day Fri. & Sat. and Sun. lunchtimes. Hot &cold food
**HONOURS:**       Isthmian Lg Div 1 75-76, (Div 1 Cup 74-75); Athenian Lg 68-69 (Div 2 62-63); London Lg 58-59 59-60 60-61 61-62, Lg Cup 58-59 60-61 61-62, R-up (3); DelphianLg 67-68 (Div 2 62-63); Essex Snr Cup 60-61 63-64 72-73 74-75 (R-up 46-47 47-48 69-70 71-72 78-79);
**PREVIOUS:**     **Leagues:** Grays & Dist. & Sth Essex (simultaneously); Kent 27-31; London 31-39 46-50 57-62; Sth Essex Comb. (war-time); Corinthian 50-57; Delphian 62-63; Athenian 63-73
**RECORDS:**     **Attendance:** 5,500 v Gorleston, FA Cup 4th Qual. Rd 19/11/49
**BEST SEASON: FA Cup:** 3rd Rd 77-78, 0-4 v Stoke City (A).
**FA Amateur Cup:** Quarter Final   FA Vase:

### FACT FILE
Founded: 1900       Nickname: Dockers
Colours: Black& white stripes,black,black
Change colours: All red
Midweek Matches: Tuesday
Reserves' League: Essex & Herts Border Comb
Programme: 32 pages, 50p
Editor: Lloyd Brown
Local Press:
Thurrock Gazette, Thurrock Recorder
Local Radio: Essex Radio, BBC Essex

### CLUB PERSONNEL
Chairman: R Nash
Vice Chairman: H.McGill
President: J B Wilson
Press Officer: Lloyd Brown (01375 409938)
Manager: TonyCross
Physio: Roger Hutton

# TRING TOWN

**Secretary:** Laurie McParland, 17 Westray, Hemel Hempstead, Herts HP3 8TE
**GROUND:** Pendley Sports Centre, Cow Lane, Tring, Herts HP23 5NS (01442 824018)
**Directions:** One mile from Tring centre on A41 - direct connection to M25 (jct20) via new A41 bypass. One and a half miles from Tring (BR). Numerous busesfrom station and Watford-Aylesbury routes serve ground
Capacity: 2,500   Seats: 150   Cover: 250   Floodlights: Yes   Club Shop: No
Clubhouse: All licensing hours. Dancehall, pool, darts, kitchen.
**HONOURS:**       Spartan Lg 67-68, R-up 68-69. Herts Charity Shield winners 4, R-up 2. Athenian Lg Div 2 R-up 76-77, Herts Snr Cup R-up 77-78
**PREVIOUS:**     **Leagues:** Gt Western Combination; Spartan 53-75; Athenian 75-77
**Names:** None   Ground: Tring Cricket Ground (40 yrs)
**RECORD:**     **Attendance:** 2,500 v West Ham, friendly
**Goalscorer & Appearances:** Gary Harthill
**BEST SEASON: FA Cup:** 3rd Qual. Rd replay 84-85, 0-5 v Fisher(A) after 1-1
**FA Vase:** 5th Rd 76-77, 0-2 v Farnborough Town (H)
98-99 -  Captain: Matt Condon   P.o.Y.: Paul Turner   Top Scorer: Steve Hale

### FACT FILE
Founded: 1904       Nickname: T's
Colours: White & red stripes/white/white
Change: Yellow & blue stripes/blue/yellow
Midweek Matchday: Tuesday
Reserves' Lge: Suburban Lge
Programme: 24 pages £1
Editor/Press Officer:
Alan Lee (01702 216063)
Local Radio: Chiltern, Mix 96
BBC Three Counties Radio

### CLUB PERSONNEL
Chairman: Harry Bowden
Manager: Mick Vipond
Asst Manager: Danny Johnson
Physio: Keith Hardy

# WARE

**Secretary:** I Bush, 42 Burnett Squ, Hertford, Herts SG14 2HD (01992 587334)
**GROUND:** Wodson Park, Wadesmill Road, Ware Herts SG12 0HZ (01920 463247)
**Directions:** A10 off at junction A602 & B1001 (Ware North), turn right at roundabout 300yds, and follow Ware sign, past Rank factory, turn left at main roundabout onto A1170 (Wadesmill Rd). After 3/4 mile stadium on right
Capacity: 3,300   Seats: 312   Cover: 500   Floodlights: Yes   Club Shop: Yes
Clubhouse: Licensed bar open matchdays. Light snacks at refreshment bar
**HONOURS:**       Herts Snr Cup 1898-99 03-04 06-07 21-22 53-54, Herts Char. Shield 26-27 56-57 58-59 62-63 85-86, Herts Char. Cup R-up 64-65 65-66 78-79 89-90, Spartan Lg 52-53 (Div 1 Sect.B 51-52, Div 2 Sect.A 26-27), Athenian Lg Div 2 Cup 65-66 72-73,East Anglian Cup 73-74, Herts Co. Lg 08-09 21-22, East Herts Lg 04-05 06-07 (LgCup 06-07), Perry Cup 26-27 28-29 37-38 51-52 52-53 53-54 55-56, Dunkels Cup 52-53, Rolleston Cup 39-40 51-52
**PREVIOUS:**     **Leagues:** East Herts; North Middx 07-08; Herts County 08-25; Spartan 25-55;Delphian 55-63; Athenian 63-75
**RECORDS**     **Attendance:** 3,800 v Hendon Amt Cup 56-57
**BEST SEASON: FA Cup:** First Round Proper 68-69 (lost 6-1 to Luton Town)

### FACT FILE
Founded: 1892       Nickname: Blues
Sponsors: Charvill Bros Ltd
Colours: Blue & white stripes/blue/red
Change colours: Amber/black
Midweek Matchday: Tuesday
Reserves' Lge:
Essex & Herts Border Comb
Programme: 24 pages, 50p
Editor/Press Officer: Tony Raisborough
(01707 656568)
Local Press: Herts Mercury, Herts Star, Herald & Post

### CLUB PERSONNEL
Chairman: W J Luck
Manager: Steve Ringrose
Coach: Dermot Drummy
Physio: Frank Roberts

# COURAGE COMBINED COUNTIES LEAGUE

**President:** Ron Monkley    **Chairman:** John Bennett   0181 568 9047 (H)
**Secretary:** Clive Tidey, 22 Silo Road, Farncombe, Godalming, Surrey GU7 3PA
Tel: 01483 428453 (H)

After four seasons of domination by Ashford Town (Middx), Ash United, everybody's pre-season favourites, overcame a sub-stantial fixture backlog, to win their first championship since 1987. Player-manager Jamie Horton used all his Conference know how and contacts to build an impressive squad that made light of having to play twice and sometimes three times a week from March onwards.

For many months it had seemed that Cobham were destined to win the championship, having turned their fortunes completely around, following the arrival of the ebullient Martin Caller but in the end too many draws was their downfall and they had to be content with a very honourable second place. Indeed to clinch the runners-up spot, they had to win their final match of the season, at Bedfont, which they did by four goals to three, the winner coming in the dying seconds of the game. That win meant that Chipstead had to settle for third place on goal difference but they too could be pleased with a season that saw them lose very few matches under the guidance of ex-Palace star Jim Cannon. Reigning champions Ashford, who had transferred Dannie Bulman to Wycombe Wanderers in pre-season for a record fee for the Combined Counties League, fielded a much younger team than in previous seasons and had to be content with fourth place, which was ironic to some extent as the club had just about brought their facilities up to the level required by the Ryman League.

At the wrong end of the table, it was once again Brook who finished bottom with a miserable ten points for their efforts, twenty points behind the next club, Hartley Wintney. Reading Town failed to match their championship aspirations of the previous season whilst newcomers AFC Wallingford managed a creditable eighth place in their first season. It could have been better though if the club had maintained its whirlwind start, spearheaded by the lethal Carl Henry up front, who finished as the League's leading scorer, despite missing much of the second half of the season.

In the Premier League Cup, sponsored by World Wide Carpets and played at Farnborough Town, it was Ashford, deter-mined to have at least one trophy to replace the Championship Trophy, who came out on top, beating Cobham by a solitary goal, scored by Des Vertannes, from the spot in the first half, after Richard McDonald had been fouled. Despite the lack of goals both teams put on an enterprising display.

In national competition, Chipstead took the eye in the FA Cup beating Redhill and Bedfont to reach the Third Qualifying Round, when they went down to Dagenham & Redbridge.

In the FA Vase, the main challenge came from Ash United, who battled their way through to the Fourth Round, over-coming the challenges of Three Bridges, Southwick, Tunbridge Wells and Melksham Town before exiting the competition at the hands of eventual winners Tiverton Town. Ash's organisation on the day against the favourites was exemplary and they even took the lead but the quality of their illustrious visitors soon became evident as they gradually got well on top, winning in the end by five goals to one. Cobham and Chipstead also enjoyed excellent runs, before losing in the Third Round to local opposition in Camberley Town and Tooting & Mitcham respectively, Tooting needing a replay.

In County competitions, Bedfont did the League proud by reaching the final of the London Senior Cup in which they nar-rowly lost to Waltham Abbey by three goals to two at Dulwich Hamlet. Ash United went one better and won the Aldershot Senior Cup, beating Fleet Town 2-0 in the Final at Aldershot. In the Surrey Senior Cup, Ashford had a notable win over a Crystal Palace team before losing just 1-2 at home to a full strength Sutton United side in the next round. Cobham also did well to reach the 1st Round Proper, only going down 3-5 to a Kingstonian side who clearly expected an easier match.

In Division One, it looked like a two horse race for much of the season between Bedfont Reserves and Cobham Reserves, the former eventually coming out on top. Cobham eventually had to settle for third place, being just nosed out by Ashford Town on goal difference, although the latter had the benefit of three points being awarded to them after Reading Town had inadvertently played an ineligible player in an earlier match.

In the Division One Cup, it was Ashford who clinched a cup double, with the score again just 1-0, over Merstham Reserves, the winner coming from skipper Mick Walter who ran virtually the length of the pitch before firing home.

From an administration point of view the season proceeded fairly smoothly, the only hiccup being the weather that saw a record 118 scheduled matches being postponed. With the co-operation of all clubs though, there was never any danger of the season not being completed.

All clubs are due to have floodlighting by 1 August 1999 and, at the time of writing, there remain two existing members who still have to achieve this, namely Cranleigh and Westfield. Both have been accepted into the constitution for 1999-2000 but on the condition that lighting must be in place by the deadline. If either fail to make it, they will drop down to the Surrey Premier League. Netherne Village had already resigned, due to the lighting problem, and will definitely be playing in the Surrey Premier next season whilst Chessington United, who finished second in the Surrey Premier, have been accepted for promotion subject to the same floodlighting deadline. This will leave the League with two clubs with very similar names, Chessington United and Chessington & Hook United, which may become an issue to be dealt with at some stage.

Referees' Secretary Ken Huckle decided to call it a day after ten year's loyal and efficient service and will take a Vice-President's role next season. His replacement is Geoff Knock, previously Secretary of Bedfont FC.

The Sportsmanship awards were taken by Farnham Town in the Premier and Westfield in Division One whilst the "Programme of the Year" award went to Chipstead with Ash United the runners up.

The Combined Counties League would like to thank its sponsors, especially Courage who have renewed their sponsor-ship for at least another season.

# FINAL LEAGUE TABLES 1998-99

## PREMIER DIVISION

| | P | W | D | L | F | A | PT |
|---|---|---|---|---|---|---|---|
| Ash United | 40 | 31 | 3 | 6 | 115 | 46 | 96 |
| Cobham | 40 | 24 | 11 | 5 | 108 | 50 | 83 |
| Chipstead | 40 | 25 | 8 | 7 | 82 | 39 | 83 |
| Ashford Town (Middx) | 40 | 24 | 7 | 9 | 102 | 50 | 79 |
| Bedfont | 40 | 23 | 5 | 12 | 97 | 66 | 74 |
| Godalming & Guildford | 40 | 23 | 3 | 14 | 79 | 58 | 72 |
| Reading Town | 40 | 21 | 7 | 12 | 73 | 55 | 70 |
| AFC Wallingford | 40 | 20 | 9 | 11 | 104 | 62 | 69 |
| Westfield | 40 | 19 | 8 | 13 | 52 | 45 | 65 |
| Chessington & Hook | 40 | 18 | 4 | 18 | 77 | 67 | 58 |
| Merstham | 40 | 16 | 8 | 16 | 75 | 67 | 56 |
| Raynes Park Vale | 40 | 16 | 8 | 16 | 73 | 70 | 56 |
| Farnham Town | 40 | 16 | 7 | 17 | 89 | 73 | 55 |
| Feltham | 40 | 16 | 7 | 17 | 53 | 57 | 55 |
| Sandhurst Town | 40 | 13 | 8 | 19 | 63 | 92 | 47 |
| Viking Sports | 40 | 12 | 5 | 23 | 56 | 97 | 41 |
| Walton Casuals | 40 | 9 | 6 | 25 | 60 | 88 | 33 |
| Cranleigh | 40 | 9 | 4 | 27 | 60 | 122 | 31 |
| Netherne Village | 40 | 9 | 4 | 27 | 60 | 122 | 31 |
| Hartley Wintney | 40 | 7 | 9 | 24 | 50 | 87 | 30 |
| Cove | 40 | 3 | 1 | 36 | 27 | 135 | 10 |

## DIVISION ONE

| | P | W | D | L | F | A | PT |
|---|---|---|---|---|---|---|---|
| Bedfont | 32 | 24 | 3 | 5 | 93 | 31 | 75 |
| Ashford Town Middx^ | 32 | 21 | 5 | 6 | 69 | 25 | 71 |
| Cobham | 32 | 20 | 8 | 4 | 98 | 25 | 68 |
| Chessington & Hook^ | 32 | 18 | 5 | 9 | 65 | 36 | 62 |
| Sandhurst Town | 32 | 15 | 10 | 7 | 65 | 44 | 55 |
| Ash Utd | 32 | 16 | 3 | 13 | 86 | 58 | 51 |
| Merstham^* | 32 | 15 | 6 | 11 | 85 | 62 | 51 |
| Farnham Town | 32 | 15 | 0 | 17 | 80 | 81 | 45 |
| Westfield | 32 | 13 | 5 | 14 | 76 | 70 | 44 |
| Reading Town* | 32 | 15 | 3 | 14 | 80 | 77 | 42 |
| Walton Casuals^ | 32 | 10 | 6 | 16 | 46 | 66 | 39 |
| AFC Wallingford | 32 | 11 | 4 | 17 | 64 | 78 | 37 |
| Netherne Villlage | 32 | 11 | 4 | 17 | 40 | 74 | 37 |
| Viking Sports* | 32 | 10 | 4 | 18 | 49 | 90 | 31 |
| Cove | 32 | 7 | 5 | 20 | 34 | 82 | 26 |
| Godalming & Guildford | 32 | 7 | 5 | 20 | 37 | 94 | 26 |
| Cranleigh | 32 | 4 | 4 | 24 | 31 | 105 | 16 |

^ points awarded
* points deducted

## PREMIER DIVISION RESULTS CHART 1998-99

| | 1 | 2 | 3 | 4 | 5 | 6 | 7 | 8 | 9 | 10 | 11 | 12 | 13 | 14 | 15 | 16 | 17 | 18 | 19 | 20 | 21 |
|---|---|---|---|---|---|---|---|---|---|---|---|---|---|---|---|---|---|---|---|---|---|
| 1 AFC Wallingford | X | 2-2 | 0-1 | 5-2 | 3-0 | 1-1 | 2-2 | 5-0 | 7-2 | 1-2 | 0-2 | 1-3 | 2-1 | 4-1 | 2-0 | 5-1 | 0-4 | 0-0 | 4-1 | 3-0 | 2-1 |
| 2 Ashford | 2-4 | X | 0-1 | 1-0 | 3-0 | 2-1 | 2-2 | 5-0 | 10-0 | 2-3 | 3-1 | 4-1 | 4-0 | 2-0 | 1-1 | 6-0 | 2-0 | 4-3 | 3-0 | 3-1 | 0-3 |
| 3 Ash United | 4-0 | 4-2 | X | 4-0 | 2-1 | 3-1 | 3-2 | 4-0 | 1-0 | 5-1 | 8-0 | 2-3 | 3-1 | 5-2 | 4-3 | 3-4 | 2-2 | 5-0 | 3-1 | 3-2 | 1-0 |
| 4 Bedfont | 3-1 | 2-2 | 2-3 | X | 2-1 | 0-0 | 3-4 | 3-1 | 4-2 | 3-1 | 3-1 | 2-1 | 4-0 | 1-3 | 3-4 | 0-1 | 3-1 | 5-0 | 2-1 | 2-1 | 0-1 |
| 5 Chessington | 1-4 | 1-4 | 3-1 | 0-1 | X | 0-2 | 2-2 | 2-0 | 7-1 | 2-4 | 2-0 | 3-0 | 1-0 | 1-2 | 2-0 | 1-1 | 2-3 | 2-3 | 6-1 | 3-0 | 1-0 |
| 6 Chipstead | 5-1 | 4-1 | 2-2 | 4-2 | 1-1 | X | 1-0 | 2-0 | 3-1 | 6-2 | 2-1 | 2-2 | 2-0 | 2-1 | 2-1 | 0-1 | 4-0 | 2-0 | 0-1 | 4-1 | 0-2 |
| 7 Cobham | 2-0 | 2-0 | 2-1 | 1-1 | 6-1 | 0-1 | X | 5-0 | 8-2 | 3-1 | 2-0 | 8-2 | 1-1 | 4-2 | 0-0 | 3-2 | 3-1 | 4-2 | 3-1 | 2-1 | 5-0 |
| 8 Cove | 0-4 | 1-4 | 0-5 | 0-8 | 1-5 | 0-5 | 1-3 | X | 1-2 | 3-4 | 0-1 | 1-4 | 3-2 | 1-5 | 0-6 | 0-0 | 0-4 | 0-2 | 0-1 | 1-5 | 1-3 |
| 9 Cranleigh | 4-3 | 0-3 | 1-2 | 2-2 | 0-2 | 1-6 | 1-4 | 2-1 | X | 3-3 | 6-3 | 1-2 | 4-1 | 1-0 | 2-4 | 3-4 | 0-3 | 0-1 | 1-2 | 2-4 | 1-1 |
| 10 Farnham | 2-2 | 3-0 | 4-0 | 2-2 | 1-2 | 0-1 | 2-6 | 9-1 | 5-0 | X | 3-0 | 4-1 | 0-1 | 4-2 | 4-0 | 2-4 | 0-3 | 1-2 | 2-2 | 4-0 | 0-1 |
| 11 Feltham | 0-0 | 0-1 | 1-2 | 2-3 | 2-1 | 0-0 | 1-1 | 4-1 | 2-0 | 2-0 | X | 1-0 | 2-2 | 0-0 | 1-0 | 0-1 | 3-0 | 4-0 | 4-0 | 2-2 | 1-0 |
| 12 Godalming & G | 1-0 | 2-1 | 0-0 | 4-2 | 5-1 | 1-3 | 2-2 | 2-0 | 4-1 | 2-0 | 0-1 | X | 3-1 | 2-0 | 3-1 | 2-1 | 0-1 | 2-0 | 4-0 | 2-1 | 3-0 |
| 13 Hartley W | 2-7 | 1-5 | 2-3 | 0-2 | 3-0 | 0-1 | 1-5 | 2-0 | 2-0 | 0-0 | 2-1 | 0-3 | X | 3-5 | 1-1 | 2-3 | 0-2 | 1-1 | 3-3 | 0-2 | 1-2 |
| 14 Merstham | 2-2 | 1-1 | 1-3 | 2-0 | 3-3 | 1-1 | 0-0 | 2-0 | 0-1 | 2-2 | 3-2 | 1-0 | 2-1 | X | 0-2 | 1-1 | 0-3 | 6-1 | 4-0 | 3-2 | 2-1 |
| 15 Netherne Vge | 2-9 | 2-6 | 1-6 | 2-4 | 0-3 | 0-1 | 3-1 | 1-5 | 0-5 | 0-6 | 1-3 | 1-5 | 2-1 | 0-7 | X | 0-3 | 0-6 | 1-5 | 1-2 | 4-0 | 2-0 |
| 16 RP Vale | 2-2 | 0-0 | 0-1 | 0-2 | 2-1 | 0-1 | 2-2 | 4-0 | 7-0 | 2-0 | 2-1 | 0-2 | 1-1 | 1-4 | 4-2 | X | 0-1 | 1-1 | 8-1 | 3-5 | 1-3 |
| 17 Reading Town | 1-2 | 1-3 | 2-1 | 3-5 | 1-0 | 3-3 | 1-1 | 1-0 | 3-1 | 0-1 | 1-1 | 2-3 | 0-1 | 2-0 | | 2-0 | X | 2-0 | 2-2 | 4-2 | 1-1 |
| 18 Sandhurst Tn | 2-7 | 1-3 | 0-6 | 3-5 | 1-3 | 0-2 | 1-3 | 2-1 | 2-1 | 2-3 | 3-1 | 2-0 | 1-3 | 3-1 | 1-1 | 4-2 | 4-1 | X | 0-0 | 1-2 | 1-1 |
| 19 Viking Sports | 0-4 | 1-4 | 0-2 | 0-3 | 2-3 | 4-1 | 1-2 | 2-3 | 2-1 | 4-2 | 0-1 | 3-1 | 1-6 | 3-1 | 4-1 | 2-0 | 1-2 | 0-2 | X | 4-1 | 0-2 |
| 20 Walton Cas | 0-2 | 0-1 | 0-2 | 1-3 | 0-6 | 2-1 | 0-1 | 3-0 | 3-3 | 0-0 | 0-1 | 3-4 | 1-1 | 1-0 | 5-0 | 2-3 | 0-1 | 4-4 | 1-1 | X | 1-2 |
| 21 Westfield | 1-1 | 0-0 | 0-4 | 1-3 | 0-1 | 1-2 | 2-1 | 2-0 | 0-1 | 1-0 | 0-0 | 2-1 | 3-0 | 1-0 | 3-0 | 2-1 | 1-1 | 2-2 | 4-2 | 2-1 | X |

## LEADING GOALSCORERS 1998-99

### PREMIER DIVISION

| | | |
|---|---|---|
| 39 | C Henry | AFC Wallingford |
| 29 | S Gorman | Godalming & Guildford |
| 28 | D Logie | Bedfont |
| 27 | H Tilbury | Cobham |
| 27 | D Bridger | Farnham Town |
| 26 | R McDonald | Ashford Town |

### DIVISION ONE

| | | |
|---|---|---|
| 25 | C Nobbs | Cobham |
| 16 | T Brooks | Reading Town |
| 16 | A Clark | Farnham Town |
| 15 | D Romain | AFC Wallingford |
| 15 | S Ellis | Sandhurst Town |
| 15 | W Dodgin | Westfield |

## FAIR PLAY TABLE 1998-99

| PREMIER DIVISION | Points |
|---|---|
| Westfield | 45 |
| Chessington & Hook | 52 |
| Feltham | 52 |
| Sandhurst Town | 52 |

| DIVISION ONE | Points |
|---|---|
| Farnham Town | 26 |
| Godalming & Guildford | 27 |
| Viking Sports | 30 |
| Ashford Town (Middx) | 32 |

# WORLDWIDE CARPETS PREMIER CHALLENGE CUP 1998-99

**FIRST ROUND**

| | | | | | | | |
|---|---|---|---|---|---|---|---|
| Ash United | v | Hartley Wintney | 4-0 | Ashford Town (Mx) | v | Walton Casuals | 6-0 |
| Chipstead | v | Sandhurst Town | 1-0 | Cove | v | Westfield | 0-0, 6-0 |
| Cranleigh | v | Viking Sports | 2-1 | | | | |

**SECOND ROUND**

| | | | | | | | |
|---|---|---|---|---|---|---|---|
| Ashford Town (Mx) | v | Godalming & G | 3*1 | Chipstead | v | Ash United | 2-3 |
| Cobham | v | Feltham | 4-0 | Merstham | v | AFC Wallingford | 6-3 |
| Netherne Village | v | Chessington & Hook | 2-3 | Raynes Park Vale | v | Cranleigh | 2-0 |
| Reading Town | v | Farnham Town | 3-0 | Westfield | v | Bedfont | 2*4 |

**THIRD ROUND**

| | | | | | | | |
|---|---|---|---|---|---|---|---|
| Ashford Town (Mx) | v | Ash United | 3-2 | Bedfont | v | Reading Town | 4*3 |
| Chessington & Hook | v | Cobham | 1*1, 0-3 | Raynes Park Vale | v | Merstham | 1-3 |

**SEMI-FINALS**

| | | | | | | | |
|---|---|---|---|---|---|---|---|
| Ashford Town (Mx) | v | Merstham | 2-0 | Cobham | v | Bedfont | 2-0 |

**FINAL**

| | | | | |
|---|---|---|---|---|
| Ashford Town (Mx) | v | Cobham | 1-0 | at Farnborough Town FC |

# DIVISION ONE CHALLENGE CUP 1998-99

**FIRST ROUND**

| | | | |
|---|---|---|---|
| Cove | v | Merstham | 3-7 |

**SECOND ROUND**

| | | | | | | | |
|---|---|---|---|---|---|---|---|
| AFC Wallingford | v | Sandhurst Town^ | 5*3 | Bedfont | v | Westfield^ | 1*1 |
| Chessington & Hook | v | Cobham | 2*1 | Farnham Town | v | Ash United | 3*2 |
| Godalming & G'ford | v | Cranleigh | 4-3 | Reading Town | v | Ashford Town (Mx) | 0-3 |
| Viking Sports | v | Netherne Village | 3-1 | Walton Casuals | v | Merstham | 0-1 |

**THIRD ROUND**

| | | | | | | | |
|---|---|---|---|---|---|---|---|
| Ashford Town (Mx)^ | v | Chessington & Hook | 0-4 | Farnham Town | v | Sandhurst Town | 1-2 |
| Godalming & G'ford | v | Westfield | 0-1 | Viking Sports | v | Merstham | 1-4 |
| ^ Match awarded | | | | | | | |

**SEMI-FINALS**

| | | | | | | | |
|---|---|---|---|---|---|---|---|
| Ashford Town (Mx) | v | Sandhurst Town | 1-0 | Westfield | v | Merstham | 1-2 |

**FINAL**

| | | | | |
|---|---|---|---|---|
| Ashford Town (Mx) | v | Merstham | 1-0 | at Farnborough Town FC |

Left: Ashford Town (Middx) celebrate their win over Cobham in the Final of the Worldwide Carpets Premier Challenge Cup, at Farnborough Town

Right:
Ash United, League Champions 1998-99

# AFC WALLINGFORD

**Secretary:** Eddie Gniadek, 17 Offas Close, Benson, Wallingford, Oxon OX10 6NR
Tel: 01491 838540 (H)  01491 838308 (B)

**Ground:** Wallingford Sports Park, Hithercroft Road, Wallingford, Oxon. Tel: 01491 835044
**Directions:**
Nearest Railway station: Cholsey & Moulsford. Bus - Thames Transit.
Capacity: 1,500    Cover: 100    Seats: 40    Floodlights: Yes
**Clubhouse:** Open evenings 7.30-11.00, Sat & Sun   Tea & snacks available  01491 835044
Club Shop: Yes
**HONOURS:** Chiltonian Prem Lge 97-98; Bon Accord Trophy 95-96
**RECORDS:** **Attendance:** 280 v Reading Town 98-99
**Goalscorere:** Carl Henry 68 97-98    **Appearances:** Anthony Hill 220
**PREVIOUS:** **Leagues:** Chiltonian Lge 95-98

### FACT FILE
Founded: 1995
Colours: Red & black hoops/black/red & black
Change colours: Blue & white
Midweek matchday: Tuesday
Programme: 20 pages; price 50p
Editor: Andy Ham  (01491 837608)

### CLUB PERSONNEL
President: K Lester
Chairman: E L Townsend
Tel: 01491 839103 (H)
Match Secretary: G Lee
21 Orchard Close, Brightwell, Wallingford,
Oxon. Tel: 01491 836921 (H)
Manager: Larry Hill    Coach: Gary Elkins

---

# ASH UNITED

**Secretary:** Alan Constable, 30 Marlborough Road, Ashford, Middlesex. TW15 3QA
Tel No: 01784 257168

**Ground:** Youngs Drive, off Shawfield Rd, Ash, Nr Aldershot Tel: 01252 320385
**Directions:** A323 towards Ash, left into Shawfield Rd, left into Youngs Drive
1 mile from both Ash and Ash Vale BR stations. Bus - Stagecoach 20A, 550
Capacity: 1,500    Seats: None    Cover: Yes    Floodlights: Yes
**HONOURS:** Prem Chall Cup 97-98; Comb Co Lge 98-99; Aldershot Sen Cup 98-99
**CLUB RECORDS Attendance;** 650 v Tiverton Town FA Vase
**Goalscorer:** Scott Joyce 40    **Appearances:** Tommy Burton 540
**BEST SEASON FA Cup:** 2nd Qual Rd v Walton & Hersham 98-99
**FA Vase:** 4th Rd v Tiverton Town 98-99
**PREVIOUS** **Ground:** Ash Common Rec. 70-71    **Leagues:** Surrey Snr, Aldershot Snr

### FACT FILE
Founded: 1911
Colours: Red & green/green/green
Change colours: All blue
Midweek Matchday: Tuesday
Admission: £2
Programme: 36 pages, 50p
Editor: Garth Watmore

### CLUB PERSONNEL
President; Mr E Britzman
Chairman: Robert J Atkins
Vice Chairman: Cliff Foster
General Manager: Alex  Smith-Gander
Manager: Jamie Horton
Asst. Manager: Angelo Barbato

---

# ASHFORD TOWN (MIDDX)

**Secretary:** Alan B J Constable, 30 Marlborough Rd, Ashford, Middx TW15 3QA 01784885092 (H)
**Ground:** Short Lane, Stanwell, Staines, Middx (01784 245908).
**Directions:** M25 jct 13, A30 towards London, 3rd left at footbridge after Ashford Hospital cross-
roads - ground signposted after 1/4 a mile on right down Short Lane. 2 miles from Ashford (BR) &
Hatton Cross (tube) stations. Bus route - Westlink 116
Capacity: 2,000    Seats: 100    Cover: 100    Floodlights: Yes    Club Shop: No
Clubhouse: Open 7 days a week. Refreshments always available - hot food on matchdays
**HONOURS:** Combined Co's Lg Champions 94-95, 95-96, 96-97, 97-8 Chall Cup R-up 92-
93 94-95, Lg Vase Cup R-up 91-92 94-95; Surrey I'mediate Lg, Surrey Prem. Cup 89-90; Middx
Prem. Cup R-up 89-90; Southern Comb Cup 95-96, World Wide Carpets Prem Ch Cup 98-99
**PREVIOUS** **Ground:** Clockhouse Lane Rec.    **Leagues:** Hounslow & Dist. 64-68;
Surrey Intermediate 68-82; Surrey Premier 82-90
**CLUB RECORD** **Attendance:** 750 v Brentford, friendly 29/7/86
**Goalscorer:** Andy Smith    **Appearances:** Alan Constable 650

### FACT FILE
Formed: 1964    Nickname: Ash Trees
Colours: Tangerine & white/white/tangerine
Change colours: All blue
Midweek matchday: Tuesday
Programme: 24 pages, £1 Editor: Secretary

### CLUB PERSONNEL
Chairman: Robert Parker
Vice Chairman: Des Vertannes
President: E Britzman
Press Secretary: Terry Vertannes
Manager: Dave Kent
98-99 - Captain: Gary Cambridge
Top Scorer:Richard McDonald (31)
P.o.Y .Graham Hill

---

# BEDFONT

**Secretary:** Leslie King, 16 Sidney Road, St Margarets, Twickenham, Middlesex. TW1 1JR
Tel No: 0181 891 1985
**Ground:** The Orchard, Hatton Rd, Bedfont, Middx. Tel: 0181 890 7264
**Directions:** Turn down Faggs Rd opposite Hatton Cross (Picadilly Line) station on Great
South Western Rd (A30), then sharp right into Hatton Rd. Ground opposite
Duke of Wellington pub. Bus - Westlink 203
Capacity:1,500    Seats: None    Cover: 50    Floodlights: Yes    Clubhouse: Yes

**HONOURS** Comb. Co's Chal. Vase 92-93 (Res. Div R-up 88-89, Res. Cup R-up 89-90),
Grant McClennan Yth Cup 91-92), Middx Lg 73-74 76-77 (Div 1 (Res) & Div 1 Cup 71-72 78-79
79-80, Surrey Prem. Lg 84-85 86-87, Middx I'mediate Cup 69-70 76-77, Inter. Contois Tour. 1992,
Liege Euromann Tour. 89, Harold Clayton Cup 90-91, Hounslow & Dist. Div 1 (Res) 86-87
**PREVIOUS Names:** Bedfont Inst.(1900), Bedfont Rangers(1950) & Fairholme Utd(1953) merged
1968. Club later merged with Interharvester(1973) & Bedfont Eagles(1988). **Ground:** Bedfont Rec.

### FACT FILE
Founded: 1968
Colours: Yellow & blue stripes/blue/blue
Change colours: All red or White/navy/navy
Midweek matches: Tuesday
Programme: 28 pages, 50p. Editors: Alan
Humphries (01932 563548) and ColinMcNeill
(0181 384 8410)

### CLUB PERSONNEL
President: Roger Cooper
Chairman: John Dollimore
Vice Chairman: K Stone
Manager: Alan Humphries
Coach: Cliff Williamson
Asst. Man.: Bob Barnes

# CHESSINGTON & HOOK UNITED

**Secretary:** Alan Warwick, 38 Hartfield Road, Chessington, Surrey. KT9 2PW
Tel:0181 397 1843 (H)

**Ground:** Chalky Lane, Chessington, Surrey. Tel: 01372 729892

**Directions:** Turn off A243 into Chalky Lane opposite Chessington World of Adventure Theme Park Railway - Chessington South. Bus - London Transport 71.

**Capacity:** Seats: Cover: Floodlights: Yes

**HONOURS:** Combined Counties Lge Prem Cup R-up 97-98, Surrey County Lge Prem Div R-up 96-97, Div 1 70-71,

**PREVIOUS** **Leagues:** Middx Lge 68-69, Surrey County 69-72, Home Counties 72-78 Comb Co 78-81, Surrey Prem, Surrey Comb, Surrey Prem.

**BEST SEASON** **FA Vase:** Do not enter      **FA Cup:** Do not enter

**FACT FILE**
Founded: 1968
Colours: All blue
Change colours: Yellow/black/yellow
Midweek Matchday:
Programme: Yes

**CLUB PERSONNEL**
Chairman: Graham Ellis
63 Stormont Way, Chessington,
Surrey. KT9 2QW
Tel: 0181 241 2832 (H)
Manager: Paul Ellis 0181 397 8499 (H)

---

# CHESSINGTON UNITED

**Secretary:** Michael Smith, 34 Sopwith Avenue, Chessington, Surrey KT9 1QE
Tel: 020 8255 8847 (H)  0797 9606125 (M)

**Ground:** Fetcham Park Utd., Riverlane, Leatherhead, Surrey. Tel: 01737 363995
Nearest Railway Station: Leatherhead
Buses: London Country 465 & 479

**FACT FILE**

Colours: Green & white/white/green & white

**CLUB PERSONNEL**

President: J F Curran

Chairman: Richard Jaramillo
19 Purbeck Close, Merstham, Redhill
Surrey RH1 1PG
Tel: 01737 644588

Match Secretary: as Secretary

---

# CHIPSTEAD

**Secretary:**Geoff Corner, 20 Sunnymede Avenue, Carshalton Beeches, Surrey SM54JF
Tel: 0181 642 0827 (H)

**Ground:** High Road, Chipstead, Surrey. Tel: 01737 553250
**Directions:** Brighton Road northbound, left into Church Lane, left into HogcrossLane, right into High Road. 1 1/2/ miles from Chipstead (BR). Bus -London County 405, 407
**Capacity: 2,000** Seats: 30 Cover: 100 Floodlights: Yes

**HONOURS** Surrey Premier Lg R-up 82-83 83-84 85-86 (Lg Cup 82-83 84-85 85-86), Combined Co's Lg 89-90 (R-up 90-91 92-93, Lg Cup 86-87 90-91 92-93, Elite Class Cup R-up 89-90, Reserve Section Cup 92-93)
**BEST SEASON** **FA Cup:** 1998-99      **FA Vase:** 1998-99
**CLUB RECORDS** Attendance: 903
Goalscorer: Appearances:
**PREVIOUS** **Leagues:** Surrey Intermediate 62-82; Surrey Premier 82-86

**FACT FILE**
Founded: 1906
Nickname: Chips
Colours: Green & white/white/green
Change colours: Purple/yellow/yellow
Midweek matchday: Tuesday
Programme: 44 pages

**CLUB PERSONNEL**
President: Clive Wood
Chairman: Derek Parsons, 32 Cannons Hill,
Old Coulsdon, Surrey. Tel.: 01737552682
Manager: S Bangs
Coach:M.Ford

---

# COBHAM

**Secretary:** Ken Reed, 29 Waterer Gardens, Tadworth, Surrey. KT20 5PB
Tel: 01737352641 (H) Fax: 01737 352259
**Ground:** Leg O'Mutton Field, Anvil Lane, Downside Bridge Rd, Cobham, Surrey
Tel: 01932 865959
**Directions:** A3 turnoff A245, A307 (Portsmouth) towards Leatherhead, right intoBetween Streets, rt into Downside Rd then rt opposite car park. Cobham & StokeD'Abernon (BR) 2 miles. Bus - Green Line 715, London Country 501, 513
**Capacity: 2,000** Seats: None Cover: Yes Floodlights: Yes Club Shop: No
Clubhouse: Yes
**HONOURS** Combined Co's Lge Cup, Res Lge (3)
**BEST SEASON** **FA Cup:**      **FA Vase:** 1998-99 3rd Rd.
**CLUB RECORDS** **Attendance: 2,000** v Showbiz XI, charity game 1975
**PREVIOUS** **League:** Surrey Senior **Grounds:** Cobham Rec

**FACT FILE**
Founded: 1892
Nickname: Hammers
Sponsor: PeterHaworth Consultancy
Colours: Red & navy/navy/navy
Change colours:Black & White stripes
Midweek matchday: Tuesday
Programme: Yes

**CLUB PERSONNEL**
Chairman: Peter Haworth
President: E D Strange
Manager: Gary Block
Coach: Tony Wilson
Physio: C Bird

# COVE

**Secretary:** Graham Brown, 6 Longfield Close,Haley Estate, Farnborough. GU14 8HQ
**Tel:** 01252 650920
**Ground:** 7 Squirrels Lane, Farnborough, Hants GU14 8PB. Tel.: 01252 543615
**Directions:** Farnborough (BR) 2 miles; right into Union Street, right at lights into Prospect Rd, left into West Heath Rd, right into Romayne Close and follow signs to Cove FC. Or, M3 jct 4, follow A325 signed Aldershot & Farnham, right into Prospect Rd. (signed Cove FC & Farnborough Town FC), then as above
**Capacity:** 3,500   **Seats:** 75   **Cover:** 475   **Floodlights:** Yes   Club Shop: No
**Clubhouse:** Mon-Fri 7-11, Sat 12-11, Sunday 12-3 & 7-11. Hot food on matchdays
**HONOURS**   Surrey I'mediate Lg; Surrey Prem. Lg x5, R-up x3, Lg Cup x3, Res.Section x4, R-up x4, Res. Cup x2; Combined Co's Lg Cup 81-82; Hants Lg Div 3,Div 4, Div 2 R-up; Aldershot - Snr Cup x5, R-up, Snr Shield x4, Snr Lg, Div 2x3, Div 2 Cup, Div 4 Cup
**PREVIOUS**   **Leagues:** AldershotJnr; Aldershot I'mediate 45-48; Surrey I'mediate 48-71; Surrey Snr 71-73; Hants 74-81; Combined Counties 81-90; Isthmian 90-95; Comb. Cos. 95-
**CLUB RECORDS Attendance:** 1,798 v Aldershot, Isthmian Lg Div 3, 1/5/93
**BEST SEASON**   **FA Cup:** 1st Qual. Rd replay 91-92, 0-4 v Burgess Hill Town (A)

**FACT FILE**
Founded: 1897
Sponsors: Sunnyside Removals
Colours: Yellow & black stripes/black/black
Change colours: Red & white stripes/red/red
Midweek Matches: Tuesday
Reserves' League: Comb. Cos. 1st Div
Programme: 30 pages, 50p
Editor: Graham Brown (01252 650920)

**CLUB PERSONNEL**
Chairman: Bob Clark, 3 Linstead Rd., Farnborough, Hants. Tel: 01276 33435
President: Ron Brown
Manager:
Asst. Manager:

**ASH UNITED** with the League Chapionship & the Aldershot Senior Cup

Photo: Eric Marsh

**MERSTHAM** L-R Back Row: Gareth Mitchell, Ben Savage, Darren Benham, Nathan McDonnell, Nathan Jupp, Paul Stanford, Russ Morgan, Lee Hill, Colin Humphries (coach). FRONT ROW: Peter Gibson, Graeme Cranford (physio), Ian Gallagher, Anthony Jupp, Joe McElligott (manager), John Penalver, Brian Jupp (captain).

Photo: Gordon Whittington

# CRANLEIGH

**Secretary:** T.Moore, Penwerris, 51 Horsham Road, Cranleigh, Surrey GU6 8DT
**Tel No:** 01483 273161 (H) 01689 874056 (W)
**Match Secretary:** Alan Pavia Tel: 01483 271233 (H) 01483 894248 (B)
**Ground:** Snoxall Playing Fields, Knowle Lane, Cranleigh Tel: 01483 275295
**Directions:** A281 from Guildford towards Horsham, at Shalford take B2128 to Cranleigh
High St., right opposite Onslow Arms into Knowle Lane, ground half mile on left.
Public transport: Guildford (BR) then bus (Alder Valley) 273 or 283

**Capacity:** 450          Seats: None          Cover: 50          Floodlights: No
**Clubhouse:** Licensed bar. Hot food on matchdays          Club Shop: No
**HONOURS**          W Sussex County Times Cup 92-93
**BEST SEASON**     FA Vase 3rd Rd 92-93          **FA Cup:**
**CLUB RECORDS**   **Attendance:** 450 v C Palace, friendly 1989
Competitive: 285 v Hailsham,FA Vase 3rd Rd 12/12/92
**PREVIOUS**          League: Surrey Intermediate

## FACT FILE
Founded: 1893
Nickname: Cranes
Sponsors: Roger Coupe, Est. Agents
Colours: Blue/black/blue
Change colours: Yellow/green/yellow
Midweek matchday: Tuesday
Programme: £1.50
Editor: Peter Slater (01483 894245)
**CLUB PERSONNEL**
Chairman: T Moore
Vice Chairman: Roy Kelsey
President: Alan Pavia
Manager: Roy Kelsey
Asst Manager: Paul Jones
Coach: Andy Clements

# FARNHAM TOWN

**Secretary:** Mrs Barbara Fripp, 70 Lower Farnham Rd., Aldershot. GU12 4EA   (01252 657184)
**Ground:** Memorial Ground, Babbs Mead, West Street, Farnham, Surrey   (01252 715305)
**Directions:** From A31, direction Winchester, take 2nd turning into town at Coxbridge roundabout.
Follow West Street until you come to new mini roundabout - the Memorial Ground is on the right.

**Capacity:** 2,000          Seats: None          Cover: 150          Floodlights: Yes
**Clubhouse:** Open every evening and match daysClub Shop: No
**HONOURS**          Combined Counties Lg 90-91 91-92, Challenge Cup Prem Div 95-96,
Challenge Tphy 91-92 (R-up 89-90).
**CLUB RECORDS**   **Attendance:** 500 v Kingstonian, Surrey Snr Cup 1960.
**PREVIOUS**          **Leagues:** Surrey Intermediate; Surrey Snr 47-71: Spartan 71-75: London
Spartan 75-80: Combined Counties 80-92.
**BEST SEASON**     FA Cup: Never past Qualifying Rounds

## FACT FILE
Founded: 1921          Nickname: The Town
Sponsors: Frazer Freight.
Colours: All  claret & blue.
Change: White, pale blue & claret/claret/claret
Midweek Matchday: Tuesday
Reserve League: Comb Counties Res Div
Programme: 32 pages 50p
Editor: Ann Butters
**CLUB PERSONNEL**
Chairman: Richard Sheppard 01252 723724 (H)
President; Paul Cooper
Press Officer: Charlie White
Manager: Peter Browning
Asst Manager: Roy Atkin
Coach: A Wyciechowski/A Metcalfe

# FELTHAM

**Secretary:** John Cronk, 37 Ruskin Ave, Feltham, Middlesex. TW14 9HY Tel: 0181 751 3663
**Ground:** Feltham Arena, Shakespeare Ave., Feltham, Middx.
Tel: 0181 384 5048 (club),  0181 890 6905 (ground)
**Directions:** BR to Feltham & 5 mins walk thro' Glebelands Park
Buses 90, 285,117, 237, H24 or H25 to Feltham station, or 116 to top of Shakespeare Ave.
By car: M3, M4, A312 Staines road towards Bedfont, 2nd left is Shakespeare Ave
**Capacity:** 10,000          Seats: 650          Cover: 1,500          Floodlights: Yes
**Clubhouse:** Open 7 days a week. 2 bars, dancehall available for hire          Club Shop: No
**HONOURS**          Surrey Snr Lg R-up 65-66 (Lg Cup 65-66, Charity Cup 63-64 65-66),Southern
Comb. Cup(2)(R-up(2)), Middx Summer Cup, Isthmian Div 2 80-81, Comb.Cos. Lge Co. 96-97
**PREVIOUS**          **Leagues:** Feltham: West Middx Sunday; Staines & Dist.; Hounslow & Dist.;
Surrey Snr 63-68; Spartan 68-73; Athenian 74-77; Isthmian 78-95
**CLUB RECORDS**   **Attendance:** 1,9 38 v Hampton,Middlesex Senior Cup 1968
**Goalscorer:** Paul Clarke 130          **Appearances:** Paul Clarke 326
**BEST SEASON**     FA Cup: 3rd Qual.Rd.77-78, 1-4 v Tilbury;  82-83, 0-1 v Chesham U

## FACT FILE
Founded: 1946
Colours: Royal blue & white halves/blue/blue
Change colours: Red & blue stripes/blue/blue
Midweek Matches: Wednesday
Programme: 20 pages, 50p
Editor: Richard Sevice
Sponsors: Cowley Security Locksmiths/
Feltham first
**CLUB PERSONNEL**
Chairman: Willi F P Seuke 0181296 9630 (H)
Press Off.: Richard Sevice
01932 - 761544(Tel) 761744 (Fax)
Manager: Bob Barnes
Asst. Man: Dave Barker

# GODALMING & GUILDFORD

**Secretary:** Eddie Russell, 31 Harts Gardens, Guildford, Surrey GU2 6QB. 01483 535287 (H & B)
**Ground:** Wey Court, Meadrow, Godalming, Surrey (01483 417520)
**Directions:** A3100 from Guildford - past Beefeater Hotel on left, then 'Save' petrol station on
right, then 1st right 50 yards on. From Godalming on A3100, grd on left by Leather Bottle pub.
Three quarters of a mile from Farncombe BR station

**Capacity:** 3,000          Seats: 200          Cover: 200          Floodlights: Yes          Club Shop: No
**Clubhouse:** Open Tues, Wed, Thurs eves, matchdays. Hot & cold snacks available
**HONOURS**          Combined Co's Lg 83-84, Lge Chall. Trophy 82-83, Res Lge 95-96 96-97, Res
Chall Cup 92-93 97-98, Chall Shield 96-97: Southern Comb Chall Cup 97-98
**PREVIOUS**          **Leagues:** Guildford & Dist 50-71; Surrey Intermediate 71-78; Surrey Co. Senior 78-79
**RECORDS**          **Attendance:** 600+ ex-Guildford City XI v ex-Football Lg XI. Tony Burge benefit 91
**Goalscorer:** Paul Hampshire 123          **Appearances:** Paul Monger 356
**BEST SEASON**     FA Cup: 1st Q.Rd.          FA Vase: 2nd Rd.

## FACT FILE
Founded: 1950
Nickname: The Gees
Colours: Green & yellow/green/yellow
Change colours: Red & blue/blue/blue
Midweek matchday: Tuesday
Programme: Yes

**CLUB PERSONNEL**
Chairman: Jane Phillips
President: W F Kyte
Press Officer: Secretary
Manager: Mick Wollen
Asst Manager: Roger Steer
Coach Roger Falconer
Physio: Steve Snelling

# HARTLEY WINTNEY

**FACT FILE**

**Secretary:** Mick Bradley, 8 Dairy Walk, Hartley Wintney, Hampshire
Tel No: 01252 845745(H/Fax)

**Ground:** Memorial Playing Fields, Green Lane, Hartley Wintney, Hants
Tel: 01252 843586

**Directions:** A30 west through Camberley, left at parade of shops at beginning of village then sharp right - ground on right. Two miles from Winchfield (BR)
Buses: Stagecoach 200, Bee Line 111, 112
Capacity: 2,000    Seats: None    Cover: No    Floodlights: No

**HONOURS:** None
**BEST SEASON** FA Cup: Do not compete    FA Vase: Do not compete
**PREVIOUS** Leagues: Basingstoke/ Aldershot

Founded: 1897
Nickname: The Row
Colours: Orange/black/black
Change colours: All white or Red/black/black
Midweek matchday: Tuesday
Programme: Yes

**CLUB PERSONNEL**

Chairman: as Secretary
President: W A Mitchell

# MERSTHAM

**FACT FILE**

**Secretary:** Richard Baxter, 2 Wood Street, Merstham, Surrey. RH1 3PF
Tel: 01737 645748 (H) 01293 432363 (B)
**Ground:** Merstham Rec., Weldon Way, Merstham, Redhill, Surrey RH1 3QB (01737 644046)
**Directions:** Leave Merstham village (A23) by School Hill, take 5th right (WeldonWay), clubhouse and car park 100m on right. 10 mins walk from Merstham (BR);down School Hill, under railway bridge, then 5th turning on right into WeldonWay. Bu98-99s - London Country 430, 432 & 435
Capacity: 2,000    Seats: 100    Cover: 100    Floodlights: Yes    Club Shop: No
Clubhouse: Across adjacent footpath. Open daily (am & pm). Snacks available
**HONOURS** Combined Co's Lg R-up 87-88 89-90 (Elite Class Cup 89-90 (R-up 90-91),
Res. Sect. 90-91), Spartan Lg 79-89 (Lg Cup 79-80), Surrey Snr Lg 71-72,
Surrey Snr Char. Cup 79-80, E. Surrey Char. Cup 80-8 98-99, Surrey I'mediate Lg 52-3
**CLUB RECORDS** Attendance: 532
**BEST SEASON** FA Cup: 3rd Q Rd    FA Vase: 4th Rd.
**PREVIOUS** Leagues: Redhill & Dist.; Surrey Co.S.E. I'mediate; Surrey Snr 64-78; London Spartan 78-85    Grounds:None

Founded: 1892
Club Sponsors: Merstham Glass
Colours: Amber & black stripes/black/amber
Change colours: All red
Midweek matches: Tuesday/Thursday
Programme: Yes  Editor:Andy Wheeler

**CLUB PERSONNEL**

Chairman: C. Humphries
President: Bill Lawton
Press Officer: Roger Peerless
Manager: Joe McElligott
Asst Manager: Colin Humphries

# RAYNES PARK VALE

**FACT FILE**

**Secretary:** Paul Armour, 68 Oaks Ave., Worcester Park, Surrey. KT4 8XD.
Tel: 0181 337 4989 (H)  0171 820 6314 (B)

**Ground:** Grand Drive, Raynes Park. SW20 9NB Tel: 0181 542 2193

**Directions:** Bus - London Transport 131 & 152
Nearest railway station - Raynes Park.

**HONOURS:** None

Colours:Claret & blue stripes/blue/red
Change colours: Green & white hoops/green/white

**CLUB PERSONNEL**

President: Robert Hallett

Chairman: Dave Brenen
22 The Crescent, Belmont, Surrey. SM2 0BJ.
Tel: 0181 2968626

# READING TOWN

**FACT FILE**

**Secretary:** Richard Grey, 6 Milestone View Court, Lowfield Road, Caversham Park, Reading RG4 6ND Tel: 0118 948 2006
**Ground:** Reading Town Spts Ground, Scours Lane, Tilehurst, Reading, Berks (0118945 3555)
**Directions:** Out of Reading on Oxford road (A329), past Battle Hosp. Scours Lane1st right after r'bout. Nearest station - Tilehurst or Reading (General). Bus -Reading Bus 17
Capacity: 2,000    Seats: No    Cover: Yes    Floodlights: Yes    Clubhouse: Yes
**PREVIOUS** Leagues: Chiltonian 89-95, Reading 66-89
Names: Lower Burghfield, XL United, Vincents Utd, Reading Garage, ITS Reading Town
**CLUB RECORDS** Attendance: 253 v Banstead Ath FA Vase 96-97
Defeat: 0-10 v Feltham(A) 96-97
Win: 7-0 v Cranleigh/Viking Spts/AFC Wallingford all Home 97-98
**BEST SEASON** FA Cup: Prelim Rd 97-98    FA Vase: 4th Rd 96-97
**HONOURS** Comb Counties Lge R-up 97-98; Chiltonian Lge Champions 94-95, Berks &Bucks Sen. Trophy 95-96, R-up 96-97

Founded: 1968
Colours: Red & black stripes/black/black
Change colours: Blue & black/white/white
Midweek Matchday: Tuesday
Programme: 20 pages 50p
Editor: Pat Monaghan

**CLUB PERSONNEL**

Chairman: Roland Ford, 103 Little Heath
Road, Tilehurst, Berkshire RG31 5TG
Tel: 0118 941 2270
Fixture Sec.: Mrs Pauline Semple, 278
Hemdean Rd., Caversham, Reading RG4 7QT
Tel: 0118 947 9394
Manager: Paul Evans

# SANDHURST TOWN

**Secretary:** Michael Roberts, 36 Constable Way, College Town, Sandhurst, Berkshire. GU47 0FE
Tel No: 01276 609038 (H) 01344 773111 (W)
**Ground:** Bottom Meadow, Memorial Ground, Yorktown Rd, Sandhurst (01252 873767)
**Directions:** A30 westwards through Camberley, right at r-bout with traffic lights onto A321, past superstore turning left the 3rd set of traffic lights onA321 towards Wokingham. Ground situated near to Town & Council offices & Community Centre. Nearest station - Sandhurst. Bus - Bee Line 193, 194
**Capacity:** 2,000      **Seats:** None      **Cover:** Yes      **Floodlights:** Yes      **Clubhouse:** open 6 days
**PREVIOUS      Leagues:** Reading & Dist.; East Berks; Aldershot Snr 79-84; Chiltonian84-90
**CLUB RECORDS      Attendance:** 353 v Aldershot Town (Friendly)
                              **Win:** 6-2 v Viking Sports      **Defeat:** 8-2 v Ashford Town (Middx)
                              **Goalscorer:** Glenn Price      **Appearances:** John Parker
**BEST SEASON      FA Vase:** 1st Rd 93-94      **FA Cup:** 1st Rd Qualifying
**HONOURS**      Combined Co's Lge Chal. Vase R-up 92-93 (Reserve Chal. Cup R-up 91-92),
Chiltonian Lg R-up 86-87, Aldershot Snr Lg R-up 83-84; Berks & Bucks Sen.Trophy R-up 92-93

### FACT FILE
Founded: 1910
Nickname: Fizzers
Colours: Red/black/black
Change colours: Blue & white hoops,blue,blue
Midweek matchday: Wednesday
Programme: Yes
Editor: Paul Varndell

### CLUB PERSONNEL
Chairman:Bob Worthington
President: Malcolm Watts
Match Sec.: as Secretary
Manager:Peter Hayward
Coach: Paul McKinnon

---

# VIKING GREENFORD

**Secretary:** Stephen Hosmer, 27 St Georges Rd., Hanworth, Middlesex. TW13 6RD
Tel. & Fax: 0181 894 1244 (M) 0831 393559
**Ground:** Avenue Park, Western Avenue, Greenford, Middx (0181 578 2706)
**Directions:** On London-bound carriageway of A40, 300 yds before Greenford flyover and slip road to A4127. 12 mins walk from Greenford (Central Line) station - turn right out of station to A40, turn right - grd 1/4 mile on rght
**Capacity:** 450      **Seats:** 50      **Cover:** 100      **Floodlights:** Yes      **Club Shop:** No
**Clubhouse:** Open every evening except Sunday. Hot & cold snacks on matchdays
**HONOURS**      Hellenic Lg Div 1 85-86 (Div 1 Cup R-up 90-91).Co.Counties Lg.(R-Up.94-95)
**CLUB RECORDS      Att:** 180 v Wealdstone,Middx.SenCup,Sept.96 **Goalscorer:** Frank Healy, 43
                              **PREVIOUS      Leagues:** Middlesex 70-80; Hellenic 80-91
**BEST SEASON      FA Cup:** 1st Q Rd 96 F,A.Vase: 2nd Rd  v Diss Town 1991
**1997-98  Captain:** Jamie Cuttica      **P.o.Y.:** Darren Fraser      **Top Scorer:** Liam White

### FACT FILE
Founded: 1945      Nickname: Vikings
Sponsors: Measham Self-Drive/ Greeene King
Colours: All tangerine, black trim
Change colours: Sky blue & maroon/sky/sky
Midweek matchday: Tuesday
Programme: 12 pages, 50p
Editor: John Bennett

### CLUB PERSONNEL
Chairman: Terry Cross
President: Roy Bartlett
Press Officer: Jamie Cuttica
Manager: Wayne Haley
Asst Man.:Steve Parsons
Physio: Ernie Stockwell

---

# WALTON CASUALS

**Secretary:** Stuart Roberts, 47 Foxholes, Weybridge, Surrey. KT13 0BN. Tel: 01932845923
**Ground:** Franklyn Road Sports Ground, Waterside Drive, Walton-on-Thames, Surrey KT12 2JG
Tel: 01932 787749 (24hrs ansaphone).
**Directions:** Next to Elmbridge Leisure Centre, left off Terrace Rd at first roundabout out of Walton centre. Hersham (BR), then bus 564 to Elmbridge Leisure Centre.
**Capacity:** 1,500      **Seats:** None      **Cover:** 80      **Floodlights:** Yes
**Clubhouse:** Matchdays only. Hot food available from Tea Bar      **Club Shop:** No
**HONOURS**      Suburban Lge (South) 82-83, (R-up 83-84); Surrey Prem Lge R-up 94-95,
S.P.L. Chall Cup 93-94, (R-up 94-95); Surrey Premier Cup R-up 86-87
**BEST SEASON      FA Vase:** 1Q 96-97(only Game)      **FA Cup:** Never entered
**PREVIOUS      Leagues:** Surrey Premier, Surrey Senior, Surrey Intermediate, Suburban.
**CLUB RECORDS      Attendance:** 178 v Pagham FA Vase 96/97

### FACT FILE
Founded: 1948
Nickname: The Stags
Sponsors: Tallents Bar
Colours: Tangerine/black/tangerine
Change colours: Red & black/white/red
Midweek Matchday: Tuesday
Programme: 36 pages 50p
Editor/Press Officer: Stuart Roberts

### CLUB PERSONNEL
Chairman: Peter Steward
General Manager: David Symonds
President: Grahan James
Managers: Mick Sullivan & Garry Clark

---

# WESTFIELD

**Secretary:**      Michael Lawrence, 19 Ash Road, Barnsbury Estate, Woking, Surrey. GU22 0BJ
                      Tel/Fax: 01483 722184 (H)

**GROUND**      Woking Park, Kingfield, Woking, Surrey Tel: 01483 771106

**Directions:**      (Adjacent to Woking FC.)
                      M25 J10 or 11, signposted from outskirts of Town.Ground 1 mile.
                      Woking B.R.Station & buses from Woking
                      Capacity: 1,000      Seats: None      Cover: Yes      Floodlights: Yes
**Clubhouse**      Yes - open matchdays when snacks are available.
**Club Shop**      No

**PREVIOUS      League:** Surrey County Senior League

### FACT FILE
Founded: 1953
Colours: All yellow
Change colours: All white
Midweek Matchday:Tuesday
Programme: No

### CLUB PERSONNEL
President: R Hill
Chairman: S P Perkins
160 Coleford Bridge Road, Mytchett,
Camberley, Surrey
Tel: 01252 547900 (B)
Manager: John Cassidy
Asst. Managers:
Alan Morton & Brian Hennessy

## HERTFORDSHIRE SENIOR COUNTY LEAGUE
### PREMIER DIVISION

| | | | | | | | |
|---|---|---|---|---|---|---|---|
| Cuffley | 28 | 21 | 2 | 5 | 78 | 29 | 65 |
| Wormley Rovers | 28 | 18 | 5 | 5 | 62 | 31 | 59 |
| Sandridge Rovers | 28 | 16 | 4 | 8 | 72 | 43 | 52 |
| Benington | 28 | 14 | 6 | 8 | 46 | 42 | 48 |
| Elliott Star | 28 | 14 | 4 | 10 | 63 | 56 | 46 |
| Bedmond Sports & S | 28 | 13 | 6 | 9 | 57 | 36 | 45 |
| Sun Postal Sports | 28 | 13 | 5 | 10 | 49 | 42 | 44 |
| Colney Heath | 28 | 11 | 5 | 12 | 62 | 62 | 38 |
| Met Police Bushey | 28 | 9 | 5 | 14 | 41 | 58 | 32 |
| Hatfield Town | 28 | 8 | 7 | 13 | 49 | 64 | 31 |
| Agrevo Sports | 28 | 7 | 7 | 14 | 38 | 57 | 28 |
| Bovingdon | 28 | 6 | 9 | 13 | 31 | 52 | 27 |
| Oxhey Jets | 28 | 8 | 2 | 18 | 48 | 80 | 26 |
| Kings Langley | 28 | 6 | 7 | 15 | 43 | 63 | 25 |
| Chipperfield Corinthians | 28 | 7 | 4 | 17 | 34 | 58 | 25 |

## MID-HERTFORDSHIRE LEAGUE
### PREMIER DIVISION

| | | | | | | | |
|---|---|---|---|---|---|---|---|
| Harpenden Rovers | 16 | 12 | 2 | 2 | 53 | 15 | 38 |
| Elizabeth Allen Old Boys | 16 | 11 | 4 | 1 | 45 | 11 | 37 |
| London Colney `A' | 16 | 9 | 1 | 6 | 45 | 49 | 28 |
| Potters Bar Town `A' | 16 | 8 | 2 | 6 | 38 | 22 | 26 |
| Caxtonians | 16 | 7 | 3 | 6 | 29 | 33 | 24 |
| Redbourn | 16 | 7 | 1 | 8 | 39 | 45 | 22 |
| Batford Old Boys | 16 | 5 | 2 | 9 | 39 | 51 | 17 |
| Hinton (Herts) | 16 | 3 | 0 | 13 | 27 | 65 | 9 |
| Cockfosters `A' | 16 | 2 | 1 | 13 | 26 | 50 | 7 |

## WEST HERTFORDSHIRE LEAGUE
### PREMIER DIVISION

| | | | | | | | |
|---|---|---|---|---|---|---|---|
| Hemel Hempstead Rvrs | 16 | 12 | 2 | 2 | 86 | 25 | 38 |
| Oxhey | 16 | 11 | 1 | 4 | 52 | 32 | 34 |
| Suburban Aerials | 16 | 10 | 3 | 3 | 58 | 20 | 33 |
| Kings Sports | 16 | 9 | 4 | 3 | 53 | 25 | 31 |
| Springwell ME Ath. C. | 16 | 6 | 5 | 5 | 41 | 46 | 23 |
| Albion Rovers (Herts) | 16 | 6 | 2 | 8 | 28 | 48 | 20 |
| Colpa Eng. Sports | 16 | 3 | 2 | 11 | 25 | 43 | 11 |
| Oxhey Wanderers | 16 | 2 | 4 | 10 | 27 | 70 | 10 |
| Oxhey Jets `A' | 16 | 1 | 1 | 14 | 15 | 76 | 4 |

# SCHWEPPES
# ESSEX SENIOR LEAGUE

**President:** Arthur Dimond    **Chairman & Publicity:** Rober Errington
**Secretary:** David Walls, 77 Thorpedene Gardens, Shoeburyness, Essex SS3 9JE
Tel/Fax: 01702 294047

In a season of two halves, Bowers United emerged as one of the most popular League Champions in the competition's history, no one seemed to mind being beaten by this bunch of ageing players who brought a style and panache all of their own and a new record holder in the shape and form of David Hope, who at the age of 34 was the leading goalscorer in the League with 45 goals. Managed by the highly motivated Tony Cross, who himself now moved on to ply his trade in the Ryman League, Bowers also won the League Cup with a 2-0 success over Great Wakering Rovers. The Rovers were eventually runners up and won with it a coveted promotion place, and with incredible work they transformed their already picturesque Burroughs Park into an extremely smart stadium.

The season was split by some horrendous wet weather and, in fact, Bowers United went fifteen weeks without a home league game but it didn't mar their spirit though it was the reason for a very unfortunate exit from the Vase at the hands of Woodbridge. But our Champions did not win an expected treble for, on the usual baking hot Bank Holiday Monday, Saffron Walden Town got the better of Bowers 2-1 to lift the Harry Fisher Trophy. They were also worthy winners of the Sportsmanship Trophy and were congratulated from many quarters on their incredible hospitality with hot sit down meals served to both teams and officials after every home game! East Ham United received a major boost when local lad Ross Weare was snapped up by QPR for a considerable fee thus creating another Senior League record . . .

Despite losing Great Wakering Rovers the League, who are indebted to Schweppes for their continuing sponsorship, welcome a brand new team from a new geographical area, Bury Football Academy from Suffolk, together with Woodford Town who return after a number of years' absence. The League are very proud of their record of promoting teams to the Ryman League, it's now more than any other feeder over the years, but the spirit and strength of the remainder of clubs hasn't wavered one iota and we look forward to another rich season of contest. There will be a Charity Cup Game at the beginning of the season between Saffron Walden Town and the double winners, Bowers United, and the League Cup will be sponsored by AOF - the Ancient Order of Foresters.

One amazing man has announced his retirement 'upstairs' to General Manager at Brentwood, and that is Derek Stittle, team Manager since 1978 and reckoned to be the second longest serving boss in the game to Roly Howard at Marine.

*Robert Errington, Chairman & Publicity Officer*

## FINAL LEAGUE TABLE 1998-99

| | P | W | D | L | F | A | PT |
|---|---|---|---|---|---|---|---|
| Bowers United | 26 | 21 | 3 | 2 | 78 | 16 | 66 |
| Gt Wakering Rovers | 26 | 20 | 2 | 4 | 73 | 26 | 62 |
| Saffron Walden Town | 26 | 16 | 8 | 2 | 49 | 20 | 56 |
| Burnham Ramblers | 26 | 14 | 6 | 6 | 61 | 25 | 48 |
| Southend Manor | 26 | 11 | 9 | 6 | 49 | 40 | 42 |
| Ilford | 26 | 13 | 3 | 10 | 49 | 44 | 42 |
| Basildon United* | 26 | 13 | 5 | 8 | 46 | 35 | 41 |
| Hullbridge Sports | 26 | 8 | 3 | 15 | 42 | 38 | 27 |
| Concord Rangers* | 26 | 8 | 7 | 11 | 33 | 48 | 27 |
| Brentwood | 26 | 5 | 6 | 15 | 30 | 60 | 21 |
| Stansted | 26 | 6 | 3 | 17 | 40 | 88 | 21 |
| East Ham United | 26 | 5 | 5 | 16 | 33 | 88 | 20 |
| Sawbridgeworth Town | 26 | 4 | 6 | 16 | 19 | 47 | 18 |
| Eton Manor | 26 | 3 | 4 | 19 | 36 | 63 | 13 |

\* points deducted

## LEAGUE CHALLENGE CUP 1998-99

**FINAL**
Bowers United    v    Gt Wakering Rvrs    2-0
at Concord Rangers FC, attendance 458

## HARRY FISHER MEMORIAL TROPHY
## 1998-99

**FINAL**
Bowers United    v    Saffron Walden Town    1-2
at Barking FC, attendance 230

# BASILDON UNITED

**Secretary:** Mrs Vivian Houghton, 66 Charlotte Ave., Wickford, Essex SS12 0DZ
Tel: 01268 571856 (H) 01268 761126 (B) 0789 9092988 (M)
**Ground:** Gardiners Close, Gardiners Lane, Basildon, Essex SS14 3AW Tel: 01268 520268
**Directions:** A176 off Southend arterial (A127), left at r'bout into Cranes FarmRoad, proceed to end of duel carriageway, left at lights, Gardiners Close is 1st left (Football Club signed). Two and a half miles from Basildon BR station
Capacity: 2,000          Seats: 400          Cover: 1,000          Floodlights: Yes
Clubhouse: Open lunchtimes, evenings, weekends. Hot food sold          Club Shop: No
**HONOURS** Isthmian Lge Div 2 83-83; Essex Senior Lge (5) 76-80 94-95, Lg Cup 77-78 94-95
97-98, Res. Cup 92-93; Essex Senior Trophy 78-79; Res. Lge &Shield 94-95
**PREVIOUS** **Leagues:** Grays & Thurrock; Gtr London 68-70; Essex Snr 70-80; Athenian 80-81;
Isthmian 81-91          **Name:** Armada Sports          **Ground:** Grosvenor Park 63-69
**CLUB RECORDS** **Attendance:** 4,000 v West Ham, ground opening 11/8/70
1998-99 Top Scorer: Ricky Finning

**FACT FILE**
Founded: 1963
Sponsors: Orsett Cock
Colours: Amber & black stripes
Change: Green & white squares/white/white
Midweek Matches: Wednesday
Programme: 16 pages, 50p
Editor: Gary Freeman

**CLUB PERSONNEL**
President: J Oakes
Chairman: John Strange
Fixture Sec. Gary Freeman
01702 712217 (H) 01474 333331 (B)
Press Officer: Frank Ford (01268 552994)
Manager:Colin Norman

# BOWERS UNITED

**Secretary:** Stephen Bond, 42 Brundish, Pitsea, Basildon, Essex SS13 3EU 01268 478035 (H)
**Ground:** Crown Avenue, off Kenneth Rd, Pitsea, Basildon (01268 452068)
**Directions:** Turn into Rectory Rd from Old London Rd (B1464) at Pitsea Broadway into Kenneth
Rd, right at top Crown Ave. 1.25 miles Pitsea (BR). Bus 5& 42 toRectory Rd, Bowers Gifford
Capacity: 2,000          Seats: 200          Stand: Yes          Floodlights: Yes
**Clubhouse:** Open every night          Club Shop: No
**PREVIOUS** **Leagues:** Thurrock & Thameside Comb.; Olympian
**Ground:** Gun Meadow, Pitsea
**HONOURS** Thurrock & Thameside Comb. 58-59; Essex Snr Lg 80-81,98-99 R-up 83-84
Div 1 Cup 90-91,Lg Cup Winners 81-82,98-99 R-up (3) Harry Fisher mem Trophy 91-92 R-up (3)
**BEST SEASON** FA Cup: 1st Rd Q          **FA Vase:** 4th Rd 98-99
**CLUB RECORDS Attendance:** 1,800 v Billericay F.A.Vase
Players progressing: Steve Tilson (Southend Utd)
**98-99 P.o.Y.:** David Hope **Captain:** Mark Kelynack **Top Scorer:** David Hope

**FACT FILE**
Founded: 1946
Colours: Red & white/red/red
Change colours: Green & black/black/black
Midweek Matches: Wednesday 7.30
Res League; Essex & Herts Border Comb
Programme: 30pages 50p
Editor:Denis Taylor

**CLUB PERSONNEL**
Chairman: Denis Taylor
Vice Chairman: Dick Dallison
Managers: John  Warner( 0181 984 9320)

# BRENTWOOD

**Secretary:**          Colin Harris, 56 Viking Way, Pilgrims Hatch, Brentwood, Essex CM15 9HY
Tel: 01277 219564 (H)
**Ground:**          Brentwood Centre, Doddinghurst Rd, Brentwood, Essex. 01277 215151 Ext.713
**Directions:** From east end High St (Wilsons Corner) turn north into Ongar Rd. 3rd mini-round-
about take right fork into Doddinghurst Rd, Centre half mile on right after A12 Bridge, ground far
right corner.
Capacity: !,000          Cover: 100          Seats:          Floodlights: Yes
Clubhouse:  Open Tues & Thur evening & matchdays          Club Shop: No
**PREVIOUS** **Names:** Manor Ath. 55-70, Brentwood Ath. 70-72
**Grounds:** King George, Hartswood, `Larkins', Ongar (pre-92), East Thurrock 92/93
**Leagues:** Romford & Dist., Sth Essex Comb., London & Essex Border,Olympian
**HONOURS** Olympian Lg Cup 67-68, Essex Inter. Cup 76-77, Essex Lg Cup 75-76 78-79 90-91;
Harry Fisher Mem. Trophy 95-96
**BEST SEASON** FA Vase: 3rd Rd Prop 95-96

**FACT FILE**

Founded: 1955          Sponsor: Parkers Cafe Bar
Nickname: Blues
Colours: All sky blue
Change colours: Pink with blue stripe
Midweek Matches: Tuesday
Programme: 50p

**CLUB PERSONNEL**

Chairman: K J O'Neale

Manager: Paul Delea  (H) 01708 550630

# BURNHAM RAMBLERS

**Secretary:** Gordon Brasted, 6 Ramblers Way, Burnham on Crouch, Essex. CM0 8LR (01621 782785
**Fixture Sec.:** Chris Dobson, 13 Chapel Rd, Burnham on Crouch Essex CM10 8JB(01621 786334)
**Ground:** Leslie Field, Springfield Rd, Burnham-on-Crouch CM0 8QL (01621 784383)
**Directions:** On B1010 from South Woodham Ferrers, turn right half mile before town.
15 mins from Burnham (BR)
Capacity: 2,000          Seats: 300          Stand: Yes          Floodlights: Yes          Club Shop: Yes/No
Clubhouse: Mon-Fri 7-11pm, Sat 12-3 & 5-11pm, Sun 12-3 & 7-9.30pm. Hot meals & snacks available
**HONOURS** Olympian Lg 65-66; Essex I'mediate Cup R-up 81-82; Essex Snr Lg Cup R-up 86-
87 89-90 97-98, (Reserve Cup 89-90 (R-up 92-93), Reserve Shield R-up 90-91;
Harry Fisher Mem. Trophy 96-97, R-up 97-98; Sportsmanship Award 96-97
**PREVIOUS** **Leagues:** N Essex, Mid-Essex, Olympian, S.E. Essex
**BEST SEASON** FA Cup:          FA Vase:
**CLUB RECORDS** **Gate:** 1,500 ?? against which club, which competition and when??

**FACT FILE**
Founded: 1900          Nickname: Ramblers
Colours: All Royal blue
Change colours: Yellow/black/yellow
Midweek matches: Tuesday
Reserves' Lge: Essex & Herts
Programme: 36 pages, 50p   Editor: Chairman
**CLUB PERSONNEL**
Chairman: Gordon Brasted
Vice-Chairman: Ron Hatcher
President: R J Cole, Esq
Press Officer: Nigel Radcliffe, 01621 783774
Manager: Colin Wallington
Physio: Cyril Tennant
1998-99; Top Scorer: Steve Harding

# BURY FOOTBALL ACADEMY

**Secretary:** Terry Clements, Olivers Barn, Donkey Lane, Stanningfield, Bury St Edmunds, Suffolk IP29 4RA. Tel: 01284 827161 (H/Fax) 0403 609446 (M)
**Fixture Sec.:** Richard Livall, Well Cottage, The Street, Lawshall, Bury St. Edmunds IP29 4QA
Tel: 01284 828504

**Ground:** Bury Town FC
Ram Meadow, Cotton Lane, Bury St Edmunds IP33 1XP Tel: 01284 754721
**Directions:** Leave A14 at sign to central Burt Sy. Edmunds, following signs to town centre at exit roundabout. At next r'about 1st exit into Northgate St., left at T junct. (lights) into Mustoe St., left immediately into Cotton Lane, ground 350 yds on right, through 'Pay & Display' car park.
Nearest Railway station: Bury St Edmunds, 10 minutes.
Bus Terminal: St Andrews Street
Capacity: 3,500    Seats: 300    Cover: 1,500    Floodlights: Yes

**FACT FILE**
Founded: 1999
Colours: Green/black/clack
Change colours: Yellow/blue/yellow
Midweek Matchday: Wednesday
Reserves' League: No reserve team
Programme Editor: Richard Livall
Tel: 01284 828504

**CLUB PERSONNEL**
Chairman: Terry Clements
Vice Chairman: Peter Olley
Joint Manager: Daniel Laws
Director of Coaching, West Suffolk College,
Out Risbygate St., Bury St Edmunds
01284 716276

# CONCORD RANGERS

**Secretary:** M.Stephens, 39 New Park Rd, Benfleet, Essex SS7 5UR
Tel: 01268 458571 or 07979 214350

**Ground:** Thames Road, Canvey Island, Essex. SS8 0HP (01268 691780/515750)

**Directions:** Follow A130 onto Canvey Island and turn right into Thorney Bay Road, then right again into Thames Road.
Capacity: 1,500    Cover: Yes    Seats: No    Floodlights: Yes
**HONOURS** Southend & Dist. Lge - Lge & Cup 84-85; Southend Alliance - Lge & Cup 87-88; Essex Intermediate Lg Div 2 90-91; Essex Sen Lge 97-98, Cup 96-97; Wirral Programme Award 93-94

**PREVIOUS Leagues:** Southend & Dist. All., Essex I'mediate (pre-1991)    **Ground:** Waterside
**CLUB RECORDS Gate:** 1,500 v Lee Chapel North, FA Sunday Cup 89-90
**Win:** 9-0 v Eton Manor, Essex Snr Lge 96-97

**FACT FILE**
Founded: 1967
Colours:Yellow & Blue/blue/yellow
Change colours: white/black/black
Midweek Matches: Tuesday
Clubhouse: Evenings & weekends
Programme: 20 pages, 50p
Editor: Mike Stephenson (01268 684638)

**CLUB PERSONNEL**
President: Albert Lant
Chairman: Eddie Brown
Manager: Steve Knott
1998-99 Top Scorer: Ian Gooden

# EAST HAM UNITED

**Secretary:** Reuben Gane, 108 Beccles Drive, Barking, Essex IG11 9HZ. 0181 594 7861 (H)
**Ground:** Ferndale Sports Ground, Pennyroyal Ave., off East Ham Manorway, Cyprus Place, Beckton E6 4NG Tel: 0171 476 5514, Fax: 0181 507 1099. **Directions:** East Ham Manorway - Cyprus Place - Beckton off A13 Newham Way from east or west.Nearest tube - East Ham, then bus 101 to ground, or Cyprus Station (DocklandsLight Railway)
Capacity: 2,500    Seats: 150    Cover: 300    Floodlights: Yes
Clubhouse: Open Evenings & weekends    Club Shop: Yes/No
**HONOURS** Metropolitan Lg; Essex Snr Tphy 76-77, Sportsmanship Trophy 97-98; Gtr London Lg Cup 69-70; London Jnr Cup 46-47; Ron Murrant Memorial Trophy 94-95; Carpathian Charity Cup 94-95; Harry Fisher Memorial Trophy 97-98,(R-u 94-95), Stepney Charity Cup 47-48,87-88
**PREVIOUS    Leagues:** Spartan, Metropolitan    **Name:** Storey Ath. 1933-55
**BEST SEASON    FA Vase:** Quarter finals    **FA Cup:**
**CLUB RECORDS Gate:** 4,250 - East Ham XI v West Ham, friendly 15/2/76 at Terrance McMillanStadium. 2,400 v Sutton United, FA Amateur Cup 14/11/53
**Goalscorer :** David Norris    **Appearances:** Ken Bowhill, 1964-84

**FACT FILE**
Founded: 1933 Nickname: Hammers
Sponsors: Stereolab Rock Band
Colours: Green/white/gold
Change colours: Red & White
hoops/black/white
Midweek Matchday: Tuesday
Programme: Yes
**CLUB PERSONNEL**
Chairman: Ted Whatmough 0181 599 4542
Press Officer: Roland Clooge
Manager: Reuben Gane
Assistant Manager/ Coach: Dorian West
Head of Coaching: Reuben Gane
Trainer: Dorian West  Top Scorer:Ross Weare

# ETON MANOR

**Secretary:** Mrs Jackie Jones, 31 Greenleaf Drive, Barkingside, Essex (0181 5509618)
**Ground:** (Share with Barkingside), Oakside, Station Rd, Barkingside, Ilford, Essex (0181 550 3611)
**Directions:** From London A12 Eastern Avenue to Green Gate, left into Hurns Rd to Barkingside, right into Craven Gardens, right again Carlton Drive leading to Station Road, under bridge and ground entrance on right. Adjacent toBarkingside station (Central Line). From Ilford station (BR) take 169 Bus to Craven Gardens.
Capacity: 1,000    Seats: 60    Cover: 60    Floodlights: Yes    Clubhouse: Yes
**HONOURS** Essex Snr Cup R-up 37-38, London Lg 33-34 37-38 52-53 53-54 (R-up 48-49 57-58, Lg Cup 55-56 (R-up 46-47 54-55)), Greater London Lg 64-65, Essex Intermediate Cup 64-65, London Intermediate Cup R-up 33-34 66-67, Essex Snr Lg Sportsmanship Award 75-76 (Div 1 Cup 90-91, Res. Div 76-77, Res. Div Cup 91-92)
**PREVIOUS    Leagues:** London 33-59; Aetolian 59-64; Greater London 64-69; Metropolitan 69-75.
**Grounds:** Wildness, Hackney; GUS Sports Ground, Clapton; Walthamstow Ave. FC; Norwegian Ground, Barking; Roding Lane, Buckhurst Hill, ThurrockHotel    **Name:** Wilderness Leyton.
**CLUB RECORDS Gate:** 600 v Leyton Orient, opening of floodlights at Roding Lane.
**Goalscorer:** Dave Sams

**FACT FILE**
Founded: 1901
Nickname: The Manor
Colours: Sky/navy/navy
Change colours: Maroon &
green/maroon/maroon
Midweek Matches: Monday
Programme: 12 pages with entry
Editor: Secretary

**CLUB PERSONNEL**
Chairman: Reg Curtis
Manager:Tony Jones Physio: Alf Jones
Top Scorers:Jamie Everton, Brad Jones

**HULLBRIDGE SPORTS**                                          Photo: Peter Barnes

**Back Row:** Cyril Gibbs (kitman), Ian Mower (physio), Nick Lowery, Rob Jones, Pat Overall, Scott Syrett, Stuart Kent, Darren Spencer, Gary Smith, Stewart Dance, Neal Hughes, Dave Hughes (joint manager).
**Front Row:** Howard Mackler (joint manager), Jamie Reynolds, Martin Gibbs, Mick Lowe, Keith Scourfield, David Kreyling (captain), Luke Slatford.
**Mascots:** Craig Hughes, Sam Hughes & James Cook

Sawbridgeworth's David Greenwood (5) sees his shot parried by Wivenhoe 'keeper Darryl Trigg during this FA Carlsberg Vase encounter last season.                                          Photo: Francis Short

# HULLBRIDGE SPORTS

**FACT FILE**

Secretary:Ron Moore, 80 Henley Crescent, Westcliff -on-Sea, Essex SS0 0NT( 01702 334677)
Ground: Lower Road, Hullbridge, Hockley, Essex SS5 6BJ (01702 230420)
Directions: Turn into Rawreth Lane from A130 (left if arriving fromChelmsford), down to
  mini-r'bout, left, across next mini-r'bout, up hill,ground signed on right just past garage
Capacity: 1,500    Seats: No    Cover: Yes    Floodlights: Yes    Club Shop: No
Clubhouse: Lounge bar, function hall with bar & changing rooms - set in 16 acres

HONOURS   Essex Intermediate Snr Div Cup 87-88, Southend & District Lg Div 1 65-66 (Div 2
51-52, Div 3 56-57), French Cup 51-52, Essex Snr Lg Sportsmanship Award 91-92 92-93 94-95

PREVIOUS      Leagues: Southend & Dist., Alliance, Essex I'mediate
              Grounds: Pooles Lane Rec

**1998-99 Top Scorer:** Kevin Scourfield

Founded: 1945
Sponsor: Thermo Shield
Colours: Royal Blue & white/white/blue
Change colours: Maroon/navy/maroon
Midweek matches: Tues/Thursday
Programme  Editor: Bryan Heggety

**CLUB PERSONNEL**

Chairman: Bryan Hegarty

Manager:David Hughes

# ILFORD

**FACT FILE**

Secretary:      Kevin Wilmot, 83 Mandeville Court, Lower Hall Lane, Chingford, London E4 8JD
                Tel: 0181 529 9475 (H), 0956 902456 (Club Mobile)
Ground: Cricklefield Stadium, High Road, Ilford, Essex. IG1 1UB Tel: 0181 514 0019
Directions: 5 min walk from Seven Kings Station. Opposite 'TheCauliflower' publ, Or 86 Bus
Capacity: 5,000         Seats - 216         Cover - Yes         Floodlights - Yes
Clubhouse:              No, but snackbar available on matchdays
HONOURS         FA Amateur Cup: 28-29 29-30, R-up 35-36 57-58 1973-74 Isthmian Lge Champ.
06-07 20-21 21-22 R-up 11-12 26-27 31-32 37-38 38-39 Essex Senior Cup x13 (record nos. of
wins), R-up x5; London Sen. Cup: x7 R-up x 5; London Charity Cup: x 6 R-up x 7: Essex I'mediate
Cup R-up x1; London I'mediate Cup R-up x1; Eastern F'lit Comp. Group Winners 96-97
PREVIOUS        League: Spartan 87-95
BEST SEASON     FA Cup: 73-74 2nd Rd, 0-2 v Southend Utd. (H)
                FA Vase: 98-99 1st Rd, 0-3 v Yaxley (H)
CLUB RECORDS Attendance: 17,000 Ilford Boys v Swansea Boys (Schools Trophy Final)

Founded: 1881      Re-Formed: 1987
Sponsor: Kelvin Hughes
Colours: Royal blue & white hoops/navy/navy
Change colours: Red & white qtrs/red/red
Midweek matches: Monday
Programme Editor: L Llewellyn
**CLUB PERSONNEL**
Chairman: George Hogarth
Vice Chairman: Melvin Attwell
President: Lord John Taylor of Warwick
Fixture Secretary: D Quinlan, 25 Burwood
Gardens, Rainham, Essex. RM13 8JS
Tel: 01708 526323
Manager: Alan Bailey (0208 5173852)

# LEYTON

**FACT FILE**

Secretary: T Hampford, 71 Clemtiana Rd., Leyton E10 7LT
  Tel: 0181 556 2665 (H)  0181 539 5405 (B)

Ground: Wingate Leyton Stadium, 282 Lea Bridge Road, Leyton, London E10 7LD
  Tel: 0181 539 5405
Directions: Lea Bridge Rd. is A104, ground next to Hare & Hounds PH.
  Leyton (Central Line) thence bus 58 or 158 to Lea Bridge Road.
  Clapton (BR) Walk 100 yds to Lea Bridge Rd. roundabout, buses 48, 55, 56 to
  ground. Bus 48 runs direct to ground from London Bridge (BR) station
  Capacity: 2,500   Seats: Yes     Cover: Yes     Floodlights: Yes

PREVIOUS      Leagues: Essex Intermediate; Spartan

Founded: 1868      Nickname: Lilywhite
Colours: Blue & white stripes/blue/blue
Change colours: Red & black halves/red/red
Midweek Matches: Tuesday
Reserves' League: No reserve team
Programme Editor: Tony Hampford
**CLUB PERSONNEL**
Chairman: Les Brown
Vice Chairman: Doug Digby
President: Peter Lewis
Fixture Sec.: as Secretary
Manager: Phil FosterTel: 0181 925 9778(H)
0181 539 5405 (B) 0956 698042 (M)

# SAFFRON WALDEN TOWN

Secretary: Peter Rule, 48 Church Street, Saffron Walden, Essex, CB10 1VQ (Tel 01799 522417)
Ground: Catons Lane, Saffron Walden, Essex CB10 2DU (01799 522789)
Directions: In Saffron Walden High St turn into Castle St, left at T-junction, 1st left by Victory pub
Capacity: 5,000    Seats: 500    Cover: 2,000    Floodlights: Yes    Club Shop: Yes
Clubhouse: Yes - opening times ?? Is food available ??
PREVIOUS    Leagues: Haverhill & Dist.; Stansted & Dist.; Cambridgeshire; Nth Essex; Herts Co.;
            Spartan 33-49 50-54; Parthenon 49-50; Essex Snr 71-74; Eastern Co's 74-84
HONOURS      Essex Snr Lg 73-74, Eastern Co's Lg 82-83, Spartan Lg Eastern Div 2 36-37,
Essex Snr Tphy 82-83 83-84 84-85, Eastern F'lit Comp. 91-92 (R-up 88-89,Nth Thames Group B
82-83), Essex Jnr Cup 1896-97 (R-up 25-26), Cambs Lg R-up 22-23, Essex & Herts Border R-up
25-26(jt), Stansted & Dist. x 7, Haverhill & Dist. x 5 ,Harry Fisher Mem& Uttlesford Ch Cup 98-99
CLUB RECORDS Scorer: John Tipputt    Appearances: Les Page, 700+
    Attendance: 6,000 v Rainham Ath., Essex Jun. Cup Final 1926 (played at Crittals, Braintree)
BEST SEASON    FA Cup: 2nd Qual. Rd  replay 84-85, 1-2 v King's Lynn (A)

**FACT FILE**
Founded: 1872
Nickname: Bloods
Club Sponsors: Tolly Cobbold
Colours: Red & black/black/black
Change cols: Blue & yellow/yellow/yellow
Midweek Matchday: Tuesday
Reserves' League: Essex & Herts Comb
Programme: 24 pages, 40p
Editor: R Smith (01799 500061)
**CLUB PERSONNEL**
Chairman: Steve Cox
Press Officer: Secretary
Manager: Tim Moylette

879

# SAWBRIDGEWORTH TOWN

**Secretary:** Barrie Mutimer, 'Ebenezer, 18 Forebury Avenue, Sawbridgeworth, Herts Cm21 9BG

**Ground:** Crofters End, West Road, Sawbridgeworth, Herts. CM21 0DE (01279 722039)

**Directions:** Three quarters of a mile from the station; up Station Road then into West Road.

Capacity: 1,500    Seats: None    Cover: 250    Floodlights: Yes    Club Shop: No
Clubhouse: Yes/No - when is it open ??? is food available ???

**HONOURS**    Essex Olympian Lg 71-72; Essex Snr Lg R-up 92-93 94-95; Harry FisherMem.
Cup 87-88; Lg Cup 94-95 R-up 92-93 93-94, Res. Div 91-92 92-93 (R-up 93-94), Res. Shield R-up 92-93); Herts Snr Tphy 90-91 93-94 (R-up 92-93);Herts Charity Shield 92-93 94-95 95-96;
Uttlesford Charity Cup 92-93; Herts Intermediate Cup R-up 93-93(res); S. Midlands F'lit Cup R.up
94-95; Res. Sect S.M Lge & Lg.Cup R-Up 94-95
**PREVIOUS**    **Leagues:** Essex Olympian, Spartan 36-53
**CLUB RECORDS Attendance:** 610 v Bishop's Stortford.
**PREVIOUS GROUNDS:** Hyde Hall, Pishiobury, Hand & Crown.

**FACT FILE**
Founded: 1890
Nickname: Robins
Colours: Red & black stripes/black/white
Change colours: Blue
Midweek Matchday;
Prog Editor:Gary Bennett (01279 830306)

**CLUB PERSONNEL**
Chairman: Barry Mutimer
President: Ron Alder
Press Officer: Gary Bennett
Manager: John Higley
Physio: Brian Latchford
1998-99 Top Scorer: Dave Dobson

---

# SOUTHEND MANOR

**Secretary:** Dave Kittle, 15 Seymour Rd, Hadleigh, Benfleet, Essex SS7 2HB. 01702 559581 (H)

**Ground:** Southchurch Park Arena, Lifstan Way, Southend-on-Sea. (01702 615577)

**Directions:** A127 then A1159 for 1 mile turn right at second roundabout by Invisible Man PH,
then due south for 1 mile, ground on right near sea front

Capacity: 2,000    Seats: 500    Cover: Yes    Floodlights: Yes
Clubhouse: Open every evening    Club Shop: No

**HONOURS**    Essex Snr Trophy 92-93; Essex Intermediate Cup 78-79; Essex Snr Lg 90-91, Cup
87-88, Challenge Cup 89-90; Harry Fisher Mem. Tphy 90-91 92-93 (R-up 91-92)

**PREVIOUS Leagues:** Southend Borough Combination, Southend Alliance
**Grounds:** Victory Spts/ Oakwood Rec

**RECORDS    Attendance:** 1,521 v Southend Utd, 22/7/91, floodlight opener

**BEST SEASON    FA Cup:**    **FA Vase:** 1996-97

**1998-99 Top Scorer:** Rob Jones    **P.O.Y.:** D.Rolfe    **Captain:** P.Dunstan

**FACT FILE**
Founded: 1955    Nickname: The Manor
Sponsors: Davlaw
Colours: Yellow/black/black
Change colours: White/red/red
Midweek Matchday: Tuesday
Reserves Lge: Essex & Herts Border Comb
Programme: 10 pages, 50p
Editor/Press Officer: Harry Cooper
(01702 308482)

**CLUB PERSONNEL**
Chairman: Robert Westley
Vice-Chairman: John Hughes
Manager: Mark Jenkins
Coach: Peter Heathcote

---

# STANSTED

**Secretary:**    Mrs Denise Murnane,    01279 815404 (H&B)
Appletree House, Fullers End, Elsenham, Bishops Stortford. CM22 6DU.

**Ground:**    Hargrave Park, Cambridge Road, Stansted, Essex. (01279 812897)

**Directions:**    B1383 north of Bishops Stortford on west side of Cambridge Rd.
Stansted (BR) - 1/2 mile

Capacity: 2,000    Seats: 200    Cover: Yes    Floodlights: Yes
Clubhouse: Matchdays till 11pm. Sandwiches available.    Club Shop: No

**HONOURS**    FA Vase Winners 83-84; Essex Snr Lg R-up 82-83; Essex Snr Lg Cup 83-84, (R-up
72-73 94-95); Harry Fisher Mem Cup 82-83 84-85 (R-up 92-93 93-94); E. Anglian
Cup 83-84; Eastern F/lit Cup 83-84; Uttlesford Char. Cup 93-84 86-87 88-89 94-95 97-98
**PREVIOUS**    **Leagues:** Spartan; London; Herts Co.  **Grounds:** Greens Meadow; ChapelHill
**RECORDS**    **Attendance:** 828 v Whickham (FA Vase 83-84)
**BEST SEASON    FA Cup:** 97-98    **FA Vase:** Winners 83-84

**FACT FILE**
Founded: 1902
Nickname: The blues
Sponsor: D C Poultons
Colours: Blue & white/blue/blue
Change: Green & red/green/black
Midweek matches: Tuesday
Reserves League: Cambridgeshire League
Programme Editor: D Murnane

**CLUB PERSONNEL**
Chairman: Terry Shoebridge
President: Percy Heal
Manager: Tony Mercer
1998-99 Top scorer: Tony Mercer

---

# WOODFORD TOWN

**FACT FILE**

**Secretary:** Bill Robertson, 2 Humphrey Close, Clayhall, Ilford, Essex IG5 0RW
0181 550 6680 (H)  07930 104076 (B&M)

**Ground:** Clapton FC ground
Old Spotted Dog Ground, Upton Lane, Forest Gate, London E7
Tel: 0181 472 0822

Nearest Railway station: Forest Gate
Buses: Any bus fron Forest Gate station

Colours: Black & white/white/black
Change colours: Red & white/red & white/red
Programme Editor: Audrey Bahari
Tel: 0181 693 8082

**CLUB PERSONNEL**

Chairman: Vincent McBean
Fixture Sec. as Secretary
Manager: Leroy Rhodes
Tel: 0181 889 7511 (H)

**Two club from THE ESSEX & SUFFOLK BORDER LEAGUE**

**KELVEDON SOCIAL F.C.**

Photo: Martin Wray

**WEST BERGHOLT F.C.**

Photo: Martin Wray

## ESSEX & SUFFOLK BORDER LEAGUE
### PREMIER DIVISION

| | P | W | D | L | F | A | Pts |
|---|---|---|---|---|---|---|---|
| Gas Recreation -3 | 30 | 24 | 2 | 4 | 94 | 26 | 71 |
| West Bergholt | 30 | 19 | 5 | 6 | 70 | 38 | 62 |
| Kelvedon Social | 30 | 15 | 8 | 7 | 80 | 45 | 53 |
| Little Oakley +3 | 30 | 14 | 7 | 9 | 77 | 57 | 52 |
| St Johns (Clacton) | 30 | 15 | 4 | 11 | 62 | 53 | 49 |
| Stowmarket Town R -1 | 30 | 13 | 10 | 7 | 49 | 38 | 48 |
| Haverhill Rovers Res. | 30 | 14 | 6 | 10 | 51 | 42 | 48 |
| Harwich & Parkeston R. | 30 | 14 | 5 | 11 | 88 | 66 | 47 |
| Sudbury Lucas Ath +2 | 30 | 11 | 6 | 13 | 32 | 46 | 41 |
| Ipswich Wanderers Res. | 30 | 10 | 6 | 14 | 59 | 68 | 36 |
| Rowhedge | 30 | 9 | 7 | 14 | 53 | 59 | 34 |
| Long Melford | 30 | 9 | 5 | 16 | 45 | 65 | 32 |
| Sudbury Wanderers Res. | 30 | 8 | 7 | 15 | 48 | 63 | 31 |
| Royal London | 30 | 8 | 4 | 18 | 43 | 95 | 28 |
| Alresford Colne Rngrs | 30 | 6 | 5 | 19 | 41 | 85 | 23 |
| Mistley United | 30 | 5 | 5 | 20 | 31 | 77 | 20 |

## ESSEX INTERMEDIATE LEAGUE
### DIVISION ONE

| | P | W | D | L | F | A | Pts |
|---|---|---|---|---|---|---|---|
| Bishop's Stortford Swifts | 22 | 14 | 6 | 2 | 64 | 22 | 34 |
| Rayleigh Town | 22 | 11 | 9 | 2 | 38 | 21 | 31 |
| Kelvedon Hatch | 22 | 12 | 6 | 4 | 37 | 19 | 30 |
| Met Police Chigwell | 22 | 13 | 4 | 5 | 33 | 23 | 30 |
| Runwell Hospital | 22 | 10 | 4 | 8 | 50 | 42 | 24 |
| Takeley | 22 | 11 | 1 | 10 | 54 | 40 | 23 |
| Frenford Senior | 22 | 9 | 5 | 8 | 37 | 31 | 23 |
| Hatfield Peverel | 22 | 8 | 5 | 9 | 42 | 43 | 21 |
| Essex Police | 22 | 8 | 5 | 9 | 29 | 35 | 21 |
| Ekco First Data | 22 | 5 | 8 | 9 | 27 | 42 | 18 |
| Writtle | 22 | 1 | 3 | 18 | 17 | 53 | 5 |
| Herongate Athletic | 22 | 1 | 2 | 19 | 18 | 75 | 4 |

**BARKINGSIDE F.C.**

Photo: Gordon Whittington

Ashford Town (Middx) celebrate with the Combined Counties Cup. Photo: Eric Marsh

# SPARTAN SOUTH MIDLANDS FOOTBALL LEAGUE

**President:** B F Smith    **Chairman:** Pat Burns

**Hon. Press Secretary:** Jim Bean, 224 The Hide, Netherfield, Milton Keynes MK6 4JE

Tel/Fax: 01908 696059

The first season of the newly-formed Premier and Senior Divisions can be considered an outstanding success, despite the disruptions caused by one of the wettest winters on record. The problems began on 24th October when more than half the fixtures had to be cancelled and it was not until 13th February that a full League programme was played again.

The new Premier Division provided an exciting finish with the final day's results establishing Barkingside as Champions, even though they only managed a home draw against Brook House. Barkingside, who suffered more than any other Club with pitch problems, arrived at the end of January having played only fifteen League games - eleven less than some other Clubs in the division. In a remarkable run they played 29 League games in fourteen weeks and by only losing four established themselves as Champions. During the second half of the season Hoddesdon Town, Potters Bar Town, Brook House and Beaconsfield SYCOB all topped the division but during the last week Barkingside's two midweek wins put them on top for the first time. London Colney, who finished third and whose defence had conceded just 26 goals in 43 League games, had to win their final game at revitalised Arlesey Town to win the title on goal difference but lost 0-2. Arlesey, FA Vase winners in 1995 and SML Champions in 1994-95 and 1995-96, had their worst season since returning to the League from the UCL in 1992, with a disastrous start which saw them second from bottom in mid-February, but ten victories and only two defeats in the last seventeen games lifted them to a mid-table position. Last year's winner of Premier Division North, Potters Bar Town, finished second, two points behind Barkingside and one ahead of London Colney. Potters Bar were the division's top goalscorers with 109. Beaconsfield finished fourth, eight points behind London Colney and last season's Premier Division South Champions, Brook House, were fifth. Brimsdown Rovers finished in last position, 21 points adrift of second from bottom club, Harpenden Town. Welwyn Garden City avoided the 'relegation spot', winning their last game 2-0 and so moved above Harpenden on goal difference. Because of fixture congestion, it was necessary to abort the Premier Division Cup Competition.

There was also an exciting finish in the Senior Division, where both Holmer Green and Hanwell Town finished level on points but Holmer Green, the League's top goalscorers with 121 goals, won the title on superior goal difference.

*Stan Eaton*

## FINAL LEAGUE TABLE 1998-99
### PREMIER DIVISION

|    |                    | P  | W  | D  | L  | F   | A   | GD   | Pts |
|----|--------------------|----|----|----|----|-----|-----|------|-----|
| 1  | Barkingside        | 44 | 30 | 6  | 8  | 97  | 44  | 53   | 96  |
| 2  | Potters Bar Town   | 44 | 29 | 7  | 8  | 109 | 30  | 79   | 94  |
| 3  | London Colney      | 44 | 29 | 5  | 10 | 98  | 28  | 70   | 92  |
| 4  | Beaconsfield SYCOB | 44 | 25 | 9  | 10 | 85  | 40  | 45   | 84  |
| 5  | Brook House        | 44 | 24 | 11 | 9  | 74  | 42  | 32   | 83  |
| 6  | Hoddesdon Town     | 44 | 24 | 7  | 13 | 80  | 60  | 20   | 79  |
| 7  | Toddington Rovers  | 44 | 22 | 12 | 10 | 72  | 48  | 24   | 78  |
| 8  | Ruislip Manor      | 44 | 22 | 10 | 12 | 89  | 60  | 29   | 76  |
| 9  | Royston Town       | 44 | 19 | 11 | 14 | 73  | 62  | 11   | 68  |
| 10 | Hillingdon Borough | 44 | 20 | 9  | 15 | 72  | 61  | 11   | 65* |
| 11 | Waltham Abbey      | 44 | 16 | 13 | 15 | 79  | 64  | 15   | 61  |
| 12 | Brache Sparta      | 44 | 17 | 6  | 21 | 80  | 74  | 6    | 57  |
| 13 | Arlesey Town       | 44 | 16 | 8  | 20 | 61  | 70  | -9   | 56  |
| 14 | New Bradwell St Peter | 44 | 15 | 11 | 18 | 56 | 70 | -14  | 56  |
| 15 | Buckingham Athletic | 44 | 15 | 9  | 20 | 65  | 101 | -36  | 54  |
| 16 | Milton Keynes City | 44 | 13 | 10 | 21 | 68  | 88  | -20  | 49  |
| 17 | Islington St Mary's | 44 | 11 | 14 | 19 | 55  | 85  | -30  | 47  |
| 18 | Somersett Ambury V & E | 44 | 13 | 6 | 25 | 50 | 103 | -53 | 45  |
| 19 | St Margaretsbury   | 44 | 12 | 10 | 22 | 75  | 98  | -23  | 43* |
| 20 | Haringey Borough   | 44 | 9  | 11 | 24 | 49  | 87  | -38  | 38  |
| 21 | Welwyn Garden City | 44 | 10 | 6  | 28 | 63  | 95  | -32  | 36  |
| 22 | Harpenden Town     | 44 | 9  | 9  | 26 | 47  | 86  | -39  | 36  |
| 23 | Brimsdown Rovers   | 44 | 3  | 6  | 35 | 35  | 136 | -101 | 15  |

# FINAL LEAGUE TABLES 1998-99

## SENIOR DIVISION

| | P | W | D | L | F | A | GD | Pts |
|---|---|---|---|---|---|---|---|---|
| Holmer Green | 42 | 30 | 6 | 6 | 121 | 42 | 79 | 96 |
| Hanwell Town | 42 | 30 | 6 | 6 | 105 | 44 | 61 | 96 |
| Tring Athletic | 42 | 28 | 8 | 6 | 109 | 35 | 74 | 92 |
| Milton Keynes | 42 | 28 | 6 | 8 | 104 | 47 | 57 | 90 |
| Biggleswade Tn | 42 | 25 | 6 | 11 | 99 | 62 | 37 | 81 |
| Bedford United | 42 | 23 | 8 | 11 | 65 | 52 | 13 | 77 |
| Letchworth | 42 | 18 | 13 | 11 | 83 | 54 | 29 | 67 |
| Biggleswade Utd | 42 | 19 | 7 | 16 | 86 | 66 | 20 | 64 |
| Leverstock Green | 42 | 17 | 13 | 12 | 73 | 63 | 10 | 64 |
| Cockfosters | 42 | 17 | 11 | 14 | 76 | 62 | 14 | 62 |
| Greenacres (H.) | 42 | 19 | 4 | 19 | 71 | 61 | 10 | 61 |
| Langford | 42 | 18 | 7 | 17 | 71 | 80 | -9 | 61 |
| Shillington | 42 | 16 | 9 | 17 | 72 | 73 | -1 | 57 |
| Amersham Town | 42 | 14 | 10 | 18 | 71 | 82 | -11 | 52 |
| Caddington | 42 | 14 | 10 | 18 | 75 | 93 | -18 | 52 |
| Totternhoe | 42 | 12 | 10 | 20 | 56 | 71 | -15 | 46 |
| Luton Old Boys | 42 | 10 | 9 | 23 | 39 | 78 | -39 | 39 |
| Stony Stratford Tn | 42 | 8 | 11 | 23 | 58 | 98 | -40 | 35 |
| Risborough Rngrs | 42 | 8 | 6 | 28 | 41 | 97 | -56 | 30 |
| Harefield United | 42 | 8 | 5 | 29 | 48 | 112 | -64 | 29 |
| Winslow United | 42 | 7 | 5 | 30 | 42 | 104 | -62 | 26 |
| Houghton Town | 42 | 6 | 4 | 32 | 43 | 132 | -89 | 22 |

## DIVISION ONE

| | P | W | D | L | F | A | GD | Pts |
|---|---|---|---|---|---|---|---|---|
| Bridger Pack'ing | 32 | 27 | 3 | 2 | 92 | 21 | 71 | 84 |
| Ampthill Town | 32 | 26 | 3 | 3 | 106 | 33 | 73 | 81 |
| de Havilland | 32 | 26 | 2 | 4 | 102 | 23 | 79 | 80 |
| Mursley United | 32 | 21 | 5 | 6 | 72 | 26 | 46 | 68 |
| Dunstable Tn '98' | 32 | 19 | 6 | 7 | 72 | 42 | 30 | 63 |
| Scot | 32 | 16 | 3 | 13 | 60 | 58 | 2 | 51 |
| Pitstone & Iv'hoe | 32 | 14 | 4 | 14 | 80 | 65 | 15 | 46 |
| Walden Rangers | 32 | 14 | 4 | 14 | 61 | 47 | 14 | 46 |
| Old Dunstablians | 32 | 14 | 4 | 14 | 65 | 59 | 6 | 46 |
| Kent Athletic | 32 | 12 | 8 | 12 | 58 | 44 | 14 | 44 |
| The 61 FC (Luton) | 32 | 10 | 7 | 15 | 57 | 87 | -30 | 37 |
| Flamstead | 32 | 10 | 4 | 18 | 63 | 84 | -21 | 33* |
| Leighton Athletic | 32 | 7 | 6 | 19 | 39 | 76 | -37 | 27 |
| Old Bradwell Utd | 32 | 9 | 3 | 20 | 49 | 96 | -47 | 27* |
| Abbey Nat'l (MK) | 32 | 4 | 8 | 20 | 41 | 75 | -34 | 20 |
| Newport Athletic | 32 | 4 | 2 | 26 | 37 | 123 | -86 | 14 |
| Markyate | 32 | 2 | 2 | 28 | 25 | 120 | -95 | 8 |

* points deducted

# PREMIER DIVISION RESULTS CHART 1998-99

| | 1 | 2 | 3 | 4 | 5 | 6 | 7 | 8 | 9 | 10 | 11 | 12 | 13 | 14 | 15 | 16 | 17 | 18 | 19 | 20 | 21 | 22 | 23 |
|---|---|---|---|---|---|---|---|---|---|---|---|---|---|---|---|---|---|---|---|---|---|---|---|
| Arlesey T | X | 1-2 | 0-1 | 0-3 | 3-2 | 1-1 | 3-0 | 3-1 | 1-0 | 0-3 | 1-2 | 1-2 | 2-0 | 4-0 | 1-0 | 0-0 | 2-1 | 0-2 | 2-1 | 0-1 | 1-2 | 0-0 | 1-4 |
| Barkingside | 1-1 | X | 2-2 | 3-0 | 6-0 | 1-1 | 6-2 | 1-0 | 2-1 | 0-0 | 0-1 | 3-1 | 1-0 | 3-1 | 5-2 | 1-1 | 1-0 | 4-1 | 2-1 | 2-0 | 1-1 | 4-0 | 2-0 |
| B. SYCOB | 5-0 | 0-3 | X | 3-1 | 6-0 | 0-1 | 2-4 | 0-1 | 2-0 | 1-1 | 2-2 | 2-1 | 0-2 | 2-1 | 1-0 | 1-1 | 1-2 | 0-2 | 1-1 | 7-0 | 0-2 | 3-1 | 4-1 |
| Brache Sp. | 3-2 | 2-0 | 0-2 | X | 7-0 | 1-2 | 3-3 | 2-0 | 3-0 | 2-0 | 5-2 | 4-0 | 0-2 | 2-1 | 1-2 | 1-2 | 1-0 | 3-2 | 0-1 | 2-4 | 2-2 | 3-3 | 3-1 |
| Brimsdown | 0-6 | 0-2 | 0-2 | 0-5 | X | 0-5 | 0-1 | 2-2 | 2-2 | 0-1 | 2-2 | 0-2 | 0-5 | 1-3 | 0-1 | 0-3 | 1-2 | 0-4 | 3-2 | 2-4 | 1-2 | 1-1 | 2-1 |
| Brook Hse | 0-0 | 1-0 | 2-0 | 4-2 | 1-0 | X | A | 2-2 | 3-1 | 7-0 | 4-3 | 1-4 | 1-0 | 2-1 | 2-1 | 0-0 | 1-0 | 0-2 | 3-0 | 5-1 | 1-2 | 1-1 | 2-1 |
| Buck Ath | 3-0 | 1-4 | 1-4 | 3-1 | 2-1 | 4-6 | X | 0-6 | 3-2 | 1-1 | 0-3 | 3-1 | 2-3 | 3-3 | 2-0 | 2-5 | 2-0 | 1-1 | 3-3 | 2-1 | 2-7 | 2-1 | 0-3 |
| Haringey B | 1-4 | 2-5 | 0-0 | 1-1 | 3-2 | 2-3 | 0-0 | X | 0-1 | 0-2 | 0-4 | 2-2 | 0-4 | 0-2 | 0-0 | 0-7 | 2-3 | 1-5 | 2-3 | 3-0 | 0-4 | 0-0 | 2-1 |
| Harpenden | 1-0 | 0-5 | 0-4 | 1-0 | 2-2 | 0-1 | 1-1 | 0-2 | X | 0-3 | 0-2 | 3-0 | 1-3 | 1-1 | 3-1 | 1-4 | 3-1 | 1-3 | 2-3 | 7-2 | 0-0 | 0-1 | 2-1 |
| Hillingdon | 1-0 | 0-1 | 1-5 | 3-0 | 4-1 | 0-2 | 6-1 | 2-2 | 2-0 | X | 1-0 | 2-3 | 0-1 | 1-1 | 6-1 | 0-1 | 2-0 | 3-1 | 1-1 | 5-1 | 0-1 | 0-2 | 1-0 |
| Hoddesdon | 1-4 | 4-1 | 3-1 | 2-0 | 2-0 | 0-0 | 1-0 | 3-0 | 2-2 | 1-0 | X | 2-1 | 2-1 | 0-2 | 2-1 | 0-2 | 2-0 | 2-1 | 2-2 | 2-0 | 0-1 | 3-1 | 3-1 |
| Islington SM | 1-1 | 0-2 | 0-3 | 1-1 | 1-1 | 4-2 | 2-1 | 0-3 | 2-1 | 1-5 | 0-2 | X | 0-4 | 2-2 | 0-0 | 1-1 | 2-2 | 2-2 | 0-1 | 1-3 | 0-2 | 3-1 | 1-1 |
| London C | 4-0 | 2-1 | 0-1 | 3-1 | 0-3 | 0-0 | 3-1 | 2-0 | 1-1 | 5-0 | 6-0 | 3-0 | X | 1-1 | 2-0 | 1-2 | 1-1 | 3-0 | 5-1 | 4-0 | 0-1 | A | 1-0 |
| MK City | 5-1 | 1-5 | 0-2 | 2-3 | 3-1 | 2-1 | 1-2 | 4-0 | 0-3 | 1-1 | 1-0 | 3-3 | 0-3 | X | 2-2 | 0-2 | 2-2 | 0-1 | 1-0 | 1-2 | 1-2 | 1-4 | 7-1 |
| New Brad | 0-1 | 2-4 | 0-1 | 2-1 | 3-0 | 1-2 | 1-2 | 0-0 | 1-0 | 0-0 | 2-5 | 1-1 | 1-5 | 1-3 | X | 1-1 | 1-1 | 1-0 | 3-2 | 2-0 | 0-0 | 3-1 | 2-0 |
| Potters Bar | 2-0 | 3-1 | 1-3 | 2-0 | 3-0 | 2-0 | 6-0 | 2-0 | 4-0 | 1-0 | 4-0 | 2-1 | 1-0 | 8-0 | 0-1 | X | 8-1 | 3-0 | 7-0 | 4-0 | 3-1 | 0-3 | 4-0 |
| Royston T | 1-1 | 3-0 | 1-1 | 2-3 | 6-1 | 0-3 | 0-1 | 1-0 | 2-0 | 5-1 | 0-3 | 2-0 | 2-1 | 1-3 | 2-2 | 1-0 | X | 0-0 | 4-0 | 4-1 | 0-0 | 2-2 | 3-1 |
| Ruislip M | 3-3 | 0-1 | 1-1 | 1-0 | 2-1 | 2-1 | 1-0 | 2-2 | 0-0 | 4-0 | 0-3 | 5-1 | 0-3 | 4-3 | 1-1 | 2-2 | 2-2 | X | 6-0 | 6-0 | 3-3 | 3-0 | 0-1 |
| St Marg'by | 5-1 | 2-4 | 1-1 | 2-4 | 7-1 | 0-1 | 1-1 | 1-0 | 6-1 | 2-2 | 3-3 | 1-2 | 1-3 | 6-0 | 0-1 | 0-6 | 2-4 | 0-1 | X | 3-3 | 1-1 | 2-4 | 3-2 |
| SA V & E | 0-2 | 0-2 | 0-3 | 2-0 | 1-0 | 1-1 | 4-2 | 1-4 | 4-1 | 0-3 | 1-0 | 1-2 | 0-4 | 2-1 | 1-5 | 1-0 | 1-2 | 4-1 | 0-0 | X | 0-0 | 0-0 | 0-0 |
| Toddington | 1-4 | 0-1 | 0-2 | 4-2 | 5-1 | 0-0 | 0-1 | 3-1 | 2-0 | 0-1 | 3-1 | 1-1 | 0-0 | 0-0 | 2-2 | 4-2 | 0-2 | 0-4 | 4-0 | 2-0 | X | 5-3 | 0-2 |
| Waltham A | 2-0 | A | 0-1 | 2-2 | 6-0 | 2-0 | 3-0 | 0-2 | 2-2 | 1-1 | 3-2 | 1-1 | 0-3 | 2-0 | 5-1 | 1-0 | 4-2 | 2-3 | 0-2 | 3-1 | 2-2 | X | 5-1 |
| Welwyn GC | 2-3 | 4-2 | 0-2 | 0-2 | 5-1 | 1-1 | 3-3 | 3-1 | 2-0 | 4-5 | 1-1 | 1-2 | 0-4 | 2-3 | 1-2 | 2-0 | 1-3 | 3-6 | 0-2 | 2-2 | 1-2 | 2-1 | X |

# CHALLENGE TROPHY 1998-99

**FOURTH ROUND**

| | | | | | | | |
|---|---|---|---|---|---|---|---|
| Ruislip Manor | v | Waltham Abbey | 1-4 | Arlesey Town | v | Hokmer Green | 1-2 |
| Hoddesdon Town | v | London Colney | 0*1 | Barkingside | v | Potters Bar Town | 2-4 |

**SEMI-FINALS**

| | | | | | | | |
|---|---|---|---|---|---|---|---|
| Potters Bar Town | v | Waltham Abbey | 3*3, 0-3 | Holmer Green | v | London Colney | 1*1, 1-0 |

**FINAL (two legs)**

Waltham Abbey v Holmer Green 0-0, 0-3 — Waltham Abbey win 3-0 on aggregate

# SENIOR DIVISION CUP 1998-99

(Holders: Holmer Green)

**FINAL**

Biggleswade Town v Tring Athletic 1-2

# DIVISION ONE CUP 1998-99

(Holders: Scot FC)

**FINAL**

Ampthill Town v de Havilland 0-3

# ARLESEY TOWN

**Secretary:** John Albon, 13 St Johns Rd, Arlesey, Beds SG15 6ST. Tel: 01462 731318 (H & B), Mob 0411 566044.
**GROUND:** Lamb Meadow, Hitchin Rd, Arlesey. Tel: 01462 731448.
**Directions:** A1 take A507 to Shefford, at 3rd roundabout turn left, 1st left follow road through village, ground 1.5miles on left
Capacity: 8,000    Seats: 150    Cover: 300    Floodlights: Yes    Club Shop: Yes
Clubhouse: Members bar & function suite Open daily 6-11.30, Sat 12-11.30, Sun12-2.30 6-11.30

**HONOURS:** FA Vase Winners 1994-5; Beds Sen Cup 65-66 78-79 96-97, Prem Cup 83-84, Interm Cup 57-58; South Mids Lge Prem Div 51-52 52-53 94-95 95-96.
**PREVIOUS:** **Leagues:** Biggleswade & Dist.; Beds. Co. (S. Mids) 22-26 ,27-28; Parthenon; London 58-60; Utd Co's 33-36 82-92.
**RECORDS:** **Attendance:** 2,000 v Luton Res, Beds Snr Cup 1906
**BEST SEASON: FA Vase:** Winners 94-95

### FACT FILE
Founded: 1891    Nickname:  Blues
Colours: Sky & navy/navy/navy
Change Colours:  All white.
Midweek matchday:  Tuesday
Reserves' Lge:  South Midlands Lge Res Div
Programme: 50p
Editor:  Pete Brennan (01462 834455)

### CLUB PERSONNEL
Chairman: Eddie Haetzman (01462 816836)
Vice-Chairman:  Scott Geekie (01462 732396)
President: M Crouch
Manager: Nicky Ironton
Asst Manager:  B Harrigan   Physio: E Turner


# BEACONSFIELD SYCOB

**Secretary:** Ken Barrett, 31 Stockley End, Abingdon, Oxon OX14 2NF. Tel: 01235202058 (H), 01235 537080 (B)
**GROUND:** Holloway Park, Slough Road, Beaconsfield, Bucks (01494 676868).
**Directions:** M40 (Jct 2), 1st exit to A355. Club 100yds on right. 1.5 miles from Beaconsfield BR Bus 441 Slough/ High Wycombe
Capacity: 3,000    Cover: 400    Seats:: 250    Floodlights: Yes    C lub Shop: Clu
Clubbhouse: Open eves & matchdays. Bar, Committee Room, Hall, Kitchen, Changing Room I
**Honours:** As Slough : Chilt.Lg R-up: 93-4,Lg Cup 92-3 Slough T Cup R-up 91-2
**PREVIOUS:** **Leagues:** Beaconsfield Utd: Wycombe & District; Maidenhead. Slough
YCOB: Windsor, Slough & District; East Berks; Chiltonian (pre 1994 )    Clubs merged 1994
**Previous Grounds:** As Slough: Haymill Community Centre,Burnham Lane,slough (pre 1944)
**Record Gate:** 300 Beaconsfield Utd v Chesham Utd, Berks & Bucks Sen Cup 1985
**BEST SEASON: FA Cup:** 3rd Q Rd 98-998 **FA Vase:** Beaconsfield: 1st Rd 83-84 85-86 87-88

### FACT FILE
Founded: 1994    Nickname:  SYCOB
Colours:Red & white quarters/black/red & black
Change colours:  All yellow
Midweek Matches: Monday or Tuesday
Reserves' League: Suburban
Programme: Yes, £1
Editor: Andy Jackson, 17 Boundary Cottages, Chipperfield Rd., Bovingdon, Herts.HP3 0JT

### CLUB PERSONNEL
President: D Piercy
Chairman: Fred Deanus
Manager: Simon Delahunty


# BIGGLESWADE TOWN

**Secretary:** Graham Arkwright, 21 Willsheres Rd, Biggleswade, Beds SG18 0BU
Tel: 01767 221574
**GROUND:** `Fairfield', Fairfield Road, Biggleswade, Beds (01767 312374).
**Directions:** A1 North r'bout, left immediately after metal bridge into car park.
10 mins walk from Biggleswade (BR).
Capacity: 2,400    Seats: 250    Cover: 400    Floodlights: Yes    Club Shop: No.
**Clubhouse:** Open all matchdays. Refreshment hut hotdogs, teas, coffees, snacks.
**HONOURS:** South Mids Lge: Res Div 2 87-88, Res Chall Trophy 88-89, S.M. Floodlit Cup 95-96; Beds Snr Cup 02-03 07-08 46-47 51-52 61-62 63-63 66-67 73-74; Beds Premier Cup 22-23 27-28; N. Beds Charity Cup x13; Utd Co's Lg Cup 73-74; Hinchingbrooke Cup 03-04 12-13 92-93 Hunts Premier Cup 92-93 93-94(joint) 94-95 97-98; Jess Piggott Trophy 87-88 89-90 91-92 92-93
**PREVIOUS: Leagues:** Biggleswade & Dist. 02-20; Bedford & Dist. 09-12; Utd Co's    (prev. Northants Lg) 20-39 51-55 63-80; Spartan 46-51; Eastern Co's 55-63   **Name:** Biggleswade F.C.
**RECORD:** **Attendance:** 2,000

### FACT FILE
Founded: 1874    Nickname:  Waders
Club Sponsors: Mantles Ford
Colours: All green
Change: Tangerine/black/black
Midweek Matchday:
Programme: 32 pages, with admission
Editor: Brian Doggett (01767 318307 (H).

### CLUB PERSONNEL
Chairman: Maurice Dorrington
Vice Chairman: M Jarvis
President: R Dorrington
Manager: David Northfield
Physio: J Maher


# BRACHE SPARTA

**Secretary:** Roy Standring, 37 Taunton Avenue, Luton, Beds. LU2 0LN. Tel: 01582 736574
**GROUND:** Foxdell Sports Ground, Dallow Rd, Luton LU1 1UP (01582 720751).
**Directions:** From M1 jct11, take A505 towards Luton. Right at Chaul End roundabout. Across A505 keep B&Q on left,  into Dallow Rd. Ground 50 yds on right by Foxdell junior school.
Capacity: 400    Cover: 100    Seats: 25    Floodlights: Yes    Club Shop: No
Clubhouse: Open daily 12-3 & 7.30-11. Light snacks & refreshments etc available
**HONOURS:** South Mids Lg R-up 92-93, 96-97 (Div 1 R-up 83-84 87-88), Lg Cup R-up 75-76 80-81 92-93 97-98, Premier Div Cup R-up 91-92, Res Div 2 R-up 75-76, Res Cup R-up 87-88; Luton & Dist. Lg 67-68 69-70 70-71 71-72; William Pease Trophy 66-67 67-68 70-71 71-72; Beds Interm Cup 71-72 (R-up 68-69 70-71), BedsJnr Cup 82-83; Leighton Challenge Cup R-up 69-70 South Mids Lg Prem Div 1 North Champions 97-98, Beds Premier Cup R-up. 97-98
**PREVIOUS:** **League:** Luton & Dist    **Record Attendance :**320
**Grounds:** Crawley Green Rd, (public park); Hitchin Town FC (share 93-94)

### FACT FILE
Founded: 1960
Nickname: The Foxes
Club Sponsors: A & E Engineering
Colours: White/navy/white
Change Colours:  All royal
Midweek matches: Tuesday
Programme: 32 pages, £2 (incl. admission)
Career Record Goalscorer: Keith Denness

### CLUB PERSONNEL
Chairman: Roy Standring
President: Doug Smith
Manager: Steve Brinkman
Physio: T.B.A.

# BROOK HOUSE

**Secretary:** Barry Crump, 19 Bradenham Road, Hayes, Middlesex UB4 8LP.
Tel: 0181 841 3959 (H), 0966 468029 (B)

**Ground:** Farm Park, Kingshill Avenue, Hayes, Middlesex (0181 845 0110)

**Directions:** From North Circular road: A40 Western Ave. to Target r'about, left towards Hayes (A312), over White Hart r'about towards Yeading/Hayes, right at traffic lights in to Kingshill Ave, ground 1 mile on right. Nearest BR stationis Hayes & Harlington, then bus 90 or 195 to Brook House pub. Nearest tube is Northolt (central line), then bus to ground

**Capacity:** 2,000    **Cover:** 100    **Seats:** 120    **Floodlights:** Yes    **Club Shop:** No
**Clubhouse:** Open weekdays 7-11pm, Sat noon-11pm, Sun noon-11.00pm

**HONOURS:**    SSM Prem South 97-98, Spartan Lge Cup R-up 91-92
**BEST SEASON:    FA Vase:** 3rd Round Proper 97-98
**FA Cup:** 1st Qual Rd 93-94
**Players progressing:** Neil Shipperley (Crystal Palace), MarkHyde (Orient), Mark Perry (QPR)

### FACT FILE
Founded: 1974
Colours: Blue & white/blue/blue
Change colours: Yellow/black/yellow
Midweek matchday: Wednesday
Reserve League: Suburban Lge
Programme: 28 pages, £3 with entry
Editor: John Handell/Dave Ball

### CLUB PERSONNEL
President: T Dean    Chairman: Mick Ralph
Vice-Chairman: J Handell
Press Officer: Lawrie Watts
Manager: M Harvey    Asst. Mge: B Strutton
Coach: R Leather

# HANWELL TOWN

**Secretary:** John A Wake, 38 Warwick Ave., South Harrow, Middx. HA2 8RD.
Tel/Fax: 0181 422 1048 (H)

**GROUND:** Reynolds Field, Perivale Lane, Perivale, Greenford, Middx (0181 998 1701)

**Directions:** A40(M) west from London, leave opp Hoover building (B456 for Ealing), turn left into Argyle Rd, left into Perivale Lane. Grd on left. 500 yards from Perivale tube station (Central line)

**Capacity:** 2,000    **Seats:** 90    **Cover:** 200    **Floodlights:** Yes    **Club Shop:** No
**Clubhouse:** Saturday matchdays 2-11pm, Tuesdays 6-11pm, Non-matchdays 7.30-11pm

**HONOURS:**    Spartan Sen Lg R-up 98-99 83-84 (Lg Cup R-up 93-94, London Snr Cup
91-92 92-93 (R-up 93-94), Middx Charity Cup R-up 92-93
**PREVIOUS:    Leagues:** Dauntless Lge
**RECORDS:    Attendance:** 600 v Spurs, Floodlight opening October 1989
**Scorer:** Trevor Canoville  **Appearances:** Phil Player, 20 seasons, 617 games
**BEST SEASON:    FA Cup:** 3rd Rd Qual 97-98

### FACT FILE
Founded: 1948    Nickname: The Town
Colours: Black & white stripes/black/black & white
Change colours: All red
Midweek matchday: Tuesday
Reserves' League: Suburban Lge
Programme: 16 pages, with entry
Editor: Bob Fisher as below

### CLUB PERSONNEL
Chairman/Press Officer: Bob Fisher
Tel: 0181 952 4142 (H) 0181 519 7511 (B)
President: Dave Iddiols
Patron: Stephen Pound MP
Manager: Ray Duffy

# HARINGEY BOROUGH

**Secretary:** George Kilikita, Unit 12A, 16-22 Seven Sisters Rd, London N7 6AE
Tel: 0171 607 7419 (H), 0181 368 2783 (B)

**GROUND:** Coles Park, White Hart Lane, Tottenham N17 (081 889 1415)

**Directions:** From M1 take North Circular Road (A406). Leave A406 turning right into Bounds Green Road (A109), proceed to end then turn left into Wood Green High Rd (A105) and then first right into White Hart Lane. Ground is on right 300 yds past New River Sports Centre. Wood Green (Picadilly Line). BR (EasternRegion) to White Hart Lane, W3 bus passes ground A105 or A10 from Nth. Circularto Wood Green

**Capacity:** 2,500    **Seats:** 280    **Cover:** Yes    **Floodlights:** Yes
**Clubhouse:** Open 7 days a week
**HONOURS:**    None
**PREVIOUS:    Leagues:** London 07-14; Isthmian 19-52 84-88; Spartan 52-54; Delphian 54-63; Athenian 63-84
**Names:** Edmonton; Tufnell Park; Tufnell Park Edmonton; Edmonton & Haringey

### FACT FILE
Colours: Green & white/green/green
Change colours: Yellow & black/black/yellow
Programme Editor: John Bacon
Tel: 01707 646797

### CLUB PERSONNEL
Chairman: Peter Lawlor
Tel: 0181 889 2726
Vice-Chairman: T O'Connell
Match Secretary: John Bacon
Tel: 01707 646797
Manager: Mike Antoniades

# HARPENDEN TOWN

**Secretary:** Neil Ludlow, 93 RussellSt.,Luton,Beds LU1 5EB( 01582 486802 (H) 0r 01582 424233)
**GROUND:** Rothamsted Park, Amenbury Lane, Harpenden (01582 715724)
**Directions:** A1081 to Harpenden. Turn left/right at George Hotel into Leyton Rd.Turn left into Amenbury Rd, then left again (50yds) into `Pay and Display' carpark - entrance is signposted thru car park to opposite corner
**Capacity:** 1,500    **Seats:** 25    **Cover:** 100    **Floodlights:** Yes    **Club Shop:** No
**Clubhouse:** open matchdays
**HONOURS:**    Sth Mids Lg 61-62 64-65, Championship Shield 67-68, Lg Cup 70-71, Div 1 89-90,Prem Div Tphy 89-90, Res Div 89-90; Herts Co. Lg 11-12 49-50 51-53 53-54(Aubrey Cup 20-21 28-29 50-51 51-52); Mid-Herts Lg 09-10 20-21; Pratt Cup 06-0708-09 10-11; Herts Jnr Cup 01-02 09-10 11-12 20-21 25-26; Herts I'mediate Cup52-53; Herts Charity Shield 07-08; Bingham Cox Cup 1896-97 1902-03 09-10 20-21
**PREVIOUS:    Leagues:** Mid-Herts; Herts County    **Best Seasons:** F.A.Cup: 1st Rd Q
**Name:** Harpenden FC 1891-1908    F.A.Vase:2nd Rd

### FACT FILE
Founded: 1891
Nickname: The Town
Colours: Yellow/blue/blue
Change:Blue & White hoops,yellow,yellow
Midweek matches: Tuesday
Programme: 50p
Editor: Chairman

### CLUB PERSONNEL
Chairman: Stephen Whiting(01582 761606)
Manager: Martin Conroy

# HILLINGDON BOROUGH

**Secretary:** Bob Bevis, Beech Cottage, Uxbridge Road, Hillingdon, Middx. UB10 0LF.

**GROUND:** Middlesex Stadium, Breakspear Road, Ruislip, Middx HA4 7SB (01895 639544)

**Directions:** From A40 take B467 (signed Ickenham), left at 2nd r'bout into Breakspear Rd South, right after 1 mile by Breakspear pub - ground half mile on left. Nearest station is Ruislip. Bus U1 passes ground

Capacity: 1,500    Seats: 150    Cover: 150    Floodlights: Yes    Club Shop: No

Clubhouse: Mon-Fri 7.30-11pm, Sat & Sun lunchtime & 7.30-10.30pm

**RECORDS:**      **Win:**  12-0 v Hanwell T. (H), S.S.M. Prem 97/98

**Defeat:** 1-11 v St. Albans City (A), FA Cup 2nd Qual. Rd. 24.9.94

**Transfer Fee Received:** ¨1,000 for Craig Johnson (Wealdstone)

**BEST SEASON:**    **FA Cup:**    **FA Vase:**

### FACT FILE

Founded: 1990            Nickname: Boro

Sponsors: Airport Motor Radiator Co

Colours: White/blue/blue

Change colours: Red/white/red

Midweek Matches: Tuesday

Reserves' League: Suburban

Programme: 20 pages  Editor/Press Off:

Alan Taylor (0181 581 0981)

### CLUB PERSONNEL

Chairman: John Mason

Commercial Mgr: Gamdoor Dhaliwal

Manager: Stuart Leavy

Asst Man.: Ian Lancaster

Physio: Dave Pook

# HODDESDON TOWN

**Secretary:** Brenda Timpson, 82 Tolmers Rd, Potters Bar, Herts EN6 4JY (01707 874028)

**GROUND:** 'Lowfield', Park View, Hoddesdon, Herts (01992 463133)

**Directions:** A10, A1170 into Hoddesdon, over 1st r'about, right at 2nd r'aboutand follow signs to Broxbourne, keeping to the left. Turn right at 1st @mini r-about into Cock Lane and 1st right is Park View. Ground 200yds on the left,entrance opposite Park Rd. BR station is Broxbourne

Capacity: 3,000 Seats: 100 Cover: 250 Floodlights: Yes Club Shop: No

Clubhouse: Bar and well-stocked Tea Bar with hot food. Open at every home game

**HONOURS:**      FA Vase 74-75 (1st winners); S.S.M. Lg Prem Div Plate 97-98 (R-up 96-97, SthMids Lge Lg Cup 85-86 86-87 91-92 (Prem Div Tphy R-up 92-93); Spartan Lg 70-71(R-up(3) 71-74), Div 1 35-36, Div 2 'B' 27-28, Lg Cup(2) 70-72;

**PREVIOUS:**     **Lges:** East Herts 1896-1908, 11-21; Herts Co. 08-25; N Middx Dist 10-22; Spartan 25-75; London Spartan 75-77; Athenian 77-84; South Midlands 84-97

**RECORDS:**      **Attendance:** 3,500 v West Ham, (Floodlight opening friendly), 1975

**BEST SEASON:** **FA Vase:** Winners 74-75

### FACT FILE

Founded: 1879

Nickname: Lilywhites/ Lowfielders

Colours: White/black/black

Change Colours: All red

Midweek matchday: Tuesday

Reserves' Lge: Essex/Herts Border Com

Programme: 88-100 pages 80p

Editor: Mrs Jane Sinden Tel: 01767

631297Fax: 01767 631562

### CLUB PERSONNEL

President: Peter Haynes

Chairman: Roger Merton

Manager: Alan Moore

Asst Man.: Paul Surridge

**Back Row** - L-R: Jeff Cross (captain), Alex Clark, Richard Evans, Spencer Knight, Neil Conner, Dave Russell, Paul Letts, Ian Barnes.    **Front Row:** Adie Bird, Barry White, Darren White, Lee Wilson, Paul Mann

# HOLMER GREEN

**Secretary:** John Anderson, 1 Jason House, Cressex Rd., High Wycombe, Bucks. HP124TT.
Tel: 01494 446128 (H), 01494 465454 (B)

**GROUND:** Watchet Lane, Holmer Green, High Wycombe (01494 711485)
**Directions:** From Amersham on A404 High Wycombe Road, after approx 2 miles turn right into Sheepcote Dell Road. Continue until end of road by Bat & Ball PH.Turn right then immediate left, continue approx 1/2 mile until 2 mini roundabouts, turn left in front of the Mandarin Duck into Watchet Lane. The ground is 150 yards on the right

Capacity: 1,000    Seats: 25      Cover:Yes    Floodlights:Yes    Club Shop:No
Clubhouse: Saturdays 12pm -11 pm midweek 7pm 11pm                Badges: Yes ( £3)

**HONOURS:**    Berks & Bucks Sen Tr.Finalists 98-99, BB Jun Cup Winners 52-53, 63-64
B&B Inter-mediate Cup Winners 76-77; S.Mid Sen Div Winners (2),
S.Mid Sen Cup Winners 96-97
**PREVIOUS**    **Leagues:** 1908-34 Chesham & Dist. 34-84 Wycombe Comb. & Lge 84-95
Chiltonian 95-98 South Midlands

**FACT FILE**

Founded: 1908
Colours: All Green
Change colours: All blue
Midweek Matchday: Tuesday (7.45)
Programme: Yes - Inc.Admission
Editor: Bill Scholes (Chairman)

**CLUB PERSONNEL**

Chairman: Bill Scholes 01494 713867 (H)
Match Secretary: T.B.A.
Manager: Jez Hodges

# LONDON COLNEY

**Secretary:** Dave Brock, 50 Seymour Rd., St Albans, Herts. AL3 5HW. Tel: 01727 761644 (H)

**Ground:** Cotslandswick, London Colney (01727 822132)
**Directions:** From London Colney r'bout (junction of A414/A1081) take A414 towards Watford, after layby (300yds) turn left (hidden turning marked `SportsGround') and follow around to gates.
Capacity: 1,000    Cover: 100    Seats: 30    Floodlights: Yes    Club Shop:
Clubhouse: Open after games. Hot food available

**HONOURS**    Sth Mids Lg Sen Div 94-95 R-up 93-94 (Chall. Tphy 93-94, Div 1 R-up 92-93,
Res.Div 1 92-93), Herts Co. Lg 56-57 59-60 86-87 88-89 (R-up 57-58 58-59).
Aubrey Cup 21-22 22-23 56-57 58-59 81-82, Res. Div 1 87-88 88-89 89-90
91-92, Res. Cup 62-63 89-90 91-92 (R-up 70-71)

**PREVIOUS**    **Leagues:** Mid Herts 1907-54; Herts Co. 07-92
**Ground:** Whitehorse Lane 07-75
**Record Attendance:** 300 v St Albans City. Herts Senior Cup 98-99

**FACT FILE**

Founded: 1907        Nickname: Blueboys
Sponsors: City Glass
Colours: Royal blue & black stripes/black/blue
Change Colours: All Red
Midweek Matchday: Tuesday
Programme: £1 with entry
Editor: Terry Hardy 01727 762705

**CLUB PERSONNEL**

Chairman: Bill Gash
Vice Chairman: P Light
President: K.Parsons
Manager: Mick Wright
Physio: J Burt

# MILTON KEYNES CITY

**Secretary:** Peter Baldwin, c/o Mercedes-Benz (UK) Ltd, Tongwell, Milton KeynesMK15 8BA
01604 870457 (H) 01908 245408 (B) 01908 245088 (Fax)
**Ground:** The Barn, Pannier Place, Downs Barn, Milton Keynes, Bucks (01908245158)
**Directions:** M1 jct 14, A509 for Milton Keynes, right onto H5 Portway at 1st island, right onto V9 Overstreet at 3rd island, 1st left into Downs Barn Boulevard, 2nd left into Pannier Place, ground at top of hill
Capacity: 300    Cover: No    Seats: None    Floodlights: No    Club Shop: No
**Clubhouse:** The Mercedes-Benz Sports & Social Club, 1 mile from ground, open normal hours

**HONOURS:**    North Bucks Lge - Div 1 90-91, Prem. Div Cup 92-93, I'mediate Tphy 91-92;
Daimler-Benz Austrian International Tournament R-up 1990
**PREVIOUS:**    **Leagues:** Milton Keynes Sunday/ North Bucks & District (pre'93)
**RECORD**    **Scorer:** Stuart Collard 132        **Appearances:** Stuart Collard 206
**Win:** 24-2 v Milton Keynes Saints, Berks & Bucks Jun Cup 1st Rd 16/10/93
**Defeat:** 1-8 v Greenleys, Milton Keynes Sun Lge Cup 1st Rd 22/11/87

**FACT FILE**

Founded: 1967        Nickname: Blues
Sponsors: Mercedes-Benz (UK) Ltd
Colours: Royal/navy/navy
Change Colours: All white
Midweek matches: Wednesday
Reserves' league: S.S.M. Reserve Div
Programme: 16 pages, 50p
Editor: Stuart Collard, 01908 660796 (H),
01908 600394 (B)

**CLUB PERSONNEL**

Chairman: Bob Flight. President: Nigel Wells
Manager: Cliff Peters
Asst Man.: Mark Collender
Coach: Kevin England    Physio: Nick Booth

# NEW BRADWELL St PETER

**Secretary:** Les Smith, 47 Rowle Close, Stantonbury, Milton Keynes MK14 6BJ.
Tel.: 01908 319522 (H)
**Ground:** Recreation Ground, Bradwell Road, New Bradwell, Milton Keynes MK13 7AT
Tel.: 01908 313835
**Directions:** From M1 Jnt 14 go towards Newport Pagnell, left at 1st r-about into H3 (A422 Monks Way). Over 5 r-abouts, right at 6th island into V6 (GraftonSt.), At 1st roundabout go right the way round (back on yourself) then take 1st left at mini-r'about into Bradwell Rd. Go straight over next mini r'about. Ground immediately on left.
Capacity:        Seats: 30    Cover: 100    Floodlights: No
**Clubhouse:** Members only (member can sign in 2 guests). Evenings & w/e mid day. No food.
**HONOURS:** Sth Mids Lg Div 1 76-77 83-84  Sen Div Champs 97-98, (Res Div 2 R-up 76-7),
**PREVIOUS:**    **League:** North Bucks
**Names:** Stantonbury St James (predecessors were New Bradwell St James);
Stantonbury St Peters (until merger with New Bradwell Corinthians in 1946)

**FACT FILE**

Founded: 1902
Nickname: Peters
Colours: Maroon & blue stripes/blue/blue
Change: Amber/black/black.
Midweek matches: Tuesday
Programme: 32 pages, £2 with entry
Editor: Paul Smith 01908 776270 (H)

**CLUB PERSONNEL**

Chairman: John Haynes
President: J P Booden
Vice-Chairman: S JBooden
Press Officer: P Smith
Manager: A Milne

# POTTERS BAR TOWN

**Secretary:** Carole Waller, 26 Queen Annes Grove, Bush Hill Park, Enfield, Middx EN1 2JR
Tel: 0181 360 7859
**GROUND:** Parkfield, The Walk, Potters Bar, Herts EN6 1QN, 01707 654833
**Directions:** M25 jct 24, enter Potters Bar along Southgate Rd (A111), at 1st lights right into the
High St (A1000), half mile left into The Walk, grd 200yds on right (opp. Potters Bar Cricket Club)
Capacity: 2,000    Seats: 25    Cover: 100    Floodlights: Yes    Club Shop: Yes    Contact Jeff
Barnes( 0170 66239902 for details of pennants,badges, car stickers and hangers etc.
**Clubhouse:** Sat 12.30-11pm, Sun noon-5pm, Tues & Thurs 7.30-11pm, midweek matchnights
**HONOURS:**        South Midlands Lge. - Prem. Div. 96-97, Plate 96-97; Herts. Sen. Co. Lge. -
Prem. Div. 90-91, Div. 1 73-74, 81-82, Div. 2 68-69; North London Comb. - Prem.Div. 67-68, Div.
1 67-68, Div. 2 R-up 65-66; SSMLg R-up 98-99  Prem Div North R-up 97-98
**PREVIOUS:**       **Leagues:** Barnet & Dist. 60-65/ N London Comb. 65-68/ Herts Snr Co. 68-91
**RECORD:**        **Attendance:** 4000 v Eastenders XI, 20.4.97. 387 v Barnet, f/light open93
                    Competitive: 200 v Cockfosters, Herts Snr Co. Lge
**BEST SEASON:**   **FA Vase:** 6th Rd 97-98

### FACT FILE
Founded: 1960
Nickname: The Grace or The Scholars
Sponsors: T.B.A.
Colours: Red & royal stripes/royal/royal
Blue & Yellow stripes/royalblue/royal blue
Midweek matchday: Tuesday or Wednesday
Programme: 20pages, £1
Editor/PRO Jeff Barnes (01707 660445)
### CLUB PERSONNEL
Chairman: Peter Waller
Vice Chairman: Alan Bolt
President: B Wright  General Mger: L Eason
Manager:DaveWhitehead.Coach:JohnMeakes
Physio: Brian Goymer

# ROYSTON TOWN

**Secretary/Press Officer:** Trevor Glasscock, 39 Poplar Drive, Royston, Herts. SG8
Tel: (01763 230783)
**GROUND:**      Garden Walk, Royston, Herts SG8 7HP (01763 241204).
**Directions:**   FromBaldock, A505 to Royston bypass, right at 2nd island onto A10 towards
London, 2nd left is Garden Walk; ground 100 yds on left.
Capacity: 4,000    Seats: 300    Cover: 300    Floodlights: Yes    Club Shop: Yes
**Clubhouse:** Mon-Thurs 7-11, Fri 11-3 & 7-11, Sat 11-3 & 4-11, Sun 12-3.
**HONOURS**       Herts Co. Lg 76-77 (Div 1 69-70 76-77); Sth Mids Lg R-up 79-80  (Div 1 78-
79,Chall. Cup R-up 78-79;
**PREVIOUS**      **Leagues:** Buntingford & Dist. 18-28; Cambs 28-50; Herts Co. 50-59 62-77;
SthMids 59-62 77-84; Isthmian 84-94
**RECORDS**       **Attendance:** 876 v Aldershot, 13/2/93
                  **Scorer:** Trevor Glasscock 289 (1968-82)    **Appearances:** Fred Bradley 713
**BEST SEASON**  **FA Cup:** 2nd Qual. Rnd 59-60, 0-9 v Barnet (A), 89-90, 0-3 V Bromley (A)

### FACT FILE
Founded: 1875    Nickname: Crows
Res League: Essex & Herts Border Comb
Sponsors: ABA Consultants
Colours: White/black/black
Change colours: Red/white/white
Midweek Matches: Tuesday
Programme: 16 pages, 30p
Editor: Steve Langridge (01438 356661)
### CLUB PERSONNEL
Chairman: Tony Moulding
Vice-Chairman: Bernard Brown
President: Alan Barlow
Manager: Kevin Pugh
Asst Mgr: S SalomonePhysio: C Mardell

# RUISLIP MANOR

**Secretary:** John Price, 1 Filey Way, Ruislip,Middlesex (01895 631933)
**Ground:** Grosvenor Vale, off West End Rd, Ruislip, Middx 01895 637487-office,676168-boardroom
Directions: A40 to Ruislip, turn off on A4180, right at r'bout into West EndRd, right into Grosvenor
Vale after a 1 1/2 miles - ground at end. From RuislipManor station (Metropolitan Line) turn left
out of station, then 1st right intoShenley Ave, 3rd left into Cranley Dr - ground 150 yds on left
Capacity: 3,000    Seats: 250    Cover: 600    Floodlights: Yes    Club Shop: Yes
**Clubhouse:** Mon-Fri 12-3.30 & 5.30-11pm, Sat & Sun 12-3 & 7.30-10.30
**HONOURS**       London Lg R-up 51-52 (Div 1 R-up 47-48), Isthmian Lg Div 2 R-up 92-93
                  (Associate Members Tphy 90-91), Athenian Lg Div 2 72-73, Middx Snr Cup
                  SF (6), Middx Charity Cup R-up 90-91 95-96
**PREVIOUS**      **Leagues:** Uxbridge 38-39; Middx Snr 39-46; London 46-58; Spartan 58-65;
                  Athenian65-84; Isthmian 84-96
**RECORDS**       **Attendance:** 2,000 v Tooting & Mitcham United, F.A. Amateur Cup 1962
                  **Appearances:** Chris Balls, 350**Goalscorer:** Kevin Quinn, 76
**BEST SEASON**  FA Cup: 4th Q Rd 90-91, 2-5 v Halesowen T (A)  F.A.Am.Cup: 1st Rd 73-74

### FACT FILE
Founded: 1938    Nickname: The Manor
Sponsors: Golf Course Management
Colours: Black & White/black/black
Change colours: Yellow & blue/yellow/yellow
Midweek Matches: Monday
Reserve League: Suburban Lge (North)
Programme: 24 Price: 50p
Editor/ Press Off.: Steve Szymanski
01895 637933
### CLUB PERSONNEL
Chairman: Tom O'Shea
Vice Chairman: George Kaplanian
Manager: Andy Waddock
Asst Manager: Fred Cummings
Physio: Gary Strudwick

# St MARGARETSBURY

**Secretary:** Keith Myall, 30 Crib St, Ware, Herts. SG12 9EX.
Tel: 01920 830356 (H), 01920 658502 (B)
**GROUND:** Station Road, Stansted St Margarets, Nr Ware, Herts (01920 870473)
**Directions:** Harlow/Chelmsford exit from A10 to A414, take B181 at Amwell after 300yds
towards Stansted Abotts, ground quarter mile on right. 300yds from St Margaretsbury BR station
(Liverpool Str.-Hertford East line)
Capacity: 1,000    Seats: 60    Cover: 60    Floodlights: Yes    Club Shop: No
**Clubhouse:** Bar open every evening 7-11, plus Sat 12-2, Sun 12-3. Bar snacks available
**HONOURS**       Herts Snr Cent Tphy 92-93; Herts Co. Lg Div 2 48-49, Div 3 78-79; Aubrey
                  Cup 48-49 71-72; Res. Div 1 82-83 86-87; Res. Cup 84-85 86-87 87-88);
                  Waltham &Dist Lg 46-47; Spartan Lge 95-96; Roy Bailey Mem Trophy 95-96
**PREVIOUS**      Lges: East Herts; Hertford & Dist.; Waltham & District 47-48; Herts Co. 48-92
**RECORD:**       Attendance: 327 v Wisbech Town, FA Vase 3rd Round 14/12/85
**BEST SEASON**  FA Vase: 5th Rd 1985

### FACT FILE
Founded: 1894    Nickname: The Bury
Sponsors: New World Builders
Colours: Red & black/black/red & black
Change colours: All white
Midweek matchday: Tuesday
Reserve Lg: Essex & Herts Border Comb.
Programme: £2.00 with entry
Editor/Match Sec.: Keith Myall
(01992 646974)
### CLUB PERSONNEL
Chairman: Trevor I Blacktin
President: R L Groucott
Manager: Colin Richards  Asst Mng:Ian Priest
Physio: John Elliott

## SOMERSETT AMBURY V & E

**Secretary:** John Venables, 156 Crossbrook St., Cheshunt, Herts. EN8 8JY Tel: 01992 636991 (H)

**Ground:** V & E Club, Goffs lane, Cheshunt, Herts. Tel: 01992 624281

**Directions:** M25 junct. 25, A10 towards Cheshunt. Take first left at first roundabout onto B198 (Cuffley & Goffs Oak). At end of road turn right off roundabout into Goffs lane. Clubhouse on immediate right.

### FACT FILE

Colours: White & blue/blue/blue
Programme Editor: Peter Harris
01992 429297 (H) 0181 345 1133 (B)

### CLUB PERSONNEL

Chairman: Doug Bacon
Tel: 01992 625830 (H)

## WALTHAM ABBEY

**Secretary:** Alex Myers, 88 The Weymarks, Weir Hall Road, Tottenham N17 8LD.
Tel/Fax: 0181 808 2706 (H)

**GROUND:** `Capershotts', Sewardstone Road, Waltham Abbey, Essex (01992 711287)
**Directions:** Just off M25 jct 26. Waltham Cross (BR Eastern Region) station three miles distant. 242 Bus
Capacity: 2,000     Seats: 100     Cover: 400     Floodlights: Yes     Club Shop: No
Clubhouse: 7-11pm Mon-Fri, 11am-11pm Sat, noon-3pm Sun. Cold snacks, pool, darts
**HONOURS:**     Middx Sen Charity Cup R-up 97-98; London Sen Cup 98-99; SSM Lge Chall Trophy 98-99
**PREVIOUS:**     Leagues: Northen Suburban
**RECORDS:**     Attendance: 1,800 v Spurs, charity game
     Scorer: Paul Holloway          Appearances: Colin Winter
**BEST SEASON:**     FA Cup: Prel. Rd 90-91
     FA Vase: Prel. Rd 87-88 88-89 89-90

### FACT FILE

Founded: 1948     Nickname: The Abbey
Colours: All green and white
Change colours: Red & black hoops/red/red
Midweek matches: Tuesday
Reserves' League: Essex & Herts Border Comb
Programme: 8 pages 50p  Editor: John Thorpe 01992 892653 (H)

### CLUB PERSONNEL

Chairman: Joe Collins
President: Dennis Cordell
Manager: Martyn Busson

## WELWYN GARDEN CITY

**Secretary:** James Bruce, 6 Autumn Grove, Welwyn G.C., Herts AL7 4DB. Tel: 01707331048 (H)
**GROUND:** Herns Lane, Welwyn Garden City (01707 328470)
**Directions:** From A1 follow signs for industrial area. Take one-way systemopposite Avdel Ltd (signed Hertford B195), take 2nd exit off one-way system.Ground 400 yards on left. One and a half miles from Welwyn GC (BR)
Capacity: 1,500     Seats: 40     Cover: 120     Floodlights: Yes     Club Shop: Yes
Clubhouse: Open every night and weekend lunchtimes. Members Bar, Hall. Steward:D Parham
**HONOURS:**     Herts Snr Centenary Tphy 84-85 (R-up 88-89), Herts Charity Shield 27-28 86-8787-88 94-95 (R-up 48-49), Sth Mids Lge 73-74 (R-up 85-86, Div 1 69-70 81-82, LgCup R-up 74-75 81-82 88-89, Reserve Cup 85-86)
**PREVIOUS:**     Leagues: Spartan; Metropolitan; Gtr London.  **Ground:** Springfields
**RECORD:**     Attendance: 600  v Welwyn Garden United
**BEST SEASON:**     FA Vase: 1st Rd 86-87          FA Cup: First Qual.Rd. 94-95

### FACT FILE

Founded: 1921     Nickname: Citzens
Colours: Maroon & blue/blue/maroon
Change Colours: Yellow/blue/yellow
Midweek Matches: Tuesday
Programme: 24 pages, 50p
Editor: Keith Browne (01707 251854)
Local Press: Welwyn & Hatfield Times, Welwyn & Hatfield Herald & Post

### CLUB PERSONNEL

Chairman: Terry Hazel
Manager: Ian Priest
Physio: Arthur Wood

**NOW IN ITS RECORD 9TH YEAR OF PUBLICATION**

# BRITAIN'S MOST POPULAR NATIONAL NON-LEAGUE FOOTBALL MONTHLY

# TEAM TALK

**BEDFORD UNITED**                                   Photo: Gordon Whittington

**BIGGLESWADE UNITED**                               Photo: Martin Wray

**RISBOROUGH RANGERS**                               Photo: Martin Wray

# AMERSHAM TOWN

**Secretary:** David Holdcroft, 147 Quarrendon Road, Amersham, Bucks. HP7 9ER(01494 582626)
**GROUND:** Spratley's Meadow, School Lane, Old Amersham, Bucks. (01494 727428)
**Directions:** From London A413 to Amersham Old town, in front of market hall, right into Church St., first left into School Lane, ground on left past Mill Lane. 1 mile from Amersham Station - BR & underground Metropolitan Line
**Capacity:** 1,500   Seats: 50   Cover: 100   Floodlights: Yes   Club Shop: No
**Clubhouse:** Open matchdays. Bar facilities. Teas, coffees and light snacks
**HONOURS:** Hellenic Lg 63-64 (R-up 64-65 65-66, Div 1 62-63, Cup 53-54), Ldn Spartan Lg R-up 79-80, St Marys Cup 89-90 96-97 (R-up 90-91,96-97), B & Bucks Jnr Cup 22-23 (Snr Cup SF 79-80 80-81), Wycombe Chal. Cup 23-24
1998-99 Leading Scorer& P.o.Y.: Satoshi Otani.   Manager's P.o.Y. John Smyth

**FACT FILE**
Founded: 1890   Nickname: Magpies
Colours: Black & white stripes/black/black
Change colours: Red/black/black
Midweek matches: Tuesday
Reserve's League: Middx Co
Prog. Editor: David Holdcroft 01494 725201

**CLUB PERSONNEL**
Chairman: Howard Lambert
President: Graham Taylor
Manager: Paul Pitfield  Coach: Richard Mount

# AMPTHILL TOWN

**Secretary:** Eric Turner, 34 Dunstable Street, Ampthill, Beds MK45 2JT.
   Tel:01525 403128 (H & B)

**Ground:** Woburn Road, Ampthill, Beds. Tel: 01525 404440

**Directions:** From Ampthill Town Centre follow signs to Woburn then take the first right into Ampthill Park

Colours: Yellow/navy/navy

Programme Editor: Eric Turner
Tel: 01525 403128 (H&B)

Chairman: Michael Lomax
Tel: 01525 755343 (H)

Manager: Alan Dunn
Tel: 01525 754330 (H)

# BEDFORD UNITED

**Secretary:** Geoff Seagrave, 16 Riverview Way, Kempston, Bedford MK42 7BB. 01234 402369
**GROUND:** McMullen Park, Meadow Lane, Cardington, Bedford MK45 3SB (01234 831024)
**Directions:** M1 jct 13, A421 to Bedford by-pass. Third exit, A603 ground 500 yards on left
**Capacity:** 5,000   Seats: 25   Cover: 100   Floodlights: Yes
**Clubhouse:** Open matchdays. Hot & cold snacks and drinks available
**HONOURS:**   Bedford & Dist Lg Premier Division & Division One, County Junior Cup, Biggleswade KO Cup, Butchers Cup(2), Britania Cup, Bedford Charity Cup
**PREVIOUS:**   Leagues: Bedford & Dist. Lge (57-70 & 80-89); United Cos. Lge 70-80
**RECORD: Attendance:** (at Fairhill) 1500 v Bedford Town, South Midlands Lge Div. 1 26/12/92
   **Scorer:** Neil Tysoe 220   **Appearances:** Simon Fordham 418

Founded: 1957   Nickname: United
Colours: Blue & White/blue/blue
Change colours: All red
Midweek matches: Wednesday
Reserves' League: S. Mids Lge Res. sect
Programme: 24 pages, £1
Editor: Robin King (01234 364654)
Chairman: John Cleverley
Vice Chairman/Press Off Jim McMullen
President: D Rostron
Manager: S Ackroyd Asst. Man.: M Ackroyd
Coach/Physio: Dave Petrie

# BIIGGLESWADE UNITED

**Secretary:** Tracey James, 17 Havelock Road, Biggleswade, Beds SG18 0DB.
   Tel: 01767 316270 (H), 0171270 6045 (B), 0467 372176 (M)
**GROUND:** Second Meadow, Fairfield Road, Biggleswade, Beds. (01767 600408)
**Directions:** From A1 Sainsbury's roundabout, cross over iron bridge and takefirst left into Sun Street. Take next turn left into Fairfield Road ground atbottom of road in lane
**Capacity:** 2,000   Seats: 25   Cover: 125   Floodlights: Yes   Club Shop: No
**Clubhouse:** Open all matchdays, rolls available. Also refreshment hut with hot snacks
**HONOURS:**   South Midlands Floodlit Cup: 95-96, Beds Sen.Cup: (8),Beds Premier Cup:(2), North Beds Charity Cup:(13), Utd Cos Lg Cup: (1) HuntsPremier Cup: (4), Hinchingbrooke Cup (3), Jess Piggott Trophy (4)   **Best Season - F.A.Vase:** 1st Rd Proper 95-96
**Record Crowd:** 250 v Biggleswade Town 28.12.98

Founded: 1959
Colours: Green/black/black
Change : Yellow & Black
Midweek Matchday: Tuesday
Prog-With admission Editor: Secretary
Chairman: David McCormick.(01767 16018)
Match Sec.: Mick Brown, 46 Glebe Road, Biggleswade, Beds. Tel: 01767 312412 (H)
Manager: Steve Wright
Physio: J.Gates

# BLETCHLEY TOWN (formerly Milton Keynes)

**Secretary:** Peter Baldwin, 1Wantage Close, Hackleton, Northants NN7 2AG
   Tel: 01604 870457 (H)  01908 245408 (B)
**GROUND:** Wolverton Park,Old Wolverton Rd.,Wolverton,Milton Keynes Mk12 5QH
**Directions:** Exit A5 trunk road at M.K. North on to Gt. Monks Way(V5).Over two roundabouts onto Old Wolverton Rd.Ground is 1m on right between two railway arches next to Wolverton BR
**Capacity:** 3,000   Seats: 160   Cover: 1,000   Floodlights: Yes   Club Shop: No
**Clubhouse:** Two bars. Upstairs bar open every evening. Snacks available
**HONOURS:**   Leighton Challenge Cup  94-95, 95-96   Sponsors: P.B.I. Intyernational
**PREVIOUS:**   Leagues: None   Names: None   Grounds: None
**RECORDS:**   Attendance: 250 v Bedford Town, S. Mids Lge 30/4/94
   Scorer: Andy McCabe   Appearances: Andy McCabe

Founded: 1967   Nickname: Blues or City
Colours: All Royal Blue
Change Colours: Old Gold,black,gold
Midweek matches: Tuesday
Reserves' Lge: Spartan S Mids Res. Div 1A
Programme: 20 pages, 50p
Editor: Stuart Collard (01908 660796)
Chairman: Bob Flight
Managing Director: A Denman
Manager: Terry Shrieves
Assistant Manager: Zane Flanagan
Coach: Steve White  Physio: Jackson Ryan

# BRIDGER PACKAGING

Colours: Sky blue & yellow stripes/sky blue/
sky blue & yellow

Secretary: Laurence Jack, 17 Curlew Close, Letchworth, Herts. SG6 4TG.
Tel: 01462 625936 (H), 0181 905 1992 (B)

Ground: Letchworth Corner Sports Club, Muddy Lane, Letchworth, Herts. SG6 3TB.
Tel: 01462 486459

Directions: A1(M) junc 9 towards Letchworth, over large roundabout, turn left at next
roundabout A505 Hitchin, through lights, turn left at pelican crossing
into Muddy Lane

Programme Editor: John Furness
Tel: 01462 627279 (H)

Chairman: Lawrence Bridger

Manager: Paul Starling
Tel: 01483 227520 (H)

# BRIMSDOWN ROVERS

Secretary: Graham Dodd, 57 Roundmoor Drive, Cheshunt, Herts EN8 9HU.
Tel: 01992 626820 (H&B), 01992 637111 (Fax)
GROUND: Brimsdown Sports & Social Club, Goldsdown Road, Enfield, Middlesex Tel: 0181 804
5491 Directions: BR from Liverpool Street to Brimsdown (half mile away) or Southbury Road.
By road off Green Street, itself off Hertford Road (A1010). Buses 191 or307
Capacity: 1,000    Seats: 25Cover: 50Floodlights: Yes    Club Shop:
Clubhouse: Large lounge & clubroom, games room & stage. 3 bars (300 capacity)
HONOURS:    Spartan Lg 92-93. Spartan Lg Cup 95-96
RECORD:    Gate: 412 v Chesham Utd, FA Cup 3rd Qual. Rd 12/10/91
BEST SEASON:    FA Vase: 3rd Rd 93-94    FA Cup: 3rd Qual. replay 91-92
PREVIOUS:    Leagues: Northern Suburban    Names: Durham Rovers; Brimsdown FC

**FACT FILE**
Founded: 1947
Colours: Black & white stripes/black/black
Change colours: All yellow & blue
Midweek Matchday:
Programme: With admission
Editor: Peter Wade
Chairman: Secreatary
Match Secretary: Tony Beasley, 80 Cobham
Road, Fetcham, Leatherhead, Surrey. KT22
9JS. Tel: 01372 376820 (H)
Manager: Nigel McGrath

# CADDINGTON

Secretary: Dave Mark, 7 Heathfield Close, Caddington, Luton, Beds. LU1 4HD
Tel: 01582 421404 (H) 01797 147968 (B)
Match Secretary: Fred Rook, 44 Clifford Crescent, Luton. LU4 9HR. Tel: 01582580453 (H)
GROUND: Caddington Recreation Club, Manor Road, Caddington (01582 450151)
Directions: On entering village turn into Manor Road (adjacent to shops andvillage green),
proceed 500 metres: Clubhouse and ground on left side next to Catholic Church
Capacity: Unknown    Seats: No    Cover: No    Floodlights: No    Club Shop: No
Clubhouse: Yes
HONOURS:    Beds Intermediate Cup 85-86 92-93
RECORD:    Gate: 150 v Barton Rvrs, Beds Snr Cup

Founded: 1971
Nickname: The Oaks
Colours: Red & black/black/black
Change colours:
Midweek matchday: Tuesday or Thursday
Programme: Yes Price
Editor: Leigh Glenister 01582 730502 (H)
Chairman: David Mark.
Tel: 01582 421404 (H)
Manager: Gary Worth

# COCKFOSTERS

Secretary: Graham Bint, 15 Chigwell Park, Chigwell, Essex IG7 5BE (0181 500 7369)
GROUND: Cockfosters Sports Ground, Chalk Lane, Cockfosters, Barnet (0181 449 5833)
Directions: M25 Jct 24 (Potters Bar), take A111 signed Cockfosters - ground 2 miles on right.
Adjacent to Cockfosters underground station (Picadilly Line). Bus 298 to Cockfosters station
Capacity: 1,000    Seats: None    Cover: 50    Floodlights: Yes    Club Shop: No
Clubhouse: 7-11pm Tues & Thurs, 4-11pm Sat, 12-3pm Sun. Hot & cold food onmatchdays
HONOURS:    London Interm Cup 70-71 89-90, Herts Snr Co. Lg 78-79 80-81 83-84 R-up
82-83 84-85, Aubrey Cup 78-79 84-85 R-up 70-71 77-78, Herts Interm Cup 78-79 R-up x3
Previous Leagues: Wood Green & Dist. 21-46/ Northern Suburban 46-66/ Herts Snr Co.66-91
BEST SEASON:    FA Vase: 2nd Round 91-92
RECORDS:    Gate: 408 v Saffron Walden, Herts Senior County Lg 68-69

Founded: 1921    Nickname: Fosters
Colours: All Red
Change colours: All White
Midweek matches: Tuesday
Reserve League: SSM Res Sect
Programme: 12 pages with entry
Editor: A Simmons (0181 440 7998)
Chairman/Press Off.: Frank Brownlie
(0181 500 5930)
President: Vic Bates
Manager: Tony Faulkner
Physio: John Walsh

# GREENACRES (Hemel Hempstead)

Secretary: Rebecca Pass, 85 Northend, H. Hempstead, Herts HP3 8TW 01442 390260 (H)

Ground: Hemel Hempstead FC, Vauxhall Rd., Adeyfield, Hemel Hempstead. 01442 259777

Directions: M1 J8; over two  roundabouts, then first right off dual carriageway. First left and
then right at roundabout
Capacity: 3,000    Seats: 100    Cover: Yes    Floodlight: Yes    Club Shop: No

Clubhouse: as for Hemel Hempstead F.C.

Colours: All Green & white
Change Colours;Red & White
Midweek Matchday: Wednesday
Programme: £1.00
Editor: Rebecca Pass (Sec.)

Chairman: David Boggins 01442 264300 (H)
Match Sec. David Lloyd 01442 259721 (H)
Manager: Mark Treadwell

# HAREFIELD UNITED

**Secretary:** Terry Devereux, 72 Williamson Way, Rickmansworth, Herts WD3 2GL.
Tel: 01923 711451 (H/B)
**GROUND:** Preston Park, Breakespeare Rd North, Harefield, Middx UB9 6DG (01895 823474)
**Directions:** M25 jct 16 to M40 East, left at 1st roundabout, then 2nd left into Harvill Rd. Follow road up the Church Hill into village, right at mini roundabout, ground on right. Denham (BR)
**Capacity:** 2,000    **Seats:** 100    **Cover:** Yes    **Floodlights:** Yes    **Club Shop:** No
**Clubhouse:** (01895 823474) Lunchtimes and evenings. Cold snacks (hot on matchdays)
**HONOURS:**    Middx Premier Cup 85-86, Athenian Lg R-up 83-84, Parthenon Lg 64-65
(Div 1 Cup 65-66), Middx Lg 66-67 68-71 (Lg Cup 66-67 68-69)
**BEST SEASON:** FA Cup: 2nd Qual. Rd replay 80-81, 86-87 **F.A.Vase:** 6th Rd 1989-90
**RECORD:**    **Gate:** 430 v Bashley, FA Vase

Founded: 1868    Nickname: Hares
Colours: Red & white/black/black
Change colours: White/blue/white
Midweek Matches: Tuesday
Reserves' League: Suburban
Programme: 12-40 pages, 30p
Editor: Terry Deveraux (Sec.)

Chairman: Keith Ronald. Tel: 01895 824287
President: Dave West
Manager: Vic Harris

# LANGFORD

**Secretary:** Frank Woodward, 4 West View, Langford, Biggleswade. Beds. SG18 9RT
Tel: 01462 701015 (H)
**GROUND:** Forde Park, Langford Road, Henlow SG16 6AF (01462 816106).
**Directions:** Halfway between Langford and Henlow on A6001 Hitchin to Biggleswade road. Bus 177 on main Hitchin-Biggleswade route stops right outside ground
**Capacity:** 4,000    **Seats:** 50    **Cover:** 250    **Floodlights:** Yes    **Club Shop:** Yes
**Clubhouse:** Weekday evenings, matchdays 11am-11pm, Sun 12-3pm. Hot food on matchdays
**HONOURS:**    S Mids Lg 88-89 (Lg Cup 73-74 75-76, Prem. Div Tphy 88-89,94-95.O'Brien Div 1Tphy 84-85), N Beds Charity Cup 27-28 30-31 69-70 75-76 86-87 92-93 94-95 98-99 Bedford & Dist. Lg 30-31 31-32 32-33, Bedford I'mediate Cup 68-69, Hinchingbrooke Cup 72-73
**RECORD:**    Gate: 450 v Q.P.R., 75th Anniversary and clubhouse opening, 22/8/85

Founded: 1910    Nickname: Reds
Sponsors: B.B & E.A. (Sandy); `The Boot'
Pub & Rest
Colours: All red with white trim
Change Colours: Blue & white
Midweek matches: Tuesday
Programme: With admission.
Editors: Bob Reed 01462 700155 (H)
Chairman: Mick Quinlan
President: Ted Rutt
Commercial Manager: Diane Woodward
Manager: Mike Olaseinde

# LETCHWORTH

**Secretary:** June Earl, 92 Bilberry Rd, Clifton, Shefford, Beds SG17 5HD.Tel: 01462 816683 (H)
**Ground:** Baldock Road, Letchworth, Herts SG6 2GN (01462 684691)
**Directions:** Jct 9 (A6141) off A1M straight over large r-about, right at next r-about, ground on right. From Luton (A505) thru Hitchin, ground 3 miles afterHitchin. 2 miles from Letchworth (BR)
**Capacity:** 3,200    **Cover:** 400 **Seats:** 200    **Floodlights:** Yes    **Clubhouse:** No:
**HONOURS:**    Herts Lg 11-12, Spartan Lg 29-30 35-36 51-52, Delphian Lg 57-58, Athenian Lg 74-75 (Mem. Shield 65-66 66-67), Herts Snr Cup 12-13 35-36 51-52, Herts Charity Shield 22-23 47-48 87-88 91-92, East Anglian Cup 76-77, Woolwich Cup 81-82, Hitchin Cup 81-82
**PREVIOUS:**    Leagues: Herts Co. 06-07; Biggleswade 07-08; Nth Herts 08-22;
S Mids 22-23 24-29; Spartan 29-56; Athenian 63-77; Isthmian 77-90

**FACT FILE**
Founded: 1906
Nickname: Bluebirds
Colours: All Blue
Change Colours: Red & white stripes/red/red
Midweek matchday: Tuesday
Programme: 24 pages, 50p Editor: Keith Brown 0385 338584
**CLUB PERSONNEL**
Chairman: Mike Abery
Match Sec.: Vikke Stutely 01462 622778 (H)
Manager: Grahaem Hopkins

# LEVERSTOCK GREEN

**Secretary:** StBrian Barter, 11 Curlew Close, Berkhamsted, Herts HP4 2HZ (01442 862322)
**GROUND:** Pancake Lane, Leverstock Green, Hemel Hempstead. Tel: 01442 246280.
**Directions:** From M1 leave at A4147 to 2nd r-about. 1st exit to LeverstockGreen, Pancake Lane is on left 300 yrds past the `Leather Bottle' pub
**Capacity:**    **Seats:** 25    **Cover:** 100    **Floodlights:** Yes **Club Shop:** Yes    **Clubhouse:** Yes, one hour before kick-off but no food

**HONOURS:**    South Midlands Lge - Sen. Div 96-97, Sen Div Cup R-up 93-94, Herts CentenaryTphy R-up 91-92, Herts Charity Shield R-up 91-92, Frank Major Tphy 1991
**PREVIOUS:**    Leagues: West Herts (pre-1950); Herts County 50-91
Players progressing to Football League: Dean Austin (Tottenham Hotspur)

Founded: 1906 Nickname: The Green
Sponsor: Sunshine Cabs
Colours: All white and green
Change Colours: Green & black/white/black
Midweek Matchday: Tuesday
Programme: 24 pages, 50p
Editor: Bill Dawes (Chairman)
Chairman: Bill Dawes, 01442 395748 (H)
Match Sec: Brian Pollard 01442 256720 (H)
Press Officer: Brian Pollard
Manager: Mark Goodson
Asst Mge: H Boycott-Brown

# LUTON OLD BOYS

Secretary    Terry Owen, 29 Elm Park Close, Houghton Regis, Dunstable, Beds. LU5 5PN
Tel: 01582 863273 (H) 01582 664264 (B)

Colours: red & black/black/black

Programme Editor: Paul Croft 01582 606625 (H)

Ground    Luton Old Boys, Dunstable Road, Luton. Tel: 01582 582060

Chairman: Terry McCabe

Directions    On the A505 Luton to Dunstable Road towards Luton, between J 11 of the M1 and Chaul End Lane. NB - there is NO right turn approaching from Dunstable direction.

Manager: Mick Justin

894

# RISBOROUGH RANGERS

**Secretary:** Derrick J Wallace, 42 Ash Road, Princes Risborough, Bucks, HP27 0BQ
**Tel:** 01844 345179 (H), 01844 345435 (B)
**GROUND:** `Windsor', Horsenden Lane, Princes Risborough. (01844 274176)
**Directions:** Rear of Princes Risborough BR Station (Chiltern Line). A4010 fromAylesbury thru
Princes Risborough, fork right onto A4009, left by thatched cottage, over railway bridge, immediate right ground 150 yds on right
**Capacity:** 2,000   **Seats:** 25   **Cover:** 100   **Floodlights:** No   **Club Shop:** No
**Clubhouse:** Yes. Snacks available matchdays
**HONOURS:**   Berks & Bucks Jnr Cup 85-86, Wycombe & Dist Lg D 2 85-86  D 3  84-85
**REVIOUS:**   **League:** Wycombe & Dist. 71 -
**RECORD:**   **Gate:** 1,200 v Showbiz XI   **Scorer:** Craig Smith

Founded: 1971
Club Sponsors: Systems 3R
Colours: Red & white/black/black
Change Colours: Blue & white
stripes/white/white
Midweek matches: Tuesday
Programme: 20+ pages, £1 with entry
Chairman: Richard Woodward
Tel: 01844 342202 (H)
Manager: Jon Franklyn

# SHILLINGTON

**Secretary:** Aubrey Cole, 32 Greenfields, Shillington, Hitchin, Herts, SG5 3NX.
**Tel:** 01462 711322 (H)
**GROUND:** Playing Field, Greenfields, Shillington, Hitchin, Herts. (01462 711757)
**Directions:**
From Luton on A6, after bypassing Barton, turn right at large r'about. Through Higham Gobian
to Shillington, From Bedford or Hitchin, A600 to RAF Henlow Camp. At `Bird in Hand' roundabout take exit to Upper Stondon
**Capacity:** 1000   **Seats:** 50   **Cover:** 100   **Floodlights:** Yes   **Club Shop:** No
**Clubhouse:** Open every evening and all week ends with food available on match days
**Previous League:** Luton & District   **Record Attendance:** 600 v Baldock Town 65-66
**Best Season - F.A.Vase:** 4th Round 85-86l

Founded: 1946
Colours: Black & white stripes/black/black
Change Colours: All white
Midweek Matchday: Tuesday
Programme: Yes
Editor: David Cole (01767 317275)

Chairman: Douglas Riggs 01462 712695 (H)
Manager: Ross Manfredi

# STONY STRATFORD TOWN

**Secretary:** Maurice J Barber, 26 Boundary Cres., Stony Stratford, Milton Keynes MK11 1DF
**Tel:** 01908 567930 (H)
**GROUND:** Sports Ground, Ostlers Lane, Stony Stratford (01908 562267).
**Directions:** From Dunstable use old A5, Watling Street. Approaching Bletchleycontinue on A5
loop road (Hinkley) to end of dual c'way to A422/A508 r'bout. First exit, thru lights, 2nd right into
Ostlers Lane.
**Capacity:** 2000   **Seats:** 30   **Cover:** 120   **Floodlights:** Yes   **Club Shop:** No
**Clubhouse:** Open evenings & weekends
**HONOURS:**   Sth Mids Lg R-up 70-71 71-72 (Div 1 93-94, Div 1 Cup 93-94)
**PREVIOUS:**   **Leagues:** North Bucks & Dist.; Northampton Combination
**RECORD:**   **Attendance:** 476 v Aston Villa u21, floodlight opening 12.11.96

Reformed: 1953
Sponsor: BILDOR Transport & BUSIPRINT
Colours: Sky blue/black/black
Change Colours: All yellow
Midweek matches: Tuesday
Reserves' League: SSM Res. Div. One
Programme: 28 pages, 50p
Editor: Maurice Barber (Sec.)
Chairman: Roger Taylor
Match Sec.: Robin Gustafson
Manager: Perry Mercer

# TOTTERNHOE

**Secretary:** Jim Basterfield, 41 Park Avenue, Totternhoe, Dunstable, Beds LU6 1QF.
**Tel:** 01582 667941 (H)
**GROUND:** Totternhoe Recreation Ground, Dunstable (01582 606738)
**Directions:** Turn off the main Dunstable to Tring Road B489. Ground on right as you enter
Totternhoe. Five miles from Leighton Buzzard (BR), 7 miles fromLuton. Bus 61 Luton-Aylesbury
**Capacity:** 1,000   **Seats:** 30   **Cover:** 200   **Floodlights:** No   **Club Shop:** No
**Clubhouse:** Evenings 8pm, Saturday after games, Sunday lunch. Tea,coffee, soups at matches
**HONOURS:**   S. Mids Lg Div 1 61-2 (R/u 68-9 85-6), Beds Sen Cup R/u 69-70 86-7  91-2,
Beds I'mediate Cup 77-8 (R/u 81-2), Luton & Dist. Lg 57-8
**PREVIOUS:**   **League:** Luton & Dist. (pre-1958)
**RECORDS:**   **Gate:** 300 v Luton Town, clubhouse opening 13/10/82

Founded: 1906   Nickname: Totts
Sponsors: Sovereign Coaches
Colours: All red
Change Colours: All Blue
Midweek matchday: Tuesday
Programme: 16 pages with entry
Editor: Steve Massey 01908 392313 (H)
Chairman: Jim Basterfield
Vice Chairman: Gifford Kelly
President: Alf Joyce
Manager:Justin Redmond
Physio: Roy Mackerness

# TRING ATHLETIC

**Secretary:** Ralph Griffiths, 42 Bedgrove, Aylesbury, Bucks HP21 7BD.
**Tel:** 0129626425 (H), 01296 393363 x 278 (B)
**Ground:** Miswell Lane, Tring, Herts. (01442 828331)   **Directions:** Through Tring on main rd
towards Aylesbury, right after Anchor PH into Miswell Lane, grd 500yds on right opposite
Beaconsfield Rd. Tring station is several miles outside town, grd by bus ortaxi
**Capacity:**   **Seats:** 25+   **Cover:** 100+   **Floodlights:** No   **Club Shop:** No
**Clubhouse:** Bar, open matchdays, training nights & Sunday lunchtimes
**HONOURS:**   West Herts Lg R-up 72-73 (Lg Cup 65-66, Div 1 61-62 64-65 65-66 (R-up
71-72 85-86), Div 2 (res) 71-72 (R-up 62-63), Div 3 R-up 83-84, Reserve Cup 72-73,
**PREVIOUS:**   **League:** West Herts 58-88
**RECORD**   **Scorer:** Ian Butler   **Appearances:** Alan Sheppard

Founded: 1958   Nickname: Athletic
Sponsors: Heygates
Colours: Red & black/black/black
Change colours: Blue & yellow/blue/blue
Midweek matchday: Wednesday
Programme: 36 pages, 50p  Editor: Sec
President: Paul Nichols
Chairman: S Thomas Tel: 01442 381633 (H)
Manager: Mick Eldridge
Asst Manager: Ray Brimson
Physio: Jean Adams

BRIDGER
PACKAGING

Baclk Row:
John Furness
Paul Starling
Jason Gornall
Tony Heath
Jason Kitchener
Mike Churchill
Paul Gittings

Front Row:
Shaun Stuart
Mike Page
Stuart Potasnick
Pete Holloway
Alan Gittings
Gareth Grant

Photo:
Gordon Whittington

DUNSTABLE TOWN - Back Row: Tony Laing (Asst. Man.), Paul Reeves (Manager), Steve Castleman, Darren Croft (Manager), Steve Bendell, Paul Orchard (Capt.), Mark Pontifract, Steve Howarth, Devon Batchelor. Front: Craig Hawkes, Dave Morgan, Graham Cooke, Clive Douglas, Aaron Smith, John Bell (Physio), Ron Ferris (Coach).
Photo: Gordon Whittington

SCOT

Photo:Gordon Whittington

## ABBEY NATIONAL (M.K.)
**Secretary:** Kerry Pearson, 25a Cruikshank Grove, Crownhill, Milton Keynes MK8 0EW
**Ground:** loughton Sports & Social Club, Lincesdale Grove, loughton, Milton Keynes. Tel: 01908 690668
**Directions:** From M1 Jct 14 follow H6, Childs Way for 5 miles until V4 Watling Way (Knowlhill r-about), right to Loughton r-about, right along H5 Portway 1st right Lineslade Grove

## CRAWLEY GREEN
**Secretary:**
**Ground:**
**Directions:**

## DE HAVILLAND
**Secretary:** Roy Ridgway, 85 Garden Ave., Hatfield, Herts AL10 8LH. Tel: 01707267327 (H)
**Ground:** De Havilland (Hatfield) Sports & Social Club, Comet Way, Hatfield(01707 263204)
**Directions:** From south leave A1(M) at Hatfield turn, A1001 to Birchwood r'bout,1st exit into car park. From north leave A1(M) at Welwyn G.C., A1001 to Birchwood r'bout and 4th exit into car park

## DUNSTABLE TOWN 1998
**Secretary:** Colin Howes, 3 Rotherwood Close, Dunstable, Beds LU6 1UA (01582478395)
**Ground:** Creasey Park, Brewers Hill Rd, Dunstable
**Directions:** Travel north on A5, Through centre Dunstable, left at 1st r/about into Brewers Hill Rd, str over mini r/about, grd on right

## FLAMSTEAD
**Secretary:** Yvonne Rutherford, 51 Parkfield, Markyate, St Albans, Herts. AL38RB. Tel: 01582 841671 (H)
**Ground:** Flamstead Sports Assoc., Friendless Lane, Flamstead, St Albans, Herts(0582 841307)
**Directions:** From Dunstable Town Centre travel south on A5 Trunk Roadtowards the M1. Follow for approximately 3 miles then turn right oppositeHertfordshire Moat House Hotel. Ground and parking approximately half a mile onthe corner of the first right turn

## HOUGHTON TOWN
**Secretary:** Dermot Mcmorrow, 70 Drury lane, Houghton Regis, Beds. LU5 5ED. Tel: 01582 865428 (H)
**Ground:** Houghton Town Association Club, Park Rd North, Houghton Regis. (01582 864862)
**Directions:** M1 jct 11, head towards Dunstable, right at island into Poynters Rd, straight over next island keeping left at small r'bout onto Park Rd North -ground on left 10yds before pelican crossing

## KENT ATHLETIC
**Secretary:** Michael Bayliss, 57 Brickley Road, Leagrave, Luton, Beds. LU4 9EF.Tel: 01582 597894 (H)
**Ground:** Kent Social Club, Tenby Drive, Leagrave, Luton (01582 582723)
**Directions:** M1 jct 11 take A505 towards Luton. Take the first turning on theleft (Stoneygate Road), straight over at the roundabout and turn right attraffic lights into Beechwood Road. Take the first road on the left and thenthe first right into Tenby Drive. Ground and car park 100 yards on left

## LEIGHTON ATHLETIC
**Secretary:** Salvatore Leotta, 28 Ashburnham Crescent, Linslade, LeightonBuzzard, Beds. LU7 7PB. Tel: 01525 382396 (H)
**Ground:** Memorial Playing Fields, Mentmore Road, Linslade, Leighton Buzzard,Beds (01525 370469)
**Directions:** On A5 north of Dunstable travelling towards Hockliffe turn left onto A505 Leighton Buzzard bypass. At end of bypass turn right towartds LeightonBuzzard and take the first right immediately after the railway bridge intoCedars Way. At 'T' Junction turn left into Mentmore Road, ground 300 yards on right

## MARKYATE
**Secretary:** John Dephley, 15 Long Meadow, Markyate, Herts AL3 8JW (01582 840855)
**Ground:** Cavendish Rd, Markyate (01582 841731)
**Directions:** M1 Junc 9, take A5 north towards Dunstable. After 2 miles left intovillage after footbridge. Right into High Street, 5th left Cavendish Rd, grd onright before school

## MURSLEY UNITED
**Secretary:** Roger Gurnett, 20 Tweedale Close, Mursley, Milton Keynes MK17 0SB.Tel: 01296 720505 (H)
**Ground:** Station Road, Mursley, Milton Keynes
**Directions:** A421 Bletchley to Buckingham Road, first right in village

## NEWPORT ATHLETIC
**Secretary:** Charles Stanley, 1 Hemingway Close, Newport Pagnell, Bucks MK16 8QP(01908 615216 H)
**Ground:** Willen Rd Sports Ground, Willen Rd, Newport Pagnell
**Directions:** M1 Junc 14, A509 to Newport Pagnell. 1st r/about turn left A422.1st r/about right into Willen Rd. 1st right Sports Ground 100 yds right

## OLD BRADWELL UNITED

Secretary: David Bird, 24 Loughton Road, Bradwell, Milton Keynes MK13 9AA. Tel:01908 315947 (H)
Ground: Abbey Road, Bradwell, Milton Keynes (01908 312355)
Directions: M1 junction 14 go towards Newport Pagnell. Turn left at firstroundabout into H3 Honks Way. Go six r'abouts then left onto V6 Grafton Street.Take 1st right at mini-r'about into Rawlins Road and then 2nd left intoLoughton Road. Take 1st right into Primrose Road and at the 'T' junction turnright into Abbey Road

## OLD DUNSTABLIANS

Secretary: Craig Renfrew, 75B Princes Street. Dunstable. LU6 3AS. Tel: 01582471794 (H), 01234 265444 (B)
Ground: Lancot Park. Dunstable Road, Totternhoe (01582 663735)
Directions: From Dunstable Town Centre take the B489 Tring Road. At the 4throundabout turn right, signposted Totternhoe. The pitch is located withinDunstable Town Cricket Club which is on the right just before entering thevillage of Totternhoe

## PITSTONE & IVINGHOE

Secretary: Jay Adlem, 22 Maud Janes Close, Ivinghoe, Leighton Buzzard. LU7 9ED.Tel: 01296 668663 (H)
Ground: Pitstone Recreation Ground, Vicarage Road, Pitstone, Bucks (01296661271)
Directions: Tring Rd (B489) from Dunstable, turn right for Ivinghoe, andcontinue through to Pitstone r-about; ground left then right. From Aylesbury -left at `Rising Sun' in Aston Clinton, keep on that road to Pitstone r'bout;ground right then right. Bus 61 from Luton or Aylesbury. Nearest BR stationsare Tring or Cheddington

## SCOT

Secretary: Mrs Ann Land, 18 Coleridge Close, Bletchley, Milton Keynes. MK3 5AF.Tel: 01908 372228 (H)
Ground: Selbourne Avenue, Bletchley, Milton Keynes (01908 368881)
Directions: Main roads to Bletchley then A421 Buckingham road, at Glen Garageright into Newton Rd, 2nd left into Selbourne Ave., through railway bridge tobottom of road

## THE 61 FC (LUTON)

Secretary/Manager: Richard Everitt, 44 Somersby Close, Luton LU1 3XB. 01582485095 (H)
Ground: Kingsway, Beverley Road, Luton, Beds. (01582 582965)
Directions: M1 jct 11, A505 to Luton centre, right at 1st island, 1st left,Beverley Rd is 3rd left, entrance in Beverley Rd, exactly 1 mile junction 11.All Luton to Dunstable buses pass ground - alight at Beech Hill Bowling Club. 1mile from both Leagrave & Luton BR stations

## WINSLOW UNITED

Secretary: David F Ward, 28 Park Road, Winslow, Buckingham MK18 3DL.
Tel: 01296713202 (H), 01865 781210 (B)
Ground: Recreation Ground, Elmfields Gate, Winslow, Bucks. (01296 713057)
Directions: A413 from Aylesbury to Winslow, in High Street turn right into ElmfieldsGate, ground on left opp. car park.A421 from Milton Keynes to Buck'ham then thro 'Gt Horwood

Craig Reynold's flick flies past Paul Orchard in the Dunstable goal for the third goal in the victory which clinched the Division One title for Bridger Packaging last season.
Photo: Gordon Whittington

# HERTS SENIOR COUNTY LEAGUE

**President:** William J R Venneear Esq.    **Chairman:** Cecil T Husdon Esq.
**Secretary:** Kevin Folds, 6 Lanthony Court, High Street, Arlesey, Beds SG15 6TU
Tel/Fax: 01462 834084

After the long wait for their first title, Cuffley decided they enjoyed the taste of success and managed, reasonably comfortably in the end, to retain the Premier Division crown. Wormley rovers got off to a tremendous start but in the end faltered - let down primarily by their home form - and finished six points back in second spot. Bedmond also started brightly and another to put up a mid-season challenge was Sandridge Rovers. Nevertheless in the end it was the reigning champions who displayed the consistency necessary to clinch their second title.

The League's Cup competitions produced a double winner. One had to look back thirty-nine seasons to 1960 to find the last occasion Colney Heath were victorious in the Aubrey Cup. For Reserve Cup success you would need to go back even further, to 1958 and the inaugural season of the competition. So the May Day Bank Holiday weekend proved a huge success for the club. On the Saturday they overcame the challenge of surprise finalists from Reserve Division Two, Sarratt, by three goals to one at Kings Langley FC. then on the Monday they saw off Benington, making a second successive Aubrey Cup Final appearance, by two goals to nil at Berkhamsted FC. For Benington not only was it a second disappointment in the Aubrey Cup but earlier they had lost their grasp on the Herts Senior Centenary Trophy. That Cup had been wrestled away from them by Elliott Star in a tense encounter at Letchworth FC which the Borehamwood based outfit eventually won 1-0.

The battle to avoid a relegation spot at the foot of the Premier Division table was the tightest it's ever been. Kings Langley held bottom spot from day one but, with almost the last kick of the season climbed off the bottom on goal difference. Indeed, had they won their last match, rather than drawn it, they would have climbed out of the bottom three altogether! So, as the final table was drawn up, it was Chipperfield Corinthians who finished bottom and were relegated with Kings Langley and Oxhey Jets next, both of whom won reprieves with adjustments to the constitution for 1999-2000.

Welwyn, on what turned out to be a one year only revival, won the Division One title by a huge ten point margin. In doing so they played some attractive football which would have graced the Premier Division. Their runners-up were newcomers Whitewebbs. The Enfield based outfit initially found the transformation from Junior soccer difficult - not least their administration - but found their feet and will be looking forward to the Premier challenge. A tight three way battle for the final promotion spot was won by Bushey Rangers as they won their games in hand at the back end of a long season. Malex and Old Parmiterians were the other challengers. the surprise in this division was the late season decline of early pacesetter St Peters who nonetheless finished with the Pauline Mary Fox Trophy as the team with the most goals (106 from 28 games). North Mymms, for the second years running, claimed the wooden spoon.

*Kevin Folds, General Secretary*

## FINAL LEAGUE TABLES 1998-99

### PREMIER DIVISION

| | P | W | D | L | F | A | Pts |
|---|---|---|---|---|---|---|---|
| Cuffley | 28 | 21 | 2 | 5 | 78 | 29 | 65 |
| Wormley Rovers | 28 | 18 | 5 | 5 | 63 | 31 | 59 |
| Sandridge Rovers | 28 | 16 | 4 | 8 | 72 | 43 | 52 |
| Benington | 28 | 14 | 6 | 8 | 46 | 42 | 48 |
| Elliott Star | 28 | 14 | 4 | 10 | 63 | 56 | 46 |
| Bedmond Sports | 28 | 13 | 6 | 9 | 57 | 36 | 45 |
| Sun Postal Sports | 28 | 13 | 5 | 10 | 49 | 42 | 44 |
| Colney Heath | 28 | 11 | 5 | 12 | 62 | 62 | 38 |
| Met. Police (Bushey) | 28 | 9 | 5 | 14 | 41 | 58 | 32 |
| Hatfield Town | 28 | 8 | 7 | 13 | 49 | 64 | 31 |
| Agrevo Sports | 28 | 7 | 7 | 14 | 38 | 57 | 28 |
| Bovingdon | 28 | 6 | 9 | 13 | 31 | 52 | 27 |
| Oxhey Jets | 28 | 8 | 2 | 18 | 48 | 80 | 26 |
| Kings Langley | 28 | 6 | 7 | 15 | 43 | 63 | 25 |
| Chipperfield Cor'ns | 28 | 7 | 4 | 17 | 34 | 58 | 25 |

### DIVISION ONE

| | P | W | D | L | F | A | Pts |
|---|---|---|---|---|---|---|---|
| Welwyn | 28 | 20 | 6 | 2 | 86 | 33 | 66 |
| Whitewebbs | 28 | 17 | 5 | 6 | 82 | 58 | 56 |
| Bushey Rangers | 28 | 16 | 5 | 7 | 86 | 48 | 53 |
| Malex | 28 | 16 | 2 | 10 | 55 | 48 | 50 |
| Old Parmiterians | 28 | 14 | 6 | 8 | 58 | 46 | 48 |
| Sarratt | 28 | 13 | 6 | 9 | 80 | 59 | 45 |
| St Peters | 28 | 13 | 5 | 10 | 106 | 68 | 44 |
| Codicote | 28 | 11 | 8 | 9 | 56 | 51 | 41 |
| Walkern Castle | 28 | 9 | 7 | 12 | 49 | 61 | 34 |
| Kimpton Rovers | 28 | 8 | 7 | 13 | 62 | 87 | 31 |
| Herts Police Athletic | 28 | 7 | 6 | 15 | 48 | 66 | 27 |
| Croxley Guild | 28 | 7 | 5 | 16 | 49 | 77 | 26 |
| Evergreen | 28 | 6 | 6 | 16 | 47 | 62 | 24 |
| Standon & Puckeridge | 28 | 6 | 6 | 16 | 44 | 85 | 24 |
| North Mymms | 28 | 4 | 6 | 19 | 41 | 103 | 18 |

# PREMIER DIVISION CLUBS

## AGREVO SPORTS
**Secretary:** Mrs Marion Howlett, 2 Bridle Way, Berkhamsted HP4 1BS 01442 872497 (H) **Ground:** Kitcheners Field, Castle Hill, Berkhamsted. 01442 864937 **Directions:** A4251 to Berkhamsted. At main lights (from Hemel H) turn right into Lower Kings Rd. Turn left under rail bridge then 2nd left. Ground on next corner

## BEDMOND S & S
**Secretary:** Peter Johnson, 101 Spring Lane, Hemel Hempstead, Herts. HP1 3RB.01442 397869 (H) **Ground:** Toms Lane Recreation Ground, Toms Lane, Bedmond. 01932 267991 **Directions:** MI to J8, A414 to 2nd r'bout, left for St. Albans A4147, bear rt. to Bedmond at church (Bedmond Rd), right in village into Toms Lane atmini r'about, grd 300 yds left. Bus 344 from Hemel or Watford

## BENINGTON
**Secretary:** Ray Edwards, 11 Badminton Close, Stevenage, Herts SG2 8SR. 01438 814535 **Ground:** Benington Recreation Ground, Town Lane, Benington. **Directions:** Leave A1(M) at Stevenage South, over 1st r'bout (A602) left at 2nd r'bout (BurgerKing), over next r'about, rt at next one by Swim Pool, follow signs to Walkern (B1037), turn rt at jcn in Walkern, past Walkern FC for approx 800yds turn left signed Benington. Thro' Benington, past Bell PH & ground is 800 yds on left

## BOVINGDON
**Secretary:** Glen Smart, 16 The Bourne, Bovingdon, Hemel Hempstead, Herts HP3 0EN. 01442 833489 (H) **Ground:** Green Lane, Bovingdon, Herts. 01442 832628. **Directions:** From Hemel Hempstead to Bovingdon, left by Halfway House, right into Green Lane, ground on left at top of hill.

## BUSHEY RANGERS
**Secretary:** Rowland Marshall, 45 Blackwell Drive, Watford, Herts. WD1 4HP. 01923461457(H), 254646(B) **Ground:** Moatfield, Bournehall Lane, Bushey, Herts. 0181 386 1875. **Directions:** A41 to Hartspring Lane, into Aldenham Rd, left at r'bout into the Avenue, rt at top into Herkomer Rd, then 4th on left. Bus - from Watford 142, 258, 306,706, 719 to Red Lion, Bushey

## COLNEY HEATH
**Secretary:** Michael Wright, 5 Grove Lea, Hatfield, Herts. AL10 8LA. 01707 880825(H) 0956 937895 (M) **Ground:** The Pavilion Rec. Ground, High St., Colney Heath, Herts. 01727 826188. **Directions:** Turn off A414 (was A405) into Colney Heath village, ground is behind school on left

## CUFFLEY
**Secretary:** Dave Chapman, 56 The Meadway, Cuffley, Herts EN6 4ES. 01707 879000 (H) 0171 360-9200 ex 401 (B) **Ground:** King George's Playing Fields, Northaw Road East, Cuffley, Herts. 01707875395. **Directions:** A121 from Potters Bar or Cheshunt, 5 miles from jcn 25or 26 on M25. Bus - 242 from Potters Bar or Cheshunt to Playing Fields, Cuffley

## ELLIOTT STAR
**Secretary:** Ray Capper, 28 Alban Crescent, Boreham Wood, Herts. WD6 5JF. 0181 207 3940 (H & B) **Ground:** Pursley Football Ground, London Rd, Shenley. **Directions:** From M25: J22 & A556 for Radlett. R'bout take B5378 to Shenley. Mini r'bout by White Horse straight over, ground 300 yds on right. From Watford A41 take B462 to Radlett. Turn rt at Watling St, lft at mini r'bout, rt in Shenley onto B5378. From A1: take A5135 to Borehamwood, follow signs to Shenley. Ground on left opposite farm.

## HATFIELD TOWN
**Secretary:** Ray Budge, 9 Drovers Way, Hatfield, Herts AL10 0PU. 01707 262974 (H) **Ground:** Birchwood Leisure Centre, Longmead, Birchwood, Hatfield, Herts 01707 270772. **Directions:** A1(M) J4, at r'bout take A414 Hertford. Next r'bout 2nd exit for Birchwood Estate, follow road to ground on right.

## KINGS LANGLEY
**Secretary:** Andy Mackness, 79 Weymouth St, Apsley, Hemel Hempstead, Herts HP3 9SJ. 01442 398186 (H) **Ground:** Kings Langley FC, Hempstead Rd., Kings Langley. **Directions:** M25, junct. 20 (Aylesbury) then A4251 to Kings Langley. Ground approx. 1 mile on right

## METROPOLITAN POLICE BUSHEY
Secretary: J R Howard, Met. Police S C, Aldenham Rd, Bushey, Herts. WD2 3TR. 01923 674373 (H), 0171 321 7903 (B) **Ground:** Met. Police Sports Club, Aldenham Road, Bushey. 01923 243947 **Directions:** M1 J5, A41 for Harrow/South Watford to 1st r'bout, rt into Hartspring Lane, leading into Aldenham Rd (A4008), ground 1/4 mile on left opp. Caledonian schl. Bus - 312 from Watford stops outside club

## OXHEY JETS
**Secretary:** J R Elliott, 7 Brampton Rd, South Oxhey, Watford, Herts. WD16PF. 0181 428 6382 (H), 0181 424 5891 (B) **Ground:** Chilwell Gardens, South Oxhey, Watford. 0181 421 4965. **Directions:** From Watford follow Bushey signs. At Bushey Arches turn rt. into Eastbury Rd, left into Brookdene Ave, cont along Prestwick Rd. past station. Right into Northwick Rd, then left into Chilwell Gdns. Bus - 348 from Watford, alight at Northwick Rd

## SANDRIDGE ROVERS
**Secretary:** G Hardwick, 21 Woodcock Hill, Sandridge, St. Albans, AL4 9EF. 01727 855334 (H), 01483 742200 (B) **Ground:** Spencer Recreation Ground. 01727 855159 or 835506 clubhouse. **Directions:** Buses 304, 357 & 358 from St. Albans. By road B651 from St Albans or Wheathampstead to High St. Ground at rear of car park

## SUN POSTAL SPORTS
**Secretary:** A Cowland, 132 Bushey Mill Lane, Watford. WD2 4PB. 01923 233045(H), 01442 229509 (B) **Ground:** Bellmount Wood Ave, Watford. 01923 227453. **Directions:** By road from Kings Langley to Watford on Hempstead Rd, right at Langley Rd lights, right at r'about, then 1st left. Ground entrance 50 yds on right

## WHITEWEBBS
**Secretary:** Miss J Kendall, 14 Oxford Rd, Enfield, Middx EN3 4BA. 0181 804 5084 (H) **Ground:** The Whitewebbs Club, Whitewebbs Lane, Enfield. 01992 718658. **Directions:** M25 J25 take A10 South, at 1st traffic lights turn right. Turn right at Pied Bull, ground 150 yds on left.

## WORMLEY ROVERS
**Secretary:** David Smith, 19 Nursery Gardens, Enfield, Middx. EN3 5NG. 0181 8043608 (H), 01992 445577 (B) **Ground:** Wormley Sports Ground, Church Lane, Wormley. 01992 460650. **Directions:** Buses 310, 316 from Hertford and London. By road from A10 take A1170, turn off for Broxbourne and Turnford. Left at `New River Arms', left again into Church Lane. Ground 1/4 mile on right

# CHERRY RED RECORDS
# CHILTONIAN FOOTBALL LEAGUE

**Secretary:** N G Stansbury
31 Colne Road, High Wycombe, Bucks HP13 7XN
Tel/Fax: 01494 521792   email: gstans@globalnet.co.uk

## HONOURS BOARD 1998-99

| | | |
|---|---|---|
| Berks & Bucks County Senior Trophy | Winners | Eton Wick |
| Cherry Red Records Bon Accord Trophy . | Winners | Eton Wick |
| | Runners Up | Harrow Hill Rovers |
| Brian Wells Memorial Cup | Winners | Peppard |
| | Runners Up | Henley Town |
| Captain Oi! Reserve League Challenge Cup | Winners | Finchampstead Reserves |
| | Runners Up | Henley Town Reserves |
| Premier Division | Champions | Eton Wick |
| | Runners Up | Peppard |
| Division One | Champions | Finchampstead Reserves |
| | Runners Up | Henley Town Reserves |
| Division Two | Champions | Stocklake Reserves |
| | Runners Up | Drayton Wanderers Reserves |
| League Shield | Champions | Drayton Wanderers Reserves |
| | Runners Up | Martin Baker Sports Reserves |

## FINAL LEAGUE TABLES 1998-99

### PREMIER DIVISION

| | P | W | D | L | F | A | Pts |
|---|---|---|---|---|---|---|---|
| Eton Wick | 24 | 18 | 2 | 4 | 73 | 27 | 56 |
| Peppard | 24 | 15 | 5 | 4 | 49 | 20 | 50 |
| Binfield | 24 | 14 | 5 | 5 | 53 | 35 | 47 |
| Rayners Lane | 24 | 13 | 6 | 5 | 75 | 31 | 45 |
| Stocklake | 24 | 13 | 3 | 8 | 62 | 38 | 42 |
| Finchampstead | 24 | 11 | 6 | 7 | 52 | 29 | 39 |
| RS Basingstoke | 24 | 12 | 1 | 11 | 53 | 42 | 37 |
| Henley Town | 24 | 10 | 6 | 8 | 50 | 32 | 36 |
| Penn & Tylers Green | 24 | 9 | 6 | 9 | 65 | 52 | 33 |
| Quarry Nomads | 24 | 7 | 2 | 15 | 31 | 65 | 23 |
| Prestwood | 24 | 6 | 3 | 15 | 31 | 71 | 21 |
| Taplow United | 24 | 2 | 2 | 20 | 27 | 119 | 8 |
| Aston Clinton | 24 | 2 | 1 | 21 | 29 | 91 | 7 |

### DIVISION ONE

| | P | W | D | L | F | A | Pts |
|---|---|---|---|---|---|---|---|
| Finchampstead Res | 24 | 18 | 2 | 4 | 69 | 33 | 56 |
| Henley Town Res | 24 | 14 | 5 | 5 | 73 | 44 | 47 |
| Drayton Wanderers | 24 | 14 | 5 | 5 | 63 | 41 | 47 |
| Martin Baker Sports | 24 | 13 | 6 | 5 | 64 | 30 | 45 |
| Chalfont Wasps | 24 | 10 | 8 | 6 | 53 | 38 | 38 |
| Englefield Green Rvrs | 24 | 10 | 7 | 7 | 59 | 37 | 37 |
| Harrow Hill Rovers | 24 | 10 | 3 | 11 | 49 | 55 | 33 |
| Iver | 24 | 10 | 2 | 12 | 60 | 55 | 32 |
| Binfield Reserves | 24 | 8 | 4 | 12 | 48 | 60 | 28 |
| Penn & Tylers G Res | 24 | 8 | 3 | 13 | 36 | 52 | 27 |
| Eton Wick Reserves | 24 | 7 | 3 | 14 | 40 | 56 | 24 |
| Wooburn Athletic | 24 | 6 | 4 | 14 | 44 | 81 | 22 |
| RS Basingstoke Res | 24 | 0 | 4 | 20 | 19 | 95 | 4 |
| Peppard Reserves | resigned mid season | | | | | | |

# PREMIER DIVISION CLUBS

## ASTON CLINTON
**Secretary:** Mrs V Cozens, 32 Beechwood Way, Aston Clinton, Aylesbury, Bucks HP22 5JP

## BINFIELD
**Secretary:** Mr V Bradshaw, 21 Audley Way, Ascot, Berkshire   Tel: 01344 886144

## CHALFONT WASPS
**Secretary:** Mr D Higgs, Stevens Mead, The Green, Chalfont St Giles, Bucks HP9 1LF

## ENGLEFIELD GREEN ROVERS
**Secretary:** Mr R D Belchamber, 100 Lancaster Avenue, Slough, Berkshire SL2 1AX

## ETON WICK
**Secretary:** Mr B Shurville, 21 the Wheatbutts, Eton Wick, Berkshire SL4 6JH

## FINCHAMPSTEAD
**Secretary:** Mr J Johnson, 21 Moulsham Lane, Yateley, Hampshire GU46 7QX

## HARROW HILL ROVERS
**Secretary:** Mr S Poules, 12 Corfe Avenue, South Harrow, Middlesex MA2 8SZ

## HENLEY TOWN
**Secretary:** Mr A Kingston, 50 Birdhill Avenue, Reading, Berkshire

## MARTIN BAKER SPORTS & SOCIAL
**Secretary:** Mr J Walford, 18 Tilehouse Way, Denham, Uxbridge, Middlesex UB9 5JA

## PENN & TYLERS GREEN
**Secretary:** Mr M James, Woodlands, Forty Green Road, Beaconsfield, Buckinghamshire

## PEPPARD
**Secretary:** Mr C Boyles, 14 Redwood Avenue, Woodley, Reading, Berkshire RG5 4DR

## PRESTWOOD
**Secretary:** Mrs B Stansbury, 31 Colne Road, High Wycombe, Buckinghamshire HP13 7XN

## QUARRY NOMADS
**Secretary:** Mr K Dolton, 58 Pitts Road, Headington, Oxford OX3 8AZ

## RAYNERS LANE
**Secretary:** Mr A Pratt, 4 Stirling Close, Cowley, Uxbridge, Middlesex. UB8 2BA

## RS BASINGSTOKE
**Secretary:** Mr M Davis, 451 Abbey Road, Popley Abbeys, Basingstoke RG24 9EN

## STOCKLAKE
**Secretary:** Mr R Simmons, 24 Wingate Walk, Aylesbury, Buckinghamshire

## TAPLOW UNITED
**Secretary:** Mr P Holt, 14 Lime Close, Wokingham, Berkshire RG41 4AW

# A QUOTE INSURANCE
# READING FOOTBALL LEAGUE

**President:** Leon Summers    **Chairman:** John Dell
**Secretary:** David Jeanes, 6 Hawkesbury Drive, Fords Farm, Calcot, Reading RG31 5ZP
Tel: 01734 413926 (H)
http://www.rdgleague.mcmail.com

A very busy April and early May was experienced with a number of teams cramming a quarter of their matches into the last five weeks of the season after the adverse weather played havoc with our scheduled fixtures.

Our Divisional Play off matches and presentation of Trophies were held at the Berkshire County Sports Ground, Sonning. Our Senior Cup Final was played at Madejski Stadium, with our other Cup Finals being held at Reading Town FC. Our thanks go to our Referees, as with their help we covered most of our matches. Our thanks are also due to the Reading Referees Association for their help and assistance.

The full League Council has met ten times this season, once at the Rendezvous Club, once at the English Martyrs Hall and the remaining meetings at the Dragon Club, Brock Barracks, and the majority of the sub committees have met on a regular basis. One committee which has been very busy is the discipline sub committee, as unfortunately a number of clubs and players have decided that the rules of the League and/or the laws of the game do not apply to them. The end result has been clubs being fined and players being informed that their registrations for next season will not be accepted; one player, having recently been dealt with, will not be allowed to register with the League until the season 2001-02. Clubs and players have been warned that the League will not accept major breaches of the rules. The majority of offences involved abuse of the Referee, which will not be tolerated under any circumstances.

Discussions have been held on a regular basis with Reading Borough Council. Our only Representative game this season resulted in a defeat by the North Berks League, and our thanks to the players who represented the League in this match.

Our promotions sub committee has again been very active, producing newsletters, programmes, League merchandise and excellent press releases to ensure that the League enjoys maximum publicity. The League's telephone news line "League Line" continues to provide a comprehensive results service and news and views to those who ring in. We are one of the few local leagues with an Internet Web Site, which provides results, fixtures, League news and details of League Sponsors. Results are on the web early Saturday evening for that day's matches.

## FINAL LEAGUE TABLES 1998-99

### SENIOR DIVISION

| | P | W | D | L | F | A | PT |
|---|---|---|---|---|---|---|---|
| Forest OB | 22 | 17 | 2 | 3 | 64 | 28 | 53 |
| Checkendon | 22 | 14 | 5 | 3 | 46 | 19 | 47 |
| Cookham Dean | 22 | 14 | 3 | 5 | 52 | 33 | 45 |
| Mortimer | 22 | 14 | 2 | 6 | 47 | 28 | 44 |
| Westwood United | 22 | 11 | 6 | 5 | 39 | 24 | 39 |
| Sonning Common | 22 | 8 | 6 | 8 | 47 | 40 | 30 |
| West Reading | 22 | 8 | 3 | 11 | 41 | 46 | 27 |
| Highmoor | 22 | 8 | 2 | 12 | 41 | 44 | 26 |
| Unity* | 22 | 8 | 2 | 12 | 34 | 51 | 23 |
| Reading Exiles | 22 | 7 | 1 | 14 | 39 | 46 | 22 |
| Emmbrook Sports | 22 | 4 | 4 | 14 | 33 | 57 | 16 |
| AFC Maidenhead | 22 | 0 | 2 | 20 | 18 | 85 | 2 |

### PREMIER DIVISION

| | P | W | D | L | F | A | PT |
|---|---|---|---|---|---|---|---|
| Reading Exiles Res | 20 | 13 | 3 | 4 | 54 | 30 | 42 |
| South End | 20 | 13 | 2 | 5 | 42 | 26 | 41 |
| REME Arborfield | 20 | 11 | 4 | 5 | 47 | 24 | 37 |
| Frilsham | 20 | 11 | 3 | 6 | 57 | 31 | 36 |
| Marlow | 20 | 11 | 3 | 6 | 33 | 27 | 36 |
| Goring | 20 | 10 | 4 | 6 | 40 | 21 | 34 |
| Round Head | 20 | 9 | 4 | 7 | 42 | 33 | 31 |
| IBIS | 20 | 5 | 4 | 11 | 38 | 46 | 19 |
| Whitley Rovers | 20 | 5 | 2 | 13 | 39 | 60 | 17 |
| Rabsons Rovers | 20 | 3 | 4 | 13 | 24 | 67 | 13 |
| Earlbourne* | 20 | 2 | 1 | 17 | 23 | 74 | 4 |

* points deducted

# SENIOR DIVISION

## CHECKENDON SPORTS
**Secretary:** Jon Sims, 39 West Chiltern, Woodcote, Reading RG8 0SG   (01491 681472)
**Ground:** Checkendon playing fields, Checkendon
**Colours:** Maroon & White/black/white

## COOKHAM DEAN
**Secretary:** Dave Johnson, 2 Palmer Close, Cox Green, Maidenhead   (01628 412626)
**Ground:** Alfred Major Rec., Hillcrest Ave, Cookham Rise, Maidenhead
**Colours:** Red & Black/Black/Red

## EMMBROOK SPORTS CLUB
**Secretary:** Steve Haynes, 15 Tilney Way, Lower Earley RG6 4AD (01189 670459)
**Ground:** Emmbrook Sports Ground, Lowther Road, Emmbrook, Wokingham   (01189 780209)
**Colours:** Blue/White

## FOREST OLD BOYS
**Secretary:** Nigel Woods, 23 Chapel Lane, Benson, Wallingford   (01491 824510)
**Ground:** Holme Park, Sonning   (0118 969 0356)
**Colours:** Yellow & Blue/Blue/Blue

## HIGHMOOR
**Secretary:** Chris Gailimore, 20 Portway Close, REading RG1 6LB   (01189 588518)
**Ground:** Highmoor Ath Grd, Highmoor, Henley
**Colours:** Yellow/Blue/White

## MORTIMER
**Secretary:** Steve Dell, 30 Croft Road, Mortimer, Reading RG7 3TS   (01189 333821)
**Ground:** Alfred Palmer Memorial PF., West End Road, Mortimer
**Colours:** Amber/Black/Black

## READING EXILES
**Secretary:** Luke Harris, 14 Pitcroft Avenue, Earley, Reading RG6 1NH   (0118 961 7577)
**Ground:** Palmer Park Sports Stadium, Wokingham Road, Reading
**Colours:** Blue & White

## SONNING COMMON
**Secretary:** Tanya Gay, 23 Valentine Crescent, Reading RG4 5JD   (0189 470400)
**Ground:** Sonning Cricket Club, Peppard Common, Peppard
**Colours:** White/Blue

## SOUTHEND
**Secretary:** Mrs S Dawson, Heath Farm Cottage, Southend Road, Southend RG7 6GP   (01189 745410)
**Ground:** Bradfield Cricket Club, Heath Road, Bradfield, Berks
**Colours:** Red/Black/White

## UNITY
**Secretary:** Trevor Lowe, 161 Cotswold Way, Tilehurst, Reading RG31 6ST   (01189 455133)
**Ground:** Cintra Park, Reading
**Colours:** Red/Black

## WEST READING
**Secretary:** Susan Porton, 6 Hampstead Court, Grovelands Rd, Reading RG3 2OO   (01189 504034)
**Ground:** Victoria Rec., Reading
**Colours:** Amber/Black

## WESTWOOD UNITED
**Secretary:** Mrs Penny Brodie, 58 Devonshire Gdns, Reading RG31 6FP   (01189 624572)
**Ground:** Cotswold Sports Centre, Downsway, Tilehurst
**Colours:** White/Jade

# PREMIER DIVISION CONSTITUTION

Frilsham & Yattendon
Goring United
Ibis
Marlow United
Forest Old Boys Reserves
Reading Old Blues
Royal Mail
R.E.M.E. Arborfield
Reading Exiles Reserves
Roundhead
Whitley Rovers

# SURREY COUNTY LEAGUE

## FINAL LEAGUE TABLES 1998-99

### PREMIER DIVISION

| | P | W | D | L | F | A | PT |
|---|---|---|---|---|---|---|---|
| Chobham & Ottershaw | 26 | 21 | 5 | 0 | 80 | 21 | 68 |
| Chessington United | 26 | 19 | 5 | 2 | 80 | 25 | 62 |
| Kingston & Ditton Town | 26 | 18 | 4 | 4 | 62 | 21 | 58 |
| Virginia Water | 26 | 12 | 7 | 7 | 49 | 43 | 43 |
| Bookham | 26 | 11 | 6 | 9 | 33 | 33 | 39 |
| Crescent Rovers | 26 | 10 | 7 | 9 | 49 | 47 | 37 |
| Bisley Sports | 26 | 9 | 8 | 9 | 60 | 53 | 35 |
| Vandyke Colliers United | 26 | 10 | 4 | 12 | 49 | 44 | 34 |
| AFC Guildford | 26 | 8 | 5 | 13 | 40 | 51 | 29 |
| Shottermill | 26 | 6 | 7 | 13 | 32 | 46 | 25 |
| Farleigh Rovers | 26 | 6 | 4 | 16 | 29 | 79 | 22 |
| Sheerwater | 26 | 5 | 5 | 16 | 23 | 56 | 20 |
| Croydon Municipal O. | 26 | 6 | 2 | 18 | 34 | 76 | 20 |
| Holmesdale | 26 | 4 | 5 | 17 | 35 | 60 | 17 |

### DIVISION ONE

| | P | W | D | L | F | A | PT |
|---|---|---|---|---|---|---|---|
| Milford & Witley Res. | 22 | 19 | 0 | 3 | 83 | 27 | 57 |
| Staines Lammas Res. | 22 | 17 | 2 | 3 | 74 | 18 | 53 |
| Tongham Res. | 22 | 13 | 2 | 7 | 48 | 36 | 41 |
| Horsley Res. | 22 | 12 | 5 | 5 | 42 | 33 | 41 |
| Ockham Res. -3 | 22 | 12 | 2 | 8 | 52 | 38 | 35 |
| Woking Pk & Horsell R. | 22 | 9 | 5 | 8 | 40 | 47 | 32 |
| Haslmere Res. | 22 | 9 | 1 | 12 | 43 | 54 | 28 |
| Marconi S & S Res. | 22 | 7 | 5 | 10 | 45 | 61 | 26 |
| Frimley Green Res. | 22 | 7 | 3 | 12 | 37 | 45 | 24 |
| Chiddingfold Res. | 22 | 4 | 5 | 13 | 35 | 58 | 17 |
| Merrow Res. | 22 | 4 | 3 | 15 | 39 | 77 | 15 |
| Worplesdon Res. | 22 | 0 | 5 | 17 | 22 | 66 | 5 |

### DIVISION TWO

| | P | W | D | L | F | A | PT |
|---|---|---|---|---|---|---|---|
| University of Surrey R. | 22 | 18 | 3 | 1 | 67 | 20 | 57 |
| Badshot Lea Res. | 22 | 16 | 4 | 2 | 72 | 28 | 52 |
| Bagshot Res. | 22 | 13 | 3 | 6 | 74 | 55 | 42 |
| Wonersh Res. | 22 | 11 | 3 | 8 | 58 | 45 | 36 |
| Fairlands Wndrs Res. | 22 | 11 | 2 | 9 | 63 | 54 | 35 |
| Elstead Res. | 22 | 10 | 2 | 10 | 53 | 48 | 32 |
| Grayshott Res. | 22 | 8 | 3 | 11 | 48 | 60 | 27 |
| Hammer United Res. | 22 | 8 | 2 | 12 | 50 | 77 | 26 |
| Farncombe Athletic R | 22 | 7 | 1 | 14 | 50 | 74 | 22 |
| G'dford C Weysiders R | 22 | 6 | 2 | 14 | 27 | 43 | 20 |
| Windlesham United R | 22 | 5 | 4 | 13 | 52 | 63 | 19 |
| Ewhurst Res. | 22 | 3 | 3 | 16 | 41 | 88 | 12 |

### DIVISION THREE

| | P | W | D | L | F | A | PT |
|---|---|---|---|---|---|---|---|
| Elmgrove Res. | 20 | 14 | 4 | 2 | 58 | 35 | 46 |
| Wrecclesham Res. | 20 | 14 | 0 | 6 | 96 | 33 | 42 |
| Lightwater United Res. | 20 | 12 | 4 | 4 | 55 | 31 | 40 |
| Ripley Village Res. | 20 | 12 | 0 | 8 | 52 | 38 | 36 |
| Royal Holloway OBR | 20 | 9 | 3 | 8 | 56 | 49 | 30 |
| Knaphill Res. | 20 | 8 | 1 | 11 | 42 | 48 | 25 |
| Shere Res. | 20 | 6 | 5 | 9 | 44 | 63 | 23 |
| Dunsfold Res. | 20 | 6 | 4 | 10 | 41 | 57 | 22 |
| Old Salesians Res. | 20 | 6 | 2 | 12 | 52 | 66 | 20 |
| Liphook Res. | 20 | 5 | 3 | 12 | 39 | 75 | 18 |
| Burymead Res. | 20 | 3 | 4 | 13 | 46 | 87 | 13 |

# OPTIMUM INTERIORS
# CAPITAL FOOTBALL LEAGUE

**Chairman:** David Free
**Secretary:** Geoff Ellis, 69 Old Woking Road, West Byfleet, Surrey KT14 6LF
Tel: 01932 345844   Fax: 01932 342585

## FINAL LEAGUE TABLE 1998-99

| | P | W | D | L | F | A | W | D | L | F | A | GD | Pts |
|---|---|---|---|---|---|---|---|---|---|---|---|---|---|
| | | *Home* | | | | | *Away* | | | | | | |
| Rushden & Diamonds | 20 | 7 | 2 | 1 | 34 | 11 | 8 | 1 | 1 | 24 | 12 | 35 | 48 |
| Stevenage Borough | 20 | 4 | 2 | 4 | 22 | 15 | 5 | 2 | 3 | 21 | 13 | 15 | 31 |
| Leyton Orient | 20 | 4 | 2 | 4 | 20 | 13 | 4 | 1 | 5 | 17 | 18 | 6 | 27 |
| Welling United | 20 | 3 | 2 | 5 | 14 | 22 | 4 | 1 | 5 | 13 | 21 | -16 | 24 |
| Woking | 20 | 4 | 2 | 4 | 18 | 17 | 2 | 2 | 6 | 10 | 29 | -18 | 22 |
| Harrow Borough | 20 | 2 | 2 | 6 | 12 | 20 | 1 | 5 | 4 | 13 | 27 | -22 | 16 |

## RESULTS CHART 1998-99

| | | 1 | 2 | 3 | 4 | 5 | 6 |
|---|---|---|---|---|---|---|---|
| 1 | Harrow Borough | X | 0-4 | 1-4 | 3-4 | 0-1 | 0-2 |
| 2 | Leyton Orient | 5-0 | X | 1-2 | 3-6 | 0-1 | 6-2 |
| 3 | Rushden & Diamonds | 5-1 | 5-0 | X | 2-2 | 5-0 | 7-1 |
| 4 | Stevenage Borough | 2-4 | 4-1 | 1-2 | X | 3-4 | 1-1 |
| 5 | Welling United | 1-1 | 0-4 | 1-2 | 0-4 | X | 2-1 |
| 6 | Woking | 4-0 | 2-1 | 1-1 | 0-1 | 3-1 | X |

## DOXHILL PRESIDENT'S CHALLENGE CUP 1998-99
Sponsored by Doxhill Limited

### FIRST ROUND
Leyton Orient   4   v   1   Welling United
Harrow Borough   4   v   7   Rushden & Diamonds
Byes: Woking and Stevenage Borough

### SEMI-FINALS
Stevenage Borough   0   v   6   Rushden & Diamonds
Woking   1   v   4   Leyton Orient

### FINAL
Rushden & Diamonds   3   v   0   Leyton Orient

## CONSTITUTION FOR SEASON 1999-2000

Aldershot Town
Aylesbury United
Boreham Wood
Harrow Borough
Rushden & Diamonds
St Albans City
Stevenage Borough

# THE CENTRAL CONFERENCE

**Chairman:** David Free

**Secretary:** Jason Mills, 25 Hewlett Road, Gloucester GL52 6AD
Tel/Fax: 01242 700496

## FINAL LEAGUE TABLE 1998-99

|  | | Home | | | | | Away | | | | | | |
| --- | --- | --- | --- | --- | --- | --- | --- | --- | --- | --- | --- | --- | --- |
|  | P | W | D | L | F | A | W | D | L | F | A | GD | Pts |
| Stoke City | 18 | 5 | 2 | 2 | 17 | 9 | 6 | 1 | 2 | 25 | 11 | 22 | 36 |
| Gloucester City | 18 | 4 | 1 | 4 | 17 | 18 | 5 | 1 | 3 | 14 | 16 | -3 | 29 |
| Rushden & Diamonds | 18 | 4 | 4 | 1 | 25 | 16 | 3 | 3 | 3 | 19 | 14 | 14 | 28 |
| Kidderminster Harriers | 18 | 5 | 1 | 3 | 27 | 19 | 3 | 2 | 4 | 21 | 19 | 10 | 27 |
| Hednesford Town | 18 | 4 | 2 | 3 | 17 | 16 | 3 | 4 | 2 | 17 | 16 | 2 | 27 |
| Worcester City | 18 | 4 | 0 | 5 | 23 | 25 | 5 | 0 | 4 | 15 | 17 | -4 | 27 |
| Cheltenham Town | 18 | 3 | 2 | 4 | 18 | 20 | 4 | 1 | 4 | 22 | 17 | 3 | 24 |
| Hereford United | 18 | 3 | 2 | 4 | 16 | 15 | 3 | 1 | 5 | 14 | 21 | -6 | 21 |
| Telford United | 18 | 3 | 2 | 4 | 8 | 18 | 1 | 3 | 5 | 23 | 30 | -17 | 17 |
| Bromsgrove Rovers | 18 | 1 | 3 | 5 | 13 | 25 | 2 | 3 | 4 | 11 | 20 | -21 | 15 |

## RESULTS CHART 1998-99

|  |  | 1 | 2 | 3 | 4 | 5 | 6 | 7 | 8 | 9 | 10 |
| --- | --- | --- | --- | --- | --- | --- | --- | --- | --- | --- | --- |
| 1 | Bromsgrove Rovers | X | 0-4 | 2-3 | 1-1 | 2-5 | 3-1 | 1-1 | 0-5 | 4-4 | 0-1 |
| 2 | Cheltenham Town | 3-4 | X | 0-1 | 1-1 | 5-4 | 3-3 | 2-1 | 1-3 | 2-1 | 1-2 |
| 3 | Gloucester City | 2-1 | 4-2 | X | 2-3 | 0-1 | 3-2 | 1-1 | 1-2 | 3-2 | 1-4 |
| 4 | Hednesford Town | 1-1 | 2-0 | 2-1 | X | 3-0 | 2-4 | 1-1 | 0-2 | 5-4 | 1-3 |
| 5 | Hereford United | 0-0 | 2-2 | 3-0 | 1-4 | X | 0-3 | 3-1 | 1-3 | 1-2 | 5-0 |
| 6 | Kidderminster Harriers | 4-0 | 3-4 | 2-3 | 4-1 | 4-1 | X | 3-6 | 1-0 | 4-4 | 2-0 |
| 7 | Rushden & Diamonds | 4-0 | 2-1 | 5-0 | 3-3 | 3-0 | 1-1 | X | 3-3 | 3-3 | 1-5 |
| 8 | Stoke City | 0-0 | 3-0 | 2-2 | 1-2 | 0-2 | 2-1 | 1-0 | X | 3-2 | 5-0 |
| 9 | Telford United | 3-5 | 1-3 | 0-3 | 0-0 | 0-0 | 1-0 | 1-5 | 1-7 | X | 1-0 |
| 10 | Worcester City | 3-5 | 0-6 | 0-1 | 3-2 | 4-1 | 4-6 | 1-3 | 3-0 | 5-1 | X |

## CONSTITUTION FOR SEASON 1999-2000

Burton Albion
Cheltenham Town
Gloucester City
Hednesford Town
Hereford United
Kidderminster Harriers
Nuneaton Borough
Rushden & Diamonds
Tamworth
Telford United
Worcester City

# DOXHILL CHALLENGE CUP 1998-99
Sponsored by Doxhill Limited

## PRELIMINARY ROUND
### (1st Leg)
Worcester City   0   v   6   Kidderminster Harriers

## PRELIMINARY ROUND
### (2nd leg)
Kidderminster Harriers   3   v   2   Worcester City
(Kidderminster won 9-2 on aggregate)

## FIRST ROUND
### (1st Leg)

| | | | |
|---|---|---|---|
| Gloucester City | 1 | v 2 | Bromsgrove Rovers |
| Telford United | 2 | v 2 | Cheltenham Town |
| Stoke City | 5 | v 0 | Hednesford Town |
| Hereford United | 3 | v 0 | Kidderminster Harriers |

## FIRST ROUND
### (2nd Leg)
Bromsgrove Rovers   1   v   1   Gloucester City
(Bromsgrove Rovers won 3-2 on aggregate)
Cheltenham Town   5   v   1   Telford United
(Cheltenham Town won 7-3 on aggregate)
Kidderminster Harriers   2   v   0   Hereford United
(Hereford United won 3-2 on aggregate)
Hednesford Town   0   v   0   Stoke City
(Stoke City won 5-0 on aggregate)

## SEMI-FINALS
### (1st Leg)
Bromsgrove Rovers   0   v   0   Stoke City
Hereford United   2   v   1   Cheltenham Town

## SEMI-FINALS
### (2nd Leg)
Stoke City   1   v   0   Bromsgrove Rovers
(Stoke City won 1-0 on aggregate)
Cheltenham Town   1   v   1   Hereford United
(Hereford United won 3-2 on aggregate)

## FINAL
Hereford United   0   v   0   Stoke City
(Hereford United won 4-3 on penalties)

# SOUTH EASTERN FINAL LEAGUE TABLES 1998-99

## ESSEX & SUFFOLK BORDER LEAGUE
### PREMIER DIVISION

| | | | | | | | |
|---|---|---|---|---|---|---|---|
| Gas Recreation -3 | 30 | 24 | 2 | 4 | 94 | 26 | 71 |
| West Bergholt | 30 | 19 | 5 | 6 | 70 | 38 | 62 |
| Kelvedon Social | 30 | 15 | 8 | 7 | 80 | 45 | 53 |
| Little Oakley +3 | 30 | 14 | 7 | 9 | 77 | 57 | 52 |
| St Johns (Clacton) | 30 | 15 | 4 | 11 | 62 | 53 | 49 |
| Stowmarket Town R -1 | 30 | 13 | 10 | 7 | 49 | 38 | 48 |
| Haverhill Rovers Res. | 30 | 14 | 6 | 10 | 51 | 42 | 48 |
| Harwich & Parkeston R. | 30 | 14 | 5 | 11 | 88 | 66 | 47 |
| Sudbury Lucas Ath +2 | 30 | 11 | 6 | 13 | 32 | 46 | 41 |
| Ipswich Wanderers Rs. | 30 | 10 | 6 | 14 | 59 | 68 | 36 |
| Rowhedge | 30 | 9 | 7 | 14 | 53 | 59 | 34 |
| Long Melford | 30 | 9 | 5 | 16 | 45 | 65 | 32 |
| Sudbury Wanderers R. | 30 | 8 | 7 | 15 | 48 | 63 | 31 |
| Royal London | 30 | 8 | 4 | 18 | 43 | 95 | 28 |
| Alresford Colne Rngrs | 30 | 6 | 5 | 19 | 41 | 85 | 23 |
| Mistley United | 30 | 5 | 5 | 20 | 31 | 77 | 20 |

## ESSEX INTERMEDIATE LEAGUE
### DIVISION ONE

| | | | | | | | |
|---|---|---|---|---|---|---|---|
| Bishop's Stortford Swifts | 22 | 14 | 6 | 2 | 64 | 22 | 34 |
| Rayleigh Town | 22 | 11 | 9 | 2 | 38 | 21 | 31 |
| Kelvedon Hatch | 22 | 12 | 6 | 4 | 37 | 19 | 30 |
| Met Police Chigwell | 22 | 13 | 4 | 5 | 33 | 23 | 30 |
| Runwell Hospital | 22 | 10 | 4 | 8 | 50 | 42 | 24 |
| Takeley | 22 | 11 | 1 | 10 | 54 | 40 | 23 |
| Frenford Senior | 22 | 9 | 5 | 8 | 37 | 31 | 23 |
| Hatfield Peverel | 22 | 8 | 5 | 9 | 42 | 43 | 21 |
| Essex Police | 22 | 8 | 5 | 9 | 29 | 35 | 21 |
| Ekco First Data | 22 | 5 | 8 | 9 | 27 | 42 | 18 |
| Writtle | 22 | 1 | 3 | 18 | 17 | 53 | 5 |
| Herongate Athletic | 22 | 1 | 2 | 19 | 18 | 75 | 4 |

## NORTH BERKSHIRE LEAGUE
### DIVISION ONE

| | | | | | | | |
|---|---|---|---|---|---|---|---|
| Saxton Rovers | 18 | 15 | 1 | 2 | 52 | 14 | 46 |
| Long Wittenham | 18 | 15 | 0 | 3 | 47 | 22 | 45 |
| Shrivenham | 18 | 11 | 3 | 4 | 50 | 25 | 36 |
| Sutton Courtenay | 18 | 8 | 3 | 7 | 40 | 42 | 27 |
| Stanford-in-the-Vale | 18 | 7 | 1 | 10 | 26 | 40 | 22 |
| Harwell International | 18 | 5 | 6 | 7 | 43 | 37 | 21 |
| Drayton | 18 | 5 | 4 | 9 | 32 | 46 | 19 |
| Faringdon Town | 18 | 4 | 4 | 10 | 30 | 40 | 16 |
| Marcham | 18 | 5 | 0 | 13 | 24 | 53 | 15 |
| Blewbury | 18 | 3 | 2 | 13 | 24 | 49 | 11 |

## AYLESBURY & DISTRICT LEAGUE
### PREMIER DIVISION

| | | | | | | | |
|---|---|---|---|---|---|---|---|
| Wing Village | 16 | 13 | 2 | 1 | 77 | 20 | 41 |
| Haddenham United | 16 | 13 | 0 | 3 | 59 | 19 | 39 |
| Bricklayers Arms | 16 | 12 | 2 | 2 | 52 | 24 | 38 |
| Wendover | 16 | 10 | 2 | 4 | 52 | 24 | 32 |
| Belgrave | 16 | 6 | 2 | 8 | 29 | 48 | 20 |
| Council Sports | 16 | 5 | 3 | 8 | 30 | 35 | 18 |
| Tring Corinthians | 16 | 4 | 2 | 10 | 23 | 32 | 14 |
| Risborough United | 16 | 1 | 1 | 14 | 19 | 75 | 4 |
| Oving SC | 16 | 1 | 0 | 15 | 11 | 75 | 3 |

## RT HARRIS OXFORD CITY FA
### PREMIER DIVISION

| | | | | | | | |
|---|---|---|---|---|---|---|---|
| Risinghurst | 18 | 15 | 2 | 1 | 92 | 24 | 32 |
| Tetsworth | 18 | 12 | 3 | 3 | 66 | 24 | 27 |
| Blackbird Leys | 18 | 13 | 1 | 4 | 76 | 42 | 27 |
| Barton | 18 | 12 | 1 | 5 | 81 | 47 | 25 |
| Great Milton | 18 | 10 | 1 | 7 | 58 | 38 | 21 |
| Fairview | 18 | 6 | 1 | 11 | 46 | 84 | 13 |
| Beckley Sports | 18 | 5 | 1 | 12 | 28 | 69 | 11 |
| Team Unipart | 18 | 5 | 0 | 13 | 44 | 68 | 10 |
| North Oxford | 18 | 4 | 0 | 14 | 46 | 85 | 8 |
| East Oxford | 18 | 3 | 0 | 15 | 35 | 98 | 6 |

## SURREY INTERMEDIATE LEAGUE (WEST)
### DIVISION ONE

| | | | | | | | |
|---|---|---|---|---|---|---|---|
| Merrow | 26 | 21 | 1 | 4 | 76 | 23 | 64 |
| Frimley Green | 26 | 19 | 0 | 7 | 92 | 33 | 57 |
| Staines Lammas | 26 | 18 | 3 | 5 | 84 | 52 | 57 |
| Lightwater United | 26 | 14 | 7 | 5 | 56 | 45 | 49 |
| Chiddingfold | 26 | 12 | 4 | 10 | 60 | 55 | 40 |
| Horsley | 26 | 9 | 7 | 10 | 48 | 53 | 34 |
| Woking Park & Horsell | 26 | 10 | 3 | 13 | 66 | 73 | 33 |
| Marconi Sports & Social | 26 | 10 | 2 | 14 | 65 | 78 | 32 |
| Tongham | 26 | 9 | 4 | 13 | 47 | 55 | 31 |
| Fairland Wanderers | 26 | 10 | 1 | 15 | 40 | 50 | 31 |
| Ockham | 26 | 9 | 3 | 14 | 52 | 51 | 30 |
| Wonersh | 26 | 7 | 4 | 15 | 55 | 82 | 25 |
| Elstead | 26 | 7 | 3 | 16 | 35 | 57 | 24 |
| Haslemere | 26 | 4 | 4 | 18 | 29 | 98 | 16 |

## SURREY SOUTH EAST COMBINATION
### INTERMEDIATE DIVISION ONE

| | | | | | | | |
|---|---|---|---|---|---|---|---|
| Worcester Park | 20 | 15 | 3 | 2 | 53 | 23 | 48 |
| Battersea Ancora | 20 | 14 | 3 | 3 | 47 | 30 | 42 |
| Godstone | 20 | 12 | 4 | 4 | 57 | 31 | 40 |
| Addington | 20 | 11 | 4 | 5 | 39 | 26 | 37 |
| Hersham RBL | 20 | 10 | 1 | 9 | 45 | 44 | 34 |
| Ashtead | 20 | 9 | 2 | 9 | 42 | 42 | 29 |
| Battersea Ironsides | 20 | 8 | 3 | 9 | 38 | 35 | 27 |
| Woodmansterne Sports | 20 | 5 | 2 | 13 | 34 | 52 | 17 |
| Oxted & District | 20 | 5 | 1 | 14 | 23 | 42 | 16 |
| Greenside | 20 | 4 | 2 | 14 | 31 | 51 | 14 |
| Coney Hall | 20 | 3 | 3 | 14 | 24 | 57 | 12 |

## LONDON INTERMEDIATE LEAGUE

| | | | | | | | |
|---|---|---|---|---|---|---|---|
| CMB Metal Box | 30 | 22 | 3 | 5 | 100 | 34 | 69 |
| Leyton County | 30 | 21 | 5 | 4 | 72 | 28 | 68 |
| Woodford Town | 30 | 20 | 5 | 5 | 103 | 38 | 65 |
| Old Roan | 30 | 18 | 5 | 7 | 96 | 50 | 59 |
| London City Athletic | 30 | 18 | 5 | 7 | 73 | 36 | 59 |
| Crown & Manor | 30 | 16 | 7 | 7 | 98 | 44 | 55 |
| Bridon Ropes | 30 | 16 | 5 | 9 | 88 | 55 | 53 |
| Cray Valley Paper Mills | 30 | 15 | 6 | 9 | 81 | 41 | 51 |
| Chestnut Trojan | 30 | 13 | 4 | 13 | 47 | 50 | 43 |
| Southwark Wanderers | 30 | 11 | 1 | 18 | 70 | 69 | 34 |
| Long Lane | 30 | 9 | 4 | 17 | 49 | 68 | 31 |
| Catford Wanderers | 30 | 8 | 4 | 18 | 47 | 97 | 28 |
| Brimsdown Rovers Res. | 30 | 6 | 7 | 17 | 41 | 82 | 25 |
| Orpington | 30 | 6 | 5 | 19 | 32 | 66 | 23 |
| Chingford Town | 30 | 5 | 4 | 21 | 35 | 96 | 19 |
| Leyton Paragon | 30 | 0 | 2 | 28 | 21 | 199 | 2 |

Lindfield FC - 100 years old.
Three former Brighton players in line up: Gerry Ryan, Neil Smillie, Andy Rowings. Chairman David Selves has the ball!
Photo: Eric Marsh

# COUNTY
# F.A.
# SECTION

*Langford FC (Minerva Spartan South Midlands League). Winners of the North Bedfordshire Charity Cup*
*Photo: Gordon Whittington*

# BEDFORDSHIRE F.A.

Tel: 01582 476163 (H)   01582 565111 (B)   Fax: 01582 565222
Century House, Skimpot Road, Dunstable LU5 4JU
**Secretary:** Peter D Brown
**Executives (Responsibility)**   Century House for
Coaching Exams/Courses, Referees, Womens Football
**Number of Affiliated Clubs**   Senior:   385   U.18:   110   **President:** K Williamson
**Number of Affiliated Leagues:** Senior:   12   Junior:   4   **Chairman:** Ray Berridge
**County Representative Teams:** Senior, U18, U16
**Inter County Competitions:**   East Anglia Counties Intermediate, East Midlands Youth, FA County Youth Cup

## BEDFORDSHIRE PREMIER CUP 1998-99
(14 entries)   (FOUNDED 1894-95)

**LAST SEASON'S FINAL:** Brache Sparta v Bedford Town  1-0
**MOST WINS:** Waterlows  10   Dunstable  9   Luton Clarence  8

**FIRST ROUND** (6 matches)

| | | | | | | | |
|---|---|---|---|---|---|---|---|
| Arlesey Town | v | Shillington | 4*3 | Langford | v | Kempston Rovers | 0-1 |
| Barton Rovers | v | Potton United | 6-0 | Wootton Blue Cross | v | Bedford Town | 2-3 |
| Bedford United | v | Leighton Town | 1-2 | Brache Sparta | v | Luton Town | 0-8 |

**SECOND ROUND** (4 matches)

| | | | | | | | |
|---|---|---|---|---|---|---|---|
| Sotfold | v | Arlesey Town | | Barton Rovers | v | Biggleswade Town | |
| Bedford Town | v | Leighton Town | | Kempston Rovers | v | Luton Town | 0-3 |

**SEMI-FINALS**

| | | | | | | | |
|---|---|---|---|---|---|---|---|
| Stotfold | v | Leighton Town | 1-0 | Biggleswade Town | v | Luton Town | 1-2 |

**FINAL**

| | | | | |
|---|---|---|---|---|
| STOTFOLD | v | LUTON TOWN | 2-1 | at Arlesey Town FC |

## BEDFORDSHIRE SENIOR CUP 1998-99
(19 entries)

**LAST SEASON'S FINAL:** Barton Rovers v Potton United  4-1

**PRELIMINARY ROUND** (3 matches)

| | | | | | | | |
|---|---|---|---|---|---|---|---|
| Biggleswade Town | v | Leighton Town | 4-6 | Caddington | v | Potton United | 3-1 |
| Houghton Town | v | Toddington Rovers | 1*3 | | | | |

**FIRST ROUND** (8 matches)

| | | | | | | | |
|---|---|---|---|---|---|---|---|
| Kempston Rovers | v | Tottenhoe | 1-2 | Wootton Blue Cross | v | Barton Rovers | 2-3 |
| Bedford Town | v | Stotfold | 3-2 | Shillington | v | Langford | 2-1 |
| Bedford United | v | Arlesey Town | 4-3 | Toddington Rovers | v | Biggleswade United | 0-1 |
| Caddington | v | Brache Sparta | 1-4 | Luton Old Boys | v | Leighton Town | 0-3 |

**SECOND ROUND** (4 matches)

| | | | | | | | |
|---|---|---|---|---|---|---|---|
| Barton Rovers | v | Bedford United | 2-0 | Brache Sparta | v | Leighton Town | 2-3 |
| Bedford Town | v | Biggleswade United | 4*3 | Tottenhoe | v | Shillington | 1-0 |

**SEMI-FINALS**

| | | | | | | | |
|---|---|---|---|---|---|---|---|
| Barton Rovers | v | Leighton Town | 5-1 | Totternhoe | v | Bedford Tn (at BT) | 1*1, 2-4 |

**FINAL**

| | | | | |
|---|---|---|---|---|
| BARTON ROVERS | v | BEDFORD TOWN | 3-0 | at Bedford Town FC |

Maidenhead United - Berks & Bucks Senior Cup Winners 1998-99    Photo: Paul Dennis LRPS

# BERKS & BUCKS F.A.

Tel: 01367 242099   Fax: 01367 242158

15a London Street, Faringdon, Oxon SN7 7HD

**Secretary:** Brian Moore          **Press Officer:** R G Woolman

**Executives (Responsibility)**     J Kelman (Coaching Exams/Courses)

                                    R J Claridge (Referees)

                                    A Glenny (Womens Football)

**Number of Affiliated Leagues:** Senior:   19     Junior:   13          **President:** D J Frost

**County Representative Teams:** U18, U16 Girls, U14 Girls          **Chairman:** J A Christopher

**Inter County Competitions:**   South/South West Counties Championship Youth

---

## BERKS & BUCKS SENIOR CUP 1998-99
### (18 entries)  (FOUNDED 1878-79)

**LAST SEASON'S FINAL:** Maidenhead United v Reading 2-1

**MOST WINS:** Wycombe  24   Maidenhead United  16   Marlow  13

**SECOND QUALIFYING ROUND** (2 matches)

| | | | | | | | |
|---|---|---|---|---|---|---|---|
| Slough Town | v | Burnham | 1-3 | Beaconsfield SYCOB | v | Hungerford Town | 1*1 3-6 |

**FIRST ROUND** (8 matches)

| | | | | | | | |
|---|---|---|---|---|---|---|---|
| Maidenhead United | v | Bracknell Town | 3-1 | Wycombe Wanderers | v | Chalfont St Peter | 3-0 |
| Marlow | v | Buckingham Town | 4-1 | Abingdon Town | v | Chesham United | 1-5 |
| Slough T/Burnham | v | Reading | 1-5 | Aylesbury United | v | Wokingham Town | 0-1 |
| Thatcham Town | v | Hungerford Town | 1-2 | Flackwell Heath | v | Windsor & Eton | 1-2 |

**SECOND ROUND** (4 matches)

| | | | | | | | |
|---|---|---|---|---|---|---|---|
| Marlow | v | Wycombe Wanderers | 0-2 | Chesham United | v | Reading | 2-1 |
| Wokingham Town | v | Windsor & Eton | 1-3 | Hungerford Town | v | Maidenhead United | 1-2 |

**SEMI-FINALS**

| | | | | | | | |
|---|---|---|---|---|---|---|---|
| Windsor & Eton | v | Maidenhead United | 1-3 | Wycombe Wanderers | v | Chesham United | 4-0 |

**FINAL**

| | | | |
|---|---|---|---|
| MAIDENHEAD UTD | v | WYCOMBE WNDRS 4*1 | at Chesham United FC |

---

## BERKS & BUCKS SENIOR TROPHY 1998-99
### (26 entries)

**LAST SEASON'S FINAL:** Abingdon United v Finchampstead 1-0

**SECOND QUALIFYING ROUND** (10 matches)

| | | | | | | | |
|---|---|---|---|---|---|---|---|
| New Bradwell St P. | v | Newport Pagnell Tn | 3-2 | Amersham Town | v | Eton Wick | 0-1 |
| Didcot Town | v | Stony Stratford Town | 2-0 | Milton Keynes City | v | Holmer Green | 0-3 |
| Penn & Tylers Green | v | Winslow United | 3-1 | Wantage Town | v | Risborough Rangers | 2-1 |
| Reading Town | v | Stocklake S & SC | 3-0 | Kintbury Rangers | v | Binfield | 2-3 |
| Milton United | v | Wallingford | 4-1 | Prestwood | v | Newbury | 1-9 |

**FIRST ROUND** (8 matches)

| | | | | | | | |
|---|---|---|---|---|---|---|---|
| Eton Wick | v | Penn & Tylers Green | 4-1 | Milton Keynes | v | Newbury | @N 0-4 |
| Abingdon United | v | Milton United | 2-4 | Buckingham Athletic | v | Olney Town | 2*3 |
| Didcot Town | v | Holmer Green | 0-1 | New Bradwell St P. | v | Binfield | 3-4 |
| Wantage Town | v | Sandhurst Town | 0-5 | Reading Town | v | Finchampstead | 0-1 |

**SECOND ROUND** (4 matches)

| | | | | | | | |
|---|---|---|---|---|---|---|---|
| Binfield | v | Sandhurst Town | 1-2 | Newbury | v | Finchampstead | 2-1 |
| Milton United | v | Eton Wick | 0*1 | Holmer Green | v | Olney Town | 3-2 |

**SEMI-FINALS**

| | | | | | | | |
|---|---|---|---|---|---|---|---|
| Holmer Green | v | Newbury | 3-2 | Sandhurst Town | v | Eton Wick | 0-4 |

**FINAL**

| | | | |
|---|---|---|---|
| ETON WICK | v | HOLMER GREEN 1-0 | at AFC Newbury. |

# BIRMINGHAM COUNTY F.A.

Tel: 0121 357 4278   Fax: 0121 358 1661
Ray Hall Lane, Great Barr, Birmingham B43 6JF
**Secretary & Press Officer:**      M Pennick F.F.A.
**Executives (Responsibility)**     T Stack (Coaching Exams/Courses, Womens Football)
                                    G J Southall (Referees)
**Number of Affiliated Clubs**      Senior:   1,685          U.18:      349          **President:** J K Horrocks
**Number of Affiliated Leagues:**   Senior:      54          Junior:      8          **Chairman:** R J Hood
**County Representative Teams:** Senior, U18, U15, Womens, U18, U15
**Inter County Competitions:**      FA County Youth, Midland County Youth (including Mitre Trophy)

## BIRMINGHAM SENIOR CUP 1998-99
### (42 entries)   (FOUNDED 1875-76)

**LAST SEASON'S FINAL:** Halesowen Town  v  Redditch United  3-1

**MOST WINS:** Aston Villa  19    Birmingham City  8
Kidderminster Harriers  7    Wolverhampton Wanderers  7

**FIRST ROUND** (10 matches)

| | | | | | | | |
|---|---|---|---|---|---|---|---|
| West Midland Police | v | Highgate United | 5-1 | Burton Albion | v | Stratford Town | 0-0 2-1 |
| Worcester City | v | Dudley Town | 3-1 | Bedworth United | v | V S Rugby | 4-1 |
| Banbury United | v | Darlaston Town | 1-1 3-4 | Halesowen Harriers | v | Kings Norton Town | 2-3 |
| Sandwell Borough | v | Gornal Athletic | 1-0 | Cradley Town | v | Wednesfield | 1-2 |
| Sutton Coldfield Tn | v | Bolehall Swifts | 0-1 | Oldbury United | v | Evesham United | 1-2 |

**SECOND ROUND** (16matches)

| | | | | | | | |
|---|---|---|---|---|---|---|---|
| Evesham United | v | Hednesford Town | 1-2 | Burton Albion | v | Kings Norton Town | 1-4 |
| Atherstone United | v | Paget Rangers | 1-1 1-2 | Boldmere St Mcls | v | Lye Town | 1-3 |
| Studley BKL | v | Brierley Hill Town | 2-3 | West Midlands Police | v | Birmingham City | 0-4 |
| Racing Warwick | v | West Brom. Alb. | 0-0 0-1 | Worcester City | v | Walsall | 1-0 |
| Tamworth | v | Bedfworth United | 2-0 | Darlaston Town | v | Redditch United | 0-4 |
| Sandwell Boro | v | Wolverhampton Wdrs | 1-4 | Solihull Borough | v | Wednesfield | 6-1 |
| Bolehall Ssifts | v | Tividale | 2-1 | Moor Green | v | Nuneaton Borough | 2-5 |
| Kings Heath | v | Stourbridge | 1-3 | Willenhall Town | v | Halesowen Town | 0-2 |

**THIRD ROUND** (8 matches)

| | | | | | | | |
|---|---|---|---|---|---|---|---|
| Redditch United | v | Solihull Borough | 0-2 | Bolehall Swifts | v | Hednesford Town | 0-2 |
| Nuneaton Borough | v | Stourbridge | 2-1 | Paget Rangers | v | Brierley Hill Town | 2-1 |
| Lye Town | v | Birmingham City | 0-4 | West Bromwich Alb. | v | Worcester City | 0-2 |
| Halesowen Town | v | Wolverhampton Wdrs | 1-2 | Kings Norton Town | v | Tamworth (at T) | 1-4 |

**FOURTH ROUND** (4 matches)

| | | | | | | | |
|---|---|---|---|---|---|---|---|
| Solihull Borough | v | Worcester C (at WC) | 2-5 | Tamworth | v | Birmingham City | 0-4 |
| Hednesford Town | v | Nuneaton Borough | 2-0 | Paget Rangers | v | Wolverhampton Wdrs | 1-2 |

**SEMI-FINALS**

| | | | | | | | |
|---|---|---|---|---|---|---|---|
| Birmingham City | v | Worcester C (at WC) | 3-1 | Hednesford Town | v | Wolverhampton Wdrs | 0-5 |

**FINAL**

BIRMINGHAM CITY  v   WOLVERHAMPTON W  4-1       at St Andrews, Birmingham City FC

# CAMBRIDGESHIRE F.A.

Tel: 01223 576770   Fax: 01223 576780

3 Signet Court, Swanns Road, Cambridge CB5 8LA

**Secretary:** Roger Pawley

**Executives (Responsibility)**   B G Manley (Coaching Exams/Courses
                                   Referees, Womens Football)

**Number of Affiliated Clubs**   Senior:   350      U.18:       50

**Number of Affiliated Leagues:** Senior:    1       Junior:      6

**County Representative Teams:** Senior, U18, U16, Womens

**Inter County Competitions:**   East Anglian Counties

**President:** W W Ashton

**Chairman:** J W Coad

---

## CAMBRIDGESHIRE INVITATION CUP 1998-99
(12 entries)  (FOUNDED 1950-51)

**LAST SEASON'S FINAL:** Soham Town Rangers  v  Wisbech Town  3-0

**MOST WINS:** Wisbech Town  9    Cambridge City  8    Chatteris Town  7

**FIRST ROUND** (4 matches)

| | | | | | | | | |
|---|---|---|---|---|---|---|---|---|
| Ely City | v | Great Shelford | 0-1 | | Mildenhall Town | v | Over Sports | 0-2 |
| Warboys Town | v | Whittlesey United 4*4 | 3-0 | | Wisbech Town | v | Histon | 3-1 |

**SECOND ROUND** (4 matches)

| | | | | | | | | |
|---|---|---|---|---|---|---|---|---|
| March Town United | v | Oversports | 1-3 | | Newmarket Town | v | Great Shelford | 3-1 |
| Wisbech Town | v | Soham Town Rangers | 2-3 | | Warboys Town | v | Chatteris Town | 1-0 |

**SEMI-FINALS**

| | | | | | | | | |
|---|---|---|---|---|---|---|---|---|
| Over Sports | v | Newmarket Town | 0-1 | | Warboys Town | v | Soham Town Rangers | 4-5 |

**FINAL**

NEWMARKET TN   v   SOHAM TN RGRS   2-3     at Abbey Stadium, Cambridge United FC

# CHESHIRE F.A.

Tel: 01606 871166   Fax: 01606 871292
The Cottage, Moss Farm Recreation Centre, Winnington, Northwich CW8 4BG

| | |
|---|---|
| **Secretary & Press Officer:** | Maureen J Dunford |
| **Executives (Responsibility)** | Sheila Goulden (Coaching Exams/Courses) |
| | Bob Cooper (Referees) |
| | Anita Gore (Women's Football) |

**Number of Affiliated Clubs**    Senior:    816         U.18:        271        **President:** Alan Burbidge
**Number of Affiliated Leagues:** Senior:    27       Junior:        13
**County Representative Teams:** U18 (Womens/Girls teams for 1999-2000)
**Inter County Competitions:**    FA County Youth, Northern Counties Youth Cup, Northern Counties Ladies Cup

## CHESHIRE SENIOR CUP 1998-99
### (17 entries)   (FOUNDED 1879-80)

**LAST SEASON'S FINAL:** Macclesfield Town   v   Runcorn  1-0
**MOST WINS:** Macclesfield Town  19    Northwich Victoria  16    Crewe Alexandra  12    Runcorn  12

**PRELIMINARY ROUND** (1 match)

| 1 Warrington Town | v | Woodley Sports | 1*2 | | | |
|---|---|---|---|---|---|---|

**FIRST ROUND** (8 matches)

| Woodley Sports | v | Runcorn (at R) | 2-3 | Congleton Town | v | Stalybridge Celtic | 1-4 |
|---|---|---|---|---|---|---|---|
| Hyde United | v | Nantwich Town | 5-1 | Witton Albion | v | Crewe Alexandra | 1-2 |
| Cheadle Town | v | Northwich Victoria | 0-2 | Winsford United | v | Altrincham | 1-2 |
| Tranmere Rovers | v | Chester City | 0-1 | Macclesfield Town | v | Vauxhall GM | 5-0 |

**SECOND ROUND** (4 matches)

| Altrincham | v | Chester City | 3-0 | Runcorn | v | Macclesfield Town | 4*2 |
|---|---|---|---|---|---|---|---|
| Stalybridge Celtic | v | Hyde United | 1*2 | Crewe Alexandra | v | Northwich Victoria | 1-6 |

**SEMI-FINALS**

| Runcorn | v | Northwich Victoria | 1-2 | Altrincham | v | Hyde United (at HU) | 1-0 |
|---|---|---|---|---|---|---|---|

**FINAL**

| ALTRINCHAM | v | NORTHWICH VIC. | 1-0 | at Witton Albion FC |
|---|---|---|---|---|

## CHESHIRE AMATEUR CUP 1998-99
### (FOUNDED 1886-87)

**LAST SEASON'S FINAL:**  Ashville   v Poulton Victoria  3-2
**MOST WINS:**  ICI Alkali  9    Cammell Laird  6    Poulton Victoria  6

**THIRD ROUND** (8 matches)

| Barnton | v | Grove United | | BICC Helsby | v | Pavillions | 5-4 |
|---|---|---|---|---|---|---|---|
| Broadheath Central | v | Poulton Vicoria | 3-3 0-4 | Castrol Social | v | Blacon Athletic | 3-1 |
| Middlewich Town | v | Vauxhalls | 2-1 | Newton | v | Christleton | 1-2 |
| Shell | v | Linotype | 2-4 | Stork | v | Ashville | 1-2 |

**FOURTH ROUND** (4 matches)

| Barnton | v | Castrol Social | 1-0 | BICC Helsby | v | Ashville | 1-2 |
|---|---|---|---|---|---|---|---|
| Christleton | v | Poulton Victoria | 0-3 | Linotype | v | Middlewich Town | |

**SEMI-FINALS**

| Barnton | v | Ashville | 2-1 | Poulton Victoria | v | Linotype | 3-1 |
|---|---|---|---|---|---|---|---|

**FINAL**

| POULTON VIC. | v | BARNTON | 1-0 | at Vauxhall GM FC |
|---|---|---|---|---|

# CORNWALL F.A.

Tel: 01726 74080   Fax: 01726 69288
1 High Cross Street, St Austell, Cornwall PL25 4AB
**Secretary:** Barry Cudmore
**Executives (Responsibility)**   John Riley (Coaching Exams/Courses)
Ian Anear (Referees)

| | | | | | |
|---|---|---|---|---|---|
| **Number of Affiliated Clubs** | Senior: | 341 | U.18: | 84 | **President:** R C Roberts |
| **Number of Affiliated Leagues:** | Senior: | 14 | Junior: | 3 | **Chairman:** D G Champion |

**County Representative Teams:** Senior, Youth U18
**Inter County Competitions:**   South West Counties Senior & Youth, FA County Youth Cup

## CORNWALL SENIOR CUP 1998-99
### (41 entries)   (FOUNDED 1892-93)

**LAST SEASON'S FINAL:** Porthleven  v  Truro City   2-2, 2-3

**MOST WINS:** Truro City   12     St Austell   11
Penzance   10     St Blazey   10     Torpoint Athletic   10

### FIRST ROUND (9 matches)

| | | | | | | | | |
|---|---|---|---|---|---|---|---|---|
| Callington Town | v | Sticker | 5-0 | | Goonhaven | v | St Ives Town | 1-2 |
| Helston Athletic | v | Penryn Athletic | 2-2 3-2 | | Illogan RBL | v | Troon | 2-3 |
| Marazion Blues | v | Wendron | 1-1 2-4 | | Padstow United | v | St Just | 2-5 |
| Roche | v | Ludgvan | 3-1 | | St Cleer | v | Mousehole | 2-2 0-2 |
| St Dennis | v | ~~Kelly Bray Athletic~~ | ~~3-0~~ | | | | | |

### SECOND ROUND (16 matches)

| | | | | | | | | |
|---|---|---|---|---|---|---|---|---|
| Callington Town | v | RNAS Culdrose | 3-1 | | Camelford | v | St Breward | 1-1 3-2 |
| Foxhole Stars | v | Bodmin Town | 0-4 | | Launceston | v | St Just | 1-2 |
| Millbrook | v | Falmouth Town | 3-1 | | Nanpean Rovers | v | Newquay | 0-1 |
| Penzance | v | Bude Town | 4-1 | | Perranwell | v | Liskeard Athletic | 2-0 |
| Roche | v | Mousehole | 7-3 | | St Austell | v | Saltash United | 1-6 |
| St Dennis | v | Mullion | 4-2 | | St Ives Town | v | Porthleven | 0-4 |
| Torpoint Athletic | v | St Agnes | 6-1 | | Troon | v | Helston Athletic | 1-2 |
| Truro City | v | Wadebridge Town | 2-3 | | Wendron | v | St Blazey | 0-12 |

### THIRD ROUND (8 matches)

| | | | | | | | | |
|---|---|---|---|---|---|---|---|---|
| Bodmin Town | v | St Just | 9-0 | | Camelford | v | Helston Athletic | 4-1 |
| Millbrook | v | Callington Town | 4-1 | | Penzance | v | Wadebridge Town | 3-2 |
| Porthleven | v | Newquay | 7-1 | | St Blazey | v | Perranwell | 7-2 |
| St Dennis | v | Roche | 4-1 | | Torpoint Athletic | v | Saltash United | 0-2 |

### QUARTER-FINALS

| | | | | | | | | |
|---|---|---|---|---|---|---|---|---|
| Bodmin Town | v | St Dennis | 6-2 | | Millbrook | v | Camelford | 1-0 |
| Porthleven | v | Saltash United | 2-1 | | St Blazey | v | Penzance | 1-1 5-2 |

### SEMI-FINALS

| | | | | | |
|---|---|---|---|---|---|
| Bodmin Town | v | Porthleven | 2-1 | | at Truro City FC |
| Millbrook | v | St Blazey | 2-1 | | at Bodmin Town |

### FINAL

# CUMBERLAND F.A.

Tel: 01900 872310   Fax: 01900 872310
17 Oxford Street, Workington, Cumbria CA14 2AL

| | |
|---|---|
| **Secretary & Press Officer:** | Albert Murphy |
| **Executives (Responsibility)** | Peter Hampton & Keith Hunton (Coaching Exams/Courses) |
| | Harry Upton & Thomas Jackson (Referees) |

**Number of Affiliated Clubs**   Senior:   187       U.18:       162       **President:** Brian Taylor
**Number of Affiliated Leagues:**  Senior:     8       Junior:       4       **Chairman:** Maurice Perkins
**County Representative Teams:** Senior, Youth, Womens
**Inter County Competitions:**   FA County Youth

## CUMBERLAND SENIOR CUP 1998-99
(38 entries)   (FOUNDED 1960-61)

**LAST SEASON'S FINAL:**  Carlisle City  v  Windscale  1-2

**MOST WINS:**  Penrith  10    Gretna  9    Haig Colliery  3

**FIRST ROUND** (6 matches)

| | | | | | | | |
|---|---|---|---|---|---|---|---|
| Longtown | v | St Bees | 4-1 | Silloth | v | Abbeytown | 1-2 |
| Windscale(wc) | v | Hearts of Liddlesdale | 2-1 | Langwathby | v | Carlisle United | 1-0 |
| Wetheriggs United | v | Windscale(w) | 4*3 | British Steel | v | Workington | 3-5 |

**SECOND ROUND** (16 matches)

| | | | | | | | |
|---|---|---|---|---|---|---|---|
| Sporting Museum | v | Dalston Athletic | 9-1 | Penrith | v | Workington | 1-2 |
| Carleton Rovers | v | Greystoke | 2-3 | Egremont St Mary's | v | Abbeytown | 1-4 |
| Whitehaven AFC(w) | v | Cockermouth | 2-1 | Gretna | v | Cleator Moor Celtic(wc) | 9-0 |
| Langwathby | v | Northbank Res(cd) | 1-0 | Wetheriggs United | v | Alston Town | 6-0 |
| Frizington White Star | v | Braithewaite | 4-0 | Cleator Mr Celtic(cd) | v | Windscale(wc) | 6-2 |
| Kirkoswald | v | Whitehaven MW(wc) | 3-2 | Northbank(na) | v | Whitehaven MW(cd) | 6-0 |
| Wigton Harriers | v | Whitehaven AFC(wc) | 9-0 | Penrith Rangers | v | Carlisle City(na) | 0-5 |
| Keswick | v | Parton United | 4-2 | Longtown | v | Mirehouse Comm. FC | 1-2 |

**THIRD ROUND** (8 matches)

| | | | | | | | | |
|---|---|---|---|---|---|---|---|---|
| Carlisle City | v | Kirkoswald | 3-0 | Wigton Harriers | v | Langwathby | | 6-1 |
| Whitehaven AFC(w) | v | Cleator Mr Celtic(cd) | 1-2 | Wetheriggs United | v | Northbank | | 3-1 |
| Frizington White Star | v | Greystoke | 1-0 | Keswick | v | Abbeytown | 1*1 | 1-4 |
| Sporting Museum | v | Gretna | 1-0 | Mirehouse Com. FC | v | Workington | | 2-3 |

**FOURTH ROUND** (4 matches)

| | | | | | | | |
|---|---|---|---|---|---|---|---|
| Cleator Mr Celtic(cd) | v | Workington | 2-0 | Abbeytown | v | Sporting Museum | 3-2 |
| Frizington White Star | v | Wetheriggs United | 2-1 | Wigton Harriers | v | Carlisle City | 1-3 |

**SEMI-FINALS**

| | | | | | | | |
|---|---|---|---|---|---|---|---|
| Carlisle City | v | Frizington White Star | 4-0 | Cleator Moor Celtic | v | Abbeytown | 4-3 |

**FINAL**

| | | | | | |
|---|---|---|---|---|---|
| CARLISLE CITY | v | CLEATOR MOOR C. | 1*1 | at Southend Road, Penrith FC |
| **REPLAY** | | | | | |
| CARLISLE CITY | v | CLEATOR MOOR C. | 2-4 | at Borough Park, Workington FC |

# DERBYSHIRE F.A.

Tel: 01332 361422   Fax: 01332 360130
The Grandstand, Moorways Stadium, Moor Lane, Derby DE2 8FB
**Secretary & Press Officer:**   K Compton
**Executives (Responsibility)**   County Secretary
   (Coaching Exams/Courses, Referees, Womens Football)
**Number of Affiliated Clubs**   Senior:   620      U.18:   220      **President:** A Brough
**Number of Affiliated Leagues:** Senior:   15      Junior:   5      **Chairman:** R F Johnson
**County Representative Teams:** U16
**Inter County Competitions:**   East Midlands Youth Football Combination

## DERBYSHIRE SENIOR CUP 1998-99
(24 entries)   (FOUNDED 1883-84)

**LAST SEASON'S FINAL:** Matlock Town  v  Glapwell  1-2

**MOST WINS:** Derby County  15    Ilkeston Town  11
Buxton  8    Chesterfield  8    Heanor Town  8

**FIRST ROUND** (3 matches)

| | | | | | | | | |
|---|---|---|---|---|---|---|---|---|
| Heanor Town | v | Stanton Ilkeston | 6-3 | | Blackwell M W | v | Long Eaton Utd | 1-1 0-3 |
| Graham St Prims | v | Shardlow St James | 1-1 0-1 | | | | | |

**SECOND ROUND** (5 matches)

| | | | | | | | | |
|---|---|---|---|---|---|---|---|---|
| Holbrook | v | Sandiacre Town | 0-1 | | Shirebrook Town | v | Long Eaton United | 1-2 |
| Mickleover Sports | v | Sheepbridge | MS W-O | | South Normanton A | v | Shardlow St James | 3-1 |
| Mickleover RBL | v | Heanor Town | 1-6 | | | | | |

**THIRD ROUND** (8 matches)

| | | | | | | | | |
|---|---|---|---|---|---|---|---|---|
| South Normanton A | v | Belper Town | 0-1 | | Buxton | v | Ilkeston Town | 1-2 |
| Borrowash Victoria | v | Alfreton Town | 1-3 | | Glapwell | v | Mickleover Sports | 6-4 |
| Town | v | Long Eaton Utd | 0-0 3-2 | | Matlock Town | v | Glossop North End | 3-1 |
| Stapenhill | v | Gresley Rovers | 2-3 | | Staveley MW | v | Sandiacre Town | 0-0 0-3 |

**QUARTER-FINALS**

| | | | | | | | | |
|---|---|---|---|---|---|---|---|---|
| Gresley Rovers | v | Sandiacre Town | 1-0 | | Matlock Town | v | Glapwell | 1-1 1-0 |
| Heanor Town | v | Belper Town | 0-0 0-7 | | Ilkeston Town | v | Alfreton Town | 3-1 |

**SEMI-FINALS**

| | | | | | | | |
|---|---|---|---|---|---|---|---|
| Ilkeston Town | v | Gresley Rovers | 1-0 | | Belper Town | v | Matlock Town | 2-1 |

**FINAL** (Two Legs)

| | | | |
|---|---|---|---|
| ILKESTON TOWN | v | BELPER TOWN | 3rd August |
| BELPER TOWN | v | ILKESTON TOWN | 10th August |

# DEVON F.A.

Tel: 01626 332077   Fax: 01626 336814
County Headquarters, Coach Road, Newton Abbot, Devon TQ12 1EJ
**Secretary & Press Officer:**   Chris J Davidson
**Executives (Responsibility)**   R Soper (Coaching Exams)   C Cox (Referees)
M Lawrence (Womens Football)   C Davey (Coaching Courses)
**Number of Affiliated Clubs**   Senior:   161       U.18:      252
**Number of Affiliated Leagues:** Senior:   50       Junior:    10       **Chairman:** Brian Williams
**County Representative Teams:** Senior, U18, Womens
**Inter County Competitions:**   South West Counties Championship
**County Publications:**   "Kick Off" - bi-monthly Newsletter

## DEVON ST LUKES BOWL 1998-99
### (13 entries)

**LAST SEASON'S FINAL:** Torquay United  v  Exeter City  1-0

**MOST WINS:** Tiverton Town  7    Bideford  3    Exmouth Town  3

### FIRST ROUND (5 matches)

| | | | | | | | |
|---|---|---|---|---|---|---|---|
| Ilfracombe Town | v | Tiverton Town | 0-3 | Clyst Rovers | v | Torrington Town | 1-2 |
| Barnstaple Town | v | Exeter City | 0-2 | Heavitree United | v | Plymouth Argyle | 1-7 |
| Elmore | v | Torquay United | 4-3 | | | | |

### QUARTER-FINALS

| | | | | | | | |
|---|---|---|---|---|---|---|---|
| Tiverton Town | v | Torrington | 4-1 | Bideford | v | Exeter City | 0-6 |
| Exmouth Town | v | Plymouth Argyle | 2*4 | Dawlish Town | v | Elmore | 0-1 |

### SEMI-FINAL

| | | | | | | | |
|---|---|---|---|---|---|---|---|
| Plymouth Argyle | v | Elmore | 3-1 | Tiverton Town | v | Exeter City | 3-5 |

### FINAL

EXETER CITY   v   PLYMOUTH ARGYLE  0-1       at St James Park, Exeter City FC.

*Devon County FA Headquarters*

# DORSET F.A.

Tel: 01202 682375   Fax: 01202 666577

County Ground, Blandford Close, Hamworthy, Poole BH15 4BF

**Secretary:** P S Hough          **Press Officer:** I Hallett

**Executives (Responsibility)**      Mrs S A Hough (Coaching Exams/Courses,
                                                        Womens Football)

                                    R J Bale (Referees)

**County Representative Teams:** Senior, Womens, Under 18          **President:** S D Miles

**Inter County Competitions:**      South West Championship Senior, Womens, Youth          **Chairman:** G Pike

---

## DORSET SENIOR CUP 1998-99
### (35 entries)   (FOUNDED 1887-88)

**LAST SEASON'S FINAL:** Poole Town  v  Hamworthy United  2-1

**MOST WINS:** Weymouth  25    Poole Town  10    Portland United  10    Bridport  9

**FIRST ROUND** (6 matches)

| | | | | | | | |
|---|---|---|---|---|---|---|---|
| Beaminster | v | EP Victoria Sports | 3-2 | Okeford United | v | Lytchett Red Triangle | 4-2 |
| Broadmayne | v | Witchampton Utd | 1-1 3-1 | Dorset Knob | v | Stourpayne | 1-1 1-3 |
| St Mary's RC | v | Dorchester YMCA | 1-4 | Moreton | v | Dorchester United | 1-3 |

**SECOND ROUND** (13 matches)

| | | | | | | | |
|---|---|---|---|---|---|---|---|
| Allendale | v | Blandford United | 1-4 | Broadmayne | v | Beaminster | 2-4 |
| Dorchester United | v | Bournemouth Sports | 3-1 | Hamworthy EFC | v | Verwood Town | 8-2 |
| Hamworthy United | v | Okeford United | 1-2 | Northerners Ath | v | Flight Refuel. | 2p4 1-1 0*0 |
| Sturminster Marshall | v | Sherborne Town | 2-2 1-3 | Sturm. Newton Utd | v | Gillingham Tn | 1-1 5-2 |
| Swanage T & Herst. | v | St Pauls Jersey | 1-3 | Wareham Rangers | v | Shaftsbury | 1-1 3-1 |
| Weymouth Sports | v | Stourpaine | 2-0 | Dorchester YMCA | v | Parley Sports | 0-8 |
| Portland United | v | Poole Town | 2-2 1-3 | | | | |

**THIRD ROUND** (8 matches)

| | | | | | | | |
|---|---|---|---|---|---|---|---|
| Weymouth Sports | v | Sherborne Town | 0*0 4-2 | Okeford United | v | Sturminster Newton U | 0-2 |
| Weymouth | v | Poole Town | 1-0 | Bridport | v | Dorchester United | 2-1 |
| Hamworthy EFC | v | Flight Refuelling | 2-1 | St Pauls | v | Blandford United | 1-0 |
| Wimborne Town | v | Beaminster | 5-0 | Parley Sports | v | Wareham Rangers | 4-0 |

**FOURTH ROUND** (4 matches)

| | | | | | | | |
|---|---|---|---|---|---|---|---|
| Weymouth | v | Bridport | 1-0 | Parley Sports | v | Wimborne Town | 2-4 |
| St Pauls | v | Sturminster Newton U | 3-1 | Weymouth Sports | v | Hamworthy EFC | 1-3 |

**SEMI-FINALS**

| | | | | | | | |
|---|---|---|---|---|---|---|---|
| Wimborne Town | v | St Pauls Jersey | 4-0 | Hamworthy EFC | v | Weymouth | 1-4 |

**FINAL**

| | | | | |
|---|---|---|---|---|
| WEYMOUTH | v | WIMBORNE TOWN | 4-1 | at Dorchester Town FC Att; 452 |

# DURHAM F.A.

Tel: 0191 384 8653   Fax: 0191 384 3234
"Codeslaw", Ferens Park, Durham DH1 1JZ
**Secretary:** John Topping
**Executives (Responsibility)**   A Philliskirk (Coaching Exams/Courses)
                                  J C Topping (Referees)
**Number of Affiliated Clubs**   Senior:   1040       Junior:   5        **President:** F D Patterson
**Number of Affiliated Leagues:** Senior:   45        Junior:   5        **Chairman:** F D Patterson
**County Representative Teams:** U18
**Inter County Competitions:**   Association of Northern Counties, FA County Youth

## DURHAM CHALLENGE CUP 1998-99
(46 entries)   (FOUNDED 1883-84)

**LAST SEASON'S FINAL:** Hartlepool United 'A'   v   Spennymoor United   2-1

**MOST WINS:** Sunderland   21     Spennymoor United   15     Bishop Auckland   14

**PRELIMINARY ROUND** (14 matches)

| | | | | | | | |
|---|---|---|---|---|---|---|---|
| Annfield Plain | v | Hebburn | 2-4 | South Shields | v | Shildon | 5-1 |
| Chester le Street Tn | v | Murton | 5-0 | Silksworth CA | v | Cleadon SC | 4-3 |
| Wolviston | v | Whickham | 1-0 | Ryhope CA | v | Norton & Stock. Anc. | 0-4 |
| Washington Nissan | v | Jarrow Roofing BCA | 4*2 | Seaham Red Star | v | Billingham Synthonia | 1-2 |
| Billingham Town | v | Esh Winning | 0-2 | Harton & Westoe | v | Jarrow | 1-2 |
| Wash. Ikeda Hoover | v | Shotton Comrades | 1-3 | Stanley United | v | Horden C W Athletic | 2-1 |
| West Auckland Town | v | Willington | 3-0 | Crook Town | v | Horden C W | 5-1 |

**FIRST ROUND** (16 matches)

| | | | | | | | |
|---|---|---|---|---|---|---|---|
| Spennymoor United | v | Silksworth CA | 5-2 | Boldon CA | v | Crook Town | 1-0 |
| Jarrow | v | Consett | 1-5 | Hartlepool BW OB | v | Billingham Synthonia | 1-0 |
| Bishop Auckland | v | Esh Winning | 9-3 | Easington Colliery | v | Sunderland Roker | 8-0 |
| Dunston F B | v | Shotton Comrades | 3-1 | Wolviston | v | Peterlee Newtown | 0-0 0-3 |
| Chester le Street Tn | v | Tow Law Town | 3-2 | Cockfield | v | Brandon United | 1-5 |
| Eppleton C W | v | West Auckland Town | 0-8 | Hebburn | v | Norton & Stock. Anc. | 2-4 |
| Durham City | v | Washington Nissan | 4-2 | Hartlepool United 'A' | v | Ryhope CW | 3-0 |
| Stanley United | v | Birtley Town | 1-2 | Evenwood Town | v | South Shields | 3*1 |

**SECOND ROUND** (8 matches)

| | | | | | | | |
|---|---|---|---|---|---|---|---|
| Birtley Town | v | Boldon C A | 1-0 | Chester le Street Tn | v | Dunston F B | 1-0 |
| Bishop Auckland | v | West Auck. T  5p4 2-2 1*1 | | | Durham City | v | Hartlepool BW OB | 3-2 |
| Norton & Stockton | v | Hartlepool United 'A' | 3V4 | Spennymoor United | v | Evenwood Town | ET W-O |
| Brandon United | v | Peterlee Newtown | 0-1 | Easington Colliery | v | Consett | 3-4 |

(Hartlepool United broke competition rules and were removed, Norton & Stockton Ancients progressing to the next round. - Spennymoor United failed to fulfill the fixture and were removed from the Competition).

**THIRD ROUND** (4 matches)

| | | | | | | | |
|---|---|---|---|---|---|---|---|
| Chester le Street Townv | | Evenwood Town | 2-1 | Bishop Auckland | v | Norton & Stock. A. | 1-1 7-2 |
| Consett | v | Birtley Town | 8-1 | Peterlee Newtown | v | Durham City | 2-5 |

**SEMI-FINALS**

| | | | | | | | |
|---|---|---|---|---|---|---|---|
| 1 Durham City | v | Chester le Street Tn | 3*2 | 2 Consett | v | Bishop Auckland | 2-3 |

**FINAL**
BISHOP AUCKLAND v   DURHAM CITY   3*2      at Crook Town FC

# EAST RIDING F.A.

Tel: 01482 221158   Fax: 01482 221159   E.Mail: ERCFA@DIAL.PIPEX.COM.
50 Boulevard, Hull HU3 2TB
**Secretary & Press Officer:** Dennis R Johnson
**Executives (Responsibility)**   T Mason (Coaching Exams/Courses)
A Youngs (Referees)
M Edge (Womens Football)

| | | | | |
|---|---|---|---|---|
| **Number of Affiliated Clubs** | Senior: | 450 | U.18: | 110 |
| **Number of Affiliated Leagues:** | Senior: | 5 | Junior: | 2 |

**President:** Denis Grout
**Chairman:** M Rawding

**County Representative Teams:** Senior, U18, Womens
**Inter County Competitions:** Association of Northern Counties, FA County Youth, East Midlands U18,

## EAST RIDING SENIOR CUP 1998-99
(23 entries)  (FOUNDED 1903-04)
**LAST SEASON'S FINAL:** North Ferriby United  v  Hull City  2-1
**MOST WINS:** Hull City  25   Bridlington Town  12   North Ferriby United  7

**FIRST ROUND**  (7 matches)

| | | | | | | | | |
|---|---|---|---|---|---|---|---|---|
| Reckitts AFC | v | Westella & Willerby | 3-2 | | Chisholms | v | Bridlington Town | 2-0 |
| Charleston AFC | v | Bulmans | | 3-6 | Kelvin Hall | v | Hider Foods | 2-1 |
| Sculcoates Amateurs | v | Cottingham Spts | SA W-O | | Walkington Wdrs | v | East Hull Amateurs | 0-2 |
| Kevmar | v | Filey Town | | 1-3 | | | | |

**SECOND ROUND**  (8 matches)

| | | | | | | | | |
|---|---|---|---|---|---|---|---|---|
| Reckitts AFC | v | Malet Lambert YC | 1-2 | | Chisholm | v | Sculcoates Amateurs | 6-0 |
| Savoy Wanderers | v | Smith & Nephew | 1-5 | | Hull City | v | Kelvin Hall | 1-3 |
| Fiveways | v | Ideal Standard | 0-4 | | East Hull Amateurs | v | Hall Road Rangers Rs | 1-0 |
| Bulmans | v | Filey Town | 1-1 0-1 | | Hall Road Rangers | v | North Ferriby Utd | 4-4 1-2 |

**THIRD ROUND** (4 matches)

| | | | | | | | |
|---|---|---|---|---|---|---|---|
| Kelvin Hall | v | Ideal Standard | 2-2 0-1 | | Malet Lambert YC | v | Chisholms | 1-3 |
| Filey Town | v | Smith & Nephew | FT W-O | | North Ferriby United | v | East Hull Amateurs | 9-0 |

**SEMI-FINALS**

| | | | | | |
|---|---|---|---|---|---|
| Chisholms | v | North Ferriby United | 0-1 | | at Dene Park, Dunswell, Hall Road Rangers FC |
| Ideal Standard | v | Filey Town | 2p4 1-1 0*0 | | at Queensgate Bridlington Town FC |

**FINAL**

| | | | | |
|---|---|---|---|---|
| FILEY TOWN | v | NORTH FERRIBY U | 1-5 | at Boothferry Park, Hull City FC |

## EAST RIDING COUNTRY CUP 1998-99
(25 entries)
**LAST SEASON'S FINAL:** Filey Town 2nd  v  Holme Rovers  3-2

**FIRST ROUND** (9 matches)

| | | | | | | | | |
|---|---|---|---|---|---|---|---|---|
| Middleton Rovers | v | Beverley O Gramm's | 2-1 | | Full Measure | v | Filey Town Res | 6-0 |
| Rillington Athletic | v | Ward | 0-4 | | Nafferton | v | North Cave | 1-3 |
| Crown | v | Bridlington Sports | 2-4 | | Beaconsfield | v | Hutton Cranswick Utd | 4-2 |
| Driffield E I | v | Bridlington T Res | BT W-O | | Pack Horse | v | Bridlington Rovers | 3-2 |
| Hutton Crans'ck SRA | v | Hornsea Town | 1-0 | | | | | |

**SECOND ROUND** (8 matches)

| | | | | | | | | |
|---|---|---|---|---|---|---|---|---|
| Middleton Rovers | v | Bridlington Spts Club | 1-0 | | Full measure | v | Bridlington Town Res | 2-0 |
| Holme Rovers | v | North Cave | 2-0 | | Hutton Crans'ck SRA | v | Market Weighton U | 4-1 |
| Withernsea | v | Pack Horse | 1-0 | | Pocklington Town | v | Flamborough AFC | 11-0 |
| Ward | v | Hilderthorpe | 3-2 | | North Ferrriby U Rs | v | Beaconsfield | 5-2 |

**THIRD ROUND** (4 matches)

| | | | | | | | |
|---|---|---|---|---|---|---|---|
| Full Measure | v | Holme Rovers | 2-3 | | Pocklington Town | v | Ward | 0-1 |
| Bridlington Sports | v | North Ferriby Utd Res | 3-2 | | Hutton Crans. SRA | v | Withernsea | 1-3 |

**SEMI-FINALS**

| | | | | | | | |
|---|---|---|---|---|---|---|---|
| Ward | v | Bridlington Sports | 3-2 | | Holme Rovers | v | Withernsea | 3-3 2-3 |

**FINAL**

| | | | | |
|---|---|---|---|---|
| WARD | v | WITHERNSEA | 6-0 | at Queensgate Bridlington Town FC |

# ESSEX F.A.

Tel: 01245 357727   Fax: 01245 344430
31 Mildmay Road, Chelmsford CM2 0DN
**Chief Executive:**            Philip Sammons
**Executives (Responsibility)**  Steve Goodsell (Coaching Exams/Course, Womens Football)
                                 Les Ives (Referees)
**Number of Affiliated Clubs**    Senior:  1604        U.18:     350         **Chairman:** G Snell
**Number of Affiliated Leagues:** Senior:   40         Junior:    15         **Vice -Chairman:** D Smith
**County Representative Teams:** Senior, Intermediate, U18, U16
**Inter County Competitions:**   East Anglian, East Midlands, Southern Counties Youth

## ESSEX SENIOR CUP 1998-99
(44 entries)   (FOUNDED 1883-84)

**LAST SEASON'S FINAL:**  Dagenham & Redbridge  v  Purfleet  2-1

**MOST WINS:**  Ilford  13    Walthamstow Avenue  12    Grays Athletic  8    Leyton  8

### FIRST ROUND (2 matches)
| | | | | | | | |
|---|---|---|---|---|---|---|---|
| Ilford | v | Concord Rangers | 2-0 | Clacton Town | v | Brightlingsea United | 3-0 |

### SECOND ROUND (10 matches)
| | | | | | | | |
|---|---|---|---|---|---|---|---|
| Brentwood | v | Burnham Rmblrs | 6p7 1*1 | Hornchurch | v | Clapton | 0-4 |
| Bowers United | v | Stansted | 10-2 | Clacton Town | v | Great Wakering Rvrs | 5-1 |
| Aveley | v | Ilford | 3-0 | Stanway Rovers | v | East Ham United | 3-2 |
| Tiptree United | v | Waltham Abbey | 0-3 | Basildon United | v | Barkingside | 1-2 |
| East Thurrock United | v | Southend Manor | 2-0 | Saffron Walden Tn | v | Hullbridge Sports | 5p4 1*1 |

### THIRD ROUND (16 matches)
| | | | | | | | |
|---|---|---|---|---|---|---|---|
| Leyton Pennant | v | East Thurrock United | 2-0 | Romford | v | Barkingside | 4-0 |
| Braintree Town | v | Maldon Town | 5-1 | Canvey Island | v | Barking | 1*0 |
| Tilbury | v | Aveley | 0-4 | Grays Athletic | v | Wivenhoe Town | 3-1 |
| Bowers United | v | Waltham Abbey | 2-1 | Saffron Walden Tn | v | Heybridge Swifts | 3*6 |
| Stanway Rovers | v | Colchester United | 0-6 | Clapton | v | Chelmsford City | 0-3 |
| Purfleet | v | Burnham Ramblers | 4-2 | Clacton Town | v | Harwich & Park. | 3p1 1*1 |
| Halstead Town | v | Dag. & Redbridge | 0-2 | Ford United | v | Southend United | 2-3 |
| Harlow Town | v | Billericay Town | 1p3 1*1 | Witham Town | v | Leyton Orient | 0-6 |

### FOURTH ROUND (8 matches)
| | | | | | | | |
|---|---|---|---|---|---|---|---|
| Aveley | v | Clacton Town | 1-2 | Colchester United | v | Leyton Orient | 3-5 |
| Grays Athletic | v | Purfleet | 0-3 | Braintree Town | v | Heybridge Swifts | 0-3 |
| Billericay Town | v | Romford | 1-3 | Dag. & Redbridge | v | Bowers United | 4-1 |
| Canvey Island | v | Chelmsford City | 4-3 | Southend United | v | Leyton Pennant | 1*2 |

### FIFTH ROUND (4 matches)
| | | | | | | | |
|---|---|---|---|---|---|---|---|
| Leyton Pennant | v | Clacton Town | 1-2 | Leyton Orient | v | Purfleet | 1-0 |
| Romford | v | Canvey Island | 1-2 | Dag. & Redbridge | v | Heybridge Swifts | 5p6 2*2 |

### SEMI-FINALS
| | | | | | | | |
|---|---|---|---|---|---|---|---|
| Leyton Orient | v | Heybridge Swifts | 4p2 2*2 | Clacton Town | v | Canvey Island | 0-3 |

### FINAL
| | | | | |
|---|---|---|---|---|
| CANVEY ISLAND | v | LEYTON ORIENT | 2-1 | at Rootes Hall, Southend United FC. |

# ESSEX THAMES-SIDE TROPHY 1998-99
## (26 entries)   (FOUNDED 1945-46)


**LAST SEASON'S FINAL:** Canvey Island  v  Aveley  1-0

**MOST WINS:** Ilford  13    Walthamstow Avenue  12    Grays Athletic  8    Leyton  8


**FIRST ROUND** (10 matches)

| | | | | | | | |
|---|---|---|---|---|---|---|---|
| Harlow Town | v | Southend Manor SM W-O | | Ford United | v | Hullbridge Sports | 3-0 |
| Basildon United | v | Leyton Pennant | 1-2 | Ilford | v | Concord Rangers | 3-1 |
| Tilbury | v | Bowers United | 2-1 | Romford | v | Barkingside | 4p2 2*2 |
| Hornchurch | v | Burnham Ramblers | 3-2 | Waltham Abbey | v | Witham Town | WT W-O |
| Clapton | v | Barking | 2*1 | East Thurrock Utd | v | Grays Athletic | 1-2 |


**SECOND ROUND** (8 matches)

| | | | | | | | |
|---|---|---|---|---|---|---|---|
| Maldon Town | v | Romford | 3-1 | Witham Town | v | Grays Athletic | 2-1 |
| Aveley | v | Clapton | 2-1 | Southend Manor | v | Ford United | 1-3 |
| Purfleet | v | Hornchurch | 5-0 | Canvey Island | v | Leyton Pennant | 2-0 |
| Tilbury | v | Ilford | 3-2 | Great Wakering Rvrs | v | Southend United | 3p5 3*3 |


**THIRD ROUND** (4 matches)

| | | | | | | | |
|---|---|---|---|---|---|---|---|
| Southend United | v | Maldon Town | 6-2 | Aveley | v | Ford United | 1-2 |
| Purfleet | v | Tilbury | 2-0 | Canvey Island | v | Witham Town | 2*0 |


**SEMI-FINALS**

| | | | | | | | |
|---|---|---|---|---|---|---|---|
| Purfleet | v | Ford United | 0-1 | Southend United | v | Canvey Island | @CI 3-0 |


**FINAL**

FORD UNITED      v      SOUTHEND UNITED  2-1        at Ford United FC  att; 270

# GLOUCESTERSHIRE F.A.

Tel: 01454 615888   Fax: 01454 618088
Oaklands Park, Almondsbury, Bristol BS32 4AG
**Secretary & Press Officer:**   Paul Britton
**Executives (Responsibility)**   Paul Brutton (Coaching Exams/Courses, Womens Football)
   J W Hawkins (Referees)

| | | | | | |
|---|---|---|---|---|---|
| **Number of Affiliated Clubs** | Senior: | 868 | U.18: | 189 | **President:** S T Rummins |
| **Number of Affiliated Leagues:** | Senior: | 21 | Junior: | 10 | **Chairman:** CH Willcox MBE JP |

**County Representative Teams:** Senior, U18, Womens
**Inter County Competitions:**   South & South West Counties Championship, FA County Youth Cup

## GLOUCESTERSHIRE SENIOR CUP 1998-99

(8 entries)   (FOUNDED 1936-37)

**LAST SEASON'S FINAL:** Bristol City  v  Forest Green Rovers  2-1

**MOST WINS:** Cheltenham Town  32   Gloucester City  18   Forest Green Rovers  3

**FIRST ROUND** (4 matches)

| | | | | | | | | |
|---|---|---|---|---|---|---|---|---|
| Cirencester Town | v | Gloucester City | 1*3 | | Yate Town | v | Bristol City | 0-6 |
| Cinderford Town | v | Cheltenham Town | 0-5 | | Forest Green Rvrs | v | Bristol Rovers | 2-0 |

**SEMI-FINALS**

| | | | | | | | | |
|---|---|---|---|---|---|---|---|---|
| Cheltenham Town | v | Bristol City | 3-2 | | Forest Green Rvrs | v | Gloucester City | 2-4 |

**FINAL**

| | | | | |
|---|---|---|---|---|
| CHELTENHAM TN | v | GLOUCESTER CITY 3-0 | | at Gloucester City FC |

# GLOUCESTERSHIRE SENIOR TROPHY 1998-99

## (35 entries)  (FOUNDED 1978-79)

**LAST SEASON'S FINAL:** DRG  v  Broadwell Amateurs  1-0

**MOST WINS:** Mangotsfield United  5    Moreton Town  3    Shortwood United  2

**PRELIMINARY ROUND** (3 matches)

| | | | | | | |
|---|---|---|---|---|---|---|
| Ellwood | v | Bristol Manor Farm | 0-3 | Totterdown POB | v | Oldlands Abbotonians  0-2 |
| 3 Winterbourne United | v | Brockworth | 2*3 | | | |

**FIRST ROUND** (16 matches)

| | | | | | | | |
|---|---|---|---|---|---|---|---|
| Tytherington Rocks | v | Fairford Town | 0-3 | EFC Cheltenham | v | Cadbury Heath | 0-1 |
| Cheltenham Saracens | v | Harrow Hill | 4-1 | Viney St Swithens | v | Patchway Town | 0-5 |
| Shortwood United | v | Tuffley Rovers | 4-2 | Broadwell Amateurs | v | Henbury Old Boys | 0-3 |
| Ellwood/Bristol MF | v | Bitton | 4-3 | Totterdown/O Abbot's | v | Pucklechurch Sp | 1-2 |
| Old Georgians | v | Wotton Rovers | 1-0 | Cirencester Acad. | v | Hallen | 0-4 |
| Shirehampton | v | Mangotsfield United | 0-2 | Robinsons | v | Highridge United | 0-2 |
| Brockworth | v | Cirencester United | 2-0 | Almondsbury Town | v | D R G | 1-0 |
| Bishops Cleeve | v | Dursley Town    @DT 1-3 | | Broad Plain House | v | Frampton Athletic | 2-1 |

**SECOND ROUND** (8 matches)

| | | | | | | | |
|---|---|---|---|---|---|---|---|
| Shortwood United | v | Cheltenham Saracens | 5-3 | Henbury O B | v | Almondsb'y T 4p2 0A0 | 2*2 |
| Brockworth | v | Hallen | 2-1 | Fairford Town | v | Pucklechurch Sports | 2-1 |
| Dursley Town | v | Bristol Manor Farm | 2-0 | Mangotsfield United | v | Highridge United | 1-2 |
| Old Georgians | v | Patchway Town | 0-5 | Broad Plain House | v | Cadbury Heath | 2-3 |

**THIRD ROUND** (4 matches)

| | | | | | | | |
|---|---|---|---|---|---|---|---|
| Cadbury Heath | v | Highridge United | 6-2 | Dursley Town | v | Shortwood United | 2-0 |
| Brockworth | v | Fairford Town    @ FT 2-3 | | Henbury OB | v | Patchway Town | 0-1 |

**SEMI-FINALS**

| | | | |
|---|---|---|---|
| Fairford Town | v | Cadbury Heath | 1-0 |
| Dursley Town | v | Patchway Town | 0-1 |

**FINAL**

FAIRFORD TOWN  v  PATCHWAY TOWN  1-0    at Glos FA HQ Oaklands Park, Almondsbury.

*Aldershot's Gary Abbot scoring his last minute winner against Basingstoke Town to win the Hampshire Senior Cup . . .*

*Photo: Ian Morsman*

*. . . and celebrating with the League Cup*

*Photo: M Sandom*

# HAMPSHIRE F.A.

Tel: 02380 791110   Fax: 02380 788340
William Pickford House, 8 Ashwood Gardens, off Winchester Road, Southampton SO16 7PW
**Secretary:** R G Barnes JP
**Executives (Responsibility)**    Ms S M Lopez (Coaching Exams/Courses, Womens Football)
                                 R G Barnes (Referees)
**Number of Affiliated Clubs**    Senior:  2000         U.18:      450          **President:** M E Turner
**County Representative Teams:** Adult, Womens, Intermediate, Girls U16, Boys U18    **Chairman:** E J Ward
**Inter County Competitions:**    South West Counties, Hants & Dorset Cup

## HAMPSHIRE SENIOR CUP 1998-99
(46 entries)   (FOUNDED 1887-88)

**LAST SEASON'S FINAL:** Newport IoW  v  Fareham Town   1-0

**MOST WINS:** Southampton  13    Newport  7    Cowes  6

**FIRST ROUND** (14 matches)

| | | | | | | | |
|---|---|---|---|---|---|---|---|
| Blackfield & Langley | v | Fleet Spurs | 7-1 | Bournemouth | v | Stockbridge | 1-2 |
| Brading Town | v | Christchurch | 4-1 | Brockenhurst | v | Colden Common | 1-0 |
| Cove | v | R S Basingstoke | 0-3 | Cowes Sports | v | Liss Athletic | 3-1 |
| Eastleigh | v | Pirelli General | 5-2 | Fleetlands | v | Vosper Thornycroft | 5-0 |
| Gosport Borough | v | Horndean | 1-2 | Hamble ASSC | v | Winchester City | 2-0 |
| Hartley Wintney | v | Bishopstoke Social | 5-2 | Locksheath | v | Hayling United | 3-2 |
| New Street | v | Mayflower West Wight | 2-4 | Romsey Town | v | Alton Town | 0-2 |

**SECOND ROUND** (16 matches)

| | | | | | | | |
|---|---|---|---|---|---|---|---|
| Totton | v | Horndean | 0-1 | Aldershot Town | v | Moneyfields | 7-0 |
| Alton Town | v | Mayflower West Wight | 5-1 | Andover | v | Cowes Sports | 4*5 |
| Basingstoke Town | v | Whitchurch United | 4-0 | Brockenhurst | v | Hamble ASSC | 3-5 |
| East Cowes Vic Ath | v | Fleetlands | 5-1 | First Tower United | v | Eastleigh | 0-3 |
| Fleet Town | v | Bashley | 1*4 | Hartley Witney | v | Locksheath | 2-3 |
| Havant & W'looville | v | Fareham Town | 5-0 | Lymington & New M. | v | B A T Sports | 1-0 |
| Newport IOW | v | Blackfield & Langley | 6-0 | Portsmouth R N | v | Farnborough Town | 0-3 |
| Stockbridge | v | R S Basingstoke | 2-1 | Sylans Sports Club | v | Bading Town | 3-2 |

**THIRD ROUND** (8 matches)

| | | | | | | | |
|---|---|---|---|---|---|---|---|
| Aldershot Town | v | Locksheath | 3-0 | Alton Town | v | Newport IOW | 2-3 |
| Bashley | v | Horndean | 5-0 | Basingstoke Town | v | Eastleigh | 7-1 |
| Cowes Sports | v | Farnborough Town | 2*1 | Havant & W'looville | v | Hamble ASSC | 5-0 |
| Lymington & New M. | v | Stockbridge | 3-2 | Sylvans Sports | v | East Cowes Vic Ath | 4-1 |

**FOURTH ROUND** (4 matches)

| | | | | | | | |
|---|---|---|---|---|---|---|---|
| Aldershot Town | v | Sylvans Sports | 6-0 | Basingstoke Town | v | Newport IOW | 2-1 |
| Cowes Sports | v | Havant & Waterlooville | 0-5 | Lymington & N Milton | v | Bashley | 1-0 |

**SEMI-FINALS** First Leg

| | | | | | | | |
|---|---|---|---|---|---|---|---|
| Basingstoke Town | v | Lymington & New M. | 3-0 | Havant & W'looville | v | Aldershot Town | 0-3 |

**SEMI-FINAL** Second Leg

| | | | | | | | |
|---|---|---|---|---|---|---|---|
| Lymington & N Milton | v | Basingstoke Tn | 0-2=0-5 | Aldershot Town | v | Havant & W'ville | 1-1=4-1 |

**FINAL**

ALDERSHOT TOWN v   BASINGSTOKE TN   1-0      at The Dell, Southampton FC

# HEREFORDSHIRE F.A.

Tel: 01432 270308 (H)
1 Muirfield Close, Holmer, Hereford HR1 1QB
**Secretary & Press Officer:** Jim Lambert
**Executives (Responsibility)**   J Layton (Coaching Exams/Courses)
                                   A Jenkins (Referees)
                                   R J Perks (Womens Football)

| | | | |
|---|---|---|---|
| **Number of Affiliated Clubs** | Senior: 125 | U.18: 114 | **President:** Sir Colin Shepherd |
| **Number of Affiliated Leagues:** | Senior: 1 | Junior: 1 | **Chairman:** E G Powell |

**County Representative Teams:** Under 18, Under 16
**Inter County Competitions:**   Midland Counties U18, East Midland U16

## HEREFORDSHIRE SENIOR CUP 1998-99
### (21 entries)  (FOUNDED 1973-74)

**LAST SEASON'S FINAL:** Ross Town  v  Kington Town  3-2

### FIRST ROUND (5 matches)

| | | | | | | | |
|---|---|---|---|---|---|---|---|
| Kington Town | v | Weston u Penyard | 4-0 | Fownhope | v | Hearts | 3-1 |
| Bulmers | v | Golden Valley Athletic | 2-3 | Ewyas Harold | v | Wellington | 0-1 |
| Pegasus Juniors | v | Bromyard Town | 3-1 | | | | |

### SECOND ROUND (8 matches)

| | | | | | | | |
|---|---|---|---|---|---|---|---|
| Ross Town | v | Leominster Town | 4-2 | Ross Utd Services | v | Pegasus Juniors | 0-6 |
| Westfields | v | Kington Town | 1-2 | Ledbury Town | v | Woofferton | 1-2 |
| Sutton United | v | Hereford Lads Club | 3-2 | Wellington | v | Fownhope | 4-1 |
| Hereford Civil Serv. | v | Golden Valley Ath | 1-2 | Hinton | v | Pencombe | 4-3 |

### THIRD ROUND (4 matches)

| | | | | | | | |
|---|---|---|---|---|---|---|---|
| Ross Town | v | Wellington | 3-1 | Pegasus Juniors | v | Kington Town | 3-1 |
| Golden Valley Athletic | v | Woofferton | 3-1 | Sutton United | v | Hinton | 1-2 |

### SEMI-FINALS

| | | | | | | | |
|---|---|---|---|---|---|---|---|
| Pegasus Juniors | v | Hinton | 6-3 | Ross Town | v | Golden Valley Athletic | 2-1 |

### FINAL

| | | | | | |
|---|---|---|---|---|---|
| PEGASUS JUNIORS | v | ROSS TOWN | 3-1 | at Edgar Street, Hereford United FC | |

# HERTFORDSHIRE F.A.

Tel: 01462 677622   Fax: 01462 677624   E.Mail: HERTSFA@Compuserve.Com
County Ground, Baldock Road, Letchworth, Herts S96 2EN
**Secretary:** R G Kibble          **Press Officer:** County HQ
**Executives (Responsibility)**      R Dowie (Coaching Exams/Courses)
                                     R G Dowden (Referees)
                                     G Phillips (Womens Football)

| | | | | | |
|---|---|---|---|---|---|
| **Number of Affiliated Clubs** | Senior: | 860 | U.18: | 190 | **President:** B W A Bayford |
| **Number of Affiliated Leagues:** | Senior: | 24 | Junior: | 11 | **Chairman:** E C Hand |

**County Representative Teams:** Senior, U18, U16
**Inter County Competitions:**   East Anglian, EMYFC

## HERTFORDSHIRE SENIOR CUP 1998-99
### (23 entries)   (FOUNDED 1886-87)

**LAST SEASON'S FINAL:** Watford  v  Boreham Wood  1-0

**MOST WINS:** Hitchin Town  21    Barnet  16    Watford  14

### FIRST ROUND (7 matches)

| | | | | | | | |
|---|---|---|---|---|---|---|---|
| Som. Ambury V&E | v | Tring Town | 0-2 | Hitchin Town | v | St Albans City | 3-4 |
| Harpenden Town | v | Bishops Stortford | 0-3 | Barnet | v | Royston Town | RT W-O |
| Hemel Hempstead | v | Stevenage Boro | 3*3 0V2 | London Colney | v | Berkhamsted Town | 2-0 |
| Sawbridgeworth Town | v | Hertford Town | 0-0 2-3 | | | | |

Stevenage In-el player HHT re-instated

### SECOND ROUND (8 matches)

| | | | | | | | |
|---|---|---|---|---|---|---|---|
| Royston Town | v | St Margaretsbury | 3-0 | Baldock Town | v | Hoddesdon Town | 0-1 |
| Hertford Town | v | Hemel Hempstead T | 3*2 | Ware | v | Boreham Wood | 0-2 |
| Potters Bar Town | v | Tring Town | 1-0 | St Albans City | v | Bishops Stortford | 3-0 |
| London Colney | v | Welwyn Garden City | 2-1 | Watford | v | Cheshunt | 6-0 |

### THIRD ROUND (4 matches)

| | | | | | | | |
|---|---|---|---|---|---|---|---|
| Potters Bar Town | v | Hertford Town | 5-1 | London Colney | v | St Albans City | 3-1 |
| Royston Town | v | Watford | 0-4 | Boreham Wood | v | Hoddesdon Town | 4-2 |

### SEMI-FINALS

| | | | | | | | |
|---|---|---|---|---|---|---|---|
| Boreham Wood | v | Potters Bar Town | 3-0 | Watford | v | London Colney (at LC) 1-0 | |

### FINAL

| | | | | |
|---|---|---|---|---|
| BOREHAM WOOD | v | WATFORD | 3-2 | at Herts FA County Ground, Baldock Road, Letchworth |

# HERTFORDSHIRE SENIOR TROPHY 1998-99
## (20 entries)

**LAST SEASON'S FINAL:** Benington v Cuffley 2-1

**FIRST ROUND** (4 matches)

| | | | | | | |
|---|---|---|---|---|---|---|
| Tring Athletic | v | Letchworth | 2*3 | Agrevo Sports | v | Sun Postal Sports | 0-4 |
| Sandridge Rovers | v | Greenacres | 4-3 | Bedmond Sports | v | Leverstock Green | 0-3 |

**SECOND ROUND** (8 matches)

| | | | | | | | |
|---|---|---|---|---|---|---|---|
| Bovingdon | v | Elliott Star | 2-4 | Oxhey Jets | v | Sun Postal Sports | 2-3 |
| Met Police Bushey | v | Sandridge Rovers | 2-3 | Leverstock Green | v | Hatfield Town | 4-1 |
| Chipperfield Corinth. | v | Wormley Rovers | 0-1 | Letchworth | v | Colney Heath | 3*2 |
| Giffen VFC | v | Benington | B W-O | Cuffley | v | Kings Langley | 4-0 |

**THIRD ROUND** (4 matches)

| | | | | | | | |
|---|---|---|---|---|---|---|---|
| Sun Postal Sports | v | Cuffley | 2-0 | Benington | v | Wormley Rovers | 3-0 |
| Elliott Star | v | Sandridge Rovers | 2-2 2-1 | Leverstock Green | v | Letchworth | @Lw 1-0 |

**SEMI-FINALS**

| | | | | | | | |
|---|---|---|---|---|---|---|---|
| Elliott Star | v | Leverstock Green | 6-0 | Sun Postal Sports | v | Benington | 1*5 |

**FINAL**

| | | | | |
|---|---|---|---|---|
| BENINGTON | v | ELLIOTT STAR | 0-1 | at Herts FA County Ground,Baldock Road,Letchworth |

# HUNTINGDONSHIRE F.A.

Tel: 01480 414422  Fax: 01480 412691
Cromwell Chambers, 8 St Johns Street, Huntingdon, Cambs. PE18 6DD

| | |
|---|---|
| **Secretary & Press Officer:** | Maurice Armstrong |
| **Executives (Responsibility)** | K J Oldham (Coaching Exams/Courses) |
| | E K Heeds (Referees) |
| | M M Armstrong (Womens Football) |

**Number of Affiliated Clubs**    Senior:   120    U.18:    25     **President:** D A Roberts
**Number of Affiliated Leagues:** Senior:   1     Junior:    1     **Chairman:** R H Carter
**County Representative Teams:** Senior, Under 18, Under 16
**Inter County Competitions:**    East Midlands Youth U18 & U16, East Anglian Championship Senior

## HUNTINGDONSHIRE SENIOR CUP 1998-99
### (15 entries)  (FOUNDED 1888-89)

**LAST SEASON'S FINAL:** St Neots Town  v  Ortonians  1-0

**MOST WINS:** St Neots  34    Eynesbury Rovers  12    Huntingdon Town  12

**FIRST ROUND** (7 matches)

| | | | | | | | | |
|---|---|---|---|---|---|---|---|---|
| St Neots Town | v | Hotpoint | 5-1 | | Warboys Town | v | Eynesbury Rovers | 1-0 |
| Yaxley | v | St Ives Town | 3-2 | | ICA Juventus | v | Somersham Town | 3-4 |
| Bluntisham Rangers | v | Alconbury U | 4p5 1-1 2*2 | | Hemingford United | v | Brampton | 2-1 |
| Ortonians | v | Godmanchester Rvrs | 4-1 | | | | | |

**SECOND ROUND** (4 matches)

| | | | | | | | | |
|---|---|---|---|---|---|---|---|---|
| Yaxley | v | Somersham Town | 1-0 | | Hemingford United | v | Ortonians | |
| Alconbury United | v | Warboys Town | 0-0 1-3 | | St Neots Town | v | Stilton United | 9-1 |

**SEMI-FINALS**

| | | | | | | | | |
|---|---|---|---|---|---|---|---|---|
| St Neots Town | v | Ortonians | 2-1 | | Warboys Town | v | Yaxley | 3-5 |

**FINAL**

| | | | | | |
|---|---|---|---|---|---|
| ST NEOTS TOWN | v | YAXLEY | 3p4 1*1 | | at Somersham Town FC |

Ramsgate - Kent Senior Trophy Winners
Photo: Roger Turner

# KENT F.A.

Tel: 01634 843824   Fax: 01634 815369
E.Mail: KCFA.Chatham@btinternet.com
69 Maidstone Road, Chatham, Kent ME4 6DT

**Secretary:** K T Masters          **Press Officer:** Tony Hudd
**Executives (Responsibility)**     Paul Holden (Coaching Exams/Courses)
                                    Keith Masters (Referees)
                                    Joanne Broadhurst (Womens Football)

**Number of Affiliated Clubs**    Senior:   1161        U.18:      211        **President:** E H Bennett
**Number of Affiliated Leagues:** Senior:    3         Junior:     39        **Chairman:** B W Bright
**County Representative Teams:** U18, U16, Womens

## KENT FACIT SENIOR CUP 1998-99
(13 entries)  (FOUNDED 1888-89)

**LAST SEASON'S FINAL:** Margate  v  Gravesend & Northfleet  1-0
**MOST WINS:** Maidstone United  15     Dartford  9     Northfleet United  9

**FIRST ROUND** (5 matches)

| | | | | | | | |
|---|---|---|---|---|---|---|---|
| Folkestone Invicta | v | Dartford | 1-0 | Welling United | v | Greenwich Borough | 19/1 |
| Bromley | v | Fisher Ath. London | 2-3 | Ashford Town | v | Erith & Belvedere | 3-1 |
| Tonbridge Angels | v | Sittingbourne | 2*3 | | | | |

**SECOND ROUND** (4 matches)

| | | | | | | | |
|---|---|---|---|---|---|---|---|
| Gravesend & N'fleet | v | Fisher Athletic | 3-4 | Margate | v | Ashford Town | 2*1 |
| Folkestone Invicta | v | Sittingbourne | 2-1 | Dover Athletic | v | Welling United | 0-2 |

**SEMI-FINALS**

| | | | | | | | |
|---|---|---|---|---|---|---|---|
| Folkestone Invicta | v | Fisher Athletic | 4*2 | Margate | v | Welling United | 2*3 |

**FINAL**
FOLKESTONE INV.  v  WELLING UNITED   0-1     at Folkestone Invicta FC

## KENT PLAAYA SENIOR TROPHY 1998-99
(23 entries)  (FOUNDED 1874-75)

**LAST SEASON'S FINAL:** Greenwich Borough  v  Folkestone Invicta  1-0
**MOST WINS:** Ramsgate  3     Alma Swanley  2     Corinthian  2
                Faversham Town  2     Fisher Athletic  2

**FIRST ROUND** (7 matches)

| | | | | | | | |
|---|---|---|---|---|---|---|---|
| Crockenhill | v | West Wickham | 2-0 | Thamesmead Town | v | Thames Polytech. | 1-1 1-2 |
| Erith Town | v | Milton Athletic | 3-2 | Hythe United | v | Swanley Furness | 2-1 |
| Chatham Town | v | Faversham Town | 0-2 | Canterbury City | v | Knatchbull | 2-4 |
| Tunbridge Wells | v | V C D Athletic | 1-3 | | | | |

**SECOND ROUND** (8 matches)

| | | | | | | | |
|---|---|---|---|---|---|---|---|
| Cray Wanderers | v | Deal Town | 1-2 | Crockenhill | v | Erith Town | 3-0 |
| Herne Bay | v | Knatchbull | 2-0 | Lordswood | v | Beckenham Town | 3-2 |
| Thames Polytechnic | v | Ramsgate | 1-3 | Whitstable Town | v | Sheppey United | 1-2 |
| Slade Green | v | V C D Athletic | 2-1 | Faversham Town | v | Hythe United | 3-1 |

**THIRD ROUND** (4 matches)

| | | | | | | | |
|---|---|---|---|---|---|---|---|
| Deal Town | v | Ramsgate | 2-2 1-3 | Herne Bay | v | Crockenhill | 3-2 |
| Lordswood | v | Slade Green | 2-0 | Sheppey United | v | Faversham Town | 2-1 |

**SEMI-FINALS**

| | | | | | | | |
|---|---|---|---|---|---|---|---|
| Herne Bay | v | Sheppey United | 0-1 | Lordswood | v | Ramsgate | 0-3 |

**FINAL**
RAMSGATE  v  SHEPPEY UTD   8p7 2*2     at Ashford Town FC

# LANCASHIRE F.A.

Tel: 01772 624000   Fax: 01772 624700
The County Ground, Thurston Road, Leyland PR5 1LF
**Secretary & Press Officer**     J Kenyon, ACIS
**Executives (Responsibility)**     D Egan (Coaching Exams/Courses)
J Kenyon (Referees)
Miss J Ashworth (Womens Football)
**Number of Affiliated Clubs**     Senior:   1600          U.18:       300          **President:** D J Lewin
**County Representative Teams:** Senior, U18, Womens
**Inter County Competitions:**     FA County Youth, Northern Counties Senior, U18 & Womens

## LANCASHIRE ATS TROPHY 1998-99
### (23 entries)   (FOUNDED 1885-86)

**LAST SEASON'S FINAL:** Southport  v  Morecambe  2-0

**FIRST ROUND** (7 matches)

| | | | | | | | |
|---|---|---|---|---|---|---|---|
| Atherton Laburnum R v | Darwen | | 0-3 | Burscough | v | Atherton Collieries | 2-1 |
| Great Harwood Town v | Bacup Borough | 1*1 | 1-0 | Leigh RMI | v | Skelmersdale United | 1-2 |
| Nelson | v | Holker O B | 3*1 | Radcliffe Borough | v | Rossendale United | 2-1 |
| Ramsbottom United | v | Fleetwood Freeport | 1-3 | | | | |

**SECOND ROUND**  (8 matches)

| | | | | | | | |
|---|---|---|---|---|---|---|---|
| Accrington Stanley | v | Skelmersdale United | 4-0 | Bamber Bridge | v | Radcliffe Borough | 4-0 |
| Burscough | v | Chorley | 0-1 | Clitheroe | v | Great Harwood Town | 1-3 |
| Fleetwood Freeport | v | Morecambe | 2-4 | Lancaster City | v | Marine | 3-2 |
| Nelson | v | Darwen | 0-2 | Southport | v | Barrow | 2-0 |

**THIRD ROUND** (4 matches)

| | | | | | | | |
|---|---|---|---|---|---|---|---|
| Chorley | v | Morecambe | 0-2 | Bamber Bridge | v | Great Harwood Town | 3-1 |
| Darwen | v | Accrington Stanley | 3-2 | Southport | v | Lancaster City | 2-0 |

**SEMI-FINALS**

| | | | | | | | |
|---|---|---|---|---|---|---|---|
| Morecambe | v | Bamber Bridge | 3-2 | Southport | v | Darwen | 0-4 |

**FINAL**

| | | | | |
|---|---|---|---|---|
| DARWEN | v | MORECAMBE | 2p4 2*2 | at Chorley FC |

# LANCASHIRE AMATEUR CUP 1998-99
## (FOUNDED 1893-94)

**LAST SEASON'S FINAL:** Merseyside Police v Crawfords UB 2-1 aet

**MOST WINS:** Liverpool/Merseyside Police 11 St Dominics 6 Marine 5

**FOURTH ROUND** (8 matches)

| | | | | | | | | |
|---|---|---|---|---|---|---|---|---|
| Accrington Amateurs | v | Old Ashtonians | | | Crawfords UB | v | St Dominics | 6-6 0-1 |
| Leigh Athletic | v | Aintree Villa | 1-3 | | Rochdale St Clem. | v | Aigburth PH | 0-3 |
| Rossendale Amat. | v | REMYCA Utd | 0-6 | | Manweb | v | Merseyside Police | 3-2 |
| Walshaw | v | East Villa | 2-3 | | Wythenshawe Am. | v | | |

**FIFTH ROUND** (4 matches)

| | | | | | | | | |
|---|---|---|---|---|---|---|---|---|
| East Villa | v | Manweb | 1-0 | | Old Ashtonians | v | Aigburth PH | 1-4 |
| St Dominics | v | REMYCA United | 2-0 | | Wythenshawe Am. | v | Aintree Villa | 0-2 |

**SEMI-FINALS**

| | | | | | | | | |
|---|---|---|---|---|---|---|---|---|
| Aigburth PH | v | Aintree Villa | 2-0 | | St Dominics | v | East Villa | 3-0 |

**FINAL**

| | | | | |
|---|---|---|---|---|
| ST DOMINICS | v | AIGBURTH PH | 1-0 | at Leyland Motors Athletic FC |

# LANCASHIRE AMATEUR SHIELD 1998-99

**FINAL**

| | | | | |
|---|---|---|---|---|
| FULWOOD AMAT. | v | GARSTANG | 4-1 | at Leyland Motors Athletic FC |

# LEICESTERSHIRE & RUTLAND F.A.

Tel: 0116 286 7828   Fax: 0116 286 7828
Holmes Park, Dog & Gun Lane, Whetstone LE8 3LJ

| | |
|---|---|
| **Secretary & Press Officer:** | R E Barston |
| **Executives (Responsibility)** | John Ball (Coaching Courses, Womens Football) |
| | J Ward (Referees) |
| | Mrs G F Wait (Womens Football) |

**Number of Affiliated Clubs**   Senior:   512   U.18:   144   **President:** G E Cooper
**Number of Affiliated Leagues:**  Senior:   1   Junior:   6   **Chairman:** J E Bray
**County Representative Teams:** Under 18, Under 16
**Inter County Competitions:**   East Midlands Youth Combination U18 & U16

## LEICESTERSHIRE 'JELSON HOMES' SENIOR CUP 1998-99
### (41 entries)  (FOUNDED 1887-88)

**LAST SEASON'S FINAL:** Birstall United  v  Ibstock Welfare   4p3, 1-1 aet

**MOST WINS:** Leicester City  27   Enderby Town  6   Shepshed Dynamo  6

**FIRST ROUND** (9 matches)

| | | | | | | | | |
|---|---|---|---|---|---|---|---|---|
| Highfield Rangers | v | Harborough Town | 4-0 | | North Kilworth | v | Castle Donington Tn | 3-2 |
| Asfordby Amateurs | v | B'stone St Giles | 1*1 1-2 | | Anstey Nomads | v | Barrow Town | 3-4 |
| Loughborough Ath. | v | Birstall United | 0-5 | | Holwell Sports | v | Saffron Dynamo | 3*2 |
| Anstey Town | v | Leic. YMCA | 2p3 2*2 3*3 | | Narborough & L | v | Aylestone Park OB | 2-1 |
| Loughborough D'mo | v | Quorn | 2-6 | | | | | |

**SECOND ROUND** (16 matches)

| | | | | | | | | |
|---|---|---|---|---|---|---|---|---|
| Blaby & W'stone Ath | v | Barlestone St Giles | 5-0 | | Ellistown | v | Quorn | 0-8 |
| Leicester YMCA | v | Fosse Imps | 2*4 | | Leicestershire Const. | v | Birstall United | 0-3 |
| Cottesmore Amats. | v | Kirby Muxloe | 4-3 | | Barrow Town | v | Oadby Town | 1-3 |
| Thurnby Rangers | v | Downes Sports | 4-3 | | Thurmaston Town | v | Stoney Stanton | 3-1 |
| Friar Lane O B | v | Highfield Rangers | 1-9 | | North Kilworth | v | Lutterworth Town | 0-6 |
| Sileby Town | v | Coalville Town | 2-4 | | Bardon Hill Sports | v | Earl Shilton Albion | 4-0 |
| Holwell Sports | v | St Andrews | 4-1 | | Narboro & L'thorpe | v | Huncote Sp | 0-4 |
| Slack & Parr | v | Thringstone United | 3-0 | | Ibstock Welfare | v | Barwell | IW W-O |

**THIRD ROUND** (8 matches)

| | | | | | | | | |
|---|---|---|---|---|---|---|---|---|
| Highfield Rangers | v | Lutterworth Town | 1*1 4-1 | | Fosse Imps | v | Thurmaston Town | 1-4 |
| Coalville Town | v | Oadby Town | 1A1 1-2 | | Slack & Parr | v | Blaby & Whetstone | 1-2 |
| Birstall United | v | Quorn | 5-0 | | Holwell Sports | v | Bardon Hill | 6-1 |
| Thurnby Rangers | v | Huncote Sports | 1-2 | | Cottesmore Amats. | v | Ibstock Welfare | 1-2 |

**FOURTH ROUND** (4 matches)

| | | | | | | | | |
|---|---|---|---|---|---|---|---|---|
| Ibstock Welfare | v | Thurmaston T (atTT) | 2-4 | | Birstall United | v | Holwell Sports | 2-1 |
| Huncote S & S | v | Highfield Rangers | 1-5 | | Blaby & Whetstone | v | Oadby Town | 0-1 |

**SEMI-FINALS**

| | | | | | |
|---|---|---|---|---|---|
| Oadby Town | v | Highfield Rangers | 1-0 | | at Friar Lane Old Boys FC |
| Birstall United | v | Thurmaston Town | 2-1 | | at Quorn FC |

**FINAL**

| | | | | | |
|---|---|---|---|---|---|
| BIRSTALL UNITED | v | OADBY TOWN | 2p0 2*2 | | at Leics FA County Ground, Holmes Park, Whetstone. |

# LEICESTERSHIRE WESTERBY CHALLENGE CUP 1998-99
## (12 entries)

**LAST SEASON'S FINAL:** Leicester City  v  Shepshed Dynamo  6-1

**FIRST ROUND** (4 matches)

| | | | | | | | |
|---|---|---|---|---|---|---|---|
| Kirby Muxloe | v | Hinckley United | 2-1 | Downes Sports | v | Barwell | 1-3 |
| Holwell Sports | v | St Andrews | 1V2 | Friar Lane OB | v | Oadby Town | 1*1 0-4 |

(St Andrews removed from Compeition for fielding an ineligible player)

**SECOND ROUND** (4 matches)

| | | | | | | | |
|---|---|---|---|---|---|---|---|
| Oadby Town | v | Barwell | 2-0 | Shepshed Dynamo | v | Leicester City | 1-3 |
| Birstall United | v | St Andrews | BU W-O | Kirby Muxloe | v | Ibstock Welfare | 1-2 |

**SEMI-FINALS**

| | | | | | | | |
|---|---|---|---|---|---|---|---|
| Birstall United | v | Leicester City | 0-6 | Oadby Town | v | Ibstock Welfare | 3-1 |

**FINAL**

| | | | | |
|---|---|---|---|---|
| LEICESTER CITY | v | OADBY TOWN | 10-1 | at Filbert Street,Leicester City FC. |

# LINCOLNSHIRE F.A.

Tel: 01522 524917  Fax: 01522 528859
PO Box 26, 12 Dean Road, Lincoln LN2 4DP

**Secretary:** J Griffin  **Press Officer:** K Weaver
**Executives (Responsibility)**  Council of the Association:
(Coaching Exams, Referees, Womens Football)
K Leedham & W Ward (Coaching Courses)

| | | | | |
|---|---|---|---|---|
| **Number of Affiliated Clubs** | Senior: | 930 | U.18: | 201 |
| **Number of Affiliated Leagues:** | Senior: | 20 | Junior: | 14 |

**President:** N A Saywell
**Chairman:** R D Teanby

**County Representative Teams:** U18, U16
**Inter County Competitions:**  East Midlands Youth Combination, FA County Youth

## LINCOLNSHIRE SENIOR CUP 1998-99
(8 entries)  (FOUNDED 1935-36)

**LAST SEASON'S FINAL:**  Lincoln City  v  Lincoln United  2-0

**MOST WINS:**  Grimsby Town  13    Lincoln City  12    Boston United  5

**FIRST ROUND** (4 matches)

| | | | | | | | |
|---|---|---|---|---|---|---|---|
| Grantham Town | v | Scunthorpe United | 0-4 | Boston United | v | Grimsby Town | 0*1 |
| Gainsborough Trinity | v | Lincoln City | 1-4 | Lincoln United | v | Stamford | 2*4 |

**SEMI-FINALS**

| | | | | | | | |
|---|---|---|---|---|---|---|---|
| Lincoln City | v | Scunthorpe United | 2-4 | Stamford | v | Grimsby Town | 3-0 |

**FINAL**

| | | | | |
|---|---|---|---|---|
| SCUNTHORPE UTD | v | STAMFORD | 2-0 | at Glanford Park, Scunthorpe United FC |

## LINCOLNSHIRE SENIOR 'A' CUP 1998-99
(9 entries)  (FOUNDED 1968-69)

**LAST SEASON'S FINAL:**  Stamford AFC  v  Spalding United  3p4 1-1 aet

**MOST WINS:**  Boston Town  6    Holbeach United  4    Skegness Town  4

**PRELIMINARY ROUND** (1 match)

| | | | |
|---|---|---|---|
| Nettleham | v | Blackstone | 1-4 |

**FIRST ROUND** (4 matches)

| | | | | | | | |
|---|---|---|---|---|---|---|---|
| Blackstone | v | Louth United | 0-1 | Spalding United | v | Bourne Town | 4-1 |
| Holbeach United | v | Brigg Town | 0-3 | Boston Town | v | Winterton Rangers | 1-0 |

**SEMI-FINALS**

| | | | | | | | |
|---|---|---|---|---|---|---|---|
| Spalding United | v | Boston Town | 5p4 3*3 0*0 | Brigg Town | v | Louth United | 0-1 |

**FINAL**

| | | | | |
|---|---|---|---|---|
| SPALDING UNITED | v | LOUTH UNITED | 5-1 | at Spalding United FC |

# LINCOLNSHIRE SENIOR 'B' CUP 1998-99
## (16 entries)   (FOUNDED 1949-50)

**LAST SEASON'S FINAL:** Sleaford Town  v  Lincoln Moorlands  2-1

**MOST WINS:** Brigg Town  5    Appleby Frodingham Athletic  4

**FIRST ROUND** (8 matches)

| | | | | | | |
|---|---|---|---|---|---|---|
| Bottesford Town | v | Grimsby Imm'ham Amt | 1-3 | Epoworth Town | v | Louth Old Boys     ET W-O |
| Alston Sports | v | Wyberton | 2-1 | Barton Town OB | v | Sleaford Town     2-1 |
| Hykeham Town | v | Horncastle Town | 1-0 | Lincoln Moorlands | v | Deeping Rangers     5-2 |
| Lymestone Rangers | v | Appleby Frodingham | 3-2 | Skegness Town | v | Harrowby United     2-0 |

**SECOND ROUND** (4 matches)

| | | | | | | | |
|---|---|---|---|---|---|---|---|
| Grimsby Im'ham Am. | v | Barton TOB | 2-4 | Alston Sports | v | Lymestone Rangers | 4-1 |
| Hykeham Town | v | Skegness Town | 1-6 | Lincoln Moorlands | v | Epworth Town | 4-0 |

**SEMI-FINALS**

| | | | | | | | |
|---|---|---|---|---|---|---|---|
| Lincoln Moorlands | v | Skegness Town | 8-0 | Alston Sports | v | Barton Town Old Boys | 0-7 |

**FINAL**

| | | | | |
|---|---|---|---|---|
| BARTON TOWN OB | v | LINCOLN M'LANDS | 2-0 | at Glanford Park, Scunthorpe United FC |

# LIVERPOOL F.A.

Tel: 0151 5234488   Fax: 0151 523 4477

Liverpool Soccer Centre, Walton Hall Park, Walton Hall Avenue, Liverpool L4 9XP

**Secretary:** F L Hunter          **Press Officer:** S Catterall

**Executives (Responsibility)**    M McGlyn (Coaching Exams/Courses)

                                   K R Naylor (Referees)

                                   Ms S Gore (Womens Football)

**Number of Affiliated Clubs**     Senior:   900        U.18:    600        **President:** J Lawson

**Number of Affiliated Leagues:**  Senior:    18        Junior:   25

**Inter County Competitions:**     All FA Competitions

## LIVERPOOL SENIOR CUP 1998-99
### (11 entries)  (FOUNDED 1977-78)

**LAST SEASON'S FINAL:** Burscough  v  Liverpool

**MOST WINS:** Marine  5    Liverpool  3    South Liverpool  3

**FIRST ROUND** (3 matches)

| | | | | | | |
|---|---|---|---|---|---|---|
| Prescot Cables | v | Bootle | 2-0 | Marine | v Warrington Town | 3-2 |
| Skelmersdale United | v | St Helens Town | 3-2 | | | |

**SECOND ROUND** (4 matches)

| | | | | | | |
|---|---|---|---|---|---|---|
| Skelmersdale United | v | Southport | 2-6 | Burscough | v Marine | 2-1 |
| Tranmere Rovers | v | Everton | 2-0 | Prescot Cables | v Liverpool | 1-0 |

**SEMI-FINALS**

| | | | | | | |
|---|---|---|---|---|---|---|
| Burscough | v | Prescot Cables | 2-0 | Southport | v Tranmere Rovers | 1*0 |

**FINAL**

Southport          v   Burscough                  at Haig Avenue, Southport FC

## ADDITIONAL 1998-99 CUP RESULTS

**LIVERPOOL JUNIOR CUP**

St Aloysius          v    St Philomenas      4-1

at Manweb FC

**LIVERPOOL INTERMEDIATE CUP**

The Anchor          v    Tapes for Industry      5-3

at Liverpool Nalgo FC

**LIVERPOOL SUNDAY PREMIER CUP**

Britannia           v    Sandon             5-2

at Marine FC

**LIVERPOOL SUNDAY JUNIOR CUP**

St Marys Old Boys    v    Moss Vale          3-2 aet

at Manweb FC

# LIVERPOOL CHALLENGE CUP 1998-99
## (FOUNDED 1908-09)

**LAST SEASON'S FINAL:** Manweb v Plessey GPT 1-0 aet

**MOST WINS:** Skelmersdale Utd 8 Prescot Cables 6 New Brighton 5 St Dominics 5

### FIRST ROUND (10 matches)

| | | | | | | | | |
|---|---|---|---|---|---|---|---|---|
| Aigburth PH | v | REMYCA United | 2-3 | Ayone | v | Cheshire Lines | 4-2 | |
| BRNESC | v | Lucas Sports | 3-4 | Collegiate OB | v | Old Cathinians | 3-3 6-3 | |
| East Villa | v | Southport Trinity | 3-2 | Liverpool Nalgo | v | Alsop OB* | 2-2 2-2 | |
| Mossley Hill Athletic | v | Old Xaverians | 4-5 | Old Holts | v | Royal Seaforth | 1-4 | |
| Quarry Bank OB | v | Stockbridge | 1-0 | South Liverpool | v | Ford Motors | 1-5 | |

### SECOND ROUND (16 matches)

| | | | | | | | |
|---|---|---|---|---|---|---|---|
| Aintree Villa | v | Garswood United | 2-3 | Ashton Town | v | Ford Motors | 3-1 |
| Crawfords UB | v | Quarry Bank OB | 6-2 | Essemmay OB | v | East Villa | 1-3 |
| Maghull | v | Alsop OB | 6-3 | Manweb | v | Collegiate OB | 5-0 |
| Old Xaverians | v | Marine Reserves | 1-0 | Plessey GPT | v | Royal Seaforth | 3-4 |
| Roma | v | REMYCA United | 2-5 | Rylands | v | Bootle Reserves | 1-0 |
| St Dominics | v | Lucas Sports | 5-0 | Speke | v | Sefton & District | 2-0 |
| Stoneycroft | v | Waterloo Dock | 1-5 | Warbreck | v | Ayone | 3-0 |
| Waterloo GSOB | v | Kirkby Boulevard | 2-5 | Yorkshire CT | v | Merseyside Police | 3-2 |

### THIRD ROUND (8 matches)

| | | | | | | | |
|---|---|---|---|---|---|---|---|
| Crawfords UB | v | Ashton Town | 5-1 | East Villa | v | Speke | 2-0 |
| Garswood United | v | Old Xaverians | 3-0 | REMYCA United | v | St Dominics | 1-2 |
| Rylands | v | Royal Seaforth | 1-4 | Warbreck | v | Maghull | 0-4 |
| Waterloo Dock | v | Kirkby Boulevard | 6-0 | Yorkshire Copper T. | v | Manweb | 0-1 |

### FOURTH ROUND (4 matches)

| | | | | | | | |
|---|---|---|---|---|---|---|---|
| East Villa | v | Waterloo Dock | 0-3 | Maghull | v | Garswood United | 2-2 1-0 |
| Manweb | v | St Dominics | 0-1 | Royal Seaforth | v | Crawfords UB | 3-0 |

### SEMI-FINALS

| | | | | | | | |
|---|---|---|---|---|---|---|---|
| Maghull | v | Waterloo Dock | 0-0 0-4 | Royal Seaforth | v | St Dominics | 0-1 |

### FINAL

| | | | | | |
|---|---|---|---|---|---|
| WATERLOO DOCK | v | ST DOMINICS | 3-2 | at Burscough FC | |

*Bottom: Dulwich Hamlet FC - London Challenge Cup winners 1998-99*
*Photo: Paul Dennis LRPS*

## LONDON F.A.

Tel: 0208 690 9626   Fax: 0208 690 9471
6 Aldworth Grove, Lewisham, London SE13 6HY
**Secretary:** D G Fowkes
**Executives (Responsibility)**   A Welsh (Coaching Exams)   B Jenkins (Referees)
                                  C Arundale (Womens Football)   D Morrison (Coaching Courses)

| | | | | | | |
|---|---|---|---|---|---|---|
| **Number of Affiliated Clubs** | Senior: | 2360 | U.18: | 510 | **President:** L A M Mackay | |
| **Number of Affiliated Leagues:** | Senior: | 165 | Junior: | 43 | **Chairman:** B M Gibbons | |

**County Representative Teams:** Senior, Womens, U16
**Inter County Competitions:**   Southern Counties Cup, Southern Counties Womens Cup, FA County Youth Cup

### LONDON CHALLENGE CUP 1998-99
(14 entries)   (Original competition founded 1908)

**LAST SEASON'S FINAL:** Boreham Wood  v  Uxbridge  3-1

**FIRST ROUND** (6 matches)

| | | | | | | | | |
|---|---|---|---|---|---|---|---|---|
| Bromley | v | Metropolitan Police | 2/2 | | Erith & Belvedere | v | Tooting & Mitcham Utd | 3-0 |
| Croydon | v | Leyton Pennant | 3*2 | | Romford | v | Fisher Athletic | 2-3 |
| Barking | v | Hampton | 0-3 | | Hendon | v | Welling United | 0-3 |

**SECOND ROUND** (4 matches)

| | | | | | | | |
|---|---|---|---|---|---|---|---|
| Hampton | v | Dulwich Hamlet | 1-2 | | Erith & Belvedere | v | Fisher Athletic | 0-2 |
| Croydon | v | Uxbridge | 0-1 | | Welling United | v | Bromley | 2-0 |

**SEMI-FINALS**

| | | | | | | | |
|---|---|---|---|---|---|---|---|
| Welling United | v | Dulwich Hamlet | 1-3 | | Fisher Athletic | v | Uxbridge | 1-2 |

**FINAL**

DULWICH HAMLET  v  UXBRIDGE        2*1        at The Valley, Charlton Athletic FC att;461

*Dean Holmes scores Dulwich Hamlet's first goal in the London Challenge Cup final against
Uxbridge at Charlton Athletic*                                          *Photo: John Egan*

947

# LONDON SENIOR CUP 1998-99
### (26 entries)   (FOUNDED 1882)

**LAST SEASON'S FINAL:** Ford United  v  Southall  2-0

**FIRST ROUND** (10 matches)

| | | | | | | | |
|---|---|---|---|---|---|---|---|
| Ilford | v | Haringey Borough | 0-1 | St Margaretsbury | v | Crown & Manor | 0-2 |
| Waltham Abbey | v | Thamesmead Town | 2-1 | Bedfont | v | Clapton | 1-0 |
| East Ham United | v | Ford United | 5p4 3*3 | Hanwell Town | v | Kingsbury Town | 3p4 1*1 |
| Barkingside | v | Cockfosters | 3-1 | Thames Polytechnic | v | Wingate & Finchley | 0-2 |
| Woodford Town | v | Islington St Mary's | 0-1 | Civil Service | v | Corinthian Casuals | 2-7 |

**SECOND ROUND** (8 matches)

| | | | | | | | |
|---|---|---|---|---|---|---|---|
| Brimsdown Rovers | v | Cray Wanderers | 3-1 | Crown & Manor | v | Waltham Abbey | 2-4 |
| Erith Town | v | Crockenhill | 0-6 | East Ham United | v | Wingate & Finchley | 0-1 |
| Croydon Athletic | v | Islington St Mary's | 0-1 | Kingsbury Town | v | Bedfont | 0-6 |
| Haringey Borough | v | Barkingside | 2-1 | Corinthian Casuals | v | Southall | 1-2 |

**THIRD ROUND** (4 matches)

| | | | | | | | |
|---|---|---|---|---|---|---|---|
| Haringey Borough | v | Brimsdown Rovers | 1-0 | Waltham Abbey | v | Wingate & Finchley | 3-2 |
| Crockenhill | v | Islington St Mary's | 2-4 | Bedfont | v | Southall | 3*1 |

**SEMI-FINALS**

| | | | | | | | |
|---|---|---|---|---|---|---|---|
| Haringey Borough | v | Waltham Abbey | 0-3 | Bedfont | v | Islington St Mary's | 2-0 |

**FINAL**

| | | | | | |
|---|---|---|---|---|---|
| WALTHAM ABBEY | v | BEDFONT | 3-2 | at Champion Hill, Dulwich Hamlet FC | |

# ADDITIONAL 1998-99 CUP RESULTS

**LFA WOMENS CUP**
Millwall Lionesses  v  Arsenal Ladies  1*0
at Ford United FC

**LFA INTERMEDIATE CUP**
Canning Town  v  Cray Valley (PM)  1-0
at Metropolitan Police FC

**LFA JUNIOR CUP**
CMB (Metal Box)  v  T.C. Sports  2-1
at Croydon Athletic FC

**LFA MIDWEEK CUP**
London Fire Brig OT  v  Shakespeare  3-0
at Corinthian Casuals FC

**LFA SUNDAY CHALLENGE CUP**
Italia Wasteels  v  Convoys  2-1
at Wingate & Finchley FC

**LFA SUNDAY INTERMEDIATE CUP**
Bricklayers Arms  v  New Salamis  4-2
at Dulwich Hamlet FC

**LFA SUNDAY JUNIOR CUP**
Black Horse  v  Greyford  4-1
at Wingate & Finchley FC

*Top: Waltham Abbey celebrate their first London Senior Cup triumph after the final held at Champion Hill, Dulwich*
*Photo: Francis Short*

# MANCHESTER F.A.

Tel: 0161 881 0299   Fax: 0161 881 6833
Brantingham Road, Chorlton, Manchester M21 0TT
**Secretary & Press Officer:**   Phil Smith
**Executives (Responsibility)**   Alan Keeling (Coaching Exams/Courses)
Phil Morris (Referees)
Phil Smith (Womens Football)

| | | | | |
|---|---|---|---|---|
| **Number of Affiliated Clubs** | Senior: | 1380 | U.18: | 180 |
| **Number of Affiliated Leagues:** | Senior: | 20 | Junior: | 10 |

**President:** Frank Hannah

**County Representative Teams:** U18, Womens
**Inter County Competitions:**   FA County Youth, Association of Northern Counties Youth Competition

## MANCHESTER PREMIER CUP 1998-99
### (17 entries)  (FOUNDED1979-80)

**LAST SEASON'S FINAL:** Glossop North End  v  Radcliffe Borough  1-0

**MOST WINS:** Curzon Ashton  5   Ashton United  3   Hyde United  3
Droylsden  2   Mossley  2

**PRELIMINARY ROUND** (1 match)

| | | | |
|---|---|---|---|
| Abbey Hey | v | Buxton | 1-0 |

**FIRST ROUND** (8 matches)

| | | | | | | | | |
|---|---|---|---|---|---|---|---|---|
| Abbey Hey | v | Radcliffe Borough | 4-1 | Chadderton | v | Ashton United | 2*1 |
| Curzon Ashton | v | Cheadle Town | 0-2 | Glossop North End | v | Trafford | 2-0 |
| Hyde United | v | Mossley | 2-0 | Maine Road | v | Droylsden | 2V4 |
| Oldham Town | v | Woodley Sports | 3-0 | Salford City | v | Flixton | 1-3 |

(Droylsden in-el Player, Maine Road reinstated)

**SECOND ROUND** (4 matches)

| | | | | | | | | |
|---|---|---|---|---|---|---|---|---|
| Flixton | v | Abbey Hey | 1-2 | Maine Road | v | Chadderton | 3-1 |
| Glossop North End | v | Woodley Sports | 2-0 | Hyde United | v | Cheadle Town | 6-1 |

**SEMI-FINALS**

| | | | | | | | | |
|---|---|---|---|---|---|---|---|---|
| Maine Road | v | Abbey Hey | 2-0 | Glossop North End | v | Hyde United | 1-3 |

**FINAL**

| | | | | | |
|---|---|---|---|---|---|
| MAINE ROAD | v | HYDE UNITED | 0-1 | at Boundary Park, Oldham Athletic FC |

# MIDDLESEX F.A.

Tel: 0181 424 8524   Fax: 0181 863 0627   E.Mail: MIDDXFA@CS.COM
39 Roxborough Road, Harrow, Middlesex HA1 1NJ
**Secretary:** Peter Clayton
**Executives (Responsibility)**   P Clayton (Coaching Exams/Courses,
                                  Womens Football, Referees)
**Number of Affiliated Clubs**   Senior:   32      U.18:    277      **President:** Dave West
**Number of Affiliated Leagues:**  Senior:   42      Junior:   37      **Chairman:** John Wake
**County Representative Teams:**  Senior, Adult, U18, U16, Womens, U16
**Inter County Competitions:**   FA County Youth, Home Counties Youth, Home Counties Championship

## MIDDLESEX SENIOR CUP 1998-99
(26 entries)   (FOUNDED 1888-89)
**LAST SEASON'S FINAL:** Enfield v Uxbridge 3-2
**MOST WINS:** Enfield 13   Southall 12   Wealdstone 11

**PRELIMINARY ROUND** (2 matches)

| | | | | | | | |
|---|---|---|---|---|---|---|---|
| Ruislip Manor | v | Cockfosters | 8-0 | Viking Sports | v | Potters Bar Town | 0-3 |

**FIRST ROUND** (8 matches)

| | | | | | | | |
|---|---|---|---|---|---|---|---|
| Hendon | v | Hanwell Town | 2-0 | Hillingdon Borough | v | Kingsbury Town | 6-1 |
| Brimsdown Rovers | v | Northwood | 0-3 | Wembley | v | Bedfont | 2-1 |
| Southall | v | Ashford Town | 3-0 | Ruislip Manor | v | Brook House | 2-1 |
| Potters Bar Town | v | Harefield United | 6-1 | Wealdstone | v | Feltham | 5-1 |

**SECOND ROUND** (8 matches)

| | | | | | | | |
|---|---|---|---|---|---|---|---|
| Hayes | v | Enfield | 4-0 | Hampton | v | Southall | 3-0 |
| Hendon | v | Uxbridge | 2*1 | Northwood | v | Yeading | 2-0 |
| Edgware Town | v | Wembley | 0-2 | Staines Town | v | Hillingdon Borough | 4-0 |
| Wealdstone | v | Harrow Borough | 2*2 2-1 | Potters Bar Town | v | Ruislip Manor | 4-2 |

**THIRD ROUND** (4 matches)

| | | | | | | | |
|---|---|---|---|---|---|---|---|
| Northwood | v | Potters Bar Town | 6-2 | Hampton | v | Hendon | 0-2 |
| Wembley | v | Staines Town | 2-0 | Hayes | v | Wealdstone | 1-2 |

**SEMI-FINALS**

| | | | | | | | |
|---|---|---|---|---|---|---|---|
| Hendon | v | Wealdstone | 3-0 | Wembley | v | Northwood | 2-1 |

**FINAL**

| | | | | |
|---|---|---|---|---|
| HENDON | v | WEMBLEY | 4p2 2*2 | at Southbury Road, Enfield FC |

## MIDDLESEX SENIOR CHARITY CUP
(19 entries)   (FOUNDED 1901-02)
**LAST SEASON'S FINAL:** Hampton v Waltham Abbey 2-1
**MOST WINS:** Wealdstone 11   Hayes 10   Southall 10

**FIRST ROUND** (3 matches)

| | | | | | | | |
|---|---|---|---|---|---|---|---|
| Kingsbury Town | v | Hanwell Town | 0-2 | Harefield United | v | Brook House | 1-4 |
| Feltham | v | Cockfosters | 8p7 0*0 | | | | |

**SECOND ROUND** (8 matches)

| | | | | | | | |
|---|---|---|---|---|---|---|---|
| Brook House | v | Feltham | 3-0 | Ashford Town | v | Wembley | 3-1 |
| Hampton | v | Waltham Abbey | H W-O | Uxbridge | v | Hanwell Town | 2-3 |
| Northwood | v | Hillingdon Borough | 0*2 | Staines Town | v | Southall | 2-3 |
| Bedfont | v | Edgware Town | 6-2 | Ruislip Manor | v | Wealdstone | 2-0 |

**THIRD ROUND** (4 matches)

| | | | | | | | |
|---|---|---|---|---|---|---|---|
| Hillingdon Borough | v | Ruislip Manor | 2p4 3*3 | Hanwell Town | v | Hampton | 0-1 |
| Bedfont | v | Brook House | 1-2 | Ashford Town | v | Southall | 2*4 |

**SEMI-FINALS**

| | | | | | | | |
|---|---|---|---|---|---|---|---|
| Hampton | v | Brook House | 3p0 2*2 | Ruislip Manor | v | Southall | 2-3 |

**FINAL**

| | | | | |
|---|---|---|---|---|
| HAMPTON | v | SOUTHALL | 3-0 | at Yeading FC |

# NORFOLK F.A.

Tel: 01603 717177    Fax: 01603 717187

Plantation Park, Blofield, Norwich NR13 4PL

**Secretary & Press Officer:**    Roger J Howlett

**Executives (Responsibility)**    Through County Office

(Coaching Exams/Courses, Referees, Womens Football)

| | | | | | |
|---|---|---|---|---|---|
| **Number of Affiliated Clubs** | Senior: | 487 | U.18: | 167 | **President:** R W Kiddell |
| **Number of Affiliated Leagues:** | Senior: | 16 | Junior: | 9 | **Chairman:** A Williams |

**County Representative Teams:** U18, Womens

**Inter County Competitions:**    FA County Youth, East Midlands Youth Combination

## NORFOLK SENIOR CUP 1998-99
### (32 entries)   (FOUNDED 1881-82)

**LAST SEASON'S FINAL:**   Wroxham  v  Swaffham Town  3-1

**MOST WINS:**  King's Lynn  19    Great Yarmouth Town  14    Gorleston  13

**FIRST ROUND** (6 matches)

| | | | | | | | |
|---|---|---|---|---|---|---|---|
| Coltishall HV | v | Loddon United | 0-1 | Horsford United | v | Hempnall | 2-1 |
| Mattishall | v | Poringland Wanderers | 1-3 | North Walsham Town | v | Anglian Windows | 2-1 |
| Town Hall Scripts | v | Scole United | 0-1 | Wells Town | v | Lakeford Rangers | 3-2 |

**SECOND ROUND** (10 matches)

| | | | | | | | |
|---|---|---|---|---|---|---|---|
| Attleborough Town | v | Stalham Town | 2-1 | Blofield United | v | Acle United | 2*2 2-3 |
| Cromer United | v | Horsford United | 3-0 | Dereham Town | v | Scole United | 2*3 |
| Norwich United | v | Loddon United | 3-1 | St Andrews | v | Poringland Wanderers | 2-1 |
| Swaffham Town | v | Mulbarton United | 5-2 | Thetford Town | v | North Walsham Town | 0-4 |
| Thorpe Village | v | Wells Town | 0-2 | Wymondham Town | v | Downham Town | 1-5 |

**THIRD ROUND** (8 matches)

| | | | | | | | |
|---|---|---|---|---|---|---|---|
| Watton United | v | Wroxham | 0-2 | Norwich United | v | Fakenham Town | 1-3 |
| Diss Town | v | Scole United | 1-0 | Wells Town | v | Gorleston | 4-1 |
| Cromer United | v | Great Yarmouth Town | 0-2 | St Andrews | v | Swaffham Town | 1-3 |
| Downham Town | v | Acle United | 3-0 | Attleborough | v | North Walsham Town | 5*2 |

**QUARTER-FINALS**

| | | | | | | | |
|---|---|---|---|---|---|---|---|
| Great Yarmouth Town | v | Diss Town | 0-1 | Attleborough Town | v | Fakenham Town | 1*2 |
| Downham Town | v | Wells Town | 2-1 | Swaffham Town | v | Wroxham | 2-1 |

**SEMI-FINALS**

| | | | | | | | |
|---|---|---|---|---|---|---|---|
| Diss Town | v | Swaffham Town | 1-2 | Downham Town | v | Fakenham Town | 0-2 |

**FINAL**

| | | | | |
|---|---|---|---|---|
| SWAFFHAM TOWN | v | FAKENHAM TOWN | 2-4 | at Carrow Road, Norwich City FC |

# NORTHAMPTONSHIRE F.A.

Tel: 01604 670741   Fax: 01604 670741
2 Duncan Close, Moulton Park, Northampton
**Secretary & Press Officer:**     B Walden
**Executives (Responsibility)**     T Clifton (Coaching Exams/Courses)
                                     B Walden (Referees)
                                     Mrs J Jeffrey (Womens Football)
**Number of Affiliated Clubs**     Senior:    460        U.18:      84        **President:** D Vernon
**Number of Affiliated Leagues:** Senior:    12         Junior:     7        **Chairman:** L Homer
**County Representative Teams:** U18
**Inter County Competitions:**     East Midland Youth Combination

## NORTHAMPTONSHIRE 'HILLIER' SENIOR CUP
(13 entries)   (FOUNDED 1883-84)

**LAST SEASON'S FINAL:** Kettering Town  v  Raunds Town  1-0
**MOST WINS:** Kettering Town  29    Northampton Town  11    Peterborough United 11

**FIRST ROUND** (5 matches)

| | | | | | | |
|---|---|---|---|---|---|---|
| Cogenhoe United | v | Corby Town | 2-1 | Long Buckby | v Brackley Town | 1-3 |
| S & L Corby | v | Ford Sports | 5-2 | Wellingborough Tn | v Raunds Town | 1-5 |
| Desborough Town | v | Norhampton Spencer | 3-2 | | | |

**SECOND ROUND** (4 matches)

| | | | | | | |
|---|---|---|---|---|---|---|
| Brackley Town | v | S & L Corby | 1-0 | Rothwell Town | v Rushden & Diamonds | 0-1 |
| Cogenhoe United | v | Desborough Town | 2-0 | Raunds Town | v Kettering Town | 1-0 |

**SEMI-FINALS**

| | | | | | | |
|---|---|---|---|---|---|---|
| Brackley Town | v | Raunds Town | 0-6 | Cogenhoe United | v Rushden & Dia. | 2*2 1-3 |

**FINAL**

| | | | | | |
|---|---|---|---|---|---|
| RAUNDS TOWN | v | RUSHDEN & DIA. | 0-2 | at Raunds Town FC | |

*Higham's Scott Freeman celebrates from a sitting position as his header beats Woodford 'keeper Mick Hemmings. However Woodford won this Northants Junior Cup tie between these UCL rivals 2-1 to progress to the semi-finals*
*Photo: Gordon Whittington*

# NORTH RIDING F.A.

Tel: 01642 224585  Fax: 0
Southlands Centre, Ormesby Road, Middlesbrough TS3 0HB
**Secretary:** Mark Jarvis
**Executives (Responsibility)**   Contact County Office for
Coaching Exams/Courses, Referees, Womens Football
**Number of Affiliated Clubs**   Senior:   500   U.18:   120
**Number of Affiliated Leagues:** Senior:   20   Junior:   10   **President:** K Boyer
**County Representative Teams:** Senior, U18, Ladies
**Inter County Competitions:**   Northern Counties Competitions, FA Youth Competition

## NORTH RIDING SENIOR CUP 1998-99
### (15 entries)  (FOUNDED 1881-82)

**LAST SEASON'S FINAL:** Whitby Town  v  York City  3-1
**MOST WINS:** Middlesbrough  46   Scarborough  17   South Bank  8   Stockton  8

**FIRST ROUND** (2 matches)
Grangetown BC   v   Stokesley SC   0-1   York R I   v   Carlin How WMC   3*2

**SECOND ROUND** (2 matches)
York Railway Inst   v   Stokesley S C   6p5 2*2   Fishburn Park   v   New Marske S C   1-2

**THIRD ROUND** (4 matches)
Pickering Town   v   New Marske S C   1-3   Stockton   v   Whitby Town   0-5
Marske United   v   Northallerton Town   1-2   Guisborough Town   v   York Railway Institute   6-0

**FOURTH ROUND** (2 matches)
Whitby Town   v   Northallerton Town   4-0   Guisborough Town   v   New Marske SC   3-1

**FIFTH/FINAL qualifier/eliminator**
Whitby Town   v   Guisborough Town   2-0

**SEMI-FINALS**
Whitby Town   v   Middlesbrough   Scarborough   v   York City
Provisional date: 17 July 1999

*North Riding FA Senior Team: Winners Northern Counties Senior Cup 1999*

*Above: Northumberland FA Senior Team - Finalists: Northern Counties Senior Cup 1999*

*Photo: J E McCormick Photography*

*Below: Northumberland FA Youth Team (U18) - Finalists: Northern Counties Youth Cup Competition*

*Photo: J E McCormick Photography*

# NORTHUMBERLAND F.A.

Tel: 0191 236 8020
10 Brenkley Way, Seaton Burn, Newcastle upon Tyne NE13 6DT
**Secretary:** R E Maughan    **Press Officer:** Bill Gardner
**Executives (Responsibility)**    B Jones (Coaching Exams/Courses)
L Hayden (Referees)
P Valentine (Womens Football)

| | | | | | |
|---|---|---|---|---|---|
| **Number of Affiliated Clubs** | Senior: | 520 | U.18: | 460 | **President:** E A Wright |
| **Number of Affiliated Leagues:** | Senior: | 11 | Junior: | 7 | |

**County Representative Teams:** Senior, U18
**Inter County Competitions:** Northern Counties Senior & Youth Cups, FA County Youth Cup
**County Publications:** "The Far Corner" - Bi-monthly Newsletter

## NORTHUMBERLAND SENIOR CUP 1998-99
### Sponsored by "Arnott Insurance"
(12 entries)   (FOUNDED 1883-84)

**LAST SEASON'S FINAL:** Bedlington Terriers  v  Blyth Spartans  2-0

**MOST WINS:** Blyth Spartans  21    Newcastle United  20    North Shields  12

**FIRST ROUND** (4 matches)

| | | | | | | | |
|---|---|---|---|---|---|---|---|
| West Allotment Celtic | v | Alnwick Town | 3-3 1-0 | Prudhoe Town | v | Morpeth Town | 5-5 1-0 |
| Newcastle Blue Star | v | Ashington | 2-0 | Newcastle Utd Res | v | Lemington Social | 8-1 |

**SECOND ROUND** (4 matches)

| | | | | | | | |
|---|---|---|---|---|---|---|---|
| Ponteland United | v | Prudhoe Town | 5-1 | West Allotment Celtic | v | Newcastle Blue Star | 3-5 |
| Bedlington Terriers | v | Newcastle Utd Res | 0-4 | Whitley Bay | v | Blyth Spartans | 0-2 |

**SEMI-FINALS**

| | | | | | | | |
|---|---|---|---|---|---|---|---|
| Ponteland United | v | Newcastle Utd Res | 2-3 | Newcastle Blue Star | v | Blyth Spartans | 0-3 |

**FINAL**

| | | | | |
|---|---|---|---|---|
| NEWCASTLE U RS | v | BLYTH SPARTANS | 2-1 | at St James' Park, Newcastle United FC |

## NORTHUMBERLAND BENEVOLENT BOWL 1998-99
### Sponsored by "Brother"
(12 entries)   (FOUNDED 1975-76)

**LAST SEASON'S FINAL:** Seaton Delaval Am  v  N/C Benfield Park  4-2 aet

**MOST WINS:** Morpeth Town  2    Stobswood Welfare  2

**FIRST ROUND** (4 matches)

| | | | | | | | |
|---|---|---|---|---|---|---|---|
| North Shields Athletic | v | Walker Ledwood F. | 2-0 | Spittal Rovers | v | Heddon Institute | 4-2 |
| Walker Central | v | Heaton Stannington | 2-0 | Newbiggin C W | v | Shankhouse | 0-5 |

**SECOND ROUND** (4 matches)

| | | | | | | | |
|---|---|---|---|---|---|---|---|
| Spittal Rovers | v | Walker Central | 3-0 | North Shields Ath. | v | Seaton Delaval Amt | 3-0 |
| N Benfield Park | v | N S St Colmubas | 1-1 2-3 | Amble Town | v | Shankhouse | 1-3 |

**SEMI-FINALS**

| | | | | | | | |
|---|---|---|---|---|---|---|---|
| Spittal Rovers | v | North Shields St C. | 2-1 | Shankhouse | v | North Shields Athletic | 0-2 |

**FINAL**

| | | | | |
|---|---|---|---|---|
| SPITTAL ROVERS | v | NORTH SHIELDS A. | 0-2 | at Craig Park, Morpeth Town FC |

# NOTTINGHAMSHIRE F.A.

Tel: 0115 941 8954   Fax: 0115 941 5254
7 Clarendon Street, Nottingham NG1 5HS
**Secretary:** Mike Kilbee
**Executives (Responsibility)**   Tom Goodwin (Referees)
Helen Bennett (Womens Football)

| | | | | |
|---|---|---|---|---|
| **Number of Affiliated Clubs** | Senior: | 681 | U.18: | 202 |
| **Number of Affiliated Leagues:** | Senior: | 11 | Junior: | 4 |

**President:** D K Ridyard
**Chairman:** J J Waterall

**County Representative Teams:** U18
**Inter County Competitions:**   FA County Youth Cup, East Midlands Youth Combination

## NOTTINGHAMSHIRE SENIOR CUP 1998-99
### (34 entries)   (FOUNDED 1883-84)

**LAST SEASON'S FINAL:** Hucknall Town  v  Pelican  2-0

**MOST WINS:** Nottingham Forest  17   Sutton Town  17   Notts County  11

**FIRST ROUND** (16 matches)

| | | | | | | | | | |
|---|---|---|---|---|---|---|---|---|---|
| Kimberley Town | v | Ruddington United | 3-2 | | Eastwood Town | v | Linby C W | | 4-1 |
| Basford United | v | Sneinton | 0-8 | | Keyworth United | v | Cotgrave C W | | 2-4 |
| Hucknall Town | v | Gedling Town | 6-1 | | Rainworth M W | v | Thoresby C W | | 4-0 |
| Arnold Town | v | Pelican | 5-2 | | Ollerton Town | v | Dunkirk | | 3-6 |
| B R S A Retford | v | Siemens | 0-2 | | Hucknall Rolls | v | Retford United | | 1-0 |
| Clipstone Welfare | v | I D P Newark | 2*3 | | Blidworth Welfare | v | Welbeck Colliery | | 1-0 |
| Greenwood Meadows | v | City-Sherwd Hospitals | 2-0 | | Collingham | v | Boots Athletic | | 0-4 |
| Radford | v | Notting'shire Police | 0*1 | | Wollaton | v | Southwell City | | 1-4 |

**SECOND ROUND** (8 matches)

| | | | | | | | | |
|---|---|---|---|---|---|---|---|---|
| Arnold Town | v | I D P Newark | 7-3 | | Sneinton | v | Eastwood Town | 1-3 |
| Boots Athletic | v | Dunkirk | 1-0 | | Cotgrave C W | v | Kimberley Town | 4-2 |
| Hucknall Rolls Roycs | v | Rainworth M W | 5-2 | | Blidworth Welfare | v | Greenwood Meadows | 4-2 |
| Hucknall Town | v | Southwell City | 7-1 | | Notting'shire Police | v | Siemens | 4-2 |

**THIRD ROUND** (4 matches)

| | | | | | | | | |
|---|---|---|---|---|---|---|---|---|
| Notts Police | v | Hucknall Rolls Royce | 1-0 | | Arnold Town | v | Cotgrave C W | 7-0 |
| Blidworth Welfare | v | Boots Athletic | 4-2 | | Hucknall Town | v | Eastwood Town | 3-1 |

**SEMI-FINALS**

| | | | | | | | | |
|---|---|---|---|---|---|---|---|---|
| Blidworth Welfare | v | Hucknall Town | 1-4 | | Arnold Town | v | Notts Police | 1-0 |

**FINAL**

| | | | | | |
|---|---|---|---|---|---|
| ARNOLD TOWN | v | HUCKNALL TOWN | 2-1 | | at Coronation Park, Eastwood Town FC |

# OXFORDSHIRE F.A.
Tel: 01865 331360   Fax: 01865 331360
Rondamician, West End Lane, Merton, Bicester, Oxon OX6 0NG
**Secretary:** Ron Leaver
**Executives (Responsibility)**   Trevor Spindler (Coaching Exams/Courses)
                                   John Abrams (Referees)
                                   R T Watts (Womens Football)
**Number of Affiliated Clubs**   350
**Number of Affiliated Leagues:**   12
**County Representative Teams:** Under 18
**Inter County Competitions:**   Under 18

**President:** J W Roughton
**Chairman:** G R Mills

## OXFORDSHIRE SENIOR CUP 1998-99
(32 entries)  (FOUNDED 1884-85)

**LAST SEASON'S FINAL:**  Witney Town  v  Oxford City  1-1 aet (Witney won on penalties)

**MOST WINS:**  Oxford City 31    Witney Town  9    Oxford United  8

**FIRST ROUND** (9 matches)

| | | | | | | |
|---|---|---|---|---|---|---|
| Peppard | v | Charlton United | 5-1 | Watlington | v | Middle Barton | 1-0 |
| Yarnton | v | Sonning Common | 1*3 | Berinsfield | v | Chinnor | 2-3 |
| Checkenden Sports | v | Goring | 4-1 | Eynsham | v | Fritwell | 1-0 |
| Hook Norton | v | | 2-1 | Easingon Sports | v | Adderbury Park | 1-0 |
| Kidlington | v | Old Woodstock T | 4p1 2*2 | | | |

**SECOND ROUND** (10 matches)

| | | | | | | |
|---|---|---|---|---|---|---|
| Henley Town | v | Checkenden Sports | 1-0 | North Leigh | v | Clanfield | 6-2 |
| Easington Sports | v | Chinnor | 3-1 | Quarry Nomads | v | Ardley United | 1-2 |
| Headington Amateurs | v | Eynsham | 4p5 3*3 | Hook Norton | v | Banbury United | 1-3 |
| Bicester Town | v | Sonning Common | 4-0 | Carterton Town | v | Worcester College OB | 5-1 |
| Peppard | v | Watlington | 1-01-0 | Kidlington | v | Launton Sports | 2-0 |

**THIRD ROUND** (5 matches)

| | | | | | | |
|---|---|---|---|---|---|---|
| Easington Sports | v | Kidlington | 1-6 | Banbury United | v | Bicester | 6-0 |
| North Leigh | v | Eynsham | 1-0 | Ardley United | v | Peppard | 1-2 |
| Carterton Town | v | Henley Town | 2-1 | | | |

**FOURTH ROUND** (4 matches)

| | | | | | | |
|---|---|---|---|---|---|---|
| North Leigh | v | Oxford City* | 0-2 | Kidlington | v | Peppard | 1-3 |
| Banbury United | v | Thame United* | 2-1 | Witney Town* | v | Carterton Town | 1-2 |

**SEMI-FINALS**

| | | | | |
|---|---|---|---|---|
| Peppard | v | Oxford City | 1-4 | at Witney Town FC |
| Carterton Town | v | Banbury United | 3-1 | at Witney Town FC |

**FINAL**

| | | | | |
|---|---|---|---|---|
| CARTERTON TOWN | v | OXFORD CITY | 0*3 | at The Manor Ground, Oxford United FC |

# SHEFFIELD & HALLAMSHIRE F.A.

Tel: 0114 267 0068   Fax: 0114 268 3348
5 Onslow Road, Sheffield S11 7AF

**Secretary:** G Thompson

**Press Officer:** J P Hope-Gill

**Executives (Responsibility)**   John Warnock (Coaching Exams/Courses)
Peter Jackson (Referees)
Julie Callaghan (Womens Football)

| | | | | | | |
|---|---|---|---|---|---|---|
| **Number of Affiliated Clubs** | Senior: | 888 | U.18: | 243 | **President:** C L Milner | |
| **Number of Affiliated Leagues:** | Senior: | 17 | Junior: | 7 | **Chairman:** M Matthews | |

**County Representative Teams:** Under 18

**Inter County Competitions:**   East Midlands Youth Combination, FA County Youth Cup

## SHEFFIELD & HALLAMSHIRE CUP 1998-99
(51 entries)   (FOUNDED 1876-77)

**LAST SEASON'S FINAL:** Emley v Parkgate 3-0

**MOST WINS:** Sheffield 10   Frickley Athletic 9   Sheffield Wednesday 9

**SECOND QUALIFYING ROUND** (19 matches)

| | | | | | | | |
|---|---|---|---|---|---|---|---|
| Harworth Colliery | v | Mexborough Main St | 3-1 | Davy | v | Parramore Sports | 2-4 |
| Yorkshire Main | v | Grapes Roy Hancock | 2-0 | Brinsworth Athletic | v | Grimethorpe M W | 1-3 |
| A B S Kilnhurst | v | Ecclesfield Red Rose | 4*3 | Sheffield Bankers | v | Sheffield Cent. | 1-1 3*2 |
| Penistone Church | v | Frecheville C A | 0-2 | Hemsworth Town | v | Mexborough Athletic | 0-1 |
| Caribbean Sports | v | Athersley Recreation | 2-3 | High Green Villa | v | Elsecar Market Hotel | 8-1 |
| Queens Hotel | v | Sheffield Lane Top | 0-1 | Phoenix | v | Wombwell Main | 2-4 |
| Wombwell Town | v | Avesta Sheffield Spts | 2-3 | Woodhouse W End | v | Thorpe Hesley | 1-2 |
| Old Edwardians | v | South Kirkby Colliery | 2-5 | H & H Hoyland Cmn | v | The Wetherby | 2-1 |
| NCB Maltby M W | v | Oughtibridge WMSC | 2-0 | Wickersley | v | Treeton Welfare | 0-3 |
| Norton Woodseats | v | Swinton Athletic | 4-5 | | | | |

**FIRST ROUND PROPER** (16 matches)

| | | | | | | | |
|---|---|---|---|---|---|---|---|
| Grimethorpe MW | v | Harworth C I | 3-5 | Worksop Town | v | Treeton Welfare | 7-1 |
| Sheffield Lane Top | v | Stocksbridge P S | 0-7 | Thorpe Hesley | v | Frecheville C A | 2-1 |
| Mexborough Athletic | v | Sheffield Bankers | 2-7 | Emley | v | Parkgate | 2-2 4-0 |
| Hallam | v | Wombwell Main | 0-1 | Worsbrough Bridge | v | High Green Villa | 1-0 |
| Parramore Sports | v | Brodsworth | 3-0 | Denaby United | v | South Kirkby Colliery | 8-1 |
| Rossington Main | v | Hare & Hounds | 3-0 | Maltby Main | v | Frickley Athletic | 0-3 |
| Avesta Sheffield | v | Doncaster Rvrs | AS W-O | Kilnhurst | v | Athersley Recreation | 1-3 |
| Norton Woodseats | v | NCB Maltby MW | 1-3 | Yorkshire Main | v | Sheffield | 1-3 |

**SECOND ROUND PROPER** (8 matches)

| | | | | | | | |
|---|---|---|---|---|---|---|---|
| Harworth Coll. Inst. | v | Worksop Town | 1-4 | Avesta Sheffield | v | Sheffield | 2-4 |
| Thorpe Hesley | v | Stocksbridge Pk Stls | 1-2 | Emley | v | NCB Malby M W | 6-0 |
| Athersley Recreation | v | Hare & Hounds | 2-1 | Parramore Sports | v | Wombwell Main | 2-3 |
| Frickley Athletic | v | Sheffield Bankers | 4-1 | Denaby United | v | Worsbrough Bridge | 4-2 |

**QUARTER-FINALS**

| | | | | | | | |
|---|---|---|---|---|---|---|---|
| Frickley Athletic | v | Denaby United | 1-0 | Worksop Town | v | Stocksbridge Pk Stls | 1-2 |
| Sheffield | v | Emley | 1-3 | Wombwell Main | v | Athersley Rec | 1-0 |

**SEMI-FINALS**

| | | | | | | |
|---|---|---|---|---|---|---|
| Wombwell Main | v | Emley (at Worsbro' Br) 0-2 | Frickley Athletic | v | Stocksbridge Pk Steels | 1-2 |

**FINAL**

| | | | | |
|---|---|---|---|---|
| EMLEY | v | STOCKSBRIDGE PS 0-1 | at Hillsborough, Sheffield Wednesday FC |

# SHROPSHIRE F.A.

Tel: 01743 362769   Fax: 01743 240474

Gay Meadow, Abbey Foregate, Shrewsbury, Shropshire SY2 6AB

**Secretary:** David Rowe          **Press Officer:** Neil Sambrook

**Executives (Responsibility)**   Alan Penton (Coaching Exams/Courses)

David Rowe (Referees/Womens Football)

**Number of Affiliated Clubs**    Senior:    569        U.18:      95        **President:** J S Constable

**Number of Affiliated Leagues:** Senior:      9        Junior:      5       **Chairman:** S T Farmer

**County Representative Teams:** U18, Womens, U16

**Inter County Competitions:**    FA County Youth, Midland County Youth, Multi-Print Trophy

## SHROPSHIRE SENIOR CUP 1998-99
### (4 entries)   (FOUNDED1877-88)

**LAST SEASON'S FINAL:** Shrewsbury Town  v  Telford United  1-0

**MOST WINS:** Shrewsbury Town  53    Telford United  34    Oswestry Town  11

**FINAL**

TELFORD UNITED  v  SHREWSBURY TN  0-1          at Buck's Head, Telford United FC.

## SHROPSHIRE COUNTY CUP 1998-99
### (20 entries)

**LAST SEASON'S FINAL:** Whitchurch Alport  v  Morda United  3-2

**FIRST ROUND** (4 matches)

| | | | | | | | |
|---|---|---|---|---|---|---|---|
| Broseley | v | Newport Town | 3p4 2*2 | Shawbury United | v | Shifnal Town Res | 0-3 |
| Tibberton United | v | Wem Town | 1-2 | Clee Hill United | v | Wellington Amateurs | 3-1 |

**SECOND ROUND** (8 matches)

| | | | | | | | |
|---|---|---|---|---|---|---|---|
| Bandon | v | Morda United | 3-0 | Belvidere | v | Oakengates Town | 4-5 |
| Belle Vue O B | v | Little Drayton Rngrs | 2-4 | Clee Hill United | v | Meole Brace | 3-2 |
| Ludlow Town | v | Star | 0-3 | Newport Town | v | Shifnal Town Res | 5-2 |
| Snailbeach White Starv | | Hanwood United | 0-7 | Wem Town | v | Whitchurch Alport | 0-1 |

**THIRD ROUND** (4 matches)

| | | | | | | | |
|---|---|---|---|---|---|---|---|
| Whitchurch Alport | v | Star | 3*4 | Little Drayton Rngrs | v | Clee Hill United | 1-0 |
| Bandon | v | Newport Town | 2-1 | Oakengates Town | v | Hanwood United | 1-0 |

**SEMI-FINALS**

| | | | | |
|---|---|---|---|---|
| Bandon | v | Little Drayton Rangers | 1-0 | at Newport Town FC |
| Oakengates Town | v | Star | 0-4 | at Ironbridge Town FC |

**FINAL**

| | | | | |
|---|---|---|---|---|
| BANDON | v | STAR | 3p0 1*1 | at Gay Meadow, Shrewsbury Town FC |

*Taunton Town and Clevedon Town (stripes) battle it out in the Somerset Premier Cup Final at Yeovil Town. Clevedon Town won 5-4 on penalties following a 3-3 draw*
*Photo: Tim Lancaster*

# SOMERSET F.A.

Tel: 01761 410280   Fax: 01761 410477

30 North Road, Midsomer Norton, Bath, Somerset BA3 2QQ

**Secretary:** Mrs H Marchment

**Executives (Responsibility)**   I Tincknell (Coaching Courses/Exams)
J H Day (Referees), L Clements (Womens Football)

**Number of Affiliated Clubs**   Senior:   78      U.18:   407         **President:** F P Hillier

**Number of Affiliated Leagues:**   Senior:   1      Junior:   22      **Chairman:** A J Hobbs

**County Representative Teams:** Senior, U18, Womens

**Inter County Competitions:**   FA County Youth, South West Counties Championship (Senior, Youth & Womens)

## SOMERSET PREMIER CUP 1998-99
### (21 entries)   (FOUNDED 1948-49)

**LAST SEASON'S FINAL:**  Yeovil Town  v  Clevedon Town   1-0

**MOST WINS:**  Bath City   17     Yeovil Town   15     Bristol City   5

**FIRST ROUND** (5 matches)

| | | | | | | |
|---|---|---|---|---|---|---|
| Wellington | v | Odd Down | 3-0 | Paulton Rovers | v Yeovil Town | 2-1 |
| Bath City | v | Backwell United | 3-1 | Keynsham Town | v Brislington | 1-3 |
| Minehead Town | v | Welton Rovers | 6-3 | | | |

**SECOND ROUND** (8 matches)

| | | | | | | |
|---|---|---|---|---|---|---|
| Bristol Manor Farm | v | Paulton Rovers | 1-2 | Frome Town | v Mangotsfield United | 0-7 |
| Chard Town | v | Wellington | 0-5 | Minehead Town | v Street | 1*3 |
| Glastonbury | v | Keynsham T/Bris'ton | 0-5 | Bridgwater Town | v Taunton Town | 4-8 |
| Bishop Sutton | v | Bath City | 1-4 | Clevedon Town | v Weston super Mare | 2-0 |

**THIRD ROUND** (4 matches)

| | | | | | | |
|---|---|---|---|---|---|---|
| Street | v | Paulton Rovers | 4p2 0*0 | Brislington | v Bath City | 2p3 2*2 |
| Clevedon Town | v | Mangotsfield United | 2-1 | Wellington | v Taunton Town | 1-2 |

**SEMI-FINALS**

| | | | | | | |
|---|---|---|---|---|---|---|
| Taunton Town | v | Street | 3-2 | Bath City | v Clevedon Town | 3p4 0*0 |

**FINAL**

| | | | | |
|---|---|---|---|---|
| Clevedon Town | v | Taunton Town | 5p4 3*3 | at Huish Park, Yeovil Town FC |

## SOMERSET SENIOR CUP 1998-99
### (57 entries)   (FOUNDED 1895-96)

**LAST SEASON'S FINAL:**  Shepton Mallet  v  Radstock Town   3-1

**MOST WINS:**  Paulton Rovers   12     Radstock Town   12     Welton Rovers   9

**SEMI-FINALS**

| | | | | | | |
|---|---|---|---|---|---|---|
| Timsbury Athletic | v | Fry Club | 1-2 | Shepton Mallet | v Backwekk United Res | 0-1 |

**FINAL**

| | | | | |
|---|---|---|---|---|
| Fry Club | v | Backwell United Res | 2-0 | at Paulton Rovers FC |

# STAFFORDSHIRE F.A.

Tel: 01785 256994  Fax: 01785 224334
County Showground, Weston Road, Stafford ST18 0DB
**Secretary:** Brian Adshead     **Press Officer:** David Shelton
**Executives (Responsibility)**   I Cooper (Coaching Exams),  N Broad (Referees)
                                  S Eccleston (Coaching Courses), D Blairs (Womens Football)
**Number of Affiliated Clubs**    Senior:    609          U.18:      556
**Number of Affiliated Leagues:** Senior:    16           Junior:    13        **Chairman:** Robert Heath
**County Representative Teams:** Under 18 Boys, Ladies, Under 16 Girls
**Inter County Competitions:**   FA County Youth Challenge Cup, Midland Counties Youth Championships

## STAFFORDSHIRE SENIOR CUP 1998-99
(25 entries)  (FOUNDED 1877-78)

**LAST SEASON'S FINAL:** Bilston Town  v  Tamworth  2-1 aggregate

**MOST WINS:** Stoke City  18     Aston Villa  16     West Bromwich Albion  13

**FIRST ROUND** (9 matches)

| | | | | | | | |
|---|---|---|---|---|---|---|---|
| Blakenall | v | Leek Town | 1-2 | Bloxwich Town | v | Rocester | 1-1 0-4 |
| Hednesford Town | v | Kidsgrove Athletic | 1-3 | Leek CSOB | v | Wednesfield | 4-1 |
| Newcastle Town | v | Shifnal Town | 2-1 | Pelsall Villa | v | Chasetown | 1-2 |
| Port Vale | v | Boldmere St Mich's | 10-0 | Rushall Olympic | v | Sutton Coldfield Town | 4-1 |
| Stourbridge | v | Oldbury United | 2-3 | | | | |

**SECOND ROUND** (8 matches)

| | | | | | | | |
|---|---|---|---|---|---|---|---|
| Bridgnorth Town | v | Leek CSOB | 4-1 | Halesowen Harriers | v | Chasetown | 0A0 2-5 |
| Oldbury United | v | Knypersley Victoria | 0-0 5*4 | Rushall Olympic | v | Stafford Rangers | 3-0 |
| Rocester | v | Newcastle Town | 0*1 | Kidsgrove Athletic | v | Port Vale | 0-2 |
| Leek Town | v | Bilston Town | 3-0 | Tamworth | v | Stoke City | 0-6 |

(Tie no 5 ordered to be re-played as Newcastle Town fielded an ineligible player)

**THIRD ROUND** (4 matches)

| | | | | | | | |
|---|---|---|---|---|---|---|---|
| Bridgnorth Town | v | Stoke City | 1-2 | Chasetown | v | Port Vale | 1-2 |
| Oldbury United | v | Rocester | 1-2 | Rushall Olympic | v | Leek Town | 1-3 |

**SEMI-FINALS**

| | | | | | | | |
|---|---|---|---|---|---|---|---|
| Rocester | v | Stoke City | 1-8 | Leek Town | v | Port Vale | 3-1 |

**FINAL**

| | | | | | |
|---|---|---|---|---|---|
| LEEK TOWN | v | STOKE CITY | 1-3 | at Harrison Park, Leek Town FC |

*Suffolk Senior Cup Round One: East Bergholt (green/black) 1 Mildenhall Town (yellow) 1*
*Mildenhall midfielder Tuck attempts to get past his East Bergholt marker in the first-half*
*Photo: M Wray*

# SUFFOLK F.A.

Tel: 01449 673481   Fax: 01449 770983
2 Millfields, Haughley, Stowmarket IP14 3PU
**Secretary:** William Steward      **Press Officer:** v
**Executives (Responsibility)**      C Rowe (Coaching Exams/Courses), Brian Thompson (Referees)
                                     Angela Locke (Womens Football)
**Number of Affiliated Clubs**    Senior:    450      U.18:    200      **President:** Ernest Brown
**Number of Affiliated Leagues:** Senior:    13       Junior:   7      **Chairman:** Gordo
Rayner
**County Representative Teams:** Intermediate (adult), U18, U16, Womens

## SUFFOLK PREMIER CUP 1998-99
### (10 entries) (FOUNDED 1958-59)

**LAST SEASON'S FINAL:** Sudbury Wanderers  v  Lowestoft Town   0-0, 5-2 aet
**MOST WINS:** Sudbury Town  12    Bury Town  10    Lowestoft Town  5

**PRELIMINARY ROUND** (2 matches)

| | | | | | | |
|---|---|---|---|---|---|---|
| Stowmarket Town | v | Woodbridge Town | 1-2 | Sudbury Town | v | Bury Town | 1-0 |

**FIRST ROUND** (4 matches)

| | | | | | | | |
|---|---|---|---|---|---|---|---|
| Cornard United | v | Ipswich Wanderers | 2-3 | Woodbridge Town | v | Sudbury Town | 1-2 |
| Felixstowe Port & T | v | Sudbury Wanderers | 1-0 | Newmarket Town | v | Lowestoft Town | 2-1 |

**SEMI-FINALS**

| | | | | | | | |
|---|---|---|---|---|---|---|---|
| Ipswich Wanderers | v | Newmarket Town | 1-3 | Sudbury Town | v | Felixstowe Port & Town | 4-2 |

**FINAL**

| | | | | |
|---|---|---|---|---|
| NEWMARKET TN | v | SUDBURY TOWN | 1-0 | at Newmarket Town FC |

## SUFFOLK SENIOR CUP 1998-99
### (33 entries) (FOUNDED 1885-86)

**LAST SEASON'S FINAL:** Grundisburgh  v  Stonham Aspal  2-1
**MOST WINS:** Ipswich Town  16    Lowestoft Town  10    Stowmarket Town  8

**PRELIMINARY ROUND** (1 match)

| | | | |
|---|---|---|---|
| Leiston | v | Framlingham Town | 1-3 |

**FIRST ROUND PROPER** (16 matches)

| | | | | | | | |
|---|---|---|---|---|---|---|---|
| Stonham Aspal | v | Grundisburgh | 0-2 | Westerfield United | v | Bungay Town | 2-3 |
| Whitton United | v | Brantham Athletic | 2-3 | Long Melford | v | Kirkley | 2-2 2-4 |
| Ipswich Wndrs Res | v | Beccles Town | 3-2 | Hadleigh United | v | Sudbury Athletic | 1-3 |
| Oulton B & L'toft Rail | v | Needham | 0-8 | Framlingham Town | v | Haughley United | 0-0 2-1 |
| Brandon Town | v | Walton United | 1-1 3-7 | East Bergholt United | v | Mildenhall Town | 1-1 0-3 |
| Capel Plough | v | Sudbury Wndrs Res | 4-2 | Stowmarket Tn Rs | v | BS Fonnereau | 1-1 0-2 |
| Ipswich Athletic | v | Old Newton United | 6-2 | Ashlea | v | BT Hollies | 3-0 |
| Walsham Le Willows | v | Lowestoft Town Res | 1-2 | Haverhill Rovers | v | Achilles | 4-1 |

**SECOND ROUND** (8 matches)

| | | | | | | | |
|---|---|---|---|---|---|---|---|
| Needham Market | v | Mildenhall Town | 2-1 | Capel Plough | v | Haverhill Rovers | 1-3 |
| Framlingham Town | v | Grundisburgh | 2-3 | Walton United | v | BS Fonnereau Athletic | 1-0 |
| Sudbury Athletic | v | Bungay Town | 3-0 | Kirkley | v | Ashlea | 3-1 |
| Brantham Athletic | v | Ipswich Wndrs Res | 5-0 | Ipswich Athletic | v | Lowestoft Town Res | 4-2 |

**QUARTER-FINALS**

| | | | | | | | |
|---|---|---|---|---|---|---|---|
| Ipswich Athletic | v | Grundisburgh | 2-0 | Sudbury Athletic | v | Walton United | 1-4 |
| Kirkley | v | Needham Market | 0-5 | Brantham Athletic | v | Haverhill Rovers | 2-0 |

**SEMI-FINALS**

| | | | | | | | |
|---|---|---|---|---|---|---|---|
| Needham Market | v | Ipswich Athletic | 1-0 | Brantham Athletic | v | Walton United | 1-4 |

**FINAL**

# SURREY F.A.

Tel: 01372 373543   Fax: 01372 361310
321 Kingston Road, Leatherhead, Surrey DT22 7TU
**Secretary:** Ray Ward
**Executives (Responsibility)**　　David Bromley (Caoching Exams/Courses)
　　　　　　　　　　　　　　　Ray Lewis (Rererees)
　　　　　　　　　　　　　　　Peter Adams (Womens Football)

**Number of Affiliated Clubs**　　Senior:　　38　　　　　　　　　　　　**President:** A P Adams
**Number of Affiliated Leagues:** Senior:　　2　　　　Junior:　　20　　**Chairman:** J A Crook
**County Representative Teams:** Under 18, Womens
**Inter County Competitions:**　　Home Counties Womens Competition, FA County Youth Cup

## SURREY SENIOR CUP 1998-99
### (FOUNDED 1882-83)

**LAST SEASON'S FINAL:** Kingstonian  v  Woking   1-1 aet, 2-1

**MOST WINS:** Worthing 20　　Eastbourne Town　12　　Southwick　10

**PRELIMINARY ROUND** (5 matches)

| | | | | | | |
|---|---|---|---|---|---|---|
| Corinthian Casuals | v | Banstead Athletic | 0-0 | Dorking | v | God'ming & G'ford 1-1, 2-1 |
| Westfield | v | Chessington & Hook | 2-1 | Dulwich Hamlet | v | Netherne  3-0 |

**FIRST ROUND**

| | | | | | | | |
|---|---|---|---|---|---|---|---|
| Ash United | v | Chertsey Town | 2-4 | Ashford Tn (Middx) | v | Crystal Palace | 2-1 |
| Camberley Town | v | Dulwich Hamlet | 0-2 | Carshalton Athletic | v | Croydon Athletic | 2-0 |
| Metropolitan Police | v | Woking | 1-3 | Redhill | v | Walton Casuals | 7-0 |
| Sutton United | v | Farnham Town | 7-0 | Tooting & Mitcham | v | Lingfield | 2-0 |
| Walton & Hersham | v | Merstham | 0-0, 0-6 | Croydon | v | Westfield | 4-0 |
| Dorking | v | Leatherhead | 1-2 | Molesey | v | Chipstead | 4-1 |
| Cranleigh | v | Epsom & Ewell | 0-4 | Kingstonian | v | Cobham | 5-3 |
| Raynes Park Vale | v | Whyteleafe | 1-6 | | | | |

**SECOND ROUND**

| | | | | | | | |
|---|---|---|---|---|---|---|---|
| Kingstonian | v | Croydon | 2-2, 4-1 | Dulwich Hamlet | v | Walton & Hersham | 0-2 |
| Woking | v | Epsom & Ewell | 5-0 | Leatherhead | v | Tooting & Mitcham U | 2-3 |
| Banstead Athletic | v | Ashford Town (Middx) | 0-1 | Chertsey Town | v | Molesey | 0-2 |
| Sutton United | v | Redhill | 6-1 | Whyteleafe | v | Carshalton Athletic | 0-3 |

**THIRD ROUND**

| | | | | | | | |
|---|---|---|---|---|---|---|---|
| Woking | v | Walton & Hersham | 3-0 | Ashford Town (Mx) | v | Sutton United | 1-2 |
| Molesey | v | Kingstonian | 0-1 | Carshalton Athletic | v | Tooting & Mitcham | 2-0 |

**SEMI FINAL**

| | | | | | | | |
|---|---|---|---|---|---|---|---|
| Kingstonian | v | Carshalton Ath | 1-1, 2-3 | Sutton United | v | Woking | 6-0 |

**FINAL**

| | | | | |
|---|---|---|---|---|
| SUTTON UNITED | v | CARSAHLTON ATH | 3-0 | at Metropolitan Police FC |

# SUSSEX ROYAL ULSTER RIFLES CHARITY CUP 1998-99
### (36 entries)   (FOUNDED 1896-97)

**LAST SEASON'S FINAL:**  Wick  v  Shoreham  3-2
**MOST WINS:**  Horsham  13   Worthing  12   Southwick  10

**PRELIMINARY ROUND** (4 matches)

| | | | | | | |
|---|---|---|---|---|---|---|
| Whitehawk | v | Burgess Hill Town | 0-2 | Three Bridges | v  Eastbourne United | 2-1 |
| Wick | v | Arundel | 3-1 | Storrington | v  Horsham YMCA | 1-3 |

**FIRST ROUND** (16 matches)

| | | | | | | |
|---|---|---|---|---|---|---|
| Crowborough Athletic | v | Crawley Down Village | 1-2 | Eastbourne Town | v  Shinewater Assoiation | 1-0 |
| Burgess Hill Town | v | Saltdean United | 2-0 | Peacehaven & Tels. | v  Hailsham Town | 2-3 |
| East Grinstead Town | v | Langney Sports | 1-4 | Three Bridges | v  Withdean | 2*2 1-3 |
| Oakwood | v | Newhaven | 2-3 | Sidley United | v  Ringmer | 3-2 |
| Chichester City | v | Broadbridge Heath | 2-0 | Hassocks | v  Sidlesham | 1-0 |
| Wick | v | Shoreham | 2*1 | Portfield | v  Lancing | 4-1 |
| East Preston | v | Littlehampton Town | 3-0 | Horsham YMCA | v  Worthing United | 3-0 |
| Pagham | v | Mile Oak | 3-0 | Southwick | v  Selsey | 0-1 |

**SECOND ROUND** (8 matches)

| | | | | | | |
|---|---|---|---|---|---|---|
| Newhaven | v | Withdean | 1-3 | Langney Sports | v  Burgess Hill Town | 0-4 |
| Crawley Down Village | v | Hailsham Town | 2-0 | Sidley United | v  Eastbourne Town | 1-5 |
| Pagham | v | Horsham YMCA | 3*4 | East Preston | v  Wick | 0-2 |
| Chichester City | v | Portfield | 0-1 | Selsey | v  Hassocks | 0-2 |

**THIRD ROUND** (4 matches)

| | | | | | | |
|---|---|---|---|---|---|---|
| Burgess Hill Town | v | Hassocks | 3-0 | Crawley Down Vlge | v  Withdean | 5-2 |
| Horsham YMCA | v | Wick | 3-6 | Portfield | v  Eastbourne Town | 2-1 |

**SEMI-FINALS**

| | | | | | | |
|---|---|---|---|---|---|---|
| Wick | v | Crawley Down Village | 5-1 | Portfield | v  Burgess Hill Town | 1-3 |

**FINAL**

| | | | | |
|---|---|---|---|---|
| BURGESS HILL TN | v | WICK | 0*1 | at Lancing FC att;250 |

*Worthing (Ryman Division One) celebrate after beating Hastings Town 3-0 in the Sussex Senior Cup Final played at Crawley's Broadfield Stadium*

*Photo: Andrew Chitty*

# SUSSEX F.A.

Tel: 01903 753547   Fax: 01903 761608
Culver Road, Lancing, West Sussex BN15 9AX
**Secretary & Press Officer:**       David Worsfold
**Executives (Responsibility)**     L Thompson (Coaching Exams)   T West (Referees)
                                     J Hemsley (Womens Football)   H Millington (Coaching Courses)
**Number of Affiliated Clubs**       Senior:     958        U.18:      262
**Number of Affiliated Leagues:**    Senior:      17        Junior:     10        **President:** John Davey
**County Representative Teams:** Senior, U18, U15, Womens, U18, U15        **Chairman:** Alan Knight
**Inter County Competitions:**       FA County Youth, Home Counties Youth,
                                     South West Counties Senior & Womens, Southern Counties Intermediate

---

Needham Market     v     Walton United          0-1         at Portman Road, Ipswich

## SUSSEX SENIOR CUP 1998-99
### (FOUNDED 1882-83)


**LAST SEASON'S FINAL:**  Hastings Town   v   Burgess Hill Town   2-1


**MOST WINS:**  Worthing 20     Eastbourne Town   12     Southwick   10


**FIRST ROUND** (12 matches)

| | | | | | | | |
|---|---|---|---|---|---|---|---|
| Oakwood | v | Chichester City | 0-3 | Sidlesham | v | Portfield | 2-3 |
| Storrington | v | Lancing | 1-4 | Shinewater Assoc. | v | Worhing United | 5-2 |
| Sidley United | v | East Preston | 1-2 | Hailsham Town | v | Newhaven | 8-2 |
| Mile Oak | v | Crawley Down Village | 2*1 | Lewes | v | Crowborough Athletic | 5-0 |
| Arundel | v | Southwick | 2-6 | East Grinstead T | v | Broadbridge Heath @B | 1-4 |
| Three Bridges | v | Peacehaven & Tels. | 1-0 | Withdean | v | Eastbourne United | 0-3 |

**SECOND ROUND** (16 matches)

| | | | | | | | |
|---|---|---|---|---|---|---|---|
| HailshamTown | v | Saltdean United | 2-4 | Mile Oak | v | Portfield | 4-5 |
| Burgess Hill Town | v | Lancing | 4-1 | Eastbourne United | v | St Leonards | 4*4 0-3 |
| Bognor Regis Town | v | Wick | 1-2 | Eastbourne Town | v | Southwick | 4-2 |
| East Preston | v | Langney Sports | 1-0 | Pagham | v | Hassocks | 2-1 |
| Broadbridge Heath | v | Hastings Town | 0-5 | Brighton & Hove Alb | v | Lewes | @W 0-3 |
| Whitehawk | v | Littlehampton Town | 3-1 | Ringmer | v | Selsey | 3-0 |
| Crawley Town | v | Shoreham | 3-0 | Horsham | v | Chichester City | 4-2 |
| Shinewater Assoc. | v | Worthing | 0-7 | Three Bridges | v | Horsham YMCA | 4-2 |

**THIRD ROUND** (8 matches)

| | | | | | | | |
|---|---|---|---|---|---|---|---|
| Wick | v | Burgess Hill Town | 2-5 | Lewes | v | Pagham | 1-0 |
| Whitehawk | v | Eastbourne Town | 4-1 | Crawley Town | v | Ringmer | 3-0 |
| East Preston | v | St Leonards | 0-3 | Hastings Town | v | Portfield | 4-0 |
| Three Bridges | v | Worthing | 0-1 | Horsham | v | Saltdean U 4p3,1V3,3*3,0*0 | |
| (Tie no. 8 ordered to be re-played) | | | | | | | |

**FOURTH ROUND** (4 matches)

| | | | | | | | |
|---|---|---|---|---|---|---|---|
| Burgess Hill Town | v | Hastings Town | 0-1 | Lewes | v | Horsham | 0-1 |
| Worthing | v | St Leonards | 3-1 | Whitehawk | v | Crawley Town | 1-2 |

**SEMI-FINALS**

| | | | | |
|---|---|---|---|---|
| Worthing | v | Crawley Town | 2-0 | at Horsham FC |
| Hastings Town | v | Horsham | 2-1 | at Lancing FC |

**FINAL**

| | | | | |
|---|---|---|---|---|
| HASTINGS TOWN | v | WORTHING | 0-3 | at Broadfield Stadium, Crawley Town FC |

# WESTMORLAND F.A.

Tel: 01539 730946   Fax: 01539 730946
Unit 1, Angle Court, 21 Highgate, Kendal, Cumbria LA9 4DA
**Secretary:** P G Ducksbury
**Executives (Responsibility)**    County Office (Coaching Exams/Courses,
                                   Womens Football, Referees)

**Number of Affiliated Clubs**    Senior:    54    U.18:    18          **President:** J B Fleming
**Number of Affiliated Leagues:** Senior:    3     Junior:    1         **Chairman:** J C L Rigg
**County Representative Teams:** Senior, U18
**Inter County Competitions:**    FA County Youth, Association of Northern Counties Senior & Youth Competitions

## WESTMORLAND 'ALBERT YOUNG' CUP
(23 entries)   (FOUNDED 1896-97)

**LAST SEASON'S FINAL:** Kirkby Lonsdale v Kirkby Stephen  1-1 aet, 1-0
**MOST WINS:** Corinthians  11    Netherfield  8    Burneside  7    Windermere  7

**FIRST ROUND** (7 matches)

| | | | | | | | |
|---|---|---|---|---|---|---|---|
| Endmoor KGR | v | Burneside | 3-2 | Kirkby Lonsdale | v | Milnthorpe Corinthians | 1*3 |
| Staveley United | v | Keswick | 2-1 | Carleton Rovers | v | Appleby | 0-1 |
| Sedburgh Wanderers | v | Victoria Sporting | 3-2 | Ambleside United | v | Netherfield Kendal | |
| Wetheriggs United | v | Windermere SC | 3-1 | | | | |

**SECOND ROUND** (8 matches)

| | | | | | | | |
|---|---|---|---|---|---|---|---|
| Burton Thistle | v | Greystoke | 0-3 | Lunesdale United | v | Appleby | 3-6 |
| Grange Amateurs | v | Corinthians | 3-5 | Kendal County | v | Ambleside United | 2-1 |
| Carvetti United | v | Sedbergh Wanderers | 2-3 | Coniston | v | Staveley United | 2-1 |
| Endmoor KGR | v | Dent | 2*1 | Wetheriggs United | v | Braithwaite | 4-0 |

**THIRD ROUND** (4 matches)

| | | | | | | | |
|---|---|---|---|---|---|---|---|
| Endmoor KGR | v | Kendal County | 1-2 | Corinthians | v | Sedburgh Wanderers | 4-1 |
| Coniston | v | Appleby | 2*2 1*2 | Wetheriggs United | v | Greystoke | 6-0 |

**SEMI-FINALS**

| | | | | | | | |
|---|---|---|---|---|---|---|---|
| Corinthians | v | Kendal County | 2*3 | Appleby | v | Wetheriggs United | 3-1 |

**FINAL**
APPLEBY      v    KENDAL COUNTY   2-5    at Parkside Road, Netherfield Kendal FC

*Westmorland County FA U18 Team 1998-99*
*Back Row (L-R): Mike Bolton (Coach), Paul Wilson (Manager), Andrew Boardley, Christopher Dixon, Daniel Bird, David Marston, Nicky Dent, Lee Waddington, Christopher Bingley, Bruce Richardson (Physiotherapist), Mike Halhead (Coach)*
*Front Row (L-R): Christopher Park, Michael Moorhead, Matthew Wardle, Luke Laddell, Daryll Tomlinson (Captain), Stephen Savage, Paul Ainsworth, Phillip Carrick*

# WEST RIDING F.A.

Tel: 01132 821222   Fax: 01132 821525
Fleet Lane, Woodlesford, Leeds LS26 8NX
**Secretary & Press Officer:** G R Carter
**Executives (Responsibility)**      Contact Secretary for:
Coaching Exams/Courses, Referees, Womens Football
**Number of Affiliated Clubs**      Senior:    950      U.18:    300      **President:** A C Taylor
**Number of Affiliated Leagues:**  Senior:    40       Junior:  12       **Chairman:** G Pawson
**County Representative Teams:** Senior, Junior U18, Womens
**Inter County Competitions:**   Association of Northern Counties Senior, Junior U18 & Womens, FA County Youth

## WEST RIDING COUNTY CUP 1998-99
(18 entries)  (FOUNDED 1924-25)
**LAST SEASON'S FINAL:** Garforth Town  v  Liversedge  2-0
**MOST WINS:** Goole Town  11    Farsley Celtic  9    Guiseley  5

**FIRST ROUND** (2 matches)

| | | | | | | | |
|---|---|---|---|---|---|---|---|
| Harrogate Town | v | Bradford Park Avenue | 0-1 | Tadcaster Albion | v | Farsley Celtic | 1-3 |

**SECOND ROUND** (8 matches)

| | | | | | | | |
|---|---|---|---|---|---|---|---|
| Ossett Albion | v | Hatfield Main | 6-1 | Garforth Town | v | Selby Town | 1-3 |
| Thackley | v | Armthorpe Welfare | 2-1 | Pontefract Collieries | v | Farsley Celtic | 2*2 rep |
| Bradford Park Ave | v | Ossett Town | 2-1 | Glasshoughton W | v | Eccleshill United | 3-2 |
| Harrogate Railway | v | Guiseley | 3-5 | Liversedge | v | Yorkshire Amateurs | 6-1 |

**QUARTER-FINALS**

| | | | | | | | |
|---|---|---|---|---|---|---|---|
| Liversedge | v | Thackley | 6-0 | Glasshoughton Welf. | v | Ossett Albion | 0-1 |
| Selby Town | v | Bradford Park Avenue | 0-1 | Farsley Celtic | v | Guiseley | 3-2 |

**SEMI-FINALS**

| | | | | | | |
|---|---|---|---|---|---|---|
| Ossett Albion | v | Farsley Celtic | 4-3 | Bradford Park Avenue | v | Liversedge 2-0 |

**FINAL**

| | | | | |
|---|---|---|---|---|
| Bradford Park Avenue | v | Ossett Albion | 0-2 | at The County FA Ground, Fleet Lane, Leeds |

## WEST RIDING COUNTY FA CHALLENGE CUP
Winners: Storthes Hall

## DISTRICT FA CUP WINNERS

| | | | |
|---|---|---|---|
| BRADFORD: | FIELDS FC | KEIGHLEY: | PHOENIX |
| HEAVY WOOLLEN: | OVERTHORPE | HALIFAX: | BRIGHOUSE TOWN |

*Headquarters of the
West Riding County
Football Association*

# WILTSHIRE F.A.

Tel: 0   Fax: 0
Wiltshire SN2 3LG
**Secretary:** E M Parry          **Press Officer:** v
**Executives (Responsibility)**    v
                                   v
**Number of Affiliated Clubs**     Senior:   v     U.18:    v        **President:** v
**Number of Affiliated Leagues:**  Senior:   v     Junior:  v        **Chairman:** v
**County Representative Teams:** v
**Inter County Competitions:**    v

---

## WILTSHIRE PREMIER SHIELD 1998-99
### (11 entries)  (FOUNDED 1926-27)

**LAST SEASON'S FINAL:** Melksham Town  v  Salisbury City  0-0 aet, 5p3
**MOST WINS:**  Swindon Town  26   Salisbury City  11   Trowbridge Town  9

**FIRST ROUND** (3 matches)
| | | | | | | |
|---|---|---|---|---|---|---|
| Bemerton Hth Hqns | v | Highworth Town | 3-4 | Devizes Town | v | Melksham Town | 1-4 |
| Calne Town | v | Warminster Town | 2-3 | | | |

**SECOND ROUND** (4 matches)
| | | | | | | | |
|---|---|---|---|---|---|---|---|
| Swindon S'marine | v | Chippenham Town | 1-0 | Highworth Town | v | Downton | 4-0 |
| Westbury United | v | Melksham Town | 2-7 | Salisbury City | v | Warminster Town | 9-0 |

**SEMI-FINALS**
| | | | | | | | |
|---|---|---|---|---|---|---|---|
| Highworth Town | v | Salisbury City | 1-2 | Swindon S'marine | v | Melksham Town | 4-2 |

**FINAL**
SALISBURY CITY  v  SWINDON S'MARINE  2-1     at The County Ground, Swindon Town FC.

---

## WILTSHIRE SENIOR CUP 1998-99
### (13 entries)  (FOUNDED 1886-87)

**LAST SEASON'S FINAL:** Highworth Town  v  Purton  2-1 aet
**MOST WINS:**  Devizes Town  14   Swindon Town  10   Chippenham Town  8

**FIRST ROUND** (5 matches)
| | | | | | | | |
|---|---|---|---|---|---|---|---|
| Raychem Mowlem | v | Shrewton United | 2-0 | Wootton Bassett Tn | v | Bradford Town | 4-1 |
| Corsham Town | v | Bromham | 2-0 | Purton | v | Cricklade Town | 1-0 |
| 5 Wroughton | v | Malmesbury Victoria | 1*0 | | | |

**SECOND ROUND** (4 matches)
| | | | | | | | |
|---|---|---|---|---|---|---|---|
| Raychem Mowlem | v | Corsham Town | 0-3 | Marlborough Town | v | Biddestone | 2-4 |
| Purton | v | Pewsey Vale | 0-2 | Wootton Bassett Tn | v | Wroughton | 6-0 |

**SEMI-FINALS**
| | | | | |
|---|---|---|---|---|
| Corsham Town | v | Wootton Bassett Town | 1-2 | at Chippenham Town FC |
| Pewsey Vale | v | Biddestone | 1-0 | at Devizes Town FC |

**FINAL**
PEWSEY VALE  v  W'TON BASSETT T  2-3     at The County Ground, Swindon Town FC.

# WORCESTERSHIRE F.A.

Tel: 01386 443215 (H)   01905 612336 (B)   Fax: 01905 729229 (B)
Fermain, 12 Worcester Road, Evesham, Worcestershire WR11 4JU
**Secretary & Press Officer:**   M R Leggett
**Executives (Responsibility)**   M J Ford (Coaching Exams/Courses)
W A Allsopp (Referees)
Lyn Kendall (Womens Football)

| | | | | | |
|---|---|---|---|---|---|
| **Number of Affiliated Clubs** | Senior: | 20 | U.18: | 264 | **President:** P Rushton |
| **Number of Affiliated Leagues:** | Senior: | 6 | Junior: | 3 | **Chairman:** K J Clifford |

**County Representative Teams:** U18
**Inter County Competitions:**   FA County Youth, Midland Counties Youth

## WORCESTERSHIRE SENIOR CUP 1998-99
(10 entries)   (FOUNDED 1893-94)

**LAST SEASON'S FINAL:** Kidderminster Harriers  v  Solihull Borough  2-1

**FIRST ROUND** (2 matches)

| | | | | | | | |
|---|---|---|---|---|---|---|---|
| Moor Green | v | Halesowen Town | 2-1 | Stourbridge | v | Solihull Borough | 2-1 |

**SECOND ROUND** (4 matches)

| | | | | | | | |
|---|---|---|---|---|---|---|---|
| Evesham United | v | Stourbridge | 1-4 | Bromsgrove Rovers | v | Moor Green | 2-2 3-0 |
| Redditch United | v | Worcester City | 2-4 | Paget Rangers | v | Kidderminster H | @KH 1-3 |

**SEMI-FINALS**

| | | | | | | | |
|---|---|---|---|---|---|---|---|
| Worcester City | v | Stourbridge | 2-1 | Kidderminster Harr. | v | Bromsgrove Rovers | 6-1 |

**FINAL First Leg**
WORCESTER CITY  v   KIDDERMINSTER H.  3-2       at St Georges Lane, Worcester City FC

**FINAL Second Leg**
KIDDERMINSTER H. v    WORCESTER C  2*0 = 4-3     at Aggborough Stadium, Kidderminster Harriers FC

## WORCESTERSHIRE SENIOR URN 1998-99
(44 entries)

**LAST SEASON'S FINAL:** Stourport Swifts  v  Worcester City Reserves  2-1 aet

**FINAL**
KID'MINSTER H RS  v   KINGS NORTON TN   1-2       at Stourport Swifts FC

*Worcestershire County FA Youth Team 1998-99*

# EAST ANGLIAN CUP 1998-99

(55 entries)

**FIRST ROUND** (23 matches)

| | | | | | | |
|---|---|---|---|---|---|---|
| Diss Town | v | Cornard United | 1p3 1*1 | Mildenhall Town | v | Soham Town Rngrs | 1-4 |
| March Town United | v | Stamford | 0-7 | Chatteris Town | v | Bourne Town | 3-1 |
| Holbeach United | v | Spalding United | 0-2 | Lowestoft Town | v | Swaffham Town | 2-1 |
| Downham Town | v | Dereham Town | 1-3 | Fakenham Town | v | Norwich United | 3-2 |
| Saffron Walden Tn | v | Ware | 3-1 | Letchworth | v | Hitchin Town | L W-O |
| Royston Town | v | Stanstead | 3-0 | Ely City | v | St Neots Town | 0-2 |
| Biggleswade Town | v | Barton Rovers | 0-2 | Biggleswade United | v | Potton United | 3-2 |
| Halstead Town | v | Romford | 2-1 | Braintree Town | v | Aveley | 4-2 |
| Hullbridge Sports | v | Tiptree United | 1-2 | Concord Rangers | v | Burnham Ramblers | 1*2 |
| Basildon United | v | Maldon Town | 2-3 | Great Wakering Rvrs | v | Southend Manor | 3-1 |
| Harwich & Parkeston | v | Wivenhoe Town | 1-5 | Clacton Town | v | Felixstowe Port & Tn | 2*3 |
| Colchester United | v | Witham Town | WT W-O | | | |

**SECOND ROUND** (16 matches)

| | | | | | | |
|---|---|---|---|---|---|---|
| Soham Town Rngrs | v | Cornard United | 4-1 | Sudbury Wanderers | v | Thetford Town | 1-2 |
| Spalding United | v | Chatteris Town | 5-0 | Stamford | v | Somersham Town | 3-1 |
| Fakenham Town | v | Dereham Town | 0-2 | Lowestoft Town | v | Mulbarton United | 5-1 |
| Royston Town | v | Letchworth | 2-1 | Saffron Walden Tn | v | Sawbridgenorth Tn | 2-0 |
| Biggleswade United | v | Barton Rovers | 1-3 | St Neots Town | v | Eynesbury Rovers | 4-0 |
| Hertford Town | v | Braintree Town | 0-3 | Halstead Town | v | Harlow Town | 3-0 |
| Gt Wakering Rovers | v | Burnham Ramblers | 1-3 | Tiptree United | v | Maldon Town | 2*3 |
| Witham Town | v | Felixstowe Port & Tn | 1-3 | Wivenhoe Town | v | Ipswich Wanderers | 0-1 |

**THIRD ROUND** (8 matches)

| | | | | | | |
|---|---|---|---|---|---|---|
| Thetford Town | v | Soham Town Rngrs | 0-4 | Stamford | v | Spalding United | 2-1 |
| Lowestoft Town | v | Dereham Town | 1-0 | Royston Town | v | Saffron Walden Town | 1-2 |
| St Neots Town | v | Barton Rovers | 5p4 1*1 | Halstead Town | v | Braintree Town | 1-2 |
| Maldon Town | v | Burnham Ramblers | 1-2 | Ipswich Wanderers | v | Felixstowe Port & Tn | 4-3 |

**QUARTER-FINALS**

| | | | | | | |
|---|---|---|---|---|---|---|
| Braintree Town | v | Soham T Rgrs | STR W-O | Saffron Walden Tn | v | Ipswich Wanderers | 0-1 |
| Stamford | v | Lowestoft Town | 6-1 | St Neots Town | v | Burnham Rmblrs | 5p4 0*0 |

**SEMI-FINALS**

| | | | | | | |
|---|---|---|---|---|---|---|
| St Neots Town | v | Soham Town Rngrs | 4-2 | Ipswich Wanderers | v | Stamford | 1-0 |

**FINAL**

| | | | | | |
|---|---|---|---|---|---|
| ST NEOTS TOWN | v | IPSWICH WNDRS | 0-2 | at St Neots Town FC |

Top: East Anglian Cup Final: St Neots on the attack against Ipswich Wanderers          Photo: Gordon Whittington

Bottom: East Anglian Cup Final: Vice-Chairman of the Cup Committee, Peter Reeve, presents the Cup to victorious Ipswich Wanderers' captain, Nicky Barker, after their 2-0 win at St Neots

Photo: Gordon Whittington

# INTERLINK EXPRESS
# MIDLAND INVITATION CUP 1998-99
### (55 entries)

**LAST SEASON'S FINAL:** Atherstone United v Blakenall 1-0

## FIRST ROUND (23 matches)

| | | | | | | |
|---|---|---|---|---|---|---|
| Bilston Com. College v | Star | 3-2 | Bolehall Swifts | v | Knypersley Victoria | 2-4 |
| Bridgnorth Town | v Stafford Town | 1-0 | Chasetown | v | Pershore Town | 0*1 |
| Cheslyn Hay | v Dudley Sports | 6-1 | Downes Sports | v | Cradley Town | 0-1 |
| Ellistown | v Barrow Town | 1-3 | Feckenham | v | Gornal Athletic | 1-0 |
| Highgate United | v Continental Star | 0-1 | Halesowen Harriers | v | Darlaston Town | 5-2 |
| Kirby Muxloe | v Studley BKL | 1-0 | Meir K A | v | Rushall Olympic | 1-2 |
| Oldbury United | v Birstall United | 2-0 | Pelsall Villa | v | Barwell | 1-3 |
| Rocester | v Aylestone Park | 3-1 | Sandwell Borough | v | Oadby Town | 2-3 |
| Southam | v Handrahan Timbers | 3-0 | St Andrews | v | Wednesfield | 1-0 |
| Stourport Swifts | v Ibstock Welfare | 3-0 | Stratford Town | v | Kings Norton Town | 1-0 |
| Tividale | v Dudley Town | 3-1 | West Midlands Police | v | Friar Lane OB | 2-0 |
| Willenhall Town | v Blakenall | 5*4 | | | | |

## SECOND ROUND (16 matches)

| | | | | | | |
|---|---|---|---|---|---|---|
| Anstey Nomads | v Stapenhill | 1-0 | Boldmere St Mi. | v | Barwell | 2-4 |
| Bridgnorth Town | v Stourport Swifts | 3-2 | Cheslyn Hay | v | Atherstone United | 1-2 |
| Cradley Town | v Pershore Town | 3-0 | Feckenham | v | Stratford Town | 1-0 |
| Kirby Muxloe | v Continental Star | 4-2 | Lutterworth Town | v | Barrow Town | 1-3 |
| Malvern Town | v West Midlands Police | 1-3 | Oadby Town | v | Bilston Com. College | 0-3 |
| Rocester | v Bandon | 0-2 | Rushall Olympic | v | Thringstone United | 1*2 |
| Tividale | v Oldbury United | 0-2 | Wednesfield | v | Southam United | 2-1 |
| Wolverhampton Cas. v | Knypersley Victoria | 3-2 | Willenhall Town | v | Halesowen Harriers | 1-2 |

## THIRD ROUND (8 matches)

| | | | | | | |
|---|---|---|---|---|---|---|
| Barrow Town | v Bilston Com. College | W-O | Bridgnorth Town | v | Barwell | 5p3 0*0 |
| Feckenham | v Cradley Town | 0-2 | Halesowen Harriers | v | Anstey Nomads | 2-1 |
| Kirby Muxloe | v Thringstone United | 5V0 | Oldbury United | v | Atherstone United | 1-2 |
| West Midlands Police v | Wednesfield (at WMP) | 2*3 | Wolverhampton Cas. | v | Bandon | 0-3 |
| (Result reversed Kirby Ineligible player) | | | | | | |

## FOURTH ROUND (4 matches)

| | | | | | |
|---|---|---|---|---|---|
| Bridgnorth Town | v Cradley Town | 2-1 | Thringstone United v | Barrow Town | 3-1 |
| Atherstone United | v Wednesfield | 2-1 | Bandon v | Halesowen Harriers | 1-0 |

## SEMI-FINALS

| | | | | | |
|---|---|---|---|---|---|
| Atherstone United | v Bridgnorth Town | 1-0 | Thringstone United v | Bandon | 2-5 |

## FINAL

| | | | |
|---|---|---|---|
| ATHERSTONE UTD v | BANDON | 2-1 | at York Road, Oldbury United FC |

# ESSEX & HERTS BORDER COMBINATION

## FINAL LEAGUE TABLES 1998-99

### EASTERN DIVISION

| | P | Home | | | Away | | | Totals | | | F | A | Pts | GD |
|---|---|---|---|---|---|---|---|---|---|---|---|---|---|---|
| | | W | D | L | W | D | L | W | D | L | | | | |
| Dagenham & Redbridge | 35 | 17 | 1 | 0 | 14 | 2 | 1 | 31 | 3 | 1 | 139 | 11 | 96 | 128 |
| Grays Athletic | 35 | 13 | 2 | 3 | 9 | 1 | 7 | 22 | 3 | 10 | 86 | 53 | 69 | 33 |
| Canvey Island | 36 | 11 | 4 | 3 | 10 | 2 | 6 | 21 | 6 | 9 | 91 | 62 | 69 | 29 |
| Braintree Town | 36 | 10 | 3 | 5 | 11 | 2 | 5 | 21 | 5 | 10 | 104 | 63 | 68 | 41 |
| Heybridge Swifts | 35 | 11 | 0 | 6 | 10 | 4 | 4 | 21 | 4 | 10 | 102 | 53 | 67 | 49 |
| East Thurrock United | 36 | 12 | 3 | 3 | 8 | 3 | 7 | 20 | 6 | 10 | 76 | 74 | 66 | 2 |
| Witham Town | 36 | 9 | 4 | 5 | 6 | 3 | 9 | 15 | 7 | 14 | 78 | 55 | 52 | 23 |
| Southend Manor | 36 | 8 | 3 | 7 | 7 | 3 | 8 | 15 | 6 | 15 | 76 | 74 | 51 | 2 |
| Aveley | 36 | 7 | 5 | 6 | 5 | 8 | 5 | 12 | 13 | 11 | 71 | 68 | 49 | 3 |
| Tilbury | 36 | 10 | 1 | 7 | 4 | 4 | 10 | 14 | 5 | 17 | 69 | 83 | 47 | -14 |
| Bowers United | 36 | 4 | 6 | 8 | 8 | 3 | 7 | 12 | 9 | 15 | 58 | 65 | 45 | -7 |
| Hullbridge Sports | 36 | 8 | 4 | 6 | 4 | 4 | 10 | 12 | 8 | 16 | 58 | 99 | 44 | -41 |
| Hornchurch | 36 | 6 | 4 | 8 | 6 | 3 | 9 | 12 | 7 | 17 | 52 | 66 | 43 | -14 |
| Halstead Town | 35 | 9 | 4 | 4 | 2 | 3 | 13 | 11 | 7 | 17 | 61 | 72 | 40 | -11 |
| Great Wakering Rovers | 36 | 7 | 2 | 9 | 4 | 3 | 11 | 11 | 5 | 20 | 50 | 83 | 38 | -33 |
| Maldon Town | 36 | 6 | 4 | 8 | 3 | 4 | 11 | 9 | 8 | 19 | 53 | 82 | 35 | -29 |
| Concord Rangers | 36 | 5 | 6 | 7 | 2 | 1 | 15 | 7 | 7 | 22 | 50 | 123 | 28 | -73 |
| Burnham Ramblers | 36 | 5 | 1 | 12 | 1 | 7 | 10 | 6 | 8 | 22 | 45 | 88 | 26 | -43 |
| Basildon United | 36 | 3 | 6 | 9 | 2 | 3 | 13 | 5 | 9 | 22 | 40 | 85 | 24 | -45 |

### WESTERN DIVISION

| | P | Home | | | Away | | | Totals | | | F | A | Pts | GD |
|---|---|---|---|---|---|---|---|---|---|---|---|---|---|---|
| | | W | D | L | W | D | L | W | D | L | | | | |
| Enfield | 30 | 11 | 2 | 2 | 11 | 2 | 2 | 22 | 4 | 4 | 106 | 36 | 70 | 70 |
| Romford | 30 | 9 | 2 | 4 | 12 | 1 | 2 | 21 | 3 | 6 | 89 | 33 | 66 | 56 |
| Ware | 30 | 12 | 2 | 1 | 8 | 2 | 5 | 20 | 4 | 6 | 82 | 41 | 64 | 41 |
| Leyton Pennant | 30 | 10 | 1 | 4 | 5 | 4 | 6 | 15 | 5 | 10 | 72 | 42 | 50 | 30 |
| Sawbridgeworth Town | 30 | 9 | 3 | 3 | 5 | 5 | 5 | 14 | 8 | 8 | 60 | 60 | 50 | 0 |
| Cheshunt | 30 | 6 | 5 | 4 | 7 | 2 | 6 | 13 | 7 | 10 | 66 | 52 | 46 | 14 |
| Potters Bar Town | 30 | 8 | 1 | 6 | 6 | 3 | 6 | 14 | 4 | 12 | 63 | 51 | 46 | 12 |
| Ford United | 30 | 8 | 2 | 5 | 4 | 6 | 5 | 12 | 8 | 10 | 46 | 51 | 44 | -5 |
| Baldock Town | 30 | 7 | 3 | 5 | 4 | 5 | 6 | 11 | 8 | 11 | 44 | 52 | 41 | -8 |
| Hertford Town | 30 | 5 | 4 | 6 | 6 | 1 | 8 | 11 | 5 | 14 | 54 | 59 | 38 | -5 |
| Harlow Town | 30 | 5 | 3 | 7 | 4 | 5 | 6 | 9 | 8 | 13 | 49 | 61 | 35 | -12 |
| Hoddesdon Town | 30 | 3 | 3 | 9 | 5 | 1 | 9 | 8 | 4 | 18 | 32 | 63 | 28 | -31 |
| St Margaretsbury | 30 | 1 | 6 | 8 | 5 | 3 | 7 | 6 | 9 | 15 | 60 | 102 | 27 | -42 |
| Waltham Abbey | 30 | 4 | 3 | 8 | 3 | 1 | 11 | 7 | 4 | 19 | 34 | 83 | 25 | -49 |
| Somersett Ambury | 30 | 5 | 3 | 7 | 0 | 3 | 12 | 5 | 6 | 19 | 35 | 75 | 21 | -40 |
| Saffron Walden Town | 30 | 2 | 6 | 7 | 1 | 5 | 9 | 3 | 11 | 16 | 43 | 74 | 20 | -31 |

Welwyn Garden City - Record expunged

| | | | | |
|---|---|---|---|---|
| CHAMPIONSHIP PLAY-OFF | Enfield | v | Dagenham & Redbridge | 0-6 |
| COMBINATION CUP FINAL | Enfield | v | Harlow Town | 2-1 |
| FRED BUDDEN TROPHY FINAL | Heybridge Swifts | v | Dagenham & Redbridge | 2-4 |
| BRIAN HITCHINGS CUP FINAL | Braintree Town | v | Dagenham & Redbridge | 1*1, 4p5 |

# SUBURBAN FOOTBALL LEAGUE

## FINAL LEAGUE TABLES 1998-99

### PREMIER DIVISION

|  | P | W | D | L | F | A | Pts |
|---|---|---|---|---|---|---|---|
| Hayes | 26 | 16 | 4 | 6 | 63 | 33 | 52 |
| Woking | 26 | 15 | 6 | 5 | 51 | 26 | 51 |
| Uxbridge | 26 | 14 | 4 | 8 | 55 | 49 | 46 |
| Oxford City | 26 | 13 | 5 | 8 | 54 | 52 | 44 |
| Dulwich Hamlet | 26 | 13 | 2 | 11 | 60 | 64 | 41 |
| Maidenhead Utd | 26 | 11 | 7 | 8 | 46 | 29 | 40 |
| Met Police | 26 | 12 | 4 | 10 | 44 | 37 | 40 |
| Sutton United | 26 | 10 | 6 | 10 | 45 | 39 | 36 |
| Fisher Athletic | 26 | 9 | 7 | 10 | 34 | 37 | 34 |
| Basingstoke Tn | 26 | 10 | 3 | 13 | 47 | 55 | 33 |
| Farnborough Tn | 26 | 9 | 5 | 12 | 35 | 47 | 32 |
| Thame United | 26 | 8 | 6 | 12 | 34 | 42 | 30 |
| Whyteleafe | 26 | 5 | 4 | 17 | 29 | 52 | 19 |
| Marlow | 26 | 3 | 5 | 18 | 29 | 84 | 14 |

### SOUTH DIVISION

|  | P | W | D | L | F | A | Pts |
|---|---|---|---|---|---|---|---|
| Hampton | 28 | 20 | 6 | 2 | 9 | 20 | 66 |
| Gravesend & N | 28 | 20 | 1 | 7 | 57 | 26 | 61 |
| Walton & Hersh. | 28 | 19 | 2 | 7 | 61 | 31 | 59 |
| Carshalton Ath | 28 | 16 | 6 | 6 | 51 | 32 | 54 |
| Tonbridge Angels | 28 | 13 | 5 | 10 | 63 | 37 | 44 |
| Tooting & Mitch. | 28 | 13 | 5 | 10 | 49 | 49 | 44 |
| Croydon Athletic | 28 | 12 | 7 | 9 | 40 | 33 | 43 |
| Corinthian Cas. | 28 | 12 | 6 | 10 | 42 | 43 | 42 |
| Chipstead | 28 | 9 | 6 | 13 | 47 | 54 | 33 |
| Banstead Ath. | 28 | 9 | 4 | 15 | 41 | 55 | 32 |
| Horsham | 28 | 8 | 5 | 25 | 39 | 70 | 29 |
| Epsom & Ewell | 28 | 7 | 5 | 16 | 37 | 56 | 26 |
| Raynes Pk Vale | 28 | 7 | 3 | 18 | 34 | 63 | 24 |
| Leatherhead | 28 | 6 | 3 | 19 | 34 | 67 | 21 |
| Croydon | 28 | 5 | 4 | 19 | 37 | 67 | 19 |

### NORTH DIVISION

|  | P | W | D | L | F | A | Pts |
|---|---|---|---|---|---|---|---|
| Hendon | 26 | 15 | 4 | 7 | 59 | 39 | 49 |
| Ruislip Manor | 26 | 14 | 6 | 6 | 56 | 33 | 48 |
| Edgware Town | 26 | 13 | 7 | 6 | 49 | 34 | 46 |
| Kingsbury Town | 26 | 12 | 7 | 7 | 46 | 46 | 43 |
| Leighton Town | 26 | 13 | 3 | 16 | 46 | 43 | 42 |
| Yeading | 26 | 11 | 6 | 9 | 47 | 44 | 39 |
| Northwood | 26 | 11 | 5 | 10 | 56 | 52 | 38 |
| Chesham Utd | 26 | 10 | 4 | 12 | 48 | 48 | 34 |
| Beaconsfield | 26 | 10 | 4 | 12 | 48 | 54 | 34 |
| Chalfont St Peter | 26 | 10 | 5 | 11 | 39 | 53 | *32 |
| Wembley | 26 | 8 | 6 | 12 | 41 | 37 | 30 |
| Wingate & F | 26 | 8 | 6 | 12 | 38 | 50 | 30 |
| Hillingdon Boro | 26 | 5 | 7 | 14 | 40 | 52 | 52 |
| Flackwell Heath | 26 | 5 | 4 | 17 | 35 | 66 | 19 |

* points deducted

### WEST DIVISION

|  | P | W | D | L | F | A | Pts |
|---|---|---|---|---|---|---|---|
| Kingstonian | 28 | 25 | 1 | 2 | 107 | 29 | 76 |
| Hungerford Tn | 28 | 20 | 3 | 5 | 93 | 27 | 63 |
| Thatcham Town | 28 | 16 | 3 | 9 | 71 | 22 | 51 |
| Staines Town | 28 | 14 | 5 | 9 | 72 | 46 | 47 |
| Alton Town | 28 | 14 | 5 | 9 | 55 | 50 | 47 |
| Molesey | 28 | 13 | 5 | 10 | 64 | 45 | 44 |
| Burnham | 28 | 14 | 2 | 12 | 62 | 60 | 44 |
| Bracknell Town | 28 | 11 | 8 | 9 | 35 | 54 | 41 |
| Camberley Tn | 28 | 13 | 2 | 13 | 44 | 54 | 41 |
| Wickingham T | 28 | 8 | 8 | 12 | 46 | 63 | 32 |
| AFC Newbury | 28 | 9 | 5 | 14 | 42 | 68 | 32 |
| Egham Town | 28 | 9 | 1 | 18 | 54 | 80 | 28 |
| Fleet Town | 28 | 7 | 3 | 18 | 43 | 72 | *23 |
| Abingdon Town | 28 | 6 | 4 | 18 | 40 | 82 | 22 |
| Whitchurch Utd | 28 | 2 | 3 | 23 | 26 | 116 | 9 |

## SUBURBAN LEAGUE CHALLENGE CUP 1998-99

**QUARTER-FINALS**

| Oxford City | v | Chalfont St Peter | 4-1 | Fisher Athletic | v | Uxbridge | 3*2 |
|---|---|---|---|---|---|---|---|
| Dulwich Hamlet | v | Hayes | 0-2 | Hampton | v | Sutton United | 1-2 |

**SEMI-FINALS**

| Oxford City | v | Fisher Athletic | 2-1 | Hayes | v | Sutton United | 2*0 |
|---|---|---|---|---|---|---|---|

**FINAL**

| Oxford City | v | Hayes | 3*2 | At Marlow FC, Attendance: 160 |
|---|---|---|---|---|

## SUBURBAN CHALLENGE SHIELD 1998-99

**FINAL**

| Wembley | v | Hampton | 1-0 | at Ruislip Manor FC, Attendance: 150 |
|---|---|---|---|---|

# NORTHERN COUNTIES CHAMPIONSHIP

## GROUP ONE RESULTS

| | | | |
|---|---|---|---|
| Liverpool | v | Lancashire | 1-1 |
| Cumberland | v | Lancashire | 1-5 |
| Cheshire | v | Cumberland | 3-0 |
| Lancashire | v | Cheshire | 1-3 |
| Lancashire | v | West Riding | 1-2 |
| West Riding | v | Liverpool | 2-2 |
| Cumberland | v | West Riding | 0-0 |
| West Riding | v | Cheshire | 0-0 |
| Liverpool | v | Cumberland | 2-2 |
| Cheshire | v | Liverpool | 1-0 |

## GROUP TWO RESULTS

| | | | |
|---|---|---|---|
| North Riding | v | Northumberland | 0-2 |
| Westmorland | v | Durham | 0-9 |
| Durham | v | North Riding | 1-1 |
| Northumberland | v | Westmorland | 3-0 |
| Manchester | v | Durham | 0-4 |
| North Riding | v | Westmorland | 6-2 |
| Manchester | v | North Riding | 0-4 |
| Westmorland | v | Manchester | 1-1 |
| Northumberland | v | Manchester | 0-0 |
| Northumberland | v | Durham | 2-0 |

## GROUP ONE

| | P | W | D | L | F | A | Pts |
|---|---|---|---|---|---|---|---|
| Cheshire | 4 | 3 | 1 | 0 | 7 | 1 | 10 |
| Lancashire | 4 | 1 | 1 | 2 | 8 | 7 | 4 |
| West Riding | 4 | 0 | 3 | 1 | 4 | 3 | 3 |
| Liverpool | 4 | 0 | 3 | 1 | 5 | 6 | 3 |
| Cumberland | 4 | 0 | 2 | 2 | 3 | 10 | 2 |

## GROUP TWO

| | P | W | D | L | F | A | Pts |
|---|---|---|---|---|---|---|---|
| Northumberland | 4 | 3 | 1 | 0 | 7 | 0 | 10 |
| Durham | 4 | 2 | 1 | 1 | 14 | 3 | 5 |
| North Riding | 4 | 2 | 1 | 1 | 11 | 5 | 5 |
| Manchester | 4 | 0 | 2 | 2 | 1 | 9 | 2 |
| Westmorland | 4 | 0 | 1 | 3 | 3 | 19 | 1 |

### FINAL TIE
Northumberland 0 v 1 Cheshire

---

# SOUTH WESTERN COUNTIES CHAMPIONSHIP

## SENIOR GROUP A RESULTS

| | | 1 | 2 | 3 | 4 | 5 | 6 |
|---|---|---|---|---|---|---|---|
| 1 | Army | X | 3-1 | 1-1 | 6-0 | 1-4 | 2-1 |
| 2 | Dorset | 1-3 | X | 2-0 | 1-1 | 0-1 | 2-2 |
| 3 | Gwent | 1-1 | 0-2 | X | 1-1 | 0-1 | 1-1 |
| 4 | Hampshire | 0-6 | 1-1 | 1-1 | X | 2-2 | 0-5 |
| 5 | Navy | 4-1 | 2-2 | 1-1 | 5-0 | X | 0-3 |
| 6 | Sussex | 1-2 | 1-0 | 1-0 | 2-2 | 3-0 | X |

## SENIOR GROUP B RESULTS

| | | 1 | 2 | 3 | 4 | 5 | 6 |
|---|---|---|---|---|---|---|---|
| 1 | Cornwall | X | 0-3 | 2-3 | 6-1 | 0-5 | 2-2 |
| 2 | Devon | 3-0 | X | 4-1 | 3-0 | 3-0 | 1-0 |
| 3 | Gloucester | 3-2 | 1-4 | X | 2-0 | 0-1 | 1-2 |
| 4 | Guernsey | 1-6 | 0-3 | 0-2 | X | 2-2 | 2-0 |
| 5 | Somerset | 5-0 | 0-3 | 1-0 | 2-2 | X | 1-1 |
| 6 | Wiltshire | 2-2 | 0-1 | 2-1 | 0-2 | 1-1 | X |

## SENIOR GROUP A

| | P | W | D | L | F | A | Pts |
|---|---|---|---|---|---|---|---|
| Army | 5 | 3 | 1 | 1 | 13 | 7 | 10 |
| Sussex | 5 | 3 | 1 | 1 | 8 | 4 | 10 |
| Navy | 5 | 2 | 2 | 1 | 12 | 7 | 8 |
| Dorset | 5 | 1 | 2 | 2 | 6 | 7 | 5 |
| Gwent | 5 | 0 | 3 | 2 | 3 | 6 | 3 |
| Hampshire | 5 | 0 | 3 | 2 | 4 | 15 | 3 |

## SENIOR GROUP B

| | P | W | D | L | F | A | Pts |
|---|---|---|---|---|---|---|---|
| Devon | 5 | 5 | 0 | 0 | 14 | 1 | 15 |
| Somerset | 5 | 2 | 2 | 1 | 9 | 6 | 8 |
| Gloucester | 5 | 2 | 0 | 3 | 7 | 9 | 6 |
| Wiltshire | 5 | 1 | 2 | 2 | 5 | 7 | 5 |
| Cornwall | 5 | 1 | 1 | 3 | 10 | 14 | 4 |
| Guernsey | 5 | 1 | 1 | 3 | 5 | 13 | 4 |

### FINAL TIE
Army 1 v 1 Devon
(Army won after penalties)

# UEFA REGIONS CUP
## England represented by Cheshire County

### RESULTS

| | | | | | | | | |
|---|---|---|---|---|---|---|---|---|
| England | v | The Netherlands | 1-2 | Republic of Ireland | v | Scotland | 2-0 |
| Republic of Ireland | v | England | 1-1 | Scotland | v | The Netherlands | 2-1 |
| England | v | Scotland | 2-0 | Republic of Ireland | v | The Netherlands | 0-2 |

### TOURNAMENT TABLE

| | | | | | | | | |
|---|---|---|---|---|---|---|---|---|
| 1 | District West II (Holland) | 3 | 2 | 0 | 1 | 5 | 3 | 6 |
| 2 | Cheshire County (England) | 3 | 1 | 1 | 1 | 4 | 3 | 4 |
| 3 | Republic of Ireland (Ireland) | 3 | 1 | 1 | 1 | 3 | 3 | 4 |
| 4 | West of Scotland Region (Scotland) | 3 | 1 | 0 | 2 | 2 | 5 | 3 |

### TOP SCORERS

| | | | | | | |
|---|---|---|---|---|---|---|
| 3 | Said Saidi Amore | District West II | 1 | Rade Trifkovic | District West II |
| 2 | Michael Grace | Republic of Ireland | 1 | Paulo Meijndershagen | District West II |
| 2 | Paul Wiggans | Cheshire County | 1 | Declan McGuinness | Republic of Ireland |
| 1 | Nicholas Dillon | Cheshire County | 1 | Garry McCann | West of Scotland Reg 1 |
| 1 | Michael Riley | Cheshire County | 1 | David Forbes | West of Scotland Reg 1 |

### SQUAD

1 John Gann (Heswall), 2 Lee Atherton (Cammell Laird), 3 Ken Burgess (Cammell Laird), 4 Craig Campbell (Heswall), 5 Neil Clarke (Shell), 6 Nicky Dillon (Heswall), 7 Chris Durkin (Heswall), 8 Mark Jones (Cammell Laird), 9 Neil Larkin (Cammell Laird), 10 Dave Mayes (Heswall), 11 Graeme Pringle (Heswall), 12 Mike Riley (Poulton Vics), 13 Mike Smith - captain (Stork), 14 Ian Dolan (Cammell Laird), 15 Graham Steele (Heswall), 16 John Thompson (Mersey Royal), 17 Paul Wiggans (Stork), 18 Dave Huyton (Heswall).
Manager - Ken Meadows (Heswall), Assistant Manager - Steve Jones (Heswall), Medical Officer - Dr Michael Freeman (Crewe Alexandra), Physiotherapist - Rick Carter (Crewe Alexandra)

# NAT WEST ISLAND GAMES 1999

| | | | P | W | D | L | F | A | GD | Pts |
|---|---|---|---|---|---|---|---|---|---|---|
| **GROUP ONE** | | | | | | | | | | |
| | 1 | Jersey | 2 | 2 | 0 | 0 | 6 | 1 | 5 | 6 |
| | 2 | Aland | 2 | 1 | 0 | 1 | 2 | 2 | 0 | 3 |
| | 3 | Gibralter | 2 | 0 | 0 | 2 | 2 | 7 | -5 | 0 |
| **GROUP TWO** | 1 | Isle of Man | 3 | 2 | 1 | 0 | 19 | 5 | 14 | 7 |
| | 2 | Gotland | 3 | 2 | 1 | 0 | 19 | 6 | 13 | 7 |
| | 3 | Shetland | 3 | 1 | 0 | 2 | 6 | 6 | 0 | 3 |
| | 4 | Hitra | 3 | 0 | 0 | 3 | 2 | 26 | -24 | 0 |
| **GROUP THREE** | 1 | Isle of Wight | 3 | 3 | 0 | 0 | 19 | 5 | 14 | 9 |
| | 2 | Greenland | 3 | 2 | 0 | 1 | 9 | 9 | 0 | 6 |
| | 3 | Froya | 3 | 1 | 0 | 2 | 7 | 10 | -3 | 3 |
| | 4 | Saaremaa | 3 | 0 | 0 | 3 | 3 | 14 | -11 | 0 |
| **GROUP FOUR** | 1 | Ynys Mon (Anglesey) | 2 | 0 | 2 | 0 | 2 | 2 | 0 | 2 |
| | 2 | Rhodos | 2 | 0 | 2 | 0 | 1 | 1 | 0 | 2 |
| | 3 | Guernsey | 2 | 0 | 2 | 0 | 1 | 1 | 0 | 2 |

### SEMI-FINALS

| | | | | |
|---|---|---|---|---|
| Isle of Man | 1 | v | 0 | Jersey |
| Ynys Mon (Anglesey) | 3 | v | 1 | Isle of Wight |

### THIRD PLACE PLAY OFF

| | | | | |
|---|---|---|---|---|
| Isle of Wight | 2 | v | 0 | Jersey |

### FINAL

| | | | | |
|---|---|---|---|---|
| Ynys Mon (Anglesey) | 1 | v | 0 | Isle of Man |

# LEAGUE OF WALES

**Chief Executive:** D G Collins
**Secretary:** J C Deakin
Plymouth Chambers, 3 Westgate Street, Cardiff CF1 1DD
Tel: 01222 372325   Fax: 01222 343961

## FINAL LEAGUE TABLE 1998-99

|   |   | P | W | D | L | F | A | W | D | L | F | A | GD | Pts |
|---|---|---|---|---|---|---|---|---|---|---|---|---|----|-----|
| 1 | Barry Town | 32 | 13 | 2 | 1 | 46 | 13 | 10 | 5 | 1 | 36 | 10 | 59 | 76 |
| 2 | Inter Cable-Tel | 32 | 9 | 2 | 5 | 35 | 14 | 10 | 4 | 2 | 26 | 12 | 35 | 63 |
| 3 | Cwmbran Town | 32 | 9 | 1 | 6 | 38 | 26 | 8 | 5 | 3 | 35 | 18 | 29 | 57 |
| 4 | Aberystwyth Town | 32 | 9 | 4 | 3 | 28 | 20 | 7 | 5 | 4 | 31 | 28 | 11 | 57 |
| 5 | Caernarfon Town | 32 | 9 | 5 | 2 | 29 | 19 | 4 | 6 | 6 | 16 | 27 | -1 | 50 |
| 6 | Newtown | 32 | 8 | 7 | 1 | 25 | 9 | 5 | 3 | 8 | 20 | 26 | 10 | 49 |
| 7 | Conwy United | 32 | 7 | 4 | 5 | 26 | 24 | 7 | 3 | 6 | 29 | 25 | 6 | 49 |
| 8 | Total Network Solutions | 32 | 7 | 5 | 4 | 28 | 19 | 5 | 6 | 5 | 27 | 23 | 13 | 47 |
| 9 | Carmarthen Town | 32 | 7 | 4 | 5 | 25 | 19 | 6 | 4 | 6 | 21 | 27 | 0 | 47 |
| 10 | Caersws | 32 | 7 | 3 | 6 | 29 | 29 | 5 | 5 | 6 | 20 | 26 | -6 | 44 |
| 11 | Bangor City | 32 | 8 | 2 | 8 | 26 | 23 | 5 | 4 | 7 | 18 | 26 | -5 | 39 |
| 12 | Connah's Quay Nomads | 32 | 6 | 5 | 5 | 28 | 23 | 4 | 3 | 9 | 16 | 24 | -3 | 38 |
| 13 | Haverfordwest County | 32 | 6 | 4 | 6 | 25 | 24 | 3 | 3 | 10 | 18 | 36 | -17 | 34 |
| 14 | Afan Lido | 32 | 3 | 4 | 9 | 14 | 27 | 4 | 6 | 6 | 14 | 19 | -18 | 31 |
| 15 | Rhayader Town | 32 | 3 | 7 | 6 | 14 | 23 | 2 | 4 | 10 | 15 | 31 | -25 | 26 |
| 16 | Rhyl | 32 | 4 | 2 | 10 | 21 | 33 | 3 | 0 | 13 | 20 | 48 | -40 | 23 |
| 17 | Holywell Town | 32 | 2 | 7 | 7 | 22 | 33 | 1 | 2 | 13 | 16 | 53 | -48 | 18 |

## LEAGUE OF WALES CHAMPIONS

| | | |
|---|---|---|
| 1992-93 | Cwmbran Town | Inter Cardiff |
| 199394 | Bangor City | Inter Cardiff |
| 1994-95 | Bangor City | Afan Lido |
| 1995-96 | Barry Town | Newtown |
| 1996-97 | Barry Town | Inter Cable-Tel |
| 1997-98 | Barry Town | Newtown |
| 1998-99 | Barry Town | Inter Cable-Tel |

## LEAGUE OF WALES CUP WINNERS

| | |
|---|---|
| 1992-93 | Afan Lido |
| 1993-94 | Afan Lido |
| 1994-95 | Llantsantffraid |
| 1995-96 | Connah's Quay Nomads |
| 1996-97 | Barry Town |
| 1997-98 | Barry Town |
| 1998-99 | Barry Town |

# ABERYSTWYTH TOWN

**Secretary:** Mr D Roberts-Young, Brynawelon, Heol y Buarth, Aberystwyth, Ceredigion SY23 1NB  Tel: 01970 617569 (H) 01970 622104 (BF)

**Ground:** Park Avenue, Aberystwyth, Dyfed Tel: 01970 612122
**Directions:** From south: A487, 1st right at Trefachan Bridge to r'bout, 1st right with Park Ave. being 3rd right. From north: A487 and follow one-way system to railway station, at r'bout 1st left with Park Avenue being 3rd right. 5 mins walk from Aberystwyth (BR) - follow as above
Capacity: 4,500     Seats: 300          Cover: 1,200          Floodlights: Yes

**Clubhouse:** Open daily noon-3 & 7-12pm. Snacks available          **Club Shop:** Yes

**HONOURS** Welsh Cup 1899-1900; Welsh I'mediate Cup 85-86 87-88; Mid Wales Lg (11) (Lg Cup(7); Welsh Amtr Cup (3); Welsh Lg Div 2 Sth 51-52; Cambrian Coast Lg (8) Central Wales Chal. Cup(6)

**PREVIOUS** **League:** Welsh 1896-97; Nth Wales Comb. 99-1900; Montgomeryshire & Dist. 04-20; Central Wales 21-25 81-87; Mid-Wales 26-32 51-81; Cambrian Coast 32-51; Welsh Lg South 51-63; Abacus 87-92

**RECORD** **Attendance:** 4,500 v Hereford, Welsh Cup 1971
**Goalscorer:** David Williams 476, 66-83
**Appearances:** David P Whitney 572, 62-81

**FACT FILE**
Founded: 1884
Nickname: Seasiders
Sponsors: Continental Cambria Tyres
Colours: Black & green/black/black
Change colours: Yellow/white/white
Midweek Matchday: Wednesday
Reserves League: Mid-Wales
Programme: 24 pages, 60p
Editor: Steve Moore (01970 617705)

**CLUB PERSONNEL**
Chairman: Donald Kane
President: D Jones
Press Officer: David Thomas
Manager: Barry Powell

# AFAN LIDO

**Secretary:** Mr P Robinson, 56 Abbeyville Avenue, Sandfields Estate, Port Talbot SA12 6PY
Tel: 01639 885638 (H)   01639 892960 (B)

**Ground:** Princess Margaret Way, Aberavon Beach, Port Talbot  Tel: 01639 892960

**FACT FILE**
Colours: Red/red/red
Change colours: White/white/white
Midweek Matchday: Tuesday

**CLUB PERSONNEL**
Chairman: David Dale
Manager: Mark Robinson

# BANGOR CITY

**Secretary:** Alun Griffiths, 12 Lon-Y-Bryn, Menai Bridge, Ynys Mon, Gwynedd LL59 5LL
Tel: 01248 712820 (H)   01248 355665 (B)

**Ground:** The Stadium, Farrar Road, Bangor, Gwynedd
Tel: 01248 355852 Fax: 01248 355852

**Directions:** Old A5 into Bangor, 1st left before railway station, ground on leftby garage
Seats: 700     Cover: 1,200          Capacity: 5,000     Floodlights: Yes

**Clubhouse:** Not on ground          **Club Shop:** Yes

**HONOURS** FA Tphy R-up 83-84; Northern Prem. Lg 81-82 (R-up 86-87, Lg Cup 68-69, Presidents Cup 88-89, Chal. Shield 87-88), Cheshire Co. Lg R-up 53-54 58-59,Lancs Comb. R-up 30-31, League of Wales 94-95 (Lg Cup R-up 94-95), WelshNational Lg 27-28 (R-up 26-27), Nth Wales Coast Lg 1895-96, Welsh Cup 1888-89 95-96 1961-62 (R-up 27-28 60-61 63-64 72-73 77-78 84-85), Nth Wales Chal. Cup 26-27 35-36 36-37 37-38 46-47 51-52 57-58 64-65 67-68, Welsh Amtr Cup 1894-9596-96 97-98 98-99 1900-01 02-03 04-05 05-06 11-12, Welsh Jnr Cup 1995-96 97-981919-20, Welsh All. Alves Cup 49-50 59-60 (Cookson Cup 61-62 68-69 84-85 86-87)

**RECORD** **Attendance:** 10,000 v Wrexham, Welsh Cup final 78-79

**PREVIOUS** **Leagues:** N Wales Coast 1893-98 1911-12; The Comb 1898-1910; N Wales Comb 30-33; WMids 32-38; Lancs Comb 38-39 46-50; Ches Co 50-68; NPL 68-79 81-82 84-92; AlliancePrem 79-81 82-84, Welsh Cup 97-98,North Wales Challenge Cup 1998-99

**FACT FILE**
Founded: 1876
Nickname: Citizens
Sponsors: Pentraeth Group
Colours: All navy blue
Change colours: All white
Midweek Matchdays: Tuesday
Reserve League: Welsh Alliance
Programme: 32 pages, 70p
Editor: Alan Monument

**CLUB PERSONNEL**
President: Gwyn Pierce Owen
Chairman: Major M.Maund
Vice Chairman: David Gareth Jones
Press Officer: Jon Jessop
Manager: Meirion Appleton
Coach: Terry Boyle
Physio: Arwel Jones

# BARRY TOWN

| | |
|---|---|
| Secretary: | Alan Whelan, 132 Westward Rise, Barry,South Glam. CF62 6NQ |
| | Tel: 01446 412938 |
| Ground: | Jenner Park, Barry   Tel: 01446 735858 |
| Directions: | M4 jct 33 via Wenvoe (A4050) to Barry. Left at 1st 2 r'bouts to Jenner Park. |
| | Nearest rail station is Cadoxton |
| | Capacity: 3,000          Seats: 3,000          Cover: Yes          Floodlights: Yes |
| Clubhouse: | Open normal licensing hours, 11.00-11.00 daily |
| HONOURS | Welsh Cup (3); Welsh Trophy 94-95; Southern Lg R-up 20-21; |
| | Western Lg R-up 11-12, Welsh Lg (7), Lg Cup (4); South Wales Senior Cup |
| | (13); SA Brain Cup (3); League of Wales 95-96 96-97 97-98; |
| | UEFA Cup 2 Qual Rds 96-97, Prel Rd 97-98 Champions Lg. prelim Rd 98-99 |
| PREVIOUS | Leagues: Western 08-13; Southern 13-82 89-93; Welsh 82-89 94-95 |
| BEST SEASON | FA Cup: 2nd Rd 29-30          FA Trophy 3rd Qualifying Rd replay 90-91 |
| RECORD | Attendance: 7,400 v Queens Park Rangers, FA Cup 1st Rd 1961 |
| | Goalscorer: Clive Ayres          Appearances: Basil Bright |

Players progressing Chris Simmonds (Millwall) 47, Derek Tapscott/Dai Ward(Arsenal) 53/54, Laurie Sheffield/Gordon Fazer/Phil Green (Newport) 62/66/84,Chris Pike (Fulham) 85, Ian Love (Swansea) 86, Tony Bird/Dave O'Gorman (SwanseaCity) 97, Mark Ovendaze (Bournemouth) 98 Eifon Williams (Torquay United) 99

**FACT FILE**

Founded: 1923
Nickname: Dragons
Sponsors: Tango
Colours: Yellow/yellow/blue
Change: Blue&white
Midweek Matchdays: Tuesday
Programme: Yes

**CLUB PERSONNEL**

Chairman: Paula O'Halloran
Player Manager: T.B.A.
1998-99 Captain: Andrew York
Top Scorer: Eifon Williams
Player of the Year: Terry Evans

---

# CAERNARFON TOWN

| | |
|---|---|
| Secretary: | Irfon Roberts, Ceris, Ffrwd Cae Du, Bontnewydd, Caernarfon Tel: 01286 830417 |
| Ground: | The Oval, Marcus Street, Caernarfon, Gwynedd Tel: 01286 675002 |
| Directions: | A55 coast road to A487 bypass to Caernarfon. At inner relief road r'bout follow |
| | Beddlegert sign, then 2nd right - ground opposite. |
| | Nearest BR station is 9 miles distant at Bangor. Local buses to Hendre estate |
| | Capacity: 3,678          Seats: 178          Cover: 1,500          Floodlights: Yes |
| Clubhouse: | 2 snooker tables, darts, pool, fruit machines , live entertainment  Club Shop: Yes |
| HONOURS | N West Co's Lg R-up 84-85 (Div 2 R-up 82-83); Lancs Comb 81-82 (Lg Cup 80-81); Welsh Lg (North)(4) 46-47 65-66 77-79, R-up (4) 56-58 72-73 79-80; Alves Cup(4) 38-39 74-75 77-79; Cookson 56-57 77-78; N Wales Combination 32-33; Welsh National Lg 26-27 29-30 (R-up 28-29); N Wales Coast Lg 11-12 |
| PREVIOUS | Leagues: North Wales Coast 06-21; Welsh National 26-30; North Wales Comb. 32-33; Welsh Lg (North) 37-76 77-80; Lancs Comb. 80-82; North West Counties 82-85; Northern Premier |
| BEST SEASON | FA Trophy: 1st Round replay 87-88 |
| | FA Cup : 3rd Rd replay 86-87, 0-1 v Barnsley (A). Also 2nd Rd 29-30 |
| RECORD | Attendance: 6,002 v Bournemouth, FA Cup 2nd Rd 1929 |
| | Goalscorer: W Jones 255 (1906-26)          Appearances: Walter Jones 306 |

Players progressing: Ernie Walley (Spurs), Gwyn Jones(Wolves 1955), Wyn Davies & Haydn Jones (Wrexham 1960 & 64), Tom Walley(Arsenal 1964), Paul Crooks (Stoke 1986), David Martindale & Steve Craven &David Higgins (Tranmere 1987), Gary Jones (Swansea City)

**FACT FILE**

Founded: 1876
Nickname: Canaries
Sponsors: T.J. Fixit
Colours: Yellow/green/yellow
Change colours: All claret
Midweek Matchday: Tuesday
Reserve Team: Yes
Programme: 48pgs 70p
Editor: Marc Roberts

**CLUB PERSONNEL**

President: Jack F Thomas
Chairman: G.Lloyd Owen
Vice-Chairmen: Eilian Angel
Press Officer: Geraint Lloyd Owen
Tel: 01286 830307
Manager: Paul Rowlands
Coach: Alan McDonald
Physio: Ian Humphreys

---

# CAERSWS

| | |
|---|---|
| Secretary: | T M B Jones, 3 Hafren Terrace, Caersws, Powys SY17 5ES |
| | Tel: 01686 688103 |
| Ground: | The Recreation Ground, Caersws, Powys. Tel: 01686 688753 |
| Directions: | Entering Caersws, which lies between Newtown & Llanidloes on the A470, the |
| | ground entrance is on the left by bridge |
| | Capacity: 3,250          Seats: 250          Cover: 300          Floodlights: Yes |
| Clubhouse: | Not on ground, but in village centre. Normal licensing hours. Food available |
| Club Shop: | No |
| HONOURS | Welsh Amtr Cup 60-61, I'mediate Cup 88-89 (R-up 91-92); Mid-Wales Lg (9) 59-61 62-63 77-78 82-83 85-86 88-90 96-97 (Lg Cup 79-80 82-83 87-88 89-90); Cent. Wales Chall. Cup 77-78 82-83 87-88 89-90 (Yth Cup 69-70 72-73); Montgomeryshire Chall. Cup (18) 52-53 59-60 62-63 69-72 74-75 76-78 83-89 90-91 94-95 94-95 96-97 97-98 98-99); Montgomeryshire Lg 77-78 |
| PREVIOUS | Leagues: Mid-Wales (pre-1989)/Cymru Alliance 90-92 |
| RECORD | Attendance: 2,795 v Swansea City, Welsh Cup 1990 |
| | Goalscorer: Gareth Davies |

Players progressing: P Woosnam (Leyton O.), M Evans (Wolverhampton W.), KLloyd (Hereford U) Graham Evans (Aston Villa)

**FACT FILE**

Founded: 1887
Nickname: Bluebirds
Sponsor: Dave Smith
Colours: Blue/white/blue
Change colour: Orange/black/black
Midweek Matchday: Tuesday
Reserve League: Mid-Wales
Programme: 44 pages, 50p
Editor: Graham Burrows

**CLUB PERSONNEL**

Chairman: Garth Williams
Vice Chairman: John Baker
President: Phil Woosnam
Press Officer: Ivor Williams
Manager: Mickey Evans
Asst Manager: Barry Harding
Physio: Wynne Jones
1998-99: Catain: Anthony Griffiths.
P.O.Y & Top Scorer: Sean Jehu.

# CARMARTHEN TOWN

**Secretary:** Alan Latham, 3 Maesdolau, Idole, Carmarthen SA32 8DQ
Tel: 01267 232432 (H), Fax 01267 222851

**Ground:** Richmond Park, Priory Street, Carmarthen Dyfed Tel: 01267 232101

**Directions:** Proceed into Carmarthen on A48, pick up 440 to Llandilo at the 1st rounabout and follow signs for 800 meters. The ground is on left in PrioryStreet

| | | | |
|---|---|---|---|
| Capacity: 3,000 | Seats: 120 | Cover: 750 | Floodlights: Yes |
| **Clubhouse:** | Yes | **Club Shop:** | Yes |

**HONOURS** Welsh Lge Div 2 59-60, Div 1 95-96, Cup Winners 95-96

**RECORD** **Attendance:** 3,000

**PREVIOUS** **Leagues:** Welsh League

### FACT FILE
Founded: 1948
Nickname: The Town
Sponsors: Jewson Carmarthen
Colours: Gold/black/black
Change colours: Red/blue/blue
Midweek Matchday: Wednesday
Reserve League: C C Sports Welsh Lge
Programme: Yes
Editor: Alun Charles

### CLUB PERSONNEL
Chairman: Jeff Thomas
President: Anthony Jenkins
Manager : Tommi Morgan
Asst Manager: Ievan John
Physio: T Poynton/A Underwood

---

# CONNAH'S QUAY NOMADS

**Secretary/Press Officer**
Robert Hunter, 40 Brookdale Ave., Connah's Quay, Deeside, Clywd CH5 4LU
Tel: 01244 831212 (H)  01244 520299 (B)

**Ground:** Deeside Stadium Connah's Quay

**Directions:** On main coast road (A548) from Chester to Rhyl west end of Connah's Quay
Deeside College.

| | | | |
|---|---|---|---|
| Capacity: 3,500 | Seats: 500 | Cover: 500 | Floodlights: Yes |
| **Clubhouse:** | Yes, in college. | **Club Shop:** No | |

**HONOURS** Welsh Amtr Cup 52-53 54-55, Nth Wales FA Amtr Cup 52-53 54-55,
North Wales Coast Challenge Cup, Welsh Intermediate Cup 80-81,
Welsh Alliance CooksonCup 87-88, Welsh Youth Cup 47-48

**PREVIOUS** **Leagues:** Clywd; Welsh Alliance; Cymru Alliance 90-92

**RECORD** **Attendance:** 1,500 v Rhyl, Welsh Cup SF 29/3/93
**Season 98-99** **Captain:** Carl Smythe    **P.O.Y.** Jamie Jardine  **Top Scorer:** Jamie Hughes

### FACT FILE
Founded: 1946
Nickname:Advantage Mortgages
Sponsors: Hallows Associatres Solicitors
Colours: White/black/black&white
Change colours: Maroon/white/maroon
Midweek Matchday: Tuesday
Reserve League: Sealink Welsh Alliance
Programme: 26 pages, £1.00
Editor: G.Thelwell

### CLUB PERSONNEL
Chairman: Mr R Morris
President: Mr R Jones
Manager s: Neville Powell
Asst Manager: Gary Wynne
Physio: Mr M Latter

---

# CONWY UNITED

**Secretary:** Mr C Jones, Iolyn, Iolyn Park, Conwy, North Wales Ll32 8UX
Tel: 01492 593496

**Ground:** Morfa Stadium, Penmaen Rd, Conwy, Gwynedd Tel: 01492 573080

**Directions:** Leave A55 on 1st slip road after river tunnel and turn left towardsConwy.
Sharp left immediately after overhead railway bridge - ground 400yds on left
off Penmaen Rd

| | | | |
|---|---|---|---|
| Capacity: 4,000 | Seats: 650 | Cover: 800 | Floodlights: Yes |
| **Club Shop:** | Yes | | |
| **Clubhouse:** | Yes,at Ground | | |

**HONOURS** UEFA Inter Toto Cup Qual 96; Welsh Alliance 84-85 85-86; Barritt Cup 84-85
96-97; Welsh Intermediate Cup 81-82; Gwynedd Lge 95-96;
Jack Owen Cup 81-82 82-83; Ron Jones Cup 87-88

**PREVIOUS** **Leagues:** Vale of Conwy; Gwynedd; Welsh Alliance;  Cymru Alliance

**RECORD** **Attendance:** 853 v Swansea City, FAW Invitation Cup 97
**Goalscorer:** Carl Dale    **Appearances:** Gwyn Williams

Players progressing: Neville Southall (via Winsford to Bury,Everton),
Carl Dale (via Rhyl and Bangor to Chester City, Cardiff City)

### FACT FILE
Founded: 1977
Nickname: Musselmen
Colours: Tangerine/black/tangerine
Change colours: All white
Midweek Matches: Wednesday
Reserves League: Welsh Alliance
Programme: 32 pages, 75p
Editor: Chris Lingwood

### CLUB PERSONNEL
Chairman: J C Davis
Vice Chairman: G Rees
President: K Davies
Press Officer: G Rees
Manager: Stan Allan
Coach: Jim Coffey
Youth Dev: Mike Roberts

# CYMBRAN TOWN

**Secretary:** Mr C Edwards, 21 Dunraven Road, Llanyravon, Cwmbran, Gwent NP44 8PW
Tel: 01633 865372 (H ) 01633 865372 (F)

**Ground:** Cwmbran Stadium, Henllys Way, Cwmbran, Gwent
Tel: 01633 866192 Fax 01633 863324

**Directions:** M4 jct 26, follow signs for Cwmbran. At 1st r/about (approx 1.5miles) take 1st
exit & proceed along Cwmbran Drive umtil passing Stadium onright. At r/about
take 1st exit, then immediately at next r/about take 3rdexit.
Ground entrance 150 yardson right.
One and a half miles from Cwmbran(BR)
Capacity: 8,201      Seats: 2,201      Cover: 1,857      Floodlights: Yes

**Club Shop:** Yes

**Clubhouse:** Pub hours, on ground. Catering facilities

**HONOURS** Lg of W. 92-93; Welsh Lg Div 1 66-67, Welsh Lg Cup 85-86 90-91

**PREVIOUS Leagues:** Monmouthshire Snr 51-59/ Welsh 60-92

**RECORD Attendance:** 8,148 v Manchester Utd Aug 1994

**Goalscorer** : Graham Reynolds  **Appearances:** Mostyn Lewis

Players progressing: Simon King (Newport 1984), Mark Waite (Bristol Rovers1984), Nathan
Wigg (Cardiff 1993), Chris Watkins (Swansea 1993)

**FACT FILE**
Founded: 1951
Nickname: The Town
Sponsors: Exide Batteries Ltd
Colours: White/blue/white
Change colours: All red
Midweek Matches: Wednesday
Reserves League: Welsh Lge Res Div East
Programme: 28 pages, 50p
Programme Editor/Press Off: Andrew Havelot

**CLUB PERSONNEL**
Chairman: J C Colley
Vice Chairman: K M McCarthy
President: John Colley
Manager: Tony Willcox
Coach: Mark Aizelwood
Physio: Terry Cutlan

# FLEXSYS CEFN DRUIDS

**Secretary:** R Davies, 7 Lancaster Terrace, Acrefair, Wrexham  Tel: 01978 823027 (H)
01978 292931 (B)   01978 823027 (F)

**Ground:** Plas Kynaston Lane, Plas Kynaston, Cefn Mawr, Wrexham
Tel: 01978 824279  Fax: 01978 824352

**FACT FILE**
Colours: Black & white/black/black
Change colours: Red & blue/red/red
Midweek Matches: Wednesday

**CLUB PERSONNEL**
Chairman: R Cottrell
Manager: Gareth Powell

*Connah's Quay Nomads FC*

# HAVERFORD WEST COUNTY

**Secretary:** Barry Vaughan, Trem y Gorwel, Chapel Rd, Keston, Haverfordwest,
Pembs SA62 6HL

**Ground:** Bridge Meadow Stadium, Haverfordwest Pembs

**Directions:** Off the Safeway roundabout near town centre

Capacity: 4,000    Covered    Seats: 500    Floodlights: Yes

**Club Shop:** Yes

**HONOURS** West Wales Sen Cup 81-82 88-89 91-92 92-93 97-98 98-99, R-up 37-38 49-50
56-57          60-61 80-81; Welsh Lge 56-57, R-up 67-70 70-71, Prem Div 80-81, National
Div             89-90, Div 1 96-97, R-up 94-95 95-96; SA Brains Cup 88-89 R-up 84-85

### FACT FILE
Nickname: Bluebirds
Sponsor: Preseli Taxis
Colours: All Blue
Change colours: Yellow/black
Midweek Matchday: Wednesday
Programme: 28 Pages £1.00
Editor: JohnThomas

### CLUB PERSONNEL
Chairman: Roger Cottrell
Press Officer: Robert Nesbitt
Manager:Mike Ellery

# INTER CARDIFF

**Secretary:** Roy Langley, 19 Duffryn Close, Roath Park, Cardiff CF23 6HT
Tel: 029 20 764381

**Ground:** Cardiff Athletic Stadium, Leckwith Road, Cardiff  Tel: 01222 225345

**Directions:** M4 Junc 33 towards Penarth, A4232 past Culverhouse Cross, turn off onto
Leckwith Road, ground on right

Capacity: 5,000    Seats: 2,500    Cover: 2,500    Floodlights: Yes

**Club Shop:** Yes

**HONOURS** Lg of W R-up 92-93 93-94 96-97, Abacus Lg Div 1 86-87, Sth Wales Amtr Lg
84-85 85-86. As Sully: Sth Wales Amtr Lg Coronation Cup 69-70, Corinthian
Cup 78-79, Abacus Lg Div 1 83-84 85-86 89-90 (Div 2 80-81), Sth Wales Snr
Cup 80-81 81-82, Lge of W R-up 1998-99, Welsh Cup winners 1998-99

**PREVIOUS** **Leagues:** Barry & District/South Wales Amateur/Abacus
**RECORD** **Attendance:** 1,500 v Everton August 96

### FACT FILE
Founded: 1990
Nickname: Seagulls
Colours: White/black/black
Change colours: Yellow/blue
Midweek Matches: Tuesday
Programme: 24 pages, £1.00
Programme Editor: Maurice Salway
Press Officer: Clive Harry
P.o.Y.: Gary Wager
Top Scorer: Paul Evans

### CLUB PERSONNEL
Chairman: Max James
Commercial Manager: Peter Hunt
Manager: Phillip Holme
Asst Manager: Paul Giles
Physio: Roy Langley

*Layham Park, Newtown*

# LLANELLI

**Team Secretary:** R Davies, 29 Pemberton Park, Llanelli, Carmarthenshire SA14 8NW
Tel: 01554 756176 (H)   01554 772973 (B)   01554 772973 (F)

**Ground:**   Stebonheath Park, Llanelli SA15 1HF   Tel: 01554 756216

**FACT FILE**
Colours: All red
Change : White/black/white
Midweek Matchdays: Wednesday

**CLUB PERSONNEL**
Chairman: Mr R Jones
Manager: Leighton James

# NEWTOWN

**Team Secretary:**  Howard Ellis, 30 Court Close, Abermull, Montgomery, Powys
(01686 630372 (H) 01686 626121 (W) )

**Ground:**  Latham Park, Newtown, Powys Tel: 01686 622666/623120, Fax: 623813
**Directions:**  A43 to Newtown, right at 1st lights into Back Lane & town centre -400yds left into
Park St., 500yds right (at Library) into Park Lane - ground at end
Capacity: 5,000        Seats:1,100        Cover: 850        Floodlights: Yes
**Clubhouse:**  Open every evening & matchday afternoons. Hot/cold snacks, pool,darts
**Club Shop:**  Yes

**HONOURS**  League of Wales R-up 95-96 97-98; Welsh Cup 1878-79 94-95 (R-up 85-65 87-
88 96-97), Welsh Amtr Cup 1954-55, Central Wales Lg 75-76 78-79 81-82 86-87
87-88 (R-up 51-52 52-53 55-56 56-57 74-75 82-83, Lg Cup 54-55 56-57 74-75
75-76 81-82 83-84), Arthur Barritt Cup 86-87, Central Wales Cup 74-75 80-81 92-
93, Emrys Morgan Cup 80-81

**PREVIOUS**  Leagues: The Combination/ Central Wales/ Northern Premier

**RECORD**  Attendance: 5,002 v Swansea City, Welsh Cup 1954

**BEST SEASON**  **FA Trophy:** 3rd Qual. 89-90
**FA Cup:** 2nd Rd 1884-85. Also 1st Rd 1885-86

**FACT FILE**
Founded: 1875
Nickname: Robins
Sponsors: ControlTechniques & Elliott Presco
Colours: All red
Change : Blue & yellow/blue/blue & yellow
Midweek Matchdays: Tuesday
Reserves League:Spar Mid Wales
Programme: 36 pages, £1
Editor: Keith Harding/ Nigel Bevan & Barry
Gardiner

**CLUB PERSONNEL**
President: Richard Edwards
Chairman: Keith Harding
Exec Co-Ordinator: Mrs Lyn Barnett
Match Sec/Press Officer: John Annereau
Manager: Brian Coyne
Asst Manager: Richard Pike
Physio: Elwyn Morgan
Res.Team Manager: Mike Pearce

*The Welsh Non-League Squad*
*Back Row (L-R): Tomi Morgan (Manager), Neil Davies, Kevin Lloyd, Craig Lima, Neil Thomas, Gary Wager, Neil*
*O'Brien, Aneurin Thomas, Jonathon Williams, George Wood (Assistant Manager)*
*Front Row: Stuart Bevis (Physio), David Barnhouse, Deiniol Graham, Adrian Needs, Andrew Thomas, Colin*
*Reynolds, Lee Congerton, Mattie Davies, Gary Shepard*                           *Photo: Peter Barnes*

# RHAYDER TOWN

**FACT FILE**

**Secretary:** P Woosnam, Bwthyn Lon, Hazelmere, Rhayader, Powys LD6 5LG
Tel: 01597 811286 (H)  01597 826620 (B)  01597 826260 (F)

**Ground:** The Weirglodd, Bridge Street, Rhayader, Powys Tel & Fax: 01597 810067

Colours: White & red/white & red/red
Change Colours: Jade & white/jade & white/jade
Midweek Matchday: Wednesday

**CLUB PERSONNEL**

Chairman: M A Pugh
Manager: R Cross

# RHYL

**FACT FILE**

**Secretary:** Dennis McNamee, 3 Maes Rhosyn, Rhuddlan. Tel: 01745 591287 (H)
**Ground:** Belle Vue, Grange Road, Rhyl, Clwyd Tel: 01745 338327
**Directions:** Leave A55 at the St Asaph/Rhyl turn off and take A525 to Rhuddlan.At roundabout take 2nd turn for Rhyl, then left at next roundabout and over next two roundabouts .After 1mile urn right into Pendyffryn Rd, then left at junction and ground is 300yds on left.
Capacity: 4,000     Cover: 1,200     Seats: 200     Floodlights: Yes
Club Shop: Yes     Clubhouse: No

Founded: 1883
Nickname: Lilywhites
Colours: White/blue/blue
Change: Blue/white/white
Midweek matches: Tuesday
Programme: 40 pages £1
Editor: Ian Johnson (01745 353976)

**HONOURS** Welsh Cup 51-52 52-53 (R-up 29-30 36-37 92-93), Welsh Amateur Cup 72-73, Northern Premier Lg Presidents Cup 84-85, North West Counties Lg R-up 82-83,North Wales Coast Challenge Cup, Cheshire County Lg 47-48 50-51 71-72 (R-up 48-49 49-50 51-52 55-56, Div 2 R-up 81-82, Lg Cup 48-49 51-52 70-71, Div 2 Shield 81-82), Cyrmu Alliance 93-94 (R-up 92-93, Lg Cup 92-93)

**CLUB PERSONNEL**

Chairman: David Simmons
President: R B G Webster
Press Officer: David Williams

**PREVIOUS** **Leagues:** Cheshire County; North West Counties; Northern Premier; Cymru Alliance 92-94

**BEST SEASON** **FA Cup :** 4th Rd Proper 56-57 (lost 0-3 at Bristol City)
**RECORD** **Attendance:** 10,000 v Cardiff City, Welsh Cup 1953
**Goalscorer:** Don Spendlove     **Appearances:** Not known
Players progressing:
Ian Edwards, Grenville Millington, Brian Lloyd, Andy Holden, Barry Horne, Andy Jones

# TOTAL NETWORK SOLUTIONS

**FACT FILE**

**Secretary:** Gwynfor Hughes, Birch Lea, Porthywaen, Oswestry, Shrops SY10 8LY
Tel: 01691 828645 (H)  Fax: 01691 828645

**Ground:** Recreation Park, Treflan, Llansantffraid Tel: 01691 828112 & Fax 01691 828862
**Directions:** A483 between Oswestry and Welshpool, right for Llansantffraid (A495) at Llynclys.
Follow signs to village. Turn opposite Mill silos towards Community Centre. Ground is behind housing estate
Capacity: 1,500     Seats: 120     Cover: 250     Floodlights: Yes
**Clubhouse:** Open weekends & evenings during week  **Club Shop:** Yes
**HONOURS** Welsh Cup 95-96; Welsh Intermediate Cup 92-93; League of Wales Cup 94-95; Cymru Alliance Lge 92-93, R-up 91-92; Central Wales Sen Cup R-up 92-93 97-98; Central Wales Lg R-up 90-91 94-95 95-96, Lge Cup 95-96; Montgomeryshire Amtr Lg (7), Village Cup (17); Montgomeryshire Cup R-up 82-83 96-97, Euro CupWinners Cup Prem Rd 96-97

Founded: 1959
Nickname: The Saints
Sponsors: Total Network Solutions
Colours: White/green/green
Change: Red/black/black
Midweek Matchdays: Tuesday
Reserves League: Montgomeryshire Lge
Programme: 36 pages, £1
Editor:Tony Williams
**CLUB PERSONNEL**
Chairman: Edgar Jones
President: Mike Hughes
Vice-Chairman: Tony Williams
Manager: Dr Andy Cale
Asst Manager: Peter Hepper
Physio: Gordon Evans
1998-99 Captain & P.o.Y.: Tim Edwards
Top Scorer: KenMcKenna

**PREVIOUS** **League:** Mid-Wales; Cymru Alliance (pre-1993)

**RECORD** **Attendance:** 2,100 v KS Ruch Chorzow Euro Cup Winners 96(at Wrexham F.C.)

Members of the Welsh Non-League team:

Top left: Jonathon Williams

Top right: Kevin Lloyd

Bottom left: Adrian Needs

Bottom right: Andrew Thomas

# SCOTTISH FOOTBALL

Thanks again to Stewart Davidson, editor and publisher of the twelfth edition of the Scottish Non-League Review, from whom most of these statistics were received.

His review costs £3 plus 40p postage, while last year's is still available at half price - now £1.50 plus 40p postage (post free if ordered with the 1998-99 edition.
Contact Stewart at 84 Gallowhill Road, Paisley PA3 4TJ                                    *TW*

## OVD SCOTTISH JUNIOR CUP

### FINAL
(Sunday, 30th May 1999. At Firhill Park, Glasgow)

KELTY HEARTS    0   v   1    KILWINNING RANGERS

H.T. 0-1    Peline

Attendance: 7,525

**KELTY HEARTS:** J Lister; D Baillie, D Arnott, S Leighton, A McKillop, D Beaumont, B Spence (captain), C Chalmers, C Reynolds, A Moffat, I Heddle. Substitute: G Bowman for Moffat 70 minutes. Substitutes (not used): R Dunlop, S Logan, C Harris, M Tanner. Yellow cards: Baillie, Arnott.

**POLLOK:** S Robertson; I Gallagher (captain), P Mullin, M Cameron, T Currie, S Farrell, T Sloan, J Duffy, G Peline, N Montgomery, A McTurk. Substitutes: C Harkness for Peline 70 minutes, A Sharkey for McTurk 89 minutes. Substitutes (not used): A McLCluckie, A Edmiston, I Jardine. Yellow cards: Farrell, Gallacher. Man of the Match: Gallacher.

**Referee:** C Mackay, Cumbernauld.

There have been better Junior Cup Finals and the main interest in this match at sun-drenched Firhill was statistical and sentimental. In their centenary year Kilwinning Rangers won the competition for the first time since 1909 - their only other success - ancd in the process of doing so gained their top honour in a season when they won all but one of the tournaments they entered with a final goals tally of an astonishing 198. It was a pity about the missing pair!

In Contrast the Fife club had only been in existence since 1980, but in that time they have won numerous honours in the Kingdom and a Taycars success in the previous season. They were also Fife champions for the fifth time this time by a five points margin over Hill of Beath Hawthorn and only one league defeat to mar their superb record. Their cup record away from the big one was disappointing, but one cannot win them all.

The only goal of the game came after a mere two minutes when Gerry Peline, who had earlier scored the only goal against holders Arthurlie in the semi-final - at Paisley. Peline was doubtful until shortly befoe the kick-off and is also a fine example of the traditional junior player - hard working, honest and not interested in the senior scene.

His goal followed a scramble in the area and his hard shot from point blank range was parried by Jock Lister in the Kelty goal only to drift gently over his helpless head and into the net. Thus Jock was ultimately unable to repeat the triumph of his father (same firts name), who had been the St Andrews United keeper against Greenock in a 3-1 victory in 1960 at Hampden Park.

The rest of the match was uninspiring with the Ayrshire club the better side, but unable to turn that superirity into goals. Stuart Robertson's work was mostly confined to fielding loose balls and the occasional comfortable cross, while at the other end orman Montgomery, a prolific scorer during the season, missed several good chances as did James Duffy. In defence Kilwinning were rock soild with skipper Iain Gallacher earning the Man of the Match award, although he was also one of the game's four booking along with colleague Farrell and Kelty's scaptain, Billy Spence, and Dick Baillie. Spence (dissent) was the only one not to go into the book for a foul in what was on the whole a good tempered game, which was well controlled by referee Craig Mackay.

Kelty can be proud of their season and their best players were defenders with the veteran Dave Beaumont, formerly of Dundee United, Hibernian and Luton Twon, for whom he played in a Wembley League Cup Final, along with Stevie Leighton, Dick Baillie and Alan McKillop - sound performers all. The side was energetic in midfield with skipper Spence trying hard, but the strkers were snuffed out and rarely threatened anything.

Kilwinning's other triumphs during the season were the Ayrshire Regional League title (only one draw and one defeat in twenty matches), the Jackie Scarlett Cup, the Irvine Times Trophy (with a 6-0 final trouncing of Troon), the 'Ardrossan & Saltcoats Herald' Ayrshire Cup and the West of Scotland Cup, in which they beat the excellent Arthurlie in the Whyte & Mackay sponsored tournament in a close game only a few days after their Firhill triumph. What a campaign! There is no improvement possible on that.                                      *Bill Mitchell*

**QUARTER-FINALS**

| Kelty Hearts | v | Montrose Roselea | 7-1 | | Kilwinning Rangers | v | Auchinleck Talbot | 1-1, 1-0 |
| Larkhall Thistle | v | Arthurlie | 1-3 | | Maryhill | v | Petershill | 0-1 |

**SEMI-FINAL** (23.4.99. At Livingstone FC)

| Kelty Hearts | v | Petershill | 3-1 |
| *Heddle (2),* | | *Walker* | |
| *Reynolds (1)* | | Attendance: 2,819 | |

**SEMI-FINAL** (30.4.99. At Love Street, Oaisley)

| Arthurie | v | Kilwinning Rangers | 0-1 |
| *Peline* | | | |
| | | Attendance: 7,387 | |

## SCOTTISH JUNIOR INTERNATIONALS
(International Tournament in Scotland - Friday & Saturday, 16th & 17th April 1999)

**SEMI-FINAL** (16.4.99. At Dunterlie Park, Arthurlie)

| Rebulic of Ireland | v | Isle of Man | 3-2 |

**SEMI-FINAL** (16.4.99. At Lochburn Park, Maryhill)

| Scotland | v | Northern Ireland | 4-0 |
| *K Cameron (3),* | | | |
| *D Flynn (1)* | | | |

**THIRD & FOURTH PLACE MATCH** (17.4.99. At Dunterlie Park, Arthurlie)

| Isle of Man | v | Northern Ireland | 3-1 |

**FINAL** (17.4.99. At Newlandfields Park, Pollok)

| Scotland | v | Republic of Ireland | 1-1 | (Republic of Ireland won 4-2 on penalty kicks) |
| *D Flynn* | | *D McGuinness* | | |

**SCOTLAND SQUAD:**
K Cameron (Tayport), D Cormack (Arthurlie), G Duncan (Arthurlie), S Farrell (Kilwinning Rangers), D Fulton (Arthurlie), D Flynn (Camelon), M Graham (Hill of Beath Hawthorn), G Gardiner (Arthurlie), D McCulloch (Auchinleck Talbot), C Milne (Whitburn), J Mitchell (Hill of Beath Hawthorn), S Quigg (Arthurlie), A Ramsay (Tayport), J Ross (Camelon), S Stewart (Tayport), T Woods (Maryhill), S Robertson (Kilwinning Rangers).

## HIGHLAND FINAL LEAGUE TABLE 1998-99

| | P | W | D | L | F | A | Pts | | | P | W | D | L | F | A | Pts |
|---|---|---|---|---|---|---|---|---|---|---|---|---|---|---|---|---|
| Peterhead | 30 | 24 | 4 | 2 | 89 | 19 | 76 | | Brora Rangers | 30 | 11 | 5 | 14 | 61 | 63 | 38 |
| Huntly | 30 | 23 | 3 | 4 | 86 | 38 | 72 | | Deveronvale | 30 | 11 | 4 | 15 | 57 | 72 | 37 |
| Keith | 30 | 22 | 4 | 4 | 92 | 41 | 70 | | Rothes | 30 | 8 | 5 | 17 | 46 | 64 | 29 |
| Elgin City | 30 | 21 | 1 | 8 | 71 | 39 | 64 | | Buckie Thistle | 30 | 8 | 4 | 18 | 36 | 60 | 28 |
| Fraserburgh | 30 | 18 | 6 | 6 | 86 | 39 | 60 | | Lossiemouth | 3O | 8 | 4 | 18 | 40 | 67 | 28 |
| Clachnacuddin | 30 | 16 | 8 | 6 | 80 | 45 | 56 | | Wick Academy | 30 | 7 | 2 | 21 | 33 | 85 | 23 |
| Cove Rangers | 30 | 16 | 5 | 9 | 88 | 48 | 53 | | Nairn County | 3O | 3 | 2 | 25 | 32 | 115 | 11 |
| Forres Mechanics | 30 | 11 | 6 | 13 | 60 | 60 | 39 | | Fort William | 30 | 1 | 1 | 28 | 24 | 127 | 4 |

## NORTH CALEDONIAN FINAL LEAGUE TABLE 1998-99

| | P | W | D | L | F | A | Pts |
|---|---|---|---|---|---|---|---|
| Golspie Sutherland | 20 | 16 | 0 | 4 | 60 | 22 | 32 |
| Balintore | 20 | 14 | 3 | 3 | 59 | 25 | 31 |
| Caledonian Thistle | 20 | 12 | 2 | 6 | 71 | 27 | 26 |
| Thurso | 20 | 10 | 4 | 6 | 57 | 25 | 24 |
| Alness United | 20 | 10 | 4 | 6 | 41 | 28 | 24 |
| Halkirk | 20 | 9 | 4 | 7 | 36 | 34 | 22 |
| Invergordon | 20 | 7 | 5 | 8 | 53 | 46 | 19 |

| | P | W | D | L | F | A | Pts |
|---|---|---|---|---|---|---|---|
| Tain | 20 | 6 | 1 | 13 | 35 | 51 | 13 |
| Bonar Bridge | 20 | 5 | 1 | 14 | 27 | 86 | 11 |
| Bunillidh | 20 | 4 | 2 | 14 | 24 | 61 | 10 |
| Dornoch | 20 | 0 | 1 | 19 | 15 | 141 | 1 |

NB: This is the most senior league in the North of
Scotland after the Highland League.

## TENNENTS HIGHLAND LEAGUE CUP

### DISTRICT 1

| | P | W | D | L | F | A | Pts |
|---|---|---|---|---|---|---|---|
| Keith | 3 | 2 | 1 | 0 | 4 | 1 | 7 |
| Peterhead | 3 | 2 | 0 | 1 | 5 | 4 | 6 |
| Fraserburgh | 3 | 1 | 0 | 2 | 8 | 5 | 3 |
| Rothes | 3 | 0 | 1 | 2 | 2 | 9 | 0 |

### DISTRICT 2

| | P | W | D | L | F | A | Pts |
|---|---|---|---|---|---|---|---|
| Huntly | 3 | 2 | 1 | 0 | 5 | 0 | 7 |
| Cove Rangers | 3 | 2 | 0 | 1 | 4 | 5 | 6 |
| Buckie Thistle | 3 | 1 | 0 | 2 | 3 | 5 | 3 |
| Deveronvale | 3 | 0 | 1 | 2 | 2 | 4 | 1 |

### DISTRICT 3

| | P | W | D | L | F | A | Pts |
|---|---|---|---|---|---|---|---|
| Forres Mech'cs | 3 | 2 | 1 | 0 | 8 | 3 | 7 |
| Lossiemouth | 3 | 2 | 1 | 0 | 5 | 1 | 7 |
| Nairn County | 3 | 1 | 0 | 2 | 4 | 9 | 3 |
| Elgin City | 3 | 0 | 0 | 3 | 1 | 5 | 0 |

### DISTRICT 4

| | P | W | D | L | F | A | Pts |
|---|---|---|---|---|---|---|---|
| Brora Rangers | 3 | 3 | 0 | 0 | 5 | 1 | 9 |
| Clachnacuddin | 3 | 2 | 0 | 1 | 8 | 1 | 6 |
| Fort William | 3 | 0 | 1 | 2 | 3 | 6 | 1 |
| Wick Academy | 3 | 0 | 1 | 2 | 2 | 10 | 1 |

**SEMI-FINALS** (Saturday, 1st May 1999)

| | | | | | | |
|---|---|---|---|---|---|---|
| Brora Rangers | v | Keith | 0-1 | Forres Mechanics | v Huntly | 2-1 |
| (attendance: 400) | | | | (attendance: 550) | | |

**FINAL** (Saturday, 8th May 1999. At Borough Briggs, Elgin)
Forres Mechanics     v     Keith   1-0
*Bavidge*

## NORTHERN CUP FINALS

### PCT NORTH CALEDONIAN CUP
(Final at Tain)
Inverness Caledonian Thistle     2     v     0     Golspie Sutherland

### CHIC ALLAN CUP
(Final at Caledonian Stadium Inverness)
Inverness Caledonian Thistle     3     v     0     Balintore

### MORRIS NEWTON CUP
(Final at Victoria Park, Dingwall)
Balintore     3     v     0     Golspie Sutherland

### FOOTBALL TIMES CUP
(Final at Alness)
Inverness Caledonian Thistle     7     v     1     Golspie Sutherland

# SCOTTISH QUALIFYING CUP

# NORTH

**FIRST ROUND**

| Deveronvale | v | Rothes | 0-2 |
|---|---|---|---|

**SECOND ROUND**

| Brora Rangers | v | Lossiemouth | 7-1 | Buckie Thistle | v | Forres Mechanics | 0-1 |
|---|---|---|---|---|---|---|---|
| Cove Rangers | v | Elgin City | 3-1 | Golspie Sutherland | v | Rothes | 0-3 |
| Huntly | v | Fort William | 3-0 | Nairn County | v | Keith | 0-7 |
| Peterhead | v | Fraserburgh | 1-1, 3-1 | Wick Academy | v | Clachnacuddin | 1-1, 0-2 |

**QUARTER-FINALS**

| Cove Rangers | v | Clachnacuddin | 1-2 | Huntly | v | Forres Mechanics | 4-1 |
|---|---|---|---|---|---|---|---|
| Keith | v | Rothes | 1-1, 4-1 | Peterhead | v | Brora Rangers | 1-0 |

**SEMI-FINALS**

| Clachnacuddin | v | Huntly | 3-2 | Keith | v | Peterhead | 2-1 |
|---|---|---|---|---|---|---|---|

**FINAL**

| Inverness Clach'din | v | Keith | 3-1 | (7th November 1998, at Borough Briggs, Elgin) |
|---|---|---|---|---|
| MacPherson (1), | | Still | H.T. 1-0 | Attendance: 1,008 |
| Keddie (1), | | | | |
| McCraw (1 pen) | | | | |

**CLACHNACUDDIN:** Rae; Skinner, Brennan, Bennett, Sinclair (captain), Douglas, Mackay, Lewis, MacPherson, McCraw, Richardson. Substuitutes: Keddie for MacPherson 66 minutes (injurde), Hercher for McCraw 88 minutes. Boyd not used. Yellow cards: Douglas, Mackay, Bennett.

**KEITH:** Thain; Brown, Patterson, Watt, Dunn, Gibson, Still (captain), Maver, McRitchie. Nicol, Simmers. Substitutes: K McKenzie for Dunn 39 minutes (injured), Hendrie for Maver 75 minutes (withdrawn), M McKenzie for Watt 86 minutes (withdrawn). Yellow card: K McKenzie.

**Referee:** A Freeland, Aberdeen

Clachnacuddin, the club which was down and out at the beginning of the decade and failed to win a match for eighteen months climaxed a wonderful recovery from crisis this season to take the North's most prestigious cup with an exhilarating display against the favourites for the event and did so in style even though their sound back Billy Skinner missed an early penalty after Lewis had been upended in the box by Patterson. Thain made a fine save high to his right to keep out the shot.

Clach shrugged off this disappointment and were by far the better team in the opening half with Keith only attacking ins spasms, although McRitchie spurned at least two good scoring chances. With half-time less than tem minutes away one of several fine corners by Clach player-manager Graeme Bennett was met beyond the far post by Alan Richardson whose return headre was neatly nodded past Thain by Jamie MacPherson.

This well earned lead was cancelled out immediately after half-time when Colin Sinclair was harshly adjudged to have fouled McRitchie and skipper Darren Still tucked away Keith's equaliser without ceremony.

This was the start of the best period of the match for Keith and it was only ended when a long clearance from the Clack defence was misjudged by Neil Gibson, whose attempted back-pass left Ian Thain in no-man's land on the edge of his area and the ball was collected by the superb Bruce McCraw, who moved to the goal-line befoe sending an inch-perfect pass to Alan Keddie, only recently on for the injured MacPherson, and he slid it home.

Desperate thrusts from Keith availed nothing and any thoughts of extra-time were demolished by McCraw, who collected a ball wide on the left and wandered cleverly into the Keith area befoe being send sprawling by Gibson. The man-of-the-match picked himself up and slammed home a low shot from the penalty to clinch victory in a superb match, which a small attendance of 1,008 mus have enjoyed thoroughly, including the losers' fans.

Apart from McCraw, who had earlier in the serason been on the Clach transfer list, Clach's stars in a fine team effort were goalkeeper Martin Rae, captain and Tony Adams look-alike Colin Sinclair, John Douglas, Andrew Mackay and Andrew Lewis. Skipper Darren Still was best of a disappointing Keith side who had lost a third final in five seasons, whereas Clach's success was their first in 24 campaigns.

# SOUTH

## FIRST ROUND

| | | | | | | | |
|---|---|---|---|---|---|---|---|
| Annan Athletic | v | Preston Athletic | 1-1, 2-1 | Edinburgh City | v | Newton Stewart | 3-1 |
| Girvan | v | Coldstream | 2-4 | Hawick Royal Albert | v | Edinburgh University | 1-2 |
| Threave Rovers | v | Whitehill Welfare | 1-3 | | | | |

## SECOND ROUND

| | | | | | | | |
|---|---|---|---|---|---|---|---|
| Burntisland Shipyard | v | St Cuthbert Wdrs | 0-0, 2-1 | Dalbeattie Star | v | Coldstream | 3-2 |
| Edinburgh City | v | Glasgow U. | 0-0, 0*0, 5p4 | Edinburgh University | v | Whitehill Welfare | 1-3 |
| Selkirk | v | Spartans | 2-2, 0-4 | Tarff Rovers | v | Annan Athletic | 5-3 |
| Vale of Leithen | v | Civil Service Strollers | 2-3 | Wigtown & Bladnoch | v | Gala Fairydean | 0-4 |

## QUARTER-FINALS

| | | | | | | | |
|---|---|---|---|---|---|---|---|
| Civil Service Strollers | v | Burntisland Shipyard | 4-1 | Edinburgh City | v | Whitehill Welfare | 1-2 |
| Spartans | v | Gala Fairydean | 7-1 | Tarff Rovers | v | Dalbeattie Star | 0-1 |

## SEMI-FINALS

| | | | | | | | |
|---|---|---|---|---|---|---|---|
| Civil Service Strollers | v | Dalbeattie Star | 3-2 | Spartans | v | Whitehill Welfare | 0-2 |

## FINAL

| | | | | |
|---|---|---|---|---|
| Whitehill Welfare | v | Civil Service Strollers | 2-0 | (14th November 1998. At Stenhousemuir FC) |
| *Thorburn, Bennett* | | | | Attendance: 239 |

# INVERNESS CUP

## PRELIMINARY ROUND

| | | | |
|---|---|---|---|
| Ross County | v | Forres Mechanics | 3-1 |

## FIRST ROUND

| | | | | | | | |
|---|---|---|---|---|---|---|---|
| Brora Rangers | v | Lossiemouth | 6-0 | Elgin City | v | Inverness C Thistle 'A' | 1-6 |
| Fort William | v | Clachnacuddin | 3*6 | Ross County | v | Nairn County | 7-1 |

## SEMI-FINALS

| | | | | | | | |
|---|---|---|---|---|---|---|---|
| Ross County 'A' | v | Brora Rangers | 4-3 | Inverness C This. A | v | Clachnacuddin | 2-0 |
| (after extra-time) | | | | | | | |

## FINAL

| | | | | |
|---|---|---|---|---|
| Inverness C Thistle 'A' | v | ROSS COUNTY | 1-0 | (26th Jan 1999. At Caledonian Stadium, Inverness) |
| *Tokely* | | | | |

# ABERDEENSHIRE SHIELD

## FIRST ROUND

| | | | | | | | |
|---|---|---|---|---|---|---|---|
| Buckie Thistle | v | Cove Rangers | 0-5 | Deveronvale | v | Fraserburgh | 3-1 |
| Huntly | v | Peterhead | 1-3 | | | | |

## SEMI-FINALS

| | | | | | | | |
|---|---|---|---|---|---|---|---|
| Keith | v | Deveronvale | 4-1 | Peterhead | v | Cove Rangers | 3-0 |

## FINAL

| | | | | |
|---|---|---|---|---|
| Keith | v | Peterhead | 1-3 | (Tuesday, 9th December 1998. At Kynoch Park, Keith) |
| *Nicol* | | *Yule (2), Yeats (1)* | | |

# NON-LEAGUE CLUBS IN SCOTTISH CUP

## SECOND ROUND

| | | | | | | | |
|---|---|---|---|---|---|---|---|
| Civil Service Strollers | v | Albion Rovers | 0-3 | Dalbeattie Star | v | East Stirlingshire | 1-2 |
| Huntly | v | Peterhead | 3-0 | Keith | v | Brechin City | 0-0, 3-1 |
| Spartans | v | Clyde | 1-1, 0-5 | Whitehill Welfare | v | Stenhousemuir | 1-1, 0-2 |
| Queen's Park | v | Clachnacuddin | 1-1, 3-2 | | | | |

## THIRD ROUND

| | | | |
|---|---|---|---|
| Falkirk | v | Huntly | 3-0 |

# JARLAW ABERDEENSHIRE CUP

**FIRST ROUND**

| | | | | | | | |
|---|---|---|---|---|---|---|---|
| Cove Rangers | v | Fraserburgh | 2-3 | Huntly | v | Deveronvale | 4-1 |
| Keith | v | Aberdeen 'A' | 1-8 | Peterhead | v | Buckie Thistle | 4-0 |

**SEMI-FINALS**

| | | | | | | | |
|---|---|---|---|---|---|---|---|
| Huntly | v | Aberdeeen 'A' | 1-1, 1-4 | Peterhead | v | Fraserburgh | 3-0 |

**FINAL**

| | | | | |
|---|---|---|---|---|
| Peterhead | v | Aberdeen 'A' | 3-1 | (at Balmoor, Peterhead) |
| Smith (1), | | Wyness | H.T. 1-0 | |
| Milne (1), | | | | |
| Livingstone (1) | | | | |

**PETERHEAD:** Pirie; Watson, Morrison, King (captain), Simpson, Yule, Smith, Baxter, Milne, Brown, Livingstone. Substitutes: Yeats for Baxter 74 minutes, G Clark for Milne 86 minutes, S Clark for Watson 88 minutes.

**ABERDEEN 'A':** Stillie; Hart, Milne, Young, Anderson, McCaffery, Gillies, Bett, Duncan, Wyness, Clark. Substitute: Mackie for Clark 54 minutes.

**Referee:** G Simpson, Aberdeen.

Peterhead confirmed to the North of Scotland public at large that they may well dethrone Huntly this season with a stunning display against a star-studded Aberdeen side which include five youth internationals.

The home team carried the match to their more vaunted opponents throughout the game and led at half-time through a well constructed goal from short range by Smith in 37 minutes.

The young Pittodrie side did draw level after a dozen minutes in the second half, but this was to be the Bluee Tonners' day and hard hit shots in the final fifteen minutes by Milne and Livingstone meant that justice was done.

# McEWAN'S NORTH OF SCOTLAND CUP

**FIRST ROUND**

| | | | | | | | |
|---|---|---|---|---|---|---|---|
| Fort William | v | Ross County 'A' | 0-1 | Nairn County | v | Inverness C Thistle 'A' | 1-0 |
| Rothes | v | Clachnacuddin | 1-0 | Wick Academy | v | Lossiemouth | 1-2 |

**SECOND ROUND**

| | | | | | | | |
|---|---|---|---|---|---|---|---|
| Elgin City | v | Golspie Sutherland | 4-0 | Nairn County | v | Brora Rangers | 0-4 |
| Ross County 'A' | v | Forres Mechanics | 2-1 | Rothes | v | Lossiemouth | 3-0 |

**SEMI-FINALS**

| | | | | | | | |
|---|---|---|---|---|---|---|---|
| Brora Rangers | v | Elgin City | 0-3 | Rothes | v | Ross County 'A' | 3-1 |

**FINAL**

| | | | | |
|---|---|---|---|---|
| Elgin City | v | Rothes | 2-0 | (at Mosset Park, Forres) |
| Cameron (1), | | | H.T. 0-0 | |
| Dunsire (1) | | | | |

**ELGIN CITY:** Pirie; Dunsire, McVicar, McLennan, McHardy, O'Brien, Whyte, Green, Polworth, Ord, Cameron. Substitutees: Maguire for McHardy 74 minutes, Grant for Ord 80 minutes, McDonald for Whyte 88 minutes.

**ROTHES:** Bowman; Aitken, Small, Esson, Coull, Smith, Thain, Pressley, Thomson, Forsyth, Goodall. Substitutes: Begg for Aitken 74 minutes, Daktas for Goodall 80 minutes, Leiper for Forsyth 83 minutes.

**Referee:** K Hadden, Keith.

In a disappointing match Elgin City were far the better of the two sides and would have been ahead before half-time had it not been for some fine work in goal by Bowman.

Early second half strikes by Cameron and Dunsire meant that the Speysiders' wait for some silverware would have to last a little bit longer, but they are a vastly improved side with good spirit and may yet cause problems to the better rated sides.

Elgin finished last season well and could be a serious threat to Huntly's recent Highland dominance.

# EAST OF SCOTLAND LEAGUE

## PREMIER DIVISION

| | P | W | D | L | F | A | Pts |
|---|---|---|---|---|---|---|---|
| Whitehill Welfare | 18 | 14 | 3 | 1 | 43 | 15 | 45 |
| Spartans | 18 | 13 | 4 | 1 | 42 | 16 | 43 |
| Annan Athletic | 18 | 11 | 4 | 3 | 39 | 26 | 37 |
| Civil Service Str | 18 | 9 | 2 | 7 | 31 | 34 | 29 |
| Edinburgh City | 18 | 6 | 5 | 7 | 23 | 26 | 23 |
| Lothian Thistle | 18 | 5 | 7 | 6 | 32 | 28 | 22 |
| Criagroyston | 18 | 5 | 3 | 10 | 29 | 39 | 18 |
| Peebles Rovers | 18 | 3 | 6 | 9 | 28 | 38 | 15 |
| Tollcross United | 18 | 2 | 3 | 13 | 14 | 32 | 9 |
| Pencaitland | 18 | 2 | 3 | 13 | 14 | 41 | 9 |

## FIRST DIVISION

| | P | W | D | L | F | A | Pts |
|---|---|---|---|---|---|---|---|
| Easthouses Lily | 24 | 16 | 7 | 1 | 45 | 20 | 55 |
| Vale of Leithen | 24 | 16 | 5 | 4 | 65 | 34 | 50 |
| Coldstream | 24 | 13 | 7 | 4 | 54 | 39 | 46 |
| Threave Rovers | 24 | 14 | 3 | 7 | 73 | 39 | 45 |
| Preston Athletic | 24 | 12 | 8 | 4 | 51 | 39 | 44 |
| Hawick Royal Albert | 24 | 9 | 6 | 9 | 49 | 52 | 33 |
| Edinburgh Univ | 24 | 8 | 8 | 8 | 38 | 39 | 32 |
| Gala Fairydean | 24 | 9 | 4 | 11 | 37 | 33 | 31 |
| Selkirk | 24 | 7 | 4 | 13 | 45 | 65 | 25 |
| Edinburgh Athletic | 24 | 6 | 6 | 12 | 31 | 52 | 24 |
| Heriot Watt Univ | 24 | 5 | 5 | 14 | 31 | 50 | 20 |
| Kelso United | 24 | 4 | 4 | 16 | 33 | 62 | 16 |
| Eyemouth United | 24 | 2 | 5 | 17 | 26 | 74 | 11 |

## EAST LEAGUE CUP

**QUARTER-FINALS**

| | | | | | | |
|---|---|---|---|---|---|---|
| Craigroyston | v | Threave R  2-2 & 2*2, 2p4 | Edinburgh City | v | Whitehill Welfare | 2-0 &1-6 |
| Hawick Royal Albert | v | Annan Athletic  2-3 & 3-8 | Spartans | v | Peebles Rovers | 2-0 & 4-0 |

**SEMI-FINALS**

| | | | |
|---|---|---|---|
| Threave Rovers | v | Annan Athletic 3-3 and 2-0 | (Aggregate 5-3) |
| Apartans | v | Whitehill Welf  0-0 and 1-3 | (Aggregate 1-3) |

**FINAL** (Sunday, 14th February 1999. At Galashiels)

| | | | | |
|---|---|---|---|---|
| Whitehill Welfare | v | Threave Rovers | 1-1 | (Whitehill Welfare won 5-4 on penalties) |
| Bird | | Hudson | | |

## IMAGE PRINTERS EAST OF SCOTLAND QUALIFYING CUP

**QUARTER-FINALS**

| | | | | | | |
|---|---|---|---|---|---|---|
| Coldstream | v | Spartans | 1-1, 1-3 | Edinburgh City | v | Whitehill Welfare  1-1, 1-1* |
| Preston Athletic | v | Lothian Thistle | 2-2, 0-1 | Tollcross United | v | Vale of Leithen  0-2 |

*Whitehill Welfare won on penalties

**SEMI-FINALS**

| | | | | | | | |
|---|---|---|---|---|---|---|---|
| Spartans | v | Lothian Thistle | 1-2 | Whitehill Welfare | v | Vale of Leithen | 3-1 |

**FINAL**

| | | | | |
|---|---|---|---|---|
| Lothian Thistle | v | Whitehill Welfare | 0-2 | (Saturday, 15th May 1999. At Preston Athletic FC) |

## ALEX JACK CUP

**FIRST ROUND**

| | | | | | | | |
|---|---|---|---|---|---|---|---|
| Peebles Rovers | v | Heriot Watt Univ | 2- 2, 4-1 | Kelso United | v | Easthouses Lily | 3-3, 2-5 |

**QUARTER-FINALS**

| | | | | | | | |
|---|---|---|---|---|---|---|---|
| Craigroyston | v | Pencaitland | 1-0 | Eyemouth United | v | Edinburgh Athletic | 2- 3 |
| Lothian Thistle | v | Peebles Rovers | 4-0 | Tollcross United | v | Easthouses Lily | 1-3 |

**SEMI-FINALS**

| | | | | | | | |
|---|---|---|---|---|---|---|---|
| Easthouses Lily | v | Edinburgh Athletic | 2-0 | Lothian Thistle | v | Craigroyatson | 3-3, 0-1 |

**FINAL**

| | | | | |
|---|---|---|---|---|
| EastHouses Lily | v | Craigroyston | 3-1 | (Sunday, 21st February 1999. At Whitehill Welfare FC) |

# CITY CUP

**SEMI-FINALS**

| | | | | |
|---|---|---|---|---|
| Berwick Rangers | v | Lothian Thistle | 1-1 | (Lothian Thistle won on penalties) |
| Livingston | v | Whitehill Welfare | 1-1 | (Whitehill Welfare won on penalties) |

**FINAL**

| | | | | |
|---|---|---|---|---|
| Whitehill Welfare | v | Lothian Thistle | 5-0 | (Wednesday, 5th May 1999. At Livingston) |

# KING CUP

**THIRD ROUND**

| | | | | | | | |
|---|---|---|---|---|---|---|---|
| Easthouses Lily | v | Preston Athletic | 2-0 | Edinburgh University v | Edinburgh Athletic | 6-0 |
| Kelso United | v | Edinburgh City | 0-4 | Whitehill Welfare v | Selkirk | 2-1 |

**SEMI-FINALS**

| | | | | | | | |
|---|---|---|---|---|---|---|---|
| Easthouses Lily | v | Edinburgh City | 0-3 | Whitehill Welfare | v | Edinburgh University | 1-2 |

**FINAL**

| | | | | |
|---|---|---|---|---|
| Edinburgh City | v | Edinburgh University | 3-1 | (Sunday, 17th May 1999. At Whitehill Welfare FC) |

NB: Whitehill Welfare won three of the five East of Scotland Cup competitions they entered plus the South Qualifying Cup and the East of Scotland League Premier Division.

# SOUTH OF SCOTLAND LEAGUE

## FINAL LEAGUE TABLE 1998-99

| | P | W | D | L | F | A | Pts | | P | W | D | L | F | A | Pts |
|---|---|---|---|---|---|---|---|---|---|---|---|---|---|---|---|
| Tarff Rovers | 24 | 20 | 0 | 4 | 106 | 27 | 60 | St Cuthbert Wands | 24 | 9 | 4 | 11 | 48 | 56 | 31 |
| Dumfries HS FP | 24 | 17 | 2 | 5 | 71 | 27 | 53 | Dalbeattie Star | 24 | 11 | 5 | 8 | 55 | 48 | 38 |
| Maxwelltown HS FP | 24 | 15 | 3 | 6 | 55 | 40 | 48 | Girvan | 24 | 9 | 4 | 11 | 65 | 86 | 31 |
| Creetown | 24 | 12 | 5 | 7 | 74 | 56 | 41 | Newton Stewart | 24 | 8 | 2 | 14 | 53 | 67 | 26 |
| Annan Athletic | 24 | 12 | 2 | 10 | 41 | 54 | 38 | Stranraer Athletic | 24 | 7 | 3 | 14 | 39 | 48 | 24 |
| Threave Rovers | 24 | 10 | 6 | 8 | 59 | 50 | 36 | Girvan | 24 | 3 | 5 | 14 | 35 | 82 | 14 |
| Dalbeattie Star | 24 | 11 | 2 | 11 | 65 | 47 | 35 | Wigtown & Bladnoch | 24 | 3 | 1 | 20 | 26 | 128 | 10 |
| Blackwood Dynamo | 24 | 8 | 7 | 9 | 67 | 57 | 31 | | | | | | | | |

# LEAGUE CUP

**SEMI-FINALS** (first legs)
WEST

| | | | |
|---|---|---|---|
| Girvan | v | Tarff Rovers | 3-9 |

EAST

| | | | |
|---|---|---|---|
| Dalbeattie Star | v | Queen of South 'A' | 0-6 |

**SEMI-FINALS** (second legs)
WEST
Tarff Rovers walked over after Girvan scratched

EAST

| | | | |
|---|---|---|---|
| Queen of South 'A' | v | Dalbeattie Star | 10-0 |

**FINAL**

(FIRST LEG)

| | | | |
|---|---|---|---|
| Tarff Rovers | v | Queen of South 'A' | 1-3 |

(SECOND LEG)

| | | | | |
|---|---|---|---|---|
| Queen of the South 'A' | v | Tarff Rovers | 1-4 | (aggregate 4-5) |

# SOUTHERN COUNTIES CHALLENGE CUP

**FIRST ROUND**

| | | | | | | | |
|---|---|---|---|---|---|---|---|
| Creetown | v | Newton Stewart | 2*2, 4p0 | Maxwelltown HS FP | v | Dalbeattie Star | 2*3 |
| St Cuthbert Wanderers | v | Dumfries High Schl FP | 3-2 | Stranraer Athletic | v | Blackwood Dynamo | 2-0 |
| Tarff Rovers | v | Threave Rovers | 1-0 | Wigtown & Bladnoch | v | Stranraer 'A' | 0-3 |

**SECOND ROUND**

| | | | | | | | |
|---|---|---|---|---|---|---|---|
| Annan Athletic | v | Queen of South 'A' | 2-1 | Creetown | v | Dalbeattie Star | 2-2, 4p1 |
| St Cuthbert Wanderers | v | Stranraer 'A' | 1-1 | Stranraer Athletic | v | Tarff Rovers | 2-0 |

**SEMI-FINALS**

| | | | | | | | |
|---|---|---|---|---|---|---|---|
| Annan Athletic | v | St Cuthbert Wndrs | 3-0 | Stranraer Athletic | v | Creetown | 3-1 |

**FINAL**

| | | | | |
|---|---|---|---|---|
| Annan Athletic | v | Stranraer Athletic | 4-0 | (Saturday, 24th April 1999. At Annan Athletic FC) |

*Proudfoot (2),*
*Paterson (1), Craig (1)*

# POTTS CUP

**SECOND ROUND**

| | | | | | | | |
|---|---|---|---|---|---|---|---|
| Annan Athletic | v | Wigton & Bladnoch | 5-1 | Newton Stewart | v | Dalbeattie Star | 1-2 |
| Tarff Rovers | v | Stranraer Athletic | 2-0 | Threave Rovers | v | Dumfries High Sch FP | 1-4 |

**SEMI-FINALS**

| | | | | | | | |
|---|---|---|---|---|---|---|---|
| Annan Athletic | v | Dalbeattie Star | 4-7 | Dumfries H Sch FP | v | Tarff Rovers | 5-4 |

**FINAL**

| | | | | |
|---|---|---|---|---|
| Dalbeattie Star | v | Dumfries High Sch FP | 1-0 | (Saturday, 24th April 1999. At Dalbeattie Star FC) |

*NcMinn*

# HAIG GORDON MEMORIAL TROPHY

**SECOND ROUND**

| | | | | | | | |
|---|---|---|---|---|---|---|---|
| Newton Stewart | v | Blackwood Dynamo | 4-0 | Queen of the Sth 'A' | v | Wigtown & Badnoch | 6-0 |
| Stranraer Athletic | v | Creetwon | 3-1 | Tarff Rovers | v | Maxwelltown H S FP | 4-1 |

**SEMI-FINALS**

| | | | | | | | |
|---|---|---|---|---|---|---|---|
| Newton Stewart | v | Stranraer Athletic | 3-0 | Tarff Rovers | v | Queen of the South 'A' | 4-2 |

**FINAL**

(Thursday, 6th May 1999. At Blairmont Park, Newton Stewart)

| | | | | |
|---|---|---|---|---|
| Newton Stewart | v | Tarff Rovers | 1-1 | (no extra-time, Tarff Rovers won 6-5 on penalties) |

# TWEEDIE CUP

**SECOND ROUND**

| | | | | | | | |
|---|---|---|---|---|---|---|---|
| Dalbeattie Star | v | Blackwood Dynamo | 5-2 | Girvan | v | Creetown | 2-8 |
| Stranraer Athletic | v | Newton Stewart | 2-0 | Tarff Rovers | v | Threave Rovers | 6-3 |

**SEMI-FINALS**

| | | | | | | | |
|---|---|---|---|---|---|---|---|
| Creetown | v | Stranraer Athletic | 4-1 | Tarff Rovers | v | Dalbeattie Star | 2-0 |

**FINAL**

| | | | | |
|---|---|---|---|---|
| | | (Saturday, 8th May 1999. At Creetown FC) | | |
| Creetown | v | Tarff Rovers | 2-2 | (after extra-time - Tarff Rovers won 6-5 on penalties) |

*McClymont (1),*   *Robinson (2)*
*Davies (1)*

# CREE LODGE CUP

## SECOND ROUND

| | | | | | | | |
|---|---|---|---|---|---|---|---|
| Annan Athletic | v | St Cuthbert Wanderers 7-2 | | Blackwood Dynamos | v | Tarff Rovers | 3-8 |
| Newton Stewart | v | Threave Rovers | 1-3 | Wigtown & Bladnoch | v | Girvan | 6-2 |

## SEMI-FINALS

| | | | | | | | |
|---|---|---|---|---|---|---|---|
| Tarff Rovers | v | Annan Athletic | 2-0 | Wigtown & Bladnoch | v | Threave Rovers | 0-4 |

## FINAL

| | | | | |
|---|---|---|---|---|
| Threave Rovers | v | Tarff Rovers | 0-1 | (11th April 1998. At Meadow Park, Castle Douglas) |
| | | Hunter | | |

NB: In the Second Round Paul Stewart (Tarff Rovers) scored seven goals and Norman Montgomery (Annan Athletic) six goals.

## DETROIT TROPHY
(Overall Champions)
Tarff Rovers

## 'WHYTE & MacKAY' WEST OF SCOTLAND CUP

### FOURTH ROUND

| | | | | | | | |
|---|---|---|---|---|---|---|---|
| Arthurlie | v | Glenafton Athletic | 3-1 | Beith | v | Pollok | 0-1 |
| Benburb | v | Auchinleck Talbot 0-0, 2-4 | | Kilwinning Rangers | v | Irvine Meadow | 3-2 |

### SEMI-FINALS

| | | | | |
|---|---|---|---|---|
| Kilwinning Rangers | v | Pollok | 5-2 | (18th May 1999. At Kilbirnie Ladeside FC) |
| Arthurlie | v | Auchinleck Talbot | 2-1 | (29th May 1999. At Newlandsfield Park, Pollok) |

### FINAL

| | | | | |
|---|---|---|---|---|
| Kilwinning Rangers | v | Arthurlie | 2-1 | (4th June 1999. At Newlandsfield Park, Pollok) |
| Sloan (1), | | Quigg | | |
| Montgomery (1) | | | | |

*Whyte & Mackay Cup Quarter Final - Auchinleck Talbot v Maryhill. Photo: JBV*

*Whyte & Mackay Cup - Billy Easton (Lugar Boswell) v Steve Quigg (Arthurlie). Photo: Alan Watson*

# AYRSHIRE DISTRICT LEAGUE

## DIVISION ONE

| | P | W | D | L | F | A | Pts |
|---|---|---|---|---|---|---|---|
| Kilwinning Rangers | 20 | 18 | 1 | 1 | 80 | 17 | 55 |
| Auchinleck Talbot | 20 | 17 | 2 | 1 | 60 | 15 | 53 |
| Cumnock Juniors | 20 | 13 | 0 | 7 | 59 | 29 | 39 |
| Kilbirnie Ladeside | 20 | 10 | 3 | 7 | 38 | 25 | 33 |
| Glenafton Athletic | 20 | 9 | 2 | 9 | 43 | 30 | 29 |
| Beith Juniors | 20 | 8 | 3 | 9 | 32 | 32 | 27 |
| Dalry Thistle | 20 | 8 | 2 | 10 | 35 | 35 | 26 |
| Troon | 20 | 7 | 3 | 10 | 43 | 50 | 34 |
| Largs Thistle | 20 | 6 | 3 | 11 | 29 | 39 | 21 |
| Ardrossan Winton R | 20 | 4 | 1 | 15 | 18 | 61 | 13 |
| Annbank United | 20 | 0 | 0 | 20 | 16 | 120 | 0 |

## DIVISION TWO

(first five positions)

| | P | W | D | L | F | A | Pts |
|---|---|---|---|---|---|---|---|
| Irvine Meadow XI | 22 | 20 | 1 | 1 | 95 | 13 | 61 |
| Irvine Victoria | 22 | 14 | 3 | 5 | 60 | 37 | 452 |
| Lugar Boswell Thist | 22 | 13 | 5 | 4 | 60 | 27 | 44 |
| Muirkirk Juniors | 22 | 12 | 7 | 3 | 50 | 26 | 43 |
| Ardeer Thistle | 22 | 12 | 4 | 6 | 59 | 44 | 40 |

Other teams and points:
Craigmark Burntonians (30), Kello Rovers (29),
Saltcoats Victoria (29), Hurlford United (20), Maybole
Juniors (15), Darvel Juniors (13), Whitletts Victoria (6)

*OVD Cup Quarter Final - Kilwinning Rangers v Auchinleck Talbot. Photo: JBV*

*Top: League First Division - Troon v Kilbirnie Ladeside. Photo: JBV*
*Bottom: Largs Thistle - Winners of the Promotion/Relegation Play Off. Photo: JBV*

# AYRSHIRE LEAGUE (JACKIE SCARLETT CUP)

**SEMI-FINALS**

| | | | | | | |
|---|---|---|---|---|---|---|
| Auchinleck Talbot | v | Cumnock | 1-0 | Irvine Meadow | v Kilwinning Rangers | 2-4 |

**FINAL**

Auchinleck Talbot    v    Kilwinning Rangers    1-2    (Monday, 5th October 1998. At Somerset Park, Ayr)
*Gallen*        *Currie (1), McTurk (1)*     Attendance: 1,700


# 'ARDROSSAN & SALTCOATS' AYRSHIRE JUNIOR CUP

**SEMI-FINALS**

| | | | | | | |
|---|---|---|---|---|---|---|
| Irvine Meadow | v | Saltcoats Victoria | 2-0 | Kilwinning Rangers | v Auchinleck Talbot | 2-0 |

**FINAL**

Kilwinning Rangers    v    Irvine Meadow    2-1    (Friday, 18th June 1999. At Meadow Park, Irvine)
*Duffy, McTurk*      *Greer pen*


# 'IRVINE TIMES' AYRSHIRE DISTRICT CUP

**SEMI-FINALS**

| | | | | | | |
|---|---|---|---|---|---|---|
| Kilwinning Rangers | v | Auchinleck Talbort | 3-2 | Troon | v Irvine Victoria | 1-0 |

**FINAL**

Kilwinning Rangers    v    Troon    6-0    (16th June 1999. At Kilwinning Rangers FC)
*McTurk (3),*
*Montgomery (2),*
*Duffy*
*Gibson, Raeburn*


# NORTH AYRSHIRE CUP

**SEMI-FINALS**

| | | | | | | |
|---|---|---|---|---|---|---|
| Beith | v | Irvine Victoria | 1-1, 2p3 | Kilbirnie Ladeside | v Kilwinning Rangers | 2-0 |

**FINAL**

Irvine Victoria    v    Kilbirnie Ladeside    2-1    (Sunday, 6th June 1999. At Irvine Meadow FC)


# EAST AYRSHIRE CUP

**SEMI-FINALS**

| | | | | | | |
|---|---|---|---|---|---|---|
| Darvel | v | Auchinleck Talbot | 0-5 | Lugar Boswell Thistle v | Cumnock | 3-2 |

**FINAL**

Auchinleck Talbot    v    Lugar Boswell Thistle    3-0    (Wednesday, 19th May 1999. At Cumnock FC)


# SOUTH AYRSHIRE CUP

**SEMI-FINALS**

| | | | | | | |
|---|---|---|---|---|---|---|
| Annbank United | v | Whitletts Victoria | 0-1 | Maybole | v Troon | 2-7 |

**FINAL**

Troon    v    Whitletts Victoria    6-2    (Monday, 12th April 1999. At Dam Park, Ayr)

# AYRSHIRE SUPER CUP

**SEMI-FINALS**

Auchinleck Talbot    v    Troon        2-1        Irvine Victoria    v    Glenafton Athletic    0-3

**FINAL**

Auchinleck Talbot    v    Glenafton Athletic    3-0        (16th June 1999. At Lugar Boswell Thistle FC)

*Ayrshire Super Cup Winners, Auchinleck Talbot, beat the holders Glenafton Athletic 3-0. Photo: JBV*

# AYRSHIRE LEAGUE PLAY-OFF

First leg:

Largs Thistle        v    Lugar Boswell Thistle   1-0

Second Leg:

Lugar Boswell Thistle    v    Largs Thistle        4-3        (Aggregate 4-3 - Largs Thistle stay in First Division)

# CENTRAL REGION

## PREMIER DIVISION FINAL LEAGUE TABLE 1998-99

| | P | W | D | L | F | A | Pts | | P | W | D | L | F | A | Pts |
|---|---|---|---|---|---|---|---|---|---|---|---|---|---|---|---|
| Shotts Bon Accord | 22 | 15 | 6 | 1 | 52 | 19 | 51 | Petershill | 22 | 7 | 7 | 8 | 31 | 30 | 28 |
| Maryhill | 22 | 14 | 3 | 5 | 45 | 32 | 45 | Pollok | 22 | 6 | 6 | 10 | 41 | 43 | 24 |
| Arthurlie | 22 | 12 | 3 | 7 | 42 | 32 | 39 | Lesmahagow | 22 | 6 | 4 | 12 | 28 | 35 | 22 |
| Benburb | 22 | 9 | 9 | 4 | 35 | 23 | 36 | Baillieston | 22 | 7 | 1 | 14 | 25 | 43 | 22 |
| Neilston | 22 | 10 | 3 | 9 | 38 | 22 | 33 | Cambuslandg Rangers | 22 | 4 | 7 | 11 | 29 | 47 | 19 |
| Lanark United | 22 | 8 | 6 | 8 | 28 | 29 | 30 | Rutherglen Glenc'n | 22 | 6 | 1 | 15 | 28 | 57 | 19 |

### DIVISION ONE
(first five posiitons)

| | P | W | D | L | F | A | Pts |
|---|---|---|---|---|---|---|---|
| Blantyre Victoria | 26 | 18 | 5 | 3 | 54 | 20 | 59 |
| Johnstone Burgh | 26 | 17 | 5 | 4 | 51 | 27 | 56* |
| Shettleston | 26 | 15 | 5 | 6 | 43 | 32 | 50 |
| Larkhall Thistle | 26 | 13 | 8 | 5 | 50 | 30 | 47 |
| Greenock | 26 | 14 | 4 | 8 | 55 | 33 | 46 |

Other teams and points:
Renfrew (38), Vale of Leven (35), Vale of Clyde (35),
Kirkintilloch Rob Roy (34), Carluke Rovers (28, Kilsyth
Rangers (24), Cumbernauld United (20), St Roch's (19),
Forth Wanderers (16).

### DIVISION TWO
(first five positions)

| | P | W | D | L | F | A | Pts |
|---|---|---|---|---|---|---|---|
| Dunipace | 24 | 17 | 6 | 1 | 63 | 23 | 57 |
| East Kilbride This | 24 | 14 | 5 | 5 | 45 | 27 | 47 |
| St Anthony's | 24 | 13 | 6 | 5 | 41 | 28 | 45 |
| Port Glasgow | 24 | 13 | 5 | 6 | 64 | 40 | 44 |
| Glasgow Perthshire | 24 | 12 | 3 | 9 | 59 | 41 | 39 |

Other teams and points:
Ashfield (34), Stonehouse Violet (33), Yoker Athletic
(32), Bellshill Athletic (30), Royal Albert (28),
Thorniewood United (23), Coltness United (14),
Wishaw (10).

## CENTRAL LEAGUE CUP

**QUARTER-FINALS**

| | | | | | | | |
|---|---|---|---|---|---|---|---|
| Blantyre Victoria | V | Ashfield | 1-1, 6p5 | Glencairn | v | Arthurlie | 2-0 |
| Kilsyth Rangers | v | Petershill | 2-0 | Shettleston | v | Lesmahagow | 2-1 |

**SEMI-FINALS**

| | | | | | | | |
|---|---|---|---|---|---|---|---|
| Blantyre Victoria | v | Glencairn | 1-3 | Shettleston | v | Kilsyth Rabgers | 2-1 |

**FINAL**

| | | | | |
|---|---|---|---|---|
| Shettleston | v | Glencairn | 1-4 | (Friday, 14th May 1999. At Newlandsfield Park, Pollok) |

## BEATONS LEAGUE CUP

**SEMI-FINALS**

| | | | | | | | |
|---|---|---|---|---|---|---|---|
| Cumbernauld Athletic | v | Neilston | 0-2 | Maryhill | v | Baillieston | 2-2, 3p4 |

**FINAL**

| | | | | |
|---|---|---|---|---|
| Neilston | v | Baillieston | 5-0 | (Tuesday, 6th October 1998. At Fir Park, Motherwell) |

## EVENING TIMES CUP WINNERS CUP

**SEMI-FINALS**

| | | | | | | | |
|---|---|---|---|---|---|---|---|
| Dunipace | v | Neilston | 2-1 | Glencairn | v | Shotts Bon Accord | 2-1 |

**FINAL**

| | | | | |
|---|---|---|---|---|
| Dunipace | v | Glencairn | 3-0 | (12th June 1999. At Cambuslang Rangers FC) |

# EAST REGION

## FINAL LEAGUE TABLES 1998-99

### DIVISION ONE

| | P | W | D | L | F | A | Pts |
|---|---|---|---|---|---|---|---|
| Linlithgow Rose | 22 | 14 | 4 | 4 | 45 | 21 | 46 |
| Whitburnow | 22 | 13 | 2 | 7 | 46 | 32 | 41 |
| Bonnyrigg Rose | 22 | 10 | 5 | 7 | 39 | 30 | 35 |
| Arniston Rangers | 22 | 10 | 5 | 7 | 31 | 31 | 35 |
| Camelon | 22 | 10 | 3 | 9 | 47 | 35 | 33 |
| Newtongrange Star | 22 | 9 | 6 | 7 | 32 | 24 | 33 |
| Bonnybridge | 22 | 8 | 4 | 10 | 39 | 37 | 28 |
| Fauldhouse United | 22 | 7 | 5 | 10 | 27 | 37 | 28 |
| Bo'ness United | 22 | 6 | 6 | 10 | 33 | 42 | 24 |
| Bathgate Thistle | 22 | 6 | 6 | 10 | 29 | 44 | 24 |
| Dunbar United | 22 | 6 | 4 | 12 | 28 | 46 | 22 |
| Musselburgh Ath'tic | 22 | 5 | 6 | 11 | 32 | 49 | 21 |

### DIVISION TWO
(first five positions)

| | P | W | D | L | F | A | Pts |
|---|---|---|---|---|---|---|---|
| Haddington Athletic | 26 | 20 | 3 | 3 | 78 | 25 | 63 |
| Stoneyburn | 26 | 18 | 3 | 5 | 62 | 31 | 57 |
| Harthill Royal | 26 | 18 | 3 | 5 | 47 | 28 | 57 |
| Pumpherston | 26 | 114 | 8 | 4 | 54 | 36 | 50 |
| Armadale thistle | 26 | 13 | 2 | 11 | 47 | 50 | 41 |

Other teams and points:
Edinburgh United (38), Ormiston Primrose (34), Tranent
(34), Blackburn United (32), Dalkeith Thistle (31),
Broxburn Athletic (25), Livingston United (23), Sauchie
(15), West Calder United (10).

## EAST LEAGUE (CARLSBERG) CUP

**SEMI-FINALS**

| Bonnyrigg Rose | v | Whitburn | 1-1, 2-1 | Newtongrange Star | v | Bonnybridge | 1-1, 4-0 |
|---|---|---|---|---|---|---|---|

**FINAL**

Newtongrange Star    v    Whitburn    1-2    (19th December 1998. At Arniston Rangers FC)

## 'CALDERS' EAST REGIONAL CUP

**SEMI-FINALS**

| Arnsiton rangers | v | Bonnyrigg Rose | 2-2, 1-0 | Trabent | v | Bo'ness United | 1-1, 1-2 |
|---|---|---|---|---|---|---|---|

**FINAL**

Bo'ness United    v    Whitburn    2-1    (Saturday, 12th June 1999. At Linlithgow Rose FC)

## DAVID MOFFAT CUP

**SEMI-FINALS**

| Armadale Thistle | v | Newtongrange Star | 2-0 | Bo'ness United | v | Linlithgow Rose | 2-0 |
|---|---|---|---|---|---|---|---|

**FINAL**

Bo'ness United    v    Armadale Thistle 1-1, 3p1    (Wednesday, 16th June 1999. At Bathgate Thistle FC)

## DALKEITH GLAZING CUP

**SEMI-FINALS**

| Bonnyrigg Rose | v | Arniston Rangers | 0-2 | Linlithgow Rose | v | Harthill Royal | 4-2 |
|---|---|---|---|---|---|---|---|

**FINAL**

Linlithgow Rose    v    Arniston Rangers    1-0    (Saturday, 12th June 1999. At Newtongrange Star FC)

## FIFE & LOTHIANS CUP

**SEMI-FINALS**

| Bo'ness United | v | Kelty Hearts | 3-2 | Oakley United | v | Whitburn | 0*2 |
|---|---|---|---|---|---|---|---|

**FINAL**

Bo'ness United    v    Whitburn    2*3    (Saturday, 5th June 1999. At Linlithgow Rose FC)

# FIFE REGION

## FINAL LEAGUE TABLE 1998-99

| | P | W | D | L | F | A | Pts | | P | W | D | L | F | A | Pts |
|---|---|---|---|---|---|---|---|---|---|---|---|---|---|---|---|
| Kelty Hearts | 30 | 26 | 3 | 1 | 96 | 19 | 81 | Lochore Welfare | 30 | 10 | 8 | 12 | 62 | 48 | 38 |
| Hill of Beath H'thn | 30 | 25 | 1 | 4 | 110 | 30 | 76 | St Andrews United | 30 | 10 | 8 | 12 | 61 | 49 | 38 |
| Glenrothes | 30 | 19 | 6 | 5 | 106 | 42 | 63 | Lochgelly Albert | 30 | 11 | 3 | 16 | 59 | 71 | 36 |
| Thornton Hibs | 30 | 18 | 5 | 7 | 82 | 39 | 59 | Crossgates Primrose | 30 | 9 | 2 | 19 | 44 | 70 | 29 |
| Newburgh | 30 | 18 | 4 | 8 | 75 | 38 | 58 | Benarty | 30 | 5 | 10 | 15 | 41 | 63 | 25 |
| Oakley United | 30 | 16 | 6 | 8 | 80 | 50 | 34 | Tulliallan Thistle | 30 | 4 | 2 | 24 | 38 | 120 | 14 |
| Rosyth Recreation | 30 | 15 | 6 | 9 | 68 | 55 | 51 | Steelend Victoria | 30 | 3 | 2 | 25 | 32 | 143 | 11 |
| Dundonald Bluebell | 30 | 13 | 6 | 11 | 63 | 54 | 45 | Kirkcaldy YMCA | 30 | 2 | 0 | 28 | 21 | 147 | 6 |

## PEDDIE SMITH MALOCCO CUP

**SEMI-FINALS**

Oakley United    V    Hill of Beath Hawthorn 1-2      Thornton Hibs    V    St Andrews United    3-1

**FINAL**

Thornton Hibs    V    Hill of Beath Hawthorn 2-0      (27th September 1998. At Dundonald Bluebell FC)

## 'BARDON AGGREGATES' FIFE CUP

**SEMI-FINALS**

Newburgh    v    Kelty Hearts    1-3      Oakley United    v    Benarty    2-0

**FINAL**

Oakley United    v    Kelty Hearts    3-3, 5p4      (Saturday, 22nd May 1999. At Dundonald Bluebell FC)

## WHITBREAD CUP

**SEMI-FINALS**

Glenrothes    v    Kelty Hearts    3-2      Oakley United    v    Thornton Heath    2-0

**FINAL**

Oakley United    v    Glenrothes    0-1      (Friday, 28th May 1999. At Kelty Hearts FC)

# TAYSIDE REGION

## FINAL LEAGUE TABLES 1998-99

### DIVISION ONE

| | P | W | D | L | F | A | Pts |
|---|---|---|---|---|---|---|---|
| Tayport | 22 | 21 | 1 | 0 | 86 | 6 | 64 |
| North End | 22 | 15 | 2 | 5 | 47 | 20 | 47 |
| Kirrie Thistle | 22 | 11 | 5 | 6 | 46 | 29 | 38 |
| Carnoustie Panmure | 22 | 11 | 5 | 6 | 49 | 37 | 38 |
| Dundee Violet | 22 | 11 | 4 | 7 | 45 | 34 | 37 |
| Lochee United | 22 | 8 | 7 | 7 | 48 | 49 | 31 |
| Downfield | 22 | 8 | 4 | 10 | 48 | 42 | 28 |
| Arbroath SC | 22 | 8 | 3 | 11 | 36 | 44 | 27 |
| Forfar West End | 22 | 7 | 2 | 13 | 29 | 49 | 23 |
| Elmwood | 22 | 6 | 4 | 12 | 35 | 61 | 22 |
| Lochee Harp | 22 | 3 | 2 | 17 | 25 | 58 | 11 |
| St Josephs | 22 | 3 | 1 | 18 | 20 | 85 | 10 |

### DIVISION TWO
(first five positions)

| | P | W | D | L | F | A | Pts |
|---|---|---|---|---|---|---|---|
| Bankfoot Athletic | 22 | 14 | 4 | 4 | 79 | 28 | 46 |
| Montrose Roselea | 22 | 13 | 7 | 2 | 60 | 21 | 46 |
| Jeanfield Swifts | 22 | 12 | 4 | 6 | 51 | 35 | 40 |
| East Craigie | 22 | 1 | 5 | 6 | 48 | 43 | 38 |
| Forfar Albion | 22 | 10 | 6 | 6 | 45 | 33 | 36 |

Other teams and points:

Scone Thistle (32), Blairgowrie (32), Kinnoull (31), Broughty Athletic (26), Brechin Victoria (23), Arbroath Victoria (11), Coupar Angus (6).

# DNEC INTER REGIONAL TROPHY
### (for North and Tayside Region clubs)

**SEMI-FINALS**

Bankfoot Athletic    v    Inverurie Loco Works   0-2      Stoneywood      v    Kirrie Thistle      0-1

**FINAL**

Kirrie Thistle    v    Inverurie Loco Works   3-2      (15th May 1999. At Sunnybank FC, Aberdeen)
*I McKenna (1),*      *Reid (1), Ross (1)*
*G McKenna (1),*
*Soutar (1)*


# HERSCHELL TROPHY

**FINAL**

North End    v    Lochee Harp      1-0      (Wednesday, 12th August 1999. At North End FC)


# TAYCARS TROPHY
### (for Tayside and Fife Region clubs)

**SEMI-FINALS**

Glenrothes    v    Tayport      0-5      Kirrie Thistle      v    St Andrews United    2-3

**FINAL**

Tayport    v    St Andrews United    5-1      (Saturday, 12th June 1999. At Glenesk Park, Dundee)
*Reilly (2), Dochard*
*Ross (2),*
*Ramsay (1)*


# DOWNFIELD SC LEAGUE CUP

**SEMI-FINALS**

Bankfoot Athletic    v    Scone Thistle      3-2      Montrose Roselea    v    Brechin Victoria    2-1

**FINAL**

Bankfoot Athletic    v    Montrose Roselea      3-1      (Sunday, 16th May 1999. At Downfield Park, Dundee)
*Millar (2), Sinclair OG*


# D J LAING HOMES TROPHY

**SEMI-FINALS**

North End    v    East Craigie      4-1      Lochee United      v    Kirrie Thistle      3-1

**FINAL**

North End    v    Lochee United      2-1      (Saturday, 5th June 1999. At Carnoustie Panmure FC)
*King (1),*      *Hutton*
*Cranston (1)*


# WHYTE & MacKAY CUP

**SEMI-FINALS**

Carnoustie Panmure    v    Forfar Albion      6-1      Tayport      v    East Craigie      3-1

**FINAL**

Tayport    v    Carnoustie Pan.   1-1, 5p3      (Friday, 28th May 1999. (At North End FC)


# ROSEBANK C.C. CUP

**SEMI-FINALS**

East Craigie    v    Bankfoot Athletic    2-4      Scone Thistle      v    Montrose Roselea    0-1

**FINAL**

Bankfoot Athletic    v    Montrose Rose.   0-0, 4p5      (Thursday, 3rd June 1999. At Forfar West End FC)

*Dave McCaffrey (Lugar Boswell Thistle) v Davie Taylor (Lochee Harp - Tayside Region Division One) during the OVD Scottish Junior Cup*

# NORTH REGION

## EAST SECTION FINAL LEAGUE TABLES 1998-99

### EAST PREMIER LEAGUE

| | P | W | D | L | F | A | Pts |
|---|---|---|---|---|---|---|---|
| Sunnybank | 22 | 15 | 4 | 3 | 60 | 22 | 49 |
| FC Stoneywood | 22 | 12 | 4 | 6 | 37 | 29 | 40 |
| Stonehaven | 22 | 11 | 5 | 6 | 33 | 28 | 38 |
| Culter | 22 | 9 | 5 | 8 | 40 | 31 | 32 |
| Inverurie Loco Wks | 22 | 9 | 5 | 8 | 48 | 41 | 32 |
| Formartine United | 22 | 9 | 4 | 9 | 42 | 37 | 31 |
| Hermes | 22 | 7 | 7 | 8 | 34 | 38 | 28 |
| Lewis United | 22 | 8 | 3 | 11 | 25 | 44 | 27 |
| Longside | 22 | 7 | 5 | 10 | 35 | 46 | 26 |
| Cruden Bay | 22 | 7 | 4 | 11 | 38 | 52 | 25 |
| Turriff United | 22 | 6 | 4 | 12 | 33 | 44 | 22 |
| Lads Club | 22 | 6 | 2 | 14 | 34 | 57 | 20 |

### EAST DIVISION TWO
(first five places)

| | P | W | D | L | F | A | Pts |
|---|---|---|---|---|---|---|---|
| Banks o' Dee | 22 | 17 | 2 | 3 | 66 | 21 | 53 |
| East End | 22 | 16 | 1 | 5 | 105 | 36 | 49 |
| Buchanhaven Hearts | 22 | 15 | 2 | 5 | 86 | 33 | 47 |
| Hall Russell Utd | 22 | 10 | 4 | 8 | 69 | 35 | 34 |
| Glentannar | 22 | 9 | 7 | 6 | 55 | 34 | 34 |

Other teams and points:
Maud (30), FrAserburgh United (30),
Banchory St Ternan (30), Parkvale (30),
Ellon United (30), Dyce (8), Inverurie Juniors (1).
Inverurie Juniors have resigned from the league.

## CHAMPIONSHIP PLAY-OFF

Sunnybank    v    Islavale    2-0    ( 5th June 1999. At Heathryfold Park, Aberdeen)

## ATLANTIC CABLE TV LEAGUE CUP

**SEMI-FINALS**
Buchanhaven Hearts    v    Inverurie Loco Works  2-4        Stonehaven    v    Formartine United    0-1

**FINAL**
Formartine United    v    Inverurie Loco Works  3-2        (12th May 1999. At Pittodrie Park, Aberdeen)

# GREAT NORTHERN REGIONAL TROPHY CUP

**SEMI-FINALS**

Stonehaven v Nairn St Ninian 1-0    Stoneywood v Culter 2-0

**FINAL**

FC Stoneywood v Stonehaven 1-0    (24th April 1999. At Heathryfold Park, Aberdeen)

# ACORN HEATING CUP

**SEMI-FINALS**

Banchory St Ternan v Stoneywood 4-2    Sunnybank v East End 4-0

**FINAL**

Sunnybank v Banchory St Ternan 4*2    (At East End FC)

# 'ROLLSTUD' ARCHIBALD CUP

**SEMI-FINALS**

Hall Russell United lost to Lewis United    Stoneywood lost to Formartine United

**FINAL**

Formartine United v Lewis United 3-2    (At Hermes FC)

# GORDON CAMPBELL CONSTRUCTION TROPHY

**SEMI-FINALS**

Formartine United v Buchanhaven Hearts 1-0    Lads Club v Stonehaven 2-5

**FINAL**

Formartine United v Stonehaven 1-0    (At Hall Russell United FC)

# MORRISON TROPHY

**SEMI-FINALS**

Banks o'Dee v Parkvale 2-3    East End v Maud 6-2

**FINAL**

Parkvale v East End 1-2    (Friday, 28th May 1999. At Spain Park, Aberdeen)

# NORTH SECTION

## FINAL LEAGUE TABLE 1998-99

| | P | W | D | L | F | A | Pts | | P | W | D | L | F | A | Pts |
|---|---|---|---|---|---|---|---|---|---|---|---|---|---|---|---|
| New Elgin | 26 | 18 | 8 | 0 | 63 | 23 | 62 | Bishopmill United | 26 | 8 | 6 | 12 | 45 | 45 | 30 |
| Islavale | 26 | 19 | 4 | 3 | 88 | 30 | 61 | Lossiemouth United | 26 | 8 | 3 | 15 | 58 | 77 | 27 |
| Buckie Rovers | 26 | 20 | 1 | 5 | 78 | 37 | 61 | Burghead Thistle | 26 | 6 | 3 | 17 | 45 | 70 | 21 |
| Deveronside | 26 | 16 | 3 | 7 | 70 | 37 | 51 | RAF Lossiemouth | 26 | 3 | 3 | 20 | 25 | 83 | 12 |
| Strathspey Thistle | 26 | 13 | 6 | 7 | 67 | 35 | 45 | Kinloss | 26 | 3 | 3 | 20 | 35 | 96 | 12 |
| Portgordon United | 26 | 12 | 5 | 9 | 64 | 49 | 41 | Fochabers | 26 | 3 | 1 | 22 | 25 | 111 | 10 |
| Nairn St Ninian | 26 | 15 | 5 | 6 | 73 | 41 | 38* | | | | | | | | |
| Forres Thistle | 26 | 10 | 5 | 11 | 48 | 50 | 35 | * Denotes 12 points deducted | | | | | | | |

# MATTHEW CUP

**SEMI-FINALS**

| | | | | | | | |
|---|---|---|---|---|---|---|---|
| Buckie Rovers | v | Islavale | 1-1, 6p5 | Forres Thistle | v | Nairn St Ninian | 2-1 |

**FINAL**

| | | | | |
|---|---|---|---|---|
| Deveronside | v | Nairn St Ninian | 1-2 | (Saturday, 12th June 1999. At Deveronside FC) |

# NICHOLSON CUP

**SEMI-FINALS**

| | | | | | | | |
|---|---|---|---|---|---|---|---|
| Burghead Thistle | v | Forres Thistle | 6-2 | Kinloss | v | Fochabers | 1-1* |

*Fochabers won on penalties

**FINAL**

| | | | | |
|---|---|---|---|---|
| Burghead Thistle | v | Kinloss | 3-1 | (Friday, 9th October 1998. at Forres Mechanics FC) |
| McKenzie (1), | | Gibson | | |
| Sim (1), | | | | |
| Davidson (1) | | | | |

# STEWART MEMORIAL CUP

**SEMI-FINALS**

| | | | | | | | |
|---|---|---|---|---|---|---|---|
| Bishopmill United | v | Portgordon United | 1-1 | Lossie United | v | New Elgin | 1-3 |

Bishopmill United won on penalties

**FINAL**

| | | | | |
|---|---|---|---|---|
| New Elgin | v | Bishopmill United | 3-0 | (1st November 1998. At Grant Park, Lossiemouth) |
| Green (2), Laing (1) | | | | |

# GORDON WILLIAMSON CUP

**SEMI-FINALS**

| | | | | | | | |
|---|---|---|---|---|---|---|---|
| Deveronside | v | Bishopmill United | 0-2 | Islavale | v | Strathspey Thistle | 3-1 |

**FINAL**

| | | | | |
|---|---|---|---|---|
| Islavale | v | Bishopmill United | 2-1 | (Friday, 11th June 1999. At Logie Park, Forres) |
| Geddes (2) | | Graham | | |

# ROBERTSON CUP

**SEMI-FINALS**

| | | | | | | | |
|---|---|---|---|---|---|---|---|
| Islavale | v | Buckie Rovers | 2*1 | Nairn St Ninian | v | Strathspey Thistle | 4-0 |

**FINAL**

| | | | | |
|---|---|---|---|---|
| Islavale | v | Nairn St Ninian | 3-1 | (Thursday, 22nd April 1999. At Kynoch Park, Keith) |
| Green (1), | | Reid | | |
| Geddes (1), | | | | |
| McLean (1) | | | | |

# ROBBIE NICOL CUP

**SEMI-FINALS**

| | | | | | | | |
|---|---|---|---|---|---|---|---|
| Buckie Rovers | v | Strathspey Thistle | 2-6 | RAF Lossiemouth | v | Portgordon United | 0-2 |

**FINAL**

| | | | | |
|---|---|---|---|---|
| Strathspey Thistle | v | Portgordon United | 5-0 | (Friday, 4th June 1999. At Pinefield, Elgin) |
| Ferguson (2), | | | | |
| McGregor (1), | | | | |
| Ross (1), Munro (1) | | | | |

# CLIVE WILLIAMSON TROPHY

**SEMI-FINALS**

| | | | | | | | |
|---|---|---|---|---|---|---|---|
| Islavale | v | RAF Lossiemouth | 4-1 | Portgordon United | v | Bishopmill United | 1-7 |

**FINAL**

| | | | | |
|---|---|---|---|---|
| Islavale | v | Bishopmill United | 3-0 | (Sunday, 13th June 1999. At Strathspey Thistle FC)) |
| *MvLean (3)* | | | | |

# MORAYSHIRE CUP

**SEMI-FINALS**

| | | | | | | | |
|---|---|---|---|---|---|---|---|
| Islavale | v | Lossiemouth United | 2*1 | Portgordon United | v | Nairn St Ninian | 3-1 |

**FINAL**

| | | | | |
|---|---|---|---|---|
| Portgordon United | v | Islavale | 2-1 | (Sunday, 15th May 1999. At Pinefield, Elgin) |
| *Nicol (1),* | | *McLean* | | |
| *Russell (1)* | | | | |

# OTHER COMPETITIONS

## SCOTTISH AMATEUR CUP

**SEMI-FINALS**

| | | | | | | | |
|---|---|---|---|---|---|---|---|
| Bearsden | v | Milton | 2-1 | Bellshill YM | v | St Patricks | 2-4 |

**FINAL**

| | | | | |
|---|---|---|---|---|
| Bearsden | v | St Patricks | 0*2 | (Sunday, 15th May 1999. At Rugby Park, Kilmarnock) |

## PRESS & JOURNAL HIGHLAND AMATEUR CUP

**SEMI-FINAL**

| | | | | |
|---|---|---|---|---|
| Brit Legion Inverness | v | Thurso Acks | | (at Brora) |
| Wick Thistle | v | Pentland United | 0-2 | (at Wick FC) |

**FINAL**

| | | | | |
|---|---|---|---|---|
| Pentland United | v | Brit Legion Inverness | 3-1 | (at Brora) |

## WESTERN ISLES CUP

**FINAL**

| | | | |
|---|---|---|---|
| Point | v | Back | 1-0 |

## MILNE CUP

| | | | | |
|---|---|---|---|---|
| Orkney | 2 | v | 3 | Shetland |

# AMATEUR FOOTBALL ALLIANCE

**President:** C R Sharp    **Chairman:** R B Rowe
**Hon Secretary:** W P Goss, 55 Islington Park Street, London N1 1QB
Tel: 0171 359 3493   Fax: 0171 359 5027

## A F A  SENIOR  CUP

**1ST ROUND PROPER**

| | | | | | | |
|---|---|---|---|---|---|---|
| Old Foresters | 0 v 2 | Old Ignatians | Pegasus | 1 v 3 | Old Aloysians |
| Parkfield | 0 v 5 | E Barnet O Gram's | Old Stationers | 2* v 3* | Old Chigwellians |
| Old Buckwellians | 3 v 4 | St Mary's College | Lancing Old Boys | 0 v 3 | Old Finchleians |
| Old Wokingians | 0 v 2 | Latymer Old Boys | Lensbury | 2* v 5* | Old Salesians |
| Bank of England | wo v wd | Old Tollingtonians | Civil Service | 2 v 1 | Alexandra Park |
| Alleyn Old Boys | 6 v 3 | Old Woodhouseians | Norsemen | 3 v 1 | South Bank |
| Old Tiffinian | 4 v 0 | Centymca | West Wickham | 3* v 1* | Old Grammarians |
| Old Sinjuns | 2 v 3 | Ealing Association | Old Hamptonians | 1 v 2 | Old Salopians |
| Wake Green | 0 v 2 | Old Suttonians | Crouch End V's | 1 v 0 | Nat'l West Bank |
| Westerns | 4 v 2 | Old Malvernian | Polytechnic | 1 v 2 | Old Reptonian |
| Old Salvatorians | 0 v 1 | Hale End Athletic | Hon. Artillery Co | 5 v 1 | Old Parmiterians |
| UCL Academicals | 1 v 4 | Old Actonians Assn | Kingsburians | 1 v 2 | Old Manorians |
| Old Bromleians | 0 v 4 | Nottsborough | Old Latymerians | 3 v 1 | Albanian |
| Midland Bank | 1 v 2 | City of London | Carshalton | 4 v 1 | William Fitt |
| Cuaco | 2 v 0 | Winchmore Hill | Old Minchendenians | 1*0 v 1*7 | Old Tenisonians |
| Mill Hill Village | 4 v 3 | Old Owens | Hadley | 0 v 4 | Old Esthameians |

(* after extra time)

**2ND ROUND PROPER**

| | | | | | | |
|---|---|---|---|---|---|---|
| Old Ignatians | 1 v 3 | Old Aloysians | E Barnet O Gram's | 2 v 0 | Old Chigwellians |
| St Mary's College | 1 v 2 | Old Finchleians | Latymer Old Boys | 1 v 2 | Old Salesians |
| Bank of England | 2* v 3* | Civil Service | Alleyn Old Boys | 0 v 1 | Norsemen |
| Old Tiffinian | 4 v 1 | West Wickham | Ealing Association | 0 v 2 | Old Salopians |
| Old Suttonians | 1 v 2 | Crouch End Vampires | Westerns | 2 v 5 | Old Reptonian |
| Hale End Athletic | 1 v 2 | Hon Artillery Co | Old Actonians Assn | 3 v 2 | Old Manorians |
| Nottsborough | 3 v 2 | City of London | Old Latymerians | 3 v 4 | Carshalton |
| Cuaco | 0 v 6 | Old Tenisonians | Mill Hill Village | 3 v 0 | Old Esthameians |

**3RD ROUND PROPER**

| | | | | | | |
|---|---|---|---|---|---|---|
| Old Aloysians | 5 v 3 | E Barnet O Gram's | Old Finchleians | 5 v 2 | Old Salesians |
| Civil Service | 4 v 1 | Norsemen | Old Tiffinian | 1 v 3 | Old Salopians |
| Crouch End V's | 3 v 1 | Old Reptonian | Hon Artillery Co | 4 v 3 | Old Actonians A |
| Nottsborough | 1 v 0 | Carshalton | Old Tenisonians | 2 v 1 | Mill Hill Village |

**4TH ROUND PROPER**

| | | | | | | |
|---|---|---|---|---|---|---|
| Old Aloysians | 1 v 2 | Old Finchleians | Civil Service | 0*2 v 0*0 | Old Salopians |
| Crouch End V's | 2* v 3* | Hon Artillery Co | Nottsborough | 3*1 v 3*0 | Old Tenisonians |

**SEMI-FINALS**

| | | | | | | |
|---|---|---|---|---|---|---|
| Old Finchleians | 4* v 2* | Civil Service | Hon Artillery Co | 3 v 2 | Nottsborough |

**FINAL**

| | | |
|---|---|---|
| Old Finchleians | 4 v 1 | Hon Artillery Co |

## OTHER AFA CUP RESULTS

**INTERMEDIATE**
Barclays Bank Res    3 v 0      Carshalton Res

**JUNIOR**
Albanian 3rd    1 v 0      Barclays Bank 3rd

**MINOR**
Barclays Bank 4th    3 v 1      Polytechnic 4th

**SENIOR NOVETS**
Polytechnic 5th    2 v 1      Old Finchleians 5

**INTERMEDIATE NOVETS**
Old Actonians 6th    1* v 2      Natwest Bank 6th

**JUNIOR NOVETS**
Old Actonians 9th    4 v 0      Midland Bank 7th

**VETERANS**
Winchmore Hill    3 v 1      Alexandra Park

**OPEN VETERANS**
P L A    2 v 1      Winchmore Hill

**YOUTH - U16**
Norsemen    4 v 0      Old Parmiterians

**ESSEX SENIOR**
Old Parkonians    2 v 0      Old Parmiterians

**MIDDLESEX SENIOR**
Old Actonians Ass'n    2 v 0      Lensbury

**SURREY SENIOR**
Carshalton    2* v 0      Old Salesians

**ESSEX INTERMEDIATE**
Old Parkonians Res    2 v 1      Old Buckwellians Res

**KENT INTERMEDIATE**
Morgan Guaranty 1st    1 v 2      Old Sedcopians Res

**MIDDLESEX INTERMEDIATE**
Old Aloysians Res    4* v 3      Barclays Bank Res

**SURREY INTERMEDIATE**
Carshalton Res    3 v 2      Nottsborough Res

**GREENLAND MEMORIAL**
Old Aloysians    5 v 1    Norsemen

(* after extra time)

## A F A REPRESENTATIVE XI

| | | | |
|---|---|---|---|
| v | Oxford University | Lost | 1-4 |
| v | Army F A | Lost | 2-3 |
| v | Royal Navy F A | Lost | 2-4 |
| v | London University | Won | 3-1 |
| v | London F A | Won | 1-0 |

## ARTHUR DUNN CUP

Old Salopians   3 v 1   Lancing Old Boys

## ARTHURIAN LEAGUE

| PREMIER DIVISION | P | W | D | L | F | A | Pts |
|---|---|---|---|---|---|---|---|
| Old Chigwellians | 16 | 12 | 1 | 3 | 32 | 19 | 25 |
| Old Foresters | 16 | 11 | 2 | 3 | 28 | 18 | 24 |
| Old Salopians | 16 | 8 | 2 | 6 | 43 | 29 | 18 |
| Old Carthusians | 16 | 9 | 0 | 7 | 28 | 18 | 18 |
| Old Brentwoods | 16 | 7 | 2 | 7 | 26 | 29 | 16 |
| Lancing Old Boys | 16 | 6 | 0 | 10 | 26 | 31 | 12 |
| Old Reptonians | 16 | 5 | 2 | 9 | 19 | 33 | 12 |
| Old Bradfieldians | 16 | 4 | 3 | 9 | 18 | 28 | 11 |
| Old Etonians | 16 | 4 | 0 | 12 | 21 | 36 | 8 |

| DIVISION ONE | P | W | D | L | F | A | Pts |
|---|---|---|---|---|---|---|---|
| Old Cholmeleians | 14 | 11 | 3 | 0 | 57 | 15 | 24 # |
| Old Malvernians | 14 | 7 | 2 | 5 | 33 | 28 | 16 |
| Old Witleians | 14 | 7 | 2 | 5 | 35 | 32 | 16 |
| Old Aldenhamians | 14 | 6 | 2 | 6 | 33 | 35 | 14 |
| Old Harrovians | 14 | 6 | 1 | 7 | 46 | 39 | 13 |
| Old Haberdashers | 14 | 5 | 2 | 7 | 17 | 37 | 12 |
| Old Wykehamists | 14 | 4 | 3 | 7 | 37 | 45 | 11 |
| Old Wellingburians | 14 | 2 | 1 | 11 | 19 | 46 | 5 |

| DIVISION TWO | P | W | D | L | F | A | Pts |
|---|---|---|---|---|---|---|---|
| Old Brentwoods Res | 16 | 11 | 4 | 1 | 44 | 21 | 26 |
| Old Etonians Res | 16 | 9 | 3 | 4 | 41 | 23 | 21 |
| Old Cholmeleians Rs* | 16 | 8 | 6 | 2 | 26 | 13 | 21 |
| Old Chigwellians Rs* | 16 | 6 | 2 | 8 | 34 | 33 | 14 |
| Old Etonians 3rd | 16 | 5 | 4 | 7 | 23 | 22 | 14 |
| Lancing O B Res | 16 | 5 | 3 | 8 | 29 | 45 | 13 |
| Old Foresters Res | 16 | 5 | 2 | 9 | 19 | 34 | 12 |
| Old Cholmeleians 3rd* | 16 | 4 | 4 | 8 | 25 | 40 | 11 |
| Old Millhillians | 16 | 4 | 2 | 10 | 29 | 39 | 10 |

| DIVISION THREE | P | W | D | L | F | A | Pts |
|---|---|---|---|---|---|---|---|
| Old Salopians Res | 14 | 8 | 2 | 4 | 52 | 22 | 18 |
| Old Carthusians Res | 14 | 8 | 2 | 4 | 45 | 20 | 18 |
| Old Westminsters | 14 | 7 | 3 | 4 | 40 | 23 | 17 |
| Old Foresters 3rd | 14 | 8 | 1 | 5 | 30 | 33 | 17 |
| Old Reptonians Res | 14 | 7 | 1 | 6 | 32 | 48 | 15 |
| Old Harrovians Res | 14 | 7 | 0 | 7 | 37 | 34 | 14 |
| Old Cholmeleians 4th* | 14 | 4 | 1 | 9 | 26 | 49 | 8 |
| Old Brentwoods 3rd | 14 | 1 | 2 | 11 | 21 | 54 | 4 |

*Points deducted

**DIVISION FOUR**
8 Teams    Won by   Old Aldenhamians Res

**DIVISION FIVE**
6 Teams    Won by   Old Carthusians 3rd

**JUNIOR LEAGUE CUP**
Old Chigwellians Res   4 v 2   Old Haberdashers Rs

**DERRIK MOORE VETERANS CUP**
Old Etonians    3 v 1      Old Ardinians

**JIM DIXSON VI A SIDE**
Won by   Old Millhillians

# LONDON FINANCIAL F.A.

## DIVISION ONE

|  | P | W | D | L | F | A | Pts |
|---|---|---|---|---|---|---|---|
| Morgan Guaranty | 14 | 9 | 2 | 3 | 49 | 26 | 29 |
| Royal Sun Alliance | 14 | 9 | 2 | 3 | 43 | 27 | 29 |
| Dresdner Kleinwort B | 14 | 6 | 4 | 4 | 34 | 26 | 22 |
| Coutts & Co | 14 | 7 | 0 | 7 | 32 | 29 | 21 |
| Granby | 14 | 5 | 6 | 3 | 23 | 28 | 21 |
| G E Capital Ins Serv | 14 | 3 | 6 | 5 | 28 | 28 | 15 |
| Bank America | 14 | 3 | 3 | 8 | 24 | 38 | 12 |
| Royal Bank of Scotland | 14 | 1 | 3 | 10 | 26 | 57 | 6 |

Allied Irish Bank withdrawn - record expunged

## DIVISION TWO

|  | P | W | D | L | F | A | Pts |
|---|---|---|---|---|---|---|---|
| Citibank | 16 | 12 | 1 | 3 | 56 | 16 | 37 |
| Eagle Star | 16 | 12 | 0 | 4 | 53 | 26 | 36 |
| Standard Chartered B | 16 | 9 | 4 | 3 | 53 | 25 | 31 |
| Chase Manhattan Bank | 16 | 10 | 1 | 5 | 47 | 25 | 31 |
| J&H Marsh & McLennan | 16 | 7 | 5 | 4 | 39 | 37 | 26 |
| Foreign & C'nwealth O | 16 | 7 | 2 | 7 | 31 | 37 | 23 |
| Temple Bar | 16 | 3 | 3 | 10 | 32 | 42 | 12 |
| Century Life | 16 | 2 | 2 | 12 | 24 | 59 | 8 |
| Salomon Smith Barney | 16 | 0 | 2 | 14 | 23 | 91 | 2 |

## DIVISION THREE

|  | P | W | D | L | F | A | Pts |
|---|---|---|---|---|---|---|---|
| Mount Pleasant P O | 14 | 12 | 1 | 1 | 74 | 18 | 37 |
| Abbey National | 14 | 10 | 1 | 3 | 54 | 24 | 31 |
| C Hoare & Co | 14 | 6 | 1 | 7 | 37 | 35 | 19 |
| Bank America Res | 14 | 6 | 1 | 7 | 29 | 42 | 19 |
| Lincoln | 14 | 5 | 3 | 6 | 38 | 35 | 18 |
| ANZ Banking Group | 14 | 5 | 1 | 8 | 19 | 32 | 16 |
| Royal Bank of Scot Res | 14 | 5 | 1 | 8 | 24 | 42 | 16 |
| Noble Lowndes | 14 | 2 | 1 | 11 | 14 | 61 | 7 |

Credit Suisse Finan'l Prds withdrawn - record expunged

## DIVISION FOUR

|  | P | W | D | L | F | A | Pts |
|---|---|---|---|---|---|---|---|
| Customs & Excise | 18 | 14 | 2 | 2 | 73 | 33 | 44 |
| Eagle Star Res | 18 | 13 | 0 | 5 | 59 | 29 | 39 |
| Royal Sun Alliance Res | 18 | 9 | 7 | 2 | 42 | 28 | 34 |
| British Gas (Bromley) | 18 | 7 | 4 | 7 | 41 | 34 | 25 |
| Granby Res | 18 | 6 | 6 | 6 | 35 | 33 | 24 |
| Citibank Res | 18 | 6 | 4 | 8 | 50 | 57 | 22 |
| J&H Marsh/McLennan R | 18 | 5 | 4 | 9 | 43 | 50 | 19 |
| Coutts & Co. Res* | 18 | 6 | 2 | 10 | 25 | 48 | 17 |
| Royal Sun Alliance 3rd | 18 | 4 | 4 | 10 | 26 | 48 | 16 |
| Temple Bar Res | 18 | 1 | 5 | 12 | 24 | 58 | 8 |

*3 pts deducted - playing ineligible player

## DIVISION FIVE

|  | P | W | D | L | F | A | Pts |
|---|---|---|---|---|---|---|---|
| Cabinet Office & Treas | 16 | 13 | 3 | 0 | 82 | 20 | 42 |
| Chelsea Exiles | 16 | 13 | 1 | 2 | 97 | 26 | 40 |
| Bank of Ireland | 16 | 11 | 3 | 2 | 67 | 22 | 36 |
| Gaflac | 16 | 8 | 0 | 8 | 56 | 53 | 24 |
| Temple Bar 3rd | 16 | 6 | 2 | 8 | 43 | 47 | 20 |
| R.Bank of Scotland 3rd | 16 | 5 | 0 | 11 | 29 | 51 | 15 |
| Noble Lowndes Res | 16 | 4 | 2 | 10 | 26 | 63 | 14 |
| Standard Chartered Res | 16 | 4 | 1 | 11 | 35 | 68 | 13 |
| Eagle Star 3rd | 16 | 2 | 0 | 14 | 30 | 115 | 6 |

## CHALLENGE CUP

| Bank England v Midland Bank | 2-1 |
|---|---|

## SENIOR CUP

| Morgan Guar'ty v G.E. Capital | 2-1 |
|---|---|

## SENIOR PLATE

| C. Manhattan v Standard C Bk | 4-1 |
|---|---|

## JUNIOR CUP

| R. Sun All'ce R v Eagle Star R | 2-1 |
|---|---|

## JUNIOR PLATE

| C. Hoare & Co v Granby Res | 4-1 |
|---|---|

## MINOR CUP

| Bank of Ireland v Cabinet O & T | 3-4 |
|---|---|

## MINOR PLATE

| C'sea Exiles v R. Bank Scot 3rd | 2-1 |
|---|---|

## VETERANS' CUP

| Lensbury v Lloyds Bank | 4-2* |
|---|---|

## W A JEWELL MEMORIAL V A SIDE

| Won by | Morgan Guaranty |
|---|---|

## SAUNDERS SHIELD V A SIDE

Won by Chase Manhattan Bank "B"

## SPORTSMANSHIP SHIELD

Won by Gaflac

## LONDON FINANCIAL F.A. REPRESENTATIVE MATCHES

| v | Southern Olympian Lge | Drawn | 1-1 |
|---|---|---|---|
| v | Royal Marines | Lost | 0-3 |
| v | Southern Amateur Lge "B" | Lost | 2-6 |
| v | Old Boys' League | Drawn | 4-6 |
| v | Bristol Insurance Institute | Lost | 1-6 |

## LONDON LEGAL LEAGUE

### DIVISION ONE

|  | P | W | D | L | F | A | Pts |
|---|---|---|---|---|---|---|---|
| Wilde Sapte | 18 | 13 | 4 | 1 | 61 | 19 | 30 |
| Clifford Chance | 18 | 10 | 5 | 3 | 37 | 20 | 25 |
| Gray's Inn | 18 | 10 | 3 | 5 | 36 | 20 | 23 |
| Slaughter & May | 18 | 10 | 2 | 6 | 53 | 28 | 22 |
| Linklaters & Paines | 18 | 9 | 4 | 5 | 25 | 30 | 22 |
| Rosling King | 18 | 9 | 3 | 6 | 41 | 34 | 21 |
| Lovell White Durrant | 18 | 7 | 4 | 7 | 29 | 31 | 18 |
| Cameron McKenna | 18 | 4 | 2 | 12 | 28 | 69 | 10 |
| Pegasus | 18 | 2 | 1 | 15 | 21 | 51 | 5 |
| Herbert Smith | 18 | 1 | 2 | 15 | 25 | 54 | 4 |

### DIVISION TWO

|  | P | W | D | L | F | A | Pts |
|---|---|---|---|---|---|---|---|
| K.P.M.G. | 18 | 15 | 0 | 3 | 69 | 19 | 30 |
| Taylor Joynson Garrett | 18 | 11 | 3 | 4 | 36 | 24 | 25 |
| Norton Rose | 18 | 11 | 2 | 5 | 41 | 27 | 24 |
| Nabarro Nathanson | 18 | 10 | 2 | 6 | 36 | 29 | 22 |
| Stephenson Harwood | 18 | 8 | 2 | 8 | 46 | 26 | 18 |
| Kennedy's | 18 | 7 | 2 | 9 | 30 | 32 | 16 |
| Freshfields | 18 | 6 | 4 | 8 | 23 | 36 | 16 |
| Denton Hall | 18 | 6 | 1 | 11 | 34 | 54 | 13 |
| D.J. Freeman | 18 | 6 | 0 | 12 | 31 | 45 | 12 |
| Allen & Overy | 18 | 2 | 0 | 16 | 17 | 71 | 4 |

London Legal League - continued

## DIVISION THREE

| | P | W | D | L | F | A | Pts |
|---|---|---|---|---|---|---|---|
| Watson Farley & Will's | 22 | 18 | 3 | 1 | 54 | 14 | 39 |
| Simmons & Simmons | 22 | 15 | 4 | 3 | 52 | 23 | 34 |
| N'son Graham & Jones | 22 | 14 | 4 | 4 | 65 | 23 | 32 |
| Barlow Lyde & Gilbert | 22 | 12 | 4 | 6 | 34 | 24 | 28 |
| Eversheds | 22 | 12 | 1 | 9 | 49 | 32 | 25 |
| Richards Butler | 22 | 9 | 3 | 10 | 43 | 46 | 21 |
| Baker & McKenzie | 22 | 10 | 1 | 11 | 35 | 55 | 21 |
| Edward Lewis | 22 | 7 | 4 | 11 | 25 | 45 | 18 |
| Titmuss Sainer Dechert | 22 | 6 | 5 | 11 | 20 | 34 | 17 |
| S.J. Berwin | 22 | 7 | 1 | 14 | 24 | 44 | 15 |
| Macfarlanes | 22 | 6 | 2 | 14 | 18 | 58 | 14 |
| Hammond Suddards | 22 | 1 | 0 | 21 | 6 | 27 | 2 |

## LEAGUE CHALLENGE CUP
Gray's Inn     2 v 1     Slaughter & May

## WEAVERS ARMS CUP
Linklaters     2 v 0     Watson Farley & Will's

# LONDON OLD BOYS' CUPS

**SENIOR**
Phoenix Old Boys   1 v 0   Old Ignatians
**INTERMEDIATE**
Old Manorians Res   2 v 1   Latymer Old Boys Res
**JUNIOR**
Phoenix Old Boys 3rd   2 v 0   Old Reigatians 3rd
**MINOR**
Old Meadonians 4th   2 v 0   Old Actonians 4th
**NOVETS**
Old Actonians A 5th   0 v 7   Old Suttonians 5th
**DRUMMOND**
Leyton County OB 6th   2 v 1   Glyn Old Boys 6th
**NEMEAN**
Old Actonins 9th   7 v 1   Old Suttonians 8th
**VETERANS'**
Old Finchleians Vets   0 v 3   Old Tenisonians Vets

# OLD BOYS' INVITATION CUPS

**SENIOR**
Old Finchleians   4 v 3   Old Tenisonians
**JUNIOR**
E Barnet O Gram's R   2 v 0   Old Stationers Res
**MINOR**
E Barnet O Gram's 3rd   2 v 3   Old Finchleians 3rd
**4TH XI**
O Esthameians 4th (wp)1 v 1 (lp)   O Tenisonians 4th
**5TH XI**
Old Minchendenians   1 v 2   Old Tenisonians 5th
**6TH XI**
E Barnet O Gram's 6th   1 v 3   Glyn Old Boys 6th
**7TH XI**
Old Bromleians 7th   4 v 1   Old Finchleians 7th
**VETERANS' XI**
Old Tenisonians Vets   6 v 2   Old Finchleians Vets
*after extra time

# OLD BOYS' LEAGUE

## PREMIER DIVISION

| | P | W | D | L | F | A | Pts |
|---|---|---|---|---|---|---|---|
| Old Ignatians | 20 | 15 | 2 | 3 | 55 | 23 | 32 |
| Old Tenisonians | 20 | 12 | 6 | 2 | 39 | 19 | 30 |
| Old Aloysians | 20 | 13 | 3 | 4 | 57 | 28 | 29 |
| Old Salvatorians | 20 | 9 | 4 | 7 | 41 | 35 | 22 |
| Old Meadonians | 20 | 10 | 2 | 8 | 38 | 33 | 22 |
| Old Hamptonians | 20 | 9 | 3 | 8 | 33 | 34 | 21 |
| Old Vaughanians | 20 | 6 | 4 | 10 | 23 | 24 | 16 |
| Cardinal Manning O B | 20 | 5 | 6 | 9 | 32 | 42 | 16 |
| Old Buckwellians | 20 | 6 | 3 | 11 | 48 | 60 | 15 |
| Glyn Old Boys | 20 | 4 | 2 | 14 | 17 | 51 | 10 |
| Enfield Old Gram's | 20 | 1 | 5 | 14 | 23 | 57 | 7 |

## SENIOR DIV ONE

| | P | W | D | L | F | A | Pts |
|---|---|---|---|---|---|---|---|
| Old Wilsonians | 20 | 16 | 2 | 2 | 67 | 24 | 34 |
| Phoenix Old Boys | 20 | 12 | 5 | 3 | 46 | 28 | 29 |
| Old Suttonians | 20 | 9 | 3 | 8 | 36 | 35 | 21 |
| Shene Old Gram's | 20 | 8 | 5 | 7 | 38 | 44 | 21 |
| Old Manorians | 20 | 7 | 5 | 8 | 35 | 35 | 19 |
| Old Dorkinians | 20 | 6 | 6 | 8 | 37 | 40 | 18 |
| Old Kingsburians | 20 | 6 | 6 | 8 | 36 | 40 | 18 |
| Old Isleworthians | 20 | 7 | 4 | 9 | 37 | 48 | 18 |
| Latymer Old Boys | 20 | 7 | 3 | 10 | 33 | 37 | 17 |
| Old Tiffinians | 20 | 3 | 7 | 8 | 21 | 35 | 13 |
| Old Reigatians | 20 | 5 | 2 | 13 | 23 | 43 | 12 |

## SENIOR DIV TWO

| | P | W | D | L | F | A | Pts |
|---|---|---|---|---|---|---|---|
| Old Minchendenians | 18 | 11 | 5 | 2 | 60 | 35 | 27 |
| Old Vaughanians Res | 18 | 11 | 3 | 4 | 40 | 24 | 25 |
| John Fisher Old Boys | 18 | 9 | 6 | 3 | 44 | 24 | 24 |
| Old Danes | 18 | 8 | 4 | 6 | 55 | 36 | 20 |
| Chertsey Old Salesians | 18 | 7 | 4 | 7 | 32 | 51 | 18 |
| Clapham Old Xaverians | 18 | 5 | 5 | 8 | 41 | 49 | 15 |
| Old Meadonians Res | 18 | 6 | 2 | 10 | 45 | 60 | 14 |
| Old Sinjuns | 18 | 5 | 3 | 10 | 52 | 51 | 13 |
| Old Tenisonians Res* | 17 | 6 | 3 | 8 | 30 | 40 | 13 |
| Old Camdenians* | 17 | 3 | 1 | 13 | 28 | 57 | 5 |

## SENIOR DIV THREE

| | P | W | D | L | F | A | Pts |
|---|---|---|---|---|---|---|---|
| Latymer Old Boys Res | 21 | 16 | 2 | 3 | 57 | 28 | 34 |
| Phoenix Old Boys Res | 22 | 11 | 5 | 6 | 50 | 39 | 27 |
| Q. Mary College O B | 22 | 10 | 5 | 7 | 55 | 49 | 25 |
| Old Uffingtonians | 22 | 11 | 2 | 9 | 59 | 49 | 24 |
| Old Aloysians Res | 22 | 10 | 3 | 9 | 57 | 51 | 23 |
| Old Addeyans | 22 | 8 | 6 | 8 | 50 | 39 | 22 |
| Old Hamptonians Res | 22 | 9 | 4 | 9 | 34 | 54 | 22 |
| Old Salvatorians Res | 21 | 6 | 8 | 7 | 31 | 43 | 20 |
| Old Sedcopians | 22 | 6 | 7 | 9 | 57 | 48 | 19 |
| Old Wokingians | 22 | 6 | 7 | 9 | 43 | 34 | 19 |
| Old Dorkinians Res* | 22 | 6 | 2 | 14 | 42 | 68 | 12 |
| Mill Hill County O B* | 22 | 5 | 3 | 14 | 42 | 75 | 11 |

## INTERMEDIATE DIVISIONS:

**NORTH**
11 Teams    Won by  Old Manorians Res

**SOUTH**
12 Teams    Won by  Old Wilsonians Res

**DIVISION ONE NORTH**
11 Teams    Won by  Old Tollingtonians

**DIVISION ONE SOUTH**
10 Teams    Won by  Old Paulines

**DIVISION ONE WEST:**
11 Teams    Won by  Old Danes Res

**DIVISION TWO NORTH**
11 Teams    Won by  Old Tollingtonians Res

**DIVISION TWO SOUTH**
11 Teams    Won by  Chertsey Old Salesians 3rd

**DIVISION TWO WEST**
11 Teams    Won by  Cardinal Manning O B 3rd

**DIVISION THREE NORTH**
11 Teams    Won by  Old Tollingtonians 3rd

**DIVISION THREE SOUTH**
11 Teams    Won by  Glyn Old Boys 4th

**DIVISION THREE WEST:**
11 Teams    Won by  Old Kingsburians 4th

**DIVISION FOUR NORTH**
11 Teams    Won by  Leyton County Old Boys 4th

**DIVISION FOUR SOUTH**
10 Teams    Won by  Old Sedcopians 3rd

**DIVISION FOUR WEST**
11 Teams    Won by  Holland Park Old Boys Res

**DIVISION FIVE NORTH**
9 Teams    Won by  Leyton County Old Boys 5th

**DIVISION FIVE SOUTH**
11 Teams    Won by  Old Sedcopians 4th

**DIVISION FIVE WEST**
12 Teams    Won by  Old Manorians 6th

**DIVISION SIX NORTH**
8 Teams    Won by  Old Buckwellians 5th

**DIVISION SIX SOUTH**
11 Teams    Won by  John Fisher Old Boys 4th

**DIVISION SIX WEST:**
10 Teams    Won by  Old Salvatorians 9th

**DIVISION SEVEN SOUTH**
10 Teams    Won by  Old Paulines Res

**DIVISION EIGHT SOUTH**
8 Teams    Won by  Old Paulines 3rd

**DIVISION NINE SOUTH**
10 Teams    Won by  Glyn Old Boys 8th

# MIDLAND AMATEUR ALLIANCE

| PREMIER DIVISION | P | W | D | L | F | A | Pts |
|---|---|---|---|---|---|---|---|
| Old Elizabethans | 20 | 16 | 3 | 1 | 63 | 21 | 51 |
| Beeston Old Boys Assn. | 20 | 16 | 1 | 3 | 75 | 29 | 49 |
| Lady Bay | 20 | 13 | 3 | 4 | 60 | 34 | 42 |
| A S C Dayncourt | 20 | 10 | 3 | 7 | 60 | 41 | 33 |
| Kirton Brick Works | 20 | 10 | 3 | 7 | 53 | 36 | 33 |
| Bassingfield | 20 | 8 | 4 | 8 | 58 | 52 | 28 |
| Pannell K F Steelers | 20 | 7 | 2 | 11 | 40 | 47 | 23 |
| Prince of Wales | 20 | 6 | 2 | 12 | 36 | 52 | 20 |
| Parkhead Academicals | 20 | 5 | 3 | 12 | 26 | 53 | 18 |
| Tibshelf Old Boys | 20 | 3 | 2 | 15 | 34 | 86 | 11 |
| Dynamo Baptist | 20 | 2 | 2 | 16 | 23 | 77 | 8 |

| DIVISION ONE | P | W | D | L | F | A | Pts |
|---|---|---|---|---|---|---|---|
| Nottingham Irish Centre | 26 | 23 | 1 | 2 | 120 | 35 | 70 |
| Beeston Town "A" | 26 | 19 | 1 | 6 | 112 | 38 | 58 |
| Caribbean Cavaliers | 26 | 17 | 5 | 4 | 69 | 26 | 56 |
| Old Elizabethans Res. | 26 | 18 | 2 | 6 | 88 | 51 | 56 |
| Ollerton Town "A" | 26 | 11 | 6 | 9 | 59 | 65 | 39 |
| Dukeries Hotel | 26 | 11 | 4 | 11 | 53 | 54 | 37 |
| Radcliffe Olympic "A" | 26 | 10 | 6 | 10 | 52 | 61 | 36 |
| Nottinghamshire | 26 | 8 | 7 | 11 | 49 | 49 | 31 |
| Magdala Amateurs "A" | 26 | 9 | 4 | 13 | 54 | 55 | 31 |
| Derbyshire Am "A" | 26 | 9 | 4 | 13 | 48 | 68 | 31 |
| Woodborough United | 26 | 7 | 4 | 15 | 45 | 76 | 25 |
| Bassingfield Res. | 26 | 7 | 3 | 16 | 48 | 85 | 24 |
| Ilkeston Rangers | 26 | 6 | 4 | 16 | 49 | 88 | 22 |
| County Nalgo | 26 | 0 | 3 | 23 | 26 | 121 | 3 |

| DIVISION TWO | P | W | D | L | F | A | Pts |
|---|---|---|---|---|---|---|---|
| Arnold & Carlton Coll | 26 | 21 | 2 | 3 | 87 | 32 | 65 |
| Hucknall Sports Y C | 26 | 18 | 5 | 3 | 96 | 38 | 59 |
| A S C Dayncourt Res | 26 | 17 | 5 | 4 | 109 | 45 | 56 |
| Gresham United | 26 | 13 | 5 | 8 | 77 | 48 | 44 |
| Cadland Chilwell | 26 | 13 | 5 | 8 | 66 | 51 | 44 |
| Nottinghamshire Res | 26 | 12 | 4 | 10 | 62 | 60 | 40 |
| Southwell Amateurs | 26 | 10 | 5 | 11 | 61 | 60 | 35 |
| Old Elizabethans 3rd | 26 | 8 | 9 | 9 | 56 | 63 | 33 |
| Lady Bay Res | 26 | 9 | 5 | 12 | 82 | 90 | 32 |
| Brunts Old Boys | 26 | 9 | 3 | 14 | 47 | 65 | 30 |
| Prince of Wales Res | 26 | 7 | 3 | 16 | 39 | 62 | 24 |
| Magdala Amateurs Res | 26 | 6 | 3 | 17 | 59 | 104 | 21 |
| Ilkeston Rangers Res | 26 | 3 | 7 | 16 | 41 | 100 | 16 |
| Beeston Old Boys Res | 26 | 4 | 3 | 19 | 42 | 106 | 15 |

| DIVISION THREE | P | W | D | L | F | A | Pts |
|---|---|---|---|---|---|---|---|
| Gedling Town Y C | 20 | 17 | 1 | 2 | 76 | 16 | 52 |
| Fleet Cars | 20 | 16 | 0 | 4 | 78 | 40 | 48 |
| Old Bemrosians | 20 | 14 | 0 | 6 | 61 | 48 | 42 |
| Acrumac | 20 | 13 | 1 | 6 | 64 | 36 | 40 |
| A S C Dayncourt 3rd | 20 | 10 | 3 | 7 | 56 | 39 | 33 |
| Prince of Wales 3rd | 20 | 10 | 0 | 10 | 58 | 46 | 30 |
| E Mid Train'g & Ed. Cntr | 20 | 8 | 2 | 10 | 55 | 63 | 26 |
| Derbyshire Amat 3rd. | 24 | 7 | 3 | 10 | 52 | 58 | 24 |
| Nottinghamshire 3rd. | 20 | 4 | 1 | 15 | 33 | 85 | 13 |
| Tibshelf Old Boys Res. | 20 | 3 | 1 | 16 | 13 | 73 | 10 |
| Dynamo Baptist Res. | 20 | 2 | 0 | 18 | 27 | 69 | 6 |

### LEAGUE CUP WINNERS

**SENIOR**
F C Beeston    2 v 1    Kirton Brick Works

**INTERMEDIATE**
Arnold & Carlton    4 v 2    Gresham United

**MINOR**
Gedling Town Y C    5 v 5    E M T E C

# SOUTHERN AMATEUR LEAGUE

## SENIOR SECTION:

| FIRST DIVISION | P | W | D | L | F | A | Pts |
|---|---|---|---|---|---|---|---|
| Old Actonians Assoc | 22 | 15 | 5 | 2 | 52 | 19 | 50 |
| Barclays Bank | 22 | 14 | 4 | 4 | 57 | 35 | 46 |
| Carshalton | 22 | 10 | 6 | 6 | 59 | 36 | 36 |
| Crouch End Vampires | 22 | 10 | 6 | 6 | 45 | 29 | 36 |
| Nat Westminster Bank | 22 | 9 | 4 | 9 | 36 | 38 | 31 |
| Polytechnic* | 22 | 9 | 5 | 8 | 45 | 37 | 29 |
| East Barnet Old Gram's | 22 | 7 | 6 | 9 | 28 | 48 | 27 |
| Lloyds Bank | 22 | 6 | 7 | 9 | 38 | 37 | 25 |
| Old Parmiterians | 22 | 8 | 1 | 13 | 34 | 44 | 25 |
| Norsemen | 22 | 5 | 7 | 10 | 35 | 50 | 22 |
| Lensbury* | 22 | 5 | 7 | 10 | 38 | 56 | 21 |
| West Wickham | 22 | 2 | 6 | 14 | 27 | 55 | 12 |

\* point deducted

| SECOND DIVISION | P | W | D | L | F | A | Pts |
|---|---|---|---|---|---|---|---|
| Old Bromleians | 22 | 12 | 8 | 2 | 53 | 26 | 44 |
| Old Owens | 22 | 12 | 7 | 3 | 45 | 28 | 43 |
| Old Salesians | 22 | 13 | 3 | 6 | 56 | 35 | 42 |
| Midland Bank | 22 | 11 | 4 | 7 | 42 | 30 | 37 |
| Old Parkonians | 22 | 11 | 3 | 8 | 38 | 31 | 36 |
| Old Esthameians | 22 | 9 | 8 | 5 | 39 | 29 | 35 |
| Civil Service | 22 | 10 | 3 | 9 | 41 | 40 | 33 |
| Alexandra Park | 22 | 8 | 7 | 7 | 44 | 44 | 31 |
| South Bank | 22 | 5 | 7 | 10 | 32 | 47 | 22 |
| Old Stationers | 22 | 4 | 5 | 13 | 32 | 55 | 17 |
| Winchmore Hill | 22 | 2 | 6 | 14 | 31 | 58 | 12 |
| Old Lyonians | 22 | 3 | 3 | 16 | 27 | 57 | 12 |

| THIRD DIVISION | P | W | D | L | F | A | Pts |
|---|---|---|---|---|---|---|---|
| Alleyn Old Boys | 22 | 16 | 4 | 2 | 73 | 21 | 52 |
| Old Finchleians | 22 | 15 | 3 | 4 | 84 | 38 | 48 |
| Broomfield | 22 | 15 | 3 | 6 | 52 | 36 | 48 |
| Bank of England | 22 | 13 | 3 | 6 | 49 | 28 | 42 |
| Cuaco | 22 | 10 | 4 | 8 | 49 | 45 | 34 |
| Merton | 22 | 8 | 5 | 9 | 41 | 43 | 29 |
| Old Latymerians | 22 | 6 | 8 | 8 | 40 | 37 | 26 |
| O Westminster Citizens | 22 | 7 | 5 | 10 | 42 | 46 | 26 |
| Southgate Olympic | 22 | 7 | 3 | 12 | 36 | 54 | 24 |
| Kew Association | 22 | 6 | 5 | 11 | 42 | 50 | 23 |
| Ibis | 22 | 2 | 7 | 13 | 30 | 69 | 13 |
| Brentham | 22 | 1 | 2 | 19 | 32 | 103 | 5 |

## RESERVE TEAMS SECTION - Divisional Champions:
**FIRST DIVISION:**
12 Teams     won by     East Barnet Old Grammarians R
**SECOND DIVISION:**
12 Teams     won by     Midland Bank Res
**THIRD DIVISION:**
12 Teams     won by     Merton Res

## 3RD TEAMS SECTION:
**FIRST DIVISION:**
12 Teams     won by     East Barnet O Grammarians 3rd
**SECOND DIVISION:**
12 Teams     won by     Old Owens 3rd
**THIRD DIVISION:**
12 Teams     won by     Old Finchleians 3rd

## 4TH TEAMS SECTION:
**FIRST DIVISION:**
12 Teams     won by     Old Actonians Association 4th
**SECOND DIVISION:**
12 Teams     won by     Old Parmiterians 4th
**THIRD DIVISION:**
12 Teams     won by     Old Finchleians 4th

## 5TH TEAMS SECTION:
**FIRST DIVISION:**
11 Teams     won by     Old Actonians Association 5th
**SECOND DIVISION:**
11 Teams     won by     Civil Service 5th
**THIRD DIVISION:**
10 Teams     won by     Old Finchleians 5th

## 6TH TEAMS SECTION:
**FIRST DIVISION:**
9 Teams     won by     Old Actonians Association 6th
**SECOND DIVISION:**
7 Teams     won by     Carshalton 6th
**THIRD DIVISION:**
7 Teams     won by     Old Finchleians 6th

## MINOR SECTION:
**FIRST DIVISION:**
10 Teams     won by     Old Stationers 7th
**SECOND DIVISION:**
10 Teams     won by     National Westminster Bank 7th
**THIRD DIVISION:**
10 Teams     won by     Old Parmiterians 8th
**FOURTH DIVISION:**
10 Teams     won by     Old Finchleians 8th

## CHALLENGE CUPS
(Entries in brackets)

**JUNIOR (22):**
Norsemen 3rd     2 v 1     Barclays Bank 3rd

**MINOR (22):**
Barclays Bank 4th     2 v 1     Crouch End Vampires

**SENIOR NOVETS (19):**
Polytechnic 5th     1:5p v 1:4p     Midland Bank 5th

**INTERMEDIATE NOVETS (16):**
Nat West Bank 6th     2 v 1     Old Parmiterians 6th

**JUNIOR NOVETS (28):**
Winchmore Hill 7th     3 v 0     Nat West Bank 7th

**HAMILTON TROPHY**
for Hospitality & Sportsmanship     Cuaco

**WILKINSON SWORD**
for Disciplinary Conduct     Cuaco

# SOUTHERN OLYMPIAN LEAGUE

**SENIOR SECTION:**

**DIVISION ONE**

|  | P | W | D | L | F | A | Pts |
|---|---|---|---|---|---|---|---|
| Nottsborough | 17 | 11 | 4 | 2 | 56 | 19 | 26 |
| Old Woodhouseians | 18 | 11 | 4 | 3 | 34 | 19 | 26 |
| Hale End Athletic | 18 | 11 | 2 | 5 | 37 | 36 | 24 |
| Old Grammarians | 18 | 8 | 5 | 5 | 36 | 25 | 20 * |
| City of London | 17 | 7 | 2 | 8 | 28 | 33 | 16 |
| Hon. Artillery Company | 17 | 6 | 3 | 8 | 32 | 30 | 15 |
| Parkfield | 17 | 6 | 2 | 9 | 39 | 41 | 14 |
| Ulysses | 18 | 5 | 4 | 9 | 27 | 36 | 14 |
| Southgate County* | 18 | 5 | 3 | 10 | 31 | 55 | 12 |
| St. Mary's College* | 18 | 2 | 3 | 13 | 34 | 50 | 5 |

**DIVISION TWO**

|  | P | W | D | L | F | A | Pts |
|---|---|---|---|---|---|---|---|
| UCL Academicals | 18 | 12 | 4 | 2 | 45 | 23 | 28 |
| Mill Hill Village | 18 | 10 | 5 | 3 | 48 | 28 | 25 |
| Pegasus | 17 | 8 | 4 | 5 | 50 | 38 | 20 |
| Fulham Compton OB* | 18 | 9 | 3 | 6 | 46 | 44 | 20 |
| Hadley | 18 | 9 | 1 | 8 | 42 | 39 | 19 |
| Old Bealonians | 18 | 8 | 3 | 7 | 43 | 41 | 19 |
| Albanian | 17 | 7 | 2 | 8 | 40 | 26 | 16 |
| Wandsworth Borough | 18 | 6 | 3 | 9 | 36 | 50 | 15 |
| Ealing Association | 18 | 4 | 3 | 11 | 24 | 44 | 11 |
| B.B.C. | 18 | 1 | 2 | 15 | 24 | 65 | 4 |

**DIVISION THREE**

|  | P | W | D | L | F | A | Pts |
|---|---|---|---|---|---|---|---|
| Old Colfeians | 18 | 14 | 2 | 2 | 55 | 20 | 30 |
| University of Hertford | 18 | 13 | 3 | 2 | 63 | 31 | 29 |
| Brent | 17 | 9 | 3 | 5 | 34 | 25 | 21 |
| Tesco Country Club* | 17 | 9 | 3 | 5 | 43 | 33 | 18 |
| London Welsh | 18 | 8 | 1 | 9 | 42 | 42 | 17 |
| Inland Revenue | 18 | 6 | 2 | 10 | 41 | 45 | 14 |
| Duncombe Sports* | 18 | 6 | 4 | 8 | 36 | 39 | 13 |
| The Comets | 18 | 5 | 3 | 10 | 36 | 55 | 13 |
| Hampstead Heathens | 18 | 5 | 0 | 13 | 40 | 63 | 10 |
| Westerns | 18 | 2 | 3 | 13 | 26 | 57 | 7 |

**DIVISION FOUR**

|  | P | W | D | L | F | A | Pts |
|---|---|---|---|---|---|---|---|
| Mayfield Athletic | 14 | 11 | 1 | 2 | 23 | 30 | 23 |
| Kings Old Boys | 14 | 8 | 3 | 3 | 23 | 26 | 19 |
| The Cheshunt Club* | 14 | 8 | 3 | 3 | 21 | 19 | 18 |
| Centymca | 14 | 4 | 6 | 4 | 26 | 32 | 14 |
| London Airways | 14 | 5 | 3 | 6 | 24 | 27 | 13 |
| Witan | 14 | 6 | 1 | 7 | 19 | 27 | 13 |
| Birkbeck College | 14 | 2 | 2 | 10 | 14 | 40 | 6 |
| Economicals | 14 | 1 | 3 | 10 | 17 | 45 | 5 |

*points deducted

## INTERMEDIATE SECTION DIVISIONAL CHAMPIONS

**DIVISION ONE:**
10 Teams     Won by  Nottsborough Res

**DIVISION TWO:**
10 Teams     Won by  Mill Hill VIllage Res.

**DIVISION THREE:**
10 Teams     Won by  Albanian 4th

**DIVISION FOUR:**
Disbanded

## JUNIOR SECTION

**DIVISION ONE N:**
10 Teams     Won by  Old Woodhouseians 3rd.

**DIVISION TWO N:**
10 Teams     Won by  Parkfield 5th.

**DIVISION THREE N:**
9 Teams     Won by  Old Woodhouseians 4th.

**DIVISION FOUR     N:**
9 Teams     Won by  Parkfield 7th.

**DIVISION ONE S&W:**
10 Teams     Won by  Centymca Res.

**DIVISION TWO S&W:**
10 Teams     Won by  Old Grammarians 3rd

**DIVISION THREE S&W:**
10 Teams     Won by  Ealing Association 4th

**SENIOR CHALLENGE BOWL:**
Won by  Albanian

**SENIOR CHALLENGE SHIELD:**
Won by  Old Colfeians

**INTERMEDIATE CHALLENGE CUP:**
Won by  Southgate County Res

**INTERMEDIATE CHALLENGE SHIELD:**
Won by  Hon Artillery Company Res

**JUNIOR CHALLENGE CUP:**
Won by  Mill Hill Village 3rd.

**JUNIOR CHALLENGE SHIELD:**
Won by  BBC 3rd

**MANDER CUP:**
Won by  Albanian 4th

**MANDER SHIELD:**
Won by  BBC 4th

**BURNTWOOD TROPHY:**
Won by  Albanian 5th

**BURNTWOOD SHIELD:**
Won by  Ealing Association 5th.

**THOMAS PARMITER CUP:**
Won by  Parkfield 6th.

**THOMAS PARMITER SHIELD:**
Won by  Old Finchleians 6th.

**VETERANS' CHALLENGE CUP:**
Won by  Old Finchleians Vets.

**VETERANS' CHALLENGE SHIELD:**
Won by  Centymca Vets.

## UNIVERSITY OF LONDON
## MENS' INTER-COLLEGIATE LEAGUE

**PREMIER DIVISION:**

|  | P | W | D | L | F | A | Pts |
|---|---|---|---|---|---|---|---|
| Imperial College | 14 | 10 | 3 | 1 | 43 | 16 | 33 |
| London School of Econ | 14 | 8 | 2 | 4 | 18 | 14 | 26 |
| University College | 14 | 8 | 1 | 5 | 32 | 17 | 25 |
| Goldsmiths' College | 14 | 6 | 1 | 7 | 18 | 22 | 19 |
| King's College | 14 | 5 | 3 | 6 | 20 | 16 | 18 |
| Royal Holloway College | 14 | 5 | 1 | 8 | 15 | 26 | 16 |
| Q. Mary Westfield Coll | 14 | 4 | 3 | 7 | 26 | 28 | 15 |
| Royal Schl of Mines (IC) | 14 | 2 | 2 | 10 | 12 | 45 | 8 |

**DIVISION ONE**

|  | P | W | D | L | F | A | Pts |
|---|---|---|---|---|---|---|---|
| GKT (ex UMDS) | 16 | 12 | 1 | 3 | 57 | 38 | 43 |
| University College Res | 18 | 13 | 2 | 3 | 49 | 27 | 41 |
| Imperial Coll Sch Med | 16 | 12 | 0 | 4 | 58 | 26 | 36 |
| London School Econ R | 18 | 8 | 2 | 8 | 28 | 25 | 26 |
| R.Lon'n & St.B's Med S | 18 | 7 | 1 | 10 | 28 | 41 | 22 |
| UCL & Middx Hosp MS | 18 | 6 | 3 | 9 | 48 | 48 | 21 |
| Goldsmiths' College Rs. | 18 | 7 | 0 | 11 | 34 | 43 | 21 |
| Q.Mary Westfield Coll R | 18 | 6 | 2 | 10 | 29 | 40 | 20 |
| Royal Holloway Coll Rs | 18 | 5 | 2 | 11 | 37 | 52 | 17 |
| Royal Veterinary College | 18 | 5 | 1 | 12 | 33 | 61 | 16 |

**DIVISION TWO**

|  | P | W | D | L | F | A | Pts |
|---|---|---|---|---|---|---|---|
| Imperial College Res. | 17 | 12 | 1 | 4 | 54 | 22 | 37 |
| Royal Holloway Coll 3rd | 18 | 11 | 3 | 4 | 51 | 19 | 36 |
| Imperial Coll Sch Med R | 18 | 11 | 3 | 4 | 30 | 20 | 36 |
| Sch Slav & E.Euro Stud | 17 | 12 | 0 | 5 | 30 | 18 | 36 |
| University College 3rd | 18 | 8 | 2 | 8 | 35 | 27 | 26 |
| London Sch. Econ 3rd. | 18 | 7 | 3 | 8 | 22 | 34 | 24 |
| King's College 3rd. | 18 | 7 | 1 | 10 | 40 | 55 | 22 |
| Royal Free Hosp. Sch M | 17 | 7 | 1 | 9 | 24 | 23 | 12 |
| Imperial College 3rd. | 17 | 5 | 3 | 9 | 19 | 41 | 18 |
| GKT Res. | 18 | 1 | 1 | 16 | 10 | 56 | 4 |

**DIVISION THREE**

|  | P | W | D | L | F | A | Pts |
|---|---|---|---|---|---|---|---|
| King's College 3rd. | 18 | 13 | 3 | 2 | 47 | 24 | 42 |
| St George's Hospital MS | 18 | 11 | 3 | 4 | 42 | 20 | 36 |
| Imperial College 4th. | 18 | 10 | 2 | 6 | 37 | 25 | 32 |
| Wye College | 18 | 10 | 1 | 7 | 38 | 21 | 31 |
| Q.Mary Westfield C 3rd. | 18 | 9 | 2 | 7 | 21 | 15 | 29 |
| U C & Middx Hosp MSR | 18 | 8 | 2 | 8 | 23 | 23 | 26 |
| London Sch. Econ 4th. | 17 | 6 | 3 | 8 | 23 | 43 | 21 |
| University College 4th | 18 | 6 | 2 | 10 | 30 | 35 | 20 |
| University College 5th. | 17 | 4 | 2 | 11 | 31 | 54 | 14 |
| Royal Holloway Coll 4th | 18 | 2 | 0 | 16 | 12 | 44 | 6 |

**DIVISION FOUR**
10 Teams    Won by  King's College 4th

**DIVISION FIVE**
9 Teams    Won by  R London & St Barts Res

**DIVISION SIX**
9 Teams    Won by  Sch Slavonic & E Euro St

---

**CHALLENGE CUP:**
Imperial          5 v 1   Queen Mary Westfield

**UPPER RESERVES CUP:**
U C Res          4 v 0    R. Holloway Coll 3rd

**LOWER RESERVES CUP:**
King's 4th       5 v 2                King's 5th

**UNITED HOSPITALS: SENIOR CUP:**
   No results advised

**JUNIOR CUP:**
   No results advised

## LONDON UNIVERSITY XI
## REPRESENTATIVE MATCH RESULTS

| Old Boys' League | Lost | 0-2 |
|---|---|---|
| Southern Amateur Lue | Lost | 0-2 |
| SE Region BUSA | Lost | 1-5 |
| Lloyds of London | Lost | 1-2 |
| Royal Navy U21 | Lost | 0-3 |
| Metropolitan Police | Won | 2-0 |
| Cambridge University | Lost | 0-3 |
| Army Crusaders | Won | 5-0 |
| Oxford University | Lost | 1-4 |
| Amateur Football All'ce | Lost | 2-3 |

## UNIVERSITY OF LONDON
## INTER-COLLEGIATE
## WOMENS' LEAGUE

**PREMIER DIVISION**

|  | P | W | D | L | F | A | Pts |
|---|---|---|---|---|---|---|---|
| R Lon Hsp & Q Mary W | 14 | 13 | 1 | 0 | 94 | 7 | 40 |
| Royal Holloway College | 14 | 11 | 1 | 2 | 100 | 9 | 34 |
| University College | 14 | 10 | 1 | 3 | 51 | 23 | 31 |
| London School of Econ | 14 | 7 | 0 | 7 | 51 | 29 | 21 |
| King's College | 14 | 5 | 1 | 7 | 33 | 43 | 16 |
| Imperial College | 14 | 5 | 0 | 9 | 28 | 57 | 15 |
| Wye College | 14 | 1 | 1 | 11 | 16 | 84 | 4 |
| St. George's Hospital | 14 | 0 | 1 | 13 | 10 | 131 | 1 |

**DIVISION ONE**

|  | P | W | D | L | F | A | Pts |
|---|---|---|---|---|---|---|---|
| SOAS | 18 | 14 | 2 | 1 | 85 | 8 | 44 |
| Goldsmiths' College | 18 | 14 | 2 | 2 | 60 | 14 | 44 |
| G K T | 18 | 11 | 0 | 6 | 66 | 30 | 33 |
| Royal Veterinary | 18 | 10 | 0 | 8 | 30 | 12 | 30 |
| Royal Free Hospital | 18 | 10 | 0 | 8 | 47 | 30 | 30 |
| University Col & Mx Hsp | 18 | 8 | 0 | 10 | 34 | 57 | 24 |
| Royal Holloway Coll Rs | 18 | 6 | 1 | 8 | 22 | 43 | 19 |
| University College Res. | 18 | 6 | 1 | 11 | 22 | 59 | 19 |
| G K T Res | 18 | 3 | 0 | 15 | 5 | 106 | 9 |
| Royal Free Hospital Rs | 18 | 2 | 0 | 15 | 6 | 18 | 6 |

**WOMENS' CHALLENGE CUP:**
Q Mary Westfield      4 v 2           Royal Holloway

# VARSITY MATCH

## OXFORD UNIVERSITY 1
## CAMBRIDGE UNIVERSITY 0

Oxford v Cambridge. Saturday, 3rd April 1999.
At Craven Cottage, Fulham

OXFORD 1-0 CAMBRIDGE
(Half-time: 0-0)

If 1997 was the ultimate in dreadful University matches it did bring one benefit to the event to prevent it from dying an unnatural death by the amount of scorn that was poured on it and the outcome has been two further matches of considerably better merit (played this year also on an excellent surface) with Oxford winning both and Cambridge unlucky on each occasion, once to lose by an unjustly wide margin and this year by being beaten at all against the run of play by a late goal well created by a fine Peter Wardle cross which was headed in by Peter Cairnes, a second year human sciences undergraduate.

Cambridge have not won the fixture since it was moved from Wembley twelve years ago and they were further handicapped by the loss of their captain, Mark Pett, with the recurrence of a knee injury after only ten minutes, but his colleagues still had more of the game although they were unable to beat Rutter in the Dark Blue goal.

The winners might have done better to make more use of the wide Craven Cottage spaces and the dribbling skills of Deji Davies, the most exciting player in the match, but in general both sides must take credit for a very much higher standard of play than has been seen in recent seasons with the ball being used with considerable intelligence - and on the ground. The influence of the arrival of several players with youth experience at professional clubs was obvious.

Much as one hates to say it, it has to be repeated that the Light Blue post Wembley hoodoo continues, and it was an irony that until the big day they had enjoyed an excellent season with more wins than losses and 61 goals scored in 22 matches before Craven Cottage.

Since the match played at Highbury in 1988 the Light Blues have drawn a blank with this result bringing the Dark Blues their sixth win in eight years. Being part of a greatly improved event with a crowd of almost 2,000 can be no consolation to Cambridge, who have also failed to score in the last three years of the fixture and have only managed three since the successful Wembley years, but there is enough determination plus good morale by the Cam for their luck to change.

Cambridge still lead overall in the fixture with 45 wins against 43 by Oxford and there have been 27 draws.


**OXFORD:** N Rutter; *W Spencer, *A O'Brien, *P Wardle,
L Humphries, K Fowler, *M Goff, L Falconer, *T Cairnes,
S Rishworth, D Davies. Substitutes: G Williams, M Fletcher, C Griffin all played. M Lowe (GK) did not play.

SCORER: Cairnes 88 minutes.


**CAMBRIDGE:** T Haines; L Hayden, A Jennings, I Mowat, A Kerr, *M
Pett (captain), *S Ball, *A Fearnley, *M Walsh, R Williamson, *T Fearnley. Substitutes: A Walford for Pett 10 minutes, G Glamokak for T Fearnley, I Brooksbank for A Fearnley. Madden (GK) did not play.

* Denotes Old Blue

**Referee:** U D Rennie, Sheffield.

# NON-LEAGUE TRAVELLER

## THE Weekly Magazine for the Non-League Follower

The magazine is published weekly throughout the season and includes up-to-date fixtures from around a hundred different leagues in England, Wales and Scotland . . . .

Plus, all the latest news from around the clubs, programme reviews, club focuses and maps, cup draws, and much, much more . . . .

All for around £1.00 per week (including first class postage) . . . .

Please write to:
Non-League Traveller, Top o' the Bank,
Evesham Road, Broadway, Worcs, WR12 7DG
(Phone 01386 853289/Fax 01386 858036)

# ENGLISH SCHOOL'S FOOTBALL ASSOCIATION

**Chief Executive:** Malcolm Berry, 112 East Gate Street, Stafford ST16 2NQ
Tel: 01785 251142
**Publicity:** Mike Simmonds, 19 The Spinney, Bulcote, Burton Joyce, Nottingham NG14 5GX
Tel: 0115 931 3299   Fax: 0115 931 2758

## THE INTERNATIONAL SEASON

### THE UNDER 18 SQUAD

With the Football Association taking over control of the Under 15 schools' side, the English Schools' F.A.'s involvement at international level was confined to the Under 18 side, which is chosen only from those in full time education. Overall, the squad had a disappointing season largely due to the difficulty they had in finding the net, although only a last minute goal from Northern Ireland's Damien McDonald robbed them of success in the Goodyear Centenary Shield.

England dominated the first half of the game against the Irish which was the opening game of the Shield and took the lead after 30 minutes through Ryan rummery but after the interval, Northern Ireland created several chances before they gained their reward which eventually came in the 94th minute. England's second match was against Wales and they fell behind when keeper Rogers allowed an Edwards cross to slip through his grasp before second half goals by Rummery and Craig Cripps brought them a 2-1 success.

These results left England needing a victory in their final match against Scotland who were competing in the Centenary Shield for the first time for several years. Once again, their lack of finishing power let them down and a 0-0 draw left Northern Ireland as champions.

The Under 18 squad also played three invitation internationals, all of which ended in defeat. A strong Hungarian side consisting mainly of professionals from the country's leading clubs won 3-0 in Budapest while the Republic of Ireland had a 2-0 success at Ipswich. The highlight of the season for the squad was, or course, the first ever Under 18 schools' international to be played at Wembley Stadium. A crowd of over 33,000 saw England put up a spirited display against a Holland side, again mainly made up of young professionals, and, when a Stephen Foster penalty cancelled out a Thijs Houwing goal, they looked to have gained the draw they deserved. Their hopes were dashed, however, when Didi Longuet (Ajax) scored a late winner after a floating cross from the left.

### RESULTS

| | | | | | | | |
|---|---|---|---|---|---|---|---|
| v | Republic of Ireland at Ipswich FC | 0-2 | | v | Northern Ireland at Darlington FC | | 1-1 |
| v | Wales at Molineux (Wolverhampton FC) | 2-1 | | v | Scotland at Hearts FC | | 0-0 |
| v | Hungary at MTK Stadium, Budapest | 0-3 | | v | Holland at Wembley Stadium | | 1-2 |

### THE CENTENARY SHIELD FINAL TABLE

| | P | W | D | L | F | A | Pts |
|---|---|---|---|---|---|---|---|
| Northern Ireland | 3 | 2 | 1 | 0 | 5 | 3 | 5 |
| England | 3 | 1 | 2 | 0 | 3 | 2 | 4 |
| Wales | 3 | 1 | 0 | 2 | 5 | 6 | 2 |
| Scotland | 3 | 0 | 1 | 2 | 1 | 3 | 1 |

### THE ENGLAND SQUAD 1998-99

| | | | |
|---|---|---|---|
| Kristian Rogers (GK) | Cheshire SFA | Bill Sobey | Devon SFA |
| James Hughes | Somerset SFA | Sam Allison | Gloucestershire SFA |
| Daniel Dawson | Greater Manchester SFA | Ryan Rummery | Surrey SFA |
| Russell Burden | West Midlands SFA | Stephen Foster | Durham SFA |
| David Duffy | Northumberland SFA | Michael Feely | Warwickshire SFA |
| Neil Morris | Gloucestershire SFA | Matthew Smith (GK) | Northumberland SFA |
| Craig Cripps | Essex SFA | Elliott Onochie | Middlesex SFA |
| Gary Fletcher | Cheshire SFA | Alan Marsh | Dorset SFA |
| Neil Dix | Wiltshire SFA | Graham Taylor | Bedfordshire SFA |

*England Schools' Under 18 Squad 1998-99*

# THE INTER-ASSOCIATION COMPETITIONS

## ENGLISH SCHOOLS F.A. HEINZ KETCHUP TROPHY

| FINAL (1st Leg) | South Notts | v | Bishop Auckland | 3-0 | at Field Mill, Mansfield |
|---|---|---|---|---|---|
| (2nd Leg) | Bishop Auckland | v | South Notts | 0-0 | at Kingsway, Bishop Auckland |

The 89th final of the premier English Schools' F.A. competition, the Inter-Association Trophy, brought together two teams who had never before gone beyond the last eight. South Notts effectively clinched victory in the second half of the first leg. Andrew Burrows put them ahead when, after appearing to lose the ball, he fought to win it back and placed a fine shot across the keeper. Bishop Auckland lost some of the defensive discipline they had shown earlier and an unnecessary tackle allowed Neil Thompson to curl a 25 yard free-kick into the top corner to make it 2-0. Thompson was also involved in the third goal when his corner was flicked on by Marshall for Carl Westcarr to head in at the far post.

In the second leg, South Notts showed no intention of sitting on their comfortable lead and could well have gone further ahead in the first ten minutes as Thompson and Burrows went close and another shot from Burrows was cleared off the line. After this frenetic start, it was not surprising that Bishop Auckland fought back with the tall David Sands dangerous in the air. This brought the outstanding moment of the second leg when keeper Simon Brocklehurst produced a stunning save from Sands downward header. After Sands had missed a fine opportunity from six yards, South Notts with Screaton and Simpson outstanding in the middle of the defence, were never seriously threatened and held on to their 3-0 aggregate lead.

*South Notts striker Carl Westcarr (right) tussles with a Bishop Auckland defender in the first leg of the Final at Field Mill, Mansfield.          Photo: Nottingham Post*

**South Notts Squad:** Simon Brocklehurst, Michael Nadjan, Marc Saric, Adam Simpson, Iaian Screaton, Nick Marshall, Peter Biggins, Neil Thompson, Matthew Hogg, Andrew Burrows, Carl Westcarr, Chris Cox, Gary Garfit, Russell Attwell, Criag Chambers, Christopher Simpson, Michael Holtham, Brett Duffy.
**Bishop Auckland Squad:** Aaron Hall, Dean Burns, Kevin Frater, Mark Batey, Criag Marley, Anthony Storey, Stephen Flockett, Carl Shippen, Neil Robinson, Gavin Bell, Craig Thorn, David Sands, Gavin Maughan, Dean Grayson, Graham Kime, Max Applegarth, Daniel Thompson, Chris Harwick.

### South Notts' Victory Run

| Round 1 | v | Leicester | (A) | | Westcarr (5), Marshall, Cox, Thompson, Cranwell |
|---|---|---|---|---|---|
| Round 2 | v | Coalville | (A) | | Westcarr (2), Thompson (2), Burrows, Cox, Cranwell |
| Round 3 | v | Mid & South Warks | (A) | 3-0 | Cox, Westcarr, Thompson |
| Round 4 | v | Erdington and Saltley | (H) | 2-1 | Westcarr (2) |
| Round 5 | v | East Riding | (A) | 2-2 | Westcarr, Burrows |
| Round 5 Rep | v | East Riding | (A) | 2-0 | Cox, Burrows |
| Round 6 | v | Liverpool | (A) | 2-0 | Burrows, Westcarr |
| Semi-final | v | Reading | (H) | 0-0 | |
| Semi-final Rep | v | Reading | (A) | 1-0 | Westcarr |

### E.S.F.A./F.A. PREMIER LEAGUE UNDER 19 COUNTY CHAMPIONSHIP

#### SEMI-FINALS

| Northumberland | 2 | v | 0 | Durham |
|---|---|---|---|---|
| Sussex | 0 | v | 3 | Dorset |

#### FINAL

Northumberland    0    v    0    Dorset 0-0
after extra time, trophy shared. At Berwick Rangers FC

### E.S.F.A./F.A. PREMIER LEAGUE UNDER 16 COUNTY CHAMPIONSHIP

**SEMI-FINALS**

Humberside   0   v   2   Northumberland
Middlesex   2   v   2   Essex
Essex won 4-2 on penalties

**FINAL**

Northumberland   3   v   2   Essex
at Middlesbrough FC

*Northumberland Schools' Under 16's, winners of the English Schools' County Championship*

### E.S.F.A. UNITED NORWEST CO-OP UNDER 16 GIRLS' COUNTY CHAMPIONSHIP

**FINAL**

Hampshire   3   v   1   Durham
at Prenton Park, Tranmere Rovers FC

Hampshire became the first holders of the United Norwest Co-op Trophy when this competition reached its initial season's climax. Durham took the lead after 22 minutes when Amanda Dobbs' shot drifted over the Hampshire keeper and dipped under the bar but Hampshire's pressure paid off when Gemma Ritchie equalised with a 25 yard shot on the stroke of half time. Hampshire's two England Under 16 players, Ritchie and Shelley Cox, played key roles as Hampshire got on top after the break with substitute Katie Wilding putting them ahead midway through the second period after Ritchie had flicked on. Despite some excellent saves by Durham's Holly Scott, Ritchie scored the clinching goal with a solo effort late in the game. Hampshire thoroughly deserved their victory but the young Durham side also deserve great credit.

**Hampshire Squad:** Aman Dosanj, Charlotte Brown, Laura Oakes, Natalie Bavister, Gemma Ryan, Corinne Yorsten, Lisa Richmond, Stephanie Webb, katie Wilding, Gemma Ritchie, Sheeley Cox, Lucy Scott, Kirsty Bell, Maggy Murphy.

### E.S.F.A. ADIDAS PREDATOR PREMIER UNDER 11 7-A-SIDE CHAMPIONSHIP

**SEMI-FINALS**

Carlisle beat Croydon     Vale of White Horse beat Brierley Hill and Dudley

**FINAL**

Vale of White Horse SFA   0   v   0   Carlisle SFA
Trophy shared. Played at Wembley Stadium

# THE INDIVIDUAL SCHOOLS' COMPETITIONS

## E.S.F.A. HEINZ KETCHUP UNDER 14 CUP

Seldom can the introduction of a new competition have been as successful as the new Heinz Ketchup Cup for Under 14 school teams. Well over a thousand schools took part in the initial year and the winners needed ten games to clinch the title in front of a 4,000 crowd at Highbury.

### THE FINAL
Cardinal Newman School (Luton)　　2　v　1　　Kingsdown School (Swindon)

Cardinal Newman snatched a fifth minute lead with a sweeping right wing move finished by Michael Macdonald who also volleyed in the second from a Glenn Marshall corner. Kingsdown rallied after the break, Aidan Doyle heading in a David Bampton cross, but they could not force an equaliser.

| Cardinal Newman School | | | | Kingsdown School | | | |
|---|---|---|---|---|---|---|---|
| Round 1 | v | Buckingham Upper School | 7-0 | Round 1 | v | St Alfred's School (Wantage) | 4-0 |
| Round 2 | v | Vandyke Upper School (Beds) | 7-1 | Round 2 | v | Gosford Hill School (Swindon) | 3-1 |
| Round 3 | v | Radcliffe School | 3-2 | Round 3 | v | St Joseph's School (Swindon) | 5-0 |
| Round 4 | v | St Paul's School (Milton Keynes) | 8-3 | Round 4 | v | Charters School (Ascot) | 5-1 |
| Round 5 | v | Notre Dame H.S. (Norwich) | 5-1 | Round 5 | v | St Thomas School (Exeter) | 2-1 |
| Round 6 | v | Neale Wade Comm Col (Cambs) | 4-2 | Round 6 | v | Liskeard School | 1-1, 3p2 |
| Round 7 | v | Bilton High School (Rugby) | 4-2 | Round 7 | v | Hurst School (Basingstoke) | 1-0 |
| Round 8 | v | Graveney School (Tooting) | 2-0 | Round 8 | v | St Thomas the Apostle Schl (Lon.) | 3-2 |
| Semi-final | v | Cardinal Heenan Schl (Liverpool) | 1-0 | Semi-final | v | Hungerhill School (Doncaster) | 1-0 |

### ROUTES TO THE FINAL:

## E.S.F.A. UNITED NORWEST CO-OP UNDER 16 GIRLS' TROPHY
### FINAL
Meole Brace School (Shropshire)　　4　v　1　　Holmfirth School (West Yorkshire)
at Prenton Park, Tranmere Rovers FC

Holmfirth School, whose school band added much to the atmosphere of the final played before a good crowd, took the lead after ten minutes through their captain Emma Schofield but that was cancelled out just before half-time by a spectacular strike by Bridgitte Titler. Holmfirth also started the second half promisingly but Meole Brace gradually got on top and Laura Appleton put them ahead from just inside the penalty box. As Holmfirth tired, excellent goals from Nicola Parry and Louella Hartshorne brought the Shropshire school a convincing victory.

*Meole Brace School*

### ROUTES TO THE FINAL:
**Meole Brace School** won five games to become Shropshire Champions
In the national rounds they beat Cheslyn Hay High School (Staffs) 10-0; Nicholas Chamberlaine School (Warwicks) 3-1; Wellsway School (Somerset) 4-2; Willingdon School (Sussex) 4-3 and Darrick Wood School (Kent) 6-1.
**Holmfirth School** won the West Yorkshire title before defeating Balby School (S Yorkshire) 6-0; Dronfield School (Derbys.) 2-1; St John Fisher (N Yorkshire) 6-1; De Lisle School (Leics.) 4-1 and Helsby High School (Cheshire) 1-0.

## E.S.F.A. UNDER 16 INDIVIDUAL SCHOOLS' CHAMPIONSHIP
For the Goodyear Trophy at Molineux
### SEMI-FINALS
Cramlington School (Northumberland)　　2　v　1　　Tupton Hall School (Derbyshire)

Crown Woods School (Inner London)　　2　v　1　　Torpoint School (Cornwall)

### FINAL
Cramlington School　　4　v　1　　Crown Woods School

## E.S.F.A. UNDER 19 SCHOOLS' CHAMPIONSHIP
For the Mars Trophy at The Hawthorns
### FINAL
Ardingley College (Sussex)  2  v  1  Archbishop Beck School (Merseyside)

Ardingly College won the Boodle and Dunthorne Independent Schools' Cup last season and they completed a unique double when they won the Mars Trophy in an exciting final. Chris Christophers, who arrived at the team's hotel having won the Sussex Under 20 triple jump title the previous day, completed an amazing 48 hours by scoring both the Ardingly goals in their narrow win over Archbishop Beck. He put them ahead after 20 minutes after being set up by Bradley Dougal but the Liverpool school fought back well and Martin Coughlin scrambled in the equaliser following a corner 15 minutes later.

Christophers scored the winner following a solo run midway through the second period but Ardingly had another hero, goalkeeper Daniel Powell, who ten minutes earlier had saved Thomas Dreve's spot kick.

*Archbishop Beck School*
*Runners-up in the Under 19 Individual Schools' Championship*

**Ardingly:** Daniel Powell, Miles Forsyth, Peter Hadden, Yuki Mihatia, Adam Virgo, Chris Christophers, Bradley Dougal, Finn Cornwall (sub. Will Barnes), Terry Swann, Drew Menzies, Chris Darkes. Unused subs: Ashley Dougal, Richard Fisher, Andrew Harker-Smith, Keisuke Yamamoto.
**Archbishop Beck:** Carl Giles, Joseph Stephens, Mark Pollock, Chris Coughlin, Andrew Glendenning, Michael Lundon, Paul Fitzpatrick, Adam Mazenko, Martin Coughlin, Lee Spike, Thomas Dreves, Lee Rowland, Thomas Morrison, Nicholas Jones, John O'Brien, Daniel Williams.

## E.S.F.A. UNDER 19 SCHOOLS' AND COLLEGES' CHAMPIONSHIP
at The Hawthorns, West Bromwich, for the Snickers Trophy
### FINAL
Cirencester College  2  v  0  Sheffield College

Cirencester College became the first team to retain the English Schools' Under 19 Championship in its 31 year history when they turned in an impressive first half display against their northern opponents. Tom Staddon gave them a twentieth minute lead following a solo effort run by Phil Corcoran and only a brave and skilful display by the Sheffield keeper David Calow kept a rampant Gloucestershire side, containing four England Schools' Under 18 international players, at bay. It was unfortunate for Calow that Cirencester's deserved second goal came from one of his own defenders, Chris Hayes, who deflected a Luke Costello cross. Sheffield welcomed the half time whistle and a reorganised side gave a much improved second half performance to produce a much more even contest, but Neil Morris and Nick McCrae in the centre of the Cirencester defence proved impassable and the Gloucestershire side were impressive victors.

Remarkably, the two sides met again two days later in the final of the British Colleges competition and Sheffield looked on target for revenge when Matt Hodson and Dale Joel put them 2-1 ahead with 20 minutes remaining. Fate was to be cruel, however, and McCrae powered in a header to add to Corcoran's first half effort to bring Cirencester level. Then, in the last minute, Dominic Dunton fired home the winner from the penalty spot and, although there was still time for Kingsley Paul to be denied a last gasp equaliser by a fine save, Sheffield were disappointed losers again.

## THE E.S.F.A. WAGON WHEELS UNDER 12 INDOOR 5-A-SIDE CHAMPIONSHIP
### BOY'S FINAL
Meadows School (Chesterfield  3  v  0  Welling School (North Kent)

### GIRL'S FINAL,
Abraham Darby School (Telford)  4  v  1  Eastlea School (Newham)

## E.S.F.A. ADIDAS PREDATOR UNDER 11 6-A-SIDE CHAMPIONSHIP
### FINAL
St Mary's Primary School (Hendon)  2  v  1  Avondale Primary School (Darwen)
at Wembley Stadium

## E.S.F.A. UNDER 11 SMALL PRIMARY SCHOOLS' CHAMPIONSHIP
### FINAL
Holy Cross Primary School (Notts)  2  v  1  Great Dalby Primary School (Leicestershire)
after extra time. Played at Filbert Street, Leicester

# NON-LEAGUE
# NEWSDESK

## FOR RESULTS, TABLES AND NEWS
## FROM THE NON-LEAGUE PYRAMID

Now entering its fifth full season, Non-League Newsdesk has become firmly established as the number one magazine for up-to-date news and statistics from the Pyramid world.

Founded in 1995 by former Non-League Club Directory editor James Wright, Non-League Newsdesk will in 1999-2000 celebrate its 200th edition. The magazine is delivered to subscribers every midweek (usually Wednesday) carrying all the previous week's results, together with current tables, from around FIFTY leagues.

For many of the more senior competitions, full match details (such as goalscorers and attendances) are supplied. County and League Cup competitions are also extensively featured, as are the FA Umbro Trophy and FA Carlsberg Vase, and the involvement of the non-League clubs in the AXA sponsored FA Cup.

But Non-League Newsdesk is not just a statistical work. Each week the magazine carries up-to-date news stories and listings of managerial changes and transfers.

The magazine is therefore particularly popular with -
* Clubs, who find much of the information extremely useful for matchday programmes and in checking on forthcoming opponents, particularly those from outside their own league.
* Statisticians, who see the weekly stats as the most extensive, accurate and up-to-date available.
* Groundhoppers, who find it invaluable in picking their games.
* The more general non-League enthusiast who likes to keep abreast of the most current news.
If you would like to see a free sample copy from 1998-99, please send an SAE to James Wright at the address below.

Leagues featured in Non-League Newsdesk include: Nationwide Conference, UniBond, Ryman, Dr Martens, First NW Trains NWCL, SGL West Lancs, Manchester, Carlsberg West Cheshire, Green Contract Services Mid-Cheshire, Arnott Insurance Northern, Northern Co's (East), Redferns Central Midlands, Powerleague Notts Alliance, West Yorkshire, Deejays Lincs, Everards Leics, Vaux Wearside, JPL Wade Northern Alliance, Herts, A Quote Insurance Reading, Courage Combined Co's, Cherry Red Chiltonian, Minerva SSML, Essex Senior, Essex Intermediate, Kent Blaxill Essex & Suffolk Border, Interlink Alliance, Endsleigh Midland Comb, Banks's West Mids, Springbank Vending Midland, Complete Music Hellenic, Glos. County, Somerset Senior, Screwfix Western, Jewson SW, Jolly's Cornwall Combination, Cornish Guardian East Cornwall, Westward Developments Devon, Jewson Wessex, Keyline Dorset Comb., Dorset Co., Hampshire, Unijet Sussex, Bass Kent, British Energy Kent Co., Jewson ECL, Lovewell Blake Anglian Combination, McGinty's Suffolk & Ipswich, Uhlsport UCL, Optimum Interiors Capital and Central Conference, League of Wales, CC Sports Welsh League, Cymru Alliance.

**JAMES WRIGHT, 13 NORTHFIELD AVENUE, TAUNTON, SOMERSET TA1 1XF**
**TEL/FAX: 01823 327720  MOBILE: 0421 004219  E-MAIL:NLNEWSDESK@ZETNET.CO.UK**

**Subscription Rates**

Non-League Newsdesk costs just 80p per week plus first class postage (26p). It is produced every Monday during the season except the week between Christmas and New Year. The table below shows how much a subscription will cost from your chosen starting date.

| FROM | to Xmas | Full season |
|---|---|---|
| Aug 9th | £21.20 | £42.40 |
| Aug 16th | £20.14 | £41.34 |
| Aug 23rd | £19.08 | £40.28 |
| Aug 30th | £18.02 | £39.22 |
| Sept 6th | £16.96 | £38.16 |
| Sept 13th | £15.90 | £37.10 |
| Sept 20th | £14.84 | £36.04 |
| Sept 27th | £13.78 | £34.98 |
| Oct 4th | £12.72 | £33.92 |
| Oct 11th | £11.66 | £32.86 |
| Oct 18th | £10.60 | £31.80 |
| Oct 25th | £9.54 | £30.74 |
| Nov 1st | £8.48 | £29.68 |
| Nov 8th | £7.42 | £28.62 |
| Nov 15th | £6.36 | £27.56 |
| Nov 22nd | £5.30 | £26.50 |
| Nov 29th | £4.24 | £25.44 |
| Dec 5th | £3.18 | £24.38 |
| Dec 12th | £2.12 | £23.32 |
| Dec 19th | £1.06 | £22.26 |
| Jan 3rd | n/a | £21.20 |
| Jan 10th | n/a | £20.14 |
| Jan 17th | n/a | £19.08 |
| Jan 24th | n/a | £18.02 |
| Jan 31st | n/a | £16.96 |
| Feb 7th | n/a | £15.90 |
| Feb 14th | n/a | £14.84 |
| Feb 21st | n/a | £13.78 |
| Feb 28th | n/a | £12.72 |
| Mar 7th | n/a | £11.66 |
| Mar 14th | n/a | £10.60 |
| Mar 21st | n/a | £9.54 |
| Mar 28th | n/a | £8.48 |
| April 4th | n/a | £7.42 |
| April 11th | n/a | £6.36 |
| April 18th | n/a | £5.30 |
| April 25th | n/a | £4.24 |
| May 2nd | n/a | £3.18 |
| May 9th | n/a | £2.12 |
| End of season issue | | £1.06 |

**TO ORDER**
Simply send your:
Name, Address, Tel. No., When you want your subscription to start and whether it is Until Christmas or until the End of the season

Please send cheque or postal order payable to Non-League Newsdesk

# CHANNEL ISLANDS REVIEW

Sylvans won the Priaulx League for the sixth year in succession. Despite losing a number of key players to other clubs (mainly St Martin's) during the close season, their winning margin of thirteen points was their second biggest to date.

After Sylvans had beaten Jersey Scottish in all of the previous three Upton Park Trophy games (Channel Island club championship) the Scots turned the tables and beat Sylvans 3-1 at Springfield in Jersey. Had Sylvans won they would have equalled St Martin's record (1964-67) as the only club to win four successive Upton's.

Cup holders Sylvans lost 5-2 aet to Vale Rec. in the Stranger Cup Final (90 mins 2-2). Vale Rec were the surprise team of the season, finishing league runners-up against many people's predictions.

The two top strikers in Guernsey football's top division were Matt Falla with 36, and David MacNab with 31. Both play for Vale Rec. Vale reached the finals of both the Jeremie Cup (Guernsey KO competition where Jersey clubs are invited to take part) and the Wheway Cup (Jersey competition with the top three Guernsey teams invited). In the Wheway Cup they lost 1-0 to Jersey's St Peter at Springfield and in the Jeremie Cup they lost by the same score to Jersey Scottish at their own Corbet Field ground.

Sylvans fell at the first hurdle in both the Jeremie and Wheway Cups. In the Jeremie they lost 3-2 to Jersey Scottish at their own St Peter's ground in September, and were knocked out of the Wheway Cup by St Paul's in Jersey, 3-2 aet in October. Remarkably it was Sylvans' first defeat in the competition for nearly four years as they had won it for the past three seasons.

After beating Brading Town, and East Cowes Victoria Athletic in the Hampshire Senior Cup, Sylvans crashed out of the competition when they lost 6-0 at Aldershot Town in late January. Sylvans' top scorers for the season were Tony Vance (19), Paul Nobes (16), and Matt Le Cras (14).

For the first time ever, Guernsey won all four inter-insulars (Senior and Junior Muratti, Women's Muratti and Under 21's Muratti). In fairness, it was only the third year that the Women's Muratti had taken place and Guernsey won 3-1 at Blanche Pierre Lane in Guernsey.

Guernsey won the Ambassadeur Bowl (Under 21's) by 2-0 at Springfield in November with goals from St Martins' Richard Herpe and Vale Rec's David MacNab.

Two goals in extra time from Sylvans' Matt Le Cras gave Guernsey their first Senior Muratti win since 1997 when they beat the old enemy 2-0 at the Track. Having lost the last four Junior Murattis (Under 18's) all by 1-0, Guernsey beat Jersey 6-0 at Springfield for their biggest win in the history of the competition. The game was played in torrential rain. Guernsey's goals were scored by Rangers' Dale Garland (2), Sylvans' Matt Warren (2), and fifteen year old Northerner, Gavin Le Page (2). Gavin is a Wycombe Wanderers trialist and son of the former Rangers and island midfielder, Colin.

Jersey won the Star Trophy (Under 15's Schoolboy Muratti) by 2-1 at the Corbet Field. This event is run by the Guernsey Schools' Football Association.

Guernsey also won the Carlsberg Victory Cup, the Malaya Cup, and the Commodores Ferries Cup (matches against invited teams). Despite being unbeaten at the NatWest Island games in Gotland, Guernsey finished ninth. The winners of each group went into the semi-finals, the second placed teams played off for fifth, and the third placed teams played off for ninth. Guernsey finished with an identical record to Rhodes in Group Four but lost out for second place by virtue of a tossed coin. The toss was done by Jersey FA President, Brian Ahier! (True story!)

Guernsey beat both Froya and Shetland to clinch ninth place. Holders Jersey, meanwhile, won Group One to reach the semi-finals where they lost 1-0 to the Isle of Man. They were beaten 2-0 in the play-off for third place by the Isle of Wight and finished fourth.

*Nigel Baudains*

# GUERNSEY FOOTBALL ASSOCIATION

## BARCLAYS FINAL LEAGUE TABLES 1998-99

### BARCLAYS PRIAULX LEAGUE

|  | P | W | D | L | F | A | Pts |
|---|---|---|---|---|---|---|---|
| Sylvans | 18 | 15 | 2 | 1 | 60 | 21 | 47 |
| Vale Recreation | 18 | 11 | 1 | 6 | 56 | 36 | 34 |
| St Martin's | 18 | 10 | 3 | 5 | 41 | 27 | 33 |
| Rovers | 18 | 6 | 4 | 8 | 31 | 40 | 22 |
| Northerners | 18 | 4 | 5 | 9 | 27 | 46 | 17 |
| Rangers | 18 | 5 | 2 | 11 | 26 | 50 | 17 |
| Belgrave's | 18 | 2 | 3 | 13 | 26 | 47 | 9 |

### BARCLAYS JACKSON LEAGUE

|  | P | W | D | L | F | A | Pts |
|---|---|---|---|---|---|---|---|
| Vale Recreation | 21 | 17 | 2 | 2 | 100 | 43 | 53 |
| St Martin's | 21 | 12 | 3 | 6 | 82 | 51 | 39 |
| Sylvans | 21 | 10 | 5 | 6 | 72 | 46 | 35 |
| Belgrave's | 21 | 10 | 3 | 8 | 66 | 38 | 33 |
| Rovers | 21 | 7 | 5 | 9 | 64 | 55 | 26 |
| Northerners | 21 | 6 | 3 | 12 | 33 | 51 | 21 |
| Rangers | 21 | 5 | 6 | 10 | 40 | 70 | 21 |
| Port City | 21 | 3 | 1 | 17 | 27 | 130 | 10 |

### BARCLAYS RAILWAY LEAGUE

|  | P | W | D | L | F | A | Pts |
|---|---|---|---|---|---|---|---|
| Sylvans | 18 | 13 | 5 | 0 | 80 | 22 | 44 |
| Belgrave's | 18 | 10 | 5 | 3 | 50 | 24 | 35 |
| Vale Recreation | 18 | 10 | 3 | 5 | 63 | 33 | 33 |
| St Martin's | 18 | 10 | 3 | 5 | 60 | 38 | 33 |
| Northerners | 18 | 7 | 3 | 8 | 32 | 34 | 24 |
| Alderney Nomads | 18 | 6 | 4 | 8 | 37 | 47 | 22 |
| Rovers | 18 | 6 | 3 | 9 | 37 | 45 | 21 |
| Police | 18 | 5 | 4 | 9 | 32 | 63 | 19 |
| Rangers | 18 | 3 | 3 | 12 | 29 | 80 | 12 |
| Port City | 18 | 2 | 3 | 13 | 37 | 71 | 9 |

### BARCLAYS YOUTH DIVISION ONE

|  | P | W | D | L | F | A | Pts |
|---|---|---|---|---|---|---|---|
| Vale Recreation | 18 | 14 | 1 | 3 | 56 | 20 | 43 |
| Rangers | 18 | 11 | 2 | 5 | 52 | 26 | 35 |
| Rovers | 18 | 9 | 2 | 7 | 39 | 33 | 29 |
| Sylvans | 18 | 9 | 1 | 8 | 43 | 35 | 28 |
| St Martin's | 18 | 7 | 1 | 10 | 33 | 37 | 22 |
| Belgrave's | 18 | 4 | 2 | 12 | 24 | 63 | 14 |
| Northerners | 18 | 4 | 1 | 13 | 26 | 59 | 13 |

### BARCLAYS YOUTH DIVISION TWO

|  | P | W | D | L | F | A | Pts |
|---|---|---|---|---|---|---|---|
| Northerners | 12 | 10 | 0 | 2 | 46 | 18 | 30 |
| St Martin's | 12 | 9 | 1 | 2 | 53 | 17 | 28 |
| Vale Recreation | 12 | 9 | 1 | 2 | 48 | 22 | 28 |
| Rangers | 12 | 4 | 0 | 8 | 27 | 43 | 12 |
| Belgrave's | 12 | 3 | 1 | 8 | 25 | 42 | 10 |
| Sylvans | 12 | 3 | 1 | 8 | 24 | 58 | 10 |
| Rovers | 12 | 2 | 0 | 10 | 14 | 37 | 6 |

# JERSEY FOOTBALL ASSOCIATION

Scottish are the kings of Jersey club football once more. They cemented a claim to being the best club side Jersey has ever seen as they captured the Jersey European Combination division One title for a record fourth consecutive season and the sixth time in eight years. Said jubilant manager Jimmy MacFarlane: "It's brilliant to win it again, especially after the number of players we'd lost for one reason or another throughout the season. But we've got some very good youngsters coming through and we'll be trying to make it five on the run next year."

Scottish needed just a point from their final game and looked about to wrap up their season in style as they raced into a 2-0 lead against Rozel Rovers - a side in with a real title shout themselves until the last three games.
Young Simon Moiani set the Scots on their way as he rifled home the first goal from 20 yards. Rozel 'keeper Chris Sheehan denied them a 2-0 lead a few minutes later when he brilliantly saved a Mark Cassidy. Yazalde Santos grabbed the second two minutes before the break after Moiani sprung Rovers' offside trap and dashed from the halfway line. His shot hit the post but Santos was on hand to slot home the rebound. Ten minutes after the break Rovers hit back as Dougie Ross scored from eighteen yards and minutes later Lee Bramley made it 2-2. Scottish responded positively as they pressed for the winner and forced Sheehan into a couple of super saves.

Scottish buried their recent Upton Park Trophy hoodoo - the annual game against Guernsey's champions - by beating Guernsey Sylvans 3-1 at Springfield. After weathering an early Sylvans storm, the Scots recovered to turn in a fine performance and lift the Channel Islands' club championship for the third time in eight years. Had Sylvans won they would have equalled the competition's record run of four successive victories by Guernsey St Martin's between 1964 and 1967.

Scottish won a third trophy when a goal from Adam Greig secured them a 1-0 win in Guernsey in the Jeremie Cup final against Vale Recreation. Greig swooped to head home a Yazalde Santos cross just before half time. And that was enough for Jimmy MacFarlane's side to win the GFA's premier competition for the fourth time.

St Peter made it an inter-insular KO cup double for Jersey when a late Barry Hardisty strike gave St Peter a deserved Wheway Cup - Jersey's premier KO - victory over Guernsey's Vale Recreation.

## JERSEY EUROPEAN FOOTBALL COMBINATION

## FINAL LEAGUE TABLES 1998-99

### DIVISION ONE

|              | P  | W  | D | L  | F  | A  | Pts |
|--------------|----|----|---|----|----|----|-----|
| Scottish     | 20 | 15 | 2 | 3  | 60 | 15 | 47  |
| St Peter     | 20 | 14 | 2 | 4  | 51 | 21 | 44  |
| Rozel Rovers | 20 | 12 | 3 | 5  | 58 | 29 | 39  |
| St Paul's    | 20 | 11 | 3 | 6  | 38 | 28 | 36  |
| First Tower  | 20 | 9  | 6 | 5  | 44 | 24 | 33  |
| Wanderers    | 20 | 9  | 2 | 9  | 27 | 32 | 29  |
| Magpies      | 20 | 8  | 3 | 9  | 35 | 37 | 27  |
| Portuguese   | 20 | 7  | 3 | 10 | 38 | 43 | 24  |
| St Martin    | 20 | 4  | 6 | 10 | 33 | 43 | 18  |
| Grouville    | 20 | 3  | 2 | 15 | 26 | 54 | 11  |
| Oaklands/SS  | 20 | 2  | 0 | 18 | 15 | 99 | 6   |

### DIVISION TWO

|               | P  | W  | D | L  | F  | A  | Pts |
|---------------|----|----|---|----|----|----|-----|
| St John       | 16 | 11 | 4 | 1  | 45 | 16 | 37  |
| St Brelade    | 16 | 10 | 2 | 4  | 33 | 14 | 32  |
| Sporting Acs  | 16 | 9  | 2 | 5  | 40 | 24 | 29  |
| Trinity       | 16 | 8  | 3 | 5  | 43 | 27 | 27  |
| Beeches OB    | 16 | 8  | 2 | 6  | 36 | 26 | 26  |
| St Clement    | 16 | 4  | 3 | 9  | 28 | 29 | 15  |
| St Lawrence   | 16 | 4  | 3 | 9  | 19 | 52 | 15  |
| St Ouen       | 16 | 3  | 3 | 10 | 19 | 37 | 12  |
| Sporting Club | 16 | 3  | 2 | 11 | 24 | 62 | 11  |

# CHANNEL ISLANDS INTER INSULAR & GUERNSEY FOOTBALL ASSOCIATION

## ROLE OF HONOUR 1998-99

| | |
|---|---|
| Muratti Vase | Guernsey FA |
| Junior Muratti (Under 18) | Guernsey FA |
| Under 21 Muratti (Ambassadeur Bowl) | Guernsey FA |
| Norman Piette Ladies Muratti | Guernsey LFA |
| Star Trophy (Under 15 Schools) | Jersey FA |
| Carlsberg Victory Cup | Guernsey FA |
| Malaya Cup (Under 21's) | Guernsey FA |
| Commodore Ferries Cup | Guernsey FA |
| Upton Park Cup | Jersey Scottish FC |
| Portsmouth Trophy (Under 18) | Vale Recreation FC |
| John Leatt Memorial Trophy (Under 16) | Rozel Rovers FC |
| Barclays Priaulx League | Sylvans SC |
| Barclays Jackson League | Vale Recreation FC |
| Barclays Railway League | Sylvans SC |
| Barclays Youth Division One | Vale Recreation FC |
| Barclays Youth Division Two | Northerners' AC |
| Deloitte & Touche Jeremie Cup | Jersey Scottish FC |
| Wheway Cup | St Peter FC |
| W J Collins Memorial Trophy | St Paul's FC |
| Barclays Stranger Cup | Vale Recreation FC |
| H E Mauger Memorial Cup | Sylvans SC |
| Ron Rouget Memorial Cup | Sylvans SC |
| Old Vic Cup | Rangers FC |
| Normandie Cup | St Martin's AC |
| Corbet Cup | Belgrave Wanderers FC |
| Le Vallee Cup | Sylvans SC |
| JW Loveridge Cup | Rovers FC |
| Bill Duquemin Memorial Trophy | St Martin's AC |
| Rawlinson Cup | Vale Recreation FC |

*Sylvans Sports FC. Back Row (L-R): Jonathon Bachelet, Matt Warren, Mike de la Haye, Joel Avery (c), Ian Drillot, Adrian Exall, Craig le Prevost, Ben Duff, Bob Avery (coach)*
*Front Row: Tom Duff, John Nobes, Martin Gauvain, Tony Vance, Paul Nobes, Dave Gilman, Andy McCarthy*
*Photo: Eric Marsh, acknowledgements to Guernsey Evening Press and Star*

# ISLE OF MAN FOOTBALL REVIEW 1998-99

## MANX FOOTBALL 1998-99

After a number of years when the dominating factors in Manx Football were teams from Douglas this time there was a complete change with all trophies going to out of town clubs whilst the top three League teams were Castletown, Peel and Rushen United.

After a season long battle Castletown eventually took the honours in the League losing only three games as they finished ahead of a Peel side which had to play a lot of matches in a short time after being caught up in a number of replays and weather delays. In the Isle of Man there is no such thing as the penalty shoot out.

Peel found the task of winning everything just too much but there can be no doubt that Castletown are worthy champions. They seemed likely to have the top scorer in Division One as well in John Palmer who notched 28 goals, that is until Peel beat St George's 17-2 with Nick Hurt their Island midfielder scoring fifteen goals to take his tally for the season to 35.

Peel ended as top scorers whilst the third place went to Rushen United from the South of the Island with the former champions St Mary's taking fourth spot. Early on after a number of defections it was obvious that St John's United would go straight back down whilst the other promoted side Marown consolidated well. The relegation therefore became a battle between the Police and Braddan with the latter going down after two narrow escapes.

The Cup ties were dominated by Peel who won the Railway Cup for the top four at the halfway stage of the season and they finished the prolonged season with wins over rivals Rushen United in both the FA Cup and Hospital Cup. The season in fact did not finish until June after TT week.

In the Second Division Laxey were in fine form throughout and after losing just one game they sealed promotion fairly early. They were one of three teams to top 100 goals with the other two having a close battle for the other promotion berth. Union Mills always looked close to promotion but it was in the last game of the season they clinched the runners up spot with the much improved Pulrose United nearly pipping them on the post while Corinthians were within two points of promotion as well but just didn't score enough goals.

The Isle of Man National Team were at their best in the Island Games in Gotland. They drew with the hosts who were the favourites to win the event and eventually reached the final where they narrowly lost to Anglesey. It really hinged in many ways on the fact that there were more teams in the Isle of Man's qualifying group.

The Isle of Man team also played in the Guinness Cup where they again showed good form in beating Northern Ireland whilst in the Isle of Man Summer Festival for the first time they played a Premiership club losing only by a single goal to Watford. The Isle of Man also lost narrowly to the Tournament winners Oldham Athletic and to Wrexham when they scored their only goal of the event.

*Dave Phillips*

*Castletown, League Division One Champions*

# TAYLOR WOODROW LEAGUE
## DIVISION ONE

| | P | W | D | L | F | A | Pts |
|---|---|---|---|---|---|---|---|
| Castletown | 24 | 20 | 1 | 3 | 78 | 31 | 61 |
| Peel | 24 | 17 | 3 | 4 | 94 | 28 | 54 |
| Rushen United | 24 | 17 | 2 | 5 | 70 | 36 | 53 |
| St Marys | 24 | 15 | 1 | 8 | 70 | 40 | 46 |
| DHSOB | 24 | 14 | 3 | 7 | 60 | 33 | 45 |
| Gymnasium | 24 | 11 | 5 | 8 | 65 | 48 | 38 |
| Marown | 24 | 10 | 2 | 12 | 47 | 62 | 32 |
| St Georges | 24 | 9 | 4 | 11 | 42 | 69 | 31 |
| Douglas Royal | 24 | 8 | 2 | 14 | 45 | 53 | 26 |
| Ayre United | 24 | 8 | 1 | 15 | 41 | 69 | 25 |
| Police | 24 | 6 | 1 | 17 | 49 | 89 | 19 |
| Braddan | 24 | 4 | 5 | 15 | 40 | 71 | 17 |
| St Johns United | 24 | 1 | 2 | 21 | 17 | 89 | 5 |

# MARSH McLENNAN LEAGUE
## DIVISION TWO

| | P | W | D | L | F | A | Pts |
|---|---|---|---|---|---|---|---|
| Laxey | 26 | 22 | 3 | 1 | 104 | 27 | 69 |
| Union Mills | 26 | 18 | 5 | 3 | 117 | 29 | 59 |
| Pulrose United | 26 | 18 | 3 | 5 | 136 | 45 | 57 |
| Corinthians | 26 | 18 | 3 | 5 | 95 | 36 | 57 |
| Ramsey | 26 | 14 | 3 | 9 | 78 | 43 | 45 |
| Ronaldsway | 26 | 13 | 4 | 9 | 65 | 49 | 43 |
| Colby | 26 | 11 | 6 | 9 | 72 | 53 | 39 |
| Ondian | 26 | 12 | 3 | 11 | 62 | 52 | 39 |
| RYCOB | 26 | 13 | 3 | 13 | 54 | 74 | 33 |
| Michael United | 26 | 9 | 5 | 12 | 57 | 47 | 32 |
| Foxdale | 26 | 8 | 5 | 13 | 71 | 76 | 29 |
| Malow | 26 | 2 | 3 | 21 | 28 | 151 | 9 |
| Barclays | 26 | 2 | 1 | 23 | 34 | 134 | 7 |
| Jurby | 26 | 1 | 1 | 24 | 15 | 172 | 4 |

## DIVISION ONE LEADING SCORERS

| | | |
|---|---|---|
| Nick Hurt | Peel | 35 |
| John Palmer | Castletown | 28 |
| Chris Hawke | Peel | 22 |
| Les Coates | Gymnasium | 20 |
| Peter Langridge | St Marys | 20 |
| Tony Duggan | Castletown | 19 |
| Brian Gartland | DHSOB | 18 |
| Steven Gardner | Police | 17 |
| Ian Kelly | Rushen United | 15 |
| Martin Kennaugh | Rushen United | 15 |
| Juan Killip | Marown | 15 |
| Brian Leavey | DHSOB | 15 |
| James Teare | Ayre United | 15 |

## DIVISION TWO LEADING SCORERS

| | | |
|---|---|---|
| Michael Dawson | Pulrose United | 41 |
| Jason Price | Union Mills | 36 |
| Nigel Moody | Corinthians | 33 |
| Peter Moore | Laxey | 24 |
| Lee Worsfold | Union Mills | 21 |
| Michael Perks | Michael United | 19 |
| Kevin Cain | Pulrose United | 18 |
| Tony Relly | Ramsey | 17 |
| Paul Thomas | Laxey | 17 |
| Joey Doyce | Corinthians | 16 |

# WOMEN'S FOOTBALL

## Compiled by Jenny Thompson

### Development Programme

Last season proved to be a fantastic campaign for women's football; it was the most exciting yet. Many new developments have been put into place to ensure that England recaptures its status as a major force in the domestic game and in the International arena.

The work carried out by Kelly Simmons, National Women's Co-ordinator, is so extensive it ranges from restructuring the league to hosting the Women's UEFA Football Conference. All of these projects and initiatives outlined are becoming a template for others to follow.

### Domestically

The structure and development of the game is vital for progression. The FA have ensured this has been one of their top priorities and they have been responsible for setting up the Women's AXA FA Premier League and the Women's AXA FA League Cup. This competition is the most prestigious in women's football and the Final earns widespread media coverage.

Other domestic competitions include the All England Fives played at senior and U16 level.

### Internationally

A number of major changes have been made to the set up of the women's game. The appointment of Hope Powell, the first full-time England Women's Manager, was the first major step forward on the ladder of development.

More significant is the creation of an U18 and an U16's England Squad. This is a part of the Talent Development Programme committed to developing the game from grassroots up to International level.

England has already hosted the European Qualifying Tournament so as to decide the quarter-finals of the UEFA U18 Championships.

Nationwide agreed to sponsor the England team and the longstanding relationship with UMBRO is still continuing. In addition to UMBRO's £20 million deal, they have made specific reference to its commitment to 'investment and product development' for the women's game.

### The Budget

Running an efficient programme costs a great deal of money and this season the budget significantly increased to over £1 million. The funds support County Grants, Centres of Excellence and the set-up of the League and Cup Competitions. £250,000 was used to fund County Grant Aid

Many other projects and initiatives have been taking place throughout the year. All of them have been there to help raise the profile of the women's game. In recent times both The Express and Sport First published weekly columns devoted to women's football while The Times regularly reported on domestic and cup matches. 'ONtheBALL' is now the official women's football magazine and the FA will be launching a web-site and newsletter to complement its current promotional information. Other projects and initiatives have been outlined below:

### Women's Football Awareness Week

This was an awareness week the FA organised to raise the profile of women's football throughout the UK.

### Active Sports

Women's football has been chosen as one of the eight minority sports for the new lottery programme. Over £10 million is being invested into these programmes.

### Awards for All

A Sports Council Scheme that will fund new projects ranging from £500 to £5000.

### FA Charter Mark for clubs and schools.

This is a new FA kite-mark given to schools and clubs who meet set criteria. The plan encompasses local authority and Football in the Community and extends up to the highest levels within the women's game. Coaches Mentoring Scheme has also been adopted where 45 female coaches have been identified to work with Centres of Excellence, four of them are to work with the International Squads.

### Regional Women's Football Awards

The FA developed a number of awards to recognised good practice. Six regions will be awarded.

### UEFA Women's Conference

This was held in London for over 140 delegates from 44 Countries. The conference concentrated on a number of issues: Euro-Club Competition, UEFA U16's competition, and seedings review were just a few items on the agenda.

# AXA FA PREMIER LEAGUE CUP
## QUARTER FINALS
**Everton 5 v 0 Blyth Spartans**
Everton cheered up a disappointing league campaign by dismissing one of the top sides in the Northern Premier Division. The Kestrels held out for most of the first half but Everton moved into the semi-finals with ease.

**Whitehawk 2 v 0 Langford**
Two stunning volleys knocked out a strong Langfod side. Whitehawk dominated for most of the game and moved towards the Semi-finals where they meet Arsenal or Croydon.

**Tranmere W/O Garswood Rovers**
Tranmere didn't have to kick a ball to progress onto the semis of the League Cup. Garswood were unable to field a side due to illness and work commitments. Somewhat controversially, they were removed from the cup, as they failed to give the required 48 hours notice.

**Arsenal 1 v 0 Croydon**
A tough match for both teams saw a stalemate through to the 89th minute. The vital strike, taking Arsenal through to the semi-finals, came from Marianne Spacey.

## SEMI FINALS
**Whitehawk 1 v 4 Arsenal**
Whitehawk put up a spirited battle, matching Arsenal kick for kick for the first 35 minutes. Angela Banks, the newest England recruit, put Whitehawk ahead after three minutes. 'The Gunners' fought back and had netted four by the final whistle.

**Everton 2 v 1 Tranmere Rovers**
Everton were out to avenge their dismal display against Rovers prior to Christmas. Immediately, they asserted pressure on Tranmere. Two goals were scored, the first one by Marley for Everton, and this was followed by another four minutes later by Jones. Tranmere did managed to pull one goal back before the whistle.

## FINAL
**Everton 1 v 3 Arsenal**
The atmosphere at Prenton Park was electrifying and a good crowd of 3,074 added to the ambience. Several internationals were competing for the coveted title and both teams had a strong line-up.

In the opening minutes both teams shared the possession, but the game stepped up a gear when Everton's Tina Mapes headed in a goal from the near post. 'The Gunners', in their usual style, battled back and equalised when Claire Grant shot from close range.

Chances in the second half were plentiful, as Everton launched an early attack on Arsenal applying relentless pressure all over the pitch. Many chances were missed and it was Arsenal who broke the deadlock. Rachel Yankey broke through the Everton defence and tapped in the winner.

In the last few minutes Everton piled on the pressure and this created a hole in the defence and Spacey chipped the Everton keeper to seal Arsenal's victory.

**Everton:** Worrall, Mason, McGuinnan, Gore, Marley, Easton, Hill, McGrady, Kenwright, Jones, McDougall, Bertie. Subs: Ryde, Sandys, Jones.
**Arsenal:** Reed, Peeling, Wheatley, Slee, Harwood, White, Williams, Grant, Spacey, Lorton, Yankey. Subs: Few, Downham, Conlon, Mapes, Rockall.

# AXA F.A. WOMENS CUP

## QUARTER FINALS
**Southampton Saints 5 v 0 Sheffield Wednesday**
Southampton Saints cruised to victory. The Yorkshire side could have been first on the score sheet when the goalkeeper made an uncharacteristic mistake. After the initial attack of nerves, Southampton settled in to a more familiar pattern and achieved a comfortable win.

**Tranmere 5 v 1 Reading Royals**
Tranmere gained the first goal but the deficit was soon cancelled out when The Royals shot into the top corner of the net. The National Premier League side were too strong for the team from the Southern Premier League and soon Tranmere built up a score line of 5-1.

**Watford 1 v 5 Arsenal**
Watford battled and tackled the fast athletic forward line of Arsenal well, despite the absence of Yankey . Arsenal took the early lead, only for the score line to be levelled by a brilliant individual effort from Watford's young talent, Ray. Arsenal moved back in front and tightened the strangle hold during the second half and cruised to an easy victory.

**Doncaster Belles 2 v 0 Croydon**
When the game was eventually played, Belles beat Croydon in front of an impressive crowd. Both goals were scored within the first ten minutes.

## SEMI FINALS
**Doncaster Belles 0 v 2 Arsenal**
The clash of the Titans proved to be a much more profitable affair for 'The Gunners'. Although Doncaster had many attempts, they could not convert any of their chances. Reid, the Arsenal keeper, said 'it was the most I had to do all season'. Despite the fact Belles had more possession and shots, they were against the best passing side in the league. Arsenal finally profited with a goal late into the first half and another well into injury time.

**Southampton 2 v 1 Tranmere Rovers**
The Saints were marching to their first F.A Cup Final even though they found themselves 1-0 down after 22 minutes. A goal was clawed back by 'The Saints' and the second goal was scored when a free kick was conceded.

## FINAL
**Arsenal 2 v 0 Southampton** Attendance: 6,450
Gould (OG), Wheatley
This auspicious occasion was held at Charlton F.C's ground and this AXA Women's F.A. Cup Final saw the biggest ever crowd for a Women's match in England. The event had great media interest; it was televised live on Sky and Radio 5 Live broadcast it to the nation.

But for a superb cross by Anne Dimsdale in the 24th minute, Arsenal had little to fight for. The occasion appeared too great for Southampton Saints and the end result seemed never in doubt.

Saints had to wait until the second half before they carved out a shooting opportunity, but none of the chances tested the Arsenal keeper. The Arsenal attacks were unrelenting and shooting chances seem to be peppering the Southampton goal.

The final score line could have been embarrassing for Southampton. For Arsenal, it seemed to be a stroll in the park, with them rarely being put under pressure and seldom breaking out into a sweat, despite the intense heat of the first half. 'The Saints' were just over-awed by the grand occasion, but they will be stronger and wiser when the next opportunity arises.

**Arsenal** (3-5-2) Reed, White, Harwood, Slee, Pealling, Grant, Williams, Lorton, Wheatley, Spacey, Yankey, SUBS: Downham, Mapes, Rockall
**Southampton** (3-5-2) Beer, Short, Hayes, Armstrong, Beastly, Fisher, McArthur, Gould, Ritchie, Dimsdale, Stainer. SUBS: O'Brien, Poore, Langrish.

# AXA F.A WOMEN'S PREMIER LEAGUE

The Football Association unveiled insurance giants AXA as their new sponsors. The deal was worth a massive £25 million over four years. AXA, as a part of the deal, will be sponsoring the Women's F.A Cup and the Women's Premiere League.

The season lost none of its excitement as it started to draw to a close. Villa, in the Northern Division, held their nerve and were virtually home and dry. Whilst Whitehawk and Three Bridges were fading, Reading Royals, in the Southern Division, continued to impress and press for promotion. Croydon slowly eased ahead of Arsenal, by winning their games in hand to complete a brilliant League campaign.

The last games of the season were the most exciting the League had witnessed in years. In their penultimate game, Aston Villa equalised in the 75th minute to gain the valuable point they needed for promotion and to celebrate in style they beat Arnold Town 7-0 the following week. Reading Royals completed a remarkable achievement of promotion to the National Division in their first attempt. Their last game of the season was a tense affair; poised at 1-1, Reading needed to win but Whitehawk only needed a draw to be promoted into the top flight. Whitehawk looked victors when Reading won a controversial free kick on the edge of the eighteen-yard box one minute from time. The Royals converted the free kick and the final whistle followed ten seconds later.

Unbeaten all season, Croydon completed the job at Tranmere and cruised to The Championship by five goals to nil. They ended with nine wins in a row, having last dropped points in mid-December against Doncaster Belles. Bampton, the team captain, put their success down to team spirit, commitment and attitude.

To celebrate the end of the season AXA sponsored the first ever awards lunch in London. The celebration provided an opportunity to recognise those who have played an important part in raising the profile of women's football. Representatives from all Premier Leagues were invited and the awards were selected via a panel of experts.

| | | |
|---|---|---|
| **NATIONWIDE INTERNATIONAL PLAYER** | Sue Smith | Tranmere Rovers |
| **WALKERS YOUNG PLAYER** | Kate Chapman | Millwall |
| **PLAYER'S PLAYER** | | |
| **National Division** | Sue Smith | Tranmere Rovers |
| **Northern Division** | Kelly Biney | Sheffied Wednesday |
| **Southern Division** | Angela Banks | Whitehawk |
| **TOP SCORER** | | |
| **National Division** | Marianne Spacey | Arsenal 17 |
| **Northern Division** | Lucy Ward | Leeds Utd. 21 |
| **Southern Division** | Angela Banks | Whitehawk 19 |
| | Emma Mead | Whitehawk 19 |
| **UMBRO MOST IMPROVED TEAM** | Southampton Saints | |
| **THE TIMES/ON THE BALL SPECIAL ACHIEVEMENT AWARD** | Sylvia Gore | |

## TOP GOALSCORERS AXA PREMIER LEAGUE - 1998-99 SEASON

| National Division | | | Northern Division | | | Southern Division | | |
|---|---|---|---|---|---|---|---|---|
| 17 | Marianne Spacey | Arsenal | 21 | Lucy Ward | Leeds | | | |
| 13 | Carmaine Walker | Croydon | 18 | Natasha Masters | Aston villa | 19 | Angela Banks | Whitehawk |
| 13 | Karen Walker | Don. Belles | 16 | Claire Mitchell | Lee Utd | 19 | Emma Mead | Whitehawk |
| 13 | Rachel Yankey | Arsenal | 15 | Katy Ward | Aston Villa | 18 | Kerry Tagg | Three Brgs |
| 12 | Kelly Shimmin | Everton | 13 | Sarah Newbould | Shef. Wed. | 18 | | |
| 10 | Karen Burke | Everton | 12 | Jakki Knight | Leed Utd | 12 | Cathy Prowse | Reading |
| 9 | Jo Broadhurst | Croydon | 12 | Donna Lanaghan | Blth SK. | 11 | Ayala Liran | Reading |
| 9 | Justine Lorton | Arsenal | 12 | Michelle Shooter | Sheff. Wed. | 10 | Susannah Abbott | Reading |
| 9 | Tara Proctor | Croydon | | | | 9 | Sarah Standbury | Wimbledon |
| 9 | Sue Smith | Tranmere | | | | | | |

# FINAL LEAGUE TABLES 1998-99

| NATIONAL DIVISION | Pld | Pts |
|---|---|---|
| Croydon | 18 | 46 |
| Arsenal | 18 | 43 |
| Doncaster Belles | 18 | 32 |
| Everton | 18 | 32 |
| Tranmere Rovers | 18 | 27 |
| Liverpool | 18 | 20 |
| Southampton Saints | 18 | 18 |
| Millwall Lionesses | 18 | 15 |
| Bradford City | 18 | 10 |
| Ilkeston Town | 18 | 8 |

| NORTHERN DIVISION | Pld | Pts |
|---|---|---|
| Aston Villa | 18 | 45 |
| Blythe Spartans | 18 | 37 |
| Leeds United | 18 | 32 |
| Wolverhampton Wanderers | 18 | 32 |
| Sheffied Wednesday | 18 | 31 |
| Garswood Saints | 18 | 29 |
| Berkhampstead Town | 18 | 22 |
| Coventry City | 18 | 10 |
| Huddersfield City | 18 | 9 |
| Arnold Town | 18 | 6 |

| SOUTHERN DIVISION | Pld | Pts |
|---|---|---|
| Reading Royals | 18 | 41 |
| Whitehawk | 18 | 39 |
| Three Bridges | 18 | 35 |
| Brighton and Hove Albion | 18 | 33 |
| Wimbleden | 18 | 28 |
| Barry Town | 18 | 26 |
| Langford | 18 | 23 |
| Barnet | 18 | 15 |
| Leyton Orient | 18 | 11 |
| Ipswich | 18 | 6 |

# WOMEN'S PYRAMID OF FOOTBALL 1998-99

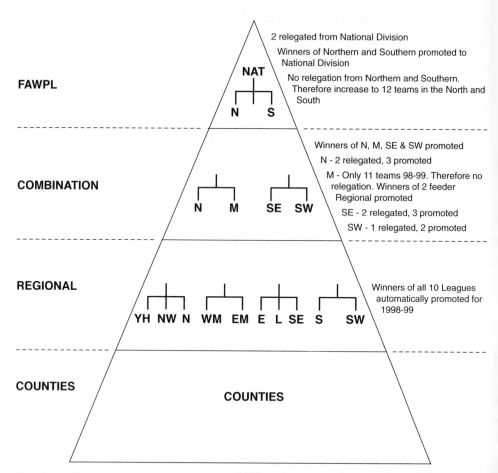

FAWPL — NAT — N  S
2 relegated from National Division
Winners of Northern and Southern promoted to National Division
No relegation from Northern and Southern. Therefore increase to 12 teams in the North and South

COMBINATION — N  M   SE  SW
Winners of N, M, SE & SW promoted
N - 2 relegated, 3 promoted
M - Only 11 teams 98-99. Therefore no relegation. Winners of 2 feeder Regional promoted
SE - 2 relegated, 3 promoted
SW - 1 relegated, 2 promoted

REGIONAL — YH NW N   WM EM E   L SE S   SW
Winners of all 10 Leagues automatically promoted for 1998-99

COUNTIES — COUNTIES

## NORTHERN COMBINATION

| | Pld | Pts |
|---|---|---|
| Bangor City | 22 | 59 |
| Stockport LFC | 22 | 46 |
| Oldham Athletic | 22 | 45 |
| Middlesbrough | 22 | 43 |
| Manchester United | 22 | 40 |
| Chester le Street | 22 | 26 |
| Doncaster Rovers | 22 | 26 |
| Preston North End | 22 | 21 |
| Blackburn Rovers | 22 | 20 |
| Sunderland | 22 | 20 |
| Scunthorpe United | 22 | 19 |
| York City | 22 | 0 |

## YORKSHIRE & HUMBERSIDE
### Premier Division

| | Pld | Pts |
|---|---|---|
| Leeds City Vixens | 14 | 42 |
| Barnsley | 14 | 31 |
| AFC Preston | 14 | 29 |
| Grimsby Town | 14 | 17 |
| Selby Town | 14 | 17 |
| Sheffield Hallam | 14 | 10 |
| Brighouse | 14 | 9 |
| Hull City | 14 | 8 |

## NORTH WEST
### Premier Division

| | Pld | Pts |
|---|---|---|
| Blackpool Wren Rvrs | 18 | 45 |
| Manchester City | 18 | 44 |
| Trafford | 18 | 34 |
| Chester City | 18 | 30 |
| Liverpool District | 18 | 25 |
| Liverpool Hope Feds | 18 | 21 |
| Wigan | 18 | 21 |
| Bolton LAFC | 18 | 15 |
| Bury | 18 | 12 |
| Newsham PH | 18 | 8 |

## NORTHERN

| | Pld | Pts |
|---|---|---|
| Newcastle | 24 | 60 |
| Carlisle Wanderers | 24 | 53 |
| Blyth Spartans K Res | 24 | 51 |
| Killingsworth YP | 24 | 45 |
| Darlington | 24 | 42 |
| Boldon | 24 | 35 |
| Middlesbrough Res | 24 | 34 |
| Guisborough | 24 | 31 |
| Sedgefield Borough | 24 | 27 |
| Workington Reds | 24 | 27 |
| Northumbria University | 24 | 25 |
| South Tyneside | 24 | 13 |
| Newton Aycliffe | 24 | 1 |

## MIDLANDS COMBINATION

| | Pld | Pts |
|---|---|---|
| Birmingham City | 20 | 50 |
| Newcastle Town | 20 | 45 |
| Mansfield Town | 20 | 44 |
| Highfield Rangers | 20 | 37 |
| Derby County | 20 | 32 |
| Chesterfield | 20 | 30 |
| Shrewsbury Town | 20 | 25 |
| Kilnhurst | 20 | 22 |
| Rea Valley Rovers | 20 | 18 |
| Bloxwich Town | 20 | 14 |
| Stratford | 20 | 4 |

## WEST MIDLANDS
### Premier Division

| | Pld | Pts |
|---|---|---|
| Telford United | 16 | 43 |
| Lichfield Diamonds | 16 | 42 |
| Hereford United | 16 | 35 |
| Tipton Town | 16 | 24 |
| Birmingham City Res | 16 | 18 |
| Worcester City | 16 | 17 |
| Banbury United | 16 | 14 |
| Willenhall Town | 16 | 12 |
| Coventry City Res | 16 | 9 |

## EAST MIDLANDS
### Premier Division

| | Pld | Pts |
|---|---|---|
| Worksop Town | 16 | 43 |
| Peterborough United | 15 | 37 |
| leicester City | 17 | 32 |
| Leicester Vixens | 16 | 28 |
| Chesterfield Res | 18 | 20 |
| Nettleham | 18 | 20 |
| Tamworth | 14 | 16 |
| Nottingham Forest | 15 | 15 |
| Belper Town | 18 | 15 |
| Derby City | 15 | 3 |

Olympia have withdrawn

## SOUTH EASTERN COMBINATION

| | Pld | Pts |
|---|---|---|
| Wembley Mill Hill | 22 | 64 |
| Chelsea | 22 | 53 |
| Hampton | 22 | 49 |
| Canary Racers | 22 | 45 |
| Bedford Bells | 22 | 34 |
| Charlton Athletic | 22 | 28 |
| Enfield | 22 | 27 |
| Clapton | 22 | 26 |
| Northampton Tn & Co | 22 | 25 |
| Crowborough Athletic | 22 | 21 |
| Walkern | 22 | 9 |
| Hassocks | 22 | 3 |

## EASTERN
### Premier Division

| | Pld | Pts |
|---|---|---|
| HP Needham Market | 18 | 52 |
| Chelmsford City | 18 | 44 |
| UG Sports | 18 | 44 |
| Colchester United | 18 | 26 |
| Luton | 18 | 23 |
| Colchester LFC | 18 | 22 |
| Statham Rangers | 18 | 20 |
| Suffolk Bluebirds | 18 | 18 |
| Norwich United | 18 | 8 |
| Bishops Stortford | 18 | 3 |

## GREATER LONDON
### Premier Division

| | Pld | Pts |
|---|---|---|
| Watford | 16 | 48 |
| Fulham | 16 | 39 |
| Tottenham Hotspur | 16 | 37 |
| Tesco Country Club | 16 | 27 |
| Barking | 16 | 21 |
| Queens Park Rangers | 16 | 15 |
| London WFC | 16 | 14 |
| Newham | 16 | 6 |

| | | |
|---|---|---|
| Romford | 16 | 4 |

## SOUTH EAST COUNTIES
### Premier Division

| | Pld | Pts |
|---|---|---|
| Abbey Rangers | 18 | 47 |
| Crawley (Oakwood) | 18 | 45 |
| Woking | 18 | 35 |
| Gillingham | 18 | 27 |
| Eastbourne | 18 | 26 |
| Sutton United | 18 | 24 |
| Maidstone United | 18 | 21 |
| Malling | 18 | 19 |
| Farnborough Town | 18 | 12 |
| Redhill | 18 | 3 |

## SOUTH WESTERN COMBINATION

| | Pld | Pts |
|---|---|---|
| Cardiff County | 22 | 53 |
| Bristol Rovers | 22 | 49 |
| Swindon Town | 22 | 43 |
| Cheltenham | 22 | 42 |
| Oxford United | 22 | 37 |
| Denham United | 22 | 34 |
| Portsmouth | 22 | 30 |
| Saltash Pilgrims | 22 | 29 |
| Sherborne | 22 | 28 |
| Bristol City | 22 | 18 |
| Bath City | 22 | 17 |
| Swindon Spitfires | 22 | 0 |

## SOUTHERN
### Premier Division

| | Pld | Pts |
|---|---|---|
| Southampton WFC | 20 | 53 |
| Launton | 20 | 44 |
| Binfield | 20 | 42 |
| Bracknell Town | 20 | 40 |
| Gosport Borough | 20 | 39 |
| Basingstoke Town | 20 | 21 |
| Ringwood Town | 19 | 21 |
| Horndean | 20 | 19 |
| Leighton Linslade | 19 | 19 |
| Wycombe Wanderers | 20 | 15 |
| Thame United | 20 | 0 |

## SOUTH WEST
### Premier Division

| | Pld | Pts |
|---|---|---|
| Newport Strikers | 16 | 48 |
| Frome Sportshouse | 16 | 35 |
| Elmore Eagles | 16 | 29 |
| Truro City | 16 | 23 |
| Clevedon | 16 | 21 |
| Barnstaple Town | 16 | 13 |
| Freeway | 16 | 13 |
| Newton Abbot | 16 | 10 |
| Bristol WFC | 16 | 5 |

# WOMEN'S WORLD CUP

'The future is definitely, definitely feminine' said the FIFA president and the World Cup in America will show to the world, just how good women's football is.

The Women's World Cup was seen to be a world wide spectacle, ticket sales a year before kick off already surpassed the 115,000 mark, these pre-match sales are more than the total sold for the last Women's World Cup in Sweden in 1995.

The World Cup when it began in June did not disappoint. The audience figures exceeded all expectations. Over 700,000 tickets were sold and over 1 billion people watched the games on T.V. The opening ceremony was broadcast to millions world wide and top celebrities, including the US President attended many of the games.

The grand final, with an attendance figure of 90,185, was the largest crowd ever, across all sports, to watch a women's sporting event and the most watched soccer game in US TV history. The US men, in participating in three games in the 1998 World Cup, did not approach the US women's appeal this year.

The final was played in soaring temperatures and the two teams displayed talent never seen before, by women, on a world stage. At the end of 90 minutes China and the USA were 0-0, after extra-time the two teams could not be separated. After bagging two penalties apiece, Scurry saved a penalty from Liu Ling. The USA netted their remaining penalties and the wall to wall crowds and the nation erupted.

## TABLES AND STANDINGS

### GROUP A

| TEAM | W | D | L | GF | GA | PTS |
|------|---|---|---|----|----|-----|
| US | 3 | 0 | 0 | 13 | 1 | 9 |
| Nigeria | 2 | 0 | 1 | 5 | 8 | 6 |
| N.Korea | 1 | 0 | 2 | 4 | 6 | 3 |
| Denmark | 0 | 0 | 3 | 1 | 8 | 0 |

### GROUP B

| TEAM | W | D | L | GF | GA | PTS |
|------|---|---|---|----|----|-----|
| Brazil | 2 | 1 | 0 | 12 | 4 | 7 |
| Germany | 1 | 2 | 0 | 10 | 4 | 5 |
| Italy | 1 | 1 | 1 | 3 | 3 | 4 |
| Mexico | 0 | 0 | 3 | 1 | 15 | 0 |

### GROUP C

| TEAM | W | D | L | GF | GA | PTS |
|------|---|---|---|----|----|-----|
| Norway | 3 | 0 | 0 | 13 | 2 | 9 |
| Russia | 2 | 0 | 1 | 10 | 3 | 6 |
| Canada | 0 | 1 | 2 | 3 | 12 | 1 |
| Japan | 0 | 1 | 2 | 1 | 10 | 1 |

### GROUP D

| TEAM | W | D | L | GF | GA | PTS |
|------|---|---|---|----|----|-----|
| China | 3 | 0 | 0 | 12 | 2 | 9 |
| Sweden | 2 | 0 | 1 | 6 | 3 | 6 |
| Australia | 0 | 1 | 2 | 1 | 10 | 1 |
| Ghana | 0 | 1 | 2 | 1 | 10 | 1 |

### QUARTER-FINALS

| | | | | |
|---|---|---|---|---|
| China | 2 | v | 0 | Russia |
| Norway | 3 | v | 1 | Sweden |
| USA | 3 | v | 2 | Germany |
| Brazil | 4 | v | 3 | Nigeria |

### SEMI-FINALS

| | | | | |
|---|---|---|---|---|
| China | 5 | v | 0 | Norway |
| USA | 2 | v | 0 | Brazil |

### FINAL

| | | | | |
|---|---|---|---|---|
| USA | 0 | v | 0 | China |

USA won on penalties AET

# INTERNATIONAL FOOTBALL

## SENIOR SQUAD

The 1998/99 season was a year of reflection and consolidation after narrowly missing out on the chance to compete in the World Cup in the USA. Despite the lack of competitive International matches this year, two of our prolific Internationals were gaining notable acclaim.

Kelly Smith, who plays her domestic soccer in America, was named 1998 BIG EAST Women's Soccer Offensive Player of the Year for the second time. The England forward is the nation's top scorer with a 3.37 game average (goals/assists).

Sue Smith's domestic performances for Tranmere this year have earned her a place amongst the FIFA World X! All Stars Team. Smith had to fly out to America to compete against the Olympic Champions in the Spartan Stadium, San Jose, in front of a 16.000 strong crowd.

## Romania    1    v    4    England

The season ahead was full of training and friendlies to unite old and new international players. The first International came in November against Romania. Hope Powell packed the midfield making it very difficult for the home team to gain possession. The constant applied pressure allowed England to score. Rachel Yankey headed the ball into the net, after Sue Smith crossed a precision ball from the by-line. Sue Smith, one of the outstanding talents in the England team, deservedly scored another goal for England on the stroke of half time.

Romania's fortunes did not change when they came out for the second half, and England scored immediately after the kick off. Karen Walker connected with Rachel Yankey's cross to make it 3-0 and assert their dominance on the game. The fourth goal for England came after 58 minutes when Sue Smith, crossed another superbly timed ball, for Karen Walker to head home. Three substitutions were made helping the debutantes gain much needed international experience. The Romanians scored the final goal of the match, when a dubious penalty was awarded.

**Team:** Pauline Cope, Becky Easton, Sue Smith, Danielle Murphy, Maureen Marley, Gillain Coultard, Karen Burke, Sammy Britton, Karen Walker, Sian Williams, Rachel Yankey.SUBS: Natasha Daley, Joanne Broadhurst, Sarah Reed

## England    2    v    1    Romania

The return match, although not packed with goals, proved to be another emphatic performance by the home side. The score line was somewhat deceiving, as England had 33 shots at goal, fifteen on target, but the Romanian keeper had an outstanding game, making some fantastic saves to make the score line a respectable one for the opposition.

Karen Walker netted another crossed ball and celebrated in style in front of more than 1500 supporters. Despite the pressure and possession England had, Romania scored the equalising goal after 31 minutes. The pressure remained and England took a well-deserved lead after 55 minutes when Joanne Broadhust scored with a well-worked free kick.

**Team:** Pauline Cope, Becky Easton, Sue Smith, Danielle Murphy, Maureen Marley, Gillian Coultard, Karen Burke, Sammy Britton, Karen Walker, Jo Broadhurst, Rachel Yankey  SUBS: Faye White, Tara Proctor, Justine Lorton

## Italy    4    v    1    England

Their first international of '99 saw England fly out to Bologna under the new sponsors Nationwide.

England had enjoyed a training session on the eve before the match. This was to be Italy's final game before they headed to the World Cup Finals in the US and they were ready and prepared to face England, who had very little match preparation.

The Italians were outstanding; their passing was clinical and their movement off the ball was something to savour. England were struggling with the talented Italians and, as the referee stopped play so frequently, there was little fluency to the game. After 20 minutes in the soaring heat of Bologna, Italy struck the first blow. Antonella Carta, one of the world's finest players, headed home an easy goal after she was left unmarked. The second duly followed when another dubious decision allowed the Italians to convert their free kick and Carta celebrated to the home crowd. The pattern soon emerged, although the Italians were ahead in the possession stakes; two more goals followed both of them from free kicks in equally dubious circumstances. Half time came just as England had upped the tempo.

A more composed display by England in the second half provided the opportunity for Hope Powell, England's coach, to give two players their England debut, Angela Banks and Julie Fletcher. Banks nearly got on the score sheet but the rebounded header went just over the cross bar.

Gillian Coultard (capt), one of England's best players, chipped the ball over the defence and Angela Banks raced after the ball as the keeper charged out to block the shot. A penalty was given, to mocking applause, and Karen Walker netted the fifth dubious goal of the game.

**Team:** Brown, Reed, White, Easton, Spacey, Lorton, Coultard, Marley, Fletcher, Burke, Britton, Murphy, Smith, Yankey, Banks: SUBS: Willoughby, Shimmin

# UNDER 18 SQUAD

With the absence of the senior squad from the world's most prestigious tournament, The World Cup, the attention had been focused on the U18 national squad seeking to qualify for the Quarter Finals of the European U18 Championships.

### Holland 1 v 1 England

At the new Britannia Stadium the two teams began their campaign nervously. After ten minutes England won a free kick, but the goal was thwarted by an outstanding save from the Dutch keeper, Bottema. The deadlock was broken when the Dutch side won a penalty, which was converted to make the score line 1-0. England applied relentless pressure and gained their reward after 69 minutes when Rahman slotted the ball into the centre of the goal. The home side pushed for a victory but to no avail and the score remained 1-1.

### England 5 v 0 Republic of Ireland

Realising the need for goals, England asserted their authority on the game and Kate Chapman was the first one to break the deadlock for the home side. At half time the score remained the same and it was left to England to add to their tally in the second half, Danielle Murphy driving the ball in off the left post. On 67 minutes, Casey Stone scored from fifteen meters out. Another soon followed when Amanda Barr headed the ball over the Irish keeper. The fifth goal came when a speculative cross was converted. A number of substitutions followed and England cruised to a 5-0 win.

### England 7 v 0 Faroe Islands

The quarter-finals were within reach and their only obstacle was the Faroe Islands. Their desire was noticeable from the first minute but it took 32 minutes before Amanda Barr scored the first goal. Rachel Unitt score just before half time, when the keeper allowed the ball to slip through her fingers to make the score 2-0.

Only eighteen seconds of the second half had passed and the home team scored another goal, Amanda Barr added to England's tally. In the 51st minute it was 4-0; Amanda Willoughby attacked the ball from 12 meters and hammered in the goal. After a number of substitutions, the sixth goal was scored in the 72nd minute and during injury time the final goal made the scoreline an impressive 7-0 and England moved on to the quarter finals.

### England 3 v 0 Finland  Friendly

The last match allowed Hope Powell to try out her young charges before the very important quarter-final clash against Norway. The young side was impressive and some of the accomplished players, Chapman, Murphy, Shimmin and Barr, were self-assured and comfortable in the national uniform. The first goal came from a set piece on 20 minutes, Shimmin delivered a precision cross for Chapman to head home. Shimmin added to the score line after 35 minutes and Barr scored the final goal in the penalty box, poking the ball into the net.

# U18 EUROPEAN CHAMPIONSHIP
## QUARTER-FINALS

1st Leg  Norway 3 v 1 England

The match was going to be a difficult prospect for Hope Powell's young talent. After only five minutes Norway landed the first blow, Kaurin lobbing over the English keeper form the edge of the box. Shimmin continued to impress and she rounded the Norweign defence, only to be brought down by the keeper. A penalty was awarded and duly converted. With the score line poised at 1-1 until the 75th minute, Norway broke the stalemate and converted a goal, and another followed four minutes from time.

2nd Leg  England 0 v 1 Norway

England bowed out of the championship after narrowly losing to Norway 0-1. Facing a deficit of 1-3 from the first leg, England had to be on top form. The uneven surface at the Sofiemyr Stadium, just outside Oslo, proved to be a telling factor for both teams. England held firm for 37 minutes, but were unable to clear a bouncing ball and the ball went into the net over Rachel Brown's head. England competed with grit and determination throughout the game but they were not able to claw back the deficit. In the second half both teams tired and the game finished 1-0 to the Norwegians.

# U16 SQUAD

The new England U16 team took its first steps in April after a series of regional trials had taken place. A summer training session awaits the successful trialists and their first competition will take place soon after in Ireland.

# WIRRAL PROGRAMME CLUB
The non-profit making Club formed in March 1967
**Secretary:** I.R.W. Runham
3 Tansley Close, Newton, West Kirby, Wirral CH48 9XH   Tel: 0151 625 9554

### 24th NON-LEAGUE FOOTBALL PROGRAMME OF THE YEAR SURVEY 1997-98

Things did not run as smoothly as I had hoped whilst I was away in New Zealand, hence the delay in the results of this season's survey. Despite rumours circulating certain parts of the country that the survey was not taking place this season, entries were received from 1120 clubs, just eleven down on the previous season. With reserve and youth programmes there were 1192 places, down ten on last season.

Again there were many superb programmes with numerous clubs showing improvement on last season. It is again pleasing to see clubs issuing for the first time plus some after a gap of many years. ALL clubs that issue a programme are to be congratulated, a single sheet is better than nothing. There would be no programmes without the hard work that the editors and any helpers they can find put in, I'm sure most supporters and many committee member s do not realise the time and effort needed to produce a programme so our special thanks go to all these people. I must also thank all those who sent in programmes for the survey and helped to spread the word, the clubs themselves, their supporters, our members, other collectors, the Football Association, all the League Secretaries, the Non League Club Directory, Team Talk, the Football Traveller, Welsh Football and all those who lent us some programmes. Sincere apologies to anyone inadvertently omitted.

Some clubs only issue for a Saturday game, some for special games, some change their style, content, price, editor, etc, during the season; some have special connections with printers, etc., and often we are not aware of these circumstances. Obviously we can only survey the programmes we receive. Some are from early in the season, others from just before the closing date, most from in between. The results always create a lot of interest with varying points being expressed; some of these we hear second or third hand but most miss our ears, so if you have any comments on the survey please let us know. I am sure the day will never come when there is complete agreement over the results, but the more discussion there is over the survey the better, as it will keep programmes to the forefront and hopefully encourage clubs at least to maintain or even improve the standards, and better still it may encourage more clubs to issue next season.

The club with the overall winning programme will receive a framed certificate; the winners of each league will also receive a certificate. Please note the programmes have been surveyed, not as many assume voted upon. Marks were awarded to each programme as follows (the maximum marks available in each section are given):
**Cover** 15 (design 10, match details 5),   **Page size** 10,   **Team layout and position** within the programme 10,
**Results** 10, **League tables** 10, **Price** 15, **Pictures** 15, **Printing and paper quality** 20, **Frequency of issue** 20,
**Value for money** 20 (this takes into account the ratio of adverts to content, the club's league etc),
**Contents** 105 (other than those listed) taking into account their relevance to the club, its league, environs etc, the size of the print used, the spacing between the lines, the size of the margins, and if the contents are original or reproduced (from League Bulletins, newspapers, magazines etc).
To gain full marks in the Frequency of issue section we needed to receive programmes from ten different current season matches for each team entered (allowances were made if ten home games were not played by the closing date and we were informed of this). The minimum entry was one programme.
As many programmes varied from issue to issue all the programmes received were surveyed, the marks in each section totalled and divided by the number of issues to get the final mark for each section, the marks from each section were then being totalled to get the final score.
A new standard of marks is set each season so this campaign's totals should not be compared with those of earlier seasons as the comparison will almost certainly be inaccurate; a programme identical to last season's will almost certainly have gained different marks.

We have already received many entries for the Specials section of the survey (for one-offs, big cup ties, friendlies, testimonials, charity matches, etc), and the closing date for receiving these is 30th June 1999. To receive the results, expected by the end of July, we would appreciate it if you could send a stamped sae. Thank you.

The results of this season's survey are as follows:

| **Best Non-League Programme Nationally 1997-98** | **1st** | Denaby United | 199 points |
| | **2nd** | Hoddesdon Town | 192 points |
| | **3rd** | Evans & Williams Sports | 191 points |

**NATIONAL TOP 30: 1** Denaby Utd 199;   **2** Hoddesdon T 192;   **3** Evans & Williams Sp 191;   **4=** Northwood, Portishead 180;   **6=** Aldershot T, Langney Sp 179;   **8** Dagenham & Redbridge 175;   **9** St Leonards 173; **10** Hayes 171;   **11** Woking 169;   **12** Norcross & Warbreck Res 168;   **13=** Kidderminster Harriers, Newton Abbot Spurs, Poole T, Reading T 166;   **17=** Lancing, Pelsall Villa 165;   **19** Willenhall T 164;   **20** Hucknall T   163; **21** Norcross & Warbreck 162;   **22=** Cwmtllery, Folkestone Invicta 161;   **24** Witney T 160;   **25=** Bridlington T, Rylands, Uxbridge, Yateley Green 157;   **29** Blackfield & Langley 156;   **30** East Preston 155

INDIVIDUAL LEAGUE RESULTS The first number after the club's name is the number of programmes received - 10 shows ten or more different programmes were received, or every programme if less than ten matches were played, the second number is the total points gained. The leagues are in no particular order.

| LEAGUE + No of entries | | | FIRST | SECOND | THIRD |
|---|---|---|---|---|---|
| Vauxhall Conference | | 21 | Hayes 10-171 | Woking 10-169 | Kidderminster Harriers 1-166 |
| Dr Martens | Overall | 58 | St Leonards 10-173 | Folkestone Invicta 10-161 | Witney Town 10-160 |
| | Prem Div | 21 | Bath City 10-150 | Tamworth 10-148 | Worcester City 10-143 |
| | Mid Div | 21 | Solihull Borough 1-153 | Stourbridge 10-145 | Hinckley United 1-138 |
| | Sth Div | 16 | St Leonards 10-173 | Folkestone Invicta 10-161 | Witney Town 10-160 |
| Rymans | Overall | 78 | Northwood 10-180 | Aldershot Town 10-179 | Dagenham & Redbridge 10-175 |
| | Prem Div | 22 | Aldershot Town 10-179 | Dagenham & Redbridge 10-175 | Bishops Stortford 10-154 |
| | Div One | 21 | Uxbridge 10-157 | Wealdstone 10-153 | Barton Rovers 10-136 |
| | Div Two | 22 | Northwood 10-180 | Harlow Town 10-145 | Wivenhoe Town 1-135 |
| | Div Three | 13 | Camberley Town 1-134 | Lewes 10-130 | Epsom & Ewell 1-128 |
| Unibond | Overall | 43 | Hucknall Town 10-163 | Bradford Park Avenue 10-151 | Blyth Spartans 10-148 |
| | Prem Div | 21 | Blyth Spartans 10-148 | Spennymoor Utd 10-132 | Bamber Bridge 10-124 |
| | Div One | 22 | Hucknall Town 10-163 | Bradford Park Avenue 10-151 | Stocksbridge PS 2-121 |
| Minerva | Overall | 50 | Hoddesdon Town 10-192 | Arlesey Town 10-144 | Cockfosters 10-138 |
| Spartan | Prem Div | 21 | Hoddesdon Town 10-192 | Arlesey Town 10-144 | Beaconsfield SYCOB 10-133 |
| South | Sen Div | 20 | Cockfosters 10-138 | Tring Athletic 10-120 | Leverstock Green 10-111 |
| Midlands | Div One | 9 | Newport Athletic 1-80 | Old Dunstablians 19-73 | Kent Athletic 1-67 |
| Courage Combined Co | | 16 | Reading Town 10-166 | Walton Casuals 10-146 | Ash United 10-133 |
| Winstonlead Kent | | 15 | Slade Green 10-128 | Canterbury City 10-126 | Whitstable Town 1-121 |
| Schweppes Essex Senior | | 10 | Concord Rangers= 10-109 / Hullbridge Sports= 10-109 | | Brentwood 1-101 |
| Unijet | Overall | 35 | Langney Sports 10-179 | Lancing 10-165 | East Preston 10-155 |
| Sussex | Div One | 13 | Langney Sports 10-179 | East Preston 10-155 | Horsham YMCA 1-133 |
| County | Div Two | 12 | Lancing 10-165 | Three Bridges 1-134 | Southwick 1-122 |
| | Div Three | 10 | Ifield 10-130 | Westfield 10-129 | Oving Social 10-121 |
| Jewson Wessex | | 14 | Brockenhurst 10-129 | Thatcham Town 10-114 | Cowes Sports 1-112 |
| Wessex Combination | | 3 | Blackfield & L Res 5-139 | Weymouth Res 7-89 | Bournemouth Res 2-62 |
| Keyline Dorset Combination | | 5 | Wareham Rangers 10-130 | Weymouth Sports 1-103 | Gillingham Town 1-60 |
| Dorset | | 3 | Dorchester YMCA 3-80 | Moreton 1-70 | Dorchester United 1-53 |
| Jewson | Overall | 24 | Sudbury Town 10-151 | Mildenhall Town 10-148 | Felixstowe Port & Town 10-137 |
| Eastern | Prem Div | 13 | Sudbury Town 10-151 | Felixstowe Port & Town 10-137 | Lowestoft Town 10-134 |
| Counties | Div One | 11 | Mildenhall Town 10-148 | Downham Town 10-135 | Thetford Town 1-117 |
| Gloucestershire County | | 6 | Highridge United 1-132 | Tytherington Rocks 10-123 | Brockworth 8-102 |
| Somerset Senior | | 3 | Portishead 10-180 | Oldland Abbotonians 1-73 | Robinsons 2-59 |
| Middlesex County | | 4 | Willesden Constantine 1-77 | Ealing Shamrock 2-63 | Northfield CAV 1-55 |
| Hampshire | Overall | 36 | Poole Town 10-166 | Yateley Green 10-157 | Blackfield & Langley 10-156 |
| | Div One | 12 | Poole Town 10-166 | Blackfield & Langley 10-156 | Colden Common 10-150 |
| | Div Two | 11 | Yateley Green 10-157 | Queens Keep 10-109 | Winchester Castle 1-106 |
| | Div Three | 13 | Amesbury Town 10-136 | Farnborough North End 10-124 | Four Marks 10-111 |
| Hampshire Combination | | 4 | Colden Common Res 10-146 | Co-op Sports Res 10-85 | Clanfield Res 3-76 |
| Skurrays Wiltshire | | 5 | Minety 10-140 | Purton Res 10-97 | Purton 'A' 2-82 |
| Screwfix | Overall | 35 | Torrington 10-151 | Paulton Rovers 10-133 | Mangotsfield United 10-128 |
| Direct | Prem Div | 17 | Paulton Rovers 10-133 | Mangotsfield United 10-128 | Backwell United 1-118 |
| Western | Div One | 18 | Torrington 10-151 | Street 1-118 | Heavitree United 1-94 |
| Westward Dev Western | | 12 | Newton Abbot Spurs 10-166 | Stoke Gabriel 10-123 | Crediton United 10-108 |
| South Devon | | 3 | Brixham United 10-130 | Brixham United Res 10-124 | Kingsteignton Athletic 1-93 |
| Devon & Exeter | | 6 | Buckland Athletic 10-120 | Exeter Civil Service 1-106 | Sidmouth Town 1-82 |
| Jewson South Western | | 7 | Saltash United 10-106 | Truro City 1-99 | St Blazey 1-91 |
| Jolly's Cornwall Combination | | 4 | Marazion Blues 7-76 | Goonhaven 1-67 | Mousehole 1-51 |
| Cherry Red | Overall | 17 | Penn & Tylers Green 10-148 | Penn & T Green Res 10-141 | Eton Wick 10-127 |
| Chiltonian | Prem Div | 10 | Penn & Tylers Green 10-148 | Eton Wick 10-127 | Rayners Lane 10-110 |
| | Divs 1 & 2 | 7 | Penn & Tylers G Res 10-141 | Englefield Green Res 1-100 | Englefield Green 1-97 |
| Complete | Overall | 21 | Burnham= 10-151 / Swindon Supermarine 10-151 | | Banbury United 10-113 |
| Musis | | | | | |
| Hellenic | Prem Div | 15 | Burnham= 10-151 / Swindon Supermarine 10-151 | | Banbury United 10-113 |
| | Div One | 6 | Purton 10-107 | Watlington Town 1-105 | Ardley United 1-97 |
| uhlsport | Overall | 18 | Northampton Spencer 2-138 | Eynesbury Rovers 10-137 | Yaxley 1-136 |
| United | Prem Div | 15 | Northampton Spencer 2-138 | Eynesbury Rovers 10-137 | Yaxley 1-136 |
| Counties | Div One | 3 | Bugbrooke St Michael 1-88 | Woodford United 1-79 | Thrapston Town 1-51 |
| Herts Senior County | | 4 | Sun Postal Sports 1-109 | Kings Langley 10-93 | Hatfield Town 1-90 |
| Channel Islands | | 4 | Belgrave Wanderers 10-114 | Sylvans 2-84 | St Peters 10-83 |
| Essex Intermediate | | 4 | Sandon Royals 10-130 | Sandon Royals Res 10-125 | Laindon Athletic 6-96 |
| Longwell | Overall | 10 | Attleborough 10-132 | Beccles Town 10-117 | East Harling 8-113 |
| Blake | Prem Div | 4 | Attleborough 10-132 | Acle United 1-109 | Wymondham Town 1-102 |
| Anglian | Div One | 3 | Beccles Town 10-117 | Loddon United 1-69 | Bungay Town 1-57 |
| Combination | Other Divs | 3 | East Harling 8-113 | East Harling Res 2-95 | Saham Toney 1-83 |
| Redferns | Overall | 32 | Mickleover Sports 10-154 | Lincoln Moorlands 1-141 | Hucknall Rolls 1-133 |
| Central | Sup Div | 17 | Mickleover Sports 10-154 | Hucknall Rolls 1-133 | Sandiacre Town 1-131 |
| Midlands | Prem Div | 15 | Lincoln Moorlands 1-141 | Selston 1-128 | Teversal Grange 1-90 |
| Interlink Ex Mid Alliance | | 15 | Pelsall Villa 10-165 | Willenhall Town 10-164 | Shifnal Town 10-149 |
| Springbank Vending Mid | | 5 | Eccleshall 10-121 | Brocton 8-119 | Stone Dominoes 1-95 |
| Endsleigh | Overall | 34 | Alvechurch 1-127 | Alvis 10-124 | Bolehall Swifts 10-112 |
| Insurance | Prem Div | 19 | Alvechurch 1-127 | Bolehall Swifts 10-112 | Kenilworth Town 1-100 |
| Midland | Div One | 6 | Alvis 10-124 | Hams Hall 5-104 | Blackheath Electrodirve 1-102 |
| Combination | Div Two | 5 | Earlswood Town 1-91 | Brownhills Town 1-84 | Kenilworth Wardens 1-81 |
| | Div Three | 4 | Barnt Green Spartak 1-82 | Burman Hi-ton 1-77 | MCL Claines 1-62 |

**Block 1**

| | | | | | | | | |
|---|---|---|---|---|---|---|---|---|
| Banks | Overall | 18 | Star | 1-108 | Shifnal Town Res | 10-107 | Ludlow Town | 2-97 |
| Brewery | Prem Div | 12 | Star | 1-108 | Ludlow Town | 2-97 | Westfields | 10-88 |
| | Div One N, S | 6 | Shifnal Town Res | 10-107 | Causeway United | 1-85 | Wolverhampton Town | 1-64 |
| Powerleague Notts Alliance | | 6 | Rainworth MW | 10-130 | Retford United | 1-109 | Nottm Police | 1-101 |
| Everards Brewery Leics | | 12 | Coalville Town | 4-139 | Oadby Town | 1-109 | Thurnby Rangers | 1-97 |
| Lincolnshire | | 3 | Sleaford Town | 10-115 | Horncastle Town | 1-101 | Barton Town Old Boys | 3-90 |
| Green C S Mid Cheshire | | 4 | Rylands | 10-157 | Rylands Res | 1-140 | Middlewich Town | 1-68 |
| Carlsberg | Over4all | 8 | New Brighton | 10-115 | Poulton Victoria | 1-86 | Capenhurst Villa | 7-82 |
| West | Div One | 3 | Poulton Victoria | 1-86 | Capenhurst Villa | 7-82 | Mond Rangers | 1-58 |
| Cheshire | Divs 2, 3 | 5 | New Brighton | 10-115 | New Brighton Res | 5-79 | Pavilions | 10-78 |
| SGL Seat | Overall | 14 | Norcross & Warbreck | 10-162 | Charnock Richard | 10-145 | Thornton Cleveleys | 10-120 |
| Cars | Prem Div | 4 | Charnock Richard | 10-145 | Vickers Sports Club | 2-84 | Padiham | 1-55 |
| West | Div One | 7 | Norcross & Warbreck | 10-162 | Thornton Cleveleys | 10-120 | Poulton Town | 1-82 |
| Lancashire | Div Two | 3 | Millom | 1-83 | S D O Rangers | 1-74 | Coppull United | 1-52 |
| East Lancashire | | 3 | Crosshills | 1-122 | Trawden Celtic | 1-89 | Ribchester Rovers | 1-64 |
| Manchester | Overall | 11 | Prestwich Heys | 10-150 | Ashton Athletic | 1-102 | Hindsford | 1-90 |
| | Prem Div | 4 | Prestwich Heys | 10-150 | Monton Amateurs | 1-82 | Atherton Town | 2-77 |
| | Divs 1, 2 | 7 | Ashton Athletic | 1-102 | Hindsford | 1-90 | Monton Amateurs Res | 1-82 |
| North | Overall | 29 | St Helens Town | 10-152 | Clitheroe | 1-139 | Skelmersdale United | 10-136 |
| Western | Div One | 17 | St Helens Town | 10-152 | Clitheroe | 1-139 | Skelmersdale United | 10-136 |
| Trains | Div Two | 12 | Darwen | 10-128 | Chadderton= | 1-113 | | |
| | | | | | Curzon Ashton= | 1-113 | | |

**Block 2**

| | | | | | | | | |
|---|---|---|---|---|---|---|---|---|
| Northern | Overall | 27 | Denaby United | 10-199 | Arnold Town | 10-152 | Sheffield | 10-146 |
| Counties | Prem Div | 17 | Denaby United | 10-199 | Arnold Town | 10-152 | Sheffield | 10-146 |
| | Div One | 10 | Brodsworth Welfare | 10-136 | Hall Road Rangers | 1-124 | Yorkshire Amateur | 1-121 |
| Arnott | Overall | 27 | Chester Le Street Tn | 10-124 | Billingham Town | 10-118 | Morpeth Town | 1-115 |
| Insurance | Div One | 17 | Chester Le Street Tn | 10-124 | Billingham Town | 10-118 | Morpeth Town | 1-15 |
| Northern | Div Two | 10 | Brandon United | 1-105 | Northallerton 94 | 1-95 | Willington | 1-81 |
| JPL Wade N Alliance | | 7 | West Allotment Celtic | 10-105 | Carlisle City | 1-78 | N Shields St Columbas | 1-75 |
| Vaux | Overall | 7 | North Shields Ath | 10-124 | Ferryhill Athletic | 10-99 | New Marske Sports Club | 1-94 |
| Wearside | Div One | 3 | North Shields Ath | 10-124 | Harton & Westoe | 1-58 | Hartlepool BWOB | 1-54 |
| | Div Two | 4 | Ferryhill Athletic | 10-99 | New Marske Sports Club | 1-94 | Herrington CW | 1-68 |
| West Riding Co Amateur | | 5 | Hemsworth MW | 10-137 | Brighouse Town | 10-120 | Phoenix | 1-88 |
| Other English Leagues | | 34 | Bridlington Town | 10-157 | Ifield Res= | 10-131 | | |
| | | | | | Taverners= | 10-131 | | |

**Block 3**

| | | | | | | | | |
|---|---|---|---|---|---|---|---|---|
| Reserves | | 42 | Norcross & Warbreck | 10-168 | Colden Common | 10-146 | Penn & Tylers Green | 10-141 |
| Youth Clubs/Schools | | 8 | St Andrews U16 | 10-150 | Askern Spa Town | 1-141 | St Andrews U14 | 10-132 |
| Club Youth XI's | | 10 | Prestwich Heys | 1-141 | Hendon U14 | 10-126 | St Leonards | 10-123 |
| FA Youth Cup | | 9 | Burgess Hill Town | 1-98 | Ipswich Wanderers | 1-77 | Hampton | 1-75 |

**Block 4**

| | | | | | | | | |
|---|---|---|---|---|---|---|---|---|
| Wales | Overall | 81 | Evans & Williams S | 10-191 | Cwmtillery | 10-161 | Cwmaman | 10-151 |
| League of Wales | | 16 | Caersws | 10-144 | Caernarfon Town | 10-135 | Rhayader Town | 1-131 |
| Cymru Alliance | | 11 | Denbigh Town | 10-150 | Flexys Cefn Druids | 10-140 | Porthmadog | 10-130 |
| CC Sports | Overall | 20 | Llanelli | 10-132 | Caerau (Ely) | 10-116 | Cardiff Corinthians | 10-94 |
| Welsh | Div One | 4 | Llanelli | 10-132 | Cardiff Corinthians | 10-94 | Cardiff Civil Service | 10-88 |
| | Div Two | 6 | Risca United | 1-69 | Chepstow Town | 1-67 | Ammanford | 1-53 |
| | Div Three | 10 | Caerau (Ely) | 10-116 | Ely Rangers | 6-84 | Newport YMCA | 1-72 |
| Fitlock Welsh Alliance | | 6 | Rhyl Delta | 10-145 | Llandymog United | 1-74 | Amlwch Town | 1-68 |
| Hyfforddiant Gwynedd T | | 7 | Llanrwst United | 10-115 | Penrhyndeudraeth | 10-114 | Glan Conwy | 2-79 |
| Welsh National (Wrexham) | | 6 | Gresford Athletic | 8-130 | Owens Corning | 1-82 | Mold Alexandra | 1-77 |
| Spar Mid Wales | | 3 | Penrhyncoch | 1-76 | Meifod | 1-65 | Guilsfield | 1-59 |
| Other Welsh Leagues | | 12 | Evans & Williams S | 10-191 | Cwmtillery | 10-161 | Cwmaman | 10-151 |

**Block 5**

| | | | | | | | | |
|---|---|---|---|---|---|---|---|---|
| Scotland | Overall | 41 | Kirkintilloch Rob R | 10-149 | Haddington Athletic | 10-131 | Tayport | 10-130 |
| Press & Journal Highland | | 7 | Lossiemouth | 10-101 | Buckie Thistle | 2-97 | Forres Mechanics | 1-82 |
| Central | Overall | 9 | Kirkintilloch Rob R | 10-149 | Renfrew | 10-98 | Cumbernauld United | 1-78 |
| Region | Prem Div | 4 | Petershill | 1-72 | Neilston | 1-71 | Maryhill | 1-59 |
| | Div One | 5 | Kirkintilloch Rob R | 10-149 | Renfrew | 10-98 | Cumbernauld United | 1-78 |
| Ayrshire Region | | 4 | Largs Thistle | 10-110 | Auchinleck Talbot | 1-87 | Irvine Meadow XI | 6-81 |
| Eastern Region | | 7 | Haddington Athletic | 10-131 | Blackburn United | 5-115 | Newtongrange Star | 1-93 |
| Fife Region | | 4 | Newburgh | 10-99 | Kelty Hearts | 6-87 | Hill of Beath Hawthorn | 1-73 |
| North Regions | | 3 | Glenatar | 7-96 | Islavale | 1-85 | Formantine United | 1-56 |
| East of Scotland | | 4 | Edinburgh City | 1-80 | Gala Fairydean | 1-76 | Tollcross United | 1-69 |
| Other Scottish Leagues | | 3 | Tayport | 10-130 | Maxwelltown HSFP | 1-58 | Blackwood Dynamos | 1-48 |

**Block 6**

| | | | | | | | | |
|---|---|---|---|---|---|---|---|---|
| Ladies | Overall | 35 | Greyhound Gunners | 10-139 | Langford | 3-138 | Stockport Celtic | 8-134 |
| Premier | Overall | 10 | Langford | 3-138 | Blyth Sp Kestrels | 10-128 | Barnet | 1-123 |
| League | Nth Div | 5 | Blyth Sp Kestrels | 10-128 | Wolverhampton Wand | 4-118 | Berkhamstead | 1-95 |
| | Sth Div | 4 | Langford | 3-138 | Barnet | 1-123 | Three Bridges | 5-101 |
| Southern Combination | | 3 | Canary Racers | 10-108 | Hampton | 10-92 | Clapton | 1-56 |
| South Regional | | 3 | Ryde | 1-96 | Risborough Rangers | 1-91 | Thatcham Town | 1-84 |
| Eastern | | 3 | Colchester | 10-118 | Chelmsford City | 8-105 | Bishops Stortford | 2-100 |
| South West | | 3 | South Bristol Wand | 10-119 | Cinderford Town | 10-104 | Cinderford Town Res | 10-90 |
| Other Ladies Leagues | | 13 | Greyhound Gunners | 10-139 | Stockport Celtic | 8-134 | Barking | 8-116 |
| FA Womens Cup | | 57 | Langford | 1-130 | Stockport Celtic | 1-120 | Wolverhampton Wand | 1-114 |

**Block 7**

| | | | | | | | | |
|---|---|---|---|---|---|---|---|---|
| Sunday Leagues Overall | | 18 | Penn Old Boys | 8-143 | Anglians | 10-141 | Worfield | 10-116 |
| Wolverhampton | | 5 | Penn Old Boys | 8-143 | Ettingshall Park Farm= | 1-82 | | |
| | | | | | Harrowby Arms= | 1-82 | | |
| Other Sunday Leagues | | 13 | Anglians | 10-141 | Worfield | 10-116 | Research Machines | 10-109 |
| FA Sunday Cup | | 49 | Pitsea | 1-97 | Shenley Hotel | 1-88 | Little Paxton | 1-86 |

# THE FOOTBALL ASSOCIATION

## FIXTURE LIST 1999-2000

**SEPTEMBER**

| | |
|---|---|
| 4 Sat | England v Luxembourg UEFA European Championship |
| | FA Cup sponsored by AXA 1Q |
| | The Times FA Youth Cup 1Q* |
| 8 Wed | Poland v England UEFA European Championship |
| 11 Sat | FA Carlsberg Vase 1Q |
| 12 Sun | AXA FA Womens Cup EP |
| 14/15 Tue/Wed | UEFA Champions League 1st Group - Match 1 |
| 15 Wed | Worthington Cup 2 (1) |
| 16 Thur | UEFA Cup 1 (1) |
| | England v France (Womens Friendly International) |
| 18 Sat | FA Cup sponsored by AXA 2Q |
| 21/22 Tue/Wed | UEFA Champions League 1st Group - Match 2 |
| 22 Wed | Worthington Cup 2 (2) |
| 25 Sat | FA Carlsberg Vase 2Q |
| | The Times FA Youth Cup 2Q* |
| 26 Sun | AXA FA Womens Cup P |
| 28/29 Tue/Wed | UEFA Champions League 1st Group - Match 3 |
| 30 Thu | UEFA Cup 1 (2) |

**OCTOBER 1999**

| | |
|---|---|
| 2 Sat | FA Cup sponsored by AXA 3Q |
| 9 Sat | FA Umbro Trophy 1 |
| | The Times FA Youth Cup 3Q* |
| | FA County Youth Cup 1* |
| 10 Sun | AXA FA Womens Cup 1 |
| | England v Belgium - Friendly International - Sunderland FC, 3.00 |
| 13 Wed | Worthington Cup 3 |
| 15 Fri | England v Northern Ireland (Victory Shield - Under 15 Schoolboy team) |
| 16 Sat | FA Cup sponsored by AXA 4Q |
| | Switzerland v England (Womens UEFA International) |
| 17 Sun | FA Umbro Sunday Cup 1 |
| 19/20 Tue/Wed | UEFA Champions League 1st Group - Match 4 |
| 21 Thu | UEFA Cup 2 (1) |
| 23 Sat | FA Carlsberg Vase 1P |
| 26/27 Tue/Wed | UEFA Champions League 1st Group - Match 5 |
| 28 Thu | England v Wales (Victory Shield - Under 15 Schoolboy teams) |
| 30 Sat | FA Cup sponsored by AXA 1P |
| | The Times FA Youth Cup 1P* |

**NOVEMBER 1999**

| | |
|---|---|
| 2/3 Tue/Wed | UEFA Champions League 1st Group - Match 6 |
| 4 Thu | UEFA Cup 2 (2) |
| 7 Sun | AXA FA Womens Cup 2 |
| 10 Wed | FA Cup sponsored by AXA 1P Replay |
| 11 Thu | Scotland v England (Victory Shield - Under 15 Schoolboy team) |
| 13 Sat | Possible Play-Off for UEFA European Championship |
| | FA Carlsberg Vase 2P |
| | The Times FA Youth Cup 2P* |
| | FA County Youth Cup 2* |
| | Under 18 UEFA Three Team Mini-tournament in England (ends 20 Nov) |
| 14 Sun | FA Umbro Sunday Cup 2 |
| 17 Wed | Possible Play-Off for UEFA European Championship |
| 20 Sat | FA Cup sponsored by AXA 2P |
| 23/24 Tue/Wed | UEFA Champions League 2nd Group- Match 1 |
| 25 Thu | UEFA Cup 3 (1) |
| 27 Sat | FA Umbro Trophy 2 |

**DECEMBER 1999**

| | |
|---|---|
| 1 Wed | Worthington Cup 4 |
| | FA Cup sponsored by AXA 2P Replay |
| 4 Sat | FA Carlsberg Vase 3P |
| 5 Sun | FA Umbro Sunday Cup 3 |
| 6 Mon | FA XI v Northern Premier League |
| 7 Tue | FIFA World Cup - Draw for Preliminary Competition |
| | FA XI v Southern League |
| 7/8 Tue/Wed | UEFA Champions League 2nd Group- Match 2 |
| 8 Wed | FA XI v Isthmian League |
| 9 Thu | UEFA Cup 3 (2) |
| 11 Sat | FA Cup sponsored by AXA 3P |
| | The Times FA Youth Cup 3P* |
| 12 Sun | AXA FA Womens Cup 3 |
| 15 Wed | Worthington Cup 5 |
| 18 Sat | FA County Youth Cup 3* |
| 22 Wed | FA Cup sponsored by AXA 3P Replay |

**JANUARY 2000**

| | |
|---|---|
| 8 Sat | FA Cup sponsored by AXA 4P |
| 9 Sun | AXA FA Womens Cup 4 |
| 10 Mon | FA XI v Combined Services |
| 12 Wed | Worthington Cup Semi-Final (1) |
| 15 Sat | FA Umbro Trophy 3 |
| 19 Wed | FA Cup sponsored by AXA 4P Replay |

| 22 Sat | FA Carlsberg Vase 4P |
| | The Times FA Youth Cup 4P* |
| 23 Sun | FA Umbro Sunday Cup 4 |
| 26 Wed | Worthington Cup Semi-Final (2) |
| 29 Sat | FA Cup sponsored by AXA 5P |
| | FA County Youth Cup 4* |

**FEBRUARY 2000**

| 5 Sat | FA Umbro Trophy 4 |
| 6 Sun | AXA FA Womens Cup 5 |
| 9 Wed | FA Cup sponsored by AXA 5P Replay |
| 12 Sat | FA Carlsberg Vase 5P |
| | The Times FA Youth Cup 5P* |
| 19 Sat | FA Cup sponsored by AXA 6P |
| 20 Sun | England v Poland (Womens UEFA International) |
| | FA Umbro Sunday Cup 5 |
| 23 Wed | International (Friendly) |
| 26 Sat | FA Umbro Trophy 5 |
| 27 Sun | AXA FA Womens Cup 6 |
| | Worthington Cup Final |
| 29 Tue | England Semi-Professional International |
| 29/1 Tue/Wed | UEFA Champions League 2nd Group-Match 3 |

**MARCH 2000**

| 1 Wed | FA Cup sponsored by AXA 6P Replay |
| 2 Thu | UEFA Cup 4 (1) |
| 4 Sat | FA Carlsberg Vase 6P |
| | The Times FA Youth Cup 6P* |
| 7 Tue | Under 16 UEFA Three Team Mini-tournament in Luxembourg (ends 12 March) |
| 7/8 Tue/Wed | UEFA Champions League 2nd Group-Match 4 |
| 9 Thu | UEFA Cup 4 (2) |
| | England v Norway (Womens UEFA International) |
| 11 Sat | FA Umbro Trophy 6 |
| | FA County Youth Cup Semi-Final* |
| 14/15 Tue/Wed | UEFA Champions League 2nd Group-Match 5 |
| 16 Thu | UEFA Cup Quarter Final (1) |
| 18 Sat | FA Carlsberg Vase SF1 |
| 19 Sun | FA Umbro Sunday Cup SF |
| 21 Tue | England Semi-Professional International |
| 21/22 Tue/Wed | UEFA Champions League 2nd Group-Match 6 |
| 23 Thu | UEFA Cup Quarter Final (2) |
| 24 Fri | England v Holland (Under 15 Schoolboy Friendly International) |
| 25 Sat | FA Carlsberg Vase SF2 |
| | The Times FA Youth Cup SF1* |
| 26 Sun | AXA FA Womens Cup SF |
| 29 Wed | International (Friendly) |

**APRIL 2000**

| 1 Sat | FA Umbro Trophy SF1 |
| 4/5 Tue/Wed | UEFA Champions League Quarter |

| | Final (1) |
| 6 Thu | UEFA Cup Semi Final (1) |
| 7 Fri | England v Italy (Under 15 Schoolboy Friendly International) |
| 9 Sun | FA Cup sponsored by AXA Semi Finals |
| 15 Sat | FA Umbro Trophy SF2 |
| | The Times FA Youth Cup SF2* |
| 18/19 Tue/Wed | UEFA Champions League Quarter Final (2) |
| 20 Thu | UEFA Cup Semi Final (2) |
| 22 Sat | Portugal v England (Womens UEFA International) |
| 26 Wed | International (Friendly) |
| 29 Sat | FA County Youth Cup Final (fixed date) |

**MAY 2000**

| 1 Mon | AXA FA Womens Cup Final |
| 3 Wed | UEFA Champions League Semi Final (1) |
| 5 Fri | The Times FA Youth Cup Final 1st Leg (fixed date) |
| 6 Sat | FA Carlsberg Vase Final |
| | Final Nationwide League fixtures Divs 2 & 3 |
| | Final Nationwide Conference fixtures |
| 7 Sun | Final Nationwide League fixtures Div 1 |
| 10 Wed | UEFA Champions League Semi Final (2) |
| 12 Fri | The Times FA Youth Cup Final 2nd Leg (fixed date) |
| 13 Sat | FA Umbro Trophy Final |
| 14 Sun | Nationwide League Play-Off Semi Final (1) |
| | Final FA Carling Premier League fixtures |
| | England v Switzerland (Womens UEFA International) |
| 17 Wed | UEFA Cup Final |
| | Nationwide League Play-Off Semi Final (2) |
| 20 Sat | FA Cup sponsored by AXA Final |
| 24 Wed | UEFA Champions League Final |
| 27 Sat | Nationwide League 3rd Division Play-Off |
| 28 Sun | Nationwide League 2nd Division Play-Off |
| 29 Mon | Nationwide League 1st Division Play-Off |

**JUNE 2000**

| 3 Sat | Possible International Friendly |
| 4 Sun | Possible International Friendly |
| | Norway v England (Womens UEFA International) |
| 10 Sat | European Championship commences (ends 2 July) |

* = closing date

# CHELTENHAM TOWN 'S
## MATCH FACTS 1998-99

| No | Date | Venue | Comp | Opponents | Att | Result | Score | Goalscorers |
|---|---|---|---|---|---|---|---|---|
| 1 | 15/08/98 | A | NC | Welling United | 820 | L | 1 - 2 | Banks 7 |
| 2 | 18/08/98 | H | NC | HEDNESFORD TOWN | 2168 | D | 0 - 0 | |
| 3 | 22/08/98 | H | NC | HAYES | 1879 | D | 3 - 3 | Eaton 53, Howells 74, Smith 89 |
| 4 | 26/08/98 | A | NC | Forest Green Rovers | 1909 | W | 2 - 1 | Eaton 59, Norton 82 |
| 5 | 29/08/98 | A | NC | Leek Town | 704 | W | 2 - 0 | Grayson 12, Victory 73 |
| 6 | 31/08/98 | H | NC | BARROW | 2005 | W | 4 - 1 | Walker 16 32, Brough 51, Eaton 87 |
| 7 | 05/09/98 | H | NC | MORECAMBE | 1959 | W | 4 - 1 | Grayson 1 65, Howells 32 69 |
| 8 | 08/09/98 | A | NC | Kettering Town | 1615 | W | 2 - 0 | Eaton 4, Grayson 70 |
| 9 | 12/09/98 | A | NC | Kingstonian | 1801 | W | 2 - 1 | Freeman 37, Eaton 56 |
| 10 | 19/09/98 | H | NC | SOUTHPORT | 2594 | W | 3 - 0 | Norton 14, Eaton 16, Walker 41 |
| 11 | 22/09/98 | H | NC | WOKING | 2406 | D | 1 - 1 | Grayson 79 |
| 12 | 26/09/98 | A | NC | Farnborough Town | 1067 | W | 4 - 2 | Freeman 2 47, Knight 28, Grayson 90 |
| 13 | 03/10/98 | H | NC | DOVER ATHLETIC | 2575 | D | 1 - 1 | Grayson 66 |
| 14 | 10/10/98 | A | NC | Yeovil Town | 2955 | D | 2 - 2 | Norton 19, Grayson 32 |
| 15 | 24/10/98 | H | NC | DONCASTER ROVERS | 2428 | W | 2 - 1 | Brough 6, Duff 30 |
| 16 | 07/11/98 | A | NC | Woking | 2738 | L | 0 - 1 | |
| 17 | 28/11/98 | H | NC | RUSHDEN & DIAMONDS | 4051 | W | 1 - 0 | Knight 32 |
| 18 | 05/12/98 | A | NC | Dover Athletic | 972 | D | 0 - 0 | |
| 19 | 12/12/98 | H | NC | LEEK TOWN | 1912 | D | 0 - 0 | |
| 20 | 19/12/98 | H | NC | STEVENAGE BOROUGH | 2772 | W | 3 - 0 | Eaton 20 33, Watkins 55 |
| 21 | 26/12/98 | A | NC | Telford United | 1304 | W | 3 - 0 | Watkins 67, Eaton 75, Jones 84[og] |
| 22 | 28/12/98 | A | NC | Kidderminster Harriers | 3295 | W | 1 - 0 | Watkins 34 |
| 23 | 02/01/99 | H | NC | TELFORD UNITED | 3027 | W | 2 - 0 | C Walker 38, Howells 69 |
| 24 | 09/01/99 | A | NC | Doncaster Rovers | 3082 | W | 2 - 2 | Watkins 28[p] 34 |
| 25 | 23/01/99 | H | NC | NORTHWICH VICTORIA | 2060 | L | 0 - 1 | |
| 26 | 30/01/99 | A | NC | Southport | 1224 | W | 2 - 0 | Howells 29, Grayson 60 |
| 27 | 13/02/99 | A | NC | Morecambe | 1354 | W | 2 - 0 | Watkins 35, Grayson 71 |
| 28 | 20/02/99 | A | NC | Hereford United | 3480 | W | 2 - 0 | Freeman 17, Victory 84 |
| 29 | 06/03/99 | A | NC | Barrow | 1773 | D | 1 - 1 | Knight 73 |
| 30 | 09/03/99 | H | NC | HEREFORD UNITED | 3341 | D | 2 - 2 | Victory 39, Brough 61 |
| 31 | 13/03/99 | A | NC | Stevenage Borough | 2576 | D | 2 - 2 | Brough 3, Howells 74 |
| 32 | 16/03/99 | H | NC | FARNBOROUGH TOWN | 2265 | D | 0 - 0 | |
| 33 | 20/03/99 | H | NC | KETTERING TOWN | 5202 | W | 3 - 0 | Matthews 36[og], Grayson 38, Hone 73[og] |
| 34 | 22/03/99 | A | NC | Hednesford Town | 1651 | L | 2 - 3 | Grayson 37, Bailey 90 |
| 35 | 03/04/99 | A | NC | Rushden & Diamonds | 6312 | W | 2 - 1 | Freeman 89, Grayson 90 |
| 36 | 05/04/99 | H | NC | KIDDERMINSTER HARRIERS | 4518 | W | 1 - 0 | Grayson 54 |
| 37 | 13/04/99 | H | NC | KINGSTONIAN | 3184 | W | 1 - 0 | Grayson 25[p] |
| 38 | 20/04/99 | H | NC | FOREST GREEN ROVERS | 3058 | D | 1 - 1 | Bailey 30 |
| 39 | 22/04/99 | H | NC | YEOVIL TOWN | 6150 | W | 3 - 2 | Victory 4, Grayson 22, Duff 90 |
| 40 | 24/04/99 | A | NC | Hayes | 2105 | L | 2 - 3 | Grayson 45, Duff 56 |
| 41 | 27/04/99 | A | NC | Northwich Victoria | 1155 | L | 0 - 1 | |
| 42 | 01/05/99 | H | NC | WELLING UNITED | 5400 | D | 0 - 0 | |

**CUP COMPETITIONS**

| | Date | Venue | Comp | Opponents | Att | Result | Score | Goalscorers |
|---|---|---|---|---|---|---|---|---|
| | 08/08/98 | A | TT Cup | Tiverton Town | 613 | L | 0 - 2 | |
| | 06/10/98 | H | Shield | HALIFAX TOWN | 1337 | L | 0 - 1 | |
| | 01/12/98 | A | ELC 2 | Stevenage Borough | 604 | W | 1 - 0 | Eaton 43 |
| | 09/02/99 | H | ELC QF | HAYES | 462 | W | 2 - 1 | Hopkins 33 80 |
| | 07/04/99 | A | ELC SF | Farnborough Town | 260 | L | 0 - 2 | |
| | 13/10/98 | A | GSC QF | Cinderford Town | 326 | W | 5 - 0 | Grayson 15, Knight 40, Watkins 41, Victory 58, Smith 88 |
| | 15/12/98 | H | GSC SF | BRISTOL CITY | 407 | W | 3 - 2 | Duff, Watkins[p], Bloomer |
| | 04/05/99 | H | GSC F | Gloucester City | 950 | W | 3 - 0 | Yates 12, Brough 49, C Walker 90 |
| | 17/10/98 | A | FA C Q3 | Barnstaple Town | 991 | W | 1 - 0 | Victory 40 |
| | 04/11/98 | H | FA C Q4 | TAUNTON TOWN | 1758 | W | 3 - 2 | Eaton 19 72, Howells 27 |
| | 14/11/98 | H | FA C 1 | LINCOLN CITY | 3589 | L | 0 - 1 | |
| | 21/11/98 | H | FAT 2 | BASHLEY | 1348 | W | 2 - 1 | Grayson 29 65 |
| | 16/01/99 | H | FAT 3 | CANVEY ISLAND | 2045 | W | 2 - 1 | Grayson 29, Freeman 90 |
| | 06/02/99 | H | FAT 4 | STEVENAGE BOROUGH | 3005 | D | 0 - 0 | |
| | 15/02/99 | H | FAT 4R | Stevenage Borough | n/k | D | 0 - 0 | (5-4 after pens) |
| | 27/02/99 | H | FAT 5 | HENDON | 2514 | W | 3 - 0 | Victory 41 45, Watkins 66 |
| | 27/03/99 | A | FAT QF | Emley | 1339 | W | 1 - 0 | Howarth 44 |
| | 10/04/99 | H | FAT SF(1) | Kingstonian | 2203 | D | 2 - 2 | Grayson 58, Brough 72 |
| | 17/04/99 | H | FAT SF(2) | KINGSTONIAN | 4425 | L | 1 - 3 | Grayson 78 |

# GLORIOUS PROMOTION SEASON
## MATCH FACTS 1998-99

| 1 | 2 | 3 | 4 | 5 | 6 | 7 | 8 | 9 | 10 | 11 | 12 14 15 | |
|---|---|---|---|---|---|---|---|---|----|----|----------|--|
| Book | Duff | Victory | Banks | Brough | Milton | Howells | Norton | Eaton | Grayson | Bloomer | Walker, Knight, Smith | 1 |
| Book | Duff | Victory | Banks | Brough | Norton | Howells | Walker | Eaton | Grayson | Milton | Knight, Smith, Jackson | 2 |
| Book | Duff | Victory | Banks | Brough | Norton | Howells | Grayson | Eaton | Milton | Walker | Jackson, Knight, Smith | 3 |
| Book | Duff | Victory | Banks | Freeman | Brough | Howells | Walker | Eaton | Grayson | Norton | Knight, Milton, Smith | 4 |
| Book | Duff | Victory | Banks | Freeman | Brough | Howells | Walker | Eaton | Grayson | Norton | Milton, Knight, Smith | 5 |
| Book | Duff | Victory | Banks | Freeman | Brough | Howells | Walker | Eaton | Grayson | Norton | Milton, Knight, Smith | 6 |
| Book | Duff | Victory | Banks | Freeman | Brough | Howells | Walker | Eaton | Grayson | Norton | Milton, Knight, Smith | 7 |
| Book | Duff | Victory | Banks | Freeman | Brough | Howells | Milton | Grayson | Eaton | Norton | Knight, Watkins, Smith | 8 |
| Book | Duff | Victory | Banks | Freeman | Brough | Howells | Walker | Eaton | Grayson | Norton | Milton, Watkins, Knight | 9 |
| Book | Duff | Victory | Banks | Freeman | Brough | Howells | Walker | Eaton | Grayson | Norton | Knight, Milton, Watkins | 10 |
| Book | Duff | Victory | Knight | Freeman | Brough | Howells | Walker | Eaton | Grayson | Norton | Bloomer, Watkins, Milton | 11 |
| Book | Duff | Victory | Knight | Freeman | Brough | Howells | Walker | Eaton | Grayson | Norton | Banks, Bloomer, Milton | 12 |
| Book | Duff | Victory | Banks | Freeman | Brough | Howells | Walker | Eaton | Grayson | Norton | Knight, Bloomer, Smith | 13 |
| Book | Duff | Victory | Banks | Freeman | Brough | Howells | Walker | Eaton | Grayson | Norton | Bloomer, Knight, Smith | 14 |
| Book | Duff | Victory | Banks | Freeman | Brough | Howells | Bloomer | Eaton | Grayson | Norton | R Walker, Smith, Knight | 15 |
| Book | Duff | Victory | Banks | Freeman | Brough | Howells | Bloomer | Eaton | Grayson | C Walker | R Walker, Knight, Milton | 16 |
| Book | Duff | Victory | Banks | Freeman | Brough | Howells | Knight | R Walker | Grayson | Norton | Watkins, Eaton, C Walker | 17 |
| Book | Duff | Victory | Banks | Freeman | Brough | Howells | Smith | R Walker | Grayson | Norton | Watkins, Eaton, Milton | 18 |
| Book | Duff | Victory | Banks | Freeman | Brough | Howells | Milton | Smith | Grayson | Norton | Eaton, C Walker, Watkins | 19 |
| Book | Duff | Victory | Banks | Freeman | R Walker | Howells | Knight | Eaton | Watkins | Norton | Milton, C Walker, Brough | 20 |
| Book | Brough | Victory | Banks | Freeman | R Walker | Howells | C Walker | Eaton | Watkins | Norton | Bloomer, Grayson, Smith | 21 |
| Book | Duff | Victory | Banks | Freeman | R Walker | Howells | C Walker | Eaton | Watkins | Norton | Brough, Bloomer, Grayson | 22 |
| Book | Duff | Victory | Banks | Freeman | Grayson | Howells | C Walker | Eaton | Watkins | Norton | Bloomer, Brough, Smith | 23 |
| Book | Duff | Victory | Banks | Brough | R Walker | Howells | Grayson | Eaton | Watkins | Norton | Bloomer , Smith, C Walker | 24 |
| Book | Duff | Victory | Banks | Freeman | C Walker | Howells | Grayson | Eaton | Watkins | Norman | Milton, Smith, Bloomer | 25 |
| Book | Duff | Victory | Banks | Freeman | R Walker | Howells | Yates | Eaton | Grayson | Norton | Brough, Watkins, Bloomer | 26 |
| Book | Duff | Victory | Banks | Freeman | R Walker | Yates | Bloomer | Grayson | Watkins | Norton | Eaton, Brough, Knight | 27 |
| Book | Duff | Victory | Brough | Freeman | R Walker | Yates | Bloomer | Grayson | Watkins | Norton | Knight, C Walker, Smith | 28 |
| Book | Duff | Victory | Brough | Freeman | R Walker | Yates | Bloomer | Grayson | Watkins | Norton | Knight, Howarth, C Walker | 29 |
| Book | Duff | Victory | Brough | Freeman | R Walker | Yates | Bloomer | Grayson | Eaton | Knight | Watkins, Howarth, C Walker | 30 |
| Book | Duff | Victory | Brough | Freeman | R Walker | Yates | Bloomer | Grayson | Eaton | Knight | Howarth, Howells, C Walker, | 31 |
| Book | Duff | Victory | Banks | Freeman | R Walker | Howells | Yates | Grayson | Brough | Knight | Eaton, Bloomer, Howarth, | 32 |
| Book | Duff | Victory | Brough | Howarth | R Walker | Howells | Yates | Grayson | Bailey | Bloomer | Eaton, C Walker, Knight | 33 |
| Book | Duff | Victory | Brough | Freeman | Howarth | Howells | Norton | Grayson | Bailey | Bloomer | C Walker, Eaton, Knight | 34 |
| Book | Duff | Victory | Banks | Brough | Howarth | Howells | Bloomer | Grayson | Bailey | Norman | Freeman, Milton, Knight | 35 |
| Book | Duff | Victory | Banks | Freeman | Howarth | Howells | Milton | Grayson | Brough | Norton | C Walker, Bloomer, Knight | 36 |
| Book | Duff | Victory | Banks | Freeman | Brough | Howells | Bloomer | Grayson | Bailey | Norton | Eaton, Milton, C Walker | 37 |
| Book | Duff | Victory | Banks | Freeman | Brough | Howells | Yates | Grayson | Bailey | Norton | Eaton, Bloomer, Knight | 38 |
| Book | Duff | Victory | Banks | Freeman | Brough | Howells | Bloomer | Grayson | Bailey | Norton | Knight, Yates, Eaton | 39 |
| Book | Duff | Victory | Banks | Freeman | Howarth | Howells | Yates | Grayson | Eaton | Knight | Brough, Bloomer, Bailey | 40 |
| Book | Duff | Victory | Banks | Freeman | Brough | Howells | Yates | Grayson | Bailey | Bloomer | Norton, Eaton, Knight | 41 |
| Book | Duff | Victory | Banks | Freeman | Yates | Howells | Bloomer | Grayson | Eaton | Norton | Brough, Watkins, Knight | 42 |

# THE TIMES F.A. YOUTH CUP

## NON LEAGUE CLUBS' INVOLVEMENT
from the First Round proper

**FIRST ROUND PROPER**

|   | | | |
|---|---|---|---|
| | Runcorn | 1 v 6 | Hull City |
| | | Att: 52 | |
| | Burscough | 2 v 3 | York City |
| | | Att: 75 | |
| | Altrincham | 0 v 1 | Hartlepool United |
| | | Att: 142 | |
| | Kidderminster Harriers | 1 v 5 | Cardiff City |
| | | Att: 100 | |
| | Rushden & Diamonds | 0 v 3 | Reading |
| | | Att: 250 | |
| | Nuneaton Borough | 2 v 2 | Swansea City |
| | | Att: 84 | |
| R | Swansea City | 3 v 1 | Nuneaton Borough |
| | | Att: 74 | |
| | Racing Club Warwick | 1 v 4 | Walsall |
| | | Att: 138 | |
| | Stoke City | 3 v 0 | Cirencester Town |
| | | Att: 204 | |
| | Notts County | 4 v 0 | Weston super Mare |
| | | Att: 167 | |
| | Bolehall Swifts | 1 v 7 | Cambridge United |
| | | Att: 91 | |
| | Wellingborough Town | 2 v 5 | Exeter City |
| | | Att: 45 | |
| | Hinckley United | 1 v 0 | Basingstoke Town |
| | | Att: 123 | |
| | Fulham | 1 v 1 | Farnborough Town |
| | | Att: 208 | |
| R | Farnborough Town | 1 v 3 | Fulham |
| | | Att: 239 | |
| | Barnet | 2 v 1 | Walton & Hersham |
| | | Att: 82 | |
| | Southend United | 7 v 0 | Sittingbourne |
| | | Att: 104 | |
| | Brighton & Hove Albion | 6 v 1 | Hitchin Town |
| | | Att: 67 | |
| | Gillingham | 3 v 1 | Chatham Town |
| | | Att: 249 | |
| | Romford | 3 v 1 | Eastleigh |
| | | Att: 90 | |
| | Burgess Hill Town | 1 v 1 | Chesham United |
| | | Att: 189 | |
| R | Chesham United | 2 v 3 | Burgess Hill Town |
| | | Att: 142 | |

|   | | | |
|---|---|---|---|
| | Langney Sports | 2 v 2 | Welling United |
| | | Att: 155 | |
| R | Welling United | 2 v 1 | Langney Sports |
| | | Att: 112 | |
| | Bishop's Stortford | 1 v 1 | Hullbridge Sports |
| | | Att: 75 | |
| R | Hullbridge Sports | 0 v 1 | Bishop's Stortford |
| | | Att: 110 | |
| | Leatherhead | 0 v 6 | Stevenage Borough |
| | | Att: 60 | |
| | Enfield | 2 v 1 | Bedford Town |
| | | Att: 71 | |
| | Millwall | 4 v 0 | Viking Sports |
| | | Att: 94 | |

**SECOND ROUND PROPER**

|   | | | |
|---|---|---|---|
| | Northampton Town | 1 v 1 | Stevenage Borough |
| | | Att: 110 | |
| R | Stevenage Borough | 0 v 2 | Northampton Town |
| | | Att: 120 | |
| | Hinckley United | 2 v 2 | Reading |
| | | Att: 165 | |
| R | Reading | 2 v 1 | Hinckley United |
| | | Att: 146 | |
| | Burgess Hill Town | 0 v 7 | Millwall |
| | | Att: 402 | |
| | Bishop's Stortford | 1 v 1 | Romford |
| | | Att: 80 | |
| R | Romford | 3 v 2 | Bishop's Stortford |
| | | Att: 103 | |
| | Welling United | 1 v 2 | Barnet |
| | | Att: 121 | |
| | Gillingham | 0 v 0 | Enfield |
| | | Att: 97 | |
| R | Enfield | 0 v 3 | Gillingham |
| | | Att: 75 | |

**THIRD ROUND PROPER**

|   | | | |
|---|---|---|---|
| | Watford | 4 v 0 | Romford |
| | | Att: 134 | |

# CLUB INDEX

| Team | No. |
|---|---|
| BRAINTREE TOWN (RYMAN 1) ιℓ | 825 |
| BRANDON UNITED (NTH 2) | 437 |
| BRENTWOOD (ESX Sen) | 876 |
| BRIDGER PACKAGING (SSM S) | 893 |
| BRIDGNORTH TOWN (M.ALL) | 732 |
| BRIDGWATER TOWN (WEST P) | 698 |
| BRIDLINGTON TOWN(NCE 1) ℕℙℙ | 395 |
| BRIDPORT (WEST P) | 698 |
| BRIERLEY HILL (W MID) | 753 |
| BRIGG TOWN (NCE P) | 388 |
| BRIGHTLINGSEA UNITED (EAST 1) | 583 |
| BRIMSDOWN ROVERS (SSM S) | 893 |
| BRISLINGTON (WEST P) | 698 |
| BRISTOL MANOR FARM (WEST P) | 699 |
| BROADBRIDGE HEATH (SSX 2) | 643 |
| BROCKENHURST (WSX) | 679 |
| BRODSWORTH M.W. (NCE 1) | 388 |
| BROMLEY (Ryman P) | 826 |
| BROMSGROVE ROVERS (DM M) | 526 |
| BROOK HOUSE (SSM P ) | 886 |
| BUCKINGHAM ATHLETIC (SSM P ) | 882 |
| BUCKINGHAM TOWN (UCL P) | 657 |
| BUGBROOKE ST MICHAELS (UCL 1) | 665 |
| BURGESS HILL TOWN (SSX 1) | 634 |
| BURNHAM (Dr M  S)) | 550 |
| BURNHAM RAMBLERS (ESX Sen) | 876 |
| BURSCOUGH (UNIB 1) ℐℓℓ | 329 |
| BURTON ALBION (DM P) ᴄℓ | 478 |
| BURTON PARK WANDERERS (UCL 1) | 665 |
| BURY FOOTBALL. ACADEMY(ESX Sen) | 877 |
| BURY TOWN  (EAST P) | 573 |
| BUSTLEHOME (W.MID P) | 753 |
| BUXTED (SSX 3) | 642 |
| BUXTON (NCE P) | 388 |
| | |
| CADDINGTON (SSM S) | 893 |
| CAERNARFON TOWN (WALES) | 980 |
| CAERSWS (WALES) | 981 |
| CALNE TOWN (WEST P) | 707 |
| CAMBERLEY TOWN (RYMAN 3) | 858 |
| CAMBRIDGE CITY (DM P) ᴄꜱ | 480 |
| CANTERBURY CITY (KENT) | 613 |
| CANVEY ISLAND (RYMAN 1) ᴄℓ | 782 |
| CARMARTHEN TOWN (WALES) | 981 |
| CARSHALTON ATHLETIC (RYMAN P) ᴄꜱ | 784 |
| CARTERTON TOWN (HELL P) | 595 |
| CASTLETON GABRIELS (NWC 2) | 360 |
| CEMAES YNYS MON (WALES) | 981 |
| CHADDERTON (NWC 2) | 360 |
| CHALFONT ST. PETER (RYMAN 2) | 845 |
| CHARD TOWN (WEST 1) | 707 |
| CHASETOWN (M.ALL) | 732 |
| CHATHAM TOWN (KENT) | 613 |
| CHATTERIS TOWN (EAST 1) | 583 |
| CHEADLE (NWC 1) | 350 |
| CHELMSFORD CITY (DM S) ιℓ | 551 |

| Team | No. |
|---|---|
| CHELTENHAM SARACENS (HELL 1) | 602 |
| CHERTSEY TOWN (RYMAN 1) | 827 |
| CHESHAM UNITED (RYMAN P) ꜱℓ | 786 |
| CHESHUNT (RYMAN 3) ιℓ | 846 |
| CHESLYN HAY (M.COMB P) | 745 |
| CHESSINGTON & HOOK UTD (C.Co P) | 869 |
| CHESSINGTON UNITED(C.Co P) | 869 |
| CHESTER-LE-STREET TOWN (NTH 1) | 428 |
| CHICHESTER CITY (SSX 1) | 634 |
| CHIPPENHAM TOWN (WEST P) ꜱℓ | 699 |
| CHIPSTEAD (C.Co P) | 869 |
| CHORLEY (UNIB 1) | 330 |
| CHRISTCHURCH (WSX) | 679 |
| CINDERFORD TOWN (DM M) | 527 |
| CIRENCESTER ACADEMY (HELL P) | 597 |
| CIRENCESTER TOWN (DM S) ꜱℓ | 528 |
| CIRENCESTER UNITED (HELL 1) | 602 |
| CLACTON TOWN (EAST P) | 573 |
| CLANFIELD (HELL 1) | 603 |
| CLAPTON TOWN (RYMAN 3) | 858 |
| CLEVEDON TOWN (DM P) | 482 |
| CLITHEROE (NWC 1) | 350 |
| CLYST ROVERS (WEST 1) | 707 |
| COBHAM (C.Co P) | 869 |
| COCKFOSTERS (SSM S) | 893 |
| COGENHOE UNITED (UCL P) | 657 |
| COLESHILL TOWN (M.COMB P) | 746 |
| COLNE (NWC 2) | 360 |
| COLWYN BAY (UNIB P) | 284 |
| CONCORD RANGERS (ESX Sen) | 877 |
| CONGLETON TOWN (UNIB 1) | 331 |
| CONNAH'S QUAY NOMADS (WALES) | 983 |
| CONSETT (NTH 1) | 428 |
| CONTINENTAL STAR (M.COMB P) | 746 |
| CONWY UNITED (WALES) | 983 |
| CORBY TOWN (DM S) | 552 |
| CORINTHIAN CASUALS (RYMAN 3) | 858 |
| CORNARD UNITED (EAST 1) | 583 |
| CORSHAM TOWN (WEST 1) | 708 |
| COTTINGHAM (UCL 1) | 665 |
| COVE (C.Co P) | 870 |
| COVENTRY SPHINX (M.COMB P) | 746 |
| COWES SPORTS (WSX) | 679 |
| CRADLEY TOWN (W.MID P) | 732 |
| CRANLEIGH (C.Co P) | 871 |
| CRAWLEY GREEN (SSM 1) | 898 |
| CRAWLEY DOWN VILLAGE (SSX 2) | 643 |
| CRAWLEY TOWN (DM P) ᐸℓ | 484 |
| CRAY WANDERERS (KENT) | 614 |
| CROCKENHILL (KENT) | 616 |
| CROOK TOWN (NTH 1) | 428 |
| CROWBOROUGH ATHLETIC (SSX 3) | 649 |
| CROYDON (RYMAN 1) | 828 |
| CROYDON ATHLETIC (RYMAN 3) | 859 |
| CURZON ASHTON (NWC 2) | 360 |
| CWMBRAN TOWN (WALES) | 983 |

| | | | |
|---|---|---|---|
| DAGENHAM & REDBRIDGE (RYMAN P) cP | 788 | EVENWOOD TOWN (NTH 2) | 438 |
| DAISY HILL (NWC 2) | 362 | EVESHAM UNITED (DM M) | 529 |
| DARLASTON TOWN (W.MID P) | 753 | EXMOUTH TOWN (WEST 1) | 708 |
| DARTFORD (DM S) | 553 | EYNESBURY ROVERS (UCL P) | 659 |
| DARWEN (NWC 2) | 362 | | |
| DAVENTRY TOWN (UCL 1) | 666 | FAIRFORD TOWN (HELL P) | 597 |
| DAVID LLOYD AFC (M.COMB P) | 712 | FAKENHAM TOWN (EAST) | 574 |
| DAWLISH TOWN (WEST 1) | 699 | FAREHAM TOWN (WSX) | 682 |
| DE HAVILAND (SSM 1) | 898 | FARNBOROUGH TOWN (GMVC) cP | 794 |
| DEAL TOWN (KENT | 614 | FARNHAM TOWN (C.Co P) | 871 |
| DENABY UNITED (NCE P) | 389 | FARSLEY CELTIC (UNIB 1) NPP | 333 |
| DEREHAM TOWN | 584 | FAVERSHAM TOWN (KENT) | 615 |
| DESBOROUGH TOWN (UCL P) | 657 | FECKENHAM (M.COMB P) | 746 |
| DEVIZES TOWN(WEST1) | 708 | FELIXSTOWE PORT & TOWN(EAST P) | 574 |
| DIDCOT TOWN (HELL P) | 597 | FELTHAM (C.Co P) | 871 |
| DISS TOWN(EAST P) | 573 | FISHER ATHLETIC LONDON (DM S) | 555 |
| DONCASTER ROVERS (NC) | 145 | FLACKWELL HEATH (ICIS 3) | 860 |
| DORCHESTER TOWN (DM P) cS | 486 | FLAMSTEAD (SSM 1) | 898 |
| DORKING (RYMAN 3) | 859 | FLEET TOWN (DM S) | 556 |
| DOVER ATHLETIC (NC) lP | 151 | FLEETWOOD WANDERERS (NWC 2) | 351 |
| DOWNHAM TOWN (EAST 1) | 584 | FLINT TOWN UNITED (WALES) | 985 |
| DOWNTON (WSX) | 680 | FLIXTON (UNIB 1) | 334 |
| DROYLSDEN (UNIB P) cN | 286 | FOLKSTONE INVICTA (DM S) lP | 557 |
| DUDLEY SPORTS (M.COMB P) | 712 | FORD SPORTS DAVENTRY (UCL P) | 659 |
| DUDLEY TOWN (W.MID P) | 753 | FORD UNITED (RYMAN 2) cS | 847 |
| DULWICH HAMLET (RYMAN P) | 790 | FOREST (SSX 3) | 649 |
| DUNSTABLE TOWN (SSM 1) SP | 893 | FOREST GREEN ROVERS (NC) cP | 157 |
| DUNSTON F.B. (NTH 1) | 429 | FOREST GREEN ROVERS RES (HELL 1) | 603 |
| DURHAM CITY (NTH 2) | 429 | FORMBY (NWC 2) | 362 |
| | | FRANKLANDS VILLAGE (SSX 3) | 649 |
| EASINGTON COLLIERY (NTH 1) | 429 | FRICKLEY ATHLETIC (UNIB P) NPP | 290 |
| EASINGTON SPORTS (HELL 1) | 603 | FROME TOWN (WEST 1) | 708 |
| EAST COWES VICTORIA (WSX) | 680 | | |
| EAST GRINSTEAD TOWN (SSX 2) | 643 | G.P.T. (COVENTRY) (M.COMB P) | 712 |
| EAST HAM UNITED (ESX Sen) | 877 | GAINSBOROUGH TRINITY (UNIB P) cN | 292 |
| EAST PRESTON (SSX 1) | 634 | GARFORTH (NCE P) | 389 |
| EAST THURROCK UNITED (RYMAN 3) | 859 | GATESHEAD (UNIB P) NPP | 294 |
| EASTBOURNE TOWN (SSX 1) cS | 635 | GLAPWELL (NCE 1) | 395 |
| EASTBOURNE UNITED (SSX 1) | 635 | GLASSHOUGHTON WELFARE (NCE P) | 391 |
| EASTLEIGH (WSX) lP | 680 | GLASTONBURY (WEST 1) | 690 |
| EASTWOOD TOWN (UNIB 1) | 332 | GLOSSOP NORTH END (NWC 1) | 351 |
| EBBW VALE (WALES) | 985 | GLOUCESTER CITY (DM P) SP | 488 |
| ECCLESHILL UNITED (NCE P) | 389 | GODALMING & GUILDFORD (C.Co P) | 871 |
| EDGWARE TOWN (RYMAN 2) | 846 | GOOLE(NCE 1) | 395 |
| EGHAM TOWN (RYMAN 3) | 860 | GORLESTON (EAST P) | 574 |
| ELMORE (WEST P) | 701 | GORNAL ATHLETIC (W.MID P) | 754 |
| ELY CITY (EAST P) | 584 | GOSPORT BOROUGH (WSX) | 682 |
| EMLEY (UNIB P) NPP HOLSFOLD @ EMLEY | 288 | GRANTHAM TOWN (DM P) | 490 |
| ENFIELD (RYMAN P) | 792 | GRAVESEND & NORTHFLEET (RYMAN P)cP | 796 |
| EPPLETON C.W. (NTH 2) | 437 | GRAYS ATHLETIC (RYMAN 1) cS | 829 |
| EPSOM & EWELL (RYMAN 3) | 860 | GREAT HARWOOD TOWN (NWC 1) | 351 |
| ERITH & BELVEDERE (DM S) | 554 | GREAT WAKERING ROVERS (RYMAN 3) | 861 |
| ERITH TOWN (KENT) | 614 | GREAT YARMOUTH TOWN | 575 |
| ESH WINNING (NTH 2) | 438 | GREENACRES (HEMEL HEMP) (SSM S) | 893 |
| ETON MANOR (ESX Sen) | 877 | GREENWICH BOROUGH (KENT) | 615 |
| ETTINGSHALL HOLY TRINITY (W.MID P) | 754 | GRESLEY ROVERS (DM P) | 530 |

| Club | No. |
|---|---|
| GRETNA (UNIB 1) | 335 |
| GUISBOROUGH (NTH 1) | 431 |
| GUISLEY (UNIB P) ↵PP | 296 |
| | |
| HADLEIGH UNITED (EAST 1) | 584 |
| HAILSHAM TOWN (SSX 2) | 644 |
| HALESOWEN HARRIERS (M.ALL) | 733 |
| HALESOWEN TOWN (DM P) SP | 492 |
| HALL ROAD RANGERS (NCE 1) | 396 |
| HALLAM (NCE P) | 391 |
| HALLEN (HELL P) | 598 |
| HALSTEAD TOWN(EAST P) | 575 |
| HAMBLE ASSC (WSX) | 682 |
| HAMPTON & RICHMOND B. (RYMAN P) rP | 798 |
| HANDRAHAN TIMBERS (M.COMB P) | 746 |
| HANWELL TOWN (SSM P ) | 886 |
| HAREFIELD UNITED (SSM S) | 894 |
| HARINGEY BOROUGH (SSM P ) | 886 |
| HARLOW TOWN (RYMAN 2) | 830 |
| HARPENDEN TOWN (SSM P ) | 886 |
| HARROGATE RAILWAY (NCE P) | 391 |
| HARROGATE TOWN (UNIB 1) cↄ | 336 |
| HARROW BOROUGH RYMAN P) rP | 800 |
| HARROW HILL (HELL P) | 598 |
| HARROWBY UNITED (UCL 1) | 666 |
| HARTLEY WINTNEY (C.Co P) | 872 |
| HARWICH & PARKESTON(EAST P) | 575 |
| HASSOCKS (SSX 1) | 635 |
| HASTINGS TOWN (DM S) | 559 |
| HATFIELD MAIN (NCE 1) | 396 |
| HAVANT & WATERLOOVILLE (DM S) cs | 494 |
| HAVERFORDWEST COUNTY (WALES) | 985 |
| HAVERHILL ROVERS (EAST 1) | 586 |
| HAYES (NC) cs | 163 |
| HAYWARDS HEATH TOWN (SSX 3) | 649 |
| HEADINGTON AMATEURS (HELL 1) | 603 |
| HEAVITREE UNITED (WEST 1) | 691 |
| HEBBURN (NTH 2) | 438 |
| HEDNESFORD TOWN (NC) SP | 169 |
| HEMEL HEMPSTEAD (RYMAN 2) SP | 847 |
| HENDON (RYMAN P) rP | 802 |
| HEREFORD UNITED (NC) cP | 175 |
| HERNE BAY (KENT) | 615 |
| HERTFORD TOWN (RYMAN 3) | 861 |
| HEYBRIDGE SWIFTS (RYMAN P) rP | 804 |
| HIGHAM TOWN (UCL 1) | 666 |
| HIGHGATE UNITED (M.COMB P) | 748 |
| HIGHWORTH TOWN (HELL P) | 598 |
| HILLINGDON BOROUGH (SSM P ) | 887 |
| HINCKLEY UNITED (DM M) cↄ | 531 |
| HITCHIN TOWN (RYMAN 1) SP | 806 |
| HISTON (EAST P) SP | 577 |
| HODDESDON TOWN (SSM P) | 887 |
| HOLBEACH UNITED (UCL P) | 659 |
| HOLKER OLD BOYS (NWC 2) | 362 |
| HOLMER GREEN (SSM P) | 888 |
| | |
| HORDEN C.W. (NTH 2) | 438 |
| HORNCHURCH (RYMAN 3) cs | 861 |
| HORSHAM (RYMAN 2) | 849 |
| HORSHAM Y.M.C.A. (SSX 1) | 636 |
| HOUGHTON TOWN (SSM1) | 898 |
| HUCKNALL TOWN (UNIB P) cↄ | 298 |
| HULLBRIDGE SPORTS (ESX Sen) | 879 |
| HUNGERFORD TOWN (RYMAN 2) | 849 |
| HURSTPIERPOINT (SSX 3) | 649 |
| HYDE UNITED (UNIB P) rPP | 300 |
| HYTHE UNITED (KENT) | 617 |
| | |
| IFIELD (SSX 3) | 649 |
| ILFORD (ESX Sen) | 879 |
| ILFRACOMBE TOWN (WEST 1) | 709 |
| ILKESTON TOWN (DM P) | 496 |
| INTER CABLE-TEL (WALES) | 985 |
| IPSWICH WANDERERS (EAST P) | 577 |
| IRCHESTER UNITED (UCL 1) | 667 |
| ISLINGTON ST MARYS (SSM P 1) | 883 |
| | |
| JARROW ROOFING BCA (NTH 1) | 431 |
| KEMPSTON ROVERS (UCL P) | 660 |
| KENILWORTH TOWN (M.COMB P) | 748 |
| KENT ATHLETIC (SSM 1) | 898 |
| KETTERING TOWN (NC) cs | 181 |
| KEYNSHAM (WEST P) | 789 |
| KIDDERMINSTER HARRIERS (NC) | 187 |
| KIDLINGTON (HELL 1) | 603 |
| KIDSGROVE ATHLETIC (NWC 1) | 351 |
| KING'S LYNN (DM P) SP | 498 |
| KINGS HEATH (M.COMB P) | 748 |
| KINGS NORTON TOWN (M.ALL) | 733 |
| KINGSBURY TOWN (RYMAN 3) | 863 |
| KINGSTONIAN (NC) rP | 193 |
| KINGTON (W.MID P) | 754 |
| KNYPERSLEY VICTORIA (M.ALL) | 733 |
| | |
| LANCASTER CITY (UNIB P) cↄ | 302 |
| LANCING (SSX 2) | 644 |
| LANGFORD (SSM S) | 894 |
| LANGNEY SPORTS (SSX 1) cs [EASTBOURNE BORO] | 636 |
| LARKHALL ATHLETIC (WEST 1) | 709 |
| LEATHERHEAD (RYMAN 1) | 831 |
| LEEK (NWC 1) | 353 |
| LEEK TOWN (NC) ↵PP | 306 |
| LEIGH RMI (UNIB P) cↄ | 304 |
| LEIGHTON TOWN (RYMAN 2) | 850 |
| LETCHWORTH (SSM S ) | 894 |
| LETCOMBE (HELL 1) | 605 |
| LEVERSTOCK GREEN (SSM S ) | 894 |
| LEWES (RYMAN 3) cs | 863 |
| LEYTON (ESX Sen) rP | 879 |
| LEYTON PENNANT (RYMAN 1) | 832 |
| LINCOLN UNITED (UNIB 1) ↵PP | 337 |
| LINGFIELD (SSX 2) | 644 |

| | | | |
|---|---|---|---|
| .EHAMPTON TOWN (SSX 1) | 636 | NEWHAVEN (SSX 3) | 649 |
| RSEDGE (NCE P) | 392 | NEWMARKET TOWN (EAST P) | 578 |
| )ON COLNEY (SSM P | 888 | NEWPORT ATHLETIC (SSM 1) | 898 |
| BUCKBY (UCL P) | 660 | NEWPORT COUNTY AFC (DM M) cS | 504 |
| )SWOOD (KENT) | 617 | NEWPORT I.O.W. (DM S) | 560 |
| TH UNITED (NCE 1) | 396 | NEWPORT PAGNELL TOWN (UCL 1) | 667 |
| ESTOFT TOWN (EAST P) | 577 | NEWTOWN (WALES) | 986 |
| OW TOWN (W.MID P) | 754 | NORTH FERRIBY UNITED (NCE P) | 392 |
| )N OLD BOYS (SSM S) | 894 | NORTHFIELD TOWN (MID COMB) | 747 |
| TOWN (W.MID P) | 755 | NORTH LEIGH (HELL P) | 599 |
| NGTON & NEW MILTON (WSX) | 683 | NORTHALLERTON (NTH 2) | 439 |
| | | NORTHAMPTON ON CHENECKS (UCL 1) | 669 |
| HULL (NWC 2) | 362 | NORTHAMPTON SPENCER (UCL P) | 660 |
| ENHEAD UNITED (RYMAN 1) cs | 833 | NORTHAMPTON VANAID (UCL 1) | 669 |
| IE ROAD (NWC 1) | 353 | NORTHWICH VICTORIA (NC) cN | 205 |
| )ON TOWN (EAST P) | 578 | NORTHWOOD (RYMAN 2) IP | 852 |
| BY MAIN (NCE P) | 392 | NORTON & STOCKTON A. (NTH 2) | 439 |
| VERN TOWN (W.MID P) | 755 | NORWICH UNITED (EAST 1) | 586 |
| GOTSFIELD UNITED (WEST P) | 701 | NUNEATON BOROUGH (NC) cN | 211 |
| CH TOWN (EAST 1) | 586 | | |
| CONI (MID COMB) | 748 | OADBY TOWN(M.All) | 735 |
| GATE (DM S) cP | 500 | OAKWOOD (SSX 2) | 645 |
| INE (UNIB P) APP | 308 | ODD DOWN (WEST P) | 702 |
| KYATE (SSM 1) | 898 | OLD BRADWELL UNITED (SSM 1) | 899 |
| LOW (RYMAN 2) | 850 | OLD DUNSTABLIANS (SSM 1) | 899 |
| SKE UNITED (NTH 1) | 431 | OLD WOODSTOCK TOWN (HELL 1) | 605 |
| SEY-FERGUSON (M.COMB P) | 748 | OLDBURY UNITED (M.ALL) | 735 |
| OCK TOWN (UNIB 1) NPP | 338 | OLDHAM TOWN (NWC 2) | 363 |
| K.A. (M.COMB P) | 747 | OLNEY TOWN (UCL 1) | 669 |
| KSHAM (WEST P) | 701 | OSSETT ALBION (NCE P) | 393 |
| STHAM (C.Co P | 872 | OSSETT TOWN (UNIB 1) | 340 |
| THYR TYDFIL (DM P) SP | 502 | OVING (SSX 2) | 645 |
| ROPOLITAN POLICE (RYMAN 2) | 851 | OXFORD CITY (RYMAN 1) | 834 |
| IURST & EASEBOURNE U (SSX 3) | 642 | | |
| )LE BARTON (HELL 1) | 605 | PAGET RANGERS (DM M) | 533 |
| ENHALL TOWN (EAST 1) | 578 | PAGHAM (SSX 1) | 638 |
| OAK (SSX 2) | 644 | PARKGATE (NCE 1) | 398 |
| ON KEYNES see Bletchley Town P892 | | PAULTON ROVERS (WEST P) | 702 |
| ON KEYNES CITY (SSM P) | 888 | PEACEHAVEN & TELSCOMBE (SSX 2) | 645 |
| ON UNITED (HELL P) | 599 | PEGASUS JUNIORS (HELL P) | 599 |
| EHEAD (WEST 1) | 702 | PELSALL VILLA (M.ALL) | 735 |
| ESEY (RYMAN 1) | 851 | PENRITH (NTH 2) | 440 |
| EYFIELDS (WSX) | 683 | PERSHORE TOWN (M.ALL) | 737 |
| R GREEN (DM M) cN | 532 | PETERLEE NEWTOWN (NTH 2) | 433 |
| ECAMBE (NC) cP | 199 | PEWSEY VALE (WEST 1) | 709 |
| PETH TOWN (NTH 1) | 433 | PICKERING TOWN (NCE 1) | 398 |
| SLEY (NWC 1) | 354 | PITSTONE & IVINGHOE (SSM 1) | 899 |
| SLEY UNITED (SSM 1) | 898 | PONTEFRACT COLLIERIES (NCE 1) | 398 |
| TON (NTH 2) | 439 | PORTFIELD (SSX 1) | 638 |
| | | PORTHMADOQ (WALES) | 986 |
| TWICH TOWN (NWC 1) | 354 | PORTSMOUTH R.N. (WSX) | 683 |
| DHAM MARKET (EAST 1) | 586 | POTTERS BAR TOWN (SSM P ) | 889 |
| SON (NWC 2) | 363 | POTTON UNITED (UCL P) | 661 |
| HERFIELD KENDAL (UNIB 1) | 389 | PRESCOT CABLES (NWC 1) NPP | 356 |
| BRADWELL ST PETER (SSM P 1) | 888 | PRUDHOE TOWN (NTH 2) | 440 |
| CASTLE BLUE STAR (NTH 1) | 439 | PURFLEET (RYMAN P) cs THURROCK | 808 |
| CASTLE TOWN (NWC 1) | 354 | PURTON (HELL 1) | 605 |